SOLUTIONS MANUAL

Kathleen Thrush Shaginaw
Community College of Philadelphia
Particular Solutions, Inc.

PRINCIPLES OF CHEMISTRY

A MOLECULAR APPROACH

Third Edition

NIVALDO J. TRO

PEARSON

Editor in Chief: Jeanne Zalesky
Senior Acquisitions Editor: Terry Haugen
Marketing Manager: Will Moore
Project Management Team Lead: David Zielonka
Project Manager: Beth Sweeten
Full-Service Project Management/Composition: CodeMantra
Operations Specialist: Maura Zaldivar-Garcia
Cover Art: Quade Paul

www.pearsonhighered.com

1 2 3 4 5 6 7 8 9 10—**V031**—17 16 15 14
ISBN-10: 0-13-389067-8; ISBN-13: 978-0-13-389067-9

Contents

Student Guide to Using This Solutions Manual

The vision behind this solutions manual is to provide guidance that is useful for both the struggling student and the advanced student.

An important feature of this solutions manual is that answers for the review questions are given. This will help in the review of the major concepts in the chapter.

The format of the solutions very closely follows the format in the textbook. Each mathematical problem includes **Given, Find, Conceptual Plan, Solution**, and **Check** sections.

Given and Find: Many students struggle with taking the written problem, parsing the information into categories, and determining the goal of the problem. It is also important to know which pieces of information in the problem are not necessary to solve the problem and if additional information needs to be gathered from sources such as tables in the textbook.

Conceptual Plan: The conceptual plan shows a step-by-step method to solve the problem. In many cases, the given quantities need to be converted to a different unit. Under each of the arrows is the equation, constant, or conversion factor needed to complete this portion of the problem. In the "Problems by Topic" section of the end-of-chapter exercises, the odd-numbered and even-numbered problems are paired. This allows you to use a conceptual plan from an odd-numbered problem in this manual as a starting point to solve the following even-numbered problem. Students should keep in mind that the examples shown are one way to solve the problems. Other mathematically equivalent solutions may be possible.

5.17   **Given:** $m\,(CO_2) = 28.8$ g, $P = 742$ mmHg, and $T = 22\,°C$ **Find:** V
Conceptual Plan: $°C \rightarrow K$ and mmHg $\rightarrow$ atm and g $\rightarrow$ mol then $n, P, T \rightarrow V$

$$K = °C + 273.15 \qquad \frac{1\ atm}{760\ mmHg} \qquad \frac{1\ mol}{44.01\ g} \qquad PV = nRT$$

Solution: $T_1 = 22\,°C + 273.15 = 295$ K, $P = 742\ \cancel{mmHg} \times \dfrac{1\ atm}{760\ \cancel{mmHg}} = 0.976316$ atm,

$n = 28.8\ \cancel{g} \times \dfrac{1\ mol}{44.01\ \cancel{g}} = 0.654397$ mol $PV = nRT$ Rearrange to solve for V.

$$V = \frac{nRT}{P} = \frac{0.654397\ \cancel{mol} \times 0.08206\ \dfrac{L \cdot \cancel{atm}}{\cancel{mol} \cdot \cancel{K}} \times 295\ \cancel{K}}{0.976316\ \cancel{atm}} = 16.2\ L$$

Check: The units (L) are correct. The magnitude of the answer (16 L) makes sense because one mole of an ideal gas under standard conditions (273 K and 1 atm) occupies 22.4 L. Although these are not standard conditions, they are close enough for a ballpark check of the answer. Because this gas sample contains 0.65 mole, a volume of 16 L is reasonable.

Solution: The Solution section walks you through solving the problem after the conceptual plan. Equations are rearranged to solve for the appropriate quantity. Intermediate results are shown with additional digits to minimize round-off error. The units are canceled in each appropriate step.

Check: The Check section confirms that the units in the answer are correct. This section also challenges the student to think about whether the magnitude of the answer makes sense. Thinking about what is a reasonable answer can help uncover errors such as calculation errors.

1 Matter, Measurement, and Problem Solving

Review Questions

The Scientific Approach to Knowledge

1.1   (a)   This statement is a theory because it attempts to explain why. It is not possible to observe individual atoms.

        (b)   This statement is an observation.

        (c)   This statement is a law because it summarizes many observations and can explain future behavior.

        (d)   This statement is an observation.

1.2   (a)   This statement is a law because it summarizes many observations and can explain future behavior.

        (b)   This statement is a law because it summarizes many observations and can explain future behavior.

        (c)   This statement is a law because it summarizes many observations and can explain future behavior.

        (d)   This statement is a theory because it attempts to explain why.

1.3   (a)   Yes, if we divide the mass of the oxygen by the mass of the carbon, the result is always 4/3, a ratio of small whole numbers.

        (b)   Yes, if we divide the mass of the oxygen by the mass of the hydrogen, the result is always 16, a ratio of small whole numbers.

        (c)   These observations suggest that the masses of elements in molecules are ratios of whole numbers (4:3 and 16:1, respectively, for parts (a) and (b)).

        (d)   Atoms combine in small whole number ratios and not as random weight ratios.

1.4   Many hypotheses may be developed. One hypothesis is that a large explosion generated galaxies that are still moving away from each other.

The Classification and Properties of Matter

1.5   (a)   Sweat is a homogeneous mixture of water, sodium chloride, and other components.

        (b)   Carbon dioxide is a pure substance that is a compound (two or more elements bonded together).

        (c)   Aluminum is a pure substance that is an element (element 13 in the periodic table).

        (d)   Vegetable soup is a heterogeneous mixture of broth, chunks of vegetables, and extracts from the vegetables.

1.6   (a)   Wine is a generally homogeneous mixture of water, ethyl alcohol, and other components from the grapes. In some cases, sediment may be present; so it would be a heterogeneous mixture.

        (b)   Beef stew is a heterogeneous mixture of thick broth with chunks of beef and vegetables.

        (c)   Iron is a pure substance that is an element (element 26 in the periodic table).

        (d)   Carbon monoxide is a pure substance that is a compound (two or more elements bonded together).

1.7

Substance	Pure or Mixture	Type
aluminum	pure	element
apple juice	mixture	mixture
hydrogen peroxide	pure	compound
chicken soup	mixture	mixture

1.8

Substance	Pure or Mixture	Type
water	pure	compound
coffee	mixture	mixture
ice	pure	compound
carbon	pure	element

1.9   (a)   pure substance that is a compound (one type of molecule that contains two different elements)
    (b)   heterogeneous mixture (two different molecules that are segregated into regions)
    (c)   homogeneous mixture (two different molecules that are randomly mixed)
    (d)   pure substance that is an element (individual atoms of one type)

1.10   (a)   pure substance that is an element (individual atoms of one type)
    (b)   homogeneous mixture (two different molecules that are randomly mixed)
    (c)   pure substance that is a compound (one type of molecule that contains two different elements)
    (d)   pure substance that is a compound (one type of molecule that contains two different elements)

1.11   (a)   physical property (color can be observed without making or breaking chemical bonds)
    (b)   chemical property (must observe by making or breaking chemical bonds)
    (c)   physical property (the phase can be observed without making or breaking chemical bonds)
    (d)   physical property (density can be observed without making or breaking chemical bonds)
    (e)   physical property (mixing does not involve making or breaking chemical bonds, so this can be observed without making or breaking chemical bonds)

1.12   (a)   physical property (color can be observed without making or breaking chemical bonds)
    (b)   physical property (odor can be observed without making or breaking chemical bonds)
    (c)   chemical property (must observe by making or breaking chemical bonds)
    (d)   chemical property (decomposition involves breaking bonds, so bonds must be broken to observe this property)
    (e)   physical property (the phase of a substance can be observed without making or breaking chemical bonds)

1.13   (a)   chemical property (burning involves breaking and making bonds, so bonds must be broken and made to observe this property)
    (b)   physical property (shininess is a physical property and so can be observed without making or breaking chemical bonds)
    (c)   physical property (odor can be observed without making or breaking chemical bonds)
    (d)   chemical property (burning involves breaking and making bonds, so bonds must be broken and made to observe this property)

1.14   (a)   physical property (vaporization is a phase change and so can be observed without making or breaking chemical bonds)
    (b)   physical property (sublimation is a phase change and so can be observed without making or breaking chemical bonds)
    (c)   chemical property (rusting involves the reaction of iron with oxygen to form iron oxide; observing this process involves making and breaking chemical bonds)
    (d)   physical property (color can be observed without making or breaking chemical bonds)

1.15   (a)   chemical change (new compounds are formed as methane and oxygen react to form carbon dioxide and water)
    (b)   physical change (vaporization is a phase change and does not involve the making or breaking of chemical bonds)
    (c)   chemical change (new compounds are formed as propane and oxygen react to form carbon dioxide and water)
    (d)   chemical change (new compounds are formed as the metal in the frame is converted to oxides)

1.16 (a) chemical change (new compounds are formed as the sugar burns)

(b) physical change (dissolution is a phase change and does not involve the making or breaking of chemical bonds)

(c) physical change (this is simply the rearrangement of the atoms)

(d) chemical change (new compounds are formed as the silver converts to an oxide)

1.17 (a) physical change (vaporization is a phase change and does not involve the making or breaking of chemical bonds)

(b) chemical change (new compounds are formed)

(c) physical change (vaporization is a phase change and does not involve the making or breaking of chemical bonds)

1.18 (a) physical change (vaporization of butane is a phase change and does not involve the making or breaking of chemical bonds)

(b) chemical change (new compounds are formed as the butane combusts)

(c) physical change (vaporization of water is a phase change and does not involve the making or breaking of chemical bonds)

Units in Measurement

1.19 (a) To convert from °F to °C, first find the equation that relates these two quantities. $°C = \dfrac{°F - 32}{1.8}$ Now substitute °F into the equation and compute the answer. Note: The number of digits reported in this answer follows significant figure conventions, covered in Section 1.6. $°C = \dfrac{°F - 32}{1.8} = \dfrac{0.}{1.8} = 0. \ °C$

(b) To convert from K to °F, first find the equations that relate these two quantities.

$K = °C + 273.15$ and $°C = \dfrac{°F - 32}{1.8}$

Because these equations do not directly express K in terms of °F, you must combine the equations and then solve the equation for °F. Substituting for °C:

$K = \dfrac{°F - 32}{1.8} + 273.15$; rearrange $K - 273.15 = \dfrac{°F - 32}{1.8}$;

rearrange $1.8(K - 273.15) = (°F - 32)$; finally, $°F = 1.8(K - 273.15) + 32$. Now substitute K into the equation and compute the answer.

$°F = 1.8(77 - 273.15) + 32 = 1.8(-196.15) + 32 = -353.07 + 32 = -321.07 \ °F = -321 \ °F$

(c) To convert from °F to °C, first find the equation that relates these two quantities. $°C = \dfrac{°F - 32}{1.8}$ Now substitute °F into the equation and compute the answer.

$°C = \dfrac{-109 \ °F - 32 \ °F}{1.8} = \dfrac{-141}{1.8} = -78.333 \ °C = -78.3 \ °C$

(d) To convert from °F to K, first find the equations that relate these two quantities.

$K = °C + 273.15$ and $°C = \dfrac{°F - 32}{1.8}$

Because these equations do not directly express K in terms of °F, you must combine the equations and then solve the equation for K. Substituting for °C: $K = \dfrac{°F - 32}{1.8} + 273.15$

Now substitute °F into the equation and compute the answer.

$K = \dfrac{(98.6 - 32)}{1.8} + 273.15 = \dfrac{66.6}{1.8} + 273.15 = 37.0 + 273.15 = 310.15 \ K = 310.2 \ K$

1.20 (a) To convert from °F to °C, first find the equation that relates these two quantities. $°C = \dfrac{°F - 32}{1.8}$

Now substitute °F into the equation and compute the answer. Note: The number of digits reported in this answer follows significant figure conventions, covered in Section 1.6.

$°C = \dfrac{212 \ °F - 32 \ °F}{1.8} = \dfrac{180.}{1.8} = 100. \ °C$

(b)   Begin by finding the equation that relates the quantity that is given (°C) and the quantity you are trying to find (K): K = °C + 273.15. Because this equation gives the temperature in K directly, simply substitute the correct value for the temperature in °C and compute the answer.

K = 22 °C + 273.15 = 295 K

(c)   To convert from K to °F, first find the equations that relate these two quantities: K = °C + 273.15 and

°C = $\dfrac{°F - 32}{1.8}$. Because these equations do not directly express K in terms of °F, you must combine the

equations and then solve the equation for °F. Substituting for °C: K = $\dfrac{°F - 32}{1.8}$ + 273.15; rearrange

K − 273.15 = $\dfrac{°F - 32}{1.8}$; rearrange 1.8(K − 273.15) = (°F − 32); rearrange °F = 1.8(K − 273.15) + 32.

Now substitute K into the equation and compute the answer.

°F = 1.8(0.00 K − 273.15) + 32 = 1.8(−273.15 K) + 32 = −491.67 + 32 = −459.67 °F

(d)   Begin by finding the equation that relates the quantity that is given (K) and the quantity you are trying to find (°C): K = °C + 273.15. Because this equation does not directly express °C in terms of K, you must solve the equation for °C: °C = K − 273.15. Now substitute K into the equation and compute the answer.

°C = 2.735 − 273.15 = −270.42 °C

1.21   To convert from °F to °C, first find the equation that relates these two quantities: °C = $\dfrac{°F - 32}{1.8}$. Now substitute °F

into the equation and compute the answer. Note: The number of digits reported in this answer follows significant fig-

ure conventions, covered in Section 1.6. °C = $\dfrac{-80.\ °F - 32\ °F}{1.8}$ = $\dfrac{-112}{1.8}$ = −62.2 °C

Begin by finding the equation that relates the quantity that is given (°C) and the quantity you are trying to find (K).
K = °C + 273.15. Because this equation gives the temperature in K directly, simply substitute the correct value for
the temperature in °C and compute the answer. K = −62.222 °C + 273.15 = 210.9 K

1.22   To convert from °F to °C, first find the equation that relates these two quantities: °C = $\dfrac{°F - 32}{1.8}$. Now substitute °F

into the equation and compute the answer. Note: The number of digits reported in this answer follows significant fig-

ure conventions, covered in Section 1.6.

°C = $\dfrac{134\ °F - 32\ °F}{1.8}$ = $\dfrac{102}{1.8}$ = 56.6667 °C = 56.7 °C

Begin by finding the equation that relates the quantity that is given (°C) and the quantity you are trying to find (K):
K = °C + 273.15. Because this equation gives the temperature in K directly, simply substitute the correct value for
the temperature in °C and compute the answer. K = 56.6667 °C + 273.15 = 329.8 K

1.23   Use Table 1.2 to determine the appropriate prefix multiplier and substitute the meaning into the expressions.
(a) 3.8×10^{-8} s = 38×10^{-9} s; 10^{-9} implies "nano," so 38×10^{-9} s = 38 nanoseconds = 38 ns
(b) 57×10^{-13} g = 5.7×10^{-12} g; 10^{-12} implies "pico," so 5.7×10^{-12} g = 5.7 picograms = 5.7 pg
(c) 5.9×10^{7} L = 59×10^{6} L; 10^{6} implies "mega," so 5.9×10^{7} L = 59 megaliters = 59 ML
(d) 9.3×10^{8} m = 930×10^{6} m; 10^{6} implies "mega," so 930×10^{6} m = 930 megameters = 930 Mm

1.24   Use Table 1.2 to determine the appropriate prefix multiplier and substitute the meaning into the expressions.
(a) 10^{-15} implies "femto," so 38 fs = 38 femtoseconds = 38×10^{-15} s = 3.8×10^{-14} s
          Remember that in scientific notation, the first number should be smaller than 10.
(b) 10^{-9} implies "nano," so 13.2 ns = 13.2 nanoseconds = 13.2×10^{-9} s = 1.32×10^{-8} s
          Remember that in scientific notation, the first number should be smaller than 10.
(c) 10^{-12} implies "pico," so 153 pm = 153×10^{-12} m = 1.53×10^{-10} m
          Remember that in scientific notation, the first number should be smaller than 10.
(d) μ implies "micro," or 10^{-6}, so 122 μm = 122 micrometers = 122×10^{-6} m = 1.22×10^{-4} m
          Remember that in scientific notation, the first number should be smaller than 10.

1.25   (b)   **Given:** 515 km   **Find:** dm
Conceptual Plan: km → m → dm

$$\frac{1000 \text{ m}}{1 \text{ km}} \quad \frac{10 \text{ dm}}{1 \text{ m}}$$

Solution: $515 \text{ km} \times \dfrac{1000 \text{ m}}{1 \text{ km}} \times \dfrac{10 \text{ dm}}{1 \text{ m}} = 5.15 \times 10^6 \text{ dm}$

Check: The units (dm) are correct. The magnitude of the answer (10^6) makes physical sense because a decimeter is a much smaller unit than a kilometer.

Given: 515 km   **Find:** cm
Conceptual Plan: km → m → cm

$$\frac{1000 \text{ m}}{1 \text{ km}} \quad \frac{100 \text{ cm}}{1 \text{ m}}$$

Solution: $515 \text{ km} \times \dfrac{1000 \text{ m}}{1 \text{ km}} \times \dfrac{100 \text{ cm}}{1 \text{ m}} = 5.15 \times 10^7 \text{ cm}$

Check: The units (cm) are correct. The magnitude of the answer (10^7) makes physical sense because a centimeter is a much smaller unit than a kilometer or a decimeter.

(c)   **Given:** 122.355 s   **Find:** ms
Conceptual Plan: s → ms

$$\frac{1000 \text{ ms}}{1 \text{ s}}$$

Solution: $122.355 \text{ s} \times \dfrac{1000 \text{ ms}}{1 \text{ s}} = 1.22355 \times 10^5 \text{ ms}$

Check: The units (ms) are correct. The magnitude of the answer (10^5) makes physical sense because a millisecond is a much smaller unit than a second.

Given: 122.355 s   **Find:** ks
Conceptual Plan: s → ks

$$\frac{1 \text{ ks}}{1000 \text{ s}}$$

Solution: $122.355 \text{ s} \times \dfrac{1 \text{ ks}}{1000 \text{ s}} = 1.22355 \times 10^{-1} \text{ ks} = 0.122355 \text{ ks}$

Check: The units (ks) are correct. The magnitude of the answer (10^{-1}) makes physical sense because a kilosecond is a much larger unit than a second.

(d)   **Given:** 3.345 kJ   **Find:** J
Conceptual Plan: kJ → J

$$\frac{1000 \text{ J}}{1 \text{ kJ}}$$

Solution: $3.345 \text{ kJ} \times \dfrac{1000 \text{ J}}{1 \text{ kJ}} = 3.345 \times 10^3 \text{ J}$

Check: The units (J) are correct. The magnitude of the answer (10^3) makes physical sense because a joule is a much smaller unit than a kilojoule.

Given: 3.345×10^3 J (from above)   **Find:** mJ
Conceptual Plan: J → mJ

$$\frac{1000 \text{ mJ}}{1 \text{ J}}$$

Solution: $3.345 \times 10^3 \text{ J} \times \dfrac{1000 \text{ mJ}}{1 \text{ J}} = 3.345 \times 10^6 \text{ mJ}$

Check: The units (mJ) are correct. The magnitude of the answer (10^6) makes physical sense because a millijoule is a much smaller unit than a joule.

1.26　　(a)　**Given:** 254,998 m　**Find:** km
　　　　　　Conceptual Plan: m → km

$$\frac{1 \text{ km}}{1000 \text{ m}}$$

　　　　　Solution: $254{,}998 \ \cancel{m} \times \dfrac{1 \text{ km}}{1000 \ \cancel{m}} = 2.54998 \times 10^2 \text{ km} = 254.998 \text{ km}$

　　　　　Check: The units (km) are correct. The magnitude of the answer (10^2) makes physical sense because a kilometer is a much larger unit than a meter.

　　　　(b)　**Given:** 254,998 m　**Find:** Mm
　　　　　　Conceptual Plan: m → Mm

$$\frac{1 \text{ Mm}}{10^6 \text{ m}}$$

　　　　　Solution: $254{,}998 \ \cancel{m} \times \dfrac{1 \text{ Mm}}{10^6 \ \cancel{m}} = 2.54998 \times 10^{-1} \text{ Mm} = 0.254998 \text{ Mm}$

　　　　　Check: The units (Mm) are correct. The magnitude of the answer (10^{-1}) makes physical sense because a megameter is a much larger unit than a meter or a kilometer.

　　　　(c)　**Given:** 254,998 m　**Find:** mm
　　　　　　Conceptual Plan: m → mm

$$\frac{1000 \text{ mm}}{1 \text{ m}}$$

　　　　　Solution: $254{,}998 \ \cancel{m} \times \dfrac{1000 \text{ mm}}{1 \ \cancel{m}} = 2.54998 \times 10^8 \text{ mm}$

　　　　　Check: The units (mm) are correct. The magnitude of the answer (10^8) makes physical sense because a millimeter is a much smaller unit than a meter.

　　　　(d)　**Given:** 254,998 m　**Find:** cm
　　　　　　Conceptual Plan: m → cm

$$\frac{100 \text{ cm}}{1 \text{ m}}$$

　　　　　Solution: $254{,}998 \ \cancel{m} \times \dfrac{100 \text{ cm}}{1 \ \cancel{m}} = 2.54998 \times 10^7 \text{ cm}$

　　　　　Check: The units (cm) are correct. The magnitude of the answer (10^7) makes physical sense because a centimeter is a much smaller unit than a meter, but larger than a millimeter.

1.27　　**Given:** 1 square meter (1 m^2)　**Find:** number of 1 cm squares in 1 square meter
　　　　Conceptual Plan: $1 \text{ m}^2 \to \text{cm}^2$

$$\frac{100 \text{ cm}}{1 \text{ m}}$$

　　　Notice that for squared units, the conversion factors must be squared.

　　　Solution: $1 \ \cancel{m}^2 \times \dfrac{(100 \text{ cm})^2}{(1 \ \cancel{m})^2} = 1 \times 10^4 \text{ cm squares} = 10{,}000. \text{ squares, so } 1 \times 10^4 \text{ cm squares}$

　　　Check: The units of the answer are correct, and the magnitude makes sense. The unit centimeter is smaller than a meter, so the value in square centimeters should be larger than in square meters.

1.28　　**Given:** 4 cm on each edge cube　**Find:** number of 1 cm cubes in a 4-cm cube
　　　　Conceptual Plan: Read the information given carefully. The 4-cm cube is 4 cm on each side.

$$l, w, h \to V$$
$$V = l \, w \, h$$
$$in \ a \ cube \ l = w = h$$

　　　Solution: $4 \text{ cm} \times 4 \text{ cm} \times 4 \text{ cm} = (4 \text{ cm})^3 = \underline{6}4 \text{ cm}^3 = 60 \text{ cm}^3$

　　　Check: The units of the answer are correct, and the magnitude makes sense. The unit 4 centimeters is larger than 1 centimeter, so the value in cubic centimeters should be larger.

Density

1.29 **Given:** $m = 2.49$ g; $V = 0.349$ cm^3 **Find:** d in g/cm^3 and compare to pure copper.
Conceptual Plan: $m, V \rightarrow d$

$$d = m/V$$

Compare to the published value: d (pure copper) $= 8.96$ g/cm^3. (This value is in Table 1.4.)

Solution: $d = \dfrac{2.49 \text{ g}}{0.349 \text{ cm}^3} = 7.13 \dfrac{\text{g}}{\text{cm}^3}$

The density of the penny is much smaller than the density of pure copper (7.13 g/cm^3; 8.96 g/cm^3), so the penny is not pure copper.

Check: The units (g/cm^3) are correct. The magnitude of the answer seems correct. Many coins are layers of metals, so it is not surprising that the penny is not pure copper.

1.30 **Given:** $m = 1.41$ kg; $V = 0.314$ L   **Find:** d in g/cm^3 and compare to pure titanium.
Conceptual Plan: $m, V \rightarrow d$ then kg $\rightarrow$ g then L $\rightarrow$ cm^3

$$d = m/V \qquad \frac{1000 \text{ g}}{1 \text{ kg}} \qquad \frac{1000 \text{ cm}^3}{1 \text{ L}}$$

Solution: $d = \dfrac{1.41 \text{ k\cancel{g}}}{0.314 \text{ \cancel{L}}} \times \dfrac{1000 \text{ g}}{1 \text{ k\cancel{g}}} \times \dfrac{1 \text{ \cancel{L}}}{1000 \text{ cm}^3} = 4.49 \dfrac{\text{g}}{\text{cm}^3}$

Check: The units (g/cm^3) are correct. The magnitude of the answer seems correct. The density of the frame is almost exactly the density of pure titanium (4.49 g/cm^3 versus 4.51 g/cm^3), so the frame could be titanium.

1.31 **Given:** $m = 4.10 \times 10^3$ g; $V = 3.25$ L   **Find:** d in g/cm^3
Conceptual Plan: $m, V \rightarrow d$ then L $\rightarrow$ cm^3

$$d = m/V \qquad \frac{1000 \text{ cm}^3}{1 \text{ L}}$$

Solution: $d = \dfrac{4.10 \times 10^3 \text{ g}}{3.25 \text{ \cancel{L}}} \times \dfrac{1 \text{ \cancel{L}}}{1000 \text{ cm}^3} = 1.26 \dfrac{\text{g}}{\text{cm}^3}$

Check: The units (g/cm^3) are correct. The magnitude of the answer seems correct.

1.32 **Given:** $m = 371$ g; $V = 19.3$ mL   **Find:** d in g/cm^3 and compare to pure gold.
Conceptual Plan: $m, V \rightarrow d$

$$d = m/V$$

Compare to the published value: (pure gold) $= 19.3$ g/mL. (This value is in Table 1.4.)

Solution: $d = \dfrac{371 \text{ g}}{19.3 \text{ mL}} = 19.2 \dfrac{\text{g}}{\text{mL}}$

The density of the nugget is essentially the same as the density of pure gold (19.2 g/mL versus 19.3 g/mL), so the nugget could be gold.

Check: The units (g/cm^3) are correct. The magnitude of the answer seems correct and is essentially the same as the density of pure gold.

1.33 (a) **Given:** $d = 1.11$ g/cm^3; $V = 417$ mL   **Find:** m
Conceptual Plan: $d, V \rightarrow m$ then cm^3 $\rightarrow$ mL

$$d = m/V \qquad \frac{1 \text{ mL}}{1 \text{ cm}^3}$$

Solution: $d = m/V$ Rearrange by multiplying both sides of the equation by V. $m = d \times V$

$m = 1.11 \dfrac{\text{g}}{\text{cm}^3} \times \dfrac{1 \text{ cm}^3}{1 \text{ mL}} \times 417 \text{ mL} = 4.63 \times 10^2$ g

Check: The units (g) are correct. The magnitude of the answer seems correct considering that the value of the density is about 1 g/cm^3.

(b) **Given:** $d = 1.11$ g/cm^3; $m = 4.1$ kg   **Find:** V in L
Conceptual Plan: $d, m \rightarrow V$ then kg $\rightarrow$ g and cm^3 $\rightarrow$ L

$$d = m/V \qquad \frac{1000 \text{ g}}{1 \text{ kg}} \qquad \frac{1 \text{ L}}{1000 \text{ cm}^3}$$

Solution: $d = m/V$ Rearrange by multiplying both sides of the equation by V and dividing both sides of the equation by d.

$$V = \frac{m}{d} = \frac{4.1 \text{ kg}}{1.11 \frac{\text{g}}{\text{cm}^3}} \times \frac{1000 \text{ g}}{1 \text{ kg}} = 3.7 \times 10^3 \text{ cm}^3 \times \frac{1 \text{ L}}{1000 \text{ cm}^3} = 3.7 \text{ L}$$

Check: The units (L) are correct. The magnitude of the answer seems correct considering that the value of the density is about 1 g/cm^3.

1.34 (a) **Given:** $d = 0.7857 \text{ g/cm}^3$; $V = 28.56 \text{ mL}$ **Find:** m

Conceptual Plan: $d, V \rightarrow m$

$$d = m/V$$

Solution: $d = m/V$ Rearrange by multiplying both sides of the equation by V. $m = d \times V$

$$m = 0.7857 \frac{\text{g}}{\text{cm}^3} \times \frac{1 \text{ cm}^3}{1 \text{ mL}} \times 28.56 \text{ mL} = 22.44 \text{ g}$$

Check: The units (g) are correct. The magnitude of the answer seems correct considering that the value of the density is less than 1 g/cm^3.

(b) **Given:** $d = 0.7857 \text{ g/cm}^3$; $m = 6.54 \text{ g}$ **Find:** V

Conceptual Plan: $d, m \rightarrow V$ then cm^3 $\rightarrow$ mL

$$d = m/V \qquad \frac{1 \text{ mL}}{1 \text{ cm}^3}$$

Solution: $d = m/V$ Rearrange by multiplying both sides of the equation by V and dividing both sides of the equation by d.

$$V = \frac{m}{d} = \frac{6.54 \text{ g}}{0.7857 \frac{\text{g}}{\text{cm}^3}} = 8.32 \text{ cm}^3 \times \frac{1 \text{ mL}}{1 \text{ cm}^3} = 8.32 \text{ mL}$$

Check: The units (mL) are correct. The magnitude of the answer seems correct considering that the value of the density is less than 1 g/cm^3.

The Reliability of a Measurement and Significant Figures

1.35 To obtain the readings, look to see where the bottom of the meniscus lies. Estimate the distance between two markings on the device.
(a) 73.3 mL—the meniscus appears to be just above the 73 mL mark.
(b) 88.2 °C—the mercury is between the 84 °C mark and the 85 °C mark, but it is closer to the lower number.
(c) 645 mL—the meniscus appears to be just above the 640 mL mark.

1.36 To obtain the readings, look to see where the bottom of the meniscus lies. Estimate the distance between two markings on the device. Use all digits on a digital device.
(a) 27.43 °C—the mercury is just above the 27.4 °C mark. Note that the 10s digit is only labeled every 10 °C.
(b) 4.47 mL—the meniscus appears to be just below the 4.5 mL mark.
(c) 0.873 g—read all of the places on the digital display.

1.37 Remember that
1. interior zeros (zeros between two numbers) are significant.
2. leading zeros (zeros to the left of the first nonzero number) are not significant. They only serve to locate the decimal point.
3. trailing zeros (zeros at the end of a number) are categorized as follows:
    - Trailing zeros after a decimal point are always significant.
    - Trailing zeros before an implied decimal point are ambiguous and should be avoided by using scientific notation or by inserting a decimal point at the end of the number.
(a) 1,050,501 km
(b) 0.0020 m
(c) 0.00000000000000002 s
(d) 0.001090 cm

1.38   Remember that
  1.   interior zeros (zeros between two numbers) are significant.
  2.   leading zeros (zeros to the left of the first nonzero number) are not significant. They only serve to locate the decimal point.
  3.   trailing zeros (zeros at the end of a number) are categorized as follows:
        • Trailing zeros after a decimal point are always significant.
        • Trailing zeros before an implied decimal point are ambiguous and should be avoided by using scientific notation or by inserting a decimal point at the end of the number.
    (a)   180,701 mi
    (b)   0.001040 m
    (c)   0.005710 km
    (d)   90,201 m

1.39   Remember all of the rules from Section 1.7.
    (a)   Three significant figures. The 3, 1, and 2 are significant (rule 1). The leading zeros only mark the decimal place and are therefore not significant (rule 3).
    (b)   Ambiguous. The 3, 1, and 2 are significant (rule 1). The trailing zeros occur before an implied decimal point and are therefore ambiguous (rule 4). Without more information, we would assume three significant figures. It is better to write this as 3.12×10^5 to indicate three significant figures or as 3.12000×10^5 to indicate six (rule 4).
    (c)   Three significant figures. The 3, 1, and 2 are significant (rule 1).
    (d)   Five significant figures. The 1s, 3, 2, and 7 are significant (rule 1).

1.40   Remember all of the rules from Section 1.7.
    (a)   Four significant figures. The 1s are significant (rule 1). The leading zero only marks the decimal place and is therefore not significant (rule 3).
    (b)   One significant figure. The 7 is significant (rule 1). The leading zeros only mark the decimal place and are therefore not significant (rule 3).
    (c)   Ambiguous. The 1, 8, and 7 are significant (rule 1). The first 0 is significant because it is an interior 0 (rule 2). The trailing zeros occur before an implied decimal point and are therefore ambiguous (rule 4). Without more information, we would assume four significant figures. It is better to write this as 1.087×10^5 to indicate four significant figures or as 1.08700×10^5 to indicate six (rule 4).
    (d)   Seven significant figures. The 1, 5, 6, and 3s are significant (rule 1). The trailing zeros are significant because they are to the right of the decimal point and nonzero numbers (rule 4).
    (e)   Ambiguous. The 3 and 8 are significant (rule 1). The first 0 is significant because it is an interior zero (rule 2). The trailing zeros occur before an implied decimal point and are therefore ambiguous (rule 4). Without more information, we would assume three significant figures. It is better to write this as 3.08×10^4 to indicate three significant figures or as 3.0800×10^4 to indicate five (rule 4).

1.41   (a)   This is not exact because π is an irrational number. The number 3.14 only shows three of the infinite number of significant figures that π has.
    (b)   This is an exact conversion because it comes from a definition of the units and so has an unlimited number of significant figures.
    (c)   This is a measured number, so it is not an exact number. There are two significant figures.
    (d)   This is an exact conversion because it comes from a definition of the units and so has an unlimited number of significant figures.

1.42   (a)   This is a measured number, so it is not an exact number. There are nine significant figures.
    (b)   This is a an exact conversion, so it has an unlimited number of significant figures.
    (c)   This is a measured number, so it is not an exact number. There are three significant figures.
    (d)   This is an exact conversion because it comes from a definition of the units and so has an unlimited number of significant figures.

1.43   (a)   156.9—The 8 is rounded up because the next digit is a 5.

    (b)   156.8—The last two digits are dropped because 4 is less than 5.

    (c)   156.8—The last two digits are dropped because 4 is less than 5.

    (d)   156.9—The 8 is rounded up because the next digit is a 9, which is greater than 5.

1.44   (a) 7.98×10^4—The last digits are dropped because 4 is less than 5.

    (b) 1.55×10^7—The 4 is rounded up because the next digit is a 8, which is greater than 5.

    (c)   2.35—The 4 is rounded up because the next digit is a 9, which is greater than 5.

    (d) 4.54×10^{-5}—The 3 is rounded up because the next digit is an 8, which is greater than 5.

Significant Figures in Calculations

1.45   (a) $9.15 \div 4.970 = 1.84$—Three significant figures are allowed to reflect the three significant figures in the least precisely known quantity (9.15).

    (b) $1.54 \times 0.03060 \times 0.69 = 0.033$—Two significant figures are allowed to reflect the two significant figures in the least precisely known quantity (0.69). The intermediate answer (0.03251556) is rounded up because the first nonsignificant digit is a 5.

    (c) $27.5 \times 1.82 \div 100.04 = 0.500$—Three significant figures are allowed to reflect the three significant figures in the least precisely known quantities (27.5 and 1.82). The intermediate answer (0.50029988) is truncated because the first nonsignificant digit is a 2, which is less than 5.

    (d) $(2.290 \times 10^6) \div (6.7 \times 10^4) = 34$—Two significant figures are allowed to reflect the two significant figures in the least precisely known quantity (6.7×10^4). The intermediate answer (34.17910448) is truncated because the first nonsignificant digit is a 1, which is less than 5.

1.46   (a) $89.3 \times 77.0 \times 0.08 = 6 \times 10^2$—One significant figure is allowed to reflect the one significant figure in the least precisely known quantity (0.08). The intermediate answer (5.50088×10^2) is rounded up because the first nonsignificant digit is a 5.

    (b) $(5.01 \times 10^5) \div (7.8 \times 10^2) = 6.4 \times 10^2$—Two significant figures are allowed to reflect the two significant figures in the least precisely known quantity (7.8×10^2). The intermediate answer (6.423076923×10^2) is truncated because the first nonsignificant digit is a 2, which is less than 5.

    (c) $4.005 \times 74 \times 0.007 = 2$—One significant figure is allowed to reflect the one significant figure in the least precisely known quantity (0.007). The intermediate answer (2.07459) is truncated because the first nonsignificant digit is a 0, which is less than 5.

    (d) $453 \div 2.031 = 223$—Three significant figures are allowed to reflect the three significant figures in the least precisely known quantity (453). The intermediate answer (223.042836) is truncated because the first nonsignificant digit is a 0, which is less than 5.

1.47   (a)

$$\begin{array}{r} 43.7 \\ -2.341 \\ \hline 41.359 \end{array} = 41.4$$

Round the intermediate answer to one decimal place to reflect the quantity with the fewest decimal places (43.7). Round the last digit up because the first nonsignificant digit is 5.

    (b)

$$\begin{array}{r} 17.6 \\ +2.838 \\ +2.3 \\ +110.77 \\ \hline 133.508 \end{array} = 133.5$$

Round the intermediate answer to one decimal place to reflect the quantity with the fewest decimal places (2.3). Truncate nonsignificant digits because the first nonsignificant digit is 0.

    (c)

$$\begin{array}{r} 19.6 \\ +58.33 \\ -4.974 \\ \hline 72.956 \end{array} = 73.0$$

Round the intermediate answer to one decimal place to reflect the quantity with the fewest decimal places (19.6). Round the last digit up because the first nonsignificant digit is 5.

(d)   5.99

$\underline{-5.572}$

0.418 = 0.42

Round the intermediate answer to two decimal places to reflect the quantity with the fewest decimal places (5.99). Round the last digit up because the first nonsignificant digit is 8.

1.48   (a)   0.004

$\underline{+0.09879}$

0.10279 = 0.103

Round the intermediate answer to three decimal places to reflect the quantity with the fewest decimal places (0.004). Round the last digit up because the first nonsignificant digit is 7.

(b)   1239.3

+9.73

$\underline{+3.42}$

1252.45 = 1252.5

Round the intermediate answer to one decimal place to reflect the quantity with the fewest decimal places (1239.3). Round the last digit up because the first nonsignificant digit is 5.

(c)   2.4

$\underline{-1.777}$

0.623 = 0.6

Round the intermediate answer to one decimal place to reflect the quantity with the fewest decimal places (2.4). Truncate nonsignificant digits because the first nonsignificant digit is 2.

(d)   532

+7.3

$\underline{-48.523}$

490.777 = 491

Round the intermediate answer to zero decimal places to reflect the quantity with the fewest decimal places (532). Round the last digit up because the first nonsignificant digit is 7.

1.49   Perform operations in parentheses first. Keep track of significant figures in each step by noting the last significant digit in an intermediate result.

(a) $(24.6681 \times 2.38) + 332.58 = 58.\underline{7}10078$

$\underline{+332.58}$

391.290078 = 391.3

The first intermediate answer has one significant digit to the right of the decimal because it is allowed three significant figures [reflecting the quantity with the fewest significant figures (2.38)]. Underline the least significant digit in this answer. Round the next intermediate answer to one decimal place to reflect the quantity with the fewest decimal places (58.7). Round the last digit up because the first nonsignificant digit is 9.

(b) $\dfrac{(85.3 - 21.489)}{0.0059} = \dfrac{63.\underline{8}11}{0.0059} = 1.\underline{0}81542 \times 10^4 = 1.1 \times 10^4$

The first intermediate answer has one significant digit to the right of the decimal to reflect the quantity with the fewest decimal places (85.3). Underline the last significant digit in this answer. Round the next intermediate answer to two significant figures to reflect the quantity with the fewest significant figures (0.0059). Round the last digit up because the first nonsignificant digit is 8.

(c) $(512 \div 986.7) + 5.44 = 0.51\underline{8}9014$

$\underline{+5.44}$

5.9589014 = 5.96

The first intermediate answer has three significant figures and three significant digits to the right of the decimal, reflecting the quantity with the fewest significant figures (512). Underline the last significant digit in this answer. Round the next intermediate answer to two decimal places to reflect the quantity with the fewest decimal places (5.44). Round the last digit up because the first nonsignificant digit is 8.

(d) $[(28.7 \times 10^5) \div 48.533] + 144.99 = 59\underline{1}35.02$

$$\frac{+144.99}{59280.01} = 59300 = 5.93 \times 10^4$$

The first intermediate answer has three significant figures, reflecting the quantity with the fewest significant figures (28.7×10^5). Underline the most significant digit in this answer. Because the number is so large, when the addition is performed, the last significant digit is the 100s place. Round the next intermediate answer to the 100s place and put in scientific notation to remove any ambiguity. Note that the last digit is rounded up because the first nonsignificant digit is 8.

1.50   Perform operations in parentheses first. Keep track of significant figures in each step by noting the last significant digit in an intermediate result.

(a) $[(1.7 \times 10^6) \div (2.63 \times 10^5)] + 7.33 = 6.4\underline{6}3878$

$$\frac{+7.33}{13.793878} = 13.8$$

The first intermediate answer has one significant digit to the right of the decimal because it is allowed two significant figures [reflecting the quantity with the fewest significant figures (1.7×10^6)]. Underline the last significant digit in this answer. Round the next intermediate answer to one decimal place to reflect the quantity with the fewest decimal places (6.5). Round the last digit up because the first nonsignificant digit is 9.

(b) $(568.99 - 232.1) \div 5.3 = 336.\underline{8}9 \div 5.3 = 63.564151 = 64$

The first intermediate answer has one significant digit to the right of the decimal to reflect the quantity with the fewest decimal places (232.1). Underline the last significant digit in this answer. Round the next intermediate answer to two significant figures to reflect the quantity with the fewest significant figures (5.3). Round the last digit up because the first nonsignificant digit is 5.

(c) $(9443 + 45 - 9.9) \times 8.1 \times 10^6 = 947\underline{8}.1 \times 8.1 \times 10^6 = 7.67726 \times 10^{10} = 7.7 \times 10^{10}$

The first intermediate answer only has significant digits to the left of the decimal, reflecting the quantities with the fewest decimal places (9443 and 45). Underline the last significant digit in this answer. Round the next intermediate answer to two significant figures to reflect the quantity with the fewest significant figures (8.1×10^6). Round the last digit up because the first nonsignificant digit is 7.

(d) $(3.14 \times 2.4367) - 2.34 = 7.6\underline{5}1238$

$$\frac{-2.34}{5.311238} = 5.31$$

The first intermediate answer has three significant figures, reflecting the quantity with the fewest significant figures (3.14). Underline the last significant digit in this answer. This number has two significant digits to the right of the decimal point. Round the next intermediate answer to two significant digits to the right of the decimal point because both numbers have two significant digits to the right of the decimal point. Note that the last digit is truncated because the first nonsignificant digit is 1.

1.51   **Given:** 11.7 mL liquid; empty flask weight $=$ 124.1 g; flask with liquid weight $=$ 132.8 g   **Find:** d in g/mL
Conceptual Plan: Empty flask weight, flask with liquid weight $\rightarrow$ liquid weight then weight, volume $\rightarrow$ d

$$\text{(flask with liquid weight)} - \text{(flask weight)} = \text{liquid weight} \qquad d = \text{mass}/\text{volume} = m/V$$

Solution: liquid weight $=$ (flask with liquid weight) $-$ (flask weight) $=$ 132.8 g $-$ 124.1 g $=$ 8.7 g liquid; then

$$\text{density}\,(d) = \frac{\text{mass}}{\text{volume}} = \frac{m}{V} = \frac{8.7\,\text{g}}{11.7\,\text{mL}} = 0.7\underline{4}358974\,\text{g/mL} = 0.74\,\text{g/mL}$$

Check: The units (g/mL) are correct. The magnitude of the answer (0.74) makes physical sense because the volume is greater than the mass.

1.52   **Given:** 9.55 mL liquid; empty flask weight $=$ 157.2 g; flask with liquid weight $=$ 148.4 g   **Find:** d in g/mL
Conceptual Plan: Empty flask weight, flask with liquid weight $\rightarrow$ liquid weight then weight, volume $\rightarrow$ d

$$\text{(flask with liquid weight)} - \text{(flask weight)} = \text{liquid weight} \qquad d = \text{mass}/\text{volume} = m/V$$

Solution: liquid weight $=$ (flask with liquid weight) $-$ (flask weight) $=$ 157.2 g $-$ 148.4 g $=$ 8.8 g liquid; then

$$\text{density}\,(d) = \frac{\text{mass}}{\text{volume}} = \frac{m}{V} = \frac{8.8\,\text{g}}{9.55\,\text{mL}} = 0.9\underline{2}146597\,\text{g/mL} = 0.92\,\text{g/mL}$$

Check: The units (g/mL) are correct. The magnitude of the answer (0.92) makes physical sense because the volume is slightly greater than the mass.

Unit Conversions

1.53 (a) **Given:** 27.8 L   **Find:** cm^3
Conceptual Plan: L $\rightarrow$ cm^3

$$\frac{1000\ cm^3}{1\ L}$$

Solution: $27.8\ \cancel{L} \times \dfrac{1000\ cm^3}{1\ \cancel{L}} = 2.78 \times 10^4\ cm^3$

Check: The units (cm^3) are correct. The magnitude of the answer (10^4) makes physical sense because cm^3 is much smaller than a liter; so the answer should go up several orders of magnitude. Three significant figures are allowed because of the limitation of 27.8 L (three significant figures).

(b) **Given:** 1898 mg   **Find:** kg
Conceptual Plan: mg $\rightarrow$ g $\rightarrow$ kg

$$\frac{1\ g}{1000\ mg}\quad \frac{1\ kg}{1000\ g}$$

Solution: $1898\ \cancel{mg} \times \dfrac{1\ \cancel{g}}{1000\ \cancel{mg}} \times \dfrac{1\ kg}{1000\ \cancel{g}} = 1.898 \times 10^{-3}\ kg$

Check: The units (kg) are correct. The magnitude of the answer (10^{-3}) makes physical sense because a kilogram is a much larger unit than a milligram. Four significant figures are allowed because 1898 mg has four significant figures.

(c) **Given:** 198 km   **Find:** cm
Conceptual Plan: km $\rightarrow$ m $\rightarrow$ cm

$$\frac{1000\ m}{1\ km}\quad \frac{100\ cm}{1\ m}$$

Solution: $198\ \cancel{km} \times \dfrac{1000\ \cancel{m}}{1\ \cancel{km}} \times \dfrac{100\ cm}{1\ \cancel{m}} = 1.98 \times 10^7\ cm$

Check: The units (cm) are correct. The magnitude of the answer (10^7) makes physical sense because a kilometer is a much larger unit than a centimeter. Three significant figures are allowed because 198 km has three significant figures.

1.54 (a) **Given:** 28.9 nm   **Find:** μm
Conceptual Plan: nm $\rightarrow$ m $\rightarrow$ μm

$$\frac{10^{-9}\ m}{1\ nm}\quad \frac{10^6\ \mu m}{1\ m}$$

Solution: $28.9\ \cancel{nm} \times \dfrac{10^{-9}\ \cancel{m}}{1\ \cancel{nm}} \times \dfrac{10^6\ \mu m}{1\ \cancel{m}} = 2.89 \times 10^{-2}\ \mu m = 0.0289\ \mu m$

Check: The units (μm) are correct. The magnitude of the answer (10^{-2}) makes physical sense because a micrometer is a much larger unit than a nanometer. Three significant figures are allowed because 28.9 nm has three significant figures.

(b) **Given:** 1432 cm^3 **Find:** L
Conceptual Plan: cm^3 $\rightarrow$ L

$$\frac{1\ L}{1000\ cm^3}$$

Solution: $1432\ \cancel{cm^3} \times \dfrac{1\ L}{1000\ \cancel{cm^3}} = 1.432\ L$

Check: The units (L) are correct. The magnitude of the answer (1) makes physical sense because cm^3 is much smaller than a liter so the answer should go down several orders of magnitude. Four significant figures are allowed because of the limitation of 1432 cm^3 (four significant figures).

(c) **Given:** 1211 Tm   **Find:** Gm
Conceptual Plan: Tm $\rightarrow$ m $\rightarrow$ Gm

$$\frac{10^{12}\ m}{1\ Tm}\quad \frac{10^{-9}\ Gm}{1\ m}$$

Solution: $1211 \text{ Tm} \times \dfrac{10^{12} \text{ m}}{1 \text{ Tm}} \times \dfrac{10^{-9} \text{ Gm}}{1 \text{ m}} = 1.211 \times 10^{6} \text{ Gm}$

Check: The units (Gm) are correct. The magnitude of the answer (10^6) makes physical sense because a terameter is a much larger unit than a gigameter. Four significant figures are allowed because 1211 Tm has four significant figures.

1.55   (a)   **Given:** 228 cm   **Find:** in
               Conceptual Plan: cm → in

$$\dfrac{1 \text{ in}}{2.54 \text{ cm}}$$

               Solution: $228 \text{ cm} \times \dfrac{1 \text{ in}}{2.54 \text{ cm}} = 89.76377953 \text{ in} = 89.8 \text{ in}$

               Check: The units (in) are correct. The magnitude of the answer (90) makes physical sense because an inch is a larger unit than a centimeter. Three significant figures are allowed because 228 cm has three significant figures.

    (b)   **Given:** 2.55 kg   **Find:** lb
               Conceptual Plan: kg → lb

$$\dfrac{2.2046 \text{ lb}}{1 \text{ kg}}$$

               Solution: $2.55 \text{ kg} \times \dfrac{2.2046 \text{ lb}}{1 \text{ kg}} = 5.62173 \text{ lb} = 5.62 \text{ lb}$

               Check: The units (lb) are correct. The magnitude of the answer (5.6) makes physical sense because a kilogram is a larger unit than a pound. Three significant figures are allowed because 2.55 kg has three significant figures.

    (c)   **Given:** 2.41 L   **Find:** qt
               Conceptual Plan: L → qt

$$\dfrac{1.057 \text{ qt}}{1 \text{ L}}$$

               Solution: $2.41 \text{ L} \times \dfrac{1.057 \text{ qt}}{1 \text{ L}} = 2.54737 \text{ qt} = 2.55 \text{ qt}$

               Check: The units (qt) are correct. The magnitude of the answer (2.6) makes physical sense because a liter is a smaller unit than a quart. Three significant figures are allowed because 2.41 L has three significant figures. Round the last digit up because the first nonsignificant digit is a 7.

    (d)   **Given:** 157 mm   **Find:** in
               Conceptual Plan: mm → m → in

$$\dfrac{1 \text{ m}}{1000 \text{ mm}} \qquad \dfrac{39.37 \text{ in}}{1 \text{ m}}$$

               Solution: $157 \text{ mm} \times \dfrac{1 \text{ m}}{1000 \text{ mm}} \times \dfrac{39.37 \text{ in}}{1 \text{ m}} = 6.18109 \text{ in} = 6.18 \text{ in}$

               Check: The units (in) are correct. The magnitude of the answer (6) makes physical sense because a millimeter is a much smaller unit than an inch. Three significant figures are allowed because 157 mm has three significant figures.

1.56   (a)   **Given:** 2.71 in   **Find:** mm
               Conceptual Plan: in → cm → m → mm

$$\dfrac{2.54 \text{ cm}}{1 \text{ in}} \qquad \dfrac{1 \text{ m}}{100 \text{ cm}} \qquad \dfrac{1000 \text{ mm}}{1 \text{ m}}$$

               Solution: $2.71 \text{ in} \times \dfrac{2.54 \text{ cm}}{1 \text{ in}} \times \dfrac{1 \text{ m}}{100 \text{ cm}} \times \dfrac{1000 \text{ mm}}{1 \text{ m}} = 68.834 \text{ mm} = 68.8 \text{ mm}$

               Check: The units (mm) are correct. The magnitude of the answer (69) makes physical sense because a millimeter is smaller than an inch. Three significant figures are allowed because 2.71 in has three significant figures. Truncate after the last significant digit because the first nonsignificant digit is a 3.

(b)   **Given:** 58 ft   **Find:** cm

Conceptual Plan: ft → in → cm

$$\frac{12\ \text{in}}{1\ \text{ft}} \quad \frac{2.54\ \text{cm}}{1\ \text{in}}$$

Solution: $58\ \text{ft} \times \dfrac{12\ \text{in}}{1\ \text{ft}} \times \dfrac{2.54\ \text{cm}}{1\ \text{in}} = 1.76784 \times 10^3\ \text{cm} = 1.8 \times 10^3\ \text{cm}$

Check: The units (cm) are correct. The magnitude of the answer (10^3) makes physical sense because a foot is a much larger unit than a centimeter. Two significant figures are allowed because 58 ft has three significant figures. Round the last digit up because the first nonsignificant digit is a 6.

(c)   **Given:** 2169 kg   **Find:** lb

Conceptual Plan: kg → g → lb

$$\frac{1000\ \text{g}}{1\ \text{kg}} \quad \frac{1\ \text{lb}}{453.59\ \text{g}}$$

Solution: $2169\ \text{kg} \times \dfrac{1000\ \text{g}}{1\ \text{kg}} \times \dfrac{1\ \text{lb}}{453.59\ \text{g}} = 4.78185145 \times 10^3\ \text{lb} = 4.782 \times 10^3\ \text{lb}$

Check: The units (lb) are correct. The magnitude of the answer (10^3) makes physical sense because a pound is a smaller unit than a kilogram. Four significant figures are allowed because 2169 kg has four significant figures. Round the last digit up because the first nonsignificant digit is an 8.

(d)   **Given:** 725 yd   **Find:** km

Conceptual Plan: yd → m → km

$$\frac{1\ \text{m}}{1.094\ \text{yd}} \quad \frac{1\ \text{km}}{1000\ \text{m}}$$

Solution: $725\ \text{yd} \times \dfrac{1\ \text{m}}{1.094\ \text{yd}} \times \dfrac{1\ \text{km}}{1000\ \text{m}} = 0.662705667\ \text{km} = 0.663\ \text{km}$

Check: The units (km) are correct. The magnitude of the answer (0.7) makes physical sense because a yard is a much smaller unit than a kilometer. Three significant figures are allowed because 725 yd has three significant figures. Round the last digit up because the first nonsignificant digit is a 7.

1.57   **Given:** 10.0 km   **Find:** minutes **Other:** running pace = 7.5 miles per hour

Conceptual Plan: km → mi → hr → min

$$\frac{0.6214\ \text{mi}}{1\ \text{km}} \quad \frac{1\ \text{hr}}{7.5\ \text{mi}} \quad \frac{60\ \text{min}}{1\ \text{hr}}$$

Solution: $10.0\ \text{km} \times \dfrac{0.6214\ \text{mi}}{1\ \text{km}} \times \dfrac{1\ \text{hr}}{7.5\ \text{mi}} \times \dfrac{60\ \text{min}}{1\ \text{hr}} = 49.712\ \text{min} = 50.\ \text{min} = 5.0 \times 10^1\ \text{min}$

Check: The units (min) are correct. The magnitude of the answer (50) makes physical sense because she is running almost 7.5 miles (which would take her 60 min = 1 hr). Two significant figures are allowed because of the limitation of 7.5 mi/hr (two significant figures). Round the last digit up because the first nonsignificant digit is a 7.

1.58   **Given:** 195 km   **Find:** hours **Other:** riding pace = 24 miles per hour

Conceptual Plan: km → mi → hr

$$\frac{0.6214\ \text{mi}}{1\ \text{km}} \quad \frac{1\ \text{hr}}{24\ \text{mi}}$$

Solution: $195\ \text{km} \times \dfrac{0.6214\ \text{mi}}{1\ \text{km}} \times \dfrac{1\ \text{hr}}{24\ \text{mi}} = 5.048875\ \text{hr} = 5.0\ \text{hr}$

Check: The units (hr) are correct. The magnitude of the answer (5) makes physical sense because she is riding over 100 miles (which would take her over 4 hr). Two significant figures are allowed because of the limitation of 24 mi/hr (two significant figures). Truncate after the last digit because the first nonsignificant digit is a 4.

1.59   **Given:** 14 km/L   **Find:** miles per gallon

Conceptual Plan: $\dfrac{\text{km}}{\text{L}} \rightarrow \dfrac{\text{mi}}{\text{L}} \rightarrow \dfrac{\text{mi}}{\text{gal}}$

$$\frac{0.6214\ \text{mi}}{1\ \text{km}} \quad \frac{3.785\ \text{L}}{1\ \text{gallon}}$$

Solution: $\dfrac{14\ \text{km}}{1\ \text{L}} \times \dfrac{0.6214\ \text{mi}}{1\ \text{km}} \times \dfrac{3.785\ \text{L}}{1\ \text{gallon}} = 32.927986\ \dfrac{\text{miles}}{\text{gallon}} = 33\ \dfrac{\text{miles}}{\text{gallon}}$

Check: The units (mi/gal) are correct. The magnitude of the answer (33) makes physical sense because the dominating factor is that a liter is much smaller than a gallon; so the answer should go up. Two significant figures are allowed because of the limitation of 14 km/L (two significant figures). Round the last digit up because the first nonsignificant digit is a 9.

1.60   **Given:** 5.0 gallons   **Find:** cm^3
Conceptual Plan: gal → L → cm^3

$$\frac{3.785\ L}{1\ gallon} \quad \frac{1000\ cm^3}{1\ L}$$

Solution: 5.0 gallons $\times \dfrac{3.785\ \cancel{L}}{1\ \cancel{gallon}} \times \dfrac{1000\ cm^3}{1\ \cancel{L}} = 1.8925 \times 10^4\ cm^3 = 1.9 \times 10^4\ cm^3$

Check: The units (cm^3) are correct. The magnitude of the answer (10^4) makes physical sense because cm^3 is much smaller than a gallon; so the answer should go up several orders of magnitude. Two significant figures are allowed because of the limitation of 5.0 gallons (two significant figures). Round the last digit up because the first nonsignificant digit is a 9.

1.61   (a)   **Given:** 195 m^2 **Find:** km^2
Conceptual Plan: m^2 → km^2

$$\frac{(1\ km)^2}{(1000\ m)^2}$$

Notice that for squared units, the conversion factors must be squared.

Solution: 195 $\cancel{m^2} \times \dfrac{(1\ km)^2}{(1000\ \cancel{m})^2} = 1.95 \times 10^{-4}\ km^2$

Check: The units (km^2) are correct. The magnitude of the answer (10^{-4}) makes physical sense because a kilometer is a much larger unit than a meter.

(b)   **Given:** 195 m^2 **Find:** dm^2
Conceptual Plan: m^2 → dm^2

$$\frac{(10\ dm)^2}{(1\ m)^2}$$

Notice that for squared units, the conversion factors must be squared.

Solution: 195 $\cancel{m^2} \times \dfrac{(10\ dm)^2}{(1\ \cancel{m})^2} = 1.95 \times 10^4\ dm^2$

Check: The units (dm^2) are correct. The magnitude of the answer (10^4) makes physical sense because a decimeter is a much smaller unit than a meter.

(c)   **Given:** 195 m^2 **Find:** cm^2
Conceptual Plan: m^2 → cm^2

$$\frac{(100\ cm)^2}{(1\ m)^2}$$

Notice that for squared units, the conversion factors must be squared.

Solution: 195 $\cancel{m^2} \times \dfrac{(100\ cm)^2}{(1\ \cancel{m})^2} = 1.95 \times 10^6\ cm^2$

Check: The units (cm^2) are correct. The magnitude of the answer (10^6) makes physical sense because a centimeter is a much smaller unit than a meter.

1.62   (a)   **Given:** 115 m^3 **Find:** km^3
Conceptual Plan: m^3 → km^3

$$\frac{(1\ km)^3}{(1000\ m)^3}$$

Notice that for cubed units, the conversion factors must be cubed.

Solution: 115 $\cancel{m^3} \times \dfrac{(1\ km)^3}{(1000\ \cancel{m})^3} = 1.15 \times 10^{-7}\ km^3$

Check: The units (km^3) are correct. The magnitude of the answer (10^{-7}) makes physical sense because a kilometer is a much larger unit than a meter.

(b)   **Given:** 115 m^3 **Find:** dm^3
Conceptual Plan: $m^3 \rightarrow dm^3$

$$\frac{(10\ dm)^3}{(1\ m)^3}$$

Notice that for cubed units, the conversion factors must be cubed.

Solution: $115\ m^3 \times \dfrac{(10\ dm)^3}{(1\ m)^3} = 1.15 \times 10^5\ dm^3$

Check: The units (dm^3) are correct. The magnitude of the answer (10^5) makes physical sense because a decimeter is a much smaller unit than a meter.

(c)   **Given:** 115 m^3 **Find:** cm^3
Conceptual Plan: $m^3 \rightarrow cm^3$

$$\frac{(100\ cm)^3}{(1\ m)^3}$$

Notice that for cubed units, the conversion factors must be cubed.

Solution: $115\ m^3 \times \dfrac{(100\ cm)^3}{(1\ m)^3} = 1.15 \times 10^8\ cm^3$

Check: The units (cm^3) are correct. The magnitude of the answer (10^8) makes physical sense because a centimeter is a much smaller unit than a meter.

1.63   **Given:** 435 acres   **Find:** square miles **Other:** 1 acre $= 43{,}560\ ft^2$; 1 mile $= 5280$ ft
Conceptual Plan: acres $\rightarrow ft^2 \rightarrow mi^2$

$$\frac{43560\ ft^2}{1\ acre} \quad \frac{(1\ mi)^2}{(5280\ ft)^2}$$

Notice that for squared units, the conversion factors must be squared.

Solution: $435\ acres \times \dfrac{43560\ ft^2}{1\ acres} \times \dfrac{(1\ mi)^2}{(5280\ ft)^2} = 0.6796875\ mi^2 = 0.680\ mi^2$

Check: The units (mi^2) are correct. The magnitude of the answer (0.7) makes physical sense because an acre is much smaller than a mi^2; so the answer should go down several orders of magnitude. Three significant figures are allowed because of the limitation of 435 acres (three significant figures). Round the last digit up because the first nonsignificant digit is a 6.

1.64   (a)   **Given:** 954 million acres   **Find:** square miles **Other:** 1 acre $= 43{,}560\ ft^2$; 1 mile $= 5280$ ft
Conceptual Plan: Substitute 10^6 for million then acres $\rightarrow ft^2 \rightarrow mi^2$

$$\frac{43560\ ft^2}{1\ acre} \quad \frac{(1\ mi)^2}{(5280\ ft)^2}$$

Notice that for squared units, the conversion factor must be squared.
Solution: 954 million acres $= 954 \times 10^6$ acres

$954 \times 10^6\ acres \times \dfrac{43560\ ft^2}{1\ acres} \times \dfrac{(1\ mi)^2}{(5280\ ft)^2} = 1.490625 \times 10^6\ mi^2 = 1.49 \times 10^6\ mi^2$

Check: The units (mi^2) are correct. The magnitude of the answer (10^6) makes physical sense because an acre is much smaller than a mi^2; so the answer should go down several orders of magnitude. Three significant figures are allowed because of the limitation of 954 million acres (three significant figures). Truncate the last digits because the first nonsignificant digit is a 0.

(b)   **Given:** 3.537 million square miles   **Find:** percentage of U.S. land is farmland
Conceptual Plan: Substitute 10^6 for million then % farm $= \dfrac{\text{farmland}}{\text{total land}} \times 100\%$

Note: Units of farmland and total land must be the same.
Solution: 3.537 million $mi^2 = 3.537 \times 10^6\ mi^2$

% farmland $= \dfrac{1.49 \times 10^6\ mi^2}{3.537 \times 10^6\ mi^2} \times 100\% = 42.12609556\%$ farmland $= 42.1\%$ farmland

Check: The units (%) are correct. The magnitude of the answer (42%) makes physical sense because less and less land is devoted to farmland. Three significant figures are allowed because of the limitation of 954 million acres (three significant figures). Truncate the last digit because the first nonsignificant digit is a 2.

1.65   **Given:** 14 lb   **Find:** mL **Other:** 80 mg/0.80 mL; 15 mg/kg body
Conceptual Plan: lb → kg body → mg → mL

$$\frac{1 \text{ kg body}}{2.205 \text{ lb}} \quad \frac{15 \text{ mg}}{1 \text{ kg body}} \quad \frac{0.80 \text{ mL}}{80 \text{ mg}}$$

Solution: $14 \text{ lb} \times \dfrac{1 \text{ kg body}}{2.205 \text{ lb}} \times \dfrac{15 \text{ mg}}{1 \text{ kg body}} \times \dfrac{0.80 \text{ mL}}{80 \text{ mg}} = 0.9523809524 \text{ mL} = 0.95 \text{ mL}$

Check: The units (mL) are correct. The magnitude of the answer (1 mL) makes physical sense because it is a reasonable amount of liquid to give to a baby. Two significant figures are allowed because of the statement in the problem. Truncate after the last significant digit because the first nonsignificant digit is a 2.

1.66   **Given:** 18 lb   **Find:** mL **Other:** 100 mg/5.0 mL; 10 mg/kg body
Conceptual Plan: lb → kg body → mg → mL

$$\frac{1 \text{ kg body}}{2.205 \text{ lb}} \quad \frac{10 \text{ mg}}{1 \text{ kg body}} \quad \frac{5.0 \text{ mL}}{100 \text{ mg}}$$

Solution: $18 \text{ lb} \times \dfrac{1 \text{ kg body}}{2.205 \text{ lb}} \times \dfrac{10 \text{ mg}}{1 \text{ kg body}} \times \dfrac{5.0 \text{ mL}}{100 \text{ mg}} = 4.081632653 \text{ mL} = 4.1 \text{ mL}$

Check: The units (mL) are correct. The magnitude of the answer (4 mL) makes physical sense because it is a reasonable amount of liquid to give to a baby.

Two significant figures are allowed because of the statement in the problem. Round the last digit up because the first nonsignificant digit is an 8.

Cumulative Problems

1.67   **Given:** solar year   **Find:** seconds
Other: 60 seconds/minute; 60 minutes/hour; 24 hours/solar day; 365.24 solar days/solar year
Conceptual Plan: yr → day → hr → min → sec

$$\frac{365.24 \text{ day}}{1 \text{ solar yr}} \quad \frac{24 \text{ hr}}{1 \text{ day}} \quad \frac{60 \text{ min}}{1 \text{ hr}} \quad \frac{60 \text{ sec}}{1 \text{ min}}$$

Solution: $1 \text{ solar yr} \times \dfrac{365.24 \text{ day}}{1 \text{ solar yr}} \times \dfrac{24 \text{ hr}}{1 \text{ day}} \times \dfrac{60 \text{ min}}{1 \text{ hr}} \times \dfrac{60 \text{ sec}}{1 \text{ min}} = 3.1556736 \times 10^7 \text{ sec} = 3.1557 \times 10^7 \text{ sec}$

Check: The units (sec) are correct. The magnitude of the answer (10^7) makes physical sense because each conversion factor increases the value of the answer—a second is many orders of magnitude smaller than a year. Five significant figures are allowed because all conversion factors are assumed to be exact except for the 365.24 days/solar year (five significant figures). Round the last digit up because the first nonsignificant digit is a 7.

1.68   **Given:** 2.0 hours   **Find:** picoseconds **Other:** 60 seconds/minute; 60 minutes/hour
Conceptual Plan: hr → min → s → ps

$$\frac{60 \text{ min}}{1 \text{ hr}} \quad \frac{60 \text{ s}}{1 \text{ min}} \quad \frac{10^{12} \text{ ps}}{1 \text{ s}}$$

Solution: $2.0 \text{ hr} \times \dfrac{60 \text{ min}}{1 \text{ hr}} \times \dfrac{60 \text{ s}}{1 \text{ min}} \times \dfrac{10^{12} \text{ ps}}{1 \text{ s}} = 7.2 \times 10^{15} \text{ ps}$

Check: The units (ps) are correct. The magnitude of the answer (10^{15}) makes physical sense because each conversion factor increases the value of the answer—a picosecond is many orders of magnitude smaller than a second. Two significant figures are allowed because all conversion factors are assumed to be exact. There are two significant figures in 2.0 hours.

1.69   (a)   Extensive—The volume of a material depends on how much is present.
(b)   Intensive—The boiling point of a material is independent of how much material you have; so these values can be published in reference tables.
(c)   Intensive—The temperature of a material is independent of how much is present.
(d)   Intensive—The electrical conductivity of a material is independent of how much material you have; so these values can be published in reference tables.

(e)   Extensive—The energy contained in material depends on how much is present. If you double the amount of material, you double the amount of energy.

1.70   **Given:** $°C = \dfrac{°F - 32}{1.8}$ **Find:** temperature where $°F = °C$

Conceptual Plan: $°C = \dfrac{°F - 32}{1.8}$ set $°C = °F = x$ **and solve for** x

Solution: $x = \dfrac{x - 32 \; °F}{1.8} \rightarrow 1.8\,x = x - 32 \rightarrow 1.8\,x - x = -32 \rightarrow 0.8\,x = -32 \rightarrow x = -32/0.8 = $

$-40. \rightarrow -40. \; °F = -40. \; °C$

Check: The units ($°F$ and $°C$) are correct. Plugging the result back into the equation confirms that the calculations were done correctly. The magnitude of the answer seems correct because it is known that the result is not between $0 \; °C$ and $100 \; °C$. The numbers are getting closer together as the temperature drops.

1.71   **Given:** $130 \; °X = 212 \; °F$ and $10 \; °X = 32 \; °F$ **Find:** temperature where $°X = °F$.
Conceptual Plan: Use data to derive an equation relating $°X$ **and** $°F$. **Then set** $°F = °X = z$ **and solve for** z.
Solution: Assume a linear relationship between the two temperatures ($y = mx + b$).
Let $y = °F$ and let $x = °X$.
The slope of the line (m) is the relative change in the two temperature scales:

$$m = \frac{\Delta \; °F}{\Delta \; °X} = \frac{212 \; °F - 32 \; °F}{130 \; °X - 10 \; °X} = \frac{180 \; °F}{120 \; °X} = 1.5$$

Solve for intercept (b) by plugging one set of temperatures into the equation:
$y = 1.5x + b \rightarrow 32 = (1.5)(10) + b \rightarrow 32 = 15 + b \rightarrow b = 17 \rightarrow °F = (1.5) \; °X + 17$
Set $°F = °X = z$ and solve for z.
$z = 1.5z + 17 \rightarrow -17 = 1.5z - z \rightarrow -17 = 0.5z \rightarrow z = -34 \rightarrow -34 \; °F = -34 \; °X$

Check: The units ($°F$ and $°X$) are correct. Plugging the result back into the equation confirms that the calculations were done correctly. The magnitude of the answer seems correct because it is known that the result is not between $32 \; °F$ and $212 \; °F$. The numbers are getting closer together as the temperature drops.

1.72   **Given:** $17 \; °J = 0 \; °H$ and $97 \; °J = 120 \; °H$ **Find:** temperature where methyl alcohol boils in $°J$
Other: methyl alcohol boils at $84 \; °H$
Conceptual Plan: Use data to derive an equation relating $°J$ **and** $°H$. **Then set** $°H = 84 \; °H$ **and solve for** $°J$.
Solution: Assume a linear relationship between the two temperatures ($y = mx + b$).
Let $y = °J$ and let $x = °H$.
The slope of the line (m) is the relative change in the two temperature scales.

$$m = \frac{\Delta \; °J}{\Delta \; °H} = \frac{97 \; °J - 17 \; °J}{120 \; °H - 0 \; °H} = \frac{80 \; °J}{120 \; °H} = 0.66\underline{7}$$

Solve for intercept (b) by plugging one set of temperatures into the equation:
$y = 0.66\underline{7}x + b \rightarrow 17 = (0.667)(0) + b \rightarrow b = 17 \rightarrow °J = (0.66\underline{7}) \; °H + 17$
Set $°H = 84 \; °H$ and solve for $°J$.
$°J = (0.667)(84) + 17 \rightarrow °J = 56 + 17 = 73 \; °J$

Check: The units ($°J$) are correct. Plugging the original data points back into the equation confirms that the calculations were done correctly. The magnitude of the answer seems correct because the result should be between $17 \; °J$ and $97 \; °J$ and closer to $97 \; °J$ than $17 \; °J$.

1.73   (a) $1.76 \times 10^{-3}/8.0 \times 10^{2} = 2.2 \times 10^{-6}$ Two significant figures are allowed to reflect the quantity with the fewest significant figures (8.0×10^{2}).

(b)   Write all figures so that the decimal points can be aligned:
         0.0187
        +0.0002 All quantities are known to four places to the right of the decimal place;
        $\underline{-0.0030}$ so the answer should be reported to four places to the right of the
         0.0159 decimal place, or three significant figures.

(c) $[(136000)(0.000322)/0.082)](129.2) = 6.899910244 \times 10^{4} = 6.9 \times 10^{4}$ Round the intermediate answer to two significant figures to reflect the quantity with the fewest significant figures (0.082). Round the last digit up because the first nonsignificant digit is 9.

1.74   **Given:** one gallon of gasoline   **Find:** US dollars **Other:** 1 euro = \$1.38 US and

1 liter of gasoline in France = 1.35 euro

Conceptual Plan: gal → L → euro → \$ US

$$\frac{3.785 \text{ L}}{1 \text{ gallon}} \quad \frac{1.35 \text{ euro}}{1 \text{ L}} \quad \frac{\$ 1.38 \text{ US}}{1 \text{ euro}}$$

Solution: $1 \text{ gallon} \times \dfrac{3.785 \text{ L}}{1 \text{ gallon}} \times \dfrac{1.35 \text{ euro}}{1 \text{ L}} \times \dfrac{\$ 1.38 \text{ US}}{1 \text{ euro}} = \$ 7.05\underline{1}455 \text{ US} = \$ 7.05 \text{ US}$

Check: The units (\$ US) are correct. The magnitude of the answer (\$7 US) makes physical sense because the domi-nating conversion factor is ~4. Three significant figures are allowed because of the limitation of 1.35 euro/L. Truncate after the last significant digit because the first nonsignificant digit is a 1.

1.75   (a)   **Given:** cylinder dimensions: length = 22 cm; radius = 3.8 cm; d(gold) = 19.3 g/cm^3; d(sand) = 3.00 g/cm^3

Find: m(gold) and m(sand)

Conceptual Plan: $l, r \rightarrow V$ **then** $d, V \rightarrow m$

$$V = l\pi r^2 \qquad d = m/V$$

Solution: V(gold) = V(sand) = $(22 \text{ cm})(\pi)(3.8 \text{ cm})^2 = 99\underline{8}.0212 \text{ cm}^3$

$d = m/V$ Rearrange by multiplying both sides of equation by $V. \rightarrow m = d \times V$

$$m\text{(gold)} = \left(19.3 \frac{\text{g}}{\text{cm}^3}\right) \times (99\underline{8}.0212 \text{ cm}^3) = 1.\underline{9}26181 \times 10^4 \text{ g} = 1.9 \times 10^4 \text{ g}$$

Check: The units (g) are correct. The magnitude of the answer seems correct considering that the value of the density is ~20 g/cm^3. Two significant figures are allowed to reflect the significant figures in 22 cm and 3.8 cm. Truncate the nonsignificant digits because the first nonsignificant digit is a 2.

$$m\text{(sand)} = \left(3.00 \frac{\text{g}}{\text{cm}^3}\right) \times (99\underline{8}.0212 \text{ cm}^3) = 2.\underline{9}9406 \times 10^3 \text{ g} = 3.0 \times 10^3 \text{ g}$$

Check: The units (g) are correct. The magnitude of the answer seems correct considering that the value of the density is 3 g/cm^3. This number is much lower than the gold mass. Two significant figures are allowed to reflect the significant figures in 22 cm and 3.8 cm. Round the last digit up because the first nonsignificant digit is a 9.

(b)   Comparing the two values 1.9×10^4 g versus 3.0×10^3 g shows a difference in weight of almost a factor of 10. This difference should be enough to trip the alarm and alert the authorities to the presence of the thief.

1.76   **Given:** $r = 1.0 \times 10^{-13}$ cm; $m = 1.7 \times 10^{-24}$ g   **Find:** density **Other:** $V = (4/3)\pi r^3$

Conceptual Plan: $r \rightarrow V$ **then** $m, V \rightarrow d$

$$V = (4/3)\pi r^3 \qquad d = m/V$$

Solution: $V = (4/3)\pi r^3 = (4/3)(\pi)(1.0 \times 10^{-13} \text{ cm})^3 = 4.1\underline{8}8790205 \times 10^{-39} \text{ cm}^3$

$$d = \frac{m}{V} = \frac{1.7 \times 10^{-24} \text{ g}}{4.188790205 \times 10^{-39} \text{ cm}^3} = 4.0\underline{5}8451049 \times 10^{14} \frac{\text{g}}{\text{cm}^3} = 4.1 \times 10^{14} \frac{\text{g}}{\text{cm}^3}$$

Check: The units (g/cm^3) are correct. The magnitude of the answer seems correct considering how small a nucleus is compared to an atom. Two significant figures are allowed to reflect the significant figures in 1.0×10^{-13} cm. Round the last digit up because the first nonsignificant digit is a 5.

1.77   **Given:** 3.5 lb of titanium; density (titanium) = 4.51 g/cm^3 **Find:** volume in in^3

Conceptual Plan: lb → g **then** $m, d \rightarrow V$ **then** cm^3 → in^3

$$\frac{453.59 \text{ g}}{1 \text{ lb}} \qquad d = m/V \qquad \frac{(1 \text{ in})^3}{(2.54 \text{ cm})^3}$$

Solution: $3.5 \text{ lb} \times \dfrac{453.59 \text{ g}}{1 \text{ lb}} = 1.\underline{5}876 \times 10^3 \text{ g}$

$d = m/V$ Rearrange by multiplying both sides of the equation by V and dividing both sides of the equation by d.

$$V = \frac{m}{d} = \frac{1.\underline{5}876 \times 10^3 \text{ g}}{4.51 \dfrac{\text{g}}{\text{cm}^3}} = 3.\underline{5}20 \times 10^2 \text{ cm}^3 = 3.5 \times 10^2 \text{ cm}^3 \times \frac{(1 \text{ in})^3}{(2.54 \text{ cm})^3} = 21.\underline{4}80 \text{ in}^3 = 21 \text{ in}^3$$

Check: The units (in^3) are correct. The magnitude of the answer seems correct considering how many grams we have. Two significant figures are allowed to reflect the significant figures in 3.5 lb. Truncate the nonsignificant digits be-cause the first nonsignificant digit is a 4.

1.78   **Given:** density (g/cm³); density (iron) = 7.86 g/cm³   **Find:** density (lb/in³)

Conceptual Plan: $\dfrac{g}{cm^3} \rightarrow \dfrac{lb}{cm^3} \rightarrow \dfrac{lb}{in^3}$

$\dfrac{1 \text{ lb}}{453.59 \text{ g}}$ $\dfrac{(2.54 \text{ cm})^3}{(1 \text{ in})^3}$

Solution: $\dfrac{7.86 \text{ g}}{cm^3} \times \dfrac{1 \text{ lb}}{453.59 \text{ g}} \times \dfrac{(2.54 \text{ cm})^3}{(1 \text{ in})^3} = 0.283961999 \dfrac{lb}{in^3} = 0.284 \dfrac{lb}{in^3}$

Check: The units (lb/in³) are correct. The magnitude of the answer seems correct considering that the dominating factor is that a gram is smaller than a pound; so the answer should go down. Three significant figures are allowed to reflect the significant figures in 7.86 (g/cm³). Round the last digit up because the first nonsignificant digit is a 9.

1.79   **Given:** cylinder dimensions: length = 2.16 in; radius = 0.22 in; m = 41 g   **Find:** density (g/m³)

Conceptual Plan: in $\rightarrow$ cm then $l, r \rightarrow V$ then $m, V \rightarrow d$

$\dfrac{2.54 \text{ cm}}{1 \text{ in}}$ $V = l\pi r^2$ $d = m/V$

Solution: $2.16 \text{ in} \times \dfrac{2.54 \text{ cm}}{1 \text{ in}} = 5.4864 \text{ cm} = l$ $\qquad 0.22 \text{ in} \times \dfrac{2.54 \text{ cm}}{1 \text{ in}} = 0.5588 \text{ cm} = r$

$V = l\pi r^2 = (5.4864 \text{ cm})(\pi)(0.5588 \text{ cm})^2 = 5.3820798 \text{ cm}^3$

$d = \dfrac{m}{V} = \dfrac{41 \text{ g}}{5.3820798 \text{ cm}^3} = 7.6178729 \dfrac{g}{cm^3} = 7.6 \dfrac{g}{cm^3}$

Check: The units (g/cm³) are correct. The magnitude of the answer seems correct considering that the value of the density of iron (a major component in steel) is 7.86 g/cm³. Two significant figures are allowed to reflect the significant figures in 0.22 in and 41 g. Truncate the nonsignificant digits because the first nonsignificant digit is a 1.

1.80   **Given:** m = 85 g; density (aluminum) = 2.70 g/cm³   **Find:** radius of the sphere (inches)

Conceptual Plan: $m, d \rightarrow V$ then $V \rightarrow r$ then cm $\rightarrow$ in

$d = m/V$ $V = (4/3)\pi r^3$ $\dfrac{1 \text{ in}}{2.54 \text{ cm}}$

Solution: $d = m/V$ Rearrange by multiplying both sides of the equation by V and dividing both sides of the equation by d.

$V = \dfrac{m}{d} = \dfrac{85 \text{ g}}{2.70 \dfrac{g}{cm^3}} = 31.48148148 \text{ cm}^3$

$V = (4/3)\pi r^3$ Rearrange by dividing both sides of the equation by $(4/3)\pi$. $r^3 = \dfrac{3V}{4\pi}$
Take the cube root of both sides of the equation.

$r = \left(\dfrac{3V}{4\pi}\right)^{1/3} = \left(\dfrac{(3)(31.48148148 \text{ cm}^3)}{4\pi}\right)^{1/3} = (7.51565009 \text{ cm}^3)^{1/3} = 1.958794386 \text{ cm}$

$1.958794386 \text{ cm} \times \dfrac{1 \text{ in}}{2.54 \text{ cm}} = 0.7711788923 \text{ in} = 0.77 \text{ in}$

Check: The units (in) are correct. The magnitude of the answer seems correct. The magnitude of the volume is about a third of the mass (density is about 3 g/cm³). The radius (in cm) seems correct considering the geometry involved. The magnitude goes down when we convert from centimeters to inches because an inch is bigger than a centimeter. Two significant figures are allowed to reflect the significant figures in 2.70 g/cm³ and 85 g. Truncate the nonsignificant digits because the first nonsignificant digit is a 1.

1.81   **Given:** 185 cubic yards (yd³) of H_2O **Find:** mass of the H_2O (pounds)
Other: $d(H_2O)$ = 1.00 g/cm³ at 4 °C
Conceptual Plan: yd³ $\rightarrow$ m³ $\rightarrow$ cm³ $\rightarrow$ g $\rightarrow$ lb

$\dfrac{(1 \text{ m})^3}{(1.094 \text{ yd})^3}$ $\dfrac{(100 \text{ cm})^3}{(1 \text{ m})^3}$ $\dfrac{1.00 \text{ g}}{1.00 \text{ cm}^3}$ $\dfrac{1 \text{ lb}}{453.59 \text{ g}}$

Solution: $185 \text{ yd}^3 \times \dfrac{(1 \text{ m})^3}{(1.094 \text{ yd})^3} \times \dfrac{(100 \text{ cm})^3}{(1 \text{ m})^3} \times \dfrac{1.00 \text{ g}}{1.00 \text{ cm}^3} \times \dfrac{1 \text{ lb}}{453.59 \text{ g}} = 3.114987377 \times 10^5 \text{ lb} = 3.11 \times 10^5 \text{ lb}$

Check: The units (lb) are correct. The magnitude of the answer (10^5) makes physical sense because a pool is not a small object. Three significant figures are allowed because the conversion factor with the least precision is the density (1.00 g/cm^3 − 3 significant figures) and the initial size has three significant figures. Truncate after the last digit because the first nonsignificant digit is a 4.

1.82   **Given:** 7655 cubic feet (ft^3) of ice   **Find:** mass of the ice (kg) **Other:** $d(\text{ice}) = 0.917 \text{ g/cm}^3$ at 0 °C.

     Conceptual Plan: $\text{ft}^3 \rightarrow \text{cm}^3 \rightarrow \text{g} \rightarrow \text{kg}$

$$\frac{(30.48 \text{ cm})^3}{(1 \text{ ft})^3} \quad \frac{0.917 \text{ g}}{1.00 \text{ cm}^3} \quad \frac{1 \text{ kg}}{1000 \text{ g}}$$

     Solution: $7655 \text{ ft}^3 \times \dfrac{(30.48 \text{ cm})^3}{(1 \text{ ft})^3} \times \dfrac{0.917 \text{ g}}{1.00 \text{ cm}^3} \times \dfrac{1 \text{ kg}}{1000 \text{ g}} = 1.9\underline{8}7739274 \times 10^5 \text{ kg} = 1.99 \times 10^5 \text{ kg}$

     Check: The units (kg) are correct. The magnitude of the answer (10^5) makes physical sense because an iceberg is a large object. Three significant figures are allowed because the conversion factor with the least precision is the density (0.917 g/cm^3 − 3 significant figures). Round the last digit up because the first nonsignificant digit is a 7.

1.83   **Given:** 15 liters of gasoline   **Find:** kilometers **Other:** 52 mi/gal in the city

     Conceptual Plan: $\text{L} \rightarrow \text{gal} \rightarrow \text{mi} \rightarrow \text{km}$

$$\frac{1 \text{ gallon}}{3.785 \text{ L}} \quad \frac{52 \text{ mi}}{1 \text{ gallon}} \quad \frac{1 \text{ km}}{0.6214 \text{ mi}}$$

     Solution: $15 \text{ L} \times \dfrac{1 \text{ gallon}}{3.785 \text{ L}} \times \dfrac{52 \text{ mi}}{1 \text{ gallon}} \times \dfrac{1 \text{ km}}{0.6214 \text{ mi}} = 3.\underline{3}16327941 \times 10^2 \text{ km} = 3.3 \times 10^2 \text{ km}$

     Check: The units (km) are correct. The magnitude of the answer (10^2) makes physical sense because the dominating conversion factor is the mileage, which increases the answer. Two significant figures are allowed because the conversion factor with the least precision is 52 mi/gallon (two significant figures) and the initial volume (15 L) has two significant figures. Truncate the last digit because the first nonsignificant digit is a 1. It is best to put the answer in scientific notation so that it is clear how many significant figures are expressed.

1.84   **Given:** 355 mL of gasoline   **Find:** kilometers **Other:** 57 mi/gal in the city

     Conceptual Plan: $\text{mL} \rightarrow \text{L} \rightarrow \text{gal} \rightarrow \text{mi} \rightarrow \text{km}$

$$\frac{1 \text{ L}}{1000 \text{ mL}} \quad \frac{1 \text{ gallon}}{3.785 \text{ L}} \quad \frac{57 \text{ mi}}{1 \text{ gallon}} \quad \frac{1 \text{ km}}{0.6214 \text{ mi}}$$

     Solution: $355 \text{ mL} \times \dfrac{1 \text{ L}}{1000 \text{ mL}} \times \dfrac{1 \text{ gallon}}{3.785 \text{ L}} \times \dfrac{57 \text{ mi}}{1 \text{ gallon}} \times \dfrac{1 \text{ km}}{0.6214 \text{ mi}} = 8.603319984 \text{ km} = 8.6 \text{ km}$

     Check: The units (km) are correct. The magnitude of the answer (8.6) makes physical sense because the dominating conversion factor is the conversion from mL to L, which decreases the answer. Two significant figures are allowed because the conversion factor with the least precision is 57 mi/gallon (two significant figures). Truncate the last digit because the first nonsignificant digit is a 0.

1.85   **Given:** radius of nucleus of the hydrogen atom $= 1.0 \times 10^{-13}$ cm; radius of the hydrogen atom $= 52.9$ pm

     Find: fractional volume occupied by nucleus

     Conceptual Plan: $\text{cm} \rightarrow \text{m}$ then $\text{pm} \rightarrow \text{m}$ then $r \rightarrow V$ then $V_{atom}, V_{nucleus} \rightarrow$ fractional volume occupied

$$\frac{1 \text{ m}}{100 \text{ cm}} \quad \frac{1 \text{ m}}{10^{12} \text{ pm}} \quad V = (4/3)\pi r^3 \quad \frac{V_{nucleus}}{V_{atom}}$$

     Solution: $1.0 \times 10^{-13} \text{ cm} \times \dfrac{1 \text{ m}}{100 \text{ cm}} = 1.0 \times 10^{-15}$ m and $52.9 \text{ pm} \times \dfrac{1 \text{ m}}{10^{12} \text{ pm}} = 5.29 \times 10^{-11}$ m

     $V = (4/3)\pi r^3$ Substitute into fractional volume equation.

     $\dfrac{V_{nucleus}}{V_{atom}} = \dfrac{(4/3)\,\pi r_{nucleus}^3}{(4/3)\,\pi r_{atom}^3}$ Simplify equation.

     $\dfrac{V_{nucleus}}{V_{atom}} = \dfrac{r_{nucleus}^3}{r_{atom}^3}$ Substitute numbers and calculate result.

     $\dfrac{V_{nucleus}}{V_{atom}} = \dfrac{(1.0 \times 10^{-15} \text{ m})^3}{(5.29 \times 10^{-11} \text{ m})^3} = (1.890359168 \times 10^{-5})^3 = 6.\underline{7}55118686 \times 10^{-15} = 6.8 \times 10^{-15}$

Check: The units (none) are correct. The magnitude of the answer seems correct (10^{-15}) because a proton is so small. Two significant figures are allowed to reflect the significant figures in 1.0×10^{-15} cm. Round the last digits up because the first nonsignificant digit is a 5.

1.86   **Given:** radius of neon = 69 pm; 2.69×10^{22} atoms per liter   **Find:** fractional volume occupied by neon
Conceptual Plan: Assume 1 L total volume.
pm $\rightarrow$ m $\rightarrow$ cm then $r \rightarrow V$ then $cm^3 \rightarrow$ L then L/atom $\rightarrow$ L then V_{Ne}, V_{Total} $\rightarrow$ fraction occupied by neon

$$\frac{1 \text{ m}}{10^{12} \text{ pm}} \quad \frac{100 \text{ cm}}{1 \text{ m}} \qquad V = (4/3)\pi r^3 = 1 \text{ atom} \qquad \frac{1 \text{ L}}{1000 \text{ cm}^3} \qquad 2.69 \times 10^{22} \text{ atoms} \qquad \frac{V_{Ne}}{V_{Total}}$$

Solution: $69 \text{ pm} \times \dfrac{1 \text{ m}}{10^{12} \text{ pm}} \times \dfrac{100 \text{ cm}}{1 \text{ m}} = 6.9 \times 10^{-9}$ cm

$V = (4/3)\pi r^3 = (4/3)\pi(6.9 \times 10^{-9} \text{ cm})^3 = 1.\underline{3}7605528 \times 10^{-24} \text{ cm}^3$

$1.\underline{3}7605528 \times 10^{-24} \text{ cm}^3 \times \dfrac{1 \text{ L}}{1000 \text{ cm}^3} = 1.\underline{3}7605528 \times 10^{-27}$ L

$\dfrac{1.\underline{3}7605528 \times 10^{-27} \text{ L}}{\text{atom}} \times 2.69 \times 10^{22} \text{ atoms} = 3.\underline{7}01588707 \times 10^{-5}$ L Substitute into fractional volume equation.

$\dfrac{V_{Ne}}{V_{Total}} = \dfrac{3.\underline{7}01588707 \times 10^{-5} \text{ L}}{1 \text{ L}} = 3.\underline{7}01588707 \times 10^{-5} = 3.7 \times 10^{-5}$

This says that the separation between atoms is very large in the gas phase.

Check: The units (none) are correct. The magnitude of the answer seems correct (10^{-5}); it is known that gases are primarily empty space. Two significant figures are allowed to reflect the significant figures in 69 pm. Truncate the nonsignificant digits because the first nonsignificant digit is a 0.

1.87   **Given:** 24.0 kg copper wire; wire is a cylinder of radius = 1.63 mm   **Find:** resistance (Ω)
Other: d(copper) = 8.96 g/cm^3; resistance = 2.061 Ω/km
Conceptual Plan: mm $\rightarrow$ m $\rightarrow$ cm and kg $\rightarrow$ g then

$$\frac{10^{-3} \text{ m}}{1 \text{ mm}} \quad \frac{100 \text{ cm}}{1 \text{ m}} \qquad \frac{1000 \text{ g}}{1 \text{ kg}}$$

$d, m \rightarrow V$ then $V, r \rightarrow l$(cm) $\rightarrow$ m $\rightarrow$ km $\rightarrow \Omega$

$$d = m/V \qquad V = l\pi r^2 \quad \frac{1 \text{ m}}{100 \text{ cm}} \quad \frac{1 \text{ km}}{1000 \text{ m}} \quad \frac{2.061 \, \Omega}{1 \text{ km}}$$

Solution: $1.63 \text{ mm} \times \dfrac{10^{-3} \text{ m}}{1 \text{ mm}} \times \dfrac{100 \text{ cm}}{1 \text{ m}} = 0.163 \text{ cm}$ $24.0 \text{ kg} \times \dfrac{1000 \text{ g}}{1 \text{ kg}} = 2.40 \times 10^4 \text{ g}$ then $d = m/V$

Rearrange by multiplying both sides of equation by V to get $m = d \times V$ then divide both sides by d.

$V = \dfrac{m}{d} = \dfrac{2.40 \times 10^4 \text{ g}}{\dfrac{8.96 \text{ g}}{1 \text{ cm}^3}} = 2.6\underline{7}85714 \times 10^3 \text{ cm}^3$ then $V = l\pi r^2$

Rearrange by dividing both sides of the equation by πr^2 to get

$l = \dfrac{V}{\pi r^2} = \dfrac{2.6\underline{7}85714 \times 10^3 \text{ cm}^3}{\pi(0.163 \text{ cm})^2} = 3.2\underline{0}90623 \times 10^4 \text{ cm}$ then

$3.2\underline{0}90623 \times 10^4 \text{ cm} \times \dfrac{1 \text{ m}}{100 \text{ cm}} \times \dfrac{1 \text{ km}}{1000 \text{ m}} \times \dfrac{2.061 \, \Omega}{1 \text{ km}} = 0.6\underline{6}13877 \, \Omega = 0.661 \, \Omega$

Check: The units (Ω) are correct. The magnitude of the answer seems correct because we expect a small resistance for a material that is commonly used for electrical wiring. Three significant figures are allowed to reflect the significant figures in 1.63 mm and 24.0 kg. Truncate the nonsignificant digits because the first nonsignificant digit is a 3.

1.88   **Given:** aluminum foil; 304 mm wide and 0.016 mm thick; 1.10 kg   **Find:** length of foil
Other: d(aluminum) = 2.70 g/cm^3
Conceptual Plan: for each dimension mm $\rightarrow$ m $\rightarrow$ cm and kg $\rightarrow$ g then

$$\frac{10^{-3} \text{ m}}{1 \text{ mm}} \quad \frac{100 \text{ cm}}{1 \text{ m}} \qquad \frac{1000 \text{ g}}{1 \text{ kg}}$$

$d, m \rightarrow V$ then $V, w, h \rightarrow l(\text{cm}) \rightarrow m$

$$d = m/V \qquad V = l\,\pi\,r^2 \qquad \frac{1\text{ m}}{100\text{ cm}}$$

Solution: $304 \text{ mm} \times \dfrac{10^{-3}\text{ m}}{1\text{ mm}} \times \dfrac{100\text{ cm}}{1\text{ m}} = 30.4\text{ cm}$ and $0.016 \text{ mm} \times \dfrac{10^{-3}\text{ m}}{1\text{ mm}} \times \dfrac{100\text{ cm}}{1\text{ m}} = 0.0016\text{ cm}$

$1.10 \text{ kg} \times \dfrac{1000\text{ g}}{1\text{ kg}} = 1.10 \times 10^3 \text{ g}$ then $d = m/V$

Rearrange by multiplying both sides of the equation by V to get

$m = d \times V$ then divide both sides by d. $V = \dfrac{m}{d} = \dfrac{1.10 \times 10^3 \text{ g}}{\dfrac{2.70 \text{ g}}{1\text{ cm}^3}} = 407.\underline{4}0741 \text{ cm}^3$ then $V = lwh$

Rearrange by dividing both sides of equation by $(w\,h)$ to get

$l = \dfrac{V}{w\,h} = \dfrac{407.\underline{4}0741 \text{ cm}^3}{(30.4\text{ cm})\,(0.0016\text{ cm})} = 8.\underline{3}7597 \times 10^3 \text{ cm}$ then

$8.\underline{3}7597 \times 10^4 \text{ cm} \times \dfrac{1\text{ m}}{100\text{ cm}} = 8.\underline{3}7597 \times 10^1 \text{ m} = 8.4 \times 10^1 \text{ m} = 84\text{ m}$

Check: The units (m) are correct. The magnitude of the answer seems correct because we expect a long length of the foil. Two significant figures are allowed to reflect the significant figures in 0.016 mm. Round the last digit up because the first nonsignificant digit is 7.

1.89   **Given:** d(liquid nitrogen) = 0.808 g/mL; d(gaseous nitrogen) = 1.15 g/L; 175 L liquid nitrogen; 10.00 m × 10.00 m × 2.50 m room   **Find:** fraction of room air displaced by nitrogen gas

Conceptual Plan: L → mL then $V_{\text{liquid}}, d_{\text{liquid}} \rightarrow m_{\text{liquid}}$ **then set** $m_{\text{liquid}} = m_{\text{gas}}$ **then** $m_{\text{gas}}, d_{\text{gas}} \rightarrow V_{\text{gas}}$ **then**

$$\frac{1000\text{ mL}}{1\text{ L}} \qquad\qquad d = m/V \qquad\qquad d = m/V$$

Calculate the $V_{\text{room}} \rightarrow \text{cm}^3 \rightarrow \text{L}$ **then calculate the fraction displaced**

$$V = l \times w \times h \quad \frac{(100\text{ cm})^3}{(1\text{ m})^3} \quad \frac{1\text{ L}}{1000\text{ cm}^3} \qquad\qquad \frac{V_{\text{gas}}}{V_{\text{room}}}$$

Solution: $175 \text{ L} \times \dfrac{1000\text{ mL}}{1\text{ L}} = 1.75 \times 10^5 \text{ mL}$. Solve for m by multiplying both sides of the equation by V.

$m = V \times d = 1.75 \times 10^5 \text{ mL} \times \dfrac{0.808\text{ g}}{1\text{ mL}} = 1.4\underline{1}4 \times 10^5 \text{ g}$ nitrogen liquid $= 1.4\underline{1}4 \times 10^5 \text{ g}$ nitrogen gas

$d = m/V$ Rearrange by multiplying both sides of the equation by V and dividing both sides of the equation by d.

$V = \dfrac{m}{d} = \dfrac{1.4\underline{1}4 \times 10^5 \text{ g}}{1.15\,\dfrac{\text{g}}{\text{L}}} = 1.2\underline{2}9565 \times 10^5 \text{ L}$ nitrogen gas

$V_{\text{room}} = l \times w \times h = 10.00 \text{ m} \times 10.00 \text{ m} \times 2.50 \text{ m} \times \dfrac{(100\text{ cm})^3}{(1\text{ m})^3} \times \dfrac{1\text{ L}}{1000\text{ cm}^3} = 2.50 \times 10^5 \text{ L}$

$\dfrac{V_{\text{gas}}}{V_{\text{room}}} = \dfrac{1.2\underline{2}9565 \times 10^5 \text{ L}}{2.50 \times 10^5 \text{ L}} = 0.491\underline{8}26 = 0.492$

Check: The units (none) are correct. The magnitude of the answer seems correct (0.5) because there is a large volume of liquid and the density of the gas is about a factor of 1000 less than the density of the liquid. Three significant figures are allowed to reflect the significant figures in the densities and the volume of the liquid given.

1.90   **Given:** d(mercury at 0.0 °C) = 13.596 g/cm³; d(mercury at 25.0 °C) = 13.534 g/cm³; 3.380 g; 0.200 mm diameter capillary   **Find:** distance mercury rises

Conceptual Plan: at each temperature $m, d \rightarrow V$ **then mm → m → cm then** $V, r \rightarrow h$

$$d = m/V \qquad \frac{1\text{ m}}{1000\text{ mm}} \quad \frac{100\text{ cm}}{1\text{ m}} \qquad V = \pi r^2 h$$

then calculate the difference between the two heights

Solution: $d = m/V$ Rearrange by multiplying both sides of the equation by V and dividing both sides of the equation by d. $V = \dfrac{m}{d}$

at 0.0 °C: $V = \dfrac{m}{d} = \dfrac{3.380 \text{ g}}{13.596 \dfrac{\text{g}}{\text{cm}^3}} = 0.24860253 \text{ cm}^3$

and at 25.0 °C: $V = \dfrac{m}{d} = \dfrac{3.380 \text{ g}}{13.534 \dfrac{\text{g}}{\text{cm}^3}} = 0.249741392 \text{ cm}^3$

$r = 0.200 \text{ mm} \times \dfrac{1 \text{ m}}{1000 \text{ mm}} \times \dfrac{100 \text{ cm}}{1 \text{ m}} = 0.0200 \text{ cm}$ then $V = \pi r^2 h$.

Rearrange by dividing both sides of the equation by πr^2. $h = \dfrac{V}{\pi r^2}$

at 0.0 °C: $h = \dfrac{V}{\pi r^2} = \dfrac{0.24860253 \text{ cm}^3}{\pi \, (0.0200 \text{ cm})^2} = 197.83161 \text{ cm}$

and at 25.0 °C: $h = \dfrac{V}{\pi r^2} = \dfrac{0.249741392 \text{ cm}^3}{\pi \, (0.0200 \text{ cm})^2} = 198.73789 \text{ cm}$

The difference in height is $198.737885 \text{ cm} - 197.831608 \text{ cm} = 0.906277 \text{ cm} = 1 \text{ cm}$.

Check: The units (cm) are correct. The magnitude of the answer seems correct (1) because there is a relatively small change in temperature and the two densities are very close to each other. Only one significant figure is allowed because the heights have four significant figures; so the error is in the ones place.

Challenge Problems

1.91   **Given:** mass of black hole (BH) = 1×10^3 suns; radius of black hole = one-half the radius of our moon
Find: density (g/cm³) **Other:** radius of our sun = 7.0×10^5 km; average density of our sun = 1.4×10^3 kg/m³; diameter of the moon = 2.16×10^3 mi
Conceptual Plan: $d_{BH} = m_{BH}/V_{BH}$
Calculate m_{BH}: $r_{sun} \rightarrow V_{sun} \text{ km}^3_{sun} \rightarrow \text{m}^3_{sun}$ then $V_{sun}, d_{sun} \rightarrow m_{sun}$ then $m_{sun} \rightarrow m_{BH} \text{ kg} \rightarrow \text{g}$

$\qquad V = (4/3)\pi r^3 \qquad \dfrac{(1000 \text{ m})^3}{(1 \text{ km})^3} \qquad d_{sun} = \dfrac{m_{sun}}{V_{sun}} \qquad m_{BH} = (1 \times 10^3) \times m_{sun} \qquad \dfrac{1000 \text{ g}}{1 \text{ kg}}$

Calculate V_{BH}: $dia_{moon} \rightarrow r_{moon} \rightarrow r_{BH} \text{ mi} \rightarrow \text{km} \rightarrow \text{m} \rightarrow \text{cm}$ then $r \rightarrow V$

$\qquad r_{moon} = 1/2 \, dia_{moon} \text{ for clarity } r_{BH} = 1/2 \, r_{moon} \qquad \dfrac{1 \text{ km}}{0.6214 \text{ mi}} \quad \dfrac{1000 \text{ m}}{1 \text{ km}} \quad \dfrac{100 \text{ cm}}{1 \text{ m}} \qquad V = (4/3)\pi r^3$

Substitute into $d_{BH} = m_{BH}/V_{BH}$

Solution: Calculate m_{BH}: $V_{sun} = (4/3)\pi r^3_{sun} = (4/3)\pi (7.0 \times 10^5 \text{ km})^3 = 1.43675504 \times 10^{18} \text{ km}^3$

$1.43675504 \times 10^{18} \text{ km}^3 \times \dfrac{(1000 \text{ m})^3}{(1 \text{ km})^3} = 1.43675504 \times 10^{27} \text{ m}^3$

$d_{sun} = m_{sun}/V_{sun}$. Solve for m by multiplying both sides of the equation by V_{sun}.
$m_{sun} = V_{sun} \times d_{sun}$
$m_{sun} = (1.43675504 \times 10^{27} \text{ m}^3)(1.4 \times 10^3 \text{ kg/m}^3) = 2.011457056 \times 10^{30} \text{ kg}$
$m_{BH} = (1 \times 10^3) \times m_{sun} = (1 \times 10^3) \times (2.011457056 \times 10^{30} \text{ kg}) = 2.011457056 \times 10^{33} \text{ kg}$

$2.011457056 \times 10^{33} \text{ kg} \times \dfrac{1000 \text{ g}}{1 \text{ kg}} = 2.011457056 \times 10^{36} \text{ g}$

Calculate V_{BH}: $r_{moon} = \dfrac{1}{2} dia_{moon} = \dfrac{1}{2}(2.16 \times 10^3 \text{ mi}) = 1.08 \times 10^3 \text{ mi}$

$r_{BH} = \dfrac{1}{2} r_{moon} = \dfrac{1}{2}(1.08 \times 10^3 \text{ mi}) = 540. \text{ mi}$

$540. \text{ mi} \times \dfrac{1 \text{ km}}{0.6214 \text{ mi}} \times \dfrac{1000 \text{ m}}{1 \text{ km}} \times \dfrac{100 \text{ cm}}{1 \text{ m}} = 8.6900547 \times 10^7 \text{ cm}$

$$V = (4/3)\pi r^3 = (4/3)\pi (8.6\underline{9}00547 \times 10^7 \text{ cm})^3 = 2.74888227 \times 10^{24} \text{ cm}^3$$

Substitute into $d_{BH} = \dfrac{m_{BH}}{V_{BH}} = \dfrac{2.011457056 \times 10^{36} \text{ g}}{2.74888227 \times 10^{24} \text{ cm}^3} = 7.\underline{3}1736342 \times 10^{11} \dfrac{\text{g}}{\text{cm}^3} = 7.3 \times 10^{11} \dfrac{\text{g}}{\text{cm}^3}$

Check: The units (g/cm^3) are correct. The magnitude of the answer seems correct (10^{12}) because we expect extremely high numbers for black holes. Two significant figures are allowed to reflect the significant figures in the radius of our sun (7.0×10^5 km) and the average density of the sun (1.4×10^3 kg/m^3). Truncate the nonsignificant digits because the first nonsignificant digit is a 1.

1.92　　**Given:** 15.0 ppm CO; eight-hour period　　**Find:** milligrams of carbon monoxide
　　　　Other: 0.50 L of air per breath; 20 breaths per minute; carbon monoxide has a density of 1.2 g/L; 15.0 ppm CO means 15.0 L CO per 10^6 L air
　　　　Conceptual Plan: hr $\rightarrow$ min $\rightarrow$ breaths $\rightarrow$ L$_{air}$ $\rightarrow$ L$_{CO}$ $\rightarrow$ g$_{CO}$ $\rightarrow$ mg$_{CO}$

$$\frac{60 \text{ min}}{1 \text{ hr}} \qquad \frac{20 \text{ breath}}{1 \text{ min}} \qquad \frac{0.50 \text{ L}_{air}}{1 \text{ breath}} \qquad \frac{15.0 \text{ L}_{CO}}{1 \times 10^6 \text{ L}_{air}} \qquad \frac{1.2 \text{ g}_{CO}}{1 \text{ L}_{CO}} \qquad \frac{1000 \text{ mg}_{CO}}{1 \text{ g}_{CO}}$$

Solution:

$$8 \text{ hr} \times \frac{60 \text{ min}}{1 \text{ hr}} \times \frac{20 \text{ breath}}{1 \text{ min}} \times \frac{0.50 \text{ L}_{air}}{1 \text{ breath}} \times \frac{15.0 \text{ L}_{CO}}{1 \times 10^6 \text{ L}_{air}} \times \frac{1.2 \text{ g}_{CO}}{1 \text{ L}_{CO}} \times \frac{1000 \text{ mg}_{CO}}{1 \text{ g}_{CO}} = \underline{8}6.4 \text{ mg}_{CO} = 9 \times 10^1 \text{ mg}_{CO}$$

Check: The units (mg) are correct. The magnitude of the answer (10^2) makes physical sense because there are more than 6 powers of 10 visible in these conversion factors in the numerator and one factor of 10^6 in the denominator. This means that most of the conversions cancel each other out, but there is still some left in the numerator. One significant figure is allowed because the conversion factor with the least precision is 20 breaths/minute (one significant figure); the starting time (8 hours) also has one significant figure. Round the last digit up because the first nonsignificant digit is a 6.

1.93　　**Given:** cubic nanocontainers with an edge length $=$ 25 nanometers
　　　　Find: (a) volume of one nanocontainer; (b) grams of oxygen could be contained by each nanocontainer; (c) grams of oxygen inhaled per hour; (d) minimum number of nanocontainers per hour; (e) minimum volume of nanocontainers.
　　　　Other: (pressurized oxygen) $=$ 85 g/L; 0.28 g of oxygen per liter; average human inhales about 0.50 L of air per breath and takes about 20 breaths per minute; adult total blood volume $=$ $\sim$5 L
　　　　Conceptual Plan:

(a)　　nm $\rightarrow$ m $\rightarrow$ cm then l $\rightarrow$ V then cm^3 $\rightarrow$ L

$$\frac{1 \text{ m}}{10^9 \text{ nm}} \qquad \frac{100 \text{ cm}}{1 \text{ m}} \qquad\qquad V = l^3 \qquad\qquad \frac{1 \text{ L}}{1000 \text{ cm}^3}$$

(b)　　L $\rightarrow$ g pressurized oxygen

$$\frac{85 \text{ g oxygen}}{1 \text{ L nanocontainers}}$$

(c)　　hr $\rightarrow$ min $\rightarrow$ breaths $\rightarrow$ L$_{air}$ $\rightarrow$ g$_{O_2}$

$$\frac{60 \text{ min}}{1 \text{ hr}} \qquad \frac{20 \text{ breath}}{1 \text{ min}} \qquad \frac{0.50 \text{ L}_{air}}{1 \text{ breath}} \qquad \frac{0.28 \text{ g}_{CO}}{1 \text{ L}_{air}}$$

(d)　　grams oxygen $\rightarrow$ number nanocontainers

$$\frac{1 \text{ nanocontainer}}{\text{part (b) grams of oxygen}}$$

(e)　　number nanocontainers $\rightarrow$ volume nanocontainers

$$\frac{\text{part(a) volume}}{\text{of 1 nanocontainer}}$$

Solution:

(a)　　$25 \text{ nm} \times \dfrac{1 \text{ m}}{10^9 \text{ nm}} \times \dfrac{100 \text{ cm}}{1 \text{ m}} = 2.5 \times 10^{-6} \text{ cm}$

$$V = l^3 = (2.5 \times 10^{-6} \text{ cm})^3 = 1.\underline{5}625 \times 10^{-17} \text{ cm}^3 \times \frac{1 \text{ L}}{1000 \text{ cm}^3} = 1.\underline{5}625 \times 10^{-20} \text{ L} = 1.6 \times 10^{-20} \text{ L}$$

(b) $1.\underline{5}625 \times 10^{-20} \, \cancel{L} \times \dfrac{85 \text{ g oxygen}}{1 \, \cancel{L} \text{ nanocontainers}} = 1.328125 \times 10^{-18} \, \dfrac{\text{g pressurized O}_2}{\text{nanocontainer}}$

$= 1.3 \times 10^{-18} \, \dfrac{\text{g pressurized O}_2}{\text{nanocontainer}}$

(c) $1 \, \cancel{hr} \times \dfrac{60 \, \cancel{\text{min}}}{1 \, \cancel{hr}} \times \dfrac{20 \, \cancel{\text{breath}}}{1 \, \cancel{\text{min}}} \times \dfrac{0.50 \, \cancel{L_{air}}}{1 \, \cancel{\text{breath}}} \times \dfrac{0.28 \text{ gO}_2}{1 \, \cancel{L_{air}}} = 1.\underline{6}8 \times 10^2 \text{ g oxygen} = 1.7 \times 10^2 \text{ g oxygen}$

(d) $1.\underline{6}8 \times 10^2 \, \cancel{\text{g oxygen}} \times \dfrac{1 \text{ nanocontainer}}{1.3 \times 10^{-18} \, \cancel{\text{g oxygen}}} = 1.292307692 \times 10^{20} \text{ nanocontainers}$

$= 1.3 \times 10^{20} \text{ nanocontainers}$

(e) $1.292307692 \times 10^{20} \, \cancel{\text{nanocontainers}} \times \dfrac{1.\underline{5}625 \times 10^{-20} \text{ L}}{\cancel{\text{nanocontainer}}} = 2.019230769 \text{ L} = 2.\underline{0} \text{ L}$

This volume is much too large to be feasible because the volume of blood in the average human is 5 L.

Check:

(a) The units (L) are correct. The magnitude of the answer (10^{-20}) makes physical sense because these are very, very tiny containers. Two significant figures are allowed, reflecting the significant figures in the starting dimension (25 nm – 2 significant figures). Round the last digit up because the first nonsignificant digit is a 6.

(b) The units (g) are correct. The magnitude of the answer (10^{-18}) makes physical sense because these are very, very tiny containers and very few molecules can fit inside. Two significant figures are allowed, reflecting the significant figures in the starting dimension (25 nm) and the given concentration (85 g/L) – 2 significant figures in each. Truncate the nonsignificant digits because the first nonsignificant digit is a 2.

(c) The units (g oxygen) are correct. The magnitude of the answer (10^2) makes physical sense because of the conversion factors involved and the fact that air is not very dense. Two significant figures are allowed because it is stated in the problem. Round the last digit up because the first nonsignificant digit is an 8.

(d) The units (nanocontainers) are correct. The magnitude of the answer (10^{20}) makes physical sense because these are very, very tiny containers and we need a macroscopic quantity of oxygen in these containers. Two significant figures are allowed, reflecting the significant figures in both of the quantities in the calculation – 2 significant figures. Round the last digit up because the first nonsignificant digit is a 9.

(e) The units (L) are correct. The magnitude of the answer (2) makes physical sense because of the magnitudes of the numbers in this step. Two significant figures are allowed, reflecting the significant figures in both of the quantities in the calculation—2 significant figures. Truncate the nonsignificant digits because the first nonsignificant digit is a 1.

1.94 Because the person weighs 155 lb and has a density of 1.0 g/cm^3, the volume of the person can be calculated as

$155 \, \cancel{lb} \times \dfrac{453.59 \, \cancel{g}}{1 \, \cancel{lb}} \times \dfrac{1 \text{ cm}^3}{1.0 \, \cancel{g}} = 7.\underline{0}30645 \times 10^4 \text{ cm}^3.$

Approximating the volume of a person as a cylinder 4.0 feet tall, $V = l\pi r^2$. Rearranging the equation, solve for r.

$r = \left(\dfrac{V}{l\pi}\right)^{\frac{1}{2}} = \sqrt{\dfrac{7.030645 \times 10^4 \text{ cm}^3}{4.0 \, \cancel{ft} \times \dfrac{30.48 \text{ cm}}{1 \, \cancel{ft}} \times \pi}} = 13.\underline{5}4831 \text{ cm}$

The circumference is $2\pi r = 2\pi(13.54831 \text{ cm}) = 85.\underline{1}2655 \text{ cm}$. When the person gains 40.0 lb of fat, the volume increase is $40.0 \, \cancel{lb} \times \dfrac{453.59 \, \cancel{g}}{1 \, \cancel{lb}} \times \dfrac{1 \text{ cm}^3}{0.918 \, \cancel{g}} = 1.9\underline{7}643 \times 10^4 \text{ cm}^3.$

Thus, the new volume is $7.\underline{0}30645 \times 10^4 \text{ cm}^3 + 1.9\underline{7}643 \times 10^4 \text{ cm}^3 = 9.\underline{0}0708 \times 10^4 \text{ cm}^3.$ So the new radius is

$r = \left(\dfrac{V}{l\pi}\right)^{\frac{1}{2}} = \sqrt{\dfrac{9.\underline{0}0708 \times 10^4 \text{ cm}^3}{4.0 \, \cancel{ft} \times \dfrac{30.48 \text{ cm}}{1 \, \cancel{ft}} \times \pi}} = 15.\underline{3}3485 \text{ cm, and the new circumference is}$

$2\pi r = 2\pi(15.33485 \text{ cm}) = 96.\underline{3}5170 \text{ cm}.$

The percent increase in circumference $\dfrac{96.35170 \text{ cm} - 85.\underline{1}2655 \text{ cm}}{85.12655 \text{ cm}} \times 100\% = 13.\underline{1}864\% = 13\%.$

1.95   Assume that all of the spheres are the same size. Let x = the percentage of spheres that are copper (expressed as a fraction); so the volume of copper = $(427 \text{ cm}^3)x$ and the volume of lead = $(427 \text{ cm}^3)(1 - x)$. Because the density of copper is 8.96 g/cm^3, the mass of copper = $(427 \text{ cm}^3)x \times \dfrac{8.96 \text{ g}}{\text{cm}^3} = 3825.92(x)$ g. Because the density of lead is 11.4 g/cm^3, the mass of lead = $(427 \text{ cm}^3)(1 - x) \times \dfrac{11.46 \text{ g}}{\text{cm}^3} = 4893.42(1 - x)$ g. Because the total mass is 4.36 kg = 4360 g, 4360 g = $3825.92(x)$ g + $4893.42(1 - x)$ g. Solving for x, $1067.50(x)$ g = 533.42 g → $x = 0.499691$, or 50.% of the spheres are copper.

Check: This answer makes sense because the average density of the spheres = 4360 g/427 cm^3 = 10.2 g/cm^3 and the average of the density of copper and the density of lead = $(8.96 + 11.4)/2$ g/cm^3 = 10.2 g/cm^3.

Conceptual Problems

1.96   No. Since the container is sealed, the atoms and molecules can move around but they cannot leave. If no atoms or molecules can leave, the mass must be constant.

1.97   (c) is the best representation. When solid carbon dioxide (dry ice) sublimes, it changes phase from a solid to a gas. Phase changes are physical changes, so no molecular bonds are broken. This diagram shows molecules with one carbon atom and two oxygen atoms bonded together in every molecule. The other diagrams have no carbon dioxide molecules.

1.98   (a)   (b)

         (c)   (d)

1.99   This problem is similar to Problem 1.28 except that the dimension is changed to 7 cm on each edge.
         Given: 7 cm on each edge cube   **Find:** cm^3
         Conceptual Plan: Read the information carefully. The cube is 7 cm on each side.
         $l, w, h \rightarrow V$
            $V = lwh$
          $in \ a \ cube \ l = w = h$

         Solution: 7 cm $\times$ 7 cm $\times$ 7 cm = $(7 \text{ cm})^3$ = 343 cm^3, or 343 cubes

1.100   To determine which number is large, the units need to be compared. There is a factor of 1000 between grams and kilograms in the numerator. There is a factor of $(100)^3$, or 1,000,000, between cm^3 and m^3. This second factor more than compensates for the first factor. Thus, Substance A with a density of 1.7 g/cm^3 is denser than Substance B with a density of 1.7 kg/m^3.

1.101   Remember that density = mass/volume.
  (a)   The darker-colored box has a heavier mass but a smaller volume, so it is denser than the lighter-colored box.
  (b)   The lighter-colored box is heavier than the darker-colored box, and both boxes have the same volume; so the lighter-colored box is denser.
  (c)   The larger box is the heavier box, so it cannot be determined with this information which box is denser.

1.102   Remember that an observation is the information collected when studying phenomena. A law is a concise statement that summarizes observed behaviors and observations and predicts future observations. A theory attempts to explain why the observed behavior is happening.
  (a)   This statement is most like a law because it summarizes many observations and can explain future behavior—many places and many days.
  (b)   This statement is a theory because it attempts to explain why (gravitational forces).
  (c)   This statement is most like an observation because it is information collected to understand tidal behavior.
  (d)   This statement is most like a law because it summarizes many observations and can explain future behavior—many places and many days and months.

Questions for Group Work

1.103

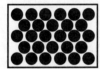 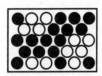

solid element   liquid compound   heterogeneous mixture

 liquid compound physical change:

 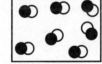

before = liquid   after = gas phase

 Solid element chemical change:

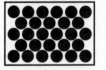 

before = solid element   after = solid compound

1.104   (a)   The average thickness of a human hair is about 100 microns (μm). Since $1\ \mu m = 10^{-6}$ m,

$$100\ \mu m \times \frac{10^{-6}\,m}{1\ \mu m} = 1 \times 10^{-4}\,m.$$

  (b) 1×10^{-4}m
  (c)   0.0001 m
  (d)   100 microns or 100 μm
  (e)   The distance between the Earth and the Sun is 149,600,000 km. Since $1\ km = 10^3$ m,

$$149,600,000\ \cancel{km} \times \frac{10^3\,m}{1\ \cancel{km}} = 149,600,000,000\ m.$$

  (f) 1.496×10^{11}m
  (g)   149,600,000,000 m
  (h)   149,600,000 km or 149.6 Mm

1.105   All of these values can be true because when we round 4.73297 km to three significant figures we get 4.73 km; and if
          we round this value to one significant figure we get 5 km. The number of digits reported indicates how accurately the
          distance was measured. The odometer on a car could be used for the first measurement. A trip meter on a car could be
          used for the second measurement. A long tape measure could be used for the last measurement.

1.106
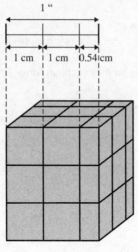

          Since 1 in = 2.54 cm, there are $\dfrac{2.54\,\text{cm}}{1\,\text{in}} \times \dfrac{2.54\,\text{cm}}{1\,\text{in}} \times \dfrac{2.54\,\text{cm}}{1\,\text{in}} = 16.397064 \text{ cm}^3/\text{in}^3$.

1.107   To convert the height of a student from feet and inches into meters: first convert the feet to inches; then add
          this to the number of inches, and finally convert the inches to centimeters and to meters. For example, if the

          height of a student is 5'8.5": $5\,\text{ft} \times \dfrac{12\,\text{in}}{1\,\text{ft}} = 60\text{ in (exactly)}$; then 60 in + 8.5 in = 68.5 in, and finally

          $68.5\,\text{in} \times \dfrac{2.54\,\text{cm}}{1\,\text{in}} \times \dfrac{1\,\text{m}}{100\,\text{cm}} = 1.7\underline{3}99 \text{ m} = 1.74 \text{ m}$.

          Add all of the heights together to get the sum for your group.

2 Atoms and Elements

Problems by Topic

The Laws of Conservation of Mass, Definite Proportions, and Multiple Proportions

2.1   **Given:** 1.50 g hydrogen; 12.0 g oxygen   **Find:** grams water vapor
Conceptual Plan: total mass reactants = total mass products
Solution: Mass of reactants = 1.50 g hydrogen + 12.0 g oxygen = 13.5 grams
Mass of products = mass of reactants = 13.5 grams water vapor

Check: According to the law of conservation of mass, matter is not created or destroyed in a chemical reaction. So because water vapor is the only product, the masses of hydrogen and oxygen must combine to form the mass of water vapor.

2.2   **Given:** 21 kg gasoline; 84 kg oxygen   **Find:** mass of carbon dioxide and water
Conceptual Plan: total mass reactants = total mass products
Solution: Mass of reactants = 21 kg gasoline + 84 kg oxygen = 105 kg mass
Mass of products = mass of reactants = 105 kg of mass of carbon dioxide and water

Check: According to the law of conservation of mass, matter is not created or destroyed in a chemical reaction. So because carbon dioxide and water are the only products, the masses of gasoline and oxygen must combine to form the mass of carbon dioxide and water.

2.3   **Given:** sample 1: 38.9 g carbon, 448 g chlorine; sample 2: 14.8 g carbon, 134 g chlorine
Find: consistent with definite proportions
Conceptual Plan: Determine mass ratio of samples 1 and 2 and compare.

$$\frac{\text{mass of chlorine}}{\text{mass of carbon}}$$

Solution: sample 1: $\dfrac{448 \text{ g chlorine}}{38.9 \text{ g carbon}} = 11.5$ sample 2: $\dfrac{134 \text{ g chlorine}}{14.8 \text{ g carbon}} = 9.05$

Results are not consistent with the law of definite proportions because the ratio of chlorine to carbon is not the same.

Check: According to the law of definite proportions, the mass ratio of one element to another is the same for all samples of the compound.

2.4   **Given:** sample 1: 6.98 grams sodium, 10.7 grams chlorine; sample 2: 11.2 g sodium, 17.3 grams chlorine
Find: consistent with definite proportions
Conceptual Plan: Determine mass ratio of samples 1 and 2 and compare.

$$\frac{\text{mass of chlorine}}{\text{mass of sodium}}$$

Solution: sample 1: $\dfrac{10.7 \text{ g chlorine}}{6.98 \text{ g sodium}} = 1.53$ sample 2: $\dfrac{17.3 \text{ g chlorine}}{11.2 \text{ g sodium}} = 1.54$

Results are consistent with the law of definite proportions.

Check: According to the law of definite proportions, the mass ratio of one element to another is the same for all samples of the compound.

2.5   **Given:** mass ratio sodium to fluorine = 1.21:1; sample = 28.8 g sodium   **Find:** g fluorine
Conceptual Plan: g sodium → g fluorine

$$\frac{\text{mass of fluorine}}{\text{mass of sodium}}$$

Solution: $28.8 \ \cancel{\text{g sodium}} \times \dfrac{1 \text{ g fluorine}}{1.21 \ \cancel{\text{g sodium}}} = 23.8$ g fluorine

Check: The units of the answer (g fluorine) are correct. The magnitude of the answer is reasonable because it is less than the grams of sodium.

2.6   **Given:** sample 1: 1.65 kg magnesium, 2.57 kg fluorine; sample 2: 1.32 kg magnesium
Find: g fluorine in Sample 2
Conceptual Plan: mass magnesium and mass fluorine → mass ratio → mass fluorine (kg) → mass fluorine (g)

$$\frac{\text{mass of fluorine}}{\text{mass of magnesium}} \qquad\qquad \frac{1000 \text{ g}}{\text{kg}}$$

Solution: mass ratio $= \dfrac{2.57 \text{ kg fluorine}}{1.65 \text{ kg magnesium}} = \dfrac{1.56 \text{ kg fluorine}}{1.00 \text{ kg magnesium}}$

$$1.32 \ \cancel{\text{kg magnesium}} \times \frac{1.56 \text{ kg fluorine}}{1.00 \ \cancel{\text{kg magnesium}}} \times \frac{1000 \text{ g}}{\text{kg}} = 2.06 \times 10^3 \text{ g fluorine}$$

Check: The units of the answer (g fluorine) are correct. The magnitude of the answer is reasonable because it is greater than the mass of magnesium and the ratio is greater than 1.

2.7   **Given:** 1 gram osmium: sample 1 = 0.168 g oxygen; sample 2 = 0.3369 g oxygen
Find: consistent with multiple proportions
Conceptual Plan: Determine mass ratio of oxygen.

$$\frac{\text{mass of oxygen sample 2}}{\text{mass of oxygen sample 1}}$$

Solution: $\dfrac{0.3369 \text{ g oxygen}}{0.168 \text{ g oxygen}} = 2.00$ Ratio is a small whole number. Results are consistent with multiple proportions.

Check: According to the law of multiple proportions, when two elements form two different compounds, the masses of element B that combine with 1 g of element A can be expressed as a ratio of small whole numbers.

2.8   **Given:** 1 g palladium: compound A: 0.603 g S; compound B: 0.301 g S; compound C: 0.151 g S
Find: consistent with multiple proportions
Conceptual Plan: Determine mass ratio of sulfur in the three compounds.

$$\frac{\text{mass of sulfur sample A}}{\text{mass of sulfur sample B}} \qquad \frac{\text{mass of sulfur sample A}}{\text{mass of sulfur sample C}} \qquad \frac{\text{mass of sulfur sample B}}{\text{mass of sulfur sample C}}$$

Solution: $\dfrac{0.603 \text{ g S in compound A}}{0.301 \text{ g S in compound B}} = 2.00 \qquad\qquad \dfrac{0.603 \text{ g S in compound A}}{0.151 \text{ g S in compound C}} = 3.99 \sim 4$

$$\frac{0.301 \text{ g S in compound B}}{0.151 \text{ g S in compound C}} = 1.99 \sim 2$$

Ratio of each is a small whole number. Results are consistent with multiple proportions.

Check: According to the law of multiple proportions, when two elements form two different compounds, the masses of element B that combine with 1 g of element A can be expressed as a ratio of small whole numbers.

2.9   **Given:** sulfur dioxide = 3.49 g oxygen and 3.50 g sulfur; sulfur trioxide = 6.75 g oxygen and 4.50 g sulfur
Find: mass oxygen per g S for each compound and then determine the mass ratio of oxygen

$$\frac{\text{mass of oxygen in sulfur dioxide}}{\text{mass of sulfur in sulfur dioxide}} \quad \frac{\text{mass of oxygen in sulfur trioxide}}{\text{mass of sulfur in sulfur trioxide}} \quad \frac{\text{mass of oxyen in sulfur trioxide}}{\text{mass of oxyen in sulfur dioxide}}$$

Solution: sulfur dioxide $= \dfrac{3.49 \text{ g oxygen}}{3.50 \text{ g sulfur}} = \dfrac{0.997 \text{ g oxygen}}{1 \text{ g sulfur}} \qquad$ sulfur trioxide $= \dfrac{6.75 \text{ g oxygen}}{4.50 \text{ g sulfur}} = \dfrac{1.50 \text{ g oxygen}}{1 \text{ g sulfur}}$

$\dfrac{1.50 \text{ g oxygen in sulfur trioxide}}{0.997 \text{ g oxygen in sulfur dioxide}} = \dfrac{1.50}{1} = \dfrac{3}{2}$. The ratio is converted from 1.50:1 to 3:2 because the law of multiple proportions states that the ratio is in small whole numbers.

Ratio is in small whole numbers and is consistent with multiple proportions.

Check: According to the law of multiple proportions, when two elements form two different compounds, the masses of element B that combine with 1 g of element A can be expressed as a ratio of small whole numbers.

2.10   **Given:** sulfur hexafluoride $= 4.45$ g fluorine and 1.25 g sulfur; sulfur tetrafluoride $= 4.43$ g fluorine and 1.87 g sulfur

Find: mass fluorine per g S for each compound and then determine the mass ratio of fluorine

$$\frac{\text{mass of fluorine in sulfur hexafluoride}}{\text{mass of sulfur in sulfur hexafluoride}} \quad \frac{\text{mass of fluorine in sulfur tetrafluoride}}{\text{mass of sulfur in sulfur tetrafluoride}} \quad \frac{\text{mass of oxyen in sulfur hexafluoride}}{\text{mass of oxyen in sulfur tetrafluoride}}$$

Solution: sulfur hexafluoride $= \dfrac{4.45 \text{ g fluorine}}{1.25 \text{ g sulfur}} = \dfrac{3.56 \text{ g fluorine}}{1 \text{ g sulfur}}$

$\qquad\qquad$ sulfur tetrafluoride $= \dfrac{4.43 \text{ g fluorine}}{1.87 \text{ g sulfur}} = \dfrac{2.3\underline{6}9 \text{ g fluorine}}{1 \text{ g sulfur}}$

$\dfrac{3.56 \text{ g fluorine in sulfur hexafluoride}}{2.3\underline{6}9 \text{ g fluorine in sulfur tetrafluoride}} = \dfrac{1.50}{1} = \dfrac{3}{2}$

Ratio is in small whole numbers and is consistent with multiple proportions.

Check: According to the law of multiple proportions, when two elements form two different compounds, the masses of element B that combine with 1 g of element A can be expressed as a ratio of small whole numbers.

Atomic Theory, Nuclear Theory, and Subatomic Particles

2.11   (a)   Sulfur and oxygen atoms have the same mass. INCONSISTENT with Dalton's atomic theory because only atoms of the same element have the same mass.

$\qquad$ (b)   All cobalt atoms are identical. CONSISTENT with Dalton's atomic theory because all atoms of a given element have the same mass and other properties that distinguish them from atoms of other elements.

$\qquad$ (c)   Potassium and chlorine atoms combine in a 1:1 ratio to form potassium chloride. CONSISTENT with Dalton's atomic theory because atoms combine in simple whole-number ratios to form compounds.

$\qquad$ (d)   Lead atoms can be converted into gold. INCONSISTENT with Dalton's atomic theory because atoms of one element cannot change into atoms of another element.

2.12   (a)   All carbon atoms are identical. CONSISTENT with Dalton's atomic theory because all atoms of a given element have the same mass and other properties that distinguish them from atoms of other elements.

$\qquad$ (b)   An oxygen atom combines with 1.5 hydrogen atoms to form a water molecule. INCONSISTENT with Dalton's atomic theory because atoms combine in simple whole-number ratios to form compounds. An oxygen atom actually combines with 2 hydrogen atoms to form a water molecule.

$\qquad$ (c)   Two oxygen atoms combine with a carbon atom to form a carbon dioxide molecule. CONSISTENT with Dalton's atomic theory because atoms combine in simple whole-number ratios to form compounds.

$\qquad$ (d)   The formation of a compound often involves the destruction of one or more atoms. INCONSISTENT with Dalton's atomic theory. Atoms change the way they are bound together with other atoms when they form a new substance, but they are neither created nor destroyed.

2.13   (a)   The volume of an atom is mostly empty space. CONSISTENT with Rutherford's nuclear theory because most of the volume of the atom is empty space, throughout which tiny, negatively charged electrons are dispersed.

$\qquad$ (b)   The nucleus of an atom is small compared to the size of the atom. CONSISTENT with Rutherford's nuclear theory because most of the atom's mass and all of its positive charge are contained in a small core called the nucleus.

$\qquad$ (c)   Neutral lithium atoms contain more neutrons than protons. INCONSISTENT with Rutherford's nuclear theory because it did not distinguish where the mass of the nucleus came from other than from the protons.

$\qquad$ (d)   Neutral lithium atoms contain more protons than electrons. INCONSISTENT with Rutherford's nuclear theory because there are as many negatively charged particles outside the nucleus as there are positively charged particles in the nucleus.

2.14   (a)   Since electrons are smaller than protons, and since a hydrogen atom contains only one proton and one electron, it must follow that the volume of a hydrogen atom is mostly due to the proton.
INCONSISTENT with Rutherford's nuclear theory because most of the volume of the atom is empty space, throughout which tiny, negatively charged electrons are dispersed.

$\qquad$ (b)   A nitrogen atom has seven protons in its nucleus and seven electrons outside of its nucleus. CONSISTENT with Rutherford's nuclear theory because there are as many negatively charged particles outside the nucleus as there are positively charged particles in the nucleus.

(c) A phosphorus atom has 15 protons in its nucleus and 150 electrons outside its nucleus. INCONSISTENT with Rutherford's nuclear theory because there are as many negatively charged particles outside the nucleus as there are positively charged particles in the nucleus.

(d) The majority of the mass of a fluorine atom is due to its nine electrons. INCONSISTENT with Rutherford's nuclear theory because most of the atom's mass and all of its positive charge are contained in a small core called the nucleus.

2.15 **Given:** drop A $= -6.9 \times 10^{-19}$ C; drop B $= -9.2 \times 10^{-19}$ C; drop C $= -11.5 \times 10^{-19}$ C; drop D $= -4.6 \times 10^{-19}$ C
Find: the charge on a single electron
Conceptual Plan: Determine the ratio of charge for each set of drops and determine the charge on an electron.

$$\frac{\text{charge on drop 1}}{\text{charge on drop 2}}$$

Solution: $\dfrac{-6.9 \times 10^{-19} \text{ C drop A}}{-4.6 \times 10^{-19} \text{ C drop D}} = 1.5$ $\dfrac{-9.2 \times 10^{-19} \text{ C drop B}}{-4.6 \times 10^{-19} \text{ C drop D}} = 2$ $\dfrac{-11.5 \times 10^{-19} \text{ C drop C}}{-4.6 \times 10^{-19} \text{ C drop D}} = 2.5$

The ratios obtained are not whole numbers, but they can be converted to whole numbers by multiplying by 2. Therefore, the charge on the electron has to be 1/2 the smallest value experimentally obtained. The charge on the electron $= -2.3 \times 10^{-19}$ C.

Check: The units of the answer (Coulombs) are correct. The magnitude of the answer is reasonable because all of the values experimentally obtained are integer multiples of -2.3×10^{-19}.

2.16 **Given:** drop A $= -4.8 \times 10^{-9}$ z; drop B $= -9.6 \times 10^{-9}$ z; drop C $= -6.4 \times 10^{-9}$ z; drop D $= -12.8 \times 10^{-9}$ z
Find: the charge on a single electron
Conceptual Plan: Determine the ratio of charge for each set of drops and determine the charge on an electron.

$$\frac{\text{charge on drop 1}}{\text{charge on drop 2}}$$

Then determine the number of electrons in each drop.

$$\frac{\text{charge on drop}}{\text{charge on one electron}}$$

Solution: $\dfrac{-9.6 \times 10^{-9} \text{ z drop B}}{-4.8 \times 10^{-9} \text{ z drop A}} = 2$ $\dfrac{-6.4 \times 10^{-9} \text{ z drop C}}{-4.8 \times 10^{-9} \text{ z drop A}} = 1.33$ $\dfrac{-12.8 \times 10^{-9} \text{ z drop D}}{-4.8 \times 10^{-9} \text{ z drop A}} = 2.66$

The ratios obtained are not all whole numbers, but they can be converted to whole numbers by multiplying by 3. Therefore, the charge on the electron has to be 1/3 the smallest value experimentally obtained. The charge on the

electron $= \dfrac{1}{3} \times -4.8 \times 10^{-9}$ z $= -1.6 \times 10^{-9}$ z.

Number of electrons in

Drop A: $\dfrac{-4.8 \times 10^{-9} \text{ z}}{-1.6 \times 10^{-9} \text{ z}} = 3$ electrons   Drop B: $\dfrac{-9.6 \times 10^{-9} \text{ z}}{-1.6 \times 10^{-9} \text{ z}} = 6$ electrons

Drop C: $\dfrac{-6.4 \times 10^{-9} \text{ z}}{-1.6 \times 10^{-9} \text{ z}} = 4$ electrons   Drop D: $\dfrac{-12.8 \times 10^{-9} \text{ z}}{-1.6 \times 10^{-9} \text{ z}} = 8$ electrons

Check: The units of the answer (zorg) are correct. The magnitude of the answer is reasonable because all of the values experimentally obtained are integer multiples of -1.6×10^{-9}.

2.17 **Given:** charge on body $= -15 \ \mu$C   **Find:** number of electrons; mass of the electrons
Conceptual Plan: μC $\rightarrow$ C $\rightarrow$ number of electrons $\rightarrow$ mass of electrons

$$\frac{1 \text{ C}}{10^6 \ \mu\text{C}} \quad \frac{1 \text{ electron}}{-1.60 \times 10^{-19} \text{ C}} \qquad \frac{9.11 \times 10^{-28} \text{ g}}{1 \text{ electron}}$$

Solution: $-15 \ \mu\cancel{C} \times \dfrac{1 \ \cancel{C}}{10^6 \ \mu\cancel{C}} \times \dfrac{1 \text{ electron}}{-1.60 \times 10^{-19} \ \cancel{C}} = 9.\underline{3}75 \times 10^{13}$ electrons $= 9.4 \times 10^{13}$ electrons

$9.\underline{3}75 \times 10^{13} \text{ electrons} \times \dfrac{9.11 \times 10^{-28} \text{ g}}{1 \text{ electron}} = 8.5 \times 10^{-14}$ g

Check: The units of the answers (number of electrons and grams) are correct. The magnitude of the answers is reasonable because the charge on an electron and the mass of an electron are very small.

2.18   **Given:** mass of proton   **Find:** number of electrons in equal mass
         Conceptual Plan: mass of protons → number of electrons

$$\frac{1.67262 \times 10^{-27} \text{ kg}}{1 \text{ proton}} \qquad \frac{1 \text{ electron}}{9.10938 \times 10^{-31} \text{ kg}}$$

Solution: $1.67262 \times 10^{-27} \text{ kg} \times \dfrac{1 \text{ electron}}{9.10938 \times 10^{-31} \text{ kg}} = 1.83615 \times 10^3$ electrons

Check: The units of the answer (electrons) are correct. The magnitude of the answer is reasonable because the mass of the electron is much less than the mass of the proton.

2.19   (a)   True: Protons and electrons have equal and opposite charges.
         (b)   True: Protons and electrons have opposite charges, so they will attract each other.
         (c)   True: The mass of the electron is much less than the mass of the neutron.
         (d)   False: The mass of the proton and the mass of the neutron are about the same.

2.20   (a)   True: Protons and electrons have equal and opposite charges.
         (b)   True: The mass of the proton and the mass of the neutron are about the same.
         (c)   False: All atoms contain protons. The lightest element, hydrogen, contains 1 proton.
         (d)   False: Protons have a positive charge, while neutrons are neutral.

Isotopes and Ions

2.21   For each of the isotopes, determine Z (the number of protons) from the periodic table and determine A (protons + neutrons). Then write the symbol in the form $^A_Z X$.
         (a)   The sodium isotope with 12 neutrons: Z = 11; A = 11 + 12 = 23 $^{23}_{11}\text{Na}$
         (b)   The oxygen isotope with 8 neutrons: Z = 8; A = 8 + 8 = 16 $^{16}_{8}\text{O}$
         (c)   The aluminum isotope with 14 neutrons: Z = 13; A = 13 + 14 = 27 $^{27}_{13}\text{Al}$
         (d)   The iodine isotope with 74 neutrons: Z = 53; A = 53 + 74 = 127 $^{127}_{53}\text{I}$

2.22   For each of the isotopes, determine Z (the number of protons) from the periodic table and determine A (protons + neutrons). Then write the symbol in the form X-A.
         (a)   The argon isotope with 22 neutrons: Z = 18; A = 18 + 22 = 40   Ar-40
         (b)   The plutonium isotope with 145 neutrons: Z = 94; A = 94 + 145 = 239   Pu-239
         (c)   The phosphorus isotope with 16 neutrons: Z = 15; A = 15 + 16 = 31   P-31
         (d)   The fluorine isotope with 10 neutrons: Z = 9; A = 9 + 10 = 19   F-19

2.23   (a) $^{14}_{7}\text{N}$:   Z = 7; A = 14; protons = Z = 7; neutrons = A − Z = 14 − 7 = 7
         (b) $^{23}_{11}\text{Na}$:   Z = 11; A = 23; protons = Z = 11; neutrons = A − Z = 23 − 11 = 12
         (c) $^{222}_{86}\text{Rn}$:   Z = 86; A = 222; protons = Z = 86; neutrons = A − Z = 222 − 86 = 136
         (d) $^{208}_{82}\text{Pb}$:   Z = 82; A = 208; protons = Z = 82; neutrons = A − Z = 208 − 82 = 126

2.24   (a) $^{40}_{19}\text{K}$:   Z = 19; A = 40; protons = Z = 19; neutrons = A − Z = 40 − 19 = 21
         (b) $^{226}_{88}\text{Ra}$:   Z = 88; A = 226; protons = Z = 88; neutrons = A − Z = 226 − 88 = 138
         (c) $^{99}_{43}\text{Tc}$:   Z = 43; A = 99; protons = Z = 43; neutrons = A − Z = 99 − 43 = 56
         (d) $^{33}_{15}\text{P}$:   Z = 15; A = 33; protons = Z = 15; neutrons = A − Z = 33 − 15 = 18

2.25   Carbon-14: A = 14, Z = 6: $^{14}_{6}\text{C}$ # protons = Z = 6   # neutrons = A − Z = 14 − 6 = 8

2.26   Uranium-235: A = 235, Z = 92: $^{235}_{92}\text{U}$ # protons = Z = 92   # neutrons = A − Z = 235 − 92 = 143

2.27   In a neutral atom, the number of protons = the number of electrons = Z. For an ion, electrons are lost (cations) or gained (anions).
         (a) Ni^{2+}: Z = 28 = protons; Z − 2 = 26 = electrons
         (b) S^{2-}: Z = 16 = protons; Z + 2 = 18 = electrons
         (c) Br^{-}: Z = 35 = protons; Z + 1 = 36 = electrons
         (d) Cr^{3+}: Z = 24 = protons; Z − 3 = 21 = electrons

2.28   In a neutral atom, the number of protons = the number of electrons = Z. For an ion, electrons are lost (cations) or gained (anions).

   (a) $Al^{3+}: Z = 13 = $ protons; $Z - 3 = 10 = $ electrons
   (b) $Se^{2-}: Z = 34 = $ protons; $Z + 2 = 36 = $ electrons
   (c) $Ga^{3+}: Z = 31 = $ protons; $Z - 3 = 28 = $ electrons
   (d) $Sr^{2+}: Z = 38 = $ protons; $Z - 2 = 36 = $ electrons

2.29   Main-group metal atoms will lose electrons to form a cation with the same number of electrons as the nearest previous noble gas.
          Nonmetal atoms will gain electrons to form an anion with the same number of electrons as the nearest noble gas.

   (a) O^{2-} O is a nonmetal and has 8 electrons. It will gain electrons to form an anion. The nearest noble gas is neon with 10 electrons, so O will gain 2 electrons.
   (b) K^{+} K is a main-group metal and has 19 electrons. It will lose electrons to form a cation. The nearest noble gas is argon with 18 electrons, so K will lose 1 electron.
   (c) Al^{3+} Al is a main-group metal and has 13 electrons. It will lose electrons to form a cation. The nearest noble gas is neon with 10 electrons, so Al will lose 3 electrons.
   (d) Rb^{+} Rb is a main-group metal and has 37 electrons. It will lose electrons to form a cation. The nearest noble gas is krypton with 36 electrons, so Rb will lose 1 electron.

2.30   Main-group metal atoms will lose electrons to form a cation with the same number of electrons as the nearest previous noble gas.
          Nonmetal atoms will gain electrons to form an anion with the same number of electrons as the nearest noble gas.

   (a) Mg^{2+} Mg is a main-group metal and has 12 electrons. It will lose electrons to form a cation. The nearest noble gas is neon with 10 electrons, so Mg will lose 2 electrons.
   (b) N^{3-} N is a nonmetal and has 7 electrons. It will gain electrons to form an anion. The nearest noble gas is neon with 10 electrons, so N will gain 3 electrons.
   (c) F^{-} F is a nonmetal and has 9 electrons. It will gain electrons to form an anion. The nearest noble gas is neon with 10 electrons, so F will gain 1 electron.
   (d) Na^{+} Na is a main-group metal and has 11 electrons. It will lose electrons to form a cation. The nearest noble gas is neon with 10 electrons, so Na will lose 1 electron.

2.31   Main-group metal atoms will lose electrons to form a cation with the same number of electrons as the nearest previous noble gas. Atoms in period 4 and higher lose electrons to form the same ion as the element at the top of the group.
          Nonmetal atoms will gain electrons to form an anion with the same number of electrons as the nearest noble gas.

Symbol	Ion Formed	Number of Electrons in Ion	Number of Protons in Ion
Ca	Ca^{2+}	**18**	**20**
Be	Be^{2+}	2	**4**
Se	Se^{2-}	**36**	34
In	In^{3+}	**46**	49

2.32   Main-group metal atoms will lose electrons to form a cation with the same number of electrons as the nearest previous noble gas.
          Nonmetal atoms will gain electrons to form an anion with the same number of electrons as the nearest noble gas.

Symbol	Ion Formed	Number of Electrons in Ion	Number of Protons in Ion
Cl	Cl^{-}	18	17
Te	Te^{2-}	54	52
Br	Br^{-}	36	35
Sr	Sr^{2+}	36	38

The Periodic Table and Atomic Mass

2.33   (a)   Na   Sodium is a metal.
          (b)   Mg   Magnesium is a metal.
          (c)   Br   Bromine is a nonmetal.
          (d)   N   Nitrogen is a nonmetal.
          (e)   As   Arsenic is a metalloid.

2.34   (a)   lead   Pb is a metal.
          (b)   iodine   I is a nonmetal.
          (c)   potassium K is a metal.
          (d)   silver   Ag is a metal.
          (e)   xenon   Xe is a nonmetal.

2.35   (a)   tellurium   Te is in group 6A and is a main-group element.
          (b)   potassium   K is in group 1A and is a main-group element.
          (c)   vanadium   V is in group 5B and is a transition element.
          (d)   manganese   Mn is in group 7B and is a transition element.

2.36   (a)   Cr   Chromium is in group 6B and is a transition element.
          (b)   Br   Bromine is in group 7A and is a main-group element.
          (c)   Mo   Molybdenum is in group 6B and is a transition element.
          (d)   Cs   Cesium is in group 1A and is a main-group element.

2.37   (a)   sodium   Na is in group 1A and is an alkali metal.
          (b)   iodine   I is in group 7A and is a halogen.
          (c)   calcium   Ca is in group 2A and is an alkaline earth metal.
          (d)   barium   Ba is in group 2A and is an alkaline earth metal.
          (e)   krypton   Kr is in group 8A and is a noble gas.

2.38   (a)   F   Fluorine is in group 7A and is a halogen.
          (b)   Sr   Strontium is in group 2A and is an alkaline earth metal.
          (c)   K   Potassium is in group 1A and is an alkali metal.
          (d)   Ne   Neon is in group 8A and is a noble gas.
          (e)   At   Astatine is in group 7A and is a halogen.

2.39   (a)   N and Ni would not be similar. Nitrogen is a nonmetal; nickel is a metal.
          (b)   Mo and Sn would not be most similar. Although both are metals, molybdenum is a transition metal and tin is a main-group metal.
          (c)   Na and Mg would not be similar. Although both are main-group metals, sodium is in group 1A and magnesium is in group 2A.
          (d)   Cl and F would be most similar. Chlorine and fluorine are both in group 7A. Elements in the same group have similar chemical properties.
          (e)   Si and P would not be most similar. Silicon is a metalloid, and phosphorus is a nonmetal.

2.40   (a)   Nitrogen and oxygen would not be most similar. Although both are nonmetals, N is in group 5A and O is in group 6A.
          (b)   Titanium and gallium would not be most similar. Although both are metals, Ti is a transition metal and Ga is a main-group metal.
          (c)   Lithium and sodium would be most similar. Li and Na are both in group 1A. Elements in the same group have similar chemical properties.
          (d)   Germanium and arsenic would not be most similar. Ge and As are both metalloids and would share some properties, but Ge is in group 4A and As is in group 5A.
          (e)   Argon and bromine would not be most similar. Although both are nonmetals, Ar is in group 8A and Br is in group 7A.

2.41 **Given:** Rb-85; mass $= 84.9118$ amu; 72.15%:Rb-87; mass $= 86.9092$ amu; 27.85%
Find: atomic mass Rb
Conceptual Plan: **% abundance → fraction and then find atomic mass**

$$\frac{\% \text{ abundance}}{100} \qquad \text{Atomic mass} = \sum_n (\text{fraction of isotope } n) \times (\text{mass of isotope } n)$$

Solution: Fraction Rb-85 $= \dfrac{72.15}{100} = 0.7215$ ⠀⠀ Fraction Rb-87 $= \dfrac{27.85}{100} = 0.2785$

$$\text{Atomic mass} = \sum_n (\text{fraction of isotope } n) \times (\text{mass of isotope } n)$$

$$= 0.7215(84.9118 \text{ amu}) + 0.2785(86.9092 \text{ amu}) = 85.47 \text{ amu}$$

Check: Units of the answer (amu) are correct. The magnitude of the answer is reasonable because it lies between 84.9118 amu and 86.9092 amu and is closer to 84.9118 amu, which has the higher % abundance.

2.42 **Given:** Si-28; mass $= 27.9769$ amu; 92.2%:Si-29; mass $= 28.9765$ amu; 4.67%:Si-30; mass $= 29.9737$ amu; 3.10%
Find: atomic mass Mg
Conceptual Plan: **% abundance → fraction and then find atomic mass**

$$\frac{\% \text{ abundance}}{100} \qquad \text{Atomic mass} = \sum_n (\text{fraction of isotope } n) \times (\text{mass of isotope } n)$$

Solution: Fraction Si-28 $= \dfrac{92.2}{100} = 0.922$;⠀ Fraction Si-29 $= \dfrac{4.67}{100} = 0.0467$;⠀ Fraction Si-30 $= \dfrac{3.10}{100} = 0.0310$

$$\text{Atomic mass} = \sum_n (\text{fraction of isotope } n) \times (\text{mass of isotope } n)$$

$$= 0.922(27.9769 \text{ amu}) + 0.0467(28.9765 \text{ amu}) + 0.0310(29.9737 \text{ amu}) = 28.1 \text{ amu}$$

Check: Units of the answer (amu) are correct. The magnitude of the answer is reasonable because it lies between 27.9769 amu and 29.9737 amu and is closer to 27.9769 amu, which has the highest % abundance.

2.43 **Given:** isotope 1, mass $= 120.9038$ amu, 57.4%. isotope 2, mass $= 122.9042$ amu.
Find: atomic mass of the element and identify the element
Conceptual Plan:
% abundance isotope 2 → and then % abundance → fraction and then find atomic mass

$$100\% - \% \text{ abundance isotope 1} \qquad \frac{\% \text{ abundance}}{100} \qquad \text{Atomic mass} = \sum_n (\text{fraction of isotope } n) \times (\text{mass of isotope } n)$$

Solution: $100.0\% - 57.4\%$ isotope $1 = 42.6\%$ isotope 2

Fraction isotope 1 $= \dfrac{57.4}{100} = 0.574$ ⠀⠀ Fraction isotope 2 $= \dfrac{42.6}{100} = 0.426$

$$\text{Atomic mass} = \sum_n (\text{fraction of isotope } n) \times (\text{mass of isotope } n)$$

$$= 0.574(120.9038 \text{ amu}) + 0.426(122.9042 \text{ amu}) = 121.8 \text{ amu}$$

From the periodic table, Sb has a mass of 121.757 amu; so it is the closest mass, and the element is antimony.

Check: The units of the answer (amu) are correct. The magnitude of the answer is reasonable because it lies between 120.9038 and 122.9042 and is slightly less than halfway between the two values because the lower value has a slightly greater abundance.

2.44 **Given:** Br-81; mass $= 80.9163$ amu; 49.31%: atomic mass Br $= 79.904$ amu
Find: mass and abundance of Br-79
Conceptual Plan: **% abundance Br-79 → then % abundance → fraction → mass Br-79**

$$100\% - \% \text{ Br-81} \qquad \frac{\% \text{ abundance}}{100} \qquad \text{Atomic mass} = \sum_n (\text{fraction of isotope } n) \times (\text{mass of isotope } n)$$

Solution: $100.00\% - 49.31\% = 50.69\%$

Fraction Br-79 $= \dfrac{50.69}{100} = 0.5069$ ⠀ Fraction Br-81 $= \dfrac{49.31}{100} = 0.4931$

Let X be the mass of Br-79.

$$\text{Atomic mass} = \sum_n (\text{fraction of isotope } n) \times (\text{mass of isotope } n)$$

$79.904 \text{ amu} = 0.5069(X \text{ amu}) + 0.4931(80.9163 \text{ amu})$
$X = 78.92 \text{ amu} = \text{mass Br-79}$

Check: The units of the answer (amu) are correct. The magnitude of the answer is reasonable because it is less than the mass of the atom and the second isotope (Br-81) has a mass greater than the mass of the atom.

The Mole Concept

2.45   **Given:** 2.7 mol sulfur   **Find:** atoms of sulfur

        Conceptual Plan: mol S $\rightarrow$ atoms S

$$\frac{6.022 \times 10^{23} \text{ atoms}}{\text{mol}}$$

        Solution: $2.7 \text{ mol S} \times \dfrac{6.022 \times 10^{23} \text{ atoms S}}{\text{mol S}} = 1.6 \times 10^{24} \text{ atoms S}$

        Check: The units of the answer (atoms S) are correct. The magnitude of the answer is reasonable because more than 1 mole of material is present.

2.46   **Given:** 1.42×10^{24} aluminum atoms   **Find:** mol Al

        Conceptual Plan: atoms Al $\rightarrow$ mol Al

$$\frac{1 \text{ mol}}{6.022 \times 10^{23} \text{ atoms}}$$

        Solution: $1.42 \times 10^{24} \text{ atoms Al} \times \dfrac{1 \text{ mol Al}}{6.022 \times 10^{23} \text{ atoms Al}} = 2.36 \text{ mol Al}$

        Check: The units of the answer (mol Al) are correct. The magnitude of the answer is reasonable because greater than Avogadro's number of atoms is present.

2.47   (a)   **Given:** 11.8 g Ar   **Find:** mol Ar

             Conceptual Plan: g Ar $\rightarrow$ mol Ar

$$\frac{1 \text{ mol Ar}}{39.95 \text{ g Ar}}$$

             Solution: $11.8 \text{ g Ar} \times \dfrac{1 \text{ mol Ar}}{39.95 \text{ g Ar}} = 0.295 \text{ mol Ar}$

             Check: The units of the answer (mol Ar) are correct. The magnitude of the answer is reasonable because less than the mass of 1 mol is present.

      (b)   **Given:** 3.55 g Zn   **Find:** mol Zn

             Conceptual Plan: g Zn $\rightarrow$ mol Zn

$$\frac{1 \text{ mol Zn}}{65.38 \text{ g Zn}}$$

             Solution: $3.55 \text{ g Zn} \times \dfrac{1 \text{ mol Zn}}{65.38 \text{ g Zn}} = 0.0543 \text{ mol Zn}$

             Check: The units of the answer (mol Zn) are correct. The magnitude of the answer is reasonable because less than the mass of 1 mol is present.

      (c)   **Given:** 26.1 g Ta   **Find:** mol Ta

             Conceptual Plan: g Ta $\rightarrow$ mol Ta

$$\frac{1 \text{ mol Ta}}{180.95 \text{ g Ta}}$$

             Solution: $26.1 \text{ g Ta} \times \dfrac{1 \text{ mol Ta}}{180.95 \text{ g Ta}} = 0.144 \text{ mol Ta}$

             Check: The units of the answer (mol Ta) are correct. The magnitude of the answer is reasonable because less than the mass of 1 mol is present.

      (d)   **Given:** 0.211 g Li   **Find:** mol Li

             Conceptual Plan: g Li $\rightarrow$ mol Li

$$\frac{1 \text{ mol Li}}{6.941 \text{ g Li}}$$

             Solution: $0.211 \text{ g Li} \times \dfrac{1 \text{ mol Li}}{6.941 \text{ g Li}} = 0.0304 \text{ mol Li}$

Check: The units of the answer (mol Li) are correct. The magnitude of the answer is reasonable because less than the mass of 1 mol is present.

2.48   (a)   **Given:** 2.3×10^{-3} mol Sb   **Find:** grams Sb

          Conceptual Plan: mol Sb → g Sb

$$\frac{121.76 \text{ g Sb}}{1 \text{ mol Sb}}$$

          Solution: $2.3 \times 10^{-3} \text{ mol Sb} \times \dfrac{121.76 \text{ g Sb}}{1 \text{ mol Sb}} = 0.28 \text{ g Sb}$

          Check: The units of the answer (grams Sb) are correct. The magnitude of the answer is reasonable because less than 1 mol of Sb is present.

    (b)   **Given:** 0.0355 mol Ba   **Find:** grams Ba

          Conceptual Plan: mol Ba → g Ba

$$\frac{137.33 \text{ g Ba}}{1 \text{ mol Ba}}$$

          Solution: $0.0355 \text{ mol Ba} \times \dfrac{137.33 \text{ g Ba}}{1 \text{ mol Ba}} = 4.88 \text{ g Ba}$

          Check: The units of the answer (grams Ba) are correct. The magnitude of the answer is reasonable because less than 1 mol of Ba is present.

    (c)   **Given:** 43.9 mol Xe   **Find:** grams Xe

          Conceptual Plan: mol Xe → g Xe

$$\frac{131.29 \text{ g Xe}}{1 \text{ mol Xe}}$$

          Solution: $43.9 \text{ mol Xe} \times \dfrac{131.29 \text{ g Xe}}{1 \text{ mol Xe}} = 5.76 \times 10^3 \text{ g Xe}$

          Check: The units of the answer (grams Xe) are correct. The magnitude of the answer is reasonable because much more than 1 mol of Xe is present.

    (d)   **Given:** 1.3 mol W   **Find:** grams W

          Conceptual Plan: mol W → g W

$$\frac{183.84 \text{ g W}}{1 \text{ mol W}}$$

          Solution: $1.3 \text{ mol W} \times \dfrac{183.84 \text{ g W}}{1 \text{ mol W}} = 2.4 \times 10^2 \text{ g W}$

          Check: The units of the answer (grams W) are correct. The magnitude of the answer is reasonable because slightly over 1 mol of W is present.

2.49   **Given:** 2.54 g silver   **Find:** atoms Ag

    Conceptual Plan: g Ag → mol Ag → atoms Ag

$$\frac{1 \text{ mol Ag}}{107.87 \text{ g Ag}} \qquad \frac{6.022 \times 10^{23} \text{ atoms}}{\text{mol}}$$

    Solution: $2.54 \text{ g Ag} \times \dfrac{1 \text{ mol Ag}}{107.87 \text{ g Ag}} \times \dfrac{6.022 \times 10^{23} \text{ atoms Ag}}{1 \text{ mol Ag}} = 1.42 \times 10^{22} \text{ atoms Ag}$

    Check: The units of the answer (atoms Ag) are correct. The magnitude of the answer is reasonable because less than the mass of 1 mol of Ag is present.

2.50   **Given:** 9.71×10^{22} Pt atoms   **Find:** grams Pt

    Conceptual Plan: atoms Pt → mol Pt → g Pt

$$\frac{1 \text{ mol}}{6.022 \times 10^{23} \text{ atoms}} \qquad \frac{195.08 \text{ g Pt}}{1 \text{ mol Pt}}$$

    Solution: $9.71 \times 10^{22} \text{ atoms Pt} \times \dfrac{1 \text{ mol Pt}}{6.022 \times 10^{23} \text{ atoms Pt}} \times \dfrac{195.08 \text{ g Pt}}{1 \text{ mol Pt}} = 31.5 \text{ g Pt}$

    Check: The units of the answer (g Pt) are correct. The magnitude of the answer is reasonable because less than 1 mol of Pt atoms is present.

2.51   (a)   **Given:** 5.18 g P   **Find:** atoms P

    Conceptual Plan: g P → mol P → atoms P

$$\frac{1 \text{ mol P}}{30.97 \text{ g P}} \qquad \frac{6.022 \times 10^{23} \text{ atoms}}{\text{mol}}$$

    Solution: $5.18 \text{ g P} \times \dfrac{1 \text{ mol P}}{30.97 \text{ g P}} \times \dfrac{6.022 \times 10^{23} \text{ atoms P}}{1 \text{ mol P}} = 1.01 \times 10^{23} \text{ atoms P}$

    Check: The units of the answer (atoms P) are correct. The magnitude of the answer is reasonable because less than the mass of 1 mol of P is present.

  (b)   **Given:** 2.26 g Hg   **Find:** atoms Hg

    Conceptual Plan: g Hg → mol Hg → atoms Hg

$$\frac{1 \text{ mol Hg}}{200.59 \text{ g Hg}} \qquad \frac{6.022 \times 10^{23} \text{ atoms}}{\text{mol}}$$

    Solution: $2.26 \text{ g Hg} \times \dfrac{1 \text{ mol Hg}}{200.59 \text{ g Hg}} \times \dfrac{6.022 \times 10^{23} \text{ atoms Hg}}{1 \text{ mol Hg}} = 6.78 \times 10^{21} \text{ atoms Hg}$

    Check: The units of the answer (atoms Hg) are correct. The magnitude of the answer is reasonable because much less than the mass of 1 mol of Hg is present.

  (c)   **Given:** 1.87 g Bi   **Find:** atoms Bi

    Conceptual Plan: g Bi → mol Bi → atoms Bi

$$\frac{1 \text{ mol Bi}}{208.98 \text{ g Bi}} \qquad \frac{6.022 \times 10^{23} \text{ atoms}}{\text{mol}}$$

    Solution: $1.87 \text{ g Bi} \times \dfrac{1 \text{ mol Bi}}{208.98 \text{ g Bi}} \times \dfrac{6.022 \times 10^{23} \text{ atoms Bi}}{1 \text{ mol Bi}} = 5.39 \times 10^{21} \text{ atoms Bi}$

    Check: The units of the answer (atoms Bi) are correct. The magnitude of the answer is reasonable because less than the mass of 1 mol of Bi is present.

  (d)   **Given:** 0.082 g Sr   **Find:** atoms Sr

    Conceptual Plan: g Sr → mol Sr → atoms Sr

$$\frac{1 \text{ mol Sr}}{87.62 \text{ g Sr}} \qquad \frac{6.022 \times 10^{23} \text{ atoms}}{\text{mol}}$$

    Solution: $0.082 \text{ g Sr} \times \dfrac{1 \text{ mol Sr}}{87.62 \text{ g Sr}} \times \dfrac{6.022 \times 10^{23} \text{ atoms Sr}}{1 \text{ mol Sr}} = 5.6 \times 10^{20} \text{ atoms Sr}$

    Check: The units of the answer (atoms Sr) are correct. The magnitude of the answer is reasonable because less than the mass of 1 mol of Sr is present.

2.52   (a)   **Given:** 1.1×10^{23} gold atoms   **Find:** grams Au

    Conceptual Plan: atoms Au → mol Au → g Au

$$\frac{1 \text{ mol}}{6.022 \times 10^{23} \text{ atoms}} \qquad \frac{196.97 \text{ g Au}}{1 \text{ mol Au}}$$

    Solution: $1.1 \times 10^{23} \text{ atoms Au} \times \dfrac{1 \text{ mol Au}}{6.022 \times 10^{23} \text{ atoms Au}} \times \dfrac{196.97 \text{ g Au}}{1 \text{ mol Au}} = 36 \text{ g Au}$

    Check: The units of the answer (g Au) are correct. The magnitude of the answer is reasonable because fewer than Avogadro's number of atoms is in the sample.

  (b)   **Given:** 2.82×10^{22} helium atoms   **Find:** grams He

    Conceptual Plan: atoms He → mol He → g He

$$\frac{1 \text{ mol}}{6.022 \times 10^{23} \text{ atoms}} \qquad \frac{4.003 \text{ g He}}{1 \text{ mol He}}$$

    Solution: $2.82 \times 10^{22} \text{ atoms He} \times \dfrac{1 \text{ mol He}}{6.022 \times 10^{23} \text{ atoms He}} \times \dfrac{4.003 \text{ g He}}{1 \text{ mol He}} = 0.187 \text{ g He}$

    Check: The units of the answer (g He) are correct. The magnitude of the answer is reasonable because fewer than Avogadro's number of atoms is in the sample.

(c)   **Given:** 1.8×10^{23} lead atoms   **Find:** grams Pb

    Conceptual Plan: atoms Pb → mol Pb → g Pb

$$\frac{1\ mol}{6.022 \times 10^{23}\ atoms} \quad \frac{207.2\ g\ Pb}{1\ mol\ Pb}$$

Solution: 1.8×10^{23} atoms Pb $\times \dfrac{1\ mol\ Pb}{6.022 \times 10^{23}\ atoms\ Pb} \times \dfrac{207.2\ g\ Pb}{1\ mol\ Pb} = 62\ g\ Pb$

Check: The units of the answer (g Pb) are correct. The magnitude of the answer is reasonable because fewer than Avogadro's number of atoms is in the sample.

(d)   **Given:** 7.9×10^{21} uranium atoms   **Find:** grams U

    Conceptual Plan: atoms U → mol U → g U

$$\frac{1\ mol}{6.022 \times 10^{23}\ atoms} \quad \frac{238.03\ g\ U}{1\ mol\ U}$$

Solution: 7.9×10^{21} atoms U $\times \dfrac{1\ mol\ U}{6.022 \times 10^{23}\ atoms\ U} \times \dfrac{238.03\ g\ U}{1\ mol\ U} = 3.1\ g\ U$

Check: The units of the answer (g U) are correct. The magnitude of the answer is reasonable because fewer than Avogadro's number of atoms is in the sample.

2.53   **Given:** 83 mg diamond (carbon)   **Find:** atoms C

    Conceptual Plan: mg C → g C → mol C → atoms C

$$\frac{1\ g\ C}{1000\ mg\ C} \quad \frac{1\ mol\ C}{12.01\ g\ C} \quad \frac{6.022 \times 10^{23}\ atoms}{mol}$$

Solution: 83 mg C $\times \dfrac{1\ g\ C}{1000\ mg\ C} \times \dfrac{1\ mol\ C}{12.01\ g\ C} \times \dfrac{6.022 \times 10^{23}\ atoms\ C}{1\ mol\ C} = 4.2 \times 10^{21}$ atoms C

Check: The units of the answer (atoms C) are correct. The magnitude of the answer is reasonable because less than the mass of 1 mol of C is present.

2.54   **Given:** 427 kg helium   **Find:** atoms He

    Conceptual Plan: kg He → g He → mol He → atoms He

$$\frac{1000\ g\ He}{1\ kg\ He} \quad \frac{1\ mol\ He}{4.003\ g\ He} \quad \frac{6.022 \times 10^{23}\ atoms}{mol}$$

Solution: 427 kg He $\times \dfrac{1000\ g\ He}{1\ kg\ He} \times \dfrac{1\ mol\ He}{4.003\ g\ He} \times \dfrac{6.022 \times 10^{23}\ atoms\ He}{1\ mol\ He} = 6.42 \times 10^{28}$ atoms He

Check: The units of the answer (atoms He) are correct. The magnitude of the answer is reasonable because much more than the mass of 1 mol of He is present.

2.55   **Given:** 1 atom platinum   **Find:** grams Pt

    Conceptual Plan: atoms Pt → mol Pt → g Pt

$$\frac{1\ mol}{6.022 \times 10^{23}\ atoms} \quad \frac{195.08\ g\ Pt}{1\ mol\ Pt}$$

Solution: 1 atom Pt $\times \dfrac{1\ mol\ Pt}{6.022 \times 10^{23}\ atoms\ Pt} \times \dfrac{195.08\ g\ Pt}{1\ mol\ Pt} = 3.239 \times 10^{-22}\ g\ Pt$

Check: The units of the answer (g Pt) are correct. The magnitude of the answer is reasonable because only 1 atom is in the sample.

2.56   **Given:** 35 atoms xenon   **Find:** grams Xe

    Conceptual Plan: atoms Xe → mol Xe → g Xe

$$\frac{1\ mol}{6.022 \times 10^{23}\ atoms} \quad \frac{131.29\ g\ Xe}{1\ mol\ Xe}$$

Solution: 35 atom Xe $\times \dfrac{1\ mol\ Xe}{6.022 \times 10^{23}\ atoms\ Xe} \times \dfrac{131.29\ g\ Xe}{1\ mol\ Xe} = 7.631 \times 10^{-21}\ g\ Xe$

Check: The units of the answer (g Xe) are correct. The magnitude of the answer is reasonable because only 35 atoms are in the sample.

Cumulative Problems

2.57   **Given:** 7.83 g HCN sample 1: 0.290 g H; 4.06 g N. 3.37 g HCN sample 2   **Find:** g C in sample 2
Conceptual Plan: g HCN sample 1 → g C in HCN sample 1 → ratio g C to g HCN → g C in HCN sample 2

$$g\,HCN - g\,H - g\,N \qquad \frac{g\,C}{g\,HCN} \qquad g\,HCN \times \frac{g\,C}{g\,HCN}$$

Solution: $7.83\,g\,HCN - 0.290\,g\,H - 4.06\,g\,N = 3.48\,g\,C$

$$3.37\,\cancel{g\,HCN} \times \frac{3.48\,g\,C}{7.83\,\cancel{g\,HCN}} = 1.50\,g\,C$$

Check: The units of the answer (g C) are correct. The magnitude of the answer is reasonable because the sample size is about half the original sample size and the g C are about half the original g C.

2.58   (a)   **Given:** mass ratio S:O = 1.0:1.0 in SO_2 **Find:** mass ratio S:O in SO_3
Conceptual Plan: Determine the ratio of O:O in SO_3 and SO_2; then determine g O per g S in SO_3.

Solution: For a fixed amount of S, the ratio of O is $\dfrac{3\,O}{2\,O} = 1.5$. So for 1 gram S, SO_3 would have 1.5 g O.

The mass ratio of S:O = 1.0:1.5, that is 2.0:3.0, in SO_3.

Check: The answer is reasonable because the ratio is smaller than the ratio for SO_2 and SO_3 has to contain more O per gram of S.

   (b)   **Given:** mass ratio S:O = 1.0:1.0 in SO_2 **Find:** mass ratio S:O in S_2O
Conceptual Plan: Determine the ratio of S:S in S_2O and SO_2; then determine g O per g S in S_2O.

Solution: For a fixed amount of O, the ratio of S is $\dfrac{2\,S}{0.5\,S} = 4.0$. So for 1 gram O, S_2O would have 4 grams S.
The mass ratio of S:O = 4.0:1.0 in S_2O.

Check: The answer is reasonable because the ratio is larger than the ratio for SO_2 and S_2O has to contain more S per gram of O.

2.59   **Given:** in CO, mass ratio O:C = 1.33:1; in compound X, mass ratio O:C = 2:1.   **Find:** formula of X
Conceptual Plan: Determine the mass ratio of O:O in the two compounds.

Solution: For 1 gram of C $\dfrac{2\,g\,O\ in\ compound\ X}{1.33\,g\,O\ in\ CO} = 1.5$

So the ratio of O to C in compound X has to be 1.5 : 1, and the formula is C_2O_3.

Check: The answer is reasonable because it fulfills the criteria of multiple proportions and the mass ratio of O:C is 2:1.

2.60   **Given:** mass ratio 1 atom N:1 atom ^{12}C = 7:6; mass ratio 2 mol N:1 mol O in N_2O = 7:4   **Find:** mass of 1 mol O
Conceptual Plan: Determine the mass ratio of O to ^{12}C from the mass ratio of N to ^{12}C and the mass ratio of N to O, determine the mol ratio of ^{12}C to O, and then use the mass of 1 mol ^{12}C to determine mass 1 mol O.

$$\frac{12.00\,g\,^{12}C}{1\,mol\,^{12}C}$$

Solution: From the mass ratios, for every 7 grams N, there are 6 grams ^{12}C and for every 7 grams N there are 4 grams O. So the mass ratio of O to ^{12}C is 4:6.

$$\frac{1\,atom\,^{12}C}{1\,atom\,N} \times \frac{6.022 \times 10^{23}\,atom\,N}{1\,mol\,N} \times \frac{1\,mol\,^{12}C}{6.022 \times 10^{23}\,atom\,^{12}C} \times \frac{2\,mol\,N}{1\,mol\,O} = \frac{2\,mol\,^{12}C}{1\,mol\,O}$$

$$\frac{2\,mol\,^{12}C}{1\,mol\,O} \times \frac{12.00\,g\,^{12}C}{1\,mol\,^{12}C} \times \frac{4\,g\,O}{6\,g\,^{12}C} = 16.00\,g\,O/mol\,O$$

Check: The units of the answer (g O/mol O) are correct. The magnitude of the answer is reasonable because it is close to the value on the periodic table.

2.61   **Given:** $^4He^{2+}$ = 4.00151 amu   **Find:** charge to mass ratio C/kg
Conceptual Plan: Determine total charge on $^4He^{2+}$ and then amu $^4He^{2+}$ → g $^4He^{2+}$ → kg $^4He^{2+}$.

$$\frac{+1.60218 \times 10^{-19}\,C}{proton} \qquad \frac{1\,g}{1.66054 \times 10^{-24}\,amu} \qquad \frac{1\,kg}{1000\,g}$$

44 **Chapter 2** Atoms and Elements

Solution: $\dfrac{2\ \text{protons}}{1\ \text{atom }^4\text{He}^{2+}} \times \dfrac{+1.60218 \times 10^{-19}\ \text{C}}{\text{proton}} = \dfrac{3.20436 \times 10^{-19}\ \text{C}}{\text{atom }^4\text{He}^{2+}}$

$$\dfrac{4.00151\ \text{amu}}{1\ \text{atom }^4\text{He}^{2+}} \times \dfrac{1.66054 \times 10^{-24}\ \text{g}}{1\ \text{amu}} \times \dfrac{1\ \text{kg}}{1000\ \text{g}} = \dfrac{6.64466742 \times 10^{-27}\ \text{kg}}{1\ \text{atom }^4\text{He}^{2+}}$$

$$\dfrac{3.20436 \times 10^{-19}\ \text{C}}{\text{atom }^4\text{He}^{2+}} \times \dfrac{1\ \text{atom }^4\text{He}^{2+}}{6.64466742 \times 10^{-27}\ \text{kg}} = 4.82245 \times 10^{7}\ \text{C/kg}$$

Check: The units of the answer (C/kg) are correct. The magnitude of the answer is reasonable when compared to the charge to mass ratio of the electron.

2.62   **Given:** 12.3849 g sample I; atomic mass I = 126.9045 amu; 1.00070g ^{129}I; mass ^{129}I = 128.9050 amu
Find: mass of contaminated sample
Conceptual Plan: total mass of sample → fraction I and ^{129}I in the sample → apparent "atomic mass"

$\text{mass I} + \text{mass }^{129}\text{I}$ $\dfrac{\text{g I}}{\text{g sample}}; \dfrac{\text{g }^{129}\text{I}}{\text{g sample}}$ $\text{Atomic mass} = \sum_{n}(\text{fraction of isotope } n) \times (\text{mass of isotope } n)$

Solution: 12.3849 g I + 1.00070 g ^{129}I = 13.3856 g sample

$$\dfrac{12.3849\ \text{g}}{13.3856\ \text{g}} = 0.925240557\ \text{fraction I} \qquad \dfrac{1.00070\ \text{g}}{13.3856\ \text{g}} = 0.07475944\ \text{fraction }^{129}\text{I}$$

$\text{Atomic mass} = \sum_{n}(\text{fraction of isotope } n) \times (\text{mass of isotope } n)$

$= (0.925240557)(126.9045\ \text{amu}) + (0.07475944)(128.9050\ \text{amu})$

$= 127.054\ \text{amu}$

Check: The units of the answer (amu) are correct. The magnitude of the answer is reasonable because it is between 126.9045 and 128.9050 and only slightly higher than the naturally occurring value.

2.63 $^{236}_{90}$Th A − Z = number of neutrons. 236 − 90 = 146 neutrons. So any nucleus with 146 neutrons is an isotone of $^{236}_{90}$Th.

Some would be $^{238}_{92}$U, $^{239}_{93}$Np, $^{241}_{95}$Am, $^{237}_{91}$Pa, $^{235}_{89}$Ac, and $^{244}_{98}$Cf.

2.64

Symbol	Z	A	Number Protons	Number Electrons	Number Neutrons	Charge
Si	14	28	14	14	14	0
S^{2-}	16	32	16	18	16	2−
Cu^{2+}	29	63	29	27	34	2+
P	15	31	15	15	16	0

2.65

Symbol	Z	A	Number Protons	Number Electrons	Number Neutrons	Charge
O^{2-}	8	16	8	10	8	2−
Ca^{2+}	20	40	20	18	20	2+
Mg^{2+}	12	25	12	10	13	2+
N^{3-}	7	14	7	10	7	3−

2.66   **Given:** r (neutron) = 1.0×10^{-13} cm; r(star piece) = 0.10 mm   **Find:** density of neutron; mass (kg) of star piece
Conceptual Plan: r (neutron) → vol (neutron) → density (neutron) and then r (star piece) → vol (star piece)

$$V = \tfrac{4}{3}\pi r^3 \qquad\qquad d = \dfrac{m}{V} \qquad\qquad V = \tfrac{4}{3}\pi r^3$$

→ **mass (star piece)**

$$m = dV$$

Copyright © 2016 Pearson Education, Inc.

Solution:

For the neutron:

$$\text{Vol(neutron)} = \frac{4}{3}\pi(1.0 \times 10^{-13}\text{cm})^3 = 4.\underline{1}9 \times 10^{-39}\text{cm}^3 \quad d = \frac{1.00866 \text{ amu}}{4.\underline{1}9 \times 10^{-39}\text{cm}^3} \times \frac{1.661 \times 10^{-24}\text{g}}{\text{amu}}$$

$$= 3.\underline{9}9 \times 10^{14} \text{ g/cm}^3$$

For the star piece:

$$\text{Vol(star piece)} = \frac{4}{3}\pi(0.10 \text{ mm})^3\frac{(1 \text{ cm})^3}{(10 \text{ mm})^3} = 4.\underline{1}9 \times 10^{-6} \text{ cm}^3; \quad m = 4.\underline{1}9 \times 10^{-6} \text{ cm}^3 \times \frac{3.\underline{9}9 \times 10^{14} \text{ g}}{\text{cm}^3} \times \frac{1 \text{ kg}}{1000 \text{ g}}$$

$$= 1.7 \times 10^6 \text{ kg}$$

Check: The units of the answer (kg) are correct. The magnitude of the answer shows the great mass of the neutron star.

2.67 **Given:** $r(\text{nucleus}) = 2.7$ fm; $r(\text{atom}) = 70$ pm (assume two significant figures)
Find: vol(nucleus); vol(atom); % vol(nucleus)
Conceptual Plan:
$r(\text{nucleus})(\text{fm}) \rightarrow r(\text{nucleus})(\text{pm}) \rightarrow \text{vol(nucleus)}$ **and then** $r(\text{atom}) \rightarrow \text{vol(atom)}$ **and then % vol**

$$\frac{10^{-15}\text{ m}}{1 \text{ fm}} \quad \frac{1 \text{ pm}}{10^{-12}\text{ m}} \qquad V = \frac{4}{3}\pi r^3 \qquad\qquad V = \frac{4}{3}\pi r^3 \quad \frac{\text{vol(nucleus)}}{\text{vol(atom)}} \times 100$$

Solution:

$$2.7 \text{ fm} \times \frac{10^{-15}\text{ m}}{\text{fm}} \times \frac{1 \text{ pm}}{10^{-12}\text{ m}} = 2.7 \times 10^{-3} \text{ pm} \qquad V_{\text{nucleus}} = \frac{4}{3}\pi(2.7 \times 10^{-3}\text{ pm})^3 = 8.2 \times 10^{-8} \text{ pm}^3$$

$$V_{\text{atom}} = \frac{4}{3}\pi(70 \text{ pm})^3 = 1.4 \times 10^6 \text{ pm}^3 \qquad \frac{8.2 \times 10^{-8}\text{ pm}^3}{1.4 \times 10^6 \text{ pm}^3} \times 100\% = 5.9 \times 10^{-12}\%$$

Check: The units of the answer (% vol) are correct. The magnitude of the answer is reasonable because the nucleus occupies only a very small % of the vol of the atom.

2.68 **Given:** 1 penny = 1.0 mm **Find:** height in km of Avogadro's number of pennies
Conceptual Plan: height of 1 penny $\rightarrow$ **height of Avogadro's number of pennies**
$$6.022 \times 10^{23}$$

Solution: $\dfrac{1.0 \text{ mm}}{\text{penny}} \times 6.022 \times 10^{23} \text{ pennies} \times \dfrac{1 \text{ m}}{1000 \text{ mm}} \times \dfrac{1 \text{ km}}{1000 \text{ m}} = 6.0 \times 10^{17} \text{ km}$

Check: The units of the answer (km) are correct. The magnitude of the answer shows just how large Avogadro's number is.

2.69 **Given:** 6.022×10^{23} pennies **Find:** the amount in dollars; the dollars/person
Conceptual Plan: pennies $\rightarrow$ **dollars** $\rightarrow$ **dollars/person**
$$\frac{1 \text{ dollar}}{100 \text{ pennies}} \qquad 6.8 \text{ billion people}$$

Solution:

$$6.022 \times 10^{23} \text{ pennies} \times \frac{1 \text{ dollar}}{100 \text{ pennies}} = 6.022 \times 10^{21}\text{dollars} \qquad \frac{6.022 \times 10^{21} \text{ dollars}}{6.8 \times 10^9 \text{ people}} = 8.9 \times 10^{11} \text{ dollars/person}$$

They are billionaires.

2.70 **Given:** 1 mol blueberries, $m = 0.75$ g; $m(\text{automobile}) = 2.0 \times 10^3$ kg **Find:** number of autos for 1 mol blueberries
Conceptual Plan:
mol blueberries $\rightarrow$ **mass blueberries (g)** $\rightarrow$ **mass blueberries (kg)** $\rightarrow$ **number of automobiles**
$$\frac{0.75 \text{ g}}{\text{blueberry}} \qquad\qquad \frac{1 \text{ kg}}{1000 \text{ g}} \qquad\qquad \frac{1 \text{ automobile}}{2.0 \times 10^3\text{kg}}$$

Solution:

$$1 \text{ mol blueberries} \times \frac{6.022 \times 10^{23} \text{ blueberries}}{\text{mol blueberries}} \times \frac{0.75 \text{ g}}{\text{blueberry}} \times \frac{1 \text{ kg}}{1000 \text{ g}} \times \frac{1 \text{ automobile}}{2.0 \times 10^3 \text{ kg}} = 2.3 \times 10^{17} \text{ automobiles}$$

Check: The units of the answer (automobiles) are correct. The magnitude of the answer is reasonable because Avogadro's number is so large.

2.71   **Given:** O = 16.00 amu when C = 12.01 amu   **Find:** mass O when C = 12.000 amu

Conceptual Plan: Determine ratio O:C for ^{12}C system; then use the same ratio when C = 12.00.

$$\frac{\text{mass O}}{\text{mass C}}$$

Solution: Based on ^{12}C = 12.00, O = 16.00 and C = 12.01; so $\dfrac{\text{mass O}}{\text{mass C}} = \dfrac{16.00 \text{ amu}}{12.01 \text{ amu}} = \dfrac{1.33\underline{2}2 \text{ amu O}}{1 \text{ amu C}}$

Based on C = 12.00, the ratio has to be the same:

$$12.000 \ \cancel{\text{amu C}} \times \frac{1.33\underline{2}2 \text{ amu O}}{1 \ \cancel{\text{amu C}}} = 15.9\underline{8}6 \text{ amu O} = 15.99 \text{ amu O}$$

Check: The units of the answer (amu O) are correct. The magnitude of the answer is reasonable because the value for the new mass basis is smaller than the original mass basis; therefore, the mass of O should be less.

2.72   **Given:** Ti cube: $d = 4.50 \text{ g/cm}^3$; $e = 2.78$ in   **Find:** number of Ti atoms

Conceptual Plan: e in inch $\rightarrow$ e in cm $\rightarrow$ vol cube $\rightarrow$ g Ti $\rightarrow$ mol Ti $\rightarrow$ atoms Ti

$$\frac{2.54 \text{ cm}}{1 \text{ in}} \qquad V = e^3 \qquad \frac{4.50 \text{ g}}{\text{cm}^3} \quad \frac{1 \text{ mol Ti}}{47.87 \text{ g}} \quad \frac{6.022 \times 10^{23} \text{ atoms}}{\text{mol}}$$

Solution: $2.78 \ \cancel{\text{in}} \times \dfrac{2.54 \text{ cm}}{\cancel{\text{in}}} = 7.0\underline{6}1 \text{ cm}$

$$(7.0\underline{6}1 \ \cancel{\text{cm}})^3 \times \frac{4.50 \ \cancel{\text{g}}}{\cancel{\text{cm}^3}} \times \frac{1 \ \cancel{\text{mol Ti}}}{47.87 \ \cancel{\text{g}}} \times \frac{6.022 \times 10^{23} \text{ atoms Ti}}{1 \ \cancel{\text{mol Ti}}} = 1.99 \times 10^{25} \text{ atoms Ti}$$

Check: The units of the answer (atoms Ti) are correct. The magnitude of the answer is reasonable because about 30 mol of Ti is in the cube.

2.73   **Given:** Cu sphere: $r = 0.935$ in; $d = 8.96 \text{ g/cm}^3$ **Find:** number of Cu atoms

Conceptual Plan: r in inch $\rightarrow$ r in cm $\rightarrow$ vol sphere $\rightarrow$ g Cu $\rightarrow$ mol Cu $\rightarrow$ atoms Cu

$$\frac{2.54 \text{ cm}}{1 \text{ in}} \qquad V = \frac{4}{3}\pi r^3 \qquad \frac{8.96 \text{ g}}{\text{cm}^3} \quad \frac{1 \text{ mol Cu}}{63.55 \text{ g}} \quad \frac{6.022 \times 10^{23} \text{ atoms}}{\text{mol}}$$

Solution: $0.935 \ \cancel{\text{in}} \times \dfrac{2.54 \text{ cm}}{\cancel{\text{in}}} = 2.3\underline{7}49 \text{ cm}$

$$\frac{4}{3}\pi(2.3\underline{7}49 \ \cancel{\text{cm}})^3 \times \frac{8.96 \ \cancel{\text{g}}}{\cancel{\text{cm}^3}} \times \frac{1 \ \cancel{\text{mol Cu}}}{63.55 \ \cancel{\text{g}}} \times \frac{6.022 \times 10^{23} \text{ atoms Cu}}{1 \ \cancel{\text{mol Cu}}} = 4.76 \times 10^{24} \text{ atoms Cu}$$

Check: The units of the answer (atoms Cu) are correct. The magnitude of the answer is reasonable because about 8 mol Cu are present.

2.74   **Given:** Cu sphere: 1.14×10^{24} copper atoms; $d = 8.96 \text{ g/cm}^3$ **Find:** r in cm

Conceptual Plan: atoms Cu $\rightarrow$ mol Cu $\rightarrow$ g Cu $\rightarrow$ vol sphere $\rightarrow$ r

$$\frac{1 \text{ mole}}{6.022 \times 10^{23} \text{ atoms}} \quad \frac{63.55 \text{ g Cu}}{1 \text{ mol Cu}} \quad \frac{1 \text{ cm}^3}{8.96 \text{ g}} \qquad V = \frac{4}{3}\pi r^3$$

Solution: $1.14 \times 10^{24} \ \cancel{\text{Cu atoms}} \times \dfrac{1 \ \cancel{\text{mol Cu}}}{6.022 \times 10^{23} \ \cancel{\text{Cu atoms}}} \times \dfrac{63.55 \ \cancel{\text{g Cu}}}{1 \ \cancel{\text{mole Cu}}} \times \dfrac{1 \text{ cm}^3}{8.96 \ \cancel{\text{g Cu}}} = 13.\underline{4}26773 \text{ cm}^3$

$V = \dfrac{4}{3}\pi r^3$ Rearrange to solve for r. $r = \sqrt[3]{\dfrac{3V}{4\pi}} = \sqrt[3]{\dfrac{3(13.\underline{4}26773 \text{ cm}^3)}{4\pi}} = 1.47 \text{ cm}$

Check: The units (cm) are correct. The magnitude of the answer (1.47) makes physical sense because there is over a mole of Cu and the density of Cu is almost 10 g/cm^3.

2.75   **Given:** Ti cube: 2.55×10^{24} titanium atoms; $d = 4.50 \text{ g/cm}^3$ **Find:** e in cm

Conceptual Plan: atoms Ti $\rightarrow$ mol Ti $\rightarrow$ g Ti $\rightarrow$ vol cube $\rightarrow$ e

$$\frac{1 \text{ mole}}{6.022 \times 10^{23} \text{ atoms}} \quad \frac{47.87 \text{ g Ti}}{1 \text{ mol Ti}} \quad \frac{1 \text{ cm}^3}{4.50 \text{ g}} \qquad V = e^3$$

Solution: 2.55×10^{24} Ti-atoms $\times \dfrac{1 \text{ mol Ti}}{6.022 \times 10^{23} \text{ Ti atoms}} \times \dfrac{47.87 \text{ g Ti}}{1 \text{ mole Ti}} \times \dfrac{1 \text{ cm}^3}{4.50 \text{ g Ti}} = 45.0\underline{4}539 \text{ cm}^3$

$V = e^3$ Rearrange to solve for e. $\quad e = \sqrt[3]{V} = \sqrt[3]{45.0\underline{4}539 \text{ cm}^3} = 3.56 \text{ cm}$

Check: The units (cm) are correct. The magnitude of the answer (3.56) makes physical sense because there is over a mole of Ti and the density of Ti is almost 5 g/cm^3.

2.76 **Given:** B-10 = 10.01294 amu; B-11 = 11.00931 amu; B = 10.81 amu **Find:** % abundance B-10 and B-11
Conceptual Plan: Let x = fraction B-10, then $1 - x$ = fraction B-11 → abundances

$$\text{Atomic mass} = \sum_n (\text{fraction of isotope } n) \times (\text{mass of isotope } n)$$

Solution: Atomic mass $= \displaystyle\sum_n (\text{fraction of isotope } n) \times (\text{mass of isotope } n)$

$10.81 = (x)(10.01294 \text{ amu}) + (1 - x)(11.00931 \text{ amu})$
$0.19\underline{9}31 = 0.99637x$
$x = 0.2\underline{0}0 \qquad 1 - x = 0.8\underline{0}0$
B-10 $= 0.2\underline{0}0 \times 100 = 20.\%$ and B-11 $= 0.8\underline{0}0 \times 100 = 80.\%$

Check: The units of the answer (%, which gives the relative abundance of each isotope) are correct.
The relative abundances are reasonable because B has an atomic mass closer to the mass of B-11 than to B-10.

2.77 **Given:** Li-6 = 6.01512 amu; Li-7 = 7.01601 amu; Li = 6.941 amu
Find: % abundance Li-6 and Li-7
Conceptual Plan: Let x = fraction Li-6 then $1 - x$ = fraction Li-7 → abundances

$$\text{Atomic mass} = \sum_n (\text{fraction of isotope } n) \times (\text{mass of isotope } n)$$

Solution: Atomic mass $= \displaystyle\sum_n (\text{fraction of isotope } n) \times (\text{mass of isotope } n)$

$6.941 = (x)(6.01512 \text{ amu}) + (1 - x)(7.01601 \text{ amu})$
$0.07\underline{5}01 = 1.00089x$
$x = 0.07\underline{4}94 \qquad 1 - x = 0.92\underline{5}06$
Li-6 $= 0.07\underline{4}94 \times 100 = 7.5\%$ and Li-7 $= 0.92\underline{5}06 \times 100\% = 92.5\%$

Check: The units of the answer (%, which gives the relative abundance of each isotope) are correct.
The relative abundances are reasonable because Li has an atomic mass closer to the mass of Li-7 than to Li-6.

2.78 **Given:** brass: 37.0% Zn; $d = 8.48$ g/cm^3; volume $= 112.5$ cm^3 **Find:** atoms of Zn and Cu
Conceptual Plan: volume sample → g sample → g Zn → mole Zn → atoms Zn

$$\dfrac{8.48 \text{ g}}{\text{cm}^3} \qquad \dfrac{37.0 \text{ g Zn}}{100.0 \text{ g sample}} \qquad \dfrac{1 \text{ mol Zn}}{65.38 \text{ g Zn}} \qquad \dfrac{6.022 \times 10^{23} \text{ atoms}}{\text{mol}}$$

→ g Cu → moles Cu → atoms Cu

$$\text{g sample} - \text{g Zn} \qquad \dfrac{1 \text{ mol Cu}}{63.55 \text{ g Cu}} \qquad \dfrac{6.022 \times 10^{23} \text{ atoms}}{\text{mol}}$$

Solution: $112.5 \text{ cm}^3 \times \dfrac{8.48 \text{ g}}{\text{cm}^3} = 95\underline{4}.0 \text{ g sample} \qquad 95\underline{4}.0 \text{ g sample} \times \dfrac{37.0 \text{ g Zn}}{100.0 \text{ g sample}} = 35\underline{2}.98 \text{ g Zn}$

$35\underline{2}.98 \text{ g Zn} \times \dfrac{1 \text{ mol Zn}}{65.38 \text{ g Zn}} \times \dfrac{6.022 \times 10^{23} \text{ atoms Zn}}{\text{mol Zn}} = 3.2\underline{5}12 \times 10^{24} \text{ atoms Zn} = 3.25 \times 10^{24} \text{ atoms Zn}$

$95\underline{4}.0 \text{ g sample} - 35\underline{2}.98 \text{ g Zn} = 60\underline{1}.02 \text{ g Cu}$

$60\underline{1}.02 \text{ g Cu} \times \dfrac{1 \text{ mol Cu}}{63.55 \text{ g Cu}} \times \dfrac{6.022 \times 10^{23} \text{ atoms Cu}}{\text{mol Cu}} = 5.6\underline{9}53 \times 10^{24} \text{ atoms Cu} = 5.70 \times 10^{24} \text{ atoms Cu}$

Check: The units of the answer (atoms of Zn and atoms of Cu) are correct. The magnitude is reasonable because there is more than 1 mole of each element in the sample.

2.79 **Given:** Alloy of Au and Pd = 67.2 g; 2.49×10^{23} atoms **Find:** % composition by mass
Conceptual Plan: atoms Au and Pd → mol Au and Pd → g Au and Pd → g Au

$$\dfrac{1 \text{ mol}}{6.022 \times 10^{23} \text{ atoms}} \qquad \dfrac{196.97 \text{ g Au}}{1 \text{ mol Au}}, \qquad \dfrac{106.42 \text{ g Pd}}{1 \text{ mol Pd}}$$

Solution: Let X = atoms Au and Y = atoms Pd; develop expressions that will permit atoms to be related to moles and then to grams.

$$(\text{X atoms Au})\left(\frac{1\text{ mol Au}}{6.022\times10^{23}\text{ atoms Au}}\right)=\frac{X}{6.022\times10^{23}}\text{ mol Au}$$

$$(\text{Y atoms Pd})\left(\frac{1\text{ mol Pd}}{6.022\times10^{23}\text{ atoms Pd}}\right)=\frac{Y}{6.022\times10^{23}}\text{ mol Pd}$$

$$X + Y = 2.49\times10^{23}\text{ atoms}; \quad Y = 2.49\times10^{23}-X$$

$$\left(\frac{X}{6.022\times10^{23}}\text{ mol Au}\right)\left(\frac{196.97\text{ g Au}}{\text{mol Au}}\right)=\frac{196.97X}{6.022\times10^{23}}\text{ g Au}$$

$$\left(\frac{2.49\times10^{23}-X}{6.022\times10^{23}}\text{ mol Pd}\right)\left(\frac{106.42\text{ g Pd}}{\text{mol Pd}}\right)=\frac{106.42(2.49\times10^{23}-X)}{6.022\times10^{23}}\text{ g Pd}$$

g Au + g Pd = 67.2 g total

$$\frac{196.97X}{6.022\times10^{23}}\text{ g Au}+\frac{106.42(2.49\times10^{23}-X)}{6.022\times10^{23}}\text{ g Pd}=67.2\text{ g}$$

$$X = 1.5426\times10^{23}\text{ atoms Au}$$

$$(1.5426\times10^{23}\text{ atoms Au})\left(\frac{1\text{ mol Au}}{6.022\times10^{23}\text{ atoms Au}}\right)\left(\frac{196.97\text{ g Au}}{\text{mol Au}}\right)=50.46\text{ g Au}$$

$$\left(\frac{50.46\text{ g Au}}{67.2\text{ g sample}}\right)\times100=75.08\%\text{ Au}=75.1\%\text{ Au}$$

% Pd = 100.0% − 75.1% Au = 24.9% Pd

Check: Units of the answer (% composition) is correct.

2.80   **Given:** Air contains 1.5 μg Pb/m³; lung volume = 5.50 L   **Find:** atoms of Pb in lungs

        Conceptual Plan: lung in L → mL → cm³ → m³ → μg Pb → g Pb → mol Pb → atoms Pb

$$\frac{1000\text{ mL}}{1\text{ L}}\quad\frac{1\text{ cm}^3}{1\text{ mL}}\quad\frac{1\text{ m}^3}{(100\text{ cm})^3}\quad\frac{1.5\ \mu g\text{ Pb}}{\text{m}^3}\quad\frac{1\text{ g Pb}}{10^6\ \mu g\text{ Pb}}\quad\frac{1\text{ mol Pb}}{207.2\text{ g Pb}}\quad\frac{6.022\times10^{23}\text{ atoms Pb}}{1\text{ mol Pb}}$$

        Solution: $5.50\text{ L}\times\left(\dfrac{1000\text{ mL}}{1\text{ L}}\right)\times\left(\dfrac{1\text{ cm}^3}{1\text{ mL}}\right)\times\left(\dfrac{1\text{ m}^3}{(100\text{ cm})^3}\right)\times\left(\dfrac{1.5\ \mu g\text{ Pb}}{\text{m}^3}\right)\times\left(\dfrac{1\text{ g Pb}}{10^6\ \mu g\text{ Pb}}\right)$

$$\times\left(\frac{1\text{ mol Pb}}{207.2\text{ g Pb}}\right)\times\left(\frac{6.022\times10^{23}\text{ atoms Pb}}{1\text{ mol Pb}}\right)=2.398\times10^{13}\text{ atoms Pb}=2.4\times10^{13}\text{ atoms Pb}$$

        Check: The units of the answer (atoms Pb) are correct. The magnitude of the answer is reasonable because about 400 nmol of Pb is present.

2.81   **Given:** 0.255 ounce 18K Au   **Find:** atoms Au   **Other:** 18K Au is 75% Au by mass

        Conceptual Plan: ounces 18K Au → ounces pure Au → g Au → mol Au → atoms Au

$$\frac{75\text{ oz Au}}{100\text{ oz 18K Au}}\qquad\frac{453.59\text{ g Au}}{16\text{ oz Au}}\quad\frac{1\text{ mol Au}}{196.97\text{ g Au}}\quad\frac{6.022\times10^{23}\text{ atoms Au}}{1\text{ mol Au}}$$

        Solution: $0.255\text{ oz 18K Au}\times\left(\dfrac{75\text{ oz pure Au}}{100\text{ oz 18K Au}}\right)\times\left(\dfrac{453.59\text{ g}}{16\text{ oz}}\right)\times\left(\dfrac{1\text{ mol Au}}{196.97\text{ g Au}}\right)\times\left(\dfrac{6.022\times10^{23}\text{ atoms Au}}{1\text{ mol Au}}\right)$

$$= 1.658\times10^{22}\text{ atoms Au}=1.7\times10^{22}\text{ atoms Au}$$

        Check: The units of the answer (atoms Au) are correct. The magnitude of the answer is reasonable because less than 1 mol of Au is in the sample.

Challenge Problems

2.82   **Given:** 1 mol sand grains; cube edge (e) = 0.10 mm; area Texas = 268,601 sq mi   **Find:** height of sand in ft

        Conceptual Plan:

        mol sand → grains sand → vol sand mm³ → vol sand ft³ and then area Texas mi² → area ft²

$$\frac{6.022\times10^{23}\text{ grains}}{1\text{ mol}}\qquad V=e^3\quad\text{mm}^3\times\left(\frac{\text{cm}}{10\text{ mm}}\right)^3\left(\frac{1\text{ in}}{2.54\text{ cm}}\right)^3\left(\frac{1\text{ ft}}{12\text{ in}}\right)^3\qquad\left(\frac{5280\text{ ft}}{1\text{ mi}}\right)^2$$

and then → height ft

$$h = \frac{\text{Volume}}{\text{Area}}$$

Solution: 1 mol sand grains $\times \dfrac{6.022 \times 10^{23} \text{ grains}}{1 \text{ mol}} \times \dfrac{(0.10 \text{ mm})^3}{1 \text{ grain}} \times \left(\dfrac{cm}{10 \text{ mm}}\right)^3 \times \left(\dfrac{1 \text{ in}}{2.54 \text{ cm}}\right)^3 \times \left(\dfrac{1 \text{ ft}}{12 \text{ in}}\right)^3$

$= 2.1266 \times 10^{13} \text{ ft}^3 \text{ sand}$

$\dfrac{2.1266 \times 10^{13} \text{ ft}^3 \text{ sand}}{268,601 \text{ mi}^2} \times \left(\dfrac{1 \text{ mi}}{5280 \text{ ft}}\right)^2 = 2.8 \text{ ft of sand}$

Check: The units of the answer (ft of sand) are correct. The magnitude of the answer seems reasonable.

2.83 **Given:** sun: $d = 1.4 \text{ g/cm}^3$, $r = 7 \times 10^8$ m; 100 billion stars/galaxy; 10 billion galaxies/universe
Find: number of atoms in the universe
Conceptual Plan: r (star) in m → r (star) in cm → vol (star) → g H/star → mol H star → atoms H/star

$$\dfrac{100 \text{ cm}}{1 \text{ m}} \qquad V = \dfrac{4}{3}\pi r^3 \qquad \dfrac{1.4 \text{ g H}}{cm^3} \qquad \dfrac{1 \text{ mol H}}{1.008 \text{ g}} \qquad \dfrac{6.022 \times 10^{23} \text{atoms}}{1 \text{ mol}}$$

→ atoms H/galaxy → atoms H/universe

$$\dfrac{100 \times 10^9 \text{ stars}}{\text{galaxy}} \qquad \dfrac{10 \times 10^9 \text{galaxies}}{\text{universe}}$$

Solution: $7 \times 10^8 \text{ m} \times \dfrac{100 \text{ cm}}{\text{m}} = 7 \times 10^{10} \text{ cm}$

$\dfrac{4}{3}\pi \dfrac{(7 \times 10^{10} \text{ cm})^3}{\text{star}} \times \dfrac{1.4 \text{ g H}}{cm^3} \times \dfrac{1 \text{ mol H}}{1.008 \text{ g H}} \times \dfrac{6.022 \times 10^{23} \text{ atoms H}}{1 \text{ mol H}} \times \dfrac{100 \times 10^9 \text{ stars}}{1 \text{ galaxy}} \times \dfrac{10 \times 10^9 \text{ galaxies}}{\text{universe}}$

$= 1 \times 10^{78} \text{ atoms/universe}$

Check: The units of the answer (atoms/universe) are correct.

2.84 (a) **Given:** 36 Wt-296; 2 Wt-297; 12 Wt-298 **Find:** % abundance of each
Conceptual Plan: total atoms → fraction of each isotope → % abundance

$$\text{Sum of atoms} \qquad \dfrac{\text{number of each isotope}}{\text{total atoms}} \qquad \text{fraction} \times 100\%$$

Solution: Total atoms $= 36 + 2 + 12 = 50$

$\dfrac{36}{50} \times 100\% = 72\% \text{ Wt-296}, \quad \dfrac{2}{50} \times 100\% = 4\% \text{ Wt-297}, \quad \dfrac{12}{50} \times 100\% = 24\% \text{ Wt-298}$

Check: The units of the answers (% abundance) are correct. The values of the answers are reasonable because they add up to 100%.

(b) **Given:** Wt-296 $m = 24.6630 \times$ mass ^{12}C, 72%:Wt-297 $m = 24.7490 \times$ mass ^{12}C, 4%:Wt-298 $m = 24.8312 \times$ mass ^{12}C; 24%.
Find: atomic mass Wt
Conceptual Plan: mass of isotope relative to ^{12}C → mass of isotope and then % abundance →

$$\text{(Mass relative to } ^{12}\text{C)}(12.00 \text{ amu)} \qquad \dfrac{\% \text{ abundance}}{100}$$

fraction abundance then determine atomic mass

$$\text{Atomic mass} = \sum_n (\text{fraction of isotope } n) \times (\text{mass of isotope } n)$$

Solution:
Wt-296 $= 24.6630 \times 12.00 \text{ amu} = 295.956 \text{ amu};$ Wt-297 $= 24.7490 \times 12.00 \text{ amu} = 296.988 \text{ amu};$
Wt-298 $= 24.8312 \times 12.00 \text{ amu} = 297.974 \text{ amu}$

fraction Wt-296 $= \dfrac{72}{100} = 0.72$ fraction Wt-297 $= \dfrac{4}{100} = 0.04$ fraction Wt-298 $= \dfrac{24}{100} = 0.24$

$\text{Atomic mass} = \sum_n (\text{fraction of isotope } n) \times (\text{mass of isotope } n)$

$= (0.72)(295.956 \text{ amu}) + (0.04)(296.988 \text{ amu}) + (0.24)(297.974 \text{ amu})$

$= 296.482 \text{ amu}$

Check: The units of the answer (amu) are correct. The magnitude of the answer is reasonable because it lies between 295.956 and 297.974 and is closer to 296, which has the highest abundance.

2.85　　**Given:** sample $= 1.5886$ g; $^{59}Co = 58.9332$ amu; $^{60}Co = 59.9338$ amu; apparent mass $= 58.9901$ amu
　　　　Find: mass of ^{60}Co in sample
　　　　Conceptual Plan: apparent mass $\rightarrow$ fraction $^{60}Co \rightarrow$ mass ^{60}Co

$$\text{Atomic mass} = \sum_n (\text{fraction of isotope } n) \times (\text{mass of isotope } n)$$

　　　　Solution: Let X $=$ fraction of ^{60}Co; so $1.00 - X =$ fraction ^{59}Co
　　　　　　　　58.9901 amu $= (1.00 - X)(58.9332 \text{ amu}) + (X)(59.9338 \text{ amu})$
　　　　　　　　$X = 0.05686$
　　　　　　　　1.5886 g sample $\times 0.05686 = 0.090328$ g $^{60}Co = 0.0903$ g ^{60}Co

　　　　Check: The units of the answer (g ^{60}Co) are correct. The magnitude of the answer is reasonable because the apparent mass is very close to the mass ^{59}Co.

2.86　　**Given:** 7.36 g Cu; 0.51 g Zn　　**Find:** apparent atomic mass of sample
　　　　Conceptual Plan: fraction Cu and Zn $\rightarrow$ atomic mass

$$\text{Atomic mass} = \sum_n (\text{fraction of atom } n) \times (\text{mass of atom } n)$$

　　　　Solution: 7.36 g Cu $+ 0.51$ g Zn $= 7.87$ g sample

$$\left(\frac{7.36 \text{ g Cu}}{7.87 \text{ g sample}} \right)\left(\frac{63.55 \text{ g Cu}}{1 \text{ mol Cu}} \right) + \left(\frac{0.51 \text{ g Zn}}{7.87 \text{ g sample}} \right)\left(\frac{65.38 \text{ g Zn}}{1 \text{ mol Zn}} \right) = 63.7 \text{ g/mol}$$

　　　　Check: Units of the answer (g/mol) are correct. The magnitude of the answer is reasonable because it is between the mass of Cu (63.55 g/mol) and Zn (65.38 g/mol) and is closer to the mass of Cu.

2.87　　**Given:** $N_2O_3 = \dfrac{\text{mass O}}{\text{mass N}} = \dfrac{12}{7}$; sample X $= \dfrac{\text{mass O}}{\text{mass N}} = \dfrac{16}{7}$　　**Find:** Formula of X, next in series

　　　　Conceptual Plan: ratio O/N for $N_2O_3 \rightarrow$ ratio O/N for X $\rightarrow$ ratio if O/O

　　　　Solution: $\dfrac{\text{mass O}}{\text{mass N}} = \dfrac{12}{7} = \dfrac{3 \text{ O}}{2 \text{ N}}$　　$\dfrac{\text{mass O}}{\text{mass N}} = \dfrac{16}{7} = \dfrac{X \text{ O}}{2 \text{ N}}$　　$\dfrac{\text{mass O}}{\text{mass O}} = \dfrac{16}{12} = \dfrac{X \text{ O}}{3 \text{ O}}$　so, X $= 4$
　　　　Therefore, the formula is N_2O_4.
　　　　The next member of the series would be N_2O_5.

$$\frac{\text{mass O}}{\text{mass O}} = \frac{5 \text{ O}}{3 \text{ O}} = \frac{Y}{12} \qquad Y = 20 \qquad \text{So } \frac{\text{mass O}}{\text{mass N}} = \frac{20}{7}$$

2.88　　**Given:** Mg $= 24.312$ amu, $^{24}Mg = 23.98504$, 78.99%, $^{26}Mg = 25.98259$ amu, $\dfrac{\text{abundance } ^{25}Mg}{\text{abundance } ^{26}Mg} = \dfrac{0.9083}{1}$

　　　　Find: mass ^{25}Mg
　　　　Conceptual Plan: abundance of ^{24}Mg and ratio $^{25}Mg/^{26}Mg \rightarrow$ abundance ^{25}Mg and $^{26}Mg \rightarrow$ mass ^{25}Mg

$$\text{Atomic mass} = \sum_n (\text{fraction of isotope } n) \times (\text{mass of isotope } n)$$

　　　　Solution: $100.00\% - \%$ abundance $^{24}Mg = \%$ abundance ^{25}Mg and ^{26}Mg
　　　　$100.00\% - 78.99\% = 21.01\%$ ^{25}Mg and ^{26}Mg

$$\text{fraction } ^{25}Mg \text{ and } ^{26}Mg = \frac{21.01}{100.0} = 0.2101$$

$$\frac{\text{abundance } ^{25}Mg}{\text{abundance } ^{26}Mg} = \frac{0.9083}{1}$$

　　　　Let X $=$ fraction ^{26}Mg, 0.9083 X $=$ fraction ^{25}Mg
　　　　fraction ^{25}Mg and $^{26}Mg = X + 0.9083$ X $= 0.2101$
　　　　X $= {}^{26}Mg = 0.1101$,　　0.9083 X $= {}^{25}Mg = 0.1000$

$$\text{Atomic mass} = \sum_n (\text{fraction of isotope } n) \times (\text{mass of isotope } n)$$

　　　　$24.312 = (0.7899)(23.98504 \text{ amu}) + (0.1000)(\text{mass } ^{25}Mg) + (0.1101)(25.98259 \text{ amu})$
　　　　mass $^{25}Mg = 25.056$ amu $= 25.06$ amu

　　　　Check: The units of the answer (amu) are correct. The magnitude of the answer is reasonable because it is between the masses of ^{24}Mg and ^{26}Mg.

Conceptual Problems

2.89   (a)   This is the law of definite proportions: All samples of a given compound, regardless of their source or how they were prepared, have the same proportions of their constituent elements.

   (b)   This is the law of conservation of mass: In a chemical reaction, matter is neither created nor destroyed.

   (c)   This is the law of multiple proportions: When two elements form two different compounds, the masses of element B that combine with 1 g of element A can be expressed as a ratio of small whole numbers. In this example the ratio of O from hydrogen peroxide to O from water $= 16:8 \rightarrow 2:1$, a small whole number ratio.

2.90   **Given:** -11.2×10^{-19} C/drop   **Find:** number of electrons on the drop

Conceptual Plan: divide total charge by the charge/electron

$$\frac{-1.602 \times 10^{-19} \text{ C}}{\text{electron}}$$

Solution: $\dfrac{-11.2 \times 10^{-19} \text{ C}}{\text{drop}} \times \dfrac{\text{electron}}{-1.602 \times 10^{-19} \text{ C}} = 6.99\underline{1}$ electrons $= 7$ electrons

2.91   Li-6 nucleus   Li-7 nucleus

Since Li-6 has an abundance of 7.5%, in a sample of 1000 atoms, there should, on average, be 75 Li-6 atoms.

2.92   The correct answer would be c. 7.00 amu. Because Li-7 with a mass of 7.0160 amu has an abundance of 92.5%, the atomic mass of Li should be close to the mass of Li-7.

2.93   If the amu and mole were not based on the same isotope, the numerical values obtained for an atom of material and a mole of material would not be the same. If, for example, the mole was based on the number of particles in C-12 but the amu was changed to a fraction of the mass of an atom of Ne-20 the number of particles and the number of amu that make up one mole of material would no longer be the same. We would no longer have the relationship where the mass of an atom in amu is numerically equal to the mass of a mole of those atoms in grams.

2.94   **Given:** a. Cr: 55.0 g; atomic mass $= 52$ g/mol b. Ti: 45.0 g; atomic mass $= 48$ g/mol and
        c. Zn: 60.0 g; atomic mass $= 65$ g/mol
Find: which has the greatest amount in moles, and which has the greatest mass
Conceptual Plan: without calculation, compare grams of material to g/mol for each.
Solution: Cr would have the greatest mole amount of the elements. It is the only one whose mass is greater than the molar mass. Zn would be the greatest mass amount because it is the largest mass value.

2.95   The different isotopes of the same element have the same number of protons and electrons, so the attractive forces between the nucleus and the electrons is constant and there is no difference in the radii of the isotopes. Ions, on the other hand, have a different number of electrons than the parent atom from which they are derived. Cations have fewer electrons than the parent atom. The attractive forces are greater because there is a larger positive charge in the nucleus than the negative charge in the electron cloud. So, cations are smaller than the parent atom from which they are derived. Anions have more electrons than the parent. The electron cloud has a greater negative charge than the nucleus, so the anions have larger radii than the parent.

Questions for Group Work

2.96

Li	Be	B	C	N	O	F
7	9	10.8	12	14	16	19
LiCl	BeCl$_2$	BH$_3$	CH$_4$	NF$_3$	H$_2$O	F$_2$
Na	Mg	Al	Si		S	Cl
23	24.3	27	28		32	35.4
NaCl	MgCl$_2$	AlH$_3$	SiH$_4$		H$_2$S	Cl$_2$
K	Ca	Ga	Ge	As	Se	Br
39	40	69.7	72.6	75	79	80
KCl	CaCl$_2$	GaH$_3$	GeH$_4$	AsF$_3$	H$_2$Se	Br$_2$

The missing element is in between Si and S. The mass should be the average of those elements $= (28+32)/2 = 30$, and the formula of the compound should be similar to the elements above and below it $= XF_3$.

2.97   Each boron atom has 5 protons. The mass of the boron atoms with 5 neutrons is ~10 amu, while the mass of the boron atoms with 6 neutrons is ~11 amu.

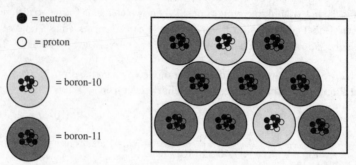

The average mass of boron in the drawing is

Atomic mass $= \sum_n$ (fraction of isotope n) $\times$ (mass of isotope n) $=$

0.2(10.01294 amu) + 0.8(11.00931 amu) = 10.810036 amu
The average mass of boron is

Atomic mass $= \sum_n$ (fraction of isotope n) $\times$ (mass of isotope n) $=$

0.198(10.01294 amu) + 0.802(11.00931 amu) = 10.8 amu

2.98   (a)   All atoms of a given element have the same number of protons and have the same chemical reactivity (except for the isotopes of hydrogen). Isotopes differ from one another by the number of neutrons, and hence the mass.

(b)   A neutral atom and an ion of the same element have the same number of protons. They have a different number of electrons, and hence different reactivity.

2.99   Electrons: $\dfrac{9.10938 \times 10^{-28}\ \text{g}}{1\ \text{electron}} \times \dfrac{6.02214179 \times 10^{23}\ \text{electrons}}{1\ \text{mole electrons}} = 5.48580 \times 10^{-4}\ \text{g/mol}$

Protons: $\dfrac{1.67262 \times 10^{-24}\ \text{g}}{1\ \text{proton}} \times \dfrac{6.02214179 \times 10^{23}\ \text{electrons}}{1\ \text{mole electrons}} = 1.00728\ \text{g/mol}$

Neutrons: $\dfrac{1.67493 \times 10^{-24}\ \text{g}}{1\ \text{neutron}} \times \dfrac{6.02214179 \times 10^{23}\ \text{neutrons}}{1\ \text{mole neutrons}} = 1.00867\ \text{g/mol}$

Carbon-12: $\dfrac{1.992646 \times 10^{-23}\ \text{g}}{1\ \text{carbon-12}} \times \dfrac{6.02214179 \times 10^{23}\ \text{carbon-12}}{1\ \text{mole carbon-12}} = 12.00000\ \text{g/mol}$

mass of components parts $= \left(6\ \text{mol protons} \times \dfrac{1.00728\ \text{g}}{1\ \text{mol protons}} \right) + \left(6\ \text{mol neutrons} \times \dfrac{1.00867\ \text{g}}{1\ \text{mol neutrons}} \right) +$

$\left(6\ \text{mol electrons} \times \dfrac{5.48580 \times 10^{-4}\ \text{g}}{1\ \text{mol electrons}} \right) = 6.04368\ \text{g} + 6.05202\ \text{g} + 0.00329148\ \text{g} = 12.09899\ \text{g}$

The total mass of the protons, neutrons, and electrons weighs 0.09899 g more than the mass of 1 mol of carbon-12 atoms.

Doughnut: $\dfrac{74\ \text{g}}{1\ \text{doughnut}} \times \dfrac{6.02214179 \times 10^{23}\ \text{doughnut}}{1\ \text{mole doughnut}} = 4.5 \times 10^{25}\ \text{g/mol}$

$74\ \text{g carbon} \times \dfrac{1\ \text{carbon atom}}{1.992646 \times 10^{-23}\ \text{g carbon}} = 3.7 \times 10^{24}\ \text{carbon atoms}$

3 Molecules, Compounds, and Chemical Equations

Problems by Topic

Chemical Formulas and Molecular View of Elements and Compounds

3.1 The chemical formula gives you the kind of atom and the number of each atom in the compound.
   - (a) $Ca_3(PO_4)_2$ contains: 3 calcium atoms, 2 phosphorus atoms, and 8 oxygen atoms.
   - (b) $SrCl_2$ contains: 1 strontium atom and 2 chlorine atoms.
   - (c) KNO_3 contains: 1 potassium atom, 1 nitrogen atom, and 3 oxygen atoms.
   - (d) $Mg(NO_2)_2$ contains: 1 magnesium atom, 2 nitrogen atoms, and 4 oxygen atoms.

3.2 The chemical formula gives you the kind of atom and the number of each atom in the compound.
   - (a) $Ba(OH)_2$ contains: 1 barium atom, 2 oxygen atoms, and 2 hydrogen atoms.
   - (b) NH_4Cl contains: 1 nitrogen atom, 4 hydrogen atoms, and 1 chlorine atom.
   - (c) $NaCN$ contains: 1 sodium atom, 1 carbon atom, and 1 nitrogen atom.
   - (d) $Ba(HCO_3)_2$ contains: 1 barium atom, 2 hydrogen atoms, 2 carbon atoms, and 6 oxygen atoms.

3.3
   - (a) 1 blue = nitrogen, 3 white = hydrogen: NH_3
   - (b) 2 black = carbon, 6 white = hydrogen: C_2H_6
   - (c) 1 yellow = sulfur, 3 red = oxygen: SO_3

3.4
   - (a) 1 blue = nitrogen, 2 red = oxygen: NO_2
   - (b) 1 yellow = sulfur, 2 white = hydrogen: H_2S
   - (c) 1 black = carbon, 4 white = hydrogen: CH_4

3.5
   - (a) Neon is an element, and it is not one of the elements that exists as diatomic molecules; therefore, it is an atomic element.
   - (b) Fluorine is one of the elements that exists as diatomic molecules; therefore, it is a molecular element.
   - (c) Potassium is not one of the elements that exists as diatomic molecules; therefore, it is an atomic element.
   - (d) Nitrogen is one of the elements that exists as diatomic molecules; therefore, it is a molecular element.

3.6
   - (a) Hydrogen is one of the elements that exists as diatomic molecules; therefore, it has a molecule as its basic unit.
   - (b) Iodine is one of the elements that exists as diatomic molecules; therefore, it has a molecule as its basic unit.
   - (c) Lead is not one of the elements that exists as a diatomic molecule; therefore, it does not have a molecule as its basic unit.
   - (d) Oxygen is one of the elements that exists as diatomic molecules; therefore, it has a molecule as its basic unit.

3.7   (a) CO_2 is a compound composed of a nonmetal and a nonmetal; therefore, it is a molecular compound.

     (b) $NiCl_2$ is a compound composed of a metal and a nonmetal; therefore, it is an ionic compound.

     (c)   NaI is a compound composed of a metal and a nonmetal; therefore, it is an ionic compound.

     (d) PCl_3 is a compound composed of a nonmetal and a nonmetal; therefore, it is a molecular compound.

3.8   (a) CF_2Cl_2 is a compound composed of a nonmetal and two other nonmetals; therefore, it is a molecular compound.

     (b) CCl_4 is a compound composed of a nonmetal and a nonmetal; therefore, it is a molecular compound.

     (c) PtO_2 is a compound composed of a metal and a nonmetal; therefore, it is an ionic compound.

     (d) SO_3 is a compound composed of a nonmetal and a nonmetal; therefore, it is a molecular compound.

3.9   (a)   white = hydrogen: a molecule composed of two of the same element; therefore, it is a molecular element.

     (b)   blue = nitrogen, white = hydrogen: a molecule composed of a nonmetal and a nonmetal; therefore, it is a molecular compound.

     (c)   purple = sodium: a substance composed of all the same atoms; therefore, it is an atomic element.

3.10   (a)   green = chlorine, purple = sodium: a compound composed of a metal and a nonmetal; therefore, it is an ionic compound.

     (b)   green = chlorine: a molecule composed of two of the same elements; therefore, it is a molecular element.

     (c)   red = oxygen, black = carbon, white = hydrogen: a molecule composed of nonmetals; therefore, it is a molecular compound.

Formulas and Names for Ionic Compounds

3.11   To write the formula for an ionic compound, do the following: (1) Write the symbol for the metal cation and its charge and the symbol for the nonmetal anion and its charge. (2) Adjust the subscript on each cation and anion to balance the overall charge. (3) Check that the sum of the charges of the cations equals the sum of the charges of the anions.

     (a)   magnesium and sulfur: Mg^{2+} S^{2-} MgS   cations 2+, anions 2−

     (b)   barium and oxygen: Ba^{2+} O^{2-} BaO   cations 2+, anions 2−

     (c)   strontium and bromine: Sr^{2+} Br^- $SrBr_2$ cations 2+, anions 2(1−) = 2−

     (d)   beryllium and chlorine: Be^{2+} Cl^- $BeCl_2$ cations 2+, anions 2(1−) = 2−

3.12   To write the formula for an ionic compound, do the following: (1) Write the symbol for the metal cation and its charge and the symbol for the nonmetal anion and its charge. (2) Adjust the subscript on each cation and anion to balance the overall charge. (3) Check that the sum of the charges of the cations equals the sum of the charges of the anions.

     (a)   aluminum and sulfur: Al^{3+} S^{2-} Al_2S_3 cations 2(3+) = 6+, anions 3(2−) = 6−

     (b)   aluminum and oxygen: Al^{3+} O^{2-} Al_2O_3 cations 2(3+) = 6+, anions 3(2−) = 6

     (c)   sodium and oxygen: Na^+ O^{2-} Na_2S cations 2(1+) = 2+, anions 2−

     (d)   strontium and iodine: Sr^{2+} I^- SrI_2 cations 2+, anions 2(1−) = 2−

3.13   To write the formula for an ionic compound, do the following: (1) Write the symbol for the metal cation and its charge and the symbol for the polyatomic anion and its charge. (2) Adjust the subscript on each cation and anion to balance the overall charge. (3) Check that the sum of the charges of the cations equals the sum of the charges of the anions. Cation = barium: Ba^{2+}

     (a)   hydroxide: OH^- $Ba(OH)_2$ cation 2+, anion 2(1−) = 2−

     (b)   chromate: CrO_4^{2-} $BaCrO_4$ cation 2+, anion 2−

     (c)   phosphate: PO_4^{3-} $Ba_3(PO_4)_2$ cation 3(2+) = 6+, anion 2(3−) = 6−

     (d)   cyanide: CN^- $Ba(CN)_2$ cation 2+, anion 2(1−) = 2−

3.14   To write the formula for an ionic compound, do the following: (1) Write the symbol for the metal cation and its charge and the symbol for the nonmetal anion and its charge. (2) Adjust the subscript on each cation and anion to balance the overall charge. (3) Check that the sum of the charges of the cations equals the sum of the charges of the anions. Cation = sodium: Na^+

     (a)   carbonate: CO_3^{2-} Na_2CO_3 cation 2(1+) = 2+, anion 2−

     (b)   phosphate: PO_4^{3-} Na_3PO_4 cation 3(1+) = 3+, anion 3−

     (c)   hydrogen phosphate: HPO_4^{2-} Na_2HPO_4 cation 2(1+) = 2+, anion 2−

     (d)   acetate: $C_2H_3O_2^-$ $NaC_2H_3O_2$ cation 1+, anion 1−

3.15   To name a binary ionic compound, provide the name of the metal cation followed by the base name of the anion +-*ide*.

    (a) Mg_3N_2:   The cation is magnesium; the anion is from nitrogen, which becomes nitride: magnesium nitride.

    (b)   KF: The cation is potassium; the anion is from fluorine, which becomes fluoride: potassium fluoride.

    (c) Na_2O: The cation is sodium; the anion is from oxygen, which becomes oxide: sodium oxide.

    (d) Li_2S: The cation is lithium; the anion is from sulfur, which becomes sulfide: lithium sulfide.

3.16   To name a binary ionic compound, provide the name of the metal cation followed by the base name of the anion +-*ide*.

    (a)   CsF: The cation is cesium; the anion is from fluorine, which becomes fluoride: cesium fluoride.

    (b)   KI: The cation is potassium; the anion is from iodine, which becomes iodide: potassium iodide.

    (c) $SrCl_2$:   The cation is strontium; the anion is from chlorine, which becomes chloride: strontium chloride.

    (d) $BaCl_2$:   The cation is barium; the anion is from chlorine, which becomes chloride: barium chloride.

3.17   To name an ionic compound with a metal cation that can have more than one charge, name the metal cation followed by parentheses with the charge in Roman numerals followed by the base name of the anion +-*ide*.

    (a) $SnCl_4$:   The charge on Sn must be 4+ for the compound to be charge neutral: The cation is tin(IV); the anion is from chlorine, which becomes chloride: tin(IV) chloride.

    (b) PbI_2:   The charge on Pb must be 2+ for the compound to be charge neutral: The cation is lead(II); the anion is from iodine, which becomes iodide: lead(II) iodide.

    (c) Fe_2O_3:   The charge on Fe must be 3+ for the compound to be charge neutral: The cation is iron(III); the anion is from oxygen, which becomes oxide: iron(III) oxide.

    (d) CuI_2:   The charge on Cu must be 2+ for the compound to be charge neutral: The cation is copper(II); the anion is from iodine, which becomes iodide: copper(II) iodide.

3.18   To name an ionic compound with a metal cation that can have more than one charge, name the metal cation followed by parentheses with the charge in Roman numerals followed by the base name of the anion +-*ide*.

    (a) SnO_2:   The charge on Sn must be 4+ for the compound to be charge neutral: The cation is tin(IV); the anion is from oxygen, which becomes oxide: tin(IV) oxide.

    (b) $HgBr_2$:   The charge of Hg must be 2+ for the compound to charge neutral: The cation is mercury(II); the anion is from bromine, which becomes bromide: mercury(II) bromide.

    (c) $CrCl_2$:   The charge on Cr must be 2+ for the compound to be charge neutral: The cation is chromium(II); the anion is from chlorine, which becomes chloride: chromium(II) chloride.

    (d) $CrCl_3$:   The charge on Cr must be 3+ for the compound to be charge neutral: The cation is chromium(III); the anion is from chlorine, which becomes chloride: chromium(III) chloride.

3.19   To name these compounds, first decide if the metal cation is invariant or can have more than one charge. Then name the metal cation followed by the base name of the anion +-*ide*.

    (a)   SnO: Sn can have more than one charge. The charge on Sn must be 2+ for the compound to be charge neutral: the cation is tin(II); the anion is from oxygen, which becomes oxide: tin(II) oxide.

    (b) Cr_2S_3:   Cr can have more than one charge. The charge on Cr must be 3+ for the compound to be charge neutral: the cation is chromium(III); the anion is from sulfur, which becomes sulfide: chromium(III) sulfide.

    (c)   RbI: Rb is invariant: the cation is rubidium; the anion is from iodine, which becomes iodide: rubidium iodide.

    (d) $BaBr_2$:   Ba is invariant: the cation is barium; the anion is from bromine, which becomes bromide: barium bromide.

3.20   To name these compounds, first decide if the metal cation is invariant or can have more than one charge. Then name the metal cation followed by the base name of the anion+-*ide*.

    (a)   BaS: Ba is invariant: The cation is barium; the anion is from sulfur, which becomes sulfide: barium sulfide.

    (b) $FeCl_3$:   Fe can have more than one charge. The charge on Fe must be 3+ for the compound to be charge neutral: The cation is iron(III); the anion is from chlorine, which becomes chloride: iron(III) chloride.

    (c) $PbCl_4$:   Pb can have more than one charge. The charge on Pb must be 4+ for the compound to be charge neutral: The cation is lead(IV); the anion is from chlorine, which becomes chloride: lead(IV) chloride.

    (d) $SrBr_2$:   Sr is invariant: The cation is strontium; the anion is from bromine, which becomes bromide: strontium bromide.

3.21   To name these compounds, first decide if the metal cation is invariant or can have more than one charge. Then name the metal cation followed by the name of the polyatomic anion.

   (a) $CuNO_2$:   Cu can have more than one charge. The charge on Cu must be 1+ for the compound to be charge neutral: The cation is copper(I); the anion is nitrite: copper(I) nitrite.

   (b) $Mg(C_2H_3O_2)_2$:   Mg is invariant: The cation is magnesium; the anion is acetate: magnesium acetate.

   (c) $Ba(NO_3)_2$:   Ba is invariant: The cation is barium; the anion is nitrate: barium nitrate.

   (d) $Pb(C_2H_3O_2)_2$:   Pb can have more than one charge. The charge on Pb must be 2+ for the compound to be charge neutral: The cation is lead(II); the anion is acetate: lead(II) acetate.

   (e) $KClO_3$:   K is invariant: The cation is potassium; the anion is chlorate: potassium chlorate.

   (f) $PbSO_4$:   Pb can have more than one charge. The charge on Pb must be 2+ for the compound to be charge neutral: The cation is lead(II); the anion is sulfate: lead(II) sulfate.

3.22   To name these compounds, first decide if the metal cation is invariant or can have more than one charge. Then name the metal cation followed by the name of the polyatomic anion.

   (a) $Ba(OH)_2$:   Ba is invariant: The cation is barium; the anion is hydroxide: barium hydroxide.

   (b) NH_4I: The cation is ammonium; the anion is from iodine, which becomes iodide: ammonium iodide.

   (c) $NaBrO_4$:   Na is invariant: The cation is sodium; the anion is perbromate: sodium perbromate.

   (d) $Fe(OH)_3$:   Fe can have more than one charge. The charge on Fe must be 3+ for the compound to be charge neutral: The cation is iron(III); the anion is hydroxide: iron(III) hydroxide.

   (e) $CoSO_4$:   Co can have more than one charge. The charge on Co must be 2+ for the compound to be charge neutral: The cation is cobalt(II); the anion is sulfate: cobalt(II) sulfate.

   (f) $KClO$:   K is invariant: The cation is potassium; the anion is hypochlorite: potassium hypochlorite.

3.23   To write the formula for an ionic compound, do the following: (1) Write the symbol for the metal cation and its charge and the symbol for the nonmetal anion or polyatomic anion and its charge. (2) Adjust the subscript on each cation and anion to balance the overall charge. (3) Check that the sum of the charges of the cations equals the sum of the charges of the anions.

   (a)   sodium hydrogen sulfite: Na^+ HSO_3^- $NaHSO_3$ cation 1+, anion 1−

   (b)   lithium permanganate: Li^+ MnO_4^- $LiMnO_4$ cation 1+, anion 1−

   (c)   silver nitrate: Ag^+ NO_3^- $AgNO_3$ cation 1+, anion 1−

   (d)   potassium sulfate: K^+ SO_4^{2-} K_2SO_4 cation 2(1+) = 2+, anion 2−

   (e)   rubidium hydrogen sulfate: Rb^+ HSO_4^- $RbHSO_4$ cation 1+, anion 1−

   (f)   potassium hydrogen carbonate: K^+ HCO_3^- $KHCO_3$ cation 1+, anion 1−

3.24   To write the formula for an ionic compound, do the following: (1) Write the symbol for the metal cation and its charge and the symbol for the nonmetal anion or polyatomic anion and its charge. (2) Adjust the subscript on each cation and anion to balance the overall charge. (3) Check that the sum of the charges of the cations equals the sum of the charges of the anions.

   (a)   copper(II) chloride: Cu^{2+} Cl^- $CuCl_2$ cation 2+, anion 2(1−) = 2−

   (b)   copper(I) iodate: Cu^+ IO_3^- $CuIO_3$ cation 1+, anion 1−

   (c)   lead(II) chromate: Pb^{2+} CrO_4^{2-} $PbCrO_4$ cation 2+, anion 2−

   (d)   calcium fluoride: Ca^{2+} F^- CaF_2 cation 2+, anion 2(1−) = 2−

   (e)   potassium hydroxide: K^+ OH^- KOH cation 1+, anion 1−

   (f)   iron(II) phosphate: Fe^{2+} PO_4^{3-} $Fe_3(PO_4)_2$ cation 3(2+) = 6+, anion 2(3−) = 6−

3.25   Hydrates are named the same way as other ionic compounds with the addition of the term *prefix*hydrate, where the prefix is the number of water molecules associated with each formula unit.

   (a) $CoSO_4 \cdot 7H_2O$ cobalt(II) sulfate heptahydrate

   (b)   iridium(III) bromide tetrahydrate $IrBr_3 \cdot 4H_2O$

   (c) $Mg(BrO_3)_2 \cdot 6H_2O$ magnesium bromate hexahydrate

   (d)   potassium carbonate dihydrate $K_2CO_3 \cdot 2H_2O$

3.26   Hydrates are named the same way as other ionic compounds with the addition of the term *prefix*hydrate, where the prefix is the number of water molecules associated with each formula unit.

   (a)   cobalt(II) phosphate octahydrate $Co_3(PO_4)_2 \cdot 8H_2O$

   (b) $BeCl_2 \cdot 2H_2O$ beryllium chloride dihydrate

   (c)   chromium(III) phosphate trihydrate $CrPO_4 \cdot 3H_2O$

   (d) $LiNO_2 \cdot H_2O$ lithium nitrite monohydrate

Formulas and Names for Molecular Compounds and Acids

3.27   (a)   CO   The name of the compound is the name of the first element, *carbon*, followed by the base name of the second element, *ox*, prefixed by *mono-* to indicate one and given the suffix *-ide*. Since the prefix ends with "o" and the base name begins with "o," the first "o" is dropped: carbon monoxide.

       (b) NI_3 The name of the compound is the name of the first element, *nitrogen*, followed by the base name of the second element, *iod*, prefixed by *tri-* to indicate three and given the suffix *-ide*: nitrogen triiodide.

       (c) $SiCl_4$ The name of the compound is the name of the first element, *silicon*, followed by the base name of the second element, *chlor*, prefixed by *tetra-* to indicate four and given the suffix *-ide*: silicon tetrachloride.

       (d) N_4Se_4 The name of the compound is the name of the first element, *nitrogen*, prefixed by *tetra-* to indicate four followed by the base name of the second element, *selen*, prefixed by *tetra-* to indicate four and given the suffix *-ide*: tetranitrogen tetraselenide.

       (e) I_2O_5 The name of the compound is the name of the first element, *iodine*, prefixed by *di-* to indicate two followed by the base name of the second element, *ox*, prefixed by *penta-* to indicate five and given the suffix *-ide*: diiodine pentaoxide.

3.28   (a) SO_3 The name of the compound is the name of the first element, *sulfur*, followed by the base name of the second element, *ox*, prefixed by *tri-* to indicate three and given the suffix *-ide*: sulfur trioxide.

       (b) SO_2 The name of the compound is the name of the first element, *sulfur*, followed by the base name of the second element, *ox*, prefixed by *di-* to indicate two and given the suffix *-ide*: sulfur dioxide.

       (c) BrF_5 The name of the compound is the name of the first element, *bromine*, followed by the base name of the second element, *fluor*, prefixed by *penta-* to indicate five and given the suffix *-ide*: bromine pentafluoride.

       (d)   NO   The name of the compound is the name of the first element, *nitrogen*, followed by the base name of the second element, *ox*, prefixed by *mono-* to indicate one and given the suffix *-ide*. Since the prefix ends with "o" and the base name begins with "o," the first "o" is dropped: nitrogen monoxide.

       (e) XeO_3 The name of the compound is the name of the first element, *xenon*, followed by the base name of the second element, *ox*, prefixed by *tri-* to indicate three and given the suffix *-ide*: xenon trioxide.

3.29   (a)   phosphorus trichloride: PCl_3
       (b)   chlorine monoxide: ClO
       (c)   disulfur tetrafluoride: S_2F_4
       (d)   phosphorus pentafluoride: PF_5
       (e)   diphosphorus pentasulfide: P_2S_5

3.30   (a)   boron tribromide: BBr_3
       (b)   dichlorine monoxide: Cl_2O
       (c)   xenon tetrafluoride: XeF_4
       (d)   carbon tetrabromide: CBr_4
       (e)   diboron tetrachloride: B_2Cl_4

3.31   (a)   HI: The base name of I is *iod*, so the name is hydroiodic acid.
       (b) HNO_3:   The oxyanion is *nitrate,* which ends in *-ate*; therefore, the name of the acid is nitric acid.
       (c) H_2CO_3:   The oxyanion is *carbonate,* which ends in *-ate*; therefore, the name of the acid is carbonic acid.
       (d) $HC_2H_3O_2$:   The oxyanion is *acetate,* which ends in *-ate*; therefore, the name of the acid is acetic acid.

3.32   (a)   HCl: The base name of Cl is *chlor*, so the name is hydrochloric acid.
       (b) $HClO_2$:   The oxyanion is *chlorite,* which ends in *-ite;* therefore, the name of the acid is chlorous acid.
       (c) H_2SO_4:   The oxyanion is *sulfate,* which ends in *-ate;* therefore, the name of the acid is sulfuric acid.
       (d) HNO_2:   The oxyanion is *nitrite,* which ends in *-ite;* therefore, the name of the acid is nitrous acid.

3.33   (a)   hydrofluoric acid: HF
       (b)   hydrobromic acid: HBr
       (c)   sulfurous acid: H_2SO_3

3.34   (a)   phosphoric acid: H_3PO_4
        (b)   hydrocyanic acid: HCN
        (c)   chlorous acid: $HClO_2$

Formula Mass and the Mole Concept for Compounds

3.35   To find the formula mass, sum the atomic masses of each atom in the chemical formula.
        (a) NO_2 formula mass = $1 \times$ (atomic mass N) + $2 \times$ (atomic mass O)
                            = $1 \times$ (14.01 amu) + $2 \times$ (16.00 amu)
                            = 46.01 amu
        (b) C_4H_{10} formula mass = $4 \times$ (atomic mass C) + $10 \times$ (atomic mass H)
                            = $4 \times$ (12.01 amu) + $10 \times$ (1.008 amu)
                            = 58.12 amu
        (c) $C_6H_{12}O_6$ formula mass = $6 \times$ (atomic mass C) + $12 \times$ (atomic mass H) + $6 \times$ (atomic mass O)
                            = $6 \times$ (12.01 amu) + $12 \times$ (1.008 amu) + $6 \times$ (16.00 amu)
                            = 180.16 amu
        (d) $Cr(NO_3)_3$ formula mass = $1 \times$ (atomic mass Cr) + $3 \times$ (atomic mass N) + $9 \times$ (atomic mass O)
                            = $1 \times$ (52.00 amu) + $3 \times$ (14.01 amu) + $9 \times$ (16.00 amu)
                            = 238.03 amu

3.36   To find the formula mass, sum the atomic masses of each atom in the chemical formula.
        (a) $MgBr_2$ formula mass = $1 \times$ (atomic mass Mg) + $2 \times$ (atomic mass Br)
                            = $1 \times$ (24.31 amu) + $2 \times$ (79.90 amu)
                            = 184.11 amu
        (b) HNO_2 formula mass = $1 \times$ (atomic mass H) + $1 \times$ (atomic mass N) + $2 \times$ (atomic mass O)
                            = $1 \times$ (1.008 amu) + $1 \times$ (14.01 amu) + $2 \times$ (16.00 amu)
                            = 47.02 amu
        (c) CBr_4 formula mass = $1 \times$ (atomic mass C) + $4 \times$ (atomic mass Br)
                            = $1 \times$ (12.01 amu) + $4 \times$ (79.90 amu)
                            = 331.61 amu
        (d) $Ca(NO_3)_2$ formula mass = $1 \times$ (atomic mass Ca) + $2 \times$ (atomic mass N) + $6 \times$ (atomic mass O)
                            = $1 \times$ (40.08 amu) + $2 \times$ (14.01 amu) + $6 \times$ (16.00 amu)
                            = 164.10 amu

3.37   (a)   **Given:** 72.5 g CCl_4 **Find:** number of moles
                Conceptual Plan: g CCl_4 → mole CCl_4

$$\frac{1 \text{ mol}}{153.81 \text{ g } CCl_4}$$

Solution: $72.5 \text{ g } CCl_4 \times \dfrac{1 \text{ mol } CCl_4}{153.81 \text{ g } CCl_4} = 0.47\underline{1}4 \text{ mol } CCl_4 = 0.471 \text{ mol } CCl_4$

Check: The units (mole CCl_4) are correct. The magnitude is appropriate because it is less than 1 mole of CCl_4.

        (b)   **Given:** 12.4 g $C_{12}H_{22}O_{11}$ **Find:** number of moles
                Conceptual Plan: g $C_{12}H_{22}O_{11}$ → mole KNO_3

$$\frac{1 \text{ mol}}{342.296 \text{ g } C_{12}H_{22}O_{11}}$$

Solution:

$$12.4 \text{ g } C_{12}H_{22}O_{11} \times \frac{1 \text{ mol } C_{12}H_{22}O_{11}}{342.296 \text{ g } C_{12}H_{22}O_{11}} = 0.036\underline{2}3 \text{ mol } C_{12}H_{22}O_{11} = 0.0362 \text{ mol } C_{12}H_{22}O_{11}$$

Check: The units (mole $C_{12}H_{22}O_{11}$) are correct. The magnitude is appropriate because there is less than 1 mole of $C_{12}H_{22}O_{11}$.

        (c)   **Given:** 25.2 kg C_2H_2 **Find:** number of moles
                Conceptual Plan: kg CO_2 → g C_2H_2 → mole C_2H_2

$$\frac{1000 \text{ g } C_2H_2}{\text{kg } C_2H_2} \qquad \frac{1 \text{ mol}}{26.036 \text{ g } C_2H_2}$$

Solution: $25.2 \text{ kg } \cancel{CO_2} \times \dfrac{1000 \text{ g } \cancel{C_2H_2}}{\text{kg } \cancel{C_2H_2}} \times \dfrac{1 \text{ mol } C_2H_2}{26.036 \text{ g} \cancel{C_2H_2}} = 96\underline{7}.9 \text{ mol } C_2H_2 = 968 \text{ mol } C_2H_2$

Check: The units (mole C_2H_2) are correct. The magnitude is appropriate because more than a kilogram of C_2H_2 is present.

(d)   **Given:** 12.3 g dinitrogen monoxide   **Find:** number of moles
        Conceptual Plan: dinitrogen monoxide → formula and then g N_2O → mole N_2O

$$\frac{1 \text{ mol}}{44.02 \text{ g } N_2O}$$

Solution: Dinitrogen monoxide is N_2O.

$$12.3 \text{ g } \cancel{N_2O} \times \frac{1 \text{ mol } N_2O}{44.02 \text{ g } \cancel{N_2O}} = 0.27\underline{9}4 \text{ mol } N_2O = 0.279 \text{ mol } N_2O$$

Check: The units (mole N_2O) are correct. The magnitude is appropriate because less than a mole of N_2O is present.

3.38   (a)   **Given:** 15.7 mol HNO_3 **Find:** number of grams
        Conceptual Plan: mole HNO_3 → g HNO_3

$$\frac{63.018 \text{ g } HNO_3}{1 \text{ mol } HNO_3}$$

Solution: $15.7 \text{ mol } \cancel{HNO_3} \times \dfrac{63.018 \text{ g } HNO_3}{1 \text{ mol } \cancel{HNO_3}} = 98\underline{9}.38 \text{ g } HNO_3 = 989 \text{ g } HNO_3$

Check: The units (g HNO_3) are correct. The magnitude is appropriate because there are more than 15 moles of HNO_3.

(b)   **Given:** 1.04×10^{-3} mol H_2O_2 **Find:** number of grams
        Conceptual Plan: mole H_2O_2 → g H_2O_2

$$\frac{34.016 \text{ g } H_2O_2}{1 \text{ mol } H_2O_2}$$

Solution: $1.04 \times 10^{-3} \text{ mol } \cancel{H_2O_2} \times \dfrac{34.016 \text{ g } H_2O_2}{1 \text{ mol } \cancel{H_2O_2}} = 0.035\underline{3}8 \text{ g } H_2O_2 = 0.0354 \text{ g } H_2O_2$

Check: The units (g H_2O_2) are correct. The magnitude is appropriate because significantly less than 1 mole of H_2O_2 is present.

(c)   **Given:** 72.1 mol SO_2 **Find:** number of grams
        Conceptual Plan: mmol SO_2 → mole SO_2 → g SO_2

$$\frac{1 \text{ mol}}{1 \text{ mmol}} \qquad \frac{64.07 \text{ g } SO_2}{1 \text{ mol } SO_2}$$

Solution: $72.1 \text{ mmol } \cancel{SO_2} \times \dfrac{1 \text{ mol } \cancel{SO_2}}{1000 \text{ mmol } \cancel{SO_2}} \times \dfrac{64.07 \text{ g } SO_2}{1 \text{ mol } \cancel{SO_2}} = 4.6\underline{1}94 \text{ g } SO_2 = 4.62 \text{ g } SO_2$

Check: The units (g SO_2) are correct. The magnitude is appropriate because significantly less than 1 mole of SO_2 is present.

(d)   **Given:** 1.23 mol xenon difluoride   **Find:** number of grams
        Conceptual Plan: xenon difluoride → formula and then mole XeF_2 → g XeF_2

$$\frac{169.29 \text{ g } XeF_2}{1 \text{ mol}}$$

Solution: $1.23 \text{ mol } \cancel{XeF_2} \times \dfrac{169.29 \text{ g } XeF_2}{1 \text{ mol} \cancel{XeF_2}} = 20\underline{8}.23 \text{ g } XeF_2 = 208 \text{ g } XeF_2$

Check: The units (g XeF_2) are correct. The magnitude is appropriate because there is more than a mole of XeF_2.

3.39   (a)   **Given:** 3.5 g H_2O **Find:** number of molecules
        Conceptual Plan: g H_2O → mole H_2O → number H_2O molecules

$$\frac{1 \text{ mol}}{18.02 \text{ g } H_2O} \qquad \frac{6.022 \times 10^{23} \text{ H}_2\text{O molecules}}{\text{mol } H_2O}$$

Solution: $3.5 \text{ g } H_2O \times \dfrac{1 \text{ mol } H_2O}{18.02 \text{ g } H_2O} \times \dfrac{6.022 \times 10^{23} \text{ H}_2\text{O molecules}}{\text{mol } H_2O} = 1.\underline{1}70 \times 10^{23} \text{ H}_2\text{O molecules}$

$= 1.2 \times 10^{23} \text{ H}_2\text{O molecules}$

Check: The units (H_2O molecules) are correct. The magnitude is appropriate: it is smaller than Avogadro's number, as expected, because there is less than 1 mole of H_2O.

(b)   **Given:** 254 g CBr_4 **Find:** number of molecules
Conceptual Plan: g CBr_4 → mole CBr_4 → number CBr_4 molecules

$$\dfrac{1 \text{ mol}}{331.6 \text{ g } CBr_4} \qquad \dfrac{6.022 \times 10^{23} \text{ CBr}_4 \text{ molecules}}{\text{mol } CBr_4}$$

Solution: $254 \text{ g } CBr_4 \times \dfrac{1 \text{ mol } CBr_4}{331.6 \text{ g } CBr_4} \times \dfrac{6.022 \times 10^{23} \text{ CBr}_4 \text{ molecules}}{\text{mol } CBr_4} = 4.6\underline{1}28 \times 10^{23} \text{ CBr}_4 \text{ molecules}$

$= 4.61 \times 10^{23} \text{ CBr}_4 \text{ molecules}$

Check: The units (CBr_4 molecules) are correct. The magnitude is appropriate: it is smaller than Avogadro's number, as expected, because there is less than 1 mole of CBr_4.

(c)   **Given:** 18.3 g O_2 **Find:** number of molecules
Conceptual Plan: g O_2 → mole O_2 → number O_2 molecules

$$\dfrac{1 \text{ mol}}{32.00 \text{ g } O_2} \qquad \dfrac{6.022 \times 10^{23} \text{ O}_2 \text{ molecules}}{\text{mol } O_2}$$

Solution: $18.3 \text{ g } O_2 \times \dfrac{1 \text{ mol } O_2}{32.00 \text{ g } O_2} \times \dfrac{6.022 \times 10^{23} \text{ O}_2 \text{ molecules}}{\text{mol } O_2} = 3.4\underline{4}38 \times 10^{23} \text{ O}_2 \text{ molecules}$

$= 3.44 \times 10^{23} \text{ O}_2 \text{ molecules}$

Check: The units (O_2 molecules) are correct. The magnitude is appropriate: it is smaller than Avogadro's number, as expected, because there is less than 1 mole of O_2.

(d)   **Given:** 26.9 g C_8H_{10} **Find:** number of molecules
Conceptual Plan: g C_8H_{10} → mole C_8H_{10} → number C_8H_{10} molecules

$$\dfrac{1 \text{ mol}}{106.16 \text{ g } C_8H_{10}} \qquad \dfrac{6.022 \times 10^{23} \text{ C}_8\text{H}_{10} \text{ molecules}}{\text{mol } C_8H_{10}}$$

Solution: $26.9 \text{ g } C_8H_{10} \times \dfrac{1 \text{ mol } C_8H_{10}}{106.16 \text{ g } C_8H_{10}} \times \dfrac{6.022 \times 10^{23} \text{ C}_8\text{H}_{10} \text{ molecules}}{\text{mol } C_8H_{10}}$

$= 1.5\underline{2}59 \times 10^{23} \text{ C}_8\text{H}_{10} \text{ molecules} = 1.53 \times 10^{23} \text{ C}_8\text{H}_{10} \text{ molecules}$

Check: The units (C_8H_{10} molecules) are correct. The magnitude is appropriate: it is smaller than Avogadro's number, as expected, because there is less than 1 mole of C_8H_{10}.

3.40   (a)   **Given:** 3.87×10^{21} SO_3 molecules   **Find:** mass in g
Conceptual Plan: number SO_3 molecules → mole SO_3 → g SO_3

$$\dfrac{1 \text{ mol } SO_3}{6.022 \times 10^{23} \text{ SO}_3 \text{ molecules}} \qquad \dfrac{80.07 \text{ g } SO_3}{1 \text{ mol } SO_3}$$

Solution: $3.87 \times 10^{21} \text{ SO}_3 \text{ molecules} \times \dfrac{1 \text{ mol } SO_3}{6.022 \times 10^{23} \text{ SO}_3 \text{ molecules}} \times \dfrac{80.07 \text{ g } SO_3}{1 \text{ mol } SO_3} = 0.51\underline{4}56 \text{ g } SO_3$

$= 0.515 \text{ g } SO_3$

Check: The units (grams SO_3) are correct. The magnitude is appropriate: there is less than Avogadro's number of molecules, so we have less than 1 mole of SO_3.

(b)   **Given:** 1.3×10^{24} H_2O molecules   **Find:** mass in g
Conceptual Plan: number H_2O molecules → mole H_2O → g H_2O

$$\dfrac{1 \text{ mol } H_2O}{6.022 \times 10^{23} \text{ H}_2\text{O molecules}} \qquad \dfrac{18.02 \text{ g } H_2O}{1 \text{ mol } H_2O}$$

Solution: $1.3 \times 10^{24} \text{ H}_2\text{O molecules} \times \dfrac{1 \text{ mol } H_2O}{6.022 \times 10^{23} \text{ H}_2\text{O molecules}} \times \dfrac{18.02 \text{ g } H_2O}{1 \text{ mol } H_2O}$

$= 38.\underline{9}01 \text{ g } H_2O = 38.9 \text{ g } H_2O$

Check: The units (g H_2O) are correct. The magnitude is appropriate: there is more than Avogadro's number of molecules, so we have more than 1 mole of H_2O.

(c) **Given:** 2.55×10^{24} O_3 molecules **Find:** mass in g
Conceptual Plan: number O_3 molecules $\rightarrow$ mole O_3 $\rightarrow$ g O_3

$$\frac{1 \text{ mol } O_3}{6.022 \times 10^{23} \text{ } O_3 \text{ molecules}} \qquad \frac{48.00 \text{ g } O_3}{1 \text{ mol } O_3}$$

Solution: 2.55×10^{24} O_3 molecules $\times \dfrac{1 \text{ mol } O_3}{6.022 \times 10^{23} \text{ } O_3 \text{ molecules}} \times \dfrac{48.00 \text{ g } O_3}{1 \text{ mol } O_3} = 203.25 \text{ g } O_3 = 203 \text{ g } O_3$

Check: The units (g O_3) are correct. The magnitude is appropriate: there is more than Avogadro's number of molecules, so we have more than 1 mole of O_3.

(d) **Given:** 1.54×10^{21} CCl_2F_2 molecules **Find:** mass in g
Conceptual Plan: number CCl_2F_2 molecules $\rightarrow$ mole CCl_2F_2 $\rightarrow$ g CCl_2F_2

$$\frac{1 \text{ mol } CCl_2F_2}{6.022 \times 10^{23} \text{ } CCl_2F_2 \text{ molecules}} \qquad \frac{120.91 \text{ g } CCl_2F_2}{1 \text{ mol } CCl_2F_2}$$

Solution:

1.54×10^{21} CCl_2F_2 molecules $\times \dfrac{1 \text{ mol } CCl_2F_2}{6.022 \times 10^{23} \text{ } CCl_2F_2 \text{ molecules}} \times \dfrac{120.91 \text{ g } CCl_2F_2}{1 \text{ mol } CCl_2F_2} = 0.30902 \text{ g } CCl_2F_2$

$= 0.309 \text{ g } CCl_2F_2$

Check: The units (g CCl_2F_2) are correct. The magnitude is appropriate: there is less than Avogadro's number of molecules, so we have less than 1 mole of CCl_2F_2.

3.41 **Given:** 1 H_2O molecule **Find:** mass in g
Conceptual Plan: number H_2O molecules $\rightarrow$ mole H_2O $\rightarrow$ g H_2O

$$\frac{1 \text{ mol } H_2O}{6.022 \times 10^{23} \text{ } H_2O \text{ molecules}} \qquad \frac{18.02 \text{ g } H_2O}{1 \text{ mol } H_2O}$$

Solution:

1 H_2O molecule $\times \dfrac{1 \text{ mol } H_2O}{6.022 \times 10^{23} \text{ } H_2O \text{ molecules}} \times \dfrac{18.02 \text{ g } H_2O}{1 \text{ mol } H_2O} = 2.99236 \times 10^{-23} \text{ g } H_2O = 2.992 \times 10^{-23} \text{ g } H_2O$

Check: The units (g H_2O) are correct. The magnitude is appropriate: there is much less than Avogadro's number of molecules, so we have much less than 1 mole of H_2O.

3.42 **Given:** 1 $C_6H_{12}O_6$ molecule **Find:** mass in g
Conceptual Plan: number $C_6H_{12}O_6$ molecules $\rightarrow$ mole $C_6H_{12}O_6$ $\rightarrow$ g $C_6H_{12}O_6$

$$\frac{1 \text{ mol } C_6H_{12}O_6}{6.022 \times 10^{23} \text{ } C_6H_{12}O_6 \text{ molecules}} \qquad \frac{180.16 \text{ g } C_6H_{12}O_6}{1 \text{ mol } C_6H_{12}O_6}$$

Solution: 1 $C_6H_{12}O_6$ molecule $\times \dfrac{1 \text{ mol } C_6H_{12}O_6}{6.022 \times 10^{23} \text{ } C_6H_{12}O_6 \text{ molecules}} \times \dfrac{180.16 \text{ g } C_6H_{12}O_6}{1 \text{ mol } C_6H_{12}O_6}$

$= 2.99170 \times 10^{-22} \text{ g } C_6H_{12}O_6 = 2.992 \times 10^{-22} \text{ g } C_6H_{12}O_6$

Check: The units (g $C_6H_{12}O_6$) are correct. The magnitude is appropriate: there is much less than Avogadro's number of molecules, so we have much less than 1 mole of $C_6H_{12}O_6$.

3.43 **Given:** 1.8×10^{17} $C_{12}H_{22}O_{11}$ molecules **Find:** moles $C_{12}H_{22}O_{11}$; mass of $C_{12}H_{22}O_{11}$ crystal
Conceptual Plan: molecules $C_{12}H_{22}O_{11}$ $\rightarrow$ mole $C_{12}H_{22}O_{11}$ $\rightarrow$ g $C_{12}H_{22}O_{11}$

$$\frac{1 \text{ mol } C_{12}H_{22}O_{11}}{6.022 \times 10^{23} \text{ } C_{12}H_{22}O_{11} \text{ molecules}} \qquad \frac{342.3 \text{ g } C_{12}H_{22}O_{11}}{1 \text{ mol } C_{12}H_{22}O_{11}}$$

Solution:

1.8×10^{17} $C_{12}H_{22}O_{11}$ molecules $\times \dfrac{1 \text{ mol } C_{12}H_{22}O_{11}}{6.022 \times 10^{23} \text{ molecules } C_{12}H_{22}O_{11}} = 2.989 \times 10^{-7} \text{ mol } C_{12}H_{22}O_{11}$

$= 3.0 \times 10^{-7} \text{ mol } C_{12}H_{22}O_{11}$

2.989×10^{-7} mol $C_{12}H_{22}O_{11} \times \dfrac{342.3 \text{ g } C_{12}H_{22}O_{11}}{1 \text{ mol } C_{12}H_{22}O_{11}} = 1.023 \times 10^{-4} \text{ g } C_{12}H_{22}O_{11} = 1.0 \times 10^{-4} \text{ g } C_{12}H_{22}O_{11}$

$= 0.010 \text{ mg } C_{12}H_{22}O_{11}$

Check: The units (mg $C_{12}H_{22}O_{11}$ and g $C_{12}H_{22}O_{11}$) are correct. The magnitude is appropriate: there is much less than Avogadro's number of molecules, so we have much less than 1 mole of $C_{12}H_{22}O_{11}$. And we expect much less than 342 g $C_{12}H_{22}O_{11}$.

3.44   **Given:** 0.12 mg NaCl   **Find:** moles of Na^+ ions; number of Na^+ ions

         Conceptual Plan: mg NaCl → g NaCl → mol NaCl → mol Na^+ then find number of Na^+ ions

$$\frac{1 \text{ g NaCl}}{1000 \text{ mg NaCl}} \qquad \frac{1 \text{ mol NaCl}}{58.44 \text{ g NaCl}} \qquad \frac{1 \text{ mol } Na^+}{1 \text{ mol NaCl}} \qquad \frac{6.022 \times 10^{23} \text{ ions } Na^+}{1 \text{ mol } Na^+}$$

         Solution:

$$0.12 \text{ mg NaCl} \times \frac{1 \text{ g NaCl}}{1000 \text{ mg NaCl}} \times \frac{1 \text{ mol NaCl}}{58.44 \text{ g NaCl}} \times \frac{1 \text{ mol } Na^+}{1 \text{ mol NaCl}} = 2.\underline{0}53 \times 10^{-6} \text{ mol } Na^+ =$$

$$2.1 \times 10^{-6} \text{ mol } Na^+$$

$$2.\underline{0}53 \times 10^{-6} \text{ mol } Na^+ \times \frac{6.022 \times 10^{23} \text{ ions } Na^+}{1 \text{ mol } Na^+} = 1.\underline{2}37 \times 10^{18} \text{ ions } Na^+ = 1.2 \times 10^{18} \text{ ions } Na^+$$

         Check: The units (moles Na^+ and ions of Na^+) are correct. The magnitude is appropriate: there is less than 1 mole of NaCl, so we have less than Avogadro's number of sodium ions.

Composition of Compounds

3.45   (a)   **Given:** CH_4 **Find:** mass percent C

         Conceptual Plan: mass % C $= \dfrac{1 \times \text{molar mass C}}{\text{molar mass } CH_4} \times 100\%$

         Solution:

         $1 \times$ molar mass C $= 1(12.01 \text{ g/mol}) = 12.01 \text{ g C}$

         molar mass $CH_4 = 1(12.01 \text{ g/mol}) + 4(1.008 \text{ g/mol}) = 16.04 \text{ g/mol}$

$$\text{mass \% C} = \frac{1 \times \text{molar mass C}}{\text{molar mass } CH_4} \times 100\%$$

$$= \frac{12.01 \text{ g/mol}}{16.04 \text{ g/mol}} \times 100\%$$

$$= 74.8\underline{7}53\% = 74.88\%$$

         Check: The units (%) are correct. The magnitude is reasonable because it is between 0 and 100% and carbon is the heaviest element.

     (b)   **Given:** C_2H_6 **Find:** mass percent C

         Conceptual Plan: mass % C $= \dfrac{2 \times \text{molar mass C}}{\text{molar mass } C_2H_6} \times 100\%$

         Solution:

         $2 \times$ molar mass C $= 2(12.01 \text{ g/mol}) = 24.02 \text{ g C}$

         molar mass $C_2H_6 = 2(12.01 \text{ g/mol}) + 6(1.008 \text{ g/mol}) = 30.07 \text{ g/mol}$

$$\text{mass \% C} = \frac{2 \times \text{molar mass C}}{\text{molar mass } C_2H_6} \times 100\%$$

$$= \frac{24.02 \text{ g/mol}}{30.07 \text{ g/mol}} \times 100\%$$

$$= 79.8\underline{8}03\% = 79.88\%$$

         Check: The units (%) are correct. The magnitude is reasonable because it is between 0 and 100% and carbon is the heaviest element.

     (c)   **Given:** C_2H_2 **Find:** mass percent C

         Conceptual Plan: mass % C $= \dfrac{2 \times \text{molar mass C}}{\text{molar mass } C_2H_2} \times 100\%$

         Solution:

         $2 \times$ molar mass C $= 2(12.01 \text{ g/mol}) = 24.02 \text{ g C}$

         molar mass $C_2H_2 = 2(12.01 \text{ g/mol}) + 2(1.008 \text{ g/mol}) = 26.04 \text{ g/mol}$

$$\text{mass \% C} = \frac{2 \times \text{molar mass C}}{\text{molar mass C}_2\text{H}_2} \times 100\%$$

$$= \frac{24.02 \text{ g/mol}}{26.04 \text{ g/mol}} \times 100\%$$

$$= 92.2\underline{4}27\% = 92.24\%$$

Check: The units (%) are correct. The magnitude is reasonable because it is between 0 and 100% and carbon is the heaviest element.

(d) **Given:** C_2H_5Cl **Find:** mass percent C

Conceptual Plan: $\text{mass \% C} = \dfrac{2 \times \text{molar mass C}}{\text{molar mass C}_2\text{H}_5\text{Cl}} \times 100\%$

Solution:

$$2 \times \text{molar mass C} = 2(12.01 \text{ g/mol}) = 24.02 \text{ g C}$$
$$\text{molar mass C}_2\text{H}_5\text{Cl} = 2(12.01 \text{ g/mol}) + 5(1.008 \text{ g/mol}) + 1(35.45 \text{ g/mol}) = 64.51 \text{ g/mol}$$

$$\text{mass \% C} = \frac{2 \times \text{molar mass C}}{\text{molar mass C}_2\text{H}_5\text{Cl}} \times 100\%$$

$$= \frac{24.02 \text{ g/mol}}{64.51 \text{ g/mol}} \times 100\%$$

$$= 37.2\underline{3}45\% = 37.23\%$$

Check: The units (%) are correct. The magnitude is reasonable because it is between 0 and 100% and chlorine is heavier than carbon.

3.46 (a) **Given:** N_2O **Find:** mass percent N

Conceptual Plan: $\text{mass \% N} = \dfrac{2 \times \text{molar mass N}}{\text{molar mass N}_2\text{O}} \times 100$

Solution:

$$2 \times \text{molar mass N} = 2(14.01 \text{ g/mol}) = 28.02 \text{ g N}$$
$$\text{molar mass N}_2\text{O} = 2(14.01 \text{ g/mol}) + (16.00 \text{ g/mol}) = 44.02 \text{ g/mol}$$

$$\text{mass \% N} = \frac{2 \times \text{molar mass N}}{\text{molar mass N}_2\text{O}} \times 100\%$$

$$= \frac{28.02 \text{ g/mol}}{44.02 \text{ g/mol}} \times 100\%$$

$$= 63.6\underline{5}29\% = 63.65\%$$

Check: The units (%) are correct. The magnitude is reasonable because it is between 0 and 100% and there are two nitrogens per molecule.

(b) **Given:** NO **Find:** mass percent N

Conceptual Plan: $\text{mass \% N} = \dfrac{1 \times \text{molar mass N}}{\text{molar mass NO}} \times 100$

Solution:

$$1 \times \text{molar mass N} = 1(14.01 \text{ g/mol}) = 14.01 \text{ g N}$$
$$\text{molar mass NO} = (14.01 \text{ g/mol}) + (16.00 \text{ g/mol}) = 30.01 \text{ g/mol}$$

$$\text{mass \% N} = \frac{1 \times \text{molar mass N}}{\text{molar mass NO}} \times 100\%$$

$$= \frac{14.01 \text{ g/mol}}{30.01 \text{ g/mol}} \times 100\%$$

$$= 46.6\underline{8}44\% = 46.68\%$$

Check: The units (%) are correct. The magnitude is reasonable because it is between 0 and 100% and the mass of nitrogen is less than the mass of oxygen.

(c) **Given:** NO_2 **Find:** mass percent N

Conceptual Plan: $\text{mass \% N} = \dfrac{1 \times \text{molar mass N}}{\text{molar mass } NO_2} \times 100\%$

Solution:

$$1 \times \text{molar mass N} = 1(14.01 \text{ g/mol}) = 14.01 \text{ g N}$$
$$\text{molar mass } NO_2 = (14.01 \text{ g/mol}) + 2(16.00 \text{ g/mol}) = 46.01 \text{ g/mol}$$
$$\begin{aligned}\text{mass \% N} &= \frac{1 \times \text{molar mass N}}{\text{molar mass } NO_2} \times 100\% \\ &= \frac{14.01 \text{ g/}\cancel{\text{mol}}}{46.01 \text{ g/}\cancel{\text{mol}}} \times 100\% \\ &= 30.4\underline{4}99\% = 30.45\%\end{aligned}$$

Check: The units (%) are correct. The magnitude is reasonable because it is between 0 and 100%. The mass of nitrogen is less than the mass of oxygen, and there are two oxygens per molecule.

(d) **Given:** HNO_3 **Find:** mass percent N

Conceptual Plan: $\text{mass \% N} = \dfrac{1 \times \text{molar mass N}}{\text{molar mass } HNO_3} \times 100\%$

Solution:

$$1 \times \text{molar mass N} = 1(14.01\text{g/mol}) = 14.01 \text{ g N}$$
$$\text{molar mass } HNO_3 = (1.008 \text{ g/mol}) + (14.01 \text{ g/mol}) + 3(16.00 \text{ g/mol}) = 63.02 \text{ g/mol}$$
$$\begin{aligned}\text{mass \% N} &= \frac{1 \times \text{molar mass N}}{\text{molar mass } HNO_3} \times 100\% \\ &= \frac{14.01 \text{ g/}\cancel{\text{mol}}}{63.02 \text{ g/}\cancel{\text{mol}}} \times 100\% \\ &= 22.2\underline{3}10\% = 22.23\%\end{aligned}$$

Check: The units (%) are correct. The magnitude is reasonable because it is between 0 and 100%. The mass of nitrogen is less than the mass of oxygen, and there are three oxygens per molecule.

3.47 **Given:** NH_3 **Find:** mass percent N

Conceptual Plan: $\text{mass \% N} = \dfrac{1 \times \text{molar mass N}}{\text{molar mass } NH_3} \times 100\%$

Solution:

$$1 \times \text{molar mass N} = 1(14.01 \text{ g/mol}) = 14.01 \text{ g N}$$
$$\text{molar mass } NH_3 = 3(1.008 \text{ g/mol}) + (14.01 \text{ g/mol}) = 17.03 \text{ g/mol}$$
$$\begin{aligned}\text{mass \% N} &= \frac{1 \times \text{molar mass N}}{\text{molar mass } NH_3} \times 100\% \\ &= \frac{14.01 \text{ g/}\cancel{\text{mol}}}{17.03 \text{ g/}\cancel{\text{mol}}} \times 100\% \\ &= 82.2\underline{6}6\% = 82.27\%\end{aligned}$$

Check: The units (%) are correct. The magnitude is reasonable because it is between 0 and 100% and nitrogen is the heaviest atom present.

Given: $CO(NH_2)_2$ **Find:** mass percent N

Conceptual Plan: $\text{mass \% N} = \dfrac{2 \times \text{molar mass N}}{\text{molar mass } CO(NH_2)_2} \times 100\%$

Solution:

$$2 \times \text{molar mass N} = 1(14.01 \text{ g/mol}) = 28.02 \text{ g N}$$
$$\text{molar mass } CO(NH_2)_2 = (12.01 \text{ g/mol}) + (16.00 \text{ g/mol}) + 2(14.01 \text{ g/mol}) + 4(1.008 \text{ g/mol}) = 60.06 \text{ g/mol}$$

$$\text{mass \% N} = \frac{2 \times \text{molar mass N}}{\text{molar mass CO(NH}_2)_2} \times 100\%$$

$$= \frac{28.02 \text{ g/mol}}{60.06 \text{ g/mol}} \times 100\%$$

$$= 46.6\underline{5}3\% = 46.65\%$$

Check: The units (%) are correct. The magnitude is reasonable because it is between 0 and 100% and there are two nitrogens and only one carbon and one oxygen per molecule.

Given: NH_4NO_3 **Find:** mass percent N

Conceptual Plan: $\text{mass \% N} = \dfrac{2 \times \text{molar mass N}}{\text{molar mass NH}_4\text{NO}_3} \times 100\%$

Solution:

$2 \times \text{molar mass N} = 2(14.01 \text{ g/mol}) = 28.02 \text{ g N}$

$\text{molar mass NH}_4\text{NO}_3 = 2(14.01 \text{ g/mol}) + 4(1.008 \text{ g/mol}) + 3(16.00 \text{ g/mol}) = 80.05 \text{ g/mol}$

$$\text{mass \% N} = \frac{2 \times \text{molar mass N}}{\text{molar mass NH}_4\text{NO}_3} \times 100\%$$

$$= \frac{28.02 \text{ g/mol}}{80.05 \text{ g/mol}} \times 100\%$$

$$= 35.0\underline{0}31\% = 35.00\%$$

Check: The units (%) are correct. The magnitude is reasonable because it is between 0 and 100%. The mass of nitrogen is less than the mass of oxygen, and there are two nitrogens and three oxygens per molecule.

Given: $(NH_4)_2SO_4$ **Find:** mass percent N

Conceptual Plan: $\text{mass \% N} = \dfrac{2 \times \text{molar mass N}}{\text{molar mass (NH}_4)_2\text{SO}_4} \times 100\%$

Solution:

$2 \times \text{molar mass N} = 2(14.01 \text{ g/mol}) = 28.02 \text{ g N}$

$\text{molar mass (NH}_4)_2\text{SO}_4 = 2(14.01 \text{ g/mol}) + 8(1.008 \text{ g/mol}) + (32.07 \text{ g/mol}) + 4(16.00 \text{ g/mol}) = 132.15 \text{ g/mol}$

$$\text{mass \% N} = \frac{2 \times \text{molar mass N}}{\text{molar mass (NH}_4)_2\text{SO}_4} \times 100\%$$

$$= \frac{28.02 \text{ g/mol}}{132.15 \text{ g/mol}} \times 100\%$$

$$= 21.2\underline{0}32\% = 21.20\%$$

Check: The units (%) are correct. The magnitude is reasonable because it is between 0 and 100% and the mass of nitrogen is less than the mass of oxygen and sulfur.

The fertilizer with the highest nitrogen content is NH_3 with a N content of 82.27%.

3.48   **Given:** Fe_2O_3 **Find:** mass percent Fe

Conceptual Plan: $\text{mass \% Fe} = \dfrac{2 \times \text{molar mass Fe}}{\text{molar mass Fe}_2\text{O}_3} \times 100\%$

Solution:

$2 \times \text{molar mass Fe} = 2(55.85 \text{ g/mol}) = 111.7 \text{ g Fe}$

$\text{molar mass Fe}_2\text{O}_3 = 2(55.85 \text{ g/mol}) + 3(16.00 \text{ g/mol}) = 159.7 \text{ g/mol}$

$$\text{mass \% Fe} = \frac{2 \times \text{molar mass Fe}}{\text{molar mass Fe}_2\text{O}_3} \times 100\%$$

$$= \frac{111.7 \text{ g/mol}}{159.7 \text{ g/mol}} \times 100\%$$

$$= 69.9\underline{4}36\% = 69.94\%$$

Check: The units (%) are correct. The magnitude is reasonable because it is between 0 and 100% and iron provides most of the formula mass.

Given: Fe_3O_4 **Find:** mass percent Fe

Conceptual Plan: mass % Fe $= \dfrac{3 \times \text{molar mass Fe}}{\text{molar mass Fe}_2O_4} \times 100\%$

Solution:

$3 \times$ molar mass Fe $= 3(55.85 \text{ g/mol}) = 167.6$ g Fe

molar mass $Fe_3O_4 = 3(55.85 \text{ g/mol}) + 4(16.00 \text{ g/mol}) = 231.6$ g/mol

$$\text{mass \% Fe} = \dfrac{3 \times \text{molar mass Fe}}{\text{molar mass Fe}_3O_4} \times 100\%$$

$$= \dfrac{167.6 \text{ g/mol}}{231.6 \text{ g/mol}} \times 100\%$$

$$= 72.3\underline{6}61\% = 72.37\%$$

Check: The units (%) are correct. The magnitude is reasonable because it is between 0 and 100% and iron provides most of the formula mass.

Given: $FeCO_3$ **Find:** mass percent Fe

Conceptual Plan: mass % Fe $= \dfrac{1 \times \text{molar mass Fe}}{\text{molar mass FeCO}_3} \times 100\%$

Solution:

$1 \times$ molar mass Fe $= (55.85 \text{ g/mol}) = 55.85$ g Fe

molar mass $FeCO_3 = 1(55.85 \text{ g/mol}) + 1(12.01 \text{ g/mol}) + 3(16.00 \text{ g/mol}) = 115.86$ g/mol

$$\text{mass \% Fe} = \dfrac{1 \times \text{molar mass Fe}}{\text{molar mass FeCO}_3} \times 100\%$$

$$= \dfrac{55.85 \text{ g/mol}}{115.86 \text{ g/mol}} \times 100\%$$

$$= 48.2\underline{0}47\% = 48.20\%$$

Check: The units (%) are correct. The magnitude is reasonable because it is between 0 and 100% and iron provides slightly less than half of the formula mass.

The ore with the highest iron content is Fe_3O_4 with an Fe content of 72.37%.

3.49   **Given:** 72.4 g CuF_2; 37.42% F in CuF_2 **Find:** g F in CuF_2

Conceptual Plan: g CuF_2 $\rightarrow$ g F

$$\dfrac{37.42 \text{ g F}}{100.0 \text{ g CuF}_2}$$

Solution: 72.4 g $\overline{CuF_2}$ $\times \dfrac{37.42 \text{ g F}}{100.0 \text{ g } \overline{CuF_2}} = 27.\underline{0}9 = 27.1$ g F

Check: The units (g F) are correct. The magnitude is reasonable because it is less than the original mass.

3.50   **Given:** 112 mg Ag; 75.27% Ag in AgCl   **Find:** mg AgCl

Conceptual Plan: mg Ag $\rightarrow$ g Ag $\rightarrow$ g AgCl $\rightarrow$ mg AgCl

$$\dfrac{1 \text{ g Ag}}{1000 \text{ mg Ag}} \quad \dfrac{100.0 \text{ g AgCl}}{75.27 \text{ g Ag}} \quad \dfrac{1000 \text{ mg AgCl}}{1 \text{ g AgCl}}$$

Solution: 112 mg $\overline{Ag}$ $\times \dfrac{1 \text{ g } \overline{Ag}}{1000 \text{ mg } \overline{Ag}} \times \dfrac{100.0 \text{ g } \overline{AgCl}}{75.27 \text{ g } \overline{Ag}} \times \dfrac{1000 \text{ mg AgCl}}{1 \text{ g } \overline{AgCl}} = 14\underline{8}.8$ mg AgCl $= 149$ mg AgCl

Check: The units (mg AgCl) are correct. The magnitude is reasonable because it is greater than the original mass.

3.51   **Given:** 150 μg I; 76.45% I in KI   **Find:** μg KI

Conceptual Plan: μg I $\rightarrow$ g I $\rightarrow$ g KI $\rightarrow$ μg KI

$$\dfrac{1 \text{ g I}}{1 \times 10^6 \ \mu\text{g I}} \quad \dfrac{100.0 \text{ g KI}}{76.45 \text{ g I}} \quad \dfrac{1 \times 10^6 \ \mu\text{g KI}}{1 \text{ g KI}}$$

Solution: 150 μg $\overline{I}$ $\times \dfrac{1 \text{ g } \overline{I}}{1 \times 10^6 \ \mu\text{g } \overline{I}} \times \dfrac{100.0 \text{ g } \overline{KI}}{76.45 \text{ g } \overline{I}} \times \dfrac{1 \times 10^6 \ \mu\text{g KI}}{1 \text{ g } \overline{KI}} = 19\underline{6}.2 \ \mu$g KI $= 196 \ \mu$g KI

Check: The units (μg KI) are correct. The magnitude is reasonable because it is greater than the original mass.

3.52   **Given:** 3.0 mg F; 45.24% F in NaF   **Find:** mg NaF
Conceptual Plan: mg F → g F → g NaF → mg NaF

$$\frac{1\ g\ F}{1000\ mg\ F} \qquad \frac{100.0\ g\ NaF}{45.24\ g\ F} \qquad \frac{1000\ mg\ NaF}{1\ g\ NaF}$$

Solution: $3.0\ \text{mg F} \times \dfrac{1\ \text{g F}}{1000\ \text{mg F}} \times \dfrac{100.0\ \text{g NaF}}{45.24\ \text{g NaF}} \times \dfrac{1000\ \text{mg NaF}}{1\ \text{g NaF}} = 6.\underline{6}3\ \text{mg NaF} = 6.6\ \text{mg NaF}$

Check: The units (mg NaF) are correct. The magnitude is reasonable because it is greater than the original mass.

3.53   (a)   red = oxygen, white = hydrogen: 2H:O H_2O
         (b)   black = carbon, white = hydrogen: C:4H CH_4
         (c)   black = carbon, white = hydrogen, red = oxygen: 2C:6H:O CH_3CH_2OH or C_2H_6O

3.54   (a)   black = carbon, red = oxygen: 2O:C CO_2
         (b)   red = oxygen, white = hydrogen: 2H:2O H_2O_2
         (c)   red = oxygen, white = hydrogen: 2H:O H_2O

3.55   (a)   **Given:** 0.0885 mol C_4H_{10} **Find:** mol H atoms
         Conceptual Plan: mol C_4H_{10} → mole H atoms

$$\frac{10\ mol\ H}{1\ mol\ C_4H_{10}}$$

Solution: $0.0885\ \text{mol } C_4H_{10} \times \dfrac{10\ \text{mol H}}{1\ \text{mol } C_4H_{10}} = 0.885\ \text{mol H atoms}$

Check: The units (mol H atoms) are correct. The magnitude is reasonable because it is greater than the original mol C_4H_{10}.

         (b)   **Given:** 1.3 mol CH_4 **Find:** mol H atoms
         Conceptual Plan: mol CH_4 → mole H atoms

$$\frac{4\ mol\ H}{1\ mol\ CH_4}$$

Solution: $1.3\ \text{mol } CH_4 \times \dfrac{4\ \text{mol H}}{1\ \text{mol } CH_4} = 5.2\ \text{mol H atoms}$

Check: The units (mol H atoms) are correct. The magnitude is reasonable because it is greater than the original mol CH_4.

         (c)   **Given:** 2.4 mol C_6H_{12} **Find:** mol H atoms
         Conceptual Plan: mol C_6H_{12} → mole H atoms

$$\frac{12\ mol\ H}{1\ mol\ C_6H_{12}}$$

Solution: $2.4\ \text{mol } C_6H_{12} \times \dfrac{12\ \text{mol H}}{1\ \text{mol } C_6H_{12}} = 28.\underline{8}\ \text{mol H atoms} = 29\ \text{mol H atoms}$

Check: The units (mol H atoms) are correct. The magnitude is reasonable because it is greater than the original mol C_6H_{12}.

         (d)   **Given:** 1.87 mol C_8H_{18} **Find:** mol H atoms
         Conceptual Plan: mol C_8H_{18} → mole H atoms

$$\frac{18\ mol\ H}{1\ mol\ C_8H_{18}}$$

Solution: $1.87\ \text{mol } C_8H_{18} \times \dfrac{18\ \text{mol H}}{1\ \text{mol } C_8H_{18}} = 33.\underline{6}6\ \text{mol H atoms} = 33.7\ \text{mol H atoms}$

Check: The units (mol H atoms) are correct. The magnitude is reasonable because it is greater than the original mol C_8H_{18}.

3.56   (a)   **Given:** 4.88 mol H_2O_2 **Find:** mol O atoms
         Conceptual Plan: mol H_2O_2 → mole O atoms

$$\frac{2\ mol\ O}{1\ mol\ H_2O_2}$$

Solution: $4.88 \; \text{mol H}_2\text{O}_2 \times \dfrac{2 \; \text{mol O}}{1 \; \text{mol H}_2\text{O}_2} = 9.76 \; \text{mol O atoms}$

Check: The units (mol O atoms) are correct. The magnitude is reasonable because it is greater than the original mol H_2O_2.

(b) **Given:** 2.15 mol N_2O **Find:** mol O atoms
Conceptual Plan: mol N_2O → mole O atoms

$$\dfrac{1 \; \text{mol O}}{1 \; \text{mol N}_2\text{O}}$$

Solution: $2.15 \; \text{mol N}_2\text{O} \times \dfrac{1 \; \text{mol O}}{1 \; \text{mol N}_2\text{O}} = 2.15 \; \text{mol O atoms}$

Check: The units (mol O atoms) are correct. The magnitude is reasonable because it is the same as the original mol N_2O.

(c) **Given:** 0.0237 mol H_2CO_3 **Find:** mol O atoms
Conceptual Plan: mol H_2CO_3 → mole O atoms

$$\dfrac{3 \; \text{mol O}}{1 \; \text{mol H}_2\text{CO}_3}$$

Solution: $0.0237 \; \text{mol H}_2\text{CO}_3 \times \dfrac{3 \; \text{mol O}}{1 \; \text{mol H}_2\text{CO}_3} = 0.0711 \; \text{mol O atoms}$

Check: The units (mol O atoms) are correct. The magnitude is reasonable because it is greater than the original mol H_2CO_3.

(d) **Given:** 24.1 mol CO_2 **Find:** mol O atoms
Conceptual Plan: mol CO_2 → mole O atoms

$$\dfrac{2 \; \text{mol O}}{1 \; \text{mol CO}_2}$$

Solution: $24.1 \; \text{mol CO}_2 \times \dfrac{2 \; \text{mol O}}{1 \; \text{mol CO}_2} = 48.2 \; \text{mol O atoms}$

Check: The units (mol O atoms) are correct. The magnitude is reasonable because it is greater than the original mol CO_2.

3.57 (a) **Given:** 8.5 g NaCl **Find:** g Na
Conceptual Plan: g NaCl → mole NaCl → mol Na → g Na

$$\dfrac{1 \; \text{mol NaCl}}{58.44 \; \text{g NaCl}} \qquad \dfrac{1 \; \text{mol Na}}{1 \; \text{mol NaCl}} \qquad \dfrac{22.99 \; \text{g Na}}{1 \; \text{mol Na}}$$

Solution: $8.5 \; \text{g NaCl} \times \dfrac{1 \; \text{mol NaCl}}{58.44 \; \text{g NaCl}} \times \dfrac{1 \; \text{mol Na}}{1 \; \text{mol NaCl}} \times \dfrac{22.99 \; \text{g Na}}{1 \; \text{mol Na}} = 3.\underline{3}44 \; \text{g Na} = 3.3 \; \text{g Na}$

Check: The units (g Na) are correct. The magnitude is reasonable because it is less than the original g NaCl.

(b) **Given:** 8.5 g Na_3PO_4 **Find:** g Na
Conceptual Plan: g Na_3PO_4 → mole Na_3PO_4 → mol Na → g Na

$$\dfrac{1 \; \text{mol Na}_3\text{PO}_4}{163.94 \; \text{g Na}_3\text{PO}_4} \qquad \dfrac{3 \; \text{mol Na}}{1 \; \text{mol Na}_3\text{PO}_4} \qquad \dfrac{22.99 \; \text{g Na}}{1 \; \text{mol Na}}$$

Solution: $8.5 \; \text{g Na}_3\text{PO}_4 \times \dfrac{1 \; \text{mol Na}_3\text{PO}_4}{163.94 \; \text{g Na}_3\text{PO}_4} \times \dfrac{3 \; \text{mol Na}}{1 \; \text{mol Na}_3\text{PO}_4} \times \dfrac{22.99 \; \text{g Na}}{1 \; \text{mol Na}} = 3.\underline{5}76 \; \text{g Na} = 3.6 \; \text{g Na}$

Check: The units (g Na) are correct. The magnitude is reasonable because it is less than the original g Na_3PO_4.

(c) **Given:** 8.5 g $NaC_7H_5O_2$ **Find:** g Na
Conceptual Plan: g $NaC_7H_5O_2$ → mole $NaC_7H_5O_2$ → mol Na → g Na

$$\dfrac{1 \; \text{mol NaC}_7\text{H}_5\text{O}_2}{144.10 \; \text{g NaC}_7\text{H}_5\text{O}_2} \qquad \dfrac{1 \; \text{mol Na}}{1 \; \text{mol NaC}_7\text{H}_5\text{O}_2} \qquad \dfrac{22.99 \; \text{g Na}}{1 \; \text{mol Na}}$$

Solution:

$8.5 \; \text{g NaC}_7\text{H}_5\text{O}_2 \times \dfrac{1 \; \text{mol NaC}_7\text{H}_5\text{O}_2}{144.10 \; \text{g NaC}_7\text{H}_5\text{O}_2} \times \dfrac{1 \; \text{mol Na}}{1 \; \text{mol NaC}_7\text{H}_5\text{O}_2} \times \dfrac{22.99 \; \text{g Na}}{1 \; \text{mol Na}} = 1.\underline{3}56 \; \text{g Na} = 1.4 \; \text{g Na}$

Check: The units (g Na) are correct. The magnitude is reasonable because it is less than the original g $NaC_7H_5O_2$.

(d)   **Given:** 8.5 g $Na_2C_6H_6O_7$ **Find:** g Na
       Conceptual Plan: g $Na_2C_6H_6O_7$ → mole $Na_2C_6H_6O_7$ → mol Na → g Na

$$\frac{1 \text{ mol } Na_2C_6H_6O_7}{236.1 \text{ g } Na_2C_6H_6O_7} \qquad \frac{2 \text{ mol Na}}{1 \text{ mol } Na_2C_6H_6O_7} \qquad \frac{22.99 \text{ g Na}}{1 \text{ mol Na}}$$

Solution:

$$8.5 \text{ g } Na_2C_6H_6O_7 \times \frac{1 \text{ mol } Na_2C_6H_6O_7}{236.1 \text{ g } Na_2C_6H_6O_7} \times \frac{2 \text{ mol Na}}{1 \text{ mol } Na_2C_6H_6O_7} \times \frac{22.99 \text{ g Na}}{1 \text{ mol Na}} = 1.\underline{6}55 \text{ g Na} = 1.7 \text{ g Na}$$

Check: The units (g Na) are correct. The magnitude is reasonable because it is less than the original g $Na_2C_6H_6O_7$.

3.58   (a)   **Given:** 25 kg CF_2Cl_2 **Find:** kg Cl
       Conceptual Plan: kg CF_2Cl_2 → g CF_2Cl_2 → mole CF_2Cl_2 → mol Cl → g Cl → kg Cl

$$\frac{1000 \text{ g } CF_2Cl_2}{1 \text{ kg } CF_2Cl_2} \quad \frac{1 \text{ mol } CF_2Cl_2}{120.91 \text{ g } CF_2Cl_2} \quad \frac{2 \text{ mol Cl}}{1 \text{ mol } CF_2Cl_2} \quad \frac{35.45 \text{ g Cl}}{1 \text{ mol Cl}} \quad \frac{1 \text{ kg Cl}}{1000 \text{ g Cl}}$$

Solution:

$$25 \text{ kg } CF_2Cl_2 \times \frac{1000 \text{ g } CF_2Cl_2}{1 \text{ kg } CF_2Cl_2} \times \frac{1 \text{ mol } CF_2Cl_2}{120.91 \text{ g } CF_2Cl_2} \times \frac{2 \text{ mol Cl}}{1 \text{ mol } CF_2Cl_2} \times \frac{35.45 \text{ g Cl}}{1 \text{ mol Cl}} \times \frac{1 \text{ kg Cl}}{1000 \text{ g Cl}}$$
$$= 14.\underline{6}6 \text{ kg Cl} = 15 \text{ kg Cl}$$

Check: The units (kg Cl) are correct. The magnitude is reasonable because it is less than the original kg CF_2Cl_2.

(b)   **Given:** 25 kg $CFCl_3$ **Find:** kg Cl
       Conceptual Plan: kg $CFCl_3$ → g $CFCl_3$ → mole $CFCl_3$ → mol Cl → g Cl → kg Cl

$$\frac{1000 \text{ g } CFCl_3}{1 \text{ kg } CFCl_3} \quad \frac{1 \text{ mol } CFCl_3}{137.4 \text{ g } CFCl_3} \quad \frac{3 \text{ mol Cl}}{1 \text{ mol } CFCl_3} \quad \frac{35.45 \text{ g Cl}}{1 \text{ mol Cl}} \quad \frac{1 \text{ kg Cl}}{1000 \text{ g Cl}}$$

Solution:

$$25 \text{ kg } CFCl_3 \times \frac{1000 \text{ g } CFCl_3}{1 \text{ kg } CFCl_3} \times \frac{1 \text{ mol } CFCl_3}{137.4 \text{ g } CFCl_3} \times \frac{3 \text{ mol Cl}}{1 \text{ mol } CFCl_3} \times \frac{35.45 \text{ g Cl}}{1 \text{ mol Cl}} \times \frac{1 \text{ kg Cl}}{1000 \text{ g Cl}}$$
$$= 19.\underline{3}5 \text{ kg Cl} = 19 \text{ kg Cl}$$

Check: The units (kg Cl) are correct. The magnitude is reasonable because it is less than the original kg $CFCl_3$.

(c)   **Given:** 25 kg $C_2F_3Cl_3$ **Find:** kg Cl
       Conceptual Plan: kg $C_2F_3Cl_3$ → g $C_2F_3Cl_3$ → mole $C_2F_3Cl_3$ → mol Cl → g Cl → kg Cl

$$\frac{1000 \text{ g } C_2F_3Cl_3}{1 \text{ kg } C_2F_3Cl_3} \quad \frac{1 \text{ mol } C_2F_3Cl_3}{187.4 \text{ g } C_2F_3Cl_3} \quad \frac{3 \text{ mol Cl}}{1 \text{ mol } C_2F_3Cl_3} \quad \frac{35.45 \text{ g Cl}}{1 \text{ mol Cl}} \quad \frac{1 \text{ kg Cl}}{1000 \text{ g Cl}}$$

Solution:

$$25 \text{ kg } C_2F_3Cl_3 \times \frac{1000 \text{ g } C_2F_3Cl_3}{1 \text{ kg } C_2F_3Cl_3} \times \frac{1 \text{ mol } C_2F_3Cl_3}{187.4 \text{ g } C_2F_3Cl_3} \times \frac{3 \text{ mol Cl}}{1 \text{ mol } C_2F_3Cl_3} \times \frac{35.45 \text{ g Cl}}{1 \text{ mol Cl}} \times \frac{1 \text{ kg Cl}}{1000 \text{ g Cl}}$$
$$= 14.\underline{1}9 \text{ kg Cl} = 14 \text{ kg Cl}$$

Check: The units (kg Cl) are correct. The magnitude is reasonable because it is less than the original kg $C_2F_3Cl_3$.

(d)   **Given:** 25 kg CF_3Cl **Find:** kg Cl
       Conceptual Plan: kg CF_3Cl → g CF_3Cl → mole CF_3Cl → mol Cl → g Cl → kg Cl

$$\frac{1000 \text{ g } CF_3Cl}{1 \text{ kg } CF_3Cl} \quad \frac{1 \text{ mol } CF_3Cl}{104.46 \text{ g } CF_3Cl} \quad \frac{1 \text{ mol Cl}}{1 \text{ mol } CF_3Cl} \quad \frac{35.45 \text{ g Cl}}{1 \text{ mol Cl}} \quad \frac{1 \text{ kg Cl}}{1000 \text{ g Cl}}$$

Solution: $25 \text{ kg } CF_3Cl \times \dfrac{1000 \text{ g } CF_3Cl}{1 \text{ kg } CF_3Cl} \times \dfrac{1 \text{ mol } CF_3Cl}{104.46 \text{ g } CF_3Cl} \times \dfrac{1 \text{ mol Cl}}{1 \text{ mol } CF_3Cl} \times \dfrac{35.45 \text{ g Cl}}{1 \text{ mol Cl}} \times \dfrac{1 \text{ kg Cl}}{1000 \text{ g Cl}}$

$$= 8.\underline{4}84 \text{ kg Cl} = 8.5 \text{ kg Cl}$$

Check: The units (kg Cl) are correct. The magnitude is reasonable because it is less than the original kg CF_3Cl.

3.59   **Given:** 5.85 g C_2F_4 **Find:** F atoms

Conceptual Plan: g C_2F_4 → mol C_2F_4 → molecules C_2F_4 → F atoms

$$\frac{1 \text{ mol } C_2F_4}{100.02 \text{ g } C_2F_4} \quad \frac{6.022 \times 10^{23} \text{ } C_2F_4 \text{ molecules}}{1 \text{ mole } C_2F_4} \quad \frac{4 \text{ F atoms}}{1 \text{ } C_2F_4 \text{ molecule}}$$

Solution: $5.85 \text{ g } C_2F_4 \times \dfrac{1 \text{ mol g } C_2F_4}{100.02 \text{ g } C_2F_4} \times \dfrac{6.022 \times 10^{23} \text{ } C_2F_4 \text{ molecules}}{1 \text{ mol } C_2F_4} \times \dfrac{4 \text{ F atoms}}{1 \text{ } C_2F_4 \text{ molecules}}$

$= 1.40\underline{8}9 \times 10^{23}$ F atoms $= 1.41 \times 10^{23}$ F atoms

Check: The units (F atoms) are correct. The magnitude of the answer (1.41×10^{23}) makes physical sense because there is ~0.06 mole of molecules and there are 4 F atoms in each molecule.

3.60   **Given:** 35.2 g CH_2Br_2 **Find:** Br atoms

Conceptual Plan: g CH_2Br_2 → mol CH_2Br_2 → molecules CH_2Br_2 → Br atoms

$$\frac{1 \text{ mol } CH_2Br_2}{173.83 \text{ g } CH_2Br_2} \quad \frac{6.022 \times 10^{23} \text{ } CH_2Br_2 \text{ molecules}}{1 \text{ mole } CH_2Br_2} \quad \frac{2 \text{ Br atoms}}{1 \text{ } CH_2Br_2 \text{ molecule}}$$

Solution: $35.2 \text{ g } CH_2Br_2 \times \dfrac{1 \text{ mol g } CH_2Br_2}{173.83 \text{ g } CH_2Br_2} \times \dfrac{6.022 \times 10^{23} CH_2Br_2 \text{ molecules}}{1 \text{ mol } CH_2Br_2} \times \dfrac{2 \text{ Br atoms}}{1 \text{ } CH_2Br_2 \text{ molecules}}$

$= 2.43\underline{8}9 \times 10^{23}$ Br atoms $= 2.44 \times 10^{23}$ Br atoms

Check: The units (Br atoms) are correct. The magnitude of the answer (2.44×10^{23}) makes physical sense because there is ~0.2 mole of molecules and there are 2 Br atoms in each molecule.

Chemical Formulas from Experimental Data

3.61   (a)   **Given:** 1.651 g Ag; 0.1224 g O   **Find:** empirical formula

Conceptual Plan:

convert mass to mol of each element → write pseudoformula → write empirical formula

$$\frac{1 \text{ mol Ag}}{107.9 \text{ g Ag}} \quad \frac{1 \text{ mol O}}{16.00 \text{ g O}} \qquad \text{divide by smallest number}$$

Solution: $1.651 \text{ g Ag} \times \dfrac{1 \text{ mol Ag}}{107.9 \text{ g Ag}} = 0.01530 \text{ mol Ag}$

$0.1224 \text{ g O} \times \dfrac{1 \text{ mol O}}{16.00 \text{ g O}} = 0.007650 \text{ mol O}$

$Ag_{0.01530} O_{0.007650}$

$Ag_{\frac{0.01530}{0.007650}} O_{\frac{0.007650}{0.007650}} \rightarrow Ag_2O$

The correct empirical formula is Ag_2O.

(b)   **Given:** 0.672 g Co; 0.569 g As; 0.486 g O   **Find:** empirical formula

Conceptual Plan:

convert mass to mol of each element → write pseudoformula → write empirical formula

$$\frac{1 \text{ mol Co}}{58.93 \text{ g Co}} \quad \frac{1 \text{ mol As}}{74.92 \text{ g As}} \quad \frac{1 \text{ mol O}}{16.00 \text{ g O}} \qquad \text{divide by smallest number}$$

Solution: $0.672 \text{ g Co} \times \dfrac{1 \text{ mol Co}}{58.93 \text{ g Co}} = 0.0114 \text{ mol Co}$

$0.569 \text{ g As} \times \dfrac{1 \text{ mol As}}{74.92 \text{ g As}} = 0.00759 \text{ mol O}$

$0.486 \text{ g O} \times \dfrac{1 \text{ mol O}}{16.00 \text{ g O}} = 0.0304 \text{ mol O}$

$Co_{0.0114} As_{0.00759} O_{0.0304}$

$Co_{\frac{0.0114}{0.00759}} As_{\frac{0.00759}{0.00759}} O_{\frac{0.0304}{0.00759}} \rightarrow Co_{1.5}As_1O_4$

$Co_{1.5}As_1O_4 \times 2 \rightarrow Co_3As_2O_8$

The correct empirical formula is $Co_3As_2O_8$.

(c) **Given:** 1.443 g Se; 5.841 g Br **Find:** empirical formula

Conceptual Plan:

convert mass to mol of each element → write pseudoformula → write empirical formula

$$\frac{1 \text{ mol Se}}{78.96 \text{ g Se}} \quad \frac{1 \text{ mol Br}}{79.90 \text{ g Br}}$$ divide by smallest number

Solution: $1.443 \text{ g Se} \times \dfrac{1 \text{ mol Se}}{78.96 \text{ g Se}} = 0.01828 \text{ mol Se}$

$5.841 \text{ g Br} \times \dfrac{1 \text{ mol Br}}{79.90 \text{ g Br}} = 0.07310 \text{ mol Br}$

$\text{Se}_{0.01828} \text{Br}_{0.07310}$

$\text{Se}_{\frac{0.01828}{0.01828}} \text{Br}_{\frac{0.07310}{0.01828}} \rightarrow \text{SeBr}_4$

The correct empirical formula is SeBr_4.

3.62   (a) **Given:** 1.245 g Ni; 5.381 g I **Find:** empirical formula

Conceptual Plan:

convert mass to mol of each element → write pseudoformula → write empirical formula

$$\frac{1 \text{ mol Ni}}{58.69 \text{ g Ni}} \quad \frac{1 \text{ mol I}}{126.9 \text{ g I}}$$ divide by smallest number

Solution: $1.245 \text{ g Ni} \times \dfrac{1 \text{ mol Ni}}{58.69 \text{ g Ni}} = 0.02121 \text{ mol Ni}$

$5.381 \text{ g I} \times \dfrac{1 \text{ mol I}}{126.9 \text{ g I}} = 0.04240 \text{ mol I}$

$\text{Ni}_{0.02121} \text{I}_{0.04240}$

$\text{Ni}_{\frac{0.02121}{0.02121}} \text{I}_{\frac{0.04240}{0.02121}} \rightarrow \text{NiI}_2$

The correct empirical formula is NiI_2.

(b) **Given:** 2.677 g Ba; 3.115 g Br **Find:** empirical formula

Conceptual Plan:

convert mass to mol of each element → write pseudoformula → write empirical formula

$$\frac{1 \text{ mol Ba}}{137.3 \text{ g Ba}} \quad \frac{1 \text{ mol Br}}{79.90 \text{ g Br}}$$ divide by smallest number

Solution: $2.677 \text{ g Ba} \times \dfrac{1 \text{ mol Ba}}{137.3 \text{ g Ba}} = 0.01950 \text{ mol Ba}$

$3.115 \text{ g Br} \times \dfrac{1 \text{ mol Br}}{79.90 \text{ g Br}} = 0.03899 \text{ mol Br}$

$\text{Ba}_{0.01950} \text{Br}_{0.03899}$

$\text{Ba}_{\frac{0.01950}{0.01950}} \text{Br}_{\frac{0.03899}{0.01950}} \rightarrow \text{BaBr}_2$

The correct empirical formula is BaBr_2.

(c) **Given:** 2.128 g Be; 7.557 g S; 15.107 g O **Find:** empirical formula

Conceptual Plan:

convert mass to mol of each element → write pseudoformula → write empirical formula

$$\frac{1 \text{ mol Be}}{9.012 \text{ g Be}} \quad \frac{1 \text{ mol S}}{32.07 \text{ g S}} \quad \frac{1 \text{ mol O}}{16.00 \text{ g O}}$$ divide by smallest number

Solution: $2.128 \text{ g Be} \times \dfrac{1 \text{ mol Be}}{9.012 \text{ g Be}} = 0.2361 \text{ mol Be}$

$7.557 \text{ g S} \times \dfrac{1 \text{ mol S}}{32.07 \text{ g S}} = 0.2356 \text{ mol S}$

$15.107 \text{ g O} \times \dfrac{1 \text{ mol O}}{16.00 \text{ g O}} = 0.9442 \text{ mol O}$

$$Be_{0.2361} S_{0.2356} O_{0.9442}$$

$$Be_{\frac{0.2361}{0.2356}} S_{\frac{0.2356}{0.2356}} O_{\frac{0.9442}{0.2356}} \rightarrow BeSO_4$$

The correct empirical formula is $BeSO_4$.

3.63   (a)   **Given:** in a 100 g sample: 74.03 g C; 8.70 g H; 17.27 g N   **Find:** empirical formula
Conceptual Plan:
convert mass to mol of each element $\rightarrow$ **write pseudoformula** $\rightarrow$ **write empirical formula**

$$\frac{1 \text{ mol C}}{12.01 \text{ g C}} \quad \frac{1 \text{ mol H}}{1.008 \text{ g H}} \quad \frac{1 \text{ mol N}}{14.01 \text{ g N}} \qquad \text{divide by smallest number}$$

Solution: $74.03 \text{ g C} \times \dfrac{1 \text{ mol C}}{12.01 \text{ g C}} = 6.164 \text{ mol C}$

$8.70 \text{ g H} \times \dfrac{1 \text{ mol H}}{1.008 \text{ g H}} = 8.63 \text{ mol H}$

$17.27 \text{ g N} \times \dfrac{1 \text{ mol N}}{14.01 \text{ g N}} = 1.233 \text{ mol N}$

$C_{6.164} H_{8.63} N_{1.233}$

$C_{\frac{6.164}{1.233}} H_{\frac{8.63}{1.233}} N_{\frac{1.233}{1.233}} \rightarrow C_5H_7N$

The correct empirical formula is C_5H_7N.

   (b)   **Given:** In a 100 g sample: 49.48 g C; 5.19 g H; 28.85 g N; 16.48 g O   **Find:** empirical formula
Conceptual Plan:
convert mass to mol of each element $\rightarrow$ **write pseudoformula** $\rightarrow$ **write empirical formula**

$$\frac{1 \text{ mol C}}{12.01 \text{ g C}} \quad \frac{1 \text{ mol H}}{1.008 \text{ g H}} \quad \frac{1 \text{ mol N}}{14.01 \text{ g N}} \quad \frac{1 \text{ mol O}}{16.00 \text{ g O}} \qquad \text{divide by smallest number}$$

Solution: $49.48 \text{ g C} \times \dfrac{1 \text{ mol C}}{12.01 \text{ g C}} = 4.120 \text{ mol C}$

$5.19 \text{ g H} \times \dfrac{1 \text{ mol H}}{1.008 \text{ g H}} = 5.15 \text{ mol H}$

$28.85 \text{ g N} \times \dfrac{1 \text{ mol N}}{14.01 \text{ g N}} = 2.059 \text{ mol N}$

$16.48 \text{ g O} \times \dfrac{1 \text{ mol O}}{16.00 \text{ g O}} = 1.030 \text{ mol O}$

$C_{4.120} H_{5.15} N_{2.059} O_{1.030}$

$C_{\frac{4.120}{1.030}} H_{\frac{5.15}{1.030}} N_{\frac{2.059}{1.030}} O_{\frac{1.030}{1.030}} \rightarrow C_4H_5N_2O$

The correct empirical formula is $C_4H_5N_2O$.

3.64   (a)   **Given:** In a 100 g sample: 58.80 g C; 9.87 g H; 31.33 g O   **Find:** empirical formula
Conceptual Plan:
convert mass to mol of each element $\rightarrow$ **write pseudoformula** $\rightarrow$ **write empirical formula**

$$\frac{1 \text{ mol C}}{12.01 \text{ g C}} \quad \frac{1 \text{ mol H}}{1.008 \text{ g H}} \quad \frac{1 \text{ mol O}}{16.00 \text{ g O}} \qquad \text{divide by smallest number}$$

Solution: $58.80 \text{ g C} \times \dfrac{1 \text{ mol C}}{12.01 \text{ g C}} = 4.896 \text{ mol C}$

$9.87 \text{ g H} \times \dfrac{1 \text{ mol H}}{1.008 \text{ g H}} = 9.79 \text{ mol H}$

$31.33 \text{ g O} \times \dfrac{1 \text{ mol O}}{16.00 \text{ g O}} = 1.958 \text{ mol O}$

$C_{4.896} H_{9.79} O_{1.958}$

$C_{\frac{4.896}{1.958}} H_{\frac{9.79}{1.958}} O_{\frac{1.958}{1.958}} \rightarrow C_{2.5}H_5O$

$$C_{2.5}H_5O \times 2 = C_5H_{10}O_2$$

The correct empirical formula is $C_5H_{10}O_2$.

(b)   **Given:** In a 100 g sample: 63.15 g C; 5.30 g H; 31.55 g O   **Find:** empirical formula
Conceptual Plan:
convert mass to mol of each element $\rightarrow$ **write pseudoformula** $\rightarrow$ **write empirical formula**

$$\frac{1 \text{ mol C}}{12.01 \text{ g C}} \quad \frac{1 \text{ mol H}}{1.008 \text{ g H}} \quad \frac{1 \text{ mol O}}{16.00 \text{ g O}} \qquad \text{divide by smallest number}$$

Solution: $63.15 \text{ g C} \times \dfrac{1 \text{ mol C}}{12.01 \text{ g C}} = 5.258 \text{ mol C}$

$5.30 \text{ g H} \times \dfrac{1 \text{ mol H}}{1.008 \text{ g H}} = 5.26 \text{ mol H}$

$31.55 \text{ g O} \times \dfrac{1 \text{ mol O}}{16.00 \text{ g O}} = 1.972 \text{ mol O}$

$C_{5.258} H_{5.26} O_{1.972}$

$C_{\frac{5.258}{1.972}} H_{\frac{5.26}{1.972}} O_{\frac{1.972}{1.972}} \rightarrow C_{2.67}H_{2.67}O$

$C_{2.67}H_{2.67}O \times 3 = C_8H_8O_3$

The correct empirical formula is $C_8H_8O_3$.

3.65   **Given:** 0.77 mg N; 6.61 mg N_xCl_y **Find:** empirical formula
Conceptual Plan: find mg Cl $\rightarrow$ **convert mg to g for each element** $\rightarrow$ **convert mass to mol of each element** $\rightarrow$

$$\text{mg } N_xCl_y - \text{mg N} \qquad\qquad \frac{1 \text{ g}}{1000 \text{ mg}} \qquad\qquad \frac{1 \text{ mol N}}{14.01 \text{ g N}} \quad \frac{1 \text{ mol Cl}}{35.45 \text{ g Cl}}$$

write pseudoformula $\rightarrow$ **write empirical formula**
            divide by smallest number

Solution: $6.61 \text{ mg } N_xCl_y - 0.77 \text{ mg N} = 5.84 \text{ mg Cl}$

$0.77 \text{ mg N} \times \dfrac{1 \text{ g N}}{1000 \text{ mg N}} \times \dfrac{1 \text{ mol N}}{14.01 \text{ g N}} = 5.5 \times 10^{-5} \text{ mol N}$

$5.84 \text{ mg Cl} \times \dfrac{1 \text{ g Cl}}{1000 \text{ mg Cl}} \times \dfrac{1 \text{ mol Cl}}{35.45 \text{ g Cl}} = 1.6 \times 10^{-4} \text{ mol Cl}$

$N_{5.5\times10^{-5}} Cl_{1.6\times10^{-4}}$

$N_{\frac{5.5\times10^{-5}}{5.5\times10^{-5}}} Cl_{\frac{1.6\times10^{-4}}{5.5\times10^{-5}}} \rightarrow NCl_3$

The correct empirical formula is NCl_3.

3.66   **Given:** 45.2 mg P; 131.6 mg P_xSe_y **Find:** empirical formula
Conceptual Plan: find mg Se $\rightarrow$ **convert mg to g for each element** $\rightarrow$ **convert mass to mol of each element** $\rightarrow$

$$\text{mg } P_xSe_y - \text{mg P} \qquad\qquad \frac{1 \text{ g}}{1000 \text{ mg}} \qquad\qquad \frac{1 \text{ mol P}}{30.97 \text{ g P}} \quad \frac{1 \text{ mol Se}}{78.96 \text{ g Se}}$$

write pseudoformula $\rightarrow$ **write empirical formula**
            divide by smallest number

Solution: $131.6 \text{ mg } P_xSe_y - 45.2 \text{ mg P} = 86.4 \text{ mg Se}$

$45.2 \text{ mg P} \times \dfrac{1 \text{ g P}}{1000 \text{ mg P}} \times \dfrac{1 \text{ mol P}}{30.97 \text{ g P}} = 0.00146 \text{ mol P}$

$86.4 \text{ g Se} \times \dfrac{1 \text{ g Se}}{1000 \text{ mg Se}} \times \dfrac{1 \text{ mol Se}}{78.96 \text{ g Se}} = 0.00109 \text{ mol Se}$

$P_{0.00146} Se_{0.00109}$

$P_{\frac{0.00146}{0.00109}} Se_{\frac{0.00109}{0.00109}} \rightarrow P_{1.34}Se$

$P_{1.34}Se \times 3 = P_4Se_3$

The correct empirical formula is P_4Se_3.

3.67 (a) **Given:** empirical formula = C_6H_7N; molar mass = 186.24 g/mol **Find:** molecular formula

Conceptual Plan: molecular formula = empirical formula $\times$ n $\quad n = \dfrac{\text{molar mass}}{\text{empirical formula mass}}$

Solution: empirical formula mass = 6(12.01 g/mol) + 7(1.008 g/mol) + 1(14.01 g/mol) = 93.13 g/mol

$$n = \frac{\text{molar mass}}{\text{formula molar mass}} = \frac{186.24 \text{ g/mol}}{93.13 \text{ g/mol}} = 1.9998 = 2$$

$$\begin{aligned}\text{molecular formula} &= C_6H_7N \times 2 \\ &= C_{12}H_{14}N_2\end{aligned}$$

(b) **Given:** empirical formula = C_2HCl; molar mass = 181.44 g/mol **Find:** molecular formula

Conceptual Plan: molecular formula = empirical formula $\times$ n $\quad n = \dfrac{\text{molar mass}}{\text{empirical formula mass}}$

Solution: empirical formula mass = 2(12.01 g/mol) + 1(1.008 g/mol) + 1(35.45 g/mol) = 60.48 g/mol

$$n = \frac{\text{molar mass}}{\text{formula molar mass}} = \frac{181.44 \text{ g/mol}}{60.48 \text{ g/mol}} = 3$$

$$\begin{aligned}\text{molecular formula} &= C_2HCl \times 3 \\ &= C_6H_3Cl_3\end{aligned}$$

(c) **Given:** empirical formula = $C_5H_{10}NS_2$; molar mass = 296.54 g/mol **Find:** molecular formula

Conceptual Plan: molecular formula = empirical formula $\times$ n $\quad n = \dfrac{\text{molar mass}}{\text{empirical formula mass}}$

Solution: empirical formula mass = 5(12.01 g/mol) + 10(1.008 g/mol)

$$+ \ 1(14.01 \text{ g/mol}) + 2(32.07) = 148.28 \text{ g/mol}$$

$$n = \frac{\text{molar mass}}{\text{formula molar mass}} = \frac{296.54 \text{ g/mol}}{148.28 \text{ g/mol}} = 2$$

$$\begin{aligned}\text{molecular formula} &= C_5H_{10}NS_2 \times 2 \\ &= C_{10}H_{20}N_2S_4\end{aligned}$$

3.68 (a) **Given:** empirical formula = C_4H_9; molar mass = 114.22 g/mol **Find:** molecular formula

Conceptual Plan: molecular formula = empirical formula $\times$ n $\quad n = \dfrac{\text{molar mass}}{\text{empirical formula mass}}$

Solution: empirical formula mass = 4(12.01 g/mol) + 9(1.008 g/mol) = 57.11 g/mol

$$n = \frac{\text{molar mass}}{\text{formula molar mass}} = \frac{114.22 \text{ g/mol}}{57.11 \text{ g/mol}} = 2$$

$$\begin{aligned}\text{molecular formula} &= C_4H_9 \times 2 \\ &= C_8H_{18}\end{aligned}$$

(b) **Given:** empirical formula = CCl; molar mass = 284.77 g/mol **Find:** molecular formula

Conceptual Plan: molecular formula = empirical formula $\times$ n $\quad n = \dfrac{\text{molar mass}}{\text{empirical formula mass}}$

Solution: empirical formula mass = 1(12.01 g/mol) + 1(35.45 g/mol) = 47.46 g/mol

$$n = \frac{\text{molar mass}}{\text{formula molar mass}} = \frac{284.77 \text{ g/mol}}{47.46 \text{ g/mol}} = 6$$

$$\begin{aligned}\text{molecular formula} &= CCl \times 6 \\ &= C_6Cl_6\end{aligned}$$

(c) **Given:** empirical formula = C_3H_2N; molar mass = 312.29 g/mol **Find:** molecular formula

Conceptual Plan: molecular formula = empirical formula $\times$ n $\quad n = \dfrac{\text{molar mass}}{\text{empirical formula mass}}$

Solution: empirical formula mass = 3(12.01 g/mol) + 2(1.008 g/mol) + 1(14.01 g/mol) = 52.06 g/mol

$$n = \frac{\text{molar mass}}{\text{formula molar mass}} = \frac{312.29 \text{ g/mol}}{52.06 \text{ g/mol}} = 6$$

$$\text{molecular formula} = C_3H_2N \times 6$$
$$= C_{18}H_{12}N_6$$

3.69　　**Given:** 33.01 g CO_2; 13.51 g H_2O　　**Find:** empirical formula

Conceptual Plan: mass CO_2, H_2O → mol CO_2, H_2O → mol C, mol H → pseudoformula → empirical formula

$$\frac{1 \text{ mol } CO_2}{44.01 \text{ g } CO_2} \quad \frac{1 \text{ mol } H_2O}{18.02 \text{ g } H_2O} \quad \frac{1 \text{ mol C}}{1 \text{ mol } CO_2} \quad \frac{2 \text{ mol H}}{1 \text{ mol } H_2O} \qquad \text{divide by smallest number}$$

Solution: $33.01 \text{ g } CO_2 \times \dfrac{1 \text{ mol } CO_2}{44.01 \text{ g } CO_2} = 0.7501 \text{ mol } CO_2$

$13.51 \text{ g } H_2O \times \dfrac{1 \text{ mol } H_2O}{18.02 \text{ g } H_2O} = 0.7497 \text{ mol } H_2O$

$0.7501 \text{ mol } CO_2 \times \dfrac{1 \text{ mol C}}{1 \text{ mol } CO_2} = 0.7501 \text{ mol C}$

$0.7497 \text{ mol } H_2O \times \dfrac{2 \text{ mol H}}{1 \text{ mol } H_2O} = 1.499 \text{ mol H}$

$C_{0.7501} H_{1.499}$

$C_{\frac{0.7501}{0.7501}} H_{\frac{1.499}{0.7501}} \rightarrow CH_2$

The correct empirical formula is CH_2.

3.70　　**Given:** 8.80 g CO_2; 1.44 g H_2O　　**Find:** empirical formula

Conceptual Plan: mass CO_2, H_2O → mol CO_2, H_2O → mol C, mol H → pseudoformula → empirical formula

$$\frac{1 \text{ mol } CO_2}{44.01 \text{ g } CO_2} \quad \frac{1 \text{ mol } H_2O}{18.02 \text{ g } H_2O} \quad \frac{1 \text{ mol C}}{1 \text{ mol } CO_2} \quad \frac{2 \text{ mol H}}{1 \text{ mol } H_2O} \qquad \text{divide by smallest number}$$

Solution: $8.80 \text{ g } CO_2 \times \dfrac{1 \text{ mol } CO_2}{44.01 \text{ g } CO_2} = 0.200 \text{ mol } CO_2$

$1.44 \text{ g } H_2O \times \dfrac{1 \text{ mol } H_2O}{18.02 \text{ g } H_2O} = 0.0799 \text{ mol } H_2O$

$0.200 \text{ mol } CO_2 \times \dfrac{1 \text{ mol C}}{1 \text{ mol } CO_2} = 0.200 \text{ mol C}$

$0.0799 \text{ mol } H_2O \times \dfrac{2 \text{ mol H}}{1 \text{ mol } H_2O} = 0.160 \text{ mol H}$

$C_{0.200} H_{0.160}$

$C_{\frac{0.200}{0.160}} H_{\frac{0.160}{0.160}} \rightarrow C_{1.25}H_1$

$C_{1.25}H_1 \times 4 = C_5H_4$

The correct empirical formula is C_5H_4.

3.71　　**Given:** 4.30 g sample; 8.59 g CO_2; 3.52 g H_2O　　**Find:** empirical formula

Conceptual Plan: mass CO_2, H_2O → mol CO_2, H_2O → mol C, mol H → mass C, mass H, mass O → mol O →

$$\frac{1 \text{ mol } CO_2}{44.01 \text{ g } CO_2} \quad \frac{1 \text{ mol } H_2O}{18.02 \text{ g } H_2O} \quad \frac{1 \text{ mol C}}{1 \text{ mol } CO_2} \quad \frac{2 \text{ mol H}}{1 \text{ mol } H_2O} \quad \frac{12.01 \text{ g C}}{1 \text{ mol C}} \quad \frac{1.008 \text{ g H}}{1 \text{ mol H}} \quad \text{g sample} - \text{g C} - \text{g H} \quad \frac{1 \text{ mol O}}{16.00 \text{ g O}}$$

pseudoformula → empirical formula

　　　　　divide by smallest number

Solution: $8.59 \text{ g } CO_2 \times \dfrac{1 \text{ mol } CO_2}{44.01 \text{ g } CO_2} = 0.195 \text{ mol } CO_2$

$3.52 \text{ g } H_2O \times \dfrac{1 \text{ mol } H_2O}{18.02 \text{ g } H_2O} = 0.195 \text{ mol } H_2O$

$$0.195 \ \cancel{\text{mol CO}_2} \times \frac{1 \ \text{mol C}}{1 \ \cancel{\text{mol CO}_2}} = 0.195 \ \text{mol C}$$

$$0.195 \ \cancel{\text{mol H}_2\text{O}} \times \frac{2 \ \text{mol H}}{1 \ \cancel{\text{mol H}_2\text{O}}} = 0.390 \ \text{mol H}$$

$$0.195 \ \cancel{\text{mol C}} \times \frac{12.01 \ \text{mol C}}{1 \ \cancel{\text{mol C}}} = 2.34 \ \text{g C}$$

$$0.390 \ \cancel{\text{mol H}} \times \frac{1.008 \ \text{g H}}{1 \ \cancel{\text{mol H}}} = 0.393 \ \text{g H}$$

$$4.30 \ \text{g} - 2.34 \ \text{g} - 0.393 \ \text{g} = 1.57 \ \text{g O}$$

$$1.57 \ \cancel{\text{g O}} \times \frac{1 \ \text{mol O}}{16.00 \ \cancel{\text{g O}}} = 0.0981 \ \text{mol O}$$

$$C_{0.195} \ H_{0.390} \ O_{0.0981}$$

$$C_{\frac{0.195}{0.0981}} \ H_{\frac{0.390}{0.0981}} \ O_{\frac{0.0981}{0.0981}} \rightarrow C_2H_4O$$

The correct empirical formula is C_2H_4O.

3.72   **Given:** 12.01 g sample; 14.08 g CO_2; 4.32 g H_2O **Find:** empirical formula
Conceptual Plan: mass CO_2, H_2O → mol CO_2, H_2O → mol C, mol H → mass C, mass H, mass O → mol O →

$$\frac{1 \ \text{mol CO}_2}{44.01 \ \text{g CO}_2} \quad \frac{1 \ \text{mol H}_2\text{O}}{18.02 \ \text{g H}_2\text{O}} \quad \frac{1 \ \text{mol C}}{1 \ \text{mol CO}_2} \quad \frac{2 \ \text{mol H}}{1 \ \text{mol H}_2\text{O}} \quad \frac{12.01 \ \text{g C}}{1 \ \text{mol C}} \quad \frac{1.008 \ \text{g H}}{1 \ \text{mol H}} \quad \text{g sample} - \text{g C} - \text{g H} \quad \frac{1 \ \text{mol O}}{16.00 \ \text{g O}}$$

mol O → pseudoformula → empirical formula
divide by smallest number

Solution: $14.08 \ \cancel{\text{g CO}_2} \times \dfrac{1 \ \text{mol CO}_2}{44.01 \ \cancel{\text{g CO}_2}} = 0.3199 \ \text{mol CO}_2$

$$4.32 \ \cancel{\text{g H}_2\text{O}} \times \frac{1 \ \text{mol H}_2\text{O}}{18.02 \ \cancel{\text{g H}_2\text{O}}} = 0.2397 \ \text{mol H}_2\text{O}$$

$$0.3199 \ \cancel{\text{mol CO}_2} \times \frac{1 \ \text{mol C}}{1 \ \cancel{\text{mol CO}_2}} = 0.3199 \ \text{mol C}$$

$$0.2397 \ \cancel{\text{mol H}_2\text{O}} \times \frac{2 \ \text{mol H}}{1 \ \cancel{\text{mol H}_2\text{O}}} = 0.4795 \ \text{mol H}$$

$$0.3199 \ \cancel{\text{mol C}} \times \frac{12.01 \ \text{g C}}{1 \ \cancel{\text{mol C}}} = 3.842 \ \text{g C}$$

$$0.4795 \ \cancel{\text{mol H}} \times \frac{1.008 \ \text{g H}}{1 \ \cancel{\text{mol H}}} = 0.4833 \ \text{g H}$$

$$12.01 \ \text{g} - 3.842 \ \text{g} - 0.4833 \ \text{g} = 7.68 \ \text{g O}$$

$$7.68 \ \cancel{\text{g O}} \times \frac{1 \ \text{mol O}}{16.00 \ \cancel{\text{g O}}} = 0.480 \ \text{mol O}$$

$$C_{0.3199} \ H_{0.4795} \ O_{0.480}$$

$$C_{\frac{0.3199}{0.3199}} \ H_{\frac{0.4795}{0.3199}} \ O_{\frac{0.480}{0.3199}} \rightarrow CH_{1.5}O_{1.5}$$

$$CH_{1.5}O_{1.5} \times 2 = C_2H_3O_3$$

The correct empirical formula is $C_2H_3O_3$.

Writing and Balancing Chemical Equations

3.73   **Conceptual Plan: write a skeletal reaction → balance atoms in more complex compounds → balance elements that occur as free elements → clear fractions**

Solution:	Skeletal reaction:	$SO_2(g) + O_2(g) + H_2O(l) \rightarrow H_2SO_4(aq)$
	Balance O:	$SO_2(g) + 1/2 \ O_2(g) + H_2O(l) \rightarrow H_2SO_4(aq)$
	Clear fraction:	$2 \ SO_2(g) + O_2(g) + 2 \ H_2O(l) \rightarrow 2 \ H_2SO_4(aq)$

Check:	left side	right side
	2 S atoms	2 S atoms
	8 O atoms	8 O atoms
	4 H atoms	4 H atoms

3.74 **Conceptual Plan: write a skeletal reaction → balance atoms in more complex compounds → balance elements that occur as free elements → clear fractions**

Solution:	Skeletal reaction:	$NO_2(g) + O_2(g) + H_2O(l) \rightarrow HNO_3(aq)$
	Balance H:	$NO_2(g) + O_2(g) + H_2O(l) \rightarrow 2\ HNO_3(aq)$
	Balance N:	$2\ NO_2(g) + O_2(g) + H_2O(l) \rightarrow 2\ HNO_3(aq)$
	Balance O:	$2\ NO_2(g) + 1/2\ O_2(g) + H_2O(l) \rightarrow 2\ HNO_3(aq)$
	Clear fraction:	$4\ NO_2(g) + O_2(g) + 2\ H_2O(l) \rightarrow 4\ HNO_3(aq)$

Check:	left side	right side
	4 N atoms	4 N atoms
	12 O atoms	12 O atoms
	4 H atoms	4 H atoms

3.75 **Conceptual Plan: write a skeletal reaction → balance atoms in more complex compounds → balance elements that occur as free elements → clear fractions**

Solution:	Skeletal reaction:	$Na(s) + H_2O(l) \rightarrow H_2(g) + NaOH(aq)$
	Balance H:	$Na(s) + H_2O(l) \rightarrow 1/2\ H_2(g) + NaOH(aq)$
	Clear fraction:	$2\ Na(s) + 2\ H_2O(l) \rightarrow H_2(g) + 2\ NaOH(aq)$

Check:	left side	right side
	2 Na atoms	2 Na atoms
	4 H atoms	4 H atoms
	2 O atoms	2 O atoms

3.76 **Conceptual Plan: write a skeletal reaction → balance atoms in more complex compounds → balance elements that occur as free elements → clear fractions**

Solution:	Skeletal reaction:	$Fe(s) + O_2(g) \rightarrow Fe_2O_3(s)$
	Balance O:	$Fe(s) + 3\ O_2(g) \rightarrow 2\ Fe_2O_3(s)$
	Balance Fe:	$4\ Fe(s) + 3\ O_2(g) \rightarrow 2\ Fe_2O_3(s)$

Check:	left side	right side
	4 Fe atoms	4 Fe atoms
	6 O atoms	6 O atoms

3.77 **Conceptual Plan: write a skeletal reaction → balance atoms in more complex compounds → balance elements that occur as free elements → clear fractions**

Solution:	Skeletal reaction:	$C_{12}H_{22}O_{11}(aq) + H_2O(l) \rightarrow C_2H_5OH(aq) + CO_2(g)$
	Balance H:	$C_{12}H_{22}O_{11}(aq) + H_2O(l) \rightarrow 4\ C_2H_5OH(aq) + CO_2(g)$
	Balance C:	$C_{12}H_{22}O_{11}(aq) + H_2O(l) \rightarrow 4\ C_2H_5OH(aq) + 4\ CO_2(g)$

Check:	left side	right side
	12 C atoms	12 C atoms
	24 H atoms	24 H atoms
	12 O atoms	12 O atoms

3.78 **Conceptual Plan: write a skeletal reaction → balance atoms in more complex compounds → balance elements that occur as free elements → clear fractions**

Solution:	Skeletal reaction:	$CO_2(g) + H_2O(l) \rightarrow C_6H_{12}O_6(aq) + O_2(g)$
	Balance C:	$6\ CO_2(g) + H_2O(l) \rightarrow C_6H_{12}O_6(aq) + O_2(g)$
	Balance H:	$6\ CO_2(g) + 6\ H_2O(l) \rightarrow C_6H_{12}O_6(aq) + O_2(g)$
	Balance O:	$6\ CO_2(g) + 6\ H_2O(l) \rightarrow C_6H_{12}O_6(aq) + 6\ O_2(g)$

Check:	left side	right side
	6 C atoms	6 C atoms
	18 O atoms	18 O atoms
	12 H atoms	12 H atoms

3.79   (a)   **Conceptual Plan: write a skeletal reaction → balance atoms in more complex compounds → balance elements that occur as free elements → clear fractions**

   Solution: Skeletal reaction: $PbS(s) + HBr(aq) \rightarrow PbBr_2(s) + H_2S(g)$
   Balance Br: $PbS(s) + 2\,HBr(aq) \rightarrow PbBr_2(s) + H_2S(g)$

   Check:

left side	right side
1 Pb atom	1 Pb atom
1 S atom	1 S atom
2 H atoms	2 H atoms
2 Br atoms	2 Br atoms

   (b)   **Conceptual Plan: write a skeletal reaction → balance atoms in more complex compounds → balance elements that occur as free elements → clear fractions**

   Solution: Skeletal reaction: $CO(g) + H_2(g) \rightarrow CH_4(g) + H_2O(l)$
   Balance H: $CO(g) + 3\,H_2(g) \rightarrow CH_4(g) + H_2O(l)$

   Check:

left side	right side
1 C atom	1 C atom
1 O atom	1 O atom
6 H atoms	6 H atoms

   (c)   **Conceptual Plan: write a skeletal reaction → balance atoms in more complex compounds → balance elements that occur as free elements → clear fractions**

   Solution: Skeletal reaction: $HCl(aq) + MnO_2(s) \rightarrow MnCl_2(aq) + H_2O(l) + Cl_2(g)$
   Balance Cl: $4\,HCl(aq) + MnO_2(s) \rightarrow MnCl_2(aq) + H_2O(l) + Cl_2(g)$
   Balance O: $4\,HCl(aq) + MnO_2(s) \rightarrow MnCl_2(aq) + 2\,H_2O(l) + Cl_2(g)$

   Check:

left side	right side
4 H atoms	4 H atoms
4 Cl atoms	4 Cl atoms
1 Mn atom	1 Mn atom
2 O atoms	2 O atoms

   (d)   **Conceptual Plan: write a skeletal reaction → balance atoms in more complex compounds → balance elements that occur as free elements → clear fractions**

   Solution: Skeletal reaction: $C_5H_{12}(l) + O_2(g) \rightarrow CO_2(g) + H_2O(l)$
   Balance C: $C_5H_{12}(l) + O_2(g) \rightarrow 5\,CO_2(g) + H_2O(l)$
   Balance H: $C_5H_{12}(l) + O_2(g) \rightarrow 5\,CO_2(g) + 6\,H_2O(l)$
   Balance O: $C_5H_{12}(l) + 8\,O_2(g) \rightarrow 5\,CO_2(g) + 6\,H_2O(l)$

   Check:

left side	right side
5 C atoms	5 C atoms
12 H atoms	12 H atoms
16 O atoms	16 O atoms

3.80   (a)   **Conceptual Plan: write a skeletal reaction → balance atoms in more complex compounds → balance elements that occur as free elements → clear fractions**

   Solution: Skeletal reaction: $Cu(s) + S(s) \rightarrow Cu_2S(s)$
   Balance Cu: $2\,Cu(s) + S(s) \rightarrow Cu_2S(s)$

   Check:

left side	right side
2 Cu atoms	2 Cu atoms
1 S atom	1 S atom

   (b)   **Conceptual Plan: write a skeletal reaction → balance atoms in more complex compounds → balance elements that occur as free elements → clear fractions**

   Solution: Skeletal reaction: $Fe_2O_3(s) + H_2(g) \rightarrow Fe(s) + H_2O(l)$
   Balance O: $Fe_2O_3(s) + H_2(g) \rightarrow Fe(s) + 3\,H_2O(l)$
   Balance Fe: $Fe_2O_3(s) + H_2(g) \rightarrow 2\,Fe(s) + 3\,H_2O(l)$
   Balance H: $Fe_2O_3(s) + 3\,H_2(g) \rightarrow 2\,Fe(s) + 3\,H_2O(l)$

	Check:	left side	right side
		2 Fe atoms	2 Fe atoms
		3 O atoms	3 O atoms
		6 H atoms	6 H atoms

(c) **Conceptual Plan: write a skeletal reaction → balance atoms in more complex compounds → balance elements that occur as free elements → clear fractions**

Solution:

Skeletal reaction:	$SO_2(g) + O_2(g) \rightarrow SO_3(g)$
Balance O:	$SO_2(g) + 1/2\ O_2(g) \rightarrow SO_3(g)$
Clear fraction:	$2\ SO_2(g) + O_2(g) \rightarrow 2\ SO_3(g)$

	Check:	left side	right side
		2 S atoms	2 S atoms
		6 O atoms	6 O atoms

(d) **Conceptual Plan: write a skeletal reaction → balance atoms in more complex compounds → balance elements that occur as free elements → clear fractions**

Solution:

Skeletal reaction:	$NH_3(g) + O_2(g) \rightarrow NO(g) + H_2O(g)$
Balance H:	$2\ NH_3(g) + O_2(g) \rightarrow NO(g) + 3\ H_2O(g)$
Balance N:	$2\ NH_3(g) + O_2(g) \rightarrow 2\ NO(g) + 3\ H_2O(g)$
Balance O:	$2\ NH_3(g) + 5/2\ O_2(g) \rightarrow 2\ NO(g) + 3\ H_2O(g)$
Clear fraction:	$4\ NH_3(g) + 5\ O_2(g) \rightarrow 4\ NO(g) + 6\ H_2O(g)$

	Check:	left side	right side
		4 N atoms	4 N atoms
		12 H atoms	12 H atoms
		10 O atoms	10 O atoms

3.81 **Conceptual Plan: write a skeletal reaction → balance atoms in more complex compounds → balance elements that occur as free elements → clear fractions**

Solution:

Skeletal reaction:	$Na_2CO_3(aq) + CuCl_2(aq) \rightarrow CuCO_3(s) + NaCl(aq)$
Balance Na:	$Na_2CO_3(aq) + CuCl_2(aq) \rightarrow CuCO_3(s) + 2\ NaCl(aq)$

	Check:	left side	right side
		2 Na atoms	2 Na atoms
		1 C atom	1 C atom
		3 O atoms	3 O atoms
		1 Cu atom	1 Cu atom
		2 Cl atoms	2 Cl atoms

3.82 **Conceptual Plan: write a skeletal reaction → balance atoms in more complex compounds → balance elements that occur as free elements → clear fractions**

Solution:

Skeletal reaction:	$KOH(aq) + FeCl_3(aq) \rightarrow Fe(OH)_3(s) + KCl(aq)$
Balance Cl:	$KOH(aq) + FeCl_3(aq) \rightarrow Fe(OH)_3(s) + 3\ KCl(aq)$
Balance K:	$3\ KOH(aq) + FeCl_3(aq) \rightarrow Fe(OH)_3(s) + 3\ KCl(aq)$

	Check:	left side	right side
		3 K atoms	3 K atoms
		3 O atoms	3 O atoms
		3 H atoms	3 H atoms
		1 Fe atom	1 Fe atom
		3 Cl atoms	3 Cl atoms

3.83 (a) **Conceptual Plan: balance atoms in more complex compounds → balance elements that occur as free elements → clear fractions**

Solution:

Skeletal reaction:	$CO_2(g) + CaSiO_3(s) + H_2O(l) \rightarrow SiO_2(s) + Ca(HCO_3)_2(aq)$
Balance C:	$2\ CO_2(g) + CaSiO_3(s) + H_2O(l) \rightarrow SiO_2(s) + Ca(HCO_3)_2(aq)$

Check:

left side	right side
2 C atoms	2 C atoms
8 O atoms	8 O atoms
1 Ca atom	1 Ca atom
1 Si atom	1 Si atom
2 H atoms	2 H atoms

(b) **Conceptual Plan: balance atoms in more complex compounds → balance elements that occur as free elements → clear fractions**

Solution:

Skeletal reaction:	$Co(NO_3)_3(aq) + (NH_4)_2S(aq) \rightarrow Co_2S_3(s) + NH_4NO_3(aq)$
Balance S:	$Co(NO_3)_3(aq) + 3\,(NH_4)_2S(aq) \rightarrow Co_2S_3(s) + NH_4NO_3(aq)$
Balance Co:	$2\,Co(NO_3)_3(aq) + 3\,(NH_4)_2S(aq) \rightarrow Co_2S_3(s) + NH_4NO_3(aq)$
Balance N:	$2\,Co(NO_3)_3(aq) + 3\,(NH_4)_2S(aq) \rightarrow Co_2S_3(s) + 6\,NH_4NO_3(aq)$

Check:

left side	right side
2 Co atoms	2 Co atoms
12 N atoms	12 N atoms
18 O atoms	18 O atoms
24 H atoms	24 H atoms
3 S atoms	3 S atoms

(c) **Conceptual Plan: balance atoms in more complex compounds → balance elements that occur as free elements → clear fractions**

Solution:

Skeletal reaction:	$Cu_2O(s) + C(s) \rightarrow Cu(s) + CO(g)$
Balance Cu:	$Cu_2O(s) + C(s) \rightarrow 2\,Cu(s) + CO(g)$

Check:

left side	right side
2 Cu atoms	2 Cu atoms
1 O atom	1 O atom
1 C atom	1 C atom

(d) **Conceptual Plan: balance atoms in more complex compounds → balance elements that occur as free elements → clear fractions**

Solution:

Skeletal reaction:	$H_2(g) + Cl_2(g) \rightarrow HCl(g)$
Balance Cl:	$H_2(g) + Cl_2(g) \rightarrow 2\,HCl(g)$

Check:

left side	right side
2 H atoms	2 H atoms
2 Cl atoms	2 Cl atoms

3.84 (a) **Conceptual Plan: balance atoms in more complex compounds → balance elements that occur as free elements → clear fractions**

Solution:

Skeletal reaction:	$Na_2S(aq) + Cu(NO_3)_2(aq) \rightarrow NaNO_3(aq) + CuS(s)$
Balance Na:	$Na_2S(aq) + Cu(NO_3)_2(aq) \rightarrow 2\,NaNO_3(aq) + CuS(s)$

Check:

left side	right side
2 Na atoms	2 Na atoms
1 S atom	1 S atom
1 Cu atom	1 Cu atom
2 N atoms	2 N atoms
6 O atoms	6 O atoms

(b) **Conceptual Plan: balance atoms in more complex compounds → balance elements that occur as free elements → clear fractions**

Solution:

Skeletal reaction:	$N_2H_4(l) \rightarrow NH_3(g) + N_2(g)$
Balance H:	$3\,N_2H_4(l) \rightarrow 4\,NH_3(g) + N_2(g)$

Check:

left side	right side
6 N atoms	6 N atoms
12 H atoms	12 H atoms

(c)   **Conceptual Plan: balance atoms in more complex compounds → balance elements that occur as free elements → clear fractions**

        Solution: Skeletal reaction: $HCl(aq) + O_2(g) \rightarrow H_2O(l) + Cl_2(g)$

                        Balance Cl: $2 HCl(aq) + O_2(g) \rightarrow H_2O(l) + Cl_2(g)$

                        Balance O: $2 HCl(aq) + 1/2\, O_2(g) \rightarrow H_2O(l) + Cl_2(g)$

                        Clear fraction: $4 HCl(aq) + O_2(g) \rightarrow 2 H_2O(l) + 2 Cl_2(g)$

        Check:

left side	right side
4 H atoms	4 H atoms
4 Cl atoms	4 Cl atoms
2 O atoms	2 O atoms

(d)   **Conceptual Plan: balance atoms in more complex compounds → balance elements that occur as free elements → clear fractions**

        Solution: Skeletal reaction: $FeS(s) + HCl(aq) \rightarrow FeCl_2(aq) + H_2S(g)$

                        Balance Cl: $FeS(s) + 2 HCl(aq) \rightarrow FeCl_2(aq) + H_2S(g)$

        Check:

left side	right side
1 Fe atom	1 Fe atom
1 S atom	1 S atom
2 H atoms	2 H atoms
2 Cl atoms	2 Cl atoms

Organic Compounds

3.85   (a)   composed of metal cation and polyatomic anion—inorganic compound

        (b)   composed of carbon and hydrogen—organic compound

        (c)   composed of carbon, hydrogen, and oxygen—organic compound

        (d)   composed of metal cation and nonmetal anion—inorganic compound

3.86   (a)   composed of carbon and hydrogen—organic compound

        (b)   composed of carbon, hydrogen, and nitrogen—organic compound

        (c)   composed of metal cation and nonmetal anion—inorganic compound

        (d)   composed of metal cation and polyatomic anion—inorganic compound

Cumulative Problems

3.87   **Given:** 165 mL C_2H_5OH; $d = 0.789 \text{g/cm}^3$ **Find:** number of molecules

        Conceptual Plan: $cm^3 \rightarrow$ mL:mL $C_2H_5OH \rightarrow$ g $C_2H_5OH \rightarrow$ mol $C_2H_5OH \rightarrow$ molecules C_2H_5OH

$$\frac{1\,cm^3}{1\,mL} \qquad \frac{1\,mL\,C_2H_5OH}{0.789\,g\,C_2H_5OH} \qquad \frac{1\,mol\,C_2H_5OH}{46.07\,g\,C_2H_5OH} \qquad \frac{6.022\times10^{23}\,molecules\,C_2H_5OH}{1\,mol\,C_2H_5OH}$$

        Solution:

$$165\,mL\,C_2H_5OH \times \frac{0.789\,g\,C_2H_5OH}{cm^3} \times \frac{1\,cm^3}{1\,mL} \times \frac{1\,mol\,C_2H_5OH}{46.07\,g\,C_2H_5OH} \times \frac{6.022\times10^{23}\,molecules\,C_2H_5OH}{1\,mol\,C_2H_5OH}$$

$$= 1.7017 \times 10^{24}\,molecules\,C_2H_5OH = 1.70 \times 10^{24}\,molecules\,C_2H_5OH$$

        Check: The units (molecules C_2H_5OH) are correct. The magnitude is reasonable because we had more than 2 moles of C_2H_5OH and we have more than two times Avogadro's number of molecules.

3.88   **Given:** 0.05 mL H_2O; $d = 1.0 \text{g/cm}^3$ **Find:** number of molecules

        Conceptual Plan: $cm^3 \rightarrow$ mL:mL $H_2O \rightarrow$ g $H_2O \rightarrow$ mol $H_2O \rightarrow$ molecules H_2O

$$\frac{1\,cm^3}{1\,mL} \qquad \frac{1\,mL\,H_2O}{1.0\,g\,H_2O} \qquad \frac{1\,mol\,H_2O}{18.02\,g\,H_2O} \qquad \frac{6.022\times10^{23}\,molecules\,H_2O}{1\,mol\,H_2O}$$

        Solution: $0.05\,mL\,H_2O \times \frac{1\,cm^3}{1\,mL} \times \frac{1.0\,g}{cm^3} \times \frac{1\,mol\,H_2O}{18.02\,g\,H_2O} \times \frac{6.022\times10^{23}\,molecules\,H_2O}{1\,mol\,H_2O}$

$$= 1.67 \times 10^{21}\,molecules\,H_2O = 2 \times 10^{21}\,molecules\,H_2O$$

        Check: The units (molecules H_2O) are correct. The magnitude is reasonable because we have less than 1 mole of H_2O and we have less than Avogadro's number of molecules.

3.89   (a)   To write the formula for an ionic compound, do the following: (1) Write the symbol for the metal cation and its charge and the symbol for the nonmetal anion or polyatomic anion and its charge. (2) Adjust the subscript on each cation and anion to balance the overall charge. (3) Check that the sum of the charges of the cations equals the sum of the charges of the anions.

potassium chromate: $K^+CrO_4^{2-}$; K_2CrO_4 cation $2(1+) = 2+$; anion $2-$

Given: K_2CrO_4 **Find:** mass percent of each element

Conceptual Plan: %K, then %Cr, then %O

$$\text{mass \% K} = \frac{2 \times \text{molar mass K}}{\text{molar mass K}_2\text{CrO}_4} \times 100\% \qquad \text{mass \% Cr} = \frac{1 \times \text{molar mass Cr}}{\text{molar mass K}_2\text{CrO}_4} \times 100\% \qquad \text{mass \% O} = \frac{4 \times \text{molar mass O}}{\text{molar mass K}_2\text{CrO}_4} \times 100\%$$

molar mass of K = 39.10 g/mol; molar mass Cr = 52.00 g/mol; molar mass O = 16.00 g/mol

Solution: molar mass K_2CrO_4 = 2(39.10 g/mol) + 1(52.00 g/mol) + 4(16.00 g/mol) = 194.20 g/mol

$$\text{mass \% K} = \frac{2 \times \text{molar mass K}}{\text{molar mass K}_2\text{CrO}_4} \times 100\% \qquad\qquad \text{mass \% Cr} = \frac{1 \times \text{molar mass Cr}}{\text{molar mass K}_2\text{CrO}_4} \times 100\%$$

$$= \frac{2(39.10 \text{ g/mol})}{194.20 \text{ g/mol}} \times 100\% \qquad\qquad = \frac{1(52.00 \text{ g/mol})}{194.20 \text{ g/mol}} \times 100\%$$

$$= \frac{78.20 \text{ g/mol}}{194.20 \text{ g/mol}} \times 100\% \qquad\qquad = \frac{52.00 \text{ g/mol}}{194.20 \text{ g/mol}} \times 100\%$$

$$= 40.27\% \qquad\qquad\qquad\qquad = 26.78\%$$

$$4 \times \text{molar mass O} = 4(16.00 \text{ g/mol}) = 64.00 \text{ g O}$$

$$\text{mass \% O} = \frac{4 \times \text{molar mass O}}{\text{molar mass K}_2\text{CrO}_4} \times 100\%$$

$$= \frac{64.00 \text{ g/mol}}{194.20 \text{ g/mol}} \times 100\%$$

$$= 32.96\%$$

Check: The units (%) are correct. The magnitude is reasonable because each is between 0 and 100% and the total is 100%.

   (b)   To write the formula for an ionic compound, do the following: (1) Write the symbol for the metal cation and its charge and the symbol for the nonmetal anion or polyatomic anion and its charge. (2) Adjust the subscript on each cation and anion to balance the overall charge. (3) Check that the sum of the charges of the cations equals the sum of the charges of the anions.

Lead(II) phosphate: Pb^{2+} PO_4^{3-}; $Pb_3(PO_4)_2$ cation $3(2+) = 6+$; anion $2(3-) = 6-$

Given: $Pb_3(PO_4)_2$ **Find:** mass percent of each element

Conceptual Plan: %Pb, then %P, then %O

$$\text{mass \% Pb} = \frac{3 \times \text{molar mass Pb}}{\text{molar mass Pb}_3(\text{PO}_4)_2} \times 100\% \qquad \text{mass \% P} = \frac{2 \times \text{molar mass P}}{\text{molar mass Pb}_3(\text{PO}_4)_2} \times 100\% \qquad \text{mass \% O} = \frac{8 \times \text{molar mass O}}{\text{molar mass Pb}_3(\text{PO}_4)_2} \times 100\%$$

Solution: molar mass $Pb_3(PO_4)_2$ = 3(207.2 g/mol) + 2(30.97 g/mol) + 8(16.00 g/mol) = 811.5 g/mol

$3 \times$ molar mass Pb = 3(207.2 g/mol) = 621.6 g Pb $2 \times$ molar mass P = 2(30.97 g/mol) = 61.94 g P

$$\text{mass \% Pb} = \frac{3 \times \text{molar mass Pb}}{\text{molar mass Pb}_3(\text{PO}_4)_2} \times 100\% \qquad\qquad \text{mass \% P} = \frac{2 \times \text{molar mass P}}{\text{molar mass Pb}_3(\text{PO}_4)_2} \times 100\%$$

$$= \frac{621.6 \text{ g/mol}}{811.5 \text{ g/mol}} \times 100\% \qquad\qquad = \frac{61.94 \text{ g/mol}}{811.5 \text{ g/mol}} \times 100\%$$

$$= 76.60\% \qquad\qquad\qquad\qquad = 7.633\%$$

$$4 \times \text{molar mass O} = 8(16.00 \text{ g/mol}) = 128.0 \text{ g O}$$

$$\text{mass \% O} = \frac{8 \times \text{molar mass O}}{\text{molar mass Pb}_3(\text{PO}_4)_2} \times 100\%$$

$$= \frac{128.0 \text{ g/mol}}{811.5 \text{ g/mol}} \times 100\%$$

$$= 15.77\%$$

Check: The units (%) are correct. The magnitude is reasonable because each is between 0 and 100% and the total is 100%.

(c) sulfurous acid: H_2SO_3

Given: H_2SO_3 **Find:** mass percent of each element

Conceptual Plan: %H, then %S, then %O

$$\text{mass \% H} = \frac{2 \times \text{molar mass H}}{\text{molar mass } H_2SO_3} \times 100\% \qquad \text{mass \% S} = \frac{1 \times \text{molar mass S}}{\text{molar mass } H_2SO_3} \times 100\% \qquad \text{mass \% O} = \frac{3 \times \text{molar mass O}}{\text{molar mass } H_2SO_3} \times 100\%$$

Solution: molar mass H_2SO_3 = 2(1.008 g/mol) + 1(32.07 g/mol) + 3(16.00 g/mol) = 82.0$\underline{8}$6 g/mol

2 × molar mass H = 2(1.008 g/mol) = 2.016 g H   1 × molar mass S = 1(32.07 g/mol) = 32.07 g S

$$\text{mass \% H} = \frac{2 \times \text{molar mass H}}{\text{molar mass } H_2SO_3} \times 100\% \qquad\qquad \text{mass \% S} = \frac{1 \times \text{molar mass S}}{\text{molar mass } H_2SO_3} \times 100\%$$

$$\qquad = \frac{2.016 \text{ g/mol}}{82.0\underline{8}6 \text{ g/mol}} \times 100\% \qquad\qquad\qquad = \frac{32.07 \text{ g/mol}}{82.0\underline{8}6 \text{ g/mol}} \times 100\%$$

$$\qquad = 2.456\% \qquad\qquad\qquad\qquad\qquad\qquad = 39.07\%$$

3 × molar mass O = 3(16.00 g/mol) = 48.00 g O

$$\text{mass \% O} = \frac{3 \times \text{molar mass O}}{\text{molar mass } H_2SO_3} \times 100\%$$

$$\qquad = \frac{48.00 \text{ g/mol}}{82.0\underline{8}6 \text{ g/mol}} \times 100\%$$

$$\qquad = 58.48\%$$

Check: The units (%) are correct. The magnitude is reasonable because each is between 0 and 100% and the total is 100%.

(d) To write the formula for an ionic compound, do the following: (1) Write the symbol for the metal cation and its charge and the symbol for the nonmetal anion or polyatomic anion and its charge. (2) Adjust the subscript on each cation and anion to balance the overall charge. (3) Check that the sum of the charges of the cations equals the sum of the charges of the anions.

cobalt(II) bromide: $Co^{2+}Br^-$; $CoBr_2$ cation 2+ = 2+; anion 2(1−) = 2−

Given: $CoBr_2$ **Find:** mass percent of each element

Conceptual Plan: %Co, then %Br

$$\text{mass \% Co} = \frac{1 \times \text{molar mass Co}}{\text{molar mass } CoBr_2} \times 100\% \qquad \text{mass \% Br} = \frac{2 \times \text{molar mass Br}}{\text{molar mass } CoBr_2} \times 100\%$$

Solution: molar mass $CoBr_2$ = (58.93 g/mol) + 2(79.90 g/mol) = 218.73 g/mol

1 × molar mass Co = 1(58.93 g/mol) = 58.93 g Co   2 × molar mass Br = 2(79.90 g/mol) = 159.80 g Br

$$\text{mass \% Co} = \frac{1 \times \text{molar mass Co}}{\text{molar mass } CoBr_2} \times 100\% \qquad\qquad \text{mass \% Br} = \frac{2 \times \text{molar mass Br}}{\text{molar mass } CoBr_2} \times 100\%$$

$$\qquad = \frac{58.93 \text{ g/mol}}{218.73 \text{ g/mol}} \times 100\% \qquad\qquad\qquad = \frac{159.80 \text{ g/mol}}{218.73 \text{ g/mol}} \times 100\%$$

$$\qquad = 26.94\% \qquad\qquad\qquad\qquad\qquad\qquad = 73.058\%$$

Check: The units (%) are correct. The magnitude is reasonable because each is between 0 and 100% and the total is 100%.

3.90 (a) perchloric acid: $HClO_4$

Given: $HClO_4$ **Find:** mass percent of each element

Conceptual Plan: %H, then %Cl, then %O

$$\text{mass \% H} = \frac{1 \times \text{molar mass H}}{\text{molar mass } HClO_4} \times 100\% \qquad \text{mass \% Cl} = \frac{1 \times \text{molar mass Cl}}{\text{molar mass } HClO_4} \times 100\% \qquad \text{mass \% O} = \frac{4 \times \text{molar mass O}}{\text{molar mass } HClO_4} \times 100\%$$

Solution: molar mass $HClO_4$ = 1(1.008 g/mol) + 1(35.45 g/mol) + 4(16.00 g/mol) = 100.46 g/mol

1 × molar mass H = 1(1.008 g/mol) = 1.008 g H   1 × molar mass Cl = 1(35.45 g/mol) = 35.45 g Cr

$$\text{mass \% H} = \frac{1 \times \text{molar mass H}}{\text{molar mass } HClO_4} \times 100\% \qquad\qquad \text{mass \% Cl} = \frac{1 \times \text{molar mass Cl}}{\text{molar mass } HClO_4} \times 100\%$$

$$\qquad = \frac{1.008 \text{ g/mol}}{100.46 \text{ g/mol}} \times 100\% \qquad\qquad\qquad = \frac{35.45 \text{ g/mol}}{100.46 \text{ g/mol}} \times 100\%$$

$$\qquad = 1.003\% \qquad\qquad\qquad\qquad\qquad\qquad = 35.29\%$$

$$4 \times \text{molar mass O} = 4(16.00 \text{ g/mol}) = 64.00 \text{ g O}$$

$$\text{mass \% O} = \frac{4 \times \text{molar mass O}}{\text{molar mass HSO}_3} \times 100\%$$

$$= \frac{64.00 \text{ g/mol}}{100.46 \text{ g/mol}} \times 100\%$$

$$= 63.71\%$$

Check: The units (%) are correct. The magnitude is reasonable because each is between 0 and 100% and the total is 100%.

(b) phosphorus pentachloride: PCl_5
Given: PCl_5 **Find:** mass percent of each element
Conceptual Plan: %P, then %Cl

$$\text{mass \% P} = \frac{1 \times \text{molar mass P}}{\text{molar mass PCl}_5} \times 100\% \qquad \text{mass \% Cl} = \frac{5 \times \text{molar mass Cl}}{\text{molar mass PCl}_5} \times 100\%$$

Solution: molar mass $PCl_5 = 1(30.97 \text{ g/mol}) + 5(35.45 \text{ g/mol}) = 208.2 \text{ g/mol}$
$1 \times \text{molar mass P} = 1(30.97 \text{ g/mol}) = 30.97 \text{ g P}$ $\qquad 5 \times \text{molar mass Cl} = 5(35.45 \text{ g/mol}) = 177.25 \text{ g Cl}$

$$\text{mass \% P} = \frac{1 \times \text{molar mass P}}{\text{molar mass PCl}_5} \times 100\% \qquad\qquad \text{mass \% Cl} = \frac{5 \times \text{molar mass Cl}}{\text{molar mass PCl}_5} \times 100\%$$

$$= \frac{30.97 \text{ g/mol}}{208.2 \text{ g/mol}} \times 100\% \qquad\qquad\qquad = \frac{177.25 \text{ g/mol}}{208.2 \text{ g/mol}} \times 100\%$$

$$= 14.88\% \qquad\qquad\qquad\qquad\qquad = 85.13\%$$

Check: The units (%) are correct. The magnitude is reasonable because each is between 0 and 100% and the total is 100%.

(c) nitrogen triiodide: NI_3
Given: NI_3 **Find:** mass percent of each element
Conceptual Plan: %N, then %I

$$\text{mass \% N} = \frac{1 \times \text{molar mass N}}{\text{molar mass NI}_3} \times 100\% \qquad \text{mass \% I} = \frac{3 \times \text{molar mass I}}{\text{molar mass NI}_3} \times 100\%$$

Solution: molar mass $NI_3 = 1(14.01 \text{ g/mol}) + 3(126.90 \text{ g/mol}) = 394.7 \text{ g/mol}$
$1 \times \text{molar mass N} = 1(14.01 \text{ g/mol}) = 14.01 \text{ g N}$ $\qquad 1 \times \text{molar mass I} = 3(126.90 \text{ g/mol}) = 380.7 \text{ g I}$

$$\text{mass \% N} = \frac{1 \times \text{molar mass N}}{\text{molar mass NI}_3} \times 100\% \qquad\qquad \text{mass \% I} = \frac{3 \times \text{molar mass I}}{\text{molar mass NI}_3} \times 100\%$$

$$= \frac{14.01 \text{ g/mol}}{394.7 \text{ g/mol}} \times 100\% \qquad\qquad\qquad = \frac{380.7 \text{ g/mol}}{394.7 \text{ g/mol}} \times 100\%$$

$$= 3.550\% \qquad\qquad\qquad\qquad\qquad = 96.45\%$$

Check: The units (%) are correct. The magnitude is reasonable because each is between 0 and 100% and the total is 100%.

(d) carbon dioxide: CO_2
Given: CO_2 **Find:** mass percent of each element
Conceptual Plan: %C, then %O

$$\text{mass \% C} = \frac{1 \times \text{molar mass C}}{\text{molar mass CO}_2} \times 100\% \qquad \text{mass \% O} = \frac{2 \times \text{molar mass O}}{\text{molar mass CO}_2} \times 100\%$$

Solution: molar mass $CO_2 = 1(12.01 \text{ g/mol}) + 2(16.00 \text{ g/mol}) = 44.01 \text{ g/mol}$
$1 \times \text{molar mass C} = 1(12.01 \text{ g/mol}) = 12.01 \text{ g C}$ $\qquad 2 \times \text{molar mass O} = 2(16.00 \text{ g/mol}) = 32.00 \text{ g O}$

$$\text{mass \% C} = \frac{1 \times \text{molar mass C}}{\text{molar mass CO}_2} \times 100\% \qquad\qquad \text{mass \% O} = \frac{2 \times \text{molar mass O}}{\text{molar mass CO}_2} \times 100\%$$

$$= \frac{12.01 \text{ g/mol}}{44.01 \text{ g/mol}} \times 100\% \qquad\qquad\qquad = \frac{32.00 \text{ g/mol}}{44.01 \text{ g/mol}} \times 100\%$$

$$= 27.29\% \qquad\qquad\qquad\qquad\qquad = 72.71\%$$

Check: The units of the answer (%) are correct. The magnitude is reasonable because each is between 0 and 100% and the total is 100%.

3.91   **Given:** 32 g CF_2Cl_2/mo   **Find:** g Cl/yr

         Conceptual Plan: g CF_2Cl_2/mo $\rightarrow$ g Cl/mo $\rightarrow$ g Cl/yr

$$\frac{70.90 \text{ g Cl}}{120.91 \text{ g } CF_2Cl_2} \qquad \frac{12 \text{ mo}}{1 \text{ yr}}$$

         Solution: $\dfrac{32 \text{ g } CF_2Cl_2}{\text{mo}} \times \dfrac{70.90 \text{ g Cl}}{120.91 \text{ g } CF_2Cl_2} \times \dfrac{12 \text{ mo}}{1 \text{ yr}} = 2.2\underline{5}2 \times 10^2 \text{ g Cl/yr} = 2.3 \times 10^2 \text{ g Cl/yr}$

         Check: The units (g Cl) are correct. Magnitude is reasonable because it is less than the total CF_2Cl_2/yr.

3.92   **Given:** 17 kg CHF_2Cl/mo   **Find:** kg Cl/yr

         Conceptual Plan: kg CHF_2Cl/mo $\rightarrow$ kg Cl/mo $\rightarrow$ kg Cl/yr

$$\frac{35.45 \text{ kg Cl}}{86.47 \text{ kg } CHF_2Cl} \qquad \frac{12 \text{ mo}}{1 \text{ yr}}$$

         Solution: $\dfrac{17 \text{ kg } CHF_2Cl}{\text{mo}} \times \dfrac{35.45 \text{ kg Cl}}{86.47 \text{ kg } CHF_2Cl} \times \dfrac{12 \text{ mo}}{1 \text{ yr}} = 83.\underline{6}3 \text{ kg Cl/yr} = 84 \text{ kg Cl/yr}$

         Check: The units (kg Cl) are correct. Magnitude is reasonable because it is less than the total CHF_2Cl/yr.

3.93   **Given:** MCl_3; 65.57% Cl in MCl_3 **Find:** identify M

         Conceptual Plan: g Cl $\rightarrow$ mol Cl $\rightarrow$ mol M $\rightarrow$ atomic mass M

$$\frac{1 \text{ mol Cl}}{35.45 \text{ g Cl}} \qquad \frac{1 \text{ mol M}}{3 \text{ mol Cl}} \qquad \frac{\text{g M}}{\text{mol M}}$$

         Solution: in 100 g sample: 65.57 g Cl; 34.43 g M

$$65.57 \text{ g Cl} \times \frac{1 \text{ mol Cl}}{35.45 \text{ g Cl}} \times \frac{1 \text{ mol M}}{3 \text{ mol Cl}} = 0.6165 \text{ mol M} \qquad \frac{34.43 \text{ g M}}{0.6165 \text{ mol M}} = 55.85 \text{ g/mol M}$$

         molar mass of 55.85 = Fe

         The identity of M = Fe.

3.94   **Given:** M_2O; 16.99% O   **Find:** identify M

         Conceptual Plan: g O $\rightarrow$ mol O $\rightarrow$ mol M $\rightarrow$ atomic mass M

$$\frac{1 \text{ mol O}}{16.00 \text{ g O}} \qquad \frac{2 \text{ mol M}}{1 \text{ mol O}} \qquad \frac{\text{g M}}{\text{mol M}}$$

         Solution: in 100 g sample: 16.99 g O; 83.01 g M

$$16.99 \text{ g O} \times \frac{1 \text{ mol O}}{16.00 \text{ g O}} \times \frac{2 \text{ mol M}}{1 \text{ mol O}} = 2.124 \text{ mol M} \qquad \frac{83.01 \text{ g M}}{2.124 \text{ mol M}} = 39.08 \text{ g/mol M}$$

         molar mass of 39.08 = K

         The identity of M = K.

3.95   **Given:** in a 100 g sample: 79.37 g C; 8.88 g H; 11.75 g O; molar mass = 272.37 g/mol   **Find:** molecular formula

         Conceptual Plan:

         convert mass to mol of each element $\rightarrow$ pseudoformula $\rightarrow$ empirical formula $\rightarrow$ molecular formula

$$\frac{1 \text{ mol C}}{12.01 \text{ g C}} \quad \frac{1 \text{ mol H}}{1.008 \text{ g H}} \quad \frac{1 \text{ mol O}}{16.00 \text{ g O}} \qquad \text{divide by smallest number} \qquad \text{empirical formula} \times n$$

         Solution: $79.37 \text{ g C} \times \dfrac{1 \text{ mol C}}{12.01 \text{ g C}} = 6.609 \text{ mol C}$

$$8.88 \text{ g H} \times \frac{1 \text{ mol H}}{1.008 \text{ g H}} = 8.81 \text{ mol H}$$

$$11.75 \text{ g O} \times \frac{1 \text{ mol O}}{16.00 \text{ g O}} = 0.7344 \text{ mol O}$$

         $C_{6.609}H_{8.81}O_{0.7344}$

         $C_{\frac{6.609}{0.7344}} H_{\frac{8.81}{0.7344}} O_{\frac{0.7344}{0.7344}} \rightarrow C_9H_{12}O$

     The correct empirical formula is $C_9H_{12}O$.

empirical formula mass = 9(12.01 g/mol) + 12(1.008 g/mol) + 1(16.00 g/mol) = 136.19 g/mol

$$n = \frac{\text{molar mass}}{\text{formula molar mass}} = \frac{272.37 \text{ g/mol}}{136.19 \text{ g/mol}} = 2$$

molecular formula = $C_9H_{12}O \times 2 = C_{18}H_{24}O_2$

3.96   **Given:** in a 100 g sample: 40.00 g C; 6.72 g H; 53.28 g O; molar mass = 180.16 g/mol   **Find:** molecular formula
Conceptual Plan:

convert mass to mol of each element → pseudoformula → empirical formula → molecular formula

$$\frac{1 \text{ mol C}}{12.01 \text{ g C}} \quad \frac{1 \text{ mol H}}{1.008 \text{ g H}} \quad \frac{1 \text{ mol O}}{16.00 \text{ g O}} \qquad \text{divide by smallest number} \qquad \text{empirical formula} \times n$$

Solution: $40.00 \text{ g C} \times \dfrac{1 \text{ mol C}}{12.01 \text{ g C}} = 3.331 \text{ mol C}$

$6.72 \text{ g H} \times \dfrac{1 \text{ mol H}}{1.008 \text{ g H}} = 6.67 \text{ mol H}$

$53.28 \text{ g O} \times \dfrac{1 \text{ mol O}}{16.00 \text{ g O}} = 3.330 \text{ mol O}$

$C_{3.331}H_{6.67}O_{3.330}$

$C_{\frac{3.331}{3.330}} H_{\frac{6.67}{3.330}} O_{\frac{3.330}{3.330}} \rightarrow CH_2O$

The correct empirical formula is CH_2O.

empirical formula mass = 1(12.01 g/mol) + 2(1.008 g/mol) + 1(16.00 g/mol) = 30.03 g/mol

$$n = \frac{\text{molar mass}}{\text{formula molar mass}} = \frac{180.16 \text{ g/mol}}{30.03 \text{ g/mol}} = 6$$

molecular formula = $CH_2O \times 6 = C_6H_{12}O_6$

3.97   **Given:** 13.42 g sample; 39.61 g CO_2; 9.01 g H_2O; molar mass = 268.34 g/mol   **Find:** molecular formula
Conceptual Plan:

mass CO_2, H_2O → mol CO_2, H_2O → mol C, mol H → mass C, mass H, mass O → mol O →

$$\frac{1 \text{ mol CO}_2}{44.01 \text{ g CO}_2} \quad \frac{1 \text{ mol H}_2O}{18.02 \text{ g H}_2O} \quad \frac{1 \text{ mol C}}{1 \text{ mol CO}_2} \quad \frac{2 \text{ mol H}}{1 \text{ mol H}_2O} \quad \frac{12.01 \text{ g C}}{1 \text{ mol C}} \quad \frac{1.008 \text{ g H}}{1 \text{ mol H}} \quad \text{g sample} - \text{g C} - \text{g H} \quad \frac{1 \text{ mol O}}{16.00 \text{ g O}}$$

pseudoformula → empirical formula → molecular formula

$$\text{divide by smallest number} \qquad \text{empirical formula} \times n$$

$39.61 \text{ g CO}_2 \times \dfrac{1 \text{ mol CO}_2}{44.01 \text{ g CO}_2} = 0.9000 \text{ mol CO}_2$

$9.01 \text{ g H}_2O \times \dfrac{1 \text{ mol H}_2O}{18.02 \text{ g H}_2O} = 0.500 \text{ mol H}_2O$

$0.9000 \text{ mol CO}_2 \times \dfrac{1 \text{ mol C}}{1 \text{ mol CO}_2} = 0.9000 \text{ mol C}$

$0.500 \text{ mol H}_2O \times \dfrac{2 \text{ mol H}}{1 \text{ mol H}_2O} = 1.00 \text{ mol H}$

$0.9000 \text{ mol C} \times \dfrac{12.01 \text{ g C}}{1 \text{ mol C}} = 10.81 \text{ g C}$

$1.00 \text{ mol H}_2O \times \dfrac{1.008 \text{ g H}}{1 \text{ mol H}} = 1.01 \text{ g H}$

$13.42 \text{ g} - 10.81 \text{ g} - 1.01 \text{ g} = 1.60 \text{ g O}$

$1.60 \text{ g O} \times \dfrac{1 \text{ mol O}}{16.00 \text{ g O}} = 0.100 \text{ mol O}$

$C_{0.9000}H_{1.000}O_{0.100}$

$C_{\frac{0.9000}{0.100}} H_{\frac{1.00}{0.100}} O_{\frac{0.100}{0.100}} \rightarrow C_9H_{10}O$

The correct empirical formula is $C_9H_{10}O$.

empirical formula mass $= 9(12.01 \text{ g/mol}) + 10(1.008 \text{ g/mol}) + 1(16.00 \text{ g/mol}) = 134.2 \text{ g/mol}$

$$n = \frac{\text{molar mass}}{\text{formula molar mass}} = \frac{268.34 \text{ g/mol}}{134.2 \text{ g/mol}} = 2$$

molecular formula $= C_9H_{10}O \times 2 = C_{18}H_{20}O_2$

3.98 **Given:** 1.893 g sample; 5.545 g CO_2; 1.388 g H_2O; molar mass $= 270.36$ g/mol   **Find:** molecular formula

Conceptual Plan:

mass CO_2, H_2O → mol CO_2, H_2O → mol C, mol H → mass C, mass H, mass O → mol O →

$$\frac{1 \text{ mol } CO_2}{44.01 \text{ g } CO_2} \quad \frac{1 \text{ mol } H_2O}{18.02 \text{ g } H_2O} \quad \frac{1 \text{ mol C}}{1 \text{ mol } CO_2} \quad \frac{2 \text{ mol H}}{1 \text{ mol } H_2O} \quad \frac{12.01 \text{ g C}}{1 \text{ mol C}} \quad \frac{1.008 \text{ g H}}{1 \text{ mol H}} \quad \text{g sample} - \text{g C} - \text{g H} \quad \frac{1 \text{ mol O}}{16.00 \text{ g O}}$$

pseudoformula → empirical formula → molecular formula

divide by smallest number   empirical formula $\times$ n

Solution:

$$5.545 \text{ g } CO_2 \times \frac{1 \text{ mol } CO_2}{44.01 \text{ g } CO_2} = 0.1260 \text{ mol } CO_2$$

$$1.388 \text{ g } H_2O \times \frac{1 \text{ mol } H_2O}{18.02 \text{ g } H_2O} = 0.07703 \text{ mol } H_2O$$

$$0.1260 \text{ mol } CO_2 \times \frac{1 \text{ mol C}}{1 \text{ mol } CO_2} = 0.1260 \text{ mol C}$$

$$0.07703 \text{ mol } H_2O \times \frac{2 \text{ mol H}}{1 \text{ mol } H_2O} = 0.1541 \text{ mol H}$$

$$0.1260 \text{ mol C} \times \frac{12.01 \text{ g C}}{1 \text{ mol C}} = 1.513 \text{ g C}$$

$$0.1541 \text{ mol } H_2O \times \frac{1.008 \text{ g H}}{1 \text{ mol H}} = 0.1553 \text{ g H}$$

$$1.893 \text{ g} - 1.513 \text{ g} - 0.1553 \text{ g} = 0.225 \text{ g O}$$

$$0.225 \text{ g O} \times \frac{1 \text{ mol O}}{16.00 \text{ g O}} = 0.0141 \text{ mol O}$$

$C_{0.1260} H_{0.1541} O_{0.0141}$

$$C_{\frac{0.1260}{0.0141}} H_{\frac{0.1541}{0.0141}} O_{\frac{0.0141}{0.0141}} \rightarrow C_9H_{11}O$$

The correct empirical formula is $C_9H_{11}O$.

empirical formula mass $= 9(12.01 \text{ g/mol}) + 11(1.008 \text{ g/mol}) + 1(16.00 \text{ g/mol}) = 135.2 \text{ g/mol}$

$$n = \frac{\text{molar mass}}{\text{formula molar mass}} = \frac{270.36 \text{ g/mol}}{135.2 \text{ g/mol}} = 2$$

molecular formula $= C_9H_{11}O \times 2$

$= C_{18}H_{22}O_2$

3.99 **Given:** 4.93 g $MgSO_4 \cdot xH_2O$; 2.41 g $MgSO_4$ **Find:** value of x

Conceptual Plan: g $MgSO_4$ → mol $MgSO_4$ then g H_2O → mol H_2O then determine mole ratio.

$$\frac{1 \text{ mol } MgSO_4}{120.38 \text{ g } MgSO_4} \qquad \frac{1 \text{ mol } H_2O}{18.02 \text{ g } H_2O} \qquad \frac{\text{mol } HO_2}{\text{mol } MgSO_4}$$

Solution:

$$2.41 \text{ g } MgSO_4 \times \frac{1 \text{ mol } MgSO_4}{120.38 \text{ g } MgSO_4} = 0.0200 \text{ mol } MgSO_4$$

Determine g H_2O: 4.93 g $MgSO_4 \cdot xH_2O$ $- 2.41$ g $MgSO_4 = 2.52$ g H_2O

$$2.52 \text{ g } H_2O \times \frac{1 \text{ mol } H_2O}{18.02 \text{ g } H_2O} = 0.140 \text{ mol } H_2O$$

$$\frac{0.140 \text{ mol } H_2O}{0.0200 \text{ mol } MgSO_4} = 7$$

$x = 7$

3.100   **Given:** 3.41 g $CuCl_2 \cdot xH_2O$; 2.69 g $CuCl_2$ **Find:** value of x

Conceptual Plan: g $CuCl_2 \rightarrow$ mol $CuCl_2$ then g $H_2O \rightarrow$ mol H_2O then determine mole ratio.

$$\frac{1 \text{ mol } CuCl_2}{134.45 \text{ g } CuCl_2} \qquad\qquad \frac{1 \text{ mol } H_2O}{18.02 \text{ g } H_2O} \qquad\qquad \frac{\text{mol } HO_2}{\text{mol } CuCl_2}$$

Solution:

$$2.69 \text{ g } CuCl_2 \times \frac{1 \text{ mol } CuCl_2}{134.45 \text{ g } CuCl_2} = 0.0200 \text{ mol } CuCl_2$$

Determine g H_2O: 3.41 g $CuCl_2 \cdot xH_2O - 2.69$ g $CuCl_2 = 0.72$ g H_2O

$$0.72 \text{ g } H_2O \times \frac{1 \text{ mol } H_2O}{18.02 \text{ g } H_2O} = 0.040 \text{ mol } H_2O$$

$$\frac{0.040 \text{ mol } H_2O}{0.0200 \text{ mol } CuCl_2} = 2$$

$$x = 2$$

3.101   **Given:** molar mass $= 177$ g/mol; g C $= 8$(g H)   **Find:** molecular formula

Conceptual Plan: C_xH_yBrO

Solution: in 1 mol compound, let $x =$ mol C and $y =$ mol H, assume mol Br $= 1$, assume mol O $= 1$

177 g/mol $= x(12.01$ g/mol$) + y(1.008$ g/mol$) + 1(79.90$ g/mol$) + 1(16.00$ g/mol$)$

$x(12.01$ g/mol$) = 8[y(1.008$ g/mol$)]$

177 g/mol $= 8y(1.008$ g/mol$) + y(1.008$ g/mol$) + 79.90$ g/mol $+ 16.00$ g/mol

$81 = 9y(1.008)$

$y = 9 =$ mol H

$x(12.01) = 8 \times 9(1.008)$

$x = 6 =$ mol C

molecular formula $= C_6H_9BrO$

Check: molar mass $= 6(12.01$ g/mol$) + 9(1.008$ g/mol$) + 1(79.90$ g/mol$) + 1(16.00$ g/mol$) = 177.0$ g/mol

3.102   **Given:** 3.54 g sample yields 8.49 g CO_2 and 2.14 g H_2O; 2.35 g sample yields 0.199 g N; molar mass $= 165$

Find: molecular formula

Conceptual Plan:

mass N $\rightarrow$ mol N; then mass CO_2, H_2O $\rightarrow$ mol CO_2, H_2O $\rightarrow$ mol C, mol H $\rightarrow$ mass C, mass H;

$$\frac{1 \text{ mol N}}{14.01 \text{ g N}} \qquad \frac{1 \text{ mol } CO_2}{44.01 \text{ g } CO_2} \quad \frac{1 \text{ mol } H_2O}{18.02 \text{ g } H_2O} \quad \frac{1 \text{ mol C}}{1 \text{ mol } CO_2} \quad \frac{2 \text{ mol H}}{1 \text{ mol } H_2O} \quad \frac{12.01 \text{ g C}}{1 \text{ mol C}} \quad \frac{1.008 \text{ g H}}{1 \text{ mol H}}$$

mass O $\rightarrow$ mol O $\rightarrow$ pseudoformula $\rightarrow$ empirical formula $\rightarrow$ molecular formula

$$\text{g sample} - \text{g C} - \text{g H} \quad \frac{1 \text{ mol O}}{16.00 \text{ g O}} \qquad\qquad \text{divide by smallest number} \qquad\qquad \text{empirical formula} \times n$$

Solution:

$$\frac{0.199 \text{ g N}}{2.35 \text{ g sample}} = \frac{x \text{ g N}}{3.54 \text{ g sample}}; x = 0.300 \text{ g N}$$

$$0.300 \text{ g N} \times \frac{1 \text{ mol N}}{14.01 \text{ g N}} = 0.0214 \text{ mol N}$$

$$8.49 \text{ g } CO_2 \times \frac{1 \text{ mol } CO_2}{44.01 \text{ g } CO_2} = 0.193 \text{ mol } CO_2$$

$$2.14 \text{ g } H_2O \times \frac{1 \text{ mol } H_2O}{18.02 \text{ g } H_2O} = 0.119 \text{ mol } H_2O$$

$$0.193 \text{ mol } CO_2 \times \frac{1 \text{ mol C}}{1 \text{ mol } CO_2} = 0.193 \text{ mol C}$$

$$0.119 \text{ mol } H_2O \times \frac{2 \text{ mol H}}{1 \text{ mol } H_2O} = 0.238 \text{ mol H}$$

$$0.193 \text{ mol C} \times \frac{12.01 \text{ g C}}{1 \text{ mol C}} = 2.32 \text{ g C}$$

$$0.238 \text{ mol } H_2O \times \frac{1.008 \text{ g H}}{1 \text{ mol H}} = 0.240 \text{ g H}$$

$$3.54 \text{ g} - 2.32 \text{ g C} - 0.240 \text{ g H} - 0.300 \text{ g N} = 0.680 \text{ g O}$$

$$0.680 \text{ g } \cancel{O} \times \frac{1 \text{ mol O}}{16.00 \text{ g } \cancel{O}} = 0.0425 \text{ mol O}$$

$$C_{0.193} H_{0.238} N_{0.0214} O_{0.0425}$$

$$C_{\underset{0.0214}{0.193}} H_{\underset{0.0214}{0.238}} N_{\underset{0.0214}{0.0214}} O_{\underset{0.0214}{0.0425}} \rightarrow C_9H_{11}NO_2$$

The correct empirical formula is $C_9H_{11}NO_2$.

empirical formula mass =
$$9(12.01 \text{ g/mol}) + 11(1.008 \text{ g/mol}) + 1(14.01 \text{ g/mol}) + 2(16.00 \text{ g/mol}) = 165.19 \text{ g/mol}$$

$$n = \frac{\text{molar mass}}{\text{formula molar mass}} = \frac{165 \text{ g/mol}}{165.19 \text{ g/mol}} = 1$$

molecular formula $= C_9H_{11}NO_2 \times 1$
$\qquad\qquad\qquad = C_9H_{11}NO_2$

3.103 **Given:** 23.5 mg $C_{17}H_{22}ClNO_4$ **Find:** total number of atoms
Conceptual Plan: mg compound $\rightarrow$ g compound $\rightarrow$ mol compound $\rightarrow$ mol atoms $\rightarrow$ number of atoms

$$\frac{1 \text{ g}}{1000 \text{ mg}} \qquad \frac{1 \text{ mol}}{339.8 \text{ g}} \qquad \frac{45 \text{ mol atoms}}{1 \text{ mol compound}} \qquad \frac{6.022 \times 10^{23} \text{ atoms}}{1 \text{ mol atoms}}$$

Solution: $23.5 \text{ m}\cancel{g} \times \dfrac{1 \text{ }\cancel{g}}{1000 \text{ m}\cancel{g}} \times \dfrac{1 \text{ }\cancel{\text{mol cpd}}}{339.8 \text{ }\cancel{g}} \times \dfrac{45 \text{ }\cancel{\text{mol atoms}}}{1 \text{ }\cancel{\text{mol cpd}}} \times \dfrac{6.022 \times 10^{23} \text{ atoms}}{\cancel{\text{mol}}}$

$\qquad\qquad = 1.8\underline{7}41 \times 10^{21} \text{ atoms} = 1.87 \times 10^{21} \text{ atoms}$

Check: The units (number of atoms) are correct. The magnitude of the answer is reasonable because the molecule is so complex.

3.104 **Given:** In a 100 g sample: 76 g V; 24 g O **Find:** formula and name
Conceptual Plan:
convert mass to mol of each element $\rightarrow$ write pseudoformula $\rightarrow$ write empirical formula

$$\frac{1 \text{ mol V}}{50.94 \text{ g V}} \quad \frac{1 \text{ mol O}}{16.00 \text{ g O}} \qquad\qquad \text{divide by smallest number}$$

Solution:

$$76 \text{ g }\cancel{V} \times \frac{1 \text{ mol V}}{50.94 \text{ g }\cancel{V}} = 1.5 \text{ mol V}$$

$$24 \text{ g }\cancel{O} \times \frac{1 \text{ mol O}}{16.00 \text{ g }\cancel{O}} = 1.5 \text{ mol O}$$

$$V_{1.5}O_{1.5}$$

$$V_{\underset{1.5}{1.5}} O_{\underset{1.5}{1.5}} \rightarrow VO$$

The correct formula is VO: vanadium(II) oxide.

Given: In a 100 g sample: 68 g V; 32 g O **Find:** formula and name
Conceptual Plan:
convert mass to mol of each element $\rightarrow$ write pseudoformula $\rightarrow$ write empirical formula

$$\frac{1 \text{ mol V}}{50.94 \text{ g V}} \quad \frac{1 \text{ mol O}}{16.00 \text{ g O}} \qquad\qquad \text{divide by smallest number}$$

Solution:

$$68 \text{ g }\cancel{V} \times \frac{1 \text{ mol V}}{50.94 \text{ g }\cancel{V}} = 1.33 \text{ mol V}$$

$$32 \text{ g }\cancel{O} \times \frac{1 \text{ mol O}}{16.00 \text{ g }\cancel{O}} = 2 \text{ mol O}$$

$$V_{1.33}O_2$$

$$V_{\underset{1.33}{1.33}} O_{\underset{1.33}{2}} \rightarrow VO_{1.5} \rightarrow V_2O_3$$

The correct formula is V_2O_3: vanadium(III) oxide.

Given: In a 100 g sample: 61 g V; 39 g O   **Find:** formula and name
Conceptual Plan:

convert mass to mol of each element → write pseudoformula → write empirical formula

$$\frac{1 \text{ mol V}}{50.94 \text{ g V}} \quad \frac{1 \text{ mol O}}{16.00 \text{ g O}}$$ divide by smallest number

Solution:

$$61 \text{ g V} \times \frac{1 \text{ mol V}}{50.94 \text{ g V}} = 1.2 \text{ mol V}$$

$$39 \text{ g O} \times \frac{1 \text{ mol O}}{16.00 \text{ g O}} = 2.4 \text{ mol O}$$

$$V_{1.2}O_{2.4}$$

$$V_{\underline{1.2}} O_{\underline{2.4}} \rightarrow VO_2$$
$$_{1.2}_{1.2}$$

The correct formula is VO_2: vanadium(IV) oxide.

Given: In a 100 g sample: 56 g V; 44 g O   **Find:** formula and name
Conceptual Plan:
convert mass to mol of each element → write pseudoformula → write empirical formula

$$\frac{1 \text{ mol V}}{50.94 \text{ g V}} \quad \frac{1 \text{ mol O}}{16.00 \text{ g O}}$$ divide by smallest number

Solution:

$$56 \text{ g V} \times \frac{1 \text{ mol V}}{50.94 \text{ g V}} = 1.1 \text{ mol V}$$

$$44 \text{ g O} \times \frac{1 \text{ mol O}}{16.00 \text{ g O}} = 2.75 \text{ mol O}$$

$$V_{1.1}O_{2.75}$$

$$V_{\underline{1.1}} O_{\underline{2.75}} \rightarrow VO_{2.5} \rightarrow V_2O_5$$
$$_{1.1}_{1.1}$$

The correct formula is V_2O_5: vanadium(V) oxide.

3.105   **Given:** MCl_3; 2.395 g sample; 3.606×10^{-2} mol Cl   **Find:** atomic mass M
Conceptual Plan: mol Cl → g Cl → g X

$$\frac{35.45 \text{ g Cl}}{1 \text{ mol Cl}} \quad \text{g sample} - \text{g Cl} = \text{g M}$$

mol Cl → mol M → atomic mass M

$$\frac{1 \text{ mol M}}{3 \text{ mol Cl}} \quad \frac{\text{g M}}{\text{mol M}}$$

Solution:

$$3.606 \times 10^{-2} \text{ mol Cl} \times \frac{35.45 \text{ g}}{1 \text{ mol Cl}} = 1.278 \text{ g Cl}$$

$$2.395 \text{ g} - 1.278 \text{ g} = 1.117 \text{ g M}$$

$$3.606 \times 10^{-2} \text{ mol Cl} \times \frac{1 \text{ mol M}}{3 \text{ mol Cl}} = 1.202 \times 10^{-2} \text{ mol M}$$

$$\frac{1.117 \text{ g M}}{0.01202 \text{ mol M}} = 92.93 \text{ g/mol M}$$

molar mass of M = 92.93 g/mol

3.106   **Given:** $Fe_xCr_yO_4$; 28.59% O   **Find:** x and y
Conceptual Plan: %O → molar mass $Fe_xCr_yO_4$ → mass Fe + Cr

$$\frac{\text{mass O}}{\text{molar mass compound}} \times 100\% = \%O \quad \text{mass cpd} - \text{mass O} = \text{mass Fe} + \text{Cr}$$

Solution: $\dfrac{28.59 \text{ g O}}{100.0 \text{ g cpd}} = \dfrac{64.00 \text{ g O}}{\text{molar mass cpd}}$ molar mass = 223.9 g/mol

Mass Fe + Cr = molar mass − (4 × molar mass O) = 223.9 − 64.00 = 159.9 g

Molar mass Fe = 55.85; molar mass Cr = 52.00

Because the mass of the two metals is close, the average mass can be used to determine the total moles of Fe

and Cr present in the compound. Average mass of Fe and Cr = 53.93. $\dfrac{159.9 \text{ g}}{53.93 \text{ g/mol}}$ = 2.965 = 3 mol metal

Let x = mol Fe and y = mol Cr

x mol Fe + y mol Cr = 3 mol total

x mol Fe(55.85 g Fe/mol) + y mol Cr(52.00 gCr/mol) = 159.9

y mol Cr = 3 − x mol Fe

x(55.85) + (3 − x)(52.00) = 159.9

So x = 1 and y = 2.

Check: Formula = $FeCr_2O_4$ would have a molar mass of Fe + 2Cr + 4O = 55.85 g/mol + 2(52.00 g/mol) + 4(16.00 g/mol) = 223.85 g/mol, and the molar mass of the compound is 223.8.

3.107 **Given:** X_3P_2; 34.00% P; 100 g sample contains 34.00 g P $\quad$ **Find:** X

Conceptual Plan: g P → mol P → mol X

$$\dfrac{1 \text{ mol P}}{30.97 \text{ g P}} \qquad \dfrac{3 \text{ mol X}}{2 \text{ mol P}}$$

and then g P → g X → molar mass X

$$100.00 \text{ g sample} - 34.00 \text{ g P} \qquad \dfrac{\text{grams X}}{\text{mol X}}$$

Solution: $34.00 \text{ g P} \times \dfrac{1 \text{ mol P}}{30.97 \text{ g P}} \times \dfrac{3 \text{ mol X}}{2 \text{ mol P}} = 1.647 \text{ mol X}$

$100.00 \text{ g sample} - 34.00 \text{ g P} = 66.00 \text{ g X}$

$\dfrac{66.00 \text{ g X}}{1.647 \text{ mol X}} = 40.07 \text{ g/mol} = \text{Ca}$

Check: The units (g/mol) are correct. The answer, Ca, is reasonable because Ca_3P_2 is a molecule that exists.

3.108 **Given:** 0.0552% $NaNO_2$; 8.00 oz bag $\quad$ **Find:** mass Na in bag

Conceptual Plan: oz bag → g bag → g $NaNO_2$ → g Na

$$\dfrac{453.6 \text{ g}}{16.00 \text{ oz}} \qquad \dfrac{0.0552 \text{ g NaNO}_2}{100.0 \text{ g bag}} \qquad \dfrac{22.99 \text{ g Na}}{69.00 \text{ g NaNO}_2}$$

Solution:

$8 \text{ oz bag} \times \dfrac{453.6 \text{ g bag}}{16.00 \text{ oz bag}} \times \dfrac{0.0552 \text{ g NaNO}_2}{100.0 \text{ g bag}} \times \dfrac{22.99 \text{ g Na}}{69.00 \text{ g NaNO}_2} \times \dfrac{1000 \text{ mg Na}}{\text{g Na}} = 41.\underline{7}12 \text{ mg Na} = 41.7 \text{ mg Na}$

Check: The units (mg Na) are correct. The magnitude of the answer is reasonable because only a small % of the total mass is Na.

3.109 **Given:** ore is 57.8% $Ca_3(PO_4)_2$ $\quad$ **Find:** mass of ore to get 1.00 kg P

Conceptual Plan: mass ore → mass $Ca_3(PO_4)_2$ → mass P

Solution: Assume a 100.0 gram sample of ore.

$100.0 \text{ g ore} \times \dfrac{57.8 \text{ g Ca}_3(PO_4)_2}{100.0 \text{ g ore}} \times \dfrac{61.94 \text{ g P}}{310.18 \text{ g Ca}_3(PO_4)_2} = 11.54 \text{ g P}$

$1.00 \text{ kg P} \times \dfrac{1000 \text{ g P}}{\text{kg P}} \times \dfrac{100.0 \text{ g ore}}{11.54 \text{ g P}} \times \dfrac{1 \text{ kg ore}}{1000 \text{ g ore}} = 8.6\underline{6}6 \text{ kg ore} = 8.67 \text{ kg ore}$

Check: The units (kg ore) are correct. The magnitude of the answer is reasonable because the amount is greater than 1 kilogram.

Challenge Problems

3.110 **Given:** g NaCl + g NaBr = 2.00 g; g Na = 0.75 g $\quad$ **Find:** g NaBr

Conceptual Plan:

let x = mol NaCl, y = mol NaBr, then x(molar mass NaCl) = g NaCl, y(molar mass NaBr) = g NaBr

Solution: x(58.4) + y(102.9) = 2.00

$\qquad x$(23.0) + y(23.0) = 0.75 $\qquad\qquad\qquad y$ = 0.0326 − x

$$58.4x + 102.9(0.0326 - x) = 2.00$$
$$58.4x + 3.354 - 102.9x = 2.00$$
$$44.5x = 1.354$$
$$x = 0.03043 \text{ mol NaCl}$$
$$y = 0.0326 - 0.03043 = 0.00217 \text{ mol NaBr}$$
$$\text{g NaBr} = (0.00217)(102.9 \text{ g/mol}) = 0.223 \text{ g NaBr} = 0.22 \text{ g NaBr}$$

Check: The units (g NaBr) are correct. The magnitude is reasonable because it is less than the total mass.

3.111   **Given:** sample 1: 1.00 g X, 0.472 g Z, X_2Z_3; sample 2: 1.00 g X, 0.630 g Z; sample 3: 1.00 g X, 0.789 g Z
Find: empirical formula for samples 2 and 3
Conceptual Plan: moles X remains constant; determine relative moles of Z for three samples.
Solution: Let X = atomic mass X, Z = atomic mass Z

$$n_X = \frac{1.00 \text{ g X}}{X} \qquad n_Z = \frac{0.472 \text{ g Z}}{Z}$$

for sample 1: $\dfrac{n_X}{n_Z} = \dfrac{2}{3}$

for sample 2: $\dfrac{0.630 \text{ g}}{0.472 \text{ g}} = 1.33$; mol = $1.33 \, n_Z$

mol ratio: $\dfrac{n_X}{1.33 \, n_Z} = \dfrac{2}{(1.33)3} = \dfrac{2}{4} = \dfrac{1}{2}$

Empirical formula sample 2: XZ_2

for sample 3: $\dfrac{0.789 \text{ g}}{0.472 \text{ g}} = 1.67$; mol = $1.67 \, n_Z$

mol ratio: $\dfrac{n_X}{1.67 \, n_Z} = \dfrac{2}{(1.67)3} = \dfrac{2}{5}$

Empirical formula sample 3: X_2Z_5

3.112   **Given:** sample of $CaCO_3$ and $(NH_4)_2CO_3$ is 61.9% CO_3^{2-} **Find:** % $CaCO_3$ by mass
Conceptual Plan: let $x = CaCO_3, y = (NH_4)_2CO_3$, then x(molar mass $CaCO_3$) = g $CaCO_3$,
   y(molar mass $(NH_4)_2CO_3$) = g $(NH_4)_2CO_3$
   then a 100.0 g sample contains x(100.0) g $CaCO_3$; y(96.1) g $(NH_4)_2CO_3$; 61.9 g CO_3^{2-}
Solution: $x(100.0) + y(96.1) = 100.0$

$$x(60.0) + y(60.0) = 61.9 \qquad\qquad y = 1.03167 - x$$
$$100.0x + 96.1(1.03 - x) = 100$$
$$100.0x + 99.0 - 96.1x = 100$$
$$3.9x = 1.0$$
$$x = 0.26 \text{ mol } CaCO_3$$
$$y = 1.032 - 0.26 = 0.77 \text{ mol } (NH_4)_2CO_3$$
$$\text{g } CaCO_3 = (0.26 \text{ mol})(100.0 \text{ g/mol}) = 26 \text{ g } CaCO_3 \text{ in a 100 g sample:}$$
mass % $CaCO_3$ = 26%

Check: The units (mass % $CaCO_3$) are correct. The magnitude is reasonable because it is between 0 and 100%.

3.113   **Given:** 50.0 g S; 1.00×10^2 g Cl_2; 150. g mixture S_2Cl_2 and SCl_2 **Find:** g S_2Cl_2
Conceptual Plan: total mol S = 2(mol S_2Cl_2) + mol SCl_2; mol $S_2Cl_2 \rightarrow$ g S_2Cl_2

$$\frac{135.04 \text{ g}}{1 \text{ mol } S_2Cl_2}$$

then S_2Cl_2 = 135.04 g/mol, SCl_2 = 102.97 g/mol, let x = mol S_2Cl_2, y = mol SCl_2
$x(135.04)$ = g S in S_2Cl_2, $y(102.97)$ = g S in SCl_2

Solution: mol S = $50.0 \text{ g S} \times \dfrac{1 \text{ mol S}}{32.1 \text{ g S}} = 1.56 \text{ mol}$

$$2x = \text{mol S in } S_2Cl_2, \, y = \text{mol S in } SCl_2$$
$$2x + y = 1.56$$
$$x(135.04) + y(102.97) = 150.0$$
$$135.04x + 102.97(1.56 - 2x) = 150.0$$

$$70.90x = 10.6$$
$$x = 0.14\underline{9}5$$
$$y = 1.26$$

$$0.14\underline{9}5 \; \text{mol S}_2\text{Cl}_2 \times \frac{135.04 \; \text{g S}_2\text{Cl}_2}{1 \; \text{mol S}_2\text{Cl}_2} = 20.\underline{1}88 \; \text{g S}_2\text{Cl}_2 = 20.2 \; \text{g S}_2\text{Cl}_2$$

Check: The units (g S_2Cl_2) are correct. The magnitude is reasonable because there would be fewer moles of S_2Cl_2 than SCl_2.

3.114   **Given:** 1.1 kg CF_2Cl_2/automobile; 25% leaked/year; 100×10^6 automobiles   **Find:** kg Cl/yr
Conceptual Plan: kg CF_2Cl_2/auto $\rightarrow$ kg CF_2Cl_2 leaked/yr $\rightarrow$ kg Cl/yr/auto $\rightarrow$ kg Cl

$$\frac{25 \; \text{kg CF}_2\text{Cl}_2}{100 \; \text{kg CF}_2\text{Cl}_2} \qquad \frac{70.9 \; \text{kg Cl}}{120.91 \; \text{kg CF}_2\text{Cl}_2} \qquad 100 \times 10^6 \; \text{auto}$$

Solution: $\dfrac{1.1 \; \text{kg CF}_2\text{Cl}_2}{\text{auto}} \times \dfrac{25 \; \text{kg CF}_2\text{Cl}_2}{100 \; \text{kg CF}_2\text{Cl}_2} \times \dfrac{70.9 \; \text{kg Cl}}{120.91 \; \text{kg CF}_2\text{Cl}_2} \times 100 \times 10^6 \; \text{auto}$

$$= 1.\underline{6}13 \times 10^7 \; \text{kg Cl/yr} = 1.6 \times 10^7 \; \text{kg Cl/yr}$$

Check: The units (kg Cl) are correct. The magnitude is reasonable because it is less than the kilogram CF_2Cl_2 leaked per year.

3.115   **Given:** coal = 2.55% S; H_2SO_4; 1.0 metric ton coal
Find: metric ton H_2SO_4 produced
Conceptual Plan: H_2SO_4 $\rightarrow$ %S

$$\frac{32.07 \; \text{g S}}{98.09 \; \text{g H}_2\text{SO}_4} \times 100\%$$

Solution: $\dfrac{32.07 \; \text{g S}}{98.09 \; \text{g H}_2\text{SO}_4} \times 100\% = 32.69\% \; \text{S}$

Conceptual Plan: metric ton coal $\rightarrow$ kg coal $\rightarrow$ kg S $\rightarrow$ kg H_2SO_4 $\rightarrow$ metric ton H_2SO_4

$$\frac{1000 \; \text{kg}}{\text{metric ton}} \qquad \frac{2.55 \; \text{kg S}}{100 \; \text{kg coal}} \qquad \frac{100 \; \text{kg H}_2\text{SO}_4}{32.69 \; \text{kg S}} \qquad \frac{\text{metric ton}}{1000 \; \text{kg}}$$

Solution: $1.0 \; \text{metric ton coal} \times \dfrac{1000 \; \text{kg coal}}{1 \; \text{metric ton coal}} \times \dfrac{2.55 \; \text{kg S}}{100 \; \text{kg coal}} \times \dfrac{100 \; \text{kg H}_2\text{SO}_4}{32.69 \; \text{kg S}} \times \dfrac{1 \; \text{metric ton H}_2\text{SO}_4}{1000 \; \text{kg H}_2\text{SO}_4}$

$$= 0.078 \; \text{metric ton H}_2\text{SO}_4$$

Check: The units (metric ton H_2SO_4) are correct. Magnitude is reasonable because it is more than 2.55% of a metric ton and the mass of H_2SO_4 is greater than the mass of S.

3.116   **Given:** rock contains: 38.0% PbS; 25.0% $PbCO_3$; 17.4% $PbSO_4$ **Find:** kg rock needed for 5.0 metric ton Pb
Conceptual Plan: determine kg Pb/100 kg rock; then ton Pb $\rightarrow$ kg Pb $\rightarrow$ kg rock

$$\frac{1000 \; \text{kg}}{\text{metric ton}} \qquad \frac{100 \; \text{kg rock}}{64.2 \; \text{kg rock}}$$

Solution: in 100 kg rock:

$$\left(38.0 \; \text{kg PbS} \times \frac{207.2 \; \text{kg Pb}}{239.3 \; \text{kg PbS}} \right) + \left(25.0 \; \text{kg PbCO}_3 \times \frac{207.2 \; \text{kg Pb}}{267.2 \; \text{kg PbCO}_3} \right) + \left(17.4 \; \text{kg PbSO}_4 \times \frac{207.2 \; \text{kg Pb}}{303.3 \; \text{kg PbSO}_4} \right)$$
$$= 64.2 \; \text{kg Pb}$$

$$5.0 \; \text{metric ton Pb} \times \frac{1000 \; \text{kg Pb}}{\text{metric ton Pb}} \times \frac{100 \; \text{kg rock}}{64.2 \; \text{kg Pb}} = 7.\underline{7}88 \times 10^3 \; \text{kg rock} = 7.8 \times 10^3 \; \text{kg rock}$$

Check: The units (kg rock) are correct. Magnitude is reasonable because it is greater than the amount of Pb needed.

3.117   **Given:** sample 1: 2.52 g sample, 4.23 g CO_2, 1.01 g H_2O; sample 2: 4.14 g, 2.11 g SO_3; sample 3: 5.66 g, 2.27 g HNO_3
Find: empirical formula of the compound
Conceptual Plan: g CO_2 $\rightarrow$ g C $\rightarrow$ %C; g H_2O $\rightarrow$ g H $\rightarrow$ %H; g SO_2 $\rightarrow$ g S $\rightarrow$ %S;

$$\frac{12.01 \; \text{g C}}{44.01 \; \text{g CO}_2} \quad \frac{\text{g C}}{\text{g sample}} \times 100\% \qquad \frac{1.01 \; \text{g H}}{18.02 \; \text{g H}_2\text{O}} \quad \frac{\text{g H}}{\text{g sample}} \times 100\% \qquad \frac{32.07 \; \text{g S}}{80.07 \; \text{g SO}_2} \quad \frac{\text{g S}}{\text{g sample}} \times 100\%$$

g HNO_3 $\rightarrow$ g N $\rightarrow$ % N and then $\rightarrow$ % O and then % composition $\rightarrow$ mol of each atom $\rightarrow$

$$\frac{14.01 \; \text{g N}}{63.02 \; \text{g HNO}_3} \qquad \frac{\text{g N}}{\text{g sample}} \times 100\% \quad 100\% - \%C - \%H - \%N - \%S = \%O$$

pseudoformula → empirical formula

divide by smallest number

Solution: $4.23 \text{ g } CO_2 \times \dfrac{12.01 \text{ g C}}{44.01 \text{ g } CO_2} = 1.15\underline{4} \text{ g C}$ $\dfrac{1.154 \text{ g C}}{2.52 \text{ g sample}} \times 100\% = 45.\underline{8}1\% \text{ C}$

$1.01 \text{ g } H_2O \times \dfrac{2.02 \text{ g H}}{18.02 \text{ g } H_2O} = 0.11\underline{3}2 \text{ g H}$ $\dfrac{0.1132 \text{ g H}}{2.52 \text{ g sample}} \times 100\% = 4.\underline{4}9\% \text{ H}$

$2.11 \text{ g } SO_3 \times \dfrac{32.07 \text{ g S}}{80.07 \text{ g } SO_3} = 0.84\underline{5}1 \text{ g S}$ $\dfrac{0.8451 \text{ g S}}{4.14 \text{ g sample}} \times 100\% = 20.\underline{4}1\% \text{ S}$

$2.27 \text{ g } HNO_3 \times \dfrac{14.01 \text{ g N}}{63.02 \text{ g } HNO_3} = 0.50\underline{4}6 \text{ g N}$ $\dfrac{0.5046 \text{ g N}}{5.66 \text{ g sample}} \times 100\% = 8.9\underline{2}\% \text{ N}$

$\% \text{ O} = 100 - 45.\underline{8}1 - 4.\underline{4}9 - 20.\underline{4}1 - 8.9\underline{2} = 20.\underline{3}7\% \text{ O}$

Assume a 100 g sample:

$45.\underline{8}1 \text{ g C} \times \dfrac{1 \text{ mol C}}{12.01 \text{ g C}} = 3.8\underline{1}4 \text{ mol C}$ $4.\underline{4}9 \text{ g H} \times \dfrac{1 \text{ mol H}}{1.008 \text{ g H}} = 4.4\underline{4}5 \text{ mol H}$

$20.\underline{4}1 \text{ g S} \times \dfrac{1 \text{ mol S}}{32.07 \text{ g S}} = 0.636\underline{4} \text{ mol S}$ $8.9\underline{2} \text{ g N} \times \dfrac{1 \text{ mol N}}{14.01 \text{ g N}} = 0.636\underline{7} \text{ mol N}$

$20.\underline{3}7 \text{ g O} \times \dfrac{1 \text{ mol O}}{16.00 \text{ g O}} = 1.2\underline{7}3 \text{ mol O}$

$C_{3.8\underline{1}4} \ H_{4.4\underline{4}5} \ S_{0.636\underline{4}} \ N_{0.636\underline{7}} \ O_{1.2\underline{7}3}$

$C_{\frac{3.814}{0.6364}} \ H_{\frac{4.445}{0.6364}} \ S_{\frac{0.6364}{0.6364}} \ N_{\frac{0.6367}{0.6364}} \ O_{\frac{1.273}{0.6364}} \rightarrow C_6H_7SNO_2$

3.118   **Given:** molar mass $= 229$ g/mol, 6 times mass C as H   **Find:** molecular formula

Conceptual Plan: Let $x =$ **mass of H, then** $6x =$ **mass of C**

Solution: in 1 mol of the compound: g C + g H + g S + g I = 229 g

Because the molar mass of I = 127, there cannot be more than 1 mol of I in the compound; so

$x + 6x + \text{g S} + 127 = 229.$

$x + 6x + \text{g S} = 102$

If the compound contains 1 mol S, then $7x = 102 - 32 = 70$ and $x = 10$ g H and $6x = 60$ g C.

$10 \text{ g H} \times \dfrac{1 \text{ mol H}}{1.008 \text{ g H}} = 10 \text{ mol H}$

$60 \text{ g C} \times \dfrac{1 \text{ mol C}}{12.01 \text{ g C}} = 5 \text{ mol C}$

1 mol I and 1 mol S; so empirical formula is $C_5H_{10}SI$

Check: Molar mass of $C_5H_{10}SI = 5(12) + 10(1.0) + 32 + 127 = 229$ g/mol, which is the mass given.

3.119   **Given:** compound is 40% X and 60% Y; atomic mass X = 2 (atomic mass Y)   **Find:** empirical formula

Conceptual Plan: mass X and Y → mass ratio X: Y and then g X → mol X and g Y → mol Y and then

$\dfrac{\text{g X}}{\text{atomic mass X}}$ $\dfrac{\text{g Y}}{\text{atomic mass Y}}$

mole ratio

Solution: $\dfrac{\text{mass X}}{\text{mass Y}} = \dfrac{40}{60} = \dfrac{2}{3}$ $\text{mol X} = \dfrac{2 \text{ g}}{\text{atomic mass X}}$ and $\text{mol Y} = \dfrac{3 \text{ g}}{\text{atomic mass Y}}$

But: atomic mass X = 2(atomic mass Y)

$\text{mol X} = \dfrac{2 \text{ g}}{2(\text{atomic mass Y})}$ and $\text{mol Y} = \dfrac{3 \text{ g}}{\text{atomic mass Y}}$

$\dfrac{\text{mol X}}{\text{mol Y}} = \dfrac{\dfrac{2 \text{ g}}{2(\text{atomic mass Y})}}{\dfrac{3 \text{ g}}{\text{atomic mass Y}}} = \dfrac{1}{3}$ empirical formula: XY_3

3.120   **Given:** Compound is 1/3 X by mass; atomic mass X is 3/4 atomic mass Y   **Find:** empirical formula
        Conceptual Plan: mass X and Y → mass ratio X: Y and then g X → mol X and g Y → mol Y and then

$$\frac{g\ X}{atomic\ mass\ X} \qquad \frac{g\ Y}{atomic\ mass\ Y}$$

        mole ratio

Solution: $\dfrac{\text{mass X}}{\text{mass Y}} = \dfrac{\frac{1}{3}}{\frac{2}{3}} = \dfrac{1}{2}$ $\text{mol X} = \dfrac{1\ g}{atomic\ mass\ X}$ and $\text{mol Y} = \dfrac{2\ g}{atomic\ mass\ Y}$

        But atomic mass X = 3/4 atomic mass Y; so:

$$\text{mol X} = \frac{1\ g}{3/4(atomic\ mass\ Y)} \text{ and mol Y} = \frac{2\ g}{atomic\ mass\ Y}$$

$$\frac{\text{mol X}}{\text{mol Y}} = \frac{\dfrac{1\ \cancel{g}}{3/4(\cancel{atomic\ mass\ Y})}}{\dfrac{2\ \cancel{g}}{\cancel{atomic\ mass\ Y}}} = \frac{2}{3}$$

        empirical formula = X_2Y_3

Conceptual Problems

3.121   The sphere in the molecular models represents the electron cloud of the atom. On this scale, the nucleus would be too small to see.

3.122   (a)   Atomic mass O > atomic mass C; % O would be higher.
        (b)   Atomic mass N and O close; molecule contains 2 N to 1 O; % N would be higher.
        (c)   Atomic mass O > atomic mass C; same number of atoms; % O would be higher.
        (d)   Atomic mass N much greater than atomic mass H; % N would be higher.

3.123   The statement is incorrect because a chemical formula is based on the ratio of atoms combined, not the ratio of grams combined. The statement should read as follows: The chemical formula for ammonia (NH_3) indicates that ammonia contains three hydrogen atoms to each nitrogen atom.

3.124   The statement is incorrect because equations are balanced based on the number and kind of atoms, not molecules. The statement should read as follows: When a chemical equation is balanced, the number of atoms of each type on both sides of the equation is equal.

3.125 H_2SO_4: Atomic mass S is approximately twice atomic mass O; both are much greater than atomic mass H. The order of % mass is % O > % S > % H.

3.126

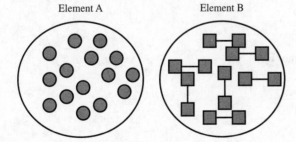

        Element A   Element B

Questions for Group Work

3.127   In an ionic bond an electron is transferred from the Na atom to the Cl atom, so a student would move from the Na atom to the Cl atom.
        For the covalent bond, a pair of electrons is shared between the O atom and each of the two H atoms.

3.128

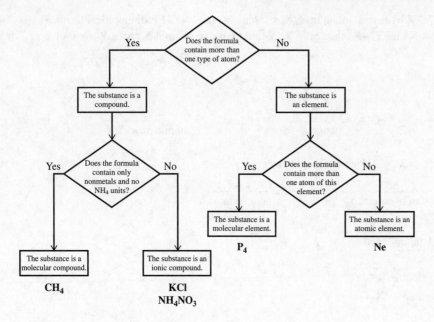

3.129   Some examples of similarities are:
- The systematic names of both binary ionic compounds and binary molecular compounds contain two words.
- The systematic names of both binary ionic compounds and binary molecular compounds end in –ide.
- The systematic names of both binary ionic compounds and binary molecular compounds indicate how many atoms of each element are in the formula.
- The systematic names of both binary ionic compounds and binary molecular compounds name the element listed first first.

Some examples of differences are:
- Only the systematic names of binary molecular compounds contain Greek prefixes.
- There are no polyatomic group names used in generating the systematic name of a binary molecular compound.
- The systematic names of only ionic compounds can have a variety of endings (-ide, -ate, and –ite).
- Binary molecular compounds end in –ide.

3.130   **Given:** In a 100 g sample: 88.14 g C; 11.86 g H; molar mass $= 136.26$ g/mol   **Find:** molecular formula
Conceptual Plan:
convert mass to mol of each element → write pseudoformula → write empirical formula

$$\frac{1 \text{ mol C}}{12.01 \text{ g C}} \qquad \frac{1 \text{ mol H}}{1.0008 \text{ g H}} \qquad \text{divide by smaller number}$$

then empirical formula → molecular formula
divide molar mass by molar mass of empirical formula

Solution: $88.14 \text{ g C} \times \dfrac{1 \text{ mol C}}{12.01 \text{ g C}} = 7.339 \text{ mol C}$

$11.86 \text{ g H} \times \dfrac{1 \text{ mol H}}{1.008 \text{ g H}} = 11.77 \text{ mol H}$

$C_{7.339} H_{11.77}$ Divide by smaller number. $C_{\frac{7.339}{7.339}} H_{\frac{11.377}{7.339}} \rightarrow C_1 H_{1.60}$

$C_1 H_{1.60} \times 2 = C_2 H_3$

The molar mass of the empirical formula is $2(12.01 \text{ g/mol}) + 3(1.008 \text{ g/mol}) = 27.04$ g/mol.

$n = \dfrac{136.26 \text{ g/mol}}{27.04 \text{ g/mol}} = 5.03$ So, $C_2 H_3 \times 5 = C_{10} H_{15}$ is the molecular formula.

The hardest part might be to determine which integer to multiply the pseudoformula by, since the atom ratio is 1:1.60 (and not 1:1.50 or 1:1.67).

3.131   **Conceptual Plan: write a skeletal reaction → balance atoms in more complex compounds → balance elements that occur as free elements → clear fractions**

          Solution:

Skeletal reaction:	$C_8H_{18}(l) + O_2(g)$	$\rightarrow CO_2(g) + H_2O(g)$
Balance C:	$C_8H_{18}(l) + O_2(g)$	$\rightarrow 8\,CO_2(g) + H_2O(g)$
Balance H:	$C_8H_{18}(l) + O_2(g)$	$\rightarrow 8\,CO_2(g) + 9\,H_2O(g)$
Balance O:	$C_8H_{18}(l) + 25/2\,O_2(g)$	$\rightarrow 8\,CO_2(g) + 9\,H_2O(g)$
Clear fraction:	$2\,C_8H_{18}(l) + 25\,O_2(g)$	$\rightarrow 16\,CO_2(g) + 18\,H_2O(g)$

          Check:

left side	right side
16 C atoms	16 C atoms
36 H atoms	36 H atoms
50 O atoms	50 O atoms

4 Chemical Quantities and Aqueous Reactions

Problems by Topic

Reaction Stoichiometry

4.1   **Given:** 4.9 moles C_6H_{14} **Find:** balanced reaction, moles O_2 required
    Conceptual Plan: balance the equation then mol $C_6H_{14} \rightarrow$ mol O_2

$$2\,C_6H_{14}(g) + 19\,O_2(g) \rightarrow 12\,CO_2(g) + 14\,H_2O(g) \qquad \frac{19\ \text{mol}\ O_2}{2\ \text{mol}\ C_6H_{14}}$$

    Solution: Skeletal reaction: $C_6H_{14}(aq) + O_2(g) \rightarrow CO_2(g) + H_2O(g)$
                  Balance C: $C_6H_{14}(aq) + O_2(g) \rightarrow 6\,CO_2(g) + H_2O(g)$
                  Balance H: $C_6H_{14}(aq) + O_2(g) \rightarrow 6\,CO_2(g) + 7\,H_2O(g)$
                  Balance O: $C_6H_{14}(aq) + 19/2\,O_2(g) \rightarrow 6\,CO_2(g) + 7\,H_2O(g)$
                  Clear fraction: $2\,C_6H_{14}(aq) + 19\,O_2(g) \rightarrow 12\,CO_2(g) + 14\,H_2O(g)$

    Check:

	left side	right side
	12 C atoms	12 C atoms
	18 H atoms	28 H atoms
	38 O atoms	38 O atoms

    Solution: $4.9\ \text{mol}\ C_6H_{14} \times \dfrac{19\ \text{mol}\ O_2}{2\ \text{mol}\ C_6H_{14}} = 46.\underline{6}\ \text{mol}\ O_2 = 47\ \text{mol}\ O_2$

    Check: The units of the answer (mol O_2) are correct. The magnitude is reasonable because much more O_2 is needed than C_6H_{14}.

4.2   **Given:** 0.107 moles $HC_2H_3O_2$ **Find:** balanced reaction, moles $Ba(OH)_2$ required
    Conceptual Plan: balance the reaction then mol $HC_2H_3O_2 \rightarrow$ mol $Ba(OH)_2$

$$2\,HC_2H_3O_2(aq) + Ba(OH)_2(aq) \rightarrow 2\,H_2O(l) + Ba(C_2H_3O_2)_2(aq) \qquad \frac{1\ \text{mol}\ Ba(OH)_2}{2\ \text{mol}\ HC_2H_3O_2}$$

    Solution: Skeletal reaction: $HC_2H_3O_2(aq) + Ba(OH)_2(aq) \rightarrow H_2O(l) + Ba(C_2H_3O_2)_2(aq)$
                  Balance C: $2\,HC_2H_3O_2(aq) + Ba(OH)_2(aq) \rightarrow H_2O(l) + Ba(C_2H_3O_2)_2(aq)$
                  Balance H: $2\,HC_2H_3O_2(aq) + Ba(OH)_2(aq) \rightarrow 2\,H_2O(l) + Ba(C_2H_3O_2)_2(aq)$

    Check:

	left side	right side
	4 C atoms	4 C atoms
	10 H atoms	10 H atoms
	6 O atoms	6 O atoms
	1 Ba atom	1 Ba atom

    Solution: $0.107\ \text{mol}\ HC_2H_3O_2 \times \dfrac{1\ \text{mol}\ Ba(OH)_2}{2\ \text{mol}\ HC_2H_3O_2} = 0.0535\underline{0}\ \text{mol}\ Ba(OH)_2 = 0.0535\ \text{mol}\ Ba(OH)_2$

    Check: The units of the answer (mol $Ba(OH)_2$) are correct. The magnitude is reasonable because much less $Ba(OH)_2$ is needed than $HC_2H_3O_2$.

4.3   (a)   **Given:** 1.3 mol N_2O_5 **Find:** mol NO_2
           Conceptual Plan: mol $N_2O_5 \rightarrow$ mol NO_2

$$\frac{4\ \text{mol}\ NO_2}{2\ \text{mol}\ N_2O_5}$$

           Solution: $1.3\ \text{mol}\ N_2O_5 \times \dfrac{4\ \text{mol}\ NO_2}{2\ \text{mol}\ N_2O_5} = 2.6\ \text{mol}\ NO_2$

Check: The units of the answer (mol NO_2) are correct. The magnitude is reasonable because it is greater than mol N_2O_5.

(b) **Given:** 5.8 mol N_2O_5 **Find:** mol NO_2

Conceptual Plan: mol N_2O_5 → mol NO_2

$$\frac{4 \text{ mol } NO_2}{2 \text{ mol } N_2O_5}$$

Solution: $5.8 \text{ mol } N_2O_5 \times \dfrac{4 \text{ mol } NO_2}{2 \text{ mol } N_2O_5} = 11.6 \text{ mol } NO_2 = 12 \text{ mol } NO_2$

Check: The units of the answer (mol NO_2) are correct. The magnitude is reasonable because it is greater than mol N_2O_5.

(c) **Given:** 10.5 g N_2O_5 **Find:** mol NO_2

Conceptual Plan: g N_2O_5 → mol N_2O_5 → mol NO_2

$$\frac{1 \text{ mol } N_2O_5}{108.02 \text{ g } N_2O_5} \quad \frac{4 \text{ mol } NO_2}{2 \text{ mol } N_2O_5}$$

Solution: $10.5 \text{ g } N_2O_5 \times \dfrac{1 \text{ mol } N_2O_5}{108.02 \text{ g } N_2O_5} \times \dfrac{4 \text{ mol } NO_2}{2 \text{ mol } N_2O_5} = 0.1944 \text{ mol } NO_2 = 0.194 \text{ mol } NO_2$

Check: The units of the answer (mol NO_2) are correct. The magnitude is reasonable because 10 g is about 0.09 mol N_2O_5 and the answer is greater than mol N_2O_5.

(d) **Given:** 1.55 kg N_2O_5 **Find:** mol NO_2

Conceptual Plan: kg N_2O_5 → g N_2O_5 → mol N_2O_5 → mol NO_2

$$\frac{1000 \text{ g } N_2O_5}{1 \text{ kg } N_2O_5} \quad \frac{1 \text{ mol } N_2O_5}{108.02 \text{ g } N_2O_5} \quad \frac{4 \text{ mol } NO_2}{2 \text{ mol } N_2O_5}$$

Solution:

$1.55 \text{ kg } N_2O_5 \times \dfrac{1000 \text{ g } N_2O_5}{1 \text{ kg } N_2O_5} \times \dfrac{1 \text{ mol } N_2O_5}{108.02 \text{ g } N_2O_5} \times \dfrac{4 \text{ mol } NO_2}{2 \text{ mol } N_2O_5} = 28.70 \text{ mol } NO_2 = 28.7 \text{ mol } NO_2$

Check: The units of the answer (mol NO_2) are correct. The magnitude is reasonable because 1.55 kg is about 14 mol N_2O_5 and the answer is greater than mol N_2O_5.

4.4 (a) **Given:** 5.3 mol N_2H_4 **Find:** mol NH_3

Conceptual Plan: mol N_2H_4 → mol NH_3

$$\frac{4 \text{ mol } NH_3}{3 \text{ mol } N_2H_4}$$

Solution: $5.3 \text{ mol } N_2H_4 \times \dfrac{4 \text{ mol } NH_3}{3 \text{ mol } N_2H_4} = 7.07 \text{ mol } NH_3 = 7.1 \text{ mol } NH_3$

Check: The units of the answer (mol NH_3) are correct. The magnitude is reasonable because it is greater than mol N_2H_4.

(b) **Given:** 2.28 mol N_2H_4 **Find:** mol NH_3

Conceptual Plan: mol N_2H_4 → mol NH_3

$$\frac{4 \text{ mol } NH_3}{3 \text{ mol } N_2H_4}$$

Solution: $2.28 \text{ mol } N_2H_4 \times \dfrac{4 \text{ mol } NH_3}{3 \text{ mol } N_2H_4} = 3.04 \text{ mol } NH_3 = 3.04 \text{ mol } NH_3$

Check: The units of the answer (mol NH_3) are correct. The magnitude is reasonable because it is greater than mol N_2H_4.

(c) **Given:** 32.5 g N_2H_4 **Find:** mol NH_3

Conceptual Plan: g N_2H_4 → mol N_2H_4 → mol NH_3

$$\frac{1 \text{ mol } N_2H_4}{32.05 \text{ g } N_2H_4} \quad \frac{4 \text{ mol } NH_3}{3 \text{ mol } N_2H_4}$$

Solution: $32.5 \text{ g } N_2H_4 \times \dfrac{1 \text{ mol } N_2H_4}{32.05 \text{ g } N_2H_4} \times \dfrac{4 \text{ mol } NH_3}{3 \text{ mol } N_2H_4} = 1.352 \text{ mol } NH_3 = 1.35 \text{ mol } NH_3$

Check: The units of the answer (mol NH_3) are correct. The magnitude is reasonable because there is about 1 mol N_2H_4 and the answer is greater than mol N_2H_4.

(d)   **Given:** 14.7 kg N_2H_4 **Find:** mol NH_3

Conceptual Plan: kg N_2H_4 → g N_2H_4 → mol N_2H_4 → mol NH_3

$$\frac{1000 \text{ g } N_2H_4}{\text{kg } N_2H_4} \qquad \frac{1 \text{ mol } N_2H_4}{32.05 \text{ g } N_2H_4} \qquad \frac{4 \text{ mol } NH_3}{3 \text{ mol } N_2H_4}$$

Solution:

$$14.7 \text{ kg } \cancel{N_2H_4} \times \frac{1000 \text{ g } \cancel{N_2H_4}}{\text{kg } \cancel{N_2H_4}} \times \frac{1 \text{ mol } \cancel{N_2H_4}}{32.05 \text{ g } \cancel{N_2H_4}} \times \frac{4 \text{ mol } NH_3}{3 \text{ mol } \cancel{N_2H_4}} = 611.5 \text{ mol } NH_3 = 612 \text{ mol } NH_3$$

Check: The units of the answer (mol NH_3) are correct. The magnitude is reasonable because 14.7 kg is about 459 mol N_2H_4 and the answer is greater than mol N_2H_4.

4.5   **Given:** 3 mol SiO_2 **Find:** mol C; mol SiC; mol CO

Conceptual Plan: mol SiO_2 → mol C → mol SiC → mol CO

$$\frac{3 \text{ mol C}}{1 \text{ mol } SiO_2} \qquad \frac{1 \text{ mol SiC}}{1 \text{ mol } SiO_2} \qquad \frac{2 \text{ mol CO}}{1 \text{ mol } SiO_2}$$

Solution: $3 \text{ mol } \cancel{SiO_2} \times \dfrac{3 \text{ mol C}}{1 \text{ mol } \cancel{SiO_2}} = 9 \text{ mol C}$ $3 \text{ mol } \cancel{SiO_2} \times \dfrac{1 \text{ mol SiC}}{1 \text{ mol } \cancel{SiO_2}} = 3 \text{ mol SiC}$

$$3 \text{ mol } \cancel{SiO_2} \times \frac{2 \text{ mol CO}}{1 \text{ mol } \cancel{SiO_2}} = 6 \text{ mol CO}$$

Given: 6 mol C   **Find:** mol SiO_2; mol SiC; mol CO

Conceptual Plan: mol C → mol SiO_2 → mol SiC → mol CO

$$\frac{1 \text{ mol } SiO_2}{3 \text{ mol C}} \qquad \frac{1 \text{ mol SiC}}{3 \text{ mol C}} \qquad \frac{2 \text{ mol CO}}{3 \text{ mol C}}$$

Solution: $6 \text{ mol } \cancel{C} \times \dfrac{1 \text{ mol } SiO_2}{3 \text{ mol } \cancel{C}} = 2 \text{ mol } SiO_2$ $6 \text{ mol } \cancel{C} \times \dfrac{1 \text{ mol SiC}}{3 \text{ mol } \cancel{C}} = 2 \text{ mol SiC}$

$$6 \text{ mol } \cancel{C} \times \frac{2 \text{ mol CO}}{3 \text{ mol } \cancel{C}} = 4 \text{ mol CO}$$

Given: 10 mol CO   **Find:** mol SiO_2; mol C; mol SiC

Conceptual Plan: mol CO → mol SiO_2 → mol C → mol SiC

$$\frac{1 \text{ mol } SiO_2}{2 \text{ mol CO}} \qquad \frac{3 \text{ mol C}}{2 \text{ mol CO}} \qquad \frac{1 \text{ mol SiC}}{2 \text{ mol CO}}$$

Solution: $10 \text{ mol } \cancel{CO} \times \dfrac{1 \text{ mol } SiO_2}{2 \text{ mol } \cancel{CO}} = 5.0 \text{ mol } SiO_2$ $10 \text{ mol } \cancel{C} \times \dfrac{3 \text{ mol C}}{2 \text{ mol } \cancel{CO}} = 15 \text{ mol C}$

$$10 \text{ mol } \cancel{CO} \times \frac{1 \text{ mol SiC}}{2 \text{ mol } \cancel{CO}} = 5.0 \text{ mol SiC}$$

Given: 2.8 mol SiO_2 **Find:** mol C; mol SiC; mol CO

Conceptual Plan: mol SiO_2 → mol C → mol SiC → mol CO

$$\frac{3 \text{ mol C}}{1 \text{ mol } SiO_2} \qquad \frac{1 \text{ mol SiC}}{1 \text{ mol } SiO_2} \qquad \frac{2 \text{ mol CO}}{1 \text{ mol } SiO_2}$$

Solution: $2.8 \text{ mol } \cancel{SiO_2} \times \dfrac{3 \text{ mol C}}{1 \text{ mol } \cancel{SiO_2}} = 8.4 \text{ mol C}$ $2.8 \text{ mol } \cancel{SiO_2} \times \dfrac{1 \text{ mol SiC}}{1 \text{ mol } \cancel{SiO_2}} = 2.8 \text{ mol SiC}$

$$2.8 \text{ mol } \cancel{SiO_2} \times \frac{2 \text{ mol CO}}{1 \text{ mol } \cancel{SiO_2}} = 5.6 \text{ mol CO}$$

Given: 1.55 mol C   **Find:** mol SiO_2; mol SiC; mol CO

Conceptual Plan: mol C → mol SiO_2 → mol SiC → mol CO

$$\frac{1 \text{ mol } SiO_2}{3 \text{ mol C}} \qquad \frac{1 \text{ mol SiC}}{3 \text{ mol C}} \qquad \frac{2 \text{ mol CO}}{3 \text{ mol C}}$$

Solution: $1.55 \text{ mol } \cancel{C} \times \dfrac{1 \text{ mol } SiO_2}{3 \text{ mol } \cancel{C}} = 0.517 \text{ mol } SiO_2$ $1.55 \text{ mol } \cancel{C} \times \dfrac{1 \text{ mol SiC}}{3 \text{ mol } \cancel{C}} = 0.517 \text{ mol SiC}$

$$1.55 \text{ mol } \cancel{C} \times \frac{2 \text{ mol CO}}{3 \text{ mol } \cancel{C}} = 1.03 \text{ mol CO}$$

SiO$_2$	C	SiC	CO
3	9	3	6
2	**6**	2	4
5.0	15	5.0	**10**
2.8	8.4	2.8	5.6
0.517	**1.55**	0.517	1.03

4.6   **Given:** 2 mol N$_2$H$_4$ **Find:** mol N$_2$O$_4$; mol N$_2$; mol H$_2$O

Conceptual Plan: mol N$_2$H$_4$ → mol N$_2$O$_4$ → mol N$_2$ → mol H$_2$O

$$\frac{1 \text{ mol N}_2\text{O}_4}{2 \text{ mol N}_2\text{H}_4} \qquad \frac{3 \text{ mol N}_2}{2 \text{ mol N}_2\text{H}_4} \qquad \frac{4 \text{ mol H}_2\text{O}}{2 \text{ mol N}_2\text{H}_4}$$

Solution: $2 \text{ mol N}_2\text{H}_4 \times \dfrac{1 \text{ mol N}_2\text{O}_4}{2 \text{ mol N}_2\text{H}_4} = 1 \text{ mol N}_2\text{O}_4 \qquad 2 \text{ mol N}_2\text{H}_4 \times \dfrac{3 \text{ mol N}_2}{2 \text{ mol N}_2\text{H}_4} = 3 \text{ mol N}_2$

$2 \text{ mol N}_2\text{H}_4 \times \dfrac{4 \text{ mol H}_2\text{O}}{2 \text{ mol N}_2\text{H}_4} = 4 \text{ mol H}_2\text{O}$

Given: 5 mol N$_2$O$_4$ **Find:** mol N$_2$H$_4$; mol N$_2$; mol H$_2$O

Conceptual Plan: mol N$_2$O$_4$ → mol N$_2$H$_4$ → mol N$_2$ → mol H$_2$O

$$\frac{2 \text{ mol N}_2\text{H}_4}{1 \text{ mol N}_2\text{O}_4} \qquad \frac{3 \text{ mol N}_2}{1 \text{ mol N}_2\text{O}_4} \qquad \frac{4 \text{ mol H}_2\text{O}}{1 \text{ mol N}_2\text{O}_4}$$

Solution: $5 \text{ mol N}_2\text{O}_4 \times \dfrac{2 \text{ mol 1 mol N}_2\text{H}_4}{1 \text{ mol N}_2\text{O}_4} = 10 \text{ mol N}_2\text{H}_4 \qquad 5 \text{ mol N}_2\text{O}_4 \times \dfrac{3 \text{ mol N}_2}{1 \text{ mol N}_2\text{O}_4} = 15 \text{ mol N}_2$

$5 \text{ mol N}_2\text{O}_4 \times \dfrac{4 \text{ mol H}_2\text{O}}{1 \text{ mol N}_2\text{O}_4} = 20 \text{ mol H}_2\text{O}$

Given: 10 mol H$_2$O   **Find:** mol N$_2$O$_4$; mol N$_2$O$_4$; mol N$_2$

Conceptual Plan: mol H$_2$O → mol N$_2$H$_4$ → mol N$_2$ → mol N$_2$O$_4$

$$\frac{2 \text{ mol N}_2\text{H}_4}{4 \text{ mol H}_2\text{O}} \qquad \frac{3 \text{ mol N}_2}{4 \text{ mol H}_2\text{O}} \qquad \frac{1 \text{ mol N}_2\text{O}_4}{4 \text{ mol H}_2\text{O}}$$

Solution: $10 \text{ mol H}_2\text{O} \times \dfrac{2 \text{ mol N}_2\text{H}_4}{4 \text{ mol H}_2\text{O}} = 5.0 \text{ mol N}_2\text{H}_4 \qquad 10 \text{ mol H}_2\text{O} \times \dfrac{3 \text{ mol N}_2}{4 \text{ mol H}_2\text{O}} = 7.5 \text{ mol N}_2$

$10 \text{ mol H}_2\text{O} \times \dfrac{1 \text{ mol N}_2\text{O}_4}{4 \text{ mol H}_2\text{O}} = 2.5 \text{ mol N}_2\text{O}_4$

Given: 2.5 mol N$_2$H$_4$ **Find:** mol N$_2$O$_4$; mol N$_2$; mol H$_2$O

Conceptual Plan: mol N$_2$H$_4$ → mol N$_2$O$_4$ → mol N$_2$ → mol H$_2$O

$$\frac{1 \text{ mol N}_2\text{O}_4}{2 \text{ mol N}_2\text{H}_4} \qquad \frac{3 \text{ mol N}_2}{2 \text{ mol N}_2\text{H}_4} \qquad \frac{4 \text{ mol H}_2\text{O}}{2 \text{ mol N}_2\text{H}_4}$$

Solution: $2.5 \text{ mol N}_2\text{H}_4 \times \dfrac{1 \text{ mol N}_2\text{O}_4}{2 \text{ mol N}_2\text{H}_4} = 1.3 \text{ mol N}_2\text{O}_4 \qquad 2.5 \text{ mol N}_2\text{H}_4 \times \dfrac{3 \text{ mol N}_2}{2 \text{ mol N}_2\text{H}_4} = 3.8 \text{ mol N}_2$

$2.5 \text{ mol N}_2\text{H}_4 \times \dfrac{4 \text{ mol H}_2\text{O}}{2 \text{ mol N}_2\text{H}_4} = 5.0 \text{ mol H}_2\text{O}$

Given: 4.2 mol N$_2$O$_4$ **Find:** mol N$_2$H$_4$; mol N$_2$; mol H$_2$O

Conceptual Plan: mol N$_2$O$_4$ → mol N$_2$H$_4$ → mol N$_2$ → mol H$_2$O

$$\frac{2 \text{ mol N}_2\text{H}_4}{1 \text{ mol N}_2\text{O}_4} \qquad \frac{3 \text{ mol N}_2}{1 \text{ mol N}_2\text{O}_4} \qquad \frac{4 \text{ mol H}_2\text{O}}{1 \text{ mol N}_2\text{O}_4}$$

Solution:

$4.2 \text{ mol N}_2\text{O}_4 \times \dfrac{2 \text{ mol N}_2\text{H}_4}{1 \text{ mol N}_2\text{O}_4} = 8.4 \text{ mol N}_2\text{H}_4 \qquad 4.2 \text{ mol N}_2\text{O}_4 \times \dfrac{3 \text{ mol N}_2}{1 \text{ mol N}_2\text{O}_4} = 12.6 \text{ mol N}_2 = 13 \text{ mol N}_2$

$4.2 \text{ mol N}_2\text{O}_4 \times \dfrac{4 \text{ mol H}_2\text{O}}{1 \text{ mol N}_2\text{O}_4} = 16.8 \text{ mol H}_2\text{O} = 17 \text{ mol H}_2\text{O}$

Given: 11.8 mol N_2 **Find:** mol N_2H_4; mol N_2O_4; mol H_2O

Conceptual Plan: mol N_2 → mol N_2H_4 → mol N_2O_4 → mol H_2O

$$\frac{2 \text{ mol } N_2H_4}{3 \text{ mol } N_2} \qquad \frac{1 \text{ mol } N_2O_4}{3 \text{ mol } N_2} \qquad \frac{4 \text{ mol } H_2O}{3 \text{ mol } N_2}$$

Solution: $11.8 \text{ mol } N_2 \times \dfrac{2 \text{ mol } N_2H_4}{3 \text{ mol } N_2} = 7.87 \text{ mol } N_2H_4 \qquad 11.8 \text{ mol } N_2 \times \dfrac{1 \text{ mol } N_2O_4}{3 \text{ mol } N_2} = 3.93 \text{ mol } N_2$

$$11.8 \text{ mol } N_2 \times \frac{4 \text{ mol } H_2O}{3 \text{ mol } N_2} = 15.7 \text{ mol } H_2O$$

N_2H_2	N_2O_4	N_2	H_2O
2	1	3	4
10	**5**	15	20
5	2.5	7.5	**10**
2.5	1.3	3.8	5.0
8.4	**4.2**	13	17
7.87	3.93	**11.8**	15.7

4.7 **Given:** 4.8 g Fe **Find:** g HBr; g H_2

Conceptual Plan: g Fe → mol Fe → mol HBr → g HBr

$$\frac{1 \text{ mol Fe}}{55.8 \text{ g Fe}} \qquad \frac{2 \text{ mol HBr}}{1 \text{ mol Fe}} \qquad \frac{80.9 \text{ g HBr}}{1 \text{ mol HBr}}$$

g Fe → mol Fe → mol H_2 → g H_2

$$\frac{1 \text{ mol Fe}}{55.8 \text{ g Fe}} \qquad \frac{1 \text{ mol } H_2}{1 \text{ mol Fe}} \qquad \frac{2.02 \text{ g } H_2}{1 \text{ mol } H_2}$$

Solution: $4.8 \text{ g Fe} \times \dfrac{1 \text{ mol Fe}}{55.8 \text{ g Fe}} \times \dfrac{2 \text{ mol HBr}}{1 \text{ mol Fe}} \times \dfrac{80.9 \text{ g HBr}}{1 \text{ mol HBr}} = 13.9 \text{ g HBr} = 14 \text{ g HBr}$

$4.8 \text{ g Fe} \times \dfrac{1 \text{ mol Fe}}{55.8 \text{ g Fe}} \times \dfrac{1 \text{ mol } H_2}{1 \text{ mol Fe}} \times \dfrac{2.02 \text{ g } H_2}{1 \text{ mol } H_2} = 0.174 \text{ g } H_2 = 0.17 \text{ g } H_2$

Check: The units of the answers (g HBr, g H_2) are correct. The magnitude of the answers is reasonable because the molar mass of HBr is greater than Fe and the molar mass of H_2 is much less than Fe.

4.8 **Given:** 12.7 g Al **Find:** g H_2SO_4; g H_2

Conceptual Plan: g Al → mol Al → mol H_2SO_4 → g H_2SO_4

$$\frac{1 \text{ mol Al}}{26.98 \text{ g Al}} \qquad \frac{3 \text{ mol } H_2SO_4}{2 \text{ mol Al}} \qquad \frac{98.09 \text{ g } H_2SO_4}{1 \text{ mol } H_2SO_4}$$

g Al → mol Al → mol H_2 → g H_2

$$\frac{1 \text{ mol Al}}{26.98 \text{ g Al}} \qquad \frac{3 \text{ mol } H_2}{2 \text{ mol Al}} \qquad \frac{2.016 \text{ g } H_2}{1 \text{ mol } H_2}$$

Solution: $12.7 \text{ g Al} \times \dfrac{1 \text{ mol Al}}{26.98 \text{ g Al}} \times \dfrac{3 \text{ mol } H_2SO_4}{2 \text{ mol Al}} \times \dfrac{98.09 \text{ g } H_2SO_4}{1 \text{ mol } H_2SO_4} = 69.26 \text{ g } H_2SO_4 = 69.3 \text{ g } H_2SO_4$

$12.7 \text{ g Al} \times \dfrac{1 \text{ mol Al}}{26.98 \text{ g Al}} \times \dfrac{3 \text{ mol } H_2}{2 \text{ mol Al}} \times \dfrac{2.016 \text{ g } H_2}{1 \text{ mol } H_2} = 1.423 \text{ g } H_2 = 1.42 \text{ g } H_2$

Check: The units of the answers (g H_2SO_4, g H_2) are correct. The magnitude of the answers is reasonable because the molar mass of H_2SO_4 is greater than Al and the molar mass of H_2 is much less than Al.

4.9 (a) **Given:** 2.5 g Ba **Find:** g $BaCl_2$

Conceptual Plan: g Ba → mol Ba → mol $BaCl_2$ → g $BaCl_2$

$$\frac{1 \text{ mol Ba}}{137.33 \text{ g Ba}} \qquad \frac{1 \text{ mol } BaCl_2}{1 \text{ mol Ba}} \qquad \frac{208.23 \text{ g } BaCl_2}{1 \text{ mol } BaCl_2}$$

Solution: $2.5 \text{ g Ba} \times \dfrac{1 \text{ mol Ba}}{137.33 \text{ g Ba}} \times \dfrac{1 \text{ mol } BaCl_2}{1 \text{ mol Ba}} \times \dfrac{208.23 \text{ g } BaCl_2}{1 \text{ mol } BaCl_2} = 3.791 \text{ g } BaCl_2 = 3.8 \text{ g } BaCl_2$

Check: The units of the answer (g BaCl$_2$) are correct. The magnitude of the answer is reasonable because it is larger than grams Ba.

(b) **Given:** 2.5 g CaO   **Find:** g CaCO$_3$
Conceptual Plan: g CaO → mol CaO → mol CaCO$_3$ → g CaCO$_3$

$$\frac{1 \text{ mol CaO}}{56.08 \text{ g CaO}} \qquad \frac{1 \text{ mol CaCO}_3}{1 \text{ mol CaO}} \qquad \frac{100.09 \text{ g CaCO}_3}{1 \text{ mol CaCO}_3}$$

Solution:

$$2.5 \text{ g CaO} \times \frac{1 \text{ mol CaO}}{56.08 \text{ g CaO}} \times \frac{1 \text{ mol CaCO}_3}{1 \text{ mol CaO}} \times \frac{100.09 \text{ g CaCO}_3}{1 \text{ mol CaCO}_3} = 4.\underline{4}62 \text{ g CaCO}_3 = 4.5 \text{ g CaCO}_3$$

Check: The units of the answer (g CaCO$_3$) are correct. The magnitude of the answer is reasonable because it is larger than grams CaO.

(c) **Given:** 2.5 g Mg   **Find:** g MgO
Conceptual Plan: g Mg → mol Mg → mol MgO → g MgO

$$\frac{1 \text{ mol Mg}}{24.31 \text{ g Mg}} \qquad \frac{1 \text{ mol MgO}}{1 \text{ mol Mg}} \qquad \frac{40.31 \text{ g MgO}}{1 \text{ mol MgO}}$$

Solution: $2.5 \text{ g Mg} \times \dfrac{1 \text{ mol Mg}}{24.31 \text{ g Mg}} \times \dfrac{1 \text{ mol MgO}}{1 \text{ mol Mg}} \times \dfrac{40.31 \text{ g MgO}}{1 \text{ mol MgO}} = 4.\underline{1}45 \text{ g MgO} = 4.1 \text{ g MgO}$

Check: The units of the answer (g MgO) are correct. The magnitude of the answer is reasonable because it is larger than grams Mg.

(d) **Given:** 2.5 g Al   **Find:** g Al$_2$O$_3$
Conceptual Plan: g Al → mol Al → mol Al$_2$O$_3$ → g Al$_2$O$_3$

$$\frac{1 \text{ mol Al}}{26.98 \text{ g Al}} \qquad \frac{2 \text{ mol Al}_2\text{O}_3}{4 \text{ mol Al}} \qquad \frac{101.96 \text{ g Al}_2\text{O}_3}{1 \text{ mol Al}_2\text{O}_3}$$

Solution: $2.5 \text{ g Al} \times \dfrac{1 \text{ mol Al}}{26.98 \text{ g Al}} \times \dfrac{2 \text{ mol Al}_2\text{O}_3}{4 \text{ mol Al}} \times \dfrac{101.96 \text{ g Al}_2\text{O}_3}{1 \text{ mol Al}_2\text{O}_3} = 4.\underline{7}24 \text{ g Al}_2\text{O}_3 = 4.7 \text{ g Al}_2\text{O}_3$

Check: The units of the answer (g Al$_2$O$_3$) are correct. The magnitude of the answer is reasonable because it is larger than grams Al.

4.10 (a) **Given:** 10.4 g Cl$_2$ **Find:** g KCl
Conceptual Plan: g Cl$_2$ → mol Cl$_2$ → mol KCl → g KCl

$$\frac{1 \text{ mol Cl}_2}{70.90 \text{ g Cl}_2} \qquad \frac{2 \text{ mol KCl}}{1 \text{ mol Cl}_2} \qquad \frac{74.55 \text{ g KCl}}{1 \text{ mol KCl}}$$

Solution: $10.4 \text{ g Cl}_2 \times \dfrac{1 \text{ mol Cl}_2}{70.90 \text{ g Cl}_2} \times \dfrac{2 \text{ mol KCl}}{1 \text{ mol Cl}_2} \times \dfrac{74.55 \text{ g KCl}}{1 \text{ mol KCl}} = 21.\underline{8}7 \text{ g KCl} = 21.9 \text{ g KCl}$

Check: The units of the answer (g KCl) are correct. The magnitude of the answer is reasonable because it is larger than grams Cl$_2$.

(b) **Given:** 10.4 g Br$_2$ **Find:** g KBr
Conceptual Plan: g Br$_2$ → mol Br$_2$ → mol KBr → g KBr

$$\frac{1 \text{ mol Br}_2}{159.80 \text{ g Br}_2} \qquad \frac{2 \text{ mol KBr}}{1 \text{ mol Br}_2} \qquad \frac{119.00 \text{ g KBr}}{1 \text{ mol KBr}}$$

Solution: $10.4 \text{ g Br}_2 \times \dfrac{1 \text{ mol Br}_2}{159.80 \text{ g Br}_2} \times \dfrac{2 \text{ mol KBr}}{1 \text{ mol Br}_2} \times \dfrac{119.00 \text{ g KBr}}{1 \text{ mol KBr}} = 15.\underline{4}9 \text{ g KBr} = 15.5 \text{ g KBr}$

Check: The units of the answer (g KBr) are correct. The magnitude of the answer is reasonable because it is larger than grams Br$_2$.

(c) **Given:** 10.4 g O$_2$ **Find:** g Cr$_2$O$_3$
Conceptual Plan: g O$_2$ → mol O$_2$ → mol Cr$_2$O$_3$ → g Cr$_2$O$_3$

$$\frac{1 \text{ mol O}_2}{32.00 \text{ g O}_2} \qquad \frac{2 \text{ mol Cr}_2\text{O}_3}{3 \text{ mol O}_2} \qquad \frac{152.00 \text{ g Cr}_2\text{O}_3}{1 \text{ mol Cr}_2\text{O}_3}$$

Solution:

$$10.4 \text{ g } \cancel{O_2} \times \frac{1 \text{ mol } \cancel{O_2}}{32.00 \text{ g } \cancel{O_2}} \times \frac{2 \text{ mol } \cancel{Cr_2O_3}}{3 \text{ mol } \cancel{O_2}} \times \frac{152.00 \text{ g } Cr_2O_3}{1 \text{ mol } \cancel{Cr_2O_3}} = 32.\underline{9}3 \text{ g } Cr_2O_3 = 32.9 \text{ g } Cr_2O_3$$

Check: The units of the answer (g Cr_2O_3) are correct. The magnitude of the answer is reasonable because it is larger than g Cr.

(d)   **Given:** 10.4 g Sr   **Find:** g SrO

       Conceptual Plan: g Sr → mol Sr → mol SrO → g SrO

$$\frac{1 \text{ mol Sr}}{87.62 \text{ g Sr}} \qquad \frac{2 \text{ mol SrO}}{2 \text{ mol Sr}} \qquad \frac{103.62 \text{ g SrO}}{1 \text{ mol SrO}}$$

       Solution: $10.4 \text{ g } \cancel{Sr} \times \dfrac{1 \text{ mol } \cancel{Sr}}{87.62 \text{ g } \cancel{Sr}} \times \dfrac{2 \text{ mol } \cancel{SrO}}{2 \text{ mol } \cancel{Sr}} \times \dfrac{103.62 \text{ g SrO}}{1 \text{ mol } \cancel{SrO}} = 12.\underline{2}99 \text{ g SrO} = 12.3 \text{ g SrO}$

       Check: The units of the answer (g SrO) are correct. The magnitude of the answer is reasonable because it is larger than g Sr.

4.11   (a)   **Given:** 4.85 g NaOH   **Find:** g HCl

       Conceptual Plan: g NaOH → mol NaOH → mol HCl → g HCl

$$\frac{1 \text{ mol NaOH}}{40.00 \text{ g NaOH}} \qquad \frac{1 \text{ mol HCl}}{1 \text{ mol NaOH}} \qquad \frac{36.46 \text{ g HCl}}{1 \text{ mol HCl}}$$

       Solution: $4.85 \text{ g } \cancel{NaOH} \times \dfrac{1 \text{ mol } \cancel{NaOH}}{40.00 \text{ g } \cancel{NaOH}} \times \dfrac{1 \text{ mol } \cancel{HCl}}{1 \text{ mol } \cancel{NaOH}} \times \dfrac{36.46 \text{ g HCl}}{1 \text{ mol } \cancel{HCl}} = 4.4\underline{2}1 \text{ g HCl} = 4.42 \text{ g HCl}$

       Check: The units of the answer (g HCl) are correct. The magnitude of the answer is reasonable because it is less than g NaOH.

(b)   **Given:** 4.85 g $Ca(OH)_2$ **Find:** g HNO_3

       Conceptual Plan: g Ca(OH)$_2$ → mol Ca(OH)$_2$ → mol HNO$_3$ → g HNO$_3$

$$\frac{1 \text{ mol Ca(OH)}_2}{74.10 \text{ g Ca(OH)}_2} \qquad \frac{2 \text{ mol HNO}_3}{1 \text{ mol Ca(OH)}_2} \qquad \frac{63.02 \text{ g HNO}_3}{1 \text{ mol HNO}_3}$$

   Solution: $4.85 \text{ g } \cancel{Ca(OH)_2} \times \dfrac{1 \text{ mol } \cancel{Ca(OH)_2}}{74.10 \text{ g } \cancel{Ca(OH)_2}} \times \dfrac{2 \text{ mol } \cancel{HNO_3}}{1 \text{ mol } \cancel{Ca(OH)_2}} \times \dfrac{63.02 \text{ g HNO}_3}{1 \text{ mol } \cancel{HNO_3}} = 8.2\underline{5}0 \text{ g HNO}_3 = 8.25 \text{ g HNO}_3$

       Check: The units of the answer (g HNO_3) are correct. The magnitude of the answer is reasonable because it is more than g $Ca(OH)_2$.

(c)   **Given:** 4.85 g KOH   **Find:** g H_2SO_4

       Conceptual Plan: g KOH → mol KOH → mol H$_2$SO$_4$ → g H$_2$SO$_4$

$$\frac{1 \text{ mol KOH}}{56.11 \text{ g KOH}} \qquad \frac{1 \text{ mol H}_2\text{SO}_4}{2 \text{ mol KOH}} \qquad \frac{98.09 \text{ g H}_2\text{SO}_4}{1 \text{ mol H}_2\text{SO}_4}$$

       Solution: $4.85 \text{ g } \cancel{KOH} \times \dfrac{1 \text{ mol } \cancel{KOH}}{56.11 \text{ g } \cancel{KOH}} \times \dfrac{1 \text{ mol } \cancel{H_2SO_4}}{2 \text{ mol } \cancel{KOH}} \times \dfrac{98.09 \text{ g H}_2\text{SO}_4}{1 \text{ mol } \cancel{H_2SO_4}} = 4.2\underline{3}9 \text{ g H}_2\text{SO}_4 = 4.24 \text{ g H}_2\text{SO}_4$

       Check: The units of the answer (g H_2SO_4) are correct. The magnitude of the answer is reasonable because it is less than g KOH.

4.12   (a)   **Given:** 55.8 g $Pb(NO_3)_2$ **Find:** g KI

       Conceptual Plan: g Pb(NO$_3$)$_2$ → mol Pb(NO$_3$)$_2$ → mol KI → g KI

$$\frac{1 \text{ mol Pb(NO}_3)_2}{331.2 \text{ g Pb(NO}_3)_2} \qquad \frac{2 \text{ mol KI}}{1 \text{ mol Pb(NO}_3)_2} \qquad \frac{166.00 \text{ g KI}}{1 \text{ mol KI}}$$

       Solution: $55.8 \text{ g } \cancel{Pb(NO_3)_2} \times \dfrac{1 \text{ mol } \cancel{Pb(NO_3)_2}}{331.2 \text{ g } \cancel{Pb(NO_3)_2}} \times \dfrac{2 \text{ mol } \cancel{KI}}{1 \text{ mol } \cancel{Pb(NO_3)_2}} \times \dfrac{166.00 \text{ g KI}}{1 \text{ mol } \cancel{KI}} = 55.\underline{9}3 \text{ g KI} = 55.9 \text{ g KI}$

       Check: The units of the answer (g KI) are correct. The magnitude of the answer is reasonable because there are 2 mol KI for each $Pb(NO_3)_2$.

(b)   **Given:** 55.8 g $CuCl_2$ **Find:** g Na_2CO_3

       Conceptual Plan: g CuCl$_2$ → mol CuCl$_2$ → mol Na$_2$CO$_3$ → g Na$_2$CO$_3$

$$\frac{1 \text{ mol CuCl}_2}{134.45 \text{ g CuCl}_2} \qquad \frac{1 \text{ mol Na}_2\text{CO}_3}{1 \text{ mol CuCl}_2} \qquad \frac{105.99 \text{ g Na}_2\text{CO}_3}{1 \text{ mol Na}_2\text{CO}_3}$$

Solution: $55.8 \text{ g } \cancel{CuCl_2} \times \dfrac{1 \text{ mol } \cancel{CuCl_2}}{134.45 \text{ g } \cancel{CuCl_2}} \times \dfrac{1 \text{ mol } Na_2CO_3}{1 \text{ mol } \cancel{CuCl_2}} \times \dfrac{105.99 \text{ g } Na_2CO_3}{1 \text{ mol } \cancel{Na_2CO_3}} = 43.\underline{9}9 \text{ g } Na_2CO_3 = 44.0 \text{ g } Na_2CO_3$

Check: The units of the answer (g Na_2CO_3) are correct. The magnitude of the answer is reasonable because it is less than g $CuCl_2$.

(c) **Given:** 55.8 g $Sr(NO_3)_2$ **Find:** g K_2SO_4

Conceptual Plan: g $Sr(NO_3)_2 \rightarrow$ mol $Sr(NO_3)_2 \rightarrow$ mol $K_2SO_4 \rightarrow$ g K_2SO_4

$$\dfrac{1 \text{ mol } Sr(NO_3)_2}{211.64 \text{ g } Sr(NO_3)_2} \qquad \dfrac{1 \text{ mol } K_2SO_4}{1 \text{ mol } Sr(NO_3)_2} \qquad \dfrac{174.27 \text{ g } K_2SO_4}{1 \text{ mol } K_2SO_4}$$

Solution: $55.8 \text{ g } \cancel{Sr(NO_3)_2} \times \dfrac{1 \text{ mol } \cancel{Sr(NO_3)_2}}{211.64 \text{ g } \cancel{Sr(NO_3)_2}} \times \dfrac{1 \text{ mol } \cancel{K_2SO_4}}{1 \text{ mol } \cancel{Sr(NO_3)_2}} \times \dfrac{174.27 \text{ g } K_2SO_4}{1 \text{ mol } \cancel{K_2SO_4}} = 45.\underline{9}47 \text{ g } K_2SO_4 = 45.9 \text{ g } K_2SO_4$

Check: The units of the answer (g K_2SO_4) are correct. The magnitude of the answer is reasonable because it is less than g $Sr(NO_3)_2$.

Limiting Reactant, Theoretical Yield, and Percent Yield

4.13   (a) **Given:** 2 mol Na; 2 mol Br_2 **Find:** limiting reactant

Conceptual Plan: mol Na $\rightarrow$ mol NaBr

$$\dfrac{2 \text{ mol NaBr}}{2 \text{ mol Na}} \qquad \rightarrow \textbf{ smallest mol amount determines limiting reactant}$$

mol $Br_2 \rightarrow$ mol NaBr

$$\dfrac{2 \text{ mol NaBr}}{1 \text{ mol } Br_2}$$

Solution: $2 \text{ } \cancel{\text{mol Na}} \times \dfrac{2 \text{ mol NaBr}}{2 \text{ } \cancel{\text{mol Na}}} = 2 \text{ mol NaBr}$

$2 \text{ } \cancel{\text{mol } Br_2} \times \dfrac{2 \text{ mol NaBr}}{1 \text{ } \cancel{\text{mol } Br_2}} = 4 \text{ mol NaBr}$

Na is the limiting reactant.

Check: The answer is reasonable because Na produced the smallest amount of product.

(b) **Given:** 1.8 mol Na; 1.4 mol Br_2 **Find:** limiting reactant

Conceptual Plan: mol Na $\rightarrow$ mol NaBr

$$\dfrac{2 \text{ mol NaBr}}{2 \text{ mol Na}} \qquad \rightarrow \textbf{ smallest mol amount determines limiting reactant}$$

mol $Br_2 \rightarrow$ mol NaBr

$$\dfrac{2 \text{ mol NaBr}}{1 \text{ mol } Br_2}$$

Solution: $1.8 \text{ } \cancel{\text{mol Na}} \times \dfrac{2 \text{ mol NaBr}}{2 \text{ } \cancel{\text{mol Na}}} = 1.8 \text{ mol NaBr}$

$1.4 \text{ } \cancel{\text{mol } Br_2} \times \dfrac{2 \text{ mol NaBr}}{1 \text{ } \cancel{\text{mol } Br_2}} = 2.8 \text{ mol NaBr}$

Na is the limiting reactant.

Check: The answer is reasonable because Na produced the smallest amount of product.

(c) **Given:** 2.5 mol Na; 1 mol Br_2 **Find:** limiting reactant

Conceptual Plan: mol Na $\rightarrow$ mol NaBr

$$\dfrac{2 \text{ mol NaBr}}{2 \text{ mol Na}} \qquad \rightarrow \textbf{ smallest mol amount determines limiting reactant}$$

mol $Br_2 \rightarrow$ mol NaBr

$$\dfrac{2 \text{ mol NaBr}}{1 \text{ mol } Br_2}$$

Solution: $2.5 \text{ } \cancel{\text{mol Na}} \times \dfrac{2 \text{ mol NaBr}}{2 \text{ } \cancel{\text{mol Na}}} = 2.5 \text{ mol NaBr}$

$1 \text{ } \cancel{\text{mol } Br_2} \times \dfrac{2 \text{ mol NaBr}}{1 \text{ } \cancel{\text{mol } Br_2}} = 2 \text{ mol NaBr}$

Br_2 is the limiting reactant.

Check: The answer is reasonable because Br_2 produced the smallest amount of product.

(d)   **Given:** 12.6 mol Na; 6.9 mol Br_2 **Find:** limiting reactant
Conceptual Plan: mol Na → mol NaBr

$$\frac{2 \text{ mol NaBr}}{2 \text{ mol Na}} \qquad \rightarrow \textbf{ smallest mol amount determines limiting reactant}$$

mol Br_2 → mol NaBr

$$\frac{2 \text{ mol NaBr}}{1 \text{ mol } Br_2}$$

Solution: $12.6 \text{ mol Na} \times \dfrac{2 \text{ mol NaBr}}{2 \text{ mol Na}} = 12.6 \text{ mol NaBr}$

$6.9 \text{ mol } Br_2 \times \dfrac{2 \text{ mol NaBr}}{1 \text{ mol } Br_2} = \underline{13.8} \text{ mol NaBr} = 14 \text{ mol NaBr}$

Na is the limiting reactant.

Check: The answer is reasonable because Na produced the smallest amount of product.

4.14   (a)   **Given:** 1 mol Al; 1 mol O_2 **Find:** limiting reactant
Conceptual Plan: mol Al → mol Al_2O_3

$$\frac{2 \text{ mol } Al_2O_3}{4 \text{ mol Al}} \qquad \rightarrow \textbf{ smallest mol amount determines limiting reactant}$$

mol O_2 → mol Al_2O_3

$$\frac{2 \text{ mol } Al_2O_3}{3 \text{ mol } O_2}$$

Solution: $1 \text{ mol Al} \times \dfrac{2 \text{ mol } Al_2O_3}{4 \text{ mol Al}} = 0.5 \text{ mol } Al_2O_3$

$1 \text{ mol } O_2 \times \dfrac{2 \text{ mol } Al_2O_3}{3 \text{ mol } O_2} = 0.67 \text{ mol } Al_2O_3$

Al is the limiting reactant.

Check: The answer is reasonable because Al produced the smallest amount of product.

(b)   **Given:** 4 mol Al; 2.6 mol O_2 **Find:** limiting reactant
Conceptual Plan: mol Al → mol Al_2O_3

$$\frac{2 \text{ mol } Al_2O_3}{4 \text{ mol Al}} \qquad \rightarrow \textbf{ smallest mol amount determines limiting reactant}$$

mol O_2 → mol Al_2O_3

$$\frac{2 \text{ mol } Al_2O_3}{3 \text{ mol } O_2}$$

Solution: $4 \text{ mol Al} \times \dfrac{2 \text{ mol } Al_2O_3}{4 \text{ mol Al}} = 2 \text{ mol } Al_2O_3$

$2.6 \text{ mol } O_2 \times \dfrac{2 \text{ mol } Al_2O_3}{3 \text{ mol } O_2} = 1.7 \text{ mol } Al_2O_3$

O_2 is the limiting reactant.

Check: The answer is reasonable because O_2 produced the smallest amount of product.

(c)   **Given:** 16 mol Al; 13 mol O_2 **Find:** limiting reactant
Conceptual Plan: mol Al → mol Al_2O_3

$$\frac{2 \text{ mol } Al_2O_3}{4 \text{ mol Al}} \qquad \rightarrow \textbf{ smallest mol amount determines limiting reactant}$$

mol O_2 → mol Al_2O_3

$$\frac{2 \text{ mol } Al_2O_3}{3 \text{ mol } O_2}$$

Solution: $16 \text{ mol Al} \times \dfrac{2 \text{ mol } Al_2O_3}{4 \text{ mol Al}} = 8.0 \text{ mol } Al_2O_3$

$13 \text{ mol } O_2 \times \dfrac{2 \text{ mol } Al_2O_3}{3 \text{ mol } O_2} = 8.67 \text{ mol } Al_2O_3$

Al is the limiting reactant.

Check: The answer is reasonable because Al produced the smallest amount of product.

(d)   **Given:** 7.4 mol Al; 6.5 mol O_2 **Find:** limiting reactant
Conceptual Plan: mol Al → mol Al_2O_3

$$\frac{2 \text{ mol Al}_2O_3}{4 \text{ mol Al}} \quad \rightarrow \textbf{ smallest mol amount determines limiting reactant}$$

mol O_2 → mol Al_2O_3

$$\frac{2 \text{ mol Al}_2O_3}{3 \text{ mol O}_2}$$

Solution: $7.4 \text{ mol Al} \times \dfrac{2 \text{ mol Al}_2O_3}{4 \text{ mol Al}} = 3.7 \text{ mol Al}_2O_3$

$6.5 \text{ mol O}_2 \times \dfrac{2 \text{ mol Al}_2O_3}{3 \text{ mol O}_2} = 4.3 \text{ mol Al}_2O_3$

Al is the limiting reactant.

Check: The answer is reasonable because Al produced the smallest amount of product.

4.15   The greatest number of Cl_2 molecules will be formed from reaction mixture b and would be 3 molecules Cl_2.

(a)   **Given:** 7 molecules HCl; 1 molecule O_2 **Find:** theoretical yield Cl_2
Conceptual Plan: molecules HCl → molecules Cl_2

$$\frac{2 \text{ molecules Cl}_2}{4 \text{ molecules HCl}} \quad \rightarrow \textbf{ smallest mol amount determines limiting reactant}$$

molecules O_2 → molecules Cl_2

$$\frac{2 \text{ molecules Cl}_2}{1 \text{ molecule O}_2}$$

Solution: $7 \text{ molecules HCl} \times \dfrac{2 \text{ molecules Cl}_2}{4 \text{ molecules HCl}} = 3 \text{ molecules Cl}_2$

$1 \text{ molecule O}_2 \times \dfrac{2 \text{ molecules Cl}_2}{1 \text{ molecule O}_2} = 2 \text{ molecules Cl}_2$

theoretical yield $= 2$ molecules Cl_2

(b)   **Given:** 6 molecules HCl; 3 molecules O_2 **Find:** theoretical yield Cl_2
Conceptual Plan: molecules HCl → molecules Cl_2

$$\frac{2 \text{ molecules Cl}_2}{4 \text{ molecules HCl}} \quad \rightarrow \textbf{ smallest mol amount determines limiting reactant}$$

molecules O_2 → molecules Cl_2

$$\frac{2 \text{ molecules Cl}_2}{1 \text{ molecule O}_2}$$

Solution: $6 \text{ molecules HCl} \times \dfrac{2 \text{ molecules Cl}_2}{4 \text{ molecules HCl}} = 3 \text{ molecules Cl}_2$

$3 \text{ molecules O}_2 \times \dfrac{2 \text{ molecules Cl}_2}{1 \text{ molecule O}_2} = 6 \text{ molecules Cl}_2$

theoretical yield $= 3$ molecules Cl_2

(c)   **Given:** 4 molecules HCl; 5 molecules O_2 **Find:** theoretical yield Cl_2
Conceptual Plan: molecules HCl → molecules Cl_2

$$\frac{2 \text{ molecules Cl}_2}{4 \text{ molecules HCl}} \quad \rightarrow \textbf{ smallest mol amount determines limiting reactant}$$

molecules O_2 → molecules Cl_2

$$\frac{2 \text{ molecules Cl}_2}{1 \text{ molecule O}_2}$$

Solution: $4 \text{ molecules HCl} \times \dfrac{2 \text{ molecules Cl}_2}{4 \text{ molecules HCl}} = 2 \text{ molecules Cl}_2$

$5 \text{ molecules O}_2 \times \dfrac{2 \text{ molecules Cl}_2}{1 \text{ molecule O}_2} = 10 \text{ molecules Cl}_2$

theoretical yield $= 2$ molecules Cl_2

Check: The units of the answer (molecules Cl_2) are correct. The answer is reasonable based on the limiting reactant in each mixture.

4.16   The greatest number of CO_2 molecules will be formed from reaction mixture a and would be 2 molecules CO_2.

(a)   **Given:** 3 molecules CH_3OH; 3 molecules O_2 **Find:** theoretical yield CO_2
Conceptual Plan: molecules CH_3OH → molecules CO_2

$$\frac{2 \text{ molecules } CO_2}{2 \text{ molecules } CH_3OH} \qquad \rightarrow \textbf{ smallest mol amount determines}$$
$$\textbf{limiting reactant}$$

molecules O_2 → molecules CO_2

$$\frac{2 \text{ molecules } CO_2}{3 \text{ molecules } O_2}$$

Solution: 3 molecules CH_3OH $\times \dfrac{2 \text{ molecules } CO_2}{2 \text{ molecules } CH_3OH} = 3$ molecules CO_2

3 molecules O_2 $\times \dfrac{2 \text{ molecules } CO_2}{3 \text{ molecules } O_2} = 2$ molecules CO_2

theoretical yield $= 2$ molecules CO_2

(b)   **Given:** 1 molecule CH_3OH; 6 molecules O_2 **Find:** theoretical yield CO_2
Conceptual Plan: molecules CH_3OH → molecules CO_2

$$\frac{2 \text{ molecules } CO_2}{2 \text{ molecules } CH_3OH} \qquad \rightarrow \textbf{ smallest mol amount determines}$$
$$\textbf{limiting reactant}$$

molecules O_2 → molecules CO_2

$$\frac{2 \text{ molecules } CO_2}{3 \text{ molecules } O_2}$$

Solution: 1 molecule CH_3OH $\times \dfrac{2 \text{ molecules } CO_2}{2 \text{ molecules } CH_3OH} = 1$ molecule CO_2

6 molecules O_2 $\times \dfrac{2 \text{ molecules } CO_2}{3 \text{ molecules } O_2} = 4$ molecules CO_2

theoretical yield $= 1$ molecule CO_2

(c)   **Given:** 4 molecules CH_3OH; 2 molecules O_2 **Find:** theoretical yield CO_2
Conceptual Plan: molecules CH_3OH → molecules CO_2

$$\frac{2 \text{ molecules } CO_2}{2 \text{ molecules } CH_3OH} \qquad \rightarrow \textbf{ smallest mol amount determines}$$
$$\textbf{limiting reactant}$$

molecules O_2 → molecules CO_2

$$\frac{2 \text{ molecules } CO_2}{3 \text{ molecules } O_2}$$

Solution: 4 molecules CH_3OH $\times \dfrac{2 \text{ molecules } CO_2}{2 \text{ molecules } CH_3OH} = 4$ molecules CO_2

2 molecules O_2 $\times \dfrac{2 \text{ molecules } CO_2}{3 \text{ molecules } O_2} = 1.3$ molecules $CO_2 = 1$ molecule CO_2 because you

cannot have a fraction of a molecule
theoretical yield $= 1$ molecule CO_2

Check: The units of the answer (molecules CO_2) are correct. The answer is reasonable based on the limiting reactant in each mixture.

4.17   (a)   **Given:** 4 mol Ti; 4 mol Cl_2 **Find:** theoretical yield $TiCl_4$
Conceptual Plan: mol Ti → mol $TiCl_4$

$$\frac{1 \text{ mol } TiCl_4}{1 \text{ mol Ti}} \qquad \rightarrow \textbf{ smallest mol amount determines limiting reactant}$$

mol Cl_2 → mol $TiCl_4$

$$\frac{1 \text{ mol } TiCl_4}{2 \text{ mol } Cl_2}$$

Solution: 4 mol Ti $\times \dfrac{1 \text{ mol } TiCl_4}{1 \text{ mol Ti}} = 4$ mol $TiCl_4$

4 mol Cl_2 $\times \dfrac{1 \text{ mol } TiCl_4}{2 \text{ mol } Cl_2} = 2$ mol $TiCl_4$

theoretical yield $= 2$ mol $TiCl_4$

Check: The units of the answer (mol $TiCl_4$) are correct. The answer is reasonable because Cl_2 produced the smallest amount of product and is the limiting reactant.

(b) **Given:** 7 mol Ti; 17 mol Cl_2 **Find:** theoretical yield $TiCl_4$
Conceptual Plan: mol Ti $\rightarrow$ mol $TiCl_4$

$$\frac{1 \text{ mol } TiCl_4}{1 \text{ mol } Ti} \qquad \rightarrow \text{ smallest mol amount determines limiting reactant}$$

mol Cl_2 $\rightarrow$ mol $TiCl_4$

$$\frac{1 \text{ mol } TiCl_4}{2 \text{ mol } Cl_2}$$

Solution: $7 \text{ mol Ti} \times \dfrac{1 \text{ mol } TiCl_4}{1 \text{ mol Ti}} = 7 \text{ mol } TiCl_4$

$17 \text{ mol } Cl_2 \times \dfrac{1 \text{ mol } TiCl_4}{2 \text{ mol } Cl_2} = 8.5 \text{ mol } TiCl_4$

theoretical yield $= 7 \text{ mol } TiCl_4$

Check: The units of the answer (mol $TiCl_4$) are correct. The answer is reasonable because Ti produced the smallest amount of product and is the limiting reactant.

(c) **Given:** 12.4 mol Ti; 18.8 mol Cl_2 **Find:** theoretical yield $TiCl_4$
Conceptual Plan: mol Ti $\rightarrow$ mol $TiCl_4$

$$\frac{1 \text{ mol } TiCl_4}{1 \text{ mol } Ti} \qquad \rightarrow \text{ smallest mol amount determines limiting reactant}$$

mol Cl_2 $\rightarrow$ mol $TiCl_4$

$$\frac{1 \text{ mol } TiCl_4}{2 \text{ mol } Cl_2}$$

Solution: $12.4 \text{ mol Ti} \times \dfrac{1 \text{ mol } TiCl_4}{1 \text{ mol Ti}} = 12.4 \text{ mol } TiCl_4$

$18.8 \text{ mol } Cl_2 \times \dfrac{1 \text{ mol } TiCl_4}{2 \text{ mol } Cl_2} = 9.40 \text{ mol } TiCl_4$

theoretical yield $= 9.40 \text{ mol } TiCl_4$

Check: The units of the answer (mol $TiCl_4$) are correct. The answer is reasonable because Cl_2 produced the smallest amount of product and is the limiting reactant.

4.18 (a) **Given:** 3 mol Mn; 3 mol O_2 **Find:** theoretical yield MnO_2
Conceptual Plan: mol Mn $\rightarrow$ mol MnO_2

$$\frac{2 \text{ mol } MnO_2}{2 \text{ mol Mn}} \qquad \rightarrow \text{ smallest mol amount determines limiting reactant}$$

mol O_2 $\rightarrow$ mol MnO_2

$$\frac{2 \text{ mol } MnO_2}{2 \text{ mol } O_2}$$

Solution: $3 \text{ mol Mn} \times \dfrac{2 \text{ mol } MnO_2}{2 \text{ mol Mn}} = 3 \text{ mol } MnO_2$

$3 \text{ mol } O_2 \times \dfrac{2 \text{ mol } MnO_2}{2 \text{ mol } O_2} = 3 \text{ mol } MnO_2$

theoretical yield $= 3 \text{ mol } MnO_2$

Check: The units of the answer (mol MnO_2) are correct. The answer is reasonable because equal mol are produced for both reactants.

(b) **Given:** 4 mol Mn; 7 mol O_2 **Find:** theoretical yield MnO_2
Conceptual Plan: mol Mn $\rightarrow$ mol MnO_2

$$\frac{2 \text{ mol } MnO_2}{2 \text{ mol Mn}} \qquad \rightarrow \text{ smallest mol amount determines limiting reactant}$$

mol O_2 $\rightarrow$ mol MnO_2

$$\frac{2 \text{ mol } MnO_2}{2 \text{ mol } O_2}$$

Solution: $4 \text{ mol Mn} \times \dfrac{2 \text{ mol } MnO_2}{2 \text{ mol Mn}} = 4 \text{ mol } MnO_2$

$7 \text{ mol } O_2 \times \dfrac{2 \text{ mol } MnO_2}{2 \text{ mol } O_2} = 7 \text{ mol } MnO_2$

theoretical yield $= 4 \text{ mol } MnO_2$

Check: The units of the answer (mol MnO_2) are correct. The answer is reasonable because Mn produced the smallest amount of product and is the limiting reactant.

(c)   **Given:** 27.5 mol Mn; 43.8 mol O_2 **Find:** theoretical yield MnO_2

Conceptual Plan: mol Mn → mol MnO_2

$$\frac{2 \text{ mol } MnO_2}{2 \text{ mol Mn}}$$ → **smallest mol amount determines limiting reactant**

mol O_2 → mol MnO_2

$$\frac{2 \text{ mol } MnO_2}{2 \text{ mol } O_2}$$

Solution: $27.5 \text{ mol Mn} \times \dfrac{2 \text{ mol } MnO_2}{2 \text{ mol Mn}} = 27.5 \text{ mol } MnO_2$

$43.8 \text{ mol } O_2 \times \dfrac{2 \text{ mol } MnO_2}{2 \text{ mol } O_2} = 43.8 \text{ mol } MnO_2$

theoretical yield $= 27.5 \text{ mol } MnO_2$

Check: The units of the answer (mol MnO_2) are correct. The answer is reasonable because Mn produced the smallest amount of product and is the limiting reactant.

4.19   (a)   **Given:** 2.0 g Al; 2.0 g Cl_2 **Find:** theoretical yield in g $AlCl_3$

Conceptual Plan: g Al → mol Al → mol $AlCl_3$

$$\frac{1 \text{ mol Al}}{26.98 \text{ g Al}} \quad \frac{2 \text{ mol } AlCl_3}{2 \text{ mol Al}}$$ → **smallest mol amount determines limiting reactant**

g Cl_2 → mol Cl_2 → mol $AlCl_3$

$$\frac{1 \text{ mol } Cl_2}{70.90 \text{ g } Cl_2} \quad \frac{2 \text{ mol } AlCl_3}{3 \text{ mol } Cl_2}$$

then mol $AlCl_3$ → g $AlCl_3$

$$\frac{133.3 \text{ g } AlCl_3}{1 \text{ mol } AlCl_3}$$

Solution: $2.0 \text{ g Al} \times \dfrac{1 \text{ mol Al}}{26.98 \text{ g Al}} \times \dfrac{2 \text{ mol } AlCl_3}{2 \text{ mol Al}} = 0.07\underline{4}1 \text{ mol } AlCl_3$

$2.0 \text{ g } Cl_2 \times \dfrac{1 \text{ mol } Cl_2}{70.90 \text{ g } Cl_2} \times \dfrac{2 \text{ mol } AlCl_3}{3 \text{ mol } Cl_2} = 0.018\underline{8} \text{ mol } AlCl_3$

$0.018\underline{8} \text{ mol } AlCl_3 \times \dfrac{133.3 \text{ g } AlCl_3}{1 \text{ mol } AlCl_3} = 2.\underline{5}1 \text{ g } AlCl_3 = 2.5 \text{ g } AlCl_3$

Check: The units of the answer (g $AlCl_3$) are correct. The answer is reasonable because Cl_2 produced the smallest amount of product and is the limiting reactant.

(b)   **Given:** 7.5 g Al; 24.8 g Cl_2 **Find:** theoretical yield in g $AlCl_3$

Conceptual Plan: g Al → mol Al → mol $AlCl_3$

$$\frac{1 \text{ mol Al}}{26.98 \text{ g Al}} \quad \frac{2 \text{ mol } AlCl_3}{2 \text{ mol Al}}$$ → **smallest mol amount determines limiting reactant**

g Cl_2 → mol Cl_2 → mol $AlCl_3$

$$\frac{1 \text{ mol } Cl_2}{70.90 \text{ g } Cl_2} \quad \frac{2 \text{ mol } AlCl_3}{3 \text{ mol } Cl_2}$$

then mol $AlCl_3$ → g $AlCl_3$

$$\frac{133.3 \text{ g } AlCl_3}{1 \text{ mol } AlCl_3}$$

Solution: $7.5 \text{ g Al} \times \dfrac{1 \text{ mol Al}}{26.98 \text{ g Al}} \times \dfrac{2 \text{ mol } AlCl_3}{2 \text{ mol Al}} = 0.2\underline{7}80 \text{ mol } AlCl_3$

$24.8 \text{ g } Cl_2 \times \dfrac{1 \text{ mol } Cl_2}{70.90 \text{ g } Cl_2} \times \dfrac{2 \text{ mol } AlCl_3}{3 \text{ mol } Cl_2} = 0.23\underline{3}2 \text{ mol } AlCl_3$

$0.23\underline{3}2 \text{ mol } AlCl_3 \times \dfrac{133.3 \text{ g } AlCl_3}{1 \text{ mol } AlCl_3} = 31.\underline{0}9 \text{ g } AlCl_3 = 31.1 \text{ g } AlCl_3$

Check: The units of the answer (g $AlCl_3$) are correct. The answer is reasonable because Cl_2 produced the smallest amount of product and is the limiting reactant.

(c)   **Given:** 0.235 g Al; 1.15 g Cl_2 **Find:** theoretical yield in g $AlCl_3$

Conceptual Plan: g A $\rightarrow$ mol Al $\rightarrow$ mol $AlCl_3$

$$\frac{1 \text{ mol Al}}{26.98 \text{ g Al}} \quad \frac{2 \text{ mol AlCl}_3}{2 \text{ mol Al}} \qquad \rightarrow \textbf{ smallest mol amount determines limiting reactant}$$

g Cl_2 $\rightarrow$ mol Cl_2 $\rightarrow$ mol $AlCl_3$

$$\frac{1 \text{ mol Cl}_2}{70.90 \text{ g Cl}_2} \quad \frac{2 \text{ mol AlCl}_3}{3 \text{ mol Cl}_2}$$

then mol $AlCl_3$ $\rightarrow$ g $AlCl_3$

$$\frac{133.3 \text{ g AlCl}_3}{1 \text{ mol AlCl}_3}$$

Solution: $0.235 \text{ g Al} \times \dfrac{1 \text{ mol Al}}{26.98 \text{ g Al}} \times \dfrac{2 \text{ mol AlCl}_3}{2 \text{ mol Al}} = 0.008710 \text{ mol AlCl}_3$

$1.15 \text{ g Cl}_2 \times \dfrac{1 \text{ mol Cl}_2}{70.90 \text{ g Cl}_2} \times \dfrac{2 \text{ mol AlCl}_3}{3 \text{ mol Cl}_2} = 0.01081 \text{ mol AlCl}_3$

$0.008710 \text{ mol AlCl}_3 \times \dfrac{133.3 \text{ g AlCl}_3}{1 \text{ mol AlCl}_3} = 1.161 \text{ g AlCl}_3 = 1.16 \text{ g AlCl}_3$

Check: The units of the answer (g $AlCl_3$) are correct. The answer is reasonable because Al produced the smallest amount of product and is the limiting reactant.

4.20   (a)   **Given:** 5.0 g Ti; 5.0 g F_2 **Find:** theoretical yield in g TiF_4

Conceptual Plan: g Ti $\rightarrow$ mol Ti $\rightarrow$ mol TiF_4

$$\frac{1 \text{ mol Ti}}{47.87 \text{ g Ti}} \quad \frac{1 \text{ mol TiF}_4}{1 \text{ mol Ti}} \qquad \rightarrow \textbf{ smallest mol amount determines limiting reactant}$$

g F_2 $\rightarrow$ mol F_2 $\rightarrow$ mol TiF_4

$$\frac{1 \text{ mol F}_2}{38.00 \text{ g F}_2} \quad \frac{1 \text{ mol TiF}_4}{2 \text{ mol F}_2}$$

then mol TiF_4 $\rightarrow$ g TiF_4

$$\frac{123.87 \text{ g TiF}_4}{1 \text{ mol TiF}_4}$$

Solution: $5.0 \text{ g Ti} \times \dfrac{1 \text{ mol Ti}}{47.87 \text{ g Ti}} \times \dfrac{1 \text{ mol TiF}_4}{1 \text{ mol Ti}} = 0.104 \text{ mol TiF}_4$

$5.0 \text{ g F}_2 \times \dfrac{1 \text{ mol F}_2}{38.00 \text{ g F}_2} \times \dfrac{1 \text{ mol TiF}_4}{2 \text{ mol F}_2} = 0.0658 \text{ mol TiF}_4$

$0.0658 \text{ mol TiF}_4 \times \dfrac{123.87 \text{ g TiF}_4}{1 \text{ mol TiF}_4} = 8.15 \text{ g TiF}_4 = 8.2 \text{ g TiF}_4$

Check: The units of the answer (g TiF_4) are correct. The answer is reasonable because F_2 produced the smallest amount of product and is the limiting reactant.

(b)   **Given:** 2.4 g Ti; 1.6 g F_2 **Find:** theoretical yield in g TiF_4

Conceptual Plan: g Ti $\rightarrow$ mol Ti $\rightarrow$ mol TiF_4

$$\frac{1 \text{ mol Ti}}{47.87 \text{ g Ti}} \quad \frac{1 \text{ mol TiF}_4}{1 \text{ mol Ti}} \qquad \rightarrow \textbf{ smallest mol amount determines limiting reactant}$$

g F_2 $\rightarrow$ mol F_2 $\rightarrow$ mol TiF_4

$$\frac{1 \text{ mol F}_2}{38.00 \text{ g F}_2} \quad \frac{1 \text{ mol TiF}_4}{2 \text{ mol F}_2}$$

then mol TiF_4 $\rightarrow$ g TiF_4

$$\frac{123.87 \text{ g TiF}_4}{1 \text{ mol TiF}_4}$$

Solution: $2.4 \text{ g Ti} \times \dfrac{1 \text{ mol Ti}}{47.87 \text{ g Ti}} \times \dfrac{1 \text{ mol TiF}_4}{1 \text{ mol Ti}} = 0.0501 \text{ mol TiF}_4$

$1.6 \text{ g F}_2 \times \dfrac{1 \text{ mol F}_2}{38.00 \text{ g F}_2} \times \dfrac{1 \text{ mol TiF}_4}{2 \text{ mol F}_2} = 0.0211 \text{ mol TiF}_4$

$0.0211 \text{ mol TiF}_4 \times \dfrac{123.87 \text{ g TiF}_4}{1 \text{ mol TiF}_4} = 2.61 \text{ g TiF}_4 = 2.6 \text{ g TiF}_4$

Check: The units of the answer (g TiF_4) are correct. The answer is reasonable because F_2 produced the smallest amount of product and is the limiting reactant.

(c)   **Given:** 0.233 g Ti; 0.288 g F_2 **Find:** theoretical yield in g TiF_4

Conceptual Plan: g Ti → mol Ti → mol TiF_4

$$\frac{1 \text{ mol Ti}}{47.87 \text{ g Ti}} \quad \frac{1 \text{ mol TiF}_4}{1 \text{ mol Ti}}$$

→ **smallest mol amount determines limiting reactant**

g F_2 → mol F_2 → mol TiF_4

$$\frac{1 \text{ mol F}_2}{38.00 \text{ g F}_2} \quad \frac{1 \text{ mol TiF}_4}{2 \text{ mol F}_2}$$

then mol TiF_4 → g TiF_4

$$\frac{123.87 \text{ g TiF}_4}{1 \text{ mol TiF}_4}$$

Solution: $0.233 \text{ g Ti} \times \dfrac{1 \text{ mol Ti}}{47.87 \text{ g Ti}} \times \dfrac{1 \text{ mol TiF}_4}{1 \text{ mol Ti}} = 0.004867 \text{ mol TiF}_4$

$0.288 \text{ g F}_2 \times \dfrac{1 \text{ mol F}_2}{38.00 \text{ g F}_2} \times \dfrac{1 \text{ mol TiF}_4}{2 \text{ mol F}_2} = 0.003789 \text{ mol TiF}_4$

$0.003789 \text{ mol TiF}_4 \times \dfrac{123.87 \text{ g TiF}_4}{1 \text{ mol TiF}_4} = 0.4693 \text{ g TiF}_4 = 0.469 \text{ g TiF}_4$

Check: The units of the answer (g TiF_4) are correct. The answer is reasonable because F_2 produced the smallest amount of product and is the limiting reactant.

4.21   **Given:** 28.5 g KCl; 25.7 g Pb^{2+}; 29.4 g $PbCl_2$ **Find:** limiting reactant; theoretical yield $PbCl_2$; % yield

Conceptual Plan: g KCl → mol KCl → mol $PbCl_2$

$$\frac{1 \text{ mol KCl}}{74.55 \text{ g KCl}} \quad \frac{1 \text{ mol PbCl}_2}{2 \text{ mol KCl}}$$

→ **smallest mol amount determines limiting reactant**

g Pb^{2+} → mol Pb^{2+} → mol $PbCl_2$

$$\frac{1 \text{ mol Pb}^{2+}}{207.2 \text{ g Pb}^{2+}} \quad \frac{1 \text{ mol PbCl}_2}{1 \text{ mol Pb}^{2+}}$$

then mol $PbCl_2$ → g $PbCl_2$ then determine % yield

$$\frac{278.1 \text{ g PbCl}_2}{\text{mol PbCl}_2} \qquad \frac{\text{actual yield g PbCl}_2}{\text{theoretical yield g PbCl}_2} \times 100\%$$

Solution: $28.5 \text{ g KCl} \times \dfrac{1 \text{ mol KCl}}{74.55 \text{ g KCl}} \times \dfrac{1 \text{ mol PbCl}_2}{2 \text{ mol KCl}} = 0.1911 \text{ mol PbCl}_2$

$25.7 \text{ g Pb}^{2+} \times \dfrac{1 \text{ mol Pb}^{2+}}{207.2 \text{ g Pb}^{2+}} \times \dfrac{1 \text{ mol PbCl}_2}{1 \text{ mol Pb}^{2+}} = 0.1240 \text{ mol PbCl}_2$ Pb^{2+} is the limiting reactant.

$0.1240 \text{ mol PbCl}_2 \times \dfrac{278.1 \text{ g PbCl}_2}{1 \text{ mol PbCl}_2} = 34.48 \text{ g PbCl}_2$

$\dfrac{29.4 \text{ g PbCl}_2}{34.48 \text{ g PbCl}_2} \times 100\% = 85.2\%$

Check: The theoretical yield has the correct units (g $PbCl_2$) and has a reasonable magnitude compared to the mass of Pb^{2+}, the limiting reactant. The % yield is reasonable, under 100%.

4.22   **Given:** 10.1 g Mg; 10.5 g O_2; 11.9 g MgO   **Find:** limiting reactant; theoretical yield MgO; % yield

Conceptual Plan: g Mg → mol Mg → mol MgO

$$\frac{1 \text{ mol Mg}}{24.31 \text{ g Mg}} \quad \frac{2 \text{ mol MgO}}{2 \text{ mol Mg}}$$

→ **smallest mol amount determines limiting reactant**

g O_2 → mol O_2 → mol MgO

$$\frac{1 \text{ mol O}_2}{32.00 \text{ g O}_2} \quad \frac{2 \text{ mol MgO}}{1 \text{ mol O}_2}$$

then mol MgO → g MgO then determine % yield

$$\frac{40.31 \text{ g MgO}}{1 \text{ mol MgO}} \qquad \frac{\text{actual yield g MgO}}{\text{theoretical yield g MgO}} \times 100\%$$

Solution: $10.1 \text{ g Mg} \times \dfrac{1 \text{ mol Mg}}{24.31 \text{ g Mg}} \times \dfrac{2 \text{ mol MgO}}{2 \text{ mol Mg}} = 0.4155 \text{ mol MgO}$ Mg is the limiting reactant.

$10.5 \text{ g O}_2 \times \dfrac{1 \text{ mol O}_2}{32.00 \text{ g O}_2} \times \dfrac{2 \text{ mol MgO}}{1 \text{ mol O}_2} = 0.6563 \text{ mol MgO}$

$$0.41\underline{5}5 \text{ mol MgO} \times \frac{40.31 \text{ g MgO}}{1 \text{ mol MgO}} = 16.75 \text{ g MgO}$$

$$\frac{11.9 \text{ g MgO}}{16.\underline{7}5 \text{ g MgO}} \times 100\% = 71.0\%$$

Check: The theoretical yield has the correct units (g MgO) and has a reasonable magnitude compared to the mass of Mg, the limiting reactant. The % yield is reasonable, under 100%.

4.23   **Given:** 136.4 kg NH_3; 211.4 kg CO_2; 168.4 kg CH_4N_2O **Find:** limiting reactant; theoretical yield CH_4N_2O; % yield

Conceptual Plan: kg NH_3 → g NH_3 → mol NH_3 → mol CH_4N_2O

$$\frac{1000 \text{ g}}{1 \text{ kg}} \qquad \frac{1 \text{ mol } NH_3}{17.03 \text{ g } NH_3} \qquad \frac{1 \text{ mol } CH_4N_2O}{2 \text{ mol } NH_3} \qquad \rightarrow \text{ smallest mol amount determines limiting reactant}$$

kg CO_2 → g CO_2 → mol CO_2 → mol CH_4N_2O

$$\frac{1000 \text{ g}}{1 \text{ kg}} \qquad \frac{1 \text{ mol } CO_2}{44.01 \text{ g } CO_2} \qquad \frac{1 \text{ mol } CH_4N_2O}{1 \text{ mol } CO_2}$$

then mol CH_4N_2O → g CH_4N_2O → kg CH_4N_2O then determine % yield

$$\frac{60.06 \text{ g } CH_4N_2O}{1 \text{ mol } CH_4N_2O} \qquad \frac{1 \text{ kg}}{1000 \text{ g}} \qquad \frac{\text{actual yield kg } CH_4N_2O}{\text{theoretical yield kg } CH_4N_2O} \times 100\%$$

Solution: $136.4 \text{ kg } NH_3 \times \dfrac{1000 \text{ g}}{1 \text{ kg}} \times \dfrac{1 \text{ mol } NH_3}{17.03 \text{ g } NH_3} \times \dfrac{1 \text{ mol } CH_4N_2O}{2 \text{ mol } NH_3} = 400\underline{4}.7 \text{ mol } CH_4N_2O$

$211.4 \text{ kg } CO_2 \times \dfrac{1000 \text{ g}}{1 \text{ kg}} \times \dfrac{1 \text{ mol } CO_2}{44.01 \text{ g } CO_2} \times \dfrac{1 \text{ mol } CH_4N_2O}{1 \text{ mol } CO_2} = 480\underline{3}.5 \text{ mol } CH_4N_2O$

NH_3 is the limiting reactant.

$$400\underline{4}.7 \text{ mol } CH_4N_2O \times \frac{60.06 \text{ g } CH_4N_2O}{1 \text{ mol } CH_4N_2O} \times \frac{1 \text{ kg}}{1000 \text{ g}} = 240.\underline{5}2 \text{ kg } CH_4N_2O$$

$$\frac{168.4 \text{ kg } CH_4N_2O}{240.\underline{5}2 \text{ kg } CH_4N_2O} \times 100\% = 70.01\%$$

Check: The theoretical yield has the correct units (kg CH_4N_2O) and has a reasonable magnitude compared to the mass of NH_3, the limiting reactant. The % yield is reasonable, under 100%.

4.24   **Given:** 155.8 kg SiO_2; 78.3 kg C; 66.1 kg Si   **Find:** limiting reactant; theoretical yield Si; % yield

Conceptual Plan: write and balance the reaction, then

kg SiO_2 → g SiO_2 → mol SiO_2 → mol Si

$$\frac{1000 \text{ g}}{1 \text{ kg}} \qquad \frac{1 \text{ mol } SiO_2}{60.09 \text{ g } SiO_2} \qquad \frac{1 \text{ mol Si}}{1 \text{ mol } SiO_2} \qquad \rightarrow \text{ smallest mol amount determines limiting reactant}$$

kg C → g C → mol C → mol Si

$$\frac{1000 \text{ g}}{1 \text{ kg}} \qquad \frac{1 \text{ mol C}}{12.01 \text{ g C}} \qquad \frac{1 \text{ mol Si}}{2 \text{ mol C}}$$

then mol Si → g Si → kg Si $\qquad$ **then determine % yield**

$$\frac{28.09 \text{ g Si}}{1 \text{ mol Si}} \qquad \frac{1 \text{ kg}}{1000 \text{ g}} \qquad \frac{\text{actual yield kg Si}}{\text{theoretical yield kg Si}} \times 100\%$$

Solution: $SiO_2(l) + 2C(s) \rightarrow Si(l) + 2CO(g)$

$155.8 \text{ kg } SiO_2 \times \dfrac{1000 \text{ g}}{\text{kg}} \times \dfrac{1 \text{ mol } SiO_2}{60.09 \text{ g } SiO_2} \times \dfrac{1 \text{ mol Si}}{1 \text{ mol } SiO_2} = 259\underline{2}.8 \text{ mol Si}$

$78.3 \text{ kg C} \times \dfrac{1000 \text{ g}}{1 \text{ kg}} \times \dfrac{1 \text{ mol C}}{12.01 \text{ g C}} \times \dfrac{1 \text{ mol Si}}{2 \text{ mol C}} = 325\underline{9}.8 \text{ mol Si.}$ SiO_2 is the limiting reactant.

$259\underline{2}.8 \text{ mol Si} \times \dfrac{28.09 \text{ g Si}}{1 \text{ mol Si}} \times \dfrac{\text{kg}}{1000 \text{ g}} = 72.8\underline{3}2 \text{ kg Si}$

$$\frac{66.1 \text{ kg Si}}{72.8\underline{3}2 \text{ kg Si}} \times 100\% = 90.8\%$$

Check: The theoretical yield has the correct units (kg Si) and has a reasonable magnitude compared to the mass of SiO_2, the limiting reactant. The % yield is reasonable, under 100%.

Solution Concentration and Solution Stoichiometry

4.25   (a)   **Given:** 4.3 mol LiCl; 2.8 L solution   **Find:** molarity LiCl
Conceptual Plan: mol LiCl, L solution → molarity

$$\text{molarity (M)} = \frac{\text{amount of solute (in moles)}}{\text{volume of solution (in L)}}$$

Solution: $\dfrac{4.3 \text{ mol LiCl}}{2.8 \text{ L solution}} = 1.\underline{5}4 \text{ M LiCl} = 1.5 \text{ M LiCl}$

Check: The units of the answer (M) are correct. The magnitude of the answer is reasonable. Concentrations are usually between 0 M and 18 M.

(b)   **Given:** 22.6 g $C_6H_{12}O_6$; 1.08 L solution   **Find:** molarity $C_6H_{12}O_6$
Conceptual Plan: g $C_6H_{12}O_6$ → mol $C_6H_{12}O_6$, L solution → molarity

$$\frac{1 \text{ mol } C_6H_{12}O_6}{180.16 \text{ g } C_6H_{12}O_6} \qquad \text{molarity (M)} = \frac{\text{amount of solute (in moles)}}{\text{volume of solution (in L)}}$$

Solution: $22.6 \text{ g } C_6H_{12}O_6 \times \dfrac{1 \text{ mol } C_6H_{12}O_6}{180.16 \text{ g } C_6H_{12}O_6} = 0.12\underline{5}4 \text{ mol } C_6H_{12}O_6$

$\dfrac{0.12\underline{5}4 \text{ mol } C_6H_{12}O_6}{1.08 \text{ L solution}} = 0.11\underline{6}1 \text{ M } C_6H_{12}O_6 = 0.116 \text{ M } C_6H_{12}O_6$

Check: The units of the answer (M) are correct. The magnitude of the answer is reasonable. Concentrations are usually between 0 M and 18 M.

(c)   **Given:** 45.5 mg NaCl; 154.4 mL solution   **Find:** molarity NaCl
Conceptual Plan: mg NaCl → g NaCl → mol NaCl, and mL solution → L solution then molarity

$$\frac{1 \text{ g NaCl}}{1000 \text{ mg NaCl}} \quad \frac{1 \text{ mol NaCl}}{58.44 \text{ g NaCl}} \quad \frac{1 \text{ L solution}}{1000 \text{ mL solution}} \quad \text{molarity (M)} = \frac{\text{amount of solute (in moles)}}{\text{volume of solution (in L)}}$$

Solution: $45.5 \text{ mg NaCl} \times \dfrac{1 \text{ g}}{1000 \text{ mg}} \times \dfrac{1 \text{ mol NaCl}}{58.44 \text{ g NaCl}} = 7.7\underline{8}6 \times 10^{-4} \text{ mol NaCl}$

$154.4 \text{ mL solution} \times \dfrac{1 \text{ L}}{1000 \text{ mL}} = 0.1544 \text{ L}$

$\dfrac{7.7\underline{8}6 \times 10^{-4} \text{ mol NaCl}}{0.1544 \text{ L}} = 0.00504\underline{3} \text{ M NaCl} = 0.00504 \text{ M NaCl}$

Check: The units of the answer (M) are correct. The magnitude of the answer is reasonable. Concentrations are usually between 0 M and 18 M.

4.26   (a)   **Given:** 0.11 mol $LiNO_3$; 5.2 L solution   **Find:** molarity $LiNO_3$
Conceptual Plan: mol $LiNO_3$; L solution → molarity

$$\text{molarity (M)} = \frac{\text{amount of solute (in moles)}}{\text{volume of solution (in L)}}$$

Solution: $\dfrac{0.11 \text{ mol } LiNO_3}{5.2 \text{ L solution}} = 0.02\underline{1}2 \text{ M } LiNO_3 = 0.021 \text{ M } LiNO_3$

Check: The units of the answer (M) are correct. The magnitude of the answer is reasonable. Concentrations are usually between 0 M and 18 M.

(b)   **Given:** 61.3 g C_2H_6O; 2.44 L solution   **Find:** molarity C_2H_6O
Conceptual Plan: g C_2H_6O → mol C_2H_6O, L solution → molarity

$$\frac{1 \text{ mol } C_2H_6O}{46.068 \text{ g } C_2H_6O} \qquad \text{molarity (M)} = \frac{\text{amount of solute (in moles)}}{\text{volume of solution (in L)}}$$

Solution: $61.3 \text{ g } C_2H_6O \times \dfrac{1 \text{ mol } C_2H_6O}{46.068 \text{ g } C_2H_6O} = 1.3\underline{3}06 \text{ mol } C_2H_6O$

$\dfrac{1.3\underline{3}06 \text{ mol } C_2H_6O}{2.44 \text{ L solution}} = 0.54\underline{5}3 \text{ M } C_2H_6O = 0.545 \text{ M } C_2H_6O$

Check: The units of the answer (M) are correct. The magnitude of the answer is reasonable. Concentrations are usually between 0 M and 18 M.

(c) **Given:** 15.2 mg KI; 102 mL solution **Find:** molarity KI

Conceptual Plan: mg KI 1 → g KI → mol KI, and mL solution → L solution then molarity

$$\frac{g\ KI}{1000\ mg\ KI} \qquad \frac{1\ mol\ KI}{166.00\ g\ KI} \qquad \frac{1\ L\ solution}{1000\ mL\ solution} \qquad molarity\ (M) = \frac{amount\ of\ solute\ (in\ moles)}{volume\ of\ solution\ (in\ L)}$$

Solution: $15.2\ \text{mg KI} \times \dfrac{1\ \cancel{g}}{1000\ \cancel{mg}} \times \dfrac{1\ mol\ KI}{166.00\ \cancel{g\ KI}} = 9.1\underline{5}7 \times 10^{-5}\ mol\ KI$

$102\ \cancel{mL\ solution} \times \dfrac{1\ L}{1000\ \cancel{mL}} = 0.102\ L$

$\dfrac{9.1\underline{5}7 \times 10^{-5}\ mol\ KI}{0.102\ L} = 8.9\underline{7}7 \times 10^{-4}\ M\ KI = 8.98 \times 10^{-4}\ M\ KI$

Check: The units of the answer (M) are correct. The magnitude of the answer is reasonable. Concentrations are usually between 0 M and 18 M.

4.27 (a) **Given:** 0.150 M KNO_3 **Find:** Molarity NO_3^-

Conceptual Plan: M KNO_3 → M NO_3^-

$$\frac{1\ M\ NO_3^-}{1\ M\ KNO_3}$$

Solution: $0.150\ \cancel{M\ KNO_3} \times \dfrac{1\ M\ NO_3^-}{1\ \cancel{M\ KNO_3}} = 0.150\ M\ NO_3^-$

Check: The units of the answer (M) are correct. The magnitude of the answer (0.150) is reasonable, since there is 1 mole of nitrate ions in each mole of potassium nitrate.

(b) **Given:** 0.150 M $Ca(NO_3)_2$ **Find:** Molarity NO_3^-

Conceptual Plan: M $Ca(NO_3)_2$ → M NO_3^-

$$\frac{2\ M\ NO_3^-}{1\ M\ Ca(NO_3)_2}$$

Solution: $0.150\ \cancel{M\ Ca(NO_3)_2} \times \dfrac{2\ M\ NO_3^-}{1\ \cancel{M\ Ca(NO_3)_2}} = 0.300\ M\ NO_3^-$

Check: The units of the answer (M) are correct. The magnitude of the answer (0.300) is reasonable, since there are 2 moles of nitrate ions in each mole of calcium nitrate.

(c) **Given:** 0.150 M $Al(NO_3)_3$ **Find:** Molarity NO_3^-

Conceptual Plan: M $Al(NO_3)_3$ → M NO_3^-

$$\frac{3\ M\ NO_3^-}{1\ M\ Al(NO_3)_3}$$

Solution: $0.150\ \cancel{M\ Al(NO_3)_3} \times \dfrac{3\ M\ NO_3^-}{1\ \cancel{M\ Al(NO_3)_3}} = 0.450\ M\ NO_3^-$

Check: The units of the answer (M) are correct. The magnitude of the answer (0.450) is reasonable, since there are 3 moles of nitrate ions in each mole of aluminum nitrate.

4.28 (a) **Given:** 0.200 M NaCl **Find:** Molarity Cl^-

Conceptual Plan: M NaCl → M Cl^-

$$\frac{1\ M\ Cl^-}{1\ M\ NaCl}$$

Solution: $0.200\ \cancel{M\ NaCl} \times \dfrac{1\ M\ Cl^-}{1\ \cancel{M\ NaCl}} = 0.200\ M\ Cl^-$

Check: The units of the answer (M) are correct. The magnitude of the answer (0.200) is reasonable, since there is 1 mole of chloride ions in each mole of sodium chloride.

(b) **Given:** 0.150 M $SrCl_2$ **Find:** Molarity Cl^-

Conceptual Plan: M $SrCl_2$ → M Cl^-

$$\frac{2\ M\ Cl^-}{1\ M\ SrCl_2}$$

Solution: $0.150\ \cancel{M\ SrCl_2} \times \dfrac{2\ M\ Cl^-}{1\ \cancel{M\ SrCl_2}} = 0.300\ M\ Cl^-$

Check: The units of the answer (M) are correct. The magnitude of the answer (0.300) is reasonable, since there are 2 moles of chloride ions in each mole of strontium chloride.

(c) **Given:** 0.100 M $AlCl_3$ **Find:** Molarity Cl^-

Conceptual Plan: M $AlCl_3$ → M Cl^-

$$\frac{3\ M\ Cl^-}{1\ M\ AlCl_3}$$

Solution: $0.100\ \text{M}\ \cancel{AlCl_3} \times \dfrac{3\ M\ Cl^-}{1\ \cancel{M\ AlCl_3}} = 0.300\ M\ Cl^-$

Check: The units of the answer (M) are correct. The magnitude of the answer (0.300) is reasonable, since there are 3 moles of chloride ions in each mole of aluminum chloride.

4.29   (a) **Given:** 0.556 L; 2.3 M KCl   **Find:** mol KCl

Conceptual Plan: volume solution × M = mol

$$\text{volume solution (L)} \times M = \text{mol}$$

Solution: $0.556\ \text{L}\ \cancel{\text{solution}} \times \dfrac{2.3\ \text{mol KCl}}{1\ \text{L}\ \cancel{\text{solution}}} = 1.2\underline{8}\ \text{mol KCl} = 1.3\ \text{mol KCl}$

Check: The units of the answer (mol KCl) are correct. The magnitude is reasonable because it is less than 1 L of solution.

(b) **Given:** 1.8 L; 0.85 M KCl   **Find:** mol KCl

Conceptual Plan: volume solution × M = mol

$$\text{volume solution (L)} \times M = \text{mol}$$

Solution: $1.8\ \text{L}\ \cancel{\text{solution}} \times \dfrac{0.85\ \text{mol KCl}}{1\ \text{L}\ \cancel{\text{solution}}} = 1.\underline{8}3\ \text{mol KCl} = 1.5\ \text{mol KCl}$

Check: The units of the answer (mol KCl) are correct. The magnitude is reasonable because it is less than 2 L of solution.

(c) **Given:** 114 mL; 1.85 M KCl   **Find:** mol KCl

Conceptual Plan: mL solution → L solution, then volume solution × M = mol

$$\frac{1\ L}{1000\ mL} \qquad\qquad \text{volume solution (L)} \times M = \text{mol}$$

Solution: $114\ \text{mL}\ \cancel{\text{solution}} \times \dfrac{1\ \cancel{L}}{1000\ \cancel{mL}} \times \dfrac{1.85\ \text{mol KCl}}{1\ \text{L}\ \cancel{\text{solution}}} = 0.210\underline{9}\ \text{mol KCl} = 0.211\ \text{mol KCl}$

Check: The units of the answer (mol KCl) are correct. The magnitude is reasonable because it is less than 1 L of solution.

4.30   (a) **Given:** 0.45 mol C_2H_5OH; 0.200 M C_2H_5OH **Find:** volume solution

Conceptual Plan: mol C_2H_5OH → volume solution

$$\frac{\text{mol } C_2H_5OH}{M\ C_2H_5OH}$$

Solution:

$$\dfrac{0.45\ \text{mol}\ \cancel{C_2H_5OH}}{0.200\ \dfrac{\text{mol}\ \cancel{C_2H_5OH}}{\text{L solution}}} = 2.2\underline{5}\ \text{L}\ C_2H_5OH = 2.3\ \text{L}\ C_2H_5OH$$

Check: The units of the answer (L C_2H_5OH) are correct. The magnitude is reasonable for the amount and volume of solution.

(b) **Given:** 1.22 mol C_2H_5OH; 0.200 M C_2H_5OH **Find:** volume solution

Conceptual Plan: mol C_2H_5OH → volume solution

$$\frac{\text{mol } C_2H_5OH}{M\ C_2H_5OH}$$

Solution:

$$\dfrac{1.22\ \text{mol}\ \cancel{C_2H_5OH}}{0.200\ \dfrac{\text{mol}\ \cancel{C_2H_5OH}}{\text{L solution}}} = 6.10\ \text{L}\ C_2H_5OH$$

Check: The units of the answer (L C_2H_5OH) are correct. The magnitude is reasonable for the amount and volume of solution.

(c)   **Given:** 1.2×0^{-2} mol C_2H_5OH; 0.200 M C_2H_5OH **Find:** volume solution
Conceptual Plan: mol C_2H_5OH $\rightarrow$ volume solution

$$\frac{\text{mol } C_2H_5OH}{\text{M } C_2H_5OH}$$

Solution:

$$\frac{1.2 \times 10^{-2} \text{ mol } C_2H_5OH}{0.200 \dfrac{\text{mol } C_2H_5OH}{\text{L solution}}} = 0.060 \text{ L } C_2H_5OH$$

Check: The units of the answer (L C_2H_5OH) are correct. The magnitude is reasonable for the amount and volume of solution.

4.31   **Given:** 500.0 mL; 1.3 M $NaNO_3$ **Find:** g $NaNO_3$
Conceptual Plan: mL solution $\rightarrow$ L solution, then volume solution $\times$ M $=$ mol $NaNO_3$

$$\frac{1 \text{ L solution}}{1000 \text{ mL solution}} \qquad\qquad \text{volume solution (L)} \times \text{M} = \text{mol}$$

then mol $NaNO_3$ $\rightarrow$ g $NaNO_3$

$$\frac{85.00 \text{ g } NaNO_3}{1 \text{ mol } NaNO_3}$$

Solution: $500.0 \text{ mL solution} \times \dfrac{1 \text{ L}}{1000 \text{ mL}} \times \dfrac{1.3 \text{ mol } NaNO_3}{1 \text{ L solution}} \times \dfrac{85.00 \text{ g}}{1 \text{ mol } NaNO_3} = 55.25 \text{ g } NaNO_3 = 55 \text{ g } NaNO_3$

Check: The units of the answer (g $NaNO_3$) are correct. The magnitude is reasonable for the concentration and volume of solution.

4.32   **Given:** 7.2 L; 0.350 M $CaCl_2$ **Find:** g $CaCl_2$
Conceptual Plan: volume solution $\times$ M $=$ mol $CaCl_2$ then mol $CaCl_2$ $\rightarrow$ g $CaCl_2$

$$\text{volume solution (L)} \times \text{M} = \text{mol} \qquad\qquad \frac{110.98 \text{ g } CaCl_2}{1 \text{ mol } CaCl_2}$$

Solution: $7.2 \text{ L solution} \times \dfrac{0.350 \text{ mol } CaCl_2}{1 \text{ L solution}} \times \dfrac{110.98 \text{ g}}{1 \text{ mol } CaCl_2} = 2.80 \times 10^2 \text{ g } CaCl_2 = 2.8 \times 10^2 \text{ g } CaCl_2$

Check: The units of the answer (g $CaCl_2$) are correct. The magnitude is reasonable for the concentration and volume of solution.

4.33   **Given:** $V_1 = 123$ mL; $M_1 = 1.1$ M glucose; $V_2 = 500.0$ mL   **Find:** M_2
Conceptual Plan: mL $\rightarrow$ L then $V_1, M_1, V_2 \rightarrow M_2$

$$\frac{1 \text{ L}}{1000 \text{ mL}} \qquad\qquad V_1 M_1 = V_2 M_2$$

Solution: $123 \text{ mL} \times \dfrac{1 \text{ L}}{1000 \text{ mL}} = 0.123 \text{ L} \qquad 500.0 \text{ mL} \times \dfrac{1 \text{ L}}{1000 \text{ mL}} = 0.5000 \text{ L}$

$$M_2 = \frac{V_1 M_1}{V_2} = \frac{(0.123 \text{ L})(1.1 \text{ M})}{(0.5000 \text{ L})} = 0.271 \text{ M glucose} = 0.27 \text{ M glucose}$$

Check: The units of the answer (M) are correct. The magnitude of the answer is reasonable because it is less than the original concentration.

4.34   **Given:** $V_1 = 3.5$ L; $M_1 = 4.8$ M; $V_2 = 45$ L   **Find:** M_2
Conceptual Plan: $V_1, M_1, V_2 \rightarrow M_2$

$$V_1 M_1 = V_2 M_2$$

Solution: $M_2 = \dfrac{V_1 M_1}{V_2} = \dfrac{(3.5 \text{ L})(4.8 \text{ M})}{(45 \text{ L})} = 0.373 \text{ M } SrCl_2 = 0.37 \text{ M } SrCl_2$

Check: The units of the answer (M) are correct. The magnitude of the answer is reasonable because it is less than the original concentration.

4.35   **Given:** $V_1 = 50.0$ mL; $M_1 = 12$ M; $M_2 = 0.100$ M   **Find:** V_2
Conceptual Plan: mL $\rightarrow$ L then $V_1, M_1, M_2 \rightarrow V_2$

$$\frac{1 \text{ L}}{1000 \text{ mL}} \qquad\qquad V_1 M_1 = V_2 M_2$$

Solution: $50.0 \text{ mL} \times \dfrac{1 \text{ L}}{1000 \text{ mL}} = 0.0500 \text{ L}$

$$V_2 = \dfrac{V_1 M_1}{M_2} = \dfrac{(0.0500 \text{ L})(12 \text{ M})}{(0.100 \text{ M})} = 6.0 \text{ L}$$

Check: The units of the answer (L) are correct. The magnitude of the answer is reasonable because the new concentration is much less than the original; the volume must be larger.

4.36   **Given:** $V_1 = 25 \text{ mL}$; $M_1 = 10.0 \text{ M}$; $M_2 = 0.150 \text{ M}$ **Find:** V_2

Conceptual Plan: $\text{mL} \rightarrow \text{L}$ then $V_1, M_1, M_2 \rightarrow V_2$

$$\dfrac{1 \text{ L}}{1000 \text{ mL}} \qquad\qquad V_1 M_1 = V_2 M_2$$

Solution: $25 \text{ mL} \times \dfrac{1 \text{ L}}{1000 \text{ mL}} = 0.025 \text{ L}$

$$V_2 = \dfrac{V_1 M_1}{M_2} = \dfrac{(0.025 \text{ L})(10.0 \text{ M})}{(0.150 \text{ M})} = 1.\underline{6}7 \text{ L} = 1.7 \text{ L}$$

Check: The units of the answer (L) are correct. The magnitude of the answer is reasonable because the new concentration is much less than the original; the volume must be larger.

4.37   **Given:** 95.4 mL; 0.102 M $CuCl_2$; 0.175 M Na_3PO_4 **Find:** volume Na_3PO_4

Conceptual Plan: $\text{mL } CuCl_2 \rightarrow \text{L } CuCl_2 \rightarrow \text{mol } CuCl_2 \rightarrow \text{mol } Na_3PO_4 \rightarrow \text{L } Na_3PO_4 \rightarrow \text{mL } Na_3PO_4$

$$\dfrac{1 \text{ L}}{1000 \text{ mL}} \qquad \dfrac{0.102 \text{ mol } CuCl_2}{1 \text{ L}} \qquad \dfrac{2 \text{ mol } Na_3PO_4}{3 \text{ mol } CuCl_2} \qquad \dfrac{1 \text{ L}}{0.175 \text{ mol } Na_3PO_4} \qquad \dfrac{1000 \text{ mL}}{1 \text{ L}}$$

Solution: $95.4 \text{ mL } CuCl_2 \times \dfrac{1 \text{ L}}{1000 \text{ mL}} \times \dfrac{0.102 \text{ mol } CuCl_2}{1 \text{ L}} \times \dfrac{2 \text{ mol } Na_3PO_4}{3 \text{ mol } CuCl_2} \times \dfrac{1 \text{ L}}{0.175 \text{ mol } Na_3PO_4} \times \dfrac{1000 \text{ mL}}{1 \text{ L}}$

$= 37.\underline{0}7 \text{ mL } Na_3PO_4 = 37.1 \text{ mL } Na_3PO_4$

Check: The units of the answer (mL Na_3PO_4) are correct. The magnitude of the answer is reasonable because the concentration of Na_3PO_4 is greater.

4.38   **Given:** 125 mL; 0.150 M $Co(NO_3)_2$; 0.150 M Li_2S **Find:** volume Li_2S

Conceptual Plan: $\text{mL } Co(NO_3)_2 \rightarrow \text{L } Co(NO_3)_2 \rightarrow \text{mol } Co(NO_3)_2 \rightarrow \text{mol } Li_2S \rightarrow \text{L } Li_2S \rightarrow \text{mL } Li_2S$

$$\dfrac{1 \text{ L}}{1000 \text{ mL}} \qquad \dfrac{0.150 \text{ mol } Co(NO_3)_2}{1 \text{ L}} \qquad \dfrac{1 \text{ mol } Li_2S}{1 \text{ mol } Co(NO_3)_2} \qquad \dfrac{1 \text{ L}}{0.150 \text{ mol } Li_2S} \qquad \dfrac{1000 \text{ mL}}{1 \text{ L}}$$

Solution:

$125 \text{ mL } Co(NO_3)_2 \times \dfrac{1 \text{ L}}{1000 \text{ mL}} \times \dfrac{0.150 \text{ mol } Co(NO_3)_2}{1 \text{ L}} \times \dfrac{1 \text{ mol } Li_2S}{1 \text{ mol } Co(NO_3)_2} \times \dfrac{1 \text{ L}}{0.150 \text{ mol } Li_2S} \times \dfrac{1000 \text{ mL}}{1 \text{ L}}$

$= 125 \text{ mL } Li_2S$

Check: The units of the answer (mL Li_2S) are correct. The magnitude of the answer is reasonable because the concentrations are the same and the mole ratio is 1:1.

4.39   **Given:** 25.0 g H_2; 6.0 M H_2SO_4 **Find:** volume H_2SO_4

Conceptual Plan: $\text{g } H_2 \rightarrow \text{mol } H_2 \rightarrow \text{mol } H_2SO_4 \rightarrow \text{L } H_2SO_4$

$$\dfrac{1 \text{ mol } H_2}{2.016 \text{ g } H_2} \qquad \dfrac{3 \text{ mol } H_2SO_4}{3 \text{ mol } H_2} \qquad \dfrac{1 \text{ L}}{6.0 \text{ mol } H_2SO_4}$$

Solution: $25.0 \text{ g } H_2 \times \dfrac{1 \text{ mol } H_2}{2.016 \text{ g } H_2} \times \dfrac{3 \text{ mol } H_2SO_4}{3 \text{ mol } H_2} \times \dfrac{1 \text{ L}}{6.0 \text{ mol } H_2SO_4} = 2.\underline{0}7 \text{ L } H_2SO_4 = 2.1 \text{ L } H_2SO_4$

Check: The units of the answer (L H_2SO_4) are correct. The magnitude is reasonable because there are approximately 12 mol H_2 and the mole ratio is 1:1.

4.40   **Given:** 25.0 g Zn; 275 mL solution   **Find:** M $ZnCl_2$

Conceptual Plan: $\text{g Zn} \rightarrow \text{mol Zn} \rightarrow \text{mol } ZnCl_2 \rightarrow \text{M } ZnCl_2$

$$\dfrac{1 \text{ mol Zn}}{65.38 \text{ g Zn}} \qquad \dfrac{1 \text{ mol } ZnCl_2}{1 \text{ mol Zn}} \qquad \dfrac{\text{mol } ZnCl_2}{\text{volume solution}}$$

Solution:

$25.0 \text{ g Zn} \times \dfrac{1 \text{ mol Zn}}{65.38 \text{ g Zn}} \times \dfrac{1 \text{ mol } ZnCl_2}{1 \text{ mol Zn}} = 0.38\underline{2}4 \text{ mol } ZnCl_2$

$$\frac{0.38\underline{2}4 \text{ mol ZnCl}_2}{275 \text{ mL}} \times \frac{1000 \text{ mL}}{1 \text{ L}} = 1.3\underline{9}1 \text{ M ZnCl}_2 = 1.39 \text{ M ZnCl}_2$$

Check: The units of the answer (M $ZnCl_2$) are correct. The magnitude is reasonable because the stoichiometry is 1:1 and the mol Zn is less than 0.5.

4.41   **Given:** 25.0 mL, 1.20 M KCl; 15.0 mL, 0.900 M $Pb(NO_3)_2$; 2.45 g $PbCl_2$
Find: limiting reactant, theoretical yield $PbCl_2$, % yield
Conceptual Plan: volume KCl solution $\times$ M $\rightarrow$ mol KCl $\rightarrow$ mol $PbCl_2$

volume solution (L) $\times$ M = mol $\frac{1 \text{ mol PbCl}_2}{2 \text{ mol KCl}}$ $\rightarrow$ **smallest mol amount determines limiting reactant**

volume $Pb(NO_3)_2$ solution $\times$ M $\rightarrow$ mol $Pb(NO_3)_2$ $\rightarrow$ mol $PbCl_2$

volume solution (L) $\times$ M = mol $\frac{1 \text{ mol PbCl}_2}{1 \text{ mol Pb(NO}_3)_2}$

then mol $PbCl_2$ $\rightarrow$ g $PbCl_2$ then determine % yield

$\frac{278.1 \text{ g PbCl}_2}{\text{mol PbCl}_2}$ $\frac{\text{actual yield g PbCl}_2}{\text{theoretical yield g PbCl}_2} \times 100\%$

Solution: $25.0 \text{ mL solution} \times \dfrac{1 \text{ L solution}}{1000 \text{ mL solution}} \times \dfrac{1.20 \text{ mol KCl}}{\text{L solution}} \times \dfrac{1 \text{ mol PbCl}_2}{2 \text{ mol KCl}} = 0.15\underline{0} \text{ mol PbCl}_2$

$15.0 \text{ mL solution} \times \dfrac{1 \text{ L solution}}{1000 \text{ mL solution}} \times \dfrac{0.900 \text{ mol Pb(NO}_3)_2}{\text{L solution}} \times \dfrac{1 \text{ mol PbCl}_2}{1 \text{ mol Pb(NO}_3)_2} = 0.013\underline{5} \text{ mol PbCl}_2$

$0.013\underline{5} \text{ mol PbCl}_2 \times \dfrac{278.1 \text{ g PbCl}_2}{1 \text{ mol PbCl}_2} = 3.7\underline{5}4 \text{ g PbCl}_2$

$\dfrac{2.45 \text{ g PbCl}_2}{3.7\underline{5}4 \text{ g PbCl}_2} \times 100\% = 65.3\%$

Check: The units are correct (g and %). The magnitude of the theoretical yield (3.75) is reasonable since we have much less than a mole of each of the reactants. The magnitude of the percent yield (65.3) is reasonable since the actual yield is a little more than half of the theoretical yield.

4.42   **Given:** 55.0 mL, 0.102 M K_2SO_4; 35.0 mL, 0.114 M $Pb(C_2H_3O_2)_2$; 1.01 g $PbSO_4$
Find: limiting reactant; theoretical yield $PbSO_4$; % yield
Conceptual Plan: volume K_2SO_4 solution $\times$ M $\rightarrow$ mol K_2SO_4 $\rightarrow$ mol $PbSO_4$

volume solution (L) $\times$ M = mol $\frac{1 \text{ mol PbSO}_4}{1 \text{ mol K}_2SO_4}$ $\rightarrow$ **smallest mol amount determines limiting reactant**

volume $Pb(C_2H_3O_2)_2$ solution $\times$ M $\rightarrow$ mol $Pb(C_2H_3O_2)_2$ $\rightarrow$ mol $PbSO_4$

volume solution (L) $\times$ M = mol $\frac{1 \text{ mol PbSO}_4}{1 \text{ mol Pb(C}_2H_3O_2)_2}$

then mol $PbSO_4$ $\rightarrow$ g $PbSO_4$ then determine % yield

$\frac{303.27 \text{ g PbSO}_4}{1 \text{ mol PbSO}_4}$ $\frac{\text{actual yield gPbSO}_4}{\text{theoretical yield gPbSO}_4} \times 100\%$

Solution:

$55.0 \text{ mL solution} \times \dfrac{1 \text{ L solution}}{1000 \text{ mL solution}} \times \dfrac{0.102 \text{ mol K}_2SO_4}{1 \text{ L solution}} \times \dfrac{1 \text{ mol PbSO}_4}{1 \text{ mol K}_2SO_4} = 0.0056\underline{1} \text{ mol PbSO}_4$

$35.0 \text{ mL solution} \times \dfrac{1 \text{ L solution}}{1000 \text{ mL solution}} \times \dfrac{0.114 \text{ mol Pb(C}_2H_3O_2)_2}{1 \text{ L solution}} \times \dfrac{1 \text{ mol PbSO}_4}{1 \text{ mol Pb(C}_2H_3O_2)_2} = 0.0039\underline{9} \text{ mol PbSO}_4$

$0.0039\underline{9} \text{ mol PbSO}_4 \times \dfrac{303.27 \text{ g PbSO}_4}{1 \text{ mol PbSO}_4} = 1.2\underline{1}0 \text{ g PbSO}_4$

$\dfrac{1.01 \text{ g PbSO}_4}{1.2\underline{1}0 \text{ g PbSO}_4} \times 100\% = 83.5\%$

Check: The units are correct (g and %). The magnitude of the theoretical yield (1.21) is reasonable since we have much less than a mole of each of the reactants. The magnitude of the percent yield (83.5) is reasonable since the actual yield is a little less than the theoretical yield.

Types of Aqueous Solutions and Solubility

4.43   (a)   CsCl is an ionic compound. An aqueous solution is an electrolyte solution, so it conducts electricity.

(b)   CH$_3$OH is a molecular compound that does not dissociate. An aqueous solution is a nonelectrolyte solution, so it does not conduct electricity.

(c)   Ca(NO$_2$)$_2$ is an ionic compound. An aqueous solution is an electrolyte solution, so it conducts electricity.

(d)   C$_6$H$_{12}$O$_6$ is a molecular compound that does not dissociate. An aqueous solution is a nonelectrolyte solution, so it does not conduct electricity.

4.44   (a)   MgBr$_2$ is an ionic compound. An aqueous solution is a strong electrolyte.

(b)   C$_{12}$H$_{22}$O$_{11}$ is a molecular compound that does not dissociate. An aqueous solution is a nonelectrolyte.

(c)   Na$_2$CO$_3$ is an ionic compound. An aqueous solution is a strong electrolyte.

(d)   KOH is a strong base. An aqueous solution is a strong electrolyte.

4.45   (a)   AgNO$_3$ is soluble. Compounds containing NO$_3^-$ are always soluble with no exceptions. The ions in the solution are Ag$^+$(aq) and NO$_3^-$(aq).

(b)   Pb(C$_2$H$_3$O$_2$)$_2$ is soluble. Compounds containing C$_2$H$_3$O$_2^-$ are always soluble with no exceptions. The ions in the solution are Pb^{2+}(aq) and C$_2$H$_3$O$_2^-$(aq).

(c)   KNO$_3$ is soluble. Compounds containing K$^+$ or NO$_3^-$ are always soluble with no exceptions. The ions in solution are K$^+$(aq) and NO$_3^-$(aq).

(d)   (NH$_4$)$_2$S is soluble. Compounds containing NH$_4^+$ are always soluble with no exceptions. The ions in solution are NH$_4^+$(aq) and S^{2-}(aq).

4.46   (a)   AgI is insoluble. Compounds containing I$^-$ are normally soluble, but Ag$^+$ is an exception.

(b)   Cu$_3$(PO$_4$)$_2$ is insoluble. Compounds containing PO$_4^{3-}$ are normally insoluble, and Cu^{2+} is not an exception.

(c)   CoCO$_3$ is insoluble. Compounds containing CO$_3^{2-}$ are normally insoluble, and Co^{2+} is not an exception.

(d)   K$_3$PO$_4$ is soluble. Compounds containing PO$_4^{3-}$ are normally insoluble, but K$^+$ is an exception. The ions in solution are K$^+$(aq) and PO$_4^{3-}$(aq).

Precipitation Reactions

4.47   (a)   LiI(aq) + BaS(aq) → Possible products: Li$_2$S and BaI$_2$. Li$_2$S is soluble. Compounds containing S^{2-} are normally insoluble, but Li$^+$ is an exception. BaI$_2$ is soluble. Compounds containing I$^-$ are normally soluble, and Ba^{2+} is not an exception. LiI(aq) + BaS(aq) → No Reaction

(b)   KCl(aq) + CaS(aq) → Possible products: K$_2$S and CaCl$_2$. K$_2$S is soluble. Compounds containing S^{2-} are normally insoluble, but K$^+$ is an exception. CaCl$_2$ is soluble. Compounds containing Cl$^-$ are normally soluble, and Ca^{2+} is not an exception. KCl(aq) + CaS(aq) → No Reaction

(c)   CrBr$_2$(aq) + Na$_2$CO$_3$(aq) → Possible products: CrCO$_3$ and NaBr. CrCO$_3$ is insoluble. Compounds containing CO$_3^{2-}$ are normally insoluble, and Cr^{2+} is not an exception. NaBr is soluble. Compounds containing Br$^-$ are normally soluble, and Na$^+$ is not an exception.
CrBr$_2$(aq) + Na$_2$CO$_3$(aq) → CrCO$_3$(s) + 2 NaBr(aq)

(d)   NaOH(aq) + FeCl$_3$(aq) → Possible products: NaCl and Fe(OH)$_3$. NaCl is soluble. Compounds containing Na$^+$ are normally soluble—no exceptions. Fe(OH)$_3$ is insoluble. Compounds containing OH$^-$ are normally insoluble, and Fe^{3+} is not an exception.
3 NaOH(aq) + FeCl$_3$(aq) → 3 NaCl(aq) + Fe(OH)$_3$(s)

4.48   (a)   NaNO$_3$(aq) + KCl(aq) → Possible products: NaCl and KNO$_3$. NaCl is soluble. Compounds containing Na$^+$ are always soluble—no exceptions. KNO$_3$ is soluble. Compounds containing K$^+$ are always soluble—no exceptions. NaNO$_3$(aq) + KCl(aq) → No Reaction

(b)   NaCl(aq) + Hg$_2$(C$_2$H$_3$O$_2$)$_2$(aq) → Possible products: NaC$_2$H$_3$O$_2$ and Hg$_2$Cl$_2$. NaC$_2$H$_3$O$_2$ is soluble. Compounds containing Na$^+$ are always soluble—no exceptions. Hg$_2$Cl$_2$ is insoluble. Compounds containing Cl$^-$ are normally soluble, but Hg$_2^{2+}$ is an exception.
2 NaCl(aq) + Hg$_2$(C$_2$H$_3$O$_2$)$_2$(aq) → 2 NaC$_2$H$_3$O$_2$(aq) + Hg$_2$Cl$_2$(s)

(c)   (NH$_4$)$_2$SO$_4$(aq) + SrCl$_2$(aq) → Possible products: NH$_4$Cl and SrSO$_4$. NH$_4$Cl is soluble. Compounds containing NH$_4^+$ are always soluble—no exceptions. SrSO$_4$ is insoluble. Compounds containing SO$_4^{2-}$ are normally soluble, but Sr^{2+} is an exception.
(NH$_4$)$_2$SO$_4$(aq) + SrCl$_2$(aq) → 2 NH$_4$Cl(aq) + SrSO$_4$(s)

(d)   NH$_4$Cl(aq) + AgNO$_3$(aq) → Possible products: NH$_4$NO$_3$ and AgCl. NH$_4$NO$_3$ is soluble. Compounds containing NH$_4^+$ are always soluble—no exceptions. AgCl is insoluble. Compounds containing Cl$^-$ are normally soluble, but Ag$^+$ is an exception.
NH$_4$Cl(aq) + AgNO$_3$(aq) → NH$_4$NO$_3$(aq) + AgCl(s)

4.49   (a) $K_2CO_3(aq) + Pb(NO_3)_2(aq) \rightarrow$ Possible products: KNO_3 and $PbCO_3$. KNO_3 is soluble. Compounds containing K^+ are always soluble—no exceptions. $PbCO_3$ is insoluble. Compounds containing CO_3^{2-} are normally insoluble, and Pb^{2+} is not an exception.

$K_2CO_3(aq) + Pb(NO_3)_2(aq) \rightarrow 2\ KNO_3(aq) + PbCO_3(s)$

        (b) $Li_2SO_4(aq) + Pb(C_2H_3O_2)_2(aq) \rightarrow$ Possible products: $LiC_2H_3O_2$ and $PbSO_4$. $LiC_2H_3O_2$ is soluble. Compounds containing Li^+ are always soluble—no exceptions. $PbSO_4$ is insoluble. Compounds containing SO_4^{2-} are normally soluble, but Pb^{2+} is an exception.

$Li_2SO_4(aq) + Pb(C_2H_3O_2)_2(aq) \rightarrow 2\ LiC_2H_3O_2(aq) + PbSO_4(s)$

        (c) $Cu(NO_3)_2(aq) + MgS(s) \rightarrow$ Possible products: CuS and $Mg(NO_3)_2$. CuS is insoluble. Compounds containing S^{2-} are normally insoluble, and Cu^{2+} is not an exception. $Mg(NO_3)_2$ is soluble. Compounds containing NO_3^- are always soluble—no exceptions.

$Cu(NO_3)_2(aq) + MgS(s) \rightarrow CuS(s) + Mg(NO_3)_2(aq)$

        (d) $Sr(NO_3)_2(aq) + KI(aq) \rightarrow$ Possible products: SrI_2 and KNO_3. SrI_2 is soluble. Compounds containing I^- are normally soluble, and Sr^{2+} is not an exception. KNO_3 is soluble. Compounds containing K^+ are always soluble—no exceptions. $Sr(NO_3)_2(aq) + KI(aq) \rightarrow$ No Reaction

4.50   (a) $NaCl(aq) + Pb(C_2H_3O_2)_2(aq) \rightarrow$ Possible products $NaC_2H_3O_2$ and $PbCl_2$. $NaC_2H_3O_2$ is soluble. Compounds containing Na^+ are always soluble—no exceptions. $PbCl_2$ is insoluble. Compounds containing Cl^- are normally soluble, but Pb^{2+} is an exception.

$2\ NaCl(aq) + Pb(C_2H_3O_2)_2(aq) \rightarrow 2\ NaC_2H_3O_2(aq) + PbCl_2(s)$

        (b) $K_2SO_4(aq) + SrI_2(aq) \rightarrow$ Possible products: KI and $SrSO_4$. KI is soluble. Compounds containing K^+ are always soluble—no exceptions. $SrSO_4$ is insoluble. Compounds containing SO_4^{2-} are normally soluble, but Sr^{2+} is an exception. $K_2SO_4(aq) + SrI_2(aq) \rightarrow 2\ KI(aq) + SrSO_4(s)$

        (c) $CsCl(aq) + CaS(aq) \rightarrow$ Possible products: Cs_2S and $CaCl_2$. Cs_2S is soluble. Compounds containing S^{2-} are normally insoluble, but Cs^+ is an exception. $CaCl_2$ is soluble. Compounds containing Cl^- are normally soluble, and Ca^{2+} is not an exception. $CsCl(aq) + CaS(aq) \rightarrow$ No Reaction

        (d) $Cr(NO_3)_3(aq) + Na_3PO_4(aq) \rightarrow$ Possible products: $CrPO_4$ and $NaNO_3$. $CrPO_4$ is insoluble. Compounds containing PO_4^{3-} are normally insoluble, and Cr^{3+} is not an exception. $NaNO_3$ is soluble. Compounds containing Na^+ are always soluble—no exceptions.

$Cr(NO_3)_3(aq) + Na_3PO_4(aq) \rightarrow CrPO_4(s) + 3\ NaNO_3(aq)$

Ionic and Net Ionic Equations

4.51   (a) $H^+(aq) + \cancel{Cl^-}(aq) + \cancel{Li^+}(aq) + OH^-(aq) \rightarrow H_2O(l) + \cancel{Li^+}(aq) + \cancel{Cl^-}(aq)$
$H^+(aq) + OH^-(aq) \rightarrow H_2O(l)$

        (b) $\cancel{Ca^{2+}}(aq) + S^{2-}(aq) + Cu^{2+}(aq) + 2\ \cancel{Cl^-}(aq) \rightarrow CuS(s) + \cancel{Ca^{2+}}(aq) + 2\ \cancel{Cl^-}(aq)$
$Cu^{2+}(aq) + S^{2-}(aq) \rightarrow CuS(s)$

        (c) $\cancel{Na^+}(aq) + OH^-(aq) + H^+(aq) + \cancel{NO_3^-}(aq) \rightarrow H_2O(l) + \cancel{Na^+}(aq) + \cancel{NO_3^-}(aq)$
$H^+(aq) + OH^-(aq) + \rightarrow H_2O(l)$

        (d) $6\ \cancel{Na^+}(aq) + 2\ PO_4^{3-}(aq) + 3\ Ni^{2+}(aq) + 6\ \cancel{Cl^-}(aq) \rightarrow Ni_3(PO_4)_2(s) + 6\ \cancel{Na^+}(aq) + 6\ \cancel{Cl^-}(aq)$
$3\ Ni^{2+}(aq) + 2\ PO_4^{3-}(aq) \rightarrow Ni_3(PO_4)_2(s)$

4.52   (a) $2\ \cancel{K^+}(aq) + SO_4^{2-}(aq) + Ca^{2+}(aq) + 2\ \cancel{I^-}(aq) \rightarrow CaSO_4(s) + 2\ \cancel{K^+}(aq) + 2\ \cancel{I^-}(aq)$
$Ca^{2+}(aq) + SO_4^{2-}(aq) \rightarrow CaSO_4(s)$

        (b) $NH_4^+(aq) + \cancel{Cl^-}(aq) + \cancel{Na^+}(aq) + OH^-(aq) \rightarrow H_2O(l) + NH_3(g) + \cancel{Na^+}(aq) + \cancel{Cl^-}(aq)$
$NH_4^+(aq) + OH^-(aq) \rightarrow H_2O(l) + NH_3(g)$

        (c) $Ag^+(aq) + \cancel{NO_3^-}(aq) + \cancel{Na^+}(aq) + Cl^-(aq) \rightarrow AgCl(s) + \cancel{Na^+}(aq) + \cancel{NO_3^-}(aq)$
$Ag^+(aq) + Cl^-(aq) \rightarrow AgCl(s)$

        (d) $2\ HC_2H_3O_2(aq) + 2\ \cancel{K^+}(aq) + CO_3^{2-}(aq) \rightarrow H_2O(l) + CO_2(g) + 2\ \cancel{K^+}(aq) + 2\ C_2H_3O_2^-(aq)$
$2\ HC_2H_3O_2(aq) + CO_3^{2-}(aq) \rightarrow H_2O(l) + CO_2(g) + 2\ C_2H_3O_2^-(aq)$

4.53 $Hg_2^{2+}(aq) + 2\ \cancel{NO_3^-}(aq) + 2\ \cancel{Na^+}(aq) + 2\ Cl^-(aq) \rightarrow Hg_2Cl_2(s) + 2\ \cancel{Na^+}(aq) + 2\ \cancel{NO_3^-}(aq)$
$Hg_2^{2+}(aq) + 2\ Cl^-(aq) \rightarrow Hg_2Cl_2(s)$

4.54 $Pb^{2+}(aq) + 2\ \cancel{NO_3^-}(aq) + 2\ \cancel{K^+}(aq) + SO_4^{2-}(aq) \rightarrow PbSO_4(s) + 2\ \cancel{K^+}(aq) + 2\ \cancel{NO_3^-}(aq)$
$Pb^{2+}(aq) + SO_4^{2-}(aq) \rightarrow PbSO_4(s)$

Acid-Base and Gas-Evolution Reactions

4.55   Skeletal reaction: $HBr(aq) + KOH(aq) \rightarrow H_2O(l) + KBr(aq)$
                                 acid   base   water   salt
          Net ionic equation: $H^+(aq) + OH^-(aq) \rightarrow H_2O(l)$

4.56   Skeletal reaction: $HNO_3(aq) + Ca(OH)_2(aq) \rightarrow H_2O(l) + Ca(NO_3)_2(aq)$
                                 acid   base   water   salt
          Balanced reaction: $2 HNO_3(aq) + Ca(OH)_2(aq) \rightarrow 2 H_2O(l) + Ca(NO_3)_2(aq)$
          Net ionic equation: $H^+(aq) + OH^-(aq) \rightarrow H_2O(l)$

4.57   (a)   Skeletal reaction: $H_2SO_4(aq) + Ca(OH)_2(aq) \rightarrow H_2O(l) + CaSO_4(s)$
                                     acid   base   water   salt
                Balanced reaction: $H_2SO_4(aq) + Ca(OH)_2(aq) \rightarrow 2 H_2O(l) + CaSO_4(s)$

           (b)   Skeletal reaction: $HClO_4(aq) + KOH(aq) \rightarrow H_2O(l) + KClO_4(aq)$
                                     acid   base   water   salt
                Balanced reaction: $HClO_4(aq) + KOH(aq) \rightarrow H_2O(l) + KClO_4(aq)$

           (c)   Skeletal reaction: $H_2SO_4(aq) + NaOH(aq) \rightarrow H_2O(l) + Na_2SO_4(aq)$
                                     acid   base   water   salt
                Balanced reaction: $H_2SO_4(aq) + 2 NaOH(aq) \rightarrow 2 H_2O(l) + Na_2SO_4(aq)$

4.58   (a)   Skeletal reaction: $HI(aq) + LiOH(aq) \rightarrow H_2O(l) + LiI(aq)$
                                     acid   base   water   salt
                Balanced reaction: $HI(aq) + LiOH(aq) \rightarrow H_2O(l) + LiI(aq)$

           (b)   Skeletal reaction: $HC_2H_3O_2(aq) + Ca(OH)_2(aq) \rightarrow H_2O(l) + Ca(C_2H_3O_2)_2(aq)$
                                     acid   base   water   salt
                Balanced reaction: $2 HC_2H_3O_2(aq) + Ca(OH)_2(aq) \rightarrow 2 H_2O(l) + Ca(C_2H_3O_2)_2(aq)$

           (c)   Skeletal reaction: $HCl(aq) + Ba(OH)_2(aq) \rightarrow H_2O(l) + BaCl_2(aq)$
                                     acid   base   water   salt
                Balanced reaction: $2 HCl(aq) + Ba(OH)_2(aq) \rightarrow 2 H_2O(l) + BaCl_2(aq)$

4.59   (a)   Skeletal reaction: $HBr(aq) + NaOH(aq) \rightarrow H_2O(l) + NaBr(aq)$
                                     acid   base   water   salt
                Balanced reaction: $HBr(aq) + NaOH(aq) \rightarrow H_2O(l) + NaBr(aq)$
                Complete ionic equation: $H^+(aq) + Br^-(aq) + Na^+(aq) + OH^-(aq) \rightarrow H_2O(l) + Na^+(aq) + Br^-(aq)$
                Net ionic equation: $H^+(aq) + OH^-(aq) \rightarrow H_2O(l)$

           (b)   Skeletal reaction: $HF(aq) + NaOH(aq) \rightarrow H_2O(l) + NaF(aq)$
                                     acid   base   water   salt
                Balanced reaction: $HF(aq) + NaOH(aq) \rightarrow H_2O(l) + NaF(aq)$
                Complete ionic equation: $H^+(aq) + F^-(aq) + Na^+(aq) + OH^-(aq) \rightarrow H_2O(l) + Na^+(aq) + F^-(aq)$
                Net ionic equation: $H^+(aq) + OH^-(aq) \rightarrow H_2O(l)$

           (c)   Skeletal reaction: $HC_2H_3O_2(aq) + RbOH(aq) \rightarrow H_2O(l) + RbC_2H_3O_2(aq)$
                                     acid   base   water   salt
                Balanced reaction: $HC_2H_3O_2(aq) + RbOH(aq) \rightarrow H_2O(l) + RbC_2H_3O_2(aq)$
                Complete ionic equation: $HC_2H_3O_2(aq) + Rb^+(aq) + OH^-(aq) \rightarrow H_2O(l) + Rb^+(aq) + C_2H_3O_2^-(aq)$
                Net ionic equation: $HC_2H_3O_2(aq) + OH^-(aq) \rightarrow H_2O(l) + C_2H_3O_2^-(aq)$

4.60   (a)   Skeletal reaction: $HI(aq) + RbOH(aq) \rightarrow H_2O(l) + RbI(aq)$
                                     acid   base   water   salt
                Balanced reaction: $HI(aq) + RbOH(aq) \rightarrow H_2O(l) + RbI(aq)$
                Complete ionic equation: $H^+(aq) + I^-(aq) + Rb^+(aq) + OH^-(aq) \rightarrow H_2O(l) + Rb^+(aq) + I^-(aq)$
                Net ionic equation: $H^+(aq) + OH^-(aq) \rightarrow H_2O(l)$

(b)   Skeletal reaction: $HCHO_2(aq) + NaOH(aq) \rightarrow H_2O(l) + NaCHO_2(aq)$
                                    acid   base   water   salt
       Balanced reaction: $HCHO_2(aq) + NaOH(aq) \rightarrow H_2O(l) + NaCHO_2(aq)$
       Complete ionic equation: $HCHO_2(aq) + Na^+(aq) + OH^-(aq) \rightarrow H_2O(l) + Na^+(aq) + CHO_2^-(aq)$
       Net ionic equation: $HCHO_2(aq) + OH^-(aq) \rightarrow H_2O(l) + CHO_2^-(aq)$

(c)   Skeletal reaction: $HC_2H_3O_2(aq) + LiOH(aq) \rightarrow H_2O(l) + LiC_2H_3O_2(aq)$
                                    acid   base   water   salt
       Balanced reaction: $HC_2H_3O_2(aq) + LiOH(aq) \rightarrow H_2O(l) + LiC_2H_3O_2(aq)$
       Complete ionic equation: $HC_2H_3O_2(aq) + Li^+(aq) + OH^-(aq) \rightarrow H_2O(l) + Li^+(aq) + C_2H_3O_2^-(aq)$
       Net ionic Equation: $HC_2H_3O_2(aq) + OH^-(aq) \rightarrow H_2O(l) + C_2H_3O_2^-(aq)$

4.61   (a)   Skeletal reaction: $HBr(aq) + NiS(s) \rightarrow NiBr_2(aq) + H_2S(g)$
                                                                                    gas
               Balanced reaction: $2\,HBr(aq) + NiS(s) \rightarrow NiBr_2(aq) + H_2S(g)$

        (b)   Skeletal reaction: $NH_4I(aq) + NaOH(aq) \rightarrow NH_4OH(aq) + NaI(aq) \rightarrow H_2O(l) + NH_3(g) + NaI(aq)$
                                                                decomposes   gas
               Balanced reaction: $NH_4I(aq) + NaOH(aq) \rightarrow H_2O(l) + NH_3(g) + NaI(aq)$

        (c)   Skeletal reaction: $HBr(aq) + Na_2S(aq) \rightarrow NaBr(aq) + H_2S(g)$
                                                                            gas
               Balanced reaction: $2\,HBr(aq) + Na_2S(aq) \rightarrow 2\,NaBr(aq) + H_2S(g)$

        (d)   Skeletal reaction:
               $HClO_4(aq) + Li_2CO_3(aq) \rightarrow H_2CO_3(aq) + LiClO_4(aq) \rightarrow H_2O(l) + CO_2(g) + LiClO_4(aq)$
                                                    decomposes   gas
               Balanced reaction: $2\,HClO_4(aq) + Li_2CO_3(aq) \rightarrow H_2O(l) + CO_2(g) + 2\,LiClO_4(aq)$

4.62   (a)   Skeletal reaction:
               $HNO_3(aq) + Na_2SO_3(aq) \rightarrow H_2SO_3(aq) + NaNO_3(aq) \rightarrow H_2O(l) + SO_2(g) + NaNO_3(aq)$
                                                    decomposes   gas
               Balanced reaction: $2\,HNO_3(aq) + Na_2SO_3(aq) \rightarrow H_2O(l) + SO_2(g) + 2\,NaNO_3(aq)$

        (b)   Skeletal reaction: $HCl(aq) + KHCO_3(aq) \rightarrow H_2CO_3(aq) + KCl(aq) \rightarrow H_2O(l) + CO_2(g) + KCl(aq)$
                                                                decomposes   gas
               Balanced reaction: $HCl(aq) + KHCO_3(aq) \rightarrow H_2O(l) + CO_2(g) + KCl(aq)$

        (c)   Skeletal reaction:
               $HC_2H_3O_2(aq) + NaHSO_3(aq) \rightarrow NaC_2H_3O_2(aq) + H_2SO_3(aq) \rightarrow H_2O(l) + SO_2(g) + NaC_2H_3O_2(aq)$
                                                                decomposes   gas
               Balanced reaction: $HC_2H_3O_2(aq) + NaHSO_3(aq) \rightarrow H_2O(l) + SO_2(g) + NaC_2H_3O_2(aq)$

        (d)   Skeletal reaction:
               $(NH_4)_2SO_4(aq) + Ca(OH)_2(aq) \rightarrow 2\,NH_4OH(aq) + CaSO_4(s) \rightarrow 2\,H_2O(l) + 2\,NH_3(g) + CaSO_4(s)$
                                                            decomposes   gas
               Balanced reaction: $(NH_4)_2SO_4(aq) + Ca(OH)_2(aq) \rightarrow 2H_2O(l) + 2NH_3(g) + CaSO_4(s)$

Oxidation–Reduction and Combustion

4.63   (a)   Ag. The oxidation state of Ag = 0. The oxidation state of an atom in a free element is 0.
        (b) Ag^+. The oxidation state of Ag^+ = +1. The oxidation state of a monatomic ion is equal to its charge.
        (c) CaF_2. The oxidation state of Ca = +2, and the oxidation state of F = −1. The oxidation state of a group 2A
               metal always has an oxidation state of +2, and the oxidation of F is −1 because the sum of the oxidation states
               in a neutral formula unit = 0.
        (d) H_2S. The oxidation state of H = +1, and the oxidation state of S = −2. The oxidation state of H when listed
               first is +1, and the oxidation state of S is −2 because S is in group 6A and the sum of the oxidation states in a
               neutral molecular unit = 0.

(e) CO_3^{2-}. The oxidation state of C = +4, and the oxidation state of O = −2. The oxidation state of O is normally −2, and the oxidation state of C is deduced from the formula because the sum of the oxidation states must equal the charge on the ion. (C ox state) + 3(O ox state) = −2; (C ox state) + 3(−2) = −2, so C ox state = +4.

(f) CrO_4^{2-}. The oxidation state of Cr = +6, and the oxidation state of O = −2. The oxidation state of O is normally −2, and the oxidation state of Cr is deduced from the formula because the sum of the oxidation states must equal the charge on the ion. (Cr ox state) + 4(O ox state) = −2; (Cr ox state) + 4(−2) = −2, so Cr ox state = +6.

4.64 (a) Cl_2. The oxidation of both Cl atoms = 0. Because Cl_2 is a free element, the oxidation state of Cl = 0.

(b) Fe^{3+}. The oxidation of Fe = +3. The oxidation state of a monatomic ion is equal to its charge.

(c) $CuCl_2$. The oxidation state of Cu = +2, and the oxidation state of each Cl = −1. The oxidation state of group 7A atoms is normally −1, and the oxidation state of Cu is deduced from the formula because the sum of the oxidation states in a neutral formula unit = 0.

(d) CH_4. The oxidation state of C = −4, and the oxidation state of H = +1. The oxidation state of H is normally +1, and the oxidation state of C is deduced for the formula because the sum of the oxidation states in a neutral molecular unit = 0. (C ox state) + 4(H ox state) = 0; (C ox state) + 4(+1) = 0, so C ox state = −4.

(e) $Cr_2O_7^{2-}$. The oxidation state of Cr = +6, and the oxidation state of O = −2. The oxidation state of O is normally −2, and the oxidation state of Cr is deduced from the formula because the sum of the oxidation states must equal the charge of the ion. 2(Cr ox state) + 7(O ox state) = −2; 2(Cr ox state) + 7(−2) = −2, so Cr ox state = +6.

(f) HSO_4^-. The oxidation state of H = +1, the oxidation state of S = +6, and the oxidation state of O = −2. The oxidation state of H is normally +1, the oxidation state of O is normally −2, and the oxidation state of S is deduced from the formula because the sum of the oxidation states must equal the charge of the ion. (H ox state) + (S ox state) + 4(O ox state) = −1; (+1) + (S ox state) + 4(−2) = −1, so S ox state = +6.

4.65 (a) CrO. The oxidation state of Cr = +2, and the oxidation state of O = −2. The oxidation state of O is normally −2, and the oxidation state of Cr is deduced from the formula because the sum of the oxidation states must = 0.
(Cr ox state) + (O ox state) = 0; (Cr ox state) + (−2) = 0, so Cr = +2.

(b) CrO_3. The oxidation state of Cr = +6, and the oxidation state of O = −2. The oxidation state of O is normally −2, and the oxidation state of Cr is deduced from the formula because the sum of the oxidation states must = 0.
(Cr ox state) + 3(O ox state) = 0; (Cr ox state) + 3 (−2) = 0, so Cr = +6.

(c) Cr_2O_3. The oxidation state of Cr = +3, and the oxidation state of O = −2. The oxidation state of O is normally −2, and the oxidation state of Cr is deduced from the formula because the sum of the oxidation states must = 0.
2(Cr ox state) + 3(O ox state) = 0; 2(Cr ox state) + 3(−2) = 0, so Cr = +3.

4.66 (a) ClO^-. The oxidation state of Cl = +1, and the oxidation state of O = −2. The oxidation state of O is normally −2, and the oxidation state of Cl is deduced from the formula because the sum of the oxidation states must equal the charge of the ion. (Cl ox state) + (O ox state) = −1; (Cl ox state) + (−2) = −1, so Cl = +1.

(b) ClO_2^-. The oxidation state of Cl = +3, and the oxidation state of O = −2. The oxidation state of O is normally −2, and the oxidation state of Cl is deduced from the formula because the sum of the oxidation states must equal the charge of the ion. (Cl ox state) + 2(O ox state) = −1; (Cl ox state) + 2(−2) = −1, so Cl = +3.

(c) ClO_3^-. The oxidation state of Cl = +5, and the oxidation state of O = −2. The oxidation state of O is normally −2, and the oxidation state of Cl is deduced from the formula because the sum of the oxidation states must equal the charge of the ion. (Cl ox state) + 3(O ox state) = −1; (Cl ox state) + 3(−2) = −1, so Cl = +5.

(d) ClO_4^-. The oxidation state of Cl = +7, and the oxidation state of O = −2. The oxidation state of O is normally −2, and the oxidation state of Cl is deduced from the formula because the sum of the oxidation states must equal the charge of the ion. (Cl ox state) + 4(O ox state) = −1; (Cl ox state) + 4(−2) = −1, so Cl = +7.

4.67 (a)
$$4\,Li(s) + O_2(g) \rightarrow 2\,Li_2O(s)$$
Oxidation states;   0   0   +1 −2
This is a redox reaction because Li increases in oxidation number (oxidation) and O decreases in number (reduction). O_2 is the oxidizing agent, and Li is the reducing agent.

(b)
$$Mg(s) + Fe^{2+}(aq) \rightarrow Mg^{2+}(aq) + Fe(s)$$
Oxidation states;   0   +2   +2   0

This is a redox reaction because Mg increases in oxidation number (oxidation) and Fe decreases in number (reduction). Fe^{2+} is the oxidizing agent, and Mg is the reducing agent.

(c) $$Pb(NO_3)_2(aq) + Na_2SO_4(aq) \rightarrow PbSO_4(s) + 2\,NaNO_3(aq)$$
Oxidation states;   +2 +5 −2   +1 +6 −2   +2 +6 −2   +1 +5 −2
This is a not a redox reaction because none of the atoms undergoes a change in oxidation number.

(d) $$HBr(aq) + KOH(aq) \rightarrow H_2O(l) + KBr(aq)$$
Oxidation states;   +1 −1   +1 −2 +1   +1 −2   +1 −1
This is a not a redox reaction because none of the atoms undergoes a change in oxidation number.

4.68   (a) $$Al(s) + 3\,Ag^+(aq) \rightarrow Al^{3+}(aq) + 3\,Ag(s)$$
Oxidation states;   0   +1   +3   0
This is a redox reaction because Al increases in oxidation number (oxidation) and Ag decreases in number (reduction). Ag^+ is the oxidizing agent, and Al is the reducing agent.

(b) $$SO_3(g) + H_2O(l) \rightarrow H_2SO_4(aq)$$
Oxidation states;   +6 −2   +1 −2   +1 +6 −2
This is a not a redox reaction because none of the atoms undergoes a change in oxidation number.

(c) $$Ba(s) + Cl_2(g) \rightarrow BaCl_2(s)$$
Oxidation states;   0   0   +2 −1
This is a redox reaction because Ba increases in oxidation number (oxidation) and Cl decreases in number (reduction). Cl_2 is the oxidizing agent, and Ba is the reducing agent.

(d) $$Mg(s) + Br_2(l) \rightarrow MgBr_2(s)$$
Oxidation states;   0   0   +2 −1
This is a redox reaction because Mg increases in oxidation number (oxidation) and Br decreases in number (reduction). Br_2 is the oxidizing agent, and Mg is the reducing agent.

4.69   (a)   Skeletal reaction: $S(s) + O_2(g) \rightarrow SO_2(g)$
Balanced reaction: $S(s) + O_2(g) \rightarrow SO_2(g)$

(b)   Skeletal reaction: $C_3H_6(g) + O_2(g) \rightarrow CO_2(g) + H_2O(g)$
Balance C: $C_3H_6(g) + O_2(g) \rightarrow 3\,CO_2(g) + H_2O(g)$
Balance H: $C_3H_6(g) + O_2(g) \rightarrow 3\,CO_2(g) + 3\,H_2O(g)$
Balance O: $C_3H_6(g) + 9/2\,O_2(g) \rightarrow 3\,CO_2(g) + 3\,H_2O(g)$
Clear fraction: $2\,C_3H_6(g) + 9\,O_2(g) \rightarrow 6\,CO_2(g) + 6\,H_2O(g)$

(c)   Skeletal reaction: $Ca(s) + O_2(g) \rightarrow CaO(s)$
Balance O: $Ca(s) + O_2(g) \rightarrow 2\,CaO(s)$
Balance Ca: $2\,Ca(s) + O_2(g) \rightarrow 2\,CaO(s)$

(d)   Skeletal reaction: $C_5H_{12}S(l) + O_2(g) \rightarrow CO_2(g) + H_2O(g) + SO_2(g)$
Balance C: $C_5H_{12}S(l) + O_2(g) \rightarrow 5\,CO_2(g) + H_2O(g) + SO_2(g)$
Balance H: $C_5H_{12}S(l) + O_2(g) \rightarrow 5\,CO_2(g) + 6\,H_2O(g) + SO_2(g)$
Balance S: $C_5H_{12}S(l) + O_2(g) \rightarrow 5\,CO_2(g) + 6\,H_2O(g) + SO_2(g)$
Balance O: $C_5H_{12}S(l) + 9\,O_2(g) \rightarrow 5\,CO_2(g) + 6\,H_2O(g) + SO_2(g)$

4.70   (a)   Skeletal reaction: $C_4H_6(g) + O_2(g) \rightarrow CO_2(g) + H_2O(g)$
Balance C: $C_4H_6(g) + O_2(g) \rightarrow 4\,CO_2(g) + H_2O(g)$
Balance H: $C_4H_6(g) + O_2(g) \rightarrow 4\,CO_2(g) + 3\,H_2O(g)$
Balance O: $C_4H_6(g) + 11/2\,O_2(g) \rightarrow 4\,CO_2(g) + 3\,H_2O(g)$
Clear fraction: $2\,C_4H_6(g) + 11\,O_2(g) \rightarrow 8\,CO_2(g) + 6\,H_2O(g)$

(b)   Skeletal reaction: $C(s) + O_2(g) \rightarrow CO_2(g)$
Balanced reaction: $C(s) + O_2(g) \rightarrow CO_2(g)$

(c)   Skeletal reaction: $CS_2(l) + O_2(g) \rightarrow CO_2(g) + SO_2(g)$
Balance C: $CS_2(l) + O_2(g) \rightarrow CO_2(g) + SO_2(g)$
Balance S: $CS_2(l) + O_2(g) \rightarrow CO_2(g) + 2\,SO_2(g)$
Balance O: $CS_2(l) + 3\,O_2(g) \rightarrow CO_2(g) + 2\,SO_2(g)$

(d)   Skeletal reaction: $C_3H_8O(l) + O_2(g) \rightarrow CO_2(g) + H_2O(g)$
Balance C: $C_3H_8O(l) + O_2(g) \rightarrow 3\,CO_2(g) + H_2O(g)$
Balance H: $C_3H_8O(l) + O_2(g) \rightarrow 3\,CO_2(g) + 4\,H_2O(g)$
Balance O: $C_3H_8O(l) + 9/2\,O_2(g) \rightarrow 3\,CO_2(g) + 4\,H_2O(g)$
Clear fraction: $2\,C_3H_8O(l) + 9\,O_2(g) \rightarrow 6\,CO_2(g) + 8\,H_2O(g)$

Cumulative Problems

4.71 **Given:** In 100 g solution, 20.0 g $C_2H_6O_2$; density of solution = 1.03 g/mL **Find:** M of solution
Conceptual Plan: g $C_2H_6O_2$ → mol $C_2H_6O_2$ and g solution → mL solution → L solution

$$\frac{1 \text{ mol } C_2H_6O_2}{62.07 \text{ g } C_2H_6O_2} \qquad \frac{1.00 \text{ mL}}{1.03 \text{ g}} \qquad \frac{1 \text{ L}}{1000 \text{ mL}}$$

then M $C_2H_6O_2$

$$M = \frac{\text{mol } C_2H_6O_2}{\text{L solution}}$$

Solution:

$$20.0 \text{ g } C_2H_6O_2 \times \frac{1 \text{ mol } C_2H_6O_2}{62.07 \text{ g } C_2H_6O_2} = 0.3222 \text{ mol } C_2H_6O_2$$

$$100.0 \text{ g solution} \times \frac{1.00 \text{ mL solution}}{1.03 \text{ g solution}} \times \frac{1 \text{ L}}{1000 \text{ mL}} = 0.09709 \text{ L}$$

$$M = \frac{0.3222 \text{ mol } C_2H_6O_2}{0.09709 \text{ L}} = 3.319 \text{ M } C_2H_6O_2 = 3.32 \text{ M } C_2H_6O_2$$

Check: The units of the answer (M $C_2H_6O_2$) are correct. The magnitude of the answer is reasonable because the concentration of solutions is usually between 0 and 18 M.

4.72 **Given:** 1.35 M NaCl; density of solution $d = 1.05$ g /mL **Find:** % NaCl by mass
Conceptual Plan: mol NaCl → g NaCl and L solution → mL solution → g solution then % NaCl

$$\frac{58.44 \text{ g NaCl}}{1 \text{ mol NaCl}} \qquad \frac{1000 \text{ mL}}{1 \text{ L}} \qquad \frac{1.05 \text{ g}}{1.00 \text{ mL}} \qquad \frac{\text{g NaCl}}{\text{g solution}} \times 100\%$$

Solution: $1.35 \text{ M} = \dfrac{1.35 \text{ mol NaCl}}{1 \text{ L solution}}$

$$1.35 \text{ mol NaCl} \times \frac{58.44 \text{ g NaCl}}{1 \text{ mol NaCl}} = 78.89 \text{ g NaCl} \qquad 1 \text{ L solution} \times \frac{1000 \text{ mL}}{\text{L}} \times \frac{1.05 \text{ g solution}}{\text{mL solution}} = 1050 \text{ g solution}$$

$$\frac{78.89 \text{ g NaCl}}{1050 \text{ g solution}} \times 100\% = 75.13\% \text{ NaCl} = 7.51\% \text{ NaCl}$$

Check: The units of the answer (% NaCl) are correct. The magnitude of the answer is reasonable for the concentration of the solution.

4.73 **Given:** 2.5 g $NaHCO_3$ **Find:** g HCl
Conceptual Plan: g $NaHCO_3$ → mol $NaHCO_3$ → mol HCl → g HCl

$$\frac{1 \text{ mol } NaHCO_3}{84.01 \text{ g } NaHCO_3} \qquad \frac{1 \text{ mol HCl}}{1 \text{ mol } NaHCO_3} \qquad \frac{36.46 \text{ g HCl}}{1 \text{ mol HCl}}$$

Solution: $HCl(aq) + NaHCO_3(aq) \rightarrow H_2O(l) + CO_2(g) + NaCl(aq)$

$$2.5 \text{ g } NaHCO_3 \times \frac{1 \text{ mol } NaHCO_3}{84.01 \text{ g } NaHCO_3} \times \frac{1 \text{ mol HCl}}{1 \text{ mol } NaHCO_3} \times \frac{36.46 \text{ g HCl}}{1 \text{ mol HCl}} = 1.08 \text{ g HCl} = 1.1 \text{ g HCl}$$

Check: The units of the answer (g HCl) are correct. The magnitude of the answer is reasonable because the molar mass of HCl is less than the molar mass of $NaHCO_3$.

4.74 **Given:** 3.8 g HCl **Find:** g $CaCO_3$
Conceptual Plan: g HCl → mol HCl → mol $CaCO_3$ → g $CaCO_3$

$$\frac{1 \text{ mol HCl}}{36.46 \text{ g HCl}} \qquad \frac{1 \text{ mol } CaCO_3}{2 \text{ mol HCl}} \qquad \frac{100.09 \text{ g } CaCO_3}{1 \text{ mol } CaCO_3}$$

Solution: $2 \text{ HCl}(aq) + CaCO_3(s) \rightarrow H_2O(l) + CO_2(g) + CaCl_2(aq)$

$$3.8 \text{ g HCl} \times \frac{\text{mol HCl}}{36.46 \text{ g HCl}} \times \frac{1 \text{ mol } CaCO_3}{2 \text{ mol HCl}} \times \frac{100.09 \text{ g } CaCO_3}{1 \text{ mol } CaCO_3} = 5.22 \text{ g } CaCO_3 = 5.2 \text{ g } CaCO_3$$

Check: The units of the answer (g $CaCO_3$) are correct. The magnitude of the answer is reasonable because the molar mass of $CaCO_3$ is greater than the molar mass of HCl.

4.75   **Given:** 1.0 kg C_8H_{18} **Find:** kg CO_2

Conceptual Plan: kg C_8H_{18} → g C_8H_{18} → mol C_8H_{18} → mol CO_2 → g CO_2 → kg CO_2

$$\frac{1000\ g}{1\ kg} \qquad \frac{1\ mol\ C_8H_{18}}{114.22\ g\ C_8H_{18}} \qquad \frac{16\ mol\ CO_2}{2\ mol\ C_8H_{18}} \qquad \frac{44.01\ g\ CO_2}{1\ mol\ CO_2} \qquad \frac{1\ kg}{1000\ g}$$

Solution: $2\ C_8H_{18}(g) + 25\ O_2(g) \rightarrow 16\ CO_2(g) + 18\ H_2O(g)$

$$1.0\ kg\ C_8H_{18} \times \frac{1000\ g}{1\ kg} \times \frac{1\ mol\ C_8H_{18}}{114.22\ g\ C_8H_{18}} \times \frac{16\ mol\ CO_2}{2\ mol\ C_8H_{18}} \times \frac{44.01\ g\ CO_2}{1\ mol\ CO_2} \times \frac{1\ kg}{1000\ g} = 3.\underline{0}8\ kg\ CO_2 = 3.1\ kg\ CO_2$$

Check: The units of the answer (kg CO_2) are correct. The magnitude of the answer is reasonable because the ratio of CO_2 to C_8H_{18} is 8:1.

4.76   **Given:** 18.9 L C_3H_8; $d = 0.621$ g/mL   **Find:** kg CO_2

Conceptual Plan: L C_3H_8 → mL C_3H_8 → g C_3H_8 → mol C_3H_8 → mol CO_2 → g CO_2 → kg CO_2

$$\frac{1000\ mL}{1\ L} \quad \frac{0.621\ g}{1\ mL} \quad \frac{1\ mol\ C_3H_8}{44.09\ g\ C_3H_8} \quad \frac{3\ mol\ CO_2}{1\ mol\ C_3H_8} \quad \frac{44.01\ g\ CO_2}{1\ mol\ CO_2} \quad \frac{1\ kg}{1000\ g}$$

Solution: $C_3H_8(g) + 5\ O_2(g) \rightarrow 3\ CO_2(g) + 4\ H_2O(g)$

$$18.9\ L\ C_3H_8 \times \frac{1000\ mL}{1\ L} \times \frac{0.621\ g}{1\ mL} \times \frac{1\ mol\ C_3H_8}{44.09\ g\ C_3H_8} \times \frac{3\ mol\ CO_2}{1\ mol\ C_3H_8} \times \frac{44.01\ g\ CO_2}{1\ mol\ CO_2} \times \frac{1\ kg}{1000\ g} = 35.147\ kg\ CO_2$$

$$= 35.1\ kg\ CO_2$$

Check: The units of the answer (kg CO_2) are correct. The magnitude of the answer is reasonable because the molar masses of CO_2 and C_3H_8 are close and the mole ratio is 1:3.

4.77   **Given:** 3.00 mL $C_4H_6O_3$, $d = 1.08$ g/mL; 1.25 g $C_7H_6O_3$; 1.22 g $C_9H_8O_4$ **Find:** limiting reactant; theoretical yield $C_9H_8O_4$; % yield $C_9H_8O_4$

Conceptual Plan: mL $C_4H_6O_3$ → g $C_4H_6O_3$ → mol $C_4H_6O_3$ → mol $C_9H_8O_4$

$$\frac{1.08\ g\ C_4H_6O_3}{1.00\ mL\ C_4H_6O_3} \quad \frac{1\ mol\ C_4H_6O_3}{102.09\ g\ C_4H_6O_3} \quad \frac{1\ mol\ C_9H_8O_4}{1\ mol\ C_4H_6O_3} \quad \rightarrow \textbf{smallest mol amount determines limiting reactant}$$

g $C_7H_6O_3$ → mol $C_7H_6O_3$ → mol $C_9H_8O_4$

$$\frac{1\ mol\ C_7H_6O_3}{138.12\ g\ C_7H_6O_3} \quad \frac{1\ mol\ C_9H_8O_4}{1\ mol\ C_7H_6O_3}$$

then mol $C_9H_8O_4$ → g $C_9H_8O_4$ then determine % yield

$$\frac{180.2\ g\ C_9H_8O_4}{1\ mol\ C_9H_8O_4} \qquad \frac{actual\ yield\ g\ C_9H_8O_4}{theoretical\ yield\ g\ C_9H_8O_4} \times 100\%$$

Solution:

$$3.00\ mL\ C_4H_6O_3 \times \frac{1.08\ g\ C_4H_6O_3}{mL\ C_4H_6O_3} \times \frac{1\ mol\ C_4H_6O_3}{102.09\ g\ C_4H_6O_3} \times \frac{1\ mol\ C_9H_8O_4}{1\ mol\ C_4H_6O_3} = 0.031\underline{7}4\ mol\ C_9H_8O_4$$

$$1.25\ g\ C_7H_6O_3 \times \frac{1\ mol\ C_7H_6O_3}{138.12\ g\ C_7H_6O_3} \times \frac{1\ mol\ C_9H_8O_4}{1\ mol\ C_7H_6O_3} = 0.00905\underline{0}\ mol\ C_9H_8O_4$$

Salicylic acid is the limiting reactant.

$$0.009050\ mol\ C_9H_8O_4 \times \frac{180.2\ g\ C_9H_8O_4}{1\ mol\ C_9H_8O_4} = 1.6\underline{3}1\ g\ C_9H_8O_4$$

$$\frac{1.22\ g\ C_9H_8O_4}{1.6\underline{3}1\ g\ C_9H_8O_4} \times 100\% = 74.8\%$$

Check: The theoretical yield has the correct units (g $C_9H_8O_4$) and has a reasonable magnitude compared to the mass of $C_7H_6O_3$, the limiting reactant. The % yield is reasonable, under 100%.

4.78   **Given:** 4.62 mL C_2H_5OH, $d = 0.789$ g/mL; 15.55 g O_2; 3.72 mL H_2O, $d = 1.00$ g/mL

Find: limiting reactant; theoretical yield H_2O; % yield H_2O

Conceptual Plan: mL C_2H_5OH → g C_2H_5OH → mol C_2H_5OH → mol H_2O

$$\frac{0.789\ g\ C_2H_5OH}{1.00\ mL\ C_2H_5OH} \quad \frac{1\ mol\ C_2H_5OH}{46.07\ g\ C_2H_5OH} \quad \frac{3\ mol\ H_2O}{1\ mol\ C_2H_5OH} \quad \rightarrow \textbf{smallest mol amount determines limiting reactant}$$

g O_2 → mol O_2 → mol H_2O

$$\frac{1\ mol\ O_2}{32.00\ g\ O_2} \quad \frac{3\ mol\ H_2O}{3\ mol\ O_2}$$

then mol H_2O → g H_2O　　　**then determine % yield**

$$\frac{18.02 \text{ g } H_2O}{1 \text{ mol } H_2O}$$ 　　　 $$\frac{\text{actual yield g } H_2O}{\text{theoretical yield g } H_2O} \times 100\%$$

Solution:

$$C_2H_5OH(l) + 3\,O_2(g) \rightarrow 2\,CO_2(g) + 3\,H_2O(l)$$

$$4.62 \text{ mL } C_2H_5OH \times \frac{0.789 \text{ g } C_2H_5OH}{\text{mL } C_2H_5OH} \times \frac{1 \text{ mol } C_2H_5OH}{46.07 \text{ g } C_2H_5OH} \times \frac{3 \text{ mol } H_2O}{1 \text{ mol } C_2H_5OH} = 0.23\underline{7}4 \text{ mol } H_2O$$

$$15.55 \text{ g } O_2 \times \frac{1 \text{ mol } O_2}{32.00 \text{ g } O_2} \times \frac{3 \text{ mol } H_2O}{3 \text{ mol } O_2} = 0.485\underline{9}4 \text{ mol } H_2O$$

C_2H_5OH is the limiting reactant.

$$0.23\underline{7}4 \text{ mol } H_2O \times \frac{18.02 \text{ g } H_2O}{1 \text{ mol } H_2O} = 4.2\underline{7}8 \text{ g } H_2O$$

$$\frac{3.72 \text{ g } H_2O}{4.2\underline{7}8 \text{ g } H_2O} \times 100\% = 87.0\%$$

Check: The theoretical yield has the correct units (g H_2O) and has a reasonable magnitude compared to the mass of C_2H_5OH, the limiting reactant. The % yield is reasonable, under 100%.

4.79　　**Given:** (a) 11 molecules H_2, 2 molecules O_2; (b) 8 molecules H_2, 4 molecules O_2; (c) 4 molecules H_2, 5 molecules O_2; (d) 3 molecules H_2, 6 molecules O_2　　**Find:** loudest explosion based on equation

Conceptual Plan: Loudest explosion will occur in the balloon with the mol ratio closest to the balanced equation that contains the most H_2.

Solution: $2H_2(g) + O_2(g) \rightarrow H_2O(l)$

Balloon (a) has enough O_2 to react with 4 molecules H_2; balloon (b) has enough O_2 to react with 8 molecules H_2; balloon (c) has enough O_2 to react with 10 molecules H_2; balloon (d) has enough O_2 for 3 molecules of H_2 to react. Balloon (b) also has the proper stoichiometric ratio of 2 H_2:1O_2 unlike the other three. Therefore balloon (b) will have the loudest explosion because it has the most H_2 that will react.

Check: Answer seems correct because it has the most H_2 with enough O_2 in the balloon to completely react.

4.80　　**Given:** Beaker containing 4 ions H^+, 4 ions Cl^-　　**Find:** which NaOH beaker will just neutralize HCl beaker

Conceptual Plan: molecules H^+ → molecules OH^- then compare to four beakers

$$\frac{1 \text{ ion } OH^-}{1 \text{ ion } H^+}$$

Solution: $HCl(aq) + NaOH(aq) \rightarrow NaCl(aq) + H_2O(l)$

Net Ionic: $H^+(aq) + OH^-(aq) \rightarrow H_2O(l)$

$$4 \text{ ions } H^+ \times \frac{1 \text{ ion } OH^-}{1 \text{ ion } H^+} = 4 \text{ ions } OH^-$$

Beaker (a) contains 2 ions OH^-; beaker (b) contains 4 ions OH^-; beaker (c) contains 5 ions OH^-; beaker (d) contains 8 ions OH^-. Beaker (b) will completely neutralize the HCl beaker with no excess.

Check: The answer is correct because it will completely neutralize the H^+ with no excess OH^-.

4.81　　(a)　Skeletal reaction:　　$HCl(aq) + Hg_2(NO_3)_2(aq) \rightarrow Hg_2Cl_2(s) + HNO_3(aq)$
　　　　　　Balance Cl:　　　　$2\,HCl(aq) + Hg_2(NO_3)_2(aq) \rightarrow Hg_2Cl_2(s) + 2\,HNO_3(aq)$
　　　　(b)　Skeletal reaction:　　$KHSO_3(aq) + HNO_3(aq) \rightarrow H_2O(l) + SO_2(g) + KNO_3(aq)$
　　　　　　Balanced reaction:　　$KHSO_3(aq) + HNO_3(aq) \rightarrow H_2O(l) + SO_2(g) + KNO_3(aq)$
　　　　(c)　Skeletal reaction:　　$NH_4Cl(aq) + Pb(NO_3)_2(aq) \rightarrow PbCl_2(s) + NH_4NO_3(aq)$
　　　　　　Balance Cl:　　　　$2\,NH_4Cl(aq) + Pb(NO_3)_2(aq) \rightarrow PbCl_2(s) + NH_4NO_3(aq)$
　　　　　　Balance N:　　　　$2\,NH_4Cl(aq) + Pb(NO_3)_2(aq) \rightarrow PbCl_2(s) + 2\,NH_4NO_3(aq)$
　　　　(d)　Skeletal reaction:　　$NH_4Cl(aq) + Ca(OH)_2(aq) \rightarrow NH_3(g) + H_2O(l) + CaCl_2(aq)$
　　　　　　Balance Cl:　　　　$2\,NH_4Cl(aq) + Ca(OH)_2(aq) \rightarrow NH_3(g) + H_2O(l) + CaCl_2(aq)$
　　　　　　Balance N:　　　　$2\,NH_4Cl(aq) + Ca(OH)_2(aq) \rightarrow 2\,NH_3(g) + H_2O(l) + CaCl_2(aq)$
　　　　　　Balance H:　　　　$2\,NH_4Cl(aq) + Ca(OH)_2(aq) \rightarrow 2\,NH_3(g) + 2\,H_2O(l) + CaCl_2(aq)$

4.82　　(a)　Skeletal reaction:　　$H_2SO_4(aq) + HNO_3(aq) \rightarrow$ No Reaction
　　　　(b)　Skeletal reaction:　　$Cr(NO_3)_3(aq) + LiOH(aq) \rightarrow Cr(OH)_3(s) + LiNO_3(aq)$

Balance OH: $Cr(NO_3)_3(aq) + 3\ LiOH(aq) \rightarrow Cr(OH)_3(s) + LiNO_3(aq)$

Balance Li: $Cr(NO_3)_3(aq) + 3\ LiOH(aq) \rightarrow Cr(OH)_3(s) + 3\ LiNO_3(aq)$

(c) Skeletal reaction: $C_5H_{12}O(l) + O_2(g) \rightarrow CO_2(g) + H_2O(g)$

Balance C: $C_5H_{12}O(l) + O_2(g) \rightarrow 5\ CO_2(g) + H_2O(g)$

Balance H: $C_5H_{12}O(l) + O_2(g) \rightarrow 5\ CO_2(g) + 6\ H_2O(g)$

Balance O: $C_5H_{12}O(l) + 15/2\ O_2(g) \rightarrow 5\ CO_2(g) + 6\ H_2O(g)$

Clear fraction: $2\ C_5H_{12}O(l) + 15\ O_2(g) \rightarrow 10\ CO_2(g) + 12\ H_2O(g)$

(d) Skeletal reaction: $SrS(aq) + CuSO_4(aq) \rightarrow SrSO_4(s) + CuS(s)$

Balanced reaction: $SrS(aq) + CuSO_4(aq) \rightarrow SrSO_4(s) + CuS(s)$

4.83 **Given:** 1.5 L solution; 0.050 M $CaCl_2$; 0.085 M $Mg(NO_3)_2$ **Find:** g Na_3PO_4

Conceptual Plan: V, M $CaCl_2 \rightarrow$ mol $CaCl_2$ and V, M $Mg(NO_3)_2 \rightarrow$ mol $Mg(NO_3)_2$

$$V \times M = \text{mol} \qquad\qquad V \times M = \text{mol}$$

then (mol $CaCl_2$ + mol $Mg(NO_3)_2$) $\rightarrow$ mol $Na_3PO_4 \rightarrow$ g Na_3PO_4

$$\frac{2\ \text{mol}\ Na_3PO_4}{3\ \text{mol}\ (CaCl_2 + Mg(NO_3)_2)} \qquad \frac{163.94\ \text{g}\ Na_3PO_4}{1\ \text{mol}\ Na_3PO_4}$$

Solution: $3\ CaCl_2(aq) + 2\ Na_3PO_4(aq) \rightarrow Ca_3(PO_4)_2(s) + 6\ NaCl(aq)$

$3\ Mg(NO_3)_2(aq) + 2\ Na_3PO_4(aq) \rightarrow Mg_3(PO_4)_2(s) + 6\ NaCl(aq)$

$1.5\ L \times 0.050\ M\ CaCl_2 = 0.07\underline{5}\ \text{mol}\ CaCl_2$

$1.5\ L \times 0.085\ M\ Mg(NO_3)_2 = 0.1\underline{2}75\ \text{mol}\ Mg(NO_3)_2$

$$0.2\underline{0}25\ \text{mol}\ CaCl_2\ \text{and}\ Mg(NO_3)_2 \times \frac{2\ \text{mol}\ Na_3PO_4}{3\ \text{mol}\ CaCl_2\ \text{and}\ Mg(NO_3)_2} \times \frac{163.94\ \text{g}\ Na_3PO_4}{1\ \text{mol}\ Na_3PO_4} = 22.1\underline{3}\ \text{g}\ Na_3PO_4$$

$= 22\ \text{g}\ Na_3PO_4$

Check: The units of the answer (g Na_3PO_4) are correct. The magnitude of the answer is reasonable because it is needed to remove both the Ca and Mg ions.

4.84 **Given:** 500.0 mL, 0.100 M HCl and 0.200 M H_2SO_4; 0.150 M KOH **Find:** volume KOH to neutralize the acid

Conceptual Plan:

mL $\rightarrow$ L, then V, M HCl $\rightarrow$ mol HCl $\rightarrow$ mol H^+ and V, M $H_2SO_4 \rightarrow$ mol $H_2SO_4 \rightarrow$ mol H^+

$$\frac{1\ L}{1000\ \text{mL}} \qquad V \times M = \text{mol} \qquad \frac{1\ \text{mol}\ H^+}{1\ \text{mol}\ HCl} \qquad\qquad V \times M = \text{mol} \qquad \frac{2\ \text{mol}\ H^+}{1\ \text{mol}\ H_2SO_4}$$

Total mol $H^+ \rightarrow$ mol $OH^- \rightarrow$ mol KOH $\rightarrow$ volume KOH

$$\frac{1\ \text{mol}\ OH^-}{1\ \text{mol}\ H^+} \qquad \frac{1\ \text{mol}\ KOH}{1\ \text{mol}\ OH^-} \qquad V = \frac{\text{mol}\ KOH}{M\ KOH}$$

Solution: $500.0\ \text{mL} \times \dfrac{1\ L}{1000\ \text{mL}} \times \dfrac{0.100\ \text{mol}\ HCl}{1\ L} \times \dfrac{1\ \text{mol}\ H^+}{1\ \text{mol}\ HCl} = 0.0500\underline{0}\ \text{mol}\ H^+$

$500.0\ \text{mL} \times \dfrac{1\ L}{1000\ \text{mL}} \times \dfrac{0.200\ \text{mol}\ H_2SO_4}{1\ L} \times \dfrac{2\ \text{mol}\ H^+}{1\ \text{mol}\ H_2SO_4} = 0.200\underline{0}\ \text{mol}\ H^+$

$(0.200\underline{0} + 0.0500\underline{0})\ \text{mol}\ H^+ \times \dfrac{1\ \text{mol}\ OH^-}{1\ \text{mol}\ H^+} \times \dfrac{1\ \text{mol}\ KOH}{1\ \text{mol}\ OH^-} \times \dfrac{1\ L\ \text{solution}}{0.150\ \text{mol}\ KOH} = 1.66\underline{7}\ L\ KOH\ \text{solution}$

$= 1.67\ L\ KOH\ \text{solution}$

Check: The units of the answer (L KOH) are correct. The magnitude of the answer is reasonable because the average concentration of acid is greater than the concentration of base.

4.85 **Given:** 1.0 L; 0.10 M OH^- **Find:** g Ba

Conceptual Plan: $V, M \rightarrow$ mol $OH^- \rightarrow$ mol $Ba(OH)_2 \rightarrow$ mol BaO $\rightarrow$ mol Ba $\rightarrow$ g Ba

$$V \times M = \text{mol} \qquad \frac{1\ \text{mol}\ Ba(OH)_2}{2\ \text{mol}\ OH^-} \qquad \frac{1\ \text{mol}\ BaO}{1\ \text{mol}\ Ba(OH)_2} \qquad \frac{1\ \text{mol}\ Ba}{1\ \text{mol}\ BaO} \qquad \frac{137.3\ \text{g}\ Ba}{1\ \text{mol}\ Ba}$$

Solution: $BaO(s) + H_2O(l) \rightarrow Ba(OH)_2(aq)$

$1.0\ L \times \dfrac{0.10\ \text{mol}\ OH^-}{L} \times \dfrac{1\ \text{mol}\ Ba(OH)_2}{2\ \text{mol}\ OH^-} \times \dfrac{1\ \text{mol}\ BaO}{1\ \text{mol}\ Ba(OH)_2} \times \dfrac{1\ \text{mol}\ Ba}{1\ \text{mol}\ BaO} \times \dfrac{137.3\ \text{g}\ Ba}{1\ \text{mol}\ Ba} = 6.86\underline{5}\ \text{g}\ Ba$

$= 6.9\ \text{g}\ Ba$

Check: The units of the answer (g Ba) are correct. The magnitude is reasonable because the molar mass of Ba is large and there are 2 moles hydroxide per mole Ba.

4.86   **Given:** 1.00 L, 1.51 M NaF; 49.6 g sample; mixture Cr^{3+} and Mg^{2+} **Find:** g Cr^{3+}

     Conceptual Plan: V, M NaF → mol NaF → mol F^- and let x = mol CrF_3 and y = mol MgF_2 → mol F

$$V \times M = mol \qquad \frac{1 \text{ mol } F^-}{1 \text{ mol NaF}} \qquad\qquad\qquad \frac{3 \text{ mol F}}{\text{mol } CrF_3} \quad \frac{2 \text{ mol F}}{\text{mol } MgF_2}$$

     and → g sample then solve for x = mol CrF_3 → mol Cr^{3+} → g Cr^{3+}

$$x \text{ (molar mass } CrF_3) = g\ CrF_3 \qquad y \text{ (molar mass } MgF_2) = g\ MgF_2 \qquad \frac{1 \text{ mol } Cr^{3+}}{1 \text{ mol } CrF_3} \quad \frac{52.00 \text{ g } Cr^{3+}}{1 \text{ mol } Cr^{3+}}$$

     Solution: $1.00\ \cancel{L} \times \dfrac{1.51\ \cancel{\text{mol NaF}}}{\cancel{L}} \times \dfrac{1 \text{ mol } F^-}{1\ \cancel{\text{mol NaF}}} = 1.51 \text{ mol } F^-$

         Let x = mol CrF_3 and y = mol MgF_2;

         $3x$ = mol F^- from CrF_3; $2y$ = mol F^- from MgF_2

         $3x + 2y = 1.51 \text{ mol } F^-$

         $2y = 1.51 - 3x$

         $y = 0.755 - 3/2x$

         $x \text{ mol } CrF_3 \times \dfrac{109.00 \text{ g } CrF_3}{\text{mol } CrF_3} = g\ CrF_3$

         $y \text{ mol } MgF_2 \times \dfrac{62.31 \text{ g } MgF_2}{\text{mol } MgF_2} = g\ MgF_2$

         $x(109.00) + y(62.31) = 49.6$ g sample

         $y = 0.755 - \dfrac{3}{2x}$

         Solve simultaneous equations by substituting for y: $x = 0.1\underline{6}45 = $ mol CrF_3.

         $0.1\underline{6}45\ \cancel{\text{mol } CrF_3} \times \dfrac{1\ \cancel{\text{mol } Cr^{3+}}}{1\ \cancel{\text{mol } CrF_3}} \times \dfrac{52.00 \text{ g } Cr^{3+}}{1\ \cancel{\text{mol } Cr^{3+}}} = 8.\underline{5}54 \text{ g } Cr^{3+} = 8.6 \text{ g } Cr^{3+}$

     Check: Units of answer (g Cr^{3+}) are correct. The magnitude of the answer is reasonable because it is less than the mass of the sample.

4.87   **Given:** 30.0% $NaNO_3$, \$9.00/100 lb; 20.0% $(NH_4)_2SO_4$, \$8.10/100 lb   **Find:** cost/lb N

     Conceptual Plan: mass fertilizer → mass $NaNO_3$ → mass N → cost/lb N

$$\frac{30.0 \text{ lb } NaNO_3}{100 \text{ lb fertilizer}} \qquad \frac{16.48 \text{ lb N}}{100 \text{ lb } NaNO_3} \qquad \frac{\$9.00}{100 \text{ lb fertilizer}}$$

     and mass fertilizer → mass $(NH_4)_2SO_4$ → mass N → cost/lb N

$$\frac{20.0 \text{ lb } (NH_4)_2SO_2}{100 \text{ lb fertilizer}} \qquad \frac{21.20 \text{ lb N}}{100 \text{ lb } (NH_4)_2SO_4} \qquad \frac{\$8.10}{100 \text{ lb fertilizer}}$$

     Solution:

         $100\ \cancel{\text{lb fertilizer}} \times \dfrac{30.0\ \cancel{\text{lb } NaNO_3}}{100\ \cancel{\text{lb fertilizer}}} \times \dfrac{16.48 \text{ lb N}}{100\ \cancel{\text{lb } NaNO_3}} = 4.9\underline{4}4 \text{ lb N}$

         $\dfrac{\$9.00}{100\ \cancel{\text{lb fertilizer}}} \times \dfrac{100\ \cancel{\text{lb fertilizer}}}{4.9\underline{4}4 \text{ lb N}} = \$1.82/\text{lb N}$

         $100\ \cancel{\text{lb fertilizer}} \times \dfrac{20.0\ \cancel{\text{lb } (NH_4)_2SO_4}}{100\ \cancel{\text{lb fertilizer}}} \times \dfrac{21.20 \text{ lb N}}{100\ \cancel{\text{lb } (NH_4)_2SO_4}} = 4.2\underline{4}0 \text{ lb N}$

         $\dfrac{\$8.10}{100\ \cancel{\text{lb fertilizer}}} \times \dfrac{100\ \cancel{\text{lb fertilizer}}}{4.2\underline{4} \text{ lb N}} = \$1.91/\text{ lb N}$

     The more economical fertilizer is the $NaNO_3$ because it costs less/lb N.

     Check: The units of the cost (\$/lb N) are correct. The answer is reasonable because you compare the cost/lb N directly.

4.88   **Given:** 0.110 M HCl; 1.52 g $Al(OH)_3$ **Find:** volume HCl needed to neutralize

     Conceptual Plan: g $Al(OH)_3$ → mol $Al(OH)_3$ → mol HCl → vol HCL

$$\frac{1 \text{ mol } Al(OH)_3}{78.00 \text{ g } Al(OH)_3} \qquad \frac{3 \text{ mol HCl}}{1 \text{ mol } Al(OH)_3} \qquad \frac{1 \text{ L HCl}}{\text{M HCl}}$$

     Solution: $3 \text{ HCl}(aq) + Al(OH)_3(aq) \rightarrow 3 \text{ H}_2O(l) + AlCl_3(aq)$

         $1.52\ \cancel{\text{g } Al(OH)_3} \times \dfrac{1\ \cancel{\text{mol } Al(OH)_3}}{78.00\ \cancel{\text{g } Al(OH)_3}} \times \dfrac{3\ \cancel{\text{mol HCl}}}{1\ \cancel{\text{mol } Al(OH)_3}} \times \dfrac{1 \text{ L}}{0.110\ \cancel{\text{mol HCl}}} = 0.531 \text{ L HCl}$

Check: The units of the answer (L HCl) are correct. The magnitude of the answer is reasonable because the mole ratio of HCl to $Al(OH)_3$ is 3:1.

4.89 **Given:** 24.5 g Au; 24.5 g BrF_3; 24.5 g KF **Find:** g $KAuF_4$
Conceptual Plan: g Au → mol Au → mol $KAuF_4$

$$\frac{1\ mol\ Au}{196.97\ g\ Au} \quad \frac{2\ mol\ KAuF_4}{2\ mol\ Au}$$

g BrF_3 → mol BrF_3 → mol $KAuF_4$ → **smallest mol amount determines limiting reactant**

$$\frac{1\ mol\ BrF_3}{136.9\ g\ BrF_3} \quad \frac{2\ mol\ KAuF_4}{2\ mol\ BrF_3}$$

g KF → mol KF → mol $KAuF_4$

$$\frac{1\ mol\ KF}{58.10\ g\ KF} \quad \frac{2\ mol\ KAuF_4}{2\ mol\ KF}$$

then mol $KAuF_4$ → g $KAuF_4$

$$\frac{312.07\ g\ KAuF_4}{1\ mol\ KAuF_4}$$

$$2\ Au(s)\ +\ 2\ BrF_3(l)\ +\ 2\ KF(s) \rightarrow Br_2(l)\ +\ 2\ KAuF_4(s)$$
Oxidation states; 0   +3 −1   +1 −1   0   +1 +3 −1

This is a redox reaction because Au increases in oxidation number (oxidation) and Br decreases in number (reduction). BrF_3 is the oxidizing agent, and Au is the reducing agent.
Solution:

$$24.5\ g\ Au \times \frac{1\ mol\ Au}{196.97\ g\ Au} \times \frac{2\ mol\ KAuF_4}{2\ mol\ Au} = 0.1244\ mol\ KAuF_4$$

$$24.5\ g\ BrF_3 \times \frac{1\ mol\ BrF_3}{136.90\ g\ BrF_3} \times \frac{2\ mol\ KAuF_4}{2\ mol\ BrF_3} = 0.1790\ mol\ KAuF$$

$$24.5\ g\ KF \times \frac{1\ mol\ KF}{58.10\ g\ KF} \times \frac{2\ mol\ KAuF_4}{2\ mol\ KF} = 0.4217\ mol\ KAuF_4$$

$$0.1244\ mol\ KAuF_4 \times \frac{312.07\ g\ KAuF_4}{1\ mol\ KAuF_4} = 38.822\ g\ KAuF_4 = 38.8\ g\ KAuF_4$$

Check: The units of the answer (g $KAuF_4$) are correct. The magnitude of the answer is reasonable compared to the mass of the limiting reactant Au.

4.90 **Given:** 0.10 L, 0.12 M NaCl; 0.23 L, 0.18 M $MgCl_2$; 0.20 M $AgNO_3$ **Find:** volume $AgNO_3$ to precipitate all of the Cl^-
Conceptual Plan : V, M NaCl → mol NaCl → mol Cl^- and V, M $MgCl_2$ → mol $MgCl_2$ → mol Cl^-

$$V \times M = mol \quad \frac{1\ mol\ Cl^-}{1\ mol\ NaCl} \qquad V \times M = mol \quad \frac{2\ mol\ Cl^-}{1\ mol\ MgCl_2}$$

then total mol Cl^- → mol Ag^+ → mol $AgNO_3$ → vol $AgNO_3$

$$\frac{1\ mol\ Ag^+}{1\ mol\ Cl^-} \quad \frac{1\ mol\ AgNO_3}{1\ mol\ Ag^+} \quad \frac{1\ L\ AgNO_3}{0.20\ mol\ AgNO_3}$$

Solution:

$$0.10\ L\ NaCl \times \frac{0.12\ mol\ NaCl}{L\ NaCl} \times \frac{1\ mol\ Cl^-}{1\ mol\ NaCl} = 0.0120\ mol\ Cl^-$$

$$0.23\ L\ NaCl \times \frac{0.18\ mol\ MgCl_2}{L\ MgCl_2} \times \frac{2\ mol\ Cl^-}{1\ mol\ MgCl_2} = 0.0828\ mol\ Cl^-$$

Total Cl^- = 0.0120 mol Cl^- + 0.0828 mol Cl^- = 0.0948 mol Cl^-

$$0.0948\ mol\ Cl^- \times \frac{1\ mol\ Ag^+}{1\ mol\ Cl^-} \times \frac{1\ mol\ AgNO_3}{1\ mol\ Ag^+} \times \frac{1\ L\ AgNO_3}{0.20\ mol\ AgNO_3} = 0.474\ L\ AgNO_3 = 0.47\ L\ AgNO_3$$

Check: Units of the answer (L $AgNO_3$) are correct. The magnitude of the answer is reasonable because the Cl^- comes from two sources.

4.91 **Given:** solution may contain Ag^+, Ca^{2+}, and Cu^{2+} **Find:** Determine which ions are present.

Conceptual Plan: Test the solution sequentially with NaCl, Na$_2$SO$_4$, and Na$_2$CO$_3$ and see if precipitates form.

Solution: Original solution + NaCl yields no reaction: Ag$^+$ is not present because chlorides are normally soluble, but Ag$^+$ is an exception.

Original solution with Na$_2$SO$_4$ yields a precipitate and solution 2. The precipitate is CaSO$_4$, so Ca^{2+} is present. Sulfates are normally soluble, but Ca^{2+} is an exception.

Solution 2 with Na$_2$CO$_3$ yields a precipitate. The precipitate is CuCO$_3$, so Cu^{2+} is present. All carbonates are insoluble.

Net Ionic Equations:
$$Ca^{2+}(aq) + SO_4{}^{2-}(aq) \rightarrow CaSO_4(s)$$
$$Cu^{2+}(aq) + CO_3{}^{2-}(aq) \rightarrow CuCO_3(s)$$

Check: The answer is reasonable because two different precipitates formed and all of the Ca^{2+} was removed before the carbonate was added.

4.92 **Given:** solution may contain Hg$_2{}^{2+}$, Ba^{2+}, and Fe^{2+} **Find:** Determine which ions are present.

Conceptual Plan: Test the solution sequentially with KCl, K$_2$SO$_4$, and K$_2$CO$_3$ and see if precipitates form.

Solution: Original solution + KCl yields a precipitate and solution 2: The precipitate is Hg$_2$Cl$_2$, so Hg$_2{}^{2+}$ is present. Chlorides are normally soluble, but Hg$_2{}^{2+}$ is an exception.

Solution 2 with K$_2$SO$_4$ yields no precipitate, so Ba^{2+} is not present. Sulfates are normally soluble, but Ba^{2+} is an exception.

Solution 2 with K$_2$CO$_3$ yields a precipitate. The precipitate is FeCO$_3$, so Fe^{2+} is present. All carbonates are insoluble.

Net Ionic Equations:
$$Hg_2{}^{2+}(aq) + 2\,Cl^-(aq) \rightarrow Hg_2Cl_2(s)$$
$$Fe^{2+}(aq) + CO_3{}^{2-}(aq) \rightarrow FeCO_3(s)$$

Check: The answer is reasonable because two different precipitates formed and all of the Hg$_2{}^{2+}$ was removed before the carbonate was added.

4.93 **Given:** 10.0 kg mixture; 30.35% hexane; 15.85% heptane; 53.80% octane **Find:** total mass CO$_2$

Conceptual Plan: kg hexane → kmol hexane → kmol CO$_2$ → kg CO$_2$

$$\frac{1\ \text{kmol C}_6\text{H}_{14}}{86.17\ \text{kg C}_6\text{H}_{14}} \qquad \frac{12\ \text{kmol CO}_2}{2\ \text{kmol C}_6\text{H}_{14}} \qquad \frac{44.01\ \text{kg CO}_2}{1\ \text{kmol CO}_2}$$

kg heptane → kmol heptane → kmol CO$_2$ → kg CO$_2$

$$\frac{1\ \text{kmol C}_7\text{H}_{16}}{100.20\ \text{kg C}_7\text{H}_{16}} \qquad \frac{7\ \text{kmol CO}_2}{1\ \text{kmol C}_7\text{H}_{16}} \qquad \frac{44.01\ \text{kg CO}_2}{1\ \text{kmol CO}_2}$$

kg octane → kmol octane → kmol CO$_2$ → kg CO$_2$

$$\frac{1\ \text{kmol C}_8\text{H}_{18}}{114.22\ \text{kg C}_8\text{H}_{18}} \qquad \frac{16\ \text{kmol CO}_2}{2\ \text{kmol C}_8\text{H}_{18}} \qquad \frac{44.01\ \text{kg CO}_2}{1\ \text{kmol CO}_2}$$

Solution: Balanced Reactions:
$$2\ C_6H_{14}(l) + 19\ O_2(g) \rightarrow 12\ CO_2(g) + 14\ H_2O(l)$$
$$C_7H_{16}(l) + 11\ O_2(g) \rightarrow 7\ CO_2(g) + 8\ H_2O(l)$$
$$2\ C_8H_{18}(l) + 25\ O_2(g) \rightarrow 16\ CO_2(g) + 18\ H_2O(l)$$

$$10.0\ \text{kg mix} \times \frac{30.35\ \text{kg C}_6\text{H}_{14}}{100.0\ \text{kg mix}} \times \frac{1\ \text{kmol C}_6\text{H}_{14}}{86.17\ \text{kg C}_6\text{H}_{14}} \times \frac{12\ \text{kmol CO}_2}{2\ \text{kmol C}_6\text{H}_{14}} \times \frac{44.01\ \text{kg CO}_2}{1\ \text{kmol CO}_2} = 9.3\underline{0}0\ \text{kg CO}_2$$

$$10.0\ \text{kg mix} \times \frac{15.85\ \text{kg C}_7\text{H}_{16}}{100.0\ \text{kg mix}} \times \frac{1\ \text{kmol C}_7\text{H}_{16}}{100.20\ \text{kg C}_7\text{H}_{16}} \times \frac{7\ \text{kmol CO}_2}{1\ \text{kmol C}_7\text{H}_{16}} \times \frac{44.01\ \text{kg CO}_2}{1\ \text{kmol CO}_2} = 4.8\underline{7}3\ \text{kg CO}_2$$

$$10.0\ \text{kg mix} \times \frac{53.80\ \text{kg C}_8\text{H}_{18}}{100.0\ \text{kg mix}} \times \frac{1\ \text{kmol C}_8\text{H}_{18}}{114.22\ \text{kg C}_8\text{H}_{18}} \times \frac{16\ \text{kmol CO}_2}{2\ \text{kmol C}_8\text{H}_{18}} \times \frac{44.01\ \text{kg CO}_2}{1\ \text{kmol CO}_2} = 16.5\underline{8}4\ \text{kg CO}_2$$

Total CO$_2$ = 9.3$\underline{0}$0 kg + 4.8$\underline{7}$3 kg + 16.5$\underline{8}$4 kg = 30.$\underline{7}$57 kg CO$_2$ = 30.8 k CO$_2$

Check: The units of the answer (kg CO$_2$) are correct. The magnitude of the answer is reasonable because a large amount of CO$_2$ is produced per mole of hydrocarbon.

4.94 **Given:** 1.00 kg sand; 22.8% ilmenite (FeTiO$_3$) **Find:** g Ti

Conceptual Plan: kg sand → g sand → g FeTiO$_3$ → mol FeTiO$_3$ → mol TiCl$_4$ → mol Ti → g Ti

$$\frac{1000\ \text{g sand}}{1\ \text{kg sand}} \quad \frac{22.8\ \text{g FeTiO}_3}{100\ \text{g sand}} \quad \frac{151.72\ \text{g FeTiO}_3}{1\ \text{mol FeTiO}_3} \quad \frac{0.908\ \text{mol TiCl}_4}{1\ \text{mol FeTiO}_3} \quad \frac{0.859\ \text{mol Ti}}{1\ \text{mol TiCl}_4} \quad \frac{47.87\ \text{g Ti}}{1\ \text{mol Ti}}$$

Solution: $1.00 \; \cancel{kg \; sand} \times \dfrac{1000 \; \cancel{g \; sand}}{1 \; \cancel{kg \; sand}} \times \dfrac{22.8 \; \cancel{g \; FeTiO_3}}{100 \; \cancel{g \; sand}} \times \dfrac{1 \; \cancel{mol \; FeTiO_3}}{151.72 \; \cancel{g \; FeTiO_3}} \times \dfrac{0.908 \; \cancel{mol \; TiCl_4}}{1 \; \cancel{mol \; FeTiO_3}} \times \dfrac{0.859 \; \cancel{mol \; Ti}}{1 \; \cancel{mol \; TiCl_4}}$

$\times \dfrac{47.87 \; g \; Ti}{1 \; \cancel{mol \; Ti}} = 56.\underline{1}09 \; g \; Ti = 56.1 \; g \; Ti$

Check: The units of the answer (g Ti) are correct. The magnitude is reasonable because the % of ilmenite in the sand is small.

Challenge Problems

4.95   **Given:** 15.2 billion L lake water; $1.8 \times 10^{-5} \, M \, H_2SO_4$; $8.7 \times 10^{-6} \, M \, HNO_3$ **Find:** kg $CaCO_3$ needed to neutralize

Conceptual Plan: vol lake $\rightarrow$ **mol** H_2SO_4 $\rightarrow$ **mol** H^+ **and vol lake** $\rightarrow$ **mol** HNO_3 $\rightarrow$ **mol** H^+

$$V \times M = \text{mol} \qquad \dfrac{2 \; \text{mol } H^+}{1 \; \text{mol } H_2SO_4} \qquad\qquad V \times M = \text{mol} \qquad \dfrac{1 \; \text{mol } H^+}{1 \; \text{mol } HNO_3}$$

then total mol H^+ $\rightarrow$ **mol** CO_3^{2-} $\rightarrow$ **mol** $CaCO_3$ $\rightarrow$ **g** $CaCO_3$ $\rightarrow$ **kg** $CaCO_3$

$$\dfrac{1 \; \text{mol } CO_3^{2-}}{2 \; \text{mol } H^+} \qquad \dfrac{1 \; \text{mol } CaCO_3}{1 \; \text{mol } CO_3^{2-}} \qquad \dfrac{100.09 \; \text{g } CaCO_3}{1 \; \text{mol } CaCO_3} \qquad \dfrac{1 \; \text{kg}}{1000 \; \text{g}}$$

Solution: $2H^+(aq) + CO_3^{2-}(aq) \rightarrow H_2O(l) + CO_2(g)$

$$15.2 \times 10^9 \; \cancel{L} \times \dfrac{1.8 \times 10^{-5} \; \cancel{mol \; H_2SO_4}}{\cancel{L \; soln}} \times \dfrac{2 \; \text{mol } H^+}{1 \; \cancel{mol \; H_2SO_4}} = 547200 \; \text{mol } H^+$$

$$15.2 \times 10^9 \; \cancel{L} \times \dfrac{8.7 \times 10^{-6} \; \cancel{mol \; HNO_3}}{\cancel{L \; soln}} \times \dfrac{1 \; \text{mol } H^+}{1 \; \cancel{mol \; HNO_3}} = 132240 \; \text{mol } H^+$$

Total $H^+ = 547200 \; \text{mol } H^+ + 132240 \; \text{mol } H^+ = 6\underline{7}9440 \; \text{mol } H^+$

$$679440 \; \cancel{mol \; H^+} \times \dfrac{1 \; \cancel{mol \; CO_3^{2-}}}{2 \; \cancel{mol \; H^+}} \times \dfrac{1 \; \cancel{mol \; CaCO_3}}{1 \; \cancel{mol \; CO_3^{2-}}} \times \dfrac{100.09 \; \cancel{g \; CaCO_3}}{1 \; \cancel{mol \; CaCO_3}} \times \dfrac{1 \; \text{kg}}{1000 \; \cancel{g}} = 3.4 \times 10^4 \; \text{kg } CaCO_3$$

Check: The units of the answer (kg $CaCO_3$) are correct. The magnitude of the answer is reasonable based on the size of the lake.

4.96   **Given:** $3.5 \times 10^{-3} \, M \, Ca^{2+}$, $1.1 \times 10^{-3} \, Mg^{2+}$, 19.5 gal H_2O; 0.65 kg detergent/load   **Find:** % by mass Na_2CO_3

Conceptual Plan: gal H_2O $\rightarrow$ **L** H_2O **then** V, M $\rightarrow$ **mol** Ca^{2+} **and** V, M $\rightarrow$ **mol** Mg^{2+}

$$\dfrac{3.785 \; \text{L}}{1 \; \text{gal}} \qquad\qquad V \times M = \text{mol} \qquad\qquad V \times M = \text{mol}$$

then total moles ions $\rightarrow$ **mol** CO_3^{2-} $\rightarrow$ **mol** Na_2CO_3 $\rightarrow$ **g** Na_2CO_3 $\rightarrow$ **kg** Na_2CO_3 $\rightarrow$ **%** Na_2CO_3

$$\dfrac{1 \; \text{mol } CO_3^{2-}}{1 \; \text{mol ion}} \qquad \dfrac{1 \; \text{mol } Na_2CO_3}{1 \; \text{mol } CO_3^{2-}} \qquad \dfrac{105.99 \; \text{g } Na_2CO_3}{1 \; \text{mol } Na_2CO_3} \qquad \dfrac{1 \; \text{kg}}{1000 \; \text{g}} \qquad \dfrac{1 \; \text{kg } Na_2CO_3}{1 \; \text{kg detergent}} \times 100\%$$

Solution: $19.5 \; \cancel{gal} \times \dfrac{3.785 \; \cancel{L}}{1 \; \cancel{gal}} \times \dfrac{3.5 \times 10^{-3} \; \text{mol } Ca^{2+}}{\cancel{L}} = 0.2\underline{5}8 \; \text{mol } Ca^{2+}$

$19.5 \; \cancel{gal} \times \dfrac{3.785 \; \cancel{L}}{1 \; \cancel{gal}} \times \dfrac{1.1 \times 10^{-3} \; \text{mol } Mg^{2+}}{\cancel{L}} = 0.08\underline{1}19 \; \text{mol } Mg^{2+}$

$0.3392 \; \cancel{mol \; ions} \times \dfrac{1 \; \cancel{mol \; CO_3^{2-}}}{1 \; \cancel{mol \; ions}} \times \dfrac{1 \; \cancel{mol \; Na_2CO_3}}{1 \; \cancel{mol \; CO_3^{2-}}} \times \dfrac{105.99 \; \cancel{g \; Na_2CO_3}}{1 \; \cancel{mol \; Na_2CO_3}} \times \dfrac{1 \; \text{kg } Na_2CO_3}{1000 \; \cancel{g \; Na_2CO_3}} = 0.03595 \; \text{kg } Na_2CO_3$

$\dfrac{0.03\underline{5}96 \; \cancel{kg \; Na_2CO_3}}{0.65 \; \cancel{kg \; detergent}} \times 100\% = 5.5\% \; Na_2CO_3$

Check: The units of the answer (% Na_2CO_3) are correct. The magnitude of the answer is reasonable. The percent is less than 100%.

4.97   **Given:** 45 μg Pb/dL blood; Vol = 5.0 L; 1 mol succimer ($C_4H_6O_4S_2$) = 1 mol Pb   **Find:** mass $C_4H_6O_4S_2$ in mg

Conceptual Plan: volume blood L $\rightarrow$ **volume blood dL** $\rightarrow$ μg **Pb** $\rightarrow$ **g Pb** $\rightarrow$ **mol Pb** $\rightarrow$

$$\dfrac{10 \; \text{dL}}{1 \; \text{L}} \qquad\qquad \dfrac{45 \; \mu g}{1 \; \text{dL}} \qquad \dfrac{1 \; \text{g}}{10^6 \mu g} \qquad \dfrac{1 \; \text{mol Pb}}{207.2 \; \text{g Pb}} \qquad \dfrac{1 \; \text{mol succimer}}{1 \; \text{mol Pb}}$$

mol succimer $\rightarrow$ **g succimer** $\rightarrow$ **mg succimer**

$$\dfrac{182.23 \; \text{g succimer}}{1 \; \text{mol succimer}} \qquad \dfrac{1000 \; \text{mg succimer}}{1 \; \text{g succimer}}$$

Solution:

$$5.0 \; \text{L blood} \times \frac{10 \; \text{dL}}{1 \; \text{L}} \times \frac{45 \; \mu\text{g}}{1 \; \text{dL}} \times \frac{1 \; \text{g}}{10^6 \; \mu\text{g}} \times \frac{1 \; \text{mol Pb}}{207.2 \; \text{g}} \times \frac{1 \; \text{mol succimer}}{1 \; \text{mol Pb}} \times \frac{182.23 \; \text{g succimer}}{1 \; \text{mol succimer}} \times \frac{1000 \; \text{mg}}{\text{g}}$$

$$= 1.9\underline{7}9 \; \text{mg succimer} = 2.0 \; \text{mg succimer}$$

Check: The units of the answer (mg succimer) are correct. The magnitude is reasonable for the volume of blood and the concentration.

4.98   In designing the unit, you would need to consider the theoretical yield and % yield of the reaction, how changing the limiting reactant would affect the reaction, and the stoichiometry between KO_2 and O_2 to determine the mass of KO_2 required to produce enough O_2 for 10 minutes. You might also consider the speed of the reaction and whether the reaction produced heat. In addition, because your body does not use 100% of the oxygen taken in with each breath, the apparatus would need to replenish only the oxygen used. The percentage of oxygen in air is about 20%, and the percentage in exhaled air is about 16%; so we will assume that 4% of the air would need to be replenished with oxygen. (NOTE: The problem can also be solved by finding the amount of KO_2 that would be required to react with all of the exhaled CO_2.)

Given: air $= 4\% \; O_2$; volume $= 5$–$8 \; \text{L/min}$; 1 mol gas $= 22.4 \; \text{L gas}$ **Find:** O_2 for 10 min breathing time
Conceptual Plan: 10 min $\rightarrow$ vol air $\rightarrow$ vol O_2 $\rightarrow$ mol O_2 $\rightarrow$ mol KO_2 $\rightarrow$ g KO_2

$$\frac{8 \; \text{L air}}{1 \; \text{min}} \qquad \frac{4 \; \text{L} \; O_2}{100 \; \text{L air}} \qquad \frac{1 \; \text{mol} \; O_2}{22.4 \; \text{L} \; O_2} \qquad \frac{4 \; \text{mol} \; KO_2}{3 \; \text{mol} \; O_2} \qquad \frac{71.10 \; \text{g} \; KO_2}{1 \; \text{mol} \; KO_2}$$

Solution: $10 \; \text{min} \times \dfrac{8 \; \text{L air}}{\text{min}} \times \dfrac{4 \; \text{L} \; O_2}{100 \; \text{L air}} \times \dfrac{1 \; \text{mol} \; O_2}{22.4 \; \text{L} \; O_2} \times \dfrac{4 \; \text{mol} \; KO_2}{3 \; \text{mol} \; O_2} \times \dfrac{71.10 \; \text{g} \; KO_2}{1 \; \text{mol} \; KO_2} = 14 \; \text{g} \; KO_2$

Check: The units of the answer (g KO_2) are correct. The magnitude of the answer is reasonable because it is an amount that could be carried in a portable device.

4.99   **Given:** 250 g sample; 67.2 mol % Al   **Find:** theoretical yield in g of Mn
Conceptual Plan: mol % Al $\rightarrow$ g Al and mol % MnO_2 $\rightarrow$ g MnO_2, then mass % Al

$$\frac{26.98 \; \text{g Al}}{1 \; \text{mol Al}} \qquad\qquad \frac{86.94 \; \text{g} \; MnO_2}{1 \; \text{mol} \; MnO_2} \qquad\qquad \frac{\text{g Al}}{\text{total g}} \times 100\%$$

then sample $\rightarrow$ g Al $\rightarrow$ mol Al $\rightarrow$ mol Mn

$$\frac{38.86 \; \text{g Al}}{100 \; \text{g sample}} \quad \frac{1 \; \text{mol Al}}{26.98 \; \text{g Al}} \quad \frac{3 \; \text{mol Mn}}{4 \; \text{mol Al}} \qquad \textbf{$\rightarrow$ smallest mol amount determines limiting reactant}$$

sample $\rightarrow$ g MnO_2 $\rightarrow$ mol MnO_2 $\rightarrow$ mol Mn

$$\frac{61.14 \; \text{g} \; MnO_2}{100 \; \text{g sample}} \quad \frac{1 \; \text{mol} \; MnO_2}{86.94 \; \text{g} \; MnO_2} \quad \frac{1 \; \text{mol Mn}}{1 \; \text{mol} \; MnO_2}$$

then mol Mn $\rightarrow$ g Mn

$$\frac{54.94 \; \text{g Mn}}{1 \; \text{mol Mn}}$$

Solution: $4 \; \text{Al}(s) + 3 \; MnO_2(s) \rightarrow 3 \; \text{Mn} + 2 \; Al_2O_3(s)$

$$\text{Assume 1 mole:} \quad 0.672 \; \text{mol Al} \times \frac{26.98 \; \text{g Al}}{1 \; \text{mol Al}} = 18.1\underline{3} \; \text{g Al}$$

$$0.328 \; \text{mol} \; MnO_2 \times \frac{86.94 \; \text{g} \; MnO_2}{1 \; \text{mol} \; MnO_2} = 28.5\underline{2} \; \text{g} \; MnO_2$$

$$\frac{18.1\underline{3} \; \text{g Al}}{(18.1\underline{3} \; \text{g Al} + 28.5\underline{2} \; \text{g} \; MnO_2)} \times 100\% = 38.8\underline{6}\% \; \text{Al}$$

So 61.1$\underline{4}$ % MnO_2

$$250 \; \text{g sample} \times \frac{38.86 \; \text{g Al}}{100 \; \text{g sample}} \times \frac{1 \; \text{mol Al}}{26.98 \; \text{g Al}} \times \frac{3 \; \text{mol Mn}}{4 \; \text{mol Al}} = 2.70\underline{1} \; \text{mol Mn}$$

$$250 \; \text{g sample} \times \frac{61.14 \; \text{g} \; MnO_2}{100 \; \text{g sample}} \times \frac{1 \; \text{mol} \; MnO_2}{86.94 \; \text{g} \; MnO_2} \times \frac{1 \; \text{mol Mn}}{1 \; \text{mol} \; MnO_2} = 1.75\underline{8} \; \text{mol Mn}$$

$$1.7\underline{5}8 \; \text{mol Mn} \times \frac{54.94 \; \text{g Mn}}{1 \; \text{mol Mn}} = 96.6 \; \text{g Mn}$$

Check: The units of the answer (g Mn) are correct. The magnitude of the answer is reasonable based on the amount of the limiting reactant, MnO_2.

4.100   **Given:** 151 g $Na_2B_4O_7$ **Find:** g B_5H_9

Conceptual Plan: g $Na_2B_4O_7$ → mol $Na_2B_4O_7$ → mol B_5H_9 → g B_5H_9

$$\frac{1 \text{ mol } Na_2B_4O_7}{201.22 \text{ g } Na_2B_4O_7} \qquad \frac{4 \text{ mol } B_5H_9}{5 \text{ mol } Na_2B_4O_7} \qquad \frac{63.12 \text{ g } B_5H_9}{\text{mol } B_5H_9}$$

Solution: All of the B in B_5H_9 goes to the $Na_2B_4O_7$, so the mole ratio between the two can be used.

$$151 \text{ g } Na_2B_4O_7 \times \frac{1 \text{ mol } Na_2B_4O_7}{201.22 \text{ g } Na_2B_4O_7} \times \frac{4 \text{ mol } B_5H_9}{5 \text{ mol } Na_2B_4O_7} \times \frac{63.12 \text{ g } B_5H_9}{1 \text{ mol } B_5H_9} = 37.\underline{8}9 \text{ g } B_5H_9 = 37.9 \text{ g } B_5H_9$$

Check: The units of the answer (g B_5H_9) are correct. The magnitude of the answer is reasonable because the molar mass of B_5H_9 is less than the molar mass of $Na_2B_4O_7$.

Conceptual Problems

4.101   The correct answer is d. The molar masses of K and O_2 are comparable. Because the stoichiometry has a ratio of 4 mol K to 1 mol O_2, K will be the limiting reactant when mass of K is less than 4 times the mass of O_2.

4.102   **Given:** 5 mol NO; 10 mol H_2 **Find:** conditions of product mixture

Conceptual Plan: mol H_2 → mol NO and mol H_2 → mol NH_3 and mol H_2 → mol H_2O

Solution: The correct answer is a. Because the mol ratio of H_2 to NO is 5:2, the 10 mol of H_2 will require 4 mol NO and H_2 is the limiting reactant. This eliminates answers b and c. Because there is excess NO, this eliminates d, leaving answer a.

4.103   **Given:** 1 M solution contains 8 particles   **Find:** amount of solute or solvent needed to obtain new concentration

Conceptual Plan: Determine amount of solute particles in each new solution; then determine whether solute (if the number is greater) or solvent (if the number is less) needs to be added to obtain the new concentration.

Solution: Solution (a) contains 12 particles solute. Concentration is greater than the original, so solute needs

to be added. $12 \text{ particles} \times \dfrac{1 \text{ mol}}{8 \text{ particles}} = 1.5 \text{ mol}$ $(1.5 \text{ mol} - 1.0 \text{ mol}) = 0.5$ mol solute added

$0.5 \text{ mol solute} \times \dfrac{8 \text{ particles}}{1 \text{ mol solute}} = 4$ solute particles added

Solution (a) is obtained by adding 4 particles solute to 1 L of original solution.

Solution (b) contains 4 particles. Concentration is less than the original, so solvent needs to be added.

$4 \text{ particles} \times \dfrac{1 \text{ mol}}{8 \text{ particles}} = 0.5$ mol solute, so 1 L solution contains 0.5 mol = 0.5 M

$(1 \text{ M})(1 \text{ L}) = (0.5 \text{ M})(x)$ $x = 2 \text{ L}$

Solution (b) is obtained by diluting 1 L of the original solution to 2 L.

Solution (c) contains 6 particles. Concentration is less than the original, so solvent needs to be added.

$6 \text{ particles} \times \dfrac{1 \text{ mol}}{8 \text{ particles}} = 0.75$ mol solute, so 1 L solution contains 0.75 mol = 0.75 M

$(1 \text{ M})(1 \text{ L}) = (0.75 \text{ M})(x)$ $x = 1.3 \text{ L}$

Solution (c) is obtained by diluting 1 L of the original solution to 1.3 L.

4.104   **Given:** 6 molecules N_2H_4; 4 molecules N_2O_4; (a) contains 9 molecules N_2, 12 molecules H_2O, and 1 molecule N_2H_4; solution (b) contains 12 molecules N_2, 16 molecules H_2O, and 2 molecules N_2H_4; solution (c) contains 9 molecules N_2, 12 molecules H_2O **Find:** theoretical yield N_2, H_2O

Conceptual Plan: molecules N_2H_4 → molecules N_2

$$\frac{3 \text{ molecules } N_2}{2 \text{ molecules } N_2H_4} \qquad \rightarrow \textbf{ smallest mol amount determines limiting reactant}$$

molecules N_2O_4 → molecules N_2

$$\frac{3 \text{ molecules } N_2}{1 \text{ molecules } N_2O_4}$$

molecules N_2H_4 → molecules H_2O

$$\frac{4 \text{ molecules } H_2O}{2 \text{ molecules } N_2H_4}$$

$$\text{molecules } N_2H_4 \rightarrow \text{molecules } N_2O_4$$

$$\frac{1 \text{ molecule } N_2O_4}{2 \text{ molecules } N_2H_4}$$

Solution: $6 \text{ molecules } N_2H_4 \times \dfrac{3 \text{ molecules } N_2}{2 \text{ molecules } N_2H_4} = 9 \text{ molecules } N_2$

$ 6 \text{ molecules } N_2O_4 \times \dfrac{3 \text{ molecules } N_2}{1 \text{ molecules } N_2O_4} = 18 \text{ molecules } N_2$

Limiting reactant $= N_2H_4$ because it produced the least molecules of N_2.

$$6 \text{ molecules } N_2H_4 \times \frac{4 \text{ molecules } H_2O}{2 \text{ molecules } N_2H_4} = 12 \text{ molecules } H_2O$$

$$6 \text{ molecules } N_2H_4 \times \frac{1 \text{ molecule } N_2O_4}{2 \text{ molecules } N_2H_4} = 3 \text{ molecules } N_2O_4 \text{ used}$$

The reaction mixture should contain 9 molecules N_2, 12 molecules H_2O, and 1 molecule N_2O_4; this is best represented by (a).

4.105   **Given:** A_2X soluble; BY_2 soluble; AY insoluble; BX soluble; 2 molecules A_2X mixed with 2 molecules BY_2
Find: a molecular representation of the mixture; an equation for the reaction
Solution:

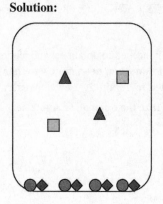

$$A_2X(aq) + BY_2(aq) \rightarrow 2AY(s) + BX(aq)$$

Questions for Group Work

4.106   (a) $CH_4(g) + 2 O_2(g) \rightarrow 2 H_2O(g) + CO_2(g)$

(b)   Calculate the number of moles of methane and oxygen:

$$16.05 \text{ g } CH_4 \times \frac{1 \text{ mol } CH_4}{16.04 \text{ g } CH_4} = 1.001 \text{ mol } CH_4 \quad \text{and} \quad 96.00 \text{ g } O_2 \times \frac{1 \text{ mol } O_2}{32.00 \text{ g } O_2} = 3.000 \text{ mol } O_2$$

 = carbon

 = hydrogen

= oxygen

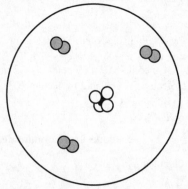

(c)   Calculate the number of moles of water and CO_2 that can be made if all of the methane reacts:

$$1.001 \text{ mol } CH_4 \times \frac{2 \text{ mol } H_2O}{1 \text{ mol } CH_4} = 2.002 \text{ mol } H_2O \quad \text{and} \quad 1.001 \text{ mol } CH_4 \times \frac{1 \text{ mol } CO_2}{1 \text{ mol } CH_4} = 1.001 \text{ mol } CO_2$$

Calculate the number of moles of water and CO_2 that can be made if all of the oxygen reacts:

$$3.000 \text{ mol } O_2 \times \frac{2 \text{ mol } H_2O}{2 \text{ mol } O_2} = 3.000 \text{ mol } H_2O \text{ and } 3.000 \text{ mol } O_2 \times \frac{1 \text{ mol } CO_2}{2 \text{ mol } O_2} = 1.500 \text{ mol } CO_2$$

The lower set of quantities is the amount that can be made: 2.002 mol water and 1.001 mol CO_2.

(d) Since the amount of methane determines the amount of the products, there will be oxygen left over.

$$2.002 \text{ mol } H_2O \times \frac{2 \text{ mol } O_2}{2 \text{ mol } H_2O} = 2.002 \text{ mol } O_2 \text{ reacted.}$$

The amount of oxygen left over $= 3.000 \text{ mol } O_2 - 2.002 \text{ mol } O_2 = 0.998 \text{ mol } O_2$ left over.

(e) The limiting reagent is methane; the excess reagent is oxygen; the theoretical yields are 2.002 mol water and 1.001 mol CO_2.

4.107 (1) Calculate the mass of NaOH needed:

$$100.0 \text{ mL solution} \times \frac{1 \text{ L solution}}{1000 \text{ mL solution}} \times \frac{12 \text{ mol NaOH}}{1 \text{ L solution}} \times \frac{40.00 \text{ g NaOH}}{1 \text{ mol NaOH}} = 48 \text{ g NaOH}$$

Weigh 48 g of solid NaOH and add to the 100.0 mL volumetric flask. Add about 50 mL of distilled water to the flask. Swirl the flask to dissolve the NaOH. Caution should be used, since the flask will become warm. Allow the flask to cool to room temperature. Add distilled water to the mark on the flask. Stopper the flask. Invert the flask several times to create a uniform solution. Allow the flask to cool and add additional distilled water if needed (stopper and agitate the flask after each addition of solvent).

(2) Calculate the volume of 12 M NaOH solution needed: $M_1 V_1 = M_2 V_2$ so

$$V_1 = \frac{M_2 V_2}{M_1} = \frac{(0.10 \text{ M})(1.00 \text{ L})}{(12 \text{ M})} = 0.0083 \text{ L} = 8.3 \text{ mL}$$

Add 8.3 mL of the 12 M NaOH solution to the 25 mL graduated cylinder. Transfer this solution to the 1.000 L volumetric flask. Add about 15 mL of distilled water to the graduated cylinder. Swirl and then transfer this solution to the 1.000 L volumetric flask. Repeat twice. (Note that the graduated cylinder is a "To Contain" device, so all of the solution in the graduated cylinder needs to be transferred to the 1.000 L volumetric flask. Add distilled water to the mark on the flask. Stopper the flask. Invert the flask several times to create a uniform solution. Allow the flask to cool and add additional distilled water if needed (stopper and agitate the flask after each addition of solvent).

4.108 Examples of soluble compounds are: NaCl, KBr, $AgNO_3$, **NH_4OH**, LiF, **Na_2S**.
Examples of insoluble compounds are: **AgBr**, $Fe(OH)_3$, ZnS, **$BaSO_4$**, $MgCO_3$, **$PbCl_2$**.
Exceptions to one of the rules are listed in **bold**.

4.109 A precipitation reaction is one in which a solid or precipitate forms upon mixing two solutions. An example is:
$2 \text{ KI}(aq) + Pb(NO_3)_2(aq) \rightarrow PbI_2(s) + 2 \text{ KNO}_3(aq)$.
In an acid–base reaction, an acid and base are mixed. The $H^+(aq)$ from the acid combines with the OH^- from the base to form $H_2O(l)$. An example is: $HCl(aq) + NaOH(aq) \rightarrow H_2O(l) + NaCl(aq)$.
A gas evolution reaction is an aqueous reaction that forms a gas upon mixing two solutions. The reactant types that give rise to gas evolution reactions are: sulfides, carbonates, bicarbonate, sulfites, bisulfites, and ammonium compounds. An example is: $H_2SO_4(aq) + Li_2S(aq) \rightarrow H_2S(g) + Li_2SO_4(aq)$.
Oxidation–reduction reactions or redox reactions are reactions in which electrons are transferred from one reactant to the other. An example is: $2 \text{ Na}(s) + Cl_2(g) \rightarrow 2 \text{ NaCl}(s)$.
Combustion reactions are characterized by the reaction of a substance with O_2 to form one or more oxygen-containing compounds, often including water. Combustion reactions emit heat.
An example is: $CH_4(g) + 2 O_2(g) \rightarrow CO_2(g) + 2 H_2O(g)$.

4.110 When a substance is oxidized it loses electrons, and there is an increase in oxidation state. When a substance is reduced it gains electrons, and there is a reduction in oxidation state. In this example, $Zn(s)$ is being oxidized to $Zn^{2+}(aq)$, while $Fe^{2+}(aq)$ is being reduced to $Fe(s)$. Electrons would move from the student representing the $Zn(s)$ to the student representing the $Fe^{2+}(aq)$. A substance that causes the oxidation of another substance is called an oxidizing agent – $Fe^{2+}(aq)$. A substance that causes the reduction of another substance is called a reducing agent – $Zn(s)$.

5 Gases

Converting Between Pressure Units

5.1   (a)   **Given:** 24.9 in Hg   **Find:** atm
       Conceptual Plan: in Hg → atm

$$\frac{1\ atm}{29.92\ in\ Hg}$$

Solution: $24.9\ \cancel{in\ Hg} \times \dfrac{1\ atm}{29.92\ \cancel{in\ Hg}} = 0.832\ atm$

Check: The units (atm) are correct. The magnitude of the answer (< 1) makes physical sense because we started with less than 29.92 in Hg.

(b)   **Given:** 24.9 in Hg   **Find:** mmHg
       Conceptual Plan: Use answer from part (a) then convert atm → mmHg

$$\frac{760\ mmHg}{1\ atm}$$

Solution: $0.832\ \cancel{atm} \times \dfrac{760\ mmHg}{1\ \cancel{atm}} = 632\ mmHg$

Check: The units (mmHg) are correct. The magnitude of the answer (< 760 mmHg) makes physical sense because we started with less than 1 atm.

(c)   **Given:** 24.9 in Hg   **Find:** psi
       Conceptual Plan: Use answer from part (a) then convert atm → psi

$$\frac{14.7\ psi}{1\ atm}$$

Solution: $0.832\ \cancel{atm} \times \dfrac{14.7\ psi}{1\ \cancel{atm}} = 12.2\ psi$

Check: The units (psi) are correct. The magnitude of the answer (< 14.7 psi) makes physical sense because we started with less than 1 atm.

(d)   **Given:** 24.9 in Hg   **Find:** Pa
       Conceptual Plan: Use answer from part (a) then convert atm → Pa

$$\frac{101,325\ Pa}{1\ atm}$$

Solution: $0.832\ \cancel{atm} \times \dfrac{101,325\ Pa}{1\ \cancel{atm}} = 8.43 \times 10^4\ Pa$

Check: The units (Pa) are correct. The magnitude of the answer ($< 101,325$ Pa) makes physical sense because we started with less than 1 atm.

5.2   (a)   **Given:** 235 mmHg   **Find:** torr
       Conceptual Plan: mmHg → torr

$$\frac{1\ torr}{1\ mmHg}$$

Solution: $235\ \cancel{mmHg} \times \dfrac{1\ torr}{1\ \cancel{mmHg}} = 235\ torr$

Check: The units (torr) are correct. The magnitude of the answer (235) makes physical sense because both units are of the same size.

(b)   **Given:** 235 mmHg   **Find:** psi
Conceptual Plan: mmHg → atm → psi

$$\frac{1 \text{ atm}}{760 \text{ mmHg}} \quad \frac{14.7 \text{ psi}}{1 \text{ atm}}$$

Solution: $235 \text{ mmHg} \times \dfrac{1 \text{ atm}}{760 \text{ mmHg}} \times \dfrac{14.7 \text{ psi}}{1 \text{ atm}} = 4.55 \text{ psi}$

Check: The units (psi) are correct. The magnitude of the answer (< 14.7 psi) makes physical sense because we started with less than 760 mmHg $= 1$ atm.

(c)   **Given:** 235 mmHg   **Find:** in Hg
Conceptual Plan: mmHg → in Hg

$$\frac{1 \text{ in Hg}}{25.4 \text{ mmHg}}$$

Solution: $235 \text{ mmHg} \times \dfrac{1 \text{ in Hg}}{25.4 \text{ mmHg}} = 9.25 \text{ in Hg}$

Check: The units (in Hg) are correct. The magnitude of the answer (9) makes physical sense because inches are larger than millimeters.

(d)   **Given:** 235 mmHg   **Find:** atm
Conceptual Plan: mmHg → atm

$$\frac{1 \text{ atm}}{760 \text{ mmHg}}$$

Solution: $235 \text{ mmHg} \times \dfrac{1 \text{ atm}}{760 \text{ mmHg}} = 0.309 \text{ atm}$

Check: The units (atm) are correct. The magnitude of the answer (< 1) makes physical sense because we started with less than 760 mmHg.

5.3   (a)   **Given:** 31.85 in Hg   **Find:** mmHg
Conceptual Plan: in Hg → mmHg

$$\frac{25.4 \text{ mmHg}}{1 \text{ in Hg}}$$

Solution: $31.85 \text{ in Hg} \times \dfrac{25.4 \text{ mmHg}}{1 \text{ in Hg}} = 809.0 \text{ mmHg}$

Check: The units (mmHg) are correct. The magnitude of the answer (809) makes physical sense because inches are larger than millimeters.

(b)   **Given:** 31.85 in Hg   **Find:** atm
Conceptual Plan: Use answer from part (a) then convert mmHg → atm

$$\frac{1 \text{ atm}}{760 \text{ mmHg}}$$

Solution: $809.0 \text{ mmHg} \times \dfrac{1 \text{ atm}}{760 \text{ mmHg}} = 1.064 \text{ atm}$

Check: The units (atm) are correct. The magnitude of the answer (>1) makes physical sense because we started with more than 760 mmHg.

(c)   **Given:** 31.85 in Hg   **Find:** torr
Conceptual Plan: Use answer from part (a) then convert mmHg → torr

$$\frac{1 \text{ torr}}{1 \text{ mmHg}}$$

Solution: $809.0 \text{ mmHg} \times \dfrac{1 \text{ torr}}{1 \text{ mmHg}} = 809.0 \text{ torr}$

Check: The units (torr) are correct. The magnitude of the answer (809) makes physical sense because both units are of the same size.

(d)   **Given:** 31.85 in Hg   **Find:** kPa

Conceptual Plan: Use answer from part (b) then convert atm $\rightarrow$ Pa $\rightarrow$ kPa

$$\frac{101,325 \text{ Pa}}{1 \text{ atm}} \quad \frac{1 \text{ kPa}}{1000 \text{ Pa}}$$

Solution: $1.064 \text{ atm} \times \dfrac{101,325 \text{ Pa}}{1 \text{ atm}} \times \dfrac{1 \text{ kPa}}{1000 \text{ Pa}} = 107.9 \text{ kPa}$

Check: The units (kPa) are correct. The magnitude of the answer (108) makes physical sense because we started with more than 1 atm and there are ~101 kPa in an atm.

5.4   (a)   **Given:** 652.5 mmHg   **Find:** torr

Conceptual Plan: mmHg $\rightarrow$ torr

$$\frac{1 \text{ torr}}{1 \text{ mmHg}}$$

Solution: $652.5 \text{ mmHg} \times \dfrac{1 \text{ torr}}{1 \text{ mmHg}} = 652.5 \text{ torr}$

Check: The units (torr) are correct. The magnitude of the answer (653) makes physical sense because both units are of the same size.

(b)   **Given:** 652.5 mmHg   **Find:** atm

Conceptual Plan: mmHg $\rightarrow$ atm

$$\frac{1 \text{ atm}}{760 \text{ mmHg}}$$

Solution: $652.5 \text{ mmHg} \times \dfrac{1 \text{ atm}}{760 \text{ mmHg}} = 0.8586 \text{ atm}$

Check: The units (atm) are correct. The magnitude of the answer (< 1 atm) makes physical sense because we started with less than 760 mmHg.

(c)   **Given:** 652.5 mmHg   **Find:** in Hg

Conceptual Plan: mmHg $\rightarrow$ in Hg

$$\frac{1 \text{ in Hg}}{25.4 \text{ mmHg}}$$

Solution: $652.5 \text{ mmHg} \times \dfrac{1 \text{ in Hg}}{25.4 \text{ mmHg}} = 25.69 \text{ in Hg}$

Check: The units (in Hg) are correct. The magnitude of the answer (26) makes physical sense because inches are larger than millimeters.

(d)   **Given:** 652.5 mmHg   **Find:** psi

Conceptual Plan: Use answer from part (b) then convert atm $\rightarrow$ psi

$$\frac{14.70 \text{ psi}}{1 \text{ atm}}$$

Solution: $0.8586 \text{ atm} \times \dfrac{14.70 \text{ psi}}{1 \text{ atm}} = 12.62 \text{ psi}$

Check: The units (psi) are correct. The magnitude of the answer (< 14.7 psi) makes physical sense because we started with less than 1 atm.

Simple Gas Laws

5.5   **Given:** $V_1 = 2.8$ L, $P_1 = 755$ mmHg, and $V_2 = 3.7$ L   **Find:** P_2

Conceptual Plan: $V_1, P_1, V_2 \rightarrow P_2$

$$P_1 V_1 = P_2 V_2$$

Solution: $P_1 V_1 = P_2 V_2$ Rearrange to solve for P_2.

$$P_2 = P_1 \frac{V_1}{V_2} = 755 \text{ mmHg} \times \frac{2.8 \text{ L}}{3.7 \text{ L}} = 5\underline{7}1.35135 \text{ mmHg} = 5.7 \times 10^2 \text{ mmHg}$$

Check: The units (mmHg) are correct. The magnitude of the answer (570 mmHg) makes physical sense because Boyle's law indicates that as the volume increases, the pressure decreases.

5.6   **Given:** $V_1 = 32.6$ L, $P_1 = 1.3$ atm, and $V_2 = 13.8$ L   **Find:** P_2
Conceptual Plan: $V_1, P_1, V_2 \rightarrow P_2$

$$P_1 V_1 = P_2 V_2$$

Solution: $P_1 V_1 = P_2 V_2$ Rearrange to solve for P_2.

$$P_2 = P_1\frac{V_1}{V_2} = 1.3 \text{ atm} \times \frac{32.6 \text{ L}}{13.8 \text{ L}} = 3.\underline{0}71 \text{ atm} = 3.1 \text{ atm}$$

Check: The units (atm) are correct. The magnitude of the answer (3 atm) makes physical sense because Boyle's law indicates that as the volume decreases, the pressure increases.

5.7   **Given:** $V_1 = 37.2$ mL, $T_1 = 22$ °C, and $T_2 = 81$ °C   **Find:** V_2
Conceptual Plan: °C $\rightarrow$ K then $V_1, T_1, T_2 \rightarrow V_2$

$$K = °C + 273.15 \qquad \frac{V_1}{T_1} = \frac{V_2}{T_2}$$

Solution: $T_1 = 22$ °C $+ 273.15 = 295$ K and $T_2 = 81$ °C $+ 273.15 = 354$ K

$$\frac{V_1}{T_1} = \frac{V_2}{T_2} \text{ Rearrange to solve for } V_2. \ V_2 = V_1\frac{T_2}{T_1} = 37.2 \text{ mL} \times \frac{354 \text{ K}}{295 \text{ K}} = 44.6 \text{ mL}$$

Check: The units (mL) are correct. The magnitude of the answer (45 mL) makes physical sense because Charles's law indicates that as the temperature increases, the volume increases.

5.8   **Given:** $V_1 = 1.25$ mL, $T_1 = 91.3$ °C, and $T_2 = 0.0$ °C   **Find:** V_2
Conceptual Plan: °C $\rightarrow$ K then $V_1, T_1, T_2 \rightarrow V_2$

$$K = °C + 273.15 \qquad \frac{V_1}{T_1} = \frac{V_2}{T_2}$$

Solution: $T_1 = 91.3$ °C $+ 273.15 = 364.5$ K and $T_2 = 0.0$ °C $+ 273.15 = 273.2$ K

$$\frac{V_1}{T_1} = \frac{V_2}{T_2} \text{ Rearrange to solve for } V_2. \ V_2 = V_1\frac{T_2}{T_1} = 1.25 \text{ mL} \times \frac{273.2 \text{ K}}{364.5 \text{ K}} = 0.937 \text{ mL}$$

Check: The units (mL) are correct. The magnitude of the answer (0.9 mL) makes physical sense because Charles's law indicates that as the temperature decreases, the volume decreases.

5.9   **Given:** $V_1 = 2.76$ L, $n_1 = 0.128$ mol, and $\Delta n = 0.073$ mol   **Find:** V_2
Conceptual Plan: $n_1 \rightarrow n_2$ then $V_1, n_1, n_2 \rightarrow V_2$

$$n_1 + \Delta n = n_2 \qquad \frac{V_1}{n_1} = \frac{V_2}{n_2}$$

Solution: $n_2 = 0.128$ mol $+ 0.073$ mol $= 0.201$ mol

$$\frac{V_1}{n_1} = \frac{V_2}{n_2} \text{ Rearrange to solve for } V_2. \ V_2 = V_1\frac{n_2}{n_1} = 2.76 \text{ L} \times \frac{0.201 \text{ mol}}{0.128 \text{ mol}} = 4.3340625 = 4.33 \text{ L}$$

Check: The units (L) are correct. The magnitude of the answer (4 L) makes physical sense because Avogadro's law indicates that as the number of moles increases, the volume increases.

5.10   **Given:** $V_1 = 334$ mL, $n_1 = 0.87$ mol, and $\Delta n = 0.22$ mol   **Find:** V_2
Conceptual Plan: $n_1 \rightarrow n_2$ then $V_1, n_1, n_2 \rightarrow V_2$

$$n_1 + \Delta n = n_2 \qquad \frac{V_1}{n_1} = \frac{V_2}{n_2}$$

Solution: $n_2 = 0.87$ mol $+ 0.22$ mol $= 1.09$ mol

$$\frac{V_1}{n_1} = \frac{V_2}{n_2} \text{ Rearrange to solve for } V_2. \ V_2 = V_1\frac{n_2}{n_1} = 334 \text{ mL} \times \frac{1.09 \text{ mol}}{0.87 \text{ mol}} = 418.4598 \text{ mL} = 4.2 \times 10^2 \text{ mL}$$

Check: The units (mL) are correct. The magnitude of the answer (420 mL) makes physical sense because Avogadro's law indicates that as the number of moles increases, the volume increases.

Ideal Gas Law

5.11   **Given:** $n = 0.128$ mol, $P = 0.97$ atm, and $T = 325$ K   **Find:** V
Conceptual Plan: $n, P, T \rightarrow V$

$$PV = nRT$$

Solution: $PV = nRT$ Rearrange to solve for V. $V = \dfrac{nRT}{P} = \dfrac{0.128 \text{ mol} \times 0.08206 \dfrac{\text{L} \cdot \text{atm}}{\text{mol} \cdot \text{K}} \times 325 \text{ K}}{0.97 \text{ atm}} = 3.5 \text{ L}$

Check: The units (L) are correct. The magnitude of the answer (3.5 L) makes sense because, as you will see in the next section, one mole of an ideal gas under standard conditions (273 K and 1 atm) occupies 22.4 L. Although these are not standard conditions, they are close enough for a ballpark check of the answer. Because this gas sample contains 0.128 moles, a volume of 3.5 L is reasonable.

5.12   **Given:** $V = 15.0 \text{ L}$, $n = 0.448 \text{ mol}$, and $T = 305 \text{ K}$ **Find:** P
       Conceptual Plan: $n, V, T \rightarrow P$
                                $PV = nRT$

Solution: $PV = nRT$ Rearrange to solve for P. $P = \dfrac{nRT}{V} = \dfrac{0.448 \text{ mol} \times 0.08206 \dfrac{\text{L} \cdot \text{atm}}{\text{mol} \cdot \text{K}} \times 305 \text{ K}}{15.0 \text{ L}} = 0.748 \text{ atm}$

Check: The units (atm) are correct. The magnitude of the answer (~1 atm) makes sense because, as you will see in the next section, one mole of an ideal gas under standard conditions (273 K and 1 atm) occupies 22.4 L. Although these are not standard conditions, they are close enough for a ballpark check of the answer. Because this gas sample contains 0.448 moles in a volume of 15 liters, a pressure of 0.75 atm is reasonable.

5.13   **Given:** $V = 28.5 \text{ L}$, $P = 1.8 \text{ atm}$, and $T = 298 \text{ K}$ **Find:** n
       Conceptual Plan: $V, P, T \rightarrow n$
                                $PV = nRT$

Solution: $PV = nRT$ Rearrange to solve for n. $n = \dfrac{PV}{RT} = \dfrac{1.8 \text{ atm} \times 28.5 \text{ L}}{0.08206 \dfrac{\text{L} \cdot \text{atm}}{\text{mol} \cdot \text{K}} \times 298 \text{ K}} = 2.1 \text{ mol}$

Check: The units (mol) are correct. The magnitude of the answer (2 mol) makes sense because, as you will see in the next section, one mole of an ideal gas under standard conditions (273 K and 1 atm) occupies 22.4 L. Although these are not standard conditions, they are close enough for a ballpark check of the answer. Because this gas sample has a volume of 28.5 L and a pressure of 1.8 atm, ~2 mol is reasonable.

5.14   **Given:** $V = 11.8 \text{ L}$, $P = 1.3 \text{ atm}$, and $n = 0.52 \text{ mol}$ **Find:** T
       Conceptual Plan: $V, P, n \rightarrow T$
                                $PV = nRT$

Solution: $PV = nRT$ Rearrange to solve for T. $T = \dfrac{PV}{nR} = \dfrac{1.3 \text{ atm} \times 11.8 \text{ L}}{0.52 \text{ mol} \times 0.08206 \dfrac{\text{L} \cdot \text{atm}}{\text{mol} \cdot \text{K}}} = 360 \text{ K}$

Check: The units (K) are correct. The magnitude of the answer (360 K) makes sense because, as you will see in the next section, one mole of an ideal gas under standard conditions (273 K and 1 atm) occupies 22.4 L. Although these are not standard conditions, they are close enough for a ballpark check of the answer. Because this gas sample has 0.52 mol, a volume of 11.8 L, and a pressure of 1.3 atm, 360 K is reasonable.

5.15   **Given:** $P_1 = 36.0 \text{ psi (gauge P)}$, $V_1 = 11.8 \text{ L}$, $T_1 = 12.0 \,°\text{C}$, $V_2 = 12.2 \text{ L}$, and $T_2 = 65.0 \,°\text{C}$ **Find:** P_2 and compare to $P_{max} = 38.0 \text{ psi (gauge P)}$
       Conceptual Plan: $°\text{C} \rightarrow \text{K}$ and gauge $\text{P} \rightarrow \text{psi} \rightarrow \text{atm}$ then $P_1, V_1, T_1, V_2, T_2 \rightarrow P_2$
            $\text{K} = °\text{C} + 273.15$ $\text{psi} = \text{gauge P} + 14.7$ $\dfrac{1 \text{ atm}}{14.7 \text{ psi}}$ $\dfrac{P_1 V_1}{T_1} = \dfrac{P_2 V_2}{T_2}$

Solution: $T_1 = 12.0 \,°\text{C} + 273.15 = 285.2 \text{ K}$ and $T_2 = 65.0 \,°\text{C} + 273.15 = 338.2 \text{ K}$

$P_1 = 36.0 \text{ psi (gauge P)} + 14.7 = 50.7 \text{ psi} \times \dfrac{1 \text{ atm}}{14.7 \text{ psi}} = 3.44898 \text{ atm}$

$P_{max} = 38.0 \text{ psi (gauge P)} + 14.7 = 52.7 \text{ psi} \times \dfrac{1 \text{ atm}}{14.7 \text{ psi}} = 3.59 \text{ atm}$

$\dfrac{P_1V_1}{T_1} = \dfrac{P_2V_2}{T_2}$ Rearrange to solve for P_2. $P_2 = P_1\dfrac{V_1}{V_2}\dfrac{T_2}{T_1} = 3.44898 \text{ atm} \times \dfrac{11.8\ \cancel{L}}{12.2\ \cancel{L}} \times \dfrac{338.2\ \cancel{K}}{285.2\ \cancel{K}} = 3.96 \text{ atm}$

This exceeds the maximum tire rating of 3.59 atm or 38.0 psi (gauge P).

Check: The units (atm) are correct. The magnitude of the answer (3.96 atm) makes physical sense because the relative increase in T is greater than the relative increase in V; so P should increase.

5.16   **Given:** $P_1 = 748$ mmHg, $V_1 = 28.5$ L, $T_1 = 28.0\ °C$, $P_2 = 385$ mmHg, and $T_2 = -15.0\ °C$ **Find:** V_2

     Conceptual Plan: $°C \rightarrow K$ then $P_1, V_1, T_1, V_2, T_2 \rightarrow P_2$

$$K = °C + 273.15 \qquad\qquad \frac{P_1V_1}{T_1} = \frac{P_2V_2}{T_2}$$

     Solution: $T_1 = 28.0\ °C + 273.15 = 301.2$ K and $T_2 = -15.0\ °C + 273.15 = 258.2$ K

$\dfrac{P_1V_1}{T_1} = \dfrac{P_2V_2}{T_2}$ Rearrange to solve for V_2. $V_2 = V_1\dfrac{P_1}{P_2}\dfrac{T_2}{T_1} = 28.5 \text{ L} \times \dfrac{748\ \cancel{\text{mmHg}}}{385\ \cancel{\text{mmHg}}} \times \dfrac{258.2\ \cancel{K}}{301.2\ \cancel{K}} = 47.5 \text{ L}$

     Check: The units (L) are correct. The magnitude of the answer (48 L) makes physical sense because the relative decrease in P is greater than the relative decrease in T; so V should increase.

5.17   **Given:** $m\ (CO_2) = 28.8$ g, $P = 742$ mmHg, and $T = 22\ °C$ **Find:** V

     Conceptual Plan: $°C \rightarrow K$ and mmHg $\rightarrow$ atm and g $\rightarrow$ mol then $n, P, T \rightarrow V$

$$K = °C + 273.15 \qquad \frac{1 \text{ atm}}{760 \text{ mmHg}} \qquad \frac{1 \text{ mol}}{44.01 \text{ g}} \qquad PV = nRT$$

     Solution: $T_1 = 22\ °C + 273.15 = 295$ K, $P = 742\ \cancel{\text{mmHg}} \times \dfrac{1 \text{ atm}}{760\ \cancel{\text{mmHg}}} = 0.976316$ atm,

$n = 28.8\ \cancel{g} \times \dfrac{1 \text{ mol}}{44.01\ \cancel{g}} = 0.654397$ mol $PV = nRT$ Rearrange to solve for V.

$V = \dfrac{nRT}{P} = \dfrac{0.654397\ \cancel{\text{mol}} \times 0.08206\ \dfrac{\text{L} \cdot \cancel{\text{atm}}}{\cancel{\text{mol}} \cdot \cancel{K}} \times 295\ \cancel{K}}{0.976316\ \cancel{\text{atm}}} = 16.2 \text{ L}$

     Check: The units (L) are correct. The magnitude of the answer (16 L) makes sense because one mole of an ideal gas under standard conditions (273 K and 1 atm) occupies 22.4 L. Although these are not standard conditions, they are close enough for a ballpark check of the answer. Because this gas sample contains 0.65 mole, a volume of 16 L is reasonable.

5.18   **Given:** 1.0 L of liquid N_2 w/$d = 0.807$ g/mL, $T = 25.0\ °C$, $P = 1.0$ atm, and closet is 1.0 m $\times$ 1.0 m $\times$ 2.0 m

     Find: $V\%$ of closet air displaced by evaporated liquid

     Conceptual Plan: $°C \rightarrow K$ and L $\rightarrow$ mL $\rightarrow$ g $\rightarrow$ mol then $n, P, T \rightarrow V_{\text{evap}}$

$$K = °C + 273.15 \qquad \frac{1000 \text{ mL}}{1 \text{ L}} \qquad d = m/V \qquad \frac{1 \text{ mol}}{28.02 \text{ g}} \qquad PV = nRT$$

     then $l, w, h \rightarrow V_{\text{closet}} \text{m}^3 \rightarrow \text{cm}^3 \rightarrow$ L finally $V_{\text{evap}}, V_{\text{closet}} \rightarrow \%\ V$ displaced

$$V = lwh \qquad \frac{(100 \text{ cm})^3}{(1 \text{ m})^3} \quad \frac{1 \text{ L}}{1000 \text{ mL}} \qquad \%\ V \text{ displaced} = \frac{V_{\text{evap}}}{V_{\text{closet}}} \times 100\%$$

     Solution: $T_1 = 25.0\ °C + 273.15 = 298.2$ K, $1.0\ \cancel{L} \times \dfrac{1000 \text{ mL}}{1\ \cancel{L}} = 1.0 \times 10^3$ mL, $d = m/V$ Rearrange to solve for m.

$m = d \times V = 0.807\dfrac{\text{g}}{\cancel{\text{mL}}} \times 1.0 \times 10^3\ \cancel{\text{mL}} = 8.07 \times 10^2\ \cancel{g} \times \dfrac{1 \text{ mol}}{28.02\ \cancel{g}} = 28.801 \text{ mol}$ $PV = nRT$

     Rearrange to solve for V.

$V_{\text{evap}} = \dfrac{nRT}{P} = \dfrac{28.801\ \cancel{\text{mol}} \times 0.08206\ \dfrac{\text{L} \cdot \cancel{\text{atm}}}{\cancel{\text{mol}} \cdot \cancel{K}} \times 298.2\ \cancel{K}}{1.0\ \cancel{\text{atm}}} = 7.0477 \times 10^2 \text{ L}$

$V_{\text{closet}} = lwh = 1.0 \text{ m} \times 1.0 \text{ m} \times 2.0 \text{ m} = 2.0 \text{ m}^3$

$V_{\text{closet}} = 2.0\ \cancel{\text{m}^3} \times \dfrac{(100 \text{ cm})^3}{(1\cancel{\text{m}})^3} \times \dfrac{1 \text{ L}}{1000\ \cancel{\text{cm}^3}} = 2.0 \times 10^3 \text{ L}$

$\%\ V$ displaced $= \dfrac{V_{\text{evap}}}{V_{\text{closet}}} \times 100\% = \dfrac{7.0477 \times 10^2\ \cancel{L}}{2.0 \times 10^3\ \cancel{L}} \times 100\% = 35\%$

Check: The units (%) are correct. The magnitude of the answer (35%) makes sense because it should be between 0 and 100%. Looking at the two volumes, when a liquid evaporates, the volume increases by several orders of magnitude; when converting from cubic meters to liters, there is an increase of 3 orders of magnitude.

5.19 **Given:** sample a = 5 gas particles, sample b = 10 gas particles, and sample c = 8 gas particles, with all temperatures and volumes the same **Find:** sample with largest P
Conceptual Plan: $n, V, T \rightarrow P$
$$PV = nRT$$

Solution: $PV = nRT$ Because V and T are constant, $P \propto n$. The sample with the largest number of gas particles will have the highest P. $P_b > P_c > P_a$.

5.20 **Given:** $P_1 = 1$ atm, $V_1 = 1$ L, $T_1 = 25\,°C$, $V_2 = 0.5$ L, and $T_2 = 250.\,°C$
Find: Draw picture and P_2
Conceptual Plan: $°C \rightarrow K$ then $P_1, V_1, T_1, V_2, T_2 \rightarrow P_2$
$$K = °C + 273.15 \qquad \frac{P_1 V_1}{T_1} = \frac{P_2 V_2}{T_2}$$

Solution: $T_1 = 25\,°C + 273.15 = 298$ K and $T_2 = 250.\,°C + 273.15 = 523$ K
$\frac{P_1 V_1}{T_1} = \frac{P_2 V_2}{T_2}$ Rearrange to solve for P_2. $P_2 = P_1 \frac{V_1}{V_2} \frac{T_2}{T_1} = 1$ atm $\times \frac{1\,L}{0.5\,L} \times \frac{523\,K}{298\,K} = 4$ atm

Check: The units (atm) are correct. The magnitude of the answer (4 atm) makes physical sense because there is an increase in T and a decrease in V, both of which increase P.

5.21 **Given:** $P_1 = 755$ mmHg, $T_1 = 25\,°C$, and $T_2 = 1155\,°C$ **Find:** P_2
Conceptual Plan: $°C \rightarrow K$ and mmHg $\rightarrow$ atm then $P_1, T_1, T_2 \rightarrow P_2$
$$K = °C + 273.15 \qquad \frac{1\,atm}{760\,mmHg} \qquad \frac{P_1}{T_1} = \frac{P_2}{T_2}$$

Solution: $T_1 = 25\,°C + 273.15 = 298$ K and $T_2 = 1155\,°C + 273.15 = 1428$ K
$P = 755$ mmHg $\times \frac{1\,atm}{760\,mmHg} = 0.993421$ atm $\quad \frac{P_1}{T_1} = \frac{P_2}{T_2}$ Rearrange to solve for P_2.
$P_2 = P_1 \frac{T_2}{T_1} = 0.993421$ atm $\times \frac{1428\,K}{298\,K} = 4.76$ atm

Check: The units (atm) are correct. The magnitude of the answer (5 atm) makes physical sense because there is a significant increase in T, which will increase P significantly.

5.22 **Given:** $V_1 = 1.75$ L, $P_1 = 1.35$ atm, $T_1 = 25\,°C$, $V_2 = 1.75$ L, and $T_2 = 355\,°C$ **Find:** P_2
Conceptual Plan: $°C \rightarrow K$ then $P_1, T_1, T_2 \rightarrow P_2$
$$K = °C + 273.15 \qquad \frac{P_1}{T_1} = \frac{P_2}{T_2}$$

Solution: $T_1 = 25\,°C + 273.15 = 298$ K and $T_2 = 355\,°C + 273.15 = 628$ K
$\frac{P_1}{T_1} = \frac{P_2}{T_2}$ Rearrange to solve for P_2. $P_2 = P_1 \frac{T_2}{T_1} = 1.35$ atm $\times \frac{628\,K}{298\,K} = 2.85$ atm

Check: The units (atm) are correct. The magnitude of the answer (3 atm) makes physical sense because there is a significant increase in T, which will increase P significantly.

Molar Volume, Density, and Molar Mass of a Gas

5.23 **Given:** STP and m (Ne) = 15.0 g **Find:** V
Conceptual Plan: g $\rightarrow$ mol $\rightarrow$ V
$$\frac{1\,mol}{20.18\,g} \qquad \frac{22.414\,L}{1\,mol}$$
Solution: 15.0 g $\times \frac{1\,mol}{20.18\,g} \times \frac{22.414\,L}{1\,mol} = 16.7$ L

Check: The units (L) are correct. The magnitude of the answer (17 L) makes sense because one mole of an ideal gas under standard conditions (273 K and 1 atm) occupies 22.4 L and we have about 0.75 mol.

5.24   **Given:** STP and CO_2 **Find:** d
         Conceptual Plan: $mol \rightarrow g$ then $m, V \rightarrow d$

$$\frac{44.01 \text{ g}}{1 \text{ mol}} \qquad d = \frac{m}{V}$$

Solution: $1 \text{ mol} \times \dfrac{44.01 \text{ g}}{1 \text{ mol}} = 44.01 \text{ g} = m$ at STP $V = 22.414 \text{ L}$ $d = \dfrac{m}{V} = \dfrac{44.01 \text{ g}}{22.414 \text{ L}} = 1.964 \text{ g/L}$

Check: The units (g/L) are correct. The magnitude of the answer (1 g/L) is reasonable for a gas density.

5.25   **Given:** H_2, $P = 1655$ psi, and $T = 20.0\,°C$ **Find:** d
         Conceptual Plan: $°C \rightarrow K$ and psi $\rightarrow$ atm then $P, T, \mathcal{M} \rightarrow d$

$$K = °C + 273.15 \qquad \frac{1 \text{ atm}}{14.70 \text{ psi}} \qquad d = \frac{P\mathcal{M}}{RT}$$

Solution: $T = 20.0\,°C + 273.15 = 293.2 \text{ K}$ $P = 1655 \text{ psi} \times \dfrac{1 \text{ atm}}{14.70 \text{ psi}} = 112.58\underline{5} \text{ atm}$

$$d = \frac{PM}{RT} = \frac{112.58\underline{5} \text{ atm} \times 2.016 \dfrac{\text{g}}{\text{mol}}}{0.08206 \dfrac{\text{L} \cdot \text{atm}}{\text{K} \cdot \text{mol}} \times 293.2 \text{ K}} = 9.434 \frac{\text{g}}{\text{L}}$$

Check: The units (g/L) are correct. The magnitude of the answer (9 g/L) makes physical sense because this is a high pressure; so the gas density will be on the high side.

5.26   **Given:** N_2O, $d = 2.85$ g/L, and $T = 298$ K   **Find:** P (mmHg)
         Conceptual Plan: $d, T, \mathcal{M} \rightarrow d$ then atm $\rightarrow$ mmHg

$$d = \frac{P\mathcal{M}}{RT} \qquad \frac{760 \text{ mmHg}}{1 \text{ atm}}$$

Solution: $d = \dfrac{P\mathcal{M}}{RT}$ Rearrange to solve for P.

$$P = \frac{dRT}{\mathcal{M}} = \frac{2.85 \dfrac{\text{g}}{\text{L}} \times 0.08206 \dfrac{\text{L} \cdot \text{atm}}{\text{K} \cdot \text{mol}} \times 298 \text{ K}}{44.02 \dfrac{\text{g}}{\text{mol}}} = 1.5832\underline{2} \text{ atm}$$

$$P = 1.5832\underline{2} \text{ atm} \times \frac{760 \text{ mmHg}}{1 \text{ atm}} = 1.20 \times 10^3 \text{ mmHg}$$

Check: The units (mmHg) are correct. The magnitude of the answer (1200 mmHg) makes physical sense because the gas density is reasonable, so we expect a $P \sim 1$ atm.

5.27   **Given:** $V = 248$ mL, $m = 0.433$ g, $P = 745$ mmHg, and $T = 28\,°C$ **Find:** $\mathcal{M}$
         Conceptual Plan: $°C \rightarrow K$ and mmHg $\rightarrow$ atm and mL $\rightarrow$ L then $V, m \rightarrow d$ then $d, P, T \rightarrow \mathcal{M}$

$$K = °C + 273.15 \qquad \frac{1 \text{ atm}}{760 \text{ mmHg}} \qquad \frac{1 \text{ L}}{1000 \text{ mL}} \qquad d = \frac{m}{V} \qquad d = \frac{p\mathcal{M}}{RT}$$

Solution: $T = 28\,°C + 273.15 = 301 \text{ K}$ $P = 745 \text{ mmHg} \times \dfrac{1 \text{ atm}}{760 \text{ mmHg}} = 0.98026\underline{3} \text{ atm}$

$V = 248 \text{ mL} \times \dfrac{1 \text{ L}}{1000 \text{ mL}} = 0.248 \text{ L}$ $d = \dfrac{m}{V} = \dfrac{0.433 \text{ g}}{0.248 \text{ L}} = 1.7459\underline{7} \text{ g/L}$ $d = \dfrac{P\mathcal{M}}{RT}$ Rearrange to solve for $\mathcal{M}$.

$$\mathcal{M} = \frac{dRT}{P} = \frac{1.7459\underline{7} \dfrac{\text{g}}{\text{L}} \times 0.08206 \dfrac{\text{L} \cdot \text{atm}}{\text{K} \cdot \text{mol}} \times 301 \text{ K}}{0.98026\underline{3} \text{ atm}} = 44.0 \text{ g/mol}$$

Check: The units (g/mol) are correct. The magnitude of the answer (44 g/mol) makes physical sense because this is a reasonable number for a molecular weight of a gas.

5.28   **Given:** $V = 113$ mL, $m = 0.171$ g, $P = 721$ mmHg, and $T = 32\,°C$ **Find:** $\mathcal{M}$
         Conceptual Plan: $°C \rightarrow K$ and mmHg $\rightarrow$ atm and mL $\rightarrow$ L then $V, m \rightarrow d$ then $d, P, T \rightarrow \mathcal{M}$

$$K = °C + 273.15 \qquad \frac{1 \text{ atm}}{760 \text{ mmHg}} \qquad \frac{1 \text{ L}}{1000 \text{ mL}} \qquad d = \frac{m}{V} \qquad d = \frac{p\mathcal{M}}{RT}$$

Solution: $T = 32\,°C + 273.15 = 305\,K$ $P = 721\,\text{mmHg} \times \dfrac{1\,\text{atm}}{760\,\text{mmHg}} = 0.948684\,\text{atm}$

$V = 113\,\text{mL} \times \dfrac{1\,L}{1000\,\text{mL}} = 0.113\,L$ $d = \dfrac{m}{V} = \dfrac{0.171\,g}{0.113\,L} = 1.51327\,g/L$ $d = \dfrac{P\mathcal{M}}{RT}$ Rearrange to solve for $\mathcal{M}$.

$$\mathcal{M} = \frac{dRT}{P} = \frac{1.51327\,\dfrac{g}{L} \times 0.08206\,\dfrac{L \cdot \text{atm}}{K \cdot \text{mol}} \times 305\,K}{0.948684\,\text{atm}} = 39.9\,g/\text{mol}$$

Check: The units (g/mol) are correct. The magnitude of the answer (40 g/mol) makes physical sense because this is a reasonable number for a molecular weight of a gas.

5.29   **Given:** $m = 38.8\,\text{mg}$, $V = 224\,\text{mL}$, $T = 55\,°C$, and $P = 886\,\text{torr}$ **Find:** $\mathcal{M}$
Conceptual Plan: mg $\rightarrow$ **g and mL** $\rightarrow$ **L and** °C $\rightarrow$ **K and torr** $\rightarrow$ **atm then** $V, m \rightarrow d$ **then** $d, P, T \rightarrow \mathcal{M}$

$\qquad\qquad\quad \dfrac{1\,g}{1000\,\text{mg}} \qquad \dfrac{1\,L}{1000\,\text{mL}} \quad K = °C + 273.15 \quad \dfrac{1\,\text{atm}}{760\,\text{torr}} \qquad\qquad d = \dfrac{m}{V} \qquad\qquad d = \dfrac{P\mathcal{M}}{RT}$

Solution:

$m = 38.8\,\text{mg} \times \dfrac{1\,g}{1000\,\text{mg}} = 0.0388\,g$ $V = 224\,\text{mL} \times \dfrac{1\,L}{1000\,\text{mL}} = 0.224\,L$ $T = 55\,°C + 273.15 = 328\,K$

$P = 886\,\text{torr} \times \dfrac{1\,\text{atm}}{760\,\text{torr}} = 1.165789\,\text{atm}$ $d = \dfrac{m}{V} = \dfrac{0.0388\,g}{0.224\,L} = 0.173214\,g/L$ $d = \dfrac{P\mathcal{M}}{RT}$

Rearrange to solve for $\mathcal{M}$. $\mathcal{M} = \dfrac{dRT}{P} = \dfrac{0.173214\,\dfrac{g}{L} \times 0.08206\,\dfrac{L \cdot \text{atm}}{K \cdot \text{mol}} \times 328\,K}{1.165789\,\text{atm}} = 4.00\,g/\text{mol}$

Check: The units (g/mol) are correct. The magnitude of the answer (4 g/mol) makes physical sense because this is a reasonable number for a molecular weight of a gas, especially because the density is on the low side.

5.30   **Given:** $m = 0.555\,g$, $V = 117\,\text{mL}$, $T = 85\,°C$, and $P = 753\,\text{mmHg}$ **Find:** $\rightarrow \mathcal{M}$
Conceptual Plan: mL $\rightarrow$ **L and** °C $\rightarrow$ **K and mmHg** $\rightarrow$ **atm then** $V, m \rightarrow d$ **then** $d, P, T \rightarrow \mathcal{M}$

$\qquad\qquad\quad \dfrac{1\,L}{1000\,\text{mL}} \quad K = °C + 273.15 \quad \dfrac{1\,\text{atm}}{760\,\text{mmHg}} \qquad\qquad d = \dfrac{m}{V} \qquad\qquad d = \dfrac{P\mathcal{M}}{RT}$

Solution: $V = 117\,\text{mL} \times \dfrac{1\,L}{1000\,\text{mL}} = 0.117\,L$ $T = 85\,°C + 273.15 = 358\,K$

$P = 753\,\text{mmHg} \times \dfrac{1\,\text{atm}}{760\,\text{mmHg}} = 0.9907895\,\text{atm}$ $d = \dfrac{m}{V} = \dfrac{0.555\,g}{0.117\,L} = 4.74359\,g/L$ $d = \dfrac{P\mathcal{M}}{RT}$

Rearrange to solve for $\mathcal{M}$. $\mathcal{M} = \dfrac{dRT}{P} = \dfrac{4.74359\,\dfrac{g}{L} \times 0.08206\,\dfrac{L \cdot \text{atm}}{K \cdot \text{mol}} \times 358\,K}{0.9907895\,\text{atm}} = 141\,g/\text{mol}$

Check: The units (g/mol) are correct. The magnitude of the answer (141 g/mol) makes physical sense because this is a reasonable number for a molecular weight of a gas, especially because the density is on the high side.

Partial Pressure

5.31   **Given:** $P_{N_2} = 315\,\text{torr}$, $P_{O_2} = 134\,\text{torr}$, $P_{He} = 219\,\text{torr}$, $V = 2.15\,L$, and $T = 25.0\,°C$ **Find:** $P_{\text{Total}}, m_{N_2}, m_{O_2}, m_{He}$
Conceptual Plan: °C $\rightarrow$ **K and torr** $\rightarrow$ **atm and** $P, V, T \rightarrow n$ **then mol** $\rightarrow$ **g**

$\qquad\qquad\quad K = °C + 273.15 \qquad \dfrac{1\,\text{atm}}{760\,\text{torr}} \qquad\qquad PV = nRT \qquad\qquad \mathcal{M}$

and $P_{N_2}, P_{O_2}, P_{He} \rightarrow P_{\text{Total}}$
$\qquad\quad P_{\text{Total}} = P_{N_2} + P_{O_2} + P_{He}$

Solution: $T_1 = 25.0\,°C + 273.15 = 298.2\,K$, $PV = nRT$ Rearrange to solve for n.

$n = \dfrac{PV}{RT}$ $P_{N_2} = 315\,\text{torr} \times \dfrac{1\,\text{atm}}{760\,\text{torr}} = 0.4144737\,\text{atm}$ $n_{N_2} = \dfrac{0.4144737\,\text{atm} \times 2.15\,L}{0.08206\,\dfrac{L \cdot \text{atm}}{\text{mol} \cdot K} \times 298.2\,K} = 0.03641634\,\text{mol}$

$0.03641634\,\text{mol} \times \dfrac{28.02\,\text{mol}}{1\,\text{mol}} = 1.02\,g\,N_2$

$$P_{O_2} = 134 \text{ torr} \times \frac{1 \text{ atm}}{760 \text{ torr}} = 0.1763158 \text{ atm} \qquad n_{O_2} = \frac{0.1763158 \text{ atm} \times 2.15 \text{ L}}{0.08206 \frac{\text{L} \cdot \text{atm}}{\text{mol} \cdot \text{K}} \times 298.2 \text{ K}} = 0.01549139 \text{ mol}$$

$$0.01549139 \text{ mol} \times \frac{32.00 \text{ mol}}{1 \text{ mol}} = 0.496 \text{ g O}_2$$

$$P_{He} = 219 \text{ torr} \times \frac{1 \text{ atm}}{760 \text{ torr}} = 0.2881579 \text{ atm} \qquad n_{He} = \frac{0.2881579 \text{ atm} \times 2.15 \text{ L}}{0.08206 \frac{\text{L} \cdot \text{atm}}{\text{mol} \cdot \text{K}} \times 298.2 \text{ K}} = 0.02531803 \text{ mol}$$

$$0.02531803 \text{ mol} \times \frac{4.003 \text{ mol}}{1 \text{ mol}} = 0.101 \text{ g He and}$$

$P_{Total} = P_{N_2} + P_{O_2} + P_{He} = 0.414 \text{ atm} + 0.176 \text{ atm} + 0.288 \text{ atm} = 0.878 \text{ atm or}$
$P_{Total} = P_{N_2} + P_{O_2} + P_{He} = 315 \text{ torr} + 134 \text{ torr} + 219 \text{ torr} = 668 \text{ torr}$

Check: The units (g, g, g, and atm or torr) are correct. The magnitude of the answer (no more than about a gram) makes sense because gases are not very dense and these pressures are < 1 atm. Because all of the pressures are small, the total is < 1 atm or 760 torr.

5.32 **Given:** $P_{Total} = 765 \text{ mmHg}$, $P_{CO_2} = 235 \text{ mmHg}$, $P_{Ar} = 112 \text{ mmHg}$, $P_{O_2} = 124 \text{ mmHg}$, $V = 20.0 \text{ L}$, and $T = 273 \text{ K}$
Find: P_{He} and m_{He}
Conceptual Plan: $P_{Total}, P_{CO_2}, P_{Ar}, P_{O_2} \rightarrow P_{He}$ then mmHg $\rightarrow$ atm then $P, V, T \rightarrow n$ then mol $\rightarrow$ g

$$P_{Total} = P_{CO_2} + P_{Ar} + P_{O_2} + P_{He} \qquad \frac{1 \text{ atm}}{760 \text{ mmHg}} \qquad PV = nRT \qquad \frac{4.003 \text{ g}}{1 \text{ mol}}$$

Solution: $P_{Total} = P_{CO_2} + P_{Ar} + P_{O2} + P_{He}$ Rearrange to solve for P_{He}.
$P_{He} = P_{Total} - P_{CO_2} + P_{Ar} + P_{O_2} = 765 \text{ mmHg} - 235 \text{ mmHg} - 112 \text{ mmHg} - 124 \text{ mmHg} = 294 \text{ mmHg}$

$$P_{He} = 294 \text{ mmHg} \times \frac{1 \text{ atm}}{760 \text{ mmHg}} = 0.387 \text{ atm} \quad PV = nRT \text{ Rearrange to solve for } n. \ n = \frac{PV}{RT}$$

$$n_{He} = \frac{0.387 \text{ atm} \times 20.0 \text{ L}}{0.08206 \frac{\text{L} \cdot \text{atm}}{\text{mol} \cdot \text{K}} \times 273 \text{ K}} = 0.3454990 \text{ mol} \quad 0.3454990 \text{ mol} \times \frac{4.003 \text{ g}}{1 \text{ mol}} = 1.38 \text{ g He}$$

Check: The units (g) are correct. The magnitude of the answer (1 g) makes sense because gases are not very dense and these pressures are < 1 atm.

5.33 **Given:** $m(CO_2) = 1.20 \text{ g}$, $V = 755 \text{ mL}$, $P_{N_2} = 725 \text{ mmHg}$, and $T = 25.0 \,°C$ **Find:** P_{Total}
Conceptual Plan: mL $\rightarrow$ L and $°C \rightarrow$ K and g $\rightarrow$ mol and $n, P, T \rightarrow V$ then atm $\rightarrow$ mmHg

$$\frac{1 \text{ L}}{1000 \text{ mL}} \qquad K = °C + 273.15 \qquad \frac{1 \text{ mol}}{44.01 \text{ g}} \qquad PV = nRT \qquad \frac{760 \text{ mmHg}}{1 \text{ atm}}$$

finally $P_{CO_2}, P_{N_2} \rightarrow P_{Total}$

$$P_{Total} = P_{CO_2} + P_{N_2}$$

Solution: $V = 755 \text{ mL} \times \frac{1 \text{ L}}{1000 \text{ mL}} = 0.755 \text{ L} \quad T = 25.0 \,°C + 273.15 = 298.2 \text{ K}$

$$n_{CO_2} = 1.20 \text{ g} \times \frac{1 \text{ mol}}{44.01 \text{ g}} = 0.0272665 \text{ mol}, \quad PV = nRT \text{ Rearrange to solve for } P.$$

$$P = \frac{nRT}{V} = \frac{0.0272665 \text{ mol} \times 0.08206 \frac{\text{L} \cdot \text{atm}}{\text{mol} \cdot \text{K}} \times 298.2 \text{ K}}{0.755 \text{ L}} = 0.883734 \text{ atm}$$

$$P_{CO_2} = 0.883734 \text{ atm} \times \frac{760 \text{ mmHg}}{1 \text{ atm}} = 672 \text{ mmHg}$$

$$P_{Total} = P_{CO_2} + P_{N_2} = 672 \text{ mmHg} + 725 \text{ mmHg} = 1397 \text{ mmHg or } 1397 \text{ torr} \times \frac{1 \text{ atm}}{760 \text{ torr}} = 1.84 \text{ atm}$$

Check: The units (mmHg) are correct. The magnitude of the answer (1400 mmHg) makes sense because it must be greater than 725 mmHg.

5.34　　**Given:** $V_{1He} = 275$ mL, $P_{1He} = 752$ torr, $V_{1Ar} = 475$ mL, and $P_{1Ar} = 722$ torr　　**Find:** P_{2He}, P_{2Ar}, and P_{Total}

Conceptual Plan: $V_{1He}, V_{1Ar} \rightarrow V_2$ and $V_1, P_1, V_2 \rightarrow P_2$ then $P_{2He}, P_{2Ar} \rightarrow P_{Total}$

$$V_{1He} + V_{1Ar} = V_2 \qquad P_1V_1 = P_2V_2 \qquad P_{Total} = P_{2He} + P_{2Ar}$$

Solution: $V_{1He} + V_{1Ar} = V_2 = 275$ mL $+ 475$ mL $= 750.$ mL, $P_1 V_1 = P_2 V_2$ Rearrange to solve for P_2.

$$P_2 = P_1 \frac{V_1}{V_2} \quad P_{2He} = P_{1He} \frac{V_{1He}}{V_2} = 752 \text{ torr} \times \frac{275 \text{ mL}}{750. \text{ mL}} = 275.733 \text{ torr} = 276 \text{ torr He}$$

$$P_{2Ar} = P_{1Ar} \frac{V_{1Ar}}{V_2} = 722 \text{ torr} \times \frac{475 \text{ mL}}{750. \text{ mL}} = 457.267 \text{ torr} = 457 \text{ torr Ar}$$

$$P_{Total} = P_{2He} + P_{2Ar} = 275.733 \text{ torr} + 457.267 \text{ torr} = 733 \text{ torr total pressure}$$

Check: The units (torr) are correct. The magnitude of the answers makes physical sense because Boyle's law indicates that as the volume increases, the pressure decreases. Because both initial pressures are ~700 torr, the final total pressure should be about the same pressure.

5.35　　**Given:** $m(N_2) = 1.25$ g, $m(O_2) = 0.85$ g, $V = 1.55$ L, and $T = 18\,°C$　　**Find:** χ_{N_2}, χ_{O_2}, P_{N_2}, P_{O_2}

Conceptual Plan: g $\rightarrow$ mol then $n_{N_2}, n_{O_2} \rightarrow \chi_{N_2}$ and $n_{N_2}, n_{O_2} \rightarrow \chi_{O_2}$ and °C $\rightarrow$ K

$$\mathcal{M} \qquad \chi_{N_2} = \frac{n_{N_2}}{n_{N_2} + n_{O_2}} \qquad \chi_{O_2} = \frac{n_{O_2}}{n_{N_2} + n_{O_2}} \qquad K = °C + 273.15$$

then $n, V, T \rightarrow P$

$$PV = nRT$$

Solution: $n_{N_2} = 1.25 \text{ g} \times \frac{1 \text{ mol}}{28.02 \text{ g}} = 0.0446110 \text{ mol}, \quad n_{O_2} = 0.85 \text{ g} \times \frac{1 \text{ mol}}{32.00 \text{ g}} = 0.026563 \text{ mol},$

$$T = 18\,°C + 273.15 = 291 \text{ K}, \chi_{N_2} = \frac{n_{N_2}}{n_{N_2} + n_{O_2}} = \frac{0.0446110 \text{ mol}}{0.0446110 \text{ mol} + 0.026563 \text{ mol}} = 0.626788 = 0.627,$$

$$\chi_{O_2} = \frac{n_{O_2}}{n_{N_2} + n_{O_2}} = \frac{0.026563 \text{ mol}}{0.0446110 \text{ mol} + 0.026563 \text{ mol}} = 0.373212 \text{ We can also calculate this as}$$

$$\chi_{O_2} = 1 - \chi_{N_2} = 1 - 0.626788 = 0.373212 = 0.373 \quad PV = nRT \text{ Rearrange to solve for } P. \ P = \frac{nRT}{V}$$

$$P_{N_2} = \frac{0.044611 \text{ mol} \times 0.08206 \frac{L \cdot atm}{mol \cdot K} \times 291 \text{ K}}{1.55 \text{ L}} = 0.687 \text{ atm}$$

$$P_{O_2} = \frac{0.026563 \text{ mol} \times 0.08206 \frac{L \cdot atm}{mol \cdot K} \times 291 \text{ K}}{1.55 \text{ L}} = 0.409 \text{ atm}$$

Check: The units (none and atm) are correct. The magnitude of the answers makes sense because the mole fractions should total 1 and because the weight of N_2 is greater than O_2, its mole fraction is larger. The number of moles is $\ll 1$, so we expect the pressures to be <1 atm, given the V (1.55 L).

5.36　　**Given:** Table 5.2, $m(O_2) = 10.0$ g, $T = 273$ K, and $P = 1.00$ atm　　**Find:** χ_{O_2} and V_{air}

Conceptual Plan: $\%V \rightarrow \chi_{O_2}$ and g $\rightarrow$ mol $\rightarrow V_{O_2} \rightarrow V_{air}$

$$\frac{1}{100\%} \qquad \frac{1 \text{ mol}}{32.00 \text{ g}} \quad \frac{22.4 \text{ L}}{1 \text{ mol}} \quad \frac{100 \text{ L air}}{21 \text{ L } O_2}$$

Solution: from Table 5.2, $\% V_{O_2} = 21\%$　$21\% \times \frac{1}{100\%} = 0.21 = \chi_{O_2}$

$$10.0 \text{ g} \times \frac{1 \text{ mol}}{32.00 \text{ g}} \times \frac{22.4 \text{ L}}{1 \text{ mol}} = 7.00 \text{ L} = V_{O_2} \text{ finally } 7.00 \text{ L } O_2 \times \frac{100 \text{ L air}}{21 \text{ L } O_2} = 33 \text{ L air}$$

Check: The units (none and L) are correct. The magnitude of the answer (0.21) makes sense because most of air is nitrogen. The magnitude of the answer (33 L) makes sense because one mole of an ideal gas under standard conditions (273 K and 1 atm) occupies 22.4 L and we have about 1/3 mol of O_2 (and so over a mole of air).

5.37　　**Given:** $T = 30.0\,°C$, $P_{Total} = 732$ mmHg, and $V = 722$ mL　　**Find:** P_{H_2} and m_{H_2}

Conceptual Plan: $T \rightarrow P_{H_2O}$ then $P_{Total}, P_{H_2O} \rightarrow P_{H_2}$ then mmHg $\rightarrow$ atm and mL $\rightarrow$ L

$$\qquad\qquad \textit{Table 5.3} \qquad\qquad P_{Total} = P_{H_2O} + P_{H_2} \qquad \frac{1 \text{ atm}}{760 \text{ mmHg}} \qquad \frac{1 \text{ L}}{1000 \text{ mL}}$$

and °C → K and P, V, T → n then mol → g

$$K = °C + 273.15 \qquad PV = nRT \qquad \frac{2.016 \text{ g}}{1 \text{ mol}}$$

Solution: Table 5.3 states that at 30 °C, $P_{H_2O} = 31.86$ mmHg $P_{Total} = P_{H_2O} + P_{H_2}$
Rearrange to solve for P_{H_2}. $P_{H_2} = P_{Total} - P_{H_2O} = 732$ mmHg $- 31.86$ mmHg $= 700.$ mmHg

$$P_{H_2} = 700. \text{ mmHg} \times \frac{1 \text{ atm}}{760 \text{ mmHg}} = 0.921052 \text{ atm} \qquad V = 722 \text{ mL} \times \frac{1 \text{ L}}{1000 \text{ mL}} = 0.722 \text{ L}$$

$$T = 30.0 °C + 273.15 = 303.2 \text{ K}, \quad PV = nRT \text{ Rearrange to solve for } n. \ n = \frac{PV}{RT}$$

$$n_{H_2} = \frac{0.921052 \text{ atm} \times 0.722 \text{ L}}{0.08206 \frac{\text{L} \cdot \text{atm}}{\text{mol} \cdot \text{K}} \times 303.2 \text{ K}} = 0.0267276 \text{ mol then } 0.0267276 \text{ mol} \times \frac{2.016 \text{ g}}{1 \text{ mol}} = 0.0539 \text{ g H}_2$$

Check: The units (g) are correct. The magnitude of the answer ($\ll 1$ g) makes sense because gases are not very dense, hydrogen is light, the volume is small, and the pressure is ~ 1 atm.

5.38 **Given:** $T = 25$ °C, $V = 5.45$ L, and $P_{Total} = 745$ mmHg   **Find:** n
Conceptual Plan: $T → P_{H_2O}$ then $P_{Total}, P_{H_2O} → P_{air}$ then mmHg → atm and °C → K

$$\text{Table 5.3} \qquad P_{Total} = P_{H_2O} + P_{air} \qquad \frac{1 \text{ atm}}{760 \text{ mmHg}} \qquad K = °C + 273.15$$

then P, V, T → n

$$PV = nRT$$

Solution: Table 5.3 states that at 25 °C, $P_{H_2O} = 23.78$ mmHg, $P_{Total} = P_{H_2O} + P_{air}$ Rearrange to solve for P_{air}.
$P_{air} = P_{Total} - P_{H_2O} = 745$ mmHg $- 23.78$ mmHg $= 721$ mmHg

$$P_{air} = 721 \text{ mmHg} \times \frac{1 \text{ atm}}{760 \text{ mmHg}} = 0.948684 \text{ atm} \quad T = 25 °C + 273.15 = 298 \text{ K}, \quad PV = nRT$$

$$\text{Rearrange to solve for } n. \ n = \frac{PV}{RT} = \frac{0.948684 \text{ atm} \times 5.45 \text{ L}}{0.08206 \frac{\text{L} \cdot \text{atm}}{\text{mol} \cdot \text{K}} \times 298 \text{ K}} = 0.211 \text{ mol}$$

Check: The units (mol) are correct. The magnitude of the answer (0.2 mol) makes sense because 22.4 L of a gas at STP contains 1 mol. We have only 5.45 L, so the answer makes sense.

5.39 **Given:** $T = 25$ °C, $P_{Total} = 748$ mmHg, and $V = 0.951$ L   **Find:** m_{H_2}
Conceptual Plan: $T → P_{H_2O}$ then $P_{Total}, P_{H_2O} → P_{H_2}$ then mmHg → atm and mL → L

$$\text{Table 5.3} \qquad P_{Total} = P_{H_2O} + P_{H_2} \qquad \frac{1 \text{ atm}}{760 \text{ mmHg}} \qquad \frac{1 \text{ L}}{1000 \text{ mL}}$$

and °C → K P, V, T → n then mol → g

$$K = °C + 273.15 \qquad PV = nRT \qquad \frac{2.016 \text{ g}}{1 \text{ mol}}$$

Solution: Table 5.3 states that at 25 °C, $P_{H_2O} = 23.78$ mmHg $P_{Total} = P_{H_2O} + P_{H_2}$
Rearrange to solve for P_{H_2}. $P_{H_2} = P_{Total} - P_{H_2O} = 748$ mmHg $- 23.78$ mmHg $= 724$ mmHg

$$P_{H_2} = 724 \text{ mmHg} \times \frac{1 \text{ atm}}{760 \text{ mmHg}} = 0.952632 \text{ atm} \quad T = 25 °C + 273.15 = 298 \text{ K}, \quad PV = nRT$$

$$\text{Rearrange to solve for } n. \ n_{H_2} = \frac{PV}{RT} = \frac{0.952632 \text{ atm} \times 0.951 \text{ L}}{0.08206 \frac{\text{L} \cdot \text{atm}}{\text{mol} \cdot \text{K}} \times 298 \text{ K}} = 0.0370474 \text{ mol}$$

$$0.0370474 \text{ mol} \times \frac{2.016 \text{ g}}{1 \text{ mol}} = 0.0747 \text{ g H}_2$$

Check: The units (g) are correct. The magnitude of the answer ($\ll 1$ g) makes sense because gases are not very dense, hydrogen is light, the volume is small, and the pressure is ~ 1 atm.

5.40 **Given:** $m (O_2) = 2.0$ g, $m (He) = 98.0$ g, $P_{Total} = 8.5$ atm   **Find:** P_{O_2}
Conceptual Plan: g → mol then $n_{O_2}, n_{He} → \chi_{O_2}$ then $\chi_{O_2}, P_{Total} → P_{O_2}$

$$\mathcal{M} \qquad \chi_{O_2} = \frac{n_{O_2}}{n_{O_2} + n_{He}} \qquad P_{O_2} = \chi_{O_2} P_{Total}$$

Solution: $n_{O_2} = 2.0 \text{ g} \times \dfrac{1 \text{ mol}}{32.00 \text{ g}} = 0.0625 \text{ mol}, \quad n_{He} = 98.0 \text{ g} \times \dfrac{1 \text{ mol}}{4.003 \text{ g}} = 24.4816 \text{ mol},$

$\chi_{O_2} = \dfrac{n_{O_2}}{n_{O_2} + n_{He}} = \dfrac{0.0625 \text{ mol}}{0.0625 \text{ mol} + 24.4816 \text{ mol}} = 0.0025464,$

$P_{O_2} = \chi_{O_2} P_{Total} = 0.0025464 \times 8.5 \text{ atm} = 0.022 \text{ atm}$

Check: The units (atm) are correct. The magnitude of the answer (0.022 atm) makes sense because at these depths, high oxygen pressures can cause toxicity.

Reaction Stoichiometry Involving Gases

5.41   **Given:** m (C) = 15.7 g, P = 1.0 atm, and T = 355 K   **Find:** V
Conceptual Plan: g C $\rightarrow$ mol C $\rightarrow$ mol H$_2$ then n (mol H$_2$), P, T $\rightarrow$ V

$$\dfrac{1 \text{ mol}}{12.01 \text{ g C}} \qquad \dfrac{1 \text{ mol H}_2}{1 \text{ mol C}} \qquad\qquad PV = nRT$$

Solution: $15.7 \text{ g C} \times \dfrac{1 \text{ mol C}}{12.01 \text{ g C}} \times \dfrac{1 \text{ mol H}_2}{1 \text{ mol C}} = 1.30724 \text{ mol H}_2$, $PV = nRT$ Rearrange to solve for V.

$$V = \dfrac{nRT}{P} = \dfrac{1.30724 \text{ mol} \times 0.08206 \dfrac{\text{L} \cdot \text{atm}}{\text{mol} \cdot \text{K}} \times 355 \text{ K}}{1.0 \text{ atm}} = 38 \text{ L}$$

Check: The units (L) are correct. The magnitude of the answer (38 L) makes sense because we have more than one mole of gas, so we expect more than 22 L.

5.42   **Given:** V_{O_2} = 1.4 L, T = 315 K, P_{O_2} = 0.957 atm   **Find:** g H$_2$O
Conceptual Plan: P(mol O$_2$), V(mol O$_2$), T $\rightarrow$ n(mol O$_2$) then mol O$_2$ $\rightarrow$ mol H$_2$O $\rightarrow$ g H$_2$O

$$PV = nRT \qquad\qquad \dfrac{2 \text{ mol H}_2\text{O}}{1 \text{ mol O}_2} \qquad \dfrac{18.02 \text{ g H}_2\text{O}}{1 \text{ mol H}_2\text{O}}$$

Solution: $PV = nRT$ Rearrange to solve for n. $n = \dfrac{PV}{RT} = \dfrac{0.957 \text{ atm} \times 1.4 \text{ L}}{0.08206 \dfrac{\text{L} \cdot \text{atm}}{\text{mol} \cdot \text{K}} \times 315 \text{ K}} = 0.051832 \text{ mol O}_2$

$0.051832 \text{ mol O}_2 \times \dfrac{2 \text{ mol H}_2\text{O}}{1 \text{ mol O}_2} \times \dfrac{18.02 \text{ g H}_2\text{O}}{1 \text{ mol H}_2\text{O}} = 1.9 \text{ g H}_2\text{O}$

Check: The units (g) are correct. The magnitude of the answer (2 g) makes sense because we have much less than a mole of oxygen.

5.43   **Given:** P = 748 mmHg, T = 86 °C, and m (CH$_3$OH) = 25.8 g   **Find:** V_{H_2} and V_{CO}
Conceptual Plan: g CH$_3$OH $\rightarrow$ mol CH$_3$OH $\rightarrow$ mol H$_2$ and mmHg $\rightarrow$ atm and °C $\rightarrow$ K

$$\dfrac{1 \text{ mol CH}_3\text{OH}}{32.04 \text{ g CH}_3\text{OH}} \qquad \dfrac{2 \text{ mol H}_2}{1 \text{ mol CH}_3\text{OH}} \qquad \dfrac{1 \text{ atm}}{760 \text{ mmHg}} \qquad K = °C + 273.15$$

then n (mol H$_2$), P, T $\rightarrow$ V and mol H$_2$ $\rightarrow$ mol CO then n (mol CO), P, T $\rightarrow$ V

$$PV = nRT \qquad\qquad \dfrac{1 \text{ mol CO}}{2 \text{ mol H}_2} \qquad\qquad PV = nRT$$

Solution: $25.8 \text{ g CH}_3\text{OH} \times \dfrac{1 \text{ mol CH}_3\text{OH}}{32.04 \text{ g CH}_3\text{OH}} \times \dfrac{2 \text{ mol H}_2}{1 \text{ mol CH}_3\text{OH}} = 1.61049 \text{ mol H}_2$,

$P_{H_2} = 748 \text{ mmHg} \times \dfrac{1 \text{ atm}}{760 \text{ mmHg}} = 0.984211 \text{ atm}, \quad T = 86 °C + 273.15 = 359 \text{ K}, \quad PV = nRT$

Rearrange to solve for V. $V = \dfrac{nRT}{P}$ $V_{H_2} = \dfrac{1.61049 \text{ mol} \times 0.08206 \dfrac{\text{L} \cdot \text{atm}}{\text{mol} \cdot \text{K}} \times 359 \text{ K}}{0.984211 \text{ atm}} = 48.2 \text{ L H}_2$

$1.61049 \text{ mol H}_2 \times \dfrac{1 \text{ mol CO}}{2 \text{ mol H}_2} = 0.80525 \text{ mol CO}$, $V_{CO} = \dfrac{0.80525 \text{ mol} \times 0.08206 \dfrac{\text{L} \cdot \text{atm}}{\text{mol} \cdot \text{K}} \times 359 \text{ K}}{0.984211 \text{ atm}} = 24.1 \text{ L CO}$

Check: The units (L) are correct. The magnitude of the answers (48 L and 24 L) makes sense because we have more than one mole of hydrogen gas and half that of CO, so we expect significantly more than 22 L for hydrogen and half that for CO.

5.44   **Given:** $P = 782$ mmHg, $T = 25\,°C$, and $m\,(Al) = 53.2$ g   **Find:** V_{O_2}

Conceptual Plan: g Al → mol Al → mol O_2 and mmHg → atm and $°C$ → K then

$$\frac{1\text{ mol Al}}{26.98\text{ g Al}} \qquad \frac{3\text{ mol }O_2}{4\text{ mol Al}} \qquad \qquad \frac{1\text{ atm}}{760\text{ mmHg}} \qquad K = °C + 273.15$$

n (mol O_2), P, T → V

$$PV = nRT$$

Solution: $53.2 \text{ g Al} \times \dfrac{1\text{ mol Al}}{26.98\text{ g Al}} \times \dfrac{3\text{ mol }O_2}{4\text{ mol Al}} = 1.478873 \text{ mol } O_2,$

$P_{O_2} = 782 \text{ mmHg} \times \dfrac{1\text{ atm}}{760\text{ mmHg}} = 1.028947 \text{ atm}, \quad T = 25\,°C + 273.15 = 298 \text{ K}, \quad PV = nRT$

Rearrange to solve for V. $V_{O_2} = \dfrac{nRT}{P} = \dfrac{1.478873 \text{ mol} \times 0.08206 \dfrac{L \cdot atm}{mol \cdot K} \times 298 \text{ K}}{1.028947 \text{ atm}} = 35.1 \text{ L } O_2$

Check: The units (L) are correct. The magnitude of the answer (35 L) makes sense because we have more than one mole of oxygen gas and more than 1 atm, so we expect significantly more than 22 L.

5.45   **Given:** $V = 11.8$ L, and STP   **Find:** $m\,(NaN_3)$

Conceptual Plan: V_{N_2} → mol N_2 → mol NaN_3 → g NaN_3

$$\frac{1\text{ mol }N_2}{22.4\text{ L }N_2} \qquad \frac{2\text{ mol }NaN_3}{3\text{ mol }N_2} \qquad \frac{65.02\text{ g }NaN_3}{1\text{ mol }NaN_3}$$

Solution: $11.8 \text{ L } N_2 \times \dfrac{1\text{ mol }N_2}{22.4\text{ L }N_2} \times \dfrac{2\text{ mol }NaN_3}{3\text{ mol }N_2} \times \dfrac{65.02\text{ g }NaN_3}{1\text{ mol }NaN_3} = 22.8 \text{ g }NaN_3$

Check: The units (g) are correct. The magnitude of the answer (23 g) makes sense because we have about half a mole of nitrogen gas, which translates to even fewer moles of NaN_3, so we expect significantly less than 65 g.

5.46   **Given:** $V = 58.5$ mL, and STP   **Find:** $m\,(Li)$

Conceptual Plan: mL N_2 → L_{N_2} → mol N_2 → mol Li → g Li

$$\frac{1\text{ L}}{1000\text{ mL}} \quad \frac{1\text{ mol }N_2}{22.4\text{ L }N_2} \quad \frac{6\text{ mol Li}}{1\text{ mol }N_2} \quad \frac{6.941\text{ g Li}}{1\text{ mol Li}}$$

Solution: $58.5 \text{ mL } N_2 \times \dfrac{1\text{ L }N_2}{1000\text{ mL }N_2} \times \dfrac{1\text{ mol }N_2}{22.4\text{ L }N_2} \times \dfrac{6\text{ mol Li}}{1\text{ mol }N_2} \times \dfrac{6.941\text{ g Li}}{1\text{ mol Li}} = 0.109 \text{ g Li}$

Check: The units (g) are correct. The magnitude of the answer (0.1 g) makes sense because we have such a small volume, which translates to a small fraction of a mole of Li, so we expect significantly less than 6.9 g.

5.47   **Given:** $V_{CH_4} = 25.5$ L, $P_{CH_4} = 732$ torr, and $T = 25\,°C$; mixed with $V_{H_2O} = 22.8$ L, $P_{H_2O} = 702$ torr, and $T = 125\,°C$; forms $V_{H_2} = 26.2$ L at STP   **Find:** % yield

Conceptual Plan: CH_4: torr → atm and $°C$ → K and P, V, T → n_{CH_4} → n_{H_2}

$$\frac{1\text{ atm}}{760\text{ torr}} \qquad K = °C + 273.15 \qquad PV = nRT \qquad \frac{3\text{ mol }H_2}{1\text{ mol }CH_4}$$

H_2O: torr → atm and $°C$ → K and P, V, T → n_{H_2O} → n_{H_2}

$$\frac{1\text{ atm}}{760\text{ torr}} \qquad K = °C + 273.15 \qquad PV = nRT \qquad \frac{3\text{ mol }H_2}{1\text{ mol }CH_4}$$

Select smaller n_{H_2} as theoretical yield,

then L_{H_2} → mol H_2 (actual yield) finally actual yield, theoretical yield → % yield

$$\frac{1\text{ mol }H_2}{22.4\text{ L }H_2} \qquad\qquad \text{\% yield} = \frac{\text{actual yield}}{\text{theoretical yield}} \times 100\%$$

Solution: CH_4: $P_{CH_4} = 732 \text{ torr} \times \dfrac{1\text{ atm}}{760\text{ torr}} = 0.963158 \text{ atm}, T = 25\,°C + 273.15 = 298 \text{ K}, PV = nRT$

Rearrange to solve for n. $n = \dfrac{PV}{RT}$ $n_{CH_4} = \dfrac{0.963158 \text{ atm} \times 25.5 \text{ L}}{0.08206 \dfrac{L \cdot atm}{mol \cdot K} \times 298 \text{ K}} = 1.00436 \text{ mol }CH_4$

$1.00436 \text{ mol }CH_4 \times \dfrac{3\text{ mol }H_2}{1\text{ mol }CH_4} = 3.01308 \text{ mol }H_2$

H_2O: $P_{H_2O} = 702 \text{ torr} \times \dfrac{1\text{ atm}}{760\text{ torr}} = 0.923684 \text{ atm}, T = 125\,°C + 273.15 = 398 \text{ K}, n = \dfrac{PV}{RT}$

$$n_{H_2O} = \frac{0.923684 \text{ atm} \times 22.8 \text{ L}}{0.08206 \frac{\text{L} \cdot \text{atm}}{\text{mol} \cdot \text{K}} \times 398 \text{ K}} = 0.644828 \text{ mol } H_2O \quad 0.644828 \text{ mol } H_2O \times \frac{3 \text{ mol } H_2}{1 \text{ mol } H_2O} = 1.93448 \text{ mol } H_2$$

Water is the limiting reagent because the moles of hydrogen generated is lower.

theoretical yield = 1.93448 mol H_2

$$26.2 \text{ L } H_2 \times \frac{1 \text{ mol } H_2}{22.414 \text{ L } H_2} = 1.16891 \text{ mol } H_2 = \text{actual yield}$$

$$\% \text{ yield} = \frac{\text{actual yield}}{\text{theoretical yield}} \times 100\% = \frac{1.16891 \text{ mol } H_2}{1.93448 \text{ mol } H_2} \times 100\% = 60.4\%$$

Check: The units (%) are correct. The magnitude of the answer (60%) makes sense because it is between 0 and 100%.

5.48 **Given:** $P = 25.0$ mmHg, $T = 225$ K, and m (CF_3Cl) = 15.0 g; and 10 cycles **Find:** V_{O_3}
Conceptual Plan: g CF_3Cl → mol CF_3Cl → mol O_3 → mol O_3 and mmHg → atm then

$$\frac{1 \text{ mol } CF_3Cl}{104.46 \text{ g } CF_3Cl} \qquad \frac{2 \text{ mol } O_3/\text{cycle}}{1 \text{ mol } CF_3Cl} \qquad 10 \text{ cycles} \qquad \frac{1 \text{ atm}}{760 \text{ mmHg}}$$

$n, P, T \rightarrow V$

$$PV = nRT$$

Solution: $15.0 \text{ g } CF_3Cl \times \dfrac{1 \text{ mol } CF_3Cl}{104.46 \text{ g } CF_3Cl} \times \dfrac{2 \text{ mol } O_3/\text{cycle}}{1 \text{ mol } CF_3Cl} \times 10 \text{ cycle} = 2.871913 \text{ mol } O_3,$

$$P_{O_3} = 25.0 \text{ mmHg} \times \frac{1 \text{ atm}}{760 \text{ mmHg}} = 0.0328947 \text{ atm}, \quad PV = nRT \text{ Rearrange to solve for } V. \; V = \frac{nRT}{P}$$

$$V_{O_3} = \frac{2.871913 \text{ mol} \times 0.08206 \frac{\text{L} \cdot \text{atm}}{\text{mol} \cdot \text{K}} \times 225 \text{ K}}{0.0328947 \text{ atm}} = 1.61 \times 10^3 \text{ L } O_3$$

Check: The units (L) are correct. The magnitude of the answer (1600 L) makes sense because we have ~3 moles of ozone gas and the pressure is so low (0.03 atm), so we expect a large volume.

5.49 **Given:** $V = 2.00$ L, $P_{Cl_2} = 337$ mmHg, $P_{F_2} = 729$ mmHg, $T = 298$ K **Find:** limiting reactant and m_{ClF_3}
Conceptual Plan: Determine limiting reactant by comparing the pressures of each reactant then

$$\frac{3 \text{ mmHg } F_2}{1 \text{ mmHg } Cl_2}$$

mmHg limiting reactant → mmHg ClF_3 and mmHg → atm then

$$\frac{2 \text{ mmHg } ClF_3}{1 \text{ mmHg } Cl_2} \text{ or } \frac{2 \text{ mmHg } ClF_3}{3 \text{ mmHg } F_2} \qquad \frac{1 \text{ atm}}{760 \text{ mmHg}}$$

$P, V, T \rightarrow n \rightarrow m$

$$PV = nRT \quad \frac{92.45 \text{ g } ClF_3}{1 \text{ mol } ClF_3}$$

Solution: To determine the limiting reactant, calculate the pressure of fluorine needed to react all of the chlorine and compare to the pressure of fluorine available.

$$337 \text{ mmHg } Cl_2 \times \frac{3 \text{ mmHg } F_2}{1 \text{ mmHg } Cl_2} = 1011 \text{ mmHg } F_2 \text{ needed.}$$

Because only 729 mmHg F_2 is available, F_2 is the limiting reactant; then

$$P_{ClF_3} = 729 \text{ mmHg } F_2 \times \frac{2 \text{ mmHg } ClF_3}{3 \text{ mmHg } F_2} \times \frac{1 \text{ atm } ClF_3}{760 \text{ mmHg } ClF_3} = 0.6394737 \text{ atm } ClF_3. \quad PV = nRT \text{ Rearrange to}$$

solve for n. $n = \dfrac{PV}{RT}$ $\quad n_{ClF_3} = \dfrac{0.6394737 \text{ atm } ClF_3 \times 2.00 \text{ L}}{0.08206 \frac{\text{L} \cdot \text{atm}}{\text{mol} \cdot \text{K}} \times 298 \text{ K}} = 0.052300387 \text{ mol } ClF_3$

Finally, $0.052300387 \text{ mol } ClF_3 \times \dfrac{92.45 \text{ g } ClF_3}{1 \text{ mol } ClF_3} = 4.8351708 \text{ g } ClF_3 = 4.84 \text{ g } ClF_3$

Check: The units (g) are correct. The magnitude of the answer (5 g) makes sense because we have much less than a mole of fluorine, so we expect a mass much less than the molar mass of ClF_3.

5.50   **Given:** $V = 1.50$ L, $P_{CO} = 232$ mmHg, $P_{H_2} = 397$ mmHg, $T = 305$ K   **Find:** limiting reactant and m_{CH_3OH}
        Conceptual Plan: Determine limiting reactant by comparing the pressures of each reactant then

$$\frac{2 \text{ mmHg H}_2}{1 \text{ mmHg CO}}$$

        mmHg limiting reactant $\rightarrow$ **mmHg ClF$_3$ and mmHg** $\rightarrow$ **atm then**

$$\frac{1 \text{ mmHg CH}_3\text{OH}}{1 \text{ mmHg CO}} \text{ or } \frac{1 \text{ mmHg CH}_3\text{OH}}{2 \text{ mmHg H}_2} \qquad \frac{1 \text{ atm}}{760 \text{ mmHg}}$$

        $P, V, T \rightarrow n \rightarrow m$

$$PV = nRT \qquad \frac{32.04 \text{ g CH}_3\text{OH}}{1 \text{ mol CH}_3\text{OH}}$$

        Solution: To determine the limiting reactant, calculate the pressure of hydrogen needed to react all of the carbon monoxide and compare to the pressure of hydrogen available.

$$232 \text{ mmHg CO} \times \frac{2 \text{ mmHg H}_2}{1 \text{ mmHg CO}} = 464 \text{ mmHg H}_2 \text{ needed.}$$

        Because only 397 mmHg H$_2$ is available, H$_2$ is the limiting reactant; then

$$P_{CH_3OH} = 397 \text{ mmHg H}_2 \times \frac{1 \text{ mmHg CH}_3\text{OH}}{2 \text{ mmHg H}_2} \times \frac{1 \text{ atm CH}_3\text{OH}}{760 \text{ mmHg CH}_3\text{OH}} = 0.261\underline{1}842 \text{ atm CH}_3\text{OH}. \quad PV = nRT$$

        Rearrange to solve for n. $n = \dfrac{PV}{RT}$ $n_{ClF_3} = \dfrac{0.261\underline{1}842 \text{ atm CH}_3\text{OH} \times 1.50 \text{ L}}{0.08206 \dfrac{\text{L} \cdot \text{atm}}{\text{mol} \cdot \text{K}} \times 305 \text{ K}} = 0.015\underline{6}53332 \text{ mol CH}_3\text{OH}$

        Finally, $0.015\underline{6}53332 \text{ mol CH}_3\text{OH} \times \dfrac{32.04 \text{ g CH}_3\text{OH}}{1 \text{ mol CH}_3\text{OH}} = 0.50\underline{1}53279 \text{ g CH}_3\text{OH} = 0.502 \text{ g CH}_3\text{OH}$

        Check: The units (g) are correct. The magnitude of the answer (0.5 g) makes sense because we have much less than a mole of hydrogen, so we expect a mass much less than the molar mass of methanol.

Kinetic Molecular Theory

5.51   (a)   Yes, because the average kinetic energy of a particle is proportional to the temperature in kelvins and the two gases are at the same temperature, they have the same average kinetic energy.

        (b)   No, because the helium atoms are lighter, they must move faster to have the same kinetic energy as argon atoms.

        (c)   No, because the Ar atoms are moving slower to compensate for their larger mass, they will exert the same pressure on the walls of the container.

        (d)   Because He is lighter, it will have the faster rate of effusion.

5.52   (a)   Because both gases have a mole fraction of 0.5, they will have the same partial pressure.

        (b)   The nitrogen molecules will have a greater velocity because they are lighter than Xe atoms.

        (c)   Because the average kinetic energy of a particle is proportional to the temperature in kelvins and the two gases are at the same temperature, they have the same average kinetic energy.

        (d)   Because nitrogen is lighter, it will have the faster rate of effusion.

5.53   **Given:** F$_2$, Cl$_2$, Br$_2$, and $T = 298$ K   **Find:** u_{rms} and KE$_{avg}$ for each gas and relative rates of effusion
        Conceptual Plan: $\mathcal{M}, T \rightarrow u_{rms} \rightarrow \text{KE}_{avg}$

$$u_{rms} = \sqrt{\frac{3RT}{\mathcal{M}}} \qquad \text{KE}_{avg} = \frac{1}{2} N_A m u_{rms}^2 = \frac{3}{2} RT$$

        Solution:

$$F_2: \mathcal{M} = \frac{38.00 \text{ g}}{1 \text{ mol}} \times \frac{1 \text{ kg}}{1000 \text{ g}} = 0.03800 \text{ kg/mol}, \quad u_{rms} = \sqrt{\frac{3RT}{\mathcal{M}}} = \sqrt{\frac{3 \times 8.314 \dfrac{\text{J}}{\text{K} \cdot \text{mol}} \times 298 \text{ K}}{0.03800 \dfrac{\text{kg}}{\text{mol}}}} = 442 \text{ m/s}$$

$$Cl_2: \mathcal{M} = \frac{70.90 \text{ g}}{1 \text{ mol}} \times \frac{1 \text{ kg}}{1000 \text{ g}} = 0.07090 \text{ kg/mol}, \quad u_{rms} = \sqrt{\frac{3RT}{\mathcal{M}}} = \sqrt{\frac{3 \times 8.314 \dfrac{\text{J}}{\text{K} \cdot \text{mol}} \times 298 \text{ K}}{0.07090 \dfrac{\text{kg}}{\text{mol}}}} = 324 \text{ m/s}$$

Br_2: $\mathcal{M} = \dfrac{159.80 \text{ g}}{1 \text{ mol}} \times \dfrac{1 \text{ kg}}{1000 \text{ g}} = 0.15980 \text{ kg/mol}$, $u_{rms} = \sqrt{\dfrac{3RT}{\mathcal{M}}} = \sqrt{\dfrac{3 \times 8.314 \dfrac{J}{K \cdot mol} \times 298 \text{ K}}{0.15980 \dfrac{kg}{mol}}} = 216 \text{ m/s}$

All molecules have the same kinetic energy:

$KE_{avg} = \dfrac{3}{2} RT = \dfrac{3}{2} \times 8.314 \dfrac{J}{K \cdot mol} \times 298 \text{ K} = 3.72 \times 10^3 \text{ J/mol}$

Because the rate of effusion is proportional to $\sqrt{\dfrac{1}{\mathcal{M}}}$, F_2 will have the fastest rate and Br_2 will have the slowest rate.

Check: The units (m/s) are correct. The magnitude of the answer (200 − 450 m/s) makes sense because it is consistent with what was seen in the text, and the heavier the molecule, the slower the molecule.

5.54 **Given:** CO, CO_2, SO_3, and $T = 298$ K
Find: u_{rms} and KE_{avg} for each gas, and rate greatest u_{rms}, KE_{avg} and rates of effusion
Conceptual Plan: $\mathcal{M}, T \rightarrow u_{rms} \rightarrow KE_{avg}$

$$u_{rms} = \sqrt{\dfrac{3RT}{\mathcal{M}}} \qquad KE_{avg} = \dfrac{1}{2} N_A m u_{rms}^2 = \dfrac{3}{2} RT$$

Solution:

CO: $\mathcal{M} = \dfrac{28.01 \text{ g}}{1 \text{ mol}} \times \dfrac{1 \text{ kg}}{1000 \text{ g}} = 0.02801 \text{ kg/mol}$

$u_{rms} = \sqrt{\dfrac{3RT}{\mathcal{M}}} = \sqrt{\dfrac{3 \times 8.314 \dfrac{J}{K \cdot mol} \times 298 \text{ K}}{0.02801 \dfrac{kg}{mol}}} = 515 \text{ m/s}$

CO_2: $\mathcal{M} = \dfrac{44.01 \text{ g}}{1 \text{ mol}} \times \dfrac{1 \text{ kg}}{1000 \text{ g}} = 0.04401 \text{ kg/mol}$

$u_{rms} = \sqrt{\dfrac{3RT}{\mathcal{M}}} = \sqrt{\dfrac{3 \times 8.314 \dfrac{J}{K \cdot mol} \times 298 \text{ K}}{0.04401 \dfrac{kg}{mol}}} = 411 \text{ m/s}$

SO_3: $\mathcal{M} = \dfrac{80.07 \text{ g}}{1 \text{ mol}} \times \dfrac{1 \text{ kg}}{1000 \text{ g}} = 0.08007 \text{ kg/mol}$

$u_{rms} = \sqrt{\dfrac{3RT}{\mathcal{M}}} = \sqrt{\dfrac{3 \times 8.314 \dfrac{J}{K \cdot mol} \times 298 \text{ K}}{0.08007 \dfrac{kg}{mol}}} = 305 \text{ m/s}$

All molecules have the same kinetic energy:

$KE_{avg} = \dfrac{3}{2} RT = \dfrac{3}{2} \times 8.314 \dfrac{J}{K \cdot mol} \times 298 \text{ K} = 3.72 \times 10^3 \text{ J/mol}$. CO has the fastest speed; all molecules have the same kinetic energy; and because the rate of effusion is proportional to $1/\sqrt{\mathcal{M}}$, CO will have the fastest rate.

Check: The units (m/s) are correct. The magnitude of the answer (300 − 520 m/s) makes sense because it is consistent with what was seen in the text, and the heavier the molecule, the slower the molecule.

5.55 **Given:** $^{238}UF_6$ and $^{235}UF_6$ U-235 = 235.054 amu, U-238 = 238.051 amu
Find: ratio of effusion rates $^{238}UF_6 / {}^{235}UF_6$
Conceptual Plan: $\mathcal{M}(^{238}UF_6), \mathcal{M}(^{235}UF_6) \rightarrow \textbf{Rate } (^{238}UF_6)/\textbf{Rate } (^{235}UF_6)$

$$\dfrac{Rate(^{238}UF_6)}{Rate(^{235}UF_6)} = \sqrt{\dfrac{\mathcal{M}(^{235}UF_6)}{\mathcal{M}(^{238}UF_6)}}$$

Solution: $^{238}UF_6$: $\mathcal{M} = \dfrac{352.05 \text{ g}}{1 \text{ mol}} \times \dfrac{1 \text{ kg}}{1000 \text{ g}} = 0.35205 \text{ kg/mol}$,

$^{235}UF_6$: $\mathcal{M} = \dfrac{349.05 \text{ g}}{1 \text{ mol}} \times \dfrac{1 \text{ kg}}{1000 \text{ g}} = 0.34905 \text{ kg/mol}$,

$\dfrac{Rate(^{238}UF_6)}{Rate(^{235}UF_6)} = \sqrt{\dfrac{\mathcal{M}(^{235}UF_6)}{\mathcal{M}(^{238}UF_6)}} = \sqrt{\dfrac{0.34905 \text{ kg/mol}}{0.35205 \text{ kg/mol}}} = 0.99573$

Check: The units (none) are correct. The magnitude of the answer (<1) makes sense because the heavier molecule has the lower effusion rate because it moves more slowly.

5.56   **Given:** Ar and Kr   **Find:** ratio of effusion rates Ar/Kr
Conceptual Plan: $\mathcal{M}(Ar), \mathcal{M}(Kr) \rightarrow$ **Rate (Ar)/Rate (Kr)**

$$\dfrac{Rate(Ar)}{Rate(Kr)} = \sqrt{\dfrac{\mathcal{M}(Kr)}{\mathcal{M}(Ar)}}$$

Solution: Ar: $\mathcal{M} = \dfrac{39.95 \text{ g}}{1 \text{ mol}} \times \dfrac{1 \text{ kg}}{1000 \text{ g}} = 0.03995 \text{ kg/mol}$, Kr: $\mathcal{M} = \dfrac{83.80 \text{ g}}{1 \text{ mol}} \times \dfrac{1 \text{ kg}}{1000 \text{ g}} = 0.08380 \text{ kg/mol}$,

$\dfrac{Rate(Ar)}{Rate(Kr)} = \sqrt{\dfrac{\mathcal{M}(Kr)}{\mathcal{M}(Ar)}} = \sqrt{\dfrac{0.08380 \text{ kg/mol}}{0.03995 \text{ kg/mol}}} = 1.448$

Check: The units (none) are correct. The magnitude of the answer (>1) makes sense because the lighter molecule has the higher effusion rate because it moves faster.

5.57   **Given:** Ne and unknown gas; Ne effusion in 76 s and unknown in 155 s   **Find:** identify unknown gas
Conceptual Plan: $\mathcal{M}(Ne),$ **Rate (Ne), Rate(Unk)** $\rightarrow \mathcal{M}(Unk)$

$$\dfrac{Rate(Ne)}{Rate(Unk)} = \sqrt{\dfrac{\mathcal{M}(Unk)}{\mathcal{M}(Ne)}}$$

Solution: Ne: $\mathcal{M} = \dfrac{20.18 \text{ g}}{1 \text{ mol}} \times \dfrac{1 \text{ kg}}{1000 \text{ g}} = 0.02018 \text{ kg/mol}$, $\dfrac{Rate(Ne)}{Rate(Unk)} = \sqrt{\dfrac{\mathcal{M}(Unk)}{\mathcal{M}(Ne)}}$ Rearrange to solve for

$\mathcal{M}(Unk)$. $\mathcal{M}(Unk) = \mathcal{M}(Ne)\left(\dfrac{Rate(Ne)}{Rate(Unk)}\right)^2$ Because Rate $\propto 1/$(effusion time),

$\mathcal{M}(Unk) = \mathcal{M}(Ne)\left(\dfrac{Time(Unk)}{Time(Ne)}\right)^2 = 0.02018 \dfrac{\text{kg}}{\text{mol}} \times \left(\dfrac{155 \text{ s}}{76 \text{ s}}\right)^2 = 0.084 \dfrac{\text{kg}}{\text{mol}} \times \dfrac{1000 \text{ g}}{1 \text{ kg}} = 84 \text{ g/mol or Kr.}$

Check: The units (g/mol) are correct. The magnitude of the answer ($>$Ne) makes sense because Ne effused faster and so must be lighter.

5.58   **Given:** N_2O and I_2 gas; N_2O effusion in 42 s   **Find:** effusion time for I_2 gas
Conceptual Plan: $\mathcal{M}(N_2O), \mathcal{M}(I_2),$ **Rate** $(N_2O), \rightarrow$ **Rate** (I_2)

$$\dfrac{Rate(N_2O)}{Rate(I_2)} = \sqrt{\dfrac{\mathcal{M}(I_2)}{\mathcal{M}(N_2O)}}$$

Solution: N_2O: $\mathcal{M} = \dfrac{44.02 \text{ g}}{1 \text{ mol}} \times \dfrac{1 \text{ kg}}{1000 \text{ g}} = 0.04402 \text{ kg/mol}$, $\mathcal{M} = \dfrac{253.8 \text{ g}}{1 \text{ mol}} \times \dfrac{1 \text{ kg}}{1000 \text{ g}} = 0.2538 \text{ kg/mol}$,

$\dfrac{Rate(N_2O)}{Rate(I_2)} = \sqrt{\dfrac{\mathcal{M}(I_2)}{\mathcal{M}(N_2O)}}$ Because Rate $\propto 1/$(effusion time), $\dfrac{Time(I_2)}{Time(N_2O)} = \sqrt{\dfrac{\mathcal{M}(I_2)}{\mathcal{M}(N_2O)}}$ Rearrange to solve for *Time*

(I_2). $Time(I_2) = Time (N_2O) \times \sqrt{\dfrac{\mathcal{M}(I_2)}{\mathcal{M}(N_2O)}} = 42 \text{ s} \times \sqrt{\dfrac{0.2538 \text{ kg/mol}}{0.04402 \text{ kg/mol}}} = 1.0 \times 10^2 \text{ s}$

Check: The units (s) are correct. The magnitude of the answer (100 s) makes sense because the mass ratio of I_2 to N_2O is ~6, so the time should be over twice as long.

5.59   Gas A has the higher molar mass because it has the slower average velocity. Gas B will have the higher effusion rate because it has the higher velocity.

5.60 T_2 is the higher temperature because it has the higher average velocity.

Real Gases

5.61 The postulate that the volume of the gas particles is small compared to the space between them breaks down at high pressure. At high pressures, the number of molecules per unit volume increases; so the volume of the gas particles becomes more significant. Because the spacing between the particles is reduced, the molecules themselves occupy a significant portion of the volume.

5.62 The postulate that the forces between the gas particles are not significant breaks down at low temperatures. At low temperatures, the molecules are not moving as fast as at higher temperatures; so when they collide, they have a greater opportunity to interact.

5.63 **Given:** Ne, $n = 1.000$ mol, $P = 500.0$ atm, and $T = 355.0$ K   **Find:** V(ideal) and V(van der Waals)
Conceptual Plan: $n, P, T \rightarrow V$ and $n, P, T \rightarrow V$

$$PV = nRT \qquad \left(P + \frac{an^2}{V^2}\right)(V - nb) = nRT$$

Solution: $PV = nRT$ Rearrange to solve for V.

$$V = \frac{nRT}{P} = \frac{1.000 \text{ mol} \times 0.08206 \dfrac{\text{L} \cdot \text{atm}}{\text{mol} \cdot \text{K}} \times 355.0 \text{ K}}{500.0 \text{ atm}} = 0.05826 \text{ L}$$

$$\left(P + \frac{an^2}{V^2}\right)(V - nb) = nRT \text{ Rearrange to solve to } V = \frac{nRT}{\left(P + \dfrac{an^2}{V^2}\right)} + nb$$

Using $a = 0.211$ L^2 atm/mol^2 and $b = 0.0171$ L/mol from Table 5.4 and the V from the ideal gas law calculation above, solve for V by successive approximations.

$$V = \frac{1.000 \text{ mol} \times 0.08206 \dfrac{\text{L} \cdot \text{atm}}{\text{mol} \cdot \text{K}} \times 355.0 \text{ K}}{500.0 \text{ atm} + \dfrac{0.211 \dfrac{\text{L}^2 \cdot \text{atm}}{\text{mol}^2} \times (1.000 \text{ mol})^2}{(0.05826 \text{ L})^2}} + \left(1.000 \text{ mol} \times 0.0171 \dfrac{\text{L}}{\text{mol}}\right) = 0.068920 \text{ L}$$

Plug in this new value.

$$V = \frac{1.000 \text{ mol} \times 0.08206 \dfrac{\text{L} \cdot \text{atm}}{\text{mol} \cdot \text{K}} \times 355.0 \text{ K}}{500.0 \text{ atm} + \dfrac{0.211 \dfrac{\text{L}^2 \cdot \text{atm}}{\text{mol}^2} \times (1.000 \text{ mol})^2}{(0.068920 \text{ L})^2}} + \left(1.000 \text{ mol} \times 0.0171 \dfrac{\text{L}}{\text{mol}}\right) = 0.070609 \text{ L}$$

Plug in this new value.

$$V = \frac{1.000 \text{ mol} \times 0.08206 \dfrac{\text{L} \cdot \text{atm}}{\text{mol} \cdot \text{K}} \times 355.0 \text{ K}}{500.0 \text{ atm} + \dfrac{0.211 \dfrac{\text{L}^2 \cdot \text{atm}}{\text{mol}^2} \times (1.000 \text{ mol})^2}{(0.070609 \text{ L})^2}} + \left(1.000 \text{ mol} \times 0.0171 \dfrac{\text{L}}{\text{mol}}\right) = 0.070816 \text{ L}$$

Plug in this new value.

$$V = \frac{1.000 \text{ mol} \times 0.08206 \dfrac{\text{L} \cdot \text{atm}}{\text{mol} \cdot \text{K}} \times 355.0 \text{ K}}{500.0 \text{ atm} + \dfrac{0.211 \dfrac{\text{L}^2 \cdot \text{atm}}{\text{mol}^2} \times (1.000 \text{ mol})^2}{(0.070816 \text{ L})^2}} + \left(1.000 \text{ mol} \times 0.0171 \dfrac{\text{L}}{\text{mol}}\right) = 0.070840 \text{ L} = 0.0708 \text{ L}$$

The two values are different because we are at very high pressures. The pressure is corrected from 500.0 atm to 542.1 atm, and the final volume correction is 0.0171 L.

Check: The units (L) are correct. The magnitude of the answer (~ 0.07 L) makes sense because we are at such a high pressure and have one mole of gas.

5.64 **Given:** Cl_2, $n = 1.000$ mol, $L = 5.000$ L, and $T = 273.0$ K   **Find:** P(ideal) and P(van der Waals)
Conceptual Plan: $n, V, T \rightarrow P$ and $n, V, T \rightarrow P$

$$PV = nRT \qquad \left(P + \frac{an^2}{V^2}\right)(V - nb) = nRT$$

Solution: $PV = nRT$ Rearrange to solve for P.

$$P = \frac{nRT}{V} = \frac{1.000 \text{ mol} \times 0.08206 \frac{L \cdot atm}{mol \cdot K} \times 273.0 \text{ K}}{5.000 \text{ L}} = 4.480 \text{ atm}$$

$\left(P + \frac{an^2}{V^2}\right)(V - nb) = nRT$ Rearrange to solve for P. $P = \frac{nRT}{(V - nb)} - \frac{an^2}{V^2}$

Using $a = 6.49$ L^2 atm/mol^2 and $b = 0.0562$ L/mol from Table 5.4,

$$P = \frac{1.000 \text{ mol} \times 0.08206 \frac{L \cdot atm}{mol \cdot K} \times 273.0 \text{ K}}{5.000 \text{ L} - \left(1.000 \text{ mol} \times 0.0562\frac{L}{mol}\right)} - \frac{6.49 \frac{L^2 \cdot atm}{mol^2} \times (1.000 \text{ mol})^2}{(5.000 \text{ L})^2} = 4.272 \text{ atm}$$

The pressure values differ slightly because of the non-ideal behavior of chlorine (a large molecule) at a slightly reduced temperature.

Check: The units (atm) are correct. The magnitude of the answers (4.5 atm and 4.3 atm) makes sense because we are at such a low temperature and small volume with one mole of gas; we expect a difference in two pressures of less than 1 atm and a $P > 1$ atm.

Cumulative Problems

5.65 **Given:** m (penny) $= 2.482$ g, $T = 25 °C$, $V = 0.899$ L, and $P_{Total} = 791$ mmHg   **Find:** % Zn in penny
Conceptual Plan: $T \rightarrow P_{H_2O}$ then $P_{Total}, P_{H_2O} \rightarrow P_{H_2}$ then mmHg $\rightarrow$ atm and $°C \rightarrow$ K

$$\text{Table 5.3} \qquad P_{Total} = P_{H_2O} + P_{H_2} \qquad \frac{1 \text{ atm}}{760 \text{ mmHg}} \qquad K = °C + 273.15$$

and $P, V, T \rightarrow n_{H_2} \rightarrow n_{Zn} \rightarrow g_{Zn} \rightarrow$ % Zn

$$PV = nRT \qquad \frac{1 \text{ mol Zn}}{1 \text{ mol } H_2} \qquad \frac{65.38 \text{ g Zn}}{1 \text{ mol Zn}} \qquad \%Zn = \frac{g_{Zn}}{g_{penny}} \times 100\%$$

Solution: Table 5.3 states that $P_{H_2O} = 23.78$ mmHg at 25 °C. $P_{Total} = P_{H_2O} + P_{H_2}$ Rearrange to solve for P_{H_2}.

$P_{H_2} = P_{Total} - P_{H_2O} = 791 \text{ mmHg} - 23.78 \text{ mmHg} = 767 \text{ mmHg}$ $P_{H_2} = 767 \text{ mmHg} \times \frac{1 \text{ atm}}{760 \text{ mmHg}} = 1.0092 \text{ atm}$

then $T = 25 °C + 273.15 = 298$ K,
$PV = nRT$
Rearrange to solve for n. $n_{H_2} = \frac{PV}{RT} = \frac{1.0092 \text{ atm} \times 0.899 \text{ L}}{0.08206 \frac{L \cdot atm}{mol \cdot K} \times 298 \text{ K}} = 0.0371013$ mol

$0.0371013 \text{ mol } H_2 \times \frac{1 \text{ mol Zn}}{1 \text{ mol } H_2} \times \frac{65.38 \text{ g Zn}}{1 \text{ mol Zn}} = 2.42568$ g Zn

$\%Zn = \frac{g_{Zn}}{g_{penny}} \times 100\% = \frac{2.42568 \text{ g}}{2.482 \text{ g}} \times 100\% = 97.7\%$ Zn

Check: The units (% Zn) are correct. The magnitude of the answer (98%) makes sense because it should be between 0 and 100%. We expect about 1/22 a mole of gas because our conditions are close to STP and we have ~1 L of gas.

5.66 **Given:** m (CFC) $= 2.85$ g, $V = 564$ mL, $P = 752$ mmHg, and $T = 298$ K   **Find:** % Cl in CFC
Conceptual Plan: mmHg $\rightarrow$ atm and mL $\rightarrow$ L and $P, V, T \rightarrow n_{Cl_2} \rightarrow g_{Cl}$

$$\frac{1 \text{ atm}}{760 \text{ mmHg}} \qquad \frac{1 \text{ L}}{1000 \text{ mL}} \qquad PV = nRT \qquad \frac{70.90 \text{ g Cl}}{1 \text{ mol } Cl_2}$$

then $g_{Cl}, g_{CFC} \rightarrow$ %Cl

$$\% Cl = \frac{g_{Cl}}{g_{CFC}} \times 100\%$$

Solution: $P_{Cl_2} = 752 \text{ mmHg} \times \dfrac{1 \text{ atm}}{760 \text{ mmHg}} = 0.98947 \text{ atm}$, $V_{Cl_2} = 564 \text{ mL} \times \dfrac{1 \text{ L}}{1000 \text{ mL}} = 0.564 \text{ L}$,

$PV = nRT$ Rearrange to solve for n. $n_{Cl_2} = \dfrac{PV}{RT} = \dfrac{0.98947 \text{ atm} \times 0.564 \text{ L}}{0.08206 \dfrac{\text{L} \cdot \text{atm}}{\text{mol} \cdot \text{K}} \times 298 \text{ K}} = 0.022821 \text{ mol Cl}_2$

$0.022821 \text{ mol Cl}_2 \times \dfrac{70.90 \text{ g Cl}}{1 \text{ mol Cl}_2} = 1.6180 \text{ g Cl}$, $\%\text{Cl} = \dfrac{g_{Cl}}{g_{CFC}} \times 100\% = \dfrac{1.6180 \text{ g}}{2.85 \text{ g}} \times 100\% = 56.8\%\text{Cl}$

Check: The units (%Cl) are correct. The magnitude of the answer (57%) makes sense because it should be between 0 and 100%. Because there will also be carbon and fluorine in the compound, we do not expect it to be extremely close to 100%.

5.67   **Given:** $V = 255$ mL, m (flask) $= 143.187$ g, m (flask + gas) $= 143.289$ g, $P = 267$ torr, and $T = 25\,°C$ **Find:** $\mathcal{M}$
Conceptual Plan: °C → K and torr → atm and mL → L and m (flask), m (flask + gas) → m (gas)

$$K = °C + 273.15 \qquad \dfrac{1 \text{ atm}}{760 \text{ torr}} \qquad \dfrac{1 \text{ L}}{1000 \text{ mL}} \qquad m \text{ (gas)} = m \text{ (flask + gas)} - m \text{ (flask)}$$

then $V, m \rightarrow d$ **then** $d, P, T, \rightarrow \mathcal{M}$

$$d = \dfrac{m}{V} \qquad d = \dfrac{P\mathcal{M}}{RT}$$

Solution: $T = 25\,°C + 273.15 = 298 \text{ K}$, $P = 267 \text{ torr} \times \dfrac{1 \text{ atm}}{760 \text{ torr}} = 0.351316 \text{ atm}$,

$V = 255 \text{ mL} \times \dfrac{1 \text{ L}}{1000 \text{ mL}} = 0.255 \text{ L}$,

$m \text{ (gas)} = m \text{ (flask + gas)} - m \text{ (flask)} = 143.289 \text{ g} - 143.187 \text{ g} = 0.102 \text{ g}$

$d = \dfrac{m}{V} = \dfrac{0.102 \text{ g}}{0.255 \text{ L}} = 0.400 \text{ g/L}$, $d = \dfrac{P\mathcal{M}}{RT}$ Rearrange to solve for $\mathcal{M}$.

$$\mathcal{M} = \dfrac{dRT}{P} = \dfrac{0.400 \dfrac{\text{g}}{\text{L}} \times 0.08206 \dfrac{\text{L} \cdot \text{atm}}{\text{K} \cdot \text{mol}} \times 298 \text{ K}}{0.351316 \text{ atm}} = 27.8 \text{ g/mol}$$

Check: The units (g/mol) are correct. The magnitude of the answer (28 g/mol) makes physical sense because this is a reasonable number for a molecular weight of a gas.

5.68   **Given:** $V = 118$ mL, m (flask) $= 97.129$ g, m (flask + gas) $= 97.171$ g, $P = 768$ torr, and $T = 35\,°C$
Find: Is gas pure?
Conceptual Plan: °C → K and torr → atm and mL → L and m (flask), m (flask + gas) → m (gas)

$$K = °C + 273.15 \qquad \dfrac{1 \text{ atm}}{760 \text{ torr}} \qquad \dfrac{1 \text{ L}}{1000 \text{ mL}} \qquad m \text{ (gas)} = m \text{ (flask + gas)} - m \text{ (flask)}$$

then $V, m \rightarrow d$ **then** $d, P, T, \rightarrow \mathcal{M}$

$$d = \dfrac{m}{V} \qquad d = \dfrac{P\mathcal{M}}{RT}$$

Solution: $T = 35\,°C + 273.15 = 308 \text{ K}$, $P = 768 \text{ torr} \times \dfrac{1 \text{ atm}}{760 \text{ torr}} = 1.01053 \text{ atm}$,

$V = 118 \text{ mL} \times \dfrac{1 \text{ L}}{1000 \text{ mL}} = 0.118 \text{ L}$

$m \text{ (gas)} = m \text{ (flask + gas)} - m \text{ (flask)} = 97.171 \text{ g} - 97.129 \text{ g} = 0.042 \text{ g}$,

$d = \dfrac{m}{V} = \dfrac{0.042 \text{ g}}{0.118 \text{ L}} = 0.35593 \text{ g/L}$, $d = \dfrac{P\mathcal{M}}{RT}$ Rearrange to solve for $\mathcal{M}$.

$$\mathcal{M} = \dfrac{dRT}{P} = \dfrac{0.35593 \dfrac{\text{g}}{\text{L}} \times 0.08206 \dfrac{\text{L} \cdot \text{atm}}{\text{K} \cdot \text{mol}} \times 308 \text{ K}}{1.01053 \text{ atm}} = 8.9 \text{ g/mol}$$

The gas is not pure because the molar mass is not 4.003 g/ml.

Check: The units (g/mol) are correct. The magnitude of the answer (9 g/mol) makes physical sense because this is a reasonable number for a molecular weight of a gas.

5.69 **Given:** $V = 158$ mL, m (gas) $= 0.275$ g, $P = 556$ mmHg, $T = 25$ °C, gas $= 82.66\%$ C and 17.34% H
Find: molecular formula
Conceptual Plan: °C $\rightarrow$ K and mmHg $\rightarrow$ atm and mL $\rightarrow$ L then $V, m \rightarrow d$

$$K = °C + 273.15 \qquad \frac{1\text{ atm}}{760\text{ mmHg}} \qquad \frac{1\text{ L}}{1000\text{ mL}} \qquad d = \frac{m}{V}$$

then $d, P, T, \rightarrow \mathcal{M}$ **then** $\% \text{ C}, \% \text{ H}, \mathcal{M} \rightarrow$ **formula**

$$d = \frac{P\mathcal{M}}{RT} \qquad \#C = \frac{\mathcal{M}\ 0.8266\text{ g C}}{12.01\ \frac{\text{g C}}{\text{mol C}}} \qquad \#H = \frac{\mathcal{M}\ 0.1734\text{ g H}}{1.008\ \frac{\text{g H}}{\text{mol H}}}$$

Solution: $T = 25$ °C $+ 273.15 = 298$ K, $P = 556$ mmHg $\times \dfrac{1\text{ atm}}{760\text{ mmHg}} = 0.731579$ atm,

$V = 158$ mL $\times \dfrac{1\text{ L}}{1000\text{ mL}} = 0.158$ L, $d = \dfrac{m}{V} = \dfrac{0.275\text{ g}}{0.158\text{ L}} = 1.74051$ g/L, $d = \dfrac{P\mathcal{M}}{RT}$ Rearrange to solve for $\mathcal{M}$.

$$\mathcal{M} = \frac{dRT}{P} = \frac{1.74051\ \frac{\text{g}}{\text{L}} \times 0.08206\ \frac{\text{L} \cdot \text{atm}}{\text{K} \cdot \text{mol}} \times 298\text{ K}}{0.731579\text{ atm}} = 58.2 \text{ g/mol},$$

$$\#C = \frac{\mathcal{M} \times 0.8266\text{ g C}}{12.01\ \frac{\text{g C}}{\text{mol C}}} = \frac{58.2\ \frac{\text{g HC}}{\text{mol HC}} \times \frac{0.8266\text{ g C}}{1\text{ g HC}}}{12.01\ \frac{\text{g C}}{\text{mol C}}} = 4.00\ \frac{\text{mol C}}{\text{mol HC}}$$

$$\#H = \frac{\mathcal{M} \times 0.1734\text{ g H}}{1.0008\ \frac{\text{g H}}{\text{mol H}}} = \frac{58.2\ \frac{\text{g HC}}{\text{mol HC}} \times \frac{0.1734\text{ g H}}{1\text{ g HC}}}{1.008\ \frac{\text{g H}}{\text{mol H}}} = 10.0\ \frac{\text{mol H}}{\text{mol HC}}$$ Formula is C_4H_{10} or butane.

Check: The answer came up with integer number of C and H atoms in the formula and a molecular weight (58 g/mol) that is reasonable for a gas.

5.70 **Given:** STP, $V = 258$ mL, m (gas) $= 0.646$ g, gas $= 85.63\%$ C and 14.37% H. **Find:** $\mathcal{M}$
Conceptual Plan: mL $\rightarrow$ L then $V, m \rightarrow d$ then $d, P, T, \rightarrow \mathcal{M}$

$$\frac{1\text{ L}}{1000\text{ mL}} \qquad d = \frac{m}{V} \qquad d = \frac{P\mathcal{M}}{RT}$$

then $\% \text{ C}, \% \text{ H}, \mathcal{M} \rightarrow$ **formula**

$$\#C = \frac{\mathcal{M}\ 0.8563\text{ g C}}{12.01\ \frac{\text{g C}}{\text{mol C}}} \qquad \#H = \frac{\mathcal{M}\ 0.1437\text{ g H}}{1.008\ \frac{\text{g H}}{\text{mol H}}}$$

Solution: $V = 258$ mL $\times \dfrac{1\text{ L}}{1000\text{ mL}} = 0.258$ L, $d = \dfrac{m}{V} = \dfrac{0.646\text{ g}}{0.258\text{ L}} = 2.50388$ g/L, $d = \dfrac{P\mathcal{M}}{RT}$

Rearrange to solve for $\mathcal{M}$. $\mathcal{M} = \dfrac{dRT}{P} = \dfrac{2.50388\ \frac{\text{g}}{\text{L}} \times 0.08206\ \frac{\text{L atm}}{\text{K mol}} \times 273.15\text{ K}}{1\text{ atm}} = 56.12$ g/mol,

$$\#C = \frac{\mathcal{M} \times 0.8563\text{ g C}}{12.01\ \frac{\text{g C}}{\text{mol C}}} = \frac{56.12\ \frac{\text{g HC}}{\text{mol HC}} \times \frac{0.8563\text{ g C}}{1\text{ g HC}}}{12.01\ \frac{\text{g C}}{\text{mol C}}} = 4.00\ \frac{\text{mol C}}{\text{mol HC}}$$

$$\#H = \frac{\mathcal{M} \times 0.1437\text{ g H}}{1.008\ \frac{\text{g H}}{\text{mol H}}} = \frac{56.12\ \frac{\text{g HC}}{\text{mol HC}} \times \frac{0.1437\text{ g H}}{1\text{ g HC}}}{1.008\ \frac{\text{g H}}{\text{mol H}}} = 8.00\ \frac{\text{mol H}}{\text{mol HC}}$$ Formula is C_4H_8 or butene.

Check: The answer came up with integer number of C and H atoms in the formula and a molecular weight (56 g/mol) that is reasonable for a gas.

5.71   **Given:** m (NiO) = 24.78 g, T = 40.0 °C, and P_{Total} = 745 mmHg   **Find:** V_{O_2}
Conceptual Plan: $T \rightarrow P_{H_2O}$ then $P_{Total}, P_{H_2O} \rightarrow P_{O_2}$ then mmHg $\rightarrow$ atm and °C $\rightarrow$ K

$$\text{Table 5.3} \qquad P_{Total} = P_{H_2O} + P_{O_2} \qquad \frac{1 \text{ atm}}{760 \text{ mmHg}} \qquad K = °C + 273.15$$

and $g_{NiO} \rightarrow n_{NiO} \rightarrow n_{O_2}$ then $P, V, T \rightarrow n_{O_2}$

$$\frac{1 \text{ mol NiO}}{74.69 \text{ g NiO}} \quad \frac{1 \text{ mol } O_2}{2 \text{ mol NiO}} \qquad PV = nRT$$

Solution: Table 5.3 states that P_{H_2O} = 55.40 mmHg at 40 °C $P_{Total} = P_{H_2O} + P_{O_2}$ Rearrange to solve for P_{O_2}.
$P_{O_2} = P_{Total} - P_{H_2O}$ = 745 mmHg − 55.40 mmHg = 689.6 mmHg

$$P_{O_2} = 689.6 \text{ mmHg} \times \frac{1 \text{ atm}}{760 \text{ mmHg}} = 0.907368 \text{ atm} \quad T = 40.0 °C + 273.15 = 313.2 \text{ K,}$$

$$24.78 \text{ g NiO} \times \frac{1 \text{ mol NiO}}{74.69 \text{ mol NiO}} \times \frac{1 \text{ mol } O_2}{2 \text{ mol NiO}} = 0.1658857 \text{ mol } O_2 \quad PV = nRT$$

Rearrange to solve for V. $V_{O_2} = \dfrac{nRT}{P} = \dfrac{0.1658857 \text{ mol} \times 0.08206 \dfrac{L \cdot atm}{mol \cdot K} \times 313.2 \text{ K}}{0.907368 \text{ atm}} = 4.70 \text{ L}$

Check: The units (L) are correct. The magnitude of the answer (5 L) makes sense because we have much less than 0.5 mole of NiO, so we get less than a mole of oxygen. Thus, we expect a volume much less than 22 L.

5.72   **Given:** m(Ag) = 15.8 g, T = 25 °C, and P_{Total} = 752 mmHg   **Find:** V_{O_2}
Conceptual Plan: $T \rightarrow P_{H_2O}$ then $P_{Total}, P_{H_2O} \rightarrow P_{O_2}$ then mmHg $\rightarrow$ atm and °C $\rightarrow$ K

$$\text{Table 5.3} \qquad P_{Total} = P_{H_2O} + P_{O_2} \qquad \frac{1 \text{ atm}}{760 \text{ mmHg}} \qquad K = °C + 273.15$$

and $g_{Ag} \rightarrow n_{Ag} \rightarrow n_{O_2}$ then $P, V, T \rightarrow n_{O_2}$

$$\frac{1 \text{ mol Ag}}{107.9 \text{ g Ag}} \quad \frac{1 \text{ mol } O_2}{4 \text{ mol Ag}} \qquad PV = nRT$$

Solution: Table 5.3 states that P_{H_2O} = 23.78 mmHg at 25 °C. $P_{Total} = P_{H_2O} + P_{O_2}$ Rearrange to solve for P_{O_2}.
$P_{O_2} = P_{Total} - P_{H_2O}$ = 752 mmHg − 23.78 mmHg = 728.22 mmHg

$$P_{O_2} = 728.22 \text{ mmHg} \times \frac{1 \text{ atm}}{760 \text{ mmHg}} = 0.958184 \text{ atm} \quad T = 25 °C + 273.15 = 298 \text{ K,}$$

$$15.8 \text{ g Ag} \times \frac{1 \text{ mol Ag}}{107.9 \text{ g Ag}} \times \frac{1 \text{ mol } O_2}{4 \text{ mol Ag}} = 0.03660797 \text{ mol } O_2 \quad PV = nRT \text{ Rearrange to solve for } V.$$

$$V_{O_2} = \frac{nRT}{P} = \frac{0.03660797 \text{ mol} \times 0.08206 \dfrac{L \cdot atm}{mol \cdot K} \times 298 \text{ K}}{0.958184 \text{ atm}} = 0.934 \text{ L}$$

Check: The units (L) are correct. The magnitude of the answer (1 L) makes sense because we have ~0.1 mole of Ag, so we get less than 0.05 mol of oxygen. Thus, we expect a volume much, much less than 22 L.

5.73   **Given:** HCl, K_2S to H_2S, V_{H_2S} = 42.9 mL, P_{H_2S} = 752 mmHg, and T = 25.8 °C   **Find:** $m(K_2S)$
Conceptual Plan: read description of reaction and convert words to equation then °C $\rightarrow$ K

$$K = °C + 273.15$$

and mmHg $\rightarrow$ atm and mL $\rightarrow$ L then $P, V, T \rightarrow n_{H_2S} \rightarrow n_{K_2S} \rightarrow m_{K_2S}$

$$\frac{1 \text{ atm}}{760 \text{ mmHg}} \qquad \frac{1 \text{ L}}{1000 \text{ mL}} \qquad PV = nRT \quad \frac{1 \text{ mol } K_2S}{1 \text{ mol } H_2S} \quad \frac{1 \text{ mol } K_2S}{110.27 \text{ g } K_2S}$$

Solution: $2 \text{ HCl}(aq) + K_2S(s) \rightarrow H_2S(g) + 2 \text{ KCl}(aq)$

$$T = 25.8 °C + 273.15 = 299.0 \text{ K}, \quad P_{H_2S} = 752 \text{ mmHg} \times \frac{1 \text{ atm}}{760 \text{ mmHg}} = 0.989474 \text{ atm,}$$

$$V_{H_2S} = 42.9 \text{ mL} \times \frac{1 \text{ L}}{1000 \text{ mL}} = 0.0429 \text{ L} \quad PV = nRT \text{ Rearrange to solve for } n_{H_2S}.$$

$$n_{H_2S} = \frac{PV}{RT} = \frac{0.989474 \text{ atm} \times 0.0429 \text{ L}}{0.08206 \dfrac{L \cdot atm}{mol \cdot K} \times 299.0 \text{ K}} = 0.00173005 \text{ mol}$$

$$0.00173005 \; \text{mol H}_2\text{S} \times \frac{1 \; \text{mol K}_2\text{S}}{1 \; \text{mol H}_2\text{S}} \times \frac{110.27 \; \text{g K}_2\text{S}}{1 \; \text{mol K}_2\text{S}} = 0.191 \; \text{g K}_2\text{S}$$

Check: The units (g) are correct. The magnitude of the answer (0.2 g) makes sense because we have such a small volume of gas generated.

5.74 (a) **Given:** $T = 315$ K, $P = 50.0$ mmHg, $V_{\text{SO}_2} = 285.5$ mL, and $V_{\text{O}_2} = 158.9$ mL
Find: limiting reagent and theoretical yield
Conceptual Plan: mmHg $\rightarrow$ atm and $\text{mL}_{\text{SO}_2} \rightarrow \text{L}_{\text{SO}_2}$ then $P, V_{\text{SO}_2}, T \rightarrow n_{\text{SO}_2}, \rightarrow n_{\text{SO}_3}$

$$\frac{1 \; \text{atm}}{760 \; \text{mmHg}} \qquad \frac{1 \; \text{L}}{1000 \; \text{mL}} \qquad PV = nRT \qquad \frac{2 \; \text{mol SO}_3}{2 \; \text{mol SO}_2}$$

and $\text{mL}_{\text{O}_2} \rightarrow \text{L}_{\text{O}_2}$ **then** $P, V_{\text{O}_2}, T \rightarrow n_{\text{O}_2} \rightarrow n_{\text{SO}_3}$

$$\frac{1 \; \text{L}}{1000 \; \text{mL}} \qquad PV = nRT \qquad \frac{2 \; \text{mol SO}_3}{1 \; \text{mol O}_2}$$

Solution: $50.0 \; \text{mmHg} \times \dfrac{1 \; \text{atm}}{760 \; \text{mmHg}} = 0.0657895 \; \text{atm}$ and $285.5 \; \text{mL SO}_2 \times \dfrac{1 \; \text{L SO}_2}{1000 \; \text{mL SO}_2} = 0.2855 \; \text{L}$

then $PV = nRT$ Rearrange to solve for n.

$$n_{\text{SO}_2} = \frac{PV}{RT} = \frac{0.0657895 \; \text{atm} \times 0.2855 \; \text{L}}{0.08206 \; \dfrac{\text{L} \cdot \text{atm}}{\text{mol} \cdot \text{K}} \times 315 \; \text{K}} = 7.26642 \times 10^{-4} \; \text{mol SO}_2$$

$$7.26642 \times 10^{-4} \; \text{mol SO}_2 \times \frac{2 \; \text{mol SO}_3}{2 \; \text{mol SO}_2} = 7.26642 \times 10^{-4} \; \text{mol SO}_3$$

then $158.9 \; \text{mL O}_2 \times \dfrac{1 \; \text{L O}_2}{1000 \; \text{mL O}_2} = 0.1589 \; \text{L O}_2$ then $PV = nRT$ Rearrange to solve for n.

$$n_{\text{O}_2} = \frac{PV}{RT} = \frac{0.0657895 \; \text{atm} \times 0.1589 \; \text{L}}{0.08206 \; \dfrac{\text{L} \cdot \text{atm}}{\text{mol} \cdot \text{K}} \times 315 \; \text{K}} = 4.04425 \times 10^{-4} \; \text{mol O}_2 \text{ then}$$

$4.04425 \times 10^{-4} \; \text{mol O}_2 \times \dfrac{2 \; \text{mol SO}_3}{1 \; \text{mol O}_2} = 8.08851 \times 10^{-4} \; \text{mol SO}_3$ Because the amount generated from the SO$_2$ is less, it is the limiting reagent and the theoretical yield is $7.27 \times 10^{-4} \; \text{mol SO}_3$.

Check: The units (mol) are correct. The magnitude of the answer (0.0007 mol) makes sense because we have small volumes of gas involved (compared to 22 L).

(b) **Given:** preceding info and $V_{\text{SO}_3} = 187.2$ mL, $T = 315$ K, and $P = 50.0$ mmHg   **Find:** % yield
Conceptual Plan: mmHg $\rightarrow$ atm and $\text{mL}_{\text{SO}_3} \rightarrow \text{L}_{\text{SO}_3}$ then $P, V_{\text{SO}_3}, T \rightarrow n_{\text{SO}_3}$

$$\frac{1 \; \text{atm}}{760 \; \text{mmHg}} \qquad \frac{1 \; \text{L}}{1000 \; \text{mL}} \qquad PV = nRT$$

then actual yield, theoretical yield $\rightarrow$ % yield

$$\% \text{ yield} = \frac{\text{actual yield}}{\text{theoretical yield}} \times 100\%$$

Solution: $50.0 \; \text{mmHg} \times \dfrac{1 \; \text{atm}}{760 \; \text{mmHg}} = 0.0657895 \; \text{atm}$ and

$187.2 \; \text{mL SO}_3 \times \dfrac{1 \; \text{L SO}_3}{1000 \; \text{mL SO}_3} = 0.1872 \; \text{L SO}_3$ then $PV = nRT$ Rearrange to solve for n.

$$n_{\text{SO}_3} = \frac{PV}{RT} = \frac{0.0657895 \; \text{atm} \times 0.1872 \; \text{L}}{0.08206 \; \dfrac{\text{L} \cdot \text{atm}}{\text{mol} \cdot \text{K}} \times 315 \; \text{K}} = 4.76453 \times 10^{-4} \; \text{mol SO}_3$$

then $\% \text{ yield} = \dfrac{\text{actual yield}}{\text{theoretical yield}} \times 100\% = \dfrac{4.76453 \times 10^{-4} \; \text{mol SO}_3}{7.26642 \times 10^{-4} \; \text{mol SO}_3} \times 100\% = 65.6\%$

Check: The units (%) are correct. The magnitude of the answer (66%) makes sense because it should be between 0 and 100%. Because the volume of product is a bit over half the volume of the limiting reagent and there is a 2:2 mole ratio of the reactant and product, we expect a number a bit over 50%.

5.75   **Given:** $T = 22\,°C$, $P = 1.02$ atm, and $m = 11.83$ g   **Find:** V_{Total}

Conceptual Plan: $°C \rightarrow K$ and $g_{(NH_4)_2CO_3} \rightarrow n_{(NH_4)_2CO_3} \rightarrow n_{Gas}$ then $p, n, T \rightarrow V$

$$K = °C + 273.15 \qquad \frac{1\ \text{mol}\ (NH_4)_2CO_3}{96.09\ \text{g}\,(NH_4)_2CO_3} \qquad \frac{(2 + 1 + 1 = 4)\ \text{mol gas}}{1\ \text{mol}\ (NH_4)_2CO_3} \qquad PV = nRT$$

Solution: $T = 22\,°C + 273.15 = 295$ K

$$11.83\ \text{g}\ (NH_4)_2CO_3 \times \frac{1\ \text{mol}\ (NH_4)_2CO_3}{96.09\ \text{g}\ (NH_4)_2CO_3} \times \frac{4\ \text{mol gas}}{1\ \text{mol}\ (NH_4)_2CO_3} = 0.49\underline{2}455\ \text{mol gas}$$

$PV = nRT$ Rearrange to solve for V_{Gas}.

$$V_{Gas} = \frac{nRT}{P} = \frac{0.49\underline{2}455\ \text{mol gas} \times 0.08206\ \dfrac{L \cdot atm}{mol \cdot K} \times 295\ K}{1.02\ atm} = 11.7\ \text{L}$$

Check: The units (L) are correct. The magnitude of the answer (12 L) makes sense because we have about half a mole of gas generated.

5.76   **Given:** $T = 125\,°C$, $P = 748$ mmHg, and $m = 1.55$ kg   **Find:** V_{Total}

Conceptual Plan: $°C \rightarrow K$ and mmHg $\rightarrow$ atm and kg $NH_4NO_3 \rightarrow$ g $NH_4NO_3 \rightarrow n_{NH_4NO_3} \rightarrow n_{Gas}$

$$K = °C + 273.15 \qquad \frac{1\ atm}{760\ mmHg} \qquad \frac{1000\ g}{1\ kg} \qquad \frac{1\ \text{mol}\ NH_4NO_3}{80.05\ \text{g}\ NH_4NO_3} \qquad \frac{(2 + 1 + 4 = 7)\ \text{mol gas}}{2\ \text{mol}\ NH_4NO_3}$$

then $P, n, T \rightarrow V$

$$PV = nRT$$

Solution: $T = 125\,°C + 273.15 = 398$ K, $748\ \text{mmHg} \times \dfrac{1\ atm}{760\ mmHg} = 0.984211\ atm$

$$1.55\ \text{kg}\ NH_4NO_3 \times \frac{1000\ \text{g}\ NH_4NO_3}{1\ \text{kg}\ NH_4NO_3} \times \frac{1\ \text{mol}\ NH_4NO_3}{80.05\ \text{g}\ NH_4NO_3} \times \frac{7\ \text{mol gas}}{2\ \text{mol}\ NH_4NO_3} = 67.7\underline{7}01\ \text{mol gas}$$

$PV = nRT$ Rearrange to solve for V_{Gas}.

$$V_{Gas} = \frac{nRT}{P} = \frac{67.7\underline{7}01\ \text{mol gas} \times 0.08206\ \dfrac{L \cdot atm}{mol \cdot K} \times 398\ K}{0.98\underline{4}211\ atm} = 2250\ \text{L}$$

Check: The units (L) are correct. The magnitude of the answer (2250 L) makes sense because we have about 67 moles of gas generated, so we expect a volume a bit above 67×22 L.

5.77   **Given:** He and air; $V = 855$ mL, $P = 125$ psi, $T = 25\,°C$, $\mathcal{M}(air) = 28.8$ g/mol   **Find:** $\Delta = m(air) - m(He)$

Conceptual Plan: mL $\rightarrow$ L and psi $\rightarrow$ atm and $°C \rightarrow K$ then $P, T, \mathcal{M} \rightarrow d$

$$\frac{1\ L}{1000\ mL} \qquad \frac{1\ atm}{14.7\ psi} \qquad K = °C + 273.15 \qquad d = \frac{P\mathcal{M}}{RT}$$

then $d, V \rightarrow m$ then $m(air), m(He) \rightarrow \Delta$

$$d = \frac{m}{V} \qquad\qquad \Delta = m(air) - m(He)$$

Solution: $V = 855\ \text{mL} \times \dfrac{1\ L}{1000\ mL} = 0.855\ \text{L}$, $P = 125\ \text{psi} \times \dfrac{1\ atm}{14.7\ psi} = 8.50\underline{3}40\ \text{atm}$,

$$T = 25\,°C + 273.15 = 298\ K, \quad d_{air} = \frac{P\mathcal{M}}{RT} = \frac{8.50\underline{3}40\ atm \times 28.8\ \dfrac{\text{g air}}{\text{mol air}}}{0.08206\ \dfrac{L \cdot atm}{K \cdot mol} \times 298\ K} = 10.0\underline{1}47\ \frac{\text{g air}}{L}, \quad d = \frac{m}{V}$$

Rearrange to solve for m. $m = dV$

$$m_{air} = 10.0\underline{1}47\ \frac{\text{g air}}{L} \times 0.855\ L = 8.56257\ \text{g air},$$

$$d_{He} = \frac{PM}{RT} = \frac{8.50\underline{3}40\ atm \times 4.03\ \dfrac{\text{g He}}{\text{mol He}}}{0.08206\ \dfrac{L \cdot atm}{K \cdot mol} \times 298\ K} = 1.40\underline{1}36\ \frac{\text{g He}}{L},$$

$$m_{He} = 1.40136 \frac{g\ He}{\cancel{L}} \times 0.855\ \cancel{L} = 1.19816\ g\ He,$$

$$\Delta = m(air) - m(He) = 8.56257\ g\ air - 1.19816\ g\ He = 7.36\ g$$

Check: The units (g) are correct. We expect the difference to be less than the difference in the molecular weights because we have less than a mole of gas.

5.78   **Given:** $V_1 = 2.95$ L, $P = 0.998$ atm, $T_1 = 25.0\ °C$, and $T_2 = -196\ °C$ **Find:** V_2 and compare to 0.61 L

Conceptual Plan: $°C \rightarrow K$ then $V_1, T_1, T_2 \rightarrow V_2$ and then compare to 0.61 L

$$K = °C + 273.15 \qquad\qquad \frac{V_1}{T_1} = \frac{V_2}{T_2}$$

Solution: $T_1 = 25\ °C + 273.15 = 298$ K, $T_2 = -196\ °C + 273.15 = 77$ K, $\dfrac{V_1}{T_1} = \dfrac{V_2}{T_2}$ Rearrange to solve for V_2.

$$V_2 = V_1 \times \frac{T_2}{T_1} = 2.95\ L \times \frac{77\ \cancel{K}}{298\ \cancel{K}} = 0.76\ L \text{ This is 25\% larger than the measured volume. We expect gases to}$$

behave non-ideally as the temperature drops. We are at the boiling point of the material, so the velocity dramatically decreases and some nitrogen will be condensing.

Check: The units (L) are correct. We expect the volume to decrease dramatically because the temperature has dropped significantly.

5.79   **Given:** flow $= 335$ L/s, $P_{NO} = 22.4$ torr, $T_{NO} = 955$ K, $P_{NH_3} = 755$ torr, $T_{NO} = 298$ K, and NH_3 purity $= 65.2\%$
Find: flow$_{NH_3}$

Conceptual Plan: torr $\rightarrow$ atm then $P_{NO}, V_{NO}/s, T_{NO} \rightarrow n_{NO}/s \rightarrow n_{NH_3}/s$ **(pure)**

$$\frac{1\ atm}{760\ torr} \qquad\qquad PV = nRT \qquad \frac{4\ mol\ NH_3}{4\ mol\ NO}$$

then n_{NH_3}/s **(pure)** $\rightarrow n_{NH_3}/s$ **(impure) then** n_{NH_3}/s **(impure)**, $P_{NH_3}, T_{NH_3} \rightarrow V_{NH_3}/s$

$$\frac{100\ mol\ NH_3\ impure}{65.2\ mol\ NH_3\ pure} \qquad\qquad\qquad PV = nRT$$

Solution: $P_{NO} = 22.4\ \cancel{torr} \times \dfrac{1\ atm}{760\ \cancel{torr}} = 0.0294737\ atm,$ $P_{NH_3} = 755\ \cancel{torr} \times \dfrac{1\ atm}{760\ \cancel{torr}} = 0.993421\ atm$

$PV = nRT$ Rearrange to solve for n_{NO}. Note that we can substitute V/s for V and get n/s as a result.

$$\frac{n_{NO}}{s} = \frac{PV}{RT} = \frac{0.0294737\ \cancel{atm} \times 335\ \cancel{L}/s}{0.08206\ \dfrac{\cancel{L} \cdot \cancel{atm}}{mol \cdot \cancel{K}} \times 955\ \cancel{K}} = 0.125992 \frac{mol\ NO}{s}$$

$$0.125992\ \frac{\cancel{mol\ NO}}{s} \times \frac{4\ \cancel{mol\ NH_3}}{4\ \cancel{mol\ NO}} \times \frac{100\ mol\ NH_3\ impure}{65.2\ \cancel{mol\ NH_3\ pure}} = 0.193240\ \frac{mol\ NH_3\ impure}{s} \qquad PV = nRT$$

Rearrange to solve for V_{NH_3}. Note that we can substitute n/s for n and get V/s as a result.

$$\frac{V_{NH_3}}{s} = \frac{nRT}{P} = \frac{0.193240\ \dfrac{\cancel{mol\ NH_3\ impure}}{s} \times 0.08206 \times \dfrac{\cancel{L} \cdot \cancel{atm}}{\cancel{mol} \cdot \cancel{K}} \times 298 \cancel{K}}{0.993421\ \cancel{atm}} = 4.76\ \frac{L}{s}\ impure\ NH_3$$

Check: The units (L) are correct. The magnitude of the answer (5 L/s) makes sense because we expect it to be less than that for the NO. The NO is at a very low concentration and a high temperature. When this converts to a much higher pressure and lower temperature, it will go down significantly even though the ammonia is impure. From a practical standpoint, a low flow rate will make it economical.

5.80   **Given:** flow$_{NO} = 2.55$ L/s, $P_{NO} = 12.4$ torr, $T_{NO} = 655$ K, and 8.0 hours   **Find:** m (urea)
Conceptual Plan: torr $\rightarrow$ atm and hr $\rightarrow$ min $\rightarrow$ s then $P_{NO}, V_{NO}/s, T_{NO} \rightarrow n_{NO}/s$

$$\frac{1\ atm}{760\ torr} \qquad \frac{60\ min}{1\ hr} \quad \frac{60\ s}{1\ min} \qquad\qquad PV = nRT$$

$n_{NO}/s \rightarrow n_{urea}/s$ **then** $s \rightarrow n_{urea} \rightarrow g_{urea}$

$$\frac{2\ mol\ urea}{4\ mol\ NO} \qquad n_{urea} = (n_{urea}/s)(s) \qquad \frac{60.06\ g\ urea}{1\ mol\ urea}$$

Solution: $P_{NO} = 12.4\ \cancel{torr} \times \dfrac{1\ atm}{760\ \cancel{torr}} = 0.01631579\ atm,$ $8.0\ \cancel{hr} \times \dfrac{60\ \cancel{min}}{1\ \cancel{hr}} \times \dfrac{60\ s}{1\ \cancel{min}} = 28800\ s$

$PV = nRT$ Rearrange to solve for n_{NO}. Note that we can substitute V/s for V and get n/s as a result.

$$\frac{n_{NO}}{s} = \frac{PV}{RT} = \frac{0.01631579 \text{ atm atm} \times 2.55 \text{ L/s}}{0.08206 \frac{\text{L} \cdot \text{atm}}{\text{mol} \cdot \text{K}} \times 655 \text{ K}} = 0.000774062 \frac{\text{mol NO}}{s},$$

$$0.000774062 \frac{\text{mol NO}}{s} \times \frac{2 \text{ mol urea}}{4 \text{ mol NO}} = 0.000387031 \frac{\text{mol urea}}{s},$$

$$28800 \text{ s} \times 0.000387031 \frac{\text{mol urea}}{s} \times \frac{60.06 \text{ g urea}}{1 \text{ mol urea}} = 670 \text{ g urea}$$

Check: The units (g) are correct. The magnitude of the answer (670 g) is not an unreasonable mass to add to a car because many more grams of gasoline are burned in 8 hours of driving.

5.81   **Given:** $l = 30.0$ cm, $w = 20.0$ cm, $h = 15.0$ cm, 14.7 psi   **Find:** Force (lb)
Conceptual Plan: $l, w, h \rightarrow$ **Surface Area, SA(cm^2)** $\rightarrow$ **Surface Area(in^2)** $\rightarrow$ **Force**

$$SA = 2(lh) + 2(wh) + 2(lw) \qquad \frac{(1 \text{ in})^2}{(2.54 \text{ cm})^2} \qquad \frac{14.7 \text{ lb}}{1 \text{ in}^2}$$

Solution: $SA = 2(lh) + 2(wh) + 2(lw) = 2(30.0 \text{ cm} \times 15.0 \text{ cm}) + 2(20.0 \text{ cm} \times 15.0 \text{ cm})$
$+ 2(30.0 \text{ cm} \times 20.0 \text{ cm}) = 2700 \text{ cm}^2$

$$2700 \text{ cm}^2 \times \frac{(1 \text{ in})^2}{(2.54 \text{ cm})^2} = 418.50 \text{ in}^2, \quad 418.50 \text{ in}^2 \times \frac{14.7 \text{ lb}}{1 \text{ in}^2} = 6150 \text{ lb}.$$ The can would be crushed.

Check: The units (lb) are correct. The magnitude of the answer (6150 lb) is not unreasonable because there is a large surface area.

5.82   **Given:** $l = 20.0$ cm, $r = 10.0$ cm, 25 mL with $d = 0.807$ g/mL, and $P_1 = 760.0$ mmHg $= 1.000$ atm, $T = 298$ K
Find: Force (lb)
Conceptual Plan: mL $\rightarrow$ g $\rightarrow$ mol then $l, r \rightarrow V(\text{cm}^3) \rightarrow V(\text{L})$ then $V, n, T \rightarrow P_{N_2}$ then

$$d = \frac{m}{V} \qquad \frac{1 \text{ mol}}{28.02 \text{ g}} \qquad V = \pi r^2 l \qquad \frac{1 \text{ L}}{1000 \text{ cm}^3} \qquad PV = nRT$$

$P_{N_2}, P_{atm} \rightarrow P_{Total}$ then atm $\rightarrow$ psi then $l, r \rightarrow$ **Surface Area(cm^2)** $\rightarrow$ **Surface Area(in^2)** $\rightarrow$ **Force**

$$P_{Total} = P_{atm} + P_{N_2} \qquad \frac{14.7 \text{ lbs}}{1 \text{ atm}} \qquad SA = 2\pi r l + 2\pi r^2 \qquad \frac{(1 \text{ in})^2}{(2.54 \text{ cm})^2} \qquad p = \frac{F}{A}$$

Solution: $d = \frac{m}{V}$ Rearrange to solve for m. $m = d V = 0.807 \frac{\text{g}}{\text{mL}} \times 25 \text{ mL} = 20.175$ g,

$$20.175 \text{ g} \times \frac{1 \text{ mol}}{28.02 \text{ g}} = 0.72002 \text{ mol}, \quad V = \pi r^2 l = \pi \times (10.0 \text{ cm})^2 \times 20.0 \text{ cm} = 6283.19 \text{ cm}^3,$$

$$6283.19 \text{ cm}^3 \times \frac{1 \text{ L}}{1000 \text{ cm}^3} = 6.28319 \text{ L}, \quad PV = nRT \text{ Rearrange to solve for } P.$$

$$P_{N_2} = \frac{nRT}{V} = \frac{0.72002 \text{ mol} \times 0.08206 \frac{\text{L} \cdot \text{atm}}{\text{mol} \cdot \text{K}} \times 298 \text{ K}}{6.28319 \text{ L}} = 2.80228 \text{ atm},$$

$$P_{Total} = P_{atm} + P_{N_2} = 1.000 \text{ atm} + 2.80228 \text{ atm} = 3.80228 \text{ atm}, \quad 3.80228 \text{ atm} \times \frac{14.7 \text{ psi}}{1 \text{ atm}} = 55.894 \text{ psi}$$

$$SA = 2\pi r l + 2\pi r^2 = (2 \times \pi \times 10.0 \text{ cm} \times 20.0 \text{ cm}) + (2 \times \pi \times (10.0 \text{ cm})^2) = 1884.956 \text{ cm}^2,$$

$$1884.956 \text{ cm}^2 \times \frac{(1 \text{ in})^2}{(2.54 \text{ cm})^2} = 292.169 \text{ in}^2, \quad P = \frac{F}{A} \text{ Rearrange to solve for } F.$$

$$292.169 \text{ in}^2 \times \frac{55.894 \text{ lbs}}{1 \text{ in}^2} = 1.6 \times 10^4 \text{ lb}$$

Check: The units (lb) are correct. The magnitude of the answer (16,000 lb) is not unreasonable because there is a large surface area and this is a high pressure.

5.83   **Given:** $V_1 = 160.0$ L, $P_1 = 1855$ psi, 3.5 L/balloon, $P_2 = 1.0$ atm $= 14.7$ psi, and $T = 298$ K   **Find:** # balloons
Conceptual Plan: $V_1, P_1, P_2 \rightarrow V_2$ then L $\rightarrow$ # balloons

$$P_1 V_1 = P_2 V_2 \qquad \frac{1 \text{ balloon}}{3.5 \text{ L}}$$

Solution: $P_1 V_1 = P_2 V_2$ Rearrange to solve for V_2. $V_2 = \dfrac{P_1}{P_2} V_1 = \dfrac{1855 \text{ psi}}{14.7 \text{ psi}} \times 160.0 \text{ L} = 20190.5 \text{ L}$,

$20190.5 \text{ L} \times \dfrac{1 \text{ balloon}}{3.5 \text{ L}} = 5800 \text{ balloons}$

Check: The units (balloons) are correct. The magnitude of the answer (5800) is reasonable because a store does not want to buy a new helium tank very often.

5.84   **Given:** 11.5 mL with $d = 0.573$ g/mL, $T = 28.5\,°C$, and $P = 892$ torr   **Find:** V

       Conceptual Plan: mL $\rightarrow$ g $\rightarrow$ mol and $°C \rightarrow K$ and torr $\rightarrow$ atm then $P, n, T \rightarrow V$

$$d = \frac{m}{V} \quad \frac{1 \text{ mol}}{58.12 \text{ g}} \qquad K = °C + 273.15 \qquad \frac{1 \text{ atm}}{760 \text{ torr}} \qquad PV = nRT$$

       Solution: $d = \dfrac{m}{V}$ Rearrange to solve for m. $m = dV = 0.573\,\dfrac{\text{g}}{\text{mL}} \times 11.5 \text{ mL} = 6.5895 \text{ g}$,

$6.5895 \text{ g} \times \dfrac{1 \text{ mol}}{58.12 \text{ g}} = 0.113377 \text{ mol}$, $T = 28.5\,°C + 273.15 = 301.7 \text{ K}$, $892 \text{ torr} \times \dfrac{1 \text{ atm}}{760 \text{ torr}} = 1.17368 \text{ atm}$

$PV = nRT$ Rearrange to solve for V.

$$V = \frac{nRT}{P} = \frac{0.113377 \text{ mol} \times 0.08206 \dfrac{\text{L} \cdot \text{atm}}{\text{mol} \cdot \text{K}} \times 301.7 \text{ K}}{1.17368 \text{ atm}} = 2.39 \text{ L}$$

       Check: The units (L) are correct. The magnitude of the answer (2 L) is reasonable because there is a lot less than one mole of butane.

5.85   **Given:** $r_1 = 2.5$ cm, $P_1 = 4.00$ atm, $T = 298$ K, and $P_2 = 1.00$ atm   **Find:** r_2

       Conceptual Plan: $r_1 \rightarrow V_1$ and $V_1, P_1, P_2 \rightarrow V_2$ then $V_2 \rightarrow r_2$

$$V = \frac{4}{3}\pi r^3 \qquad P_1 V_1 = P_2 V_2 \qquad V = \frac{4}{3}\pi r^3$$

       Solution: $V = \dfrac{4}{3}\pi r^3 = \dfrac{4}{3} \times \pi \times (2.5 \text{ cm})^3 = 65.450 \text{ cm}^3$ $P_1 V_1 = P_2 V_2$ Rearrange to solve for V_2.

$V_2 = \dfrac{P_1}{P_2} V_1 = \dfrac{4.00 \text{ atm}}{1.00 \text{ atm}} \times 65.450 \text{ cm}^3 = 261.80 \text{ cm}^3$, $V = \dfrac{4}{3}\pi r^3$

Rearrange to solve for r. $r = \sqrt[3]{\dfrac{3V}{4\pi}} = \sqrt[3]{\dfrac{3 \times 261.80 \text{ cm}^3}{4 \times \pi}} = 4.0 \text{ cm}$

       Check: The units (cm) are correct. The magnitude of the answer (4 cm) is reasonable because the bubble will expand as the pressure is decreased.

5.86   **Given:** max $SA = 1257 \text{ cm}^2$, $V_1 = 3.0$ L, $P_1 = 755$ torr, $T_1 = 298$ K, and $T_2 = 273$ K   **Find:** P_2 to burst balloon

       Conceptual Plan: torr $\rightarrow$ atm and $A \rightarrow r \rightarrow V \text{ (cm}^3) \rightarrow V(\text{L})$ then

$$\frac{1 \text{ atm}}{760 \text{ torr}} \qquad SA = 4\pi r^2 \quad V = \frac{4}{3}\pi r^3 \qquad \frac{1 \text{ L}}{1000 \text{ cm}^3}$$

       $P_1, V_1, P_2, T_1, V_2, T_2 \rightarrow P_2$

$$\frac{P_1 V_1}{T_1} = \frac{P_2 V_2}{T_2}$$

       Solution: $P_1 = 755 \text{ torr} \times \dfrac{1 \text{ atm}}{760 \text{ torr}} = 0.993421 \text{ atm}$, $SA = 4\pi r^2$ Rearrange to solve for r.

$r = \sqrt{\dfrac{SA}{4\pi}} = \sqrt{\dfrac{1257 \text{ cm}^2}{4\pi}} = 10.00144 \text{ cm}$, $V = \dfrac{4}{3}\pi r^3 = \dfrac{4}{3} \times \pi \times (10.00144 \text{ cm})^3 = 4190.600 \text{ cm}^3$

$4190.600 \text{ cm}^3 \times \dfrac{1 \text{ L}}{1000 \text{ cm}^3} = 4.190600 \text{ L}$ $\dfrac{P_1 V_1}{T_1} = \dfrac{P_2 V_2}{T_2}$ Rearrange to solve for P_2.

$P_2 = P_1 \dfrac{V_1 T_2}{V_2 T_1} = 0.993421 \text{ atm} \times \dfrac{3.00 \text{ L}}{4.190600 \text{ L}} \times \dfrac{273 \text{ K}}{298 \text{ K}} = 0.652 \text{ atm}$

       Check: The units (atm) are correct. The magnitude of the answer (0.65 atm) is reasonable because the pressure must decrease for the balloon to expand.

5.87 **Given:** 2.0 mol CO: 1.0 mol O_2, $V = 2.45$ L, $P_1 = 745$ torr, $P_2 = 552$ torr, and $T = 552\,°C$ **Find:** %reacted
Conceptual Plan: From $PV = nRT$, we know that $P \propto n$; looking at the chemical reaction, we see that $2 + 1 = 3$ moles of gas gets converted to 2 moles of gas. If all of the gas reacts, $P_2 = 2/3\, P_1$. Calculate $-\Delta P$ for 100% reacted and for actual case. Then calculate % reacted.

$$-\Delta P_{100\% \text{ reacted}} = P_1 - \frac{2}{3}P_1 \quad -\Delta P_{\text{actual}} = P_1 - P_2 \quad \%\text{reacted} = \frac{\Delta P_{\text{actual}}}{\Delta P_{100\% \text{ reacted}}} \times 100\%$$

Solution: $-\Delta P_{100\% \text{ reacted}} = P_1 - \frac{2}{3}P_1 = 745\ \text{torr} - \frac{2}{3}745\ \text{torr} = 248.\underline{3}33\ \text{torr}$,

$-\Delta P_{\text{actual}} = P_1 - P_2 = 745\ \text{torr} - 552\ \text{torr} = 193\ \text{torr}$,

$\%\text{reacted} = \dfrac{\Delta P_{\text{actual}}}{\Delta P_{100\% \text{ reacted}}} \times 100\% = \dfrac{193\ \text{torr}}{248.333\ \text{torr}} \times 100\% = 77.7\%$

Check: The units (%) are correct. The magnitude of the answer (78%) makes sense because the pressure would have dropped to $2/3(745\ \text{torr}) = 497$ torr if all of the reactants had reacted. **Note: There are many ways to solve this problem, including calculating the moles of reactants and products using $PV = nRT$.**

5.88 **Given:** N_2, $V_1 = 1.0$ L, $P_1 = 1.0$ atm, $T_1 = 300.$ K, and $V_2 = 3.0$ L **Find:** d_2
Conceptual Plan: $\mathcal{M}, V_1, P_1, T_1 \rightarrow d_1 \rightarrow d_2$

$$d = \frac{P\mathcal{M}}{RT} \quad d = \frac{m}{V}$$

Solution: $d_1 = \dfrac{P\mathcal{M}}{RT} = \dfrac{1.0\ \text{atm} \times 28.02\ \dfrac{\text{g}}{\text{mol}}}{0.08206\ \dfrac{\text{L} \cdot \text{atm}}{\text{K} \cdot \text{mol}} \times 300.\ \text{K}} = 1.\underline{1}3819\ \dfrac{\text{g}}{\text{L}}, d = \dfrac{m}{V}$

Because we have a sealed container, $m_1 = m_2$. Rearrange to solve for m. $m = dV$ or $m = d_1 V_1 = d_2 V_2$

Rearrange to solve for d_2. $d_2 = d_1 \dfrac{V_1}{V_2} = 1.\underline{1}3819\ \dfrac{\text{g}}{\text{L}} \times \dfrac{1.0\ \text{L}}{3.0\ \text{L}} = 0.38\ \dfrac{\text{g}}{\text{L}}$

Check: The units (g/L) are correct. The magnitude of the answer (0.4 g/L) is a typical gas density. The density dropped as the volume went up.

5.89 **Given:**
$P(\text{Total})_1 = 2.2$ atm $= P(\text{CO}) + P(O_2)$, $P(\text{Total})_2 = 1.9$ atm $= P(\text{CO}) + P(O_2) + P(CO_2)$, $V = 1.0$ L, and $T = 1.0 \times 10^3$ K
Find: mass CO_2 made
Conceptual Plan: $P(\text{Total})_1 = 2.2\ \text{atm} = P(\text{CO})_1 + P(O_2)_1, P(\text{Total})_2 = 1.9\ \text{atm} = P(\text{CO})_2 + P(O_2)_2 + P(CO_2)_2$. Let $x = $ amount of $P(O_2)$ reacted. From stoichiometry: $P(\text{CO})_2 = P(\text{CO})_1 - 2x, P(O_2)_2 = P(O_2)_1 - x, P(CO_2)_2 = 2x$. Thus, $P(\text{Total})_2 = 1.9\ \text{atm} = P(\text{CO})_1 - 2x + P(O_2)_1 - x + 2x = P(\text{Total})_1 - x$. Using the initial conditions: $1.9\ \text{atm} = 2.2\ \text{atm} - x$. So $x = 0.3$ atm, and because $2x = P(CO_2)_2 = 0.6$ atm, then $P, V, T \rightarrow n \rightarrow$ g.

$$PV = nRT \quad \frac{44.01\ \text{g}}{1\ \text{mol}}$$

Solution: $PV = nRT$ Rearrange to solve for n.

$n = \dfrac{PV}{RT} = \dfrac{0.6\ \text{atm} \times 1.0\ \text{L}}{0.08206\ \dfrac{\text{L} \cdot \text{atm}}{\text{mol} \cdot \text{K}} \times 1000\ \text{K}} = 0.00\underline{7}3117\ \text{mol}$

$0.00\underline{7}3117\ \text{mol} \times \dfrac{44.01\ \text{g}}{1\ \text{mol}} = 0.\underline{3}21788\ \text{g}\ CO_2 = 0.3\ \text{g}\ CO_2$

Check: The units (g) are correct. The magnitude of the answer (0.3 g) makes sense because we have such a small volume at a very high temperature and such a small pressure. This leads us to expect a very small number of moles.

5.90 **Given:** $r = 1.3 \times 10^{-8}$ cm, $V = 100.$ mL, $P = 1.0$ atm, and $T_1 = 273$ K **Find:** V fraction occupied by Xe atoms
Conceptual Plan: mL $\rightarrow$ L then $V \rightarrow n \rightarrow$ atoms then $r \rightarrow V(\text{cm}^3)/\text{atom}$

$$\frac{1\ \text{L}}{1000\ \text{mL}} \qquad \frac{1\ \text{mol}}{22.4\ \text{L}}\ \text{at STP} \quad 6.022 \times 10^{23}\ \text{atoms/mol} \quad V = \frac{4}{3}\pi r^3$$

then atoms, $V(\text{cm}^3)/\text{atom} \rightarrow V(\text{Xe})$ then $V(\text{Xe}), V(\text{container}) \rightarrow$ Fraction Xe

$$V(\text{Xe}) = (V/\text{atom})(\text{atoms}) \qquad \%V(\text{Xe}) = \frac{V(\text{Xe})}{V(\text{container})} \times 100\%$$

Solution: $100 \; \cancel{mL} \times \dfrac{1 \; L}{1000 \; \cancel{mL}} = 0.100 \; L,$

$0.100 \; \cancel{L} \times \dfrac{1 \; mol}{22.4 \; \cancel{L}} = 0.00446\underline{1}50 \; mol, \; 0.00446\underline{1}50 \; \cancel{mol} \times 6.022 \times 10^{23} \; \dfrac{atoms}{\cancel{mol}} = 2.68839 \times 10^{21} \; atoms$

$V = \dfrac{4}{3} \pi r^3 = \dfrac{4}{3} \times \pi \times (1.3 \times 10^{-8} \; cm)^3 = 9.\underline{2}028 \times 10^{-24} \; cm^3/atom,$

$V(Xe) = (V/atom)(atoms) = \dfrac{9.\underline{2}028 \times 10^{-24} \; cm^3}{\cancel{atom}} \times 2.6\underline{8}839 \times 10^{21} \; \cancel{atoms} = 0.024\underline{7}41 \; cm^3$

$\% \; V(Xe) = \dfrac{V(Xe)}{V(\text{container})} \times 100\% = \dfrac{0.024\underline{7}41 \; \cancel{cm^3}}{100 \; \cancel{cm^3}} \times 100\% = 0.025\%V$

Check: The units ($\%V$) are correct. The magnitude of the answer (0.025 $\%V$) is reasonable because we expect the molecules to take up very little of the volume of a container of a gas.

5.91   **Given:** $h_1 = 22.6 \; m$, $T_1 = 22 \; °C$, and $h_2 = 23.8 \; m$ **Find:** T_2
         Conceptual Plan: °C → K because $V_{\text{cylinder}} \propto h$ we do not need to know r to use $V_1, T_1, T_2 \rightarrow V_2$

$$K = °C + 273.15 \qquad V = \pi r^2 h \qquad \dfrac{V_1}{T_1} = \dfrac{V_2}{T_2}$$

         Solution: $T_1 = 22 \; °C + 273.15 = 295 \; K, \; \dfrac{V_1}{T_1} = \dfrac{V_2}{T_2}$ Rearrange to solve for T_2.

$$T_2 = T_1 \times \dfrac{V_2}{V_1} = T_1 \times \dfrac{\pi r^2 h_2}{\pi r^2 h_1} = 295 \; K \times \dfrac{23.8 \; \cancel{m}}{22.6 \; \cancel{m}} = 311 \; K$$

         Check: The units (K) are correct. We expect the temperature to increase because the volume increased.

5.92   **Given:** $m \; (CH_4) = 8.0 \; g$, $m \; (Xe) = 8.0 \; g$, and $P_{\text{Total}} = 0.44 \; atm$ **Find:** P_{CH_4}
         Conceptual Plan: g → mol then $n_{CH_4}, n_{Xe} \rightarrow \chi_{CH_4}$ then $\chi_{CH_4}, P_{\text{Total}} \rightarrow P_{CH_4}$

$$\mathcal{M} \qquad\qquad \chi_{CH_4} = \dfrac{n_{CH_4}}{n_{CH_4} + n_{Xe}} \qquad\qquad P_{CH_4} = \chi_{CH_4} P_{\text{Total}}$$

         Solution: $n_{CH_4} = 8.0 \; \cancel{g} \times \dfrac{1 \; mol}{16.04 \; \cancel{g}} = 0.49\underline{8}75 \; mol, \; n_{Xe} = 8.0 \; \cancel{g} \times \dfrac{1 \; mol}{131.3 \; \cancel{g}} = 0.060\underline{9}29 \; mol,$

$$\chi_{CH_4} = \dfrac{n_{CH_4}}{n_{CH_4} + n_{Xe}} = \dfrac{0.49\underline{8}75 \; mol}{0.49\underline{8}75 \; mol + 0.060\underline{9}29 \; mol} = 0.89\underline{1}14,$$

$$P_{CH_4} = \chi_{CH_4} P_{\text{Total}} = 0.89\underline{1}14 \times 0.44 \; atm = 0.39 \; atm$$

         Check: The units (atm) are correct. The magnitude of the answer (0.4 atm) makes sense because the molecular weight of methane is so much lower than that of xenon, so we have many more moles of methane. The partial pressure of methane is almost as large as the total pressure.

5.93   **Given:** He, $V = 0.35 \; L$, $P_{\text{max}} = 88 \; atm$, and $T = 299 \; K$ **Find:** m_{He}
         Conceptual Plan: $P, V, T \rightarrow n$ then mol → g

$$P \, V = nRT \qquad\qquad \mathcal{M}$$

         Solution: $PV = nRT$ Rearrange to solve for n.

$$n_{He} = \dfrac{PV}{RT} = \dfrac{88 \; \cancel{atm} \times 0.35 \; \cancel{L}}{0.08206 \; \dfrac{\cancel{L} \cdot \cancel{atm}}{mol \cdot \cancel{K}} \times 299 \; \cancel{K}} = 1.2\underline{5}53 \; mol, \; 1.2\underline{5}53 \; \cancel{mol} \times \dfrac{4.003 \; g}{1 \; \cancel{mol}} = 5.0 \; g \; He$$

         Check: The units (g) are correct. The magnitude of the answer (5 g) makes sense because the high pressure and the low volume cancel out (remember 22 L/mol at STP). So we expect ~1 mol and so ~4 g.

5.94   **Given:** NaH + water, $V = 0.490 \; L$, $P_{\text{Total}} = 758 \; mmHg$, and $T = 35 \; °C$ **Find:** m_{H_2} and m_{NaH}
         Other: $P_{H_2O} = 42.23 \; mmHg$ at 35 °C
         Conceptual Plan: °C → K and $P_{\text{Total}}(mmHg) \rightarrow P_{H_2}(mmHg) \rightarrow P_{H_2}(atm)$ then

$$K = °C + 273.15 \qquad P_{\text{Total}} = P_{H_2O} + P_{H_2} \qquad \dfrac{1 \; atm}{760 \; mmHg}$$

         Write balanced reaction

         $NaH(s) + H_2O(l) \rightarrow NaOH(aq) + H_2(g)$

$P, V, T \rightarrow n_{H_2}$ then $mol_{H_2} \rightarrow g_{H_2}$ then $mol_{H_2} \rightarrow mol_{NaH} \rightarrow g_{NaH}$

$$PV = nRT \qquad \frac{2.016\ g}{1\ mol} \qquad \frac{1\ mol\ NaH}{1\ mol\ H_2} \qquad \frac{24.0\ g}{1\ mol}$$

Solution: $T = 35\ °C + 273.15 = 308$ K, $P_{Total} = P_{H_2O} + P_{H_2}$ Rearrange to solve for P_{H_2}.

$$P_{H_2} = 758\ mmHg - 42.23\ mmHg = 715.77\ mmHg, \quad 715.77\ \cancel{mmHg} \times \frac{1\ atm}{760\ \cancel{mmHg}} = 0.941803\ atm \quad PV = nRT$$

Rearrange to solve for n. $n_{H_2} = \dfrac{PV}{RT} = \dfrac{0.941803\ \cancel{atm} \times 0.490\ \cancel{L}}{0.08206\ \dfrac{\cancel{L} \cdot \cancel{atm}}{mol \cdot \cancel{K}} \times 308\ \cancel{K}} = 0.0182589$ mol,

$0.0182589\ \cancel{mol} \times \dfrac{2.016\ g}{1\ \cancel{mol}} = 0.0368$ g H_2 and $0.0182589\ \cancel{mol\ H_2} \times \dfrac{1\ mol\ NaH}{1\ \cancel{mol\ H_2}} = 0.0182589$ mol NaH,

0.0182589 mol NaH $\times \dfrac{24.0\ g}{1\ mol} = 0.438$ g NaH

Check: The units (g) are correct. The magnitude of the answers (0.04 g and 0.4 g) makes sense because we have much less than a mole of each material (remember 22 L/mol at STP), so we expect <2 g gas and <24 g solid.

5.95   **Given:** 15.0 mL HBr in 1.0 min and 20.3 mL unknown hydrocarbon gas in 1.0 min
Find: formula of unknown gas
Conceptual Plan: Because these gases are under the same conditions, $V \propto n$, V, time $\rightarrow$ Rate then

$$Rate = \frac{V}{time}$$

$\mathcal{M}$(HBr), Rate (HBr), Rate (Unk) $\rightarrow$ $\mathcal{M}$(Unk)

$$\frac{Rate\ (HBr)}{Rate\ (U)} = \sqrt{\frac{\mathcal{M}(U)}{\mathcal{M}(HBr)}}$$

Solution: Rate (HBr) $= \dfrac{V}{time} = \dfrac{15.0\ mL}{1.0\ min} = 15.0\ \dfrac{mL}{min}$, Rate(Unk) $= \dfrac{V}{time} = \dfrac{20.3\ mL}{1.0\ min} = 20.3\ \dfrac{mL}{min}$,

$\dfrac{Rate(HBr)}{Rate(Unk)} = \sqrt{\dfrac{\mathcal{M}(Unk)}{\mathcal{M}(HBr)}}$ Rearrange to solve for $\mathcal{M}$(Unk).

$$\mathcal{M}(Unk) = M(HBr)\left(\frac{Rate\ (HBr)}{Rate\ (Unk)}\right)^2 = 80.91\ \frac{g}{mol} \times \left(\frac{15.0\ \dfrac{m\cancel{L}}{\cancel{min}}}{20.3\ \dfrac{m\cancel{L}}{\cancel{min}}}\right)^2 = 44.2\ \frac{g}{mol}$$ The formula is C_3H_8, or propane.

Check: The units (g/mol) are correct. The magnitude of the answer (<HBr) makes sense because the unknown diffused faster and so must be lighter.

5.96   **Given:** helium + argon density 0.670 g/L, $P = 755$ mmHg, and $T = 298$ K   **Find:** composition
Solution: Assume that 22.414 L; so number of moles of gas $= 755$ mmHg/760 mmHg $= 0.9934211$ moles of gas

and the mass of the gas $= \dfrac{0.670\ g}{1\ \cancel{L}} \times 22.414\ \cancel{L} = 15.01738$ g total. Let $x = n_{He}$, so

$m_{Total} = 15.01738$ g total $= x\ \dfrac{4.003\ g}{1\ mol} + (0.9934211 - x)\ \dfrac{39.95\ g}{1\ mol}$ Solve for x.

x mol $\left(\dfrac{39.95\ g}{1\ mol} - \dfrac{4.003\ g}{1\ mol}\right) = (39.68717 - 15.01738)$ g $\rightarrow x$ mol $= \dfrac{(24.66979)\ \cancel{g}}{\left(\dfrac{35.947\ \cancel{g}}{1\ mol}\right)} = 0.6862823$ mol He and

$(0.9934211 - 0.6862823)$ mol Ar $= 0.3071388$ mol Ar. The composition on a volume basis is the same as the composition on a molar basis.

$\dfrac{0.6862823\ \cancel{mol\ He}}{0.9934211\ \cancel{mol\ total}} \times 100\% = 69.1\%$ He and $100\% - 69.1\% = 30.9\%$ Ar

Check: The units (%) are correct. The magnitude of the answer (70% He) makes sense because the average molar mass is ~15 g/mol, which is closer to the molar mass of He than to Ar.

5.97   **Given:** 75.2% by mass nitrogen + 24.8% by mass krypton and P_{Total} = 745 mmHg   **Find:** P_{Kr}
Solution: Assume that 100 g total, so we have 75.2 g N_2 and 24.8 g Kr. Converting these masses to moles,

$$75.2 \text{ g } N_2 \times \frac{1 \text{ mol } N_2}{28.02 \text{ g } N_2} = 2.683797 \text{ mol } N_2 \text{ and } 24.8 \text{ g Kr} \times \frac{1 \text{ mol Kr}}{83.80 \text{ g Kr}} = 0.2959427 \text{ mol Kr}$$

$$P_{Kr} = \chi_{Kr} P_{Total} = \frac{0.2959427 \text{ mol Kr}}{2.683797 \text{ mol } N_2 + 0.2959427 \text{ mol Kr}} \times 745 \text{ mmHg Kr} = 74.0 \text{ mmHg Kr}$$

Check: The units (mmHg) are correct. The magnitude of the answer (74 mmHg) makes sense because the mixture is mostly nitrogen by mass and this dominance is magnified because the molar mass of krypton is larger than the molar mass of nitrogen.

Challenge Problems

5.98   **Given:** 3.7×10^{12} kg/yr octane; atm = 399 ppm CO_2 by volume; atm thickness = 15 km; r_{Earth} = 6371 km; P_{atm} = 381 torr; T_{atm} = 275 K   **Find:** $m(CO_2)$ and % increase in CO_2
Conceptual Plan: write a balanced chemical reaction $kg_{C_8H_{18}} \rightarrow g_{C_8H_{18}} \rightarrow mol_{C_8H_{18}} \rightarrow mol_{CO_2}$

$$2 C_8H_{18}(g) + 25 O_2(g) \rightarrow 16 CO_2(g) + 18 H_2O(l) \qquad \frac{1000 \text{ g}}{1 \text{ kg}} \quad \frac{1 \text{ mol}}{114.22 \text{ g}} \quad \frac{16 \text{ mol } CO_2}{2 \text{ mol } C_8H_{18}}$$

then $mol_{CO_2} \rightarrow g_{CO_2}$ **and** $ppm_{CO_2} \rightarrow \chi_{CO_2} \rightarrow P_{CO_2}$ **torr** $\rightarrow$ **atm then** $r_{Earth} \rightarrow V_{Earth}$ **and**

$$\frac{44.01 \text{ g}}{1 \text{ mol}} \qquad\qquad \frac{1 \text{ part}}{10^6 \text{ parts}} \quad P_{CO_2} = \chi_{CO_2} P_{atm} \quad \frac{1 \text{ atm}}{760 \text{ torr}} \qquad V = \frac{4}{3}\pi r^3$$

r_{Earth}, **atm thickness** $\rightarrow r_{Earth+atm}$ **then** $r_{Earth+atm} \rightarrow V_{Earth+atm}$ $V_{Earth+atm}, V_{Earth} \rightarrow V_{atm}$ **then**

$$r_{Earth+atm} = r_{Earth} + r_{atm} \qquad V = \frac{4}{3}\pi r^3 \qquad V_{atm} = V_{Earth+atm} - V_{Earth}$$

$km^3 \rightarrow m^3 \rightarrow cm^3 \rightarrow$ **L then** $V_{atm}, P_{CO_2}, T_{atm} \rightarrow n_{CO_2} \rightarrow g_{CO_2}$ **and**

$$\left(\frac{1000 \text{ cm}}{1 \text{ km}}\right)^3 \left(\frac{100 \text{ cm}}{1 \text{ m}}\right)^3 \frac{1 \text{ L}}{1000 \text{ cm}^3} \qquad PV = nRT \qquad \frac{44.01 \text{ g}}{1 \text{ mol}}$$

$g_{CO_2 added}, g_{CO_2 initially,} \rightarrow \%\text{increase}_{CO_2}$

$$\%\text{increase} = \frac{\text{added}}{\text{initial}} \times 100\%$$

Solution: $3.7 \times 10^{12} \text{ kg} \times \frac{1000 \text{ g}}{1 \text{ kg}} \times \frac{1 \text{ mol}}{114.22 \text{ g}} \times \frac{16 \text{ mol } CO_2}{2 \text{ mol } C_8H_{18}} \times \frac{44.01 \text{ g}}{1 \text{ mol}} = 1.1405 \times 10^{16} \text{ g } CO_2 \text{ added,}$

$399 \text{ parts } CO_2 \frac{1 \text{ part}}{10^6 \text{ parts}} = 3.99 \times 10^{-4} = \chi_{CO_2}, P_{CO_2} = \chi_{CO_2} P_{atm} = 3.99 \times 10^{-4} \times 381 \text{ torr} = 0.152019 \text{ torr,}$

$0.152019 \text{ torr} \times \frac{1 \text{ atm}}{760 \text{ torr}} = 0.00020003 \text{ atm, } V_{Earth} = \frac{4}{3}\pi r^3 = \frac{4}{3} \times \pi \times (6371 \text{ km})^3 = 1.08321 \times 10^{12} \text{ km}^3,$

$r_{Earth+atm} = r_{Earth} + r_{atm} = 6371 \text{ km} + 15 \text{ km} = 6386 \text{ km,}$

$V_{Earth+atm} = \frac{4}{3}\pi r^3 = \frac{4}{3} \times \pi \times (6386 \text{ km})^3 = 1.09088 \times 10^{12} \text{ km}^3,$

$V_{atm} = V_{Earth+atm} - V_{Earth} = 1.09088 \times 10^{12} \text{ km}^3 - 1.08321 \times 10^{12} \text{ km}^3 = 7.670 \times 10^9 \text{ km}^3,$

$7.670 \times 10^9 \text{ km}^3 \times \left(\frac{1000 \text{ m}}{1 \text{ km}}\right)^3 \times \left(\frac{100 \text{ cm}}{1 \text{ m}}\right)^3 \times \frac{1 \text{ L}}{1000 \text{ cm}^3} = 7.670 \times 10^{21} \text{ L, } PV = nRT$

Rearrange to solve for n. $n_{CO_2 \text{ initial}} = \frac{PV}{RT} = \dfrac{0.00020003 \text{ atm} \times 7.670 \times 10^{21} \text{ L}}{0.08206 \dfrac{\text{L} \cdot \text{atm}}{\text{mol} \cdot \text{K}} \times 275 \text{ K}} = 6.799 \times 10^{16} \text{ mol,}$

$6.799 \times 10^{16} \text{ mol} \times \frac{44.01 \text{ g}}{1 \text{ mol}} = 2.9922 \times 10^{18} \text{ g } CO_2$

% increase $= \frac{\text{added}}{\text{initial}} \times 100\% = \frac{1.1405 \times 10^{16} \text{ g } CO_2}{2.9922 \times 10^{18} \text{ g } CO_2} \times 100 = 0.3812\%$ increase $= 0.4\%$ increase

Check: The units (g and %) are correct. The magnitude of the answer (10^{16} g) is reasonable because we started with so much octane and the mass of CO_2 will be larger than the original octane weight because there is so much added oxygen. The % increase is reasonable because the volume of the atmosphere is so large.

5.99 **Given:** CH$_4$: $V = 155$ mL at STP; O$_2$: $V = 885$ mL at STP; NO: $V = 55.5$ mL at STP; mixed in a flask: $V = 2.0$ L, $T = 275$ K, and 90.0% of limiting reagent used. **Find:** Ps of all components and P_{Total}

Conceptual Plan: CH$_4$: mL $\rightarrow$ L $\rightarrow$ mol$_{CH_4}$ $\rightarrow$ mol$_{CO_2}$ and

$$\frac{1 \text{ L}}{1000 \text{ mL}} \quad \frac{1 \text{ mol}}{22.414 \text{ L}} \quad \frac{1 \text{ mol CO}_2}{1 \text{ mol CH}_4}$$

O$_2$: mL $\rightarrow$ L $\rightarrow$ mol$_{O_2}$ $\rightarrow$ mol$_{CO_2}$ and NO: mL $\rightarrow$ L $\rightarrow$ mol$_{NO}$ $\rightarrow$ mol$_{CO_2}$

$$\frac{1 \text{ L}}{1000 \text{ mL}} \quad \frac{1 \text{ mol}}{22.414 \text{ L}} \quad \frac{1 \text{ mol CO}_2}{5 \text{ mol O}_2} \quad \frac{1 \text{ L}}{1000 \text{ mL}} \quad \frac{1 \text{ mol}}{22.414 \text{ L}} \quad \frac{1 \text{ mol CO}_2}{5 \text{ mol NO}}$$

the smallest yield determines the limiting reagent then initial mol$_{NO}$ $\rightarrow$ reacted mol$_{NO}$ $\rightarrow$ final mol$_{NO}$

NO is the limiting reagent 90.0% 0.100 $\times$ initial mol$_{NO}$

reacted mol$_{NO}$ $\rightarrow$ reacted mol$_{CH_4}$ then initial mol$_{CH_4}$, reacted mol$_{CH_4}$ $\rightarrow$ final mol$_{CH_4}$ then

$$\frac{1 \text{ mol CH}_4}{5 \text{ mol NO}}$$

initial mol$_{CH_4}$ $-$ reacted mol$_{CH_4}$ = final mol$_{CH_4}$

final mol$_{CH_4}$, V, T $\rightarrow$ final P_{CH_4} and reacted mol$_{NO}$ $\rightarrow$ reacted mol$_{O_2}$ then

$$PV = nRT \qquad \frac{5 \text{ mol O}_2}{5 \text{ mol NO}}$$

initial mol$_{O_2}$, reacted mol$_{O_2}$ $\rightarrow$ final mol$_{O_2}$ then final mol$_{O_2}$, V, T $\rightarrow$ final P_{O_2} and

initial mol$_{O_2}$ $-$ reacted mol$_{O_2}$ = final mol$_{O_2}$ $\qquad PV = nRT$

final mol$_{NO}$, V, T $\rightarrow$ final P_{NO} and theoretical mol$_{CO_2}$ from NO $\rightarrow$ final mol$_{CO_2}$

$PV = nRT$ 90.0%

final mol$_{CO_2}$, V, T $\rightarrow$ P_{CO_2} then final mol$_{CO_2}$ $\rightarrow$ mol$_{H_2O}$, V, T $\rightarrow$ P_{H_2O} and

$$PV = nRT \qquad \frac{1 \text{ mol H}_2O}{1 \text{ mol CO}_2} \qquad PV = nRT$$

final mol$_{CO_2}$ $\rightarrow$ mol$_{NO_2}$ then mol$_{NO_2}$, V, T $\rightarrow$ P_{NO_2} and final mol$_{CO_2}$ $\rightarrow$ mol$_{OH}$ then

$$\frac{1 \text{ mol NO}_2}{1 \text{ mol CO}_2} \qquad PV = nRT \qquad \frac{2 \text{ mol OH}}{1 \text{ mol CO}_2}$$

mol$_{OH}$, V, T $\rightarrow$ P_{OH} finaly P_{CH_4}, P_{O_2}, P_{NO}, P_{CO_2}, P_{H_2O}, P_{NO_2}, P_{OH} $\rightarrow$ $P_{T \text{ total}}$

$PV = nRT$ $\qquad$ P$_{Total}$ = $\sum P$

Solution: CH$_4$: $155 \text{ mL} \times \dfrac{1 \text{ L}}{1000 \text{ mL}} \times \dfrac{1 \text{ mol CH}_4}{22.414 \text{ L}} \times \dfrac{1 \text{ mol CO}_2}{1 \text{ mol CH}_4} = 0.00691532 \text{ mol CO}_2$,

O$_2$: $885 \text{ mL} \times \dfrac{1 \text{ L}}{1000 \text{ mL}} \times \dfrac{1 \text{ mol O}_2}{22.414 \text{ L}} = 0.0394843 \text{ mol O}_2 \times \dfrac{1 \text{ mol CO}_2}{5 \text{ mol O}_2} = 0.00789686 \text{ mol CO}_2$

NO: $55.5 \text{ mL} \times \dfrac{1 \text{ L}}{1000 \text{ mL}} \times \dfrac{1 \text{ mol NO}}{22.414 \text{ L}} \times \dfrac{1 \text{ mol CO}_2}{5 \text{ mol NO}} = 0.000495226 \text{ mol CO}_2$.

0.000495226 mol CO$_2$ is the smallest yield, so NO is the limiting reagent.

$55.5 \text{ mL} \times \dfrac{1 \text{ L}}{1000 \text{ mL}} \times \dfrac{1 \text{ mol NO}}{22.414 \text{ L}} = 0.00247613 \text{ mol NO}$

reacted mol NO = $0.900 \times$ mol NO = 0.900×0.00247613 mol NO = 0.00222852 mol NO,

unreacted mol NO = $0.100 \times$ mol NO = 0.100×0.00247613 mol NO = 0.000247613 mol NO,

$0.00222852 \text{ mol NO} \times \dfrac{1 \text{ mol CH}_4}{5 \text{ mol NO}} = 0.000445704 \text{ mol CH}_4$ reacted,

0.00691532 mol CH$_4$ $-$ 0.000445704 mol CH$_4$ reacted = 0.00646962 mol CH$_4$ then $PV = nRT$

Rearrange to solve for P. $P = \dfrac{nRT}{V} = \dfrac{0.00646962 \text{ mol} \times 0.08206 \dfrac{\text{L} \cdot \text{atm}}{\text{mol} \cdot \text{K}} \times 275 \text{ K}}{2.0 \text{ L}} = 0.0730$ atm CH$_4$ remaining

$0.00222852 \text{ mol NO} \times \dfrac{5 \text{ mol O}_2}{5 \text{ mol NO}} = 0.00222852 \text{ mol O}_2$ reacted

0.0394843 mol O$_2$ $-$ 0.00222852 mol O$_2$ reacted = 0.0372558 mol O$_2$

$P = \dfrac{nRT}{V} = \dfrac{0.0372558 \text{ mol} \times 0.08206 \dfrac{\text{L} \cdot \text{atm}}{\text{mol} \cdot \text{K}} \times 275 \text{ K}}{2.0 \text{ L}} = 0.420$ atm O$_2$ remaining

$$P = \frac{nRT}{V} = \frac{0.000247613 \text{ mol} \times 0.08206 \dfrac{L \cdot atm}{mol \cdot K} \times 275 \text{ K}}{2.0 \text{ L}} = 0.00279 \text{ atm NO remaining}$$

$$0.00222852 \text{ mol NO} \times \frac{1 \text{ mol } CO_2}{5 \text{ mol NO}} = 0.000445704 \text{ mol } CO_2$$

$$P = \frac{nRT}{V} = \frac{0.000445704 \text{ mol} \times 0.08206 \dfrac{L \cdot atm}{mol \cdot K} \times 275 \text{ K}}{2.0 \text{ L}} = 0.00503 \text{ atm } CO_2 \text{ produced}$$

$$0.00222852 \text{ mol NO} \times \frac{1 \text{ mol } H_2O}{5 \text{ mol NO}} = 0.000445704 \text{ mol } H_2O$$

$$P = \frac{nRT}{V} = \frac{0.000445704 \text{ mol} \times 0.08206 \dfrac{L \cdot atm}{mol \cdot K} \times 275 \text{ K}}{2.0 \text{ L}} = 0.00503 \text{ atm } H_2O \text{ produced}$$

$$0.00222852 \text{ mol NO} \times \frac{5 \text{ mol } NO_2}{5 \text{ mol NO}} = 0.00222852 \text{ mol } NO_2$$

$$P = \frac{nRT}{V} = \frac{0.00222852 \text{ mol} \times 0.08206 \dfrac{L \cdot atm}{mol \cdot K} \times 275 \text{ K}}{2.0 \text{ L}} = 0.0251 \text{ atm } NO_2 \text{ produced}$$

$$0.00222852 \text{ mol NO} \times \frac{2 \text{ mol OH}}{5 \text{ mol NO}} = 0.000891408 \text{ mol OH}$$

$$P = \frac{nRT}{V} = \frac{0.000891408 \text{ mol} \times 0.08206 \dfrac{L \cdot atm}{mol \cdot K} \times 275 \text{ K}}{2.0 \text{ L}} = 0.0101 \text{ atm OH produced}$$

$$P_{Total} = \sum P$$
$$= 0.0730 \text{ atm} + 0.420 \text{ atm} + 0.00279 \text{ atm} + 0.00503 \text{ atm} + 0.00503 \text{ atm} + 0.0251 \text{ atm} + 0.0101 \text{ atm}$$
$$= 0.541 \text{ atm}$$

Check: The units (atm) are correct. The magnitude of the answers is reasonable. The limiting reagent has the lowest pressure. The product pressures are in line with the ratios of the stoichiometric coefficients.

5.100   **Given:** He and air   **Find:** % He diffused through balloon wall
      Conceptual Plan: $\mathcal{M}(N_2), \mathcal{M}(O_2) \rightarrow \mathcal{M}(air)$ then $\mathcal{M}(air), \mathcal{M}(He)$, % air diffused $\rightarrow$ % He diffused

$$\mathcal{M}(air) = \chi(N_2)\mathcal{M}(N_2) + \chi(O_2)\mathcal{M}(O_2) \qquad \frac{Rate(He)}{Rate(air)} = \sqrt{\frac{\mathcal{M}(air)}{\mathcal{M}(He)}}$$

      Solution: $\mathcal{M}(air) = \chi(N_2)\mathcal{M}(N_2) + \chi(O_2)\mathcal{M}(O_2) = \left(\dfrac{4}{5} \times 28.02 \text{ g/mol}\right) + \left(\dfrac{1}{5} \times 32.00 \text{ g/mol}\right) = 28.82 \text{ g/mol}$

$\dfrac{Rate(He)}{Rate(air)} = \sqrt{\dfrac{\mathcal{M}(air)}{\mathcal{M}(He)}}$ Because rate $\propto$ % diffused, substitute % diffused for rate and rearrange to solve for % He

diffused. % He diffused $= $ % air diffused $\sqrt{\dfrac{\mathcal{M}(air)}{\mathcal{M}(He)}} = 5.0\% \sqrt{\dfrac{28.82 \text{ g/mol}}{4.003 \text{ g/mol}}} = 13\%$

Check: The units (%) are correct. The magnitude of the answer (>5%) makes sense because He is lighter, so it has the higher diffusion rate.

5.101   **Given:** $P_{CH_4} + P_{C_2H_4} = 0.53 \text{ atm}$ and $P_{CO_2} + P_{H_2O} = 2.2 \text{ atm}$ **Find:** χ_{CH_4}
      Conceptual Plan: Write balanced reactions to determine change in moles of gas for CH_4 and C_2H_6.

$$2 \, CH_4(g) + 4 \, O_2(g) \rightarrow 4 \, H_2O(g) + 2 \, CO_2(g) \text{ and } 2 \, C_2H_6(g) + 7 \, O_2(g) \rightarrow 6 \, H_2O(g) + 4 \, CO_2(g) \text{ thus} \qquad \frac{6 \text{ mol gases}}{2 \text{ mol } CH_4} \qquad \frac{10 \text{ mol gases}}{2 \text{ mol } C_2H_6}$$

      Write expression for final pressure, substituting in data given $\rightarrow \chi_{CH_4}$.

$$\chi_{CH_4} = \frac{n_{CH_4}}{n_{CH_4} + n_{C_2H_6}} \text{ and } \chi_{C_2H_6} = 1 - \chi_{CH_4}$$

$$P_{CH_4} = \chi_{CH_4} P_{Total} \qquad P_{C_2H_6} = \chi_{C_2H_6} P_{Total} \qquad P_{Final} = \left(\chi_{CH_4} P_{Total} \times \frac{6 \text{ mol gases}}{2 \text{ mol } CH_4}\right) + \left((1 - \chi_{CH_4}) P_{Total} \times \frac{10 \text{ mol gases}}{2 \text{ mol } C_2H_6}\right)$$

Solution:

$$P_{\text{Final}} = \left(\chi_{CH_4} \times 0.53 \text{ atm} \times \frac{6 \text{ mol gases}}{2 \text{ mol } CH_4} \right) + \left((1 - \chi_{CH_4}) \times 0.53 \text{ atm} \times \frac{10 \text{ mol gases}}{2 \text{ mol } C_2H_6} \right) = 2.2 \text{ atm}$$

Substitute as above for $\chi_{C_2H_6}$, then to solve for $\chi_{CH_4} = 0.42$.

Check: The units (none) are correct. The magnitude of the answer (0.42) makes sense because if it were all methane, the final pressure would have been 1.59 atm and if it were all ethane, the final pressure would have been 2.65 atm. Because we are closer to the latter pressure, we expect the mole fraction of methane to be less than 0.5.

5.102   **Given:** $P_{C_2H_2} = 7.8$ kPa initially, $P_{C_2H_2} + P_{C_6H_6} = 3.9$ kPa   **Find:** fraction of C_2H_2 reacted
          Conceptual Plan: Write balanced reaction to determine change in moles of gas.

$3 C_2H_2(g) \rightarrow C_6H_6(g)$ thus $\dfrac{1 \text{ mol } C_6H_6}{3 \text{ mol } C_2H_2 \text{ reacted}}$ Because $P_{C_2H_2} \alpha\, n_{C_2H_2}$, the pressure will drop 2 kPa for every 3 kPa of ethylene that reacts.

$P_{\text{initial}}, P_{\text{final}} \rightarrow P_{\text{drop}}$ write expression for reacted $P_{C_2H_2}$, then

$$P_{\text{drop}} = P_{\text{initial}} - P_{\text{final}} \qquad\qquad \text{reacted } P_{C_2H_2} = \Delta P \, \frac{3 \text{ kPa } C_2H_2 \text{ reacted}}{2 \text{ kPa pressure drop}}$$

reacted $P_{C_2H_2}$, initial $P_{C_2H_2} \rightarrow$ % C_2H_2 reacted

$$\%C_2H_2 \text{ reacted} = \frac{\text{reacted } P_{C_2H_2}}{\text{initial } P_{C_2H_2}} \times 100\%$$

Solution: $P_{\text{drop}} = P_{\text{initial}} - P_{\text{final}} = 7.8 \text{ kPa} - 3.9 \text{ kPa} = 3.9 \text{ kPa}$,

$$\text{reacted } P_{C_2H_2} = \Delta P \, \frac{3 \text{ kPa } C_2H_2 \text{ reacted}}{2 \text{ kPa pressure drop}} = 3.9 \text{ kPa} \times \frac{3 \text{ kPa } C_2H_2 \text{ reacted}}{2 \text{ kPa pressure drop}} = 5.85 \text{ kPa}$$

$$\%C_2H_2 \text{ reacted} = \frac{\text{reacted } P_{C_2H_2}}{\text{initial } P_{C_2H_2}} \times 100\% = \frac{5.85 \text{ kPa}}{7.8 \text{ kPa}} \times 100\% = 75\%$$

Check: The units (%) are correct. The magnitude of the answer (75%) makes sense because if all of the ethylene reacted, the final pressure would have been 2.6 kPa. Because we are most of the way to that, we expect the amount reacted to be higher than 50%.

5.103   **Given:** $V = 10$ L, 0.10 mol H_2 initially, $T = 3000$ K, and $P_{\text{final}} = 3.0$ atm   **Find:** P_H
          Conceptual Plan: Write balanced reaction to determine change in moles of gas.

$H_2(g) \rightarrow 2 H(g)$ thus $\dfrac{2 \text{ mol } H}{1 \text{ mol } H_2 \text{ reacted}}$. Since $P_{H_2} \alpha\, n_{H_2}$, the pressure will increase 1 atm for every 1 atm of H_2 that reacts.

$n, T, V \rightarrow P_{\text{initial}}$ $P_{\text{initial}}, P_{\text{final}} \rightarrow \Delta P$ write expression for P_H

$$PV = nRT \qquad\qquad \Delta P = P_{\text{final}} - P_{\text{initial}} \qquad\qquad P_H = \Delta P \, \frac{2 \text{ mol } H}{1 \text{ mol } H_2 \text{ reacted}}$$

Solution: $PV = nRT$ Rearrange to solve for P.

$$P = \frac{nRT}{V} = \frac{0.10 \text{ mol} \times 0.08206 \, \dfrac{L \cdot \text{atm}}{\text{mol} \cdot K} \times 3000 \, K}{10 \, L} = 2.4618 \text{ atm } H_2$$

$$\Delta P = P_{\text{final}} - P_{\text{initial}} = 3.0 \text{ atm} - 2.4618 \text{ atm} = 0.5382 \text{ atm and}$$

$$P_H = \Delta P \, \frac{2 \text{ mol } H}{1 \text{ atm reacted}} = 0.5382 \text{ atm} \times \frac{2 \text{ mol } H}{1 \text{ atm reacted}} = 1.0764 \text{ atm} = 1.1 \text{ atm } H$$

Check: The units (atm) are correct. The magnitude of the answer (1 atm) makes sense because if all of the hydrogen dissociated, the final pressure would have been 5 atm. Because we are closer to the initial pressure than this maximum pressure, less than half of the hydrogen has dissociated.

5.104   **Given:** $2 NH_3(g) \rightarrow N_2(g) + 3 H_2(g)$; $N_2H_4(g) \rightarrow N_2(g) + 2 H_2(g)$; initially $P = 0.50$ atm, $T = 300$ K; finally
          $P = 4.5$ atm, $T = 1200$ K   **Find:** N_2H_4 percent initially
          Conceptual Plan: $P_{\text{initial}}, T_{\text{initial}}, T_{\text{final}} \rightarrow P_{\text{final}}$ then determine change in moles of gas

$$\frac{P_{\text{initial}}}{T_{\text{initial}}} = \frac{P_{\text{final}}}{T_{\text{final}}} \qquad\qquad \frac{2 \text{ atm added gas}}{2 \text{ atm } NH_3 \text{ reacted}} \text{ and } \frac{2 \text{ atm added gas}}{1 \text{ atm } N_2H_4 \text{ reacted}}$$

$P_1, P_2 \rightarrow \Delta P$ write expression for ΔP then solve for $P_{1N_2H_4}$ and P_{1NH_3} finally $P_{1N_2H_4}, P_{1NH_3} \rightarrow \%N_2H_4$

$$\Delta P = P_2 - P_1 \quad \Delta P = P_{1NH_3} \frac{2 \text{ atm added gas}}{2 \text{ atm reacted}} + P_{1N_2H_4} \frac{2 \text{ atm added gas}}{1 \text{ atm reacted}} \text{ where } P_{1,1200\,K} = P_{1NH_3} + P_{1N_2H_4} \quad \%N_2H_4 = \frac{P_{N_2H_4}}{P_{N_2H_4} + P_{NH_3}} \times 100\%$$

Solution: $\dfrac{P_{initial}}{T_{initial}} = \dfrac{P_{final}}{T_{final}}$ Rearrange to solve for P_{final}. $P_2 = P_1 \times \dfrac{T_2}{T_1} = 0.50 \text{ atm} \times \dfrac{1200 \text{ K}}{300 \text{ K}} = 2.0 \text{ atm}$ if no reaction occurred.

$\Delta P = P_{final} - P_{initial} = 4.5 \text{ atm} - 2.0 \text{ atm} = 2.5 \text{ atm}$, and $P_{1,1200 \text{ K}} = 2.0 \text{ atm} = P_{1NH_3} + P_{1N_2H_4}$ or $P_{1NH_3} = 2.0 \text{ atm} - P_{1N_2H_4}$.

Substitute this into $\Delta P = P_{1NH_2} \dfrac{2 \text{ atm added gas}}{2 \text{ atm reacted}} + P_{1N_2H_4} \dfrac{2 \text{ atm added gas}}{1 \text{ atm reacted}}$ and solve for $P_{1N_2H_4}$.

$\Delta P = 2.5 \text{ atm} = (2.0 \text{ atm} - P_{1N_2H_4}) \dfrac{2 \text{ atm added gas}}{2 \text{ atm reacted}} + P_{1N_2H_4} \dfrac{2 \text{ atm added gas}}{1 \text{ atm reacted}} \rightarrow$

$P_{1N_2H_4} = 2.5 \text{ atm} - 2.0 \text{ atm} = 0.5 \text{ atm}$ and $P_{NH_3} = 2.0 \text{ atm} - 0.5 \text{ atm} = 1.5 \text{ atm}$; finally

$\%N_2H_4 = \dfrac{P_{N_2H_4}}{P_{N_2H_4} + P_{NH_3}} \times 100\% = \dfrac{0.5 \text{ atm}}{0.5 \text{ atm} + 1.5 \text{ atm}} \times 100\% = \underline{2}5\% \text{ N}_2\text{H}_4 = 30\% \text{ N}_2\text{H}_4$

Check: The units (%) are correct. The magnitude of the answer (30%) makes sense because if it were all N_2H_4, the final pressure would have been 6 atm. Because we are closer to the initial pressure than this maximum pressure, less than half of the gas is N_2H_4.

5.105   **Given:** CO gas; initial: $V = 0.48$ L, $P = 1.0$ atm, and $T = 275$ K; **final:** $V = 1.3$ L   **Find:** final gas density
Conceptual Plan: $P, V, T \rightarrow n \rightarrow m$ then $m, V \rightarrow d$

$$PV = nRT \qquad \frac{28.01 \text{ g}}{1 \text{ mol}} \qquad\qquad d = m/V$$

Solution: $PV = nRT$ Rearrange to solve for n. $n = \dfrac{PV}{RT} = \dfrac{1.0 \text{ atm} \times 0.48 \text{ L}}{0.08206 \dfrac{\text{L} \cdot \text{atm}}{\text{mol} \cdot \text{K}} \times 275 \text{ K}} = 0.02\underline{1}27047 \text{ mol}$

$0.02\underline{1}27047 \text{ mol} \times \dfrac{28.01 \text{ g}}{1 \text{ mol}} = 0.59\underline{5}7859 \text{ g}$ then $d = \dfrac{m}{V} = \dfrac{0.59\underline{5}7859 \text{ g}}{1.3 \text{ L}} = 0.45\underline{8}2968 \text{ g/L} = 0.46 \text{ g/L}$

Check: The units (g/L) are correct. The magnitude of the answer (0.5 g/L) makes sense because this is typical for a gas density.

5.106   **Given:** $2 \text{ CO}_2(g) \rightarrow 2 \text{ CO}(g) + \text{O}_2(g)$; initially $P = 10.0$ atm, $T = 701$ K; finally $P = 22.5$ atm, $T = 1401$ K
Find: mole percent decomposed
Conceptual Plan: $P_{initial}, T_{initial}, T_{final} \rightarrow P_{final}$ then determine change in moles of gas

$$\frac{P_{initial}}{T_{initial}} = \frac{P_{final}}{T_{final}} \qquad\qquad \frac{1 \text{ atm added gas}}{2 \text{ atm CO}_2 \text{ reacted}}$$

$P_1, P_2 \rightarrow \Delta P$ **write expression for** ΔP **then solve for** $P_{CO_2 \text{reacted}}$ **finally**

$$\Delta P = P_2 - P_1 \qquad \Delta P = P_{CO_2 \text{ reacted}} \frac{1 \text{ atm added gas}}{2 \text{ atm CO}_2 \text{ reacted}}$$

$P_{final}, P_{CO_2 \text{ reacted}} \rightarrow \% \text{ CO}_2$ **decomposed**

$$\%CO_2 \text{ decomposed} = \frac{P_{CO_2 \text{ reacted}}}{P_{final}} \times 100\%$$

Solution: $\dfrac{P_{initial}}{T_{initial}} = \dfrac{P_{final}}{T_{final}}$ Rearrange to solve for P_{final}. $P_2 = P_1 \times \dfrac{T_2}{T_1} = 10.0 \text{ atm} \times \dfrac{1401 \text{ K}}{701 \text{ K}} = 19.98\underline{5}735 \text{ atm}$

$\Delta P = P_{final} - P_{initial} = 22.5 \text{ atm} - 19.98\underline{5}735 \text{ atm} = 2.51\underline{4}265 \text{ atm}$,

$\Delta P = P_{CO_2 \text{ reacted}} \dfrac{1 \text{ atm added gas}}{2 \text{ atm CO}_2 \text{ reacted}}$ or the pressure increases 1 atm for each 2 atm of gas decomposed, so

$5.0\underline{2}853$ atm decomposes and then

$\%CO_2 \text{ decomposed} = \dfrac{P_{CO_2 \text{ reacted}}}{P_{final}} \times 100\% = \dfrac{5.0\underline{2}853 \text{ atm}}{19.98\underline{5}735 \text{ atm}} \times 100\% = 2\underline{5}.1606\% \text{ CO}_2 \text{ decomposed} =$

$25\% \text{ CO}_2 \text{ decomposed}$

Check: The units (%) are correct. The magnitude of the answer (25%) makes sense because if all of the gas decomposed, the final pressure would have been 40 atm. Because we are much closer to the initial pressure than this maximum pressure, much less than half of the gas decomposed.

Conceptual Problems

5.107   Because the passengers have more mass than the balloon, they have more momentum than the balloon. The passengers will continue to travel in their original direction longer. The car is slowing, so the relative position of the passengers is to move forward and the balloon to move backwards. The opposite happens upon acceleration.

5.108   B is the limiting reactant (2.0 L of B requires 1.0 L A to completely react). The final container will have 0.5 L A and 2.0 L C, so the final volume will be 2.5 L. The change will be ((2.5 L/3.5 L) × 100%) − 100% = −29%.

5.109   Because each gas will occupy 22.4 L/mole at STP and we have 2 moles of gas, we will have a volume of 44.828 L.

5.110   (a)   False—All gases have the same average kinetic energy at the same temperature.

(b)   False—The gases will have the same partial pressures because we have the same number of moles of each.

(c)   False—The average velocity of the B molecules will be less than that of the A molecules because the Bs are heavier.

(d)   True—Since B molecules are heavier, they will contribute more to the density ($d = m/V$).

5.111 Br_2 would deviate the most from ideal behavior because it is the largest of the three.

5.112   When the volume of a gas is cut in half, the pressure doubles. When the temperature of a gas in Kelvins doubles, the pressure doubles. The net effect is that the pressure increases by a factor of four.

5.113   Because He has the lowest molar mass, it will have the most number of moles and the greatest volume.

5.114   Because the velocity is inversely proportional to the molar mass, the tails on the helium are $\sqrt{20/4} = $ ~2.2 times as long as those for neon and $\sqrt{84/4} = $ ~4.6 times as long as those for krypton.

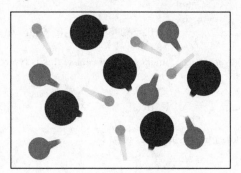

Questions for Group Work

5.115   Boyle's law states that the volume of the gas varies inversely to the pressure on the gas, while temperature and number of moles are kept constant ($V \propto 1/P$ or $P_1V_1 = P_2V_2$). Charles's law states that the volume of a gas is directly proportional to the temperature of the gas, while pressure and number of moles are kept constant ($V \propto T$ or $V_1/T_1 = V_2/T_2$). All temperatures must be in degree Kelvin when used in math calculations. Avogadro's law states that the volume of a gas is directly proportional to the number of moles of the gas, while pressure and temperature are kept constant ($V \propto n$ or $V_1/n_1 = V_2/n_2$).

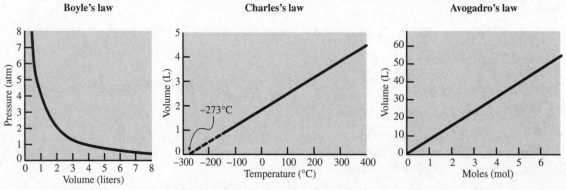

5.116   Ideal gas law: $PV = nRT$.
Rearranging, we can get: $P = nRT/V$; $V = nRT/P$; $n = PV/RT$; and $T = PV/nR$.

5.117   (a) $2 H_2O_2(aq) \rightarrow 2 H_2O(l) + O_2(g)$
(b)   Table 5.3 states that $P_{H_2O} = 23.78$ mmHg
(c) $P_{Total} = P_{H_2O} + P_{O_2}$ Rearrange to solve for P_{O_2}.
$P_{O_2} = P_{Total} - P_{H_2O} = 763.8$ mmHg $- 23.78$ mmHg $= 740.\underline{0}2$ mmHg
(d) $P_{O_2} = 740.\underline{0}2 \text{ mmHg} \times \dfrac{1 \text{ atm}}{760 \text{ mmHg}} = 0.973710526$ atm; $V = 49.5 \text{ mL} \times \dfrac{1 \text{ L}}{1000 \text{ mL}} = 0.0495$ L;

$T = 25.0\,°C + 273.15 = 298.\underline{1}5$ K.

$n_{O_2} = \dfrac{PV}{RT} = \dfrac{0.973710526 \text{ atm} \times 0.0495 \text{ L}}{0.08206 \dfrac{\text{L}\cdot\text{atm}}{\text{mol}\cdot\text{K}} \times 298.\underline{1}5 \text{ K}} = 0.00\underline{1}97001139 \text{ mol } O_2$

(e) $0.00\underline{1}97001139 \text{ mol } O_2 \times \dfrac{2 \text{ mol } H_2O_2}{1 \text{ mol } O_2} \times \dfrac{34.02 \text{ g } H_2O_2}{1 \text{ mol } H_2O_2} = 0.13\underline{4}02381 \text{ g } H_2O_2 = 0.1340 \text{ g } H_2O_2$

(f) $5.00 \text{ mL} \times \dfrac{1 \text{ L}}{1000 \text{ mL}} = 0.0500$ L; $0.00\underline{1}97001139 \text{ mol } O_2 \times \dfrac{2 \text{ mol } H_2O_2}{1 \text{ mol } O_2} = 0.00\underline{3}94002278 \text{ mol } H_2O_2$

$[H_2O_2] = \dfrac{0.00\underline{3}94002278 \text{ mol } H_2O_2}{0.00500 \text{ L}} = 0.788 \text{ M } H_2O_2$

(g)   Perhaps the most difficult part was keeping track of which volumes were liquids and which were gases.

5.118   All of the gases are in the same container, so they have the same temperature and the same average kinetic energy. If there are equal amounts (in moles) of He, Ar, and Kr, then the mass ratios are $4.003 : 39.95 : 83.80$ for He : Ar : Kr, respectively. This is roughly a $1 : 10 : 20$ mass ratio for He : Ar : Kr, respectively. The average velocities will be inversely proportional to the square root of the molar masses. Thus, helium will have the highest average velocity; argon's average velocity will be about a third of helium's average velocity; and krypton's average velocity will be between a fifth and a quarter of helium's average velocity. All three gasses have a common number of particles, temperature, and average kinetic energy. All of the other properties will be different.

5.119   For an ideal gas, $P = \dfrac{nRT}{V} = \dfrac{1.000 \text{ mol} \times 0.08206 \dfrac{\text{L}\cdot\text{atm}}{\text{mol}\cdot\text{K}} \times 298 \text{ K}}{0.500 \text{ L}} = 48.\underline{9}0776$ atm

For van der Waals gas, $\left(P + \dfrac{an^2}{V^2} \right)(V - nb) = nRT$ Rearrange to solve for P.

$P = \dfrac{nRT}{(V - nb)} - \dfrac{an^2}{V^2}$ For He, $a = 0.0342$ L^2 atm/mol^2 and $b = 0.02370$ L/mol from Table 5.4:

$P = \dfrac{1.000 \text{ mol} \times 0.08206 \dfrac{\text{L}\cdot\text{atm}}{\text{mol}\cdot\text{K}} \times 298 \text{ K}}{0.500 \text{ L} - \left(1.000 \text{ mol} \times 0.02370 \dfrac{\text{L}}{\text{mol}} \right)} - \dfrac{0.0342 \dfrac{\text{L}^2 \cdot \text{atm}}{\text{mol}^2} \times (1.000 \text{ mol})^2}{(0.500 \text{ L})^2} = 51.\underline{2}05 \text{ atm} = 51.2 \text{ atm}$

The pressure is higher than the ideal gas because there are weak intermolecular forces and the atoms are small.
For Ne, $a = 0.211$ L^2 atm/mol^2 and $b = 0.0171$ L/mol from Table 5.4:

$P = \dfrac{1.000 \text{ mol} \times 0.08206 \dfrac{\text{L}\cdot\text{atm}}{\text{mol}\cdot\text{K}} \times 298 \text{ K}}{0.500 \text{ L} - \left(1.000 \text{ mol} \times 0.0171 \dfrac{\text{L}}{\text{mol}} \right)} - \dfrac{0.211 \dfrac{\text{L}^2 \cdot \text{atm}}{\text{mol}^2} \times (1.000 \text{ mol})^2}{(0.500 \text{ L})^2} = 49.\underline{7}96 \text{ atm} = 49.8 \text{ atm}$

The pressure is higher than the ideal gas because there are weak intermolecular forces and the atoms are small.

For H_2, $a = 0.244$ L^2 atm/mol^2 and $b = 0.0266$ L/mol from Table 5.4:

$$P = \frac{1.000 \text{ mol} \times 0.08206 \frac{\text{L} \cdot \text{atm}}{\text{mol} \cdot \text{K}} \times 298 \text{ K}}{0.500 \text{ L} - \left(1.000 \text{ mol} \times 0.0266 \frac{\text{L}}{\text{mol}}\right)} - \frac{0.244 \frac{\text{L}^2 \cdot \text{atm}}{\text{mol}^2} \times (1.000 \text{ mol})^2}{(0.500 \text{ L})^2} = 50.680 \text{ atm} = 50.7 \text{ atm}$$

The pressure is higher than the ideal gas because there are weak intermolecular forces and the atoms are small.
For CH_4, $a = 2.25$ L^2 atm/mol^2 and $b = 0.0428$ L/mol from Table 5.4:

$$P = \frac{1.000 \text{ mol} \times 0.08206 \frac{\text{L} \cdot \text{atm}}{\text{mol} \cdot \text{K}} \times 298 \text{ K}}{0.500 \text{ L} - \left(1.000 \text{ mol} \times 0.0428 \frac{\text{L}}{\text{mol}}\right)} - \frac{2.25 \frac{\text{L}^2 \cdot \text{atm}}{\text{mol}^2} \times (1.000 \text{ mol})^2}{(0.500 \text{ L})^2} = 44.486 \text{ atm} = 44.5 \text{ atm}$$

The pressure is lower than the ideal gas because there are stronger intermolecular forces and the atoms are larger.
For CO_2, $a = 3.59$ L^2 atm/mol^2 and $b = 0.0427$ L/mol from Table 5.4:

$$P = \frac{1.000 \text{ mol} \times 0.08206 \frac{\text{L} \cdot \text{atm}}{\text{mol} \cdot \text{K}} \times 298 \text{ K}}{0.500 \text{ L} - \left(1.000 \text{ mol} \times 0.0427 \frac{\text{L}}{\text{mol}}\right)} - \frac{3.59 \frac{\text{L}^2 \cdot \text{atm}}{\text{mol}^2} \times (1.000 \text{ mol})^2}{(0.500 \text{ L})^2} = 39.114 \text{ atm} = 39.1 \text{ atm}$$

The pressure is lower than the ideal gas because there are stronger intermolecular forces and the atoms are larger.

6 Thermochemistry

Energy Units

6.1   (a)   **Given:** 3.55×10^4 J   **Find:** cal

             Conceptual Plan: J → cal

$$\frac{1\ \text{cal}}{4.184\ \text{J}}$$

             Solution: $3.55 \times 10^4\ \text{J} \times \dfrac{1\ \text{cal}}{4.184\ \text{J}} = 8.48 \times 10^3\ \text{cal}$

             Check: The units (cal) are correct. The magnitude of the answer (8000) makes physical sense because a calorie is larger than a joule, so the answer decreases.

    (b)   **Given:** 1025 Cal   **Find:** J

             Conceptual Plan: Cal → J

$$\frac{4184\ \text{J}}{1\ \text{Cal}}$$

             Solution: $1025\ \text{Cal} \times \dfrac{4184\ \text{J}}{1\ \text{Cal}} = 4.289 \times 10^6\ \text{J}$

             Check: The units (J) are correct. The magnitude of the answer (10^6) makes physical sense because a Calorie is much larger than a joule, so the answer increases.

    (c)   **Given:** 355 kJ   **Find:** cal

             Conceptual Plan: kJ → J → cal

$$\frac{1000\ \text{J}}{1\ \text{kJ}} \quad \frac{1\ \text{cal}}{4.184\ \text{J}}$$

             Solution: $355\ \text{kJ} \times \dfrac{1000\ \text{J}}{1\ \text{kJ}} \times \dfrac{1\ \text{cal}}{4.184\ \text{J}} = 8.48 \times 10^4\ \text{cal}$

             Check: The units (cal) are correct. The magnitude of the answer (10^4) makes physical sense because a calorie is much smaller than a kJ, so the answer increases.

    (d)   **Given:** 125 kWh   **Find:** J

             Conceptual Plan: kWh → J

$$\frac{3.60 \times 10^6\ \text{J}}{1\ \text{kWh}}$$

             Solution: $125\ \text{kWh} \times \dfrac{3.60 \times 10^6\ \text{J}}{1\ \text{kWh}} = 4.50 \times 10^8\ \text{J}$

             Check: The units (J) are correct. The magnitude of the answer (10^8) makes physical sense because a kWh is much larger than a joule, so the answer increases.

6.2   (a)   **Given:** 1.58×10^3 kJ   **Find:** kcal

             Conceptual Plan: kJ → J → cal → kcal

$$\frac{1000\ \text{J}}{1\ \text{kJ}} \quad \frac{1\ \text{cal}}{4.184\ \text{J}} \quad \frac{1\ \text{kcal}}{1000\ \text{cal}}$$

             Solution: $1.58 \times 10^3\ \text{kJ} \times \dfrac{1000\ \text{J}}{1\ \text{kJ}} \times \dfrac{1\ \text{cal}}{4.184\ \text{J}} \times \dfrac{1\ \text{kcal}}{1000\ \text{cal}} = 3.78 \times 10^2\ \text{kcal} = 378\ \text{kcal}$

             Check: The units (kcal) are correct. The magnitude of the answer (400) makes physical sense because a kcal is larger than a kJ, so the answer decreases.

177

(b) **Given:** 865 cal   **Find:** kJ
Conceptual Plan: cal → J → kJ

$$\frac{4.184 \text{ J}}{1 \text{ cal}} \quad \frac{1 \text{ kJ}}{1000 \text{ J}}$$

Solution: $865 \text{ cal} \times \dfrac{4.184 \text{ J}}{1 \text{ cal}} \times \dfrac{1 \text{ kJ}}{1000 \text{ J}} = 3.62 \text{ kJ}$

Check: The units (kJ) are correct. The magnitude of the answer (4) makes physical sense because a kJ is much larger than a cal, so the answer decreases.

(c) **Given:** 1.93×10^4 J   **Find:** Cal
Conceptual Plan: J → Cal

$$\frac{1 \text{ Cal}}{4184 \text{ J}}$$

Solution: $1.93 \times 10^4 \text{ J} \times \dfrac{1 \text{ Cal}}{4184 \text{ J}} = 4.61 \text{ Cal}$

Check: The units (Cal) are correct. The magnitude of the answer (5) makes physical sense because a J is much smaller than a Cal, so the answer decreases.

(d) **Given:** 1.8×10^4 kJ   **Find:** kWh
Conceptual Plan: kJ → J → kWh

$$\frac{1000 \text{ J}}{1 \text{ kJ}} \quad \frac{1 \text{ kWh}}{3.60 \times 10^6 \text{ J}}$$

Solution: $1.8 \times 10^4 \text{ kJ} \times \dfrac{1000 \text{ J}}{1 \text{ kJ}} \times \dfrac{1 \text{ kWh}}{3.60 \times 10^6 \text{ J}} = 5.0 \text{ kWh}$

Check: The units (kWh) are correct. The magnitude of the answer (5) makes physical sense because a kWh is much larger than a joule, so the answer decreases.

6.3   (a) **Given:** 2285 Cal   **Find:** J
Conceptual Plan: Cal → J

$$\frac{4184 \text{ J}}{1 \text{ Cal}}$$

Solution: $2285 \text{ Cal} \times \dfrac{4184 \text{ J}}{1 \text{ Cal}} = 9.560 \times 10^6 \text{ J}$

Check: The units (J) are correct. The magnitude of the answer (10^7) makes physical sense because a Calorie is much larger than a joule, so the answer increases.

(b) **Given:** 2285 Cal   **Find:** kJ
Conceptual Plan: Cal → J → kWh

$$\frac{4184 \text{ J}}{1 \text{ Cal}} \quad \frac{1 \text{ kJ}}{1000 \text{ J}}$$

Solution: $2285 \text{ Cal} \times \dfrac{4184 \text{ J}}{1 \text{ Cal}} \times \dfrac{1 \text{ kJ}}{1000 \text{ J}} = 9.560 \times 10^3 \text{ kJ}$

Check: The units (kJ) are correct. The magnitude of the answer (10^4) makes physical sense because a Calorie is larger than a kJ, so the answer increases.

(c) **Given:** 2285 Cal   **Find:** kWh
Conceptual Plan: Cal → J → kWh

$$\frac{4184 \text{ J}}{1 \text{ Cal}} \quad \frac{1 \text{ kWh}}{3.60 \times 10^6 \text{ J}}$$

Solution: $2285 \text{ Cal} \times \dfrac{4184 \text{ J}}{1 \text{ Cal}} \times \dfrac{1 \text{ kWh}}{3.60 \times 10^6 \text{ J}} = 2.656 \text{ kWh}$

Check: The units (kWh) are correct. The magnitude of the answer (3) makes physical sense because a Calorie is much smaller than a kWh, so the answer decreases.

6.4　　(a)　**Given:** 685 kWh　**Find:** J
　　　　　　Conceptual Plan: kWh → J

$$\frac{3.60 \times 10^6 \text{ J}}{1 \text{ kWh}}$$

　　　　　　Solution: $685 \text{ kWh} \times \dfrac{3.60 \times 10^6 \text{ J}}{1 \text{ kWh}} = 2.47 \times 10^9 \text{ J}$

　　　　　　Check: The units (J) are correct. The magnitude of the answer (10^9) makes physical sense because a kWh is much larger than a joule, so the answer increases.

　　　　(b)　**Given:** 685 kWh　**Find:** kJ
　　　　　　Conceptual Plan: kWh → J → kJ

$$\frac{3.60 \times 10^6 \text{ J}}{1 \text{ kWh}} \quad \frac{1 \text{ kJ}}{1000 \text{ J}}$$

　　　　　　Solution: $685 \text{ kWh} \times \dfrac{3.60 \times 10^6 \text{ J}}{1 \text{ kWh}} \times \dfrac{1 \text{ kJ}}{1000 \text{ J}} = 2.47 \times 10^6 \text{ kJ}$

　　　　　　Check: The units (kJ) are correct. The magnitude of the answer (10^6) makes physical sense because a kWh is much larger than a kJ, so the answer increases.

　　　　(c)　**Given:** 685 kWh　**Find:** Cal
　　　　　　Conceptual Plan: kWh → J → Cal

$$\frac{3.60 \times 10^6 \text{ J}}{1 \text{ kWh}} \quad \frac{1 \text{ Cal}}{4184 \text{ J}}$$

　　　　　　Solution: $685 \text{ kWh} \times \dfrac{3.60 \times 10^6 \text{ J}}{1 \text{ kWh}} \times \dfrac{1 \text{ Cal}}{4184 \text{ J}} = 5.89 \times 10^5 \text{ Cal}$

　　　　　　Check: The units (Cal) are correct. The magnitude of the answer (10^5) makes physical sense because a kWh is much larger than a Cal, so the answer increases.

Internal Energy, Heat, and Work

6.5　　(d)　$\Delta E_{sys} = -\Delta E_{surr}$ If energy change of the system is negative, energy is being transferred from the system to the surroundings, decreasing the energy of the system and increasing the energy of the surroundings. The amount of energy lost by the system must go somewhere, so the amount gained by the surroundings is equal and opposite to that lost by the system.

6.6　　The sign is positive because the energy is being taken in by or deposited into the system.

6.7　　(a)　The energy exchange is primarily heat because the skin (part of the surroundings) is cooled. There is a small expansion (work) because water is being converted from a liquid to a gas. The sign of ΔE_{sys} is positive because the surroundings cool.

　　　　(b)　The energy exchange is primarily work. The sign of ΔE_{sys} is negative because the system is expanding (doing work on the surroundings).

　　　　(c)　The energy exchange is primarily heat. The sign of ΔE_{sys} is positive because the system is being heated by the flame.

6.8　　(a)　The energy exchange is primarily work because there is a lot of motion. There is a small amount of heat transferred because there is some friction as the balls roll. The sign of ΔE_{sys} is negative because the kinetic energy of the first ball is transferred to the second ball.

　　　　(b)　The energy exchange is primarily work. The sign of ΔE_{sys} is negative because the potential energy of the book decreases as it falls.

　　　　(c)　The energy exchange is primarily work. The sign of ΔE_{sys} is positive because the father is doing work to move the girl and the swing.

6.9　　**Given:** 625 kJ heat released; 105 kJ work done on surroundings　**Find:** ΔE_{sys}
　　　　Conceptual Plan: interpret language to determine the sign of the two terms then $q, w \rightarrow \Delta E_{sys}$

$$\Delta E = q + w$$

Solution: Because heat is released from the system to the surroundings, $q = -625$ kJ; because the system is doing work on the surroundings, $w = -105$ kJ. $\Delta E = q + w = -625$ kJ $- 105$ kJ $= -730$ kJ $= -7.30 \times 10^2$ kJ

Check: The units (kJ) are correct. The magnitude of the answer (-730) makes physical sense because both terms are negative.

6.10   **Given:** 272 kJ heat absorbed; surroundings do 125 kJ work   **Find:** ΔE_{sys}
Conceptual Plan: interpret language to determine the sign of the two terms then $q, w \rightarrow \Delta E_{sys}$

$$\Delta E = q + w$$

Solution: Because heat is absorbed by the system, $q = +272$ kJ; because the surroundings are doing work on the system, $w = +125$ kJ. $\Delta E = q + w = 272$ kJ $+ 125$ J $= 397$ kJ $= 3.97 \times 10^2$ kJ

Check: The units (kJ) are correct. The magnitude of the answer (400) makes physical sense because both terms are positive.

6.11   **Given:** 655 J heat absorbed; 344 J work done on surroundings   **Find:** ΔE_{sys}
Conceptual Plan: interpret language to determine the sign of the two terms then $q, w \rightarrow \Delta E_{sys}$

$$\Delta E = q + w$$

Solution: Because heat is absorbed by the system, $q = +655$ J; because the system is doing work on the surroundings, $w = -344$ J. $\Delta E = q + w = 655$ J $- 344$ J $= 311$ J.

Check: The units (J) are correct. The magnitude of the answer ($+300$) makes physical sense because the heat term dominates over the work term.

6.12   **Given:** 155 J heat absorbed; 77 kJ work done on surroundings   **Find:** ΔE_{sys}
Conceptual Plan: interpret language to determine the sign of the two terms kJ $\rightarrow$ J **then** $q, w \rightarrow \Delta E_{sys}$

$$\frac{1 \text{ kJ}}{1000 \text{ J}} \qquad \Delta E = q + w$$

Solution: Because heat is absorbed by the system, $q = +155$ J; because the system is doing work on the surroundings, $w = -77$ kJ. Thus, $-77 \text{ kJ} \times \dfrac{1000 \text{ J}}{1 \text{ kJ}} = -77{,}000$ J and

$\Delta E = q + w = 155$ J $- 77{,}000$ J $= -76{,}845$ J $= -77$ kJ.

Check: The units (kJ) are correct. The magnitude of the answer (-77 kJ) makes physical sense because the work term dominates over the heat term. In fact, the heat term is negligible compared to the work term.

Heat, Heat Capacity, and Work

6.13   Cooler A had more ice after 3 hours because most of the ice in cooler B was melted to cool the soft drinks that started at room temperature. In cooler A, the drinks were already cold; so the ice only needed to maintain this cool temperature.

6.14   Because the specific heat capacity of water is much larger than the specific heat capacity of aluminum, much more heat needs to be released by the water than the aluminum for each 1 °C of temperature drop. This means that more heat is stored in each kg of water than aluminum.

6.15   **Given:** 1.75 L water; $T_i = 25.0$ °C; $T_f = 100.0$ °C; $d = 1.0$ g/mL   **Find:** q
Conceptual Plan: L $\rightarrow$ mL $\rightarrow$ g **and pull** C_s **from Table 6.4 and** $T_i, T_f \rightarrow \Delta T$ **then** $m, C_s, \Delta T \rightarrow q$

$$\frac{1000 \text{ mL}}{1 \text{ L}} \quad \frac{1.0 \text{ g}}{1.0 \text{ mL}} \qquad 4.18 \frac{\text{J}}{\text{g} \cdot \text{°C}} \qquad\qquad \Delta T = T_f - T_i \qquad q = m C_s \Delta T$$

Solution: $1.75 \text{ L} \times \dfrac{1000 \text{ mL}}{1 \text{ L}} \times \dfrac{1.0 \text{ g}}{1.0 \text{ mL}} = 1\underline{7}50$ g and $\Delta T = T_f - T_i = 100.0$ °C $- 25.0$ °C $= 75.0$ °C

then $q = m C_s \Delta T = 1\underline{7}50 \text{ g} \times 4.18 \dfrac{\text{J}}{\text{g} \cdot \text{°C}} \times 75.0 \text{ °C} = 5.5 \times 10^5$ J

Check: The units (J) are correct. The magnitude of the answer (10^6) makes physical sense because there are a large mass, a significant temperature change, and a high specific heat capacity material.

6.16   **Given:** 1.75 kg sand; $T_i = 25.0\,°C$; $T_f = 100.0\,°C$ **Find:** q

Conceptual Plan: kg → g and pull C_s from Table 6.4 and T_i, T_f → ΔT then m, C_s, ΔT → q

$$\frac{1000\ g}{1\,kg} \qquad 0.84\,\frac{J}{g\cdot°C} \qquad\qquad \Delta T = T_f - T_i \qquad\qquad q = mC_s\Delta T$$

Solution: $1.75\ \cancel{kg} \times \dfrac{1000\ g}{1\ \cancel{kg}} = 17\underline{5}0$ g and $\Delta T = T_f - T_i = 100.0\,°C - 25.0\,°C = 75.0\,°C$

then $q = mC_s\Delta T = 17\underline{5}0\ \cancel{g} \times 0.84\,\dfrac{J}{\cancel{g}\cdot\cancel{°C}} \times 75.0\,\cancel{°C} = 1.1 \times 10^5$ J

Check: The units (J) are correct. The magnitude of the answer (10^5) makes physical sense because there are a large mass and a significant temperature change.

6.17   (a)   **Given:** 25 g gold; $T_i = 27.0\,°C$; $q = 2.35$ kJ   **Find:** T_f

Conceptual Plan: kJ → J and pull C_s from Table 6.4 then m, C_s, q → ΔT then T_i, ΔT → T_f

$$\frac{1000\ J}{1\ kJ} \qquad 0.128\,\frac{J}{g\cdot°C} \qquad\qquad q = mC_s\Delta T \qquad\qquad \Delta T = T_f - T_i$$

Solution: $2.35\ \cancel{kJ} \times \dfrac{1000\ J}{1\ \cancel{kJ}} = 23\underline{5}0$ J then $q = mC_s\Delta T$. Rearrange to solve for ΔT.

$$\Delta T = \frac{q}{mC_s} = \frac{23\underline{5}0\ J}{25\ \cancel{g} \times 0.128\,\dfrac{J}{\cancel{g}\cdot°C}} = 7\underline{3}4.375\,°C \text{ finally } \Delta T = T_f - T_i. \text{ Rearrange to solve for } T_f.$$

$T_f = \Delta T + T_i = 7\underline{3}4.375\,°C + 27.0\,°C = 760\,°C$

Check: The units (°C) are correct. The magnitude of the answer (760) makes physical sense because such a large amount of heat is absorbed and there are a small mass and specific heat capacity. The temperature change should be very large.

(b)   **Given:** 25 g silver; $T_i = 27.0\,°C$; $q = 2.35$ kJ   **Find:** T_f

Conceptual Plan: kJ → J and pull C_s from Table 6.4 then m, C_s, q → ΔT then T_i, ΔT → T_f

$$\frac{1000\ J}{1\ kJ} \qquad 0.235\,\frac{J}{g\cdot°C} \qquad\qquad q = mC_s\Delta T \qquad\qquad \Delta T = T_f - T_i$$

Solution: $2.35\ \cancel{kJ} \times \dfrac{1000\ J}{1\ \cancel{kJ}} = 23\underline{5}0$ J then $q = mC_s\Delta T$. Rearrange to solve for ΔT.

$$\Delta T = \frac{q}{mC_s} = \frac{23\underline{5}0\ J}{25\ \cancel{g} \times 0.235\,\dfrac{J}{\cancel{g}\cdot°C}} = 4\underline{0}0\,°C \text{ finally } \Delta T = T_f - T_i. \text{ Rearrange to solve for } T_f.$$

$T_f = \Delta T + T_i = 4\underline{0}0\,°C + 27.0\,°C = 430\,°C$

Check: The units (°C) are correct. The magnitude of the answer (430) makes physical sense because such a large amount of heat is absorbed and there are a small mass and specific heat capacity. The temperature change should be very large. The temperature change should be less than that of the gold because the specific heat capacity is greater.

(c)   **Given:** 25 g aluminum; $T_i = 27.0\,°C$; $q = 2.35$ kJ   **Find:** T_f

Conceptual Plan: kJ → J and pull C_s from Table 6.4 then m, C_s, q → ΔT then T_i, ΔT → T_f

$$\frac{1000\ J}{1\ kJ} \qquad 0.903\,\frac{J}{g\cdot°C} \qquad\qquad q = mC_s\Delta T \qquad\qquad \Delta T = T_f - T_i$$

Solution: $2.35\ \cancel{kJ} \times \dfrac{1000\ J}{1\ \cancel{kJ}} = 23\underline{5}0$ J then $q = mC_s\Delta T$. Rearrange to solve for ΔT.

$$\Delta T = \frac{q}{mC_s} = \frac{23\underline{5}0\ J}{25\ \cancel{g} \times 0.903\,\dfrac{J}{\cancel{g}\cdot°C}} = 1\underline{0}4.10\,°C \text{ finally } \Delta T = T_f - T_i. \text{ Rearrange to solve for } T_f.$$

$T_f = \Delta T + T_i = 1\underline{0}4.10\,°C + 27.0\,°C = 130\,°C$

Check: The units (°C) are correct. The magnitude of the answer (130) makes physical sense because such a large amount of heat is absorbed and there is such a small mass. The temperature change should be less than that of the silver because the specific heat capacity is greater.

(d) **Given:** 25 g water; $T_i = 27.0\,°C$; $q = 2.35$ kJ   **Find:** T_f

Conceptual Plan: kJ $\rightarrow$ J and pull C_s from Table 6.4 then $m, C_s, q \rightarrow \Delta T$ then $T_i, \Delta T \rightarrow T_f$

$$\frac{1000\,J}{1\,kJ} \qquad 4.18\frac{J}{g\cdot°C} \qquad\qquad q = mC_s\Delta T \qquad\qquad \Delta T = T_f - T_i$$

Solution: $2.35\,\text{kJ} \times \dfrac{1000\,J}{1\,\text{kJ}} = 23\underline{5}0\,J$ then $q = mC_s\Delta T$. Rearrange to solve for ΔT.

$$\Delta T = \frac{q}{mC_s} = \frac{23\underline{5}0\,J}{25\,\text{g} \times 4.18\dfrac{J}{\text{g}\cdot°C}} = 22.\underline{4}88\,°C \text{ finally } \Delta T = T_f - T_i. \text{ Rearrange to solve for } T_f.$$

$$T_f = \Delta T + T_i = 22.\underline{4}88\,°C + 27.0\,°C = 49\,°C$$

Check: The units (°C) are correct. The magnitude of the answer (49) makes physical sense because such a large amount of heat is absorbed and there is such a small mass. The temperature change should be less than that of the aluminum because the specific heat capacity is greater.

6.18   (a)   **Given:** Pyrex glass; $q = 1.95 \times 10^3$ J; $T_i = 23.0\,°C$; $T_f = 55.4\,°C$ **Find:** m

Conceptual Plan: pull C_s from Table 6.4 then $T_i, T_f \rightarrow \Delta T$ then $\Delta T, C_s, q \rightarrow m$

$$0.75\frac{J}{g\cdot°C} \qquad\qquad \Delta T = T_f - T_i \qquad\qquad q = mC_s\Delta T$$

Solution: $\Delta T = T_f - T_i = 55.4\,°C - 23.0\,°C = 32.4\,°C$ and $q = mC_s\Delta T$. Rearrange to solve for m.

$$m = \frac{q}{C_s\Delta T} = \frac{1.95 \times 10^3\,J}{0.75\dfrac{J}{g\cdot°C} \times 32.4\,°C} = 80.\,\text{g, or } 8.0 \times 10^1\,\text{g}$$

Check: The units (g) are correct. The magnitude of the answer (80) makes physical sense because such a large amount of heat is absorbed and there are a moderate temperature rise and specific heat capacity.

(b)   **Given:** sand; $q = 1.95 \times 10^3$ J; $T_i = 23.0\,°C$; $T_f = 62.1\,°C$ **Find:** m

Conceptual Plan: pull C_s from Table 6.4 then $T_i, T_f \rightarrow \Delta T$ then $\Delta T, C_s, q \rightarrow m$

$$0.84\frac{J}{g\cdot°C} \qquad\qquad \Delta T = T_f - T_i \qquad\qquad q = mC_s\Delta T$$

Solution: $\Delta T = T_f - T_i = 62.1\,°C - 23.0\,°C = 39.1\,°C$ then $q = mC_s\Delta T$. Rearrange to solve for m.

$$m = \frac{q}{C_s\Delta T} = \frac{1.95 \times 10^3\,J}{0.84\dfrac{J}{g\cdot°C} \times 39.1\,°C} = 59\,\text{g}$$

Check: The units (g) are correct. The magnitude of the answer (60) makes physical sense because such a large amount of heat is absorbed and there are a moderate temperature rise and specific heat capacity.

(c)   **Given:** ethanol; $q = 1.95 \times 10^3$ J; $T_i = 23.0\,°C$; $T_f = 44.2\,°C$ **Find:** m

Conceptual Plan: pull C_s from Table 6.4 then $T_i, T_f \rightarrow \Delta T$ then $\Delta T, C_s, q \rightarrow m$

$$2.42\frac{J}{g\cdot°C} \qquad\qquad \Delta T = T_f - T_i \qquad\qquad q = mC_s\Delta T$$

Solution: $\Delta T = T_f - T_i = 44.2\,°C - 23.0\,°C = 21.2\,°C$ then $q = mC_s\Delta T$. Rearrange to solve for m.

$$m = \frac{q}{C_s\Delta T} = \frac{1.95 \times 10^3\,J}{2.42\dfrac{J}{g\cdot°C} \times 21.2\,°C} = 38.0\,\text{g}$$

Check: The units (g) are correct. The magnitude of the answer (40) makes physical sense because such a large amount of heat is absorbed and there are a small temperature rise and specific heat capacity.

(d)   **Given:** water; $q = 1.95 \times 10^3$ J; $T_i = 23.0\,°C$; $T_f = 32.4\,°C$ **Find:** m

Conceptual Plan: pull C_s from Table 6.4 then $T_i, T_f \rightarrow \Delta T$ then $\Delta T, C_s, q \rightarrow m$

$$4.18\frac{J}{g\cdot°C} \qquad\qquad \Delta T = T_f - T_i \qquad\qquad q = mC_s\Delta T$$

Solution: $\Delta T = T_f - T_i = 32.4\,°C - 23.0\,°C = 9.4\,°C$ then $q = mC_s\Delta T$. Rearrange to solve for m.

$$m = \frac{q}{C_s \Delta T} = \frac{1.95 \times 10^3 \, \text{J}}{4.18 \, \dfrac{\text{J}}{\text{g} \cdot \text{°C}} \times 9.4 \, \text{°C}} = 50. \, \text{g or } 5.0 \times 10^1 \, \text{g}$$

Check: The units (g) are correct. The magnitude of the answer (50) makes physical sense because such a large amount of heat is absorbed and there are a small temperature rise and very specific heat capacity.

6.19 **Given:** $V_i = 0.0 \, \text{L}$; $V_f = 2.5 \, \text{L}$; $P = 1.1 \, \text{atm}$ **Find:** w (J)
Conceptual Plan: $V_i, V_f \rightarrow \Delta V$ **then** $P, \Delta V \rightarrow w$ **(L atm)** $\rightarrow w$ **(J)**

$$\Delta V = V_f - V_i \qquad w = -P\Delta V \qquad \frac{101.3 \, \text{J}}{1 \, \text{L} \cdot \text{atm}}$$

Solution: $\Delta V = V_f - V_i = 2.5 \, \text{L} - 0.0 \, \text{L} = 2.5 \, \text{L}$ then

$$w = -P\Delta V = -1.1 \, \text{atm} \times 2.5 \, \text{L} \times \frac{101.3 \, \text{J}}{1 \, \text{L} \cdot \text{atm}} = -2.8 \times 10^2 \, \text{J}$$

Check: The units (J) are correct. The magnitude of the answer (-280) makes physical sense because this is an expansion (negative work) and we have $\sim$ atmospheric pressure and a small volume of expansion.

6.20 **Given:** $\Delta V = 0.50 \, \text{L}$; $P = 1.0 \, \text{atm}$ **Find:** w (J)
Conceptual Plan: $P, \Delta V \rightarrow w$ **(L atm)** $\rightarrow w$ **(J)**

$$w = -P\Delta V \qquad \frac{101.3 \, \text{J}}{1 \, \text{L} \cdot \text{atm}}$$

Solution: $w = -P\Delta V = -1.0 \, \text{atm} \times 0.50 \, \text{L} \times \dfrac{101.3 \, \text{J}}{1 \, \text{L} \cdot \text{atm}} = -51 \, \text{J}$

Check: The units (J) are correct. The magnitude of the answer (-51) makes physical sense because this is a small expansion (negative work) and we do not expect breathing to take much energy.

6.21 **Given:** $q = 565 \, \text{J}$ absorbed; $V_i = 0.10 \, \text{L}$; $V_f = 0.85 \, \text{L}$; $P = 1.0 \, \text{atm}$ **Find:** ΔE_{sys}
Conceptual Plan: $V_i, V_f \rightarrow \Delta V$ **and interpret language to determine the sign of the heat**

$$\Delta V = V_f - V_i \qquad\qquad q = +565 \, \text{J}$$

then $P, \Delta V \rightarrow w$ **(L atm)** $\rightarrow w$ **(J)** **finally** $q, w \rightarrow \Delta E_{sys}$

$$w = -P\Delta V \qquad \frac{101.3 \, \text{J}}{1 \, \text{L} \cdot \text{atm}} \qquad \Delta E = q + w$$

Solution: $\Delta V = V_f - V_i = 0.85 \, \text{L} - 0.10 \, \text{L} = 0.75 \, \text{L}$ then

$$w = -P\Delta V = -1.0 \, \text{atm} \times 0.75 \, \text{L} \times \frac{101.3 \, \text{J}}{1 \, \text{L} \cdot \text{atm}} = -75.975 \, \text{J} \quad \Delta E = q + w = +565 \, \text{J} - 75.\underline{9}75 \, \text{J} = 489 \, \text{J}$$

Check: The units (J) are correct. The magnitude of the answer (500) makes physical sense because the heat absorbed dominated the small expansion work (negative work).

6.22 **Given:** $q = 124 \, \text{J}$ released; $V_i = 5.55 \, \text{L}$; $V_f = 1.22 \, \text{L}$; $P = 1.00 \, \text{atm}$ **Find:** ΔE_{sys}
Conceptual Plan: $V_i, V_f \rightarrow \Delta V$ **and interpret language to determine the sign of the heat**

$$\Delta V = V_f - V_i \qquad\qquad q = -124 \, \text{J}$$

then $P, \Delta V \rightarrow w$ **(L atm)** $\rightarrow w$ **(J)** **finally** $q, w \rightarrow \Delta E_{sys}$

$$w = -P\Delta V \qquad \frac{101.3 \, \text{J}}{1 \, \text{L} \cdot \text{atm}} \qquad \Delta E = q + w$$

Solution: $\Delta V = V_f - V_i = 1.22 \, \text{L} - 5.55 \, \text{L} = -4.33 \, \text{L}$ then

$$w = -P\Delta V = -1.00 \, \text{atm} \times (-4.33 \, \text{L}) \times \frac{101.3 \, \text{J}}{1 \, \text{L} \cdot \text{atm}} = +438.\underline{6}29 \, \text{J} \text{ then}$$

$$\Delta E = q + w = -124 \, \text{J} + 438.\underline{6}29 \, \text{J} = 315 \, \text{J}$$

Check: The units (J) are correct. The magnitude of the answer (300) makes physical sense because the compression work dominated the small amount of heat released.

Enthalpy and Thermochemical Stoichiometry

6.23 **Given:** 1 mol fuel, 3452 kJ heat produced; 11 kJ work done on surroundings **Find:** ΔE_{sys}, ΔH
Conceptual Plan: interpret language to determine the sign of the two terms then $q \rightarrow \Delta H$ **and** $q, w \rightarrow \Delta E_{sys}$

$$\Delta H = q_p \qquad\qquad \Delta E = q + w$$

Solution: Because heat is produced by the system to the surroundings, $q = -3452$ kJ; because the system is doing work on the surroundings, $w = -11$ kJ. $\Delta H = q_p = -3452$ kJ and
$\Delta E = q + w = -3452$ kJ $- 11$ kJ $= -3463$ kJ.

Check: The units (kJ) are correct. The magnitude of the answer (-3500) makes physical sense because both terms are negative. We expect significant amounts of energy from fuels.

6.24   **Given:** 1 mol octane, $P = 1.0$ atm, $\Delta E_{sys} = 5084.3$ kJ; $\Delta H = 5074.1$ kJ   **Find:** w
Conceptual Plan: interpret language to determine the sign of the two terms then $q \rightarrow \Delta H$ **and** $q, \Delta E_{sys} \rightarrow w$
$$\Delta E_{sys} = -5084.3 \text{ kJ}; \Delta H = -5074.1 \text{ kJ} \qquad\qquad\qquad \Delta H = q_p \qquad\qquad \Delta E = q + w$$

Solution: Because heat is produced by the system to the surroundings, $\Delta H = q_p = -5074.1$ kJ;
$\Delta E_{sys} = -5084.3$ kJ $\Delta E = q + w$. Rearrange to solve for w.
$w = \Delta E - q = -5084.3$ kJ $- (-5074.1$ kJ$) = -10.2$ kJ

Check: The units (kJ) are correct. The magnitude of the answer (-10) makes physical sense because the work should be negative in an expansion. We expect more heat than work in an engine.

6.25   (a)   Combustion is an exothermic process; ΔH is negative.
(b)   Evaporation requires an input of energy, so it is endothermic; ΔH is positive.
(c)   Condensation is the reverse of evaporation, so it is exothermic; ΔH is negative.

6.26   (a)   Sublimation requires an input of energy, so it is endothermic; ΔH is positive.
(b)   Combustion is an exothermic process; ΔH is negative.
(c)   Because the temperature drops, this is an endothermic process; ΔH is positive.

6.27   **Given:** 177 mL acetone (C_3H_6O), $\Delta H_{rxn}^\circ = -1658$ kJ; $d = 0.788$ g/mL   **Find:** q
Conceptual Plan: mL acetone $\rightarrow$ **g acetone** $\rightarrow$ **mol acetone** $\rightarrow q$
$$\frac{0.788 \text{ g}}{1 \text{ mL}} \qquad \frac{1 \text{ mol}}{58.08 \text{ g}} \qquad \frac{-1658 \text{ kJ}}{1 \text{ mol}}$$

Solution: 177 mL $\times \dfrac{0.788 \text{ g}}{1 \text{ mL}} \times \dfrac{1 \text{ mol}}{58.08 \text{ g}} \times \dfrac{-1658 \text{ kJ}}{1 \text{ mol}} = -3.98 \times 10^3$ kJ or 3.98×10^3 kJ released

Check: The units (kJ) are correct. The magnitude of the answer ($\sim -10^3$) makes physical sense because the enthalpy change is negative and we have more than a mole of acetone. We expect more than 1658 kJ to be released.

6.28   **Given:** natural gas (CH_4), $\Delta H_{rxn}^\circ = -802.3$ kJ; $q = 267$ kJ   **Find:** m
Conceptual Plan: $q \rightarrow$ **mol natural gas** $\rightarrow$ **g natural gas**
$$\frac{1 \text{ mol}}{-802.3 \text{ kJ}} \qquad \frac{16.04 \text{ g}}{1 \text{ mol}}$$

Solution: -267 kJ $\times \dfrac{1 \text{ mol}}{-802.3 \text{ kJ}} \times \dfrac{16.04 \text{ g}}{1 \text{ mol}} = 5.34$ g

Check: The units (g) are correct. The magnitude of the answer (5) makes physical sense because the enthalpy change per mole is so large and we need to burn less than a mole.

6.29   **Given:** 5.56 kg nitromethane (CH_3NO_2); $\Delta H_{rxn}^\circ = -1418$ kJ/2 mol nitromethane   **Find:** q
Conceptual Plan: kg nitromethane $\rightarrow$ **g nitromethane** $\rightarrow$ **mol nitromethane** $\rightarrow q$
$$\frac{1000 \text{ g}}{1 \text{ kg}} \qquad \frac{1 \text{ mol}}{61.04 \text{ g}} \qquad \frac{-1418 \text{ kJ}}{2 \text{ mol}}$$

Solution: 5.56 kg $\times \dfrac{1000 \text{ g}}{1 \text{ kg}} \times \dfrac{1 \text{ mol}}{61.04 \text{ g}} \times \dfrac{-1418 \text{ kJ}}{2 \text{ mol}} = -6.46 \times 10^4$ kJ or 6.46×10^4 kJ released

Check: The units (kJ) are correct. The magnitude of the answer (-10^4) makes physical sense because the enthalpy change is negative and we have more than a mole of nitromethane. We expect more than 709 kJ to be released.

6.30   **Given:** titanium and iodine, $\Delta H_{rxn}^\circ = -839$ kJ; $q = 1.55 \times 10^3$ kJ   **Find:** m (Ti) and m (I_2)
Conceptual Plan: $q \rightarrow$ **mol Ti** $\rightarrow$ **g Ti and** $q \rightarrow$ **mol** I_2 $\rightarrow$ **g** I_2
$$\frac{2 \text{ mol}}{-839 \text{ kJ}} \qquad \frac{47.87 \text{ g}}{1 \text{ mol}} \qquad \frac{3 \text{ mol}}{-839 \text{ kJ}} \qquad \frac{253.80 \text{ g}}{1 \text{ mol}}$$

Solution: $-1.55 \times 10^3 \text{ kJ} \times \dfrac{2 \text{ mol Ti}}{-839 \text{ kJ}} \times \dfrac{47.87 \text{ g Ti}}{1 \text{ mol Ti}} = 1.77 \times 10^2 \text{ g Ti}$ and

$$-1.55 \times 10^3 \text{ kJ} \times \dfrac{3 \text{ mol I}_2}{-839 \text{ kJ}} \times \dfrac{253.80 \text{ g I}_2}{1 \text{ mol I}_2} = 1.41 \times 10^3 \text{ g I}_2$$

Check: The units (g and g) are correct. The magnitudes of the answers (10^2 and 10^3) make physical sense because the heat emitted is much more than the enthalpy of the reaction; so the reaction will consume much more than a mole of titanium and iodine.

6.31 **Given:** pork roast, $\Delta H^\circ_{\text{rxn}} = -2044 \text{ kJ}$; q needed $= 1.6 \times 10^3 \text{ kJ}$, 10% efficiency   **Find:** $m(CO_2)$

Conceptual Plan: q used $\rightarrow$ q generated $\rightarrow$ mol CO_2 $\rightarrow$ g CO_2

$$\dfrac{100 \text{ kJ generated}}{10 \text{ kJ used}} \qquad \dfrac{3 \text{ mol CO}_2}{2044 \text{ kJ}} \qquad \dfrac{44.01 \text{ g}}{1 \text{ mol}}$$

Solution: $1.6 \times 10^3 \text{ kJ} \times \dfrac{100 \text{ kJ generated}}{10 \text{ kJ used}} \times \dfrac{3 \text{ mol CO}_2}{2044 \text{ kJ}} \times \dfrac{44.01 \text{ g CO}_2}{1 \text{ mol CO}_2} = 1.0 \times 10^3 \text{ g CO}_2$

Check: The units (g) are correct. The magnitude of the answer (1000) makes physical sense because the process is not very efficient and a lot of energy is needed.

6.32 **Given:** carbon, $\Delta H^\circ_{\text{rxn}} = -393.5 \text{ kJ}$; q needed $= 5.00 \times 10^2 \text{ kJ}$ **Find:** $m(CO_2)$

Conceptual Plan: q needed $\rightarrow$ mol CO_2 $\rightarrow$ g CO_2

$$\dfrac{1 \text{ mol}}{393.5 \text{ kJ}} \qquad \dfrac{44.01 \text{ g}}{1 \text{ mol}}$$

Solution: $5.00 \times 10^2 \text{ kJ} \times \dfrac{1 \text{ mol CO}_2}{393.5 \text{ kJ}} \times \dfrac{44.01 \text{ g CO}_2}{1 \text{ mol CO}_2} = 55.9 \text{ g CO}_2$

Check: The units (g) are correct. The magnitude of the answer (~ 60) makes physical sense as there is a 1:1 mol ratio between the carbon burned and the carbon dioxide produced.

6.33 **Given:** silver block; $T_{\text{Agi}} = 58.5 \,^\circ\text{C}$; 100.0 g water; $T_{\text{H}_2\text{Oi}} = 24.8 \,^\circ\text{C}$; $T_f = 26.2 \,^\circ\text{C}$ **Find:** mass of silver block

Conceptual Plan: pull C_s values from table then H_2O: $m, C_s, T_i, T_f \rightarrow q$ Ag: $C_s, T_i, T_f \rightarrow m$

$$\text{Ag: } 0.235 \dfrac{\text{J}}{\text{g}\cdot{}^\circ\text{C}} \quad \text{H}_2\text{O: } 4.18 \dfrac{\text{J}}{\text{g}\cdot{}^\circ\text{C}} \qquad\qquad q = mC_s(T_f - T_i) \text{ then set } q_{\text{Ag}} = -q_{\text{H}_2\text{O}}$$

Solution: $q = mC_s(T_f - T_i)$ substitute in values and set $q_{\text{Ag}} = -q_{\text{H}_2\text{O}}$.

$$q_{\text{Ag}} = m_{\text{Ag}}C_{\text{Ag}}(T_f - T_{\text{Agi}}) = m_{\text{Ag}} \times 0.235 \dfrac{\text{J}}{\text{g}\cdot{}^\circ\text{C}} \times (26.2 \,{}^\circ\text{C} - 58.5 \,{}^\circ\text{C}) =$$

$$-q_{\text{H}_2\text{O}} = -m_{\text{H}_2\text{O}}C_{\text{H}_2\text{O}}(T_f - T_{\text{H}_2\text{Oi}}) = -100.0 \text{ g} \times 4.18 \dfrac{\text{J}}{\text{g}\cdot{}^\circ\text{C}} \times (26.2 \,{}^\circ\text{C} - 24.8 \,{}^\circ\text{C})$$

Rearrange to solve for m_{Ag}.

$$m_{\text{Ag}} \times \left(-7.5\underline{9}05 \dfrac{\text{J}}{\text{g}}\right) = -58\underline{5}.2 \text{ J} \rightarrow m_{\text{Ag}} = \dfrac{-58\underline{5}.2 \text{ J}}{-7.5\underline{9}05 \dfrac{\text{J}}{\text{g}}} = 77.0\underline{9}64 \text{ g Ag} = 77.1 \text{ g Ag}$$

Check: The units (g) are correct. The magnitude of the answer (77 g) makes physical sense because the heat capacity of water is much greater than the heat capacity of silver.

6.34 **Given:** 32.5 g iron rod; $T_{\text{Fei}} = 22.7 \,^\circ\text{C}$; $T_{\text{H}_2\text{Oi}} = 63.2 \,^\circ\text{C}$; $T_f = 59.5 \,^\circ\text{C}$ **Find:** mass of water

Conceptual Plan: pull C_s values from table then Fe: $m, C_s, T_i, T_f \rightarrow q$ H_2O: $C_s, T_i, T_f \rightarrow m$

$$\text{Fe: } 0.449 \dfrac{\text{J}}{\text{g}\cdot{}^\circ\text{C}} \quad \text{H}_2\text{O: } 4.18 \dfrac{\text{J}}{\text{g}\cdot{}^\circ\text{C}} \qquad\qquad q = mC_s(T_f - T_i) \text{ then set } q_{\text{Fe}} = -q_{\text{H}_2\text{O}}$$

Solution: $q = mC_s(T_f - T_i)$ substitute in values and set $q_{\text{Fe}} = -q_{\text{H}_2\text{O}}$.

$$q_{\text{Fe}} = m_{\text{Fe}}C_{\text{Fe}}(T_f - T_{\text{Fei}}) = 32.5 \text{ g} \times 0.449 \dfrac{\text{J}}{\text{g}\cdot{}^\circ\text{C}} \times (59.5 \,{}^\circ\text{C} - 22.7 \,{}^\circ\text{C}) =$$

$$-q_{\text{H}_2\text{O}} = -m_{\text{H}_2\text{O}}C_{\text{H}_2\text{O}}(T_f - T_{\text{H}_2\text{Oi}}) = -m_{\text{H}_2\text{O}} \times 4.18 \dfrac{\text{J}}{\text{g}\cdot{}^\circ\text{C}} \times (59.5 \,{}^\circ\text{C} - 63.2 \,{}^\circ\text{C})$$

Rearrange to solve for $m_{\text{H}_2\text{O}}$.

$$537.004 \text{ J} = -m_{H_2O} \times \left(15.\underline{4}66 \frac{\text{J}}{\text{g}}\right) \rightarrow m_{H_2O} = \frac{537.004 \text{ J}}{15.\underline{4}66 \frac{\text{J}}{\text{g}}} = 34.\underline{7}2158 \text{ g H}_2\text{O} = 34.7 \text{ g H}_2\text{O}$$

Check: The units (g) are correct. The magnitude of the answer (35 g) makes physical sense because the heat capacity of water is much greater than the heat capacity of iron.

6.35   **Given:** 31.1 g gold; $T_{Au\,i} = 69.3 \,°C$; 64.2 g water; $T_{H_2O\,i} = 27.8 \,°C$ **Find:** T_f

     Conceptual Plan: pull C_s values from table then $m, C_s, T_i \rightarrow T_f$

         Au: $0.128 \frac{\text{J}}{\text{g} \cdot °C}$ H$_2$O: $4.18 \frac{\text{J}}{\text{g} \cdot °C}$ $q = mC_s(T_f - T_i)$ then set $q_{Au} = -q_{H_2O}$

     Solution: $q = mC_s(T_f - T_i)$ substitute in values and set $q_{Au} = -q_{H_2O}$.

$$q_{Au} = m_{Au}C_{Au}(T_f - T_{Au\,i}) = 31.1 \text{ g} \times 0.128 \frac{\text{J}}{\text{g} \cdot °C} \times (T_f - 69.3 \,°C) =$$

$$-q_{H_2O} = -m_{H_2O}C_{H_2O}(T_f - T_{H_2O\,i}) = -64.2 \text{ g} \times 4.18 \frac{\text{J}}{\text{g} \cdot °C} \times (T_f - 27.8°C)$$

Rearrange to solve for T_f.

$$3.9\underline{8}08 \frac{\text{J}}{°C} \times (T_f - 69.3 \,°C) = -268.356 \frac{\text{J}}{°C} \times (T_f - 27.8 \,°C) \rightarrow$$

$$3.9\underline{8}08 \frac{\text{J}}{°C} T_f - 275.8694 \text{ J} = -268.356 \frac{\text{J}}{°C} T_f + 74\underline{6}0.2968 \text{ J} \rightarrow$$

$$268.356 \frac{\text{J}}{°C} T_f + 3.9\underline{8}08 \frac{\text{J}}{°C} T_f = 275.8694 \text{ J} + 74\underline{6}0.2968 \text{ J} \rightarrow 272.\underline{3}368 \frac{\text{J}}{°C} T_f = 77\underline{3}6.1662 \text{ J} \rightarrow$$

$$T_f = \frac{77\underline{3}6.1662 \text{ J}}{272.\underline{3}368 \frac{\text{J}}{°C}} = 28.4 \,°C$$

Check: The units (°C) are correct. The magnitude of the answer (28) makes physical sense because the heat transfer is dominated by the water (larger mass and larger specific heat capacity). The final temperature should be closer to the initial temperature of water than of gold.

6.36   **Given:** 2.85 lead; $T_{Pb\,i} = 10.3 \,°C$; 7.55 g water; $T_{H_2O\,i} = 52.3 \,°C$ **Find:** T_f

     Conceptual Plan: pull C_s values from table then $m, C_s, T_i \rightarrow T_f$

         Pb: $0.128 \frac{\text{J}}{\text{g} \cdot °C}$ H$_2$O: $4.18 \frac{\text{J}}{\text{g} \cdot °C}$ $q = mC_s(T_f - T_i)$ then set $q_{Pb} = -q_{H_2O}$

     Solution: $q = mC_s(T_f - T_i)$ substitute in values and set $q_{Pb} = -q_{H_2O}$.

$$q_{Pb} = m_{Pb}C_{Pb}(T_f - T_{Pb\,i}) = 2.85 \text{ g} \times 0.128 \frac{\text{J}}{\text{g} \cdot °C} \times (T_f - 10.3 \,°C) =$$

$$-q_{H_2O} = -m_{H_2O}C_{H_2O}(T_f - T_{H_2O\,i}) = -7.55 \text{ g} \times 4.18 \frac{\text{J}}{\text{g} \cdot °C} \times (T_f - 52.3 \,°C)$$

Rearrange to solve for T_f.

$$0.36\underline{4}8 \frac{\text{J}}{°C} \times (T_f - 10.3 \,°C) = -31.\underline{5}59 \frac{\text{J}}{°C} \times (T_f - 52.3 \,°C) \rightarrow$$

$$0.36\underline{4}8 \frac{\text{J}}{°C} T_f - 3.7\underline{5}744 \text{ J} = -31.\underline{5}59 \frac{\text{J}}{°C} T_f + 16\underline{5}0.5357 \text{ J} \rightarrow$$

$$0.36\underline{4}8 \frac{\text{J}}{°C} T_f + 31.\underline{5}59 \frac{\text{J}}{°C} T_f = 3.7\underline{5}744 \text{ J} + 16\underline{5}0.5357 \text{ J} \rightarrow 31.\underline{9}238 \frac{\text{J}}{°C} T_f = 16\underline{5}4.2931 \text{ J} \rightarrow$$

$$T_f = \frac{16\underline{5}4.2931 \text{ J}}{31.\underline{9}238 \frac{\text{J}}{°C}} = 51.8 \,°C$$

Check: The units (°C) are correct. The magnitude of the answer (52) makes physical sense because the heat transfer is dominated by the water (larger mass and larger specific heat capacity). The final temperature should be closer to the initial temperature of water than of lead.

6.37   **Given:** 6.15 g substance A; T_{Ai} = 20.5 °C; 25.2 g substance B; T_{Bi} = 52.7 °C; C_s = 1.17 J/g · °C, T_f = 46.7 °C
Find: specific heat capacity of substance A
Conceptual Plan: $A: m, T_i, T_f \rightarrow q$ $B: m, C_s, T_i, T_f \rightarrow q$ **and solve for** C_A

$$q = mC_s(T_f - T_i) \qquad \text{then set } q_A = -q_B$$

Solution: $q = mC_s(T_f - T_i)$ substitute in values and set $q_A = -q_B$.
$$q_A = m_A C_A(T_f - T_{Ai}) = 6.15 \text{ g} \times C_A \times (46.7 \text{ °C} - 20.5 \text{ °C}) =$$

$$-q_B = -m_B C_B(T_f - T_{Bi}) = -25.2 \text{ g} \times 1.17 \frac{\text{J}}{\text{g} \cdot \text{°C}} \times (46.7 \text{ °C} - 52.7 \text{ °C})$$

Rearrange to solve for C_A.

$$C_A \times (16\underline{1}.13 \text{ g} \cdot \text{°C}) = 17\underline{6}.904 \text{ J} \rightarrow C_A = \frac{176.904 \text{ J}}{161.13 \text{ g} \cdot \text{°C}} = 1.09\underline{7}896 \frac{\text{J}}{\text{g} \cdot \text{°C}} = 1.10 \frac{\text{J}}{\text{g} \cdot \text{°C}}$$

Check: The units (J/g · °C) are correct. The magnitude of the answer (1 J/g · °C) makes physical sense because the mass of substance B is greater than the mass of substance A by a factor of ~4.1 and the temperature change for substance A is greater than the temperature change of substance B by a factor of ~4.4; so the heat capacity of substance A will be a little smaller.

6.38   **Given:** 2.74 g substance that may be gold; $T_{Au?i}$ = 72.1 °C; 15.2 g water; T_{H_2Oi} = 24.7 °C; T_f = 26.3 °C
Find: heat capacity of substance that may be gold, and could it be gold
Conceptual Plan: pull C_s **values from Table 6.4 substance :** $m, T_i, T_f \rightarrow q$ $H_2O: m, C_s, T_i, T_f \rightarrow q$

$$\text{Au: } 0.128 \frac{\text{J}}{\text{g} \cdot \text{°C}} \text{ H}_2\text{O: } 4.18 \frac{\text{J}}{\text{g} \cdot \text{°C}} \qquad q = mC_s(T_f - T_i) \qquad \text{then set } q_{Au?} = -q_{H_2O}.$$

and solve for C
Solution: $q = mC_s(T_f - T_i)$ substitute in values and set $q_{Au?} = -q_{H_2O}$.
$$q_{Au?} = m_{Au?}C_{Au?}(T_f - T_{Au?i}) = 2.74 \text{ g} \times C_{Au?} \times (26.3 \text{ °C} - 72.1 \text{ °C}) =$$

$$-q_{H_2O} = -m_{H_2O}C_{H_2O}(T_f - T_{H_2Oi}) = -15.2 \text{ g} \times 4.18 \frac{\text{J}}{\text{g} \cdot \text{°C}} \times (26.3 \text{ °C} - 24.7 \text{ °C})$$

Rearrange to solve for $C_{Au?}$.

$$C_{Au?} \times (-12\underline{5}.492 \text{ g} \cdot \text{°C}) = -10\underline{1}.6576 \text{ J} \rightarrow C_{Au?} = \frac{-101.6576 \text{ J}}{-125.492 \text{ g} \cdot \text{°C}} = 0.8\underline{1}00724 \frac{\text{J}}{\text{g} \cdot \text{°C}} = 0.81 \frac{\text{J}}{\text{g} \cdot \text{°C}}$$

Because the specific heat capacity of gold is 0.128 J/g · °C, this substance is not gold.

Check: The units (J/g · °C) are correct. The magnitude of the answer (1 J/g · °C) makes physical sense because the mass of the substance is much less than the mass of the water by a factor of ~5.5 and the temperature change for the substance is greater than the temperature change of the water by a factor of ~29; so the heat capacity of the unknown substance will be a factor of ~5.2 smaller than the water, but not as low as 0.128 J/g · °C.

Calorimetry

6.39 $\Delta H_{rxn} = q_p$ and $\Delta E_{rxn} = q_V = \Delta H - P\Delta V$. Because combustions always involve expansions, expansions do work and therefore have a negative value. Combustions are always exothermic and therefore have a negative value. This means that ΔE_{rxn} is more negative than $\Delta H°_{rxn}$; so A (−25.9 kJ) is the constant volume process, and B (−23.3 kJ) is the constant pressure process.

6.40   Constant volume conditions should be used. Because $\Delta E = q + w$ and $w = -P\Delta V$, at constant V, $w = 0$ and all of the energy is released at heat ($\Delta E_{rxn} = q_V$). At constant P, $\Delta H_{rxn} = q_p$ and $\Delta E_{rxn} = q_p = \Delta H - P\Delta V$. Because combustions always involve expansions, expansions do work; so they have a negative value. Combustions are always exothermic, so they have a negative value. This means that ΔE_{rxn} is more negative than $\Delta H°_{rxn}$, so more heat will be generated in a constant V process.

6.41   **Given:** 0.514 g biphenyl ($C_{12}H_{10}$); bomb calorimeter; T_i = 25.8 °C; T_f = 29.4 °C; C_{cal} = 5.86 kJ/°C   **Find:** ΔE_{rxn}
Conceptual Plan: $T_i, T_f \rightarrow \Delta T$ then $\Delta T, C_{cal} \rightarrow q_{cal} \rightarrow q_{rxn}$ then g $C_{12}H_{10} \rightarrow$ mol $C_{12}H_{10}$

$$\Delta T = T_f - T_i \qquad q_{cal} = C_{cal}\Delta T \quad q_{cal} = -q_{rxn} \qquad \frac{1 \text{ mol}}{154.20 \text{ g}}$$

then q_{rxn}, **mol** $C_{12}H_{10} \rightarrow \Delta E_{rxn}$

$$\Delta E_{rxn} = \frac{q_V}{\text{mol } C_{12}H_{10}}$$

Solution: $\Delta T = T_f - T_i = 29.4\ °C - 25.8\ °C = 3.6\ °C$ then $q_{cal} = C_{cal}\Delta T = 5.86\ \dfrac{kJ}{°C} \times 3.6\ °C = 2\underline{1}.096\ kJ$

then $q_{cal} = -q_{rxn} = -2\underline{1}.096\ kJ$ and $0.514\ \text{g}\ C_{12}H_{10} \times \dfrac{1\ mol\ C_{12}H_{10}}{154.20\ \text{g}\ C_{12}H_{10}} = 0.003333\underline{3}33\ mol\ C_{12}H_{10}$ then

$\Delta E_{rxn} = \dfrac{q_V}{mol\ C_{12}H_{10}} = \dfrac{-2\underline{1}.096\ kJ}{0.003333\underline{3}33\ mol\ C_{12}H_{10}} = -6.3 \times 10^3\ kJ/mol$

Check: The units (kJ/mol) are correct. The magnitude of the answer (-6000) makes physical sense because such a large amount of heat is generated from a very small amount of biphenyl.

6.42 **Given:** 1.025 g naphthalene ($C_{10}H_8$); bomb calorimeter; $T_i = 24.25\ °C$; $T_f = 32.33\ °C$; $C_{cal} = 5.11\ kJ/°C$
Find: ΔE_{rxn}
Conceptual Plan: $T_i, T_f \rightarrow \Delta T$ then $\Delta T, C_{cal} \rightarrow q_{cal} \rightarrow q_{rxn}$ then g $C_{10}H_8 \rightarrow$ mol $C_{10}H_8$

$$\Delta T = T_f - T_i \qquad\qquad q_{cal} = C_{cal}\Delta T \quad q_{cal} = -q_{rxn} \qquad\qquad \dfrac{1\ mol}{128.16\ g}$$

then q_{rxn}, mol $C_{10}H_8 \rightarrow \Delta E_{rxn}$

$$\Delta E_{rxn} = \dfrac{q_V}{mol\ C_{10}H_8}$$

Solution: $\Delta T = T_f - T_i = 32.33\ °C - 24.25\ °C = 8.08\ °C$ then $q_{cal} = C_{cal}\Delta T = 5.11\ \dfrac{kJ}{°C} \times 8.08\ °C = 41.2\underline{8}88\ kJ$

then $q_{cal} = -q_{rxn} = -41.2\underline{8}88\ kJ$ and $1.025\ \text{g}\ C_{10}H_8 \times \dfrac{1\ mol\ C_{10}H_8}{128.16\ \text{g}\ C_{10}H_8} = 0.007997\underline{8}15\ mol\ C_{10}H_8$ then

$\Delta E_{rxn} = \dfrac{q_V}{mol\ C_{10}H_8} = \dfrac{-41.2\underline{8}88\ kJ}{0.007997\underline{8}15\ mol\ C_{10}H_8} = -5.16 \times 10^3\ kJ/mol$

Check: The units (kJ/mol) are correct. The magnitude of the answer (-5000) makes physical sense because such a large amount of heat is generated from a very small amount of naphthalene.

6.43 **Given:** 0.103 g zinc; coffee-cup calorimeter; $T_i = 22.5\ °C$; $T_f = 23.7\ °C$; 50.0 mL solution; $d(\text{solution}) = 1.0\ \text{g/mL}$;
$C_{soln} = 4.18\ kJ/g \cdot °C$ **Find:** ΔH_{rxn}
Conceptual Plan: $T_i, T_f \rightarrow \Delta T$ and mL soln $\rightarrow$ g soln then $\Delta T, C_{soln} \rightarrow q_{cal} \rightarrow q_{rxn}$ then

$$\Delta T = T_f - T_i \qquad\qquad \dfrac{1.0\ g}{1.0\ mL} \qquad\qquad q_{soln} = m\ C_{soln}\ \Delta T \quad q_{soln} = -q_{rxn}$$

g Zn $\rightarrow$ mol Zn then q_{rxn}, mol Zn $\rightarrow \Delta H_{rxn}$

$$\dfrac{1\ mol}{65.38\ g} \qquad\qquad \Delta H_{rxn} = \dfrac{q_p}{mol\ Zn}$$

Solution: $\Delta T = T_f - T_i = 23.7\ °C - 22.5\ °C = 1.2\ °C$ and $50.0\ \text{mL} \times \dfrac{1.0\ g}{1.0\ \text{mL}} = 50.0\ g$ then

$q_{soln} = m\ C_{soln}\ \Delta T = 50.0\ \text{g} \times 4.18\ \dfrac{J}{\text{g} \cdot °C} \times 1.2\ °C = 2\underline{5}0.8\ J$ then $q_{soln} = -q_{rxn} = -2\underline{5}0.8\ J$ and

$0.103\ \text{g}\ Zn \times \dfrac{1\ mol\ Zn}{65.38\ \text{g}\ Zn} = 0.00157\underline{5}41\ mol\ Zn$ then

$\Delta H_{rxn} = \dfrac{q_p}{mol\ Zn} = \dfrac{-2\underline{5}0.8\ J}{0.00157\underline{5}41\ mol\ Zn} = -1.6 \times 10^5\ J/mol = -1.6 \times 10^2\ kJ/mol$

Check: The units (kJ/mol) are correct. The magnitude of the answer (-160) makes physical sense because such a large amount of heat is generated from a very small amount of zinc.

6.44 **Given:** 1.25 g NH_4NO_3; coffee-cup calorimeter; $T_i = 25.8\ °C$; $T_f = 21.9\ °C$; 25.0 mL solution; $d(\text{solution}) = 1.0\ \text{g/mL}$; $C_{soln} = 4.18\ kJ/g\ °C$ **Find:** ΔH_{rxn}
Conceptual Plan: $T_i, T_f \rightarrow \Delta T$ and mL soln $\rightarrow$ g soln then $\Delta T, C_{soln} \rightarrow q_{cal} \rightarrow q_{rxn}$ then

$$\Delta T = T_f - T_i \qquad\qquad \dfrac{1.0\ g}{1.0\ mL} \qquad\qquad q_{soln} = m\ C_{soln}\ \Delta T \quad q_{soln} = -q_{rxn}$$

g $NH_4NO_3 \rightarrow$ mol NH_4NO_3 then q_{rxn}, mol $NH_4NO_3 \rightarrow \Delta H_{rxn}$

$$\dfrac{1\ mol}{80.05\ g} \qquad\qquad \Delta H_{rxn} = \dfrac{q_p}{mol\ NH_4NO_3}$$

Solution: $\Delta T = T_f - T_i = 21.9\,°C - 25.8\,°C = -3.9\,°C$ and $25.0\ \cancel{mL} \times \dfrac{1.0\ g}{1.0\ \cancel{mL}} = 25.0\ g$ then

$q_{soln} = mC_{soln}\Delta T = 25.0\ \cancel{g} \times 4.18\ \dfrac{J}{\cancel{g}\cdot\cancel{°C}} \times (-3.9\ \cancel{°C}) = -4\underline{0}7.55\ J$ then $q_{soln} = -q_{rxn} = 4\underline{0}7.55\ J$ and

$1.25\ \cancel{g\ NH_4NO_3} \times \dfrac{1\ mol\ NH_4NO_3}{80.05\ \cancel{g\ NH_4NO_3}} = 0.015\underline{6}152\ mol\ NH_4NO_3$ then

$\Delta H_{rxn} = \dfrac{q_P}{mol\ NH_4NO_3} = \dfrac{4\underline{0}7.55\ J}{0.015\underline{6}152\ mol\ NH_4NO_3} = 2.6 \times 10^4\ J/mol = 26\ kJ/mol$

Check: The units (kJ/mol) are correct. The magnitude of the answer (26) makes physical sense because such a small amount of heat is absorbed.

Quantitative Relationships Involving ΔH and Hess's Law

6.45   (a)   Because $A + B \rightarrow 2\,C$ has ΔH_1, then $2\,C \rightarrow A + B$ will have a $\Delta H_2 = -\Delta H_1$. When the reaction direction is reversed, it changes from exothermic to endothermic (or vice versa); so the sign of ΔH changes.

        (b)   Because $A + \frac{1}{2}B \rightarrow C$ has ΔH_1, then $2\,A + B \rightarrow 2\,C$ will have a $\Delta H_2 = 2\,\Delta H_1$. When the reaction amount doubles, the amount of heat (or ΔH) doubles.

        (c)   Because $A \rightarrow B + 2\,C$ has ΔH_1, then $\frac{1}{2}A \rightarrow \frac{1}{2}B + C$ will have a $\Delta H_{1'} = \frac{1}{2}\Delta H_1$. When the reaction amount is cut in half, the amount of heat (or ΔH) is cut in half. Then $\frac{1}{2}B + C \rightarrow \frac{1}{2}A$ will have a $\Delta H_2 = -\Delta H_{1'} = -\frac{1}{2}\Delta H_1$ When the reaction direction is reversed, it changes from exothermic to endothermic (or vice versa); so the sign of ΔH changes.

6.46   (a)   Because $A + 2\,B \rightarrow C + 3\,D$ has $\Delta H = 155\ kJ$, then $3A + 6\,B \rightarrow 3\,C + 9\,D$ will have a $\Delta H' = 3\,\Delta H = 3(155\ kJ) = 465\ kJ$. When the reaction amount triples, the amount of heat (or ΔH) triples.

        (b)   Because $A + 2\,B \rightarrow C + 3\,D$ has $\Delta H = 155\ kJ$, then $C + 3\,D \rightarrow 3\,A + 6\,B$ will have a $\Delta H' = -\Delta H = -155\ kJ$. When the reaction direction is reversed, it changes from endothermic to exothermic; so the sign of ΔH changes.

        (c)   Because $A + 2\,B \rightarrow C + 3\,D$ has $\Delta H = 155\ kJ$, then $\frac{1}{2}A + B \rightarrow \frac{1}{2}C + \frac{3}{2}D$ will have a $\Delta H' = \frac{1}{2}\Delta H = \frac{1}{2}(155\ kJ) = 77.5\ kJ$. When the reaction amount is cut in half, the amount of heat (or ΔH) is cut in half. Then $\frac{1}{2}C + \frac{3}{2}D \rightarrow \frac{1}{2}A + B$ will have a $\Delta H'' = -H' = -77.5\ kJ$. When the reaction direction is reversed, the sign of it changes from endothermic to exothermic; so the sign of ΔH changes.

6.47   Because the first reaction has Fe_2O_3 as a product and the reaction of interest has it as a reactant, we need to reverse the first reaction. When the reaction direction is reversed, ΔH changes.
       $Fe_2O_3(s) \rightarrow 2\,Fe(s) + \frac{3}{2}O_2(g)$ $\Delta H = +824.2\ kJ$
       Because the second reaction has 1 mole of CO as a reactant and the reaction of interest has 3 moles of CO as a reactant, we need to multiply the second reaction and the ΔH by 3.
       $3[CO(g) + \frac{1}{2}O_2(g) \rightarrow CO_2(g)]$ $\Delta H = 3(-282.7\ kJ) = -848.1\ kJ$
       Hess's law states that the ΔH of the net reaction is the sum of the ΔH of the steps.
       The rewritten reactions are as follows:

       $Fe_2O_3(s) \rightarrow 2\,Fe(s) + \frac{3}{2}\cancel{O_2(g)}$ $\Delta H = +824.2\ kJ$
       $3\,CO(g) + \frac{3}{2}\cancel{O_2(g)} \rightarrow 3\,CO_2(g)$ $\Delta H = -848.1\ kJ$
       $\overline{Fe_2O_3(s) + 3\,CO(g) \rightarrow 2\,Fe(s) + 3\,CO_2(g)}$ $\Delta H_{rxn} = -23.9\ kJ$

6.48   Because the first reaction has $CaCO_3$ as a product and the reaction of interest has it as a product, we simply write the first reaction and the ΔH unchanged.
       $Ca(s) + CO_2(g) + \frac{1}{2}O_2(g) \rightarrow CaCO_3(s)$ $\Delta H = -814.1\ kJ$
       Because the second reaction has 2 moles of CaO as a product and the reaction of interest has 1 mole of CaO as a reactant, we need to reverse the direction of the second reaction and multiply it by $\frac{1}{2}$. The sign of the ΔH in the second reaction is changed and is multiplied by $\frac{1}{2}$.
       $\frac{1}{2}[2\,CaO(s) \rightarrow 2\,Ca(s) + O_2(g)]$ $\Delta H = -\frac{1}{2}(-1269.8\ kJ) = +634.9\ kJ$
       Hess's law states that the ΔH of the net reaction is the sum of the ΔH of the steps.

The rewritten reactions are as follows:

$$\cancel{Ca(s)} + CO_2(g) + \tfrac{1}{2}\cancel{O_2(g)} \rightarrow CaCO_3(s) \qquad \Delta H = -814.1 \text{ kJ}$$
$$\underline{CaO(s) \rightarrow \cancel{Ca(s)} + \tfrac{1}{2}\cancel{O_2(g)} \qquad\qquad \Delta H = +634.9 \text{ kJ}}$$
$$CaO(s) + CO_2(g) \rightarrow CaCO_3(s) \qquad \Delta H_{rxn} = -179.2 \text{ kJ}$$

6.49 Because the first reaction has C_5H_{12} as a reactant and the reaction of interest has it as a product, we need to reverse the first reaction. When the reaction direction is reversed, the sign of ΔH changes.

$$5\,CO_2(g) + 6\,H_2O(g) \rightarrow C_5H_{12}(l) + 8\,O_2(g) \qquad \Delta H = +3271.5 \text{ kJ}$$

Because the second reaction has 1 mole of C as a reactant and the reaction of interest has 5 moles of C as a reactant, we need to multiply the second reaction and the ΔH by 5.

$$5[C(s) + O_2(g) \rightarrow CO_2(g)] \qquad \Delta H = 5(-393.5 \text{ kJ}) = -1967.5 \text{ kJ}$$

Because the third reaction has 2 moles of H_2 as a reactant and the reaction of interest has 6 moles of H_2 as a reactant, we need to multiply the third reaction and the ΔH by 3.

$$3[2\,H_2(g) + O_2(g) \rightarrow 2\,H_2O(g)] \qquad \Delta H = 3(-483.5 \text{ kJ}) = -1450.5 \text{ kJ}$$

Hess's law states that the ΔH of the net reaction is the sum of the ΔH of the steps.

The rewritten reactions are as follows:

$$5\,\cancel{CO_2(g)} + 6\,\cancel{H_2O(g)} \rightarrow C_5H_{12}(l) + 8\,\cancel{O_2(g)} \qquad \Delta H = +3271.5 \text{ kJ}$$
$$5\,C(s) + 5\,\cancel{O_2(g)} \rightarrow 5\,\cancel{CO_2(g)} \qquad\qquad \Delta H = -1967.5 \text{ kJ}$$
$$\underline{6\,H_2(g) + 3\,\cancel{O_2(g)} \rightarrow 6\,\cancel{H_2O(g)} \qquad\qquad \Delta H = -1450.5 \text{ kJ}}$$
$$5\,C(s) + 6\,H_2(g) \rightarrow C_5H_{12}(l) \qquad \Delta H_{rxn} = -146.5 \text{ kJ}$$

6.50 Because the first reaction has CH_4 as a product and the reaction of interest has it as a reactant, we need to reverse the first reaction. When the reaction direction is reversed, ΔH changes.

$$CH_4(g) \rightarrow C(s) + 2\,H_2(g) \qquad \Delta H = +74.6 \text{ kJ}$$

Because the second reaction has CCl_4 as a product and the reaction of interest has it as a product, we simply write the first reaction and the ΔH is unchanged.

$$C(s) + 2\,Cl_2(g) \rightarrow CCl_4(g) \qquad \Delta H = -95.7 \text{ kJ}$$

Because the third reaction has 2 moles of HCl as a product and the reaction of interest has 4 moles of HCl as a product, we need to multiply the third reaction and the ΔH by 2.

$$2[H_2(g) + Cl_2(g) \rightarrow 2\,HCl(g)] \qquad \Delta H = 2(-184.6 \text{ kJ}) = -369.2 \text{ kJ}$$

Hess's law states that the ΔH of the net reaction is the sum of the ΔH of the steps.

The rewritten reactions are as follows:

$$CH_4(g) \rightarrow \cancel{C(s)} + 2\,\cancel{H_2(g)} \qquad\qquad \Delta H = +74.6 \text{ kJ}$$
$$\cancel{C(s)} + 2\,Cl_2(g) \rightarrow CCl_4(g) \qquad\qquad \Delta H = -95.7 \text{ kJ}$$
$$\underline{2\,\cancel{H_2(g)} + 2\,Cl_2(g) \rightarrow 4\,HCl(g) \qquad\quad \Delta H = -369.2 \text{ kJ}}$$
$$CH_4(g) + 4\,Cl_2(g) \rightarrow CCl_4(g) + 4\,HCl(g) \qquad \Delta H_{rxn} = -390.3 \text{ kJ}$$

Enthalpies of Formation and ΔH

6.51 (a) $\tfrac{1}{2}N_2(g) + \tfrac{3}{2}H_2(g) \rightarrow NH_3(g) \qquad \Delta H_f^\circ = -45.9 \text{ kJ/mol}$

(b) $C(s) + O_2(g) \rightarrow CO_2(g) \qquad \Delta H_f^\circ = -393.5 \text{ kJ/mol}$

(c) $2\,Fe(s) + \tfrac{3}{2}O_2(g) \rightarrow Fe_2O_3(s) \qquad \Delta H_f^\circ = -824.2 \text{ kJ/mol}$

(d) $C(s) + 2\,H_2(g) \rightarrow CH_4(g) \qquad \Delta H_f^\circ = -74.6 \text{ kJ/mol}$

6.52 (a) $\tfrac{1}{2}N_2(g) + O_2(g) \rightarrow NO_2(g) \qquad \Delta H_f^\circ = 33.2 \text{ kJ/mol}$

(b) $Mg(s) + C(s) + \tfrac{3}{2}O_2(g) \rightarrow MgCO_3(s) \qquad \Delta H_f^\circ = -1095.8 \text{ kJ/mol}$

(c) $2\,C(s) + 2\,H_2(g) \rightarrow C_2H_4(g) \qquad \Delta H_f^\circ = 52.4 \text{ kJ/mol}$

(d) $C(s) + 2\,H_2(g) + \tfrac{1}{2}O_2(g) \rightarrow CH_3OH(l) \qquad \Delta H_f^\circ = -238.6 \text{ kJ/mol}$

6.53 **Given:** $N_2H_4(l) + N_2O_4(g) \rightarrow 2\,N_2O(g) + 2\,H_2O(g)$ **Find:** ΔH_{rxn}°
Conceptual Plan: $\Delta H_{rxn}^\circ = \sum n_P \Delta H_f^\circ(\text{products}) - \sum n_R \Delta H_f^\circ(\text{reactants})$

Solution:

Reactant/Product	ΔH_f° (kJ/mol, from Appendix IIB)
$N_2H_4(l)$	50.6
$N_2O_4(g)$	9.16
$N_2O(g)$	81.6
$H_2O(g)$	−241.8

Be sure to pull data for the correct formula and phase.

$$\Delta H_{rxn}^\circ = \sum n_P \Delta H_f^\circ (\text{products}) - \sum n_R \Delta H_f^\circ (\text{reactants})$$
$$= [2(\Delta H_f^\circ(N_2O(g))) + 2(\Delta H_f^\circ(H_2O(g)))] - [1(\Delta H_f^\circ(N_2H_4(l))) + 1(\Delta H_f^\circ(N_2O_4(g)))]$$
$$= [2(81.6 \text{ kJ}) + 2(-241.8 \text{ kJ})] - [1(50.6 \text{ kJ}) + 1(9.16 \text{ kJ})]$$
$$= [-320.4 \text{ kJ}] - [59.76 \text{ kJ}]$$
$$= -380.2 \text{ kJ}$$

Check: The units (kJ) are correct. The answer is negative, which means that the reaction is exothermic. The answer is dominated by the negative heat of formation of water.

6.54   **Given:** $C_5H_{12}(l) + 8 O_2(g) \rightarrow 5 CO_2(g) + 6 H_2O(g)$ **Find:** ΔH_{rxn}°
Conceptual Plan: $\Delta H_{rxn}^\circ = \sum n_P \Delta H_f^\circ (\text{products}) - \sum n_R \Delta H_f^\circ (\text{reactants})$
Solution:

Reactant/Product	ΔH_f° (kJ/mol, from Appendix IIB)
$C_5H_{12}(l)$	−146.8
$O_2(g)$	0.0
$CO_2(g)$	−393.5
$H_2O(g)$	−241.8

Be sure to pull data for the correct formula and phase.

$$\Delta H_{rxn}^\circ = \sum n_P \Delta H_f^\circ (\text{products}) - \sum n_R \Delta H_f^\circ (\text{reactants})$$
$$= [5(\Delta H_f^\circ(CO_2(g))) + 6(\Delta H_f^\circ(H_2O(g)))] - [1(\Delta H_f^\circ(C_5H_{12}(l))) + 8(\Delta H_f^\circ(O_2(g)))]$$
$$= [5(-393.5 \text{ kJ}) + 6(-241.8 \text{ kJ})] - [1(-146.8 \text{ kJ}) + 8(0.0 \text{ kJ})]$$
$$= [-3418.3 \text{ kJ}] - [-146.8 \text{ kJ}]$$
$$= -3271.5 \text{ kJ}$$

Check: The units (kJ) are correct. The answer is negative, which means that the reaction is exothermic, which is typical for combustion reactions.

6.55   (a)   **Given:** $C_2H_4(g) + H_2(g) \rightarrow C_2H_6(g)$ **Find:** ΔH_{rxn}°
Conceptual Plan: $\Delta H_{rxn}^\circ = \sum n_P \Delta H_f^\circ (\text{products}) - \sum n_R \Delta H_f^\circ (\text{reactants})$
Solution:

Reactant/Product	ΔH_f° (kJ/mol, from Appendix IIB)
$C_2H_4(g)$	52.4
$H_2(g)$	0.0
$C_2H_6(g)$	−84.68

Be sure to pull data for the correct formula and phase.

$$\Delta H_{rxn}^\circ = \sum n_P \Delta H_f^\circ (\text{products}) - \sum n_R \Delta H_f^\circ (\text{reactants})$$
$$= [1(\Delta H_f^\circ(C_2H_6(g)))] - [1(\Delta H_f^\circ(C_2H_4(g))) + 1(\Delta H_f^\circ(H_2(g)))]$$
$$= [1(-84.68 \text{ kJ})] - [1(52.4 \text{ kJ}) + 1(0.0 \text{ kJ})]$$
$$= [-84.68 \text{ kJ}] - [52.4 \text{ kJ}]$$
$$= -137.1 \text{ kJ}$$

Check: The units (kJ) are correct. The answer is negative, which means that the reaction is exothermic. Both hydrocarbon terms are negative, so the final answer is negative.

(b)   **Given:** $CO(g) + H_2O(g) \rightarrow H_2(g) + CO_2(g)$ **Find:** ΔH_{rxn}°
Conceptual Plan: $\Delta H_{rxn}^\circ = \sum n_P \Delta H_f^\circ (\text{products}) - \sum n_R \Delta H_f^\circ (\text{reactants})$

Solution:

Reactant/Product	ΔH_f° (kJ/mol, from Appendix IIB)
$CO(g)$	-110.5
$H_2O(g)$	-241.8
$H_2(g)$	0.0
$CO_2(g)$	-393.5

Be sure to pull data for the correct formula and phase.

$$\Delta H_{rxn}^\circ = \sum n_P \Delta H_f^\circ (\text{products}) - \sum n_R \Delta H_f^\circ (\text{reactants})$$
$$= [1(\Delta H_f^\circ(H_2(g))) + 1(\Delta H_f^\circ(CO_2(g)))] - [1(\Delta H_f^\circ(CO(g))) + 1(\Delta H_f^\circ(H_2O(g)))]$$
$$= [1(0.0 \text{ kJ}) + 1(-393.5 \text{ kJ})] - [1(-110.5 \text{ kJ}) + 1(-241.8 \text{ kJ})]$$
$$= [-393.5 \text{ kJ}] - [-352.3 \text{ kJ}]$$
$$= -41.2 \text{ kJ}$$

Check: The units (kJ) are correct. The answer is negative, which means that the reaction is exothermic.

(c)   **Given:** $3 NO_2(g) + H_2O(l) \rightarrow 2 HNO_3(aq) + NO(g)$ **Find:** ΔH_{rxn}°
       Conceptual Plan: $\Delta H_{rxn}^\circ = \sum n_P \Delta H_f^\circ (\text{products}) - \sum n_R \Delta H_f^\circ (\text{reactants})$
       Solution:

Reactant/Product	ΔH_f° (kJ/mol, from Appendix IIB)
$NO_2(g)$	33.2
$H_2O(l)$	-285.8
$HNO_3(aq)$	-207
$NO(g)$	91.3

Be sure to pull data for the correct formula and phase.

$$\Delta H_{rxn}^\circ = \sum n_P \Delta H_f^\circ (\text{products}) - \sum n_R \Delta H_f^\circ (\text{reactants})$$
$$= [2(\Delta H_f^\circ(HNO_3(aq))) + 1(\Delta H_f^\circ(NO(g)))] - [3(\Delta H_f^\circ(NO_2(g))) + 1(\Delta H_f^\circ(H_2O(l)))]$$
$$= [2(-207 \text{ kJ}) + 1(91.3 \text{ kJ})] - [3(33.2 \text{ kJ}) + 1(-285.8 \text{ kJ})]$$
$$= [-322.7 \text{ kJ}] - [-186.2 \text{ kJ}]$$
$$= -137 \text{ kJ}$$

Check: The units (kJ) are correct. The answer is negative, which means that the reaction is exothermic.

(d)   **Given:** $Cr_2O_3(s) + 3 CO(g) \rightarrow 2 Cr(s) + 3 CO_2(g)$ **Find:** ΔH_{rxn}°
       Conceptual Plan: $\Delta H_{rxn}^\circ = \sum n_P \Delta H_f^\circ (\text{products}) - \sum n_R \Delta H_f^\circ (\text{reactants})$
       Solution:

Reactant/Product	ΔH_f° (kJ/mol, from Appendix IIB)
$Cr_2O_3(s)$	-1139.7
$CO(g)$	-110.5
$Cr(s)$	0.0
$CO_2(g)$	-393.5

Be sure to pull data for the correct formula and phase.

$$\Delta H_{rxn}^\circ = \sum n_P \Delta H_f^\circ (\text{products}) - \sum n_R \Delta H_f^\circ (\text{reactants})$$
$$= [2(\Delta H_f^\circ(Cr(s))) + 3(\Delta H_f^\circ(CO_2(g)))] - [1(\Delta H_f^\circ(Cr_2O_3(s))) + 3(\Delta H_f^\circ(CO(g)))]$$
$$= [2(0.0 \text{ kJ}) + 3(-393.5 \text{ kJ})] - [1(-1139.7 \text{ kJ}) + 3(-110.5 \text{ kJ})]$$
$$= [-1180.5 \text{ kJ}] - [-1471.2 \text{ kJ}]$$
$$= 290.7 \text{ kJ}$$

Check: The units (kJ) are correct. The answer is positive, which means that the reaction is endothermic.

6.56   (a)   **Given:** $2 H_2S(g) + 3 O_2(g) \rightarrow 2 H_2O(l) + 2 SO_2(g)$ **Find:** ΔH_{rxn}°
               Conceptual Plan: $\Delta H_{rxn}^\circ = \sum n_P \Delta H_f^\circ (\text{products}) - \sum n_R \Delta H_f^\circ (\text{reactants})$

Solution:

Reactant/Product	ΔH_f° (kJ/mol, from Appendix IIB)
$H_2S(g)$	-20.6
$O_2(g)$	0.0
$H_2O(l)$	-285.8
$SO_2(g)$	-296.8

Be sure to pull data for the correct formula and phase.

$$\Delta H_{rxn}^\circ = \sum n_P \Delta H_f^\circ (\text{products}) - \sum n_R \Delta H_f^\circ (\text{reactants})$$
$$= [2(\Delta H_f^\circ(H_2O(l))) + 2(\Delta H_f^\circ(SO_2(g)))] - [2(\Delta H_f^\circ(H_2S(g))) + 3(\Delta H_f^\circ(O_2(g)))]$$
$$= [2(-285.8 \text{ kJ}) + 2(-296.8 \text{ kJ})] - [2(-20.6 \text{ kJ}) + 3(0.0 \text{ kJ})]$$
$$= [-1165.2 \text{ kJ}] - [-41.2 \text{ kJ}]$$
$$= -1124.0 \text{ kJ}$$

Check: The units (kJ) are correct. The answer is negative, which means that the reaction is exothermic.

(b)   **Given:** $SO_2(g) + 1/2\,O_2(g) \rightarrow SO_3(g)$ **Find:** ΔH_{rxn}°
Conceptual Plan: $\Delta H_{rxn}^\circ = \sum n_P \Delta H_f^\circ (\text{products}) - \sum n_R \Delta H_f^\circ (\text{reactants})$
Solution:

Reactant/Product	ΔH_f° (kJ/mol, from Appendix IIB)
$SO_2(g)$	-296.8
$O_2(g)$	0.0
$SO_3(g)$	-395.7

Be sure to pull data for the correct formula and phase.

$$\Delta H_{rxn}^\circ = \sum n_P \Delta H_f^\circ (\text{products}) - \sum n_R \Delta H_f^\circ (\text{reactants})$$
$$= [1(\Delta H_f^\circ(SO_3(g)))] - [1(\Delta H_f^\circ(SO_2(g))) + 1/2(\Delta H_f^\circ(O_2(g)))]$$
$$= [1(-395.7 \text{ kJ})] - [1(-296.8 \text{ kJ}) + 1/2(0.0 \text{ kJ})]$$
$$= [-395.7 \text{ kJ}] - [-296.8 \text{ kJ}]$$
$$= -98.9 \text{ kJ}$$

Check: The units (kJ) are correct. The answer is negative, which means that the reaction is exothermic. The SO_3 has a lower heat of formation than SO_2, so we expect an exothermic reaction.

(c)   **Given:** $C(s) + H_2O(g) \rightarrow CO(g) + H_2(g)$ **Find:** ΔH_{rxn}°
Conceptual Plan: $\Delta H_{rxn}^\circ = \sum n_P \Delta H_f^\circ (\text{products}) - \sum n_R \Delta H_f^\circ (\text{reactants})$
Solution:

Reactant/Product	ΔH_f° (kJ/mol, from Appendix IIB)
$C(s)$	0.0
$H_2O(g)$	-241.8
$CO(g)$	-110.5
$H_2(g)$	0.0

Be sure to pull data for the correct formula and phase.

$$\Delta H_{rxn}^\circ = \sum n_P \Delta H_f^\circ (\text{products}) - \sum n_R \Delta H_f^\circ (\text{reactants})$$
$$= [1(\Delta H_f^\circ(CO(g))) + 1(\Delta H_f^\circ(H_2(g)))] - [1(\Delta H_f^\circ(C(s))) + 1(\Delta H_f^\circ(H_2O(g)))]$$
$$= [1(-110.5 \text{ kJ}) + 1(0.0 \text{ kJ})] - [1(0.0 \text{ kJ}) + 1(-241.8 \text{ kJ})]$$
$$= [-110.5 \text{ kJ}] - [-241.8 \text{ kJ}]$$
$$= 131.3 \text{ kJ}$$

Check: The units (kJ) are correct. The answer is positive, which means that the reaction is endothermic. The CO has a smaller (less negative) heat of formation than H_2O, so we expect an endothermic reaction.

(d)   **Given:** $N_2O_4(g) + 4\,H_2(g) \rightarrow N_2(g) + 4\,H_2O(g)$ **Find:** ΔH_{rxn}°
Conceptual Plan: $\Delta H_{rxn}^\circ = \sum n_P \Delta H_f^\circ (\text{products}) - \sum n_R \Delta H_f^\circ (\text{reactants})$

Solution:

Reactant/Product	ΔH_f° (kJ/mol, from Appendix IIB)
$N_2O_4(g)$	9.16
$H_2(g)$	0.0
$N_2(g)$	0.0
$H_2O(g)$	−241.8

Be sure to pull data for the correct formula and phase.

$\Delta H_{rxn}^\circ = \sum n_P \Delta H_f^\circ (\text{products}) - \sum n_R \Delta H_f^\circ (\text{reactants})$

$= [1(\Delta H_f^\circ(N_2(g))) + 4(\Delta H_f^\circ(H_2O(g)))] - [1(\Delta H_f^\circ(N_2O_4(g))) + 4(\Delta H_f^\circ(H_2(g)))]$

$= [1(0.0 \text{ kJ}) + 4(-241.8 \text{ kJ})] - [1(9.16 \text{ kJ}) + 4(0.0 \text{ kJ})]$

$= [-967.2 \text{ kJ}] - [9.16 \text{ kJ}]$

$= -973.4 \text{ kJ}$

Check: The units (kJ) are correct. The answer is negative, which means that the reaction is exothermic. The H_2O has a lower heat of formation than N_2O_4, so we expect an exothermic reaction.

6.57   **Given:** form glucose ($C_6H_{12}O_6$) and oxygen from sunlight, carbon dioxide, and water   **Find:** ΔH_{rxn}°
Conceptual Plan: write balanced reaction then $\Delta H_{rxn}^\circ = \sum n_P \Delta H_f^\circ (\text{products}) - \sum n_R \Delta H_f^\circ (\text{reactants})$
Solution: $6 CO_2(g) + 6 H_2O(l) \rightarrow C_6H_{12}O_6(s) + 6 O_2(g)$

Reactant/Product	ΔH_f° (kJ/mol, from Appendix IIB)
$CO_2(g)$	−393.5
$H_2O(l)$	−285.8
$C_6H_{12}O(s)$	−1273.3
$O_2(g)$	0.0

Be sure to pull data for the correct formula and phase.

$\Delta H_{rxn}^\circ = \sum n_P \Delta H_f^\circ (\text{products}) - \sum n_R \Delta H_f^\circ (\text{reactants})$

$= [1(\Delta H_f^\circ(C_6H_{12}O(s))) + 6(\Delta H_f^\circ(O_2(g)))] - [6(\Delta H_f^\circ(CO_2(g))) + 6(\Delta H_f^\circ(H_2O(l)))]$

$= [1(-1273.3 \text{ kJ}) + 6(0.0 \text{ kJ})] - [6(-393.5 \text{ kJ}) + 6(-285.8 \text{ kJ})]$

$= [-1273.3 \text{ kJ}] - [-4075.8 \text{ kJ}]$

$= +2802.5 \text{ kJ}$

Check: The units (kJ) are correct. The answer is positive, which means that the reaction is endothermic. The reaction requires the input of light energy, so we expect that this will be an endothermic reaction.

6.58   **Given:** ethanol (C_2H_5OH) combustion   **Find:** ΔH_{rxn}°
Conceptual Plan: write balanced reaction then $\Delta H_{rxn}^\circ = \sum n_P \Delta H_f^\circ (\text{products}) - \sum n_R \Delta H_f^\circ (\text{reactants})$
Solution: Combustion is the combination with oxygen to form carbon dioxide and water:
$C_2H_5OH(l) + 3 O_2(g) \rightarrow 2 CO_2(g) + 3 H_2O(g)$

Reactant/Product	ΔH_f° (kJ/mol, from Appendix IIB)
$C_2H_5OH(l)$	−277.6
$O_2(g)$	0.0
$CO_2(g)$	−393.5
$H_2O(g)$	−241.8

Be sure to pull data for the correct formula and phase.

$\Delta H_{rxn}^\circ = \sum n_P \Delta H_f^\circ (\text{products}) - \sum n_R \Delta H_f^\circ (\text{reactants})$

$= [2(\Delta H_f^\circ(CO_2(g))) + 3(\Delta H_f^\circ(H_2O(g)))] - [1(\Delta H_f^\circ(C_2H_5OH(l))) + 3(\Delta H_f^\circ(O_2(g)))]$

$= [2(-393.5 \text{ kJ}) + 3(-241.8 \text{ kJ})] - [1(-277.6 \text{ kJ}) + 3(0.0 \text{ kJ})]$

$= [-1512.4 \text{ kJ}] - [-277.6 \text{ kJ}]$

$= -1234.8 \text{ kJ}$

Check: The units (kJ) are correct. The answer is negative, which means that the reaction is exothermic; this is typical for combustion reactions.

6.59   **Given:** $2\ CH_3NO_2(l) + 3/2\ O_2(g) \rightarrow 2\ CO_2(g) + 3\ H_2O(l) + N_2(g)$ and $\Delta H°_{rxn} = -1418.4$ kJ/mol
        Find: $\Delta H°_f(CH_3NO_2(l))$
        Conceptual Plan: Fill known values into $\Delta H°_{rxn} = \sum n_P \Delta H°_f(\text{products}) - \sum n_R \Delta H°_f(\text{reactants})$ **and rearrange to solve for** $\Delta H°_f(CH_3NO_2(l))$.
        Solution:

Reactant/Product	$\Delta H°_f$(kJ/mol, from Appendix IIB)
$O_2(g)$	0.0
$CO_2(g)$	−393.5
$H_2O(l)$	−285.8
$N_2(g)$	0.0

Be sure to pull data for the correct formula and phase.
$$\Delta H°_{rxn} = \sum n_P \Delta H°_f(\text{products}) - \sum n_R \Delta H°_f(\text{reactants})$$
$$= [2(\Delta H°_f(CO_2(g))) + 3(\Delta H°_f(H_2O(l))) + 1(\Delta H°_f(N_2(g)))] - [2(\Delta H°_f(CH_3NO_2(l))) + 3/2(\Delta H°_f(O_2(g)))]$$
$$2(-709.2\ kJ) = [2(-393.5\ kJ) + 3(-285.8\ kJ) + 1(0.0\ kJ)] - [2(\Delta H°_f(CH_3NO_2(l))) + 3/2(0.0\ kJ)]$$
$$-1418.4\ kJ = [-1644.4\ kJ] - [2(\Delta H°_f(CH_3NO_2(l)))]$$
$$\Delta H°_f(CH_3NO_2(l)) = -113\ kJ/mol$$

Check: The units (kJ/mol) are correct. The answer is negative (but not as negative as water and carbon dioxide), which is consistent with an exothermic combustion reaction.

6.60   **Given:** $4\ C_3H_5N_3O_9(l) \rightarrow 12\ CO_2(g) + 10\ H_2O(g) + 6\ N_2(g) + O_2(g)$ and $\Delta H°_{rxn} = -5678$ kJ/mol
        Find: $\Delta H°_f(C_3H_5N_3O_9(l))$
        Conceptual Plan: Fill known values into $\Delta H°_{rxn} = \sum n_P \Delta H°_f(\text{products}) - \sum n_R \Delta H°_f(\text{reactants})$ **and rearrange to solve for** $\Delta H°_f(C_3H_5N_3O_9(l))$.
        Solution:

Reactant/Product	$\Delta H°_f$(kJ/mol, from Appendix IIB)
$CO_2(g)$	−393.5
$H_2O(g)$	−241.8
$N_2(g)$	0.0
$O_2(g)$	0.0

Be sure to pull data for the correct formula and phase.
$$\Delta H°_{rxn} = \sum n_P \Delta H°_f(\text{products}) - \sum n_R \Delta H°_f(\text{reactants})$$
$$= [12(\Delta H°_f(CO_2(g))) + 10(\Delta H°_f(H_2O(g))) + 6(\Delta H°_f(N_2(g))) + 1(\Delta H°_f(O_2(g)))]$$
$$-[4(\Delta H°_f(C_3H_5N_3O_9(l)))]$$
$$(-5678\ kJ) = [12(-393.5\ kJ) + 10(-241.8\ kJ) + 6(0.0\ kJ) + 1(0.0\ kJ)] - [4(\Delta H°_f(C_3H_5N_3O_9(l)))]$$
$$-5678\ kJ = [-7140.\ kJ] - [4(\Delta H°_f(C_3H_5N_3O_9(l)))]$$
$$\Delta H°_f(C_3H_5N_3O_9(l)) = -365.5\ kJ/mol$$

Check: The units (kJ/mol) are correct. The answer is negative, but not as negative as carbon dioxide and significantly more water and carbon dioxide are formed than moles of nitroglycerin combusted as we would expect for an extremely exothermic reaction.

Cumulative Problems

6.61   **Given:** billiard ball$_A$ = system: $m_A = 0.17$ kg, $v_{A1} = 4.5$ m/s slows to $v_{A2} = 3.8$ m/s and $v_{A3} = 0$;
        ball$_B$: $m_B = 0.17$ kg, $v_{B1} = 0$ and $v_{B2} = 3.8$ m/s, and KE $= \frac{1}{2}mv^2$ **Find:** $w, q, \Delta E_{sys}$
        Conceptual Plan: $m, v \rightarrow$ **KE** then $KE_{A3}, KE_{A1} \rightarrow \Delta E_{sys}$ and $KE_{A2}, KE_{A1} \rightarrow q$ and $KE_{B2}, KE_{B1} \rightarrow w_B$

$$KE = \frac{1}{2}mv^2 \qquad \Delta E_{sys} = KE_{A3} - KE_{A1} \qquad q = KE_{A2} - KE_{A1} \qquad w_B = KE_{B2} - KE_{B1}$$

$\Delta E_{sys}, q \rightarrow w_A$ **verify that** $w_A = -w_B$ **so that no heat is transferred to ball$_B$**
        $\Delta E = q + w$

Solution: $KE = \frac{1}{2}mv^2$ because m is in kg and v is in m/s; KE will be in kg $\cdot$ m^2/s^2, which is the definition of a joule.

$$KE_{A1} = \frac{1}{2}(0.17 \text{ kg})\left(4.5 \frac{\text{m}}{\text{s}}\right)^2 = 1.\underline{7}213 \frac{\text{kg} \cdot \text{m}^2}{\text{s}^2} = 1.\underline{7}213 \text{ J}$$

$$KE_{A2} = \frac{1}{2}(0.17 \text{ kg})\left(3.8 \frac{\text{m}}{\text{s}}\right)^2 = 1.\underline{2}274 \frac{\text{kg} \cdot \text{m}^2}{\text{s}^2} = 1.\underline{2}274 \text{ J}$$

$$KE_{A3} = \frac{1}{2}(0.17 \text{ kg})\left(0 \frac{\text{m}}{\text{s}}\right)^2 = 0 \frac{\text{kg} \cdot \text{m}^2}{\text{s}^2} = 0 \text{ J},$$

$$KE_{B1} = \frac{1}{2}(0.17 \text{ kg})\left(0 \frac{\text{m}}{\text{s}}\right)^2 = 0 \frac{\text{kg} \cdot \text{m}^2}{\text{s}^2} = 0 \text{ J}$$

$$KE_{B2} = \frac{1}{2}(0.17 \text{ kg})\left(3.8 \frac{\text{m}}{\text{s}}\right)^2 = 1.\underline{2}274 \frac{\text{kg} \cdot \text{m}^2}{\text{s}^2} = 1.\underline{2}274 \text{ J}$$

$\Delta E_{sys} = KE_{A3} - KE_{A1} = 0 \text{ J} - 1.\underline{7}213 \text{ J} = -1.\underline{7}213 \text{ J} = -1.7 \text{ J}$
$q = KE_{A2} - KE_{A1} = 1.\underline{2}274 \text{ J} - 1.\underline{7}213 \text{ J} = -0.\underline{4}939 \text{ J} = -0.5 \text{ J}$
$w_B = KE_{B2} - KE_{B1} = 1.\underline{2}274 \text{ J} - 0 \text{ J} = 1.\underline{2}274 \text{ J}$
$w = \Delta E - q = -1.\underline{7}213 \text{ J} - (-0.\underline{4}939 \text{ J}) = -1.\underline{2}274 \text{ J} = -1.2 \text{ J}$
Because $w_A = -w_B$, no heat is transferred to ball$_B$.

Check: The units (J) are correct. Because the ball is initially moving and is stopped at the end, it has lost energy (negative ΔE_{sys}). As the ball slows due to friction, it is releasing heat (negative q). The kinetic energy is transferred to a second ball, so it does work (w negative).

6.62 **Given:** 100 W lightbulb in a piston; bulb on for 0.015 hr, $V_i = 0.85$ L, $V_f = 5.88$ L, $P = 1.0$ atm
Find: w, q, ΔE_{sys}
Conceptual Plan: bulb wattage, time $\rightarrow$ ΔE_{sys}(Wh) $\rightarrow$ ΔE_{sys}(kWh) $\rightarrow$ ΔE_{sys}(J) and $V_i, V_f \rightarrow \Delta V$ then

$$\Delta E = (wattage)(time) \qquad \frac{1 \text{ kW}}{1000 \text{ W}} \qquad \frac{3.60 \times 10^6 \text{J}}{1 \text{ kWh}} \qquad \Delta V = V_f - V_i$$

$P, \Delta V \rightarrow w$(L atm) $\rightarrow$ w(J) finally $\Delta E_{sys}, w \rightarrow q$

$$w = -P\Delta V \qquad \frac{101.3 \text{ J}}{1 \text{ L atm}} \qquad \Delta E = q + w$$

Solution: $\Delta E = (wattage)(time) = (100 \text{ W})(0.015 \text{ hr}) = 1.5 \text{ Wh} \times \dfrac{1 \text{ kW}}{1000 \text{ W}} \times \dfrac{3.60 \times 10^6 \text{ J}}{1 \text{ kWh}} = 5400 \text{ J}$ and

$\Delta V = V_f - V_i = 5.88 \text{ L} - 0.85 \text{ L} = 5.03 \text{ L}$ then

$w = -P\Delta V = -1.0 \text{ atm} \times 5.03 \text{ L} \times \dfrac{101.3 \text{ J}}{1 \text{ L atm}} = -5\underline{0}9.539 \text{ J} = -5.1 \times 10^2 \text{ J}$

$\Delta E = q + w$
Rearrange to solve for q. $q = \Delta E_{sys} - w = +54\underline{0}0 \text{ J} - (-5\underline{0}9.539 \text{ J}) = 5900 \text{ J}$

Check: The units (J) are correct. Electricity is added, so energy is added (positive ΔE_{sys}). The piston expands, so it does work (negative work). For the lightbulb to generate light, it must be heated or it must absorb energy (positive q).

6.63 **Given:** $H_2O(l) \rightarrow H_2O(g)$ $\Delta H^\circ_{rxn} = +44.01$ kJ/mol; $\Delta T_{body} = -0.50 \text{ °C}$, $m_{body} = 95$ kg, $C_{body} = 4.0$ J/g °C
Find: m_{H_2O}
Conceptual Plan: kg $\rightarrow$ **g** then $m_{body}, \Delta T, C_{body} \rightarrow q_{body} \rightarrow q_{rxn}$(J) $\rightarrow q_{rxn}$(kJ) $\rightarrow$ mol H_2O $\rightarrow$ g H_2O

$$\frac{1000 \text{ g}}{1 \text{ kg}} \qquad q_{body} = m_{body}C_{body}\Delta T_{body} \quad q_{rxn} = -q_{body} \quad \frac{1 \text{ kJ}}{1000 \text{ J}} \qquad \frac{1 \text{ mol}}{44.01 \text{ kJ}} \qquad \frac{18.02 \text{ g}}{1 \text{ mol}}$$

Solution: $95 \text{ kg} \times \dfrac{1000 \text{ g}}{1 \text{ kg}} = 95000 \text{ g}$ then

$q_{body} = m_{body}C_{body}\Delta T_{body} = 95000 \text{ g} \times 4.0 \dfrac{\text{J}}{\text{g} \cdot \text{°C}} \times (-0.50 \text{ °C}) = -19\underline{0}000 \text{ J}$ then

$q_{rxn} = -q_{body} = 19\underline{0}000 \text{ J} \times \dfrac{1 \text{ kJ}}{1000 \text{ J}} \times \dfrac{1 \text{ mol}}{44.01 \text{ kJ}} \times \dfrac{18.02 \text{ g}}{1 \text{ mol}} = 78 \text{ g } H_2O$

Check: The units (g) are correct. The magnitude of the answer (78) makes physical sense because a person can sweat this much on a hot day.

6.64 **Given:** LP gas combustion, $\Delta H^\circ_{rxn} = -2044$ kJ; 1.5 L water, $T_{H_2Oi} = 25.0 \text{ °C}$, $T_{H_2Of} = 100.0 \text{ °C}$, 15% efficiency
Find: $m_{\text{LP gas}}$

Conceptual Plan: $L \rightarrow mL \rightarrow g$ and $T_i, T_f \rightarrow \Delta T$ then, $m_{H_2O}, C_{H_2O} \rightarrow q_{H_2O} \rightarrow q_{rxn}$

$$\frac{1000 \text{ mL}}{1 \text{ L}} \qquad \frac{1.0 \text{ g}}{1.0 \text{ mL}} \qquad \qquad \Delta T = T_f - T_i \qquad \qquad q_{H_2O} = m_{H_2O}C_{H_2O}\Delta T_{H_2O} \quad q_{rxn} = -q_{H_2O}$$

then q_{rxn} needed $\rightarrow q_{rxn}$ generated (J) $\rightarrow q_{rxn}$ (kJ) $\rightarrow$ **mol LP gas** $\rightarrow$ **g LP gas**

$$\frac{100 \text{ J generated}}{15 \text{ J needed}} \qquad \frac{1 \text{ kJ}}{1000 \text{ J}} \qquad \frac{1 \text{ mol}}{-2044 \text{ kJ}} \qquad \frac{44.09 \text{ g}}{1 \text{ mol}}$$

Solution: $1.5 \cancel{L} \times \dfrac{1000 \cancel{mL}}{1 \cancel{L}} \times \dfrac{1.0 \text{ g}}{1.0 \cancel{mL}} = 1500 \text{ g}$

and $\Delta T = T_f - T_i = 100.0\,°C - 25.0\,°C = 75.0\,°C$ then

$q_{H_2O} = m_{H_2O}C_{H_2O}\Delta T_{H_2O} = 1500 \cancel{g} \times 4.184 \dfrac{J}{\cancel{g} \cdot \cancel{°C}} \times (75.0 \cancel{°C}) = 4\underline{7}0700 \text{ J}$ then

$q_{rxn} = -q_{H_2O} = -4\underline{7}0700 \cancel{\text{J generated}} \times \dfrac{100 \cancel{\text{J generated}}}{15 \cancel{\text{J needed}}} \times \dfrac{1 \cancel{kJ}}{1000 \cancel{J}} \times \dfrac{1 \cancel{mol}}{-2044 \cancel{kJ}} \times \dfrac{44.09 \text{ g}}{1 \cancel{mol}} = 68 \text{ g LP gas}$

Check: The units (g) are correct. The magnitude of the answer (68) makes physical sense because a tank of LP gas contains many orders of magnitude more than this amount.

6.65   **Given:** $H_2O(s) \rightarrow H_2O(l)$ $\Delta H_f°(H_2O(s)) = -291.8$ kJ/mol; 355 mL beverage $T_{Bevi} = 25.0\,°C$, $T_{Bevf} = 0.0\,°C$, $C_{Bev} = 4.184$ J/g $°C$, $d_{Bev} = 1.0$ g/mL   **Find:** $\Delta H_{rxn}°$ (ice melting) and m_{ice}
Conceptual Plan: $\Delta H_{rxn}° = \sum n_P \Delta H_f°(\text{products}) - \sum n_R \Delta H_f°(\text{reactants})$ **mL** $\rightarrow$ **g** and $T_i, T_f \rightarrow \Delta T$ then

$$\frac{1.0 \text{ g}}{1.0 \text{ mL}} \qquad \qquad \Delta T = T_f - T_i$$

$m_{H_2O}, \Delta T_{H_2O}, C_{H_2O} \rightarrow q_{H_2O} \rightarrow q_{rxn}(J) \rightarrow q_{rxn}$ (kJ) $\rightarrow$ **mol ice** $\rightarrow$ **g ice**

$$q_{Bev} = m_{Bev}C_{Bev}\Delta T_{Bev} \quad q_{rxn} = -q_{Bev} \qquad \frac{1 \text{ kJ}}{1000 \text{ J}} \qquad \frac{1 \text{ mol}}{\Delta H_{rxn}°} \qquad \frac{18.02 \text{ g}}{1 \text{ mol}}$$

Solution:

Reactant/Product	$\Delta H_f°$(kJ/mol, from Appendix IIB)
$H_2O(s)$	-291.8
$H_2O(l)$	-285.8

Be sure to pull data for the correct formula and phase.

$\Delta H_{rxn}° = \sum n_P \Delta H_f°(\text{products}) - \sum n_R \Delta H_f°(\text{reactants})$
$\qquad\quad = [1(\Delta H_f°(H_2O(l)))] - [1(\Delta H_f°(H_2O(s)))]$
$\qquad\quad = [1(-285.8 \text{ kJ})] - [1(-291.8 \text{ kJ})]$
$\qquad\quad = +6.0 \text{ kJ}$

$355 \cancel{mL} \times \dfrac{1.0 \text{ g}}{1.0 \cancel{mL}} = 355 \text{ g}$ and $\Delta T = T_f - T_i = 0.0\,°C - 25.0\,°C = -25.0\,°C$ then

$q_{Bev} = m_{Bev}C_{Bev}\Delta T_{Bev} = 355 \cancel{g} \times 4.184 \dfrac{J}{\cancel{g} \cdot \cancel{°C}} \times (-25.0 \cancel{°C}) = -37\underline{1}33 \text{ J}$ then

$q_{rxn} = -q_{Bev} = -37\underline{1}33 \cancel{J} \times \dfrac{1 \cancel{kJ}}{1000 \cancel{J}} \times \dfrac{1 \cancel{mol}}{-6.0 \cancel{kJ}} \times \dfrac{18.02 \text{ g}}{1 \cancel{mol}} = 110 \text{ g ice}$

Check: The units (kJ and g) are correct. The answer is positive, which means that the reaction is endothermic. We expect an endothermic reaction because we know that heat must be added to melt ice. The magnitude of the answer (110 g) makes physical sense because it is much smaller than the weight of the beverage and it would fit in a glass with the beverage.

6.66   **Given:** $CO_2(s) \rightarrow CO_2(g)$ $\Delta H_f°(CO_2(s)) = -427.4$ kJ/mol; 15.0 L water, $T_{H_2Oi} = 85\,°C$, $T_{H_2Of} = 25\,°C$
Find: $\Delta H_{rxn}°$ (dry ice sublimation) and m_{dryice}
Conceptual Plan: $\Delta H_{rxn}° = \sum n_P \Delta H_f°(\text{products}) - \sum n_R \Delta H_f°(\text{reactants})$ **L** $\rightarrow$ **mL** $\rightarrow$ **g** and $T_i, T_f \rightarrow \Delta T$ then

$$\frac{1000 \text{ mL}}{1 \text{ L}} \qquad \frac{1.00 \text{ g}}{1.00 \text{ mL}} \qquad \qquad \Delta T = T_f - T_i$$

$m_{H_2O}, \Delta T_{H_2O}, C_{H_2O} \rightarrow q_{H_2O} \rightarrow q_{rxn}(J) \rightarrow q_{rxn}$ (kJ) $\rightarrow$ **mol ice** $\rightarrow$ **g ice**

$$q_{H_2O} = m_{H_2O}C_{H_2O}\Delta T_{H_2O} \quad q_{rxn} = -q_{H_2O} \qquad \frac{1 \text{ kJ}}{1000 \text{ J}} \qquad \frac{1 \text{ mol}}{\Delta H_{rxn}°} \qquad \frac{44.01 \text{ g}}{1 \text{ mol}}$$

Solution:

Reactant/Product	ΔH_f° (kJ/mol, from Appendix IIB)
$CO_2(s)$	-427.4
$CO_2(g)$	-393.5

Be sure to pull data for the correct formula and phase.

$$\Delta H_{rxn}^\circ = \sum n_P \Delta H_f^\circ (\text{products}) - \sum n_R \Delta H_f^\circ (\text{reactants})$$
$$= [1(\Delta H_f^\circ(CO_2(g)))] - [1(\Delta H_f^\circ(CO_2(s)))]$$
$$= [1(-393.5 \text{ kJ})] - [1(-427.4 \text{ kJ})]$$
$$= +33.9 \text{ kJ}$$

$$15.0 \, \cancel{L} \times \frac{1000 \, \cancel{mL}}{1 \, \cancel{L}} \times \frac{1.00 \text{ g}}{1.00 \, \cancel{mL}} = 15\underline{0}00 \text{ g and } \Delta T = T_f - T_i = 25 \, ^\circ C - 85 \, ^\circ C = -60. \, ^\circ C \text{ then}$$

$$q_{H_2O} = m_{H_2O} C_{H_2O} \Delta T_{H_2O} = 15\underline{0}00 \, \cancel{g} \times 4.184 \, \frac{J}{\cancel{g} \cdot \cancel{^\circ C}} \times (-60. \, \cancel{^\circ C}) = -37\underline{6}5600 \text{ J then}$$

$$q_{rxn} = -q_{H_2O} = 37\underline{6}5600 \, \cancel{J} \times \frac{1 \, \cancel{kJ}}{1000 \, \cancel{J}} \times \frac{1 \, \cancel{mol}}{33.9 \, \cancel{kJ}} \times \frac{44.01 \text{ g}}{1 \, \cancel{mol}} = 4900 \text{ g dry ice}$$

Check: The units (kJ and g) are correct. The answer is positive, which means that the reaction is endothermic. We expect an endothermic reaction because we know that heat must be added to sublime dry ice. The magnitude of the answer (4900 g) makes physical sense because the temperature change of the water is fairly large and the volume of water is large. It is a reasonable amount to put in a cooler.

6.67   **Given:** 25.5 g aluminum; $T_{Ali} = 65.4 \, ^\circ C$; 55.2 g water; $T_{H_2Oi} = 22.2 \, ^\circ C$ **Find:** T_f
Conceptual Plan: pull C_s values from table then $m, C_s, T_i \rightarrow T_f$

$$\text{Al: } 0.903 \, \frac{J}{g \cdot ^\circ C} \qquad H_2O: 4.18 \, \frac{J}{g \cdot ^\circ C} \qquad q = mC_s(T_f - T_i) \text{ then set } q_{Al} = -q_{H_2O}$$

Solution: $q = mC_s(T_f - T_i)$ substitute in values and set $q_{Al} = -q_{H_2O}$.

$$q_{Al} = m_{Al} C_{Al}(T_f - T_{Ali}) = 25.5 \, \cancel{g} \times 0.903 \, \frac{J}{\cancel{g} \cdot ^\circ C} \times (T_f - 65.4 \, ^\circ C) =$$

$$-q_{H_2O} = -m_{H_2O} C_{H_2O}(T_f - T_{H_2Oi}) = -55.2 \, \cancel{g} \times 4.18 \, \frac{J}{\cancel{g} \cdot ^\circ C} \times (T_f - 22.2 \, ^\circ C)$$

Rearrange to solve for T_f.

$$23.\underline{0}265 \, \frac{J}{^\circ C} \times (T_f - 65.4 \, ^\circ C) = -230.\underline{7}36 \, \frac{J}{^\circ C} \times (T_f - 22.2 \, ^\circ C) \rightarrow$$

$$23.\underline{0}265 \, \frac{J}{^\circ C} T_f - 15\underline{0}5.93 \text{ J} = -230.\underline{7}36 \, \frac{J}{^\circ C} T_f + 51\underline{2}2.34 \text{ J} \rightarrow$$

$$-51\underline{2}2.34 \text{ J} - 15\underline{0}5.93 \text{ J} = -230.\underline{7}36 \, \frac{J}{^\circ C} T_f - 23.\underline{0}265 \, \frac{J}{^\circ C} T_f \rightarrow 66\underline{2}8.27 \text{ J} = 253.\underline{7}625 \, \frac{J}{^\circ C} T_f \rightarrow$$

$$T_f = \frac{66\underline{2}8.27 \, \cancel{J}}{253.\underline{7}625 \, \frac{\cancel{J}}{^\circ C}} = 26.1 \, ^\circ C$$

Check: The units ($^\circ C$) are correct. The magnitude of the answer (26) makes physical sense because the heat transfer is dominated by the water (larger mass and larger specific heat capacity). The final temperature should be closer to the initial temperature of water than of aluminum.

6.68   **Given:** ethanol: 50.0 mL; $d = 0.789$ g/mL, $T_{EtOHi} = 7.0 \, ^\circ C$, water: 50.0 mL; $d = 1.0$ g/mL, $T_{H_2Oi} = 28.4 \, ^\circ C$
Find: T_f
Conceptual Plan: pull C_s values from Table 6.4 mL $\rightarrow$ g then $m, C_s, T_i \rightarrow T_f$

$$\text{EtOH: } 2.42 \, \frac{J}{g \cdot ^\circ C} \quad H_2O: 4.18 \, \frac{J}{g \cdot ^\circ C} \quad \text{EtOH: } \frac{0.789 \text{ g}}{1.0 \text{ mL}} \quad H_2O: \frac{1.0 \text{ g}}{1.0 \text{ mL}} \quad q = mC_s(T_f - T_i) \text{ then set } q_{EtOH} = -q_{H_2O}$$

Solution: $50.0 \, \cancel{mL} \times \frac{0.789 \text{ g}}{1.0 \, \cancel{mL}} = 39.\underline{4}5 \text{ g EtOH and } 50.0 \, \cancel{mL} \times \frac{1.0 \text{ g}}{1.0 \, \cancel{mL}} = 50.0 \text{ g } H_2O \text{ then}$

$q = mC_s(T_f - T_i)$ substitute in values and set $q_{EtOH} = -q_{H_2O}$.

$$q_{EtOH} = m_{EtOH}C_{EtOH}(T_f - T_{EtOHi}) = 39.\underline{4}5 \text{ g} \times 2.42 \frac{J}{\text{g} \cdot {}^{\circ}\text{C}} \times (T_f - 7.0\,{}^{\circ}\text{C}) =$$

$$-q_{H_2O} = -m_{H_2O}C_{H_2O}(T_f - T_{H_2Oi}) = -50.0 \text{ g} \times 4.18 \frac{J}{\text{g} \cdot {}^{\circ}\text{C}} \times (T_f - 28.4\,{}^{\circ}\text{C})$$

Rearrange to solve for T_f. $95.\underline{4}69 \frac{J}{{}^{\circ}\text{C}} \times (T_f - 7.0\,{}^{\circ}\text{C}) = -20\underline{9}.0 \frac{J}{{}^{\circ}\text{C}} \times (T_f - 28.4\,{}^{\circ}\text{C}) \rightarrow$

$$95.\underline{4}69 \frac{J}{{}^{\circ}\text{C}} T_f - 6\underline{6}8.283 \text{ J} = -20\underline{9}.0 \frac{J}{{}^{\circ}\text{C}} T_f + 59\underline{3}5.6 \text{ J} \rightarrow$$

$$-6\underline{6}8.283 \text{ J} - 59\underline{3}5.6 \text{ J} = -20\underline{9}.0 \frac{J}{{}^{\circ}\text{C}} T_f - 95.\underline{4}69 \frac{J}{{}^{\circ}\text{C}} T_f \rightarrow 660\underline{3}.883 \text{ J} = 30\underline{4}.469 \frac{J}{{}^{\circ}\text{C}} T_f \rightarrow$$

$$T_f = \frac{660\underline{3}.883 \text{ J}}{30\underline{4}.469 \frac{J}{{}^{\circ}\text{C}}} = 21.7\,{}^{\circ}\text{C}$$

Check: The units (°C) are correct. The magnitude of the answer (22) makes physical sense because the heat transfer is dominated by the water (larger mass and larger specific heat capacity). The final temperature should be closer to the initial temperature of water than of ethanol.

6.69   **Given:** palmitic acid ($C_{16}H_{32}O_2$) $\Delta H_f^{\circ}(C_{16}H_{32}O_2(s)) = -208$ kJ/mol; sucrose ($C_{12}H_{22}O_{11}$)
$\Delta H_f^{\circ}(C_{12}H_{22}O_{11}(s)) = -2226.1$ kJ/mol   **Find:** ΔH_{rxn}° in kJ/mol and Cal/g
Conceptual Plan: write balanced reaction then $\Delta H_{rxn}^{\circ} = \sum n_P \Delta H_f^{\circ}(\text{products}) - \sum n_R \Delta H_f^{\circ}(\text{reactants})$ **then**
kJ/mol → J/mol → Cal/mol → Cal/g

$$\frac{1000 \text{ J}}{1 \text{ kJ}} \qquad \frac{1 \text{ Cal}}{4184 \text{ J}} \qquad \text{PA: } \frac{1 \text{ mol}}{256.42 \text{ g}} \qquad \text{S: } \frac{1 \text{ mol}}{342.30 \text{ g}}$$

Solution: Combustion is the combination with oxygen to form carbon dioxide and water (*l*):
$C_{16}H_{32}O_2(s) + 23\,O_2(g) \rightarrow 16\,CO_2(g) + 16\,H_2O(l)$

Reactant/Product	ΔH_f° (kJ/mol, from Appendix IIB)
$C_{16}H_{32}O_2(s)$	−208
$O_2(g)$	0.0
$CO_2(g)$	−393.5
$H_2O(l)$	−285.8

Be sure to pull data for the correct formula and phase.
$$\begin{aligned}
\Delta H_{rxn}^{\circ} &= \sum n_P \Delta H_f^{\circ}(\text{products}) - \sum n_R \Delta H_f^{\circ}(\text{reactants}) \\
&= [16(\Delta H_f^{\circ}(CO_2(g))) + 16(\Delta H_f^{\circ}(H_2O(l)))] - [1(\Delta H_f^{\circ}(C_{16}H_{32}O_2(s))) + 23(\Delta H_f^{\circ}(O_2(g)))] \\
&= [16(-393.5 \text{ kJ}) + 16(-285.8 \text{ kJ})] - [1(-208 \text{ kJ}) + 23(0.0 \text{ kJ})] \\
&= [-10868.8 \text{ kJ}] - [-208 \text{ kJ}] \\
&= -1066\underline{0}.8 \text{ kJ/mol} = -10661 \text{ kJ/mol}
\end{aligned}$$

$$-1066\underline{0}.8 \frac{\text{kJ}}{\text{mol}} \times \frac{1000 \text{ J}}{1 \text{ kJ}} \times \frac{1 \text{ Cal}}{4184 \text{ J}} \times \frac{1 \text{ mol}}{256.42 \text{ g}} = -9.9368 \text{ Cal/g}$$

$C_{12}H_{22}O_{11}(s) + 12\,O_2(g) \rightarrow 12\,CO_2(g) + 11\,H_2O(l)$

Reactant/Product	ΔH_f° (kJ/mol, from Appendix IIB)
$C_{12}H_{22}O_{11}(s)$	−2226.1
$O_2(g)$	0.0
$CO_2(g)$	−393.5
$H_2O(l)$	−285.8

Be sure to pull data for the correct formula and phase.
$$\begin{aligned}
\Delta H_{rxn}^{\circ} &= \sum n_P \Delta H_f^{\circ}(\text{products}) - \sum n_R \Delta H_f^{\circ}(\text{reactants}) \\
&= [12(\Delta H_f^{\circ}(CO_2(g))) + 11(\Delta H_f^{\circ}(H_2O(l)))] - [1(\Delta H_f^{\circ}(C_{12}H_{22}O_{11}(s))) + 12(\Delta H_f^{\circ}(O_2(g)))] \\
&= [12(-393.5 \text{ kJ}) + 11(-285.8 \text{ kJ})] - [1(-2226.1 \text{ kJ}) + 12(0.0 \text{ kJ})] \\
&= [-7865.8 \text{ kJ}] - [-2226.1 \text{ kJ}] \\
&= -5639.7 \text{ kJ/mol}
\end{aligned}$$

$$-5639.7 \; \frac{kJ}{mol} \times \frac{1000 \; J}{1 \; kJ} \times \frac{1 \; Cal}{4184 \; J} \times \frac{1 \; mol}{342.30 \; g} = -3.938 \; Cal/g$$

Palmitic acid gives more Cal/g than sucrose.

Check: The units (kJ/mol and Cal/g) are correct. The magnitudes of the answers are consistent with the food labels we see every day.

6.70   **Given:** hydrogen, methanol (CH_3OH), and octane combustion   **Find:** q released in kJ/kg

Conceptual Plan: write balanced reaction then $\Delta H^\circ_{rxn} = \sum n_P \Delta H^\circ_f(\text{products}) - \sum n_R \Delta H^\circ_f(\text{reactants})$

then kJ/mol   →   kJ/g → kJ/kg

$H_2: \dfrac{1 \; mol}{2.016 \; g}$ $MeOH: \dfrac{1 \; mol}{32.04 \; g}$ $O: \dfrac{1 \; mol}{114.22 \; g}$ $\dfrac{1000 \; g}{1 \; kg}$

Solution: Combustion is the combination with oxygen to form carbon dioxide and water:

$H_2(g) + \dfrac{1}{2} O_2(g) \rightarrow H_2O(g)$. This reaction is the heat of formation of gaseous water, so

$\Delta H^\circ_{rxn} = -241.8$ kJ/mol.

$$-241.8 \; \frac{kJ}{mol} \times \frac{1 \; mol}{2.016 \; g} \times \frac{1000 \; g}{1 \; kg} = -1.199 \times 10^5 \; kJ/kg \; H_2 \; \text{and}$$

$CH_3OH(l) + 3/2 \; O_2(g) \rightarrow CO_2(g) + 2 \; H_2O(g)$

Reactant/Product	ΔH°_f (kJ/mol, from Appendix IIB)
$CH_3OH(l)$	−238.6
$O_2(g)$	0.0
$CO_2(g)$	−393.5
$H_2O(g)$	−241.8

Be sure to pull data for the correct formula and phase.

$\Delta H^\circ_{rxn} = \sum n_P \Delta H^\circ_f(\text{products}) - \sum n_R \Delta H^\circ_f(\text{reactants})$

$\qquad = [1(\Delta H^\circ_f(CO_2(g))) + 2(\Delta H^\circ_f(H_2O(g)))] - [1(\Delta H^\circ_f(CH_3OH(l))) + 3/2(\Delta H^\circ_f(O_2(g)))]$

$\qquad = [1(-393.5 \; kJ) + 2(-241.8 \; kJ)] - [1(-238.6 \; kJ) + 3/2(0.0 \; kJ)]$

$\qquad = [-877.1 \; kJ] - [-238.6 \; kJ]$

$\qquad = -638.5 \; kJ$

$$-638.5 \; \frac{kJ}{mol} \times \frac{1 \; mol}{32.04 \; g} \times \frac{1000 \; g}{1 \; kg} = -1.993 \times 10^4 \; kJ/kg \; CH_3OH \; \text{and}$$

$$-5074.1 \; \frac{kJ}{mol} \times \frac{1 \; mol}{114.22 \; g} \times \frac{1000 \; g}{1 \; kg} = -4.4424 \times 10^4 \; kJ/kg \; C_8H_{18}.$$

Hydrogen delivers the most energy per weight of fuel. This is not surprising because hydrogen is so light. Octane delivers more energy per gram than methanol.

Check: The units (kJ/kg fuel) are correct. The magnitude of the answers ($10^4 - 10^5$) makes physical sense because there are many moles of fuel in a kilogram and the heat of reactions is high.

6.71   At constant pressure $\Delta H_{rxn} = q_P$ and at constant volume $\Delta E_{rxn} = q_V = \Delta H_{rxn} - P\Delta V$. Recall that $PV = nRT$. Because the conditions are constant P and a constant number of moles of gas, as T changes the only variable that can change is V. This means that $P\Delta V = nR\Delta T$. Substituting into the equation for ΔE_{rxn}, we get $\Delta E_{rxn} = \Delta H_{rxn} - nR\Delta T$ or $\Delta H_{rxn} = \Delta E_{rxn} + nR\Delta T$.

6.72   **Given:** $SO_2(g) + 1/2 \; O_2(g) \rightarrow SO_3(g)$, $\Delta H_{rxn} = +89.5$ kJ, and $\Delta H_f(SO_3(g)) = -204.2$ kJ

Find: $\Delta H_{rxn}(SO_2(g))$

Conceptual Plan: Fill known values into $\Delta H^\circ_{rxn} = \sum n_P \Delta H^\circ_f(\text{products}) - \sum n_R \Delta H^\circ_f(\text{reactants})$ **and rearrange to solve for** $\Delta H^\circ_f(SO_2(g))$.

Solution:

Reactant/Product	ΔH°_f (kJ/mol, from Appendix IIB)
$O_2(g)$	0.0
$SO_3(g)$	−204.2

$$\Delta H^\circ_{rxn} = \sum n_P \Delta H^\circ_f (\text{products}) - \sum n_R \Delta H^\circ_f (\text{reactants})$$
$$= [1(\Delta H^\circ_f(SO_3(g)))] - [1(\Delta H^\circ_f(SO_2(g))) + 1/2(\Delta H^\circ_f(O_2(g)))]$$
$$= [1(-204.2 \text{ kJ})] - [1(\Delta H^\circ_f(SO_2(g))) + 1/2(0.0 \text{ kJ})]$$
$$+89.5 \text{ kJ} = [-204.2 \text{ kJ}] - [\Delta H^\circ_f(SO_2(g))]$$
$$\Delta H^\circ_f(SO_2(g)) = -293.7 \text{ kJ}$$

Check: The units (kJ) are correct. The answer is more negative than $\Delta H^\circ_f(SO_3(g))$, which makes sense because the reaction is endothermic.

6.73   **Given:** 16 g peanut butter; bomb calorimeter; $T_i = 22.2 \,°C$; $T_f = 25.4 \,°C$; $C_{cal} = 120.0 \text{ kJ/}°C$
Find: calories in peanut butter
Conceptual Plan: $T_i, T_f \rightarrow \Delta T$ then $\Delta T, C_{cal} \rightarrow q_{cal} \rightarrow q_{rxn} \text{(kJ)} \rightarrow q_{rxn} \text{(kJ)} \rightarrow q_{rxn}\text{(Cal)}$

$$\Delta T = T_f - T_i \qquad q_{cal} = -C_{cal}\Delta T \quad q_{rxn} = -q_{cal} \qquad \frac{1000 \text{ J}}{1 \text{ kJ}} \qquad \frac{1 \text{ Cal}}{4184 \text{ J}}$$

then $q_{rxn} \text{ (Cal)} \rightarrow \textbf{Cal/g}$

$\div$ 16 g peanut butter

Solution: $\Delta T = T_f - T_i = 25.4 \,°C - 22.2 \,°C = 3.2 \,°C$ then $q_{cal} = C_{cal}\Delta T = 120.0 \dfrac{\text{kJ}}{°C} \times 3.2 \,°C = 3\underline{8}4 \text{ kJ}$

then $q_{rxn} = -q_{cal} = -384 \text{ kJ} \times \dfrac{1000 \text{ J}}{1 \text{ kJ}} \times \dfrac{1 \text{ Cal}}{4184 \text{ J}} = -9\underline{1}.778 \text{ Cal}$ then $\dfrac{-91.778 \text{ Cal}}{16 \text{ g}} = -5.7 \text{ Cal/g}$

Check: The units (Cal/g) are correct. The magnitude of the answer (6) makes physical sense because there is a significant percentage of fat and sugar in peanut butter. The answer is in line with the answers in Problem 6.69.

6.74   **Given:** 2.0 mol $H_2(g)$ + 1.0 mol $O_2(g)$ at 25 °C   **Find:** temperature of water
Conceptual Plan: write balanced reaction then $\Delta H^\circ_{rxn} = \sum n_P \Delta H^\circ_f (\text{products}) - \sum n_R \Delta H^\circ_f (\text{reactants})$
then kJ/mol $\rightarrow q\text{(kJ)} \rightarrow q\text{(J)}$ **then** 2.0 mol H_2 + 1.0 mol $O_2 \rightarrow$ **mol** $H_2O \rightarrow$ **g** H_2O **then**

x mol of limiting reagent $\qquad \dfrac{1000 \text{ J}}{1 \text{ kJ}} \qquad\qquad\qquad\qquad \dfrac{1 \text{ mol } H_2O}{1 \text{ mol } H_2} \quad \dfrac{18.02 \text{ g}}{1 \text{ mol}}$

$q_{rxn} \rightarrow q_{H_2O}$ **then pull** C_s **for** H_2O **(***l***) then** $q, m, C_s, T_i \rightarrow T_f$

$q_{rxn} = -q_{H_2O} \qquad\qquad 4.18 \dfrac{\text{J}}{\text{g} \cdot °C} \qquad\qquad q = mC_s(T_f - T_i)$

Solution: Combustion is the combination with oxygen to form water; choose liquid water because $T = 25 \,°C$.

$H_2(g) + \dfrac{1}{2} O_2(g) \rightarrow H_2O(l)$. This reaction is the heat of formation of liquid water, so

$\Delta H^\circ_{rxn} = -285.8 \text{ kJ/mol}$. The two reactants are in the stoichiometric ratio, so either amount can be used.

$-285.8 \dfrac{\text{kJ}}{1 \text{ mol } H_2} \times 2.0 \text{ mol } H_2 \times \dfrac{1000 \text{ J}}{1 \text{ kJ}} = -5\underline{7}1600 \text{ J}$ and $q_{H_2O} = -q_{rxn} = 5\underline{7}1600 \text{ J}$

$2.0 \text{ mol } H_2 \times \dfrac{1 \text{ mol } H_2O}{1 \text{ mol } H_2} \times \dfrac{18.02 \text{ g}}{1 \text{ mol } H_2O} = 36.04 \text{ g } H_2O$ then $q = mC_s(T_f - T_i)$. Rearrange to solve for T_f.

$T_f = \dfrac{mC_sT_i + q}{mC_s} = \dfrac{\left(36.02 \text{ g} \times 4.18 \dfrac{\text{J}}{\text{g} \cdot °C} \times 25 \,°C\right) + 5\underline{7}1600 \text{ J}}{36.02 \text{ g} \times 4.18 \dfrac{\text{J}}{\text{g} \cdot °C}} = 3821 \,°C.$ This is much higher than the boiling

point of water. The heat needed to raise the water to 100 °C is

$q = mC_s(T_f - T_i) = 36.02 \text{ g} \times 4.18 \dfrac{\text{J}}{\text{g} \cdot °C} \times (100 \,°C - 25 \,°C) = 1\underline{1}292 \text{ J}$, so $5\underline{7}1600 \text{ J} - 1\underline{1}292 \text{ J} = 5\underline{6}0308 \text{ J}$ is

still available. 2.0 moles H_2O utilizes $8\underline{1},400 \text{ J}$ ($= 40.7 \text{ kJ/mol}$), so $4\underline{7}8,908 \text{ J}$ ($= 5\underline{6}0,308 \text{ J} - 8\underline{1},400 \text{ J}$) is available to heat steam. Note: $C_s(\text{steam}) = 2.04 \text{ J/g} \cdot °C$.

Using equation from above $T_f = \dfrac{mC_sT_i + q}{mC_s} = \dfrac{\left(36.04 \text{ g} \times 2.04 \dfrac{\text{J}}{\text{g} \cdot °C} \times 100. \,°C\right) + 4\underline{7}8,908 \text{ J}}{36.04 \text{ g} \times 2.04 \dfrac{\text{J}}{\text{g} \cdot °C}} = 6,600 \,°C$

Check: The units (°C) are correct. The temperature is extremely high. A large amount of heat is liberated, and only a relatively small amount of mass absorbs it.

6.75   **Given:** $V_1 = 20.0$ L at $P_1 = 3.0$ atm; $P_2 = 1.5$ atm let expand at constant T **Find:** w, q, ΔE_{sys}
         Conceptual Plan: $V_1, P_1, P_2 \rightarrow V_2$ then $V_1, V_2 \rightarrow \Delta V$ then $P, \Delta V \rightarrow w$ (L atm) $\rightarrow w$ (J)

$$P_1V_1 = P_2V_2 \qquad\qquad \Delta V = V_2 - V_1 \qquad\qquad w = -P\Delta V \qquad\qquad \frac{101.3\ \text{J}}{1\ \text{L atm}}$$

for an ideal gas $\Delta E_{sys} \propto T$; so because this is a constant temperature process, $\Delta E_{sys} = 0$ finally $\Delta E_{sys}, w \rightarrow q$

$$\Delta E = q + w$$

Solution: $P_1V_1 = P_2V_2$. Rearrange to solve for V_2. $V_2 = V_1\dfrac{P_1}{P_2} = (20.0\ \text{L}) \times \dfrac{3.0\ \text{atm}}{1.5\ \text{atm}} = 40.$ L and

$\Delta V = V_2 - V_1 = 40.\ \text{L} - 20.0\ \text{L} = 20.$ L then

$w = -P\Delta V = -1.5\ \text{atm} \times 20.\ \text{L} \times \dfrac{101.3\ \text{J}}{1\ \text{L} \cdot \text{atm}} = -3039\ \text{J} = -3.0 \times 10^3\ \text{J}\ \Delta E = q + w$

Rearrange to solve for q. $q = \Delta E_{sys} - w = +\ 0\ \text{J} - (-3039\ \text{J}) = 3.0 \times 10^3\ \text{J}$

Check: The units (J) are correct. Because there is no temperature change, we expect no energy change ($\Delta E_{sys} = 0$). The piston expands as it does work (negative work), so heat is absorbed (positive q).

6.76   **Given:** 10.00 g $P_4(s)$ + $O_2(g)$ to form $P_4O_{10}(s)$; q released heats 2950 g water from $T_i = 18.0\ ^\circ$C to $T_f = 38.0\ ^\circ$C
         Find: $\Delta H_f^\circ(P_4O_{10}(s))$
         Conceptual Plan: write balanced reaction then $\Delta H_{rxn}^\circ = \sum n_P \Delta H_f^\circ(\text{products}) - \sum n_R \Delta H_f^\circ(\text{reactants})$ **then**
         $m, C_s, T_i, T_f \rightarrow q_{H_2O} \rightarrow q_{rxn}(\text{J}) \rightarrow q(\text{kJ})$ **then** g (P_4) $\rightarrow$ **mol (P_4) finally**

$$q = mC_s(T_f - T_i) \quad q_{rxn} = -q_{H_2O} \qquad \frac{1\ \text{kJ}}{1000\ \text{J}} \qquad\qquad \frac{123.90\ \text{g}}{1\ \text{mol}}$$

$q(\text{kJ})$, mol (P_4) $\rightarrow \Delta H_f^\circ(P_4O_{10}(s))$

$$\Delta H_f^\circ(P_4O_{10}(s)) = \frac{q}{\text{mol}\ P_4}$$

Solution: $P_4(s) + 5\ O_2(g) \rightarrow P_4O_{10}(s)$. This reaction is the heat of formation of $P_4O_{10}(s)$, so $\Delta H_{rxn}^\circ = \Delta H_f^\circ(P_4O_{10}(s))$

then $q = mC_s(T_f - T_i) = 2950\ \text{g} \times 4.18\ \dfrac{\text{J}}{\text{g} \cdot ^\circ\text{C}} \times (38.0\ ^\circ\text{C} - 18.0\ ^\circ\text{C}) = 246620\ \text{J}$

then $q_{rxn} = -q_{H_2O} = -246620\ \text{J} \times \dfrac{1\ \text{kJ}}{1000\ \text{J}} = -246.620\ \text{kJ}$ then $10.00\ \text{g}\ P_4 \times \dfrac{1\ \text{mol}\ P_4}{123.90\ \text{g}\ P_4} = 0.080710\ \text{mol}\ P_4$

then $\Delta H_f^\circ(P_4O_{10}(s)) = \dfrac{q}{\text{mol}\ P_4} = \dfrac{-246.620\ \text{kJ}}{0.080710\ \text{mol}} = -3.06 \times 10^3\ \text{kJ/mol}$

Check: The units (kJ/mol) are correct. The negative sign is consistent with the fact that heat was released to heat a large amount of water. The magnitude (3000) is not surprising because a small amount of phosphorous heated a lot of water (a high heat capacity material).

6.77   **Given:** 25.3% methane (CH_4), 38.2% ethane (C_2H_6), and the rest propane (C_3H_8) by volume; $V = 1.55$ L tank, $P = 755$ mmHg, and $T = 298$ K   **Find:** heat for combustion
         Conceptual Plan: percent composition $\rightarrow$ **mmHg** $\rightarrow$ **atm then** $P, V, T \rightarrow n$ **then**

$$\text{Dalton's law of partial pressures} \qquad \frac{1\ \text{atm}}{760\ \text{mmHg}} \qquad\qquad PV = nRT$$

use data in Problem 6.28 for methane and calculate heat of combustion for ethane and propane

$\Delta H_{rxn}^\circ(CH_4) = -802.3$ kJ; $\Delta H_{rxn}^\circ(C_3H_8) = -2217$ kJ write balanced reaction then $\Delta H_{rxn}^\circ = \sum n_P \Delta H_f^\circ(\text{products}) - \sum n_R \Delta H_f^\circ(\text{reactants})$

then $n, \Delta H \rightarrow q$

Solution: $P_{CH_4} = \dfrac{25.3\ \text{mmHg}\ CH_4}{100\ \text{mmHg gas}} \times 755\ \text{mmHg gas} \times \dfrac{1\ \text{atm}\ CH_4}{760\ \text{mmHg}} = 0.2513355\ \text{atm}\ CH_4$

$P_{C_2H_6} = \dfrac{38.2\ \text{mmHg}\ C_2H_6}{100\ \text{mmHg gas}} \times 755\ \text{mmHg gas} \times \dfrac{1\ \text{atm}\ C_2H_6}{760\ \text{mmHg}} = 0.37948684\ \text{atm}\ C_2H_6$

$P_{C_3H_8} = \dfrac{100 - (25.3 + 38.2)\ \text{mmHg}\ C_3H_8}{100\ \text{mmHg gas}} \times 755\ \text{mmHg gas} \times \dfrac{1\ \text{atm}\ C_3H_8}{760\ \text{mmHg}} = 0.36259868\ \text{atm}\ C_3H_8$

$PV = nRT$ Rearrange to solve for n.

$n_{CH_4} = \dfrac{PV}{RT} = \dfrac{0.2513355\ \text{atm}\ CH_4 \times 1.55\ \text{L}}{0.08206\ \dfrac{\text{L} \cdot \text{atm}}{\text{mol} \cdot \text{K}} \times 298\ \text{K}} = 0.01593081\ \text{mol}\ CH_4$

$$n_{C_2H_6} = \frac{PV}{RT} = \frac{0.37948684 \text{ atm } C_2H_6 \times 1.55 \text{ L}}{0.08206 \dfrac{\text{L} \cdot \text{atm}}{\text{mol} \cdot \text{K}} \times 298 \text{ K}} = 0.02405363 \text{ mol } C_2H_6$$

$$n_{C_2H_6} = \frac{PV}{RT} = \frac{0.36259868 \text{ atm } C_3H_8 \times 1.55 \text{ L}}{0.08206 \dfrac{\text{L} \cdot \text{atm}}{\text{mol} \cdot \text{K}} \times 298 \text{ K}} = 0.022983181 \text{ mol } C_3H_8$$

$C_2H_6(g) + 7/2\,O_2(g) \rightarrow 2\,CO_2(g) + 3\,H_2O(g)$

Reactant/Product	ΔH_f° (kJ/mol, from Appendix IIB)
$C_2H_6(g)$	−84.68
$O_2(g)$	0.0
$CO_2(g)$	−393.5
$H_2O(g)$	−241.8

Be sure to pull data for the correct formula and phase.

$$\begin{aligned}
\Delta H_{rxn}^\circ &= \sum n_P \Delta H_f^\circ (\text{products}) - \sum n_R \Delta H_f^\circ (\text{reactants}) \\
&= [2(\Delta H_f^\circ(CO_2(g))) + 3(\Delta H_f^\circ(H_2O(g)))] - [1(\Delta H_f^\circ(C_2H_6(g))) + 7/2(\Delta H_f^\circ(O_2(g)))] \\
&= [2(-393.5 \text{ kJ}) + 3(-241.8 \text{ kJ})] - [1(-84.68 \text{ kJ}) + 7/2(0.0 \text{ kJ})] \\
&= [-1512.4 \text{ kJ}] - [-84.68 \text{ kJ}] \\
&= -1427.7 \text{ kJ}
\end{aligned}$$

$C_3H_8(g) + 5\,O_2(g) \rightarrow 3\,CO_2(g) + 4\,H_2O(g)$

Reactant/Product	ΔH_f° (kJ/mol, from Appendix IIB)
$C_3H_8(g)$	−103.85
$O_2(g)$	0.0
$CO_2(g)$	−393.5
$H_2O(g)$	−241.8

Be sure to pull data for the correct formula and phase.

$$\begin{aligned}
\Delta H_{rxn}^\circ &= \sum n_P \Delta H_f^\circ (\text{products}) - \sum n_R \Delta H_f^\circ (\text{reactants}) \\
&= [3(\Delta H_f^\circ(CO_2(g))) + 4(\Delta H_f^\circ(H_2O(g)))] - [1(\Delta H_f^\circ(C_3H_8(g))) + 5(\Delta H_f^\circ(O_2(g)))] \\
&= [3(-393.5 \text{ kJ}) + 4(-241.8 \text{ kJ})] - [1(-103.85 \text{ kJ}) + 5(0.0 \text{ kJ})] \\
&= [-2147.7 \text{ kJ}] - [-103.85 \text{ kJ}] \\
&= -2043.9 \text{ kJ}
\end{aligned}$$

$$0.01593081 \text{ mol } CH_4 \times \frac{-802.3 \text{ kJ}}{1 \text{ mol } CH_4} = -12.781289 \text{ kJ}$$

$$0.02405363 \text{ mol } C_2H_6 \times \frac{-1427.7 \text{ kJ}}{1 \text{ mol } C_2H_6} = -34.34137 \text{ kJ}$$

$$0.022983181 \text{ mol } C_3H_8 \times \frac{-2043.9 \text{ kJ}}{1 \text{ mol } C_3H_8} = -46.97532 \text{ kJ}$$

The total heat is $-12.781289 \text{ kJ} - 34.34137 \text{ kJ} - 46.97532 \text{ kJ} = -94.09798 \text{ kJ} = -94.1 \text{ kJ}$

Check: The units (kJ) are correct. The magnitude of the answer (−100 kJ) makes sense because heats of combustion are typically large and negative.

6.78   **Given:** methane (CH_4) + propane (C_3H_8); $V = 11.7$ L, $P = 745$ mmHg, and $T = 298$ K, 769 kJ released

Find: mole fraction of methane in mixture

Conceptual Plan: let x = mole fraction methane $\rightarrow$ mmHg $\rightarrow$ atm then $P, V, T \rightarrow n$ then

$$\underset{\text{Dalton's law of partial pressures}}{} \qquad \frac{1 \text{ atm}}{760 \text{ mmHg}} \qquad PV = nRT$$

use data in Problems 6.28 and 6.64 for methane and propane, then $q, \Delta H \rightarrow x$

$\Delta H_{rxn}^\circ\,(CH_4) = -802.3$ kJ; $\quad \Delta H_{rxn}^\circ\,(C_3H_8) = -2043.9$ kJ

Solution: Let x = mole fraction methane, then

$$P_{CH_4} = \chi_{CH_4} P_{Total} = x \times 745 \text{ mmHg gas} \times \frac{1 \text{ atm } CH_4}{760 \text{ mmHg}} = x(0.98026316) \text{ atm } CH_4$$

$$P_{C_3H_8} = \chi_{C_3H_8}P_{Total} = (1 - x) \times 745 \text{ mmHg gas} \times \frac{1 \text{ atm } C_3H_8}{760 \text{ mmHg}} = (0.98\underline{0}26316 - 0.98\underline{0}26316x) \text{ atm } C_3H_8$$

$PV = nRT$. Rearrange to solve for n.

$$n_{CH_4} = \frac{PV}{RT} = \frac{x(0.98\underline{0}26316) \text{ atm } CH_4 \times 11.7 \text{ L}}{0.08206 \dfrac{\text{L} \cdot \text{atm}}{\text{mol} \cdot \text{K}} \times 298 \text{ K}} = x(0.46\underline{9}00856) \text{ mol } CH_4$$

$$n_{C_2H_6} = \frac{PV}{RT} = \frac{(0.98\underline{0}26316 - 0.98\underline{0}26316x) \text{ atm } C_3H_8 \times 11.7 \text{ L}}{0.08206 \dfrac{\text{L} \cdot \text{atm}}{\text{mol} \cdot \text{K}} \times 298 \text{ K}} = (0.46\underline{9}00856 - 0.46\underline{9}00856x) \text{ mol } C_3H_8$$

The total heat is the sum of the combustion of the two components.

$$\Delta H = -769 \text{ kJ} = x(0.46\underline{9}00856) \text{ mol } CH_4 \times \frac{-802.3 \text{ kJ}}{1 \text{ mol } CH_4} + (0.46\underline{9}00856 - 0.46\underline{9}00856x) \text{ mol } C_3H_8 \times \frac{-2043.9 \text{ kJ}}{1 \text{ mol } C_3H_8}$$

Solve for x. $-769 \text{ kJ} = x(-37\underline{6}.2856) \text{ kJ} + (-958\underline{.}6066 \text{ kJ}) + x(958\underline{.}6066 \text{ kJ}) \rightarrow$

$$+189\underline{.}6066 \text{ kJ} = x(+582\underline{.}3209 \text{ kJ}) \rightarrow x = \frac{+189\underline{.}6066 \text{ kJ}}{+582\underline{.}3209 \text{ kJ}} = 0.32\underline{5}605 = 0.326 \text{ mole fraction methane}$$

Check: The units (none) are correct. The magnitude of the answer (0.3) makes sense because if the mixture were all methane, the amount of heat would have been –376 kJ and if the mixture were all propane, the amount of heat would have been −1040 kJ. Because the heat released is closer to the all-propane amount, the mixture must be mostly propane.

Challenge Problems

6.79   **Given:** 655 kWh/yr; coal is 3.2% S; remainder is C; S emitted as $SO_2(g)$ and gets converted to H_2SO_4 when reacting with water   **Find:** $m(H_2SO_4)$/yr
   Conceptual Plan: write balanced reaction then $\Delta H°_{rxn} = \sum n_P \Delta H°_f(\text{products}) - \sum n_R \Delta H°_f(\text{reactants})$
   (because the form of sulfur is not given, assume that all heat is from combustion of only carbon) then
   kWh $\rightarrow$ J $\rightarrow$ kJ $\rightarrow$ mol (C) $\rightarrow$ g (C) $\rightarrow$ g (S) $\rightarrow$ mol (S) $\rightarrow$ mol (H_2SO_4) $\rightarrow$ g (H_2SO_4)

   $$\frac{3.60 \times 10^6 \text{ J}}{1 \text{ kWh}} \quad \frac{1 \text{ kJ}}{1000 \text{ J}} \quad \frac{\text{mol C}}{\Delta H°_f(CO_2(g))} \quad \frac{12.01 \text{ g}}{1 \text{ mol}} \quad \frac{3.2 \text{ g S}}{(100.0 - 3.2) \text{ g C}} \quad \frac{1 \text{ mol}}{32.07 \text{ g}} \quad \frac{1 \text{ mol } H_2SO_4}{1 \text{ mol S}} \quad \frac{98.09 \text{ g}}{1 \text{ mol}}$$

   Solution: $C(s) + O_2(g) \rightarrow CO_2(g)$. This reaction is the heat of formation of $CO_2(g)$, so $\Delta H°_{rxn} = \Delta H°_f(CO_2(g)) = -393.5 \text{ kJ/mol}$ then

   $$655 \text{ kWh} \times \frac{3.60 \times 10^6 \text{ J}}{1 \text{ kWh}} \times \frac{1 \text{ kJ}}{1000 \text{ J}} \times \frac{\text{mol C}}{393.5 \text{ kJ}} \times \frac{12.01 \text{ g C}}{1 \text{ mol C}} \times \frac{3.2 \text{ g S}}{(100.0 - 3.2) \text{ g C}} \times \frac{1 \text{ mol S}}{32.07 \text{ g S}}$$

   $$\times \frac{1 \text{ mol } H_2SO_4}{1 \text{ mol S}} \times \frac{98.09 \text{ g } H_2SO_4}{1 \text{ mol } H_2SO_4} = 7.3 \times 10^3 \text{ g } H_2SO_4$$

   Check: The units (g) are correct. The magnitude (7300) is reasonable, considering this is just one home.

6.80   **Given:** $2.5 \times 10^3 \text{ kg SUV}; v_1 = 0.0 \text{ mph}; v_2 = 65.0 \text{ mph}$; octane combustion, 30% efficiency   **Find:** $m(CO_2)$
   Conceptual Plan: mi/hr $\rightarrow$ m/hr $\rightarrow$ m/min $\rightarrow$ m/s then $m, v \rightarrow$ **KE then**

   $$\frac{1000 \text{ m}}{0.6214 \text{ mi}} \quad \frac{1 \text{ hr}}{60 \text{ min}} \quad \frac{1 \text{ min}}{60 \text{ sec}} \qquad KE = \frac{1}{2}mv^2$$

   $KE_1, KE_2 \rightarrow \Delta E$ used $\rightarrow \Delta E$ generated

   $$\Delta E_{sys} = KE_2 - KE_1 \qquad \frac{100 \text{ J generated}}{30 \text{ J used}}$$

   write balanced reaction similar to the reaction in Problem 6.77. $C_8H_{18}(l) + 25/2 \, O_2(g) \rightarrow 8 \, CO_2(g) + 9 \, H_2O(g)$

   with $\Delta H°_{rxn} = -5074.1 \text{ kJ}$

   ΔE generated (J) $\rightarrow$ kJ $\rightarrow$ mol(C_8H_{18}) $\rightarrow$ mol $CO_2 \rightarrow$ g CO_2

   $$\frac{1 \text{ kJ}}{1000 \text{ J}} \quad \frac{1 \text{ mol } C_8H_{18}}{5074.1 \text{ kJ}} \quad \frac{8 \text{ mol } CO_2}{1 \text{ mol } C_8H_{18}} \quad \frac{44.01 \text{ g}}{1 \text{ mol}}$$

   Solution: $v_1 = 0.0 \text{ m/s}, 65.0 \dfrac{\text{mi}}{\text{hr}} \times \dfrac{1000 \text{ m}}{0.6214 \text{ mi}} \times \dfrac{1 \text{ hr}}{60 \text{ min}} \times \dfrac{1 \text{ min}}{60 \text{ sec}} = 29.\underline{0}563 \dfrac{\text{m}}{\text{s}}$ then $KE = \dfrac{1}{2}mv^2$

   $$KE_1 = \frac{1}{2}(2.5 \times 10^3 \text{ kg})(0)^2 = 0$$

$$KE_2 = \frac{1}{2}(2.5 \times 10^3 \, kg)\left(29.\underline{0}563 \, \frac{m}{s}\right)^2 = 1.\underline{0}5534 \times 10^6 \, \frac{kg \, m^2}{s^2} = 1.\underline{0}5534 \times 10^6 \, J$$

$$\Delta E_{sys} = KE_2 - KE_1 = 1.\underline{0}5534 \times 10^6 \, J - 0 \, J = 1.\underline{0}5534 \times 10^6 \, \cancel{J \, used} \times \frac{100 \, J \, generated}{30 \, \cancel{J \, used}} =$$

$$= 3.\underline{5}1780 \times 10^6 \, J \, generated$$

$$3.\underline{5}1780 \times 10^6 \, \cancel{J \, generated} \times \frac{1 \, kJ}{1000 \, \cancel{J}} \times \frac{1 \, \cancel{mol \, C_8H_{18}}}{5074.1 \, \cancel{kJ}} \times \frac{8 \, \cancel{mol \, CO_2}}{1 \, \cancel{mol \, C_8H_{18}}} \times \frac{44.01 \, g \, CO_2}{1 \, \cancel{mol \, CO_2}} = 2.4 \times 10^2 \, g \, CO_2$$

Check: The units (g) are correct. The magnitude (240) is reasonable, considering the vehicle is so heavy and we generate 8 moles of CO_2 for each mole of octane.

6.81 **Given:** methane combustion, 100% efficiency; $\Delta T = 10.0 \, °C$; house = 30.0 m × 30.0 m × 3.0 m; $C_s(air) = 30 \, J/K \cdot mol$; 1.00 mol air = 22.4 L   **Find:** $m \, (CH_4)$

Conceptual Plan: $l, w, h \rightarrow V(m^3) \rightarrow V(cm^3) \rightarrow V(L) \rightarrow mol \, (air)$ then $m, C_s, \Delta T \rightarrow q_{air} \, (J)$

$$V = lwh \qquad \frac{(100 \, cm)^3}{(1 \, m)^3} \qquad \frac{1 \, L}{1000 \, cm^3} \qquad \frac{1 \, mol \, air}{22.4 \, L} \qquad \qquad q = mC_s\Delta T$$

then $q_{air} \, (J) \rightarrow q_{rxn} \, (J) \rightarrow q(kJ)$ then write balanced reaction for methane combustion

$$q_{rxn} = -q_{air} \qquad \frac{1 \, kJ}{1000 \, J}$$

then $\Delta H^\circ_{rxn} = \sum n_P \Delta H^\circ_f (products) - \sum n_R \Delta H^\circ_f (reactants)$, and then $q(kJ) \rightarrow mol \, (CH_4) \rightarrow g(CH_4)$

$$\Delta H^\circ_{rxn} \qquad \qquad \frac{16.04 \, g}{1 \, mol}$$

Solution: $V = lwh = 30.0 \, m \times 30.0 \, m \times 3.0 \, m = 2\underline{7}00 \, m^3$, then

$$2\underline{7}00 \, \cancel{m^3} \times \frac{(100 \, \cancel{cm})^3}{(1 \, \cancel{m^3})} \times \frac{1 \, \cancel{L}}{1000 \, \cancel{cm^3}} \times \frac{1 \, mol \, air}{22.4 \, \cancel{L}} = 1.\underline{2}0536 \times 10^5 \, mol \, air, \text{ and then}$$

$$q = mC_s\Delta T = 1.\underline{2}0536 \times 10^5 \, \cancel{mol} \times 30 \, \frac{J}{\cancel{mol} \cdot \cancel{°C}} \times 10.0 \, \cancel{°C} = 3.\underline{6}161 \times 10^7 \, J \times \frac{1 \, kJ}{1000 \, \cancel{J}} = 3.\underline{6}161 \times 10^4 \, kJ$$

needed

$$CH_4(g) + 2 \, O_2(g) \rightarrow CO_2(g) + 2 \, H_2O(g)$$

Reactant/Product	ΔH°_f(kJ/mol, from Appendix IIB)
$CH_4(g)$	-74.6
$O_2(g)$	0.0
$CO_2(g)$	-393.5
$H_2O(g)$	-241.8

Be sure to pull data for the correct formula and phase.

$$\Delta H^\circ_{rxn} = \sum n_P \Delta H^\circ_f (products) - \sum n_R \Delta H^\circ_f (reactants)$$
$$= [1(\Delta H^\circ_f(CO_2(g))) + 2(\Delta H^\circ_f(H_2O(g)))] - [1(\Delta H^\circ_f(CH_4(g))) + 2(\Delta H^\circ_f(O_2(g)))]$$
$$= [(-393.5 \, kJ) + 2(-241.8 \, kJ)] - [1(-74.6 \, kJ) + 2(0.0 \, kJ)]$$
$$= [-877.1 \, kJ] - [-74.6 \, kJ]$$
$$= -802.5 \, kJ$$

$$q_{rxn} = -q_{air} = -3.\underline{6}161 \times 10^4 \, kJ \times \frac{1 \, \cancel{mol \, CH_4}}{-802.5 \, \cancel{kJ}} \times \frac{16.04 \, g \, CH_4}{1 \, \cancel{mol \, CH_4}} = 7\underline{2}2.8 \, g \, CH_4 = 7 \times 10^2 \, g \, CH_4$$

Check: The units (g) are correct. The magnitude (700) is not surprising because the volume of a house is large.

6.82 **Given:** water: $V = 35 \, L$, $T_i = 25.0 \, °C$, $T_f = 100.0 \, °C$; fuel = C_7H_{16}, 15% efficiency, $d = 0.78 \, g/ml$
$\Delta H^\circ_f(C_7H_{16}(l)) = -224.4 \, kJ$

Find: V (fuel)

Conceptual Plan: write balanced reaction then $\Delta H^\circ_{rxn} = \sum n_P \Delta H^\circ_f (products) - \sum n_R \Delta H^\circ_f (reactants)$ then
$L \rightarrow mL \rightarrow g$ then $T_i, T_f \rightarrow \Delta T$ then $m, C_s, \Delta T \rightarrow q_{H_2O}(J) \rightarrow q_{H_2O}(kJ) \rightarrow q_{rxn}(kJ)$

$$\frac{1000 \, mL}{1 \, L} \quad \frac{1.0 \, g}{1.0 \, mL} \qquad \qquad \Delta T = T_f - T_i \qquad q_{H_2O} = m_{H_2O}C_{H_2O}\Delta T_{H_2O} \quad \frac{1 \, kJ}{1000 \, J} \qquad q_{rxn} = -q_{H_2O}$$

then q_{rxn} generated (kJ) $\rightarrow q_{rxn}$ used (kJ) $\rightarrow mol \, C_7H_{16} \rightarrow g \, C_7H_{16} \rightarrow mL \, C_7H_{16}$

$$\frac{100 \, kJ \, generated}{15 \, kJ \, needed} \qquad \frac{1 \, mol \, C_7H_{16}}{\Delta H^\circ_{rxn}} \qquad \frac{100.20 \, g}{1 \, mol} \qquad \frac{1.0 \, mL}{0.78 \, g}$$

Solution: Combustion is the combination with oxygen to form carbon dioxide and water:

$C_7H_{16}(l) + 11\ O_2(g) \rightarrow 7\ CO_2(g) + 8\ H_2O(g)$

Reactant/Product	ΔH_f°(kJ/mol, from Appendix IIB)
$C_7H_{16}(l)$	−224.4
$O_2(g)$	0.0
$CO_2(g)$	−393.5
$H_2O(g)$	−241.8

Be sure to pull data for the correct formula and phase.

$\Delta H_{rxn}^\circ = \sum n_P \Delta H_f^\circ(\text{products}) - \sum n_R \Delta H_f^\circ(\text{reactants})$

$= [7(\Delta H_f^\circ(CO_2(g))) + 8(\Delta H_f^\circ(H_2O(g)))] - [1(\Delta H_f^\circ(C_7H_{16}(l))) + 11(\Delta H_f^\circ(O_2(g)))]$

$= [7(-393.5\ \text{kJ}) + 8(-241.8\ \text{kJ})] - [1(-224.4\ \text{kJ}) + 11(0.0\ \text{kJ})]$

$= [-4688.9\ \text{kJ}] - [-224.4\ \text{kJ}]$

$= -4464.5\ \text{kJ}$

$35\ \text{L} \times \dfrac{1000\ \text{mL}}{1\ \text{L}} \times \dfrac{1.0\ \text{g}}{1.0\ \text{mL}} = 35000\ \text{g}$ then $\Delta T = T_f - T_i = 100.0\ ^\circ\text{C} - 25.0\ ^\circ\text{C} = 75.0\ ^\circ\text{C}$ then

$q_{H_2O} = m_{H_2O}C_{H_2O}\Delta T_{H_2O} = 35000\ \text{g} \times 4.18\ \dfrac{\text{J}}{\text{g}\cdot\ ^\circ\text{C}} \times 75.0\ ^\circ\text{C} = 1.09725 \times 10^7\ \text{J} \times \dfrac{1\ \text{kJ}}{1000\ \text{J}} = 1.09725 \times 10^4\ \text{kJ}$

$q_{rxn} = -q_{H_2O} = -1.09725 \times 10^4\ \text{kJ} \times \dfrac{100\ \text{kJ generated}}{15\ \text{kJ used}} \times \dfrac{1\ \text{mol}\ C_7H_{16}}{-4464.5\ \text{kJ}} \times \dfrac{100.20\ \text{g}\ C_7H_{16}}{1\ \text{mol}\ C_7H_{16}} \times \dfrac{1.0\ \text{mL}\ C_7H_{16}}{0.78\ \text{g}\ C_7H_{16}} =$

$2100\ \text{mL}\ C_7H_{16} = 2.1\ \text{L}\ C_7H_{16}$

Check: The units (mL) are correct. The magnitude (2 L) is a reasonable volume to have to take on a back-packing trip.

6.83   **Given:** $m(\text{ice}) = 9.0$ g; coffee: $T_1 = 90.0\ ^\circ\text{C}$, $m = 120.0$ g, $C_s = C_{H_2O}$, $\Delta H_{fus}^\circ = 6.0$ kJ/mol   **Find:** T_f of coffee
Conceptual Plan: $q_{ice} = -q_{coffee}$ so g(ice) → mol (ice) → q_{fus}(kJ) → q_{fus} (J) → q_{coffee} (J) then

$\dfrac{1\ \text{mol}}{18.01\ \text{g}} \qquad \dfrac{6.0\ \text{kJ}}{1\ \text{mol}} \qquad \dfrac{1000\ \text{J}}{1\ \text{kJ}} \qquad q_{coffee} = -q_{ice}$

$q, m, C_s \rightarrow \Delta T$ then $T_i, \Delta T \rightarrow T_2$; now we have slightly cooled coffee in contact with 0.0 °C water

$q = mC_s\Delta T \qquad \Delta T = T_2 - T_i$

so $q_{ice} = -q_{coffee}$ with $m, C_s, T_i \rightarrow T_f$

$q = mC_s(T_f - T_i)$ then set $q_{ice} = -q_{coffee}$

Solution: $9.0\ \text{g} \times \dfrac{1\ \text{mol}}{18.01\ \text{g}} \times \dfrac{6.0\ \text{kJ}}{1\ \text{mol}} \times \dfrac{1000\ \text{J}}{1\ \text{kJ}} = 2.9983 \times 10^3\ \text{J}$, $q_{coffee} = -q_{ice} = -2.9983 \times 10^3\ \text{J}$

$q = mC_s\Delta T$ Rearrange to solve for ΔT. $\Delta T = \dfrac{q}{mC_s} = \dfrac{-2.9983 \times 10^3\ \text{J}}{120.0\ \text{g} \times 4.18\ \dfrac{\text{J}}{\text{g}\cdot\ ^\circ\text{C}}} = -5.9775\ ^\circ\text{C}$ then

$\Delta T = T_2 - T_i$. Rearrange to solve for T_2. $T_2 = \Delta T + T_i = -5.9775\ ^\circ\text{C} + 90.0\ ^\circ\text{C} = 84.0225\ ^\circ\text{C}$
$q = mC_s(T_f - T_i)$ substitute in values and set $q_{H_2O} = -q_{coffee}$.

$q_{H_2O} = m_{H_2O}C_{H_2O}(T_f - T_{H_2Oi}) = 9.0\ \text{g} \times 4.18\ \dfrac{\text{J}}{\text{g}\cdot\ ^\circ\text{C}} \times (T_f - 0.0\ ^\circ\text{C}) =$

$-q_{coffee} = -m_{coffee}C_{coffee}(T_f - T_{coffee2}) = -120.0\ \text{g} \times 4.18\ \dfrac{\text{J}}{\text{g}\cdot\ ^\circ\text{C}} \times (T_f - 84.0225\ ^\circ\text{C})$

Rearrange to solve for T_f.
$9.0\ \text{g}\ T_f = -120.0\ \text{g}\ (T_f - 84.0225\ ^\circ\text{C}) \rightarrow 9.0\ \text{g}\ T_f = -120.0\ \text{g}\ T_f + 10082.7\ \text{g} \rightarrow$

$-10082.7\ \text{g} = -129.0\ \dfrac{\text{g}}{^\circ\text{C}}\ T_f \rightarrow T_f = \dfrac{-10082.7\ \text{g}}{-129.0\ \dfrac{\text{g}}{^\circ\text{C}}} = 78.2\ ^\circ\text{C}$

Check: The units (°C) are correct. The temperature is closer to the original coffee temperature because the mass of coffee is so much larger than the ice mass.

6.84   **Given:** liquid water at −10.0 °C, C_s (ice) = 2.04 J/g · °C; $\Delta H_{fus}^\circ = -332$ J/g (at 0.0 °C)
Find: ΔH, ΔE, q, and w for freezing at −10.0 °C

Conceptual Plan: Assume exactly 1 g H_2O for all calculations (report answers as J/g) and constant $P = 1$ atm. Construct the following path: According to Hess's law $\Delta H_1 + \Delta H_2 + \Delta H_3 = \Delta H_4 = \Delta H^\circ_{fus}$ at $-10.0\,°C$

$$
\begin{array}{ccc}
 & \text{step 2} & \\
\text{Liquid at 0.0 °C} & \longrightarrow & \text{solid at 0.0 °C} \\
\uparrow \text{ step 1} & & \downarrow \text{ step 3} \quad\quad \text{at constant } P,\ \Delta H = q \\
\text{Liquid at } -10.0\,°C & \longrightarrow & \text{solid at } -10.0\,°C \quad \text{For steps 1 and 3, } q = mC_s\Delta T \\
 & \text{step 4} &
\end{array}
$$

Look up the density of liquid and solid water at 0.0 °C. (Assume that the density of each phase does not change significantly at -10.0 °C.)

$d_L = 0.9998$ g/mL and $d_S = 0.917$ g/mL

$$\text{g} \rightarrow \text{mL} \rightarrow \text{L then } V_L, V_S \rightarrow \Delta V \text{ then } P, \Delta V \rightarrow w(\text{L atm}) \rightarrow w(\text{J}) \text{ then } q, w \rightarrow \Delta E$$

L: $\dfrac{1\ \text{mL}}{0.9998\ \text{g}}$ S: $\dfrac{1\ \text{mL}}{0.917\ \text{g}}$ $\dfrac{1\ \text{L}}{1000\ \text{mL}}$ $\Delta V = V_S - V_L$ $w = -P\Delta V$ $\dfrac{101.3\ \text{J}}{1\ \text{L atm}}$ $\Delta E = q + w$

Solution: $\Delta H_1 = q_1 = mC_S\Delta T = 1\ \text{g} \times 4.18\ \dfrac{\text{J}}{\text{g}\cdot°C} \times (0.00\,°C - (-10.0\,°C)) = +41.8$ J

$\Delta H_2 = q_2 = m\Delta H = 1\ \text{g} \times -332\ \dfrac{\text{J}}{\text{g}} = -332$ J

$\Delta H_3 = q_3 = mC_S\Delta T = 1\ \text{g} \times 2.04\ \dfrac{\text{J}}{\text{g}\cdot°C} \times (-10.00\,°C - 0.0\,°C) = -20.4$ J

so $\Delta H_4 = q_4 = \Delta H_1 + \Delta H_2 + \Delta H_3 = +41.8\ \text{J} - 332\ \text{J} - 20.4\ \text{J} = -310.6\ \text{J} = -311$ J/g

$V_L = 1\ \text{g} \times \dfrac{1\ \text{mL}}{0.9998\ \text{g}} \times \dfrac{1\ \text{L}}{1000\ \text{mL}} = 0.00100020004\ \text{L}$ and $V_S = 1\ \text{g} \times \dfrac{1\ \text{mL}}{0.917\ \text{g}} \times \dfrac{1\ \text{L}}{1000\ \text{mL}} = 0.0010905$ L

then $\Delta V = V_S - V_L = 0.0010905\ \text{L} - 0.00100020004\ \text{L} = 9.029996 \times 10^{-5}$ L

then $w = -P\Delta V = -1\ \text{atm} \times 9.029996 \times 10^{-5}\ \text{L} \times \dfrac{101.3\ \text{J}}{1\ \text{L atm}} = -0.009147\ \text{J} = -0.009$ J/g

and $\Delta E = q + w = -310.6\ \text{J} - 0.009147\ \text{J} = -311$ J/g

Check: The units (J/g) are correct. We expect freezing to release less energy at $-10\,°C$ because we are below the normal freezing point. The work is negligible because the volume change is so small.

6.85 $KE = \dfrac{1}{2}mv^2$. For an ideal gas. $v = u_{rms} = \sqrt{\dfrac{3RT}{\mathcal{M}}}$; so $KE_{avg} = \dfrac{1}{2}N_A m u_{rms}^2 = \dfrac{3}{2}RT$ then

$\Delta E_{sys} = KE_2 - KE_1 = \dfrac{3}{2}RT_2 - \dfrac{3}{2}RT_1 = \dfrac{3}{2}R\Delta T$. At constant V, $\Delta E_{sys} = C_V\Delta T$; so $C_V = \dfrac{3}{2}R$.

At constant P, $\Delta E_{sys} = q + w = q_P - P\Delta V = \Delta H - P\Delta V$. Because $PV = nRT$, for one mole of an ideal

gas at constant P, $P\Delta V = R\Delta T$; so $\Delta E_{sys} = q + w = q_P - P\Delta V = \Delta H - P\Delta V = \Delta H - R\Delta T$. This gives

$\dfrac{3}{2}R\Delta T = \Delta H - R\Delta T$ or $\Delta H = \dfrac{5}{2}R\Delta T = C_P\Delta T$, so $C_P = \dfrac{5}{2}R$.

6.86   **Given:** fixed amount of an ideal gas; step 1: $V_1 = 12.0$ L to $V_2 = 24.0$ L at constant $P = 1.0$ atm; step 2: gas cooled at constant $V = 24.0$ L to original T; step 3: $V_1 = 24.0$ L to $V_2 = 12.0$ L
Find: q for entire process
Solution: For the expansion: $w_1 = -(24.0\ \text{L} - 12.0\ \text{L})(1.0\ \text{atm}) = -12.0$ L atm; for the constant V step: $w_2 = 0$ because there is no PV work at constant volume; for the contraction: $w_3 = -nRT \ln (V_2/V_1) = -PV \ln (V_2/V_1) = -(1.0\ \text{atm})(12.0\ \text{L}) \ln (12.0\ \text{L}/24.0\ \text{L}) = 8.3\ \text{L}\cdot\text{atm}$, then $w_{total} = w_1 + w_2 + w_3 = -12.0\ \text{L atm} + 0 + 8.3$ L atm

$w_{total} = -3.7\ \text{L}\cdot\text{atm} \times \dfrac{101\ \text{J}}{\text{L}\cdot\text{atm}} = 370$ J. Because the system ends where it started, $\Delta E = 0$; therefore,

$q = -w = 370$ J.

Check: The units (J) are correct. The total energy change over the entire cycle is 0 because we end where we started, but this does not mean that q has to be 0.

6.87 $q = \Delta H = 454\ \text{g} \times \dfrac{1\ \text{mol}}{18.02\ \text{g}} \times \dfrac{40.7\ \text{kJ}}{1\ \text{mol}} = 1025.405\ \text{kJ} = 1030$ kJ and $w = -P\Delta V$. Assume that $P = 1$ atm

(exactly) and $\Delta V = V_G - V_L$, where $V_L = 454\ \text{g} \times \dfrac{1\ \text{mL}}{0.9998\ \text{g}} \times \dfrac{1\ \text{L}}{1000\ \text{mL}} = 0.4540908\ \text{L}$ and $PV = nRT$.

Rearrange to solve for V_G.

$$V_G = \frac{nRT}{P} = \frac{454\ \cancel{g} \times \dfrac{1\ \cancel{mol}}{18.02\ \cancel{g}} \times 0.08206\ \dfrac{L \cdot \cancel{atm}}{\cancel{mol} \cdot \cancel{K}} \times 373\ \cancel{K}}{1\ \cancel{atm}} = 77\underline{1}.1545\ L$$

$\Delta V = V_G - V_L = 77\underline{1}.1545\ L - 0.4540908\ L = 770.7004\ L$ and so

$$w = -P\Delta V = -1.0\ \cancel{atm} \times 770.7004\ \cancel{L} \times \frac{101.3\ J}{1\ \cancel{L \cdot atm}} = -7807\underline{1}.9515\ J = -7.81 \times 10^4\ J = -78.1\ kJ$$

Finally, $\Delta E = q + w = 1025.405\ kJ - 78.0719515\ kJ = 94\underline{7}.333\ kJ = 950\ kJ$.

6.88 $q = q_1 + q_2 + q_3 = \Delta H$, where

$$q_1 = nC\Delta T = 1.0\ \cancel{mol} \times 75.3\ \frac{J}{\cancel{mol} \cdot \cancel{°C}} \times (100\ °C - 80\ °C) = +1\underline{5}06\ J$$

$$q_2 = n\Delta H = 1.0\ \cancel{mol} \times 40.7 \times 10^3\ \frac{J}{\cancel{mol}} = 4.07 \times 10^4\ J$$

$$q_3 = nC\Delta T = 1.0\ \cancel{mol} \times 25.0\ \frac{J}{\cancel{mol} \cdot \cancel{°C}} \times (110\ °C - 100\ °C) = +2\underline{5}0\ J;\ so$$

$q = q_1 + q_2 + q_3 = \Delta H = +1\underline{5}06\ J + 4.07 \times 10^4\ J + 2\underline{5}0\ J = 424\underline{5}6\ J = 42500\ J = 42.5\ kJ$ and

$w = -P\Delta V$. Assume that $P = 1$ atm (exactly) and $\Delta V = V_G - V_L$ where

$$V_L = 1.0\ \cancel{mol} \times \frac{18.02\ \cancel{g}}{1\ \cancel{mol}} \times \frac{1\ \cancel{mL}}{0.9998\ \cancel{g}} \times \frac{1\ L}{1000\ \cancel{mL}} = 0.0180\underline{2}\ L$$ and $PV = nRT$. Rearrange to solve for V_G.

$$V_G = \frac{nRT}{P} = \frac{1.0\ \cancel{mol} \times 0.08206\ \dfrac{L \cdot \cancel{atm}}{\cancel{mol} \cdot \cancel{K}} \times (110 + 273)\ \cancel{K}}{1\,\cancel{atm}} = 3\underline{1}.42898\ L$$ and so

$\Delta V = V_G - V_L = 3\underline{1}.42898\ L - 0.0180\underline{2}\ L = 31.41096\ L$ and

$$w = -P\Delta V = -1.0\ \cancel{atm} \times 31.41096\ \cancel{L} \times \frac{101.3\ J}{1\ \cancel{L \cdot atm}} = -3\underline{1}81.930\ J = -3200\ J = -3.2\ kJ$$

Finally, $\Delta E = q + w = 424\underline{5}6\ J - 3\underline{1}81.930\ J = 392\underline{7}4.07\ J = 39300\ J = 39.3\ kJ$

Conceptual Problems

6.89   (a)   False. When ΔE_{sys} is positive, the system gains energy.

(b)   False. The first law of thermodynamics states that the energy of the universe is constant. Therefore, the energy being gained by the system has to come from the surroundings, and the surroundings lose energy.

(c)   False. When ΔE_{sys} is positive, the system gains energy.

(d)   True. According to the first law of thermodynamics, the energy of the universe is constant. Therefore, the energy gained by the system comes from the surroundings, and the surroundings lose energy equal to the energy gained by the system.

6.90   (a)   False. An isothermal process has $\Delta E_{sys} = 0$.

(b)   False. $w < 0$ for expansions.

(c)   True. If $\Delta E_{sys} = 0$ and $\Delta E_{sys} = q + w$ and $w < 0$, then $q > 0$.

(d)   False. An isothermal process has $\Delta E_{sys} = 0$.

6.91   (a)   At constant P, $\Delta E_{sys} = q + w = q_P + w = \Delta H + w$; so $\Delta E_{sys} - w = \Delta H = q$.

6.92   Refrigerator A contains only air, which will cool quickly but will not stabilize the temperature. Refrigerator B contains containers of water, which require a great deal of energy to cool on day 1 but will remain stable at a cold temperature on day 2.

6.93   The aluminum cylinder will be cooler after 1 hour because it has a lower heat capacity than does water (less heat needs to be pulled out for every °C temperature change).

6.94   Because $q = mC_S\Delta T$, $m_A = 2\ m_B$, $C_B = 4\ C_A$, $q_A = -q_B$, we can substitute into the equation to get
$q_A = mC_S\Delta T_A = -q_B = -m_B C_B \Delta T_B \rightarrow (2\ m_B)C_A\Delta T_A = -m_B(4\ C_A)\Delta T_B$

$$\rightarrow \Delta T_A = \frac{-m_B\,(4\,C_A)}{(2\,m_B)\,C_A}\,\Delta T_B = \frac{-4}{2}\,\Delta T_B = -2\Delta T_B, \text{ or the temperature change for substance A is twice the}$$

magnitude of the temperature change for substance B.

6.95   **Given:** 2418 J heat produced; 5 J work done on surroundings at constant P **Find:** ΔE, ΔH, q, and w
        Conceptual Plan: interpret language to determine the sign of the two terms then q, $w \rightarrow \Delta E_{sys}$
$$\Delta E = q + w$$

Solution: Because heat is released from the system to the surroundings, $q = -2418\,\text{J}$;
because the system is doing work on the surroundings, $w = -5\,\text{kJ}$. At constant P,
$\Delta H = q = -2.418\,\text{kJ}$; $\Delta E = q + w = -2418\,\text{J} - 5\,\text{J} = -2423\,\text{J} = -2\,\text{kJ}$.

Check: The units (kJ) are correct. The magnitude of the answer (–2) makes physical sense because both terms are
negative and the amount of work done is negligibly small.

6.96   The internal energy of a chemical system is the sum of its kinetic energy and its potential energy. This potential energy is the energy source in an exothermic chemical reaction. Under normal circumstances, chemical potential energy (or simply chemical energy) arises primarily from the electrostatic forces between the protons and electrons that compose the atoms and molecules within the system. In an exothermic reaction, some bonds break and new ones form, and the protons and electrons go from an arrangement of higher potential energy to one of lower potential energy. As they rearrange, their potential energy is converted into kinetic energy. Heat is emitted in the reaction, so it feels hot to the touch.

6.97   (a)   If ΔV is positive, then $w = -P\Delta V < 0$. Because $\Delta E_{sys} = q + w = q_P + w = \Delta H + w$; if w is negative, then $\Delta H > \Delta E_{sys}$.

Questions for Group Work

6.98   Examples of heat transfer problems can be seen in Problems 6.33–6.38. All of the problems use the equations $q = m\,C_s\,\Delta T$ where $\Delta T = T_f - T_i$. The difference can include different masses of the two object/substances, different initial and final temperatures, and different identities of the two object/substances (which changes the heat capacities).

6.99   (a)   Gasoline burning is a combustion reaction, which is always exothermic (gasoline engines get very hot when running). $\Delta H < 0$
        (b)   Steam condensing is an exothermic process, since the steam loses a lot of heat when it condenses (which is why you can get severely burned from steam). $\Delta H < 0$
        (c)   Water boiling is an endothermic process, since the water molecules in steam have more kinetic energy than the molecules in the liquid phase. $\Delta H > 0$
        Additional examples of exothermic processes are:
        • Liquid water freezing on a cold winter day;
        • Reacting an acid and a base, such as HCl with NaOH solutions;
        • Any combustion reaction, such as propane burning in a gas grill, alcohol burning in a flaming dessert, or burning wood in a fireplace.
        Additional examples of endothermic processes are:
        • Snow melting on a spring day;
        • Photosynthesis, which converts carbon dioxide and water into glucose and oxygen;
        • The reaction in an instant cold pack.

6.100   (a) $C_3H_8(g) + 5\,O_2(g) \rightarrow 3\,CO_2(g) + 4\,H_2O(g)$

        (b) $10.4 \times 10^3 \; g\,C_3H_8 \times \dfrac{1\;mol\,C_3H_8}{44.09\;g\,C_3H_8} \times \dfrac{-2044\;kJ}{1\;mol\,C_3H_8} = -4.82 \times 10^5\;kJ$

        (c) $q = m\,C_s\,\Delta T$ so $m = \dfrac{q}{C_s\,\Delta T} = \dfrac{-4.82 \times 10^5\;kJ \times \dfrac{1000\;J}{1\;kJ}}{4.184\;\dfrac{J}{g \times \mathcal{C}} \times (100.\,\mathcal{C} - 25\,\mathcal{C})} = 1.5 \times 10^6\;g\;water$

6.101   The reactions in the calorimeter are:
- $C(s, \text{graphite}) + O_2(g) \rightarrow CO_2(g)$ ΔH_1
- $2 H_2(g) + O_2(g) \rightarrow 2 H_2O(g)$ ΔH_2
- $C_6H_{12}O_6(s) + 6 O_2(g) \rightarrow 6 CO_2(g) + 6 H_2O(g)$ ΔH_3

The desired reaction is $6 C(s, \text{graphite}) + 3 O_2(g) + 6 H_2(g) \rightarrow C_6H_{12}O_6(s)$. We can get this reaction with the following scheme:

$6 C(s, \text{graphite}) + \cancel{6 O_2(g)} \rightarrow \cancel{6 CO_2(g)}$ $6\Delta H_1$

$6 H_2(g) + 3 O_2(g) \rightarrow \cancel{6 H_2O(g)}$ $3\Delta H_2$

$\cancel{6 CO_2(g)} + \cancel{6 H_2O(g)} \rightarrow C_6H_{12}O_6(s) + \cancel{6 O_2(g)}$ $-\Delta H_3$

$6 C(s, \text{graphite}) + 3 O_2(g) + 6 H_2(g) \rightarrow C_6H_{12}O_6(s)$ $\Delta H = 6\Delta H_1 + 3\Delta H_2 - \Delta H_3$

Plug the results from the three individual reactions into the above equation to calculate the heat of formation of glucose.

6.102   The decomposition of hydrogen peroxide is $2 H_2O_2(l) \rightarrow 2 H_2O(l) + O_2(g)$.
(a)   The heat of formation of hydrogen peroxide is $H_2(g) + O_2(g) \rightarrow H_2O_2(l)$ $\Delta H = -187.8$ kJ
(b)   The heat of formation of water is $H_2(g) + 1/2 O_2(g) \rightarrow H_2O(l)$ $\Delta H = -285.8$ kJ
(c)   The heat of formation of oxygen gas is defined as zero, since it is an element in its most stable state at 25 °C.
(d)   See above.
(e) $2 H_2O_2(l) \rightarrow 2 H_2O(l) + O_2(g)$.
(f)   The heat of the reaction in part (e) is

$$\Delta H^{\circ}_{rxn} = \sum n_P \Delta H^{\circ}_f (\text{products}) - \sum n_R \Delta H^{\circ}_f (\text{reactants})$$
$$= [2(\Delta H^{\circ}_f(H_2O(l))) + 1(\Delta H^{\circ}_f(O_2(g)))] - [2(\Delta H^{\circ}_f(H_2O_2(l)))]$$
$$= [2(-285.8 \text{ kJ}) + 1(0.0 \text{ kJ})] - [2(-187.8 \text{ kJ})]$$
$$= [-571.6 \text{ kJ}] - [-375.6 \text{ kJ}]$$
$$= -196.0 \text{ kJ}$$

(g)

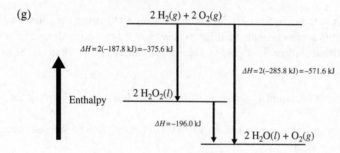

Enthalpy

$2 H_2(g) + 2 O_2(g)$

$\Delta H = 2(-187.8 \text{ kJ}) = -375.6 \text{ kJ}$

$\Delta H = 2(-285.8 \text{ kJ}) = -571.6 \text{ kJ}$

$2 H_2O_2(l)$

$\Delta H = -196.0 \text{ kJ}$

$2 H_2O(l) + O_2(g)$

7 The Quantum-Mechanical Model of the Atom

Problems by Topic

Electromagnetic Radiation

7.1   **Given:** distance to sun $= 1.496 \times 10^8$ km   **Find:** time for light to travel from sun to Earth
Conceptual Plan: distance km → distance m → time

$$\frac{1000 \text{ m}}{1 \text{ km}} \qquad \text{time} = \frac{\text{distance}}{3.00 \times 10^8 \text{ m/s}}$$

Solution: $1.496 \times 10^8 \text{ km} \times \dfrac{1000 \text{ m}}{1 \text{ km}} \times \dfrac{\text{s}}{3.00 \times 10^8 \text{ m}} = 499 \text{ s}$

Check: The units of the answer (s) are correct. The magnitude of the answer is reasonable because it corresponds to about 8 minutes.

7.2   **Given:** 4.3 light-years to star   **Find:** distance in km
Conceptual Plan: light-years → days → hours → seconds → m → km

$$\frac{365 \text{ days}}{1 \text{ yr}} \qquad \frac{24 \text{ hr}}{1 \text{ day}} \qquad \frac{3600 \text{ s}}{1 \text{ hr}} \qquad \frac{3.00 \times 10^8 \text{ m}}{\text{s}} \qquad \frac{1 \text{ km}}{1000 \text{ m}}$$

Solution: $4.3 \text{ light yr} \times \dfrac{365 \text{ days}}{1 \text{ yr}} \times \dfrac{24 \text{ hrs}}{1 \text{ day}} \times \dfrac{3600 \text{ s}}{1 \text{ hr}} \times \dfrac{3.00 \times 10^8 \text{ m}}{\text{s}} \times \dfrac{1 \text{ km}}{1000 \text{ m}} = 4.1 \times 10^{13} \text{ km}$

Check: The units of the answer (km) are correct. The magnitude of the answer is reasonable because it takes much longer for the light to reach Earth from Proxima Centauri than from the sun; so the distance should be much greater.

7.3   (i)   By increasing wavelength, the order is d) ultraviolet $<$ c) infrared $<$ b) microwave $<$ a) radio waves.

(ii)   By increasing energy, the order is a) radio waves $<$ b) microwaves $<$ c) infrared $<$ d) ultraviolet.

7.4   (i)   By increasing frequency, the order is b) radio waves $<$ c) microwaves $<$ d) visible light $<$ a) gamma rays.

(ii)   By decreasing energy, the order is a) gamma rays $>$ d) visible light $>$ c) microwaves $>$ b) radio waves.

7.5   (a)   **Given:** $\lambda = 632.8$ nm   **Find:** frequency (ν)
Conceptual Plan: nm → m → ν

$$\frac{1 \text{ m}}{10^9 \text{ nm}} \qquad \nu = \frac{c}{\lambda}$$

Solution:

$$632.8 \text{ nm} \times \frac{\text{m}}{10^9 \text{ nm}} = 6.328 \times 10^{-7} \text{m}; \quad \nu = \frac{3.00 \times 10^8 \text{ m}}{\text{s}} \times \frac{1}{6.328 \times 10^{-7} \text{ m}} = 4.74 \times 10^{14} \text{ s}^{-1}$$

Check: The units of the answer (s^{-1}) are correct. The magnitude of the answer seems reasonable because wavelength and frequency are inversely proportional.

(b) **Given:** $\lambda = 503$ nm   **Find:** frequency (ν)
Conceptual Plan: nm $\rightarrow$ m $\rightarrow$ ν

$$\frac{1\,m}{10^9\,nm} \qquad \nu = \frac{c}{\lambda}$$

Solution: $503\;\text{nm} \times \dfrac{1\,m}{10^9\,nm} = 5.03 \times 10^{-7}\,m; \quad \nu = \dfrac{3.00 \times 10^8\,m}{s} \times \dfrac{1}{5.03 \times 10^{-7}\,m} = 5.96 \times 10^{14}\,s^{-1}$

Check: The units of the answer (s^{-1}) are correct. The magnitude of the answer seems reasonable because wavelength and frequency are inversely proportional.

(c) **Given:** $\lambda = 0.052$ nm   **Find:** frequency (ν)
Conceptual Plan: nm $\rightarrow$ m $\rightarrow$ ν

$$\frac{1\,m}{10^9\,nm} \qquad \nu = \frac{c}{\lambda}$$

Solution: $0.052\;\text{nm} \times \dfrac{1\,m}{10^9\,nm} = 5.2 \times 10^{-11}\,m; \quad \nu = \dfrac{3.00 \times 10^8\,m}{s} \times \dfrac{1}{5.2 \times 10^{-11}\,m} = 5.8 \times 10^{18}\,s^{-1}$

Check: The units of the answer (s^{-1}) are correct. The magnitude of the answer seems reasonable because wavelength and frequency are inversely proportional.

7.6   (a) **Given:** $\nu = 100.2$ MHz   **Find:** wavelength (λ)
Conceptual Plan: MHz $\rightarrow$ Hz $\rightarrow$ s^{-1} $\rightarrow$ λ

$$\frac{10^6\,Hz}{1\,MHz} \qquad 1\,Hz = 1\,s^{-1} \qquad \lambda = \frac{c}{\nu}$$

Solution:

$100.2\;\text{MHz} \times \dfrac{10^6\,Hz}{1\,MHz} \times \dfrac{1\,s^{-1}}{1\,Hz} = 1.002 \times 10^8\,s^{-1}; \quad \lambda = \dfrac{3.00 \times 10^8\,m}{s} \times \dfrac{s}{1.002 \times 10^8} = 2.99\,m$

Check: The units of the answer (m) are correct. The magnitude of the answer is reasonable because FM wavelengths are generally in the 3–8 m range.

(b) **Given:** $\nu = 1070$ kHz   **Find:** wavelength (λ)
Conceptual Plan: kHz $\rightarrow$ Hz $\rightarrow$ s^{-1} $\rightarrow$ λ

$$\frac{10^3\,Hz}{1\,kHz} \qquad 1\,Hz = 1\,s^{-1} \qquad \lambda = \frac{c}{\nu}$$

Solution: $1070\;\text{kHz} \times \dfrac{10^3\,Hz}{1\,kHz} \times \dfrac{1\,s^{-1}}{1\,Hz} = 1.070 \times 10^6\,s^{-1}; \quad \lambda = \dfrac{3.00 \times 10^8\,m}{s} \times \dfrac{s}{1.070 \times 10^6} = 280.\,m$

Check: The units of the answer (m) are correct. The magnitude of the answer is reasonable because AM wavelengths are generally in the 100–1000 m range.

(c) **Given:** $\nu = 835.6$ MHz   **Find:** wavelength (λ)
Conceptual Plan: MHz $\rightarrow$ Hz $\rightarrow$ s^{-1} $\rightarrow$ λ

$$\frac{10^6\,Hz}{1\,MHz} \qquad 1\,Hz = 1\,s^{-1} \qquad \lambda = \frac{c}{\nu}$$

Solution:

$835.6\;\text{MHz} \times \dfrac{10^6\,Hz}{1\,MHz} \times \dfrac{1\,s^{-1}}{1\,Hz} = 8.356 \times 10^8\,s^{-1}; \quad \lambda = \dfrac{3.00 \times 10^8\,m}{s} \times \dfrac{s}{8.356 \times 10^8} = 3.59 \times 10^{-1}\,m$

Check: The units of the answer (m) are correct. The magnitude of the answer is reasonable because cell phone wavelengths are generally in the 0.1–0.5 m range.

7.7   (a) **Given:** frequency (ν) from Problem 7.5(a) $= 4.74 \times 10^{14}\,s^{-1}$ **Find:** Energy
Conceptual Plan: $\nu \rightarrow E$

$$E = h\nu \qquad h = 6.626 \times 10^{-34}\,J \cdot s$$

Solution: $6.626 \times 10^{-34}\,J \cdot s \times \dfrac{4.74 \times 10^{14}}{s} = 3.14 \times 10^{-19}\,J$

Check: The units of the answer (J) are correct. The magnitude of the answer is reasonable because we are talking about the energy of one photon.

(b) **Given:** frequency (ν) from Problem 7.5(b) = 5.96×10^{14} s^{-1} **Find:** Energy
Conceptual Plan: $\nu \rightarrow E$

$$E = h\nu \quad h = 6.626 \times 10^{-34}\,\text{J}\cdot\text{s}$$

Solution: $6.626 \times 10^{-34}\,\text{J}\cdot\text{s} \times \dfrac{5.96 \times 10^{14}}{\text{s}} = 3.95 \times 10^{-19}$ J

Check: The units of the answer (J) are correct. The magnitude of the answer is reasonable because we are talking about the energy of one photon.

(c) **Given:** frequency (ν) from Problem 7.5(c) = 5.8×10^{18} s^{-1} **Find:** Energy
Conceptual Plan: $\nu \rightarrow E$

$$E = h\nu \quad h = 6.626 \times 10^{-34}\,\text{J}\cdot\text{s}$$

Solution: $6.626 \times 10^{-34}\,\text{J}\cdot\text{s} \times \dfrac{5.8 \times 10^{18}}{\text{s}} = 3.8 \times 10^{-15}$ J

Check: The units of the answer (J) are correct. The magnitude of the answer is reasonable because we are talking about the energy of one photon.

7.8   (a) **Given:** frequency (ν) from Problem 7.6(a) = 100.2 MHz   **Find:** Energy
Conceptual Plan: MHz $\rightarrow$ Hz $\rightarrow$ s^{-1} $\rightarrow$ E

$$\frac{10^6\,\text{Hz}}{1\,\text{MHz}} \quad 1\,\text{Hz} = 1\,\text{s}^{-1} \quad E = h\nu \quad h = 6.626 \times 10^{-34}\,\text{J}\cdot\text{s}$$

Solution:

$$100.2\,\text{MHz} \times \frac{10^6\,\text{Hz}}{1\,\text{MHz}} \times \frac{1\,\text{s}^{-1}}{1\,\text{Hz}} = 1.002 \times 10^8\,\text{s}^{-1} \quad 6.626 \times 10^{-34}\,\text{J}\cdot\text{s} \times \frac{1.002 \times 10^8}{\text{s}} = 6.639 \times 10^{-26}\,\text{J}$$

Check: The units of the answer (J) are correct. The magnitude of the answer is reasonable because we are talking about the energy of one photon and have a relatively long wavelength.

(b) **Given:** $\nu = 1070$ kHz   **Find:** Energy
Conceptual Plan: kHz $\rightarrow$ Hz $\rightarrow$ s^{-1} $\rightarrow$ E

$$\frac{10^3\,\text{Hz}}{1\,\text{kHz}} \quad 1\,\text{Hz} = 1\,\text{s}^{-1} \quad E = h\nu \quad h = 6.626 \times 10^{-34}\,\text{J}\cdot\text{s}$$

Solution:

$$1070\,\text{kHz} \times \frac{10^3\,\text{Hz}}{1\,\text{kHz}} \times \frac{1\,\text{s}^{-1}}{1\,\text{Hz}} = 1.070 \times 10^6\,\text{s}^{-1}; \quad 6.626 \times 10^{-34}\,\text{J}\cdot\text{s} \times \frac{1.070 \times 10^6}{\text{s}} = 7.090 \times 10^{-28}\,\text{J}$$

Check: The units of the answer (J) are correct. The magnitude of the answer is reasonable because we are talking about the energy of one photon and have a relatively long wavelength.

(c) **Given:** $\nu = 835.6$ MHz   **Find:** Energy
Conceptual Plan: MHz $\rightarrow$ Hz $\rightarrow$ s^{-1} $\rightarrow$ E

$$\frac{10^6\,\text{Hz}}{1\,\text{MHz}} \quad 1\,\text{Hz} = 1\,\text{s}^{-1} \quad E = h\nu \quad h = 6.626 \times 10^{-34}\,\text{J}\cdot\text{s}$$

Solution:

$$835.6\,\text{MHz} \times \frac{10^6\,\text{Hz}}{1\,\text{MHz}} \times \frac{1\,\text{s}^{-1}}{1\,\text{Hz}} = 8.356 \times 10^8\,\text{s}^{-1} \quad 6.626 \times 10^{-34}\,\text{J}\cdot\text{s} \times \frac{8.356 \times 10^8}{\text{s}} = 5.537 \times 10^{-25}\,\text{J}$$

Check: The units of the answer (J) are correct. The magnitude of the answer is reasonable because we are talking about the energy of one photon and have a relatively long wavelength.

7.9   **Given:** $\lambda = 532$ nm and $E_{\text{pulse}} = 4.88$ mJ   **Find:** number of photons
Conceptual Plan: nm $\rightarrow$ m $\rightarrow$ E_{photon} $\rightarrow$ number of photons

$$\frac{1\,\text{m}}{10^9\,\text{nm}} \quad E = \frac{hc}{\lambda}; h = 6.626 \times 10^{-34}\,\text{J}\cdot\text{s} \quad \frac{E_{\text{pulse}}}{E_{\text{photon}}}$$

Solution:

$$532\,\text{nm} \times \frac{1\,\text{m}}{10^9\,\text{nm}} = 5.32 \times 10^{-7}\,\text{m}; \quad E = \frac{6.626 \times 10^{-34}\,\text{J}\cdot\text{s} \times \dfrac{3.00 \times 10^8\,\text{m}}{\text{s}}}{5.32 \times 10^{-7}\,\text{m}} = 3.7\underline{3}65 \times 10^{-19}\,\text{J/photon}$$

$$4.88 \text{ mJ} \times \frac{1 \text{ J}}{1000 \text{ mJ}} \times \frac{1 \text{ photon}}{3.7\underline{3}65 \times 10^{-19} \text{ J}} = 1.31 \times 10^{16} \text{ photons}$$

Check: The units of the answer (number of photons) are correct. The magnitude of the answer is reasonable for the amount of energy involved.

7.10   **Given:** $\lambda = 6.5 \ \mu\text{m}$; power = 41.7 watts   **Find:** photons/second

Conceptual Plan: $\mu\text{m} \rightarrow \text{m} \rightarrow E_{\text{photon}} \rightarrow$ and then watts $\rightarrow$ J/s $\rightarrow$ number of photons

$$\frac{1 \text{ m}}{10^6 \ \mu\text{m}} \qquad E = \frac{hc}{\lambda}; h = 6.626 \times 10^{-34} \text{ J} \cdot \text{s} \qquad \frac{\text{J/sec}}{\text{watt}} \qquad \frac{\text{J/sec}}{\text{J/photon}}$$

Solution:

$$6.5 \ \mu\text{m} \times \frac{1 \text{ m}}{10^6 \ \mu\text{m}} = 6.5 \times 10^{-6} \text{ m}; \quad E = \frac{6.626 \times 10^{-34} \text{ J} \cdot \text{s} \times \dfrac{3.00 \times 10^8 \text{ m}}{\text{s}}}{6.5 \times 10^{-6} \text{ m}} = 3.0\underline{5}8 \times 10^{-20} \text{ J/photon}$$

$$41.7 \text{ watts} \times \frac{\text{J/s}}{1 \text{ watt}} \times \frac{1 \text{ photon}}{3.0\underline{5}8 \times 10^{-20} \text{ J}} = 1.4 \times 10^{21} \text{ photons/s}$$

Check: The units of the answer (photons/s) are correct. The magnitude of the answer is reasonable for the amount of energy involved.

7.11   (a)   **Given:** $\lambda = 1500 \text{ nm}$ **Find:** E for 1 mol photons

Conceptual Plan: nm $\rightarrow$ m $\rightarrow E_{\text{photon}} \rightarrow E(\text{J})_{\text{mol}} \rightarrow E(\text{kJ})_{\text{mol}}$

$$\frac{1 \text{ m}}{10^9 \text{ nm}} \qquad E = \frac{hc}{\lambda}; h = 6.626 \times 10^{-34} \text{ J} \cdot \text{s} \qquad \frac{1 \text{ mol}}{6.022 \times 10^{23} \text{ photons}} \qquad \frac{1 \text{ kJ}}{1000 \text{ J}}$$

Solution:

$$1500 \text{ nm} \times \frac{1 \text{ m}}{10^9 \text{ nm}} = 1.500 \times 10^{-6} \text{ m}; \quad E = \frac{6.626 \times 10^{-34} \text{ J} \cdot \text{s} \times \dfrac{3.00 \times 10^8 \text{ m}}{\text{s}}}{1.500 \times 10^{-6} \text{ m}} = 1.3\underline{2}52 \times 10^{-19} \text{ J/photon}$$

$$\frac{1.3\underline{2}52 \times 10^{-19} \text{ J}}{\text{photon}} \times \frac{6.022 \times 10^{23} \text{ photons}}{1 \text{ mol}} \times \frac{1 \text{ kJ}}{1000 \text{ J}} = 79.8 \text{ kJ/mol}$$

Check: The units of the answer (kJ/mol) are correct. The magnitude of the answer is reasonable for a wavelength in the infrared region.

(b)   **Given:** $\lambda = 500 \text{ nm}$ **Find:** E for 1 mol photons

Conceptual Plan: nm $\rightarrow$ m $\rightarrow E_{\text{photon}} \rightarrow E_{\text{mol}} \rightarrow E(\text{kJ})_{\text{mol}}$

$$\frac{1 \text{ m}}{10^9 \text{ nm}} \qquad E = \frac{hc}{\lambda}; h = 6.626 \times 10^{-34} \text{ J} \cdot \text{s} \qquad \frac{1 \text{ mol}}{6.022 \times 10^{23} \text{ photons}} \qquad \frac{1 \text{ kJ}}{1000 \text{ J}}$$

Solution:

$$500 \text{ nm} \times \frac{1 \text{ m}}{10^9 \text{ nm}} = 5.00 \times 10^{-7} \text{ m}; \quad E = \frac{6.626 \times 10^{-34} \text{ J} \cdot \text{s} \times \dfrac{3.00 \times 10^8 \text{ m}}{\text{s}}}{5.00 \times 10^{-7} \text{ m}} = 3.9\underline{7}56 \times 10^{-19} \text{ J/photon}$$

$$\frac{3.9\underline{7}56 \times 10^{-19} \text{ J}}{\text{photon}} \times \frac{6.022 \times 10^{23} \text{ photons}}{1 \text{ mol}} \times \frac{1 \text{ kJ}}{1000 \text{ J}} = 239 \text{ kJ/mol}$$

Check: The units of the answer (kJ/mol) are correct. The magnitude of the answer is reasonable for a wavelength in the visible region.

(c)   **Given:** $\lambda = 150 \text{ nm}$ **Find:** E for 1 mol photons

Conceptual Plan: nm $\rightarrow$ m $\rightarrow E_{\text{photon}} \rightarrow E_{\text{mol}} \rightarrow E(\text{kJ})_{\text{mol}}$

$$\frac{1 \text{ m}}{10^9 \text{ nm}} \qquad E = \frac{hc}{\lambda}; h = 6.626 \times 10^{-34} \text{ J} \cdot \text{s} \qquad \frac{1 \text{ mol}}{6.022 \times 10^{23} \text{ photons}} \qquad \frac{1 \text{ kJ}}{1000 \text{ J}}$$

Solution:

$$1.50 \text{ nm} \times \frac{1 \text{ m}}{10^9 \text{ nm}} = 1.50 \times 10^{-7} \text{ m}; \quad E = \frac{6.626 \times 10^{-34} \text{ J} \cdot \text{s} \times \dfrac{3.00 \times 10^8 \text{ m}}{\text{s}}}{1.50 \times 10^{-7} \text{ m}} = 1.3\underline{2}52 \times 10^{-18} \text{ J/photon}$$

$$\frac{1.3\underline{2}52 \times 10^{-18} \text{ J}}{\text{photon}} \times \frac{6.022 \times 10^{23} \text{ photons}}{1 \text{ mol}} \times \frac{1 \text{ kJ}}{1000 \text{ J}} = 798 \text{ kJ/mol}$$

Check: The units of the answer (kJ/mol) are correct. The magnitude of the answer is reasonable for a wavelength in the ultraviolet region. Note: The energy increases from the IR to the Vis to the UV as expected.

7.12   (a)   **Given:** $\lambda = 0.155$ nm   **Find:** E for 1 mol photons

         Conceptual Plan: nm $\rightarrow$ m $\rightarrow$ E_{photon} $\rightarrow$ E_{mol} $\rightarrow$ $E(kJ)_{mol}$

$$\frac{1 \text{ m}}{10^9 \text{ nm}} \quad E = \frac{hc}{\lambda}; \quad h = 6.626 \times 10^{-34} \text{ J} \cdot \text{s} \quad \frac{1 \text{ mol}}{6.022 \times 10^{23} \text{ photons}} \quad \frac{1 \text{ kJ}}{1000 \text{ J}}$$

         Solution:

$$0.155 \text{ nm} \times \frac{1 \text{ m}}{10^9 \text{ nm}} = 1.55 \times 10^{-10} \text{ m}; \quad E = \frac{6.626 \times 10^{-34} \text{ J} \cdot \text{s} \times \dfrac{3.00 \times 10^8 \text{ m}}{\text{s}}}{1.55 \times 10^{-10} \text{ m}} = 1.2\underline{8}2 \times 10^{-15} \text{ J/photon}$$

$$\frac{1.2\underline{8}2 \times 10^{-15} \text{ J}}{\text{photon}} \times \frac{6.022 \times 10^{23} \text{ photons}}{1 \text{ mol}} \times \frac{1 \text{ kJ}}{1000 \text{ J}} = 7.72 \times 10^5 \text{ kJ/mol}$$

         Check: The units of the answer (kJ/mol) are correct. The magnitude of the answer is reasonable for a wavelength in the X-ray region.

   (b)   **Given:** $\lambda = 2.55 \times 10^{-5}$ nm   **Find:** E for 1 mol photons

         Conceptual Plan: nm $\rightarrow$ m $\rightarrow$ E_{photon} $\rightarrow$ E_{mol} $\rightarrow$ $E(kJ)_{mol}$

$$\frac{1 \text{ m}}{10^9 \text{ nm}} \quad E = \frac{hc}{\lambda}; \quad h = 6.626 \times 10^{-34} \text{ J} \cdot \text{s} \quad \frac{1 \text{ mol}}{6.022 \times 10^{23} \text{ photons}} \quad \frac{1 \text{ kJ}}{1000 \text{ J}}$$

         Solution:

$$2.55 \times 10^{-5} \text{ nm} \times \frac{1 \text{ m}}{10^9 \text{ nm}} = 2.55 \times 10^{-14} \text{ m}; \quad E = \frac{6.626 \times 10^{-34} \text{ J} \cdot \text{s} \times \dfrac{3.00 \times 10^8 \text{ m}}{\text{s}}}{2.55 \times 10^{-14} \text{ m}} = 7.7\underline{9}5 \times 10^{-12} \text{ J/photon}$$

$$\frac{7.7\underline{9}5 \times 10^{-12} \text{ J}}{\text{photon}} \times \frac{6.022 \times 10^{23} \text{ photons}}{1 \text{ mol}} \times \frac{1 \text{ kJ}}{1000 \text{ J}} = 4.69 \times 10^9 \text{ kJ/mol}$$

         Check: The units of the answer (kJ/mol) are correct. The magnitude of the answer is reasonable for a wavelength in the gamma ray region.

The Wave Nature of Matter and the Uncertainty Principle

7.13   The interference pattern would be a series of light and dark lines.

7.14   Because the interference pattern is caused by single electrons interfering with themselves, the pattern remains the same even when the rate of the electrons passing through the slits is one electron per hour. It will simply take longer for the full pattern to develop. When a laser is placed behind the slits to determine which hole the electron passes through, the laser flashes when a photon is scattered at the point of crossing, indicating the slit used, but the interference pattern is now absent. With the laser on, the electrons hit positions directly behind each slit, as if they were ordinary particles.

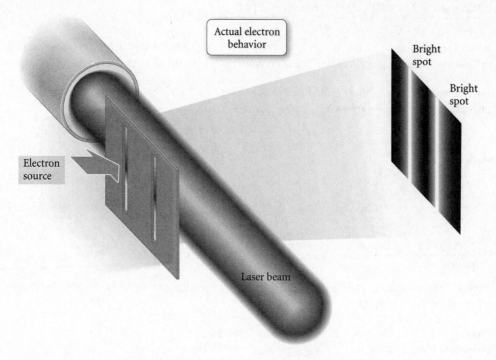

7.15 **Given:** $m = 9.109 \times 10^{-31}$ kg; $v = 1.55 \times 10^5$ m/s **Find:** λ
Conceptual Plan: $m, v \rightarrow \lambda$

$$\lambda = \frac{h}{mv}$$

Solution: $\dfrac{6.626 \times 10^{-34} \dfrac{kg \cdot m^2}{s^2} \cdot s}{(9.109 \times 10^{-31}\ kg)\left(\dfrac{1.55 \times 10^5\ m}{s}\right)} = 4.69 \times 10^{-9}$ m $= 4.69$ nm

Check: The units of the answer (m) are correct. The magnitude is reasonable because we are looking at an electron.

7.16 **Given:** $m = 9.109 \times 10^{-31}$ kg; $\lambda = 225$ nm **Find:** v
Conceptual Plan: $m, v \rightarrow \lambda$

$$v = \frac{h}{m\lambda}$$

Solution: $\dfrac{6.626 \times 10^{-34} \dfrac{kg \cdot m^2}{s^2} \cdot s}{(9.109 \times 10^{-31}\ kg)(225\ nm)\left(\dfrac{1\ m}{10^9\ nm}\right)} = 3.23 \times 10^3$ m/s

Check: The units of the answer (m/s) are correct. The magnitude is reasonable because we are looking at an electron.

7.17 **Given:** $m = 143$ g; $v = 95$ mph **Find:** λ
Conceptual Plan: $m, v \rightarrow \lambda$

$$\lambda = \frac{h}{mv}$$

Solution: $\dfrac{6.626 \times 10^{-34} \dfrac{kg \cdot m^2}{s^2} \cdot s}{(143\ g)\left(\dfrac{1\ kg}{1000\ g}\right)\left(\dfrac{95\ mi}{1\ hr}\right)\left(\dfrac{1.609\ km}{1\ mi}\right)\left(\dfrac{1000\ m}{1\ km}\right)\left(\dfrac{1\ hr}{3600\ s}\right)} = 1.1 \times 10^{-34}$ m

The value of the wavelength (1.1×10^{-34} m) is so small that it will not have an effect on the trajectory of the baseball.

Check: The units of the answer (m) are correct. The magnitude of the answer is very small, as would be expected for the de Broglie wavelength of a baseball.

7.18   **Given:** $m = 2.7$ g; $v = 765$ m/s   **Find:** λ
Conceptual Plan: $m, v \rightarrow \lambda$

$$\lambda = \frac{h}{mv}$$

Solution: $\dfrac{6.626 \times 10^{-34} \frac{\text{kg} \cdot \text{m}^2}{\text{s}^2} \cdot \text{s}}{(2.7 \text{ g})\left(\dfrac{1\text{kg}}{1000 \text{ g}}\right)\left(\dfrac{765 \text{ m}}{\text{s}}\right)} = 3.2 \times 10^{-34} \text{ m}$

The value of the wavelength (3.2×10^{-34} m) is so small that it will not have an effect on the trajectory of the bullet. The wave nature of matter is irrelevant to bullets.

Check: The units of the answer (m) are correct. The magnitude of the answer is very small, as would be expected for the de Broglie wavelength of a bullet.

Orbitals and Quantum Numbers

7.19   Because the size of the orbital is determined by the n quantum number, with the size increasing with increasing n, an electron in a $2s$ orbital is closer, on average, to the nucleus than is an electron in a $3s$ orbital.

7.20   Because the size of the orbital is determined by the n quantum number, with the size increasing with increasing n, an electron in a $4p$ orbital is further away, on average, from the nucleus than is an electron in a $3p$ orbital.

7.21   The value of l is an integer that lies between 0 and $n - 1$.
(a)   When $n = 1$, l can only be $l = 0$.
(b)   When $n = 2$, l can be $l = 0$ or $l = 1$.
(c)   When $n = 3$, l can be $l = 0$, $l = 1$, or $l = 2$.
(d)   When $n = 4$, l can be $l = 0$, $l = 1$, $l = 2$, or $l = 3$.

7.22   The value of m_l is an integer that lies between $-l$ and $+l$.
(a)   When $l = 0$, m_l can only be $m_l = 0$.
(b)   When $l = 1$, m_l can be $m_l = -1$, $m_l = 0$, or $m_l = +1$.
(c)   When $l = 2$, m_l can be $m_l = -2$, $m_l = -1$, $m_l = 0$, $m_l = +1$, or $m_l = +2$.
(d)   When $l = 3$, m_l can be $m_l = -3$, $m_l = -2$, $m_l = -1$, $m_l = 0$, $m_l = +1$, $m_l = +2$, or $m_l = +3$.

7.23   When $n = 3$: $l = 2$, $m_l = -2, -1, 0, 1, 2$
$\qquad\qquad\qquad l = 1$, $m_l = -1, 0, 1$
$\qquad\qquad\qquad l = 0$ $m_l = 0$
for a total of 9 orbitals.

7.24   When $n = 4$: $l = 3$, $m_l = -3, -2, -1, 0, 1, 2, 3$
$\qquad\qquad\qquad l = 2$, $m_l = -2, -1, 0, 1, 2$
$\qquad\qquad\qquad l = 1$, $m_l = -1, 0, 1$
$\qquad\qquad\qquad l = 0$ $m_l = 0$
for a total of 16 orbitals.

7.25   The spin quantum number m_s has only two possible values: $m_s = +\frac{1}{2}$ and $m_s = -\frac{1}{2}$.

7.26   The spin quantum number m_s specifies the orientation of the spin of the electron. The $m_s = +\frac{1}{2}$ is called spin up, and $m_s = -\frac{1}{2}$ is called spin down.

7.27   Set c cannot occur together as a set of quantum numbers to specify an orbital. l must lie between 0 and $n - 1$; so for $n = 3$, l can only be as high as 2.

7.28   (a) $1s$ is a real orbital, $n = 1$, $l = 0$.
(b) $2p$ is a real orbital, $n = 2$, $l = 1$.
(c) $4s$ is a real orbital, $n = 4$, $l = 0$.
(d) $2d$ is an impossible representation. $n = 2$, $l = 2$ is not allowed. l must lie between 0 and $n - 1$; so for $n = 2$, l can only be as high as $1(p)$.

7.29   The 2*s* orbital would be the same shape as the 1*s* orbital but would be larger in size, and the 3*p* orbitals would have the same shape as the 2*p* orbitals but would be larger in size. Also, the 2*s* and 3*p* orbitals would have more nodes.

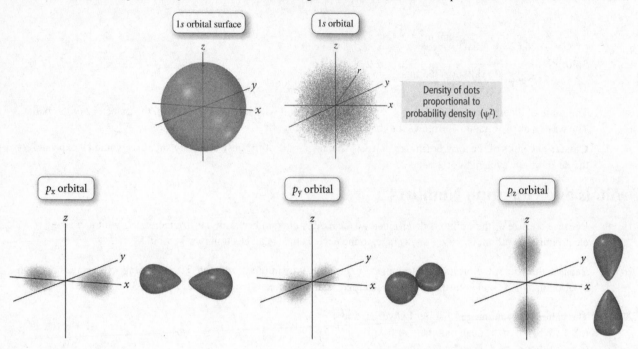

7.30   The 4*d* orbitals would be the same shape as the 3*d* orbitals but would be larger in size, and the 4*d* orbital would have more nodes.

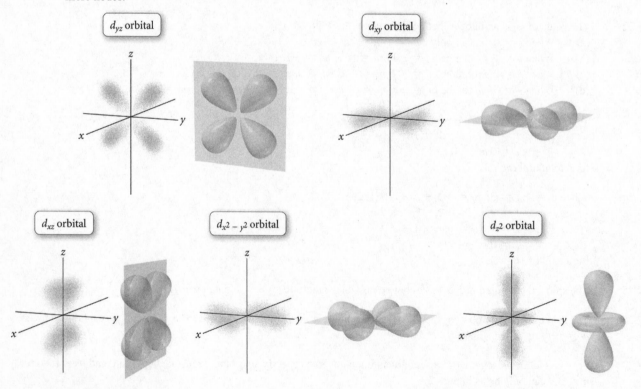

Atomic Spectroscopy

7.31   When the atom emits the photon of energy that was needed to raise the electron to the $n = 2$ level, the photon has the same energy as the energy absorbed to move the electron to the excited state. Therefore, the electron has to be in $n = 1$ (the ground state) following the emission of the photon.

7.32 (a) From $n = 3 \rightarrow n = 1$, the electron is moving to a lower energy, therefore, there is an emission of energy.
      (b) From $n = 2 \rightarrow n = 4$, the electron is moving to a higher energy, therefore, there is an absorption of energy.
      (c) From $n = 4 \rightarrow n = 3$, the electron is moving to a lower energy, therefore, there is an emission of energy.

7.33 According to the quantum-mechanical model, the higher the n level, the higher the energy. So the transition from $3p \rightarrow 1s$ would be a greater energy difference than a transition from $2p \rightarrow 1s$. The lower energy transition would have the longer wavelength. Therefore, the $2p \rightarrow 1s$ transition would produce a longer wavelength.

7.34 According to the quantum-mechanical model, the higher the n level, the higher the energy and the higher in energy, the closer the levels are to each other. So the transition from $3p \rightarrow 2s$ would be a greater energy difference than the transition from $4p \rightarrow 3p$. The lower energy transition would have the longer wavelength. Therefore, the $4p \rightarrow 3p$ transition would produce a longer wavelength.

7.35 (a) **Given:** $n = 2 \rightarrow n = 1$ **Find:** λ
      Conceptual Plan: $n = 1, n = 2 \rightarrow \Delta E_{\text{atom}} \rightarrow \Delta E_{\text{photon}} \rightarrow \lambda$

$$\Delta E_{\text{atom}} = E_1 - E_2 \quad \Delta E_{\text{atom}} \rightarrow -\Delta E_{\text{photon}} \quad E = \frac{hc}{\lambda}$$

Solution:
$$\Delta E = E_1 - E_2$$

$$= -2.18 \times 10^{-18} \text{ J}\left(\frac{1}{1^2}\right) - \left[-2.18 \times 10^{-18}\left(\frac{1}{2^2}\right)\right] = -2.18 \times 10^{-18} \text{ J}\left[\left(\frac{1}{1^2}\right) - \left(\frac{1}{2^2}\right)\right]$$

$$= -1.6\underline{3}5 \times 10^{-18} \text{ J}$$

$$\Delta E_{\text{photon}} = -\Delta E_{\text{atom}} = 1.6\underline{3}5 \times 10^{-18} \text{ J}; \lambda = \frac{hc}{E} = \frac{(6.626 \times 10^{-34} \text{ J} \cdot \text{s})(3.00 \times 10^8 \text{ m/s})}{1.6\underline{3}5 \times 10^{-18} \text{ J}} = 1.22 \times 10^{-7} \text{ m}$$

This transition would produce a wavelength in the UV region.

Check: The units of the answer (m) are correct. The magnitude of the answer is reasonable because it is in the region of UV radiation.

      (b) **Given:** $n = 3 \rightarrow n = 1$ **Find:** λ
      Conceptual Plan: $n = 1, n = 3 \rightarrow \Delta E_{\text{atom}} \rightarrow \Delta E_{\text{photon}} \rightarrow \lambda$

$$\Delta E_{\text{atom}} = E_1 - E_3 \quad \Delta E_{\text{atom}} \rightarrow -\Delta E_{\text{photon}} \quad E = \frac{hc}{\lambda}$$

Solution:
$$\Delta E = E_1 - E_3$$

$$= -2.18 \times 10^{-18} \text{ J}\left(\frac{1}{1^2}\right) - \left[-2.18 \times 10^{-18}\left(\frac{1}{3^2}\right)\right] = -2.18 \times 10^{-18} \text{ J}\left[\left(\frac{1}{1^2}\right) - \left(\frac{1}{3^2}\right)\right]$$

$$= -1.9\underline{3}8 \times 10^{-18} \text{ J}$$

$$\Delta E_{\text{photon}} = -\Delta E_{\text{atom}} = 1.9\underline{3}8 \times 10^{-18} \text{ J}; \lambda = \frac{hc}{E} = \frac{(6.626 \times 10^{-34} \text{ J} \cdot \text{s})(3.00 \times 10^8 \text{ m/s})}{1.9\underline{3}8 \times 10^{-18} \text{ J}} = 1.03 \times 10^{-7} \text{ m}$$

This transition would produce a wavelength in the UV region.

Check: The units of the answer (m) are correct. The magnitude of the answer is reasonable because it is in the region of UV radiation.

      (c) **Given:** $n = 4 \rightarrow n = 2$ **Find:** λ
      Conceptual Plan: $n = 2, n = 4 \rightarrow \Delta E_{\text{atom}} \rightarrow \Delta E_{\text{photon}} \rightarrow \lambda$

$$\Delta E_{\text{atom}} = E_2 - E_4 \quad \Delta E_{\text{atom}} \rightarrow -\Delta E_{\text{photom}} \quad E = \frac{hc}{\lambda}$$

Solution:
$$\Delta E = E_2 - E_4$$

$$= -2.18 \times 10^{-18} \text{ J}\left(\frac{1}{2^2}\right) - \left[-2.18 \times 10^{-18}\left(\frac{1}{4^2}\right)\right] = -2.18 \times 10^{-18} \text{ J}\left[\left(\frac{1}{2^2}\right) - \left(\frac{1}{4^2}\right)\right]$$

$$= -4.0\underline{8}8 \times 10^{-19} \text{ J}$$

$$\Delta E_{photon} = -\Delta E_{atom} = 4.0\underline{8}8 \times 10^{-19} \text{ J}; \lambda = \frac{hc}{E} = \frac{(6.626 \times 10^{-34} \text{ J} \cdot \text{s})(3.00 \times 10^8 \text{ m/s})}{4.0\underline{8}8 \times 10^{-19} \text{ J}} = 4.86 \times 10^{-7} \text{ m}$$

This transition would produce a wavelength in the visible region.

Check: The units of the answer (m) are correct. The magnitude of the answer is reasonable because it is in the region of visible light.

(d)   **Given:** $n = 5 \rightarrow n = 2$ **Find:** λ

Conceptual Plan: $n = 2, n = 5 \rightarrow \Delta E_{atom} \rightarrow \Delta E_{photon} \rightarrow \lambda$

$$\Delta E_{atom} = E_2 - E_5 \quad \Delta E_{atom} \rightarrow -\Delta E_{photon} \quad E = \frac{hc}{\lambda}$$

Solution:

$\Delta E = E_2 - E_5$

$$= -2.18 \times 10^{-18} \text{ J}\left(\frac{1}{2^2}\right) - \left[-2.18 \times 10^{-18}\left(\frac{1}{5^2}\right)\right] = -2.18 \times 10^{-18} \text{ J}\left[\left(\frac{1}{2^2}\right) - \left(\frac{1}{5^2}\right)\right]$$

$$= -4.5\underline{7}8 \times 10^{-19} \text{ J}$$

$$\Delta E_{photon} = -\Delta E_{atom} = 4.5\underline{7}8 \times 10^{-19} \text{ J}; \lambda = \frac{hc}{E} = \frac{(6.626 \times 10^{-34} \text{ J} \cdot \text{s})(3.00 \times 10^8 \text{ m/s})}{4.5\underline{7}8 \times 10^{-19} \text{ J}} = 4.34 \times 10^{-7} \text{ m}$$

This transition would produce a wavelength in the visible region.

Check: The units of the answer (m) are correct. The magnitude of the answer is reasonable because it is in the region of visible light.

7.36   (a)   **Given:** $n = 4 \rightarrow n = 3$ **Find:** ν

Conceptual Plan: $n = 3, n = 4 \rightarrow \Delta E_{atom} \rightarrow \Delta E_{photon} \rightarrow \nu$

$$\Delta E_{atom} = E_3 - E_4 \quad \Delta E_{atom} \rightarrow -\Delta E_{photon} \quad E = h\nu$$

Solution:

$\Delta E = E_3 - E_4$

$$= -2.18 \times 10^{-18} \text{ J}\left(\frac{1}{3^2}\right) - \left[-2.18 \times 10^{-18}\left(\frac{1}{4^2}\right)\right] = -2.18 \times 10^{-18} \text{ J}\left[\left(\frac{1}{3^2}\right) - \left(\frac{1}{4^2}\right)\right]$$

$$= -1.0\underline{6}0 \times 10^{-19} \text{ J}$$

$$\Delta E_{photon} = -\Delta E_{atom} = 1.0\underline{6}0 \times 10^{-19} \text{ J}; \nu = \frac{E}{h} = \frac{(1.0\underline{6}0 \times 10^{-19} \text{ J})}{6.626 \times 10^{-34} \text{ J} \cdot \text{s})} = 1.60 \times 10^{14} \text{ s}^{-1}$$

Check: The units of the answer (s^{-1}) are correct. The magnitude of the answer is reasonable because it is a transition between two close levels and the levels become closer as the n value increases. Therefore, the energy difference is smaller and the frequency is smaller.

(b)   **Given:** $n = 5 \rightarrow n = 1$ **Find:** ν

Conceptual Plan: $n = 1, n = 5 \rightarrow \Delta E_{atom} \rightarrow \Delta E_{photon} \rightarrow \nu$

$$\Delta E_{atom} = E_1 - E_5 \quad \Delta E_{atom} \rightarrow -\Delta E_{photon} \quad E = h\nu$$

Solution:

$\Delta E = E_1 - E_5$

$$= -2.18 \times 10^{-18} \text{ J}\left(\frac{1}{1^2}\right) - \left[-2.18 \times 10^{-18}\left(\frac{1}{5^2}\right)\right] = -2.18 \times 10^{-18} \text{ J}\left[\left(\frac{1}{1^2}\right) - \left(\frac{1}{5^2}\right)\right]$$

$$= -2.0\underline{9}3 \times 10^{-18} \text{ J}$$

$$\Delta E_{photon} = -\Delta E_{atom} = 2.0\underline{9}3 \times 10^{-18} \text{ J}; \nu = \frac{E}{h} = \frac{(2.0\underline{9}3 \times 10^{-18} \text{ J})}{6.626 \times 10^{-34} \text{ J} \cdot \text{s}} = 3.16 \times 10^{15} \text{ s}^{-1}$$

Check: The units of the answer (s^{-1}) are correct. The magnitude of the answer is reasonable because it is a transition that will produce a wavelength in the UV region and the frequency is correct for the UV region.

(c)   **Given:** $n = 5 \rightarrow n = 4$ **Find:** ν

Conceptual Plan: $n = 4, n = 5 \rightarrow \Delta E_{atom} \rightarrow \Delta E_{photon} \rightarrow \nu$

$$\Delta E_{atom} = E_4 - E_5 \quad \Delta E_{atom} \rightarrow -\Delta E_{photon} \quad E = h\nu$$

Solution:

$\Delta E = E_4 - E_5$

$= -2.18 \times 10^{-18} \text{ J} \left(\frac{1}{4^2} \right) - \left[-2.18 \times 10^{-18} \left(\frac{1}{5^2} \right) \right] = -2.18 \times 10^{-18} \text{ J} \left[\left(\frac{1}{4^2} \right) - \left(\frac{1}{5^2} \right) \right]$

$= -4.9\underline{0}5 \times 10^{-20} \text{ J}$

$\Delta E_{photon} = -\Delta E_{atom} = 4.9\underline{0}5 \times 10^{-20} \text{ J}; \nu = \frac{E}{h} = \frac{4.9\underline{0}5 \times 10^{-20} \text{ J}}{6.626 \times 10^{-34} \text{ J} \cdot \text{s}} = 7.40 \times 10^{13} \text{ s}^{-1}$

Check: The units of the answer (s^{-1}) are correct. The magnitude of the answer is reasonable because it is a transition between two close levels and the levels become closer as the n value increases. Therefore, the energy difference is smaller and the frequency is smaller.

(d) **Given:** $n = 6 \rightarrow n = 5$ **Find:** ν
Conceptual Plan: $n = 5, n = 6 \rightarrow \Delta E_{atom} \rightarrow \Delta E_{photon} \rightarrow \nu$

$$\Delta E_{atom} = E_5 - E_6 \quad \Delta E_{atom} \rightarrow -\Delta E_{photom} \quad E = h\nu$$

Solution:

$\Delta E = E_5 - E_6$

$= -2.18 \times 10^{-18} \text{ J} \left(\frac{1}{5^2} \right) - \left[-2.18 \times 10^{-18} \left(\frac{1}{6^2} \right) \right] = -2.18 \times 10^{-18} \text{ J} \left[\left(\frac{1}{5^2} \right) - \left(\frac{1}{6^2} \right) \right]$

$= -2.6\underline{6}4 \times 10^{-20} \text{ J}$

$\Delta E_{photon} = -\Delta E_{atom} = 2.6\underline{6}4 \times 10^{-20} \text{ J}; \nu = \frac{E}{h} = \frac{2.6\underline{6}4 \times 10^{-20} \text{ J}}{6.626 \times 10^{-34} \text{ J} \cdot \text{s}} = 4.02 \times 10^{13} \text{ s}^{-1}$

Check: The units of the answer (s^{-1}) are correct. The magnitude of the answer is reasonable because it is a transition between two close levels and the levels become closer as the n value increases. Therefore, the energy difference is smaller and the frequency is smaller.

7.37 **Given:** n (initial) $= 7; \lambda = 397 \text{ nm}$ **Find:** n (final)
Conceptual Plan: $\lambda \rightarrow \Delta E_{photon} \rightarrow \Delta E_{atom} \rightarrow n = x, n = 7$

$$E = \frac{hc}{\lambda} \quad \Delta E_{photon} \rightarrow -\Delta E_{atom} \quad \Delta E_{atom} = E_x - E_7$$

Solution: $E = \frac{hc}{\lambda} = \frac{(6.626 \times 10^{-34} \text{ J} \cdot \text{s})(3.00 \times 10^8 \text{ m/s})}{(397 \text{ nm}) \left(\frac{1 \text{ m}}{10^9 \text{ nm}} \right)} = 5.0\underline{0}7 \times 10^{-19} \text{ J}$

$\Delta E_{atom} = -\Delta E_{photon} = -5.0\underline{0}7 \times 10^{-19} \text{ J}$

$\Delta E = E_x - E_7 = -5.0\underline{0}7 \times 10^{-19} = -2.18 \times 10^{-18} \text{ J} \left(\frac{1}{x^2} \right) - \left[-2.18 \times 10^{-18} \left(\frac{1}{7^2} \right) \right]$

$= -2.18 \times 10^{-18} \text{ J} \left[\left(\frac{1}{x^2} \right) - \left(\frac{1}{7^2} \right) \right]$

$0.2297 = \left(\frac{1}{x^2} \right) - \left(\frac{1}{7^2} \right); \quad 0.25011 = \left(\frac{1}{x^2} \right); \quad x^2 = 3.998; \quad x = 2$

Check: The answer is reasonable because it is an integer less than the initial value of 7.

7.38 **Given:** n (final) $= 4; \nu = 114 \text{ THz}$ **Find:** n (initial)
Conceptual Plan: $\nu \rightarrow \Delta E_{photon} \rightarrow \Delta E_{atom} \rightarrow n = 4, n = x$

$$E = h\nu \quad \Delta E_{photon} \rightarrow -\Delta E_{atom} \quad \Delta E_{atom} = E_4 - E_x$$

Solution: $E = h\nu = (6.626 \times 10^{-34} \text{ J} \cdot \text{s})(114 \text{ THz}) \left(\frac{10^{12} \text{ Hz}}{\text{Hz}} \right) \left(\frac{\text{s}^{-1}}{\text{Hz}} \right) = 7.5\underline{5}4 \times 10^{-20} \text{ J}$

$\Delta E_{atom} = -\Delta E_{photon} = -7.5\underline{5}4 \times 10^{-20} \text{ J}$

$$\Delta E = E_4 - E_x = -7.5\underline{5}4 \times 10^{-20} \text{ J} = -2.18 \times 10^{-18} \text{ J}\left(\frac{1}{4^2}\right) - \left[-2.18 \times 10^{-18}\left(\frac{1}{x^2}\right)\right]$$

$$= -2.18 \times 10^{-18} \text{ J}\left[\left(\frac{1}{4^2}\right) - \left(\frac{1}{x^2}\right)\right]$$

$$0.03465 = \left(\frac{1}{4^2}\right) - \left(\frac{1}{x^2}\right); \quad 0.02785 = \left(\frac{1}{x^2}\right); \quad x^2 = 35.9; \text{ so } x = 6$$

Check: The answer is reasonable because it is an integer greater than the final value of 4.

Cumulative Problems

7.39   **Given:** 348 kJ/mol   **Find:** λ

Conceptual Plan: kJ/mol → kJ/molec → J/molec → λ

$$\frac{\text{mol C} - \text{C bonds}}{6.022 \times 10^{23} \text{ C} - \text{C bonds}} \qquad \frac{1000 \text{ J}}{1 \text{ kJ}} \qquad E = \frac{hc}{\lambda}$$

Solution: $\dfrac{348 \text{ kJ}}{\text{mol C} - \text{C bonds}} \times \dfrac{\text{mol C} - \text{C bonds}}{6.022 \times 10^{23} \text{ C} - \text{C bonds}} \times \dfrac{1000 \text{ J}}{\text{kJ}} = 5.7\underline{7}9 \times 10^{-19} \text{ J}$

$$\lambda = \frac{(6.626 \times 10^{-34} \text{ J} \cdot \text{s})(3.00 \times 10^8 \text{ m/s})}{5.7\underline{7}9 \times 10^{-19} \text{ J}} = 3.44 \times 10^{-7} \text{ m} = 344 \text{ nm}$$

Check: The units of the answer (m or nm) are correct. The magnitude of the answer is reasonable because this wavelength is in the UV region.

7.40   **Given:** 164 kJ/mol   **Find:** λ

Conceptual Plan: kJ/mol → kJ/molec → J/molec → λ

$$\frac{1 \text{ mol}}{6.022 \times 10^{23} \text{ molec}} \qquad \frac{1000 \text{ J}}{1 \text{ kJ}} \qquad E = \frac{hc}{\lambda}$$

Solution: $\dfrac{164 \text{ kJ}}{1 \text{ mol}} \times \dfrac{1 \text{ mol}}{6.022 \times 10^{23} \text{ molecules}} \times \dfrac{1000 \text{ J}}{1 \text{ kJ}} = 2.7\underline{2}3 \times 10^{-19} \text{ J}$

$$\lambda = \frac{(6.626 \times 10^{-34} \text{ J} \cdot \text{s})(3.00 \times 10^8 \text{ m/s})}{2.7\underline{2}3 \times 10^{-19} \text{ J}} = 7.30 \times 10^{-7} \text{ m} = 730 \text{ nm}$$

Check: The units of the answer (m or nm) are correct. The magnitude of the answer is reasonable because this wavelength is in the red region of visible light.

7.41   **Given:** $E_{\text{pulse}} = 5.0$ watts; $d = 5.5$ mm; hole $= 1.2$ mm; $\lambda = 532$ nm   **Find:** photons/s

Conceptual Plan: fraction of beam through hole → fraction of power and then E_{photon} → number photons/s

$$\frac{\text{area hole}}{\text{area beam}} \qquad \text{fraction} \times \text{power} \qquad E = \frac{hc}{\lambda} \qquad \frac{\text{power/s}}{E/\text{photon}}$$

Solution: $A = \pi r^2; \ \dfrac{\pi(0.60 \text{ mm})^2}{\pi(2.75 \text{ mm})^2} = 0.0476 \qquad 0.0476 \times 5.0 \text{ watts} \times \dfrac{\text{J/s}}{\text{watt}} = 0.23\underline{8} \text{ J/s}$

$$E_{\text{photon}} = \frac{(6.626 \times 10^{-34} \text{ J} \cdot \text{s})(3.00 \times 10^8 \text{ m/s})}{(532 \text{ nm})\left(\dfrac{1 \text{ m}}{10^9 \text{ nm}}\right)} = 3.7\underline{3}6 \times 10^{-19} \text{ J/photon}$$

$$\frac{0.23\underline{8} \text{ J/s}}{3.7\underline{3}6 \times 10^{-19} \text{ J/photon}} = 6.4 \times 10^{17} \text{ photons/s}$$

Check: The units of the answer (number of photons/s) are correct. The magnitude of the answer is reasonable.

7.42   **Given:** $A_{\text{leaf}} = 2.50 \text{ cm}^2; E_{\text{rad}} = 1000 \text{ W/m}^2; \lambda = 504 \text{ nm}$ **Find:** photons/s

Conceptual Plan: E_{rad}/s → E_{leaf}/s and then E_{photon} → number photons/s

$$E_{\text{rad}} \times A_{\text{leaf}} \qquad E = \frac{hc}{\lambda} \qquad \frac{E_{\text{leaf}}/\text{s}}{E/\text{photon}}$$

Solution: $E_{\text{rad}} = 2.50 \text{ cm}^2 \times \dfrac{1000 \text{ W}}{1 \text{ m}^2} \times \dfrac{1 \text{ m}^2}{(100 \text{ cm})^2} \times \dfrac{1 \text{ J/s}}{1 \text{ W}} = 0.250 \text{ J/s}$

$$E_{photon} = \frac{hc}{\lambda} = \frac{(6.626 \times 10^{-34}\,\text{J}\cdot\text{s})(3.00 \times 10^8\,\text{m/s})}{(504\,\text{nm})\left(\dfrac{1\,\text{m}}{10^9\,\text{nm}}\right)} = 3.9\underline{4}4 \times 10^{-19}\,\text{J/photon}$$

$$\frac{E_{rad}}{E_{photon}} = \frac{0.250\,\text{J/s}}{3.9\underline{4}4 \times 10^{-19}\,\text{J/photon}} = 6.34 \times 10^{17}\,\text{photons/s}$$

Check: The units of the answer (photons/s) are correct. The magnitude of the answer is reasonable compared to the radiation from the sun.

7.43 **Given:** KE = 506 eV **Find:** λ

Conceptual Plan: $KE_{eV} \rightarrow KE_J \rightarrow v \rightarrow \lambda$

$$\frac{1.602 \times 10^{-19}\,\text{J}}{1\,\text{eV}} \qquad KE = 1/2\,mv^2 \qquad \lambda = \frac{h}{mv}$$

Solution:

$$506\,\text{eV}\left(\frac{1.602 \times 10^{-19}\,\text{J}}{1\,\text{eV}}\right)\left(\frac{\text{kg}\cdot\text{m}^2}{\dfrac{\text{s}^2}{\text{J}}}\right) = \frac{1}{2}\,(9.11 \times 10^{-31}\,\text{kg})\,v^2$$

$$v^2 = \frac{506\,\text{eV}\left(\dfrac{1.602 \times 10^{-19}\,\text{J}}{1\,\text{eV}}\right)\left(\dfrac{\text{kg}\cdot\text{m}^2}{\dfrac{\text{s}^2}{\text{J}}}\right)}{\dfrac{1}{2}\,(9.11 \times 10^{-31}\,\text{kg})} = 1.7796 \times 10^{14}\,\frac{\text{m}^2}{\text{s}^2}$$

$$v = 1.33 \times 10^7\,\text{m/s} \qquad \lambda = \frac{h}{mv} = \frac{6.626 \times 10^{-34}\,\dfrac{\text{kg}\cdot\text{m}^2}{\text{s}^2}\cdot\text{s}}{(9.11 \times 10^{-31}\,\text{kg})(1.33 \times 10^7\,\text{m/s})} = 5.47 \times 10^{-11}\,\text{m} = 0.0547\,\text{nm}$$

Check: The units of the answer (m or nm) are correct. The magnitude of the answer is reasonable because a de Broglie wavelength is usually a very small number.

7.44 **Given:** λ = 0.989 nm; KE = 969 eV **Find:** *BE*/mol

Conceptual Plan: $\lambda \rightarrow E_{photon} \rightarrow BE_{photon} \rightarrow BE_{mol}$

$$E = \frac{hc}{\lambda} \qquad BE_{photon} = E_{photon} - KE \qquad \frac{6.022 \times 10^{23}\,\text{photons}}{1\,\text{mol}}$$

Solution: $E_{photon} = \dfrac{hc}{\lambda} = \dfrac{(6.626 \times 10^{-34}\,\text{J}\cdot\text{s})(3.00 \times 10^8\,\text{m/s})}{(0.989\,\text{nm})\left(\dfrac{1\,\text{m}}{10^9\,\text{nm}}\right)} = 2.0\underline{1}0 \times 10^{-16}\,\text{J/photon}$

$$BE_{photon} = 2.0\underline{1}0 \times 10^{-16}\,\text{J/photon} - \left[(969\,\text{eV})\left(\frac{1.602 \times 10^{-19}\,\text{J}}{\text{eV}}\right)\right] = 4.5\underline{7}6 \times 10^{-17}\,\text{J/photon}$$

$$\frac{4.5\underline{7}6 \times 10^{-17}\,\text{J}}{\text{photon}} \times \frac{6.022 \times 10^{23}\,\text{photons}}{1\,\text{mol}} \times \frac{\text{kJ}}{1000\,\text{J}} = 2.76 \times 10^4\,\text{kJ/mol}$$

Check: The units of the answer (kJ/mol) are correct. The magnitude of the answer is reasonable because it should require a large amount of energy to remove an electron from a metal surface.

7.45 **Given:** $n = 1 \rightarrow n = \infty$ **Find:** *E*; λ

Conceptual Plan: $n = \infty, n = 1 \rightarrow \Delta E_{atom} \rightarrow \Delta E_{photon} \rightarrow \lambda$

$$\Delta E_{atom} = E_\infty - E_1 \qquad \Delta E_{atom} = \Delta E_{photon} \qquad E = \frac{hc}{\lambda}$$

Solution: $\Delta E = E_\infty - E_1 = 0 - \left[-2.18 \times 10^{-18}\left(\dfrac{1}{1^2}\right)\right] = +2.18 \times 10^{-18}\,\text{J}$

$$\Delta E_{photon} = \Delta E_{atom} = +2.18 \times 10^{-18}\,\text{J}$$

$$\lambda = \frac{hc}{E} = \frac{(6.626 \times 10^{-34}\,\text{J}\cdot\text{s})(3.00 \times 10^8\,\text{m/s})}{2.18 \times 10^{-18}\,\text{J}} = 9.12 \times 10^{-8}\,\text{m} = 91.2\,\text{nm}$$

Check: The units of the answers (J for E and m or nm for part 1) are correct. The magnitude of the answer is reasonable because it would require more energy to completely remove the electron than just moving it to a higher n level. This results in a shorter wavelength.

7.46   **Given:** E = 496 kJ/mol   **Find:** ν
Conceptual Plan: kJ/mol $\rightarrow$ **kJ/molecule** $\rightarrow$ **J/molecule** $\rightarrow$ ν

$$\frac{1 \text{ mol}}{6.022 \times 10^{23} \text{ atoms}} \qquad \frac{1000 \text{ J}}{1 \text{ kJ}} \qquad E = h\nu$$

Solution: $\nu = \dfrac{E}{h} = \dfrac{\left(\dfrac{496 \text{ kJ}}{\text{mol}}\right)\left(\dfrac{1 \text{ mol}}{6.022 \times 10^{23} \text{ atom}}\right)\left(\dfrac{1000 \text{ J}}{1 \text{ kJ}}\right)}{6.626 \times 10^{-34} \text{ J}} = 1.24 \times 10^{15} \text{ s}^{-1}$

Check: The units of the answer (s^{-1}) are correct. The magnitude of the answer is reasonable because the frequency is slightly higher than the visible region of the spectrum, and this is expected because the excitation of sodium produces a line in the visible region.

7.47   (a)   **Given:** $n = 1$ **Find:** number of orbitals if $l = 0 \rightarrow n$
Conceptual Plan: value n $\rightarrow$ **values** l $\rightarrow$ **values** m_l $\rightarrow$ **number of orbitals**

$l = 0 \rightarrow n$ $\qquad\qquad m_l = -1 \rightarrow +1$ total m_l

Solution:
$n = \quad 1$
$l = \quad 0 \qquad\qquad 1$
$m_l = \quad 0 \qquad\qquad -1, 0, +1$
total 4 orbitals

Check: The total orbitals will be equal to the number of l sublevels^2.

(b)   **Given:** $n = 2$ **Find:** number of orbitals if $l = 0 \rightarrow n$
Conceptual Plan: value n $\rightarrow$ **values** l $\rightarrow$ **values** m_l $\rightarrow$ **number of orbitals**

$l = 0 \rightarrow n$ $\qquad\qquad m_l = -1 \rightarrow +1$ total m_l

Solution:
$n = \quad 2$
$l = \quad 0 \qquad\qquad 1 \qquad\qquad 2$
$m_l = \quad 0 \qquad\qquad -1, 0, +1 \qquad -2, -1, 0, 1, 2$
total 9 orbitals

Check: The total orbitals will be equal to the number of l sublevels^2.

(c)   **Given:** $n = 3$ **Find:** number of orbitals if $l = 0 \rightarrow n$
Conceptual Plan: value n $\rightarrow$ **values** l $\rightarrow$ **values** m_l $\rightarrow$ **number of orbitals**

$l = 0 \rightarrow n$ $\qquad\qquad m_l = -1 \rightarrow +1$ total m_l

Solution:
$n = \quad 3$
$l = \quad 0 \qquad\qquad 1 \qquad\qquad 2 \qquad\qquad\qquad 3$
$m_l = \quad 0 \qquad -1, 0, +1 \quad -2, -1, 0, 1, 2 \quad -3, -2, -1, 0, 1, 2, 3$
total 16 orbitals

Check: The total orbitals will be equal to the number of l sublevels^2.

7.48   (a)   **Given:** s sublevel   **Find:** number of orbitals if $m_l = -l - 1 \rightarrow l + 1$
Conceptual Plan: value l $\rightarrow$ **values** m_l $\rightarrow$ **number of orbitals**

$m_l = -l - 1 \rightarrow +l + 1$ $\qquad$ total m_l

Solution: sublevel $s \rightarrow l = 0$
$m_l = -1, 0, +1$
total 3 orbitals

(b)   **Given:** p sublevel   **Find:** number of orbitals if $m_l = -l - 1 \rightarrow l + 1$
Conceptual Plan: value l $\rightarrow$ **values** m_l $\rightarrow$ **number of orbitals**

$m_l = -l - 1 \rightarrow +l + 1$ $\qquad$ total m_l

Solution: sublevel $p \rightarrow l = 1$
$m_l = -2, -1, 0, +1, +2$
total 5 orbitals

(c)   **Given:** d sublevel   **Find:** number of orbitals if $m_l = -l - 1 \rightarrow l + 1$

Conceptual Plan: value l → values m_l → number of orbitals

$$m_l = -l - 1 \rightarrow +l + 1 \;\; \text{total } m_l$$

Solution: sublevel $d \rightarrow l = 2$

$m_l = -3, -2, -1, 0, +1, +2, +3$

total 7 orbitals

7.49   **Given:** $\lambda = 1875$ nm; 1282 nm; 1093 nm   **Find:** equivalent transitions

Conceptual Plan: $\lambda \rightarrow E_{photon} \rightarrow E_{atom} \rightarrow n$

$$E = \frac{hc}{\lambda} \quad E_{photon} = -E_{atom} \quad E = -2.18 \times 10^{-18} \, J \left(\frac{1}{n_f^2} - \frac{1}{n_i^2} \right)$$

Solution: Because the wavelengths of the transitions are longer wavelengths than those obtained in the visual region, the electron must relax to a higher n level. Therefore, we can assume that the electron returns to the $n = 3$ level.

For $\lambda = 1875$ nm: $E = \dfrac{(6.626 \times 10^{-34} \, J \cdot s)(3.00 \times 10^8 \, m/s)}{1875 \, nm \left(\dfrac{1 \, m}{10^9 \, nm} \right)} = 1.060 \times 10^{-19}$ J; 1.060×10^{-19} J $= -1.060 \times 10^{-19}$ J

-1.060×10^{-19} J $= -2.18 \times 10^{-18} \left(\dfrac{1}{3^2} - \dfrac{1}{n^2} \right)$; $n = 4$

For $\lambda = 1282$ nm: $E = \dfrac{(6.626 \times 10^{-34} \, J \cdot s)(3.00 \times 10^8 \, m/s)}{1282 \, nm \left(\dfrac{1 \, m}{10^9 \, nm} \right)} = 1.551 \times 10^{-19}$ J; 1.551×10^{-19} J $= -1.551 \times 10^{-19}$ J

$-1.551 \times 10^{-19} = -2.18 \times 10^{-18} \left(\dfrac{1}{3^2} - \dfrac{1}{n^2} \right)$; $n = 5$

For $\lambda = 1093$ nm: $E = \dfrac{(6.626 \times 10^{-34} \, J \cdot s)(3.00 \times 10^8 \, m/s)}{1093 \, nm \left(\dfrac{1 \, m}{10^9 \, nm} \right)} = 1.819 \times 10^{-19}$ J; 1.819×10^{-19} J $= -1.819 \times 10^{-19}$ J

-1.819×10^{-19} J $= -2.18 \times 10^{-18} \left(\dfrac{1}{3^2} - \dfrac{1}{n^2} \right)$; $n = 6$

Check: The values obtained are all integers, which is correct. The values of n (4, 5, and 6) are reasonable. The values of n increase as the wavelength decreases because the two n levels involved are further apart and more energy is released as the electron relaxes to the $n = 3$ level.

7.50   **Given:** $\lambda = 121.5$ nm; 102.6 nm; 97.23 nm   **Find:** equivalent transitions

Conceptual Plan: $\lambda \rightarrow E_{photon} \rightarrow E_{atom} \rightarrow n$

$$E = \frac{hc}{\lambda} \quad E_{photon} = -E_{atom} \quad E = -2.18 \times 10^{-18} \, J \left(\frac{1}{n_f^2} - \frac{1}{n_i^2} \right)$$

Solution: Because the wavelengths of the transitions are shorter wavelengths than those obtained in the visual region, the electron must relax to a lower n level. Therefore, we can assume that the electron returns to the $n = 1$ level.

For $\lambda = 121.5$ nm: $E = \dfrac{(6.626 \times 10^{-34} \, J \cdot s)(3.00 \times 10^8 \, m/s)}{121.5 \, nm \left(\dfrac{1 \, m}{10^9 \, nm} \right)} = 1.636 \times 10^{-18}$ J; 1.636×10^{-18} J $= -1.636 \times 10^{-18}$ J

-1.636×10^{-18} J $= -2.18 \times 10^{-18} \left(\dfrac{1}{1^2} - \dfrac{1}{n^2} \right)$; $n = 2$

For $\lambda = 102.6$ nm: $E = \dfrac{(6.626 \times 10^{-34} \, J \cdot s)(3.00 \times 10^8 \, m/s)}{102.6 \, nm \left(\dfrac{1 \, m}{10^9 \, nm} \right)} = 1.937 \times 10^{-18}$ J; 1.937×10^{-18} J $= -1.937 \times 10^{-18}$ J

-1.937×10^{-18} J $= -2.18 \times 10^{-18} \left(\dfrac{1}{1^2} - \dfrac{1}{n^2} \right)$; $n = 3$

For $\lambda = 97.23$ nm: $E = \dfrac{(6.626 \times 10^{-34}\,\text{J} \cdot \text{s})(3.00 \times 10^8\,\text{m/s})}{97.23\,\text{nm}\left(\dfrac{1\,\text{m}}{10^9\,\text{nm}}\right)} = 2.044 \times 10^{-18}\,\text{J}$ $2.044 \times 10^{-18}\,\text{J} = -2.044 \times 10^{-18}\,\text{J}$

$-2.044 \times 10^{-18}\,\text{J} = -2.18 \times 10^{-18}\left(\dfrac{1}{1^2} - \dfrac{1}{n^2}\right); n = 4$

Check: The values obtained are all integers, which is correct. The values of n (2, 3, and 4) are reasonable. The values of n increase as the wavelength decreases because the two n levels involved are further apart and more energy is released as the electron relaxes to the $n = 1$ level.

7.51   **Given:** $\Phi = 193$ kJ/mol   **Find:** threshold frequency (ν)
Conceptual Plan: Φ kJ/ mol $\rightarrow$ Φ kJ/ atom $\rightarrow$ Φ J/ atom $\rightarrow$ ν

$$\frac{1\,\text{mol}}{6.022 \times 10^{23}\,\text{atoms}} \qquad \frac{1000\,\text{J}}{1\,\text{kJ}} \qquad \Phi = h\nu$$

Solution: $\nu = \dfrac{\Phi}{h} = \dfrac{\left(\dfrac{193\,\text{kJ}}{1\,\text{mol}}\right)\left(\dfrac{1\,\text{mol}}{6.022 \times 10^{23}\,\text{atoms}}\right)\left(\dfrac{1000\,\text{J}}{1\,\text{kJ}}\right)}{6.626 \times 10^{-34}\,\text{J} \cdot \text{s}} = 4.84 \times 10^{14}\,\text{s}^{-1}$

Check: The units of the answer (s^{-1}) are correct. The magnitude of the answer puts the frequency in the infrared range and is a reasonable answer.

7.52   **Given:** $m = 2$ amu; $\nu = 1 \times 10^6$ m/s   **Find:** λ
Conceptual Plan: $m(\text{amu}) \rightarrow m(\text{g}) \rightarrow m(\text{kg})$ and then $m, \nu \rightarrow \lambda$

$$\frac{1.661 \times 10^{-24}\,\text{g}}{1\,\text{amu}} \quad \frac{1\,\text{kg}}{1000\,\text{g}} \qquad \lambda = \frac{h}{m\nu}$$

Solution: $\dfrac{6.626 \times 10^{-34}\,\dfrac{\text{kg} \cdot \text{m}^2}{\text{s}^2} \cdot \text{s}}{(2\,\text{amu})\left(\dfrac{1.661 \times 10^{-24}\,\text{g}}{1\,\text{amu}}\right)\left(\dfrac{1\,\text{kg}}{1000\,\text{g}}\right)(1 \times 10^6\,\text{m/s})} = 2 \times 10^{-13}\,\text{m}$

Check: The units of the answer (m) are correct. The magnitude of the answer is reasonable because it is a smaller wavelength than for an electron and a deuteron has a much larger mass than an electron.

7.53   **Given:** $\nu_{\text{low}} = 30\,\text{s}^{-1}$; $\nu_{\text{hi}} = 1.5 \times 10^4\,\text{s}^{-1}$; speed $= 344$ m/s   **Find:** $\lambda_{\text{low}} - \lambda_{\text{hi}}$
Conceptual Plan: $\nu_{\text{low}} \rightarrow \lambda_{\text{low}}$ and $\nu_{\text{hi}} = \lambda_{\text{hi}}$ then $\lambda_{\text{low}} - \lambda_{\text{hi}}$

$$\lambda\nu = \text{speed}$$

Solution: $\lambda = \dfrac{\text{speed}}{\nu}$; $\lambda_{\text{low}} = \dfrac{344\,\text{m/s}}{30\,\text{s}^{-1}} = 11$ m; $\lambda_{\text{hi}} = \dfrac{344\,\text{m/s}}{1.5 \times 10^4\,\text{s}^{-1}} = 0.023$ m; $11\,\text{m} - 0.023\,\text{m} = 11$ m

Check: The units of the answer (m) are correct. The magnitude is reasonable because the value is only determined by the low frequency value because of significant figures.

7.54   **Given:** $d = 1.5 \times 10^8$ km; $\nu = 1.0 \times 10^{14}\,\text{s}^{-1}$ **Find:** number of wave crests
Conceptual Plan: $\nu \rightarrow \lambda$ and then $d(\text{km}) \rightarrow d(\text{m}) \rightarrow$ number of waves $\rightarrow$ number of crests

$$\nu = \frac{c}{\lambda} \qquad \frac{1000\,\text{m}}{\text{km}} \qquad \frac{d}{\lambda}$$

Solution: $\dfrac{3.00 \times 10^8\,\text{m/s}}{1.0 \times 10^{14}\,\text{s}^{-1}} = 3.0 \times 10^{-6}$ m; $\dfrac{1.5 \times 10^8\,\text{km} \times \dfrac{1000\,\text{m}}{1\,\text{km}}}{3.0 \times 10^{-6}\,\text{m}} = 5.0 \times 10^{16}$ waves

Because wavelength is measured crest to crest, the number of wave crests would be $5.0 \times 10^{16} + 1$.

Check: The answer is reasonable because the wavelength is small and the distance traveled is large.

7.55   **Given:** $\lambda = 792$ nm; $V = 100.0$ mL; $P = 55.7$ mtorr; $T = 25\,°\text{C}$ **Find:** E to dissociate 15.0%
Conceptual Plan: $\lambda \rightarrow E/\text{molecule}$ and then $P, V, T \rightarrow n \rightarrow$ molecules

$$E = \frac{hc}{\lambda} \qquad\qquad n = \frac{PV}{RT}\,\frac{6.022 \times 10^{23}\,\text{molecules}}{1\,\text{mole}}$$

Solution: $E = \dfrac{(6.626 \times 10^{-34}\,\text{J} \cdot \text{s})(3.00 \times 10^8\,\text{m/s})}{792\,\text{nm}\left(\dfrac{1\,\text{m}}{10^9\,\text{nm}}\right)} = 2.51 \times 10^{-19}\,\text{J/molecule}$

$$\dfrac{(55.7\,\text{mtorr})\left(\dfrac{1\,\text{torr}}{1000\,\text{mtorr}}\right)\left(\dfrac{1\,\text{atm}}{760\,\text{torr}}\right)(100.0\,\text{mL})\left(\dfrac{1\,\text{L}}{1000\,\text{mL}}\right)\left(\dfrac{6.022 \times 10^{23}\,\text{molecules}}{1\,\text{mol}}\right)}{\left(\dfrac{0.0821\,\text{L} \cdot \text{atm}}{\text{mol} \cdot \text{K}}\right)(298\,\text{K})} = 1.80 \times 10^{17}\,\text{molecules}$$

$(1.80 \times 10^{17}\,\text{molecules})(0.150) = 2.70 \times 10^{16}\,\text{molecules dissociated}$

$(2.51 \times 10^{-19}\,\text{J/molecule})\,(2.70 \times 10^{16}\,\text{molecules}) = 6.777 \times 10^{-3}\,\text{J} = 6.78 \times 10^{-3}\,\text{J}$

Check: The units of the answer (J) are correct. The magnitude is reasonable because it is for a part of a mole of molecules.

7.56   **Given:** 5.00 mL; 0.100 M; E = 15.5 J; λ = 349 nm   **Find:** % molecules emitting a photon

Conceptual Plan: mL, M → mol → molecules and then λ → E/molecule and then E → % molecules

$VM \qquad \dfrac{6.022 \times 10^{23}\,\text{molecules}}{1\,\text{mole}} \qquad\qquad E = \dfrac{hc}{\lambda} \qquad (E\,\text{given}/(E \times \text{molecules})) \times 100\%$

Solution: $(5.00\,\text{mL})\left(\dfrac{1\,\text{L}}{1000\,\text{mL}}\right)\left(\dfrac{0.100\,\text{mol}}{1\,\text{L}}\right)\left(\dfrac{6.022 \times 10^{23}\,\text{molecules}}{1\,\text{mol}}\right) = 3.011 \times 10^{20}\,\text{molecules}$

$E = \dfrac{(6.626 \times 10^{-34}\,\text{J} \cdot \text{s})(3.00 \times 10^8\,\text{m/s})}{349\,\text{nm}\left(\dfrac{1\,\text{m}}{10^9\,\text{nm}}\right)} = 5.696 \times 10^{-19}\,\text{J/molecule}$

$(3.01 \times 10^{20}\,\text{molecules})(5.70 \times 10^{-19}\,\text{J/molecule}) = 171.57\,\text{J} = 172\,\text{J}$

$\dfrac{15.5\,\text{J}}{172\,\text{J}} \times 100\% = 9.01\%$

Check: The units of the answer are correct; the magnitude is reasonable because it is less than 100%.

7.57   **Given:** 20.0 mW; 1.00 hr.; 2.29×10^{20} photons   **Find:** λ

Conceptual Plan: mW → W → J → J/photon → λ

$\dfrac{\text{W}}{1000\,\text{mW}} \qquad E = \text{W} \times \text{s} \qquad \dfrac{E}{\text{number of photons}} \qquad \lambda = \dfrac{hc}{E}$

Solution: $(20.0\,\text{mW})\left(\dfrac{1\,\text{W}}{1000\,\text{mW}}\right)\left(\dfrac{\dfrac{1\,\text{J}}{1\,\text{s}}}{1\,\text{W}}\right)\left(\dfrac{3600\,\text{s}}{2.29 \times 10^{20}\,\text{photons}}\right) = 3.14 \times 10^{-19}\,\text{J/photon}$

$\dfrac{(6.626 \times 10^{-34}\,\text{J} \cdot \text{s})(3.00 \times 10^8\,\text{m/s})\left(\dfrac{10^9\,\text{nm}}{1\,\text{m}}\right)}{3.14 \times 10^{-19}\,\text{J}} = 632\,\text{nm}$

Check: The units of the answer (nm) are correct. The magnitude is reasonable because it is in the red range.

7.58   **Given:** 150.0 W; 1.33×10^{19} photons/s; λ = 1064 nm   **Find:** % efficiency

Conceptual Plan: λ → E/photon → E → W → %

$E = \dfrac{hc}{\lambda} \times \text{Photons} \qquad 1.33 \times 10^{19}\,\dfrac{\text{photons}}{1\,\text{s}} \qquad (\text{W}/\text{W}_{\text{total}}) \times 100\%$

Solution: $E = \dfrac{\left(6.626 \times 10^{-34}\,\dfrac{\text{J}}{\text{photon}} \cdot \text{s}\right)(3.00 \times 10^8\,\text{m/s})\left(1.33 \times 10^{19}\,\dfrac{\text{photon}}{\text{s}}\right)\left(\dfrac{1\,\text{W}}{1\,\text{J/s}}\right)}{1064\,\text{nm}\left(\dfrac{1\,\text{m}}{10^9\,\text{nm}}\right)} = 2.484\,\text{W}$

$\dfrac{2.48\,\text{W}}{150.0\,\text{W}} \times 100\% = 1.65\%$

Check: The units of the answer (%) are correct. The magnitude is reasonable because it is less than 100%.

7.59   **Given:** $\lambda = 280$ nm, $E_{available} = 885$ mW for 10. minutes; $\Phi = 0.24$ **Find:** Maximum mol CH_3X dissociated
     Conceptual Plan: $\lambda(nm) \rightarrow \lambda(m) \rightarrow E_{photon}$ and $mW \rightarrow W$, $min \rightarrow s$ then $W, s \rightarrow E_{available}$

$$\frac{1\ m}{10^9\ nm} \qquad E = \frac{hc}{\lambda} \qquad \frac{1\ W}{10^3\ mW} \qquad \frac{60\ s}{1\ min} \qquad 1\ W = 1\ \frac{J}{s}$$

     then E_{photon}, $E_{used} \rightarrow$ **photons** $\rightarrow$ **mol CH_3X dissociated ideal** $\rightarrow$ **mol CH_3X dissociated actual**

$$\frac{E_{used}}{E/\ photon} \qquad \frac{1\ mole\ photons}{6.022 \times 10^{23}\ photons} \qquad \Phi = \frac{number\ of\ reaction\ events}{number\ of\ photons\ absorbed}$$

Solution:

$$E_{photon} = \frac{(6.626 \times 10^{-34}\ J \cdot s)(3.00 \times 10^8\ m/s)}{(280\ nm)\left(\dfrac{m}{10^9\ nm}\right)} = 7.09929 \times 10^{-19}\ J/photon; \quad 885\ mW \times \frac{1\ W}{10^3\ mW} = 0.885\ W$$

$$10.\ min \times \frac{60\ s}{1\ min} = 6.0 \times 10^2\ s \text{ then } 0.885\ W \times \frac{1\ J/s}{1\ W} \times 6.0 \times 10^2\ s = 531\ J$$

$$\frac{531\ J}{7.09929 \times 10^{-19}\ J/photon} \times \frac{1\ mole\ photons}{6.022 \times 10^{23}\ photons} = 1.2420 \times 10^{-3}\ mol\ photons$$

$$mol\ CH_3X\ dissociated\ ideal = 1.2420 \times 10^{-3}\ mol\ photons \times \frac{0.24\ mol\ CH_3X}{1.00\ mol\ photons} = 3.0 \times 10^{-4}\ mol\ CH_3X\ actual$$

Check: The units of the answer (mol CH_3X dissociated) are correct. The magnitude of the answer is reasonable, since the power and quantum yield are low.

7.60   **Given:** $\lambda = 590$ nm, $E_{available} = 255$ mW for 35 s, 0.0256 mmol I formed   **Find:** Φ
     Conceptual Plan: $\lambda(nm) \rightarrow \lambda(m) \rightarrow E_{photon}$ and $mW \rightarrow W$, then

$$\frac{1\ m}{10^9\ nm} \qquad E = \frac{hc}{\lambda} \qquad \frac{1\ W}{10^3\ mW}$$

$W, s \rightarrow E_{available}$, $E_{photon} \rightarrow$ photons $\rightarrow$ mol photons $\rightarrow$ max mol I formed then

$$1\ W = 1\ \frac{J}{s} \qquad \frac{E_{used}}{E/\ photon} \qquad \frac{1\ mole\ photons}{6.022 \times 10^{23}\ photons} \qquad \frac{2\ mole\ I}{1\ mol\ photons}$$

max mol I formed, mol I formed? $\rightarrow \Phi$

$$\Phi = \frac{number\ of\ reaction\ events}{number\ of\ photons\ absorbed}$$

Solution:

$$E_{photon} = \frac{(6.626 \times 10^{-34}\ J \cdot s)(3.00 \times 10^8\ m/s)}{(590\ nm)\left(\dfrac{m}{10^9\ nm}\right)} = 3.36915 \times 10^{-19}\ J/photon \quad 255\ mW \times \frac{1\ W}{10^3\ mW} = 0.255\ W$$

$$\text{then } 0.255\ W \times \frac{1\ J/s}{1\ W} \times 35\ s = 8.925\ J$$

$$\frac{8.925\ J}{3.36915 \times 10^{-19}\ J/photon} \times \frac{1\ mol\ photons}{6.022 \times 10^{23}\ photons} \times \frac{2\ mole\ I}{1\ mol\ photons} = 8.7979 \times 10^{-5}\ mol\ I = 0.087979\ mmol\ I$$

$$\Phi = \frac{number\ of\ reaction\ events}{number\ of\ photons\ absorbed} = \frac{0.0256\ mmol\ I}{0.087979\ mmol\ I} = 0.29098 = 0.29$$

Check: The units of the answer (unitless) are correct. The magnitude of the answer is reasonable, since the power and time are low.

Challenge Problems

7.61   (a)   **Given:** $n = 1$; $n = 2$; $n = 3$; $L = 155$ pm   **Find:** E_1, E_2, E_3
         Conceptual Plan: $n \rightarrow E$

$$E_n = \frac{n^2 h^2}{8\ m\ L^2}$$

         Solution:

$$E_1 = \frac{1^2(6.626 \times 10^{-34}\ J \cdot s)^2}{8(9.11 \times 10^{-31}\ kg)(155\ pm)^2\left(\dfrac{1\ m}{10^{12}\ pm}\right)^2} = \frac{1(6.626 \times 10^{-34})^2\ J^2 s^2}{8(9.11 \times 10^{-31}\ kg)(155 \times 10^{-12})^2\ m^2}$$

$$= \frac{1(6.626 \times 10^{-34})^2 \left(\frac{kg \cdot m^2}{s^2}\right)Js^2}{8(9.11 \times 10^{-31} \, kg)(155 \times 10^{-12})^2 \, m^2} = 2.51 \times 10^{-18} \, J$$

$$E_2 = \frac{2^2(6.626 \times 10^{-34} \, J \cdot s)^2}{8(9.11 \times 10^{-31} \, kg)(155 \, pm)^2 \left(\frac{1 \, m}{10^{12} \, pm}\right)^2} = \frac{4(6.626 \times 10^{-34})^2 \, J^2 s^2}{8(9.11 \times 10^{-31} \, kg)(155 \times 10^{-12})^2 \, m^2}$$

$$= \frac{4(6.626 \times 10^{-34})^2 \left(\frac{kg \cdot m^2}{s^2}\right)Js^2}{8(9.11 \times 10^{-31} \, kg)(155 \times 10^{-12})^2 \, m^2} = 1.00 \times 10^{-17} \, J$$

$$E_3 = \frac{3^2(6.626 \times 10^{-34} \, J \cdot s)^2}{8(9.11 \times 10^{-31} \, kg)(155 \, pm)^2 \left(\frac{1 \, m}{10^{12} \, pm}\right)^2} = \frac{9(6.626 \times 10^{-34})^2 \, J^2 s^2}{8(9.11 \times 10^{-31} \, kg)(155 \times 10^{-12})^2 \, m^2}$$

$$= \frac{9(6.626 \times 10^{-34})^2 \left(\frac{kg \cdot m^2}{s^2}\right)Js^2}{8(9.11 \times 10^{-31} \, kg)(155 \times 10^{-12})^2 \, m^2} = 2.26 \times 10^{-17} \, J$$

Check: The units of the answers (J) are correct. The answers seem reasonable because the energy is increasing with increasing n level.

(b)   **Given:** $n = 1 \rightarrow n = 2$ and $n = 2 \rightarrow n = 3$ **Find:** λ

Conceptual Plan: $n = 1, n = 2 \rightarrow \Delta E_{atom} \rightarrow \Delta E_{photon} \rightarrow \lambda$

$$\Delta E_{atom} = E_2 - E_1 \qquad \Delta E_{atom} \rightarrow -\Delta E_{photon} \qquad E = \frac{hc}{\lambda}$$

Solution: Use the energies calculated in part (a).

$$E_2 - E_1 = (1.00 \times 10^{-17} \, J - 2.51 \times 10^{-18} \, J) = 7.49 \times 10^{-18} \, J$$

$$\lambda = \frac{(6.626 \times 10^{-34} \, J \cdot s)(3.00 \times 10^8 \, m/s)}{7.49 \times 10^{-18} \, J} = 2.65 \times 10^{-8} \, m = 26.5 \, nm$$

$$E_3 - E_2 = (2.26 \times 10^{-17} \, J - 1.00 \times 10^{-17} \, J) = 1.26 \times 10^{-17} \, J$$

$$\lambda = \frac{(6.626 \times 10^{-34} \, J \cdot s)(3.00 \times 10^8 \, m/s)}{1.26 \times 10^{-17} \, J} = 1.58 \times 10^{-8} \, m = 15.8 \, nm$$

These wavelengths are in the UV region.

Check: The units of the answers (m) are correct. The magnitude of the answers is reasonable based on the energies obtained for the levels.

7.62   **Given:** $n = 1; \nu = 8.85 \times 10^{13} \, s^{-1}$ **Find:** E, λ

Conceptual Plan: $n, \nu \rightarrow E \rightarrow \lambda$

$$E = \left(n + \frac{1}{2}\right)h\nu \qquad E = \frac{hc}{\lambda}$$

Solution: $E = \left(1 + \frac{1}{2}\right)(6.626 \times 10^{-34} \, J \cdot s)(8.85 \times 10^{13} \, s^{-1}) = 8.80 \times 10^{-20} \, J$

$$\lambda = \frac{hc}{E} = \frac{(6.626 \times 10^{-34} \, J \cdot s)(3.00 \times 10^8 \, m/s)}{8.80 \times 10^{-20} \, J} = 2.26 \times 10^{-6} \, m$$

Check: The units of the answer (J and m) are correct. The magnitude of the answer puts the vibrational frequency in the infrared region, which is reasonable.

7.63   For the $1s$ orbital in the Excel® spreadsheet, call the columns as follows: column A as r and column B as $\Psi(1s)$. Make the values for r column A as follows: $0 - 200$. In column B, put the equation for the wave function written as follows: = (POWER(1/3.1415, 1/2))*(1/POWER(53, 3/2))*(EXP(−A2/53)). Go to make chart, choose xy scatter.

e.g., sample values	
r	$\Psi\,(1s)$
0	7.000146224
1	7.000143491
2	7.000140809
3	7.000138177
4	7.000135594
5	7.00013306
6	7.000130573

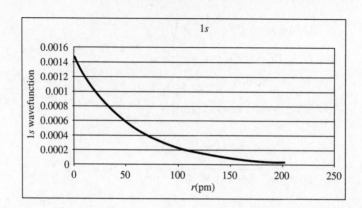

For the 2s orbital in the same Excel® spreadsheet, call the columns as follows: column A as r and column C as $\Psi(2s)$. Use the same values for r in column A: 0–200. In column C, put the equation for the wave function written as follows: = (POWER(1/((32)*(3.1415)), 1/2))*(1/POWER(53,3/2))*(2 − (A2/53))*(EXP(−A2/53)). Go to make chart, choose xy scatter.

e.g., sample values	
r	$\Psi\,(2s)$
0	7. 0000516979
1	7. 000050253
2	7. 0000488441
3	7. 0000474702
4	7. 0000461307
5	7. 0000448247
6	7. 0000435513

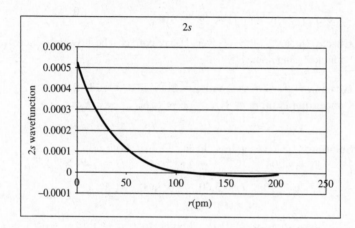

The plot for the 2s orbital extends below the x-axis. The x-intercept represents the radial node of the orbital. The plots differ in that the 1s plot does not contain a node and the slope of the plots are different.

7.64 **Given:** $\Delta E = E_m - E_n = -2.18 \times 10^{-18}(1/m^2) - [-2.18 \times 10^{-18}(1/n^2)]$; $E = hc/\lambda$ **Find:** $1/\lambda = R(1/m^2 - 1/n^2)$
Conceptual Plan: $\Delta E_{atom} \rightarrow \Delta E_{photon} \rightarrow 1/\lambda$

$$\Delta E_{atom} = E_m - E_n \quad \Delta E_{atom} \rightarrow -\Delta E_{photon} \quad E = \frac{hc}{\lambda}$$

Solution:

$$\Delta E = E_m - E_n = -2.18 \times 10^{-18}\left(\frac{1}{m^2}\right) - \left[-2.18 \times 10^{-18}\left(\frac{1}{n^2}\right)\right] = -2.18 \times 10^{-18}\left(\frac{1}{m^2} - \frac{1}{n^2}\right)$$

$$\Delta E_{atom} = -\Delta E_{photon}$$

$$E_{photon} = -\left[-2.18 \times 10^{-18}\left(\frac{1}{m^2} - \frac{1}{n^2}\right)\right] = \frac{hc}{\lambda}; \frac{1}{\lambda} = \frac{2.18 \times 10^{-18}}{hc}\left(\frac{1}{m^2} - \frac{1}{n^2}\right) = 1.1 \times 10^7\left(\frac{1}{m^2} - \frac{1}{n^2}\right)$$

$$\frac{1}{\lambda} = R\left(\frac{1}{m^2} - \frac{1}{n^2}\right)$$

7.65 **Given:** threshold frequency = 2.25×10^{14} s^{-1}; $\lambda = 5.00 \times 10^{-7}$ m **Find:** v of electron
Conceptual Plan: $v \rightarrow \Phi$ and then $\lambda \rightarrow E$ and then $\rightarrow KE \rightarrow v$

$$\Phi = hv \qquad E = \frac{hc}{\lambda} \qquad KE = E - \Phi \quad KE = 1/2\,mv^2$$

Solution:
$$\Phi = (6.626 \times 10^{-34}\,J \cdot s)(2.25 \times 10^{14}\,s^{-1}) = 1.491 \times 10^{-19}\,J;$$

$$E = \frac{(6.626 \times 10^{-34}\,J \cdot s)(3.00 \times 10^8\,m/s)}{5.00 \times 10^{-7}\,m} = 3.976 \times 10^{-19}\,J$$

$$KE = 3.9\underline{7}6 \times 10^{-19} \text{ J} - 1.4\underline{9}1 \times 10^{-19} \text{ J} = 2.485 \times 10^{-19} \text{ J}; \quad v^2 = \frac{2.485 \times 10^{-19} \frac{\text{kg} \cdot \text{m}^2}{\text{s}^2}}{\frac{1}{2}(9.11 \times 10^{-31} \text{ kg})} = 5.455 \times 10^{11} \frac{\text{m}^2}{\text{s}^2}$$

$v = 7.39 \times 10^5$ m/s

Check: The units of the answer (m/s) are correct. The magnitude of the answer is reasonable for the speed of an electron.

7.66   **Given:** $\lambda = 2.8 \times 10^{-4}$ cm; $m = 2.0$ g; $\Delta T = 2.0$ K   **Find:** number of photons
Conceptual Plan: λ(cm) $\rightarrow$ λ(m) $\rightarrow$ E_{photon} and m, $\Delta T \rightarrow q_{water}$ and then $\rightarrow$ number photons

$$\frac{1 \text{ m}}{100 \text{ cm}} \qquad E = \frac{hc}{\lambda} \qquad\qquad q = mC_s \Delta T \qquad\qquad \frac{q_{water}}{E_{photon}}$$

Solution: $E_{photon} = \dfrac{(6.626 \times 10^{-34} \text{ J} \cdot \text{s})(3.00 \times 10^8 \text{ m/s})}{(2.8 \times 10^{-4} \text{ cm})\left(\dfrac{1 \text{ m}}{100 \text{ cm}}\right)} = 7.1 \times 10^{-20}$ J/photon

$q = (2.0 \text{ g})\left(4.18 \dfrac{\text{J}}{\text{g} \cdot {}^\circ\text{C}}\right)\left(\dfrac{1 {}^\circ\text{C}}{1 \text{ K}}\right)(2.0 \text{ K}) = 1\underline{6}.7$ J; number of photons $= \dfrac{16.7 \text{ J}}{7.1 \times 10^{-20} \text{ J/photon}} = 2.4 \times 10^{20}$ photons

Check: The units of the answer (photons) are correct. The magnitude of the answer seems reasonable because a large amount of heat energy is needed to raise the temperature of the water.

7.67   **Given:** $t = 5.0$ fs; $\lambda_{low} = 722$ nm   **Find:** ΔE and λ_{high}
Conceptual Plan: $t \rightarrow \Delta E$ and then $\lambda_{low} \rightarrow E_{high} \rightarrow E_{low} \rightarrow \lambda_{high}$

$$\Delta t \times \Delta E \geq \frac{h}{4\pi} \qquad\qquad E = \frac{hc}{\lambda} \qquad E - \Delta E \qquad \lambda = \frac{hc}{E}$$

Solution: $\dfrac{6.626 \times 10^{-34} \text{ J} \cdot \text{s}}{4(3.141)(5.0 \text{ fs})\left(\dfrac{1 \text{ s}}{1 \times 10^{15} \text{ fs}}\right)} = 1.\underline{0}55 \times 10^{-20}$ J

$E = \dfrac{(6.626 \times 10^{-34} \text{ J} \cdot \text{s})(3.00 \times 10^8 \text{ m/s})}{722 \text{ nm}\left(\dfrac{1 \text{ m}}{10^9 \text{ nm}}\right)} = 2.7\underline{5}32 \times 10^{-19}$ J

$2.7\underline{5}32 \times 10^{-19}$ J $+ 1.\underline{0}55 \times 10^{-20}$ J $= 2.8\underline{5}87 \times 10^{-19}$ J

$\lambda = \dfrac{(6.626 \times 10^{-34} \text{ J} \cdot \text{s})\left(3.00 \times 10^8 \dfrac{\text{m}}{\text{s}}\right)\left(\dfrac{10^9 \text{ nm}}{1 \text{ m}}\right)}{(2.8\underline{5}87 \times 10^{-19} \text{ J})} = 69\underline{5}.35 \text{ nm} = 695$ nm

Check: The units of the answer (nm) are correct. The magnitude of the answer is reasonable because it is a shorter wavelength but it is close to the original wavelength.

7.68   **Given:** threshold $v = 6.71 \times 10^{14}$ s^{-1}; $v = 6.95 \times 10^5$ m/s; $\nu = 1.01 \times 10^{15}$ s^{-1} **Find:** mass of electron
Conceptual Plan: $\nu \rightarrow \Phi$ and then $\nu \rightarrow E$ and then $KE \rightarrow m$

$$\Phi = h\nu \qquad\qquad E = h\nu \qquad KE = E - \Phi \qquad m = \frac{2 \text{ KE}}{v^2}$$

Solution: $\Phi = (6.626 \times 10^{-34} \text{ J s})(6.71 \times 10^{14} \text{ s}^{-1}) = 4.4\underline{4}60 \times 10^{-19}$ J
$E = (6.626 \times 10^{-34} \text{ J s})(1.01 \times 10^{15} \text{ s}^{-1}) = 6.6\underline{9}23 \times 10^{-19}$ J
$KE = E - \Phi = 2.2\underline{4}63 \times 10^{-19}$ J

$$m = \frac{2\left(2.2\underline{4}63 \times 10^{-19} \dfrac{\text{kg m}^2}{\text{s}^2}\right)}{\left(6.95 \times 10^5 \dfrac{\text{m}}{\text{s}}\right)^2} = 9.30 \times 10^{-31} \text{ kg}$$

Check: The units of the answer (kg) are correct. The magnitude of the answer is reasonable because it is very close to the accepted mass of an electron.

Conceptual Problems

7.69   In the Bohr model of the atom, the electron travels in a circular orbit around the nucleus. It is a two-dimensional model. The electron is constrained to move only from one orbit to another orbit. But the electron is treated as a particle that behaves according to the laws of classical physics. The quantum-mechanical model of the atom is three-dimensional. In this model, we treat the electron, an absolutely small particle, differently than we treat particles with classical physics. The electron is in an orbital, which gives us the probability of finding the electron within a volume of space.

Because the electron in the Bohr model is constrained to a circular orbit, it would theoretically be possible to know both the position and the velocity of the electron simultaneously. This contradicts the Heisenberg uncertainty principle, which states that position and velocity are complementary terms that cannot both be known with precision.

7.70   The transition from $n = 3 \rightarrow n = 2$ would cause the photoelectric effect, while the transition from $n = 4 \rightarrow n = 3$ would not. Because the n levels get closer together as n increases, the energy difference between the 4 and 3 levels would be less than the energy difference between the 3 and 2 levels. Therefore, the energy of the photon emitted when the electron moves from 4 to 3 would not be above the threshold energy for the metal. The energy of the photon emitted when the electron makes the transition from $n = 3$ to $n = 2$ is larger and surpasses the threshold energy, thus causing the photoelectric effect.

7.71   The transition from a, $n = 4 \rightarrow n = 3$, would result in emitted light with the longest wavelength. Because the n levels get closer together as n increases, the energy difference between the $n = 4$ and 3 levels would be less energy than the energy difference between the $n = 3$ and 2 levels and the $n = 2$ and 1 levels. Because energy and wavelength are inversely proportional, the smaller the energy, the longer the wavelength.

7.72   (a)   Because the interference pattern is caused by single electrons interfering with themselves, the pattern remains the same even when the rate of the electrons passing through the slits is one electron per minute. It will simply take longer for the full pattern to develop.

(b)   When a light is placed behind the slits, it flashes to indicate which hole the electron passed through, but the interference pattern is now absent. With the laser on, the electrons hit positions directly behind each slit, as if they were ordinary particles.

(c)   Diffraction occurs when a wave encounters an obstacle of a slit that is comparable in size to its wavelength. The wave bends around the slit. The diffraction of light through two slits separated by a distance comparable to the wavelength of the light results in an interference pattern. Each slit acts as a new wave source, and the two new waves interfere with each other, which results in a pattern of bright and dark lines.

(d)   Because the mass of the bullets and their particle size are not absolutely small, the bullets will not produce an interference pattern when they pass through the slits. The de Broglie wavelength produced by the bullets will not be sufficiently large enough to interfere with the bullet trajectory, and no interference pattern will be observed.

Questions for Group Work

7.73   Light is electromagnetic radiation, a type of energy embodied in oscillating electric and magnetic fields. Light in a vacuum travels at 3.00×10^8 m/s.

Electromagnetic radiation can be characterized by wavelength, amplitude, and frequency. The wavelength (λ) of the wave is the distance in space between adjacent crests and is measured in units of distance. The amplitude of the wave is the vertical height of a crest. The more closely spaced the waves, that is, the shorter the wavelength, the more energy there is. The amplitude of the electric and magnetic field wave in light determines the intensity or brightness of the light. The higher the amplitude, the more photons are in the want and so the more energy the wave has. The frequency, (ν), is the number of cycles (or wave crests) that pass through a stationary point in a given period of time. The units of frequency are cycles per second. The frequency is inversely proportional to the wavelength (λ). Frequency and wavelength are related by the equation: $\nu = \dfrac{c}{\lambda}$.

For visible light, wavelength determines the color. Red light has a wavelength of 750 nm, the longest wavelength of visible light, and blue has a wavelength of 500 nm. The presence of a variety of wavelengths in white light is responsible for the way we perceive colors in objects. When a substance absorbs some colors while reflecting others, it appears colored. Grass appears green because it reflects primarily the wavelength associated with green light and absorbs the others.

7.74 The baseball and the electron are alike in that they can both be described by the de Broglie relation. You can measure the position of a baseball by observing the light that strikes the ball, bounces off it, and enters your eye. The baseball is so large in comparison to the disturbance caused by the light that it is virtually unaffected by your observation. By contrast, if you attempt to measure the position of an electron using light, the light itself disturbs the electron. The interaction of the light with the electron actually changes its position.

7.75 The magnetic quantum number (m_l) is an integer ranging from $-l$ to $+l$.
(a)   When $l = 0$, $m_l = 0$.
(b)   When $l = 1$, $m_l = -1, 0$, or $+1$.
(c)   When $l = 2$, $m_l = -2, -1, 0, +1$ or $+2$.
(d)   When $l = 20$, $m_l = -20, -19, ..., 0, ...19$, or 20, so there are 41 values for m_l.
In the general case, the number of possible values for $m_l = 2l + 1$.

7.76 For the hydrogen atom, the energy levels depend only on the value of n.

$$\Delta E = E_{final} - E_{initial} = -2.18 \times 10^{-18} \, J \left[\left(\frac{1}{n_{final}^2} - \frac{1}{n_{initial}^2} \right) \right] \text{ and } \lambda = \frac{hc}{\Delta E}.$$ The shorter the wavelength, the higher the energy, so we get the following combinations for $n \leq 7$.

$n_{initial}$	n_{final}	$\lambda(m)$	$\lambda(nm)$
6	5	7.46×10^{-6}	7.46×10^3
5	4	4.05×10^{-6}	4.05×10^3
6	4	2.63×10^{-6}	2.63×10^3
4	3	1.88×10^{-6}	1.88×10^3
5	3	1.28×10^{-6}	1.28×10^3
6	3	1.09×10^{-6}	1.09×10^3
3	2	6.57×10^{-7}	6.57×10^2
4	2	4.86×10^{-7}	4.86×10^2
5	2	4.34×10^{-7}	4.34×10^2
6	2	4.10×10^{-7}	4.10×10^2
2	1	1.22×10^{-7}	1.22×10^2
3	1	1.03×10^{-7}	1.03×10^2
4	1	9.73×10^{-8}	9.73×10^1
5	1	9.50×10^{-8}	9.50×10^1
6	1	9.38×10^{-8}	9.38×10^1

7.77 The $1s$ orbital does not have any nodes. The $2p$ orbitals have a node at the nucleus. Four of the $3d$ orbitals have a cloverleaf shape, with four lobes of electron density around the nucleus and two perpendicular nodal planes. The f orbitals are even more complex. The $4f$ orbitals are shown here. The number of nodes (and nodal planes) depends on the specific orbital.

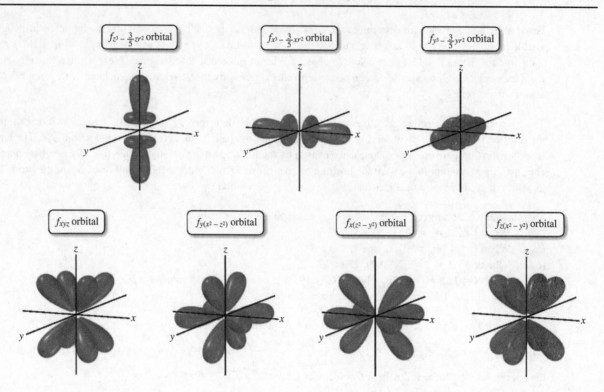

8 Periodic Properties of the Elements

Problems by Topic

Electron Configurations

8.1   (a)   P   Phosphorus has 15 electrons. Distribute two of these into the $1s$ orbital, two into the $2s$ orbital, six into the $2p$ orbital, two into the $3s$ orbital, and three into the $3p$ orbital. $1s^2 2s^2 2p^6 3s^2 3p^3$

      (b)   C   Carbon has six electrons. Distribute two of these into the $1s$ orbital, two into the $2s$ orbital, and two into the $2p$ orbital. $1s^2 2s^2 2p^2$

      (c)   Na   Sodium has 11 electrons. Distribute two of these into the $1s$ orbital, two into the $2s$ orbital, six into the $2p$ orbital, and one into the $3s$ orbital. $1s^2 2s^2 2p^6 3s^1$

      (d)   Ar   Argon has 18 electrons. Distribute two of these into the $1s$ orbital, two into the $2s$ orbital, six into the $2p$ orbital, two into the $3s$ orbital, and six into the $3p$ orbital. $1s^2 2s^2 2p^6 3s^2 3p^6$

8.2   (a)   O   Oxygen has eight electrons. Distribute two of these into the $1s$ orbital, two into the $2s$ orbital, and four into the $2p$ orbital. $1s^2 2s^2 2p^4$

      (b)   Si   Silicon has 14 electrons. Distribute two of these into the $1s$ orbital, two into the $2s$ orbital, six into the $2p$ orbital, two into the $3s$ orbital, and two into the $3p$ orbital. $1s^2 2s^2 2p^6 3s^2 3p^2$

      (c)   Ne   Neon has ten electrons. Distribute two of these into the $1s$ orbital, two into the $2s$ orbital, and six into the $2p$ orbital. $1s^2 2s^2 2p^6$

      (d)   K   Potassium has 19 electrons. Distribute two of these into the $1s$ orbital, two into the $2s$ orbital, six into the $2p$ orbital, two into the $3s$ orbital, six into the $3p$ orbital, and one into the $4s$ orbital. $1s^2 2s^2 2p^6 3s^2 3p^6 4s^1$

8.3   (a)   N   Nitrogen has seven electrons and has the electron configuration $1s^2 2s^2 2p^3$. Draw a box for each orbital, putting the lowest energy orbital ($1s$) on the far left and proceeding to orbitals of higher energy to the right. Distribute the seven electrons into the boxes representing the orbitals, allowing a maximum of two electrons per orbital and remembering Hund's rule. You can see from the diagram that nitrogen has three unpaired electrons.

           ↓↑   ↓↑   ↑ ↑ ↑
           $1s$ $2s$ $2p$

      (b)   F   Fluorine has nine electrons and has the electron configuration $1s^2 2s^2 2p^5$. Draw a box for each orbital, putting the lowest energy orbital ($1s$) on the far left and proceeding to orbitals of higher energy to the right. Distribute the nine electrons into the boxes representing the orbitals, allowing a maximum of two electrons per orbital and remembering Hund's rule. You can see from the diagram that fluorine has one unpaired electron.

           ↓↑   ↓↑   ↓↑ ↓↑ ↑
           $1s$ $2s$ $2p$

      (c)   Mg   Magnesium has 12 electrons and has the electron configuration $1s^2 2s^2 2p^6 3s^2$. Draw a box for each orbital, putting the lowest energy orbital ($1s$) on the far left and proceeding to orbitals of higher energy to the right. Distribute the 12 electrons into the boxes representing the orbitals, allowing a maximum of two electrons per orbital and remembering Hund's rule. You can see from the diagram that magnesium has no unpaired electrons.

           ↓↑   ↓↑   ↓↑ ↓↑ ↓↑   ↓↑
           $1s$ $2s$ $2p$ $3s$

(d)   Al   Aluminum has 13 electrons and has the electron configuration $1s^2 2s^2 2p^6 3s^2 3p^1$. Draw a box for each orbital, putting the lowest energy orbital ($1s$) on the far left and proceeding to orbitals of higher energy to the right. Distribute the 13 electrons into the boxes representing the orbitals, allowing a maximum of two electrons per orbital and remembering Hund's rule. You can see from the diagram that aluminum has one unpaired electron.

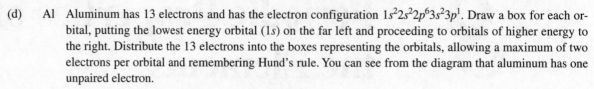

8.4   (a)   S   Sulfur has 16 electrons and has the electron configuration $1s^2 2s^2 2p^6 3s^2 3p^4$. Draw a box for each orbital, putting the lowest energy orbital ($1s$) on the far left and proceeding to orbitals of higher energy to the right. Distribute the 16 electrons into the boxes representing the orbitals, allowing a maximum of two electrons per orbital and remembering Hund's rule. You can see from the diagram that sulfur has two unpaired electrons.

(b)   Ca   Calcium has 20 electrons and has the electron configuration $1s^2 2s^2 2p^6 3s^2 3p^6 4s^2$. Draw a box for each orbital, putting the lowest energy orbital ($1s$) on the far left and proceeding to orbitals of higher energy to the right. Distribute the 20 electrons into the boxes representing the orbitals, allowing a maximum of two electrons per orbital and remembering Hund's rule. You can see from the diagram that nitrogen has no unpaired electrons.

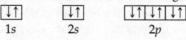

(c)   Ne   Neon has ten electrons and has the electron configuration $1s^2 2s^2 2p^6$. Draw a box for each orbital, putting the lowest energy orbital ($1s$) on the far left and proceeding to orbitals of higher energy to the right. Distribute the ten electrons into the boxes representing the orbitals, allowing a maximum of two electrons per orbital and remembering Hund's rule. You can see from the diagram that neon has no unpaired electrons.

(d)   He   Helium has two electrons and has the electron configuration $1s^2$. Draw a box for each orbital, putting the lowest energy orbital ($1s$) on the far left and proceeding to orbitals of higher energy to the right. Distribute the two electrons into the boxes representing the orbitals, allowing a maximum of two electrons per orbital and remembering Hund's rule. You can see from the diagram that helium has no unpaired electrons.

8.5   (a)   P   The atomic number of P is 15. The noble gas that precedes P in the periodic table is neon, so the inner electron configuration is [Ne]. Obtain the outer electron configuration by tracing the elements between Ne and P and assigning electrons to the appropriate orbitals. Begin with [Ne]. Because P is in row 3, add two $3s$ electrons. Next, add three $3p$ electrons as you trace across the p block to P, which is in the third column of the p block.

$$\text{P [Ne] } 3s^2 3p^3$$

(b)   Ge   The atomic number of Ge is 32. The noble gas that precedes Ge in the periodic table is argon, so the inner electron configuration is [Ar]. Obtain the outer electron configuration by tracing the elements between Ar and Ge and assigning electrons to the appropriate orbitals. Begin with [Ar]. Because Ge is in row 4, add two $4s$ electrons. Next, add ten $3d$ electrons as you trace across the d block. Finally, add two $4p$ electrons as you trace across the p block to Ge, which is in the second column of the p block.

$$\text{Ge [Ar] } 4s^2 3d^{10} 4p^2$$

(c)   Zr   The atomic number of Zr is 40. The noble gas that precedes Zr in the periodic table is krypton, so the inner electron configuration is [Kr]. Obtain the outer electron configuration by tracing the elements between Kr and Zr and assigning electrons to the appropriate orbitals. Begin with [Kr]. Because Zr is in row 5, add two $5s$ electrons. Next, add two $4d$ electrons as you trace across the d block to Zr, which is in the second column.

$$\text{Zr [Kr] } 5s^2 4d^2$$

(d)   I   The atomic number of I is 53. The noble gas that precedes I in the periodic table is krypton, so the inner electron configuration is [Kr]. Obtain the outer electron configuration by tracing the elements between Kr and I and assigning electrons to the appropriate orbitals. Begin with [Kr]. Because I is in row 5, add two $5s$ electrons. Next, add ten $4d$ electrons as you trace across the d block. Finally, add five $5p$ electrons as you trace across the p block to I, which is in the fifth column of the p block.

$$\text{I [Kr] } 5s^2 4d^{10} 5p^5$$

8.6   (a) $[Ar] 4s^2 3d^{10} 4p^6$ To determine the element corresponding to the electron configuration, begin with Ar; then trace across the $4s$ block, the $3d$ block, and the $4p$ block until you come to the sixth column The element is Kr.

       (b) $[Ar] 4s^2 3d^2$ To determine the element corresponding to the electron configuration, begin with Ar; then trace across the $4s$ block and the $3d$ block until you come to the second column. The element is Ti.

       (c) $[Kr] 5s^2 4d^{10} 5p^2$ To determine the element corresponding to the electron configuration, begin with Kr; then trace across the $5s$ block, the $4d$ block, and the $5p$ block until you come to the second column. The element is Sn.

       (d) $[Kr] 5s^2$ To determine the element corresponding to the electron configuration, begin with Kr; then trace across the $5s$ block to the second column. The element is Sr.

8.7   (a)   Li is in period 2, and the first column in the s block, so Li has one $2s$ electron.

       (b)   Cu is in period 4, and the ninth column in the d block ($n-1$), so Cu should have nine $3d$ electrons. However, it is one of our exceptions, so it has ten $3d$ electrons.

       (c)   Br is in period 4, and the fifth column of the p block, so Br has five $4p$ electrons.

       (d)   Zr is in period 5, and the second column of the d block ($n-1$), so Zr has two $4d$ electrons.

8.8   (a)   Mg is in period 3, and the second column of the s block, so Mg has two $3s$ electrons.

       (b)   Cr is in period 4, and the fourth column of the d block ($n-1$), so Cr should have four $3d$ electrons. However, Cr is one of our exceptions, so it has five $3d$ electrons.

       (c)   Y is in period 5, and the first column of the d block ($n-1$), so Y has one $4d$ electron.

       (d)   Pb is in period 6, and the second column of the p block, so Pb has two $6p$ electrons.

8.9   (a)   In period 4, an element with five valence electrons could be V or As.

       (b)   In period 4, an element with four $4p$ electrons would be in the fourth column of the p block and is Se.

       (c)   In period 4, an element with three $3d$ electrons would be in the third column of the d block ($n-1$) and is V.

       (d)   In period 4, an element with a complete outer shell would be in the sixth column of the p block and is Kr.

8.10   (a)   In period 3, an element with three valence electrons would be in the first column of the p block and is Al.

       (b)   In period 3, an element with four $3p$ electrons would be in the fourth column of the p block and is S.

       (c)   In period 3, an element with six $3p$ electrons would be in the sixth column of the p block and is Ar.

       (d)   In period 3, an element with two $3s$ electrons and no $3p$ electrons would be in the second column of the s block and is Mg.

Valence Electrons and Simple Chemical Behavior Form the Periodic Table

8.11   (a)   Ba is in column 2A, so it has two valence electrons.

       (b)   Cs is in column 1A, so it has one valence electron.

       (c)   Ni is in column 8 of the d block, so it has ten valence electrons (eight from the d block and two from the s block).

       (d)   S is in column 6A, so it has six valence electrons.

8.12   (a)   Al is in column 3A, so it has three valence electrons. Al is a metal and will tend to lose the three valence electrons to achieve the noble gas configuration of Ne.

       (b)   Sn is in column 4A, so it has four valence electrons. Sn is a metal and will tend to lose the valence electrons to obtain a completely filled $n = 3$ level.

       (c)   Br is in column 7A, so it has seven valence electrons. Br is a nonmetal and will tend to gain an electron to achieve the noble gas configuration of Kr.

       (d)   Se is in column 6A, so it has six valence electrons. Se is a nonmetal and will tend to gain electrons to achieve the noble gas configuration of Kr.

8.13   (a)   The outer electron configuration ns^2 would belong to a reactive metal in the alkaline earth family.

        (b)   The outer electron configuration ns^2np^6 would belong to an unreactive nonmetal in the noble gas family.

        (c)   The outer electron configuration ns^2np^5 would belong to a reactive nonmetal in the halogen family.

        (d)   The outer electron configuration ns^2np^2 would belong to an element in the carbon family. If $n = 2$, the element is a nonmetal, if $n = 3$ or 4, the element is a metalloid, and if $n = 5$ or 6, the element is a metal.

8.14   (a)   The outer electron configuration ns^2 would belong to a metal in the alkaline earth family for period $n = 2$ and greater. He is a noble gas with a $1s^2$ electron configuration.

        (b)   The outer electron configuration ns^2np^6 would belong to a nonmetal in the noble gas family.

        (c)   The outer electron configuration ns^2np^5 would belong to a nonmetal in the halogen family.

        (d)   The outer electron configuration ns^2np^2 would belong to an element in the carbon family. If $n = 2$, the element is a nonmetal, if $n = 3$ or 4, the element is a metalloid, and if $n = 5$ or 6, the element is a metal.

8.15   Coulomb's law states that the potential energy (E) of two charge particles depends on their charges (q_1 and q_2) and on their separation (r). $E = \dfrac{1}{4\pi\varepsilon_o}\dfrac{q_1q_2}{r}$. The potential energy is positive for charges of the same sign and negative for charges of opposite signs. The magnitude of the potential energy depends inversely on the separation between the charged particles.

        (a)   **Given:** $q_1 = 1-;\ q_2 = 2+;\ r = 150$ pm   **Find:** E

           Conceptual Plan: Magnitude of Potential Energy depends on the charge and the separation.

$$E = \frac{1}{4\pi\varepsilon_o}\frac{q_1q_2}{r}$$

           Solution: $E = \dfrac{1}{4\pi\varepsilon_o}\dfrac{(1-)(2+)}{150} = \dfrac{-0.0133}{4\pi\varepsilon_o}$

        (b)   **Given:** $q_1 = 1-;\ q_2 = 1+;\ r = 150$ pm   **Find:** E

           Conceptual Plan: Magnitude of Potential Energy depends on the charge and the separation.

$$E = \frac{1}{4\pi\varepsilon_o}\frac{q_1q_2}{r}$$

           Solution: $E = \dfrac{1}{4\pi\varepsilon_o}\dfrac{(1-)(1+)}{150} = \dfrac{-0.00667}{4\pi\varepsilon_o}$

        (c)   **Given:** $q_1 = 1-;\ q_2 = 3+;\ r = 150$ pm   **Find:** E

           Conceptual Plan: Magnitude of Potential Energy depends on the charge and the separation.

$$E = \frac{1}{4\pi\varepsilon_o}\frac{q_1q_2}{r}$$

           Solution: $E = \dfrac{1}{4\pi\varepsilon_o}\dfrac{(1-)(3+)}{100} = \dfrac{-0.0300}{4\pi\varepsilon_o}$

           c is most negative and will have the lowest potential energy.

8.16   According to Coulomb's law, for opposite charges, the potential energy increases (becomes less negative) with increasing distance; so c is greater than a.

        Because the charge of b is twice the charge of a at the same distance and is the opposite charge, it would have the lowest (most negative) potential energy. Ranking from lowest to highest: $b < a < c$.

Coulomb's Law and Effective Nuclear Charge

8.17   The valence electrons in nitrogen would experience a greater effective nuclear charge. Be has four protons, and N has seven protons. Both atoms have two core electrons that predominantly contribute to the shielding, while the valence electrons will contribute a slight shielding effect. So Be has an effective nuclear charge of slightly more than 2+, and N has an effective nuclear charge of slightly more than 5+.

8.18 $S(16) = [Ne]\ 3s^23p^4$ $Mg(12) = [Ne]\ 3s^2$ $Al(13) = [Ne]\ 3s^23p^1$ $Si(14) = [Ne]\ 3s^23p^2$

        All four atoms have the same number of core electrons that contribute to shielding. So the effective nuclear charge will decrease with a decreasing number of protons. $S > Si > Al > Mg$

8.19   (a)   K(19) [Ar] $4s^1$ $Z_{eff} = Z - \text{core electrons} = 19 - 18 = 1+$

        (b)   Ca(20) [Ar] $4s^2$ $Z_{eff} = Z - \text{core electrons} = 20 - 18 = 2+$

        (c)   O(8) [He] $2s^22p^4$ $Z_{eff} = Z - \text{core electrons} = 8 - 2 = 6+$

        (d)   C(6) [He] $2s^22p^2$ $Z_{eff} = Z - \text{core electrons} = 6 - 2 = 4+$

8.20   B has an electron configuration of $1s^2 2s^2 2p^1$. To estimate the effective nuclear charge experienced by the outer electrons, we need to distinguish between two types of shielding: (1) the shielding of the outermost electrons by the core electrons and (2) the shielding of the outermost electrons by each other. The three outermost electrons in boron experience the 5+ charge of the nucleus through the shield of the two $1s$ core electrons. We can estimate that the shielding experienced by any one of the outermost electrons due to the core electrons is nearly 2. For the $2s$ electrons, the shielding due to the other $2s$ electron is nearly zero. For the $2p$ electron, however, we would expect that the $2s$ electrons would contribute some shielding because although the $2p$ orbital penetrates the $2s$ orbital to some degree, most of the $2p$ orbital lies outside the $2s$ orbital. So the effective nuclear charge would be slightly greater than 3+, and the effective nuclear charge felt by the $2s$ electrons would be greater than the effective nuclear charge felt by the $2p$ electrons.

Atomic Radius

8.21   (a)   Al or In   In atoms are larger than Al atoms because as you trace the path between Al and In on the periodic table, you move down a column. Atomic size increases as you move down a column because the outermost electrons occupy orbitals with a higher principal quantum number that are larger, resulting in a larger atom.

         (b)   Si or N   Si atoms are larger than N atoms because as you trace the path between N and Si on the periodic table, you move down a column (atomic size increases) and then to the left across a period (atomic size increases). These effects add together for an overall increase.

         (c)   P or Pb   Pb atoms are larger than P atoms because as you trace the path between P and Pb on the periodic table, you move down a column (atomic size increases) and then to the left across a period (atomic size increases). These effects add together for an overall increase.

         (d)   C or F   C atoms are larger than F atoms because as you trace the path between C and F on the periodic table, you move to the right within the same period. As you move to the right across a period, the effective nuclear charge experienced by the outermost electrons increases, which results in a smaller size.

8.22   (a)   Sn or Si   Sn atoms are larger than Si atoms because as you trace the path between Si and Sn on the periodic table, you move down a column. Atomic size increases as you move down a column because the outermost electrons occupy orbitals with a higher principal quantum number that is larger, resulting in a larger atom.

         (b)   Br or Ga   Ga atoms are larger than Br atoms because as you trace the path between Ga and Br on the periodic table, you move to the right within the same period. As you move to the right across a period, the effective nuclear charge experienced by the outermost electrons increases, which results in a smaller size.

         (c)   Sn or Bi   Based on periodic trends alone, you cannot tell which atom is larger because as you trace the path between Sn and Bi, you move to the right across a period (atomic size decreases) and then down a column (atomic size increases). These effects tend to oppose each other, and it is not easy to tell which will predominate.

         (d)   Se or Sn   Sn atoms are larger than Se atoms because as you trace the path between Se and Sn on the periodic table, you move down a column (atomic size increases) and then to the left across a period (atomic size increases). These effects add together for an overall increase.

8.23   Ca, Rb, S, Si, Ge, F   F is above and to the right of the other elements, so we start with F as the smallest atom. As you trace a path from F to S, you move to the left (size increases) and down (size increases). Next, you move left from S to Si (size increases), then down to Ge (size increases), then to the left to Ca (size increases), and then to the left and down to Rb (size increases). So in order of increasing atomic radii, F<S<Si<Ge<Ca<Rb.

8.24   Cs, Sb, S, Pb, Se   Cs is below and to the left of the other elements, so we start with Cs as the largest atom. As you trace a path from Cs to Pb, you move to the right in the same period (size decreases). Next, going from Pb to Sb, you move up a column and then to the right (size decreases); from Sb to Se, you move up the column and then to the right (size decreases); and finally, from Se to S, you move up the column (size decreases). So in order of decreasing radii, Cs>Pb>Sb>Se>S.

Ionic Electron Configurations, Ionic Radii, Magnetic Properties, and Ionization Energy

8.25   (a) O^{2-} Begin by writing the electron configuration of the neutral atom.

O $1s^2 2s^2 2p^4$

Because this ion has a 2− charge, add two electrons to write the electron configuration of the ion.

O^{2-} $1s^2 2s^2 2p^6$ This is isoelectronic with Ne.

(b) Br^- Begin by writing the electron configuration of the neutral atom.

Br $[Ar] 4s^2 3d^{10} 4p^5$

Because this ion has a 1− charge, add one electron to write the electron configuration of the ion.

Br^- $[Ar] 4s^2 3d^{10} 4p^6$ This is isoelectronic with Kr.

(c) Sr^{2+} Begin by writing the electron configuration of the neutral atom.

Sr $[Kr] 5s^2$

Because this ion has a 2+ charge, remove two electrons to write the electron configuration of the ion.

Sr^{2+} $[Kr]$

(d) Co^{3+} Begin by writing the electron configuration of the neutral atom.

Co $[Ar] 4s^2 3d^7$

Because this ion has a 3+ charge, remove three electrons to write the electron configuration of the ion. Because it is a transition metal, remove the electrons from the 4s orbital before removing electrons from the 3d orbitals.

Co^{3+} $[Ar] 4s^0 3d^6$

(e) Cu^{2+} Begin by writing the electron configuration of the neutral atom. Remember, Cu is one of our exceptions.

Cu $[Ar] 4s^1 3d^{10}$

Because this ion has a 2+ charge, remove two electrons to write the electron configuration of the ion. Because it is a transition metal, remove the electron from the 4s orbital before removing electrons from the 3d orbitals.

Cu^{2+} $[Ar] 4s^0 3d^9$

8.26   (a) Cl^- Begin by writing the electron configuration of the neutral atom.

Cl $[Ne] 3s^2 3p^5$

Because this ion has a 1− charge, add one electron to write the electron configuration of the ion.

Cl^- $[Ne] 3s^2 3p^6$ This is isoelectronic with Ar.

(b) P^{3-} Begin by writing the electron configuration of the neutral atom.

P $[Ne] 3s^2 3p^3$

Because this ion has a 3− charge, add three electrons to write the electron configuration of the ion.

P^{3-} $[Ne] 3s^2 3p^6$ This is isoelectronic with Ar.

(c) K^+ Begin by writing the electron configuration of the neutral atom.

K $[Ar] 4s^1$

Because this ion has a 1+ charge, remove one electron to write the electron configuration of the ion.

K^+ $[Ar]$

(d) Mo^{3+} Begin by writing the electron configuration of the neutral atom. Remember, Mo is one of our exceptions.

Mo $[Kr] 5s^1 4d^5$

Because this ion has a 3+ charge, remove three electrons to write the electron configuration of the ion. Because it is a transition metal, remove the electron from the 5s orbital before removing electrons from the 4d orbitals.

Mo^{3+} $[Kr] 5s^0 4d^3$

(e) V^{3+} Begin by writing the electron configuration of the neutral atom.

V $[Ar] 4s^2 3d^3$

Because this ion has a 3+ charge, remove three electrons to write the electron configuration of the ion. Because it is a transition metal, remove the electrons from the 4s orbital before removing electrons from the 3d orbitals.

V^{3+} $[Ar] 4s^0 3d^2$

8.27 (a) V^{5+} Begin by writing the electron configuration of the neutral atom.

V   [Ar] $4s^2 3d^3$

Because this ion has a 5+ charge, remove five electrons to write the electron configuration of the ion. Because it is a transition metal, remove the electrons from the 4s orbital before removing electrons from the 3d orbitals.

V^{5+} [Ar] $4s^0 3d^0$ = [Ne] $3s^2 3p^6$

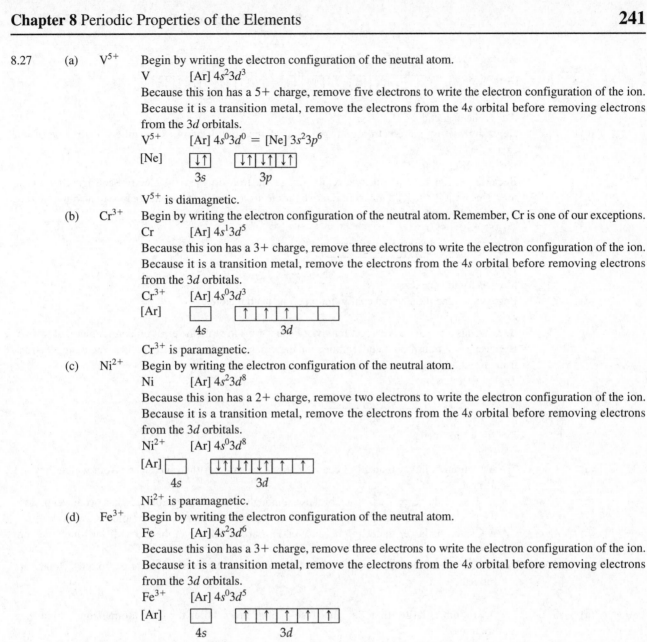

[Ne]

     3s   3p

V^{5+} is diamagnetic.

(b) Cr^{3+} Begin by writing the electron configuration of the neutral atom. Remember, Cr is one of our exceptions.

Cr   [Ar] $4s^1 3d^5$

Because this ion has a 3+ charge, remove three electrons to write the electron configuration of the ion. Because it is a transition metal, remove the electrons from the 4s orbital before removing electrons from the 3d orbitals.

Cr^{3+} [Ar] $4s^0 3d^3$

[Ar]

     4s   3d

Cr^{3+} is paramagnetic.

(c) Ni^{2+} Begin by writing the electron configuration of the neutral atom.

Ni   [Ar] $4s^2 3d^8$

Because this ion has a 2+ charge, remove two electrons to write the electron configuration of the ion. Because it is a transition metal, remove the electrons from the 4s orbital before removing electrons from the 3d orbitals.

Ni^{2+} [Ar] $4s^0 3d^8$

[Ar]

     4s   3d

Ni^{2+} is paramagnetic.

(d) Fe^{3+} Begin by writing the electron configuration of the neutral atom.

Fe   [Ar] $4s^2 3d^6$

Because this ion has a 3+ charge, remove three electrons to write the electron configuration of the ion. Because it is a transition metal, remove the electrons from the 4s orbital before removing electrons from the 3d orbitals.

Fe^{3+} [Ar] $4s^0 3d^5$

[Ar]

     4s   3d

Fe^{3+} is paramagnetic.

8.28 (a) Cd^{2+} Begin by writing the electron configuration of the neutral atom.

Cd   [Kr] $5s^2 4d^{10}$

Because this ion has a 2+ charge, remove two electrons to write the electron configuration of the ion. Because it is a transition metal, remove the electrons from the 5s orbital before removing electrons from the 4d orbitals.

Cd^{2+} [Kr] $5s^0 4d^{10}$

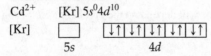

[Kr]

     5s   4d

Cd^{2+} is diamagnetic.

(b) Au^+ Begin by writing the electron configuration of the neutral atom. Remember, Au is one of our exceptions.

Au   [Xe] $6s^1 4f^{14} 5d^{10}$

Because this ion has a 1+ charge, remove one electron to write the electron configuration of the ion. Because it is a transition metal, remove the electrons from the 6s orbital before removing electrons from the 5d or 4f orbitals.

Au$^+$ [Xe] $6s^0 4f^{14} 5d^{10}$

[Xe] $\boxed{}$ $\boxed{\uparrow\downarrow|\uparrow\downarrow|\uparrow\downarrow|\uparrow\downarrow|\uparrow\downarrow|\uparrow\downarrow|\uparrow\downarrow}$ $\boxed{\uparrow\downarrow|\uparrow\downarrow|\uparrow\downarrow|\uparrow\downarrow|\uparrow\downarrow}$

    $6s$ $4f$ $5d$

Au$^+$ is diamagnetic.

(c)   Mo^{3+} Begin by writing the electron configuration of the neutral atom. Remember, Mo is one of our exceptions.

Mo   [Kr] $5s^1 4d^5$

Because this ion has a 3+ charge, remove three electrons to write the electron configuration of the ion. Because it is a transition metal, remove the electron from the $5s$ orbital before removing electrons from the $4d$ orbitals.

Mo^{3+} [Kr] $5s^0 4d^3$

[Kr] $\boxed{}$ $\boxed{\uparrow|\uparrow|\uparrow||}$

    $5s$ $4d$

Mo^{3+} is paramagnetic.

(d)   Zr^{2+} Begin by writing the electron configuration of the neutral atom.

Zr   [Kr]$5s^2 4d^2$

Because this ion has a 2+ charge, remove two electrons to write the electron configuration of the ion. Because it is a transition metal, remove the electrons from the $5s$ orbital before removing electrons from the $4d$ orbitals.

Zr^{2+} [Kr] $5s^0 4d^2$

[Kr] $\boxed{}$ $\boxed{\uparrow|\uparrow|||}$

    $5s$ $4d$

Zr^{2+} is paramagnetic.

8.29   (a)   Li or Li$^+$ A Li atom is larger than Li$^+$ because cations are smaller than the atoms from which they are formed.

        (b)   I$^-$ or Cs$^+$ An I$^-$ ion is larger than a Cs$^+$ ion because, although they are isoelectronic, I$^-$ has two fewer protons than Cs$^+$, resulting in a lesser pull on the electrons and therefore a larger radius.

        (c)   Cr or Cr^{3+} A Cr atom is larger than Cr^{3+} because cations are smaller than the atoms from which they are formed.

        (d)   O or O^{2-} An O^{2-} ion is larger than an O atom because anions are larger than the atoms from which they are formed.

8.30   (a)   Sr or Sr^{2+} A Sr atom is larger than Sr^{2+} because cations are smaller than the atoms from which they are formed.

        (b)   N or N^{3-} A N^{3-} ion is larger than a N atom because anions are larger than the atoms from which they are formed.

        (c)   Ni or Ni^{2+} A Ni atom is larger than Ni^{2+} because cations are smaller than the atoms from which they are formed.

        (d)   S^{2-} or Ca^{2+} A S^{2-} ion is larger than a Ca^{2+} ion because, although they are isoelectronic, S^{2-} has four fewer protons than Ca^{2+}, resulting in a lesser pull on the electrons and therefore a larger radius.

8.31   Because all of the species are isoelectronic, the radius will depend on the number of protons in each species. The fewer the protons, the larger the radius.

F: $Z = 9$; O: $Z = 8$; Mg: $Z = 12$; Na: $Z = 11$

So: O^{2-} > F$^-$ > Na$^+$ > Mg^{2+}

8.32   Because all of the species are isoelectronic, the radius will depend on the number of protons in each species. The fewer the protons, the larger the radius.

Se: $Z = 34$; Sr: $Z = 38$; Rb: $Z = 37$; Br: $Z = 35$

So: Sr^{2+} < Rb$^+$ < Br$^-$ < Se^{2-}

8.33   (a)   Br or Bi   Br has a higher ionization energy than Bi because as you trace the path between Br and Bi on the periodic table, you move down a column (ionization energy decreases) and then to the left across a period (ionization energy decreases). These effects sum together for an overall decrease.

        (b)   Na or Rb   Na has a higher ionization energy than Rb because as you trace a path between Na and Rb on the periodic table, you move down a column. Ionization energy decreases as you go down a column because of the increasing size of orbitals with increasing n.

        (c)   As or At   Based on periodic trends alone, it is impossible to tell which has a higher ionization energy because as you trace the path between As and At, you move to the right across a period (ionization energy increases) and then down a column (ionization energy decreases). These effects tend to oppose each other, and it is not obvious which will dominate.

        (d)   P or Sn   P has a higher ionization energy than Sn because as you trace the path between P and Sn on the periodic table, you move down a column (ionization energy decreases) and then to the left across a period (ionization energy decreases). These effects sum together for an overall decrease.

8.34   (a)   P or I   Based on periodic trends alone, it is impossible to tell which has a higher ionization energy because as you trace the path between P and I, you move to the right across a period (ionization energy increases) and then down a column (ionization energy decreases). These effects tend to oppose each other, and it is not obvious which will dominate.

        (b)   Si or Cl   Cl has a higher ionization energy than Si because as you trace the path between Si and Cl on the periodic table you move right across a period. Ionization energy increases as you go to the right because of increasing nuclear charge.

        (c)   P or Sb   P has a higher ionization energy than Sb because as you trace a path between P and Sb on the periodic table, you move down a column. Ionization energy decreases as you go down a column because of the increasing size of orbitals with increasing n.

        (d)   Ga or Ge   Ge has a higher ionization energy than Ga because as you trace a path between Ga and Ge on the periodic table, you move to the right within the same period. Ionization energy increases as you move to the right because of increasing effective nuclear charge.

8.35   Because ionization energy increases as you move to the right across a period and increases as you move up a column, the element with the smallest first ionization energy would be the element farthest to the left and lowest on the periodic table. So In has the smallest ionization energy. As you trace a path to the right and up on the periodic table, the next element you reach is Si; continuing up and to the right, you reach N; and continuing to the right, you reach F. So in the order of increasing first ionization energy, the elements are In < Si < N < F.

8.36   Because ionization energy increases as you move to the right across a period and increases as you move up a column, the element with the largest first ionization energy would be the element farthest to the right and highest on the periodic table. So Cl has the largest ionization energy. As you trace a path to the left on the periodic table, you reach S; as you move down a column and to the left, you reach Sn; and as you move down the column, you reach Pb. So in the order of decreasing first ionization energy, the elements are Cl > S > Sn > Pb.

8.37   The jump in ionization energy occurs when you change from removing a valence electron to removing a core electron. To determine where this jump occurs, you need to look at the electron configuration of the atom.

        (a)   Be $1s^2 2s^2$ The first and second ionization energies involve removing $2s$ electrons, while the third ionization energy removes a core electron; so the jump will occur between the second and third ionization energies.

        (b)   N $1s^2 2s^2 2p^3$ The first five ionization energies involve removing the $2p$ and $2s$ electrons, while the sixth ionization energy removes a core electron; so the jump will occur between the fifth and sixth ionization energies.

        (c)   O $1s^2 2s^2 2p^4$ The first six ionization energies involve removing the $2p$ and $2s$ electrons, while the seventh ionization energy removes a core electron; so the jump will occur between the sixth and seventh ionization energies.

        (d)   Li $1s^2 2s^1$ The first ionization energy involves removing a $2s$ electron, while the second ionization energy removes a core electron; so the jump will occur between the first and second ionization energies.

8.38   The jump occurs between IE_3 and IE_4. So removing the first three electrons involves removing valence electrons, and the fourth electron is a core electron; so the valence electron configuration would be ns^2np^1. This puts the element in column 3A and would be Al.

Electron Affinities and Metallic Character

8.39   (a)   Na or Rb   Na has a more negative electron affinity than Rb. In column 1A, electron affinity becomes less negative as you go down the column.

(b)   B or S   S has a more negative electron affinity than B. As you trace from B to S in the periodic table, you move to the right, which shows the value of the electron affinity becoming more negative. Also, as you move from period 2 to period 3, the value of the electron affinity becomes more negative. Both of these trends sum together for the value of the electron affinity to become more negative.

(c)   C or N   C has the more negative electron affinity. As you trace from C to N across the periodic table, you would normally expect N to have the more negative electron affinity. However, N has a half-filled p sublevel, which lends it extra stability; therefore, it is harder to add an electron.

(d)   Li or F   F has the more negative electron affinity. As you trace from Li to F on the periodic table, you move to the right in the period. As you move to the right across a period, the value of the electron affinity generally becomes more negative.

8.40   (a)   Mg or S   S has the more negative electron affinity. As you trace from Mg to S on the periodic table, you move to the right in the period. As you move to the right across a period, the value of the electron affinity generally becomes more negative.

(b)   K or Cs   K has the more negative electron affinity. In column 1A, as you go down the column, the electron affinity becomes less negative.

(c)   Si or P   Si has the more negative electron affinity. As you trace from Si to P across the periodic table, you would normally expect P to have the more negative electron affinity. However, P has a half-filled p sublevel, which lends extra stability; therefore, it is harder to add an electron.

(d)   Ga or Br   Br has the more negative electron affinity. As you trace from Ga to Br on the periodic table, you move to the right in the period. As you move to the right across a period, the value of the electron affinity generally becomes more negative.

8.41   (a)   Sr or Sb   Sr is more metallic than Sb because as we trace the path between Sr and Sb on the periodic table, we move to the right within the same period. Metallic character decreases as you move to the right.

(b)   As or Bi   Bi is more metallic because as we trace a path between As and Bi on the periodic table, we move down a column in the same family (metallic character increases).

(c)   Cl or O   Based on periodic trends alone, we cannot tell which is more metallic because as we trace the path between O and Cl, we move to the right across a period (metallic character decreases) and then down a column (metallic character increases). These effects tend to oppose each other, and it is not easy to tell which will predominate.

(d)   S or As   As is more metallic than S because as we trace the path between S and As on the periodic table, we move down a column (metallic character increases) and then to the left across a period (metallic character increases). These effects add together for an overall increase.

8.42   (a)   Sb or Pb   Pb is more metallic than Sb because as we trace the path between Sb and Pb on the periodic table, we move down a column (metallic character increases) and then to the left across a period (metallic character increases). These effects add together for an overall increase.

(b)   K or Ge   K is more metallic than Ge because as we trace the path between K and Ge on the periodic table, we move to the right within the same period. Metallic character decreases as you move to the right.

(c)   Ge or Sb   Based on periodic trends alone, we cannot tell which is more metallic because as we trace the path between Ge and Sb, we move to the right across a period (metallic character decreases) and then down a column (metallic character increases). These effects tend to oppose each other, and it is not easy to tell which will predominate.

(d)   As or Sn   Sn is more metallic than As because as we trace the path between As and Sn on the periodic table, we move down a column (metallic character increases) and then to the left across a period (metallic character increases). These effects add together for an overall increase.

8.43   The order of increasing metallic character is S < Se < Sb < In < Ba < Fr. Metallic character decreases as you move left to right across a period and decreases as you move up a column; therefore, the element with the least metallic character will be to the top right of the periodic table. So of these elements, S has the least metallic character. As you move down the column, the next element is Se. As you continue down and to the right, you reach Sb; continuing to the right, you reach In; moving down the column and to the right, you come to Ba; and down the column and to the right is Fr.

8.44   The order of decreasing metallic character is Sr > Ga > Al > Si > P > N. Metallic character decreases as you move left to right across a period and decreases as you move up a column; therefore, the element with the greatest metallic character will be at the bottom left of the periodic table. So of these elements, Sr has the most metallic character. As you trace up the column and then to the right across the period, the next element is Ga; trace up the column to Al, then to the right to Si and P; finally, trace up the column to N.

Cumulative Problems

8.45   Br: $1s^2 2s^2 2p^6 3s^2 3p^6 4s^2 3d^{10} 4p^5$
        Kr: $1s^2 2s^2 2p^6 3s^2 3p^6 4s^2 3d^{10} 4p^6$
        Krypton has a completely filled p sublevel, giving it chemical stability. Bromine needs one electron to achieve a completely filled p sublevel and thus has a highly negative electron affinity. Therefore, it easily takes on an electron and is reduced to the bromide ion, giving it the added stability of the filled p sublevel.

8.46   K: $1s^2 2s^2 2p^6 3s^2 3p^6 4s^1$
        Ar: $1s^2 2s^2 2p^6 3s^2 3p^6$
        Argon has a completely filled p sublevel, giving it chemical stability. Potassium has one electron in the $4s$ sublevel and can easily lose this electron, so it has a low first ionization energy. Therefore, it loses the $4s$ electron to achieve an argon electron configuration, giving it the added stability of the filled p sublevel.

8.47   Write the electron configuration of vanadium.
        V: $[\text{Ar}]\, 4s^2 3d^3$
        Because this ion has a 3+ charge, remove three electrons to write the electron configuration of the ion. Because it is a transition metal, remove the electrons from the $4s$ orbital before removing electrons from the $3d$ orbitals.
        V^{3+}: $[\text{Ar}]\, 4s^0 3d^2$
        Both vanadium and the V^{3+} ion have unpaired electrons and are paramagnetic.

8.48   Begin by writing the electron configuration of the neutral atom. Remember, Cu is one of our exceptions.
        Cu: $[\text{Ar}]\, 4s^1 3d^{10}$
        Because this ion has a 1+ charge, remove one electron to write the electron configuration of the ion. Because it is a transition metal, remove the electrons from the $4s$ orbital before removing electrons from the $3d$ orbitals.
        Cu^+: $[\text{Ar}]\, 4s^0 3d^{10}$
        Cu contains one unpaired electron in the $4s$ orbital and is paramagnetic; Cu^+ has all paired electrons in the $3d$ orbitals and is diamagnetic.

8.49   Because K^+ has a 1+ charge, you would need a cation with a similar size and a 1+ charge. Looking at the ions in the same family, Na^+ would be too small and Rb^+ would be too large. If we consider Ar^+ and Ca^+, we would have ions of similar size and charge. Between these two, Ca^+ would be easier to achieve because the first ionization energy of Ca is similar to that of K, while the first ionization energy of Ar is much larger. However, the second ionization energy of Ca is relatively low, making it easy to lose the second electron.

8.50   Because Na^+ has a 1+ charge, you would need a cation with a similar size and a 1+ charge. Looking at the ions in the same family, Li^+ would be too small and K^+ would be too large. If we consider Ne^+ and Mg^+, we would have ions of similar size and charge. Between these two, Mg^+ would be easier to achieve because the first ionization energy of Mg is similar to that of Na, while the first ionization energy of Ne is much larger. However, the second ionization energy of Mg is relatively low, making it easy to lose the second electron.

8.51   C has an outer shell electron configuration of $ns^2 np^2$; based on this, you would expect Si and Ge, which are in the same family, to be most like carbon. Ionization energies for both Si and Ge are similar and tend to be slightly lower than that of C, but all are intermediate in the range of first ionization energies. The electron affinities of Si and Ge are close to the electron affinity of C.

8.52   (a)   Si and Ga   Ga would be larger than Si because as you trace from Si to Ga on the periodic table, you move down a column (radius increases) and then to the left across the period (radius increases). The sum of these two trends would give you a larger radius for Ga.

        (b)   Si and Ge   Ge would be larger than Si because as you trace from Si to Ge on the periodic table, you move down a column and the radius increases.

        (c)   Si and As   As would be most similar to Si in atomic radius because as you trace from Si to As on the periodic table, you move down the column (radius increase) and then to the right across the period (radius decreases). The sum of these two trends would make As smaller than Ga and Ge and thus closer to the radius of Si.

8.53   (a)   N: [He] $2s^2 2p^3$ Mg: [Ne] $3s^2$ O: [He] $2s^2 2p^4$
               F: [He] $2s^2 2p^5$ Al: [Ne] $3s^2 3p^1$

        (b)   Mg > Al > N > O > F

        (c)   Al < Mg < O < N < F (from the table)

        (d)   Mg and Al would have the largest radius because they are in period $n = 3$; Al is smaller than Mg because radius decreases as you move to the right across the period. F is smaller than O and O is smaller than N because as you move to the right across the period, radius decreases.

               The first ionization energy of Al is smaller than the first ionization energy of Mg because Al loses the electron from the $3p$ orbital, which is shielded by the electrons in the $3s$ orbital. Mg loses the electron from the filled $3s$ orbital, which has added stability because it is a filled orbital. The first ionization energy of O is lower than the first ionization energy of N because N has a half-filled $2p$ orbitals, which adds extra stability, thus making it harder to remove the electron. The fourth electron in the O $2p$ orbitals experiences added electron–electron repulsion because it must pair with another electron in the same $2p$ orbital, thus making it easier to remove.

8.54   (a)   P: [Ne] $3s^2 3p^3$ Ca: [Ar] $4s^2$ Si: [Ne] $3s^2 3p^2$
               S: [Ne] $3s^2 3p^4$ Ga: [Ar] $4s^2 3d^{10} 4p^1$

        (b)   Ca > Ga > Si > P > S

        (c)   Ga < Ca < Si < S < P (from table)

        (d)   Ca and Ga would have the largest radius because they are in period $n = 4$; Ga is smaller than Ca because radius increases as you move to the left across the period. S is smaller than P and P is smaller than Si because as you move to the right across the period, radius decreases.

               The first ionization energy of Ga is smaller than the first ionization energy of Ca because Ga loses the electron from the $4p$ orbital, which is shielded by the electrons in the $4s$ orbital. Ca loses the electron from the filled $4s$ orbital, which has added stability because it is a filled orbital. The first ionization energy of S is lower than the first ionization energy of P because P has a half-filled $3p$ orbital, which adds extra stability, thus making it harder to remove the electron. The fourth electron in the S $3p$ orbitals experiences added electron–electron repulsion because it must pair with another electron in the same $3p$ orbital, thus making it easier to remove.

8.55   As you move to the right across a row in the periodic table for the main-group elements, the effective nuclear charge (Z_{eff}) experienced by the electrons in the outermost principal energy level increases, resulting in a stronger attraction between the outermost electrons and the nucleus and therefore a smaller atomic radii.

        Across the row of transition elements, the number of electrons in the outermost principal energy level (highest n value) is nearly constant. As another proton is added to the nucleus with each successive element, another electron is added, but that electron goes into an $n_{highest} - 1$ orbital (a core level). The number of outermost electrons stays constant, and they experience a roughly constant effective nuclear charge, keeping the radius approximately constant after the first couple of elements in the series.

8.56   Across the row of transition elements, the number of electrons in the outermost principal energy level (highest n value) is nearly constant. As another proton is added to the nucleus with each successive element, another electron is added, but the electron goes into an $n_{highest} - 1$ orbital. So even though the atomic number of Cu is higher than that of V, the outermost electron experiences roughly the same effective nuclear charge; thus, the radii of the two elements are nearly the same. Because the radii of the two elements are nearly the same, the volume occupied by the element will be nearly the same. Because the mass increases as the atomic number increases, the mass of Cu is greater than the mass of V; density is mass/volume, so the density of Cu should be greater than the density of V. We find that the densities are Cu = 8.96 g/cm^3 and V = 6.11 g/cm^3, and our prediction was correct.

8.57   All of the noble gases have a filled outer quantum level, very high first ionization energies, and positive values for the electron affinity; thus, the noble gases are particularly unreactive. The lighter noble gases will not form any compounds because the ionization energies of both He and Ne are over 2000 kJ/mol. Because ionization energy decreases as you move down a column, you find that the heavier noble gases (Ar, Kr, and Xe) do form some compounds. They have ionization energies that are close to the ionization energy of H and can thus be forced to lose an electron.

8.58   All of the halogens will add an electron to achieve the stability of the noble gas configuration; thus, they are all powerful oxidizing agents (they are reduced). F would be the strongest because it adds the electron to the $n = 2$ level, achieving the electron configuration of Ne. Because the $n = 2$ level lies lower in energy than the outermost level of the other halogens, it is more energetically favorable for F to gain the noble gas configuration than for the other halogens. This, combined with the high ionization energy and relatively exothermic electron affinity, makes F very reactive. As you move down the column, the n level of the outermost electrons increases, making it less energetically favorable for each of the successive halogens to gain an electron.

8.59   Group 6A: ns^2np^4 Group 7A: ns^2np^5
The electron affinity of the group 7A elements is more negative than that of the group 6A elements in the same period because group 7A requires only one electron to achieve the noble gas configuration ns^2np^6, while the group 6A elements require two electrons. Adding one electron to the group 6A element will not give them any added stability and leads to extra electron–electron repulsions, so the value of the electron affinity is less negative than that for group 7A.

8.60   Group 5A: ns^2np^3 Group 4A: ns^2np^2
The electron affinity of the group 5A elements is more positive than that of the group 4A elements in the same period because group 5A has a half-filled p sublevel. Adding an electron to this group adds a fourth electron to the p sublevel and increases the electron–electron repulsions. It also eliminates the stability of the half-filled sublevel. Adding an electron to a group 4A element, however, adds a third electron to the p sublevel, giving it the added stability of the half-filled sublevel.

8.61 $35 = Br = [Ar]\,4s^23d^{10}4p^5$ $53 = I = [Kr]\,5s^24d^{10}5p^5$
Br and I are both halogens with an outermost electron configuration of ns^2np^5; the next element with the same outermost electron configuration is 85, At.

8.62   Begin by writing the electron configuration of the neutral atom. $S = 1s^22s^22p^63s^23p^4$

S^+ loses one electron: $1s^22s^22p^63s^23p^3$

S^{2+} loses two electrons: $1s^22s^22p^63s^23p^2$

S^{3+} loses three electrons: $1s^22s^22p^63s^23p^1$

S^{4+} loses four electrons: $1s^22s^22p^63s^23p^0$

S^{5+} loses five electrons: $1s^22s^22p^63s^13p^0$

S^{6+} loses six electrons: $1s^22s^22p^63s^03p^0$

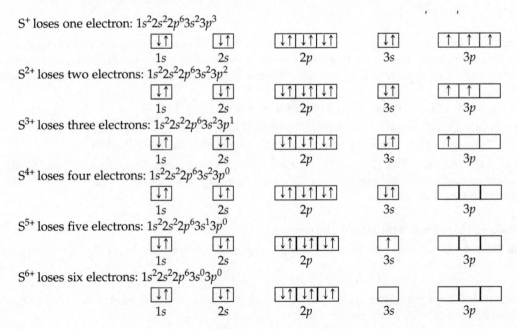

8.63   **Given:** $r = 100.00$ pm, $q_{proton} = 1.60218 \times 10^{-19}$ C, and $q_{electron} = -1.60218 \times 10^{-19}$ C

Find: IE in kJ/mol and λ of ionization

Conceptual Plan: $r, q_{proton}, q_{electron}, \rightarrow E_{atom} \rightarrow E_{mol}$ and then $E_{atom} \rightarrow \lambda$

$$E = \frac{1}{4\pi\varepsilon_0} \frac{q_p q_e}{r} \qquad \frac{1000 \text{ J}}{1 \text{kJ}} \qquad \frac{6.022 \times 10^{23} \text{ atom}}{1 \text{mol}} \qquad\qquad \lambda = \frac{hc}{E}$$

Solution:

$$E = \frac{1}{(4)(3.141)\left(8.85 \times 10^{-12} \frac{C^2}{J \cdot m}\right)} \times \frac{(1.60218 \times 10^{-19} \text{ C})(-1.60218 \times 10^{-19} \text{ C})}{(100.00 \text{ pm})\left(\frac{1 \text{ m}}{1 \times 10^{12} \text{ pm}}\right)} = -2.3086 \times 10^{-18} \text{ J/atom}$$

$$-2.3086 \times 10^{-18} \text{ J/atom} \times \frac{6.022 \times 10^{23} \text{ atom}}{1 \text{ mol}} \times \frac{1 \text{ kJ}}{(1000 \text{ J})} = -1.39 \times 10^3 \text{ kJ/mol}$$

IE $= 0 - (-1.39 \times 10^3 \text{ kJ/mol}) = 1.39 \times 10^3 \text{ kJ/mol}$

$$\lambda = \frac{(6.626 \times 10^{-34} \text{ J} \cdot \text{s})(3.00 \times 10^8 \text{ m/s})\left(\frac{1 \times 10^9 \text{ nm}}{1 \text{m}}\right)}{(2.3086 \times 10^{-18} \text{ J})} = 86.1 \text{ nm}$$

Check: The units of the answer (kJ/mol) are correct. The magnitude of the answer is reasonable because the value is positive and energy must be added to the atom to remove the electron. The units of the wavelength (nm) are correct, and the magnitude is reasonable based on the ionization energy.

8.64   **Given:** IE $= 496$ kJ/mol, $q_{proton} = 1.60218 \times 10^{-19}$ C, and $q_{electron} = -1.60218 \times 10^{-19}$ C   **Find:** r

Conceptual Plan: kJ/mol $\rightarrow$ J/mol $\rightarrow$ J/atom $\rightarrow$ r

$$\frac{1000 \text{ J}}{1 \text{ kJ}} \qquad \frac{1 \text{ mol}}{6.022 \times 10^{23} \text{ atom}} \qquad r = \frac{1}{4\pi\varepsilon_0} \frac{q_p q_e}{E}$$

Solution: E $= -$IE $= -496$ kJ/mol

$$-496 \frac{\text{kJ}}{\text{mol}} \times \frac{1000 \text{ J}}{1 \text{kJ}} \times \frac{1 \text{ mol}}{6.022 \times 10^{23} \text{ atoms}} = -8.236 \times 10^{-19} \text{ J/atom}$$

$$r = \frac{1}{(4)(3.141)\left(8.85 \times 10^{-12} \frac{C^2}{J \cdot m}\right)\left(\frac{1 \text{ m}}{1 \times 10^{12} \text{ pm}}\right)} \times \frac{(1.60218 \times 10^{-19} \text{ C})(-1.60218 \times 10^{-19} \text{ C})}{(-8.236 \times 10^{-19} \text{ J})} = 280. \text{ pm}$$

The actual atomic radius of sodium is 186 pm. The $3s^1$ electron that is being removed is shielded from the nuclear charge by the core electrons. Thus, the energy of the electron in the $3s$ orbital is less negative than what would be expected for an electron at a distance of 186 pm. Because the energy is less negative, the ionization energy is smaller.

8.65   **Given:** Ra, $Z = 88$ **Find:** Z for next two alkaline earth metals

Solution: The next element would lie in period 8, column 2A. The largest currently known element is 116 in period 7, column 6A. To reach period 8, column 2A, you need to add 4 protons and would have $Z = 120$.

The alkaline earth metal following 120 would lie in period 9, column 2A. To reach this column, you need to add 10 d block element protons, 14 f block element protons, 18 g block element protons, 6 p block element protons, and 2 s block element protons. This would give $Z = 170$.

8.66   **Given:** Element 165   **Find:** What group would it be in?

Solution: Element 165 would have the electron configuration [Rn] $7s^2 6d^{10} 5f^{14} 7p^6 8s^2 7d^{10} 6f^{14} 5g^{18} 8p^3$. The element would be in the p block in column 15.

8.67   (a)   Because ionization energy increases as you move to the right across a period, the element with the highest first ionization energy would be the element farthest to the right, F.

(b)   Because the effective nuclear charge experienced by the outermost electrons increases as you move to the right across a period, which results in a smaller size, the element with the largest atomic radius is the element farthest to the left, B.

(c)   Because metallic character decreases as you move left to right across a period, the most metallic element will be the element farthest to the left, B.

(d)   In this series of elements we are filling the $2p$ orbitals, the element with three unpaired electrons will have an electron configuration of $1s^2 2s^2 2p^3$, N.

8.68   (a)   Because the second ionization energy is very high for elements with one valence electron, the element with the highest second ionization energy would be the element in group 1A, Na.

(b)   Because the effective nuclear charge experienced by the outermost electrons increases as you move to the right across a period, which results in a smaller size, the element with the smallest atomic radius is the element farthest to the right, P.

(c)   Because metallic character decreases as you move left to right across a period, the least metallic element will be the element farthest to the right, P.

(d)   Because an element is diamagnetic when all of the electrons are paired, we are looking for an element that has completely filled or completely empty subshells; Mg has an electron configuration of $1s^2 2s^2 2p^6 4s^2$.

Challenge Problems

8.69   (a)   Using Excel®, make a table of radius, atomic number, and density. Using xy scatter, make a chart of radius versus density. With an exponential trendline, estimate the density of argon and xenon. Also make a chart of atomic number versus density. With a linear trendline, estimate the density of argon and xenon.

Element	Atomic Radius (pm)	Atomic Number	Density g/L
He	32	2	0.18
Ne	70	10	0.90
Ar	98	18	
Kr	112	36	3.75
Xe	130	54	
Rn		86	9.73
		118	

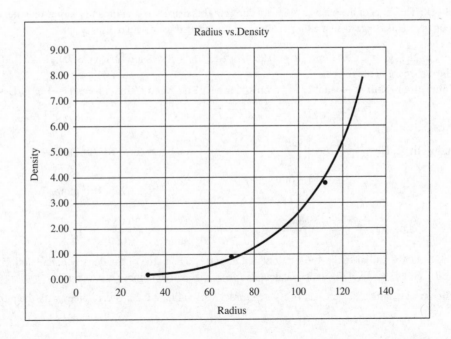

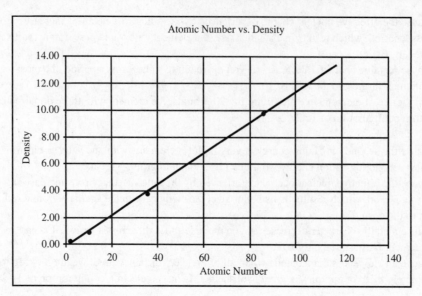

From the radius versus density chart, Ar has a density of ~2 g/L and Xe has a density of ~7.7 g/L. From the atomic number versus density chart, Ar has a density of ~1.8 g/L and Xe has a density of ~6 g/L.

(b)   Using the chart of atomic number versus density, element 118 would be predicted to have a density of ~13 g/L.

(c)   **Given:** Ne: $\mathcal{M} = 20.18$ g/mol; $r = 70$ pm   **Find:** mass of neon; d of neon in g/L
Conceptual Plan: $\mathcal{M} \rightarrow m_{\text{atom}}$ and then $r \rightarrow \text{vol}_{\text{atom}}$ and then $\rightarrow d$

$$\frac{1\ \text{mol}}{6.022 \times 10^{23}\ \text{atoms}} \qquad V = \frac{4}{3}\pi r^3 \qquad d = \frac{m}{V}$$

Solution: $\dfrac{20.18\ \text{g}}{1\ \text{mol}} \times \dfrac{1\ \text{mol}}{6.022 \times 10^{23}\ \text{atoms}} = 3.35 \times 10^{-23}$ g/atom

$$V = \frac{4}{3} \times 3.14 \times (70\ \text{pm})^3 \times \left(\frac{1\ \text{m}}{10^{12}\ \text{pm}}\right)^3 \times \frac{1\ \text{L}}{0.0010\ \text{m}^3} = 1.\underline{4}4 \times 10^{-27}\ \text{L}$$

$$d = \frac{3.35 \times 10^{-23}\ \text{g}}{1.44 \times 10^{-27}\ \text{L}} = 2.\underline{3}3 \times 10^4 = 2.3 \times 10^4\ \text{g/L}$$

Check: The units of the answer (g/L) are correct. This density is significantly larger than the actual density of neon gas. This suggests that a liter L of neon is composed primarily of empty space.

(d)   **Given:** Ne: $\mathcal{M} = 20.18$ g/mol, $d = 0.90$ g/L; Kr: $\mathcal{M} = 83.80$ g/mol, $d = 3.75$ g/L; Ar: $\mathcal{M} = 39.95$ g/mol
Find: d of argon in g/L
Conceptual Plan: $d \rightarrow$ mol/L $\rightarrow$ atoms/L for Kr and Ne and then atoms/L $\rightarrow$ mol/L $\rightarrow d$ for Ar

$$\text{mol} = \frac{\text{mass}}{\text{molar mass}} \quad \frac{6.022 \times 10^{23}\ \text{atoms}}{1\ \text{mol}} \qquad\qquad \frac{1\ \text{mol}}{6.022 \times 10^{23}\ \text{atoms}} \quad \frac{39.95\ \text{g}}{1\ \text{mol}}$$

Solution: for Ne: $\dfrac{0.90\ \text{g}}{\text{L}} \times \dfrac{1\ \text{mol}}{20.18\ \text{g}} \times \dfrac{6.022 \times 10^{23}\ \text{atoms}}{1\ \text{mol}} = 2.69 \times 10^{22}$ atoms/L

for Kr: $\dfrac{3.75\ \text{g}}{\text{L}} \times \dfrac{1\ \text{mol}}{83.80\ \text{g}} \times \dfrac{6.022 \times 10^{23}\ \text{atoms}}{1\ \text{mol}} = 2.69 \times 10^{22}$ atoms/L

for Ar: $\dfrac{2.69 \times 10^{22}\ \text{atoms}}{\text{L}} \times \dfrac{1\ \text{mol}}{6.022 \times 10^{23}\ \text{atoms}} \times \dfrac{39.95\ \text{g}}{1\ \text{mol}} = 1.78$ g/L

This value is similar to the value calculated in part a. The value of the density calculated from the radius was 2 g/L, and the value of the density calculated from the atomic number was 1.8 g/L.

Check: The units of the answer (g/L) are correct. The value of the answer agrees with the published value.

8.70   If there were only two *p* orbitals, there would only be four *p* block columns, and if there were only three *d* orbitals, there would be only six *d* block columns. So the periodic table would have 12 columns.

H											He
Li	Be							B	C	N	O
F	Ne							Na	Mg	Al	Si
P	S	Cl	Ar	K	Ca	Sc	Ti	V	Cr	Mn	Fe

The noble gas equivalent elements would be He, O, Si, and Fe.
The halogen equivalent elements would be N, Al, and Mn.
The alkali metal equivalent elements would be Li, F, and P.

8.71   The density increases as you move to the right across the first transition series. For the first transition series, the mass increases as you move to the right across the periodic table. However, the radius of the transition series elements stays nearly constant as you move to the right across the periodic table; thus, the volume will remain nearly constant. Because density is mass/volume, the density of the elements increases.

8.72   If there are three possible spin quantum numbers, there will be 3*s* electrons, 9*p* electrons, and 15*d* electrons.
   (a)   Ne(10 e): $1s^3 2s^3 2p^4$
   (b)   Completed $n = 2$ level: $1s^3 2s^3 2p^9$ Atomic number $= 15$
   (c)   F(9 e): $1s^3 2s^3 2p^3$ There will be one unpaired electron in the 1*s* and 2*s* and three unpaired electrons in the 2*p*; therefore, there are five unpaired electrons.

8.73   The longest wavelength would be associated with the lowest energy state next to the ground state of carbon, which has two unpaired electrons. Ground state of carbon:

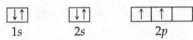

Longest wavelength: One of the *p* electrons flipped in its orbital, which requires the least amount of energy.

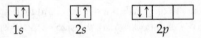

The next wavelength would be associated with the pairing of the two *p* electrons in the same orbital because this requires energy and raises the energy.

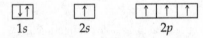

The next wavelength would be associated with the energy needed to promote one of the *s* electrons to a *p* orbital.

8.74   Element darmstadtium (110) would be in the column with Ni, Pd, and Pt; so it might be expected to have an electron configuration similar to that of Ni, Pd, or Pt.
Similar to Ni: [Rn] $7s^2 5f^{14} 6d^8$
Similar to Pd: [Rn] $7s^0 5f^{14} 6d^{10}$
Similar to Pt: [Rn] $7s^1 5f^{14} 6d^9$

8.75   The element that would fill the 8*s* and 8*p* orbitals would have atomic number 168. The element is in the noble gas family and would have the properties of noble gases. It would have the electron configuration of [118] $8s^2 5g^{18} 6f^{14} 7d^{10} 8p^6$. The outer shell electron (highest *n* level) configuration would be $8s^2 8p^6$. The element would be relatively inert, have a first ionization energy less than 1037 kJ/mol (the first ionization energy of Rn), and have a positive electron affinity. It would be difficult to form compounds with most elements but would be able to form compounds with fluorine.

8.76   To determine the second ionization energies, look at the electron configuration of the 1+ ions.

First, write the electron configuration of   Then write the electron configuration
the atom: of the 1+ ion:

Li $1s^2 2s^1$ Li^+ $1s^2 2s^0$
Be $1s^2 2s^2$ Be^+ $1s^2 2s^1$
B $1s^2 2s^2 2p^1$ B^+ $1s^2 2s^2$
C $1s^2 2s^2 2p^2$ C^+ $1s^2 2s^2 2p^1$
N $1s^2 2s^2 2p^3$ N^+ $1s^2 2s^2 2p^2$
O $1s^2 2s^2 2p^4$ O^+ $1s^2 2s^2 2p^3$
F $1s^2 2s^2 2p^5$ F^+ $1s^2 2s^2 2p^4$

Based on the electron configuration of the ions, Li^+ should have the highest second ionization energy because the removal of the second electron involves removing a core electron. The lowest second ionization energy should be Be^+ because removing the second electron takes you to the $1s^2$ (stable) configuration.

O would have the highest second ionization energy because the electron configuration of O^+ has a half-filled p orbital, which is particularly stable; therefore, it would require more energy to remove the second electron. N^+ would have the lowest second ionization energy because the size of N^+ would be larger than the radius of the F^+; so the attraction between the outer electron and the nucleus would be less in N^+ than in F^+, making it easier to remove the electron.

8.77   When you move down the column from Al to Ga, the size of the atom actually decreases because not much shielding is contributed by the $3d$ electrons in the Ga atom, while there is a large increase in the nuclear charge. Therefore, the effective nuclear charge is greater for Ga than for Al, so the ionization energy does not decrease. As you go from In to Tl, the ionization energy actually increases because the $4f$ electrons do not contribute to the shielding of the outermost electrons and there is a large increase in the effective nuclear charge.

8.78 ΔE for the reaction based on the ionization energy and the electron affinity $= +147$ kJ/mol
$Na(g) \rightarrow Na^+(g) + e^-$ IE $= +496$ kJ/mol
$Na(g) + e^- \rightarrow Cl^-(g)$ EA $= -349$ kJ/mol
$Na(g) + Cl(g) \rightarrow Na^+(g) + Cl^-(g)$ $\Delta E = +147$ kJ/mol

8.79   The second electron is added to an ion with a $1-$ charge, so a large repulsive force has to be overcome to add the second electron. Thus, it will require energy to add the second electron, and the second electron affinity will have a positive value.

8.80   The diagonal relationship between some elements could be explained because the atomic size of the atoms on the diagonal would be about the same. On the diagonal, the radius would increase as you go down the column but would decrease as you move to the right across the period. Also, the size of the ion formed would be about the same. Therefore, you might expect the elements to have similar behavior.

Conceptual Problems

8.81   If six electrons rather than eight electrons led to a stable configuration, the electron configuration of the stable configuration would be $ns^2 np^4$.
(a)   A noble gas would have the electron configuration $ns^2 np^4$. This could correspond to the O atom.
(b)   A reactive nonmetal would have one less electron than the stable configuration. This would have the electron configuration $ns^2 np^3$. This could correspond to the N atom.
(c)   A reactive metal would have one more electron than the stable configuration. This would have the electron configuration of ns^1. This could correspond to the Li atom.

8.82   Atom B would have the higher first ionization energy. Even though the effective nuclear charge is less, the outermost electron is closer to the nucleus and the potential energy becomes more negative with decreasing distance, making it harder to remove and requiring a larger ionization energy.

8.83   (a)   True: An electron in a $3s$ orbital is more shielded than an electron in a $2s$ orbital. This is true because there are more core electrons below a $3s$ orbital.

(b)　True:　An electron in a 3s orbital penetrates the region occupied by the core electrons more than electrons in a 3p orbital. Examine Figure 8.5 showing the radial distribution functions for the 3s, 3p, and 3d orbitals. You will see that the 3s electrons penetrate more deeply than the 3p electrons and more than the 3d electrons.

(c)　False:　An electron in an orbital that penetrates closer to the nucleus will experience *less* shielding than an electron in an orbital that does not penetrate as far.

(d)　True:　An electron in an orbital that penetrates close to the nucleus will tend to experience a higher effective nuclear charge than one that does not. Because the orbital penetrates closer to the nucleus, the electron will experience less shielding and therefore a higher effective nuclear charge.

8.84　　An electron in a 5p orbital could have any one of the following combinations of quantum numbers:
5,1,−1,+1/2　　　5,1,−1,−1/2　　　5,1,0,+1/2　　　5,1,0,−1/2　　　5,1,1,+1/2　　　5,1,1,−1/2
An electron in a 6d orbital could have any one of the following combinations of quantum numbers:
6,2,−2,+1/2　　　6,2,−2,−1/2　　　6,2,−1,+1/2　　　6,2,−1,−1/2　　　6,2,0,+1/2　　　6,2,0,−1/2
6,2,1,+1/2　　　6,2,1,−1/2　　　6,2,2,+1/2　　　6,2,2,−1/2

8.85　　The 4s electrons in calcium have relatively low ionization energies (IE_1 = 590 kJ/mol; IE_2 = 1145 kJ/mol) because they are valence electrons. The energetic cost for calcium to lose a third electron is extraordinarily high because the next electron to be lost is a core electron. Similarly, the electron affinity of fluorine to gain one electron (−328 kJ/mol) is highly exothermic because the added electron completes fluoride's valence shell. The gain of a second electron by the negatively charged fluoride anion would not be favorable. Therefore, we would expect calcium and fluoride to combine in a 1:2 ratio.

Questions for Group Work

8.86　　Shielding or screening occurs when one electron is blocked from the full effects of the nuclear charge so that the electron experiences only a part of the nuclear charge. Penetration occurs when an electron penetrates the electron cloud of the 1s orbital and now experiences the full effect of the nuclear charge.

8.87　　The orbitals fill in order of increasing energy of the orbitals, which is 1s<2s<2p<3s<3p<4s<3d<4p<5s<4d< 5p<6s. Keep in mind that s subshells can contain two electrons, p subshells can contain six electrons, and d subshells can contain ten electrons.

8.88

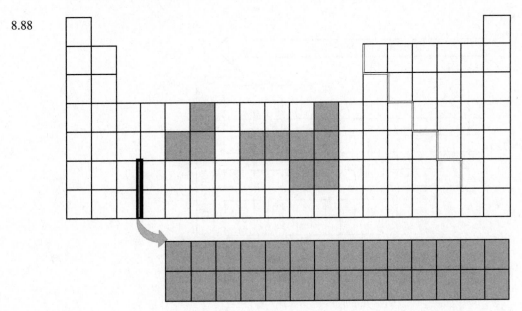

8.89   (a)   The Br^- and Se^{2-} ions are about the same size because the ions are an isoelectric pair.

(b)   The Br^- ion is smaller than the Se^{2-} ion because the Br^- ion has a larger nuclear charge and fewer extra electrons than the Se^{2-} ion.

(c)   The Fr^+ (194 pm) ion is the singly charged cation that is closest in size to the Br^- (195 pm) and Se^{2-} (198 pm) ions because cations are much smaller than their corresponding atoms.

8.90   The atomic radius decreases as you move to the right across a period in the periodic table, as the effective nuclear charge increases. The atomic radius increases as you move down a column in the periodic table, as larger and larger shells are filled with electrons.

The first ionization energy generally decreases as you move down a column in the periodic table because electrons in the outermost principal level become farther away from the positively charged nucleus and are therefore held less tightly. The first ionization energy generally increases as you move to the right across a period in the periodic table because electrons in the outermost principal energy level generally experience a greater effective nuclear charge.

The metallic character (how easy is it to move electrons) decreases as you move to the right across a period in the periodic table, as electrons are held tighter and tighter. The metallic character increases as you move down a column in the periodic table, as the valence electrons are at increasing distances from the nucleus.

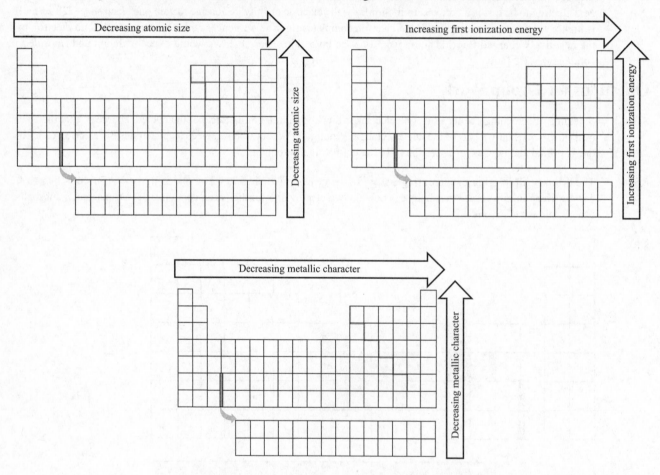

9 Chemical Bonding I: Lewis Theory

Problems by Topic

Valence Electrons and Dot Structures

9.1   N: $1s^2 2s^2 2p^3$ $\cdot \ddot{N} :$ The electrons included in the Lewis structure are $2s^2 2p^3$.

9.2   Ne: $1s^2 2s^2 2p^6$ $: \ddot{Ne} :$ The electrons included in the Lewis structure are $2s^2 2p^6$.

9.3   (a)   Al: $1s^2 2s^2 2p^6 3s^2 3p^1$

$\cdot \dot{Al} \cdot$

(b)   Na$^+$: $1s^2 2s^2 2p^6$

Na$^+$

(c)   Cl: $1s^2 2s^2 2p^6 3s^2 3p^5$

$: \ddot{Cl} \cdot$

(d)   Cl$^-$: $1s^2 2s^2 2p^6 3s^2 3p^6$

$\left[: \ddot{Cl} : \right]^-$

9.4   (a)   S^{2-}: $1s^2 2s^2 2p^6 3s^2 3p^6$

$\left[: \ddot{S} : \right]^{2-}$

(b)   Mg: $1s^2 2s^2 2p^6 3s^2$

$\cdot Mg \cdot$

(c)   Mg^{2+}: $1s^2 2s^2 2p^6$

Mg^{2+}

(d)   P: $1s^2 2s^2 2p^6 3s^2 3p^3$

$\cdot \ddot{P} \cdot$

Ionic Lewis Symbols and Lattice Energy

9.5   (a)   NaF: Draw the Lewis symbols for Na and F based on their valence electrons.
Na: $3s^1$ F: $2s^2 2p^5$

Na$\cdot$ $: \ddot{F} \cdot$

Sodium must lose one electron and be left with the octet from the previous shell, while fluorine needs to gain one electron to get an octet.

Na$^+$ $\left[: \ddot{F} : \right]^-$

(b)   CaO: Draw the Lewis symbols for Ca and O based on their valence electrons.
Ca: $4s^2$ O: $2s^2 2p^4$

$\cdot Ca \cdot$ $: \ddot{O} \cdot$

Calcium must lose two electrons and be left with the octet from the previous shell, while oxygen needs to gain two electrons to get an octet.

$$\text{Ca}^{2+} \quad \left[:\ddot{\text{O}}: \right]^{2-}$$

(c) $SrBr_2$: Draw the Lewis symbols for Sr and Br based on their valence electrons. Sr: $5s^2$ Br: $4s^24p^5$

·Sr·   :B̈r·

Strontium must lose two electrons and be left with the octet from the previous shell, while bromine needs to gain one electron to get an octet.

$$\text{Sr}^{2+} \ 2\left[:\ddot{\text{B}}\text{r}: \right]^{-}$$

(d) K_2O: Draw the Lewis symbols for K and O based on their valence electrons. K: $4s^1$ O: $2s^22p^4$

K·   :Ö·

Potassium must lose one electron and be left with the octet from the previous shell, while oxygen needs to gain two electrons to get an octet.

$$2\text{K}^{+} \quad \left[:\ddot{\text{O}}: \right]^{2-}$$

9.6 (a) SrO: Draw the Lewis symbols for Sr and O based on their valence electrons. Sr: $5s^2$ O: $2s^22p^4$

·Sr·   :Ö·

Strontium must lose two electrons and be left with the octet from the previous shell, while oxygen needs to gain two electrons to get an octet.

$$\text{Sr}^{2+} \quad \left[:\ddot{\text{O}}: \right]^{2-}$$

(b) Li_2S: Draw the Lewis symbols for Li and S based on their valence electrons. Li: $2s^1$ S: $3s^23p^4$

Li·   :S̈·

Lithium must lose one electron and be left with two $1s$ electrons from the previous shell, while sulfur needs to gain two electrons to get an octet.

$$2\,\text{Li}^{+} \quad \left[:\ddot{\text{S}}: \right]^{2-}$$

(c) CaI_2: Draw the Lewis symbols for Ca and I based on their valence electrons. Ca: $4s^2$ I: $5s^25p^5$

·Ca·   :Ï·

Calcium must lose two electrons and be left with the octet from the previous shell, while iodine needs to gain one electron to get an octet.

$$\text{Ca}^{2+} \quad 2\left[:\ddot{\text{I}}: \right]^{-}$$

(d) RbF: Draw the Lewis symbols for Rb and F based on their valence electrons. Rb: $5s^1$ F: $2s^22p^5$

Rb·   :F̈·

Rubidium must lose one electron and be left with the octet from the previous shell, while fluorine needs to gain one electron to get an octet.

$$\text{Rb}^{+} \quad \left[:\ddot{\text{F}}: \right]^{-}$$

9.7 (a) Sr and Se: Draw the Lewis symbols for Sr and Se based on their valence electrons.

Sr: $5s^2$ Se: $4s^24p^4$

·Sr·   :S̈e·

Strontium must lose two electrons and be left with the octet from the previous shell, while selenium needs to gain two electrons to get an octet.

$$\text{Sr}^{2+} \quad \left[:\ddot{\text{S}}\text{e}: \right]^{2-}$$

Thus, we need one Sr^{2+} and one Se^{2-}. Write the formula with subscripts (if necessary) to indicate the number of atoms.

SrSe

(b)   Ba and Cl: Draw the Lewis symbols for Ba and Cl based on their valence electrons.

Ba: $6s^2$ Cl: $3s^23p^5$

·Ba·   :C̈l·

Barium must lose two electrons and be left with the octet from the previous shell, while chlorine needs to gain one electron to get an octet.

$$Ba^{2+}\quad 2\left[:\ddot{\underset{..}{C}}l:\right]^-$$

Thus, we need one Ba^{2+} and two Cl^-. Write the formula with subscripts (if necessary) to indicate the number of atoms.

$BaCl_2$

(c)   Na and S: Draw the Lewis symbols for Na and S based on their valence electrons.

Na:$3s^1$ S:$3s^23p^4$

Na·   :S̈·

Sodium must lose one electron and be left with the octet from the previous shell, while sulfur needs to gain two electrons to get an octet.

$$2\,Na^+\quad \left[:\ddot{\underset{..}{S}}:\right]^{2-}$$

Thus, we need two Na^+ and one S^{2-}. Write the formula with subscripts (if necessary) to indicate the number of atoms.

Na_2S

(d)   Al and O: Draw the Lewis symbols for Al and O based on their valence electrons.

Al:$3s^23p^1$ O:$2s^22p^4$

·Al̇·   :Ö·

Aluminum must lose three electrons and be left with the octet from the previous shell, while oxygen needs to gain two electrons to get an octet.

$$2\,Al^{3+}\quad 3\left[:\ddot{\underset{..}{O}}:\right]^{2-}$$

Thus, we need two Al^{3+} and three O^{2-} to lose and gain the same number of electrons. Write the formula with subscripts (if necessary) to indicate the number of atoms.

Al_2O_3

9.8   (a)   Ca and N: Draw the Lewis symbols for Ca and N based on their valence electrons.

Ca:$4s^2$ N:$2s^22p^3$

·Ca·   ·N̈·

Calcium must lose two electrons and be left with the octet from the previous shell, while nitrogen needs to gain three electrons to get an octet.

$$3\,Ca^{2+}\quad 2\left[:\ddot{\underset{..}{N}}:\right]^{3-}$$

Thus, we need three Ca^{2+} and two N^{3-} to lose and gain the same number of electrons. Write the formula with subscripts (if necessary) to indicate the number of atoms.

Ca_3N_2

(b)   Mg and I: Draw the Lewis symbols for Mg and I based on their valence electrons.

Mg:$3s^2$ I:$5s^25p^5$

·Mg·   :Ï·

Magnesium must lose two electrons and be left with the octet from the previous shell, while iodine needs to gain one electron to get an octet.

$$Mg^{2+}\quad 2\left[:\ddot{\underset{..}{I}}:\right]^-$$

Thus, we need one Mg^{2+} and two I^-. Write the formula with subscripts (if necessary) to indicate the number of atoms.

MgI_2

(c)　Ca and S:　Draw the Lewis symbols for Ca and S based on their valence electrons.

$$Ca: 4s^2 \qquad S: 3s^2 3p^4$$

$$\cdot Ca \cdot \qquad :\ddot{S}\cdot$$

Calcium must lose two electrons and be left with the octet from the previous shell, while sulfur needs to gain two electrons to get an octet.

$$Ca^{2+} \qquad \left[:\ddot{\ddot{S}}: \right]^{2-}$$

Thus, we need one Ca^{2+} and one S^{2-}. Write the formula with subscripts (if necessary) to indicate the number of atoms.

CaS

(d)　Cs and F:　Draw the Lewis symbols for Cs and F based on their valence electrons.

$$Cs: 6s^1 \qquad F: 2s^2 2p^5$$

$$Cs \cdot \qquad :\ddot{F}\cdot$$

Cesium must lose one electron and be left with the octet from the previous shell, while fluorine needs to gain one electron to get an octet.

$$Cs^+ \qquad \left[:\ddot{\ddot{F}}: \right]^-$$

Thus, we need one Cs^+ and one F^-. Write the formula with subscripts (if necessary) to indicate the number of atoms.

CsF

9.9　As the size of the alkaline metal ions increases down the column, so does the distance between the metal cation and the oxide anion. Therefore, the magnitude of the lattice energy of the oxides decreases, making the formation of the oxides less exothermic and the compounds less stable. Because the ions cannot get as close to each other, they do not release as much energy.

9.10　Rubidium is below potassium on the periodic table, and iodine is below bromine on the periodic table. Therefore, both the rubidium ion and the iodide ion are larger than the potassium ion and the bromide ion. So the rubidium ion and the iodide ion cannot get as close to each other as the potassium ion and the bromide ion can; thus, the rubidium and iodide ions do not release as much energy, and the lattice energy of potassium bromide is more exothermic.

9.11　Cesium is slightly larger than barium, but oxygen is slightly larger than fluorine; so we cannot use size to explain the difference in the lattice energy. However, the charge on the cesium ion is 1+ and the charge on the fluoride ion is 1−, while the charge on the barium ion is 2+ and the charge on the oxide ion is 2−. The coulombic equation states that the magnitude of the potential also depends on the product of the charges. Because the product of the charges for CsF = 1− and the product of the charges for BaO = 4−, the stabilization for BaO relative to CsF should be about four times greater, which is what we see in its much more exothermic lattice energy.

9.12　RbBr < KCl < SrO < CaO. KCl and RbBr both have a product of the charges of 1−, while SrO and CaO have a product of the charges of 4−. So the lattice energies of KCl and RbBr are less than those of SrO and CaO. Within KCl and RbBr, the rubidium ion is larger than the potassium ion, and the bromide ion is larger than the chloride ion. Therefore, the rubidium ion and the bromide ion will be farther apart, leading to a smaller lattice energy. Between SrO and CaO, the strontium ion is larger than the calcium ion; so the strontium oxide will have a smaller (less negative) lattice energy.

Simple Covalent Lewis Structures, Electronegativity, and Bond Polarity

9.13　(a)　Hydrogen:　Write the Lewis symbol of each atom based on the number of valence electrons.

$$H \cdot \qquad \cdot H$$

When the two hydrogen atoms share their electrons, they each get a duet, which is a stable configuration for hydrogen.

$$H—H$$

(b)　The halogens:　Write the Lewis symbol of each atom based on the number of valence electrons.

$$:\ddot{X}\cdot \qquad \cdot\ddot{X}:$$

If the two halogens pair together, each can achieve an octet, which is a stable configuration. So the halogens are predicted to exist as diatomic molecules.

$$:\ddot{\ddot{X}}-\ddot{\ddot{X}}:$$

(c)   Oxygen: Write the Lewis symbol of each atom based on the number of valence electrons.

$$:\ddot{O}\cdot \quad \cdot\ddot{O}:$$

To achieve a stable octet on each oxygen, the oxygen atoms will need to share two electron pairs. So oxygen is predicted to exist as a diatomic molecule with a double bond.

$$:\ddot{O}=\ddot{O}:$$

(d)   Nitrogen: Write the Lewis symbol of each atom based on the number of valence electrons.

$$\cdot\ddot{N}\cdot \quad \cdot\ddot{N}\cdot$$

To achieve a stable octet on each nitrogen, the nitrogen atoms will need to share three electron pairs. So nitrogen is predicted to exist as a diatomic molecule with a triple bond.

$$\ddot{N}\equiv\ddot{N}$$

9.14   Write the Lewis symbol for N and H based on the number of valence electrons.

$$\cdot\ddot{N}\cdot \quad \cdot H$$

$$H-\underset{\underset{H}{|}}{\overset{..}{N}}-H$$

$$\underset{\underset{H}{|}}{\cdot\ddot{N}}-H$$

$$H-\underset{\underset{H}{|}}{\overset{\overset{H}{|}}{\cdot N}}-H$$

If nitrogen combines with three hydrogen atoms, the nitrogen will achieve a stable octet and each hydrogen will have a duet of electrons. This is a stable configuration. If the nitrogen were to combine with only two hydrogen atoms, the nitrogen could only achieve a seven electron configuration, which is not stable. Also, if the nitrogen were to combine with four hydrogen atoms, the nitrogen would have a nine electron configuration, which is not stable. So Lewis theory predicts that nitrogen will combine with three hydrogen atoms.

9.15   (a) PH_3:   Write the Lewis symbol for each atom based on the number of valence electrons.

$$\cdot\ddot{P}\cdot \quad \cdot H$$

Phosphorus will share an electron pair with each hydrogen to achieve a stable octet.

$$H-\underset{\underset{H}{|}}{\overset{..}{P}}-H$$

(b) SCl_2:   Write the Lewis symbol for each atom based on the number of valence electrons.

$$:\ddot{S}\cdot \quad :\ddot{Cl}\cdot$$

The sulfur will share an electron pair with each chlorine to achieve a stable octet.

$$:\underset{\underset{:\ddot{Cl}:}{|}}{\ddot{S}}-\ddot{Cl}:$$

(c)   HI: Write the Lewis symbol for each atom based on the number of valence electrons.

$$H\cdot \quad \cdot\ddot{I}:$$

The iodine will share an electron pair with hydrogen to achieve a stable octet.

$$H-\ddot{I}:$$

(d)   CH₄: Write the Lewis symbol for each atom based on the number of valence electrons.

·Ċ·   H·

The carbon will share an electron pair with each hydrogen to achieve a stable octet.

$$
\begin{array}{c}
\text{H} \\
| \\
\text{H}\!-\!\text{C}\!-\!\text{H} \\
| \\
\text{H}
\end{array}
$$

9.16   (a)   NF₃: Write the Lewis symbol for each atom based on the number of valence electrons.

·N̈·   ·F̈:

The nitrogen will share an electron pair with each fluorine to achieve a stable octet.

$$
\begin{array}{c}
:\!\ddot{\text{F}}\!-\!\ddot{\text{N}}\!-\!\ddot{\text{F}}\!: \\
| \\
:\!\ddot{\text{F}}\!:
\end{array}
$$

(b)   HBr: Write the Lewis symbol for each atom based on the number of valence electrons.

H·   ·B̈r:

The bromine will share an electron pair with hydrogen to achieve a stable octet.

H—B̈r:

(c)   SBr₂: Write the Lewis symbol for each atom based on the number of valence electrons.

:S̈·   :B̈r·

The sulfur will share an electron pair with each bromine to achieve a stable octet.

$$
\begin{array}{c}
:\!\ddot{\text{S}}\!-\!\ddot{\text{B}}\text{r}\!: \\
| \\
:\!\ddot{\text{B}}\text{r}\!:
\end{array}
$$

(d)   CCl₄: Write the Lewis symbol for each atom based on the number of valence electrons.

·Ċ·   :C̈l·

The carbon will share an electron pair with each chlorine to achieve a stable octet.

$$
\begin{array}{c}
:\!\ddot{\text{C}}\text{l}\!: \\
| \\
:\!\ddot{\text{C}}\text{l}\!-\!\text{C}\!-\!\ddot{\text{C}}\text{l}\!: \\
| \\
:\!\ddot{\text{C}}\text{l}\!:
\end{array}
$$

9.17   (a)   Br and Br: pure covalent From Figure 9.7, we find that the electronegativity of Br is 2.8. Because both atoms are the same, the electronegativity difference (ΔEN) = 0, and using Table 9.1, we classify this bond as pure covalent.

(b)   C and Cl: polar covalent From Figure 9.7, we find that the electronegativity of C is 2.5 and Cl is 3.0. The electronegativity difference (ΔEN) is ΔEN = 3.0 − 2.5 = 0.5. Using Table 9.1, we classify this bond as polar covalent.

(c)   C and S: pure covalent From Figure 9.7, we find that the electronegativity of C is 2.5 and S is 2.5. The electronegativity difference (ΔEN) is ΔEN = 2.5 − 2.5 = 0. Using Table 9.1, we classify this bond as pure covalent.

(d)   Sr and O: ionic From Figure 9.7, we find that the electronegativity of Sr is 1.0 and O is 3.5. The electronegativity difference (ΔEN) is ΔEN = 3.5 − 1.0 = 2.5. Using Table 9.1, we classify this bond as ionic.

9.18   (a)   C and N: polar covalent From Figure 9.7, we find that the electronegativity of C is 2.5 and N is 3.0. The electronegativity difference (ΔEN) is ΔEN = 3.0 − 2.5 = 0.5. Using Table 9.1, we classify this bond as polar covalent.

(b)   N and S: polar covalent From Figure 9.7, we find that the electronegativity of S is 2.5 and N is 3.0. The electronegativity difference (ΔEN) is ΔEN = 3.0 − 2.5 = 0.5. Using Table 9.1, we classify this bond as polar covalent.

(c)   K and F: ionic From Figure 9.7, we find that the electronegativity of K is 0.8 and F is 4.0. The electronegativity difference (ΔEN) is ΔEN = 4.0 − 0.8 = 3.2. Using Table 9.1, we classify this bond as ionic.

(d)   N and N: pure covalent From Figure 9.7, we find that the electronegativity of N is 3.0. Because both atoms are the same, the electronegativity difference (ΔEN) = 0, and using Table 9.1, we classify this bond as pure covalent.

9.19   CO: Write the Lewis symbol for each atom based on the number of valence electrons.

·Ċ·   :Ö·

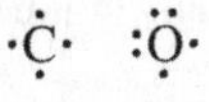

The carbon will share three electron pairs with oxygen to achieve a stable octet.

The oxygen atom is more electronegative than the carbon atom; so the oxygen will have a partial negative charge, and the carbon will have a partial positive charge.

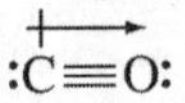

:C≡O:

To estimate the percent ionic character, determine the difference in electronegativity between carbon and oxygen. From Figure 9.7, we find that the electronegativity of C is 2.5 and O is 3.5. The electronegativity difference (ΔEN) is ΔEN = 3.5 − 2.5 = 1.0. From Figure 9.9, we can estimate a percent ionic character of 25%.

9.20   BrF: Write the Lewis symbol for each atom based on the number of valence electrons.

:B̈r·   ·F̈:

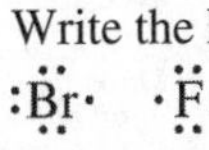

The bromine and fluorine will share an electron pair to achieve a stable octet.
The fluorine atom is more electronegative than the bromine atom; so the fluorine will have a partial negative charge, and the bromine will have a partial positive charge.

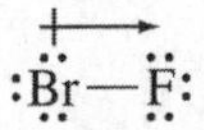

:B̈r—F̈:

To estimate the percent ionic character, determine the difference in electronegativity between bromine and fluorine. From Figure 9.7 we find that the electronegativity of Br = 2.8 and F = 4.0. The electronegativity difference (ΔEN) is ΔEN = 4.0 − 2.8 = 1.2. From Figure 9.9, we can estimate a percent ionic character of 30%.

Covalent Lewis Structures, Resonance, and Formal Charge

9.21   (a)   CI$_4$:   Write the correct skeletal structure for the molecule.

$$
\begin{array}{c}
I \\
| \\
I-C-I \\
| \\
I
\end{array}
$$

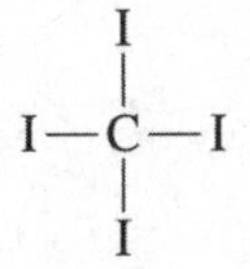

Calculate the total number of electrons for the Lewis structure by summing the number of valence electrons of each atom in the molecule.

(number of valence e⁻ for C) + 4(number of valence e⁻ for I) = 4 + 4(7) = 32

Distribute the electrons among the atoms, giving octets to as many atoms as possible. Begin with the bonding electrons; then proceed to lone pairs on terminal atoms and finally to lone pairs on the central atom.

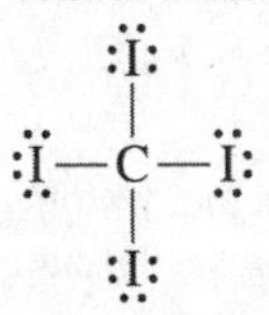

$$
\begin{array}{c}
:\ddot{I}: \\
| \\
:\ddot{I}-C-\ddot{I}: \\
| \\
:\ddot{I}:
\end{array}
$$

All 32 valence electrons are used.

If any atom lacks an octet, form double or triple bonds as necessary to give them octets. All atoms have octets; the structure is complete.

(b)   N$_2$O: Write the correct skeletal structure for the molecule.

N is less electronegative, so it is central.

N—N—O

Calculate the total number of electrons for the Lewis structure by summing the number of valence electrons of each atom in the molecule.

$$2(\text{number of valence e}^- \text{ for N}) + (\text{number of valence e}^- \text{ for O}) = 2(5) + 6 = 16$$

Distribute the electrons among the atoms, giving octets to as many atoms as possible. Begin with the bonding electrons; then proceed to lone pairs on terminal atoms and finally to lone pairs on the central atom.

$$:\ddot{N}—N—\ddot{O}:$$

All 16 valence electrons are used.

If any atom lacks an octet, form double or triple bonds as necessary.

$$:N≡N—\ddot{O}:$$

All atoms have octets; the structure is complete.

(c)   SiH$_4$:   Write the correct skeletal structure for the molecule.

H is always terminal, so Si is the central atom.

$$\begin{array}{c} H \\ | \\ H—Si—H \\ | \\ H \end{array}$$

Calculate the total number of electrons for the Lewis structure by summing the number of valence electrons of each atom in the molecule.

$$(\text{number of valence e}^- \text{ for Si}) + 4(\text{number of valence e}^- \text{ for H}) = 4 + 4(1) = 8$$

Distribute the electrons among the atoms, giving octets (or duets for H) to as many atoms as possible. Begin with the bonding electrons; then proceed to lone pairs on terminal atoms and finally to lone pairs on the central atom.

$$\begin{array}{c} H \\ | \\ H—Si—H \\ | \\ H \end{array}$$

All eight valence electrons are used.

If any atom lacks an octet, form double or triple bonds as necessary to give them octets. All atoms have octets; the structure is complete.

(d)   Cl$_2$CO: Write the correct skeletal structure for the molecule. C is least electronegative, so it is the central atom.

$$\begin{array}{c} O \\ | \\ Cl—C—Cl \end{array}$$

Calculate the total number of electrons for the Lewis structure by summing the number of valence electrons of each atom in the molecule.

$$(\text{number of valence e}^- \text{ for C}) + 2(\text{number of valence e}^- \text{ for Cl}) + (\text{number of valence e}^- \text{ for O})$$
$$= 4 + 2(7) + 6 = 24$$

Distribute the electrons among the atoms, giving octets to as many atoms as possible. Begin with the bonding electrons; then proceed to lone pairs on terminal atoms and finally to lone pairs on the central atom.

$$\begin{array}{c} :\ddot{O}: \\ | \\ :\ddot{C}l—C—\ddot{C}l: \end{array}$$

All 24 valence electrons are used.

If any atom lacks an octet, form double or triple bonds as necessary.

$$:\!\overset{\displaystyle :O:}{\underset{\displaystyle }{\overset{\displaystyle \|}{\!\!}}}$$

$$:\ddot{C}l\!-\!C\!-\!\ddot{C}l:$$

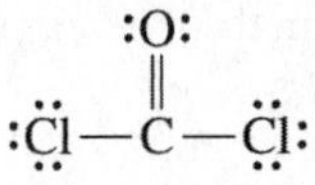

All atoms have octets; the structure is complete.

(e) H_3COH: Write the correct skeletal structure for the molecule. C is less electronegative, and H is terminal.

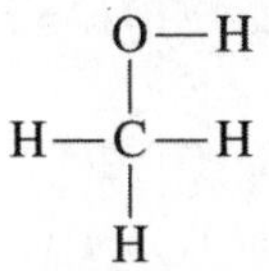

$$\begin{array}{c} O\!-\!H \\ | \\ H\!-\!C\!-\!H \\ | \\ H \end{array}$$

Calculate the total number of electrons for the Lewis structure by summing the number of valence electrons of each atom in the molecule.

(number of valence e^- for C) $+ 4$(number of valence e^- for H) $+$ (number of valence e^- for O)
$= 4 + 4(1) + 6 = 14$

Distribute the electrons among the atoms, giving octets (or duets for H) to as many atoms as possible. Begin with the bonding electrons; then proceed to lone pairs on terminal atoms and finally to lone pairs on the central atoms.

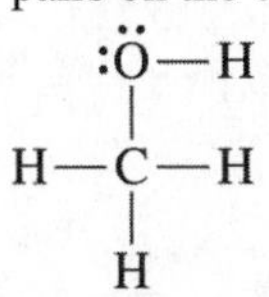

$$\begin{array}{c} :\ddot{O}\!-\!H \\ | \\ H\!-\!C\!-\!H \\ | \\ H \end{array}$$

All 14 valence electrons are used.

If any atom lacks an octet, form double or triple bonds as necessary to give them octets. All atoms have octets (duets for H); the structure is complete.

(f) OH^-:   Write the correct skeletal structure for the ion.

O—H

Calculate the total number of electrons for the Lewis structure by summing the number of valence electrons of each atom in the ion and adding 1 for the 1− charge.

(number of valence e^- for O) $+$ (number of valence e^- for H) $+ 1 = 6 + 1 + 1 = 8$

Distribute the electrons among the atoms, giving octets (or duets for H) to as many atoms as possible. Begin with the bonding electrons; then proceed to lone pairs on terminal atoms and finally to lone pairs on the central atom.

$:\ddot{O}\!-\!H$

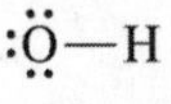

All eight valence electrons are used.

If any atom lacks an octet, form double or triple bonds as necessary to give them octets. Finally, write the Lewis structure in brackets with the charge of the ion in the upper right-hand corner.

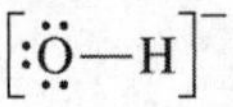

$$\left[:\ddot{O}\!-\!H\right]^-$$

(g) BrO^-:   Write the correct skeletal structure for the ion.

Br—O

Calculate the total number of electrons for the Lewis structure by summing the number of valence electrons of each atom in the ion and adding 1 for the 1− charge.

(number of valence e^- for O) $+$ (number of valence e^- for Br) $+ 1 = 6 + 7 + 1 = 14$

Distribute the electrons among the atoms, giving octets to as many atoms as possible. Begin with the bonding electrons; then proceed to lone pairs on terminal atoms and finally to lone pairs on the central atom.

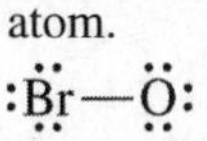

$:\ddot{B}r\!-\!\ddot{O}:$

All 14 valence electrons are used.

If any atom lacks an octet, form double or triple bonds as necessary to give them octets. Finally, write the Lewis structure in brackets with the charge of the ion in the upper right-hand corner.

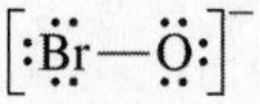

$$\left[:\ddot{Br}—\ddot{O}:\right]^{-}$$

9.22   (a) N_2H_2:   Write the correct skeletal structure for the molecule.

H—N—N—H

Calculate the total number of electrons for the Lewis structure by summing the number of valence electrons of each atom in the molecule.

2(number of valence e⁻ for N) + 2(number of valence e⁻ for H) = 2(5) + 2(1) = 12

Distribute the electrons among the atoms, giving octets (or duets for H) to as many atoms as possible. Begin with the bonding electrons; then proceed to lone pairs on terminal atoms and finally to lone pairs on the central atom.

H—$\ddot{N}$—$\ddot{N}$—H

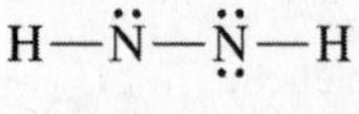

All 12 valence electrons are used.

If any atom lacks an octet, form double or triple bonds as necessary.

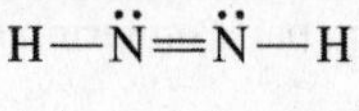

H—$\ddot{N}$=$\ddot{N}$—H

All atoms have octets (duets for H); the structure is complete.

   (b) N_2H_4:   Write the correct skeletal structure for the molecule.

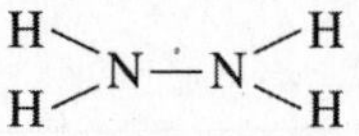

$$\begin{matrix} H\searrow & & \nearrow H \\ & N—N & \\ H\nearrow & & \searrow H \end{matrix}$$

Calculate the total number of electrons for the Lewis structure by summing the valence electrons of each atom in the molecule.

2(number of valence e⁻ for N) + 4(number of valence e⁻ for H) = 2(5) + 4(1) = 14

Distribute the electrons among the atoms, giving octets (or duets for H) to as many atoms as possible. Begin with the bonding electrons; then proceed to lone pairs on terminal atoms and finally to lone pairs on the central atom.

$$\begin{matrix} H\searrow & & \nearrow H \\ & \ddot{N}—\ddot{N} & \\ H\nearrow & & \searrow H \end{matrix}$$

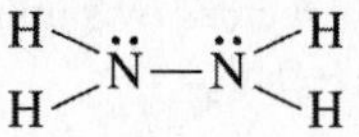

All 14 valence electrons are used.

If any atom lacks an octet, form double or triple bonds as necessary to give them octets.

All atoms have octets (duets for H); the structure is complete.

   (c) C_2H_2:   Write the correct skeletal structure for the molecule.

H—C—C—H

Calculate the total number of electrons for the Lewis structure by summing the number of valence electrons of each atom in the molecule.

2(number of valence e⁻ for C) + 2(number of valence e⁻ for H) = 2(4) + 2(1) = 10

Distribute the electrons among the atoms, giving octets (or duets for H) to as many atoms as possible. Begin with the bonding electrons; then proceed to lone pairs on terminal atoms and finally to lone pairs on the central atom.

H—C—$\ddot{C}$—H

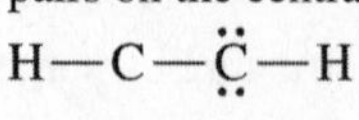

All ten valence electrons are used.

If any atom lacks an octet, form double or triple bonds as necessary.

H—C≡C—H

All atoms have octets (duets for H); the structure is complete.

(d) C_2H_4:   Write the correct skeletal structure for the molecule.

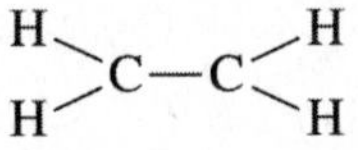

H\ ⟍   H
    C—C⟋
H⟋   ⟍H

Calculate the total number of electrons for the Lewis structure by summing the number of valence electrons of each atom in the molecule.

2(number of valence e⁻ for C) + 4(number of valence e⁻ for H) = 2(4) + 4(1) = 12

Distribute the electrons among the atoms, giving octets (or duets for H) to as many atoms as possible. Begin with the bonding electrons; then proceed to lone pairs on terminal atoms and finally to lone pairs on the central atom.

H\ ⟍ ..   H
    C—C⟋
H⟋   ⟍H

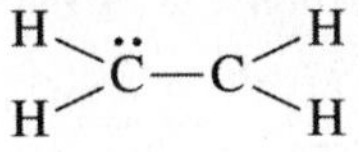

All 12 valence electrons are used.

If any atom lacks an octet, form double or triple bonds as necessary.

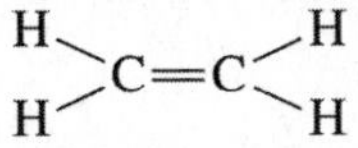

H\ ⟍   H
    C=C⟋
H⟋   ⟍H

All atoms have octets (duets for H); the structure is complete.

(e) H_3COCH_3:   Write the correct skeletal structure for the molecule.

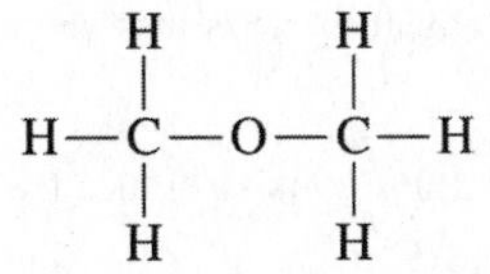

$$\begin{array}{ccc} H & & H \\ | & & | \\ H—C—O—C—H \\ | & & | \\ H & & H \end{array}$$

Calculate the total number of electrons for the Lewis structure by summing the number of valence electrons of each atom in the molecule.

2(number of valence e⁻ for C) + (number of valence e⁻ for O) + 6(number of valence e⁻ for H) = 2(4) + 6 + 6(1) = 20

Distribute the electrons among the atoms, giving octets (or duets for H) to as many atoms as possible. Begin with the bonding electrons; then proceed to lone pairs on terminal atoms and finally to lone pairs on the central atom.

$$\begin{array}{ccc} H & & H \\ | & & | \\ H—C—\overset{..}{\underset{..}{O}}—C—H \\ | & & | \\ H & & H \end{array}$$

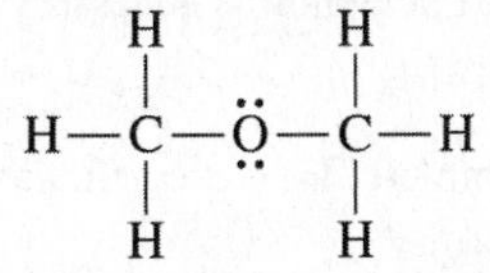

All 20 valence electrons are used.

If any atom lacks an octet, form double or triple bonds as necessary to give them octets. All atoms have octets (duets for H); the structure is complete.

(f) CN^-:   Write the correct skeletal structure for the ion.

C—N

Calculate the total number of electrons for the Lewis structure by summing the number of valence electrons of each atom in the ion and adding 1 for the 1− charge.

(number of valence e⁻ for C) + (number of valence e⁻ for N) + 1 = 4 + 5 + 1 = 10

Distribute the electrons among the atoms, giving octets to as many atoms as possible. Begin with the bonding electrons; then proceed to lone pairs on terminal atoms and finally to lone pairs on the central atom.

$\overset{..}{C}—\overset{..}{\underset{..}{N}}:$

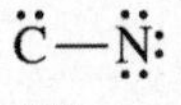

All ten valence electrons are used.

If any atom lacks an octet, form double or triple bonds as necessary.

$:C≡N:$

Finally, write the Lewis structure in brackets with the charge of the ion in the upper right-hand corner.

$$\left[\,:\!C\!\equiv\!N\!:\right]^{-}$$

(g) NO_2^-:   Write the correct skeletal structure for the ion.

O—N—O

Calculate the total number of electrons for the Lewis structure by summing the number of valence electrons of each atom in the ion and adding 1 for the 1− charge.

2(number of valence e⁻ for O) + (number of valence e⁻ for N) + 1 = 2(6) + 5 + 1 = 18

Distribute the electrons among the atoms, giving octets to as many atoms as possible. Begin with the bonding electrons; then proceed to lone pairs on terminal atoms and finally to lone pairs on the central atom.

$:\!\ddot{O}\!-\!\ddot{N}\!-\!\ddot{O}\!:$

All 18 valence electrons are used.

If any atom lacks an octet, form double or triple bonds as necessary.

$:\!\ddot{O}\!-\!\ddot{N}\!=\!\ddot{O}\!:$

Finally, write the Lewis structure in brackets with the charge of the ion in the upper right-hand corner.

$$\left[\,:\!\ddot{O}\!-\!\ddot{N}\!=\!\ddot{O}\!:\right]^{-}$$

9.23   (a) SeO_2:   Write the correct skeletal structure for the molecule. Se is less electronegative, so it is central.

O—Se—O

Calculate the total number of electrons for the Lewis structure by summing the number of valence electrons of each atom in the molecule.

(number of valence e⁻ for Se) + 2(number of valence e⁻ for O) = 6 + 2(6) = 18

Distribute the electrons among the atoms, giving octets to as many atoms as possible. Begin with the bonding electrons; then proceed to lone pairs on terminal atoms and finally to lone pairs on the central atom.

$:\!\ddot{O}\!-\!\ddot{Se}\!-\!\ddot{O}\!:$

All 18 valence electrons are used.

If any atom lacks an octet, form double or triple bonds as necessary.

$:\!\ddot{O}\!-\!\ddot{Se}\!=\!\ddot{O}\!:$

All atoms have octets; the structure is complete. However, the double bond can form from either oxygen atom, so there are two resonance forms.

$:\!\ddot{O}\!-\!\ddot{Se}\!=\!\ddot{O}\!: \longleftrightarrow :\!\ddot{O}\!=\!\ddot{Se}\!-\!\ddot{O}\!:$

Calculate the formal charge on each atom by finding the number of valence electrons and subtracting the number of lone pair electrons and one-half the number of bonding electrons.

	$:\!\ddot{O}\!-\!\ddot{Se}\!=\!\ddot{O}\!:$		$\longleftrightarrow$	$:\!\ddot{O}\!=\!\ddot{Se}\!-\!\ddot{O}\!:$		
number of valence electrons	6	6	6	6	6	6
− number of lone pair electrons	6	2	4	4	2	6
− 1/2(number of bonding electrons)	1	3	2	2	3	1
Formal charge	−1	+1	0	0	+1	−1

(b) CO_3^{2-}:   Write the correct skeletal structure for the ion.

O
|
O—C—O

Calculate the total number of electrons for the Lewis structure by summing the number of valence electrons of each atom in the ion and adding 2 for the 2− charge.

3(number of valence e⁻ for O) + (number of valence e⁻ for C) + 2 = 3(6) + 4 + 2 = 24

Distribute the electrons among the atoms, giving octets to as many atoms as possible. Begin with the bonding electrons; then proceed to lone pairs on terminal atoms and finally to lone pairs on the central atom.

$$\ddot{:}\ddot{O}\ddot{:}$$
$$\ |$$
$$:\ddot{O}-C-\ddot{O}:$$

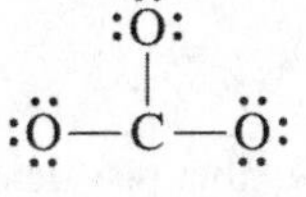

All 24 valence electrons are used.

If any atom lacks an octet, form double or triple bonds as necessary.

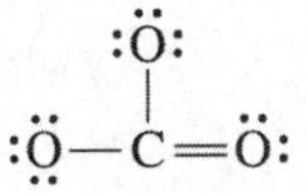

$$\ddot{:}\ddot{O}\ddot{:}$$
$$\ |$$
$$:\ddot{O}-C=\ddot{O}:$$

Finally, write the Lewis structure in brackets with the charge of the ion in the upper right-hand corner.

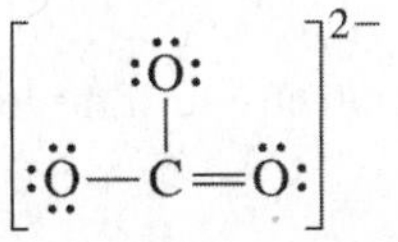

$$\left[\ \begin{matrix} :\ddot{O}: \\ | \\ :\ddot{O}-C=\ddot{O}: \end{matrix}\ \right]^{2-}$$

All atoms have octets; the structure is complete. However, the double bond can form from any oxygen atom, so there are three resonance forms.

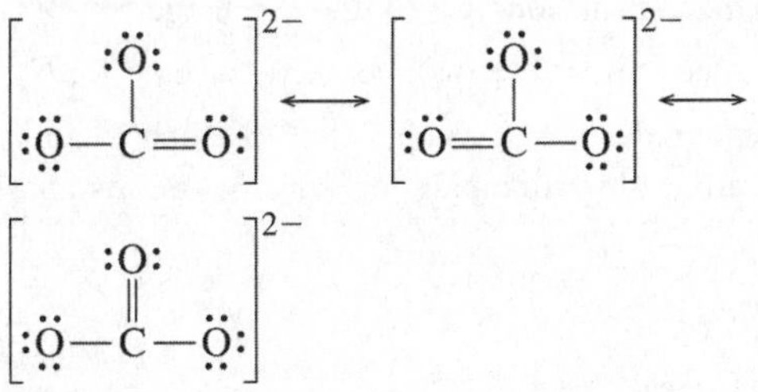

$$\left[\ \begin{matrix} :\ddot{O}: \\ | \\ :\ddot{O}-C=\ddot{O}: \end{matrix}\ \right]^{2-} \longleftrightarrow \left[\ \begin{matrix} :\ddot{O}: \\ | \\ :\ddot{O}=C-\ddot{O}: \end{matrix}\ \right]^{2-} \longleftrightarrow$$

$$\left[\ \begin{matrix} :O: \\ \| \\ :\ddot{O}-C-\ddot{O}: \end{matrix}\ \right]^{2-}$$

Calculate the formal charge on each atom by finding the number of valence electrons and subtracting the number of lone pair electrons and one-half the number of bonding electrons.

$$\left[\ \begin{matrix} :\ddot{O}: \\ | \\ :\ddot{O}-C=\ddot{O}: \end{matrix}\ \right]^{2-}$$

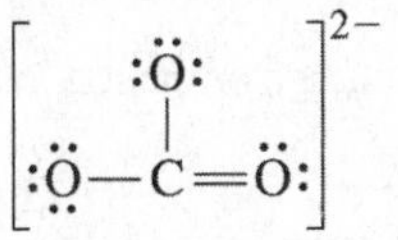

	O_{left}	O_{top}	O_{right}	C
number of valence electrons	6	6	6	4
− number of lone pair electrons	6	6	4	0
− 1/2(number of bonding electrons)	1	1	2	4
Formal charge	−1	−1	0	0

The sum of the formal charges is −2, which is the overall charge of the ion. The other resonance forms would have the same values for the single- and double-bonded oxygen atoms.

(c) ClO^-:   Write the correct skeletal structure for the ion.

Cl—O

Calculate the total number of electrons for the Lewis structure by summing the number of valence electrons of each atom in the ion and adding 1 for the 1− charge.

(number of valence e⁻ for O) + (number of valence e⁻ for Cl) + 1 = 6 + 7 + 1 = 14

Distribute the electrons among the atoms, giving octets to as many atoms as possible. Begin with the bonding electrons; then proceed to lone pairs on terminal atoms and finally to lone pairs on the central atom.

$$:\ddot{C}l-\ddot{O}:$$

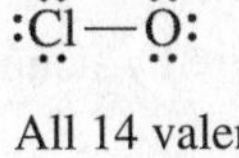

All 14 valence electrons are used.

If any atom lacks an octet, form double or triple bonds as necessary to give them octets. Finally, write the Lewis structure in brackets with the charge of the ion in the upper right-hand corner.

$$\left[:\ddot{C}l\!-\!\ddot{O}:\right]^{-}$$

All atoms have octets; the structure is complete.

Calculate the formal charge on each atom by finding the number of valence electrons and subtracting the number of lone pair electrons and one-half the number of bonding electrons.

	Cl	**O**
number of valence electrons	7	6
− number of lone pair electrons	6	6
− 1/2(number of bonding electrons)	1	1
Formal charge	0	−1

The sum of the formal charges is −1, which is the overall charge of the ion.

(d) NO_2^-:   Write the correct skeletal structure for the ion.

O—N—O

Calculate the total number of electrons for the Lewis structure by summing the number of valence electrons of each atom in the ion and adding 1 for the 1− charge.

$$2(\text{number of valence e}^-\text{ for O}) + (\text{number of valence e}^-\text{ for N}) + 1 = 2(6) + 5 + 1 = 18$$

Distribute the electrons among the atoms, giving octets to as many atoms as possible. Begin with the bonding electrons; then proceed to lone pairs on terminal atoms and finally to lone pairs on the central atom.

$$:\ddot{O}\!-\!\ddot{N}\!-\!\ddot{O}:$$

All 18 valence electrons are used.

If any atom lacks an octet, form double or triple bonds as necessary.

$$:\ddot{O}\!=\!\ddot{N}\!-\!\ddot{O}:$$

Finally, write the Lewis structure in brackets with the charge of the ion in the upper right-hand corner.

$$\left[:\ddot{O}\!=\!\ddot{N}\!-\!\ddot{O}:\right]^{-}$$

All atoms have octets; the structure is complete. However, the double bond can form from either oxygen atom, so there are two resonance forms.

$$\left[:\ddot{O}\!=\!\ddot{N}\!-\!\ddot{O}:\right]^{-} \longleftrightarrow \left[:\ddot{O}\!-\!\ddot{N}\!=\!\ddot{O}:\right]^{-}$$

Calculate the formal charge on each atom by finding the number of valence electrons and subtracting the number of lone pair electrons and one-half the number of bonding electrons. Using the left-side structure:

	O	**N**	**O**
number of valence electrons	6	5	6
− number of lone pair electrons	4	2	6
− 1/2(number of bonding electrons)	2	3	1
Formal charge	0	0	−1

The sum of the formal charges is −1, which is the overall charge of the ion.

9.24   (a) ClO_3^-:   Write the correct skeletal structure for the ion.

O
|
O—Cl—O

Calculate the total number of electrons for the Lewis structure by summing the number of valence electrons of each atom in the ion and adding 1 for the 1− charge.

$$3(\text{number of valence e}^-\text{ for O}) + (\text{number of valence e}^-\text{ for Cl}) + 1 = 3(6) + 7 + 1 = 26$$

Distribute the electrons among the atoms, giving octets to as many atoms as possible. Begin with the bonding electrons; then proceed to lone pairs on terminal atoms and finally to lone pairs on the central atom.

$$:\ddot{O}:$$
$$|$$
$$:\ddot{O}-\ddot{C}l-\ddot{O}:$$

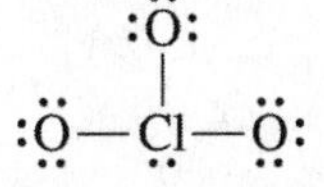

All 26 valence electrons are used.

If any atom lacks an octet, form double or triple bonds as necessary to give them octets.

Finally, write the Lewis structure in brackets with the charge of the ion in the upper right-hand corner.

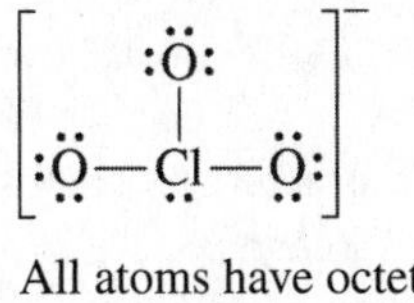

$$\left[\ :\ddot{O}: \atop :\ddot{O}-\ddot{C}l-\ddot{O}: \right]^{-}$$

All atoms have octets; the structure is complete.

Calculate the formal charge on each atom by finding the number of valence electrons and subtracting the number of lone pair electrons and one-half the number of bonding electrons.

	O_{left}	O_{top}	O_{right}	Cl
number of valence electrons	6	6	6	7
− number of lone pair electrons	6	6	6	2
− 1/2(number of bonding electrons)	1	1	1	3
Formal charge	−1	−1	−1	+2

The sum of the formal charges is −1, which is the overall charge of the ion.

(b) ClO_4^-: Write the correct skeletal structure for the ion.

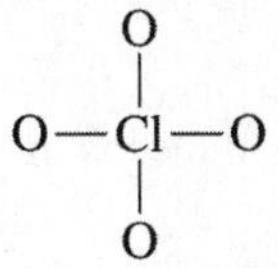

$$O$$
$$|$$
$$O-Cl-O$$
$$|$$
$$O$$

Calculate the total number of electrons for the Lewis structure by summing the number of valence electrons of each atom in the ion and adding 1 for the 1− charge.

4(number of valence e^- for O) + (number of valence e^- for Cl) + 1 = 4(6) + 7 + 1 = 32

Distribute the electrons among the atoms, giving octets to as many atoms as possible. Begin with the bonding electrons; then proceed to lone pairs on terminal atoms and finally to lone pairs on the central atom.

$$:\ddot{O}:$$
$$|$$
$$:\ddot{O}-Cl-\ddot{O}:$$
$$|$$
$$:\ddot{O}:$$

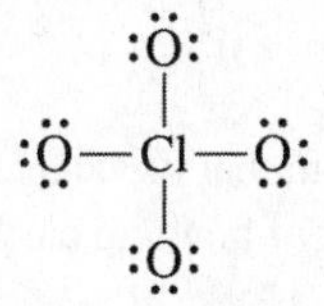

All 32 valence electrons are used.

If any atom lacks an octet, form double or triple bonds as necessary to give them octets. Finally, write the Lewis structure in brackets with the charge of the ion in the upper right-hand corner.

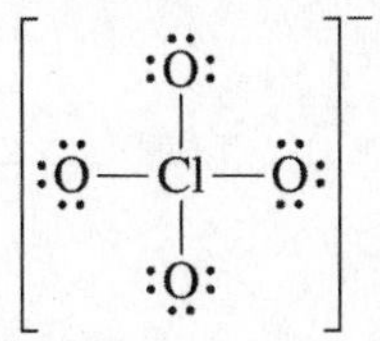

$$\left[\ :\ddot{O}: \atop :\ddot{O}-Cl-\ddot{O}: \atop :\ddot{O}: \right]^{-}$$

All atoms have octets; the structure is complete.

Calculate the formal charge on each atom by finding the number of valence electrons and subtracting the number of lone pair electrons and one-half the number of bonding electrons.

Using the left-side structure:

	O_{left}	O_{top}	O_{right}	O_{bottom}	Cl
number of valence electrons	6	6	6	6	7
− number of lone pair electrons	6	6	6	6	0
− 1/2(number of bonding electrons)	1	1	1	1	4
Formal charge	−1	−1	−1	−1	+3

The sum of the formal charges is −1, which is the overall charge of the ion.

(c) NO_3^-:   Write the correct skeletal structure for the ion.

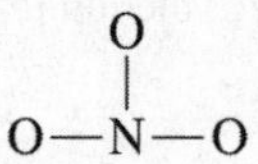

$$O$$
$$|$$
$$O—N—O$$

Calculate the total number of electrons for the Lewis structure by summing the number of valence electrons of each atom in the ion and adding 1 for the 1− charge.

3(number of valence e⁻ for O) + (number of valence e⁻ for N) + 1 = 3(6) + 5 + 1 = 24

Distribute the electrons among the atoms, giving octets to as many atoms as possible. Begin with the bonding electrons; then proceed to lone pairs on terminal atoms and finally to lone pairs on the central atom.

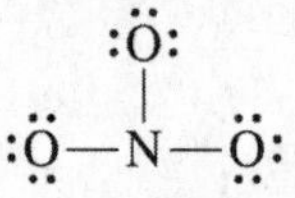

$$:\ddot{O}:$$
$$|$$
$$:\ddot{O}—N—\ddot{O}:$$

All 24 valence electrons are used.

If any atom lacks an octet, form double or triple bonds as necessary.

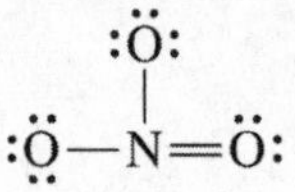

$$:\ddot{O}:$$
$$|$$
$$:\ddot{O}—N=\ddot{O}:$$

Finally, write the Lewis structure in brackets with the charge of the ion in the upper right-hand corner.

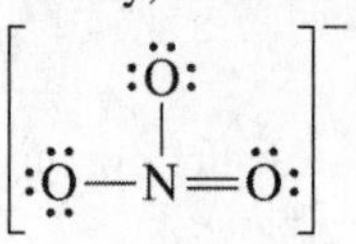

$$\left[\begin{array}{c} :\ddot{O}: \\ | \\ :\ddot{O}—N=\ddot{O}: \end{array} \right]^-$$

All atoms have octets; the structure is complete. However, the double bond can form from any oxygen atom, so there are three resonance forms.

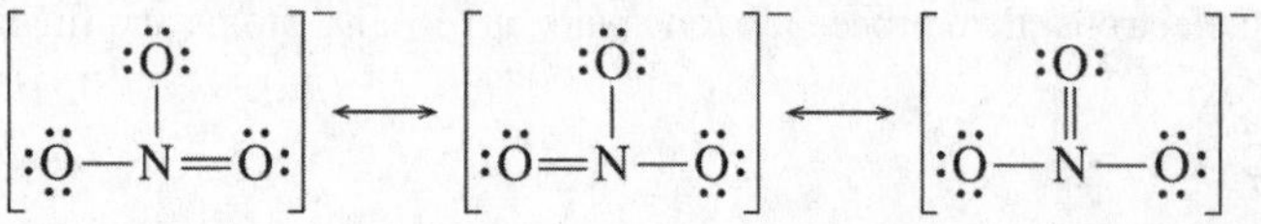

$$\left[\begin{array}{c} :\ddot{O}: \\ | \\ :\ddot{O}—N=\ddot{O}: \end{array} \right]^- \longleftrightarrow \left[\begin{array}{c} :\ddot{O}: \\ | \\ :\ddot{O}=N—\ddot{O}: \end{array} \right]^- \longleftrightarrow \left[\begin{array}{c} :O: \\ || \\ :\ddot{O}—N—\ddot{O}: \end{array} \right]^-$$

Calculate the formal charge on each atom by finding the number of valence electrons and subtracting the number of lone pair electrons and one-half the number of bonding electrons.

Using the left-hand structure:

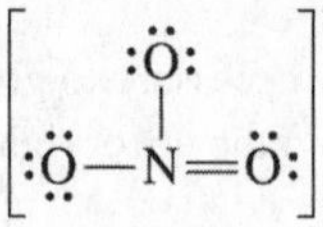

$$\left[\begin{array}{c} :\ddot{O}: \\ | \\ :\ddot{O}—N=\ddot{O}: \end{array} \right]^-$$

	O_{left}	O_{top}	O_{right}	N
number of valence electrons	6	6	6	5
− number of lone pair electrons	6	6	4	0
− 1/2(number of bonding electrons)	1	1	2	4
Formal charge	−1	−1	0	+1

The sum of the formal charges is −1, which is the overall charge of the ion. The other resonance forms would have the same values for the single- and double-bonded oxygen atoms.

(d) NH_4^+:   Write the correct skeletal structure for the ion.

$$
\begin{array}{c}
\text{H} \\
| \\
\text{H}-\text{N}-\text{H} \\
| \\
\text{H}
\end{array}
$$

Calculate the total number of electrons for the Lewis structure by summing the valence electrons of each atom in the ion and subtracting 1 for the 1+ charge.

$$4(\text{number of valence } e^- \text{ for H}) + (\text{number of valence } e^- \text{ for N}) - 1 = 4(1) + 5 - 1 = 8$$

Distribute the electrons among the atoms, giving octets (or duets for H) to as many atoms as possible. Begin with the bonding electrons; then proceed to lone pairs on terminal atoms and finally to lone pairs on the central atom.

$$
\begin{array}{c}
\text{H} \\
| \\
\text{H}-\text{N}-\text{H} \\
| \\
\text{H}
\end{array}
$$

All eight valence electrons are used.

If any atom lacks an octet, form double or triple bonds as necessary to give them octets.

Finally, write the Lewis structure in brackets with the charge of the ion in the upper right-hand corner.

$$
\left[
\begin{array}{c}
\text{H} \\
| \\
\text{H}-\text{N}-\text{H} \\
| \\
\text{H}
\end{array}
\right]^+
$$

All atoms have octets (duets for H); the structure is complete.

Calculate the formal charge on each atom by finding the number of valence electrons and subtracting the number of lone pair electrons and one-half the number of bonding electrons.

	H_{left}	H_{top}	H_{right}	H_{bottom}	N
number of valence electrons	1	1	1	1	5
− number of lone pair electrons	0	0	0	0	0
− 1/2(number of bonding electrons)	1	1	1	1	4
Formal charge	0	0	0	0	+1

The sum of the formal charges is +1, which is the overall charge of the ion.

9.25

$$
\begin{array}{cc}
\begin{array}{c}
\text{H} \\
| \\
\text{H}-\text{C}=\overset{\cdot\cdot}{\underset{\cdot\cdot}{\text{S}}} \\
\text{I}
\end{array}
&
\begin{array}{c}
\text{H} \\
| \\
\text{H}-\text{S}=\overset{\cdot\cdot}{\text{C}} \\
\text{II}
\end{array}
\end{array}
$$

Calculate the formal charge on each atom in structure I by finding the number of valence electrons and subtracting the number of lone pair electrons and one-half the number of bonding electrons.

	H_{left}	H_{top}	C	S
number of valence electrons	1	1	4	6
− number of lone pair electrons	0	0	0	4
− 1/2(number of bonding electrons)	1	1	4	2
Formal charge	0	0	0	0

The sum of the formal charges is 0, which is the overall charge of the molecule. Calculate the formal charge on each atom in structure II by finding the number of valence electrons and subtracting the number of lone pair electrons and one-half the number of bonding electrons.

	H_{left}	H_{top}	S	C
number of valence electrons	1	1	6	4
− number of lone pair electrons	0	0	0	4
− 1/2(number of bonding electrons)	1	1	4	2
Formal charge	0	0	+2	−2

The sum of the formal charges is 0, which is the overall charge of the molecule.

Structure I is the better Lewis structure because it has the least amount of formal charge on each atom.

9.26

Calculate the formal charge on each atom in structure I by finding the number of valence electrons and subtracting the number of lone pair electrons and one-half the number of bonding electrons.

	H_{left}	H_{top}	H_{right}	H_{bottom}	S	C
number of valence electrons	1	1	1	1	6	4
− number of lone pair electrons	0	0	0	0	0	4
− 1/2(number of bonding electrons)	1	1	1	1	4	2
Formal charge	0	0	0	0	+2	−2

The sum of the formal charges is 0, which is the overall charge of the molecule.

Calculate the formal charge on each atom in structure II by finding the number of valence electrons and subtracting the number of lone pair electrons and one-half the number of bonding electrons.

	H_{left}	H_{top}	H_{right}	H_{bottom}	C	S
number of valence electrons	1	1	1	1	4	6
− number of lone pair electrons	0	0	0	0	0	4
− 1/2(number of bonding electrons)	1	1	1	1	4	2
Formal charge	0	0	0	0	0	0

The sum of the formal charges is 0, which is the overall charge of the molecule.

Structure II is the better Lewis structure because it has the least amount of formal charge on each atom.

9.27 $:O\equiv C-\ddot{O}:$ does not provide a significant contribution to the resonance hybrid as it has a +1 formal charge on a very electronegative oxygen.

	O_{left}	O_{right}	C
number of valence electrons	6	6	4
− number of lone pair electrons	2	6	0
− 1/2(number of bonding electrons)	3	1	4
Formal charge	+1	−1	0

9.28   Compare the two forms of each molecule with O as a central atom and a terminal atom. Determine the formal charge on the central atom for all of the structures.

	I	**II**	**III**	**IV**
	N	O	O	F
number of valence electrons	5	6	6	7
− number of lone pair electrons	0	0	4	4
− 1/2(number of bonding electrons)	4	4	4	2
Formal charge	+1	+2	0	+1

For the N_2O molecule, when O is the central atom, it has a +2 formal charge and it is the more electronegative atom. So this would not be a good structure. For the OF_2 molecule, O has to be the central atom. When O is central, it has a formal charge of 0; when F is central, it has a formal charge of +1. This puts a positive formal charge on the most electronegative atom, which is not acceptable.

9.29 CH_3COO^-:   Write the correct skeletal structure for the molecule

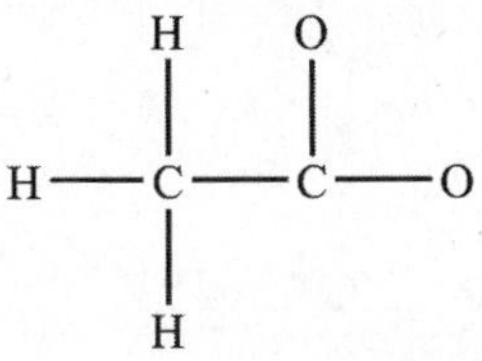

H   O
| |
H — C — C — O
|
H

Calculate the total number of electrons for the Lewis structure by summing the valence electrons of each atom in the ion and adding 1 for the 1 − charge.

2(number of valence e⁻ for C) + 2(number of valence e⁻ for O) + 3(number of valence e⁻ for H) + 1 = 2(4) + 2(6) + 3(1) + 1 = 24

Distribute the electrons among the atoms, giving octets (or duets for H) to as many atoms as possible. Begin with the bonding electrons, and then proceed to lone pairs on terminal atoms and finally to lone pairs of the central atom.

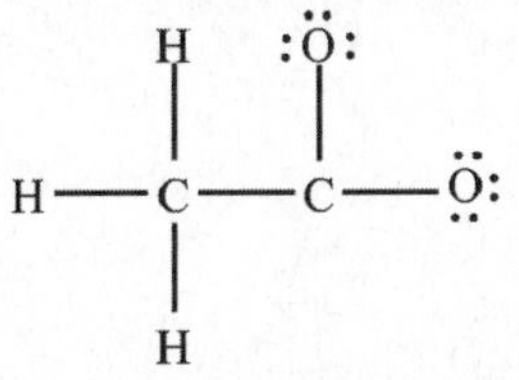

H   :Ö:
| |
H — C — C — Ö:
|
H

All 24 valence electrons are used.

If any atom lacks an octet, form double or triple bonds as necessary to give them octets.

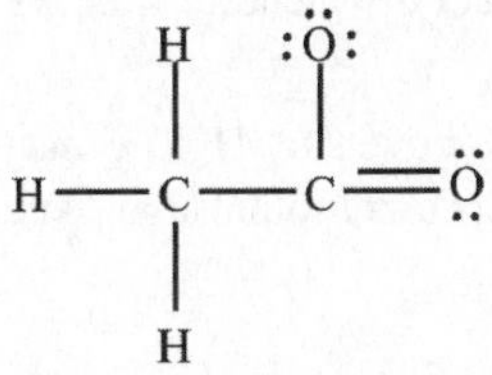

H   :Ö:
| |
H — C — C = Ö
|
H

Lastly, write the Lewis structure in brackets with the charge of the ion in the upper right-hand corner.

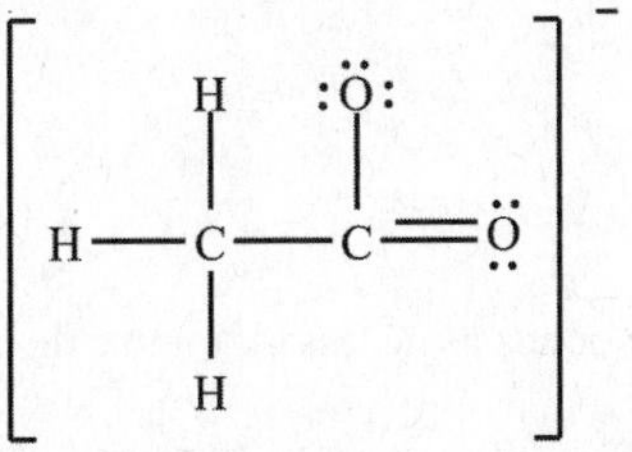

[H   :Ö:
  | |
  H — C — C = Ö]⁻
  |
  H

All atoms have octets (duets for H); the structure is complete. However, the double bond can form from either oxygen atom, so there are two resonance forms.

$$
\left[\begin{array}{c} \text{structure} \end{array}\right]^{-} \longleftrightarrow \left[\begin{array}{c} \text{structure} \end{array}\right]^{-}
$$

Calculate the formal charge on each atom by finding the number of valence electrons and subtracting the number of lone pair electrons and one-half the number of bonding electrons.

$$
\left[\begin{array}{c} \text{structure} \end{array}\right]^{-}
$$

	H	**O**$_{top}$	**O**$_{right}$	**C**
number of valence electrons	1	6	6	4
− number of lone pair electrons	0	6	4	0
− 1/2(number of bonding electrons)	1	1	2	4
Formal charge	0	−1	0	0

The sum of the formal charges is −1, which is the overall charge of the ion. The other resonance form would be the same.

9.30 CH_3N_3:   Write the correct skeletal structure for the molecule

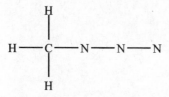

Calculate the total number of electrons for the Lewis structure by summing the valence electrons of each atom in the molecule.

1(number of valence e$^-$ for C) + 3(number of valence e$^-$ for H) + 3(number of valence e$^-$ for N) = 1(4) + 3(1) + 3(5) = 22

Distribute the electrons among the atoms, giving octets (or duets for H) to as many atoms as possible. Begin with the bonding electrons, and then proceed to lone pairs on terminal atoms and finally to lone pairs of the central atom.

$$
\begin{array}{c}
\text{H} \\
| \\
\text{H} - \text{C} - \ddot{\text{N}} - \ddot{\text{N}} - \ddot{\text{N}} \\
| \\
\text{H}
\end{array}
$$

All 22 valence electrons are used.

If any atom lacks an octet, form double or triple bonds as necessary to give them octets.

$$
\begin{array}{c}
\text{H} \\
| \\
\text{H} - \text{C} - \ddot{\text{N}} = \text{N} = \ddot{\text{N}} \\
| \\
\text{H}
\end{array}
$$

All atoms have octets (duets for H); the structure is complete. However, the double bonds can be changed to a single bond and a triple bond, so there are three resonance forms.

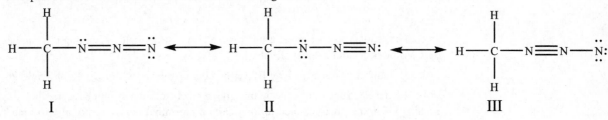

Calculate the formal charge on each atom by finding the number of valence electrons and subtracting the number of lone pair electrons and one-half the number of bonding electrons.

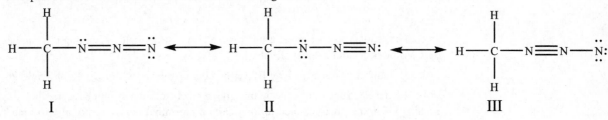

	H	**C**	**N$_{1 bond}$**	**N$_{2 bond}$**	**N$_{3 bond}$**	**N$_{4 bond}$**
number of valence electrons	1	4	5	5	5	5
− number of lone pair electrons	0	0	6	4	2	0
− 1/2(number of bonding electrons)	1	4	1	2	3	4
Formal charge	0	0	−2	−1	0	+1

The sums of the formal charges are:

Structure I = 3(0) + 0 + 0 + (+1) + (−1) = 0

Structure II = 3(0) + 0 + (−1) + (+1) + 0 = 0

Structure III = 3(0) + 0 + (+1) + (+1) + (−2) = 0

Thus, all structures have no overall charge. Structure III is the least likely because it has a formal charge of −2 on one of the N atoms.

9.31   Calculate the formal charge on each atom by finding the number of valence electrons and subtracting the number of lone pair electrons and one-half the number of bonding electrons.

	N	**O**
number of valence electrons	5	6
− number of lone pair electrons	0	6
− 1/2(number of bonding electrons)	4	1
Formal charge	+1	−1

$$CH_3-N-\ddot{O}:$$

with CH_3 groups above and below the N.

9.32   Calculate the formal charge on each atom by finding the number of valence electrons and subtracting the number of lone pair electrons and one-half the number of bonding electrons.

	S	**O**
number of valence electrons	6	6
− number of lone pair electrons	2	6
− 1/2(number of bonding electrons)	3	1
Formal charge	+1	−1

$$\overset{\displaystyle :\overset{\displaystyle ..}{O}:}{\underset{}{\text{CH}_3-\overset{|}{\underset{..}{S}}-\text{CH}_3}}$$

Odd-Electron Species, Incomplete Octets, and Expanded Octets

9.33   (a) BCl_3:   Write the correct skeletal structure for the molecule.

B is less electronegative, so it is central.

$$\begin{array}{c} \text{Cl} \\ | \\ \text{Cl}-\text{B}-\text{Cl} \end{array}$$

Calculate the total number of electrons for the Lewis structure by summing the number of valence electrons of each atom in the molecule.

(number of valence e^- for B) + 3(number of valence e^- for Cl) = 3 + 3(7) = 24

Distribute the electrons among the atoms, giving octets to as many atoms as possible. Begin with the bonding electrons; then proceed to lone pairs on terminal atoms and finally to lone pairs on the central atom.

$$\begin{array}{c} :\overset{..}{\underset{}{\text{Cl}}}: \\ | \\ :\overset{..}{\underset{..}{\text{Cl}}}-\text{B}-\overset{..}{\underset{..}{\text{Cl}}}: \end{array}$$

All 24 valence electrons are used.

B has an incomplete octet. If we complete the octet, there is a formal charge of −1 on the B, which is less electronegative than Cl.

(b) NO_2:   Write the correct skeletal structure for the molecule.

N is less electronegative, so it is central.

O—N—O

Calculate the total number of electrons for the Lewis structure by summing the number of valence electrons of each atom in the molecule.

(number of valence e^- for N) + 2(number of valence e^- for O) = 5 + 2(6) = 17

Distribute the electrons among the atoms, giving octets to as many atoms as possible. Begin with the bonding electrons; then proceed to lone pairs on terminal atoms and finally to lone pairs on the central atom.

$$\overset{..}{\underset{..}{O}}=\overset{\cdot}{N}-\overset{..}{\underset{..}{O}}:$$

$$\longleftrightarrow \;\; :\overset{..}{\underset{..}{O}}-\overset{\cdot}{N}=\overset{..}{\underset{..}{O}}$$

All 17 valence electrons are used.

N has an incomplete octet. It has seven electrons because we have an odd number of valence electrons.

(c) BH_3:   Write the correct skeletal structure for the molecule.

B is less electronegative, so it is central.

$$\begin{array}{c} \text{H} \\ | \\ \text{H}-\text{B}-\text{H} \end{array}$$

Calculate the total number of electrons for the Lewis structure by summing the number of valence electrons of each atom in the molecule.

(number of valence e^- for B) + 3(number of valence e^- for H) = 3 + 3(1) = 6

Distribute the electrons among the atoms, giving octets (or duets for H) to as many atoms as possible. Begin with the bonding electrons; then proceed to lone pairs on terminal atoms and finally to lone pairs on the central atom.

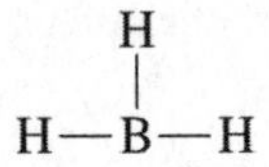

$$
\begin{array}{c}
\text{H} \\
| \\
\text{H——B——H}
\end{array}
$$

All six valence electrons are used.

B has an incomplete octet. H cannot double-bond, so it is not possible to complete the octet on B with a double bond.

9.34   (a)   BBr₃: Write the correct skeletal structure for the molecule.

B is less electronegative, so it is central.

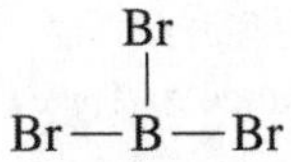

$$
\begin{array}{c}
\text{Br} \\
| \\
\text{Br——B——Br}
\end{array}
$$

Calculate the total number of electrons for the Lewis structure by summing the number of valence electrons of each atom in the molecule.

(number of valence e⁻ for B) + 3(number of valence e⁻ for Br) = 3 + 3(7) = 24

Distribute the electrons among the atoms, giving octets to as many atoms as possible. Begin with the bonding electrons; then proceed to lone pairs on terminal atoms and finally to lone pairs on the central atom.

$$
\begin{array}{c}
:\!\ddot{\text{Br}}\!: \\
| \\
:\!\ddot{\text{Br}}\!——\text{B}——\ddot{\text{Br}}\!:
\end{array}
$$

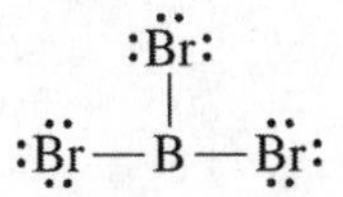

All 24 valence electrons are used.

B has an incomplete octet. If we complete the octet, there is a formal charge of −1 on the B, which is less electronegative than Br.

(b)   NO: Write the correct skeletal structure for the molecule.

N——O

Calculate the total number of electrons for the Lewis structure by summing the number of valence electrons of each atom in the molecule.

(number of valence e⁻ for N) + (number of valence e⁻ for O) = 5 + 6 = 11

Distribute the electrons among the atoms, giving octets to as many atoms as possible. Begin with the bonding electrons; then proceed to lone pairs on terminal atoms and finally to lone pairs on the central atom.

$\dot{\text{N}}\!=\!\ddot{\text{O}}\!:$

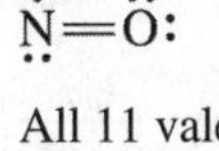

All 11 valence electrons are used.

N has an incomplete octet. It has seven electrons because we have an odd number of valence electrons.

(c)   ClO₂: Write the correct skeletal structure for the molecule.

Cl is less electronegative, so it is central.

O——Cl——O

Calculate the total number of electrons for the Lewis structure by summing the number of valence electrons of each atom in the molecule.

(number of valence e⁻ for Cl) + 2(number of valence e⁻ for O) = 7 + 2(6) = 19

Distribute the electrons among the atoms, giving octets to as many atoms as possible. Begin with the bonding electrons; then proceed to lone pairs on terminal atoms and finally to lone pairs on the central atom.

$:\!\ddot{\text{O}}\!——\dot{\ddot{\text{Cl}}}\!——\ddot{\text{O}}\!:$

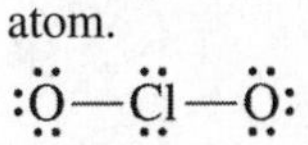

All 19 valence electrons are used.

Cl will have either an incomplete octet or an expanded octet. Because Cl brings seven electrons, there is an odd number of electrons in either structure.

9.35   (a) PO_4^{3-}:   Write the correct skeletal structure for the ion.

$$
\begin{array}{c}
O \\
| \\
O{-}P{-}O \\
| \\
O
\end{array}
$$

Calculate the total number of electrons for the Lewis structure by summing the number of valence electrons of each atom in the ion and adding 3 for the 3− charge.

$$4(\text{number of valence } e^- \text{ for O}) + (\text{number of valence } e^- \text{ for P}) + 3 = 4(6) + 5 + 3 = 32$$

Distribute the electrons among the atoms, giving octets to as many atoms as possible. Begin with the bonding electrons; then proceed to lone pairs on terminal atoms and finally to lone pairs on the central atom.

$$
\begin{array}{c}
:\ddot{O}: \\
| \\
:\ddot{O}{-}P{-}\ddot{O}: \\
| \\
:\ddot{O}:
\end{array}
$$

All 32 valence electrons are used.

Finally, write the Lewis structure in brackets with the charge of the ion in the upper right-hand corner.

$$
\left[
\begin{array}{c}
:\ddot{O}: \\
| \\
:\ddot{O}{-}P{-}\ddot{O}: \\
| \\
:\ddot{O}:
\end{array}
\right]^{3-}
$$

All atoms have octets (duets for H); the structure is complete.

Calculate the formal charge on each atom by finding the number of valence electrons and subtracting the number of lone pair electrons and one-half the number of bonding electrons.

$$
\left[
\begin{array}{c}
:\ddot{O}: \\
| \\
:\ddot{O}{-}P{-}\ddot{O}: \\
| \\
:\ddot{O}:
\end{array}
\right]^{3-}
$$

	O_{left}	O_{top}	O_{right}	O_{bottom}	P
number of valence electrons	6	6	6	6	5
− number of lone pair electrons	6	6	6	6	0
− 1/2(number of bonding electrons)	1	1	1	1	4
Formal charge	−1	−1	−1	−1	+1

The sum of the formal charges is −3, which is the overall charge of the ion. However, we can write a resonance structure with a double bond to an oxygen because P can expand its octet. This leads to lower formal charges on P and O.

$$
\left[
\begin{array}{c}
:\ddot{O}: \\
| \\
\ddot{O}{=}P{-}\ddot{O}: \\
| \\
:\ddot{O}:
\end{array}
\right]^{3-}
\longleftrightarrow
\left[
\begin{array}{c}
:O: \\
|| \\
:\ddot{O}{-}P{-}\ddot{O}: \\
| \\
:\ddot{O}:
\end{array}
\right]^{3-}
\longleftrightarrow
\left[
\begin{array}{c}
:\ddot{O}: \\
| \\
:\ddot{O}{-}P{=}\ddot{O} \\
| \\
:\ddot{O}:
\end{array}
\right]^{3-}
\longleftrightarrow
\left[
\begin{array}{c}
:\ddot{O}: \\
| \\
:\ddot{O}{-}P{-}\ddot{O}: \\
|| \\
:O:
\end{array}
\right]^{3-}
$$

Using the leftmost structure, calculate the formal charge on each atom by finding the number of valence electrons and subtracting the number of lone pair electrons and one-half the number of bonding electrons.

	O_{left}	O_{top}	O_{right}	O_{bottom}	P
number of valence electrons	6	6	6	6	5
− number of lone pair electrons	4	6	6	6	0
− 1/2(number of bonding electrons)	2	1	1	1	5
Formal charge	0	−1	−1	−1	0

The sum of the formal charges is −3, which is the overall charge of the ion. These resonance forms would all have the lower formal charges associated with the double-bonded O and P.

(b) CN^-:   Write the correct skeletal structure for the ion.

C—N

Calculate the total number of electrons for the Lewis structure by summing the number of valence electrons of each atom in the ion and adding 1 for the 1− charge.

(number of valence e^- for C) + (number of valence e^- for N) + 1 = 4 + 5 + 1 = 10

Distribute the electrons among the atoms, giving octets to as many atoms as possible. Begin with the bonding electrons; then proceed to lone pairs on terminal atoms and finally to lone pairs on the central atom.

:C—N̈:

All ten valence electrons are used.

If any atom lacks an octet, form double or triple bonds as necessary.

:C≡N:

Finally, write the Lewis structure in brackets with the charge of the ion in the upper right-hand corner.

$\left[:C≡N: \right]^-$

All atoms have octets; the structure is complete.

Calculate the formal charge on each atom by finding the number of valence electrons and subtracting the number of lone pair electrons and one-half the number of bonding electrons.

$\left[:C≡N: \right]^-$

	C	N
number of valence electrons	4	5
− number of lone pair electrons	2	2
− 1/2(number of bonding electrons)	3	3
Formal charge	−1	0

The sum of the formal charges is −1, which is the overall charge of the ion.

(c) $SO_3{}^{2-}$:   Write the correct skeletal structure for the ion.

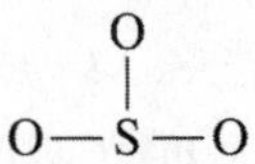

O
|
O—S—O

Calculate the total number of electrons for the Lewis structure by summing the valence electrons of each atom in the ion and adding 2 for the 2− charge.

3(number of valence e^- for O) + (number of valence e^- for S) + 2 = 3(6) + 6 + 2 = 26

Distribute the electrons among the atoms, giving octets to as many atoms as possible. Begin with the bonding electrons; then proceed to lone pairs on terminal atoms and finally to lone pairs on the central atom.

:Ö:
|
:Ö—S—Ö:

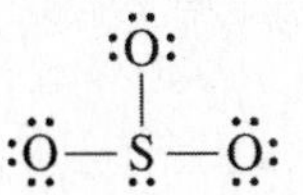

All 26 valence electrons are used.

Finally, write the Lewis structure in brackets with the charge of the ion in the upper right-hand corner.

$$\left[\begin{array}{c} :\ddot{O}: \\ | \\ :\ddot{O}-S-\ddot{O}: \end{array} \right]^{2-}$$

Calculate the formal charge on each atom by finding the number of valence electrons and subtracting the number of lone pair electrons and one-half the number of bonding electrons.

$$\left[\begin{array}{c} :\ddot{O}: \\ | \\ :\ddot{O}-S-\ddot{O}: \end{array} \right]^{2-}$$

	O_{left}	O_{top}	O_{right}	S
number of valence electrons	6	6	6	6
− number of lone pair electrons	6	6	6	2
− 1/2(number of bonding electrons)	1	1	1	3
Formal charge	−1	−1	−1	+1

The sum of the formal charges is −2, which is the overall charge of the ion. However, we can write a resonance structure with a double bond to an oxygen because S can expand its octet. This leads to a lower formal charge.

$$\left[\begin{array}{c} :\ddot{O}: \\ | \\ \ddot{O}=S-\ddot{O}: \end{array} \right]^{2-} \longleftrightarrow \left[\begin{array}{c} :O: \\ \| \\ :\ddot{O}-S-\ddot{O}: \end{array} \right]^{2-} \longleftrightarrow \left[\begin{array}{c} :\ddot{O}: \\ | \\ :\ddot{O}-S=\ddot{O} \end{array} \right]^{2-}$$

Using the leftmost resonance form, calculate the formal charge on each atom by finding the number of valence electrons and subtracting the number of lone pair electrons and one-half the number of bonding electrons.

	O_{left}	O_{top}	O_{right}	S
number of valence electrons	6	6	6	6
− number of lone pair electrons	4	6	6	2
− 1/2(number of bonding electrons)	2	1	1	4
Formal charge	0	−1	−1	0

The sum of the formal charges is −2, which is the overall charge of the ion. These resonance forms would all have the lower formal charge on the double-bonded O and S.

(d) ClO_2^-:   Write the correct skeletal structure for the ion.

O—Cl—O

Calculate the total number of electrons for the Lewis structure by summing the number of valence electrons of each atom in the ion and adding 1 for the 1− charge.

2(number of valence e⁻ for O) + (number of valence e⁻ for Cl) + 1 = 2(6) + 7 + 1 = 20

Distribute the electrons among the atoms, giving octets to as many atoms as possible. Begin with the bonding electrons; then proceed to lone pairs on terminal atoms and finally to lone pairs on the central atom.

$:\ddot{O}-\ddot{Cl}-\ddot{O}:$

All 20 valence electrons are used.

Finally, write the Lewis structure in brackets with the charge of the ion in the upper right-hand corner.

$\left[:\ddot{O}-\ddot{Cl}-\ddot{O}: \right]^{-}$

All atoms have octets; the structure is complete.

Calculate the formal charge on each atom by finding the number of valence electrons and subtracting the number of lone pair electrons and one-half the number of bonding electrons.

$$\left[:\ddot{O}-\ddot{Cl}-\ddot{O}: \right]^{-}$$

	O_{left}	O_{right}	Cl
number of valence electrons	6	6	7
− number of lone pair electrons	6	6	4
− 1/2(number of bonding electrons)	1	1	2
Formal charge	−1	−1	+1

The sum of the formal charges is −1, which is the overall charge of the ion. However, we can write a resonance structure with a double bond to an oxygen because Cl can expand its octet. This leads to a lower formal charge.

$$\left[\ddot{O}=\ddot{Cl}-\ddot{O}: \right]^{-} \longleftrightarrow \left[:\ddot{O}-\ddot{Cl}=\ddot{O} \right]^{-}$$

Using the leftmost resonance form, calculate the formal charge on each atom by finding the number of valence electrons and subtracting the number of lone pair electrons and one-half the number of bonding electrons.

	O_{left}	O_{right}	Cl
number of valence electrons	6	6	7
− number of lone pair electrons	4	6	4
− 1/2(number of bonding electrons)	2	1	3
Formal charge	0	−1	0

The sum of the formal charges is −1, which is the overall charge of the ion. These resonance forms would all have the lower formal charge on the double-bonded O and Cl.

9.36   (a) SO_4^{2-}:   Write the correct skeletal structure for the ion.

$$\begin{array}{c} O \\ | \\ O-S-O \\ | \\ O \end{array}$$

Calculate the total number of electrons for the Lewis structure by summing the valence electrons of each atom in the molecule and adding 2 for the 2− charge.

$$4(\text{number of valence e}^- \text{ for O}) + (\text{number of valence e}^- \text{ for S}) + 2 = 4(6) + 6 + 2 = 32$$

Distribute the electrons among the atoms, giving octets to as many atoms as possible. Begin with the bonding electrons; then proceed to lone pairs on terminal atoms and finally to lone pairs on the central atom.

$$\begin{array}{c} :\ddot{O}: \\ | \\ :\ddot{O}-S-\ddot{O}: \\ | \\ :\ddot{O}: \end{array}$$

All 32 valence electrons are used.

Finally, write the Lewis structure in brackets with the charge of the ion in the upper right-hand corner.

$$\left[\begin{array}{c} :\ddot{O}: \\ | \\ :\ddot{O}-S-\ddot{O}: \\ | \\ :\ddot{O}: \end{array} \right]^{2-}$$

All atoms have octets; the structure is complete.

Calculate the formal charge on each atom by finding the number of valence electrons and subtracting the number of lone pair electrons and one-half the number of bonding electrons.

	O_{left}	O_{top}	O_{right}	O_{bottom}	S
number of valence electrons	6	6	6	6	6
− number of lone pair electrons	6	6	6	6	0
− 1/2(number of bonding electrons)	1	1	1	1	4
Formal charge	−1	−1	−1	−1	+2

The sum of the formal charges is −2, which is the overall charge of the ion. However, we can write a resonance structure with double bonds to two oxygen atoms because S can expand its octet. This leads to lower formal charges.

Using the leftmost resonance form, calculate the formal charge on each atom by finding the number of valence electrons and subtracting the number of lone pair electrons and one-half the number of bonding electrons.

	O_{left}	O_{top}	O_{right}	O_{bottom}	S
number of valence electrons	6	6	6	6	6
− number of lone pair electrons	4	4	6	6	0
− 1/2(number of bonding electrons)	2	2	1	1	6
Formal charge	0	0	−1	−1	0

The sum of the formal charges is −2, which is the overall charge of the ion. These resonance forms would all have the lower formal charges on the double-bonded O and S.

(b) HSO_4^-:   Write the correct skeletal structure for the ion.

Calculate the total number of electrons for the Lewis structure by summing the valence electrons of each atom in the ion and adding 1 for the 1− charge.

4(number of valence e^- for O) + (number of valence e^- for S) + (number of valence e^- for H) + 1 = 4(6) + 6 + 1 + 1 = 32

Distribute the electrons among the atoms, giving octets (or duets for H) to as many atoms as possible. Begin with the bonding electrons; then proceed to lone pairs on terminal atoms and finally to lone pairs on the central atoms.

$$
\begin{array}{c}
\text{:O:} \\
| \\
\text{:O—S—O—H} \\
| \\
\text{:O:}
\end{array}
$$

All 32 valence electrons are used.

Finally, write the Lewis structure in brackets with the charge of the ion in the upper right-hand corner.

$$
\left[
\begin{array}{c}
\text{:O:} \\
| \\
\text{:O—S—O—H} \\
| \\
\text{:O:}
\end{array}
\right]^{-}
$$

All atoms have octets (duets for H); the structure is complete.

Calculate the formal charge on each atom by finding the number of valence electrons and subtracting the number of lone pair electrons and one-half the number of bonding electrons.

$$
\left[
\begin{array}{c}
\text{:O:} \\
| \\
\text{:O—S—O—H} \\
| \\
\text{:O:}
\end{array}
\right]^{-}
$$

	O_{left}	O_{top}	O_{right}	O_{bottom}	S	H
number of valence electrons	6	6	6	6	6	1
− number of lone pair electrons	6	6	4	6	0	0
− 1/2(number of bonding electrons)	1	1	2	2	4	1
Formal charge	−1	−1	0	−1	+2	0

The sum of the formal charges is −1, which is the overall charge of the ion. However, we can write a resonance structure with double bonds to two oxygen atoms because S can expand its octet. This leads to lower formal charges.

$$
\left[
\begin{array}{c}
\text{:O:} \\
\| \\
\text{O=S—O—H} \\
\| \\
\text{:O:}
\end{array}
\right]^{-}
\longleftrightarrow
\left[
\begin{array}{c}
\text{:O:} \\
\| \\
\text{O=S—O—H} \\
\| \\
\text{:O:}
\end{array}
\right]^{-}
\longleftrightarrow
\left[
\begin{array}{c}
\text{:O:} \\
| \\
\text{:O—S—O—H} \\
\| \\
\text{:O:}
\end{array}
\right]^{-}
$$

Using the leftmost resonance form, calculate the formal charge on each atom by finding the number of valence electrons and subtracting the number of lone pair electrons and one-half the number of bonding electrons.

	O_{left}	O_{top}	O_{right}	O_{bottom}	S	H
number of valence electrons	6	6	6	6	6	1
− number of lone pair electrons	4	4	4	6	0	0
− 1/2(number of bonding electrons)	2	2	2	2	6	1
Formal charge	0	0	0	−1	0	0

The sum of the formal charges is −1, which is the overall charge of the ion. Each of these resonance forms would have lower formal charges on O and S.

(c) SO_3:   Write the correct skeletal structure for the molecule.

$$
\begin{array}{c}
\text{O} \\
| \\
\text{O—S—O}
\end{array}
$$

Calculate the total number of electrons for the Lewis structure by summing the number of valence electrons of each atom in the molecule.

$$
3(\text{number of valence e}^- \text{ for O}) + (\text{number of valence e}^- \text{ for S}) = 3(6) + 6 = 24
$$

Distribute the electrons among the atoms, giving octets to as many atoms as possible. Begin with the bonding electrons; then proceed to lone pairs on terminal atoms and finally to lone pairs on the central atom.

$$:\overset{\displaystyle ..}{\underset{\displaystyle |}{O}}:$$
$$:\ddot{O}\!-\!S\!-\!\ddot{O}:$$

All 24 valence electrons are used.

If any atoms lack an octet, form double or triple bonds as necessary to give them octets.

$$:\overset{\displaystyle ..}{\underset{\displaystyle |}{O}}:$$
$$:\ddot{O}\!-\!S\!=\!\ddot{O}$$

All atoms have octets; the structure is complete.

Calculate the formal charge on each atom by finding the number of valence electrons and subtracting the number of lone pair electrons and one-half the number of bonding electrons.

$$:\overset{\displaystyle ..}{\underset{\displaystyle |}{O}}:$$
$$:\ddot{O}\!-\!S\!=\!\ddot{O}$$

	O_{left}	O_{top}	O_{right}	S
number of valence electrons	6	6	6	6
− number of lone pair electrons	6	6	4	0
− 1/2(number of bonding electrons)	1	1	2	4
Formal charge	−1	−1	0	+2

The sum of the formal charges is 0, which is the overall charge of the molecule. However, we can write a resonance structure with a double bond to all oxygen atoms because S can expand its octet. This leads to lower formal charges.

$$:O:$$
$$\ddot{O}\!=\!S\!=\!\ddot{O}$$

Calculate the formal charge on each atom by finding the number of valence electrons and subtracting the number of lone pair electrons and one-half the number of bonding electrons.

	O_{left}	O_{top}	O_{right}	S
number of valence electrons	6	6	6	6
− number of lone pair electrons	4	4	4	0
− 1/2(number of bonding electrons)	2	2	2	6
Formal charge	0	0	0	0

The sum of the formal charges is 0, which is the overall charge of the molecule. This resonance form would have the lower formal charges on each atom.

(d) BrO_2^-:   Write the correct skeletal structure for the ion.

O—Br—O

Calculate the total number of electrons for the Lewis structure by summing the number of valence electrons of each atom in the molecule and adding 1 for the 1− charge.

$$2(\text{number of valence e}^- \text{ for O}) + (\text{number of valence e}^- \text{ for Br}) + 1 = 2(6) + 7 + 1 = 20$$

Distribute the electrons among the atoms, giving octets to as many atoms as possible. Begin with the bonding electrons; then proceed to lone pairs on terminal atoms and finally to lone pairs on the central atom.

$$:\ddot{O}\!-\!\ddot{B}r\!-\!\ddot{O}:$$

All 20 valence electrons are used.

Finally, write the Lewis structure in brackets with the charge of the ion in the upper right-hand corner.

$$\left[:\ddot{O}-\ddot{Br}-\ddot{O}:\right]^{-}$$

All atoms have octets; the structure is complete.

Calculate the formal charge on each atom by finding the number of valence electrons and subtracting the number of lone pair electrons and one-half the number of bonding electrons.

$$\left[:\ddot{O}-\ddot{Br}-\ddot{O}:\right]^{-}$$

	O_{left}	O_{right}	Br
number of valence electrons	6	6	7
− number of lone pair electrons	6	6	4
− 1/2(number of bonding electrons)	1	1	2
Formal charge	−1	−1	+1

The sum of the formal charges is −1, which is the overall charge of the ion. However, we can write a resonance structure with a double bond to an oxygen because Br can expand its octet. This leads to a lower formal charge.

$$\left[\ddot{O}=\ddot{Br}-\ddot{O}:\right]^{-} \longleftrightarrow \left[:\ddot{O}-\ddot{Br}=\ddot{O}\right]^{-}$$

Using the leftmost resonance form, calculate the formal charge on each atom by finding the number of valence electrons and subtracting the number of lone pair electrons and one-half the number of bonding electrons.

	O_{left}	O_{right}	Br
number of valence electrons	6	6	7
− number of lone pair electrons	4	6	4
− 1/2(number of bonding electrons)	2	1	3
Formal charge	0	−1	0

The sum of the formal charges is −1, which is the overall charge of the ion. These resonance forms would both have the lower formal charges on the double-bonded O and Br.

9.37   (a) PF_5:   Write the correct skeletal structure for the molecule.

$$F-\underset{\underset{F}{|}}{\overset{\overset{F}{|}}{P}}\diagup^{F}_{F}$$

Calculate the total number of electrons for the Lewis structure by summing the number of valence electrons of each atom in the molecule.

(number of valence e⁻ for P) + 5(number of valence e⁻ for F) = 5 + 5(7) = 40

Distribute the electrons among the atoms, giving octets to as many atoms as possible. Begin with the bonding electrons; then proceed to lone pairs on terminal atoms and finally to lone pairs on the central atom. Arrange additional electrons around the central atom, giving it an expanded octet of up to 12 electrons.

$$:\ddot{F}-\underset{\underset{\ddot{F}:}{|}}{\overset{\overset{:\ddot{F}:}{|}}{P}}\diagup^{\ddot{F}:}_{\ddot{F}:}$$

(b) I_3^-:   Write the correct skeletal structure for the ion.

I—I—I

Calculate the total number of electrons for the Lewis structure by summing the number of valence electrons of each atom in the ion and adding 1 for the 1− charge.

3(number of valence e⁻ for I) + 1 = 3(7) + 1 = 22

Distribute the electrons among the atoms, giving octets to as many atoms as possible. Begin with the bonding electrons; then proceed to lone pairs on terminal atoms and finally to lone pairs on the central atom. Arrange additional electrons around the central atom, giving it an expanded octet of up to 12 electrons.

:Ï—Ï—Ï:

Finally, write the Lewis structure in brackets with the charge of the ion in the upper right-hand corner.

$$\left[\ddot{\underset{..}{I}} - \ddot{\underset{..}{I}} - \ddot{\underset{..}{I}} \right]^{-}$$

(c)   SF₄: Write the correct skeletal structure for the molecule.

$$\begin{array}{c} F \\ | \\ F-S-F \\ | \\ F \end{array}$$

Calculate the total number of electrons for the Lewis structure by summing the number of valence electrons of each atom in the molecule.

(number of valence e⁻ for S) + 4(number of valence e⁻ for F) = 6 + 4(7) = 34

Distribute the electrons among the atoms, giving octets (or duets for H) to as many atoms as possible. Begin with the bonding electrons; then proceed to lone pairs on terminal atoms and finally to lone pairs on the central atom. Arrange additional electrons around the central atom, giving it an expanded octet of up to 12 electrons.

$$\begin{array}{c} :\ddot{F}: \\ | \\ :\ddot{F}-\underset{..}{S}-\ddot{F}: \\ | \\ :\ddot{F}: \end{array}$$

(d)   GeF₄: Write the correct skeletal structure for the molecule.

$$\begin{array}{c} F \\ | \\ F-Ge-F \\ | \\ F \end{array}$$

Calculate the total number of electrons for the Lewis structure by summing the number of valence electrons of each atom in the molecule.

(number of valence e⁻ for Ge) + 4(number of valence e⁻ for F) = 4 + 4(7) = 32

Distribute the electrons among the atoms, giving octets to as many atoms as possible. Begin with the bonding electrons; then proceed to lone pairs on terminal atoms and finally to lone pairs on the central atom.

$$\begin{array}{c} :\ddot{F}: \\ | \\ :\ddot{F}-Ge-\ddot{F}: \\ | \\ :\ddot{F}: \end{array}$$

9.38   (a)   ClF₅: Write the correct skeletal structure for the molecule.

$$\begin{array}{c} F \\ | \quad F \\ F-Cl \\ | \quad F \\ F \end{array}$$

Calculate the total number of electrons for the Lewis structure by summing the valence electrons of each atom in the molecule.

(number of valence e⁻ for Cl) + 5(number of valence e⁻ for F) = 7 + 5(7) = 42

Distribute the electrons among the atoms, giving octets to as many atoms as possible. Begin with the bonding electrons; then proceed to lone pairs on terminal atoms and finally to lone pairs on the central atom. Arrange additional electrons around the central atom, giving it an expanded octet of up to 12 electrons.

$$\ddot{\text{:F:}}$$
$$\ddot{\text{:F}}—\underset{\underset{\ddot{\text{:F:}}}{|}}{\overset{|}{\text{Cl}}}\overset{\diagup\ddot{\text{F:}}}{\diagdown\ddot{\text{F:}}}$$

(b) AsF_6^-:   Write the correct skeletal structure for the ion.

$$\begin{array}{ccc} & F & \\ F\diagdown & | & \diagup F \\ & As & \\ F\diagup & | & \diagdown F \\ & F & \end{array}$$

Calculate the total number of electrons for the Lewis structure by summing the valence electrons of each atom in the ion and adding one for the 1− charge.

(number of valence e^- for As) + 6(number of valence e^- for F) + 1 = 5 + 6(7) + 1 = 48

Distribute the electrons among the atoms, giving octets to as many atoms as possible. Begin with the bonding electrons; then proceed to lone pairs on terminal atoms and finally to lone pairs on the central atom.

$$\ddot{\text{:F:}}$$
$$\ddot{\text{:F}}\diagdown\;|\;\diagup\ddot{\text{F:}}$$
$$\qquad \text{As}$$
$$\ddot{\text{:F}}\diagup\;|\;\diagdown\ddot{\text{F:}}$$
$$\ddot{\text{:F:}}$$

Finally, write the Lewis structure in brackets with the charge of the ion in the upper right-hand corner.

$$\left[\begin{array}{c} \ddot{\text{:F:}} \\ \ddot{\text{:F}}\diagdown\;|\;\diagup\ddot{\text{F:}} \\ \text{As} \\ \ddot{\text{:F}}\diagup\;|\;\diagdown\ddot{\text{F:}} \\ \ddot{\text{:F:}} \end{array}\right]^-$$

(c) Cl_3PO: Write the correct skeletal structure for the molecule.

$$\begin{array}{c} O \\ | \\ Cl—P—Cl \\ | \\ Cl \end{array}$$

Calculate the total number of electrons for the Lewis structure by summing the valence electrons of each atom in the molecule.

(number of valence e^- for P) + (number of valence e^- for O) + 3(number of valence e^- for Cl) = 5 + 6 + 3(7) = 32

Distribute the electrons among the atoms, giving octets to as many atoms as possible. Begin with the bonding electrons; then proceed to lone pairs on terminal atoms and finally to lone pairs on the central atom.

$$\ddot{\text{:O:}}$$
$$\ddot{\text{:Cl}}—\underset{\underset{\ddot{\text{:Cl:}}}{|}}{\overset{|}{\text{P}}}—\ddot{\text{Cl:}}$$

$$\longleftrightarrow \quad :\overset{\cdot\cdot}{\underset{\cdot\cdot}{Cl}}-\overset{\overset{\displaystyle :O:}{\|}}{\underset{\underset{\displaystyle :\overset{\cdot\cdot}{Cl}:}{|}}{P}}-\overset{\cdot\cdot}{\underset{\cdot\cdot}{Cl}}:$$

(d) IF_5:   Write the correct skeletal structure for the molecule.

$$F-\overset{\overset{\displaystyle F}{|}}{\underset{\underset{\displaystyle F}{|}}{I}}\overset{\displaystyle \diagup F}{\diagdown F}$$

Calculate the total number of electrons for the Lewis structure by summing the valence electrons of each atom in the molecule.

(number of valence e⁻ for I) + 5(number of valence e⁻ for F) = 7 + 5(7) = 42

Distribute the electrons among the atoms, giving octets to as many atoms as possible. Begin with the bonding electrons; then proceed to lone pairs on terminal atoms and finally to lone pairs on the central atom. Arrange additional electrons around the central atom, giving it an expanded octet of up to 12 electrons.

$$\underset{\underset{\displaystyle :\overset{\cdot\cdot}{F}:}{}}{\overset{:\overset{\cdot\cdot}{F}\diagdown\,\cdot\cdot\,\diagup\overset{\cdot\cdot}{F}:}{:\overset{\cdot\cdot}{F}\diagup\,|\,\diagdown\overset{\cdot\cdot}{F}:}}$$

Bond Energies and Bond Lengths

9.39   Bond strength: $H_3CCH_3 < H_2CCH_2 < HCCH$
Bond length: $H_3CCH_3 > H_2CCH_2 > HCCH$
Write the Lewis structures for the three compounds. Compare the C—C bonds. Triple bonds are stronger than double bonds, double bonds are stronger than single bonds. Also, single bonds are longer than double bonds, which are longer than triple bonds.

HCCH (10 e⁻)   **H₂CCH₂ (12 e⁻)**   **H₃CCH₃(14 e⁻)**

$$H-C\equiv C-H$$

$$\underset{H}{\overset{H}{\diagdown}}C=C\underset{\diagdown H}{\overset{\diagup H}{}}$$

$$H-\overset{\overset{\displaystyle H}{|}}{\underset{\underset{\displaystyle H}{|}}{C}}-\overset{\overset{\displaystyle H}{|}}{\underset{\underset{\displaystyle H}{|}}{C}}-H$$

9.40   Stronger bond: HNNH
Shorter bond: HNNH
Write the Lewis structures for the two compounds. Compare the N—N bonds. Double bonds are stronger than single bonds. Also, single bonds are longer than double bonds.

H₂NNH₂(14 e⁻)   **HNNH(12 e⁻)**

$$\underset{H}{\overset{H}{\diagdown}}\overset{\cdot\cdot}{N}-\overset{\cdot\cdot}{N}\underset{\diagdown H}{\overset{\diagup H}{}}$$

$$H-\overset{\cdot\cdot}{N}=\overset{\cdot\cdot}{N}-H$$

9.41   Rewrite the reaction using the Lewis structures of the molecules involved.

$$\underset{H}{\overset{H}{\diagdown}}C=C\underset{\diagdown H}{\overset{\diagup H}{}} + H-H \longrightarrow H-\overset{\overset{\displaystyle H}{|}}{\underset{\underset{\displaystyle H}{|}}{C}}-\overset{\overset{\displaystyle H}{|}}{\underset{\underset{\displaystyle H}{|}}{C}}-H$$

Determine which bonds are broken in the reaction and sum the bond energies of the following:

$\Sigma(\Delta H's$ bonds broken)

= 4 mol(C—H) + 1 mol(C=C) + 1 mol(H—H)

= 4 mol(414 kJ/mol) + 1 mol(611 kJ/mol) + 1 mol(436 kJ/mol)

= 2703 kJ/mol

Determine which bonds are formed in the reaction and sum the negatives of the bond energies of the following:

$$\Sigma(-\Delta H\text{'s bonds formed})$$
$$= -6\ \text{mol}(C\text{—}H) - 1\ \text{mol}(C\text{—}C)$$
$$= -6\ \text{mol}(414\ \text{kJ/mol}) - 1\text{mol}(347\ \text{kJ/mol})$$
$$= -2831\ \text{kJ/mol}$$

Find ΔH_{rxn} by summing the results of the two steps.

$$\Delta H_{rxn} = \sum(\Delta H\text{'s bonds broken}) + \sum(-\Delta H\text{'s bonds formed})$$
$$= 2703\ \text{kJ/mol} - 2831\ \text{kJ/mol}$$
$$= -128\ \text{kJ/mol}$$

9.42   Rewrite the reaction using the Lewis structures of the molecules involved.

$$\text{H—}\overset{\displaystyle H}{\underset{\displaystyle H}{C}}\text{—}\overset{\displaystyle H}{\underset{\displaystyle H}{C}}\text{—}\ddot{\underset{\cdot\cdot}{O}}\text{—H} + 3\ \ddot{\underset{\cdot\cdot}{O}}\text{=}\ddot{\underset{\cdot\cdot}{O}} \longrightarrow 2\ \ddot{\underset{\cdot\cdot}{O}}\text{=C=}\ddot{\underset{\cdot\cdot}{O}} + 3\ \text{H—}\ddot{\underset{\cdot\cdot}{O}}\text{—H}$$

Determine which bonds are broken in the reaction and sum the bond energies of the following:

$$\Sigma(\Delta H\text{'s bonds broken})$$
$$= 5(C\text{—}H) + 1(C\text{—}C) + 1(C\text{—}O) + 1(O\text{—}H) + 3(O\text{=}O)$$
$$= 5(414\ \text{kJ/mol}) + 1(347\ \text{kJ/mol}) + 1(360\ \text{kJ/mol}) + 1(464\ \text{kJ/mol}) + 3(498\text{kJ/mol})$$
$$= 4735\ \text{kJ/mol}$$

Determine which bonds are formed in the reaction and sum the negatives of the bond energies of the following:

$$\Sigma(-\Delta H\text{'s bonds formed})$$
$$= -4(C\text{=}O) - 6(O\text{—}H)$$
$$= -4(799\ \text{kJ/mol}) - 6(464\ \text{kJ/mol})$$
$$= -5980\ \text{kJ/mol}$$

Find ΔH_{rxn} by summing the results of the two steps.

$$\Delta H_{rxn} = \sum(\Delta H\text{'s bonds broken}) + \sum(-\Delta H\text{'s bonds formed})$$
$$= 4735\ \text{kJ/mol} - 5980\ \text{kJ/mol}$$
$$= -1245\ \text{kJ/mol}$$

Cumulative Problems

9.43   (a) BI_3:   This is a covalent compound between two nonmetals.
Write the correct skeletal structure for the molecule.

Calculate the total number of electrons for the Lewis structure by summing the number of valence electrons of each atom in the molecule.

(number of valence e^- for B) + 3(number of valence e^- for I) = 3 + 3(7) = 24

Distribute the electrons among the atoms, giving octets to as many atoms as possible. Begin with the bonding electrons; then proceed to lone pairs on terminal atoms and finally to lone pairs on the central atom.

$$:\ddot{I}:$$
$$:\ddot{I}\text{—B—}\ddot{I}:$$

(b) K_2S: This is an ionic compound between a metal and nonmetal.
Draw the Lewis symbols for K and S based on their valence electrons. K: $4s^1$ S: $3s^2 3p^4$

$$\text{K}\cdot \quad \cdot\ddot{S}:$$

Potassium must lose one electron and be left with the octet from the previous shell, while sulfur needs to gain two electrons to get an octet.

$$2\text{K}^+ \quad \left[:\ddot{S}:\right]^{2-}$$

(c)   HCFO: This is a covalent compound between nonmetals.
Write the correct skeletal structure for the molecule.

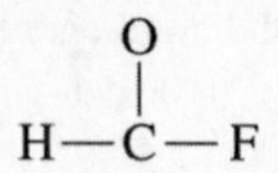

$$
\begin{array}{c}
\text{O} \\
| \\
\text{H—C—F}
\end{array}
$$

Calculate the total number of electrons for the Lewis structure by summing the number of valence electrons of each atom in the molecule.

(number of valence e⁻ for H) + (number of valence e⁻ for C) + (number of valence e⁻ for F) +

(number of valence e⁻ for O) = 1 + 4 + 7 + 6 = 18

Distribute the electrons among the atoms, giving octets to as many atoms as possible. Begin with the bonding electrons; then proceed to lone pairs on terminal atoms and finally to lone pairs on the central atom.

$$
\begin{array}{c}
:\ddot{\text{O}}: \\
| \\
\text{H—C—}\ddot{\text{F}}:
\end{array}
$$

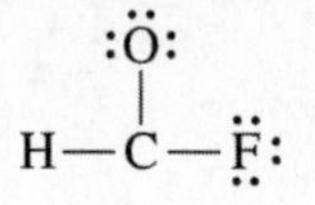

If any atom lacks an octet, form double or triple bonds as necessary to give them octets.

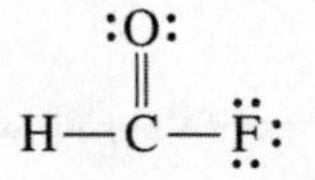

$$
\begin{array}{c}
:\text{O}: \\
\| \\
\text{H—C—}\ddot{\text{F}}:
\end{array}
$$

(d)   PBr₃: This is a covalent compound between two nonmetals.

Write the correct skeletal structure for the molecule.

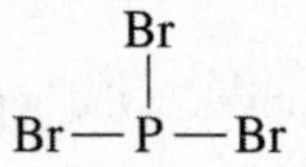

$$
\begin{array}{c}
\text{Br} \\
| \\
\text{Br—P—Br}
\end{array}
$$

Calculate the total number of electrons for the Lewis structure by summing the number of valence electrons of each atom in the molecule.

(number of valence e⁻ for P) + 3(number of valence e⁻ for Br) = 5 + 3(7) = 26

Distribute the electrons among the atoms, giving octets to as many atoms as possible. Begin with the bonding electrons; then proceed to lone pairs on terminal atoms and finally to lone pairs on the central atom.

$$
\begin{array}{c}
:\ddot{\text{Br}}: \\
| \\
:\ddot{\text{Br}}—\ddot{\text{P}}—\ddot{\text{Br}}:
\end{array}
$$

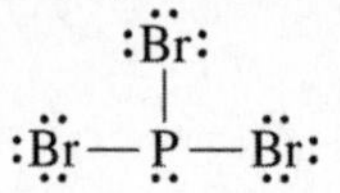

9.44   (a)   Al₂O₃: This is an ionic compound between a metal and nonmetal.

Draw the Lewis symbols for Al and O based on their valence electrons. Al: $3s^2 3p^1$ O: $2s^2 2p^4$

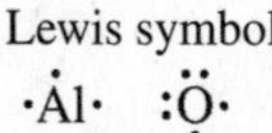

·Al·   :Ö·

Aluminum must lose three electrons and be left with the octet from the previous shell, while oxygen needs to gain two electrons to get an octet.

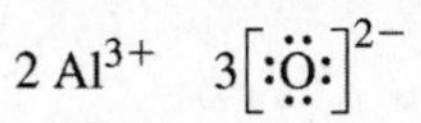

$$
2\,\text{Al}^{3+}\quad 3\left[:\ddot{\text{O}}:\right]^{2-}
$$

(b)   ClF₅: This is a covalent compound between two nonmetals.

Write the correct skeletal structure for the molecule.

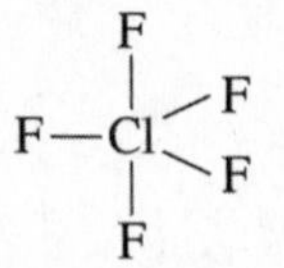

$$
\begin{array}{c}
\text{F} \\
| \\
\text{F—Cl}\begin{array}{c}\nearrow\text{F}\\\searrow\text{F}\end{array} \\
| \\
\text{F}
\end{array}
$$

Calculate the total number of electrons for the Lewis structure by summing the number of valence electrons of each atom in the molecule.

(number of valence e⁻ for Cl) + 5(number of valence e⁻ for F) = 7 + 5(7) = 42

Distribute the electrons among the atoms, giving octets to as many atoms as possible. Begin with the bonding electrons; then proceed to lone pairs on terminal atoms and finally to lone pairs on the central atom. Arrange additional electrons around the central atom, giving it an expanded octet of up to 12 electrons.

$$:\ddot{F}:$$
$$\underset{\displaystyle :\ddot{F}:}{\overset{\displaystyle |}{:\ddot{F}-\underset{\displaystyle |}{Cl}}} \overset{\displaystyle \ddot{F}:}{\underset{\displaystyle \ddot{F}:}{<}}$$

(c) MgI$_2$: This is an ionic compound between a metal and nonmetal.

Draw the Lewis symbols for Mg and I based on their valence electrons. Mg: $3s^2$ I:$5s^25p^5$.

$$\cdot Mg\cdot \quad \cdot\ddot{I}:$$

Magnesium must lose two electrons and be left with the octet from the previous shell, while iodine needs to gain one electron to get an octet.

$$Mg^{2+} \quad 2\left[:\ddot{I}:\right]^{-}$$

(d) XeO$_4$: This is a covalent compound between two nonmetals.

Write the correct skeletal structure for the molecule.

$$\overset{\displaystyle O}{\underset{\displaystyle O}{O-\underset{\displaystyle |}{\overset{\displaystyle |}{Xe}}-O}}$$

Calculate the total number of electrons for the Lewis structure by summing the valence electrons of each atom in the molecule.

$$\text{(number of valence e}^- \text{ for Xe)} + 4\text{(number of valence e}^- \text{ for O)} = 8 + 4(6) = 32$$

Distribute the electrons among the atoms, giving octets to as many atoms as possible. Begin with the bonding electrons; then proceed to lone pairs on terminal atoms and finally to lone pairs on the central atom.

$$\overset{\displaystyle :\ddot{O}:}{\underset{\displaystyle :\ddot{O}:}{:\ddot{O}-\underset{\displaystyle |}{\overset{\displaystyle |}{Xe}}-\ddot{O}:}}$$

The structure as shown is an appropriate Lewis structure. However, this structure would leave a formal charge on Xe. It can be drawn with all double bonds, which would eliminate all of the formal charge.

9.45 (a) BaCO$_3$: Ba^{2+}

$$\left[\overset{\displaystyle :\ddot{O}:}{\ddot{O}=\underset{\displaystyle |}{C}-\ddot{O}:}\right]^{2-}$$

Determine the cation and anion.

$$Ba^{2+} \quad CO_3^{2-}$$

Write the Lewis symbol for the barium cation based on the valence electrons.

$$Ba \quad 5s^2 \qquad Ba^{2+} \quad 5s^0$$
$$\cdot Ba\cdot \qquad Ba^{2+}$$

Ba must lose two electrons and be left with the octet from the previous shell.

Write the Lewis structure for the covalent anion.

Write the correct skeletal structure for the ion.

$$\overset{\displaystyle O}{\underset{}{O-\underset{\displaystyle |}{\overset{\displaystyle |}{C}}-O}}$$

Calculate the total number of electrons for the Lewis structure by summing the number of valence electrons of each atom in the ion and adding two for the 2− charge.

(number of valence e⁻ for C) + 3(number of valence e⁻ for O) + 2 = 4 + 3(6) + 2 = 24

Distribute the electrons among the atoms, giving octets to as many atoms as possible. Begin with the bonding electrons; then proceed to lone pairs on terminal atoms and finally to lone pairs on the central atom.

$$\ddot{O} - \overset{\displaystyle :\ddot{O}:}{\underset{}{C}} - \ddot{O}$$

If any atom lacks an octet, form double or triple bonds as necessary.

$$\ddot{O} = \overset{\displaystyle :\ddot{O}:}{\underset{}{C}} - \ddot{O}$$

Finally, write the Lewis structure in brackets with the charge of the ion in the upper right-hand corner.

$$\left[\ddot{O} = \overset{\displaystyle :\ddot{O}:}{\underset{}{C}} - \ddot{O} \right]^{2-}$$

The double bond can be between the C and any of the oxygen atoms, so there are resonance structures.

$$\left[\ddot{O} = \overset{:\ddot{O}:}{C} - \ddot{O} \right]^{2-} \longleftrightarrow \left[\ddot{O} - \overset{:O:}{\underset{\|}{C}} - \ddot{O} \right]^{2-} \longleftrightarrow \left[\ddot{O} - \overset{:\ddot{O}:}{C} = \ddot{O} \right]^{2-}$$

(b) $Ca(OH)_2$: Ca^{2+}

$$2\left[:\ddot{O} - H \right]^{-}$$

Determine the cation and anion.

$$Ca^{2+} \qquad OH^{-}$$

Write the Lewis symbol for the calcium cation based on the valence electrons.

$$Ca \quad 4s^2 \qquad Ca^{2+} \quad 4s^0$$

$$\cdot Ca \cdot \qquad Ca^{2+}$$

Ca must lose two electrons and be left with the octet from the previous shell.

Write the Lewis structure for the covalent anion.

Write the correct skeletal structure for the ion.

$$O - H$$

Calculate the total number of electrons for the Lewis structure by summing the valence electrons of each atom in the ion and adding one for the 1− charge.

(number of valence e⁻ for H) + (number of valence e⁻ for O) + 1 = 1 + 6 + 1 = 8

Distribute the electrons among the atoms, giving octets (or duets for H) to as many atoms as possible. Begin with the bonding electrons; then proceed to lone pairs on terminal atoms and finally to lone pairs on the central atom.

$$:\ddot{O} - H$$

Finally, write the Lewis structure in brackets with the charge of the ion in the upper right-hand corner.

$$\left[:\ddot{O} - H \right]^{-}$$

(c) KNO_3: K^+

$$\left[\ddot{O} = \overset{\displaystyle :\ddot{O}:}{\underset{}{N}} - \ddot{O} \right]^{-}$$

Determine the cation and anion.

$$K^+ \qquad NO_3^{-}$$

Write the Lewis symbol for the potassium cation based on the valence electrons.

K $4s^1$ K$^+$ $4s^0$

K·   K$^+$

K must lose one electron and be left with the octet from the previous shell.

Write the Lewis structure for the covalent anion.

Write the correct skeletal structure for the ion.

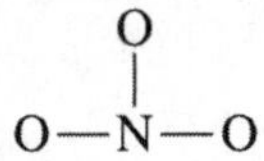

$$\begin{array}{c} \text{O} \\ | \\ \text{O—N—O} \end{array}$$

Calculate the total number of electrons for the Lewis structure by summing the valence electrons of each atom in the ion and adding one for the 1− charge.

(number of valence e⁻ for N) + 3(number of valence e⁻ for O) + 1 = 5 + 3(6) + 1 = 24

Distribute the electrons among the atoms, giving octets to as many atoms as possible. Begin with the bonding electrons; then proceed to lone pairs on terminal atoms and finally to lone pairs on the central atom.

$$\begin{array}{c} :\ddot{\text{O}}: \\ | \\ :\ddot{\text{O}}\text{—N—}\ddot{\text{O}}: \end{array}$$

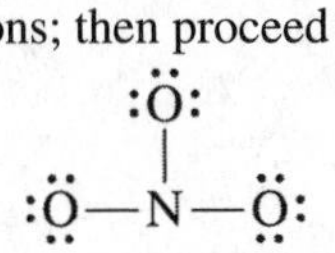

If any atom lacks an octet, form double or triple bonds as necessary.

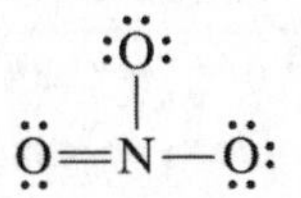

$$\begin{array}{c} :\ddot{\text{O}}: \\ | \\ \ddot{\text{O}}\text{=N—}\ddot{\text{O}}: \end{array}$$

Finally, write the Lewis symbol in brackets with the charge of the ion in the upper right-hand corner.

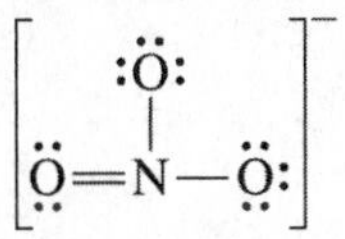

$$\left[\begin{array}{c} :\ddot{\text{O}}: \\ | \\ \ddot{\text{O}}\text{=N—}\ddot{\text{O}}: \end{array} \right]^-$$

The double bond can be between the N and any of the oxygen atoms, so there are resonance structures.

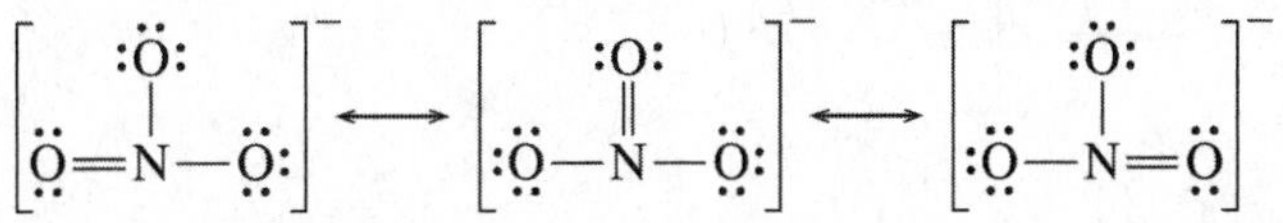

$$\left[\begin{array}{c} :\ddot{\text{O}}: \\ | \\ \ddot{\text{O}}\text{=N—}\ddot{\text{O}}: \end{array} \right]^- \longleftrightarrow \left[\begin{array}{c} :\text{O}: \\ \| \\ :\ddot{\text{O}}\text{—N—}\ddot{\text{O}}: \end{array} \right]^- \longleftrightarrow \left[\begin{array}{c} :\ddot{\text{O}}: \\ | \\ :\ddot{\text{O}}\text{—N=}\ddot{\text{O}} \end{array} \right]^-$$

(d)   LiIO: Li$^+$

$$\left[:\ddot{\text{I}}\text{—}\ddot{\text{O}}: \right]^-$$

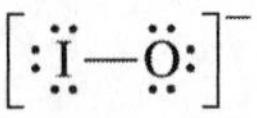

Determine the cation and anion.

Li$^+$ IO$^-$

Write the Lewis structure for the lithium cation based on the valence electrons.

Li $2s^1$ Li$^+$ $2s^0$

Li·   Li$^+$

Li must lose one electron and be left with the octet from the previous shell.

Write the Lewis structure for the covalent anion.

Write the correct skeletal structure for the ion.

I—O

Calculate the total number of electrons for the Lewis structure by summing the number of valence electrons of each atom in the ion and adding one for the 1− charge.

(number of valence e⁻ for I) + (number of valence e⁻ for O) = 7 + 6 + 1 = 14

Distribute the electrons among the atoms, giving octets to as many atoms as possible. Begin with the bonding electrons; then proceed to lone pairs on terminal atoms and finally to lone pairs on the central atom.

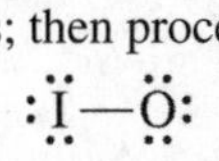

$$:\ddot{\text{I}}\text{—}\ddot{\text{O}}:$$

Finally, write the Lewis structure in brackets with the charge of the ion in the upper right-hand corner.

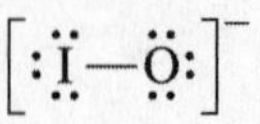

$$\left[\, :\ddot{\text{I}}-\ddot{\text{O}}: \,\right]^{-}$$

9.46   (a) $RbIO_2$: Rb^+

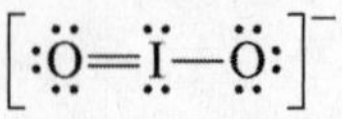

$$\left[\, :\ddot{\text{O}}=\ddot{\text{I}}-\ddot{\text{O}}: \,\right]^{-}$$

Determine the cation and anion.

$\quad Rb^+ \qquad IO_2^-$

Write the Lewis symbol for the rubidium cation based on the valence electrons.

$\quad$ Rb $\ 5s^1 \qquad Rb^+ \ 5s^0$

$\quad$ Rb$\cdot \qquad\qquad Rb^+$

Rb must lose one electron and be left with the octet from the previous shell.

Write the Lewis structure for the covalent anion.

Write the correct skeletal structure for the ion.

$\quad$ O—I—O

Calculate the total number of electrons for the Lewis structure by summing the valence electrons of each atom in the ion and adding one for the 1− charge.

$\quad$ (number of valence e$^-$ for I) + 2(number of valence e$^-$ for O) = 7 + 2(6) + 1 = 20

Distribute the electrons among the atoms, giving octets to as many atoms as possible. Begin with the bonding electrons; then proceed to lone pairs on terminal atoms and finally to lone pairs on the central atom.

$$:\ddot{\text{O}}-\ddot{\text{I}}-\ddot{\text{O}}:$$

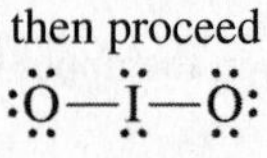

Then form double bonds to eliminate formal charge on I.

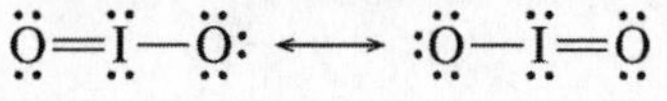

$$\ddot{\text{O}}=\ddot{\text{I}}-\ddot{\text{O}}: \longleftrightarrow :\ddot{\text{O}}-\ddot{\text{I}}=\ddot{\text{O}}$$

Finally, write the Lewis structure in brackets with the charge of the ion in the upper right-hand corner.

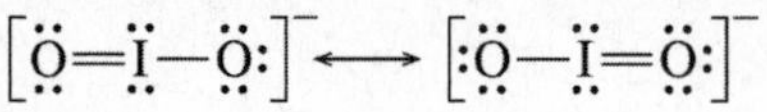

$$\left[\, \ddot{\text{O}}=\ddot{\text{I}}-\ddot{\text{O}}: \,\right]^{-} \longleftrightarrow \left[\, :\ddot{\text{O}}-\ddot{\text{I}}=\ddot{\text{O}}: \,\right]^{-}$$

(b) NH_4Cl:

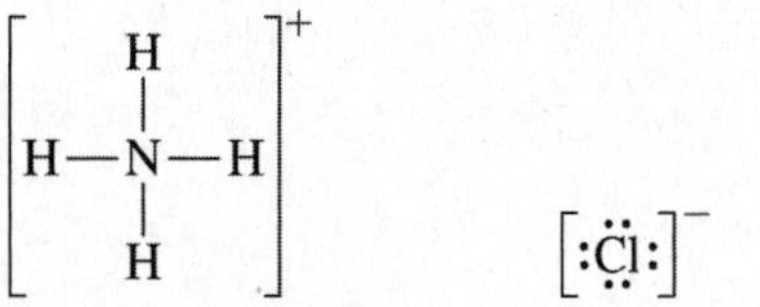

$$\left[\begin{array}{c} \text{H} \\ | \\ \text{H}-\text{N}-\text{H} \\ | \\ \text{H} \end{array}\right]^{+} \qquad\qquad \left[\, :\ddot{\text{C}}\text{l}: \,\right]^{-}$$

Determine the cation and anion.

$\quad NH_4^+ \qquad Cl^-$

Write the Lewis structure for the covalent cation.

Write the correct skeletal structure for the ion.

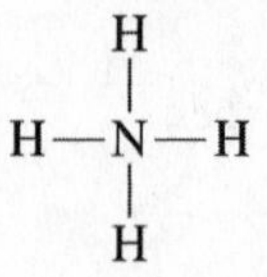

$$\begin{array}{c} \text{H} \\ | \\ \text{H}-\text{N}-\text{H} \\ | \\ \text{H} \end{array}$$

Calculate the total number of electrons for the Lewis structure by summing the number of valence electrons of each atom in the ion and subtracting one for the 1+ charge.

$\quad$ (number of valence e$^-$ for N) + 4(number of valence e$^-$ for H) − 1 = 5 + 4(1) − 1 = 8

Distribute the electrons among the atoms, giving octets (or duets for H) to as many atoms as possible. Begin with the bonding electrons; then proceed to lone pairs on terminal atoms and finally to lone pairs on the central atom.

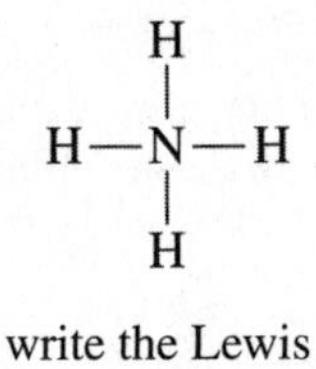

$$\begin{array}{c} H \\ | \\ H{-}N{-}H \\ | \\ H \end{array}$$

Finally, write the Lewis structure in brackets with the charge of the ion in the upper right-hand corner.

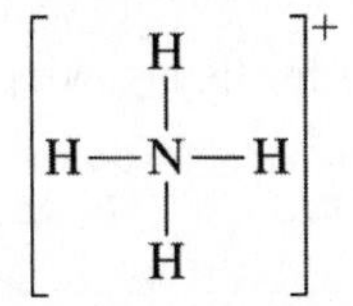

$$\left[\begin{array}{c} H \\ | \\ H{-}N{-}H \\ | \\ H \end{array}\right]^{+}$$

Write the Lewis symbol for the chlorine anion based on the valence electrons.

Cl $3s^2 3p^5$

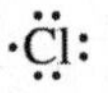

·C̈l:

Cl must gain one electron to complete its octet.

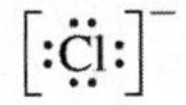

$$\left[:\ddot{\text{C}}\text{l}:\right]^{-}$$

(c)   KOH: K^+

$$\left[:\ddot{\text{O}}{-}\text{H}\right]^{-}$$

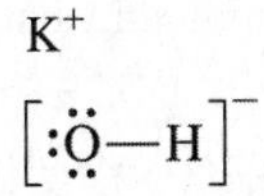

Determine the cation and anion.

K^+ OH^-

Write the Lewis symbol for the potassium cation based on the valence electrons.

K $4s^1$ K^+ $4s^0$
K· K^+

K must lose one electron and be left with the octet from the previous shell.
Write the Lewis structure for the covalent anion.
Write the correct skeletal structure for the ion.

O—H

Calculate the total number of electrons for the Lewis structure by summing the valence electrons of each atom in the ion and adding one for the 1− charge.

(number of valence e^- for H) + (number of valence e^- for O) + 1 = 1 + 6 + 1 = 8

Distribute the electrons among the atoms, giving octets (or duets for H) to as many atoms as possible. Begin with the bonding electrons; then proceed to lone pairs on terminal atoms and finally to lone pairs on the central atom.

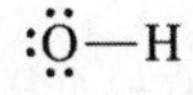

:Ö—H

Finally, write the Lewis structure in brackets with the charge of the ion in the upper right-hand corner.

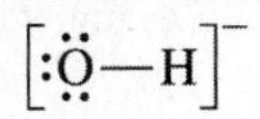

$$\left[:\ddot{\text{O}}{-}\text{H}\right]^{-}$$

(d) $Sr(CN)_2$: Sr^{2+}

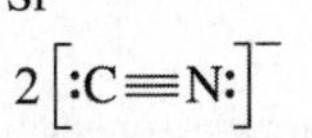

$$2\left[:\text{C}\equiv\text{N}:\right]^{-}$$

Determine the cation and anion.

Sr^{2+} $2\,CN^-$

Write the Lewis symbol for the strontium cation based on the valence electrons.

Sr $5s^2$ Sr^{2+} $5s^0$
·Sr· Sr^{2+}

Sr must lose two electrons and be left with the octet from the previous shell.
Write the Lewis structure for the covalent anion.
Write the correct skeletal structure for the ion.

C—N

Calculate the total number of electrons for the Lewis structure by summing the valence electrons of each atom in the ion and adding one for the 1− charge.

(number of valence e⁻ for N) + (number of valence e⁻ for C) + 1 = 5 + 4 + 1 = 10

Distribute the electrons among the atoms, giving octets to as many atoms as possible. Begin with the bonding electrons; then proceed to lone pairs on terminal atoms and finally to lone pairs on the central atom.

$$:C-\ddot{N}:$$

Complete octets on both atoms by forming a triple bond.

$$:C\equiv N:$$

Finally, write the Lewis structure in brackets with the charge of the ion in the upper right-hand corner.

$$\left[:C\equiv N:\right]^-$$

9.47   (a) C_4H_8:   Write the correct skeletal structure for the molecule.

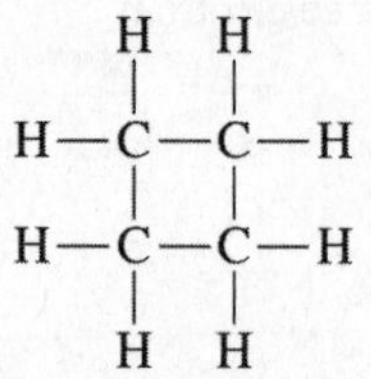

$$
\begin{array}{ccc}
 & H & H \\
 & | & | \\
H- & C- & C-H \\
 & | & | \\
H- & C- & C-H \\
 & | & | \\
 & H & H \\
\end{array}
$$

Calculate the total number of electrons for the Lewis structure by summing the number of valence electrons of each atom in the molecule.

4(number of valence e⁻ for C) + 8(number of valence e⁻ for H) = 4(4) + 8(1) = 24

Distribute the electrons among the atoms, giving octets (or duets for H) to as many atoms as possible.

$$
\begin{array}{ccc}
 & H & H \\
 & | & | \\
H- & C- & C-H \\
 & | & | \\
H- & C- & C-H \\
 & | & | \\
 & H & H \\
\end{array}
$$

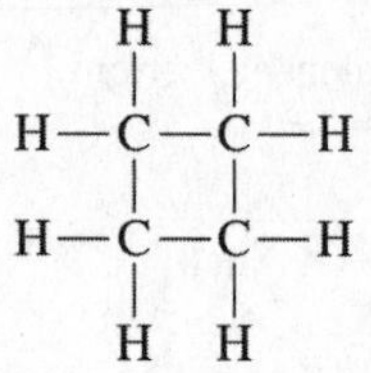

All atoms have octets or duets for H.

(b) C_4H_4:   Write the correct skeletal structure for the molecule.

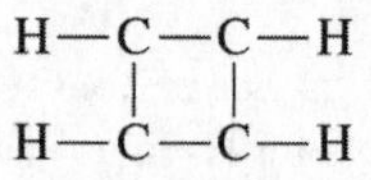

$$
\begin{array}{ccc}
H- & C- & C-H \\
 & | & | \\
H- & C- & C-H \\
\end{array}
$$

Calculate the total number of electrons for the Lewis structure by summing the number of valence electrons of each atom in the molecule.

4(number of valence e⁻ for C) + 4(number of valence e⁻ for H) = 4(4) + 4(1) = 20

Distribute the electrons among the atoms, giving octets (or duets for H) to as many atoms as possible.

$$
\begin{array}{ccc}
H- & \ddot{C}- & \ddot{C}-H \\
 & | & | \\
H- & C- & C-H \\
\end{array}
$$

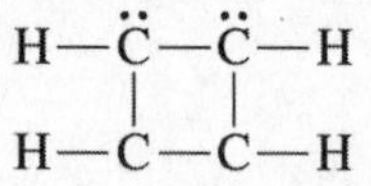

Complete octets by forming double bonds on alternating carbons; draw resonance structures.

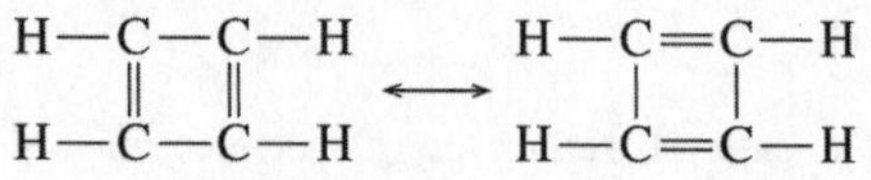

$$
\begin{array}{ccc}
H-C-C-H & & H-C=C-H \\
\parallel \quad \parallel & \longleftrightarrow & | \quad\quad | \\
H-C-C-H & & H-C=C-H \\
\end{array}
$$

(c) C_6H_{12}:   Write the correct skeletal structure for the molecule.

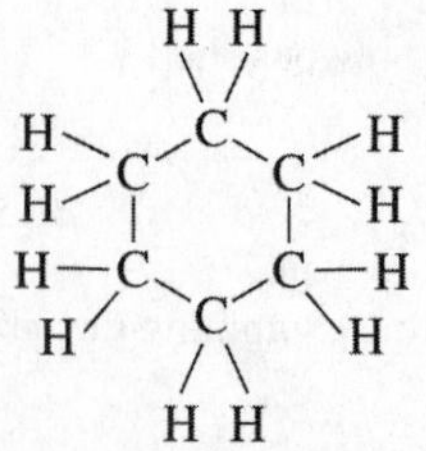

$$
\begin{array}{c}
H\ H \\
\diagdown\diagup \\
H\diagdown \quad C \quad \diagup H \\
H\diagup C \qquad C \diagdown H \\
H-C \diagdown \quad\quad \diagup C-H \\
H\diagup \quad C \quad \diagdown H \\
\diagup\diagdown \\
H\ H
\end{array}
$$

Calculate the total number of electrons for the Lewis structure by summing the valence electrons of each atom in the molecule.

6(number of valence e⁻ for C) + 12(number of valence e⁻ for H) = 6(4) + 12(1) = 36

Distribute the electrons among the atoms, giving octets (or duets for H) to as many atoms as possible. Begin with the bonding.

All 36 electrons are used, and all atoms have octets or duets for H.

(d) C_6H_6:   Write the correct skeletal structure for the molecule.

Calculate the total number of electrons for the Lewis structure by summing the number of valence electrons of each atom in the molecule.

6(number of valence e⁻ for C) + 6(number of valence e⁻ for H) = 6(4) + 6(1) = 30

Distribute the electrons among the atoms, giving octets (or duets for H) to as many atoms as possible.

Complete octets by forming double bonds on alternating carbons; draw resonance structures.

9.48 H_2NCH_2COOH Write the correct skeletal structure for the molecule.

Calculate the total number of electrons for the Lewis structure by summing the number of valence electrons of each atom in the molecule.

2(number of valence e⁻ for C) + 2(number of valence e⁻ for O) + (number of valence e⁻ for N) +
5(number of valence e⁻ for H) = 2(4) + 2(6) + 5 + 5(1) = 30

Distribute the electrons among the atoms, giving octets (or duets for H) to as many atoms as possible. Begin with the bonding electrons; then proceed to lone pairs on terminal atoms and finally to lone pairs on the central atoms.

$$
\begin{array}{c}
\text{H} \quad :\!\ddot{\text{O}}\!: \\
\text{H}\!\diagdown \\
\qquad :\!\text{N}\!-\!\text{C}\!-\!\text{C}\!-\!\ddot{\text{O}}\!-\!\text{H} \\
\text{H}\!\diagup \\
\qquad\quad \text{H}
\end{array}
$$

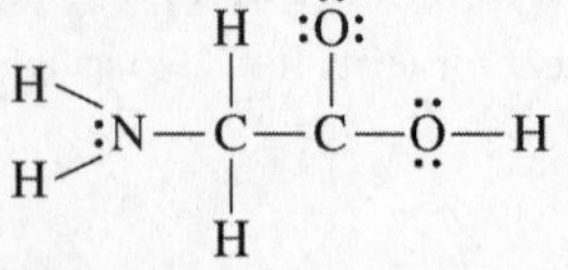

All 30 electrons are used.

Draw a double bond to satisfy the octet on C.

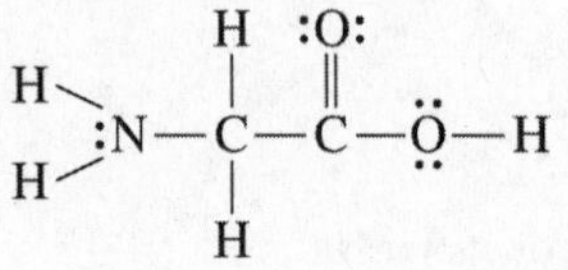

$$
\begin{array}{c}
\text{H} \quad :\!\text{O}\!: \\
\text{H}\!\diagdown \\
\qquad :\!\text{N}\!-\!\text{C}\!=\!\text{C}\!-\!\ddot{\text{O}}\!-\!\text{H} \\
\text{H}\!\diagup \\
\qquad\quad \text{H}
\end{array}
$$

9.49   **Given:** 26.01% C; 4.38% H; 69.52% O; molar mass = 46.02 g/mol

Find: molecular formula and Lewis structure

Conceptual Plan: convert mass to mol of each element $\rightarrow$ pseudoformula $\rightarrow$ empirical formula

$$\frac{1 \text{ mol C}}{12.01 \text{ g C}} \qquad \frac{1 \text{ mol H}}{1.008 \text{ g H}} \qquad \frac{1 \text{ mol O}}{16.00 \text{ g O}} \qquad\qquad \text{divide by smallest number}$$

$\rightarrow$ **molecular formula** $\rightarrow$ **Lewis structure**

empirical formula $\times$ n

Solution: $26.01 \text{ g C} \times \dfrac{1 \text{ mol C}}{12.01 \text{ g C}} = 2.166 \text{ mol C}$

$4.38 \text{ g H} \times \dfrac{1 \text{ mol H}}{1.008 \text{ g H}} = 4.345 \text{ mol H}$

$69.52 \text{ g O} \times \dfrac{1 \text{ mol O}}{16.00 \text{ g O}} = 4.345 \text{ mol O}$

$C_{2.166}H_{4.345}O_{4.345}$

$C_{\frac{2.166}{2.166}}H_{\frac{4.345}{2.166}}O_{\frac{4.345}{2.166}} \rightarrow CH_2O_2$

The correct empirical formula is CH_2O_2.

empirical formula mass = (12.01 g/mol) + 2(1.008 g/mol) + 2(16.00 g/mol) = 46.03 g/mol

$$n = \frac{\text{molar mass}}{\text{formula molar mass}} = \frac{46.02 \text{ g/mol}}{46.03 \text{ g/mol}} = 1$$

molecular formula = $CH_2O_2 \times 1$

$= CH_2O_2$

Write the correct skeletal structure for the molecule.

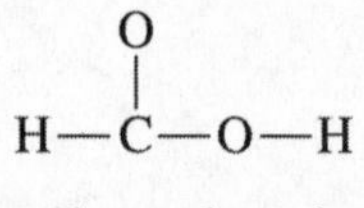

$$
\begin{array}{c}
\text{O} \\
\| \\
\text{H}\!-\!\text{C}\!-\!\text{O}\!-\!\text{H}
\end{array}
$$

Calculate the total number of electrons for the Lewis structure by summing the number of valence electrons of each atom in the molecule.

(number of valence e^- for C) + 2(number of valence e^- for O) + 2(number of valence e^- for H)
$= 4 + 2(6) + 2(1) = 18$

Distribute the electrons among the atoms, giving octets (or duets for H) to as many atoms as possible. Begin with the bonding electrons; then proceed to lone pairs on terminal atoms and finally to lone pairs on the central atoms.

$$
\begin{array}{c}
:\!\ddot{\text{O}}\!: \\
| \\
\text{H}\!-\!\text{C}\!-\!\ddot{\text{O}}\!-\!\text{H}
\end{array}
$$

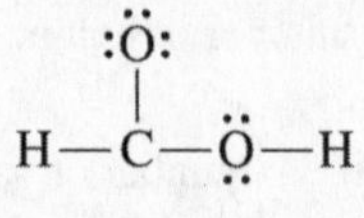

Complete the octet on C by forming a double bond.

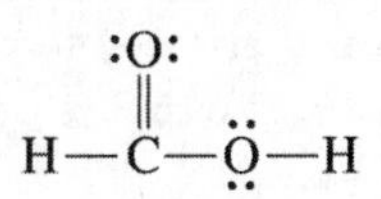

$$:O:$$
$$\|$$
$$H-C-\ddot{O}-H$$

9.50   **Given:** 28.57% C; 4.80% H; 66.64% N; molar mass m $=$ 42.04 g/mol
Find: molecular formula and Lewis structure
Conceptual Plan: convert mass to mol of each element $\rightarrow$ **pseudoformula** $\rightarrow$ **empirical formula**

$$\frac{1 \text{mol C}}{12.01 \text{ g C}} \qquad \frac{1 \text{mol H}}{1.008 \text{ g H}} \qquad \frac{1 \text{mol N}}{14.01 \text{ g N}}$$ divide by smallest number

$\rightarrow$ **molecular formula** $\rightarrow$ **Lewis structure**

empirical formula $\times$ n

Solution: $28.57 \text{ g C} \times \dfrac{1 \text{ mol C}}{12.01 \text{ g C}} = 2.379 \text{ mol C}$

$4.80 \text{ g H} \times \dfrac{1 \text{mol H}}{1.008 \text{ g H}} = 4.7\underline{6}2 \text{ mol H}$

$66.64 \text{ g N} \times \dfrac{1 \text{ mol N}}{14.01 \text{ g N}} = 4.757 \text{ mol N}$

$C_{2.379}H_{4.762}N_{4.757}$

$\underset{2.379 \quad 2.379 \quad 2.379}{C_{2.379}H_{4.762}N_{4.757}} \rightarrow CH_2N_2$

The correct empirical formula is CH_2N_2.

empirical formula mass $=$ (12.01 g/mol) $+$ 2(1.008 g/mol) $+$ 2(14.01 g/mol) $=$ 42.05 g/mol

$$n = \frac{\text{molar mass}}{\text{formula molar mass}} = \frac{42.04 \text{ g/mol}}{42.05 \text{ g/mol}} = 1$$

molecular formula $=$ $CH_2N_2 \times 1 = CH_2N_2$

Write the correct skeletal structure for the molecule.

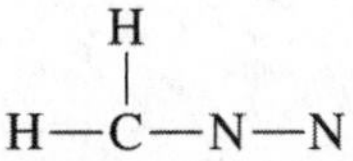

$$\overset{\displaystyle H}{\underset{\displaystyle |}{H-C-N-N}}$$

Calculate the total number of electrons for the Lewis structure by summing the number of valence electrons of each atom in the molecule.

(number of valence e$^-$ for C) $+$ 2(number of valence e$^-$ for N) $+$ 2(number of valence e$^-$ for H)
$= 4 + 2(5) + 2(1) = 16$

Distribute the electrons among the atoms, giving octets (or duets for H) to as many atoms as possible. Begin with the bonding electrons; then proceed to lone pairs on terminal atoms and finally to lone pairs on the central atoms.

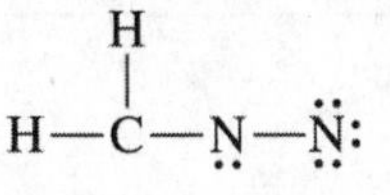

$$\overset{\displaystyle H}{\underset{\displaystyle |}{H-C-N-\ddot{\underset{\cdot\cdot}{N}}:}}$$

Complete the octet on C and N by forming double bonds.

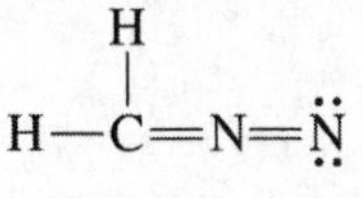

$$\overset{\displaystyle H}{\underset{\displaystyle |}{H-C=N=\ddot{\underset{\cdot\cdot}{N}}}}$$

Calculate the formal charge on each atom in the structure by finding the number of valence electrons and subtracting the number of lone pair electrons and one-half the number of bonding electrons.

	H_{left}	H_{top}	C	N_{left}	N_{right}
number of valence electrons	1	1	4	5	5
$-$ number of lone pair electrons	0	0	0	0	4
$-$ 1/2(number of bonding electrons)	1	1	4	4	2
Formal charge	0	0	0	+1	-1

The diazomethane molecule has nitrogen atoms next to each other with a +1 and a −1 formal charge. Nitrogen is more electronegative than C, which has a 0 formal charge. The nitrogen with the +1 charge is not a very stable configuration for nitrogen, particularly next to the 0 formal charge C atom.

9.51 To determine the values of the lattice energy, it is necessary to look them up online. The lattice energy of Al_2O_3 is −15,916 kJ/mol; the value for Fe_2O_3 is −14,774 kJ/mol. The thermite reaction is exothermic due to the energy released when the Al_2O_3 lattice forms. The lattice energy of Al_2O_3 is more negative than the lattice energy of Fe_2O_3.

9.52 For NaCl, E is proportional to $(1+)(1-) = -1$, while for XY, E is proportional to $(3+)(3-) = -9$. So the relative stabilization for XY relative to NaCl should be roughly nine times greater.
$\Delta H_{lattice}(XY) = 9 \times \Delta H_{lattice}(NaCl) = 9(-787 \text{ kJ/mol}) = -7083 \text{ kJ/mol}$.

9.53 HNO_3 Write the correct skeletal structure for the molecule.

$$\begin{array}{c} O \\ | \\ H-O-N-O \end{array}$$

Calculate the total number of electrons for the Lewis structure by summing the number of valence electrons of each atom in the molecule.

3(number of valence e⁻ for O) + (number of valence e⁻ for N) + (number of valence e⁻ for H) = 3(6) + 5 + 1 = 24

Distribute the electrons among the atoms, giving octets (or duets for H) to as many atoms as possible. Begin with the bonding electrons; then proceed to lone pairs on terminal atoms and finally to lone pairs on the central atom.

$$\begin{array}{c} :\ddot{O}: \\ | \\ H-\ddot{O}-N-\ddot{O}: \end{array}$$

All 24 valence electrons are used.

If any atoms lack an octet, form double or triple bonds as necessary. The double bond can be formed to any of the three oxygen atoms, so there are three resonance forms.

$$\underset{I}{H-\ddot{\underset{..}{O}}-\overset{\overset{\textstyle :O:}{\|}}{N}-\ddot{\underset{..}{O}}:} \longleftrightarrow \underset{II}{H-\ddot{\underset{..}{O}}-\overset{\overset{\textstyle :\ddot{O}:}{|}}{N}=\ddot{O}} \longleftrightarrow \underset{III}{H-\ddot{O}=\overset{\overset{\textstyle :\ddot{O}:}{|}}{N}-\ddot{\underset{..}{O}}:}$$

All atoms have octets (duets for H); the structure is complete.

To determine which resonance hybrid(s) is most important, calculate the formal charge on each atom in each structure by finding the number of valence electrons and subtracting the number of lone pair electrons and one-half the number of bonding electrons.

	Structure I						**Structure II**				
	O_{left}	O_{top}	O_{right}	N	H		O_{left}	O_{top}	O_{right}	N	H
number of valence electrons	6	6	6	5	1		6	6	6	5	1
− number of lone pair electrons	4	4	6	0	0		4	6	4	0	0
− 1/2(number of bonding electrons)	2	2	1	4	1		2	1	2	4	1
Formal charge	0	0	−1	+1	0		0	−1	0	+1	0

	Structure III				
	O_{left}	O_{top}	O_{right}	N	H
number of valence electrons	6	6	6	5	1
− number of lone pair electrons	2	6	6	0	0
− 1/2(number of bonding electrons)	3	1	1	4	1
Formal charge	+1	−1	−1	+1	0

The sum of the formal charges is 0 for each structure, which is the overall charge of the molecule. However, in structures I and II, the individual formal charges are lower. These two forms would contribute equally to the structure of HNO_3. Structure III would be less important because the individual formal charges are higher.

9.54   Cl₂CO   Write the correct skeletal structure for the molecule.

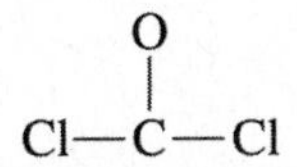

$$
\begin{array}{c}
\text{O} \\
| \\
\text{Cl—C—Cl}
\end{array}
$$

Calculate the total number of electrons for the Lewis structure by summing the number of valence electrons of each atom in the molecule.

1(number of valence e⁻ for O) + (number of valence e⁻ for C) + 2(number of valence e⁻ for Cl)
    = 6 + 4 + 2(7) = 24

Distribute the electrons among the atoms, giving octets to as many atoms as possible. Begin with the bonding electrons; then proceed to lone pairs on terminal atoms and finally to lone pairs on the central atom.

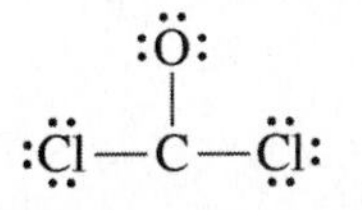

$$
\begin{array}{c}
\text{:Ö:} \\
| \\
\text{:C̈l—C—C̈l:}
\end{array}
$$

All 24 valence electrons are used.

If any atoms lack an octet, form double or triple bonds as necessary. The double bond can be formed to any of the three terminal atoms, so there are three resonance forms.

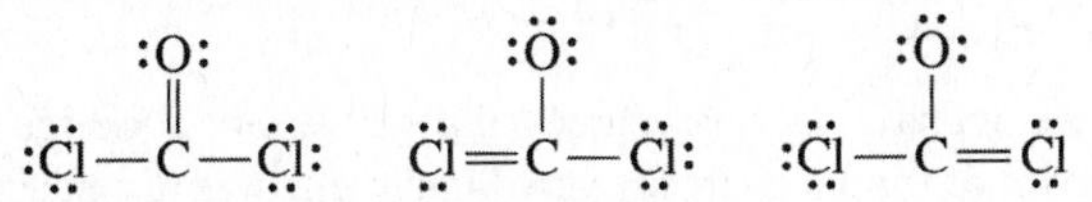

$$
\begin{array}{ccc}
\text{:O:} & \text{:Ö:} & \text{:Ö:} \\
\| & | & | \\
\text{:C̈l—C—C̈l:} & \text{C̈l=C—C̈l:} & \text{:C̈l—C=C̈l} \\
\text{I} & \text{II} & \text{III}
\end{array}
$$

All atoms have octets; the structures are complete.

To determine which resonance hybrids(s) is most important, calculate the formal charge on each atom in each structure by finding the number of valence electrons and subtracting the number of lone pair electrons and one-half the number of bonding electrons.

	Structure I					Structure II			
	Cl_right	Cl_left	O	C		Cl_right	Cl_left	O	C
number of valence electrons	7	7	6	4		7	7	6	4
− number of lone pair electrons	6	6	4	0		4	6	6	0
− 1/2(number of bonding electrons)	1	1	2	4		2	1	1	4
Formal charge	0	0	0	0		+1	0	−1	0

	Structure III			
	Cl_left	Cl_right	O	C
number of valence electrons	7	7	6	4
− number of lone pair electrons	6	4	6	0
− 1/2(number of bonding electrons)	1	2	1	4
Formal charge	0	+1	−1	0

The sum of the formal charges is 0 for each structure, which is the overall charge of the molecule. However, in structure I, the individual formal charges are lower, and this form would be more important to Cl₂CO than structure II and structure III.

9.55   CNO⁻   Write the skeletal structure:

C—N—O

Determine the number of valence electrons.

(valence e⁻ from C) + (valence e⁻ from N) + (valence e⁻ from O) + 1(from the negative charge)

4 + 5 + 6 + 1 = 16

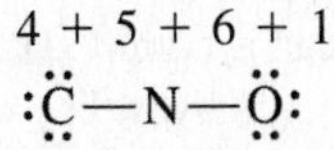

:C̈—N—Ö:

Distribute the electrons to complete octets if possible.

$$\left[\ddot{C}=N=\ddot{O}\right]^{-} \longleftrightarrow \left[:C\equiv N-\ddot{O}:\right]^{-} \longleftrightarrow \left[:\ddot{C}-N\equiv O:\right]^{-}$$
$$\text{I} \qquad\qquad\qquad \text{II} \qquad\qquad\qquad \text{III}$$

Determine the formal charge on each atom for each structure.

| | **Structure I** | | | **Structure II** | | |
	C	N	O	C	N	O
number of valence electrons	4	5	6	4	5	6
− number of lone pair electrons	4	0	4	2	0	6
− 1/2(number of bonding electrons)	2	4	2	3	4	1
Formal charge	−2	+1	0	−1	+1	−1

| | **Structure III** | | |
	C	N	O
number of valence electrons	4	5	6
− number of lone pair electrons	6	0	2
− 1/2(number of bonding electrons)	1	4	3
Formal charge	−3	+1	+1

Structures I, II, and III all follow the octet rule but have varying degrees of negative formal charge on carbon, which is the least electronegative atom. Also, the amount of formal charge is very high in all three resonance forms. Although structure II is the best of the resonance forms, it has a −1 charge on the least electronegative atom, C, and a +1 charge on the more electronegative atom, N. Therefore, none of these resonance forms contributes strongly to the stability of the fulminate ion and the ion is not very stable.

9.56   The Lewis structures for the three ions will be similar. So we can write the Lewis structure for one ion and use it to determine the other two.

Br_3^-:   Write the correct skeletal structure for the ion.

    Br — Br — Br

Calculate the total number of electrons for the Lewis structure by summing the number of valence electrons of each atom in the ion and adding 1 for the 1− charge.

    3(number of valence e^- for Br) + 1 = 3(7) + 1 = 22

Distribute the electrons among the atoms, giving octets to as many atoms as possible. Begin with the bonding electrons; then proceed to lone pairs on terminal atoms and finally to lone pairs on the central atom. Assign electrons above 8 to the central atom.

    $:\ddot{Br}-\ddot{Br}-\ddot{Br}:$

Finally, place the ion in brackets and place the charge in the upper right-hand corner.

$$\left[:\ddot{Br}-\ddot{Br}-\ddot{Br}:\right]^{-}$$

Because Br, I, and F are all in the same family, each of these ions would have 22 electrons and should have the same Lewis structure.

$$\left[:\ddot{Br}-\ddot{Br}-\ddot{Br}:\right]^{-}$$

$$\left[:\ddot{I}-\ddot{I}-\ddot{I}:\right]^{-}$$

$$\left[:\ddot{F}-\ddot{F}-\ddot{F}:\right]^{-}$$

All three ions are written with five electron groups around the central atom. Bromine and iodine can accommodate ten electrons around the central atom; fluorine cannot. Fluorine is in period 2 and can accommodate, at most, eight electrons around the central atom because there are no orbitals low enough in energy to hybridize with the 2s and 2p orbitals. Therefore, F_3^- does not exist.

9.57   (a) C_3H_8:   Write the correct skeletal structure for the molecule.

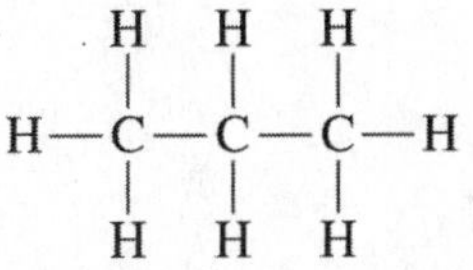

$$
\begin{array}{ccccccc}
 & H & & H & & H & \\
 & | & & | & & | & \\
H- & C & - & C & - & C & -H \\
 & | & & | & & | & \\
 & H & & H & & H &
\end{array}
$$

Calculate the total number of electrons for the Lewis structure by summing the valence electrons of each atom in the molecule.

3(number of valence e⁻ for C) + 8(number of valence e⁻ for H) = 3(4) + 8(1) = 20

Distribute the electrons among the atoms, giving octets (or duets for H) to as many atoms as possible. Begin with the bonding electrons; then proceed to lone pairs on terminal atoms and finally to lone pairs on the central atom.

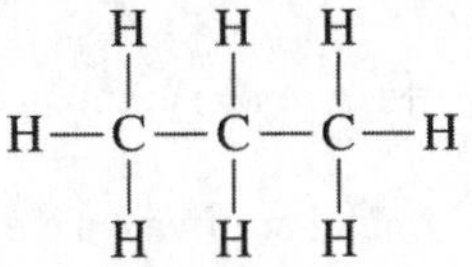

$$
\begin{array}{ccccccc}
 & H & & H & & H & \\
 & | & & | & & | & \\
H- & C & - & C & - & C & -H \\
 & | & & | & & | & \\
 & H & & H & & H &
\end{array}
$$

All 20 valence electrons are used.

       (b) CH_3OCH_3:   Write the correct skeletal structure for the molecule.

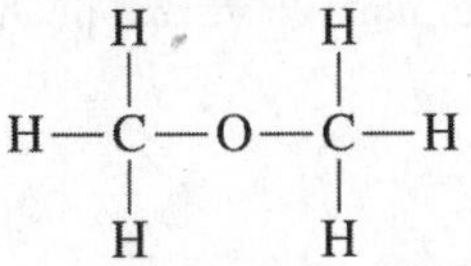

$$
\begin{array}{ccccccc}
 & H & & & & H & \\
 & | & & & & | & \\
H- & C & - & O & - & C & -H \\
 & | & & & & | & \\
 & H & & & & H &
\end{array}
$$

Calculate the total number of electrons for the Lewis structure by summing the valence electrons of each atom in the molecule.

2(number of valence e⁻ for C) + 6(number of valence e⁻ for H) + (number of valence electrons for O) = 2(4) + 6(1) + 6 = 20

Distribute the electrons among the atoms, giving octets (or duets for H) to as many atoms as possible. Begin with the bonding electrons; then proceed to lone pairs on terminal atoms and finally to lone pairs on the central atom.

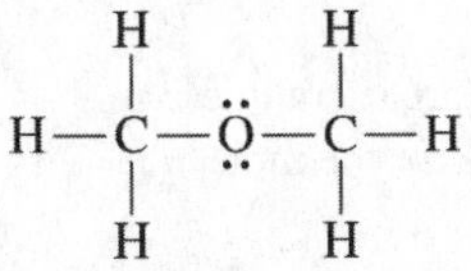

$$
\begin{array}{ccccccc}
 & H & & & & H & \\
 & | & & & & | & \\
H- & C & - & \ddot{\underset{..}{O}} & - & C & -H \\
 & | & & & & | & \\
 & H & & & & H &
\end{array}
$$

All 20 valence electrons are used.

       (c) CH_3COCH_3:   Write the correct skeletal structure for the molecule.

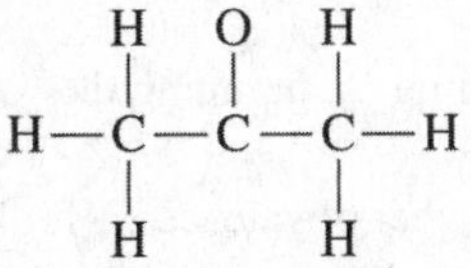

$$
\begin{array}{ccccccc}
 & H & & O & & H & \\
 & | & & | & & | & \\
H- & C & - & C & - & C & -H \\
 & | & & | & & | & \\
 & H & & H & & H &
\end{array}
$$

Calculate the total number of electrons for the Lewis structure by summing the valence electrons of each atom in the molecule.

3(number of valence e⁻ for C) + 6(number of valence e⁻ for H) + (number of valence electrons for O) = 3(4) + 6(1) + 6 = 24

Distribute the electrons among the atoms, giving octets (or duets for H) to as many atoms as possible. Begin with the bonding electrons; then proceed to lone pairs on terminal atoms and finally to lone pairs on the central atom.

$$
\begin{array}{ccccccc}
 & H & & :\ddot{O}: & & H & \\
 & | & & | & & | & \\
H- & C & - & C & - & C & -H \\
 & | & & | & & | & \\
 & H & & H & & H &
\end{array}
$$

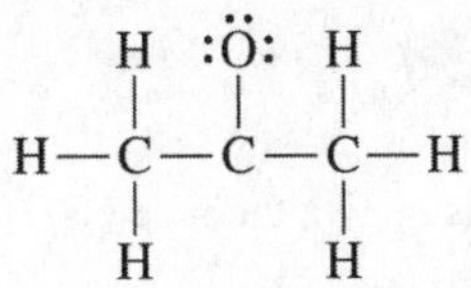

All 24 valence electrons are used.

If any atom lacks an octet, form double or triple bonds to give them octets.

$$\begin{array}{ccc} H & :O: & H \\ | & \| & | \\ H-C- & C- & C-H \\ | & & | \\ H & & H \end{array}$$

All atoms have octets (duets for hydrogen); the structure is complete.

(d)   CH$_3$COOH: Write the correct skeletal structure for the molecule.

$$\begin{array}{cc} H & O \\ | & | \\ H-C-C & -O-H \\ | & \\ H & \end{array}$$

Calculate the total number of electrons for the Lewis structure by summing the valence electrons of each atom in the molecule.

2(number of valence e$^-$ for C) + 4(number of valence e$^-$ for H) + 2(number of valence electrons for O) = 2(4) + 4(1) + 2(6) = 24

Distribute the electrons among the atoms, giving octets (or duets for H) to as many atoms as possible. Begin with the bonding electrons; then proceed to lone pairs on terminal atoms and finally to lone pairs on the central atom.

$$\begin{array}{cc} H & :\ddot{O}: \\ | & | \\ H-C-C & -\ddot{O}-H \\ | & \\ H & \end{array}$$

All 24 valence electrons are used.
If any atom lacks an octet, form double or triple bonds to give them octets.

$$\begin{array}{cc} H & :O: \\ | & \| \\ H-C-C & -\ddot{O}-H \\ | & \\ H & \end{array}$$

All atoms have octets (duets for hydrogen); the structure is complete.

(e)   CH$_3$CHO: Write the correct skeletal structure for the molecule.

$$\begin{array}{cc} H & O \\ | & | \\ H-C-C & -H \\ | & \\ H & \end{array}$$

Calculate the total number of electrons for the Lewis structure by summing the valence electrons of each atom in the molecule.

2(number of valence e$^-$ for C) + 4(number of valence e$^-$ for H) + (number of valence electrons for O) = 2(4) + 4(1) + (6) = 18

Distribute the electrons among the atoms, giving octets (or duets for H) to as many atoms as possible. Begin with the bonding electrons; then proceed to lone pairs on terminal atoms and finally to lone pairs on the central atom.

$$\begin{array}{cc} H & :\ddot{O}: \\ | & | \\ H-C-C & -H \\ | & \\ H & \end{array}$$

All 18 valence electrons are used.
If any atom lacks an octet, form double or triple bonds to give them octets.

$$\begin{array}{cc} H & :O: \\ | & \| \\ H-C-C & -H \\ | & \\ H & \end{array}$$

All atoms have octets (duets for hydrogen); the structure is complete.

9.58   (a) C_2H_4:   Write the correct skeletal structure for the molecule.

$$H-\underset{\underset{H}{|}}{C}-\underset{\underset{H}{|}}{C}-H$$

Calculate the total number of electrons for the Lewis structure by summing the valence electrons of each atom in the molecule.

2(number of valence e⁻ for C) + 4(number of valence e⁻ for H) = 2(4) + 4(1) = 12

Distribute the electrons among the atoms, giving octets (or duets for H) to as many atoms as possible. Begin with the bonding electrons; then proceed to lone pairs on terminal atoms and finally to lone pairs on the central atom.

$$H-\underset{\underset{H}{|}}{\overset{..}{C}}-\underset{\underset{H}{|}}{C}-H$$

All 12 valence electrons are used.

If any atom lacks an octet, form double or triple bonds to give them octets.

$$H-\underset{\underset{H}{|}}{C}=\underset{\underset{H}{|}}{C}-H$$

All atoms have octets (duets for hydrogen); the structure is complete.

    (b) CH_3NH_2:   Write the correct skeletal structure for the molecule.

$$H-\underset{\underset{H}{|}}{\overset{\overset{H}{|}}{C}}-\underset{\underset{H}{|}}{N}-H$$

Calculate the total number of electrons for the Lewis structure by summing the valence electrons of each atom in the molecule.

number of valence e⁻ for C + 5(number of valence e⁻ for H) + number of valence

electrons for N = 4 + 5(1) + 5 = 14

Distribute the electrons among the atoms, giving octets (or duets for H) to as many atoms as possible. Begin with the bonding electrons; then proceed to lone pairs on terminal atoms and finally to lone pairs on the central atom.

$$H-\underset{\underset{H}{|}}{\overset{\overset{H}{|}}{C}}-\underset{\underset{H}{|}}{\overset{..}{N}}-H$$

All 14 valence electrons are used. All atoms have octets (duets for hydrogen); the structure is complete.

    (c)   HCHO: Write the correct skeletal structure for the molecule.

$$H-\underset{}{\overset{\overset{O}{|}}{C}}-H$$

Calculate the total number of electrons for the Lewis structure by summing the valence electrons of each atom in the molecule.

number of valence e⁻ for C + 2(number of valence e⁻ for H) + number of valence

electrons for O = 4 + 2(1) + 6 = 12

Distribute the electrons among the atoms, giving octets (or duets for H) to as many atoms as possible. Begin with the bonding electrons; then proceed to lone pairs on terminal atoms and finally to lone pairs on the central atom.

$$H-\overset{\overset{..}{\overset{\displaystyle :\ddot{O}:}{|}}}{C}-H$$

All 12 valence electrons are used.

If any atom lacks an octet, form double or triple bonds to give them octets.

$$H-\overset{\overset{:O:}{\|}}{C}-H$$

All atoms have octets (duets for hydrogen); the structure is complete.

(d) CH_3CH_2OH: Write the correct skeletal structure for the molecule.

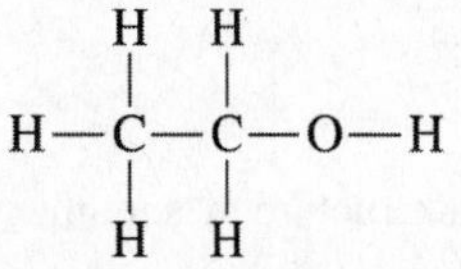

$$
\begin{array}{cccc}
 & H & H & \\
 & | & | & \\
H - & C - & C - & O - H \\
 & | & | & \\
 & H & H &
\end{array}
$$

Calculate the total number of electrons for the Lewis structure by summing the valence electrons of each atom in the molecule.

2(number of valence e⁻ for C) + 6(number of valence e⁻ for H) + number of electrons
for O = 2(4) + 6(1) + 6 = 20

Distribute the electrons among the atoms, giving octets (or duets for H) to as many atoms as possible. Begin with the bonding electrons; then proceed to lone pairs on terminal atoms and finally to lone pairs on the central atom.

$$
\begin{array}{cccc}
 & H & H & \\
 & | & | & \\
H - & C - & C - & \ddot{O} - H \\
 & | & | & \\
 & H & H &
\end{array}
$$

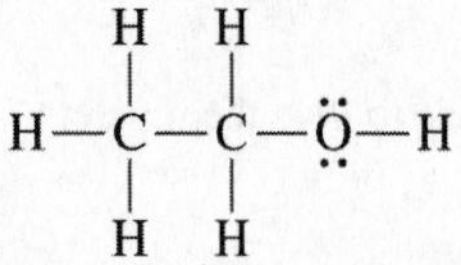

All 20 valence electrons are used. All atoms have octets (duets for hydrogen); the structure is complete.

(e) HCOOH: Write the correct skeletal structure for the molecule.

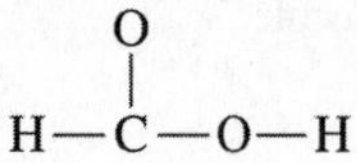

$$
\begin{array}{c}
O \\
\| \\
H - C - O - H
\end{array}
$$

Calculate the total number of electrons for the Lewis structure by summing the valence electrons of each atom in the molecule.

number of valence e⁻ for C + 2(number of valence e⁻ for H) + 2(number of electrons
for O) = 4 + 2(1) + 2(6) = 18

Distribute the electrons among the atoms, giving octets (or duets for H) to as many atoms as possible. Begin with the bonding electrons; then proceed to lone pairs on terminal atoms and finally to lone pairs on the central atom.

$$
\begin{array}{c}
:\ddot{O}: \\
| \\
H - C - \ddot{O} - H
\end{array}
$$

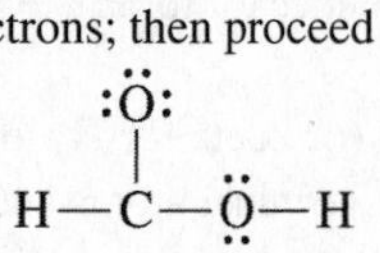

All 18 valence electrons are used.

If any atom lacks an octet, form double or triple bonds to give them octets.

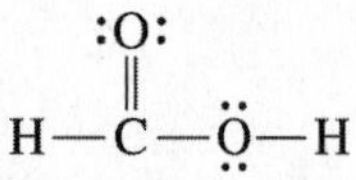

$$
\begin{array}{c}
:O: \\
\| \\
H - C - \ddot{O} - H
\end{array}
$$

All atoms have octets (duets for hydrogen); the structure is complete.

9.59 $HCSNH_2$:   Write the correct skeletal structure for the molecule.

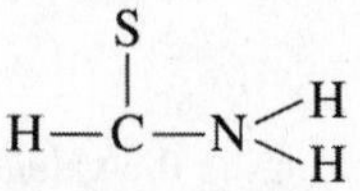

$$
\begin{array}{c}
S \\
\| \\
H - C - N \diagup\!\!\diagdown\, {}^H_H
\end{array}
$$

Calculate the total number of electrons for the Lewis structure by summing the number of valence electrons of each atom in the molecule.

(number of valence e⁻ for N) + (number of valence e⁻ for S) + (number of valence e⁻ for C) +
3(number of valence e⁻ for H) = 5 + 6 + 4 + 3(1) = 18

Distribute the electrons among the atoms, giving octets (or duets for H) to as many atoms as possible. Begin with the bonding electrons; then proceed to lone pairs on terminal atoms and finally to lone pairs on the central atoms.

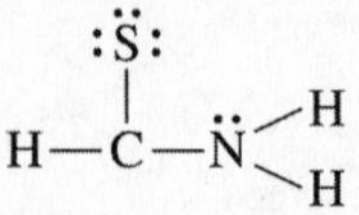

$$
\begin{array}{c}
:\ddot{S}: \\
| \\
H - C - \ddot{N} \diagup\!\!\diagdown\, {}^H_H
\end{array}
$$

Complete the octet on C by forming a double bond.

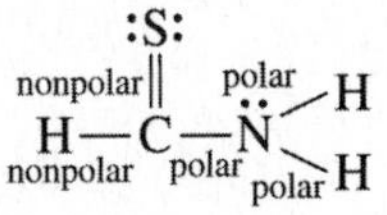

:S:
nonpolar ‖   polar ⟍H
H—C—N⟨
nonpolar polar polar ⟋H

9.60   H₂NCONH₂   Write the correct skeletal structure for the molecule.

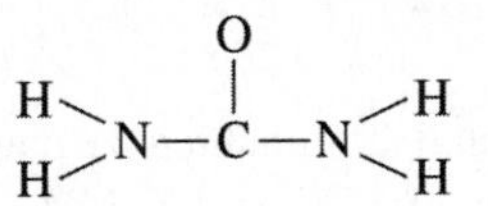

$$
\begin{array}{c}
O \\
\| \\
H{\searrow}N{-}C{-}N{\swarrow}H \\
H{\nearrow}\qquad\qquad{\nwarrow}H
\end{array}
$$

Calculate the total number of electrons for the Lewis structure by summing the number of valence electrons of each atom in the molecule.

2(number of valence e⁻ for N) + (number of valence e⁻ for O) + 4(number of valence e⁻ for H) + (number of valence e⁻ for C)
= 2(5) + 6 + 4(1) + 4 = 24

Distribute the electrons among the atoms, giving octets (or duets for H) to as many atoms as possible. Begin with the bonding electrons; then proceed to lone pairs on terminal atoms and finally to lone pairs on the central atoms.

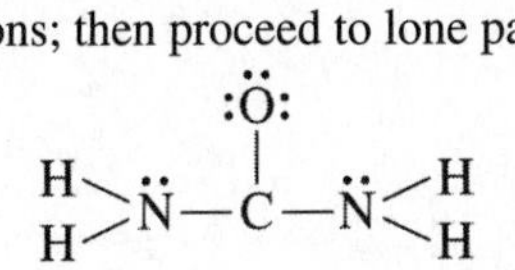

$$
\begin{array}{c}
:\ddot{O}: \\
| \\
H{\searrow}\ddot{N}{-}C{-}\ddot{N}{\swarrow}H \\
H{\nearrow}\qquad\qquad{\nwarrow}H
\end{array}
$$

Complete the octet on C with a double bond.

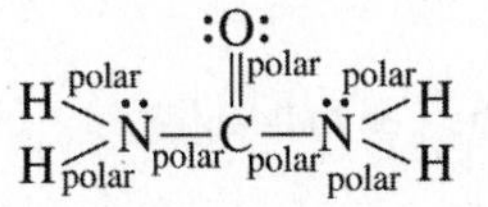

$$
\begin{array}{c}
:O: \\
\| \\
H{\searrow}^{polar}\ddot{N}{-}^{polar}C{-}^{polar}\ddot{N}{\swarrow}^{polar}H \\
H{\nearrow}_{polar}\quad_{polar}\quad_{polar}{\nwarrow}_{polar}H
\end{array}
$$

The C — O bond would be most polar because it has the greatest difference in electronegativity. From Figure 9.7,

ΔEN C—O = 1.0   ΔEN C—N = 0.5   ΔEN N—H = 0.9

9.61   (a)   O₂⁻:   Write the correct skeletal structure for the radical.
O—O

Calculate the total number of electrons for the Lewis structure by summing the number of valence electrons of each atom in the radical and adding 1 for the 1− charge.

2(number of valence e⁻ for O) + 1 = 2(6) + 1 = 13

Distribute the electrons among the atoms, giving octets to as many atoms as possible. Begin with the bonding electrons; then proceed to lone pairs on terminal atoms and finally to lone pairs on the central atom.

$$\left[\cdot\ddot{O}{-}\ddot{O}:\right]^{-}$$

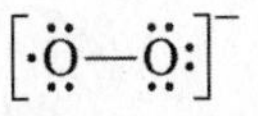

All 13 valence electrons are used.
O has an incomplete octet. It has seven electrons because we have an odd number of valence electrons.

(b)   O⁻:   Write the Lewis symbol based on the valence electrons $2s^2 2p^5$.

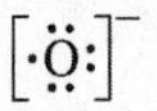

$$\left[\cdot\ddot{\underset{..}{O}}:\right]^{-}$$

(c)   OH: Write the correct skeletal structure for the molecule.
H—O

Calculate the total number of electrons for the Lewis structure by summing the number of valence electrons of each atom in the molecule.

(number of valence e⁻ for O) + (number of valence e⁻ for H) = 6 + 1 = 7

Distribute the electrons among the atoms, giving octets (or duets for H) to as many atoms as possible. Begin with the bonding electrons; then proceed to lone pairs on terminal atoms and finally to lone pairs on the central atom.

H—Ö·

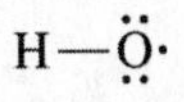

All seven valence electrons are used.
O has an incomplete octet. It has seven electrons because we have an odd number of valence electrons.

(d) CH_3OO: Write the correct skeletal structure for the radical.

C is the least electronegative atom, so it is central.

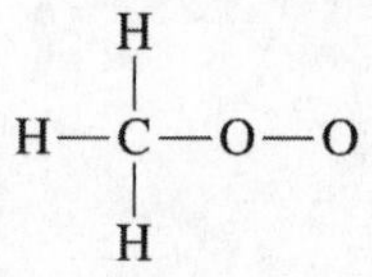

$$
\begin{array}{c}
H \\
| \\
H-C-O-O \\
| \\
H
\end{array}
$$

Calculate the total number of electrons for the Lewis structure by summing the number of valence electrons of each atom in the molecule.

3(number of valence e⁻ for H) + (number of valence e⁻ for C) + 2(number of valence

e⁻ for O) = 3(1) + 4 + 2(6) = 19

Distribute the electrons among the atoms, giving octets (or duets for H) to as many atoms as possible. Begin with the bonding electrons; then proceed to lone pairs on terminal atoms and finally to lone pairs on the central atoms.

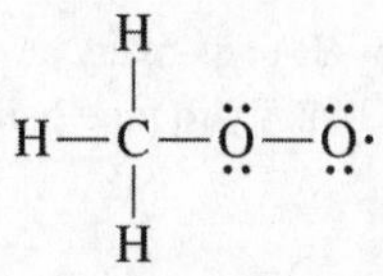

$$
\begin{array}{c}
H \\
| \\
H-C-\ddot{\text{O}}-\ddot{\text{O}}\cdot \\
| \\
H
\end{array}
$$

All 19 valence electrons are used.

O has an incomplete octet. It has seven electrons because we have an odd number of valence electrons.

9.62 $\ddot{\text{O}}=\dot{\text{N}}-\ddot{\text{O}}\colon \rightarrow \dot{\text{N}}=\ddot{\text{O}}\colon + \cdot\dot{\text{O}}\colon$

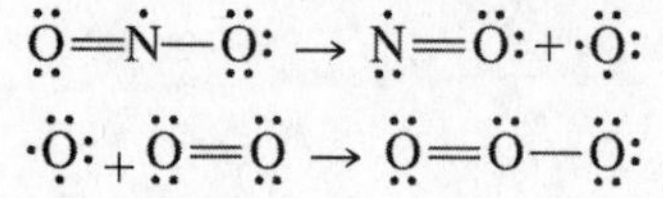

$\cdot\ddot{\text{O}}\colon + \ddot{\text{O}}=\ddot{\text{O}} \rightarrow \ddot{\text{O}}=\ddot{\text{O}}-\ddot{\text{O}}\colon$ where NO_2, O, and NO are the free radicals.

9.63   Rewrite the reaction using the Lewis structures of the molecules involved.

$$\text{H}-\text{H}(g) + 1/2\,\ddot{\text{O}}=\ddot{\text{O}}(g) \longrightarrow \text{H}-\ddot{\text{O}}-\text{H}(g)$$

Determine which bonds are broken in the reaction and sum the bond energies of the following:

$\Sigma(\Delta H$'s bonds broken)

= 1(H—H) + 1/2(O=O)

= 1(436 kJ/mol) + 1/2(498)

= 685 kJ/mol

Determine which bonds are formed in the reaction and sum the negatives of the bond energies of the following:

$\Sigma(-\Delta H$'s bonds formed)

= −2 mol(O—H)

= −2 mol(464 kJ/mol)

= −928 kJ/mol

Find $\Delta H^\circ_{\text{rxn}}$ by summing the results of the two steps.

$\Delta H^\circ_{\text{rxn}} = \Sigma(\Delta H$'s bonds broken) + $\Sigma(-\Delta H$'s bonds formed)

= 685 kJ/mol − 928 kJ/mol

= −243 kJ/mol

$CH_4(g) + 2O_2(g) \rightarrow CO_2(g) + 2H_2O(g)$

Rewrite the reaction using the Lewis structures of the molecules involved.

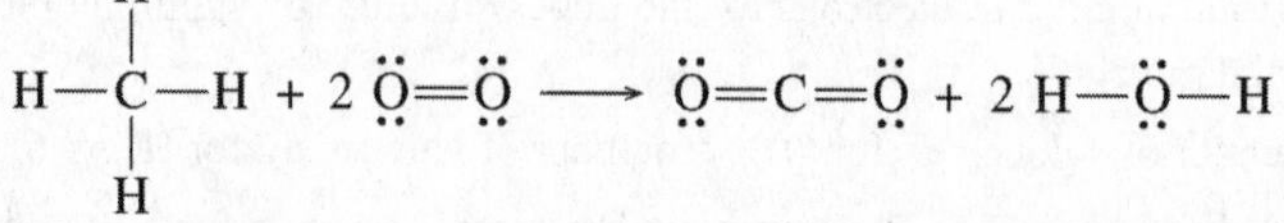

$$
\begin{array}{c}
H \\
| \\
H-C-H + 2\,\ddot{\text{O}}=\ddot{\text{O}} \longrightarrow \ddot{\text{O}}=C=\ddot{\text{O}} + 2\,H-\ddot{\text{O}}-H \\
| \\
H
\end{array}
$$

Determine which bonds are broken in the reaction and sum the bond energies of the following:

$\Sigma(\Delta H$'s bonds broken)

= 4(C—H) + 2(O=O)

= 4(414 kJ/mol) + 2(498)

= 2652 kJ/mol

Determine which bonds are formed in the reaction and sum the negatives of the bond energies of the following:

$$\Sigma(-\Delta H\text{'s bonds formed})$$
$$= -2(C{=}O) - 4(O{-}H)$$
$$= -2(799 \text{ kJ/mol}) - 4(464 \text{ kJ/mol})$$
$$= -3454 \text{ kJ/mol}$$

Find ΔH°_{rxn} by summing the results of the two steps.

$$\Delta H^\circ_{rxn} = \Sigma(\Delta H\text{'s bonds broken}) + \Sigma(-\Delta H\text{'s bonds formed})$$
$$= 2652 \text{ kJ/mol} - 3454 \text{ kJ/mol}$$
$$= -802 \text{ kJ/mol}$$

Compare the following:

	kJ/mol	kJ/g
H_2	-243	-121 (using a molar mass of 2.016)
CH_4	-802	-50.0 (using a molar mass of 16.04)

$$\frac{-243 \text{ kJ}}{\text{mol } H_2} \times \frac{1 \text{ mol } H_2}{2.016 \text{ g } H_2} = \frac{-121 \text{ kJ}}{\text{g } H_2} \qquad \frac{-802 \text{ kJ}}{\text{mol } CH_4} \times \frac{1 \text{ mol } CH_4}{16.04 \text{ g } CH_4} = \frac{-50.0 \text{ kJ}}{\text{g } CH_4}$$

So methane yields more energy per mole, but hydrogen yields more energy per gram.

9.64   octane $= C_8H_{18}$

$C_8H_{18}(l) + 25/2 \, O_2(g) \rightarrow 8CO_2(g) + 9H_2O(g)$

Rewrite the reaction using the Lewis structures of the molecules involved.

Determine which bonds are broken in the reaction and sum the bond energies of the following:

$$\Sigma(\Delta H\text{'s bonds broken})$$
$$= 18(C{-}H) + 25/2(O{=}O) + 7(C{-}C)$$
$$= 18(414 \text{ kJ/mol}) + 25/2(498 \text{ kJ/mol}) + 7(347 \text{ kJ/mol})$$
$$= 16106 \text{ kJ/mol}$$

Determine which bonds are formed in the reaction and sum the negatives of the bond energies of the following:

$$\Sigma(-\Delta H\text{'s bonds formed})$$
$$= -16(C{=}O) - 18(O{-}H)$$
$$= -16(799 \text{ kJ/mol}) - 18(464 \text{ kJ/mol})$$
$$= -21136 \text{ kJ/mol}$$

Find ΔH°_{rxn} by summing the results of the two steps.

$$\Delta H^\circ_{rxn} = \Sigma(\Delta H\text{'s bonds broken}) + \Sigma(-\Delta H\text{'s bonds formed})$$
$$= 16106 \text{ kJ/mol} - 21136 \text{ kJ/mol}$$
$$= -5030 \text{ kJ/mol}$$

From Appendix IIB ΔH°_f for octane. $\Delta H^\circ_f = -250.1 \text{ kJ/mol}$

$$\Delta H^\circ_{rxn} = \sum n_P \Delta H^\circ_f (\text{products}) - \sum n_R \Delta H^\circ_f (\text{reactants})$$
$$= [8\Delta H^\circ_f(CO_2(g)) + 9\Delta H^\circ_f(H_2O(g))] - [1\Delta H^\circ_f(C_8H_{18}(l)) + 25/2\Delta H^\circ_f(O_2(g))]$$
$$= [8(-393.5 \text{ kJ/mol}) + 9(-241.8 \text{ kJ/mol})] - [1(-250.1 \text{ kJ/mol}) + 25/2(0)]$$
$$= -5074 \text{ kJ/mol}$$

$$\% \text{ difference} = \frac{-5074 \text{ kJ} - (-5030 \text{ kJ})}{-5074 \text{ kJ}} \times 100\% = 0.8672\%$$

You would expect the value calculated from the heats of formation data to be more accurate. The bond energy values are average values, not values for a specific molecule. The heats of formation are for specific compounds.

9.65   (a) Cl_2O_7:   Write the correct skeletal structure for the molecule.

```
        O           O
        |           |
   O — Cl — O — Cl — O
        |           |
        O           O
```

Calculate the total number of electrons for the Lewis structure by summing the valence electrons of each atom in the molecule.

$$2(\text{number of valence e}^- \text{ for Cl}) + 7(\text{number of valence e}^- \text{ for O}) = 2(7) + 7(6) = 56$$

Distribute the electrons among the atoms, giving octets (or duets for H) to as many atoms as possible. Begin with the bonding electrons; then proceed to lone pairs on terminal atoms and finally to lone pairs on the central atom.

```
       ːÖː        ːÖː
        |          |
   ːÖ — Cl — Ö — Cl — Öː
        |          |
       ːOː        ːOː
```

Form double bonds to minimize formal charge.

```
       ːOː        ːOː
        ‖          ‖
   Ö = Cl — Ö — Cl = Ö
        ‖          ‖
       ːOː        ːOː
```

(b) H_3PO_3:   Write the correct skeletal structure for the molecule.

```
        O
        ‖
   H — P — O — H
        |
        O
        |
        H
```

Calculate the total number of electrons for the Lewis structure by summing the valence electrons of each atom in the molecule.

$$(\text{number of valence e}^- \text{ for P}) + 3(\text{number of valence e}^- \text{ for O}) + 3(\text{number of valence e}^- \text{ for H}) = 5 + 3(6) + 3(1) = 26$$

Distribute the electrons among the atoms, giving octets (or duets for H) to as many atoms as possible. Begin with the bonding electrons; then proceed to lone pairs on terminal atoms and finally to lone pairs on central atoms.

```
       ːÖː
        |
   H — P — Ö — H
        |
       ːOː
        |
        H
```

Form double bonds to minimize formal charge.

```
       ːOː
        ‖
   H — P — Ö — H
        |
       ːOː
        |
        H
```

(c)   H₃AsO₄: Write the correct skeletal structure for the molecule.

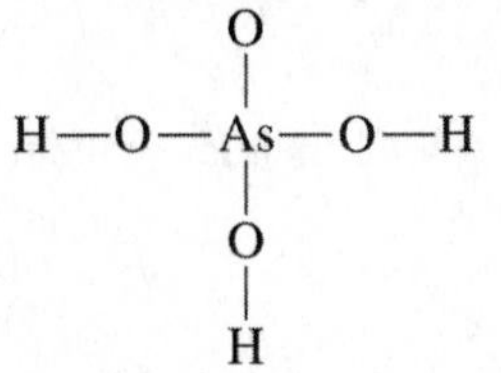

$$
\begin{array}{c}
O \\
\parallel \\
H-O-As-O-H \\
| \\
O \\
| \\
H
\end{array}
$$

Calculate the total number of electrons for the Lewis structure by summing the valence electrons of each atom in the molecule.

(number of valence e⁻ for As) + 4(number of valence e⁻ for O) + 3(number of valence e⁻ for H)
= 5 + 4(6) + 3(1) = 32

Distribute the electrons among the atoms, giving octets (or duets for H) to as many atoms as possible. Begin with the bonding electrons; then proceed to lone pairs on terminal atoms and finally to lone pairs on the central atom.

$$
\begin{array}{c}
:\ddot{O}: \\
| \\
H-\ddot{O}-As-\ddot{O}-H \\
| \\
:\ddot{O}: \\
| \\
H
\end{array}
$$

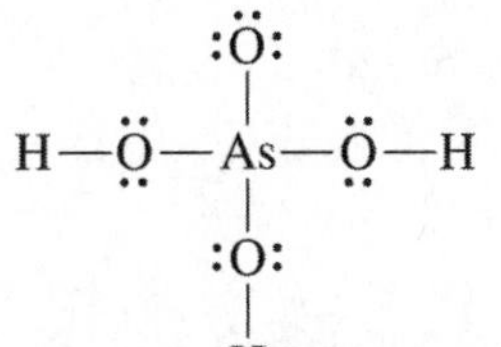

Form double bonds to minimize formal charge.

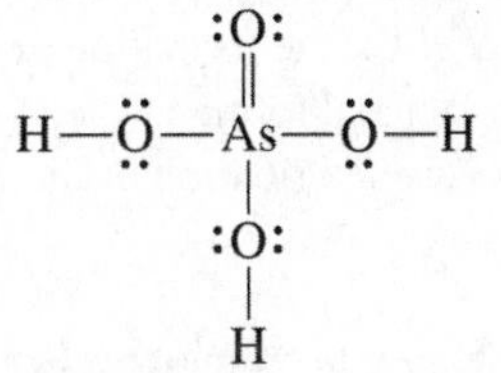

$$
\begin{array}{c}
:O: \\
\parallel \\
H-\ddot{O}-As-\ddot{O}-H \\
| \\
:O: \\
| \\
H
\end{array}
$$

9.66   N₃⁻:   Write the correct skeletal structure for the ion.

N—N—N

Calculate the total number of electrons for the Lewis structure by summing the valence electrons of each atom in the ion and adding 1 for the 1− charge.

3(number of valence e⁻ for N) + 1 = 3(5) + 1 = 16

Distribute the electrons among the atoms, giving octets to as many atoms as possible. Begin with the bonding electrons; then proceed to lone pairs on terminal atoms and finally to lone pairs on the central atom.

:N̈—N—N̈:

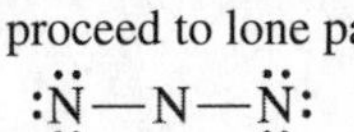

Complete octets with double or triple bonds.

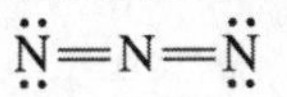

N̈=N=N̈

Finally, write the ion in brackets with the charge in the upper right-hand corner.

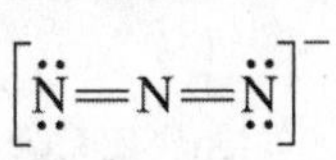

$$
\left[\ddot{N}=N=\ddot{N} \right]^{-}
$$

Write the resonance forms.

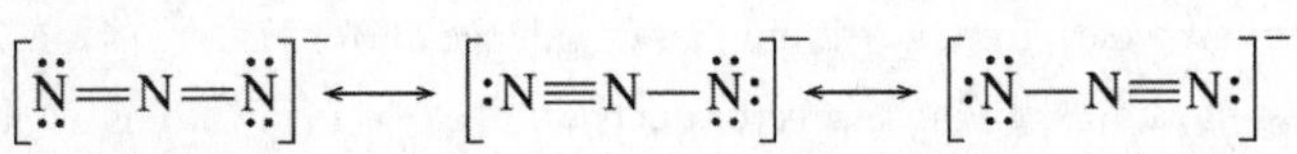

$$
\left[\ddot{N}=N=\ddot{N} \right]^{-} \longleftrightarrow \left[:N\equiv N-\ddot{N}: \right]^{-} \longleftrightarrow \left[:\ddot{N}-N\equiv N: \right]^{-}
$$

9.67 $Na^{+}F^{-} < Na^{+}O^{2-} < Mg^{2+}F^{-} < Mg^{2+}O^{2-} < Al^{3+}O^{2-}$

The lattice energy is proportional to the magnitude of the charge and inversely proportional to the distance between the atoms. $Na^{+}F^{-}$ would have the smallest lattice energy because the magnitude of the charges on Na and F are the smallest. $Mg^{2+}F^{-}$ and $Na^{+}O^{2-}$ both have the same magnitude formal charge, the O^{2-} is larger than F^{-} in size, and Na^{+} is larger than Mg^{2+}; so $Na^{+}O^{2-}$ should be less than $Mg^{2+}F^{-}$. The magnitude of the charge makes $Mg^{2+}O^{2-} < Al^{3+}O^{2-}$.

9.68   Rewrite the reaction using the Lewis structures of the molecules involved.

$$\text{H—H} + \ddot{\underset{..}{\text{B}}}\text{r}\text{—}\ddot{\underset{..}{\text{B}}}\text{r}: \longrightarrow 2\ \text{H—}\ddot{\underset{..}{\text{B}}}\text{r}:$$

Determine which bonds are broken in the reaction and sum the bond energies of the following:

$\Sigma(\Delta H$'s bonds broken)
$= 1(\text{H—H}) + 1(\text{Br—Br})$
$= 1(436\ \text{kJ/mol}) + 1(193\ \text{kJ/mol})$
$= 629\ \text{kJ/mol}$

Determine which bonds are formed in the reaction and sum the negatives of the bond energies of the following:

$\Sigma(-\Delta H$'s bonds formed)
$= -2(\text{H—Br})$
$= -2(364\ \text{kJ/mol})$
$= -728\ \text{kJ/mol}$

Find $\Delta H^\circ_\text{rxn}$ by summing the results of the two steps.
$\Delta H^\circ_\text{rxn} = \Sigma(\Delta H$'s bonds broken) $+ \Sigma(-\Delta H$'s bonds formed)
$= 629\ \text{kJ/mol} - 728\ \text{kJ/mol}$
$= -99\ \text{kJ/mol}$
ΔH°_f from the table $= -36.3\ \text{kJ/mol}$

The value for ΔH°_f would be expected to be one-half the value calculated from the bond energies but it is not. ΔH°_f is for the formation of HBr from elements in the standard state. The standard state of Br is $\text{Br}_2(l)$, while we used bond energies for $\text{Br}_2(g)$. If you include the value for the formation of $\text{Br}_2(g)$, ($-30.9\ \text{kJ/mol}$), we obtain a value of -51.8 kJ/mol for the reaction. This is still not one-half the value of ΔH°_f for the formation of HBr. Because it is not, we can account for the difference by looking at the types of bonds broken and formed. The H_2 and Br_2 bonds are pure covalent bonds, while the HBr bond formed will be polar covalent. The distribution of the electron density will be unequal.

9.69   **Given:** 7.743% H   **Find:** Lewis structure
            Conceptual Plan: %H → %C → mass C, H → mol C, H → pseudoformula → empirical formula

$$100\% - \%\text{H} \quad \text{Assume 100 g sample} \quad \frac{1\ \text{mol C}}{12.01\ \text{g}} \quad \frac{1\ \text{mol H}}{1.008\ \text{g}} \quad \text{divide by smallest number}$$

Solution: $\%\text{C} = 100\% - 7.743\% = 92.257\%\ \text{C}$
In a 100.00 g sample: 7.743 g H, 92.257 g C

$$7.743\ \cancel{\text{g H}} \times \frac{1\ \text{mol H}}{1.008\ \cancel{\text{g H}}} = 7.682\ \text{mol}$$

$$92.257\ \cancel{\text{g C}} \times \frac{1\ \text{mol C}}{12.01\ \cancel{\text{g C}}} = 7.682\ \text{mol C}$$

$\text{C}_{7.682}\text{H}_{7.682}$

$\text{C}_{\frac{7.682}{7.682}}\text{H}_{\frac{7.682}{7.682}} \rightarrow \text{CH}$

The smallest molecular formula would be C_2H_2.

Write the correct skeletal structure for the molecule.

$$\text{H—C—C—H}$$

Calculate the total number of electrons for the Lewis structure by summing the valence electrons of each atom in the molecule.

2(number of valence e^- for C) + 2(number of valence e^- for H) = 2(4) + 2(1) = 10

Distribute the electrons among the atoms, giving octets (or duets for H) to as many atoms as possible. Begin with the bonding electrons; then proceed to lone pairs on terminal atoms and finally to lone pairs on the central atom.

$$\text{H—}\underset{..}{\text{C}}\text{—}\underset{..}{\text{C}}\text{—H}$$

Complete the octet on C by forming a triple bond.

$$\text{H—C}\equiv\text{C—H}$$

9.70   **Given:** 85.5% Cl   **Find:** Lewis structure
Conceptual Plan: %Cl → %C → mass Cl, C → mol Cl, C → pseudoformula → empirical formula

$\underset{\text{100\% - \%Cl}}{} \qquad \underset{\text{Assume 100 g sample}}{} \qquad \underset{\dfrac{1 \text{ mol Cl}}{35.45 \text{ g}}}{} \qquad \underset{\dfrac{1 \text{ mol C}}{12.01 \text{ g}}}{} \qquad \underset{\text{divide by smallest number}}{}$

Solution: $\%C = 100\% - 85.5\% = 14.5\% \text{ C}$

In a 100.00 g sample: 85.5 g Cl, 14.5 g C

$85.5 \text{ g Cl} \times \dfrac{1 \text{ mol Cl}}{35.45 \text{ g Cl}} = 2.41 \text{ mol}$

$14.5 \text{ g C} \times \dfrac{1 \text{ mol C}}{12.01 \text{ g C}} = 1.21 \text{ mol C}$

$C_{1.21}Cl_{2.41}$

$C_{\frac{1.21}{1.21}}Cl_{\frac{2.41}{1.21}} \rightarrow CCl_2$

The smallest molecular formula would be C_2Cl_4.

Write the correct skeletal structure for the molecule.

$$\begin{array}{c} \text{Cl} \quad \text{Cl} \\ | \qquad | \\ \text{Cl}-\text{C}-\text{C}-\text{Cl} \end{array}$$

Calculate the total number of electrons for the Lewis structure by summing the valence electrons of each atom in the molecule.

$2(\text{number of valence e}^- \text{ for C}) + 4(\text{number of valence e}^- \text{ for Cl}) = 2(4) + 4(7) = 36$

Distribute the electrons among the atoms, giving octets to as many atoms as possible. Begin with the bonding electrons; then proceed to lone pairs on terminal atoms and finally to lone pairs on the central atoms.

$$\begin{array}{c} :\!\ddot{\text{Cl}}\!: \ :\!\ddot{\text{Cl}}\!: \\ | \qquad | \\ :\!\ddot{\text{Cl}}\!-\!\text{C}\!-\!\text{C}\!-\!\ddot{\text{Cl}}\!: \end{array}$$

Complete the octet on C by forming a double bond.

$$\begin{array}{c} :\!\ddot{\text{Cl}}\!: \ :\!\ddot{\text{Cl}}\!: \\ | \qquad | \\ :\!\ddot{\text{Cl}}\!-\!\text{C}\!=\!\text{C}\!-\!\ddot{\text{Cl}}\!: \end{array}$$

Challenge Problems

9.71

$$1 \ \ddot{\text{O}}\!=\!\ddot{\text{S}}\!=\!\ddot{\text{O}} + \text{H}-\ddot{\text{O}}\!\cdot \longrightarrow \ :\!\ddot{\text{O}}\!-\!\overset{\overset{\textstyle :\!\text{O}:}{\|}}{\text{S}}\!-\!\ddot{\text{O}}\!-\!\text{H}$$

$$2 \ :\!\ddot{\text{O}}\!-\!\overset{\overset{\textstyle :\text{O}:}{\|}}{\text{S}}\!-\!\ddot{\text{O}}\!-\!\text{H} + \ddot{\text{O}}\!=\!\ddot{\text{O}} \longrightarrow \ :\!\ddot{\text{O}}\!-\!\overset{\overset{\textstyle :\text{O}:}{\|}}{\text{S}}\!-\!\ddot{\text{O}}\!: + \ \cdot\text{H}-\ddot{\text{O}}\!-\!\ddot{\text{O}}\!\cdot$$

$$3 \ :\!\ddot{\text{O}}\!-\!\overset{\overset{\textstyle :\text{O}:}{\|}}{\text{S}}\!-\!\ddot{\text{O}} + \text{H}-\ddot{\text{O}}\!-\!\text{H} \longrightarrow \ \ddot{\text{O}}\!=\!\overset{\overset{\textstyle :\text{O}:}{\|}}{\underset{\underset{\textstyle \text{H}}{\underset{\textstyle |}{:\text{O}:}}}{\text{S}}}\!-\!\ddot{\text{O}}\!-\!\text{H}$$

Step 1:
   Bonds broken: $2(\text{S}=\text{O}) + 1(\text{H}-\text{O}) = 2(523 \text{ kJ/mol}) + 1(464 \text{ kJ/mol}) = 1510 \text{ kJ/mol}$
   Bonds formed: $-2(\text{S}-\text{O}) - 1(\text{S}=\text{O}) - 1(\text{O}-\text{H}) =$
   $-2(265 \text{ kJ/mol}) - 1(523 \text{ kJ/mol}) - 1(464 \text{ kJ/mol}) = -1517 \text{ kJ/mol}$
   $$\Delta H_{\text{step}} = -7 \text{ kJ/mol}$$

Step 2:

Bonds broken: $2(S-O) + 1(S=O) + 1(O-H) + 1(O=O) =$
$2(265 \text{ kJ/mol}) + 1(523 \text{ kJ/mol}) + 1(464 \text{ kJ/mol}) + 1(498 \text{ kJ/mol}) = 2015 \text{ kJ/mol}$
Bonds formed: $-2(S-O) - 1(S=O) - 1(O-H) - 1(O-O) =$
$-2(265 \text{ kJ/mol}) - 1(523 \text{ kJ/mol}) - 1(464 \text{ kJ/mol}) - 1(142 \text{ kJ/mol}) = -1659 \text{ kJ/mol}$
$$\Delta H_{step} = +356 \text{ kJ/mol}$$

Step 3:

Bonds broken: $2(S-O) + 1(S=O) + 2(O-H) =$
$2(265 \text{ kJ/mol}) + 1(523 \text{ kJ/mol}) + 2(464 \text{ kJ/mol}) = 1981 \text{ kJ/mol}$
Bonds formed: $-2(S-O) - 2(S=O) - 2(O-H) =$
$-2(265 \text{ kJ/mol}) + -2(523 \text{ kJ/mol}) + -2(464 \text{ kJ/mol}) = -2504 \text{ kJ/mol}$
$$\Delta H_{step} = -523 \text{ kJ/mol}$$

Hess's law states that ΔH for the reaction is the sum of ΔH of the steps:
$\Delta H^{\circ}_{rxn} = (-7 \text{ kJ/mol}) + (+356 \text{ kJ/mol}) + (-523 \text{ kJ/mol}) = -174 \text{ kJ/mol}$

9.72   **Given:** 0.167 g acid; 27.8 mL 0.100 M NaOH; 40.00% C; 6.71% H; 53.29% O
Find: molar mass, molecular formula, Lewis structure
Conceptual Plan: mL → L → mol NaOH → mol acid → molar mass and then:

$$\frac{1 \text{L}}{1000 \text{ mL}} \text{ mol} = VM \quad \text{mol acid} = \text{mol base} \qquad \frac{\text{mass}}{\text{mol}}$$

convert mass to mol of each element → pseudoformula → empirical formula → molecular formula

$$\frac{1 \text{ mol C}}{12.01 \text{ g C}} \frac{1 \text{ mol H}}{1.008 \text{ g H}} \frac{1 \text{ mol O}}{16.00 \text{ g O}} \qquad \text{divide by smallest number} \qquad \text{empirical formula} \times n$$

→ Lewis structure

Solution: $27.8 \text{ mL} \times \dfrac{1 \text{ L}}{1000 \text{ mL}} \times \dfrac{0.100 \text{ mol NaOH}}{1 \text{ L}} \times \dfrac{1 \text{ mol acid}}{1 \text{ mol NaOH}} = 0.00278 \text{ mol acid}$

$\dfrac{0.167 \text{ g acid}}{0.00278 \text{ mol acid}} = 60.1 \text{ g/mol}$

$40.00 \text{ g C} \times \dfrac{1 \text{ mol C}}{12.01 \text{ g C}} = 3.331 \text{ mol C}$

$6.71 \text{ g H} \times \dfrac{1 \text{ mol H}}{1.008 \text{ g H}} = 6.657 \text{ mol H}$

$53.29 \text{ g O} \times \dfrac{1 \text{ mol O}}{16.00 \text{ g O}} = 3.331 \text{ mol O}$

$C_{3.331}H_{6.657}O_{3.331}$

$C_{\frac{3.331}{3.331}}H_{\frac{6.657}{3.331}}O_{\frac{3.331}{3.331}} \rightarrow CH_2O$

The correct empirical formula is CH_2O.

empirical formula mass = $(12.01 \text{ g/mol}) + 2(1.008 \text{ g/mol}) + (16.00 \text{ g/mol}) = 30.03 \text{ g/mol}$

$$n = \frac{\text{molar mass}}{\text{formula molar mass}} = \frac{60.1 \text{ g/mol}}{30.03 \text{ g/mol}} = 2$$

$$\text{molecular formula} = CH_2O \times 2$$
$$= C_2H_4O_2$$

Write the correct skeletal structure for the molecule.

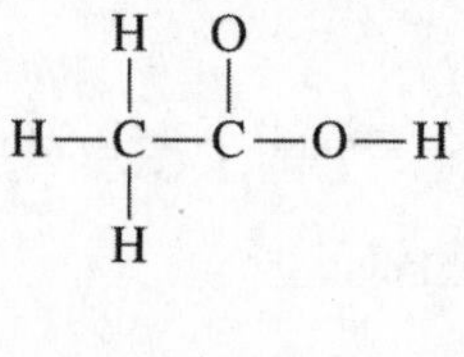

```
      H   O
      |   |
  H — C — C — O — H
      |
      H
```

Calculate the total number of electrons for the Lewis structure by summing the number of valence electrons of each atom in the molecule.

2(number of valence e⁻ for C) + 2(number of valence e⁻ for O) + 4(number of valence e⁻ for H)
= 2(4) + 2(6) + 4(1) = 24

Distribute the electrons among the atoms, giving octets (or duets for H) to as many atoms as possible. Begin with the bonding electrons; then proceed to lone pairs on terminal atoms and finally to lone pairs on the central atoms.

Complete the octet on C by forming a double bond.

9.73   **Given:** $\mu = 1.08$ D HCl, 20% ionic and $\mu = 1.82$ D HF, 45% ionic   **Find:** r

Conceptual Plan: $\mu \rightarrow \mu_{calc} \rightarrow r$

% ionic character $= \dfrac{\mu}{\mu_{calc}} \times 100\%$

Solution: For HCl $\mu_{calc} = \dfrac{1.08}{0.20} = 5.4$ D

$$\dfrac{5.4 \cancel{D} \times \dfrac{3.34 \times 10^{-30}\ \cancel{C} \cdot \cancel{m}}{\cancel{D}} \times \dfrac{10^{12}\ pm}{1\ \cancel{m}}}{1.6 \times 10^{-19}\ \cancel{C}} = 113\ pm$$

For HF $\mu_{calc} = \dfrac{1.82}{0.45} = 4.04$ D

$$\dfrac{4.04 \cancel{D} \times \dfrac{3.34 \times 10^{-30}\ \cancel{C} \cdot \cancel{m}}{\cancel{D}} \times \dfrac{10^{12}\ pm}{1\ \cancel{m}}}{1.6 \times 10^{-19}\ \cancel{C}} = 84\ pm$$

From Table 9.4, the bond length of HCl = 127 pm, and HF = 92 pm. Both of these values are slightly higher than the calculated values.

9.74   Formation reaction: $6\ C(s) + 3\ H_2(g) \rightarrow C_6H_6(g)$ $\Delta H_f^\circ = 82.9$ kJ/mol

Using bond energies, we would have the reaction $6\ C(g) + 3\ H_2(g) \rightarrow C_6H_6(g)$; so we have to include in the bond energy calculation the energy needed to convert $C(s) \rightarrow C(g)$(718.4 kJ/mol). 6 mol C(s) →
6 mol C(g) 6 mol(718.4 kJ/mol) = 4310.4 kJ/mol

Rewrite the reaction with the Lewis structures.

$6C(g) + 3\ H - H(g) \rightarrow$

(g)

Bonds broken: 3(H—H) = 3(436 kJ/mol) = 1308 kJ/mol

Bonds formed: −3(C═C) − 3(C—C) − 6(C—H) =

−3(611 kJ/mol) − 3(347 kJ/mol) − 6(414 kJ/mol) = −5358 kJ/mol

ΔH from bond energies = +(4310 kJ) + (1308 kJ) − 5358 kJ = +260 kJ/mol

The difference between the value calculated from bond energies (260 kJ/mol) and $\Delta H_f^\circ = 82.9$ kJ/mol for benzene leads us to conclude that there is a great deal of stabilization from the two resonance forms and that they contribute much to the formation of benzene.

9.75 For the four P atoms to be equivalent, they must all be in the same electronic environment. That is, they must all see the same number of bonds and lone pair electrons. The only way to achieve this is with a tetrahedral configuration where the P atoms are at the four points of the tetrahedron.

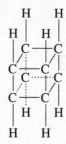

9.76 **Given:** C_8H_8 all C's identical, all H's identical **Find:** Lewis structure

For the eight C atoms to be equivalent, they must all be in the same electronic environment, and for the eight H atoms to be equivalent, they must all be in the same electronic environment as well. That is, they must all see the same number and kinds of bonds. One way to achieve this is with a cubic arrangement of the C atoms and then a H atom attached to each C.

9.77 **Given:** H_2S_4 linear **Find:** oxidation number of each S

Write the correct skeletal structure for the molecule.

$$H-S-S-S-S-H$$

Calculate the total number of electrons for the Lewis structure by summing the number of valence electrons of each atom in the molecule.

$$4(\text{number of valence e}^- \text{ for S}) + 2(\text{number of valence e}^- \text{ for H}) = 4(6) + 2(1) = 26$$

Distribute the electrons among the atoms, giving octets (or duets for H) to as many atoms as possible.

$$H-\overset{..}{\underset{..}{S}}-\overset{..}{\underset{..}{S}}-\overset{..}{\underset{..}{S}}-\overset{..}{\underset{..}{S}}-H$$

Determine the oxidation number on each atom. EN(H) < EN(S), so the electrons in the H—S bond belong to the S atom, while the electrons in the S—S bonds split between the two S atoms.

$$\text{O. N.} = \text{valence electrons} - \text{electrons that belong to the atom}$$

$$H-\overset{..}{\underset{..}{S}}_A-\overset{..}{\underset{..}{S}}_B-\overset{..}{\underset{..}{S}}_C-\overset{..}{\underset{..}{S}}_D-H$$

$$H = 1 - 0 = +1 \text{ for each H}$$
$$S_A = 6 - 7 = -1$$
$$S_B = 6 - 6 = 0$$
$$S_C = 6 - 6 = 0$$
$$S_D = 6 - 7 = -1$$

9.78 O^{2-} anion has eight electrons and therefore a complete octet, which makes it a stable anion in an ionic solid.

O^- anion has seven electrons. Because it does not have a complete octet, it will not be a stable anion in an ionic solid.

O^{3-} anion has nine electrons. Because O cannot accommodate more than eight electrons, this anion will not form.

9.79 **Given:** $\Delta H_f^\circ(SO_2) = -296.8$ kJ/mol, $S(g) = 277.2$ kJ/mol, break $O{=}O$ bond $= 498$ kJ

Find: $S{=}O$ bond energy

Conceptual Plan: Use ΔH_f for SO_2 and $S(g)$ and the bond energy of O_2 to determine heat of atomization of SO_2.

Reaction			ΔH (kJ/mol)
$SO_2(g)$	$\rightarrow$	~~$S(s, \text{rhombic})$~~ $+$ ~~$O_2(g)$~~	$+296.8$
~~$S(s, \text{rhombic})$~~	$\rightarrow$	$S(g)$	$+277.2$
~~$O{=}O(g)$~~	$\rightarrow$	$2 O(g)$	$+498$
$SO_2(g)$	$\rightarrow$	$S(g) + 2 O(g)$	$+1072$

Write the reaction using the Lewis structure.

$$\ddot{\text{O}}=\ddot{\text{S}}=\ddot{\text{O}}(g) \longrightarrow \text{S}(g) + 2\,\text{O}(g)$$

Determine the number and kinds of bonds broken and then ΔH atomization = bonds broken.

ΔH atomization = $2\sum$ (S=O) bonds broken.

1072 kJ/mol = 2 (S=O) bonds broken.

S=O bond energy = 536 kJ/mol.

Check: The S=O bond energy is close to the table value of 523 kJ/mol.

Conceptual Problems

9.80   (a) is true: Strong bonds break, and weak bonds form. In an endothermic reaction, the energy required to break the bonds is greater than the energy given off when the bonds are formed ($\Delta H > 0$); therefore, in an endothermic reaction, the bonds that are breaking are stronger than the bonds that are forming.

9.81   When we say that a compound is "energy rich," we mean that it gives off a great amount of energy when it reacts. It means that a lot of energy is stored in the compound. This energy is released when the weak bonds in the compound break and much stronger bonds are formed in the product, thereby releasing energy.

9.82   In solid covalent compounds, the electrons in the bonds are shared directly between the atoms involved in the molecule. Each molecule is a distinct unit. Ionic compounds, on the other hand, are not distinct units. Rather, they are composed of alternating positive and negative ions in a three-dimensional crystalline array.

9.83   Lewis theory is successful because it allows us to understand and predict many chemical observations. We can use it to determine the formulas of ionic compounds and to account for the low melting points and boiling points of molecular compounds compared to ionic compounds. Lewis theory allows us to predict what molecules or ions will be stable, which will be more reactive, and which will not exist. Lewis theory, however, does not tell us anything about how the bonds in the molecules and ions form. It does not give us a way to account for the paramagnetism of oxygen. And, by itself, Lewis theory does not tell us anything about the shape of the molecule or ion.

Questions for Group Work

9.84   Each group member should have a coin for each of the valence electrons in the atom that they represent. The nonmetal atoms will be the most reluctant to give up a coin. The metal atoms will be less reluctant to give up a coin. A bond between a metal and a nonmetal would be an ionic bond, while a bond between two nonmetals will be a covalent bond, and a bond between two metals will be a metallic bond. Some examples could be:

Atom 1	Atom 2	Type of Bonding
Na	Br	Ionic bonding
Rb	O	Ionic bonding
Ca	Cl	Ionic bonding
Cl	F	Covalent bonding
C	O	Covalent bonding
Mg	S	Covalent bonding
Mg	Mg	Metallic bonding

Atom 1	Atom 2	Type of Bonding
Al	F	Ionic bonding
Li	N	Ionic bonding
Sr	Cl	Covalent bonding
N	O	Covalent bonding
P	I	Covalent bonding
Na	K	Metallic bonding
Pt	Au	Metallic bonding

9.85   The Lewis dot symbols for the atoms are:

$$\text{Li}\cdot \quad \cdot\text{Be}\cdot \quad \cdot\dot{\text{B}}\cdot \quad \cdot\dot{\text{C}}\cdot \quad \cdot\ddot{\text{N}}: \quad \cdot\ddot{\text{O}}: \quad :\ddot{\text{F}}: \quad :\ddot{\text{Ne}}:$$

The formal charge on each atom is the number of valence electrons minus the number of lone pair electrons and one-half the number of bonding electrons. The formal charge is equal to the number of valence electrons because there are no bonds.

9.86   Draw the Lewis structures for Al and O based on their valence electrons. Al: $3s^2 3p^1$ O: $2s^2 2p^4$.

$\cdot \dot{Al} \cdot$ $: \ddot{O} \cdot$

Aluminum must lose three electrons and be left with the octet from the previous shell, while oxygen needs to gain two electrons to get an octet.

$2\ Al^{3+}$ $3 \left[: \ddot{O} : \right]^{2-}$

Thus, we need two Al^{3+} and three O^{2-} in order to lose and gain the same number of electrons. Write the formula with subscripts (if necessary) to indicate the number of atoms.

$Al_2 O_3$

9.87   The steps for writing a Lewis structure are:
1.   Write the correct skeletal structure for the molecule or ion.
2.   Calculate the total number of electrons for the Lewis structure by summing the valence electrons of each atom in the molecule or ion. Add an electron for each negative charge on an ion and subtract an electron for each charge on a cation.
3.   Distribute the electrons among the atoms, giving octets (or duets for hydrogen) to as many atoms as possible.
4.   If any atoms lack an octet, form double or triple bonds as necessary to give them octets.
5.   Consider forming resonance structures if it is possible to write two or more Lewis structures for the same molecule or ion. Remember that only electrons move when generating resonance structures. The formal charges of atoms can be used to determine which resonance structures are better than others. The formal charge of an atom in a Lewis structure is the charge it would have if all bonding electrons were shared equally between the bonded atoms. Formal charge = number of valence electrons − (number of lone pair electron +1/2 number of bonding electrons).

9.88 $N_2 H_4$: Write the correct skeletal structure for the molecule.

$$\begin{array}{c} H \quad\quad\quad H \\ \diagdown \quad\quad\quad \diagup \\ N - N \\ \diagup \quad\quad\quad \diagdown \\ H \quad\quad\quad H \end{array}$$

Calculate the total number of electrons for the Lewis structure by summing the valence electrons of each atom in the molecule

2(number of valence e − for N) + 4(number of valence e − for H) = 2(5) + 4(1) = 14

Distribute the electrons among the atoms, giving octets (or duets for H) to as many atoms as possible. Begin with the bonding electrons, and then proceed to lone pairs on terminal atoms and finally to lone pairs of the central atom.

$$\begin{array}{c} H \quad\quad \cdot\cdot \quad\quad \cdot\cdot \quad\quad H \\ \diagdown \quad\quad\quad\quad\quad\quad \diagup \\ N - N \\ \diagup \quad\quad\quad\quad\quad\quad \diagdown \\ H \quad\quad\quad\quad\quad\quad H \end{array}$$

All 14 valence electrons are used.

If any atom lacks an octet, form double or triple bonds as necessary to give them octets. All atoms have octets (duets for hydrogen); the structure is complete.

CCl_4:   Write the Lewis symbol for each atom based on the valence electron.

$\cdot \dot{C} \cdot$ $: \ddot{Cl} \cdot$

The carbon will share an electron pair with each chlorine in order to achieve a stable octet.

$$\begin{array}{c} : \ddot{Cl} : \\ | \\ : \ddot{Cl} - C - \ddot{Cl} : \\ | \\ : \ddot{Cl} : \end{array}$$

$CO_3{}^{2-}$:   Write the correct skeletal structure for the ion.

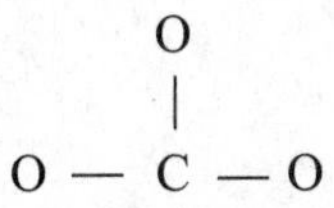

$$O$$
$$|$$
$$O - C - O$$

Calculate the total number of electrons for the Lewis structure by summing the valence electrons of each atom in the ion and adding 2 for the 2 − charge.

3(number of valence e ⁻ for O) + (number of valence e ⁻ for C) + 2 = 3(6) + 4 + 2 = 24

Distribute the electrons among the atoms, giving octets (or duets for H) to as many atoms as possible. Begin with the bonding electrons, and then proceed to lone pairs on terminal atoms and finally to lone pairs of the central atom.

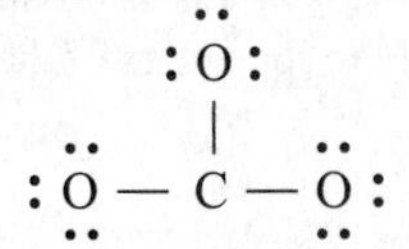

$$:O:$$
$$|$$
$$:O - C - O:$$

All 24 valence electrons are used.

If any atom lacks an octet, form double or triple bonds as necessary to give them octets.

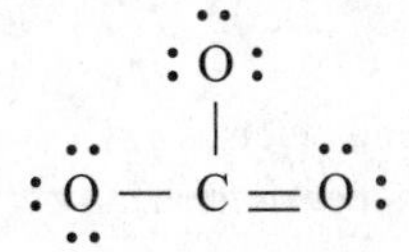

$$:O:$$
$$|$$
$$:O - C = O:$$

Lastly, write the Lewis structure in brackets with the charge of the ion in the upper right-hand corner.

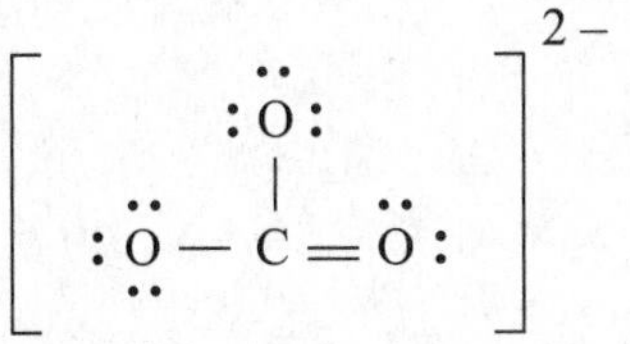

$$\left[\begin{array}{c} :O: \\ | \\ :O - C = O: \end{array} \right]^{2-}$$

All atoms have octets (duets for H); the structure is complete. However, the double bond can form from any oxygen atom, so there are three resonance forms.

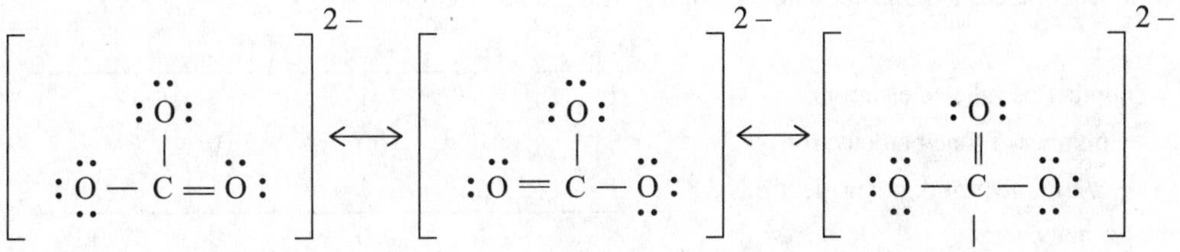

$$\left[\begin{array}{c} :O: \\ | \\ :O - C = O: \end{array} \right]^{2-} \longleftrightarrow \left[\begin{array}{c} :O: \\ | \\ :O = C - O: \end{array} \right]^{2-} \longleftrightarrow \left[\begin{array}{c} :O: \\ \| \\ :O - C - O: \end{array} \right]^{2-}$$

Calculate the formal charge on each atom by finding the number of valence electrons and subtracting the number of lone pair electrons and one-half the number of bonding electrons.

$$\left[\begin{array}{c} :O: \\ | \\ :O - C = O: \end{array} \right]^{2-}$$

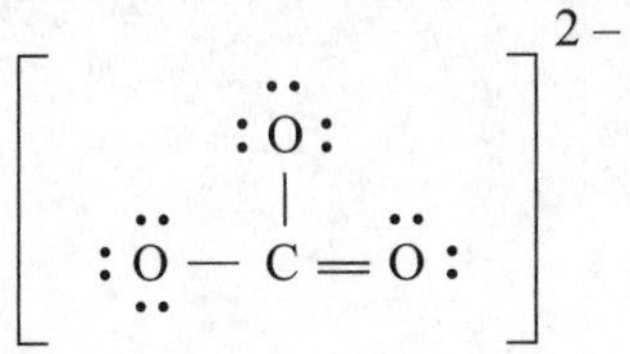

	O_{left}	O_{top}	O_{right}	C
number of valence electrons	6	6	6	4
− number of lone pair electrons	6	6	4	0
− 1/2(number of bonding electrons)	1	1	2	4
Formal charge	−1	−1	0	0

The sum of the formal charges is − 2, which is the overall charge of the ion. The other resonance forms would be the same.

NH_4^+:   Write the correct skeletal structure for the ion.

$$
\begin{array}{c}
\text{H} \\
| \\
\text{H} - \text{N} - \text{H} \\
| \\
\text{H}
\end{array}
$$

Calculate the total number of electrons for the Lewis structure by summing the valence electrons of each atom in the ion and subtracting 1 for the 1+ charge.

$$4(\text{number of valence e}^- \text{ for H}) + (\text{number of valence e}^- \text{ for N}) - 1 = 4(1) + 5 - 1 = 8$$

Distribute the electrons among the atoms, giving octets (or duets for H) to as many atoms as possible. Begin with the bonding electrons, and then proceed to lone pairs on terminal atoms and finally to lone pairs of the central atom.

$$
\begin{array}{c}
\text{H} \\
| \\
\text{H} - \text{N} - \text{H} \\
| \\
\text{H}
\end{array}
$$

All eight valence electrons are used.
If any atom lacks an octet, form double or triple bonds as necessary to give them octets.
Lastly, write the Lewis structure in brackets with the charge of the ion in the upper right–hand corner.

$$
\left[
\begin{array}{c}
\text{H} \\
| \\
\text{H} - \text{N} - \text{H} \\
| \\
\text{H}
\end{array}
\right]^{+}
$$

All atoms have octets (duets for H); the structure is complete.
Calculate the formal charge on each atom by finding the number of valence electrons and subtracting the number of lone pair electrons and one-half the number of bonding electrons.

	H_{left}	H_{top}	H_{right}	H_{bottom}	N
number of valence electrons	1	1	1	1	5
− number of lone pair electrons	0	0	0	0	0
− 1/2(number of bonding electrons)	1	1	1	1	4
Formal charge	0	0	0	0	+1

The sum of the formal charges is +1, which is the overall charge of the ion.

10 Chemical Bonding II: Molecular Shapes, Valence Bond Theory, and Molecular Orbital Theory

Problems by Topic

VSEPR Theory and Molecular Geometry

10.1   Four electron groups: A trigonal pyramidal molecular geometry has three bonding groups and one lone pair of electrons, so there are four electron groups on atom A.

10.2   Three electron groups: A trigonal planar molecular geometry has three bonding groups and no lone pairs of electrons, so there are three electron groups on atom A.

10.3   (a)   4 total electron groups, 4 bonding groups, 0 lone pairs
              A tetrahedral molecular geometry has four bonding groups and no lone pairs. So there are four total electron groups, four bonding groups, and no lone pairs.
        (b)   5 total electron groups, 3 bonding groups, 2 lone pairs
              A T-shaped molecular geometry has three bonding groups and two lone pairs. So there are five total electron groups, three bonding groups, and two lone pairs.
        (c)   6 total electron groups, 5 bonding groups, 1 lone pair
              A square pyramidal molecular geometry has five bonding groups and one lone pair. So there are six total electron groups, five bonding groups, and one lone pair.

10.4   (a)   6 total electron groups, 6 bonding groups, 0 lone pairs
              An octahedral molecular geometry has six bonding groups and no lone pairs. So there are six total electron groups, six bonding groups, and no lone pairs.
        (b)   6 electron groups, 4 bonding groups, 2 lone pairs
              A square planar molecular geometry has four bonding groups and two lone pairs. So there are six total electron groups, four bonding groups, and two lone pairs.
        (c)   5 electron groups, 4 bonding groups, 1 lone pair
              A seesaw molecular geometry has four bonding groups and one lone pair. So there are five total electron groups, four bonding groups, and one lone pair.

10.5   (a) PF_3: Electron geometry—tetrahedral; molecular geometry—trigonal pyramidal; bond angle = 109.5°
              Because of the lone pair, the bond angle will be less than 109.5°.
              Draw a Lewis structure for the molecule:
              PF_3 has 26 valence electrons.

Determine the total number of electron groups around the central atom:
There are four electron groups on P.
Determine the number of bonding groups and the number of lone pairs around the central atom:
There are three bonding groups and one lone pair.
Use Table 10.1 to determine the electron geometry, molecular geometry, and bond angles:
Four electron groups give a tetrahedral electron geometry; three bonding groups and one lone pair give a trigonal pyramidal molecular geometry; the idealized bond angles for tetrahedral geometry are 109.5°. The lone pair will make the bond angle less than idealized.

(b) SBr_2:   Electron geometry—tetrahedral; molecular geometry—bent; bond angle = 109.5°
Because of the lone pairs, the bond angle will be less than 109.5°.
Draw a Lewis structure for the molecule:
SBr_2 has 20 valence electrons.

$$\ddot{S}-\ddot{Br}:$$
$$|$$
$$:\ddot{Br}:$$

Determine the total number of electron groups around the central atom:
There are four electron groups on S.
Determine the number of bonding groups and the number of lone pairs around the central atom:
There are two bonding groups and two lone pairs.
Use Table 10.1 to determine the electron geometry, molecular geometry, and bond angles:
Four electron groups give a tetrahedral electron geometry; two bonding groups and two lone pairs give a bent molecular geometry; the idealized bond angles for tetrahedral geometry are 109.5°. The lone pairs will make the bond angle less than idealized.

(c) $CHCl_3$:   Electron geometry—tetrahedral; molecular geometry—tetrahedral; bond angle = 109.5°
Because there are no lone pairs, the bond angle will be 109.5°.
Draw a Lewis structure for the molecule:
$CHCl_3$ has 26 valence electrons.

$$H$$
$$|$$
$$:\ddot{Cl}-C-\ddot{Cl}:$$
$$|$$
$$:\ddot{Cl}:$$

Determine the total number of electron groups around the central atom:
There are four electron groups on C.
Determine the number of bonding groups and the number of lone pairs around the central atom:
There are four bonding groups and no lone pairs.
Use Table 10.1 to determine the electron geometry, molecular geometry, and bond angles:
Four electron groups give a tetrahedral electron geometry; four bonding groups and no lone pairs give a tetrahedral molecular geometry; the idealized bond angles for tetrahedral geometry are 109.5°. However, because the attached atoms have different electronegativities, the bond angles are less than idealized.

(d) CS_2:   Electron geometry—linear; molecular geometry—linear; bond angle = 180°
Because there are no lone pairs, the bond angle will be 180°.
Draw a Lewis structure for the molecule:
CS_2 has 16 valence electrons.

$$\ddot{S}=C=\ddot{S}$$

Determine the total number of electron groups around the central atom:
There are two electron groups on C.
Determine the number of bonding groups and the number of lone pairs around the central atom:
There are two bonding groups and no lone pairs.
Use Table 10.1 to determine the electron geometry, molecular geometry, and bond angles:
Two electron groups give a linear geometry; two bonding groups and no lone pairs give a linear molecular geometry; the idealized bond angle is 180°. The molecule will not deviate from this.

10.6   (a) CF_4:   Electron geometry—tetrahedral; molecular geometry—tetrahedral; bond angle = 109.5°
                Draw a Lewis structure for the molecule:
                CF_4 has 32 valence electrons.

$$:\!\ddot{\text{F}}\!:$$
$$|$$
$$:\!\ddot{\text{F}}\!-\!\text{C}\!-\!\ddot{\text{F}}\!:$$
$$|$$
$$:\!\ddot{\text{F}}\!:$$

Determine the total number of electron groups around the central atom:
There are four electron groups on C.
Determine the number of bonding groups and the number of lone pairs around the central atom:
There are four bonding groups and no lone pairs.
Use Table 10.1 to determine the electron geometry, molecular geometry, and bond angles:
Four electron groups give a tetrahedral electron geometry; four bonding groups and no lone pairs give a tetrahedral molecular geometry; idealized bond angles for tetrahedral geometry are 109.5°.

(b) NF_3:   Electron geometry—tetrahedral; molecular geometry—trigonal pyramidal; bond angle = 109.5°
                Because of the lone pair, the bond angle will be less than 109.5°.
                Draw a Lewis structure for the molecule:
                NF_3 has 26 valence electrons.

$$:\!\ddot{\text{F}}\!-\!\ddot{\text{N}}\!-\!\ddot{\text{F}}\!:$$
$$|$$
$$:\!\ddot{\text{F}}\!:$$

Determine the total number of electron groups around the central atom:
There are four electron groups on N.
Determine the number of bonding groups and the number of lone pairs around the central atom:
There are three bonding groups and one lone pair.
Use Table 10.1 to determine the electron geometry, molecular geometry, and bond angles:
Four electron groups give a tetrahedral electron geometry; three bonding groups and one lone pair give a trigonal pyramidal molecular geometry; the idealized bond angles for tetrahedral geometry are 109.5°. The lone pair will make the bond angles less than idealized.

(c) OF_2:   Electron geometry—tetrahedral; molecular geometry—bent; bond angle = 109.5°
                Because of the lone pairs, the bond angle will be less than 109.5°.
                Draw a Lewis structure for the molecule:
                OF_2 has 20 valence electrons.

$$:\!\ddot{\text{F}}\!-\!\ddot{\text{O}}\!-\!\ddot{\text{F}}\!:$$

Determine the total number of electron groups around the central atom:
There are four electron groups on O.
Determine the number of bonding groups and the number of lone pairs around the central atom:
There are two bonding groups and two lone pairs.
Use Table 10.1 to determine the electron geometry, molecular geometry, and bond angles:
Four electron groups give a tetrahedral electron geometry; two bonding groups and two lone pairs give a bent molecular geometry; the idealized bond angles for tetrahedral geometry are 109.5°. The lone pairs will make the bond angle less than idealized.

(d) H_2S: Electron geometry—tetrahedral; molecular geometry—bent; bond angle = 109.5°
                Because of the lone pair, the bond angle will be less than 109.5°.
                Draw a Lewis structure for the molecule:
                H_2S has eight valence electrons.

$$\text{H}\!-\!\ddot{\text{S}}\!-\!\text{H}$$

Determine the total number of electron groups around the central atom:
There are four electron groups on S.
Determine the number of bonding groups and the number of lone pairs around the central atom:
There are two bonding groups and two lone pairs.
Use Table 10.1 to determine the electron geometry, molecular geometry, and bond angles:

Four electron groups give a tetrahedral electron geometry; two bonding groups and two lone pairs give a bent molecular geometry; the idealized bond angles for tetrahedral geometry are 109.5°. However, the lone pairs will make the bond angle less than idealized.

10.7 H_2O will have the smaller bond angle because lone pair–lone pair repulsions are greater than lone pair–bonding pair repulsions.

Draw the Lewis structures for both structures:

H_3O^+ has eight valence electrons. H_2O has eight valence electrons.

There are three bonding groups and one lone pair.

There are two bonding groups and two lone pairs.

Both have four electron groups, but the two lone pairs in H_2O will cause the bond angle to be smaller because of the lone pair–lone pair repulsions.

10.8 ClO_3^- will have the smaller bond angle because lone pair–bonding pair repulsions are greater than bonding pair–bonding pair repulsions.

Draw the Lewis structures for both structures:

ClO_3^- has 26 valence electrons. ClO_4^- has 32 valence electrons.

There are three bonding groups and one lone pair.

There are four bonding groups and no lone pairs.

Both have four electron groups, but the lone pair in ClO_3^- will cause the bond angle to be smaller because of the lone pair–bonding pair repulsions.

10.9   (a) SF_4 Draw a Lewis structure for the molecule:

SF_4 has 34 valence electrons.

Determine the total number of electron groups around the central atom:
There are five electron groups on S.
Determine the number of bonding groups and the number of lone pairs around the central atom:
There are four bonding groups and one lone pair.
Use Table 10.1 to determine the electron geometry and molecular geometry:
The electron geometry is trigonal bipyramidal, so the molecular geometry is seesaw.
Sketch the molecule:

(b) ClF_3 Draw a Lewis structure for the molecule:

ClF_3 has 28 valence electrons.

Determine the total number of electron groups around the central atom:
There are five electron groups on Cl.
Determine the number of bonding groups and the number of lone pairs around the central atom:
There are three bonding groups and two lone pairs.
Use Table 10.1 to determine the electron geometry and molecular geometry:
The electron geometry is trigonal bipyramidal, so the molecular geometry is T-shaped.
Sketch the molecule:

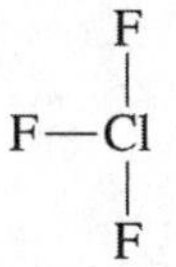

$$
\begin{array}{c}
\text{F} \\
| \\
\text{F—Cl} \\
| \\
\text{F}
\end{array}
$$

(c)　IF_2^-　Draw a Lewis structure for the ion:
IF_2^- has 22 valence electrons.

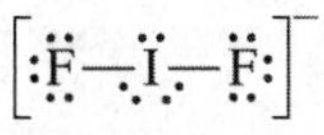

$$\left[:\ddot{\text{F}}—\ddot{\text{I}}—\ddot{\text{F}}: \right]^-$$

Determine the total number of electron groups around the central atom:
There are five electron groups on I.
Determine the number of bonding groups and the number of lone pairs around the central atom:
There are two bonding groups and three lone pairs.
Use Table 10.1 to determine the electron geometry and molecular geometry:
The electron geometry is trigonal bipyramidal, so the molecular geometry is linear.
Sketch the ion:

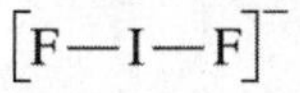

$$\left[\text{F—I—F} \right]^-$$

(d)　IBr_4^-　Draw a Lewis structure for the ion:
IBr_4^- has 36 valence electrons.

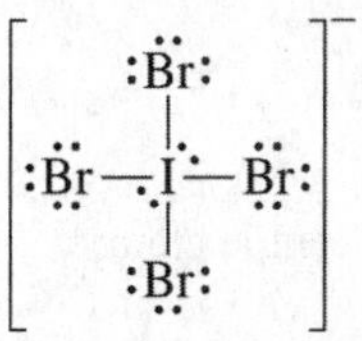

$$
\left[
\begin{array}{c}
:\ddot{\text{Br}}: \\
| \\
:\ddot{\text{Br}}—\ddot{\text{I}}—\ddot{\text{Br}}: \\
| \\
:\ddot{\text{Br}}:
\end{array}
\right]^-
$$

Determine the total number of electron groups around the central atom:
There are six electron groups on I.
Determine the number of bonding groups and the number of lone pairs around the central atom:
There are four bonding groups and two lone pairs.
Use Table 10.1 to determine the electron geometry and molecular geometry:
The electron geometry is octahedral, so the molecular geometry is square planar.
Sketch the ion:

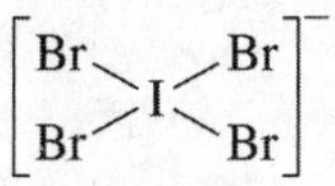

$$
\left[
\begin{array}{c}
\text{Br} \diagdown \quad \diagup \text{Br} \\
\quad \text{I} \\
\text{Br} \diagup \quad \diagdown \text{Br}
\end{array}
\right]^-
$$

10.10　(a)　BrF_5　Draw a Lewis structure for the molecule:
BrF_5 has 42 valence electrons.

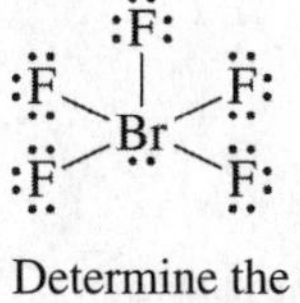

$$
\begin{array}{c}
:\ddot{\text{F}}: \\
:\ddot{\text{F}} \diagdown \ | \ \diagup \ddot{\text{F}}: \\
\text{Br} \\
:\ddot{\text{F}} \diagup \ \ddot{} \ \diagdown \ddot{\text{F}}:
\end{array}
$$

Determine the total number of electron groups around the central atom:
There are six electron groups on Br.
Determine the number of bonding groups and the number of lone pairs around the central atom:
There are five bonding groups and one lone pair.
Use Table 10.1 to determine the electron geometry and molecular geometry:
The electron geometry is octahedral, so the molecular geometry is square pyramidal.

Sketch the molecule:

F\\\...F ... Br ... F ... F ... F

(b) SCl_6 Draw a Lewis structure for the molecule:

SCl_6 has 48 valence electrons.

Determine the total number of electron groups around the central atom:

There are six electron groups on S.

Determine the number of bonding groups and the number of lone pairs around the central atom:

There are six bonding groups and no lone pairs.

Use Table 10.1 to determine the electron geometry and molecular geometry:

The electron geometry is octahedral, so the molecular geometry is octahedral.

Sketch the molecule:

(c) PF_5 Draw a Lewis structure for the molecule:

PF_5 has 40 valence electrons.

Determine the total number of electron groups around the central atom:

There are five electron groups on P.

Determine the number of bonding groups and the number of lone pairs around the central atom:

There are five bonding groups and no lone pairs.

Use Table 10.1 to determine the electron geometry and molecular geometry:

The electron geometry is trigonal bipyramidal, so the molecular geometry is trigonal bipyramidal.

Sketch the molecule:

(d) IF_4^+ Draw a Lewis structure for the ion:

IF_4^+ has 34 valence electrons.

Determine the total number of electron groups around the central atom:

There are five electron groups on I.

Determine the number of bonding groups and the number of lone pairs around the central atom:

There are four bonding groups and one lone pair.

Use Table 10.1 to determine the electron geometry and molecular geometry:

The electron geometry is trigonal bipyramidal, so the molecular geometry is seesaw.

Sketch the ion:

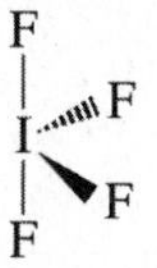

$$
\begin{array}{c}
\text{F} \\
| \\
\text{I} \cdots\cdots \text{F} \\
| \quad \blacktriangledown \text{F} \\
\text{F}
\end{array}
$$

10.11   (a) C_2H_2 Draw the Lewis structure:

$$H—C\equiv C—H$$

Atom	Number of Electron Groups	Number of Lone Pairs	Molecular Geometry
Left C	2	0	Linear
Right C	2	0	Linear

Sketch the molecule:

$$H—C\equiv C—H$$

(b) C_2H_4 Draw the Lewis structure:

$$
\begin{array}{c}
\text{H} \qquad\qquad \text{H} \\
\diagdown\diagup \\
\text{C}=\text{C} \\
\diagup\diagdown \\
\text{H} \qquad\qquad \text{H}
\end{array}
$$

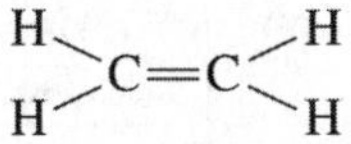

Atom	Number of Electron Groups	Number of Lone Pairs	Molecular Geometry
Left C	3	0	Trigonal planar
Right C	3	0	Trigonal planar

Sketch the molecule:

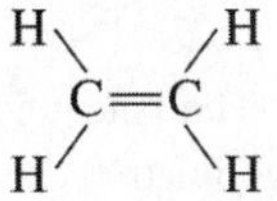

$$
\begin{array}{c}
\text{H} \qquad\qquad \text{H} \\
\diagdown\diagup \\
\text{C}=\text{C} \\
\diagup\diagdown \\
\text{H} \qquad\qquad \text{H}
\end{array}
$$

(c) C_2H_6 Draw the Lewis structure:

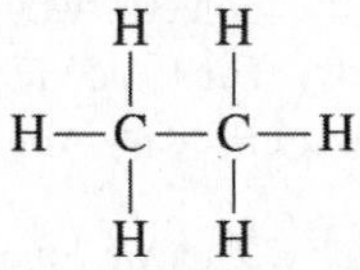

$$
\begin{array}{c}
\text{H} \quad \text{H} \\
| \quad\ | \\
\text{H}—\text{C}—\text{C}—\text{H} \\
| \quad\ | \\
\text{H} \quad \text{H}
\end{array}
$$

Atom	Number of Electron Groups	Number of Lone Pairs	Molecular Geometry
Left C	4	0	Tetrahedral
Right C	4	0	Tetrahedral

Sketch the molecule:

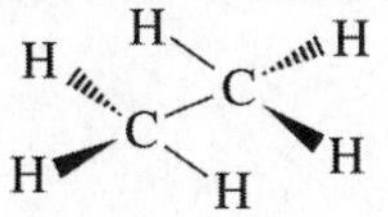

$$
\begin{array}{c}
\text{H} \quad\ \ \text{H} \\
\text{H} \cdots \text{C}\text{---}\text{C} \cdots \text{H} \\
\text{H} \quad \text{H} \quad \text{H}
\end{array}
$$

10.12   (a) N_2 Draw the Lewis structure:

$$:N\equiv N:$$

Atom	Number of Electron Groups	Number of Lone Pairs	Molecular Geometry
Left N	2	1	Linear
Right N	2	1	Linear

Sketch the molecule:

N≡N

(b) N_2H_2 Draw the Lewis structure:

H—N̈=N̈—H

Atom	Number of Electron Groups	Number of Lone Pairs	Molecular Geometry
Left N	3	1	Bent
Right N	3	1	Bent

Sketch the molecule:

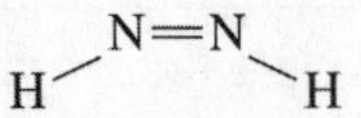

N=N
H   H

(c) N_2H_4 Draw the Lewis structure:

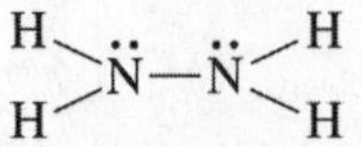

H   H
  N̈—N̈
H   H

Atom	Number of Electron Groups	Number of Lone Pairs	Molecular Geometry
Left N	4	1	Trigonal pyramidal
Right C	4	1	Trigonal pyramidal

Sketch the molecule:

H   N—N   H
H   H

10.13 (a) Four pairs of electrons give a tetrahedral electron geometry. The lone pair would cause lone pair–bonded pair repulsions and would have a trigonal pyramidal molecular geometry.

(b) Five pairs of electrons give a trigonal bipyramidal electron geometry. The lone pair occupies an equatorial position to minimize lone pair–bonded pair repulsions, and the molecule would have a seesaw molecular geometry.

(c) Six pairs of electrons give an octahedral electron geometry. The two lone pairs would occupy opposite positions to minimize lone pair–lone pair repulsions. The molecular geometry would be square planar.

10.14 (a) Four pairs of electrons give a tetrahedral electron geometry. The two lone pairs would cause repulsions that would lead to a bent molecular geometry.

(b) Five pairs of electrons give a trigonal bipyramidal geometry. The three lone pairs would occupy equatorial positions to minimize the lone pair–lone pair repulsions. This would give a linear molecular geometry.

(c) Six pairs of electrons give an octahedral electron geometry. The lone pair would occupy a position to minimize the lone pair–bonded pair repulsions. This would give a square pyramidal molecular geometry.

10.15 (a) CH_3OH Draw the Lewis structure and determine the geometry about each interior atom:

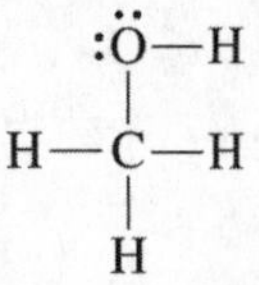

:Ö—H
|
H—C—H
|
H

Atom	Number of Electron Groups	Number of Lone Pairs	Molecular Geometry
C	4	0	Tetrahedral
O	4	2	Bent

Sketch the molecule:

(b) CH_3OCH_3 Draw the Lewis structure and determine the geometry about each interior atom:

Atom	Number of Electron Groups	Number of Lone Pairs	Molecular Geometry
C	4	0	Tetrahedral
O	4	2	Bent
C	4	0	Tetrahedral

Sketch the molecule:

(c) H_2O_2 Draw the Lewis structure and determine the geometry about each interior atom:

$$H-\ddot{O}-\ddot{O}-H$$

Atom	Number of Electron Groups	Number of Lone Pairs	Molecular Geometry
O	4	2	Bent
O	4	2	Bent

Sketch the molecule:

10.16   (a) CH_3NH_2 Draw the Lewis structure and determine the geometry about each interior atom:

Atom	Number of Electron Groups	Number of Lone Pairs	Molecular Geometry
C	4	0	Tetrahedral
N	4	1	Trigonal pyramidal

Sketch the molecule:

(b) $CH_3CO_2CH_3$ Draw the Lewis structure and determine the geometry about each interior atom:

Atom	Number of Electron Groups	Number of Lone Pairs	Molecular Geometry
Left C	4	0	Tetrahedral
Center C	3	0	Trigonal planar
O	4	2	Bent
Right C	4	0	Tetrahedral

Sketch the molecule:

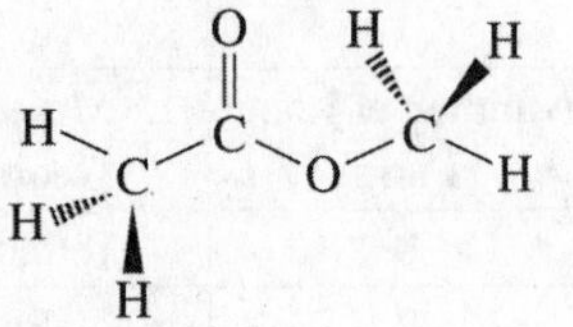

(c) NH_2CO_2H Draw the Lewis structure and determine the geometry about each interior atom:

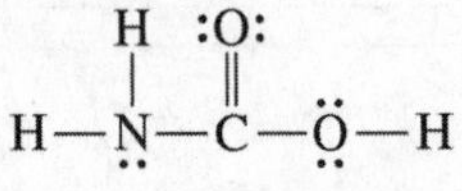

Atom	Number of Electron Groups	Number of Lone Pairs	Molecular Geometry
N	4	1	Trigonal pyramidal
C	3	0	Trigonal planar
O	4	2	Bent

Sketch the molecule:

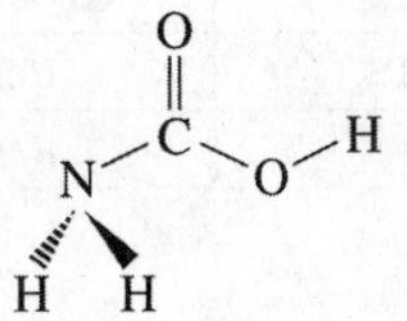

Molecular Shape and Polarity

10.17   Draw the Lewis structure for CO_2 and CCl_4; determine the molecular geometry and then the polarity.

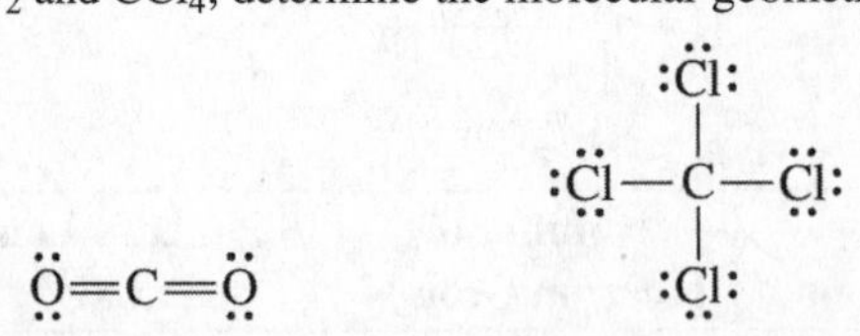

Number of electron groups on C	2	4
Number of lone pairs	0	0
Molecular geometry	linear	tetrahedral

Even though each molecule contains polar bonds, the sum of the bond dipoles gives a net dipole of zero for each molecule.

The linear molecular geometry of CO_2 will have bond vectors that are equal and opposite. ⟵————⟶

The tetrahedral molecular geometry of CCl_4 will have bond vectors that are equal and have a net dipole of zero.

10.18   Draw the Lewis structure of CH_3F; determine the molecular geometry and then the polarity.

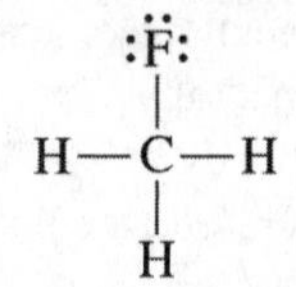

$$:\ddot{F}:$$
$$H—C—H$$
$$|$$
$$H$$

Number of electron groups on C	4
Number of lone pairs	0
Molecular geometry	tetrahedral

The molecule is tetrahedral but is polar because the C—H bond dipoles are different from the C—F bond dipole because the electronegativities of C = 2.5, H = 2.1, and F = 4.0. Because the bond dipoles are different (ΔEN (C—H) = 0.4 versus delta EN (C—F) = 1.5), the sum of the bond dipoles is *not* zero. Therefore, the molecule is polar.

The tetrahedral molecular geometry of CH_3F will have unequal bond vectors, so the molecule will have a net dipole.

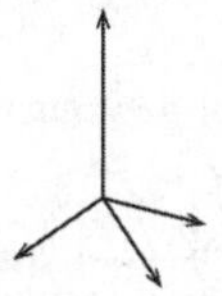

10.19   (a) PF_3—polar

Draw the Lewis structure and determine the molecular geometry:
The molecular geometry from Problem 5 is trigonal pyramidal.
Determine whether the molecule contains polar bonds:
The electronegativity of P = 2.1 and F = 4. Therefore, the bonds are polar.

Determine whether the polar bonds add together to form a net dipole:

Because the molecule is trigonal pyramidal, the three dipole moments sum to a nonzero net dipole moment. The molecule is polar. See Table 10.2, in the text to see how dipole moments add to determine polarity.

    (b) SBr_2—nonpolar

Draw the Lewis structure and determine the molecular geometry:
The molecular geometry from Problem 5 is bent.
Determine whether the molecule contains polar bonds:
The electronegativity of S = 2.5 and Br = 2.8. Therefore, the bonds are nonpolar.

Even though the molecule is bent, because the bonds are nonpolar, the molecule is nonpolar.

    (c) $CHCl_3$—polar

Draw the Lewis structure and determine the molecular geometry:
The molecular geometry from Problem 5 is tetrahedral.
Determine whether the molecule contains polar bonds:
The electronegativity of C = 2.5, H = 2.1, and Cl = 3.0. Therefore, the bonds are polar.

Determine whether the polar bonds add together to form a net dipole:

Because the bonds have different dipole moments due to the different atoms involved, the four dipole moments sum to a nonzero net dipole moment. The molecule is polar. See Table 10.2, in the text to see how dipole moments add to determine polarity.

    (d) CS_2—nonpolar

Draw the Lewis structure and determine the molecular geometry:
The molecular geometry from Problem 5 is linear.

Determine whether the molecule contains polar bonds:

The electronegativity of C = 2.5 and S = 2.5. Therefore, the bonds are nonpolar. Also, the molecule is linear, which would result in a zero net dipole even if the bonds were polar.

The molecule is nonpolar. See Table 10.2, in the text to see how dipole moments add to determine polarity.

10.20   (a) CF_4—nonpolar

Draw the Lewis structure and determine the molecular geometry:

The molecular geometry from Problem 6 is tetrahedral.

Determine whether the molecule contains polar bonds:

The electronegativity of C = 2.5 and F = 4.0. Therefore, the bonds are polar.

Determine whether the polar bonds add together to form a net dipole:

Because the molecular geometry is tetrahedral, the four equal dipole moments sum to a zero net dipole moment. The molecule is nonpolar. See Table 10.2, in the text to see how dipole moments add to determine polarity.

   (b) NF_3—polar

Draw the Lewis structure and determine the molecular geometry:

The molecular geometry from Problem 6 is trigonal pyramidal.

Determine whether the molecule contains polar bonds:

The electronegativity of N = 3.0 and F = 4.0. Therefore, the bonds are polar.

Determine whether the polar bonds add together to form a net dipole:

Because the molecular geometry is trigonal pyramidal, the three dipole moments sum to a nonzero net dipole moment. The molecule is polar. See Table 10.2, in the text to see how dipole moments add to determine polarity.

   (c) OF_2—polar

Draw the Lewis structure and determine the molecular geometry:

The molecular geometry from Problem 6 is bent.

Determine whether the molecule contains polar bonds:

The electronegativity of O = 3.5 and F = 4.0. Therefore, the bonds are polar.

Determine whether the polar bonds add together to form a net dipole:

Because the molecular geometry is bent, the two dipole moments sum to a nonzero net dipole moment. The molecule is polar. See Table 10.2, in the text to see how dipole moments add to determine polarity.

   (d) H_2S—polar

Draw the Lewis structure and determine the molecular geometry:

The molecular geometry from Problem 6 is bent.

Determine whether the molecule contains polar bonds:

The electronegativity of H = 2.1 and S = 2.5. Therefore, the bonds are polar.

Determine whether the polar bonds add together to form a net dipole:

Because the molecular geometry is bent, the two dipole moments sum to a nonzero net dipole moment. The molecule is polar. See Table 10.2, in the text to see how dipole moments add to determine polarity.

10.21   (a) SCl_2—polar

Draw the Lewis structure and determine the molecular geometry:

$$:\ddot{S}-\ddot{C}l:$$
$$\;\;|$$
$$:\ddot{C}l:$$

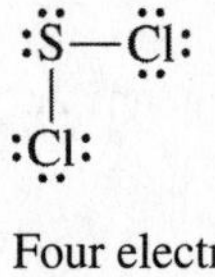

Four electron pairs with two lone pairs give a bent molecular geometry.

Determine whether the molecule contains polar bonds:

The electronegativity of S = 2.5 and Cl = 3.0. Therefore, the bonds are polar.

Determine whether the polar bonds add together to form a net dipole:

Because the molecular geometry is bent, the two dipole moments sum to a nonzero net dipole moment. The molecule is polar. See Table 10.2, in the text to see how dipole moments add to determine polarity.

   (b) SCl_4—polar

Draw the Lewis structure and determine the molecular geometry:

$$:\ddot{C}l:$$
$$\;\;|$$
$$:\ddot{C}l-\ddot{S}-\ddot{C}l:$$
$$\;\;|$$
$$:\ddot{C}l:$$

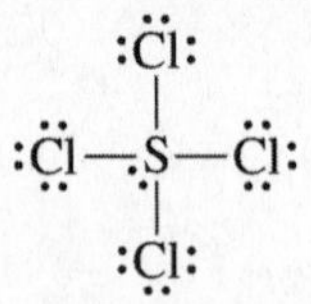

Five electron pairs with one lone pair give a seesaw molecular geometry.

Determine whether the molecule contains polar bonds:

The electronegativity of S = 2.5 and Cl = 3.0. Therefore, the bonds are polar.

Determine whether the polar bonds add together to form a net dipole:

Because the molecular geometry is seesaw, the four equal dipole moments sum to a nonzero net dipole moment. The molecule is polar.

The seesaw molecular geometry will not have offsetting bond vectors.

(c) $BrCl_5$—nonpolar

Draw the Lewis structure and determine the molecular geometry.

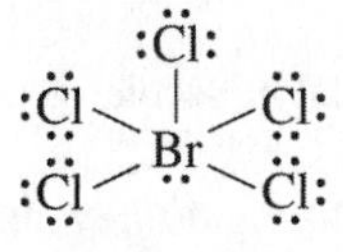

Six electron pairs with one lone pair give square pyramidal molecular geometry.

Determine whether the molecule contains polar bonds:

The electronegativity of Br = 2.8 and Cl = 3.0. The difference is only 0.2; therefore, the bonds are nonpolar. Even though the molecular geometry is square pyramidal, the five bonds are nonpolar; so there is no net dipole. The molecule is nonpolar.

10.22   (a) $SiCl_4$—nonpolar

Draw the Lewis structure and determine the molecular geometry:

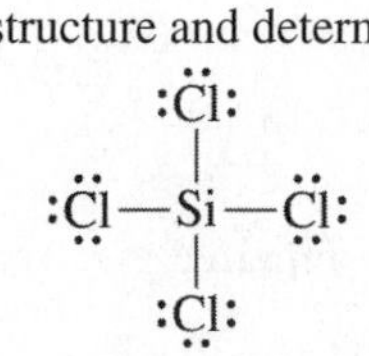

Four electron pairs with no lone pairs give a tetrahedral molecular geometry.

Determine whether the molecule contains polar bonds:

The electronegativity of Cl = 3.0 and Si = 1.8. Therefore, the bonds are polar.

Determine whether the polar bonds add together to form a net dipole:

Because the molecular geometry is tetrahedral, the four equal dipole moments sum to a zero net dipole moment. The molecule is nonpolar. See Table 10.2, in the text to see how dipole moments add to determine polarity.

(b) CF_2Cl_2—polar

Draw the Lewis structure and determine the molecular geometry:

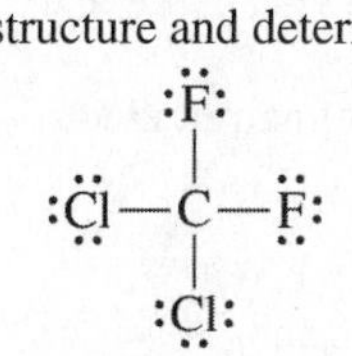

Four electron pairs with no lone pairs give a tetrahedral molecular geometry.

Determine whether the molecule contains polar bonds:

The electronegativity of C = 2.5, F = 4.0, and Cl = 3.0. Therefore, the bonds are polar.

Determine whether the polar bonds add together to form a net dipole:

Even though the molecular geometry is tetrahedral, which normally yields a nonpolar molecule, the four dipole moments sum to a nonzero net dipole moment because of the different electronegativities of Cl and F. The molecule is polar. See Table 10.2, in the text to see how dipole moments add to determine polarity.

(c) SeF_6—nonpolar

Draw the Lewis structure and determine the molecular geometry:

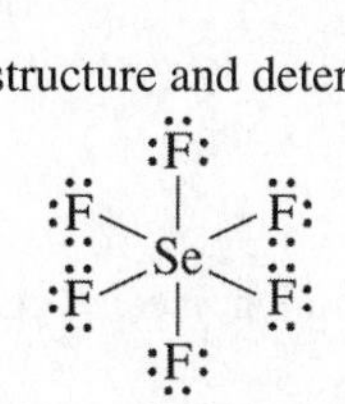

Six electron pairs with no lone pairs give an octahedral molecular geometry.

Determine whether the molecule contains polar bonds:

The electronegativity of Se = 3.0 and F = 4.0. Therefore, the bonds are polar.

Determine whether the polar bonds add together to form a net dipole:

Because the molecular geometry is octahedral, the six equal dipole moments sum to a zero net dipole moment. The molecule is nonpolar. See Table 10.2, in the text to see how dipole moments add to determine polarity.

(d)   IF₅—polar

Draw the Lewis structure and determine the molecular geometry:

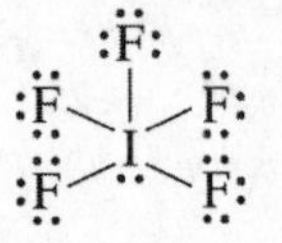

Six electron pairs with one lone pair give square pyramidal molecular geometry.

Determine whether the molecule contains polar bonds:

The electronegativity of I = 2.0 and F = 4.0. Therefore, the bonds are polar.

Determine whether the polar bonds add together to form a net dipole:

Because the molecular geometry is square pyramidal, the five dipole moments sum to a nonzero net dipole moment. The molecule is polar.

The square pyramid structure has offsetting bond vectors in the equatorial plane but not in the axial positions.

Valence Bond Theory

10.23   (a)   Be $2s^2$ No bonds can form. Beryllium contains no unpaired electrons, so no bonds can form without hybridization.

    (b)   P $3s^23p^3$ Three bonds can form. Phosphorus contains three unpaired electrons, so three bonds can form without hybridization.

    (c)   F $2s^22p^5$ One bond can form. Fluorine contains one unpaired electron, so one bond can form without hybridization.

10.24   (a)   B $2s^22p^1$ One bond can form. Boron contains one unpaired electron, so one bond can form without hybridization.

    (b)   N $2s^22p^3$ Three bonds can form. Nitrogen contains three unpaired electrons, so three bonds can form without hybridization.

    (c)   O $2s^22p^4$ Two bonds can form. Oxygen contains two unpaired electrons, so two bonds can form without hybridization.

10.25   PH₃

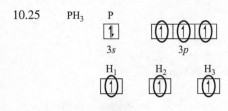

The unhybridized bond angles should be 90°. So without hybridization, there is good agreement between valence bond theory and the actual bond angle of 93.3°.

10.26   SF$_2$

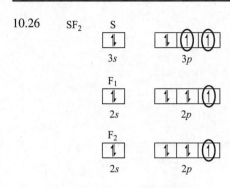

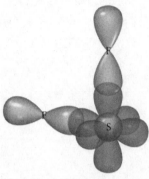

The unhybridized bond angles should be 90°. So without hybridization, there is not very good agreement between valence bond theory and the actual bond angle of 98.2°.

10.27   C $2s^2 2p^2$

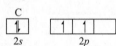

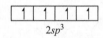

10.28   C $2s^2 2p^2$

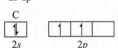

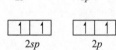

10.29 sp^2 Only sp^2 hybridization of this set of orbitals has a remaining p orbital to form a π bond.
sp^3 hybridization utilizes all three p orbitals.
$sp^3 d^2$ hybridization utilizes all three p orbitals and two d orbitals.

10.30 $sp^3 d$ $sp^3 d$ hybridization utilizes an s orbital, three p orbitals, and a d orbital. Because five orbitals are used, five hybrid orbitals form and five bonds can form.
sp^3 hybridization utilizes an s orbital and three p orbitals. Four orbitals are used, so four hybrid orbitals form and four bonds can form.
sp^2 hybridization utilizes an s orbital and two p orbitals. Three orbitals are used, so three hybrid orbitals form. This allows three σ and one π bond to form, for a total of four bonds formed.

10.31   (a)   CCl₄   Write the Lewis structure for the molecule:

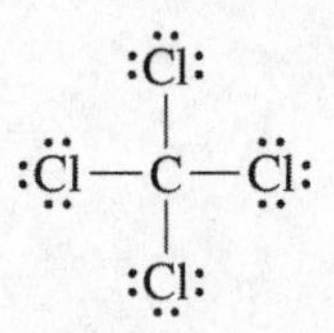

$$\ddot{:}\overset{\displaystyle \ddot{\underset{\cdot\cdot}{Cl}}}{\underset{\displaystyle \ddot{\underset{\cdot\cdot}{Cl}}}{\overset{|}{\underset{|}{C}}}}\ddot{Cl}:$$

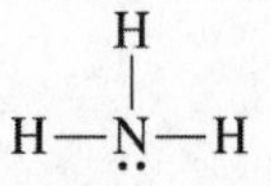

Use VSEPR to predict the electron geometry:
Four electron groups around the central atom give a tetrahedral electron geometry.
Select the correct hybridization for the central atom based on the electron geometry:
Tetrahedral electron geometry has sp^3 hybridization.
Sketch the molecule and label the bonds:

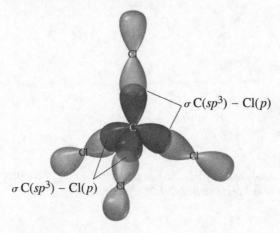

$\sigma\ C(sp^3) - Cl(p)$

$\sigma\ C(sp^3) - Cl(p)$

          (b)   NH₃   Write the Lewis structure for the molecule:

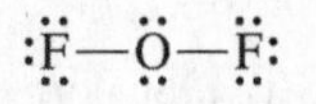

$$H-\underset{\cdot\cdot}{\overset{\displaystyle \overset{|}{H}}{N}}-H$$

Use VSEPR to predict the electron geometry:
Four electron groups around the central atom give a tetrahedral electron geometry.
Select the correct hybridization for the central atom based on the electron geometry:
Tetrahedral electron geometry has sp^3 hybridization.
Sketch the molecule and label the bonds:

Lone pair in N sp^3

$\sigma\ N(sp^3) - H(s)$ $\sigma\ N(sp^3) - H(s)$

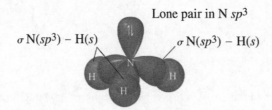

          (c)   OF₂   Write the Lewis structure for the molecule:

$$\ddot{:}\ddot{F}-\ddot{O}-\ddot{F}:$$

Use VSEPR to predict the electron geometry:
Four electron groups around the central atom give a tetrahedral electron geometry.
Select the correct hybridization for the central atom based on the electron geometry:
Tetrahedral electron geometry has sp^3 hybridization.

Sketch the molecule and label the bonds:

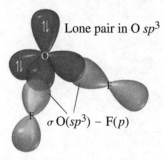

Lone pair in O sp^3

$\sigma\,O(sp^3) - F(p)$

(d) CO_2 Write the Lewis structure for the molecule:

$$\ddot{O}\!=\!C\!=\!\ddot{O}$$

Use VSEPR to predict the electron geometry:
Two electron groups around the central atom give a linear electron geometry.
Select the correct hybridization for the central atom based on the electron geometry:
Linear electron geometry has sp hybridization.
Sketch the molecule and label the bonds:

$\pi\,C(p_y) - O(p_y)$ $\pi\,C(p_z) - O(p_z)$

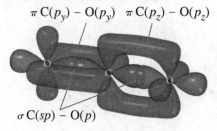

$\sigma\,C(sp) - O(p)$

10.32   (a) CH_2Br_2 Write the Lewis structure for the molecule:

$$\begin{array}{c} H \\ | \\ :\!\ddot{B}r\!-\!C\!-\!H \\ | \\ :\!\ddot{B}r\!: \end{array}$$

Use VSEPR to predict the electron geometry:
Four electron groups around the central atom give a tetrahedral electron geometry.
Select the correct hybridization for the central atom based on the electron geometry:
Tetrahedral electron geometry has sp^3 hybridization.
Sketch the molecule and label the bonds:

$\sigma\,C(sp^3) - H(s)$

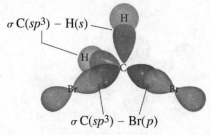

$\sigma\,C(sp^3) - Br(p)$

(b) SO_2 Write the Lewis structure for the molecule:

$$\ddot{O}\!=\!\underset{..}{S}\!-\!\ddot{O}\!:$$

Use VSEPR to predict the electron geometry:
Three electron groups around the central atom give a trigonal planar electron geometry.
Select the correct hybridization for the central atom based on the electron geometry:
Trigonal planar electron geometry has sp^2 hybridization.

Sketch the molecule and label the bonds:

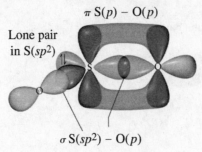

$\pi\, S(p) - O(p)$

Lone pair
in $S(sp^2)$

$\sigma\, S(sp^2) - O(p)$

(c) NF_3 Write the Lewis structure for the molecule:

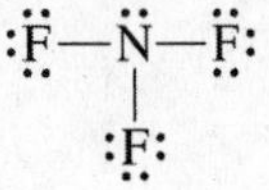

$$:\!\ddot{F}\!-\!\ddot{N}\!-\!\ddot{F}\!:$$
$$\underset{\displaystyle :\!\ddot{F}\!:}{|}$$

Use VSEPR to predict the electron geometry:
Four electron groups around the central atom give a tetrahedral electron geometry.
Select the correct hybridization for the central atom based on the electron geometry:
Tetrahedral electron geometry has sp^3 hybridization.
Sketch the molecule and label the bonds:

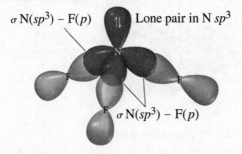

$\sigma\, N(sp^3) - F(p)$ Lone pair in N sp^3

$\sigma\, N(sp^3) - F(p)$

(d) BF_3 Write the Lewis structure for the molecule:

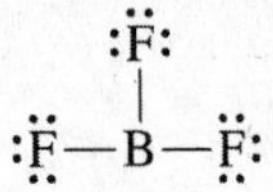

$$:\!\ddot{F}\!:$$
$$\underset{\displaystyle :\!\ddot{F}\!-\!B\!-\!\ddot{F}\!:}{|}$$

Use VSEPR to predict the electron geometry:
Three electron groups around the central atom give a trigonal planar electron geometry.
Select the correct hybridization for the central atom based on the electron geometry:
Trigonal planar electron geometry has sp^2 hybridization.
Sketch the molecule and label the bonds:

Empty p orbital

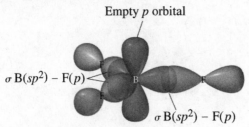

$\sigma\, B(sp^2) - F(p)$

$\sigma\, B(sp^2) - F(p)$

10.33   (a) $COCl_2$ Write the Lewis structure for the molecule:

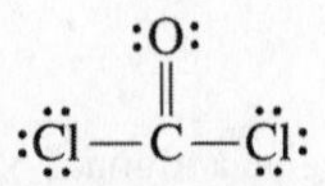

$$:\!O\!:$$
$$\underset{\displaystyle :\!\ddot{Cl}\!-\!C\!-\!\ddot{Cl}\!:}{\|}$$

Use VSEPR to predict the electron geometry:
Three electron groups around the central atom give a trigonal planar electron geometry.
Select the correct hybridization for the central atom based on the electron geometry:
Trigonal planar electron geometry has sp^2 hybridization.

Sketch the molecule and label the bonds:

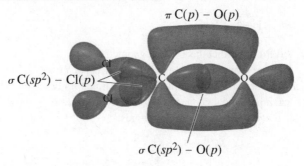

(b) BrF_5 Write the Lewis structure for the molecule:

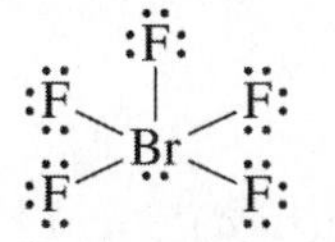

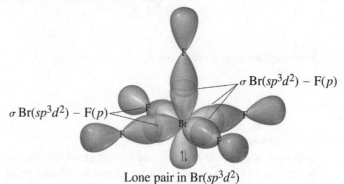

Use VSEPR to predict the electron geometry:
Six electron pairs around the central atoms gives an octahedral electron geometry.
Select the correct hybridization for the central atom based on the electron geometry:
Octahedral electron geometry has sp^3d^2 hybridization.
Sketch the molecule and label the bonds:

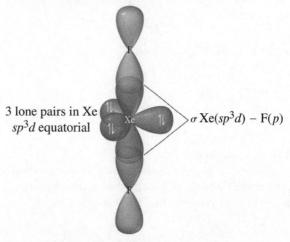

Lone pair in $Br(sp^3d^2)$

(c) XeF_2 Write the Lewis structure for the molecule:

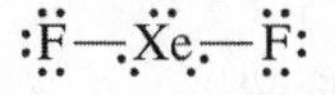

$$:\ddot{F} - \ddot{Xe} - \ddot{F}:$$

Use VSEPR to predict the electron geometry:
Five electron groups around the central atom give a trigonal bipyramidal geometry.
Select the correct hybridization for the central atom based on the electron geometry:
Trigonal bipyramidal geometry has sp^3d hybridization.
Sketch the molecule and label the bonds:

3 lone pairs in Xe
sp^3d equatorial

σ Xe(sp^3d) – F(p)

(d) I_3^- Write the Lewis structure for the molecule:

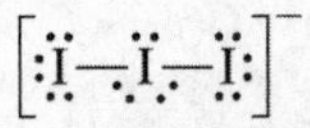

$$\left[\,\ddot{\underset{\displaystyle\cdot\cdot}{I}}-\ddot{\underset{\displaystyle\cdot\cdot}{I}}-\ddot{\underset{\displaystyle\cdot\cdot}{I}}\,\right]^-$$

Use VSEPR to predict the electron geometry:
Five electron groups around the central atom give a trigonal bipyramidal geometry.
Select the correct hybridization for the central atom based on the electron geometry:
Trigonal bipyramidal geometry has sp^3d hybridization.
Sketch the molecule and label the bonds:

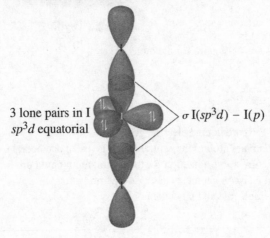

3 lone pairs in I
sp^3d equatorial

$\sigma\ I(sp^3d) - I(p)$

10.34   (a) SO_3^{2-} Write the Lewis structure for the ion:

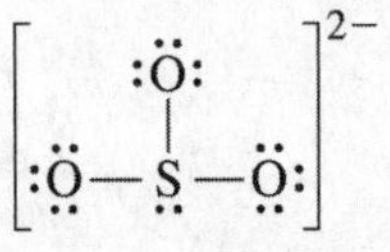

$$\left[\,\begin{array}{c}\ddot{O}:\\|\\:\ddot{O}-S-\ddot{O}:\end{array}\,\right]^{2-}$$

Use VSEPR to predict the electron geometry:
Four electron groups around the central atom give a tetrahedral electron geometry.
Select the correct hybridization for the central atom based on the electron geometry:
Tetrahedral electron geometry has sp^3 hybridization.
Sketch the molecule and label the bonds:

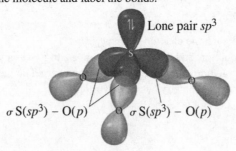

Lone pair sp^3

$\sigma\ S(sp^3) - O(p)$ $\sigma\ S(sp^3) - O(p)$

(b) PF_6^- Write the Lewis structure for the ion:

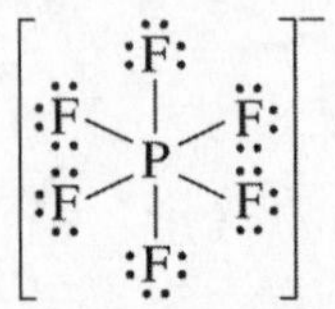

$$\left[\,\begin{array}{c}:\ddot{F}:\\:\ddot{F}\diagdown\,|\,\diagup\ddot{F}:\\\quad P\\:\ddot{F}\diagup\,|\,\diagdown\ddot{F}:\\:\ddot{F}:\end{array}\,\right]^-$$

Use VSEPR to predict the electron geometry:
Six electron pairs around the central atoms give an octahedral electron geometry.
Select the correct hybridization for the central atom based on the electron geometry:
Octahedral electron geometry has sp^3d^2 hybridization.

Sketch the molecule and label the bonds:

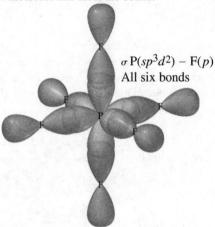

$\sigma\,P(sp^3d^2) - F(p)$
All six bonds

(c) BrF_3 Write the Lewis structure for the molecule:

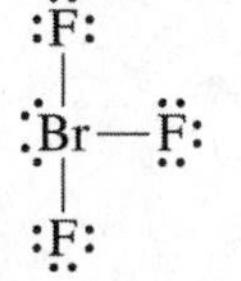

:F̈:
|
:Br̈—F̈:
|
:F̈:

Use VSEPR to predict the electron geometry:
Five electron groups around the central atom give a trigonal bipyramidal geometry.
Select the correct hybridization for the central atom based on the electron geometry:
Trigonal bipyramidal geometry has sp^3d hybridization.
Sketch the molecule and label the bonds:

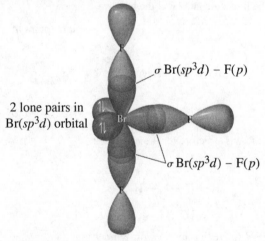

$\sigma\,Br(sp^3d) - F(p)$

2 lone pairs in
$Br(sp^3d)$ orbital

$\sigma\,Br(sp^3d) - F(p)$

(d)   HCN   Write the Lewis structure for the molecule:

H—C≡N:

Use VSEPR to predict the electron geometry:
Two electron groups around the central atom give a linear electron geometry.
Select the correct hybridization for the central atom based on the electron geometry:
Linear electron geometry has sp hybridization.
Sketch the molecule and label the bonds:

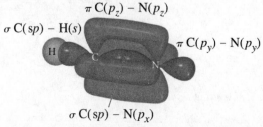

$\pi\,C(p_z) - N(p_z)$

$\sigma\,C(sp) - H(s)$

$\pi\,C(p_y) - N(p_y)$

$\sigma\,C(sp) - N(p_x)$

10.35   (a) N_2H_2 Write the Lewis structure for the molecule:

$$H—\ddot{N}=\ddot{N}—H$$

Use VSEPR to predict the electron geometry:
Three electron groups around each interior atom give a trigonal planar electron geometry.
Select the correct hybridization for the central atoms based on the electron geometry:
Trigonal planar electron geometry has sp^2 hybridization.
Sketch the molecule and label the bonds:

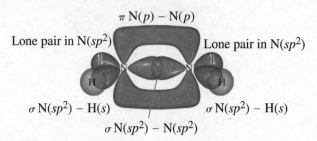

π N(p) – N(p)
Lone pair in N(sp^2)
Lone pair in N(sp^2)
σ N(sp^2) – H(s)
σ N(sp^2) – H(s)
σ N(sp^2) – N(sp^2)

(b) N_2H_4 Write the Lewis structure for the molecule:

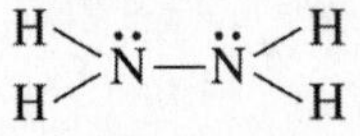

$$\begin{array}{c} H \\ \diagdown \\ H \diagup \end{array} \ddot{N}—\ddot{N} \begin{array}{c} H \\ \diagup \\ \diagdown H \end{array}$$

Use VSEPR to predict the electron geometry:
Four electron groups around each interior atom give tetrahedral electron geometry.
Select the correct hybridization for the central atoms based on the electron geometry:
Tetrahedral electron geometry has sp^3 hybridization.
Sketch the molecule and label the bonds:

2 lone pairs in
N(sp^3)
σ N(sp^3) – H(s)
σ N(sp^3) – H(s)
σ N(sp^3) – N(sp^3)

(c) CH_3NH_2 Write the Lewis structure for the molecule:

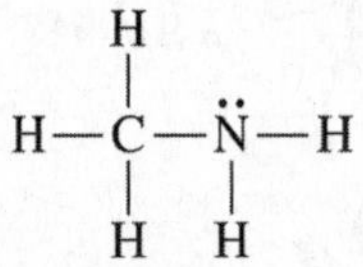

$$\begin{array}{c} H \\ | \\ H—C—\ddot{N}—H \\ | \quad | \\ H \quad H \end{array}$$

Use VSEPR to predict the electron geometry:
Four electron groups around the C give a tetrahedral electron geometry around the C atom, and
four electron groups around the N give a tetrahedral geometry around the N atom.
Select the correct hybridization for the central atoms based on the electron geometry:
Tetrahedral electron geometry has sp^3 hybridization of both C and N.
Sketch the molecule and label the bonds:

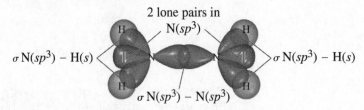

Lone pair in N(sp^3)
σ C(sp^3) – H(s)
σ N(sp^3) – H(s)
σ C(sp^3) – N(sp^3)

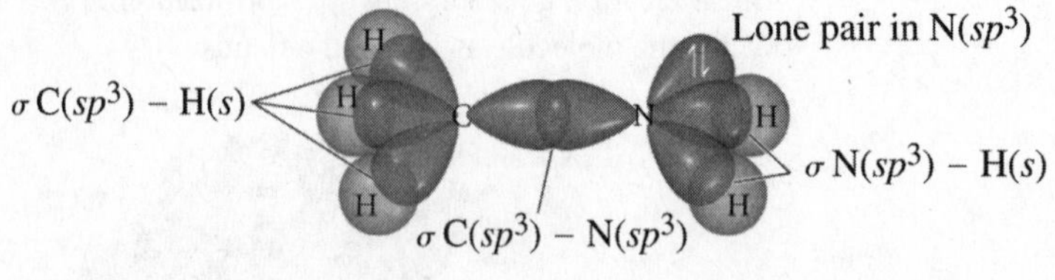

10.36   (a) C_2H_2 Write the Lewis structure for the molecule:

$$H—C≡C—H$$

Use VSEPR to predict the electron geometry:
Two electron groups around each interior atom give a linear electron geometry.
Select the correct hybridization for the central atoms based on the electron geometry:
Linear electron geometry has *sp* hybridization.
Sketch the molecule and label the bonds:

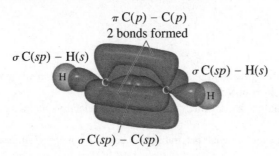

π C(*p*) – C(*p*)
2 bonds formed

σ C(*sp*) – H(*s*)

σ C(*sp*) – H(*s*)

σ C(*sp*) – C(*sp*)

(b)   C$_2$H$_4$ Write the Lewis structure for the molecule:

$$\begin{array}{c} \text{H} \\ \text{H} \end{array} \!\!\!\! {>} \text{C} {=} \text{C} {<} \!\!\!\! \begin{array}{c} \text{H} \\ \text{H} \end{array}$$

Use VSEPR to predict the electron geometry:
Three electron groups around each interior atom give a trigonal planar electron geometry.
Select the correct hybridization for the central atoms based on the electron geometry:
Trigonal planar electron geometry has *sp^2* hybridization.
Sketch the molecule and label the bonds:

π C(*p*) – C(*p*)

σ C(*sp^2*) – H(*s*)

σ C(*sp^2*) – H(*s*)

σ C(*sp^2*) – C(*sp^2*)

(c)   C$_2$H$_6$ Write the Lewis structure for the molecule:

$$\begin{array}{ccc} \text{H} & & \text{H} \\ | & & | \\ \text{H} - \text{C} & - & \text{C} - \text{H} \\ | & & | \\ \text{H} & & \text{H} \end{array}$$

Use VSEPR to predict the electron geometry:
Four electron groups around each interior atom give a tetrahedral electron geometry.
Select the correct hybridization for the central atoms based on the electron geometry:
Tetrahedral electron geometry has *sp^3* hybridization.
Sketch the molecule and label the bonds:

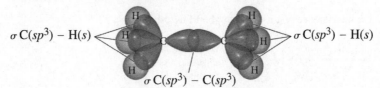

σ C(*sp^3*) – H(*s*)

σ C(*sp^3*) – H(*s*)

σ C(*sp^3*) – C(*sp^3*)

10.37

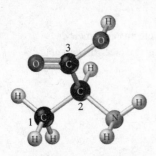

C – 1 and C – 2 each have four electron groups around the atom, which is tetrahedral electron geometry. Tetrahedral electron geometry is sp^3 hybridization.
C – 3 has three electron groups around the atom, which is trigonal planar electron geometry. Trigonal planar electron geometry is sp^2 hybridization.
O has four electron groups around the atom, which is tetrahedral electron geometry. Tetrahedral electron geometry is sp^3 hybridization.
N has four electron groups around the atom, which is tetrahedral electron geometry. Tetrahedral electron geometry is sp^3 hybridization.

10.38

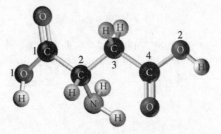

C – 1 and C – 4 each have three electron groups around the atom, which is trigonal planar electron geometry. Trigonal planar electron geometry is sp^2 hybridization.
C – 2 and C – 3 each have four electron groups around the atom, which is tetrahedral electron geometry. Tetrahedral electron geometry is sp^3 hybridization.
O – 1 and O – 2 each have four electron groups around the atom, which is tetrahedral electron geometry. Tetrahedral electron geometry is sp^3 hybridization.
N has four electron groups around the atom, which is tetrahedral electron geometry. Tetrahedral electron geometry is sp^3 hybridization.

Molecular Orbital Theory

10.39 $1s + 1s$ constructive interference results in a bonding orbital:

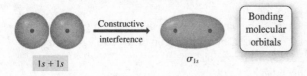

10.40 $1s - 1s$ destructive interference results in an antibonding orbital:

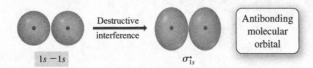

10.41 Be_2^+ has seven electrons. Be_2^- has nine electrons.

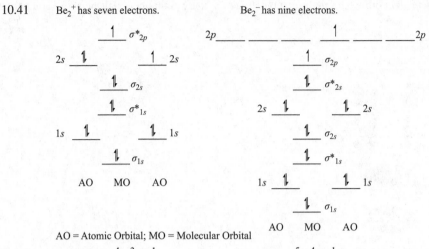

AO = Atomic Orbital; MO = Molecular Orbital

Bond order = $\dfrac{4-3}{2} = \dfrac{1}{2}$ stable   Bond order = $\dfrac{5-4}{2} = \dfrac{1}{2}$ stable

10.42 Li_2^+ has five electrons. Li_2^- has seven electrons.

AO = Atomic Orbital; MO = Molecular Orbital

Bond order = $\dfrac{3-2}{2} = \dfrac{1}{2}$ stable   Bond order = $\dfrac{4-3}{2} = \dfrac{1}{2}$ stable

10.43   The bonding and antibonding molecular orbitals from the combination of p_x and p_x atomic orbitals lie along the internuclear axis.

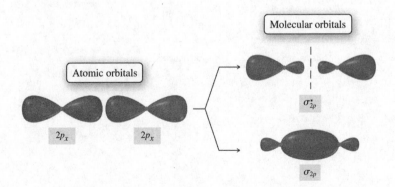

10.44   The bonding and antibonding molecular orbitals from the combination of p_y and p_y atomic orbitals lie above and below the internuclear axis.

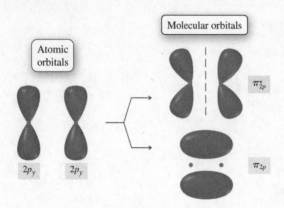

When the p_z and the p_z orbitals combine, similar bonding and antibonding molecular orbitals form. The only difference between the resulting MOs is a rotation about the internuclear axis. The energies and the names of the bonding and antibonding MOs obtained from the combination of the p_z atomic orbitals are identical to those obtained from the combination of the p_y atomic orbitals, which lie in front and in back of the internuclear axis.

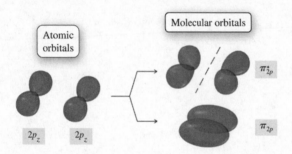

10.45   (a) 4 valence electrons   (b) 6 valence electrons   (c) 8 valence electrons   (d) 9 valence electrons

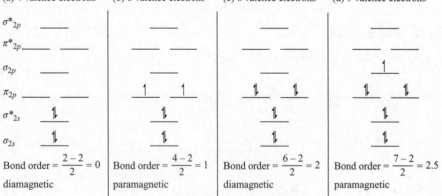

10.46   (a) 10 valence electrons   (b) 12 valence electrons   (c) 13 valence electrons   (d) 14 valence electrons

$$\text{Bond order} = \frac{8-2}{2} = 3$$
diamagnetic

$$\text{Bond order} = \frac{8-4}{2} = 2$$
paramagnetic

$$\text{Bond order} = \frac{8-5}{2} = 1.5$$
paramagnetic

$$\text{Bond order} = \frac{8-6}{2} = 1$$
diamagnetic

10.47   (a)   Write an energy-level diagram for the molecular orbitals in H_2^{2-}. The ion has four valence electrons. Assign the electrons to the molecular orbitals beginning with the lowest energy orbitals and following Hund's rule.

$$\text{Bond order} = \frac{2-2}{2} = 0.$$ With a bond order of 0, the ion will not exist.

(b)   Write an energy-level diagram for the molecular orbitals in Ne_2. The molecule has 16 valence electrons. Assign the electrons to the molecular orbitals beginning with the lowest energy orbitals and following Hund's rule.

$$\text{Bond order} = \frac{8-8}{2} = 0.$$ With a bond order of 0, the molecule will not exist.

(c)   Write an energy-level diagram for the molecular orbitals in He_2^{2+}. The ion has two valence electrons. Assign the electrons to the molecular orbitals beginning with the lowest energy orbitals and following Hund's rule.

$$\text{Bond order} = \frac{2-0}{2} = 1.$$ With a bond order of 1, the ion will exist.

(d)   Write an energy-level diagram for the molecular orbitals in F_2^{2-}. The molecule has 16 valence electrons. Assign the electrons to the molecular orbitals beginning with the lowest energy orbitals and following Hund's rule.

$$\text{Bond order} = \frac{8-8}{2} = 0.$$ With a bond order of 0, the ion will not exist.

10.48   (a)   Write an energy-level diagram for the molecular orbitals in C_2^{2+}. The ion has six valence electrons. Assign the electrons to the molecular orbitals beginning with the lowest energy orbitals and following Hund's rule.

σ^*_{2p} ____

π^*_{2p} ____ ____

σ_{2p} ____

π_{2p} ↑ ↑

σ^*_{2s} ↑↓

σ_{2s} ↑↓

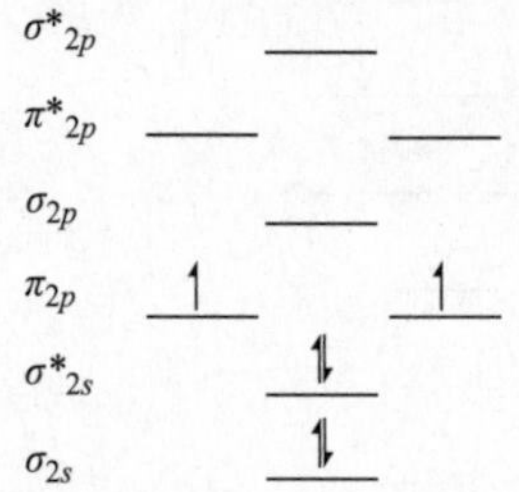

Bond order $= \dfrac{4-2}{2} = 1$. With a bond order of 1, the ion will exist.

(b)   Write an energy-level diagram for the molecular orbitals in Li_2. The ion has two valence electrons. Assign the electrons to the molecular orbitals beginning with the lowest energy orbitals and following Hund's rule.

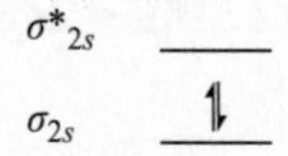

σ^*_{2s} ____

σ_{2s} ↑↓

Bond order $= \dfrac{2-0}{2} = 1$. With a bond order of 1, the molecule will exist.

(c)   Write an energy-level diagram for the molecular orbitals in Be_2^{2+}. The ion has two valence electrons. Assign the electrons to the molecular orbitals beginning with the lowest energy orbitals and following Hund's rule.

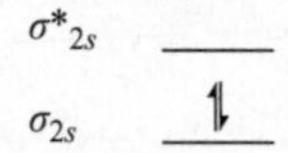

σ^*_{2s} ____

σ_{2s} ↑↓

Bond order $= \dfrac{2-0}{2} = 1$. With a bond order of 1, the ion will exist.

(d)   Write an energy-level diagram for the molecular orbitals in Li_2^{2-}. The ion has four valence electrons. Assign the electrons to the molecular orbitals beginning with the lowest energy orbitals and following Hund's rule.

σ^*_{2s} ↑↓

σ_{2s} ↑↓

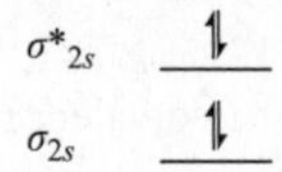

Bond order $= \dfrac{2-2}{2} = 0$. With a bond order of 0, the ion will not exist.

10.49 C_2^- has the highest bond order, the highest bond energy, and the shortest bond.
Write an energy-level diagram for the molecular orbitals in each of the C_2 species.
Assign the electrons to the molecular orbitals beginning with the lowest energy orbitals and following Hund's rule for each of the species.

C_2 (8 valence electrons) C_2^+ (7 valence electrons) C_2^- (9 valence electrons)

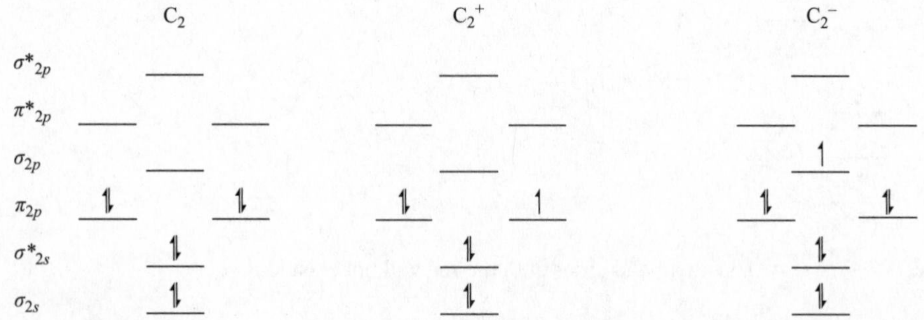

	C_2		C_2^+		C_2^-	
σ^*_{2p}	____		____		____	
π^*_{2p}	____ ____		____ ____		____ ____	
σ_{2p}	____		____		↑	
π_{2p}	↑↓ ↑↓		↑↓ ↑		↑↓ ↑↓	
σ^*_{2s}	↑↓		↑↓		↑↓	
σ_{2s}	↑↓		↑↓		↑↓	

Bond order $= \dfrac{6-2}{2} = 2$ Bond order $= \dfrac{5-2}{2} = 1.5$ Bond order $= \dfrac{7-2}{2} = 2.5$

C_2^- has the highest bond order at 2.5. Bond order is directly related to bond energy, so C_2^- has the largest bond energy; bond order is inversely related to bond length, so C_2^- has the shortest bond length.

10.50 O_2 has the highest bond order, the highest bond energy, and the shortest bond.
Write an energy-level diagram for the molecular orbitals in each of the O_2 species.
Assign the electrons to the molecular orbitals beginning with the lowest energy orbitals and following Hund's rule for each of the species.

| O_2 (12 valence electrons) | O_2^- (13 valence electrons) | O_2^{2-} (14 valence electrons) |

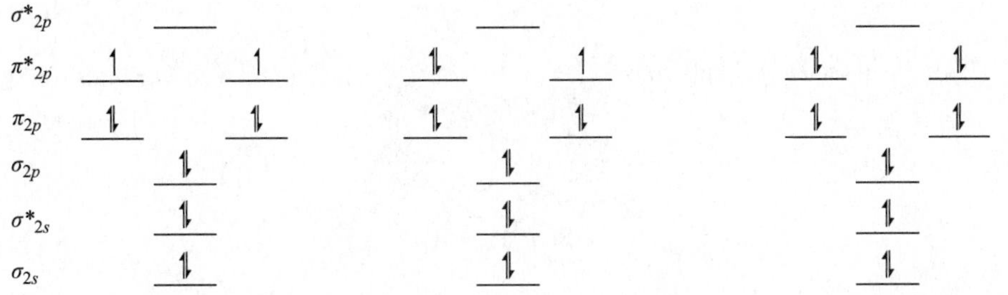

$$\text{Bond order} = \frac{8-4}{2} = 2 \qquad \text{Bond order} = \frac{8-5}{2} = 1.5 \qquad \text{Bond order} = \frac{8-6}{2} = 1$$

O_2 has the highest bond order at 2. Bond order is directly related to bond energy, so O_2 has the largest bond energy, and bond order is inversely related to bond length, so O_2 has the shortest bond length.

Cumulative Problems

10.51   (a) COF_2 Write the Lewis structure for the molecule:

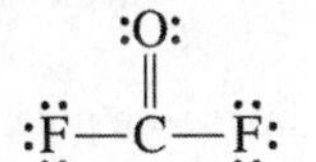

Use VSEPR to predict the electron geometry:
Three electron groups around the central atom give a trigonal planar electron geometry. Three bonding pairs of electrons give a trigonal planar molecular geometry.
Determine whether the molecule contains polar bonds:
The electronegativity of C = 2.5, O = 3.5, and F = 4.0. Therefore, the bonds are polar.
Determine whether the polar bonds add together to form a net dipole:
Even though a trigonal planar molecular geometry normally is nonpolar, because the bonds have different dipole moments, the sum of the dipole moments is not zero. The molecule is polar. See Table 10.2, in the text to see how dipole moments add to determine polarity.
Select the correct hybridization for the central atom based on the electron geometry:
Trigonal planar geometry has sp^2 hybridization.
Sketch the molecule and label the bonds:

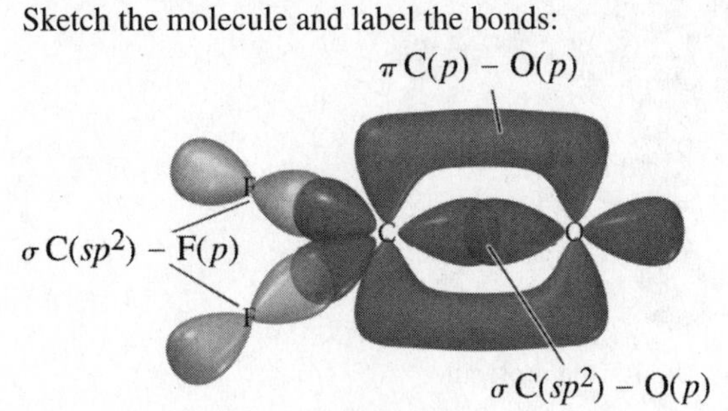

(b) S_2Cl_2 Write the Lewis structure for the molecule:

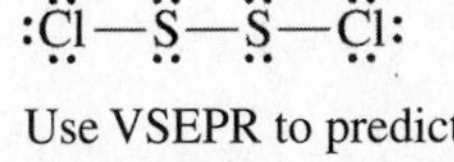

Use VSEPR to predict the electron geometry:
Four electron groups around the central atom give a tetrahedral electron geometry. Two bonding pairs and two lone pairs of electrons give a bent molecular geometry.

Determine whether the molecule contains polar bonds:

The electronegativity of S = 2.5 and Cl = 3.0. Therefore, the bonds are polar.

Determine whether the polar bonds add together to form a net dipole:

In a bent molecular geometry, the sum of the dipole moments is not zero. As drawn the molecule is polar, however, there is free rotation around the S—S bond, so the molecule can also take on a conformation that is nonpolar. See Table 10.2, in the text to see how dipole moments add to determine polarity.

Select the correct hybridization for the central atom based on the electron geometry:

Tetrahedral geometry has sp^3 hybridization.

Sketch the molecule and label the bonds:

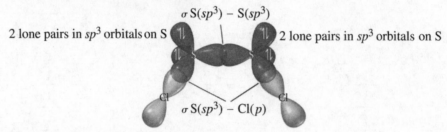

$$\sigma\, S(sp^3) - S(sp^3)$$

2 lone pairs in sp^3 orbitals on S

2 lone pairs in sp^3 orbitals on S

$$\sigma\, S(sp^3) - Cl(p)$$

(c) SF_4 Write the Lewis structure for the molecule:

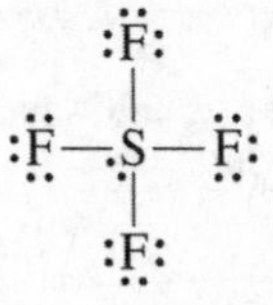

$$\ddot{\underset{\ldots}{F}} $$

$$:\!\ddot{F}\!-\!\underset{\underset{\displaystyle :\ddot{F}:}{|}}{\overset{\displaystyle |}{S}}\!-\!\ddot{F}\!:$$

Use VSEPR to predict the electron geometry:

Five electron groups around the central atom give a trigonal bipyramidal electron geometry.

Four bonding pairs and one lone pair of electrons give a seesaw molecular geometry.

Determine whether the molecule contains polar bonds:

The electronegativity of S = 2.5 and F = 4.0. Therefore, the bonds are polar.

Determine whether the polar bonds add together to form a net dipole:

In a seesaw molecular geometry, the sum of the dipole moments is not zero. The molecule is polar. See Table 10.2, in the text to see how dipole moments add to determine polarity.

Select the correct hybridization for the central atom based on the electron geometry:

Trigonal bipyramidal electron geometry has sp^3d hybridization.

Sketch the molecule and label the bonds:

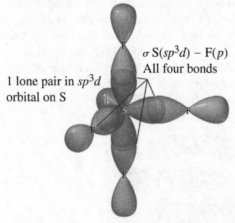

$$\sigma\, S(sp^3d) - F(p)$$
All four bonds

1 lone pair in sp^3d
orbital on S

10.52   (a) IF_5 Write the Lewis structure for the molecule:

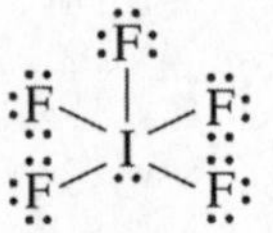

$$:\!\ddot{F}\!:$$

Use VSEPR to predict the electron geometry:

Six electron groups around the central atom give an octahedral electron geometry. Five bonding pairs and one lone pair of electrons give a square pyramidal molecular geometry.

Determine whether the molecule contains polar bonds:

The electronegativity of I = 2.5 and F = 4.0. Therefore, the bonds are polar.

Determine whether the polar bonds add together to form a net dipole:

In a square pyramidal molecular geometry, the sum of the dipole moments is not zero. The molecule is polar. See Table 10.2, in the text to see how dipole moments add to determine polarity.

Select the correct hybridization for the interior atoms based on the electron geometry:

Octahedral electron geometry has sp^3d^2 hybridization.

Sketch the molecule and label the bonds:

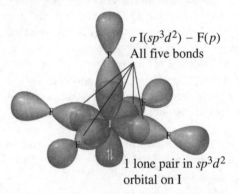

$\sigma\, I(sp^3d^2) - F(p)$
All five bonds

1 lone pair in sp^3d^2
orbital on I

(b) CH_2CHCH_3 Write the Lewis structure for the molecule:

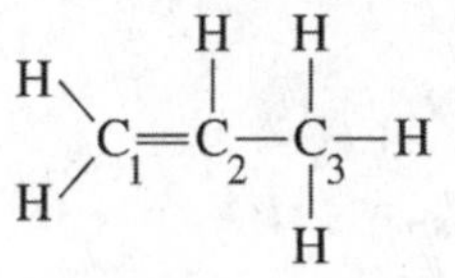

$$\underset{H}{\overset{H}{\diagdown}}\underset{1}{C}=\underset{2}{C}\underset{|}{\overset{H}{\overset{|}{\underset{3}{C}}}}-H$$

Use VSEPR to predict the electron geometry:

C – 1 and C – 2 each have three electron groups around the atom, which is trigonal planar electron geometry. Three bonding pairs of electrons give a trigonal planar molecular geometry.

C – 3 has four electron groups around the C atom; four electron groups give a tetrahedral electron geometry. Four bonding groups give a tetrahedral molecular geometry.

Determine whether the molecule contains polar bonds:

The electronegativity of C = 2.5 and H = 2.1. Therefore, the bonds are slightly polar because the difference in electronegativity is less than 0.5.

Determine whether the polar bonds add together to form a net dipole:

The trigonal planar molecular geometry and the tetrahedral molecular geometry give a net dipole moment of zero. The molecule is nonpolar.

Select the correct hybridization for the interior atoms based on the electron geometry:

Trigonal planar electron geometry has sp^2 hybridization, and the tetrahedral electron geometry has sp^3 hybridization.

Sketch the molecule and label the bonds:

$\pi\, C(p) - C(p)$ $\sigma\, C(sp^2) - H(s)$
$\sigma\, C(sp^3) - C(sp^3)$

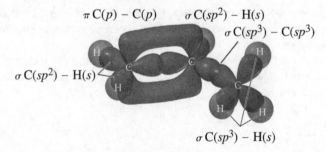

$\sigma\, C(sp^2) - H(s)$

$\sigma\, C(sp^3) - H(s)$

(c) CH_3SH Write the Lewis structure for the molecule:

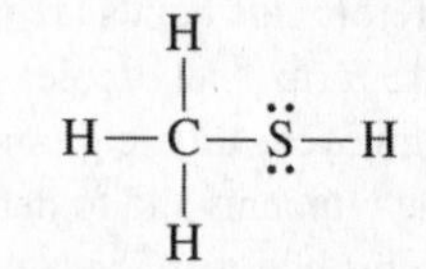

$$H-\overset{\overset{\displaystyle H}{|}}{\underset{\underset{\displaystyle H}{|}}{C}}-\ddot{\overset{..}{S}}-H$$

Use VSEPR to predict the electron geometry:
Four electron groups around the C atom and the S atom give a tetrahedral electron geometry.
Four bonding pairs of electrons around the C give a tetrahedral molecular geometry, and two
bonding groups and two lone pairs around the S give a bent molecular geometry.
Determine whether the molecule contains polar bonds:
The electronegativity of C = 2.5, S = 2.5, and H = 2.1. The C—H bonds and the S—H bond
will be slightly polar, and the C—S bond will be nonpolar.
Determine whether the polar bonds add together to form a net dipole:
In both molecular geometries, the sum of the dipole moments is not zero. The molecule is
polar.
Select the correct hybridization for the central atom based on the electron geometry:
Tetrahedral electron geometry has sp^3 hybridization on both C and S.
Sketch the molecule and label the bonds:

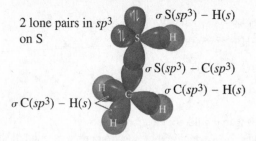

2 lone pairs in sp^3 on S

$\sigma\ S(sp^3) - H(s)$

$\sigma\ S(sp^3) - C(sp^3)$

$\sigma\ C(sp^3) - H(s)$

$\sigma\ C(sp^3) - H(s)$

10.53   (a)   serine

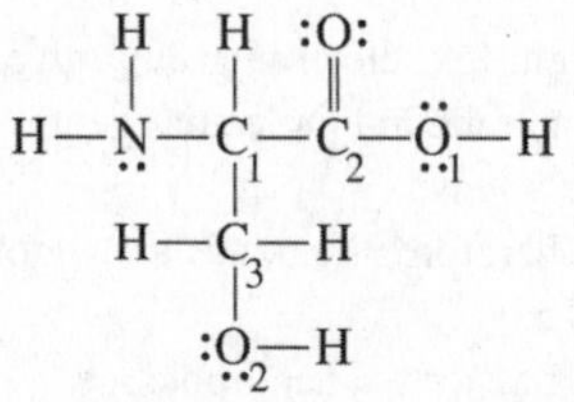

$$H-\overset{\overset{\displaystyle H}{|}}{\underset{..}{N}}-\overset{\overset{\displaystyle H}{|}}{\underset{|}{C}}_1-\overset{\overset{\displaystyle :O:}{\|}}{C}_2-\overset{..}{\underset{..}{O}}_1-H$$
$$H-\overset{|}{\underset{|}{C}}_3-H$$
$$:\overset{..}{\underset{..}{O}}_2-H$$

C – 1 and C – 3 each have four electron groups around the atom. Four electron groups give a tetrahedral electron geometry; tetrahedral electron geometry has sp^3 hybridization. Four bonding groups and zero lone pairs
give a tetrahedral molecular geometry.
C – 2 has three electron groups around the atom. Three electron groups give a trigonal planar geometry;
trigonal planar geometry has sp^2 hybridization. Three bonding groups and zero lone pairs give a trigonal planar
molecular geometry.
N has four electron groups around the atom. Four electron groups give a tetrahedral electron geometry; tetrahedral electron geometry has sp^3 hybridization. Three bonding groups and one lone pair give a trigonal pyramidal
molecular geometry.
O – 1 and O – 2 each have four electron groups around the atom. Four electron groups give a tetrahedral
electron geometry; tetrahedral electron geometry has sp^3 hybridization. Two bonding groups and two lone pairs
give a bent molecular geometry.

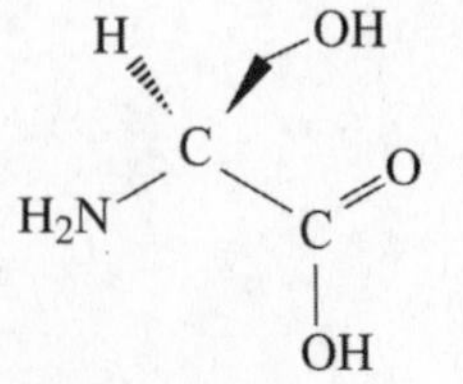

$$H_2N-\overset{\overset{\displaystyle H}{\cdots}}{\underset{\underset{\displaystyle C}{|}}{C}}\overset{\diagup OH}{\diagdown}\underset{\underset{\displaystyle OH}{|}}{C}=O$$

(b)   asparagine

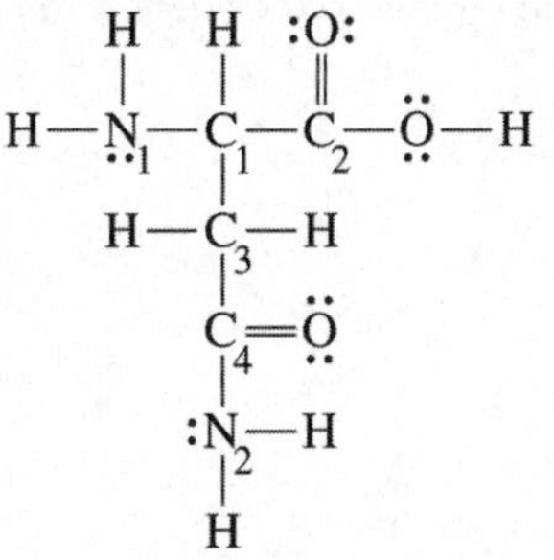

$$
\begin{array}{c}
\text{H} \quad \text{H} \quad :\!\text{O}: \\
| \qquad | \qquad \| \\
\text{H}-\underset{\cdot\cdot 1}{\text{N}}-\underset{1}{\text{C}}-\underset{2}{\text{C}}-\ddot{\text{O}}-\text{H} \\
| \\
\text{H}-\underset{3}{\text{C}}-\text{H} \\
| \\
\underset{4}{\text{C}}=\ddot{\text{O}}: \\
| \\
:\underset{2}{\text{N}}-\text{H} \\
| \\
\text{H}
\end{array}
$$

C – 1 and C – 3 each have four electron groups around the atom. Four electron groups give a tetrahedral electron geometry; tetrahedral electron geometry has sp^3 hybridization. Four bonding groups and zero lone pairs give a tetrahedral molecular geometry.

C – 2 and C – 4 each have three electron groups around the atom. Three electron groups give a trigonal planar geometry; trigonal planar geometry has sp^2 hybridization. Three bonding groups and zero lone pairs give a trigonal planar molecular geometry.

N – 1 and N – 2 each have four electron groups around the atom. Four electron groups give a tetrahedral electron geometry; tetrahedral electron geometry has sp^3 hybridization. Three bonding groups and one lone pair give a trigonal pyramidal molecular geometry.

O has four electron groups around the atom. Four electron groups give a tetrahedral electron geometry; tetrahedral electron geometry has sp^3 hybridization. Two bonding groups and two lone pairs give a bent molecular geometry.

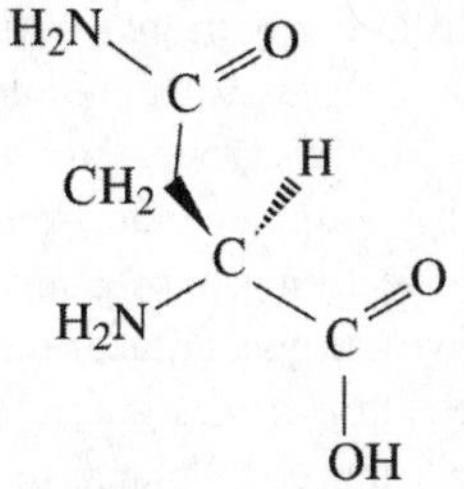

$$
\begin{array}{c}
\text{H}_2\text{N} \qquad\qquad \text{O} \\
\diagdown \qquad \diagup\!\!\diagup \\
\text{C} \\
\text{CH}_2 \qquad\qquad \text{H} \\
\diagdown \qquad \diagup \\
\text{C} \\
\text{H}_2\text{N} \diagup \quad \diagdown \qquad \text{O} \\
\qquad\qquad \text{C}\diagup\!\!\diagup \\
\qquad\qquad | \\
\qquad\qquad \text{OH}
\end{array}
$$

(c)   cysteine

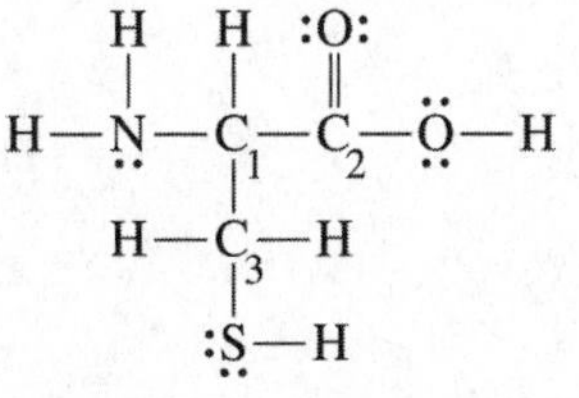

$$
\begin{array}{c}
\text{H} \quad \text{H} \quad :\!\text{O}: \\
| \qquad | \qquad \| \\
\text{H}-\underset{\cdot\cdot}{\text{N}}-\underset{1}{\text{C}}-\underset{2}{\text{C}}-\ddot{\text{O}}-\text{H} \\
| \\
\text{H}-\underset{3}{\text{C}}-\text{H} \\
| \\
:\underset{\cdot\cdot}{\text{S}}-\text{H}
\end{array}
$$

C – 1 and C – 3 each have four electron groups around the atom. Four electron groups give a tetrahedral electron geometry; tetrahedral electron geometry has sp^3 hybridization. Four bonding groups and zero lone pairs give a tetrahedral molecular geometry.

C – 2 has three electron groups around the atom. Three electron groups give a trigonal planar geometry; trigonal planar geometry has sp^2 hybridization. Three bonding groups and zero lone pairs give a trigonal planar molecular geometry.

N has four electron groups around the atom. Four electron groups give a tetrahedral electron geometry; tetrahedral electron geometry has sp^3 hybridization. Three bonding groups and one lone pair give a trigonal pyramidal molecular geometry.

O and S have four electron groups around the atom. Four electron groups give a tetrahedral electron geometry; tetrahedral electron geometry has sp^3 hybridization. Two bonding groups and two lone pairs give bent molecular geometry.

10.54   (a)   cytosine

N – 1 has three bonding groups of electrons and one lone pair; four electron groups give a tetrahedral electron geometry and sp^3 hybridization. Three bonding groups of electrons and one lone pair give a trigonal pyramidal molecular geometry.
C – 2 has three bonding groups of electrons and zero lone pairs; three electron groups give a trigonal planar geometry and sp^2 hybridization. Three bonding groups of electrons give a trigonal planar molecular geometry.
N – 3 has two bonding groups of electrons and one lone pair; three electron groups give a trigonal planar electron geometry and sp^2 hybridization. Two bonding groups and one lone pair give a bent molecular geometry.
C – 4 has three bonding groups of electrons and zero lone pairs; three electron groups give a trigonal planar geometry and sp^2 hybridization. Three bonding groups of electrons give a trigonal planar molecular geometry.
C – 5 has three bonding groups of electrons and zero lone pairs; three electron groups give a trigonal planar geometry and sp^2 hybridization. Three bonding groups of electrons give a trigonal planar molecular geometry.
C – 6 has three bonding pairs of electrons and zero lone pairs; three electron groups give a trigonal planar geometry and sp^2 hybridization. Three bonding groups of electrons give a trigonal planar molecular geometry.
N outside the ring has three bonding groups of electrons and one lone pair; four electron groups give a tetrahedral electron geometry and sp^3 hybridization. Three bonding groups of electrons give a trigonal pyramidal molecular geometry.

(b)   adenine

N – 1 has two bonding groups of electrons and one lone pair; three electron groups give a trigonal planar electron geometry and sp^2 hybridization. Two bonding groups and one lone pair give a bent molecular geometry.
C – 2 has three bonding groups of electrons and zero lone groups; three electron groups give a trigonal planar geometry and sp^2 hybridization. Three bonding groups of electrons give a trigonal planar molecular geometry.
N – 3 has two bonding groups of electrons and one lone pair; three electron groups give a trigonal planar electron geometry and sp^2 hybridization. Two bonding groups and one lone pair give a bent molecular geometry.
C – 4 has three bonding groups of electrons and zero lone groups; three electron groups give a trigonal planar geometry and sp^2 hybridization. Three bonding groups of electrons give a trigonal planar molecular geometry.
C – 5 has three bonding groups of electrons and zero lone groups; three electron groups give a trigonal planar geometry and sp^2 hybridization. Three bonding groups of electrons give a trigonal planar molecular geometry.
C – 6 has three bonding groups of electrons and zero lone groups; three electron groups give a trigonal planar geometry and sp^2 hybridization. Three bonding groups of electrons give a trigonal planar molecular geometry.

N – 7 has two bonding groups of electrons and one lone pair; three electron groups give a trigonal planar electron geometry and sp^2 hybridization. Two bonding groups and one lone pair give a bent molecular geometry.
C – 8 has three bonding groups of electrons and zero lone groups; three electron groups give a trigonal planar geometry and sp^2 hybridization. Three bonding groups of electrons give a trigonal planar molecular geometry.
N – 9 has three bonding groups of electrons and one lone pair; four electron groups give a tetrahedral electron geometry and sp^3 hybridization. Three bonding groups of electrons give a trigonal pyramidal molecular geometry.
N outside the ring has three bonding groups of electrons and one lone pair; four electron groups give a tetrahedral electron geometry and sp^3 hybridization. Three bonding groups of electrons give a trigonal pyramidal molecular geometry.

(c)   thymine

N – 1 has three bonding groups of electrons and one lone pair; four electron groups give a tetrahedral electron geometry and sp^3 hybridization. Three bonding groups and one lone pair give a trigonal pyramidal molecular geometry.
C – 2 has three bonding groups of electrons and zero lone pairs; three electron groups give a trigonal planar geometry and sp^2 hybridization. Three bonding groups of electrons give a trigonal planar molecular geometry.
N – 3 has three bonding groups of electrons and one lone pair; four electron pairs give a tetrahedral electron geometry and sp^3 hybridization. Three bonding groups and one lone pair give a trigonal pyramidal molecular geometry.
C – 4 has three bonding groups of electrons and zero lone pairs; three electron groups give a trigonal planar geometry and sp^2 hybridization. Three bonding groups of electrons give a trigonal planar molecular geometry.
C – 5 has three bonding groups of electrons and zero lone pairs; three electron groups give a trigonal planar geometry and sp^2 hybridization. Three bonding groups of electrons give a trigonal planar molecular geometry.
C – 6 has three bonding groups of electrons and zero lone pairs; three electron groups give a trigonal planar geometry and sp^2 hybridization. Three bonding groups of electrons give a trigonal planar molecular geometry.
C outside the ring has four bonding groups of electrons and zero lone pairs; four electron groups give a tetrahedral electron geometry and sp^3 hybridization. Four bonding groups of electrons give a tetrahedral molecular geometry.

(d)   guanine

N – 1 has three bonding groups of electrons and one lone pair; four electron groups give a tetrahedral electron geometry and sp^3 hybridization. Three bonding groups and one lone pair give a trigonal pyramidal molecular geometry.
C – 2 has three bonding groups of electrons and zero lone pairs; three electron groups give a trigonal planar geometry and sp^2 hybridization. Three bonding groups of electrons give a trigonal planar molecular geometry.
N – 3 has two bonding groups of electrons and one lone pair; three electron groups give a trigonal planar electron geometry and sp^2 hybridization. Two bonding groups and one lone pair give a bent molecular geometry.
C – 4 has three bonding groups of electrons and zero lone pairs; three electron groups give a trigonal planar geometry and sp^2 hybridization. Three bonding groups of electrons give a trigonal planar molecular geometry.
C – 5 has three bonding groups of electrons and zero lone pairs; three electron groups give a trigonal planar geometry and sp^2 hybridization. Three bonding groups of electrons give a trigonal planar molecular geometry.
C – 6 has three bonding groups of electrons and zero lone pairs; three electron groups give a trigonal planar geometry and sp^2 hybridization. Three bonding groups of electrons give a trigonal planar molecular geometry.

N – 7 has two bonding groups of electrons and one lone pair; three electron groups give a trigonal planar electron geometry and sp^2 hybridization. Two bonding groups and one lone pair give a bent molecular geometry.

C – 8 has three bonding groups of electrons and zero lone pair; three electron groups give a trigonal planar geometry and sp^2 hybridization. Three bonding groups and one lone pair give a trigonal planar molecular geometry.

N – 9 has three bonding groups of electrons and one lone pair; four electron groups give a tetrahedral electron geometry and sp^3 hybridization. Three bonding groups and one lone pair give a trigonal pyramidal molecular geometry.

N outside the ring has three bonding groups of electrons and one lone pair; four electron groups give a tetrahedral electron geometry and sp^3 hybridization. Three bonding groups and one lone pair give a trigonal pyramidal molecular geometry.

10.55 4π bonds, 25σ bonds; the lone pairs on the Os occupy unhybridized p orbitals, the lone pair on N – 2 occupies an sp^2 orbital; the lone pairs on N – 1, N – 3, and N – 4 occupy sp^3 orbitals.

caffeine

10.56 5π bonds, 21σ bonds

aspirin

There is rotation around the bond from C – 1 to the ring and from C – 1 to the OH bond. There is rotation around the O – 2 to the ring bond and around the O – 2 to C – 2 bond. There is rotation around the C – 2 to C – 3 bond. The C – 1 to O – 1 bond is rigid, the ring structure is rigid, and the C – 2 to O – 3 bond is rigid.

10.57   (a)   Water-soluble: The 4 C—OH bonds, the C = O bond, and the C—O bonds in the ring make the molecule polar. Because of the large electronegativity difference between the C and O, each of the bonds will have a dipole moment. The sum of the dipole moments does *not* give a net zero dipole moment, so the molecule is polar. Because it is polar, it will be water-soluble.

          (b)   Fat-soluble: There is only one C—O bond in the molecule. The dipole moment from this bond is not enough to make the molecule polar because of all of the nonpolar components of the molecule. The C—H bonds in the structure lead to a net dipole of zero for most of the sites in the molecule. Because the molecule is nonpolar, it is fat-soluble.

          (c)   Water-soluble: The carboxylic acid function (COOH group) along with the N atom in the ring make the molecule polar. Because of the electronegativity difference between the C and O and the C and N atoms, the bonds will have a dipole moment and the net dipole moment of the molecule is *not* zero; so the molecule is polar. Because the molecule is polar, it is water-soluble.

          (d)   Fat-soluble: The two O atoms in the structure contribute a very small amount to the net dipole moment of this molecule. The majority of the molecule is nonpolar because there is no net dipole moment around the interior C atoms. Because the molecule is nonpolar, it is fat-soluble.

10.58   The soap molecule has a nonpolar hydrocarbon end and an anionic end when it is dissolved in water. When it dissolves in water, the sodium stearate congregates to form small spheres (called micelles) with the nonpolar ends on the insides and the anionic ends on the surface. The anionic end interacts with the polar water molecules, while the nonpolar hydrocarbon end can attract and interact with the nonpolar grease. This allows the soapy water to remove the grease by trapping the grease inside the micelle.

10.59   BrF (14 valence electrons)

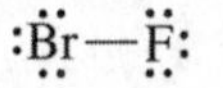

:B̈r—F̈:   no central atom, no hybridization, no electron structure

BrF_2^- (22 valence electrons)

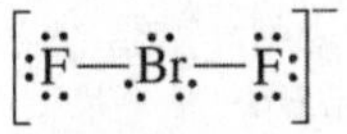

[:F̈—B̈r—F̈:]¯   There are five electron groups on the central atom, so the electron geometry is trigonal bipyramidal. The two bonding groups and three lone pairs give a linear molecular geometry. An electron geometry of trigonal bipyramidal has sp^3d hybridization.

BrF_3 (28 valence electrons)

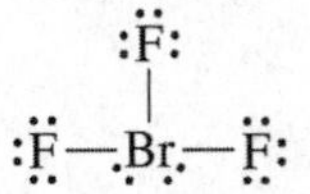

:F̈:
|
:F̈—B̈r—F̈:   There are five electron groups on the central atom, so the electron geometry is trigonal bipyramidal. The three bonding groups and two lone pairs give a T-shaped molecular geometry. An electron geometry of trigonal bipyramidal has sp^3d hybridization.

BrF_4^- (36 valence electrons)

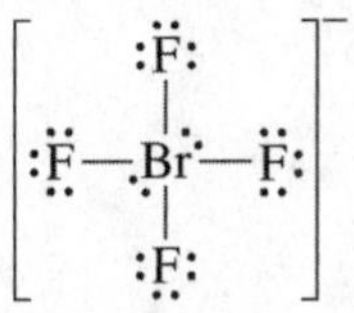

[:F̈:
  |
:F̈—Br—F̈:
  |
  :F̈:]   There are six electron groups on the central atom, so the electron geometry is octahedral. The four bonding groups and two lone pairs give a square planar molecular geometry. An electron geometry of octahedral has sp^3d^2 hybridization.

BrF_5 (42 valence electrons)

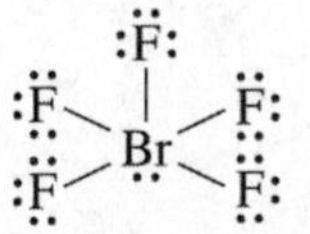

:F̈:
:F̈\ | /F̈:
    Br
:F̈/ ·· \F̈:   There are six electron groups on the central atom, so the electron geometry is octahedral. The five bonding groups and one lone pair give a square pyramidal molecular geometry. An electron geometry of octahedral has sp^3d^2 hybridization.

10.60   Write the Lewis structure:

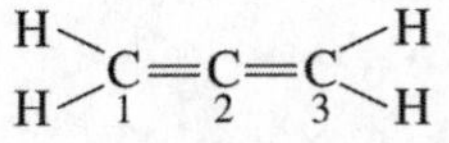

H\   /H
   C=C=C
H/ 1 2 3 \H

C – 1 and C – 3 each have three groups of electrons and a trigonal planar structure giving sp^2 hybridization on the C with a p orbital left for the π bond. C – 2 has two groups of electrons and is linear, which shows sp hybridization and two p orbitals left for the π bonds. According to valence bond theory, the π bonds are formed by the sideways overlap of p orbitals. Because the remaining p orbitals on C – 2 are perpendicular to each other, the π bonds formed between C – 1 and C – 2 and between C – 2 and C – 3 also must be perpendicular to each other. Therefore, the two trigonal planar structures at C – 1 and C – 3 will be perpendicular to each other.

10.61   Draw the Lewis structure: $C_4H_6Cl_2$ (36 valence electrons)

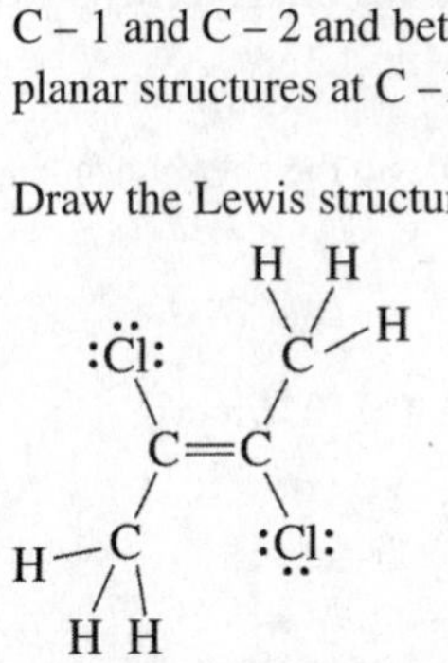

H H
\ /
:C̈l: C—H
  \   /
   C=C
  /   \
H—C   :C̈l:
 / \
H   H

Even though the C—Cl bonds are polar, the net dipole will be zero because the C—Cl bonds and the C—CH₃ bonds are on opposite sides of the double bond. This will result in bond vectors that cancel each other.

10.62   (a) $BeBr_2$ Draw the Lewis structure: (16 valence electrons)

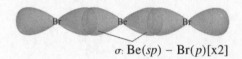

$$\sigma: Be(sp) - Br(p)[\times 2]$$

The two σ bonds form between a hybrid sp orbital on Be and a p orbital on Br.

(b) $HgCl_2$ Draw the Lewis structure: (16 valence electrons)

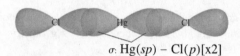

$$\sigma: Hg(sp) - Cl(p)[\times 2]$$

The two σ bonds form between a hybrid sp orbital on Hg and a p orbital on Cl.

(c)   ICN   Draw the Lewis structure: (16 valence electrons)

Sketch the molecule.

$$\pi: C(p) - N(p)[\times 2]$$
$$\sigma: C(sp) - I(p)$$

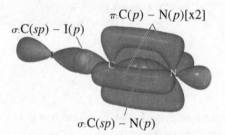

$$\sigma: C(sp) - N(p)$$

One σ bond forms between a hybrid sp orbital on C and a p orbital on I; one σ bond forms between a hybrid sp orbital on C and a p orbital on N; two π bonds form between unhybridized p orbitals on C and p orbitals on N.

Challenge Problems

10.63   According to valence bond theory, CH_4, NH_3, and H_2O are all sp^3 hybridized. This hybridization results in a tetrahedral electron group configuration with a 109.5° bond angle. NH_3 and H_2O deviate from this idealized bond angle because their lone electron pairs exist in their own sp^3 orbitals. The presence of lone pairs lowers the tendency for the central atom's orbitals to hybridize. As a result, as lone pairs are added, the bond angle moves from the 109.5° hybrid angle toward the 90° unhybridized angle.

10.64   (a)   In the isomerization, you need to break the C—C π bond but not the σ bond. So the energy needed would be the difference between the bond energy of a C=C bond and a C—C bond.

C=C   611 kJ/mol
C—C   347 kJ/mol

Therefore, the energy needed to break the π bond would be 264 kJ/mol = 2.64×10^5 J/mol

$$\frac{264 \text{ kJ}}{\text{mol}} \times \frac{1000 \text{ J}}{1 \text{ kJ}} \times \frac{1 \text{ mol}}{6.022 \times 10^{23} \text{ molecules}} = 4.38 \times 10^{-19} \frac{\text{J}}{\text{molecule}}$$

(b)   **Given:** 4.38×10^{-19} J/molecule   **Find:** ν and part of the spectrum

Conceptual Plan: $E \to \nu$

Solution: $\nu = \dfrac{E}{h} = \dfrac{4.38 \times 10^{-19} \text{ J}}{6.626 \times 10^{-34} \text{ J} \cdot \text{s}} = 6.61 \times 10^{14} \text{ s}^{-1}$

This frequency is near the border of the ultraviolet-visible region of the electromagnetic spectrum.

10.65   For each write the Lewis structure:
Determine electron pair geometry around each central atom.
Determine the molecular geometry, determine idealized bond angles, and predict actual bond angles.
NO_2

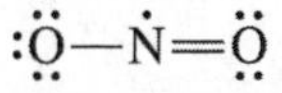

:Ö—Ṅ=Ö

Two bonding groups and a lone electron give a trigonal planar electron geometry; the molecular geometry will be bent. Trigonal planar electron geometry has idealized bond angles of 120°. The bond angle is expected to be slightly less than 120° because of the lone electron occupying the third sp^2 orbital.
NO_2^+

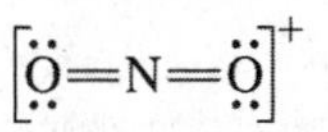

$\left[\ddot{\text{O}}=\text{N}=\ddot{\text{O}} \right]^+$

Two bonding groups of electrons and no lone pairs give a linear electron geometry and molecular geometry. Linear electron geometry has a bond angle of 180°.
NO_2^-

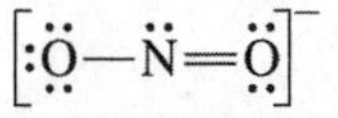

$\left[:\ddot{\text{O}}—\ddot{\text{N}}=\ddot{\text{O}} \right]^-$

Two bonding groups of electrons and one lone pair give a trigonal planar electron geometry; the molecular geometry will be bent.
Trigonal planar electron geometry has idealized bond angles of 120°. The bond angle is expected to be less than 120° because of the lone pair electrons occupying the third sp^2 orbital. Further, the bond angle should be less than the bond angle in NO_2 because the presence of lone pairs lowers the tendency for the central atom's orbitals to hybridize. As a result, as lone pairs are added, the bond angle moves further from the 120° hybrid angle to the 90° unhybridized angle, and the two electrons will increase this tendency.

10.66   As you move down the column from F to Cl to Br to I, the atomic radius of the atoms increases. Because of this, the larger atoms cannot be accommodated with the smaller bond angle. The attached atoms themselves would begin to overlap their orbitals. So as the size of the attached atom increases, the bond angle becomes larger, approaching the hybridized 109.5° angle.

10.67 CH_3CONH_2 Draw the Lewis structure: (24 valence electrons)

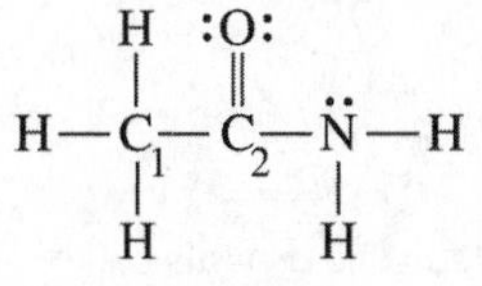

H   :O:
| ‖
H—C₁—C₂—N̈—H
| |
H   H

Structure I

In structure I: C_1 has four σ bonds and no lone pair. The electron geometry would be tetrahedral.
C_2 has three σ bonds, one π bond, and no lone pair. The electron geometry would be trigonal planar.
N has three σ bonds and one lone pair. The electron geometry would be tetrahedral.
This structure would have a trigonal pyramidal molecular geometry around the nitrogen and would not be planar. A second resonance form can be drawn.

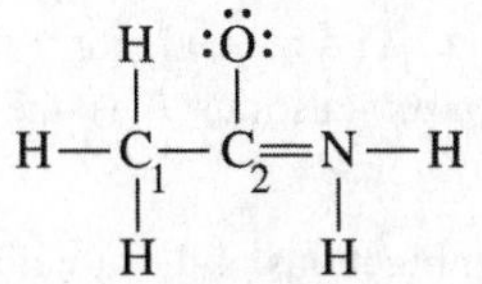

H   :Ö:
| |
H—C₁—C₂=N—H
| |
H   H

Structure II

In structure II: C$_1$ has four σ bonds and no lone pair. The electron geometry would be tetrahedral.

C$_2$ has three σ bonds, one π bond, and no lone pair. The electron geometry would be trigonal planar.

N has three σ bonds, one π bond, and no lone pair. The electron geometry would be trigonal planar. This resonance form would account for a planar configuration around the N.

10.68   CH$_3$NO$_2$ Draw the Lewis structure: (24 valence electrons)

$$
\begin{array}{c}
H \\
| \\
H-C-N \\
| \\
H
\end{array}
\begin{array}{c}
\ddot{\text{O}}: \\
\diagup \\
\diagdown \\
\ddot{\text{O}}
\end{array}
$$

Structure I

$$
\begin{array}{c}
H \\
| \\
H-C-\ddot{\text{O}}-\ddot{\text{N}} \\
| \\
H
\end{array}
\begin{array}{c}
\\
\diagdown \\
\ddot{\text{O}}
\end{array}
$$

Structure II

In structure I, the N has a trigonal planar electron geometry with three bonds to the N and sp^2 hybridization. This will give an O—N—O bond angle of about 120°. In structure II, the N also has trigonal planar electron geometry and sp^2 hybridization. However, the lone pair of electrons on the N will cause the O—N—O bond angle to be less than 120°.

Conceptual Problems

10.69   Statement a is the best statement.
Statement b neglects the lowering of potential energy that arises from the interaction of the lone pair electrons with the bonding electrons.
Statement c neglects the interaction of the electrons altogether. The molecular geometries are determined by the number and types of electron groups around the central atom.

10.70   A molecule with four bond groups and one lone pair would need five equivalent positions around the central atom. In two dimensions, this could be accommodated with a pentagon shape around the central atom. The idealized bond angles would be 72°; however, because of the lone pair occupying one of the positions, the bond angles would be less than 72°.

10.71   In Lewis theory, a covalent bond comes from the sharing of electrons.

A single bond shares two electrons (one pair).
A double bond shares four electrons (two pairs).
A triple bond shares six electrons (three pairs).

In valence bond theory, a covalent bond forms when orbitals overlap. The orbitals can be unhybridized or hybridized orbitals.

A single bond forms when a σ bond is formed from the overlap of an s orbital with an s orbital, an s orbital with a p orbital, or a p orbital and a p orbital overlapping end to end. A σ can also form from the overlap of a hybridized orbital on the central atom with an s orbital or with a p orbital overlapping end to end.
A double bond is a combination of a σ bond and a π bond. The π bond forms from the sideways overlap of a p orbital on each of the atoms involved in the bond. The p orbitals must have the same orientation.
A triple bond is a combination of a σ bond and two π bonds. The π bonds form from the sideways overlap of a p orbital on each of the atoms involved in the bond. The p orbitals must have the same orientation, so each π bond is formed from a different set of p orbitals.

In molecular orbital theory, molecular orbitals form. These are combinations of the atomic orbitals of the atoms involved in the bond. The bonds form when the valence electrons occupy more bonding molecular orbitals than antibonding molecular orbitals. This is calculated by the bond order.

A single bond has a bond order of 1.
A double bond has a bond order of 2.
A triple bond has a bond order of 3.

All three models show the formation of bonds between two atoms. All three models show the formation of the same number of bonds between the atoms involved. Lewis theory tells us only about the number of bonds formed and, combined with VSEPR theory, allows us to predict the shape of the molecule. It does not, however, tell us anything about how the bonds are formed. Valence bond theory addresses the formation of the different types of bonds, sigma and pi. In valence bond theory, the bonds form from the overlap of atomic orbitals on the individual atoms involved in the bonds, and the atoms are localized between the two atoms involved in the bond. Molecular orbital theory approaches the formation of bonds by looking at the entire molecule. The electrons are not restricted to any two individual atoms but are treated as belonging to the whole molecule. The electrons reside in molecular orbitals that are part of the entire molecule rather than being restricted to individual atoms. Each model gives us information about the molecule. The amount and type of information we need determines the model we choose to use.

10.72   In period 2, the atoms are smaller and do not have *d* orbitals available to hybridize; so they cannot accommodate as many atoms around the central atom. To complete the octet of electrons, multiple bonds must form. In the period 3 and higher atoms, more atoms can surround the central atom, which is larger, and the *d* orbitals can hybridize with the *s* and *p* orbitals. There are now more orbitals available to overlap, and there is space for them to do so. The central atom, therefore, can attain a stable configuration of eight or more electrons without having to multiple-bond.

Questions for Group Work

10.73   Someone might expect methane to have 90° angles because we typically draw Lewis structures with 90° angles. The format to arrange an octet of electrons around an atom is top, bottom, left, and right, implying 90° angles.

10.74   Linear molecules can be derived from two different electron geometries:
  • Two electron groups, with both groups being bonding groups; CO_2 is a common example of this geometry.
  • Five electron groups, with two bonding groups and three lone pairs; XeF_2 is a common example of this geometry.

10.75 CS_2: (a) Draw a Lewis structure for the molecule:
          CS_2 has 16 valence electrons

          $$\ddot{S}=C=\ddot{S}$$

          (b) Electron geometry – linear; molecular geometry – linear; bond angle = 180°
          (c) Because both C and S have en electronegativity of 2.5, there are no polar bonds.
          (d) Because there are no polar bonds and no lone pairs, the molecule is nonpolar.

        NCl_3: (a) Draw a Lewis structure for the molecule:
          NCl_3 has 26 valence electrons

          $$:\ddot{Cl}-\ddot{N}-\ddot{Cl}:$$
          $$|$$
          $$:\ddot{Cl}:$$

          (b) Electron geometry – tetrahedral; there are three bonding atoms and one lone pair so the molecular geometry – trigonal pyramid; bond angle < 109.5°

          (c) Because both N and Cl have en electronegativity of 3.0, there are no polar bonds.
          (d) There are no polar bonds, but there is one lone pair, the molecule is polar.

CF$_4$:   (a)   Draw a Lewis structure for the molecule:

CF$_4$ has 32 valence electrons

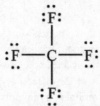

(b)   Electron geometry – tetrahedral; there are four bonding atoms and no lone pair so the molecular geometry – tetrahedral; bond angle = 109.5°

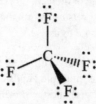

(c)   C and F have electronegativities of 2.5 and 4.0, respectively, so there are four polar bonds.

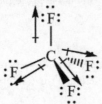

(d)   There are four polar bonds, but they cancel each other out, the molecule is nonpolar.

CH$_2$F$_2$:   (a)   Draw a Lewis structure for the molecule:

CH$_2$F$_2$ has 20 valence electrons

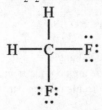

(b)   Electron geometry – tetrahedral; there are four bonding atoms and no lone pair so the molecular geometry – tetrahedral; bond angle = 109.5°

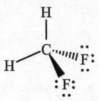

(c)   C, H, and F have electronegativities of 2.5, 2.1, and 4.0, respectively, so there are four polar bonds.

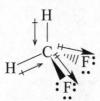

(d)   There are four polar bonds and they do not cancel each other out, the molecule is polar.

10.76   There are four atomic orbitals needed to form a set of sp^3 orbitals. There are three atomic orbitals needed to form a set of sp^2 orbitals. There are two atomic orbitals needed to form a set of sp orbitals. The number of atomic orbitals needed is the same as the number of electron groups around a central atom.

10.77   Both N_2^+ and N_2^- have a bond order of 2.5, so the bond lengths and strengths should be similar to each other. For N_2 the bond order = 3, so it has the shortest and strongest bond of these three species. Notice that for N_2 the bonding molecular orbitals are filled with the last valence electron, for N_2^+ the bonding molecular orbital is not filled, and for N_2^- the last electron is in an antibonding molecular orbital (destabilizing).

11 Liquids, Solids, and Intermolecular Forces

Intermolecular Forces

11.1   (a)   dispersion forces
        (b)   dispersion forces, dipole–dipole forces, and hydrogen bonding
        (c)   dispersion forces and dipole–dipole forces
        (d)   dispersion forces

11.2   (a)   dispersion forces
        (b)   dispersion forces and dipole–dipole forces
        (c)   dispersion forces
        (d)   dispersion forces, dipole–dipole forces, and hydrogen bonding

11.3   (a)   dispersion forces and dipole–dipole forces
        (b)   dispersion forces, dipole–dipole forces, and hydrogen bonding
        (c)   dispersion forces
        (d)   dispersion forces

11.4   (a)   dispersion forces and dipole–dipole forces
        (b)   dispersion forces and dipole–dipole forces
        (c)   dispersion forces, dipole–dipole forces, and hydrogen bonding
        (d)   dispersion forces

11.5   (a) CH_4 < (b) CH_3CH_3 < (c) CH_3CH_2Cl < (d) CH_3CH_2OH. The first two molecules only exhibit dispersion forces, so the boiling point increases with increasing molar mass. The third molecule also exhibits dipole–dipole forces, which are stronger than dispersion forces. The last molecule exhibits hydrogen bonding. Because these are by far the strongest intermolecular forces in this group, the last molecule has the highest boiling point.

11.6   (a) H_2S < (b) H_2Se < (c) H_2O. The first two molecules only exhibit dispersion forces and dipole–dipole forces, so the boiling point increases with increasing molar mass. The third molecule also exhibits hydrogen bonding. Because these are by far the strongest intermolecular forces in this group, the last molecule has the highest boiling point.

11.7   (a) CH_3OH has the higher boiling point because it exhibits hydrogen bonding.
        (b) CH_3CH_2OH has the higher boiling point because it exhibits hydrogen bonding.
        (c) CH_3CH_3 has the higher boiling point because it has the larger molar mass.

11.8   (a) NH_3 has the higher boiling point because it exhibits hydrogen bonding.
        (b) CS_2 has the higher boiling point because it has the larger molar mass.
        (c) NO_2 has the higher boiling point because it exhibits dipole–dipole forces.

11.9   (a) Br_2 has the higher vapor pressure because it has the smaller molar mass.
        (b) H_2S has the higher vapor pressure because it does not exhibit hydrogen bonding.
        (c) PH_3 has the higher vapor pressure because it does not exhibit hydrogen bonding.

11.10   (a) CH_4 has the higher vapor pressure because it has the smaller molar mass and it does not exhibit dipole–dipole forces.

       (b) CH_3OH has the higher vapor pressure because it has the smaller molar mass, and both exhibit hydrogen bonding.

       (c) H_2CO has the higher vapor pressure because it has the smaller molar mass and it does not exhibit hydrogen bonding.

11.11   (a)   This will not form a homogeneous solution because one is polar and one is nonpolar.

       (b)   This will form a homogeneous solution. There will be ion–dipole interactions between the K^+ and Cl^- ions and the water molecules. There will also be dispersion forces, dipole–dipole forces, and hydrogen bonding between the water molecules.

       (c)   This will form a homogeneous solution. Dispersion forces will be present among all of the molecules.

       (d)   This will form a homogeneous solution. There will be dispersion forces, dipole–dipole forces, and hydrogen bonding among all of the molecules.

11.12   (a)   This will form a homogeneous solution. Only dispersion forces will be present.

       (b)   This will not form a homogeneous solution because one is polar and one is nonpolar.

       (c)   This will form a homogeneous solution. There will be ion–dipole interactions between the Li^+ and NO_3^- ions and the water molecules. There will also be dispersion forces, dipole–dipole forces, and hydrogen bonding between the water molecules.

       (d)   This will not form a homogeneous solution because one is polar and one is nonpolar.

Surface Tension, Viscosity, and Capillary Action

11.13   Water will have the higher surface tension because it exhibits hydrogen bonding, a strong intermolecular force. Acetone does not engage in hydrogen bonding.

11.14   (a)   Water "wets" surfaces that are capable of dipole–dipole interactions. The water will form strong adhesive forces with the surface when these dipole–dipole forces are present; so the water will spread to cover as much of the surface as possible. Water does not experience strong intermolecular forces with oil and other nonpolar surfaces. The water will bead up, maximizing the cohesive interactions, which involve strong hydrogen bonds. So water will bead up on surfaces that can exhibit only dispersion forces.

       (b)   Mercury will bead up on surfaces because it is not capable of strong intermolecular interactions (only dispersion forces).

11.15   Compound A will have the higher viscosity because it can interact with other molecules along the entire molecule. The more branched isomer has a smaller surface area, allowing for fewer interactions. Also, Compound A is very flexible, and the molecules can get tangled with each other.

11.16   Multigrade oils contain polymers (long molecules made up of repeating structural units) that coil at low temperatures but unwind at high temperatures. At low temperatures, the coiled polymers—because of their compact shape—do not contribute very much to the viscosity of the oil. As the temperature increases, however, the molecules unwind and their long shape results in intermolecular forces and molecular entanglements that prevent the viscosity from decreasing as much as it would normally. The result is an oil whose viscosity is less temperature-dependent than it would be otherwise, allowing the same oil to be used over a wider range of temperatures.

11.17   In a clean glass tube, the water can generate strong adhesive interactions with the glass (due to the dipoles at the surface of the glass). Water experiences adhesive forces with glass that are stronger than its cohesive forces, causing it to climb the surface of a glass tube. When grease or oil coats the glass, this interferes with the formation of these adhesive interactions with the glass because oils are nonpolar and cannot interact strongly with the dipoles in the water. Without experiencing these strong intermolecular interactions with oil, the water's cohesive forces will be greater and water will be drawn away from the surface of the tube.

11.18   Water can generate strong adhesive interactions with the glass (due to the dipoles at the surface of the glass), but hexane is nonpolar and cannot interact strongly with the glass surface.

Vaporization and Vapor Pressure

11.19   The water in the 12-cm diameter beaker will evaporate more quickly because there is more surface area for the molecules to evaporate from. The vapor pressure will be the same in the two containers because the vapor pressure is the pressure of the gas when it is in dynamic equilibrium with the liquid (evaporation rate = condensation rate). The vapor pressure is dependent only on the substance and the temperature. The 12-cm diameter container will reach this dynamic equilibrium faster.

11.20   The acetone will evaporate more quickly because it is not capable of hydrogen bonding, so the intermolecular forces are much weaker. This will result in a larger vapor pressure at the same temperature as the water.

11.21   The boiling point and heat of vaporization of oil are much higher than that of water, so it will not vaporize as quickly as the water. The evaporation of water cools your skin because evaporation is an endothermic process.

11.22   Water molecules have a lower kinetic energy at room temperature than at 100 °C. The heat of vaporization is the energy difference between the molecules in the liquid phase and the gas phase. Because the energy of the liquid is lower at room temperature, the energy difference that must be overcome to become steam is greater; so the heat of vaporization is greater.

11.23   **Given:** 1065 kJ from candy bar; water $d = 1.00$ g/mL   **Find:** L(H_2O) vaporized at 100.0 °C
            Other: $\Delta H^\circ_{vap} = 40.7$ kJ/mol
            Conceptual Plan: $q \rightarrow$ **mol H_2O** $\rightarrow$ **g H_2O** $\rightarrow$ **mL H_2O** $\rightarrow$ **L H_2O**

$$\frac{1 \text{ mol}}{40.7 \text{ kJ}} \quad \frac{18.02 \text{ g}}{1 \text{ mol}} \quad \frac{1.00 \text{ mL}}{1.00 \text{ g}} \quad \frac{1 \text{ L}}{1000 \text{ mL}}$$

Solution: $1065 \text{ kJ} \times \dfrac{1 \text{ mol}}{40.7 \text{ kJ}} \times \dfrac{18.02 \text{ g}}{1 \text{ mol}} \times \dfrac{1.00 \text{ mL}}{1 \text{ g}} \times \dfrac{1 \text{ L}}{1000 \text{ mL}} = 0.472 \text{ L } H_2O$

Check: The units (L) are correct. The magnitude of the answer (<1 L) makes physical sense because we are vaporizing about 26 moles of water.

11.24   **Given:** 45.0 mL water, $d = 1.00$ g/mL, heated to 100.0 °C   **Find:** heat (kJ) to vaporize at 100.0 °C
            Other: $\Delta H^\circ_{vap} = 40.7$ kJ/mol
            Conceptual Plan: mL H_2O $\rightarrow$ **g H_2O** $\rightarrow$ **mol H_2O** $\rightarrow$ q

$$\frac{1.00 \text{ g}}{1.00 \text{ mL}} \quad \frac{1 \text{ mol}}{18.02 \text{ g}} \quad \frac{40.7 \text{ kJ}}{1 \text{ mol}}$$

Solution: $45.0 \text{ mL} \times \dfrac{1.00 \text{ g}}{1.00 \text{ mL}} \times \dfrac{1 \text{ mol}}{18.02 \text{ g}} \times \dfrac{40.7 \text{ kJ}}{1 \text{ mol}} = 102 \text{ kJ}$

Check: The units (kJ) are correct. The magnitude of the answer (102 kJ) makes physical sense because we are vaporizing about 2.5 moles of water.

11.25   **Given:** 0.88 g water condenses on iron block 75.0 g at $T_i = 22$ °C   **Find:** T_f (iron block)
            Other: $\Delta H^\circ_{vap} = 44.0$ kJ/mol; $C_{Fe} = 0.449$ J/g · °C from text
            Conceptual Plan: g H_2O $\rightarrow$ **mol H_2O** $\rightarrow$ q_{H_2O}(kJ) $\rightarrow$ q_{H_2O}(J) $\rightarrow$ q_{Fe} **then** $q_{Fe}, m_{Fe}, T_i \rightarrow T_f$

$$\frac{1 \text{ mol}}{18.02 \text{ g}} \quad \frac{-44.0 \text{ kJ}}{1 \text{ mol}} \quad \frac{1000 \text{ J}}{1 \text{ kJ}} \quad -q_{H_2O} = q_{Fe} \quad q = mC_s(T_f - T_i)$$

Solution: $0.88 \text{ g} \times \dfrac{1 \text{ mol}}{18.02 \text{ g}} \times \dfrac{-44.0 \text{ kJ}}{1 \text{ mol}} \times \dfrac{1000 \text{ J}}{1 \text{ kJ}} = -2148.72 \text{ J}$ then $-q_{H_2O} = q_{Fe} = 2148.72$ J then

$q = m \, C_s(T_f - T_i)$. Rearrange to solve for T_f.

$$T_f = \frac{m \, C_s T_i + q}{m \, C_s} = \frac{\left(75.0 \text{ g} \times 0.449 \dfrac{J}{g \cdot °C} \times 22 \text{ °C}\right) + 2148.72 \text{ J}}{75.0 \text{ g} \times 0.449 \dfrac{J}{g \cdot °C}} = 86 \text{ °C}$$

Check: The units (°C) are correct. The temperature rose, which is consistent with heat being added to the block. The magnitude of the answer (86 °C) makes physical sense because even though we have $\sim\frac{1}{20}$ of a mole, the energy involved in condensation is very large.

11.26   **Given:** 1.02 g rubbing alcohol (C_3H_8O) evaporated from aluminum block 55.0 g at $T_i = 25\ °C$
Find: T_f (aluminum block) **Other:** $\Delta H^\circ_{vap} = 45.4$ kJ/mol; $C_{Al} = 0.903$ J/g·°C from text
Conceptual Plan: g $C_3H_8O \to$ mol $C_3H_8O \to q_{C_3H_8O}(kJ) \to q_{C_3H_8O}(J) \to q_{Al}$ then $q_{Al}, m_{Al}, T_i \to T_f$

$$\frac{1\ mol}{60.09\ g} \qquad \frac{45.4\ kJ}{1\ mol} \qquad \frac{1000\ J}{1\ kJ} \qquad -q_{H_2O} = q_{Al} \qquad q = m\,C_s(T_f - T_i)$$

Solution: $1.02\ \cancel{g} \times \dfrac{1\ \cancel{mol}}{60.09\ \cancel{g}} \times \dfrac{45.4\ \cancel{kJ}}{1\ \cancel{mol}} \times \dfrac{1000\ J}{1\ \cancel{kJ}} = 77\underline{0}.644$ J then $-q_{H_2O} = q_{Al} = -77\underline{0}.644$ J then

$q = m\,C_s(T_f - T_i)$. Rearrange to solve for T_f.

$$T_f = \frac{m\,C_s T_i + q}{m\,C_s} = \frac{\left(55.0\ \cancel{g} \times 0.903\ \dfrac{J}{\cancel{g}\cdot\cancel{°C}} \times 25\ \cancel{°C}\right) - 77\underline{0}.644\ J}{55.0\ \cancel{g} \times 0.903\ \dfrac{J}{\cancel{g}\cdot°C}} = 9.\underline{4}8316\ °C = 9.5\ °C$$

Check: The units (°C) are correct. The temperature dropped, which is consistent with heat being removed from the block. The magnitude of the answer (9.5 °C) makes physical sense because even though we have only a fraction of a mole, the energy involved in vaporization is very large.

11.27   **Given:**

Temperature (K)	Vapor Pressure (torr)
200	65.3
210	134.3
220	255.7
230	456.0
235	597.0

Find: $\Delta H^\circ_{vap}(NH_3)$ and normal boiling point

Conceptual Plan: To find the heat of vaporization, use Excel or similar software to make a plot of the natural log of vapor pressure (ln P) as a function of the inverse of the temperature in K ($1/T$). Then fit the points to a line and determine the slope of the line. Because the *slope* $= -\Delta H_{vap}/R$, we find the heat of vaporization as follows:

slope $= -\Delta H_{vap}/R \to \Delta H_{vap} = -slope \times R$ then J $\to$ kJ

$$\frac{1\ kJ}{1000\ J}$$

For the normal boiling point, use the equation of the best fit line, substitute 760 torr for the pressure, and calculate the temperature.

Solution: Data was plotted in Excel.
The slope of the best fitting line is $-29\underline{6}9.9$ K.

$$\Delta H_{vap} = -slope \times R = -(-29\underline{6}9.9\ \cancel{K}) \times \frac{8.314\ J}{\cancel{K}\ mol} = \frac{2.4\underline{6}917 \times 10^4\ J}{mol} \times \frac{1\ kJ}{1000\ \cancel{J}} = 24.7\ \frac{kJ}{mol}$$

$$\ln P = -29\underline{6}9.9\ K\left(\frac{1}{T}\right) + 19.03\underline{6} \to$$

$$\ln 760 = -29\underline{6}9.9\ K\left(\frac{1}{T}\right) + 19.03\underline{6} \to$$

$$29\underline{6}9.9\ K\left(\frac{1}{T}\right) = 19.03\underline{6} - 6.63\underline{3}32 \to$$

$$T = \frac{29\underline{6}9.9\ K}{12.402\underline{6}8} = 239\ K$$

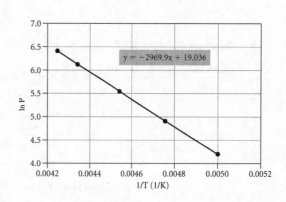

y = −2969.9x + 19.036

Check: The units (kJ/mol) are correct. The magnitude of the answer (25 kJ/mol) is consistent with other values in the text.

11.28 **Given:**

Temperature (K)	Vapor Pressure (torr)
65	130.5
70	289.5
75	570.8
80	1028
85	1718

Find: $\Delta H^\circ_{vap}(N_2)$ and normal boiling point

Conceptual Plan: To find the heat of vaporization, use Excel or similar software to make a plot of the natural log of vapor pressure (ln P) as a function of the inverse of the temperature in K (1/T). Then fit the points to a line and determine the slope of the line. Because the *slope* $= -\Delta H_{vap}/R$, we find the heat of vaporization as follows:

$$slope = -\Delta H_{vap}/R \rightarrow \Delta H_{vap} = -slope \times R \text{ then J} \rightarrow \text{kJ}$$

$$\frac{1 \text{ kJ}}{1000 \text{ J}}$$

For the normal boiling point, use the equation of the best fit line, substitute 760 torr for the pressure, and calculate the temperature.

Solution: Data was plotted in Excel.
The slope of the best fitting line is -711.98 K.

$$\Delta H_{vap} = -slope \times R = -(-711.98 \text{ K}) \times \frac{8.314 \text{ J}}{\text{K mol}} =$$

$$\frac{5.91940 \times 10^3 \text{ J}}{\text{mol}} \times \frac{1 \text{ kJ}}{1000 \text{ J}} = 5.92 \frac{\text{kJ}}{\text{mol}}$$

$$\ln P = -711.98 \text{ K}\left(\frac{1}{T}\right) + 15.833 \rightarrow$$

$$\ln 760 = -711.98 \text{ K}\left(\frac{1}{T}\right) + 15.833 \rightarrow$$

$$711.98 \text{ K}\left(\frac{1}{T}\right) = 15.833 - 6.63332 \rightarrow$$

$$T = \frac{711.98 \text{ K}}{9.19968} = 77.4 \text{ K}$$

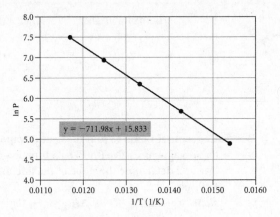

$$y = -711.98x + 15.833$$

Check: The units (kJ/mol) are correct. The magnitude of the answer is lower than other values quoted in the text. This is consistent with the fact that nitrogen boils at such a low temperature.

11.29 **Given:** ethanol, $\Delta H^\circ_{vap} = 38.56$ kJ/mol; normal boiling point $= 78.4\,°C$ **Find:** $P_{Ethanol}$ at $15\,°C$
Conceptual Plan: $°C \rightarrow K$ and $kJ \rightarrow J$ then $\Delta H^\circ_{vap}, T_1, P_1, T_2 \rightarrow P_2$

$$K = °C + 273.15 \qquad \frac{1000 \text{ J}}{1 \text{ kJ}} \qquad \ln \frac{P_2}{P_1} = \frac{-\Delta H_{vap}}{R}\left(\frac{1}{T_2} - \frac{1}{T_1}\right)$$

Solution: $T_1 = 78.4\,°C + 273.15 = 351.6$ K; $T_2 = 15\,°C + 273.15 = 288$ K;

$$\frac{38.56 \text{ kJ}}{\text{mol}} \times \frac{1000 \text{ J}}{1 \text{ kJ}} = 3.856 \times 10^4 \frac{\text{J}}{\text{mol}}; \quad P_1 = 760 \text{ torr}; \quad \ln \frac{P_2}{P_1} = \frac{-\Delta H_{vap}}{R}\left(\frac{1}{T_2} - \frac{1}{T_1}\right). \text{ Substitute values in}$$

$$\text{equation. } \ln \frac{P_2}{760 \text{ torr}} = \frac{-3.856 \times 10^4 \dfrac{\text{J}}{\text{mol}}}{8.314 \dfrac{\text{J}}{\text{K} \cdot \text{mol}}}\left(\frac{1}{288 \text{ K}} - \frac{1}{351.6 \text{ K}}\right) = -2.91302 \rightarrow$$

$$\frac{P_2}{760 \text{ torr}} = e^{-2.91302} = 0.054311 \rightarrow P_2 = 0.054311 \times 760 \text{ torr} = 41 \text{ torr}$$

Check: The units (torr) are correct. Because 15 °C is significantly below the boiling point, we expect the answer to be much less than 760 torr.

11.30   **Given:** benzene, $\Delta H^\circ_{vap} = 30.72$ kJ/mol; normal boiling point $= 80.1\ ^\circ$C; $P_2 = 445$ torr   **Find:** T_2
Conceptual Plan: $^\circ$C $\rightarrow$ K and kJ $\rightarrow$ J then $\Delta H^\circ_{vap}, T_1, P_1, P_2 \rightarrow T_2$

$$K = \,^\circ C + 273.15 \qquad \frac{1000\ J}{1\ kJ} \qquad \ln\frac{P_2}{P_1} = \frac{-\Delta H_{vap}}{R}\left(\frac{1}{T_2} - \frac{1}{T_1}\right)$$

Solution: $T_1 = 80.1\ ^\circ$C $+ 273.15 = 353.3$ K; $\dfrac{30.72\ kJ}{mol} \times \dfrac{1000\ J}{1\ kJ} = 3.072 \times 10^4\ \dfrac{J}{mol}$; $P_1 = 760$ torr;

$P_2 = 445$ torr $\ln\dfrac{P_2}{P_1} = \dfrac{-\Delta H_{vap}}{R}\left(\dfrac{1}{T_2} - \dfrac{1}{T_1}\right)$. Substitute values in equation.

$$\ln\frac{445\ torr}{760\ torr} = \frac{-3.072 \times 10^4\,\frac{J}{mol}}{8.314\,\frac{J}{K \cdot mol}}\left(\frac{1}{T_2} - \frac{1}{353.3\ K}\right) \rightarrow -0.535\underline{2}44 = -3.69\underline{4}972 \times 10^3\ K\left(\frac{1}{T_2} - 0.002830456\right)$$

$$\rightarrow \frac{1.4\underline{4}857 \times 10^{-4}}{K} = \left(\frac{1}{T_2} - \frac{0.002830456}{K}\right) \rightarrow \frac{1}{T_2} = \frac{2.9\underline{7}531 \times 10^{-3}}{K} \rightarrow T_2 = 336.0990\ K = 63\ ^\circ C.$$

Check: The units ($^\circ$C) are correct. Because the pressure is over half of 760 torr, we expect a temperature a little lower than the boiling point.

11.31   **Given:** CS_2, $P_{CS_2} = 363$ torr at 25 $^\circ$C; normal boiling point $= 46.3\ ^\circ$C   **Find:** ΔH_{vap}
Conceptual Plan: $^\circ$C $\rightarrow$ K and then $T_1, P_1, T_2, P_2 \rightarrow \Delta H_{vap}$

$$K = \,^\circ C + 273.15 \qquad \ln\frac{P_2}{P_1} = \frac{-\Delta H_{vap}}{R}\left(\frac{1}{T_2} - \frac{1}{T_1}\right)$$

Solution: $T_1 = 25\ ^\circ$C $+ 273.15 = 298.15$ K; $T_2 = 46.3\ ^\circ$C $+ 273.15 = 319.\underline{4}5$ K; $P_2 = 760$ torr;

$\ln\dfrac{P_2}{P_1} = \dfrac{-\Delta H_{vap}}{R}\left(\dfrac{1}{T_2} - \dfrac{1}{T_1}\right)$. Rearrange to solve for ΔH_{vap}.

$$\Delta H_{vap} = -\frac{R\ln\frac{P_2}{P_1}}{\left(\frac{1}{T_2} - \frac{1}{T_1}\right)} = -\frac{8.314\,\frac{J}{K \cdot mol}\ln\frac{760\ torr}{363\ torr}}{\left(\frac{1}{319.\underline{4}5\ K} - \frac{1}{298.15\ K}\right)} = +2\underline{7},470.27\,\frac{J}{mol} = +27\,\frac{kJ}{mol}$$

Check: The units (kJ/mol) are correct. The value is reasonable compared to other values seen in this chapter. It also is close to the published value of +27.65 kJ/mol.

11.32   **Given:** methylamine, $P_{methylamine} = 344$ torr at $-25\ ^\circ$C; normal boiling point $= -6.4\ ^\circ$C   **Find:** ΔH_{vap}
Conceptual Plan: $^\circ$C $\rightarrow$ K and then $T_1, P_1, T_2, P_2 \rightarrow \Delta H_{vap}$

$$K = \,^\circ C + 273.15 \qquad \ln\frac{P_2}{P_1} = \frac{-\Delta H_{vap}}{R}\left(\frac{1}{T_2} - \frac{1}{T_1}\right)$$

Solution: $T_1 = -25\ ^\circ$C $+ 273.15 = 248.15$ K; $T_2 = -6.4\ ^\circ$C $+ 273.15 = 266.\underline{7}5$ K; $P_2 = 760$ torr;

$\ln\dfrac{P_2}{P_1} = \dfrac{-\Delta H_{vap}}{R}\left(\dfrac{1}{T_2} - \dfrac{1}{T_1}\right)$. Rearrange to solve for ΔH_{vap}.

$$\Delta H_{vap} = -\frac{R\ln\frac{P_2}{P_1}}{\left(\frac{1}{T_2} - \frac{1}{T_1}\right)} = -\frac{8.314\,\frac{J}{K \cdot mol}\ln\frac{760\ torr}{344\ torr}}{\left(\frac{1}{266.\underline{7}5\ K} - \frac{1}{248.15\ K}\right)} = +2\underline{3},453.73\,\frac{J}{mol} = +23\,\frac{kJ}{mol}$$

Check: The units (kJ/mol) are correct. The value is reasonable compared to other values seen in this chapter. It also is close to the published value of +23.85 kJ/mol.

Sublimation and Fusion

11.33   **Given:** 47.5 g water freezes   **Find:** energy released   **Other:** $\Delta H^\circ_{fus} = 6.02$ kJ/mol from text
Conceptual Plan: g $H_2O \rightarrow$ mol $H_2O \rightarrow q_{H_2O}$(kJ) $\rightarrow q_{H_2O}$(J)

$$\frac{1\ mol}{18.02\ g} \qquad \frac{-6.02\ kJ}{1\ mol} \qquad \frac{1000\ J}{1\ kJ}$$

Solution: $47.5 \, \cancel{g} \times \dfrac{1 \, \cancel{mol}}{18.02 \, \cancel{g}} \times \dfrac{-6.02 \, \cancel{kJ}}{1 \, \cancel{mol}} \times \dfrac{1000 \, J}{1 \, \cancel{kJ}} = -15\underline{8}68.48 \, J = 1.59 \times 10^4 \, J$ or $1.59 \times 10^4 \, J$ released

or 15.9 kJ released

Check: The units (J) are correct. The magnitude (15,900 J) makes sense because we are freezing about 2.5 moles of water. Freezing is exothermic, so heat is released.

11.34   **Given:** 25.0 g dry ice (CO_2) sublimation   **Find:** heat required **Other:** $\Delta H^{\circ}_{sub} = 32.3$ kJ/mol
Conceptual Plan: g dry ice $\rightarrow$ mol dry ice $\rightarrow q_{dry \, ice}$(kJ) $\rightarrow q_{dry \, ice}$(J)

$$\dfrac{1 \, mol}{44.01 \, g} \qquad \dfrac{32.3 \, kJ}{1 \, mol} \qquad \dfrac{1000 \, J}{1 \, kJ}$$

Solution: $25.0 \, \cancel{g} \times \dfrac{1 \, \cancel{mol}}{44.01 \, \cancel{g}} \times \dfrac{32.3 \, \cancel{kJ}}{1 \, \cancel{mol}} \times \dfrac{1000 \, J}{1 \, \cancel{kJ}} = 18\underline{3}48 \, J$ required $= 18,300 \, J$ required or 18.3 kJ absorbed

Check: The units (J) are correct. The magnitude (18,300 J) makes sense because we are subliming just over 0.5 mole of dry ice. Sublimation is endothermic, so heat is required.

11.35   **Given:** 8.5 g ice; 255 g water   **Find:** ΔT of water
Other: $\Delta H^{\circ}_{fus} = 6.02$ kJ/mol; $C_{H_2O} = 4.18$ J/g $\cdot$ °C from text
Conceptual Plan: The first step is to calculate how much heat is removed from the water to melt the ice.
$q_{ice} = -q_{water}$ so g(ice) $\rightarrow$ mol(ice) $\rightarrow q_{fus}$(kJ) $\rightarrow q_{fus}$(J) $\rightarrow q_{water}$(J) then $q, m, C_s \rightarrow \Delta T_1$

$$\dfrac{1 \, mol}{18.02 \, g} \qquad \dfrac{6.02 \, kJ}{1 \, mol} \qquad \dfrac{1000 \, J}{1 \, kJ} \qquad q_{water} = -q_{ice} \qquad q = mC_s\Delta T_1$$

Now we have slightly cooled water (at a temperature of T_1) in contact with 0.0 °C water, and we can calculate a second temperature drop of the water due to mixing of the water that was ice with the water that was initially room temperature; so $q_{ice} = -q_{water}$ with $m, C_s \rightarrow \Delta T_2$ with $\Delta T_1 \, \Delta T_2 \rightarrow \Delta T_{Total}$.

$$q = m \, C_s\Delta T_2 \text{ then set } q_{ice} = -q_{water} \qquad \Delta T_{Total} = \Delta T_1 + \Delta T_2$$

Solution: $8.5 \, \cancel{g} \times \dfrac{1 \, \cancel{mol}}{18.02 \, \cancel{g}} \times \dfrac{6.02 \, \cancel{kJ}}{1 \, \cancel{mol}} \times \dfrac{1000 \, J}{1 \, \cancel{kJ}} = 2.\underline{8}3962 \times 10^3 \, J$, $q_{water} = -q_{ice} = -2.\underline{8}3962 \times 10^3 \, J$

$q = mC_s\Delta T$. Rearrange to solve for ΔT. $\Delta T_1 = \dfrac{q}{mC_s} = \dfrac{-2.\underline{8}3962 \times 10^3 \, \cancel{J}}{255 \, \cancel{g} \times 4.18 \, \dfrac{\cancel{J}}{\cancel{g} \cdot °C}} = -2.\underline{6}641 \, °C$

$q = mC_s\Delta T$ substitute in values and set $q_{ice} = -q_{H_2O}$

$q_{ice} = m_{ice}C_{ice}(T_f - T_{icei}) = 8.5 \, \cancel{g} \times 4.18 \, \dfrac{\cancel{J}}{\cancel{g} \cdot °C} \times (T_f - 0.0 \, °C) =$

$-q_{water} = -m_{water}C_{water}\Delta T_{water2} = -255 \, \cancel{g} \times 4.18 \, \dfrac{\cancel{J}}{\cancel{g} \cdot °C} \times \Delta T_{water2} \rightarrow$

$8.5 \, T_f = -255\Delta T_{water2} = -255(T_f - T_{f1})$. Rearrange to solve for T_f. $8.5 \, T_f + 255 \, T_f = 255 \, T_{f1} \rightarrow$
$26\underline{3}.5 \, T_f = 255 \, T_{f1} \rightarrow T_f = 0.96\underline{7}74 \, T_{f1}$ but $\Delta T_1 = (T_{f1} - T_{i1}) = -2.\underline{6}641 \, °C$, which says that
$T_{f1} = T_{i1} - 2.6641 \, °C$ and $\Delta T_{Total} = (T_f - T_{i1})$; so
$\Delta T_{Total} = 0.96\underline{7}74 \, T_{f1} - T_{i1} = 0.96\underline{7}74(T_{i1} - 2.\underline{6}641 \, °C) - T_{i1} = -2.\underline{5}782 \, °C - 0.03\underline{2}26 \, T_{i1}$.
This implies that the larger the initial temperature of the water, the larger the temperature drop. If the initial temperature was 90 °C, the temperature drop would be 5.6 °C. If the initial temperature was 25 °C, the temperature drop would be 3.5 °C. If the initial temperature was 5 °C, the temperature drop would be 2.8 °C. This makes physical sense because the lower the initial temperature of the water, the less kinetic energy it initially has and the smaller the heat transfer from the water to the melted ice will be.

Check: The units (°C) are correct. The temperature drop from the melting of the ice is only 2.7 °C because the mass of the water is so much larger than that of the ice.

11.36   **Given:** 352 mL water, $T_i = 25$ °C, $T_f = 5$ °C, $d = 1.0$ g/mL; ice $T_i = 0$ °C, $T_f = 5$ °C   **Find:** g (ice)
Other: $\Delta H^{\circ}_{fus} = 6.02$ kJ/mol; $C_{H_2O} = 4.18$ J/g $\cdot$ °C from text
Conceptual Plan: mL $\rightarrow$ g then $m, C_s, T_i, T_f \rightarrow q_{water}$(J) $\rightarrow q_{ice}$(J) then $q_{ice}, \Delta H^{\circ}_{fus}, C_{H_2O}, T_i, T_f \rightarrow$ g(ice)

$$\dfrac{1.0 \, g}{1.0 \, mL} \qquad q = m \, C_s(T_f - T_i) \quad q_{ice} = -q_{water} \qquad q_{ice} = mC_s(T_f - T_i) + m \times \dfrac{1 \, mol}{18.02 \, g} \times \dfrac{6.02 \, kJ}{1 \, mol} \times \dfrac{1000 \, J}{1 \, kJ}$$

Solution: $352 \; \cancel{mL} \times \dfrac{1.0 \; g}{1.0 \; \cancel{mL}} = 3\underline{5}2 \; g$

$q_{water} = m_{water} \, C_{water}(T_f - T_i) = 3\underline{5}2 \; \cancel{g} \times 4.18 \dfrac{J}{\cancel{g} \cdot \cancel{°C}} \times (5 \; \cancel{°C} - 25 \; \cancel{°C}) = -2.\underline{9}4272 \times 10^4 \; J$

$q_{ice} = -q_{water} = 2.\underline{9}4272 \times 10^4 \; J$ then $q_{ice} = mC_s(T_f - T_i) + m \times \dfrac{1 \; mol}{18.02 \; g} \times \dfrac{6.02 \; kJ}{1 \; mol} \times \dfrac{1000 \; J}{1 \; kJ}$

Substitute values. $2.\underline{9}4272 \times 10^4 \; J = m \times 4.18 \dfrac{J}{g \cdot °C} \times (5 \; °C - 0 \; °C) + m \times \dfrac{334.26 \; J}{1 \; g}$. Rearrange to solve for m.

$m = \dfrac{2.\underline{9}4272 \times 10^4 \; \cancel{J}}{\dfrac{35\underline{5}.16 \; \cancel{J}}{1 \; g}} = 83 \; g$

Check: The units (g) are correct. The temperature drop is large as is the amount of water we want to cool; so the mass seems reasonable.

11.37 **Given:** 10.0 g ice $T_i = -10.0 \; °C$ to steam at $T_f = 110.0 \; °C$ **Find:** heat required (kJ)
Other: $\Delta H^{\circ}_{fus} = 6.02 \; kJ/mol$; $\Delta H^{\circ}_{vap} = 40.7 \; kJ/mol$; $C_{ice} = 2.09 \; J/g \cdot °C$; $C_{water} = 4.18 \; J/g \cdot °C$; $C_{steam} = 2.01 \; J/g \cdot °C$
Conceptual Plan: Follow the heating curve in Figure 11.24. $q_{Total} = q_1 + q_2 + q_3 + q_4 + q_5$ where q_1, q_3, and q_5 are heating of a single phase then $J \rightarrow kJ$ and q_2 and q_4 are phase transitions.

$\qquad q = m \, C_s(T_f - T_i) \qquad\qquad \dfrac{1 \; kJ}{1000 \; J} \qquad\qquad q = m \times \dfrac{1 \; mol}{18.02 \; g} \times \dfrac{\Delta H}{1 \; mol}$

Solution:

$q_1 = m_{ice}C_{ice}(T_{icef} - T_{icei}) = 10.0 \; \cancel{g} \times 2.09 \dfrac{J}{\cancel{g} \cdot \cancel{°C}} \times (0.0 \; \cancel{°C} - (-10.0 \; \cancel{°C})) = 209 \; \cancel{J} \times \dfrac{1 \; kJ}{1000 \; \cancel{J}} = 0.209 \; kJ$

$q_2 = m \times \dfrac{1 \; \cancel{mol}}{18.02 \; g} \times \dfrac{\Delta H_{fus}}{1 \; \cancel{mol}} = 10.0 \; \cancel{g} \times \dfrac{1 \; \cancel{mol}}{18.02 \; \cancel{g}} \times \dfrac{6.02 \; kJ}{1 \; \cancel{mol}} = 3.3\underline{4}1 \; kJ$

$q_3 = m_{water}C_{water}(T_{waterf} - T_{wateri}) = 10.0 \; \cancel{g} \times 4.18 \dfrac{J}{\cancel{g} \cdot \cancel{°C}} \times (100.0 \; \cancel{°C} - 0.0 \; \cancel{°C}) = 4180 \; \cancel{J} \times \dfrac{1 \; kJ}{1000 \; \cancel{J}} = 4.18 \; kJ$

$q_4 = m \times \dfrac{1 \; \cancel{mol}}{18.02 \; g} \times \dfrac{\Delta H_{vap}}{1 \; \cancel{mol}} = 10.0 \; \cancel{g} \times \dfrac{1 \; \cancel{mol}}{18.02 \; \cancel{g}} \times \dfrac{40.7 \; kJ}{1 \; \cancel{mol}} = 22.\underline{5}86 \; kJ$

$q_5 = m_{steam}C_{steam}(T_{steamf} - T_{steami}) = 10.0 \; \cancel{g} \times 2.01 \dfrac{J}{\cancel{g} \cdot \cancel{°C}} \times (110.0 \; \cancel{°C} - 100.0 \; \cancel{°C})$

$= 201 \; \cancel{J} \times \dfrac{1 \; kJ}{1000 \; \cancel{J}} = 0.201 \; kJ$

$q_{Total} = q_1 + q_2 + q_3 + q_4 + q_5 = 0.209 \; kJ + 3.3\underline{4}1 \; kJ + 4.18 \; kJ + 22.\underline{5}86 \; kJ + 0.201 \; kJ = 30.5 \; kJ$

Check: The units (kJ) are correct. The total amount of heat is dominated by the vaporization step. Because we have less than 1 mole, we expect less than 41 kJ.

11.38 **Given:** 1.00 mole steam $T_i = 145.0 \; °C$ to ice at $T_f = -50.0 \; °C$ **Find:** heat evolved (kJ) **Other:** $\Delta H^{\circ}_{fus} = 6.02 \; kJ/mol$; $\Delta H^{\circ}_{vap} = 40.7 \; kJ/mol$; $C_{ice} = 2.09 \; J/g \cdot °C$; $C_{water} = 4.18 \; J/g \cdot °C$; $C_{steam} = 2.01 \; J/g \cdot °C$
Conceptual Plan: mol $\rightarrow$ g Follow the heating curve in Figure 11.24, but in reverse.

$\qquad\qquad \dfrac{18.02 \; g}{1 \; mol}$

$q_{Total} = q_1 + q_2 + q_3 + q_4 + q_5$ where q_1, q_3, and q_5 are heating of a single phase then $J \rightarrow kJ$

$\qquad\qquad q = m \, C_s(T_f - T_i) \qquad\qquad \dfrac{1 \; kJ}{1000 \; J}$

and q_2 and q_4 are phase transitions.

$\qquad q = n \times \dfrac{\Delta H}{1 \; mol}$

Solution: $1.00 \; \cancel{mol} \times \dfrac{18.02 \; g}{1 \; \cancel{mol}} = 18.\underline{0}2 \; g$

$$q_1 = m_{steam}C_{steam}(T_{steamf} - T_{steami}) = 18.\underline{0}2 \text{ g} \times 2.01 \frac{\text{J}}{\text{g} \cdot {}^{\circ}\text{C}} \times (100.0 \, {}^{\circ}\text{C} - 145.0 \, {}^{\circ}\text{C}) = -16\underline{2}9.91 \text{ J} \times \frac{1 \text{ kJ}}{1000 \text{ J}}$$

$$= -1.6\underline{3}0 \text{ kJ}$$

$$q_2 = n \times \frac{-\Delta H_{vap}}{1 \text{ mol}} = 1.00 \text{ mol} \times \frac{-40.7 \text{ kJ}}{1 \text{ mol}} = -40.7 \text{ kJ}$$

$$q_3 = m_{water}C_{water}(T_{waterf} - T_{wateri}) = 18.\underline{0}2 \text{ g} \times 4.18 \frac{\text{J}}{\text{g} \cdot {}^{\circ}\text{C}} \times (0.0 \, {}^{\circ}\text{C} - 100.0 \, {}^{\circ}\text{C}) = -75\underline{3}2.4 \text{ J} \times \frac{1 \text{ kJ}}{1000 \text{ J}}$$

$$= -7.5\underline{3}24 \text{ kJ}$$

$$q_4 = n \times \frac{-\Delta H_{fus}}{1 \text{ mol}} = 1.00 \text{ mol} \times \frac{-6.02 \text{ kJ}}{1 \text{ mol}} = -6.02 \text{ kJ}$$

$$q_5 = m_{ice}C_{ice}(T_{icef} - T_{icei}) = 18.\underline{0}2 \text{ g} \times 2.09 \frac{\text{J}}{\text{g} \cdot {}^{\circ}\text{C}} \times (-50.0 \, {}^{\circ}\text{C} - 0.0 \, {}^{\circ}\text{C}) = -18\underline{8}3.1 \text{ J} \times \frac{1 \text{ kJ}}{1000 \text{ J}}$$

$$= -1.8\underline{8}31 \text{ kJ}$$

$$q_{Total} = q_1 + q_2 + q_3 + q_4 + q_5 = -1.6\underline{3}0 \text{ kJ} - 40.7 \text{ kJ} - 7.5\underline{3}24 \text{ kJ} - 6.02 \text{ kJ} - 1.8\underline{8}31 \text{ kJ}$$
$$= -57.8 \text{ kJ or } 57.8 \text{ kJ released.}$$

Check: The units (kJ) are correct. The amount of heat is dominated by the vaporization step. Because we have exactly 1 mole, we expect more than 41 kJ.

Phase Diagrams

11.39   (a)   solid
        (b)   liquid
        (c)   gas
        (d)   supercritical fluid
        (e)   solid/liquid equilibrium
        (f)   liquid/gas equilibrium
        (g)   solid/liquid/gas equilibrium

11.40   (a)   184.4 °C
        (b)   113.6 °C
        (c)   solid
        (d)   gas

11.41   **Given:** nitrogen; normal boiling point = 77.3 K; normal melting point = 63.1 K; critical temperature = 126.2 K; critical pressure = 2.55×10^4 torr; triple point at 63.1 K and 94.0 torr
        Find: Sketch phase diagram. Does nitrogen have a stable liquid phase at 1 atm?

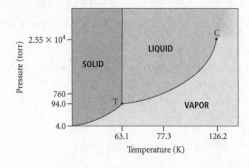

Nitrogen has a stable liquid phase at 1 atm.
Note that the axes are not to scale.

11.42   **Given:** argon; normal boiling point = 87.2 K; normal melting point = 84.1 K; critical temperature = 150.8 K; critical pressure = 48.3 atm; triple point at 83.7 K and 0.68 atm
        Find: Sketch phase diagram. Which has the greater density, solid or liquid argon?

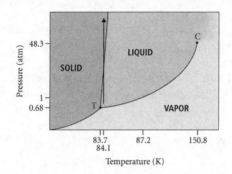

The solid has the higher density because the slope of the solid/liquid equilibrium line is positive. If we start in the liquid and increase the pressure, we will cross into the solid phase, the dense phase.

Note that the axes are not to scale.

11.43   (a)   0.027 mmHg, the higher of the two triple points

       (b)   The rhombic phase is denser because if we start in the monoclinic phase at 100 °C and increase the pressure, we will cross into the rhombic phase.

11.44   The triple point marked "O" shows the equilibrium of Ice II, Ice III, and Ice V. Ice II is denser than Ice I because you can generate Ice II from Ice I by increasing the pressure (pushing the molecules closer together). Ice III would sink in liquid water. Note that the slope of the Ice III/liquid line has the typical positive slope.

The Uniqueness of Water

11.45   Water has a low molar mass (18.02 g/mol), yet it is a liquid at room temperature. Water's high boiling point for its molar mass can be understood by examining the structure of the water molecule. The bent geometry of the water molecule and the highly polar nature of the O—H bonds result in a molecule with a significant dipole moment. Water's two O—H bonds (hydrogen directly bonded to oxygen) allow a water molecule to engage in hydrogen bonding with four other water molecules, resulting in a relatively high boiling point.

11.46   Water's high polarity also allows it to dissolve many other polar and ionic compounds—and even a number of nonpolar gases such as oxygen and carbon dioxide (by inducing a dipole moment in their molecules). Consequently, water is the main solvent in living organisms, transporting nutrients and other important compounds throughout the body. Water is also the main solvent of the environment, allowing aquatic animals, for example, to survive by breathing dissolved oxygen and allowing aquatic plants to survive by using dissolved carbon dioxide for photosynthesis.

11.47   Water has an exceptionally high specific heat capacity, which has a moderating effect on the climate of coastal cities. Also, its high ΔH_{vap} causes water evaporation and condensation to have a strong effect on temperature. A tremendous amount of heat can be stored in large bodies of water. Heat will be absorbed or released from large bodies of water preferentially over land around it. In some cities, such as San Francisco, for example, the daily fluctuation in temperature can be less than 10 °C. This same moderating effect occurs over the entire planet, two-thirds of which is covered by water. In other words, without water, the daily temperature fluctuations on our planet might be more like those on Mars, where temperature fluctuations of 63 °C (113 °F) have been measured between early morning and midday.

11.48   One significant difference between the phase diagram of water and that of other substances is the fusion curve for water, which has a negative slope. The fusion curve in the phase diagrams for most substances has a positive slope because increasing pressure favors the denser phase, which for most substances is the solid phase. This negative slope means that ice is less dense than liquid water, so ice floats. The solids sink in the liquids of most other substances. The frozen layer of ice at the surface of a winter lake insulates the water in the lake from further freezing. If this ice layer sank, it would kill bottom-dwelling aquatic life and possibly allow the lake to freeze solid, eliminating virtually all life in the lake.

Types of Solids and Their Structures

11.49   (a)   8 corner atoms × (1/8 atom/unit cell) = 1 atom/unit cell

       (b)   8 corner atoms × (1/8 atom/unit cell) + 1 atom in center = (1 + 1) atoms/unit cell = 2 atoms/unit cell

       (c)   8 corner atoms × (1/8 atom/unit cell) + 6 face-centered atoms × (1/2 atom/unit cell) = (1 + 3) atoms/unit cell = 4 atoms/unit cell

11.50   (a)   coordination number of 12 because this is a face-centered cubic structure

      (b)   coordination number of 12 because this is a hexagonal closest-packed structure

      (c)   coordination number of 8 because this is a body-centered cubic structure

11.51   **Given:** platinum; face-centered cubic structure; $r = 139$ pm   **Find:** edge length of unit cell and density (g/cm³)

Conceptual Plan: $r \rightarrow l$ and $l \rightarrow V(\text{pm}^3) \rightarrow V(\text{cm}^3)$ and $\mathcal{M}$, FCC structure $\rightarrow m$ then $m, V \rightarrow d$

$$l = 2\sqrt{2}\,r \quad V = l^3 \quad \frac{(1\,\text{cm})^3}{(10^{10}\,\text{pm})^3} \quad m = \frac{4\,\text{atoms}}{\text{unit cell}} \times \frac{\mathcal{M}}{N_A} \quad d = m/V$$

Solution: $l = 2\sqrt{2}\,r = 2\sqrt{2} \times 139\,\text{pm} = 393.151\,\text{pm} = 393\,\text{pm}$ and

$$V = l^3 = (393.151\,\text{pm})^3 \times \frac{(1\,\text{cm})^3}{(10^{10}\,\text{pm})^3} = 6.07684 \times 10^{-23}\,\text{cm}^3 \text{ and}$$

$$m = \frac{4\,\text{atoms}}{\text{unit cell}} \times \frac{\mathcal{M}}{N_A} = \frac{4\,\text{atoms}}{\text{unit cell}} \times \frac{195.08\,\text{g}}{1\,\text{mol}} \times \frac{1\,\text{mol}}{6.022 \times 10^{23}\,\text{atoms}} = 1.295782 \times 10^{-21}\,\frac{\text{g}}{\text{unit cell}} \text{ then}$$

$$d = \frac{m}{V} = \frac{1.295782 \times 10^{-21}\,\dfrac{\text{g}}{\text{unit cell}}}{6.07684 \times 10^{-23}\,\dfrac{\text{cm}^3}{\text{unit cell}}} = 21.3\,\frac{\text{g}}{\text{cm}^3}$$

Check: The units (pm and g/cm³) are correct. The magnitude (393 pm) makes sense because it must be larger than the radius of an atom. The magnitude (21 g/cm³) is consistent for Pt from Chapter 1.

11.52   **Given:** molybdenum; body-centered cubic structure; $r = 136$ pm

Find: edge length of unit cell and density (g/cm³)

Conceptual Plan: $r \rightarrow l$ and $l \rightarrow V(\text{pm}^3) \rightarrow V(\text{cm}^3)$ and $\mathcal{M}$, BCC structure $\rightarrow m$ then $m, V \rightarrow d$

$$l = \frac{4r}{\sqrt{3}} \quad V = l^3 \quad \frac{(1\,\text{cm})^3}{(10^{10}\,\text{pm})^3} \quad m = \frac{2\,\text{atoms}}{\text{unit cell}} \times \frac{\mathcal{M}}{N_A} \quad d = m/V$$

Solution: $l = \dfrac{4r}{\sqrt{3}} = \dfrac{4 \times 136\,\text{pm}}{\sqrt{3}} = 314.079\,\text{pm} = 314\,\text{pm}$ and

$$V = l^3 = (314.079\,\text{pm})^3 \times \frac{(1\,\text{cm})^3}{(10^{10}\,\text{pm})^3} = 3.09825 \times 10^{-23}\,\text{cm}^3 \text{ and}$$

$$m = \frac{2\,\text{atoms}}{\text{unit cell}} \times \frac{\mathcal{M}}{N_A} = \frac{2\,\text{atoms}}{\text{unit cell}} \times \frac{95.96\,\text{g}}{1\,\text{mol}} \times \frac{1\,\text{mol}}{6.022 \times 10^{23}\,\text{atoms}} = 3.186981 \times 10^{-22}\,\frac{\text{g}}{\text{unit cell}} \text{ then}$$

$$d = \frac{m}{V} = \frac{3.186981 \times 10^{-22}\,\dfrac{\text{g}}{\text{unit cell}}}{3.09825 \times 10^{-23}\,\dfrac{\text{cm}^3}{\text{unit cell}}} = 10.3\,\frac{\text{g}}{\text{cm}^3}$$

Check: The units (pm and g/cm³) are correct. The magnitude (314 pm) makes sense because it must be larger than the radius of an atom. The magnitude (10 g/cm³) is reasonable for a metal density.

11.53   **Given:** rhodium; face-centered cubic structure; $d = 12.41$ g/cm³   **Find:** r(Rh)

Conceptual Plan: $\mathcal{M}$, FCC structure $\rightarrow m$ then $m, V \rightarrow d$ then $V(\text{cm}^3) \rightarrow l(\text{cm}) \rightarrow l(\text{pm})$ then $l \rightarrow r$

$$m = \frac{4\,\text{atoms}}{\text{unit cell}} \times \frac{\mathcal{M}}{N_A} \quad d = m/V \quad V = l^3 \quad \frac{10^{10}\,\text{pm}}{1\,\text{cm}} \quad l = 2\sqrt{2}\,r$$

Solution: $m = \dfrac{4\,\text{atoms}}{\text{unit cell}} \times \dfrac{\mathcal{M}}{N_A} = \dfrac{4\,\text{atoms}}{\text{unit cell}} \times \dfrac{102.91\,\text{g}}{1\,\text{mol}} \times \dfrac{1\,\text{mol}}{6.022 \times 10^{23}\,\text{atoms}} = 6.835603 \times 10^{-22}\,\dfrac{\text{g}}{\text{unit cell}}$

then $d = \dfrac{m}{V}$. Rearrange to solve for V. $V = \dfrac{m}{d} = \dfrac{6.835603 \times 10^{-22}\,\dfrac{\text{g}}{\text{unit cell}}}{12.41\,\dfrac{\text{g}}{\text{cm}^3}} = 5.508141 \times 10^{-23}\,\dfrac{\text{cm}^3}{\text{unit cell}}$

then $V = l^3$. Rearrange to solve for l.

$l = \sqrt[3]{V} = \sqrt[3]{5.508141 \times 10^{-23}\,\text{cm}^3} = 3.804828 \times 10^{-8}\,\text{cm} \times \dfrac{10^{10}\,\text{pm}}{1\,\text{cm}} = 380.4828\,\text{pm}$ then $l = 2\sqrt{2}\,r$

Rearrange to solve for r. $r = \dfrac{1}{2\sqrt{2}} = \dfrac{380.\underline{4}828 \text{ pm}}{2\sqrt{2}} = 134.5 \text{ pm}$

Check: The units (pm) are correct. The magnitude (135 pm) is consistent with an atomic diameter.

11.54   **Given:** barium; body-centered cubic structure; $d = 3.59 \text{ g/cm}^3$ **Find:** r (Ba)

        Conceptual Plan: $\mathcal{M}$, **BCC structure** $\rightarrow m$ then $m, V \rightarrow d$ then $V(\text{cm}^3) \rightarrow l(\text{cm}) \rightarrow l(\text{pm})$ then $l \rightarrow r$

$$m = \frac{2 \text{ atoms}}{\text{unit cell}} \times \frac{\mathcal{M}}{N_A} \qquad d = m/V \qquad V = l^3 \qquad \frac{10^{10}\,\text{pm}}{1\,\text{cm}} \qquad l = \frac{4r}{\sqrt{3}}$$

        Solution: $m = \dfrac{2 \text{ atoms}}{\text{unit cell}} \times \dfrac{\mathcal{M}}{N_A} = \dfrac{2 \text{ atoms}}{\text{unit cell}} \times \dfrac{137.33 \text{ g}}{1 \text{ mol}} \times \dfrac{1 \text{ mol}}{6.022 \times 10^{23} \text{ atoms}} = 4.56\underline{0}943 \times 10^{-22} \dfrac{\text{g}}{\text{unit cell}}$ then

$d = \dfrac{m}{V}$. Rearrange to solve for V. $V = \dfrac{m}{d} = \dfrac{4.56\underline{0}943 \times 10^{-22} \dfrac{\text{g}}{\text{unit cell}}}{3.59 \dfrac{\text{g}}{\text{cm}^3}} = 1.27\underline{0}458 \times 10^{-22} \dfrac{\text{cm}^3}{\text{unit cell}}$

then $V = l^3$. Rearrange to solve for l.

$l = \sqrt[3]{V} = \sqrt[3]{1.27\underline{0}458 \times 10^{-22} \text{ cm}^3} = 5.02\underline{7}129 \times 10^{-8} \text{ cm} \times \dfrac{10^{10}\,\text{pm}}{1 \text{ cm}} = 502.\underline{7}129 \text{ pm}$

then $l = \dfrac{4r}{\sqrt{3}}$. Rearrange to solve for r. $r = \dfrac{l\sqrt{3}}{4} = \dfrac{502.\underline{7}129 \text{ pm} \times \sqrt{3}}{4} = 217.7 \text{ pm}$

        Check: The units (pm) are correct. The magnitude (218 pm) is consistent with an atomic diameter.

11.55   **Given:** polonium, simple cubic structure $d = 9.3 \text{ g/cm}^3$; $r = 167 \text{ pm}$; $\mathcal{M} = 209 \text{ g/mol}$ **Find:** estimate N_A

        Conceptual Plan: $r \rightarrow l$ and $l \rightarrow V(\text{pm}^3) \rightarrow V(\text{cm}^3)$ then $d, V \rightarrow m$ then $\mathcal{M}$, **SC structure** $\rightarrow m$

$$l = 2r \qquad V = l^3 \qquad \frac{(1\,\text{cm})^3}{(10^{10}\,\text{pm})^3} \qquad d = m/V \qquad m = \frac{1 \text{ atom}}{\text{unit cell}} \times \frac{\mathcal{M}}{N_A}$$

        Solution: $l = 2r = 2 \times 167 \text{ pm} = 334 \text{ pm}$ and $V = l^3 = (334 \text{ pm})^3 \times \dfrac{(1 \text{ cm})^3}{(10^{10} \text{ pm})^3} = 3.7\underline{2}597 \times 10^{-23} \text{ cm}^3$ then

$d = \dfrac{m}{V}$. Rearrange to solve for m. $m = dV = 9.3 \dfrac{\text{g}}{\text{cm}^3} \times \dfrac{3.7\underline{2}597 \times 10^{-23} \text{ cm}^3}{\text{unit cell}} = 3.4\underline{6}515 \times 10^{-22} \dfrac{\text{g}}{\text{unit cell}}$

then $m = \dfrac{1 \text{ atom}}{\text{unit cell}} \times \dfrac{\mathcal{M}}{N_A}$. Rearrange to solve for N_A.

$N_A = \dfrac{1 \text{ atom}}{\text{unit cell}} \times \dfrac{\mathcal{M}}{m} = \dfrac{1 \text{ atom}}{\text{unit cell}} \times \dfrac{209 \text{ g}}{1 \text{ mol}} \times \dfrac{1 \text{ unit cell}}{3.4\underline{6}515 \times 10^{-22} \text{ g}} = 6.0 \times 10^{23} \dfrac{\text{atoms}}{\text{mol}}$

        Check: The units (atoms/mol) are correct. The magnitude (6×10^{23} atoms/mol) is consistent with Avogadro's number.

11.56   **Given:** palladium, face-centered cubic structure, $d = 12.0 \text{ g/cm}^3$; $r = 138 \text{ pm}$; $\mathcal{M} = 106.42 \text{ g/mol}$

        Find: estimate N_A

        Conceptual Plan: $r \rightarrow l$ and $l \rightarrow V(\text{pm}^3) \rightarrow V(\text{cm}^3)$ then $d, V \rightarrow m$ then $\mathcal{M}$, **FCC structure** $\rightarrow m$

$$l = 2\sqrt{2}r \qquad V = l^3 \qquad \frac{(1\,\text{cm})^3}{(10^{10}\,\text{pm})^3} \qquad m = \frac{4 \text{ atoms}}{\text{unit cell}} \times \frac{\mathcal{M}}{N_A}$$

        Solution: $l = 2\sqrt{2}r = 2\sqrt{2} \times 138 \text{ pm} = 39\underline{0}.323 \text{ pm}$ and

$V = l^3 = (39\underline{0}.323 \text{ pm})^3 \times \dfrac{(1 \text{ cm})^3}{(10^{10} \text{ pm})^3} = 5.9\underline{4}665 \times 10^{-23} \text{ cm}^3$ then $d = \dfrac{m}{V}$. Rearrange to solve for m.

$m = dV = 12.0 \dfrac{\text{g}}{\text{cm}^3} \times \dfrac{5.9\underline{4}665 \times 10^{-23} \text{ cm}^3}{\text{unit cell}} = 7.1\underline{3}598 \times 10^{-22} \dfrac{\text{g}}{\text{unit cell}}$ then $m = \dfrac{4 \text{ atoms}}{\text{unit cell}} \times \dfrac{\mathcal{M}}{N_A}$

Rearrange to solve for N_A. $N_A = \dfrac{4 \text{ atoms}}{\text{unit cell}} \times \dfrac{\mathcal{M}}{m} = \dfrac{4 \text{ atoms}}{\text{unit cell}} \times \dfrac{106.42 \text{ g}}{1 \text{ mol}} \times \dfrac{1 \text{ unit cell}}{7.1\underline{3}598 \times 10^{-22} \text{ g}} = 5.97 \times 10^{23} \dfrac{\text{atoms}}{\text{mol}}$

        Check: The units (atoms/mol) are correct. The magnitude (6×10^{23} atoms/mol) is consistent with Avogadro's number.

11.57   (a)   atomic because argon (Ar) is an atom

        (b)   molecular because water (H_2O) is a molecule

        (c)   ionic because potassium oxide (K_2O) is an ionic solid

        (d)   atomic because iron (Fe) is an atom

11.58   (a)   ionic because calcium chloride ($CaCl_2$) is an ionic solid

        (b)   molecular because carbon dioxide (CO_2) is a molecule

        (c)   atomic because nickel (Ni) is an atom

        (d)   molecular because iodine (I_2) is a molecule

11.59   LiCl has the highest melting point because it is the only ionic solid in the group. The other three solids are held together by intermolecular forces, while LiCl is held together by stronger coulombic interactions between the cations and anions of the crystal lattice.

11.60   C (diamond) has the highest melting point (3800 °C). Both covalent network solids and ionic solids have high melting points. NaCl has a melting point of 801 °C. In diamond (Figure 11.48a), each carbon atom forms four covalent bonds to four other carbon atoms in a tetrahedral geometry. This structure extends throughout the entire crystal; so a diamond crystal can be thought of as a giant molecule held together by these covalent bonds. Because covalent bonds are very strong, covalent atomic solids have high melting points.

11.61   (a) TiO_2 because it is an ionic solid

        (b) $SiCl_4$ because it has a higher molar mass and therefore has stronger dispersion forces

        (c)   Xe because it has a higher molar mass and therefore has stronger dispersion forces

        (d)   CaO because the ions have greater charge and therefore stronger electrostatic interactions

11.62   (a)   Fe because it is an atomic solid held together by metallic bonding

        (b)   KCl because it is an ionic solid

        (c)   Ti because it is an atomic solid held together by metallic bonding

        (d) H_2O because it is capable of hydrogen bonding

11.63   The Ti atoms occupy the corner positions and the center of the unit cell: 8 corner atoms $\times$ (1/8 atom/unit cell) $+1$ atom in center $= (1 + 1)$ Ti atoms/unit cell $= 2$ Ti atoms/unit cell. The O atoms occupy four positions on the top and bottom faces and two positions inside the unit cell: 4 face-centered atoms $\times$ (1/2 atom/unit cell) $+2$ atoms in the interior $= (2 + 2)$ O atoms/unit cell $= 4$ O atoms/unit cell. Therefore, there are 2 Ti atoms/ unit cell and 4 O atoms/unit cell, so the ratio Ti:O is 2:4, or 1:2. The formula for the compound is TiO_2.

11.64   The Re atoms occupy the corner positions of the unit cell: 8 corner atoms $\times$ (1/8 atom/unit cell) $= 1$ Re atom/unit cell. The O atoms occupy 12 edge positions: 12 edge atoms $\times$ (1/4 atom/unit cell) $= 3$ O atoms/unit cell. Therefore, there are 1 Re atom/unit cell and 3 O atoms/unit cell, so the ratio Re:O is 1:3. The formula for the compound is ReO_3.

11.65   In CsCl: The Cs atoms occupy the center of the unit cell: 1 atom in center $= 1$ Cs atom/unit cell. The Cl atoms occupy corner positions of the unit cell: 8 corner atoms $\times$ (1/8 atom/unit cell) $= 1$ Cl atom/unit cell. Therefore, there are 1 Cs atom/unit cell and 1 Cl atom/unit cell, so the ratio Cs:Cl is 1:1. The formula for the compound is CsCl, as expected.

        In $BaCl_2$: The Ba atoms occupy the corner positions and the face-centered positions of the unit cell: 8 corner atoms $\times$ (1/8 atom/unit cell) + 6 face-centered atoms $\times$ (1/2 atom/unit cell) $= (1 + 3)$ Ba atoms/unit cell $= 4$ Ba atoms/unit cell. The Cl atoms occupy the eight tetrahedral holes within the unit cell: 8 Cl atoms/unit cell. Therefore, there are 4 Ba atoms/unit cell and 8 Cl atoms/unit cell, so the ratio Ba:Cl is 4:8, or 1:2. The formula for the compound is $BaCl_2$, as expected.

11.66   In Li_2O: The Li atoms occupy the eight tetrahedral holes within the unit cell: 8 Li atoms/unit cell. The O atoms occupy the corner positions and the face-centered positions of the unit cell: 8 corner atoms $\times$ (1/8) atom/unit cell) + 6 face-centered atoms $\times$ (1/2 atom/unit cell) $= (1 + 3)$ O atoms/unit cell $= 4$ O atoms/unit cell. Therefore, there are 4 O atoms/unit cell and 8 Li atoms/unit cell, so the ratio Li:O is 8:4, or 2:1. The formula for the compound is Li_2O, as expected.

In AgI : The Ag atoms occupy four of the eight tetrahedral holes within the unit cell: 4 Ag atoms/unit cell. The I atoms occupy the corner positions and the face-centered positions of the unit cell: 8 corner atoms $\times$ (1/8 atom/unit cell) +6 face-centered atoms $\times$ (1/2 atom/unit cell) = (1 + 3) I atoms/unit cell = 4 I atoms/unit cell. Therefore, there are 4 I atoms/unit cell and 4 Ag atoms/unit cell, so the ratio Ag:I is 4:4, or 1:1. The formula for the compound is AgI, as expected.

Band Theory

11.67   (a)   Zn should have little or no band gap because it is the only metal in the group.

11.68   **Given:** 5.45 g sodium crystal   **Find:** number of molecular orbitals in the valence band

Conceptual Plan: g $\rightarrow$ mol $\rightarrow$ Na$_N$ $\rightarrow$ number of valence electrons $\rightarrow$ number of molecular orbitals

$$\frac{1\ mol}{22.99\ g} \quad \frac{6.022 \times 10^{23}\ atoms}{1\ mol} \quad \frac{1\ 3s\ electron}{1\ Na\ atom} \qquad \frac{1\ molecular\ orbital}{1\ 3s\ electron}$$

Solution: $5.45\ \cancel{g\ Na} \times \dfrac{1\ \cancel{mol\ Na}}{22.99\ \cancel{g\ Na}} \times \dfrac{6.022 \times 10^{23}\ \cancel{Na\ atoms}}{1\ \cancel{mol\ Na}} \times \dfrac{1\ \cancel{3s\ electron}}{1\ \cancel{Na\ atom}} \times \dfrac{1\ molecular\ orbital}{1\ \cancel{3s\ electron}}$

$= 1.43 \times 10^{23}$ molecular orbitals

Check: The units (number of molecular orbitals) are correct. The magnitude (10^{23} molecular orbitals) is expected because there are so many orbitals because we have about $\frac{1}{4}$ mole of atoms. Metals can conduct electricity because of these large numbers of orbitals.

Cumulative Problems

11.69   The general trend is that melting point increases with increasing molar mass. This is because the electrons of the larger molecules are held more loosely and a stronger dipole moment can be induced more easily. HF is the exception to the rule. It has a relatively high melting point due to strong intermolecular forces due to hydrogen bonding.

11.70   The general trend is that boiling point increases with increasing molar mass. This is because the electrons of the larger molecules are held more loosely and a stronger dipole moment can be induced more easily. H_2O is the exception to the rule. It has a relatively high boiling point due to strong intermolecular forces due to hydrogen bonding.

11.71   **Given:** P_{H_2O} = 23.76 torr at 25 °C; 1.25 g water in 1.5 L container   **Find:** m (H_2O) as liquid

Conceptual Plan: °C $\rightarrow$ K and torr $\rightarrow$ atm then P, V, T $\rightarrow$ mol (g) $\rightarrow$ g (g) then g (g), g (l)$_i$ $\rightarrow$ g (l)$_f$

$$K = °C + 273.15 \quad \frac{1\ atm}{760\ torr} \qquad PV = nRT \qquad \frac{18.02\ g}{1\ mol} \qquad g\ (l)_f = g(l)_i - g(g)$$

Solution: $T = 25\ °C + 273.15 = 298\ K$, $23.76\ \cancel{torr} \times \dfrac{1\ atm}{760\ \cancel{torr}} = 0.0312\underline{6}32$ atm then $PV = nRT$

Rearrange to solve for n. $n = \dfrac{PV}{RT} = \dfrac{0.0312\underline{6}32\ \cancel{atm} \times 1.5\ \cancel{L}}{0.08206\ \dfrac{\cancel{L} \cdot \cancel{atm}}{\cancel{K} \cdot mol} \times 298\ \cancel{K}} = 0.00191768$ mol in the gas phase then

$0.0019\underline{1}768\ \cancel{mol} \times \dfrac{18.02\ g}{1\ \cancel{mol}} = 0.034\underline{5}566$ g in the gas phase then

$g\ (l)_f = g\ (l)_i - g\ (g) = 1.25\ g - 0.034\underline{5}566\ g = 1.22$ g remaining as liquid. Yes, there is 1.22 g of liquid.

Check: The units (g) are correct. The magnitude (1.2 g) is expected because very little material is expected to be in the gas phase.

11.72   **Given:** P_{CCl_3F} = 856 torr at 300 K; 11.5 g CCl_3F in 1.0 L container   **Find:** m (CCl_3F) as liquid

Conceptual Plan: torr $\rightarrow$ atm then P, V, T $\rightarrow$ mol (g) $\rightarrow$ g (g) then g (g), g (l)$_i$ $\rightarrow$ g (l)$_f$

$$\frac{1\ atm}{760\ torr} \qquad PV = nRT \qquad \frac{137.36\ g}{1\ mol} \qquad g\ (l)_f = g(l)_i - g(g)$$

Solution: $856\ \cancel{torr} \times \dfrac{1\ atm}{760\ \cancel{torr}} = 1.12\underline{6}32$ atm then $PV = nRT$. Rearrange to solve for n.

$$n = \frac{PV}{RT} = \frac{1.12632 \text{ atm} \times 1.0 \text{ L}}{0.08206 \dfrac{\text{L} \cdot \text{atm}}{\text{K} \cdot \text{mol}} \times 300 \text{ K}} = 0.0457519 \text{ mol in the gas phase then}$$

$$0.0457519 \text{ mol} \times \frac{137.36 \text{ g}}{1 \text{ mol}} = 6.2845 \text{ g in the gas phase then}$$

$g(l)_f = g(l)_i - g(g) = 11.5 \text{ g} - 6.2845 \text{ g} = 5.2 \text{ g remaining as liquid. Yes, there is 5.2 g of liquid.}$

Check: The units (g) are correct. The magnitude (5 g) is expected because even at moderate pressures, little material is expected to be in the gas phase.

11.73   Because we are starting at a temperature that is higher and a pressure that is lower than the triple point, the phase transitions will be gas $\rightarrow$ liquid $\rightarrow$ solid, or condensation followed by freezing.

11.74   The solid is denser than the liquid. Because the triple point temperature is lower than the normal melting point, the slope of the fusion curve must be positive. This means that as you start in the liquid phase and increase the pressure, you will eventually cross into the solid phase. As pressure increases, the phases get denser and the atoms, molecules, or ions are pushed closer and closer together.

11.75   **Given:** ice: $T_i = 0 \,°C$ exactly, $m = 53.5 \text{ g}$; water: $T_1 = 75 \,°C$, $m = 115 \text{ g}$ **Find:** T_f
       Other: $\Delta H_{fus}^\circ = 6.02 \text{ kJ/mol}$; $C_{water} = 4.18 \text{ J/g} \cdot °C$
       Conceptual Plan: $q_{ice} = -q_{water}$ so g(ice) $\rightarrow$ mol(ice) $\rightarrow q_{fus}(\text{kJ}) \rightarrow q_{fus}(\text{J}) \rightarrow q_{water}(\text{J})$ then

$$\frac{1 \text{ mol}}{18.02 \text{ g}} \qquad \frac{6.02 \text{ kJ}}{1 \text{ mol}} \qquad \frac{1000 \text{ J}}{1 \text{ kJ}} \qquad q_{water} = -q_{ice}$$

       $q, m, C_s \rightarrow \Delta T$ then $T_i, \Delta T \rightarrow T_2$ now we have slightly cooled water in contact with 0.0 °C water

$$q = mC_s \Delta T \qquad\qquad \Delta T = T_2 - T_i$$

       so $q_{ice} = -q_{water}$ with $m, C_s, T_i \rightarrow T_f$

$$q = mC_s(T_f - T_i) \text{ then set } q_{ice} = -q_{water}$$

       Solution: $53.5 \text{ g} \times \dfrac{1 \text{ mol}}{18.02 \text{ g}} \times \dfrac{6.02 \text{ kJ}}{1 \text{ mol}} \times \dfrac{1000 \text{ J}}{1 \text{ kJ}} = 1.78729 \times 10^4 \text{ J}, q_{water} = -q_{ice} = -1.78729 \times 10^4 \text{ J}$

$q_{water} = mC_s \Delta T.$ Rearrange to solve for ΔT. $\Delta T = \dfrac{q}{mC_s} = \dfrac{-1.78729 \times 10^4 \text{ J}}{115 \text{ g} \times 4.18 \dfrac{\text{J}}{\text{g} \cdot °C}} = -37.1810 \,°C$ then

$\Delta T = T_2 - T_i.$ Rearrange to solve for T_2. $T_2 = \Delta T + T_i = -37.1810 \,°C + 75 \,°C = 37.819 \,°C$
$q = m \, C_s(T_f - T_i)$ substitute in values and set $q_{ice} = -q_{water}$.

$$q_{ice} = m_{ice}C_{ice}(T_f - T_{icei}) = 53.5 \text{ g} \times 4.18 \frac{\text{J}}{\text{g} \cdot °C} \times (T_f - 0.0 \,°C) =$$

$$-q_{water} = -m_{water} C_{water}(T_f - T_{water2}) = -115 \text{ g} \times 4.18 \frac{\text{J}}{\text{g} \cdot °C} \times (T_f - 37.819 \,°C)$$

Rearrange to solve for T_f.
$53.5 \, T_f = -115(T_f - 37.819 \,°C) \rightarrow 53.5 \, T_f = -115 \, T_f + 4349.2 \,°C$

$$\rightarrow -4346.8 \,°C = -168.5 \, T_f \rightarrow T_f = \frac{-4349.2 \,°C}{-168.5} = 25.8 \,°C = 26 \,°C$$

Check: The units (°C) are correct. The temperature is between the two initial temperatures. Because the ice mass is about half the water mass, we are not surprised that the temperature is closer to the original ice temperature.

11.76   **Given:** steam: $T_i = 100 \,°C$, $m = 0.552 \text{ g}$; water: $T_i = 5.0 \,°C$, $m = 4.25 \text{ g}$ **Find:** T_f
       Other: $\Delta H_{vap}^\circ = 40.7 \text{ kJ/mol}$; $C_{water} = 4.18 \text{ J/g} \cdot °C$
       Conceptual Plan: $q_{steam} = -q_{water}$ so g(steam) $\rightarrow$ mol(steam) $\rightarrow -q_{vap}(\text{kJ}) \rightarrow -q_{vap}(\text{J}) \rightarrow q_{water}(\text{J})$ then

$$\frac{1 \text{ mol}}{18.02 \text{ g}} \qquad \frac{-40.7 \text{ kJ}}{1 \text{ mol}} \qquad \frac{1000 \text{ J}}{1 \text{ kJ}} \qquad q_{steam} = -q_{ice}$$

       $q, m, C_s \rightarrow \Delta T$ then $T_i, \Delta T \rightarrow T_2$ now we have slightly warmed water in contact with 100.0 °C water

$$q = mC_s \Delta T \qquad\qquad \Delta T = T_2 - T_i$$

       so $q_{steam} = -q_{water}$ with $m, C_s, T_i \rightarrow T_f$

$$q = mC_s(T_f - T_i) \text{ then set } q_{ice} = -q_{water}$$

Solution: $0.552 \text{ g} \times \dfrac{1 \text{ mol}}{18.02 \text{ g}} \times \dfrac{-40.7 \text{ kJ}}{1 \text{ mol}} \times \dfrac{1000 \text{ J}}{1 \text{ kJ}} = -1.2\underline{4}675 \times 10^3 \text{ J}$

$q_{water} = -q_{steam} = -(-1.2\underline{4}675 \times 10^3 \text{ J})$

$q = mC_s\Delta T$. Rearrange to solve for ΔT.

$\Delta T = \dfrac{q}{mC_s} = \dfrac{1.2\underline{4}675 \times 10^3 \text{ J}}{4.25 \text{ g} \times 4.18 \dfrac{\text{J}}{\text{g} \cdot {}^\circ\text{C}}} = 70.\underline{1}800 \,{}^\circ\text{C}$ then $\Delta T = T_2 - T_i$

Rearrange to solve for T_2. $T_2 = \Delta T + T_i = 70.\underline{1}800 \,{}^\circ\text{C} + 5.0 \,{}^\circ\text{C} = 75.\underline{1}800 \,{}^\circ\text{C}$

Recall that $q = mC_s(T_f - T_i)$ and substitute in values and set $q_{steam} = -q_{water}$

$q_{steam} = m_{steam}C_{steam}(T_f - T_{steami}) = 0.552 \text{ g} \times 4.18 \dfrac{\text{J}}{\text{g} \cdot {}^\circ\text{C}} \times (T_f - 100.0 \,{}^\circ\text{C}) =$

$-q_{water} = -m_{water}C_{water}(T_f - T_{water2}) = -4.25 \text{ g} \times 4.18 \dfrac{\text{J}}{\text{g} \cdot {}^\circ\text{C}} \times (T_f - 75.\underline{1}800 \,{}^\circ\text{C})$

Rearrange to solve for T_f.

$0.552(T_f - 100.0 \,{}^\circ\text{C}) = -4.25(T_f - 75.\underline{1}800 \,{}^\circ\text{C}) \rightarrow 0.552 \, T_f - 55.2 \,{}^\circ\text{C} = -4.25 \, T_f + 31\underline{9}.515 \,{}^\circ\text{C}$

$\rightarrow -37\underline{4}.715 \,{}^\circ\text{C} = -4.8\underline{0}2 \, T_f \rightarrow T_f = \dfrac{-37\underline{4}.715 \,{}^\circ\text{C}}{-4.8\underline{0}2} = 78.0 \,{}^\circ\text{C}$

Check: The units (${}^\circ\text{C}$) are correct. The temperature is between the two initial temperatures. Because so much heat is involved in the vaporization process, we are not surprised that the temperature is closer to the original steam temperature.

11.77 **Given:** 1 mole of methanol   **Find:** Draw a heating curve beginning at 170 K and ending at 350 K
Other: melting point = 176 K, boiling point = 338 K, $\Delta H_{fus} = 2.2$ kJ/mol, $\Delta H_{vap} = 35.2$ kJ/mol,
$C_{s,solid} = 105$ J/mol $\cdot$ K, $C_{s,liquid} = 81.3$ J/mol $\cdot$ K, $C_{s,gas} = 48$ J/mol $\cdot$ K
Conceptual Plan:
Calculate the temperature range of each phase:

$T_{Starting}, T_{Melting} \rightarrow \Delta T_{Solid}$ and $T_{Melting}, T_{Boiling} \rightarrow \Delta T_{Liquid}$ and $T_{Boiling}, T_{Ending} \rightarrow \Delta T_{Gas}$

$\qquad \Delta T_{Solid} = T_{Melting} - T_{Starting} \qquad\qquad \Delta T_{Liquid} = T_{Boiling} - T_{Melting} \qquad\qquad \Delta T_{Gas} = T_{Ending} - T_{Boiling}$

Because there is 1 mole of methanol, the heat for each phase change is simply the ΔH for that phase change.
Calculate the heat required for each step:

$\Delta T_{Solid}, C_{s,solid} \rightarrow q_{Solid}$ and $\Delta T_{Liquid}, C_{s,liquid} \rightarrow q_{Liquid}$ and $\Delta T_{Gas}, C_{s,gas} \rightarrow q_{Gas}$

$\qquad q = C_s \times \Delta T \qquad\qquad\qquad q = C_s \times \Delta T \qquad\qquad\qquad q = C_s \times \Delta T$

Finally, plot each of the segments.
Solution:

$\Delta T_{Solid} = T_{Melting} - T_{Starting} = 176 \text{ K} - 170 \text{ K} = 6 \text{ K}; \quad \Delta T_{Liquid} = T_{Boiling} - T_{Melting} = 338 \text{ K} - 176 \text{ K} = 162 \text{ K}$
and $\Delta T_{Gas} = T_{Ending} - T_{Boiling} = 350 \text{ K} - 338 \text{ K} = 12 \text{ K}$

$q_{fus} = \Delta H_{fus} = 2.2$ kJ/mol and $q_{vap} = \Delta H_{vap} = 35.2$ kJ/mol

$q_{Solid} = C_{s,Solid} \times \Delta T_{Solid} = 105 \dfrac{\text{J}}{\text{mol} \cdot \text{K}} \times 6 \text{ K} = \underline{6}30$ J/mol $= 0.\underline{6}3$ kJ/mol

$q_{Liquid} = C_{s,Liquid} \times \Delta T_{Liquid} = 81.3 \dfrac{\text{J}}{\text{mol} \cdot \text{K}} \times 162 \text{ K} = 131\underline{7}0.6$ J/mol $= 13.\underline{1}706$ kJ/mol and

$q_{Gas} = C_{s,Gas} \times \Delta T_{Gas} = 48 \dfrac{\text{J}}{\text{mol} \cdot \text{K}} \times 12 \text{ K} = 5\underline{7}6$ J/mol $= 0.5\underline{0}76$ kJ/mol

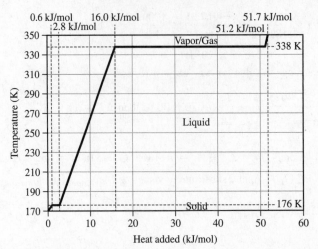

Check: The heating curve has a shape that is similar to that of water.

11.78   **Given:** 1 mole of benzene   **Find:** Draw a heating curve beginning at 0 °C and ending at 100 °C.

Other: melting point = 5.4 °C, boiling point = 80.1 °C, ΔH_{fus} = 9.9 kJ/mol, ΔH_{vap} = 30.7 kJ/mol, $C_{s,solid}$ = 118 J/mol · °C, $C_{s,liquid}$ = 135 J/mol · °C, $C_{s,gas}$ = 104 J/mol · °C

Conceptual Plan:

Calculate the temperature range of each phase:

$$T_{Starting}, T_{Melting} \rightarrow \Delta T_{Solid} \text{ and } T_{Melting}, T_{Boiling} \rightarrow \Delta T_{Liquid} \text{ and } T_{Boiling}, T_{Ending} \rightarrow \Delta T_{Gas}$$

$$\Delta T_{Solid} = T_{Melting} - T_{Starting} \qquad \Delta T_{Liquid} = T_{Boiling} - T_{Melting} \qquad \Delta T_{Gas} = T_{Ending} - T_{Boiling}$$

Because there is 1 mole of benzene, the heat for each phase change is simply the ΔH for that phase change.

Calculate the heat required for each step:

$$\Delta T_{Solid}, C_{s,solid} \rightarrow q_{Solid} \text{ and } \Delta T_{Liquid}, C_{s,liquid} \rightarrow q_{Liquid} \text{ and } \Delta T_{Gas}, C_{s,gas} \rightarrow q_{Gas}$$

$$q = C_s \times \Delta T \qquad q = C_s \times \Delta T \qquad q = C_s \times \Delta T$$

Finally, plot each of the segments.

Solution:

$$\Delta T_{Solid} = T_{Melting} - T_{Starting} = 5.4 \text{ °C} - 0.0 \text{ °C} = 5.4 \text{ °C}$$

$$\Delta T_{Liquid} = T_{Boiling} - T_{Melting} = 80.1 \text{ °C} - 5.4 \text{ °C} = 74.7 \text{ °C}$$

$$\Delta T_{Gas} = T_{Ending} - T_{Boiling} = 100.0 \text{ °C} - 80.1 \text{ °C} = 19.9 \text{ °C}$$

$$q_{fus} = \Delta H_{fus} = 9.9 \text{ kJ/mol} \text{ and } q_{vap} = \Delta H_{vap} = 30.7 \text{ kJ/mol}$$

$$q_{Solid} = C_{s,Solid} \times \Delta T_{Solid} = 118 \frac{\text{J}}{\text{mol} \cdot \text{°C}} \times 5.4 \text{ °C} = 63\underline{7}.2 \text{ J/mol} = 0.6\underline{3}72 \text{ kJ/mol}$$

$$q_{Liquid} = C_{s,Liquid} \times \Delta T_{Liquid} = 135 \frac{\text{J}}{\text{mol} \cdot \text{°C}} \times 74.7 \text{ °C} = 100\underline{8}4.5 \text{ J/mol} = 10.0\underline{8}45 \text{ kJ/mol}$$

$$q_{Gas} = C_{s,Gas} \times \Delta T_{Gas} = 104 \frac{\text{J}}{\text{mol} \cdot \text{°C}} \times 19.9 \text{ °C} = 206\underline{9}.6 \text{ J/mol} = 2.0\underline{6}96 \text{ kJ/mol}$$

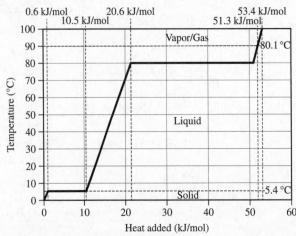

Check: The heating curve has a shape that is similar to that of water.

11.79 **Given:** home: $6.0 \text{ m} \times 10.0 \text{ m} \times 2.2 \text{ m}$; $T = 30 \,°C$, $P_{H_2O} = 85\%$ of $P°_{H_2O}$ **Find:** $m(H_2O)$ removed
Other: $P°_{H_2O} = 31.8$ mmHg from text
Conceptual Plan: $l, w, h \rightarrow V(\text{m}^3) \rightarrow V(\text{cm}^3) \rightarrow V(\text{L})$ and $P°_{H_2O} \rightarrow P_{H_2O}(\text{mmHg}) \rightarrow P_{H_2O}(\text{atm})$ and

$$V = l\,w\,h \qquad \frac{(100 \text{ cm})^3}{(1 \text{ m})^3} \qquad \frac{1 \text{ L}}{1000 \text{ cm}^3} \qquad\qquad P_{H_2O} = 0.85\, P°_{H_2O} \qquad \frac{1 \text{ atm}}{760 \text{ mmHg}}$$

$°C \rightarrow K$ then $P, V, T \rightarrow \text{mol}(H_2O) \rightarrow g(H_2O)$

$$K = °C + 273.15 \qquad PV = nRT \qquad \frac{18.02 \text{ g}}{1 \text{ mol}}$$

Solution: $V = l\,w\,h = 6.0 \text{ m} \times 10.0 \text{ m} \times 2.2 \text{ m} = 132 \text{ m}^3 \times \dfrac{(100 \text{ cm})^3}{(1 \text{ m})^3} \times \dfrac{1 \text{ L}}{1000 \text{ cm}^3} = 1.\underline{3}2 \times 10^5 \text{ L}$,

$P_{H_2O} = 0.85\, P°_{H_2O} = 0.85 \times 31.8 \text{ mmHg} \times \dfrac{1 \text{ atm}}{760 \text{ mmHg}} = 0.035\underline{5}66 \text{ atm}$, $T = 30 \,°C + 273.15 = 3\underline{0}3 \text{ K}$,

then $PV = nRT$. Rearrange to solve for n.

$n = \dfrac{PV}{RT} = \dfrac{0.035\underline{5}66 \text{ atm} \times 1.\underline{3}2 \times 10^5 \text{ L}}{0.08206 \dfrac{\text{L} \cdot \text{atm}}{\text{K} \cdot \text{mol}} \times 3\underline{0}3 \text{ K}} = 18\underline{8}.81 \text{ mol}$ then $18\underline{8}.81 \text{ mol} \times \dfrac{18.02 \text{ g}}{1 \text{ mol}} = 3400 \text{ g to remove}$

Check: The units (g) are correct. The magnitude of the answer (3400 g) makes sense because the volume of the house is so large. We are removing almost 200 moles of water.

11.80 **Given:** flask with 0.55 g water at $T = 28 \,°C$, $P_{H_2O} = 28.36$ mmHg **Find:** minimum V of flask for all vapor
Conceptual Plan: $g(H_2O) \rightarrow \text{mol}(H_2O)$ and $P_{H_2O}(\text{mmHg}) \rightarrow P_{H_2O}(\text{atm})$ and $°C \rightarrow K$ then $P, n, T \rightarrow V$

$$\frac{1 \text{ mol}}{18.02 \text{ g}} \qquad\qquad \frac{1 \text{ atm}}{760 \text{ mmHg}} \qquad\qquad K = °C + 273.15 \qquad PV = nRT$$

Solution: $0.55 \text{ g} \times \dfrac{1 \text{ mol}}{18.02 \text{ g}} = 0.030\underline{5}22 \text{ mol}$,

$P_{H_2O} = 28.36 \text{ mmHg} \times \dfrac{1 \text{ atm}}{760 \text{ mmHg}} = 0.0373\underline{1}579 \text{ atm}$,

$T = 28 \,°C + 273.15 = 301 \text{ K}$, then $PV = nRT$. Rearrange to solve for V.

$V = \dfrac{nRT}{P} = \dfrac{0.030\underline{5}22 \text{ mol} \times 0.08206 \dfrac{\text{L} \cdot \text{atm}}{\text{K} \cdot \text{mol}} \times 301 \text{ K}}{0.0373\underline{1}579 \text{ atm}} = 2\underline{0}.20 \text{ L} = 2.0 \times 10^1 \text{ L}$

Check: The units (L) are correct. The magnitude of the answer (20 L) makes sense because we have about 1/30 mole and a pressure of about 1/30 atm and because at STP, one mole of a gas occupies 22 L.

11.81 CsCl has a higher melting point than AgI because of its higher coordination number. In CsCl, one anion bonds to eight cations (and vice versa), while in AgI, one anion bonds only to four cations.

11.82 KCl has a higher melting point than copper iodide because of its higher coordination number. In KCl, one anion bonds to six cations (and vice versa) while in copper iodide, one anion bonds only to four cations.

11.83 (a) Atoms are connected across the face diagonal (c), so $c = 4r$.
 (b) From the Pythagorean Theorem, $c^2 = a^2 + b^2$; from part (a), $c = 4r$; and for a cubic structure, $a = l, b = l$. So $(4r)^2 = l^2 + l^2 \rightarrow 16r^2 = 2l^2 \rightarrow 8r^2 = l^2 \rightarrow l = \sqrt{8r^2} \rightarrow l = 2\sqrt{2}r$.

11.84 (a) Atoms are connected across the cube diagonal (c), so $c = 4r$.
 (b) Because b forms the diagonal of the face, where each edge length $a = l$, and combining this with the Pythagorean Theorem, $b^2 = l^2 + l^2 \rightarrow b^2 = 2l^2 \rightarrow b = \sqrt{2}l$.
 (c) From the Pythagorean Theorem, $c^2 = a^2 + b^2$; from part (a), $c = 4r$; from part (b), $b = \sqrt{2}l$; and for a cubic structure, $a = l$. So $(4r)^2 = l^2 + (\sqrt{2}l)^2 \rightarrow 16r^2 = l^2 + 2l^2 \rightarrow 16r^2 = 3l^2 \rightarrow 4r = \sqrt{3}l \rightarrow l = \dfrac{4r}{\sqrt{3}}$.

11.85 **Given:** diamond, $V(\text{unit cell}) = 0.0454 \text{ nm}^3$; $d = 3.52 \text{ g/cm}^3$ **Find:** number of carbon atoms/unit cell
Conceptual Plan: $V(\text{nm}^3) \rightarrow V(\text{cm}^3)$ then $d, V \rightarrow m \rightarrow \text{mol} \rightarrow$ atoms

$$\frac{(1 \text{ cm})^3}{(10^7 \text{ nm})^3} \qquad\qquad d = m/V \qquad \frac{1 \text{ mol}}{12.01 \text{ g}} \qquad \frac{6.022 \times 10^{23} \text{ atoms}}{1 \text{ mol}}$$

Solution: $0.0454 \ \text{nm}^3 \times \dfrac{(1 \ \text{cm})^3}{(10^7 \ \text{nm})^3} = 4.54 \times 10^{-23} \ \text{cm}^3$ then $d = \dfrac{m}{V}$. Rearrange to solve for m.

$$m = d\,V = 3.52 \ \frac{\text{g}}{\text{cm}^3} \times 4.54 \times 10^{-23} \ \text{cm}^3 = 1.59808 \times 10^{-22} \ \text{g then}$$

$$\frac{1.59808 \times 10^{-22} \ \text{g}}{\text{unit cell}} \times \frac{1 \ \text{mol}}{12.01 \ \text{g}} \times \frac{6.022 \times 10^{23} \ \text{atoms}}{1 \ \text{mol}} = 8.01 \ \frac{\text{C atoms}}{\text{unit cell}} = 8 \ \frac{\text{C atoms}}{\text{unit cell}}$$

Check: The units (atoms) are correct. The magnitude (8 atoms) makes sense because it is a fairly small number and our answer is within calculation error of an integer.

11.86   **Given:** metal, $d = 12.3 \ \text{g/cm}^3$; $r = 0.134$ nm, face-centered cubic lattice   **Find:** $\mathcal{M}$
Conceptual Plan: $r \rightarrow l \rightarrow V(\text{nm}^3) \rightarrow V(\text{cm}^3)$ then $d, V \rightarrow m$ then m, FCC structure $\rightarrow \mathcal{M}$

$$l = 2\sqrt{2}r \quad V = l^3 \qquad \frac{(1 \ \text{cm})^3}{(10^7 \ \text{nm})^3} \qquad\qquad d = m/V \qquad\qquad m = \frac{4 \ \text{atoms}}{\text{unit cell}} \times \frac{\mathcal{M}}{N_A}$$

Solution: $l = 2\sqrt{2}r = 2\sqrt{2} \times 0.134 \ \text{nm} = 0.379009 \ \text{nm}$

$$V = l^3 = (0.379009 \ \text{nm})^3 = 0.0544438 \ \text{nm}^3 \times \frac{(1 \ \text{cm})^3}{(10^7 \ \text{nm})^3} = 5.44438 \times 10^{-23} \ \text{cm}^3 \text{ then } d = \frac{m}{V}. \text{ Rearrange to}$$

solve for m. $m = dV = 12.3 \ \dfrac{\text{g}}{\text{cm}^3} \times 5.44438 \times 10^{-23} \ \text{cm}^3 = 6.69659 \times 10^{-22} \ \text{g then } m = \dfrac{4 \ \text{atoms}}{\text{unit cell}} \times \dfrac{\mathcal{M}}{N_A}$.

Rearrange to solve for $\mathcal{M}$.

$$\mathcal{M} = \frac{\text{unit cell}}{4 \ \text{atoms}} \times N_A \times m = \frac{\text{unit cell}}{4 \ \text{atoms}} \times \frac{6.022 \times 10^{23} \ \text{atoms}}{1 \ \text{mol}} \times \frac{6.69659 \times 10^{-22} \ \text{g}}{\text{unit cell}} = 101 \frac{\text{g}}{\text{mol}} \text{ Ruthenium}$$

Check: The units (g/mol) are correct. The magnitude (101 g/mol) makes sense because it is a reasonable atomic mass for a metal and it is close to Ruthenium.

11.87   (a) $CO_2(s) \rightarrow CO_2(g)$ at 194.7 K

(b) $CO_2(s) \rightarrow$ triple point at 216.5 K $\rightarrow CO_2(g)$ just above 216.5 K

(c) $CO_2(s) \rightarrow CO_2(l)$ at somewhat above 216 K $\rightarrow CO_2(g)$ at around 250 K

(d) $CO_2(s) \rightarrow CO_2(l) \rightarrow$ super critical CO_2. Above the critical point where there is no distinction between liquid and gas. This change occurs at about 300 K.

11.88   If atmospheric pressure was 2500 mmHg, water would still be a liquid. At a higher atmospheric pressure, water would remain a liquid to a lower temperature than 0 °C; this could reduce the damage done to organisms that are exposed to cold temperatures. At a higher atmospheric pressure, there would be more molecules in the gas phase and the atmosphere would not behave as ideally; water might condense more readily, lowering the vapor pressure of water. This could have an adverse effect on living organisms. At higher atmospheric pressures, cell walls would need to be stronger to withstand higher pressures. This would most likely make the cell walls less permeable and affect many biological systems.

11.89   **Given:** metal, $d = 7.8748 \ \text{g/cm}^3$; $l = 0.28664$ nm, body-centered cubic lattice   **Find:** $\mathcal{M}$
Conceptual Plan: $l \rightarrow V(\text{nm}^3) \rightarrow V(\text{cm}^3)$ then $d, V \rightarrow m$ then m, FCC structure $\rightarrow \mathcal{M}$

$$V = l^3 \qquad \frac{(1 \ \text{cm})^3}{(10^7 \ \text{nm})^3} \qquad d = m/V \qquad\qquad m = \frac{2 \ \text{atoms}}{\text{unit cell}} \times \frac{\mathcal{M}}{N_A}$$

Solution: $V = l^3 = (0.28664 \ \text{nm})^3 = 0.02355105602 \ \text{nm}^3 \times \dfrac{(1 \ \text{cm})^3}{(10^7 \ \text{nm})^3} = 2.355105602 \times 10^{-23} \ \text{cm}^3 \text{ then } d = \dfrac{m}{V}.$

Rearrange to solve for m. $m = d\,V = 7.8748 \ \dfrac{\text{g}}{\text{cm}^3} \times 2.355105602 \times 10^{-23} \ \text{cm}^3 = 1.854598559 \times 10^{-22} \ \text{g}$

then $m = \dfrac{2 \ \text{atoms}}{\text{unit cell}} \times \dfrac{\mathcal{M}}{N_A}$. Rearrange to solve for $\mathcal{M}$.

$$\mathcal{M} = \frac{\text{unit cell}}{2 \ \text{atoms}} \times N_A \times m = \frac{\text{unit cell}}{2 \ \text{atoms}} \times \frac{6.022 \times 10^{23} \ \text{atoms}}{1 \ \text{mol}} \times \frac{1.854598559 \times 10^{-22} \ \text{g}}{\text{unit cell}} = 55.842 \ \frac{\text{g}}{\text{mol}}$$

$= 55.84 \ \dfrac{\text{g}}{\text{mol}}$ iron

Check: The units (g/mol) are correct. The magnitude (55.8 g/mol) makes sense because it is a reasonable atomic mass for a metal and it is close to iron.

11.90   There are two spheres in each unit cell. The volume of the unit cell $V = a^3$. Because the spheres occupy 68.0% of the available volume and the volume of a sphere $= \frac{4}{3}\pi r^3$, $0.680V = 0.680a^3 = 2\left(\frac{4}{3}\pi r^3\right)$. Rearranging this to solve

for a, we have $a^3 = \dfrac{2\left(\dfrac{4}{3}\pi r^3\right)}{0.680} \rightarrow a = \sqrt[3]{\dfrac{2\left(\dfrac{4}{3}\pi\right)}{0.680}}\, r \rightarrow a = 1.58\,\sqrt[3]{\pi}\,r \rightarrow a = 2.31\,r$, which agrees with the

solution in Problem 6.80.

Challenge Problems

11.91   **Given:** KCl, rock salt structure   **Find:** density (g/cm^3) **Other:** $r(K^+) = 133$ pm; $r(Cl^-) = 181$ pm from Chapter 8
Conceptual Plan: Rock salt structure is a face-centered cubic structure with anions at the lattice points and cations in the holes between lattice sites $\rightarrow$ assume $r = r(Cl^-)$, but $\mathcal{M} = \mathcal{M}(KCl)$
$r(K^+), r(Cl^-) \rightarrow l$ and $l \rightarrow V(pm^3) \rightarrow V(cm^3)$, and FCC structure $\rightarrow m$ then $m, V \rightarrow d$.

$$\text{from Figure 11.43} \quad l = 2r(Cl^-) + 2r(K^+) \quad V = l^3 \quad \frac{(1\text{ cm})^3}{(10^{10}\text{ pm})^3} \quad m = \frac{4\text{ formula units}}{\text{unit cell}} \times \frac{\mathcal{M}}{N_A} \quad d = m/V$$

Solution: $l = 2r(Cl^-) + 2r(K^+) = 2(181\text{ pm}) + 2(133\text{ pm}) = 628\text{ pm}$ and

$$V = l^3 = (628\text{ pm})^3 \times \frac{(1\text{ cm})^3}{(10^{10}\text{ pm})^3} = 2.47673 \times 10^{-22}\text{ cm}^3 \text{ and}$$

$$m = \frac{4\text{ formula units}}{\text{unit cell}} \times \frac{\mathcal{M}}{N_A} = \frac{4\text{ formula units}}{\text{unit cell}} \times \frac{74.55\text{ g}}{1\text{ mol}} \times \frac{1\text{ mol}}{6.022 \times 10^{23}\text{ formula units}}$$

$$= 4.951843 \times 10^{-22}\ \frac{\text{g}}{\text{unit cell}}$$

$$\text{then } d = \frac{m}{V} = \frac{4.951843 \times 10^{-22}\ \dfrac{\text{g}}{\text{unit cell}}}{2.47673 \times 10^{-22}\ \dfrac{\text{cm}^3}{\text{unit cell}}} = 1.99935\ \frac{\text{g}}{\text{cm}^3} = 2.00\ \frac{\text{g}}{\text{cm}^3}$$

Check: The units (g/cm^3) are correct. The magnitude (2 g/cm^3) is reasonable for a salt density. The published value is 1.98 g/cm^3. This method of estimating the density gives a value that is close to the experimentally measured density.

11.92   **Given:** butane (C_4H_{10}), $\Delta H^\circ_{vap} = 22.44$ kJ/mol; normal boiling point $= -0.4\,°C$, 0.55 g; 250 mL flask
Find: amount of butane present as a liquid at $-22\,°C$ and at 25 °C
Conceptual Plan: at each temperature: °C $\rightarrow$ K and kJ $\rightarrow$ J then $\Delta H^\circ_{vap}, T_1, P_1, T_2 \rightarrow P_2$

$$\text{K} = °\text{C} + 273.15 \qquad \frac{1000\text{ J}}{1\text{ kJ}} \qquad \ln\frac{P_2}{P_1} = \frac{-\Delta H_{vap}}{R}\left(\frac{1}{T_2} - \frac{1}{T_1}\right)$$

and mL $\rightarrow$ L then $P_2, V, T_2 \rightarrow$ mol $\rightarrow$ g(g) $\rightarrow$ g(l)

$$\frac{1\text{ L}}{1000\text{ mL}} \qquad PV = nRT \qquad \frac{58.12\text{ g}}{1\text{ mol}} \qquad g(l) = g_{Total} - g(g)$$

Solution: $T_1 = -0.4\,°C + 273.15 = 272.8$ K; $T_2 = -22\,°C + 273.15 = 251$ K

$$\frac{22.44\text{ kJ}}{\text{mol}} \times \frac{1000\text{ J}}{1\text{ kJ}} = 2.244 \times 10^4\ \frac{\text{J}}{\text{mol}} \qquad P_1 = 1\text{ atm} \qquad \ln\frac{P_2}{P_1} = \frac{-\Delta H_{vap}}{R}\left(\frac{1}{T_2} - \frac{1}{T_1}\right)$$

Substitute values in equation.

$$\ln\frac{P_2}{1\text{ atm}} = \frac{-2.244 \times 10^4\ \dfrac{\text{J}}{\text{mol}}}{8.314\ \dfrac{\text{J}}{\text{K}\cdot\text{mol}}}\left(\frac{1}{251\text{ K}} - \frac{1}{272.8\text{ K}}\right) = -0.859313 \rightarrow \frac{P_2}{1\text{ atm}} = e^{-0.859312} = 0.42345 \rightarrow$$

$$P_2 = 0.42345 \times 1\text{ atm} = 0.42345\text{ atm and } 250\text{ mL} \times \frac{1\text{ L}}{1000\text{ mL}} = 0.25\text{ L then } PV = nRT.$$

Rearrange to solve for n. $n = \dfrac{PV}{RT} = \dfrac{0.42\underline{3}45 \text{ atm} \times 0.25 \text{ L}}{0.08206 \dfrac{\text{L} \cdot \text{atm}}{\text{K} \cdot \text{mol}} \times 251 \text{ K}} = 0.005\underline{1}397 \text{ mol}$ then

$0.005\underline{1}397 \text{ mol} \times \dfrac{58.12 \text{ g}}{1 \text{ mol}} = 0.2\underline{9}872 \text{ g}$ in the gas phase then

$g(l) = g_{\text{Total}} - g(g) = 0.55 \text{ g} - 0.2\underline{9}872 \text{ g} = 0.25$ gas liquid at $-22 \,^\circ\text{C}$

$T_1 = -0.4 \,^\circ\text{C} + 273.15 = 272.8 \text{ K}; T_2 = 25 \,^\circ\text{C} + 273.15 = 298 \text{ K}; \dfrac{22.44 \text{ kJ}}{\text{mol}} \times \dfrac{1000 \text{ J}}{1 \text{ kJ}} = 2.244 \times 10^4 \dfrac{\text{J}}{\text{mol}}$

$P_1 = 1 \text{ atm} \qquad \ln \dfrac{P_2}{P_1} = \dfrac{-\Delta H_{\text{vap}}}{R} \left(\dfrac{1}{T_2} - \dfrac{1}{T_1} \right)$. Substitute values in equation.

$\ln \dfrac{P_2}{1 \text{ atm}} = \dfrac{-2.244 \times 10^4 \dfrac{\text{J}}{\text{mol}}}{8.314 \dfrac{\text{J}}{\text{K} \cdot \text{mol}}} \left(\dfrac{1}{298 \text{ K}} - \dfrac{1}{272.8 \text{ K}} \right) = 0.83\underline{6}667 \rightarrow \dfrac{P_2}{1 \text{ atm}} = e^{0.836667} = 2.3\underline{0}866 \rightarrow$

$P_2 = 2.3\underline{0}866 \times 1 \text{ atm} = 2.3\underline{0}866 \text{ atm}$ and $250 \text{ mL} \times \dfrac{1 \text{ L}}{1000 \text{ mL}} = 0.25 \text{ L}$ then $PV = nRT$.

Rearrange to solve for n. $n = \dfrac{PV}{RT} = \dfrac{2.3\underline{0}866 \text{ atm} \times 0.25 \text{ L}}{0.08206 \dfrac{\text{L} \cdot \text{atm}}{\text{K} \cdot \text{mol}} \times 298 \text{ K}} = 0.02\underline{3}602 \text{ mol}$ then

$0.02\underline{3}602 \text{ mol} \times \dfrac{58.12 \text{ g}}{1 \text{ mol}} = 1.\underline{3}718 \text{ g}$ in the gas phase. Because the amount that can be put in the gas phase is greater than the available amount, no liquid is present at 25 °C.

Check: The units (g) are correct. The magnitude of the answers (0.25 g and 0 g) makes sense because we expect less to be in the liquid phase at a higher temperature. The second temperature is over the boiling point, so we expect a lot in the gas phase.

11.93   Decreasing the pressure will decrease the temperature of liquid nitrogen. Because the nitrogen is boiling, its temperature must be constant at a given pressure. As the pressure decreases, the boiling point decreases, and so does the temperature. Remember that vaporization is an endothermic process, so as the nitrogen vaporizes, it removes heat from the liquid, dropping its temperature. If the pressure drops below the pressure of the triple point, the phase change will shift from vaporization to sublimation and the liquid nitrogen will become solid.

11.94   **Given:** cubic closest packing structure   **Find:** fraction of empty space to five significant figures
        Conceptual Plan: cubic closest packing is the same as face-centered cubic structure, so calculate the volume of the atoms and the volume of the unit cell then $V_{\text{atoms}}, V_{\text{unit cell}} \rightarrow \% \, V_{\text{empty}}$

$\dfrac{4 \text{ atoms}}{\text{unit cell}}$ and $V_{\text{atom}} = \dfrac{\frac{4}{3}\pi r^3}{\text{atom}}$ $\quad V_{\text{unit cell}} = l^3$ and $l = 2\sqrt{2}r$ $\qquad \% \, V_{\text{empty}} = \dfrac{V_{\text{unit cell}} - V_{\text{atoms}}}{V_{\text{unit cell}}} \times 100\%$

Solution: $V_{\text{atoms}} = \dfrac{4 \text{ atoms}}{\text{unit cell}} \times \dfrac{\frac{4}{3}\pi r^3}{\text{atom}} = \dfrac{\frac{16}{3}\pi r^3}{\text{unit cell}}$ and $V_{\text{unit cell}} = l^3 = (2\sqrt{2}r)^3$ so

$\% \, V_{\text{empty}} = \dfrac{V_{\text{unit cell}} - V_{\text{atoms}}}{V_{\text{unit cell}}} \times 100\%$ or

$\% \, V_{\text{empty}} = \dfrac{(2\sqrt{2}r)^3 - \frac{16}{3}\pi r^3}{(2\sqrt{2}r)^3} \times 100\% = \dfrac{2^3 2^{3/2} r^3 - \frac{2^4}{3}\pi r^3}{2^3 2^{3/2} r^3} \times 100\% = \dfrac{\sqrt{2} - \frac{\pi}{3}}{\sqrt{2}} \times 100\% = 25.952\%$

Check: The units (%) are correct. The magnitude (26%) is consistent with what is stated in the text.

11.95   **Given:** cubic closest packing structure = cube with touching spheres of radius = r on alternating corners of a cube
        Find: body diagonal of cube and radius of tetrahedral hole

Solution: The cell edge length = l and $l^2 + l^2 = (2r)^2 \rightarrow 2l^2 = 4r^2 \rightarrow l^2 = 2r^2$. Because body diagonal = BD is the hypotenuse of the right triangle formed by the face diagonal and the cell edge, we have

$(BD)^2 = l^2 + (2r)^2 = 2r^2 + 4r^2 = 6r^2 \rightarrow BD = \sqrt{6}r$. The radius of the tetrahedral hole $= r_T$ is half the body diagonal minus the radius of the sphere, or

$$r_T = \frac{BD}{2} - r = \frac{\sqrt{6}r}{2} - r = \left(\frac{\sqrt{6}}{2} - 1\right)r = \left(\frac{\sqrt{6} - 2}{2}\right)r = \left(\frac{\sqrt{3}\sqrt{2} - \sqrt{2}\sqrt{2}}{\sqrt{2}\sqrt{2}}\right)r$$

$$= \left(\frac{\sqrt{3} - \sqrt{2}}{\sqrt{2}}\right)r \approx 0.22474r.$$

11.96   **Given:** $\Delta H^\circ_{fus} = -6.02 \text{ kJ/mol}$ @ 0.0 °C; C_s(liquid water) $= 75.2 \text{ J/mol} \cdot \text{K}$; C_s(ice) $= 37.7 \text{ J/mol} \cdot \text{K}$
Find: ΔH_{fus} at -10.0 °C
Conceptual Plan: Assume exactly 1 mol H_2O for all calculations (report answer as kJ/mol). Because K $=$ °C $+$ 273.13, ΔT(°C) $= \Delta T$(K). Construct the following path:

	step 2	
Liquid @ 0.0 °C $\rightarrow$ solid @ 0.0 °C	According to Hess's law, $\Delta H_1 + \Delta H_2 + \Delta H_3 = \Delta H_4$	
$\uparrow$ step 1 $\downarrow$ step 3	$= \Delta H^\circ_{fus}$ @ -10.0 °C	
Liquid @ $\cdot10.0$ °C $\rightarrow$ solid @ $\cdot10.0$ °C	at constant P, $\Delta H = q$	
step 4	for steps 1 and 3 $q = nC_s\Delta T$	

for steps 1 and 3 J $\rightarrow$ kJ

$$\frac{1 \text{ kJ}}{1000 \text{ J}}$$

Solution:

$$\Delta H_1 = q_1 = nC_s\Delta T = 1 \text{ mol} \times 75.2 \frac{J}{mol \cdot °C} \times (0.00 °C - 10.0 °C) = +752 \text{ J} \times \frac{1 \text{ kJ}}{1000 \text{ J}} = +0.752 \text{ kJ},$$

$$\Delta H_2 = q_2 = n\Delta H = 1 \text{ mol} \times -6.02 \frac{kJ}{mol} = -6.02 \text{ kJ},$$

$$\Delta H_3 = q_3 = nC_s\Delta T = 1 \text{ mol} \times 37.7 \frac{J}{mol \cdot °C} \times (-10.00 °C - 0.0 °C) = -377 \text{ J} \times \frac{1 \text{ kJ}}{1000 \text{ J}} = -0.377 \text{ kJ so}$$

$$\Delta H_4 = \Delta H_1 + \Delta H_2 + \Delta H_3 = 0.752 \text{ kJ} - 6.02 \text{ kJ} - 0.377 \text{ kJ} = -5.65 \text{ kJ}$$

Check: The units (kJ) are correct. We expect freezing to release less energy at -10 °C because we are below the normal freezing point.

11.97   **Given:** 1.00 L water, $T_i = 298 \text{ K}$, $T_f = 373 \text{ K-vapor}$; $P_{CH_4} = 1.00 \text{ atm}$ **Find:** $V(CH_4)$
Other: $\Delta H^\circ_{comb}(CH_4) = 890.4 \text{ kJ/mol}$; $C_{water} = 75.2 \text{ J/mol} \cdot \text{K}$; $\Delta H^\circ_{vap}(H_2O) = 40.7 \text{ kJ/mol}$, $d = 1.00 \text{ g/mL}$
Conceptual Plan: L $\rightarrow$ mL $\rightarrow$ g $\rightarrow$ mol then heat liquid water: $n, C_s, T_i, T_f \rightarrow q_{1water}$(J)

$$\frac{1000 \text{ mL}}{1 \text{ L}} \quad \frac{1.00 \text{ g}}{1.00 \text{ mL}} \quad \frac{1 \text{ mol}}{18.02 \text{ g}} \qquad q = mC_s(T_f - T_i)$$

vaporize water: $n_{water}, \Delta H^\circ_{vap} \rightarrow q_{2water}$(J) then calculate total heat $q_{1water}, q_{2water} \rightarrow q_{water}$(J) then

$$q = n\Delta H \qquad\qquad q_{1water} + q_{2water} = q_{water}$$

q_{water}(J) $\rightarrow -q_{CH_4comb}$(J) $\rightarrow n_{CH_4}$ finally $n_{CH_4}, P, T \rightarrow V$

$$q_{water} = -q_{CH_4comb} \qquad q = n\Delta H \qquad\qquad PV = nRT$$

Solution: $1.00 \text{ L} \times \frac{1000 \text{ mL}}{1 \text{ L}} \times \frac{1.00 \text{ g}}{1.00 \text{ mL}} \times \frac{1 \text{ mol}}{18.02 \text{ g}} = 55.\underline{4}939 \text{ mol } H_2O$

$q_{1water} = n_{water}C_{water}(T_f - T_i) = 55.\underline{4}939 \text{ mol} \times 75.2 \frac{J}{mol \cdot K} \times (373 \text{ K} - 298 \text{ K}) = 3.1\underline{2}98557 \times 10^5 \text{ J}$

$= 312.98557 \text{ kJ}$

$q_{2water} = n\Delta H = 55.\underline{4}939 \text{ mol} \times 40.7 \frac{kJ}{mol} = 2.2\underline{5}8602 \times 10^3 \text{ kJ}$

$q_{1water} + q_{2water} = q_{water} = 312.98557 \text{ kJ} + 2.2\underline{5}8602 \times 10^3 \text{ kJ} = 2.5\underline{7}158757 \times 10^3 \text{ kJ}$

$q_{water} = -q_{CH_4comb} = 2.5\underline{7}158757 \times 10^3 \text{ kJ}$ then $q_{CH_4comb} = n\Delta H$. Rearrange to solve for n.

$$n_{CH_4} = \frac{q_{CH_4}}{\Delta H_{CH_4comb}} = \frac{-2.5\underline{7}158757 \times 10^3 \text{ kJ}}{-890.4 \frac{kJ}{mol}} = 2.8\underline{8}81262 \text{ mol then } PV = nRT$$

$$Rearrange\ to\ solve\ for\ V.\ V = \frac{nRT}{P} = \frac{2.8881262\ \cancel{mol} \times 0.08206\ \frac{L \cdot \cancel{atm}}{\cancel{mol} \cdot \cancel{K}} \times 298\ \cancel{K}}{1.00\ \cancel{atm}} = 70.\underline{6}25892\ L = 70.6\ L$$

Check: The units (L) are correct. The volume (71 L) is reasonable because we are using about 3 moles of methane.

11.98 $P_{Total} = P_{N_2} + P_{H_2O} + P_{ethanol}$

P_{N_2}: Use Boyle's law to calculate $P_1V_1 = P_2V_2$. Rearrange to solve for P_2.

$$P_2 = P_1 \frac{V_1}{V_2} = 1.0\ \cancel{atm} \times \frac{1.0\ \cancel{L}}{3.0\ \cancel{L}} \times \frac{760\ mmHg}{1\ \cancel{atm}} = 25\underline{3}.333\ mmHg$$

For water and ethanol, we need to calculate the pressure if all of the liquid were to vaporize in the 3.0 L apparatus.

$PV = nRT$. Rearrange to solve for P.

$$P = \frac{nRT}{V} = \frac{2.0\ \cancel{g} \times \frac{1\ \cancel{mol}}{18.02\ \cancel{g}} \times 0.08206\ \frac{\cancel{L} \cdot \cancel{atm}}{\cancel{mol} \cdot \cancel{K}} \times \frac{760\ mmHg}{1\ \cancel{atm}} \times 308\ \cancel{K}}{3.00\ \cancel{L}} = 71\underline{0}.640\ mmHg\ H_2O.$$ Because this

pressure is greater than the vapor pressure of water at this temperature, $P_{H_2O} = 42\ mmHg.$

$$P = \frac{nRT}{V} = \frac{0.50\ \cancel{g} \times \frac{1\ \cancel{mol}}{46.07\ \cancel{g}} \times 0.08206 \frac{\cancel{L} \cdot \cancel{atm}}{\cancel{mol} \cdot \cancel{K}} \times \frac{760\ mmHg}{1\ \cancel{atm}} \times 308\ \cancel{K}}{3.00\ \cancel{L}} = 69.\underline{4}937\ mmHg\ ethanol.$$ Because this

pressure is less than the vapor pressure of ethanol at this temperature (102 mmHg), all of the liquid will vaporize and $P_{ethanol} = 69.\underline{4}937\ mmHg.$

Finally, the total pressure is

$P_{Total} = P_{N_2} + P_{H_2O} + P_{ethanol} = 25\underline{3}.333\ mmHg + 42\ mmHg + 69.\underline{4}937\ mmHg = 3\underline{6}4.827\ mmHg = 360\ mmHg.$

Conceptual Problems

11.99   The melting of an ice cube in a glass of water will not raise or lower the level of the liquid in the glass as long as the ice is always floating in the liquid. This is because the ice will displace a volume of water based on its mass. By the same logic, melting floating icebergs will not raise the ocean levels (assuming that the dissolved solids content, and thus the density, will not change when the icebergs melt). Dissolving ice formations that are supported by land will raise the ocean levels, just as pouring more water into a glass will raise the liquid level in the glass.

11.100   The water in a container with a larger surface area will evaporate more quickly because there is more surface area for the molecules to evaporate from. Vapor pressure is the pressure of the gas when it is in dynamic equilibrium with the liquid (evaporation rate = condensation rate). The vapor pressure is dependent only on the substance and the temperature. The larger the surface area, the more quickly it will reach this equilibrium state.

11.101   Substance A will have the larger change in vapor pressure with the same temperature change. To understand this, consider the Clausius–Clapeyron equation: $\ln \frac{P_2}{P_1} = \frac{-\Delta H_{vap}}{R}\left(\frac{1}{T_2} - \frac{1}{T_1}\right)$. If we use the same temperatures, we see that $\frac{P_2}{P_1} \alpha\ e^{-\Delta H_{vap}}$. So the smaller the heat of vaporization, the larger the final vapor pressure. We can also consider that the lower the heat of vaporization, the easier to convert the substance from a liquid to a gas. This again leads to Substance A having the larger change in vapor pressure.

11.102   The triple point will be at a lower temperature because the fusion equilibrium line has a positive slope. This means that we will be increasing both temperature and pressure as we travel from the triple point to the normal melting point.

11.103 $\Delta H_{sub} = \Delta H_{fus} + \Delta H_{vap}$ as long as the heats of fusion and vaporization are measured at the same temperatures.

11.104   The liquid segment will have the least steep slope because it takes the most kJ/mol to raise the temperature of the phase.

11.105   Water has an exceptionally high specific heat capacity, which has a moderating effect on the temperature of the root cellar. A large amount of heat can be stored in a large vat of water. The heat will be absorbed or released from the large bodies of water preferentially over the area around it. As the temperature of the air drops, the water will release heat, keeping the temperature more constant. If the temperature of the cellar falls enough to begin to freeze the water, the heat given off during the freezing will further protect the food in the cellar.

11.106   The heat of fusion of a substance is always smaller than the heat of vaporization because the number of interactions between particles that are broken is less in fusion than in vaporization. When we melt a solid, the particles have increased mobility but are still strongly interacting with other liquid particles. In vaporization, all of the interactions between particles must be broken (gas particles have essentially no intermolecular interactions), and the particles must absorb enough energy to move much more rapidly.

11.107   (a)   In moving from line segment 5 to line segment 4, the water is condensing. Heat is being released, and q is negative.

   (b)   This line represents the heat absorbed when melting ice. The heat is converted to increased kinetic energy of the water molecules as they become more mobile in the liquid phase.

   (c)   For other substances, the following things would change: the melting point, the boiling point, the length of segments, and the slopes of line segments 1, 3, and 5.

11.108   The oxygen atoms would be attracted to the —CH_2 groups through dipole–dipole forces.

Questions for Group Work

11.109   1-hexnaol exhibits hydrogen bonding — it has the highest boiling point. 2-hexanone is polar, but cannot exhibit hydrogen bonding — it has the next highest boiling point. Heptane is nonpolar — it has the lowest boiling point.

11.110   Since the slope $= -\Delta H_{vap}/R$ this can be rearranged to give $\Delta H_{vap} = -\text{slope} \times R$.

Water: $\Delta H_{vap} = -4895 \, K \times \dfrac{8.314 \, J}{K \, \text{mol}} \times \dfrac{1 \, \text{kJ}}{1000 \, J} = 40.70 \, \dfrac{\text{kJ}}{\text{mol}}$

Acetone: $\Delta H_{vap} = -3636 \, K \times \dfrac{8.314 \, J}{K \, \text{mol}} \times \dfrac{1 \, \text{kJ}}{1000 \, J} = 30.23 \, \dfrac{\text{kJ}}{\text{mol}}$

These values are consistent with the values in Table 11.7. Water is capable of hydrogen bonding, while acetone is only not. The stronger intermolecular attractions of hydrogen bonding in water result in a higher heat of vaporization.

11.111   Referring to Figure 11.30, the amount of heat needed to melt one mole of water is 6.02 kJ and the amount of heat needed to boil one mole of water is 40.7 kJ — it takes a lot more heat to boil water than to melt ice, because all of the intermolecular interactions need to be completely broken when boiling but not to melt.

Referring to Figure 11.30, the amount of heat needed to warm one mole of ice 10 °C is 0.38 kJ (0.941 kJ ×
(10 °C/25 °C), the amount of heat needed to warm one mole of water 10 °C is 0.75 kJ (7.52 kJ × (10 °C/100 °C) and
the amount of heat needed to warm one mole of steam 10 °C is 0.36 kJ (0.905 kJ × (10 °C/25 °C). It takes more heat
to warm water than to warm ice or steam, because there is more motion and disorder in the liquid and gas phases.

11.112   The phase diagram for carbon dioxide is in Figure 11.32. Referring to line A, as the gas is cooled it will go directly
from a gas to a solid. Referring to line B, as the pressure of the gas is increased it will go from a gas to a liquid. Referring to line C, 37 °C is greater than the critical temperature, so as the pressure of the gas is increased it will go from a
gas to a supercritical fluid, not a liquid.

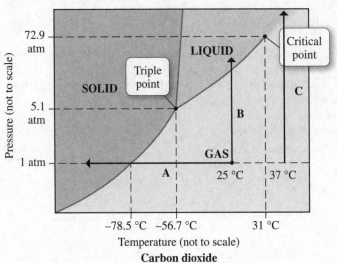

11.113   The characteristics of the various cubic crystalline lattices are presented in Figure 11.35.

Cubic Cell Name	Atoms per Unit Cell	Structure	Coordination Number	Edge Length in terms of r	Packing Efficiency (fraction of volume occupied)
Simple Cubic	1		6	$2r$	52%
Body-centered Cubic	2		8	$\dfrac{4r}{\sqrt{3}}$	68%
Face-centered Cubic	4		12	$2\sqrt{2}r$	74%

Note: All of the spheres are identical.

12 Solutions

Solubility

12.1   (a)   hexane, toluene, or CCl_4; dispersion forces
(b)   water, methanol, acetone; dispersion, dipole–dipole, hydrogen bonding (except for acetone)
(c)   hexane, toluene, or CCl_4; dispersion forces
(d)   water, acetone, methanol, ethanol; dispersion, ion–dipole

12.2   (a)   water, acetone, methanol, ethanol; dispersion, dipole–dipole, hydrogen bonding (except for acetone)
(b)   water, acetone, methanol, ethanol; dispersion, ion–dipole
(c)   hexane, toluene, or CCl_4; dispersion forces
(d)   water, acetone, methanol, ethanol; dispersion, ion–dipole

12.3 $HOCH_2CH_2CH_2OH$ would be more soluble in water because it has –OH groups on both ends of the molecule; so it can hydrogen-bond on both ends.

12.4 CH_2Cl_2 would be more soluble in water because it is a polar molecule and can exhibit dipole–dipole interactions with the water molecules. CCl_4 is a nonpolar molecule.

12.5   (a)   water; dispersion, dipole–dipole, hydrogen bonding
(b)   hexane; dispersion forces
(c)   water; dispersion, dipole–dipole
(d)   water; dispersion, dipole–dipole, hydrogen bonding

12.6   (a)   hexane; dispersion forces
(b)   water; dispersion, dipole–dipole, hydrogen bonding
(c)   hexane; dispersion forces
(d)   water; dispersion, dipole–dipole, hydrogen bonding

Energetics of Solution Formation

12.7   (a)   endothermic
(b)   The lattice energy is greater in magnitude than is the heat of hydration.
(c)

(d)   The solution forms because chemical systems tend toward greater entropy.

12.8   (a)   exothermic
        (b)   The lattice energy is smaller in magnitude than is the heat of hydration.
        (c)

        (d)   The solution forms because chemical systems tend toward lower energy and greater entropy.

12.9   **Given:** $AgNO_3$: lattice energy $= -820.$ kJ/mol, $\Delta H_{soln} = +22.6$ kJ/mol   **Find:** $\Delta H_{hydration}$
        Conceptual Plan: lattice energy, $\Delta H_{soln} \rightarrow \Delta H_{hydration}$

$$\Delta H_{soln} = \Delta H_{solute} + \Delta H_{hydration} \text{ where } \Delta H_{solute} = -\Delta H_{lattice}$$

        Solution: $\Delta H_{soln} = \Delta H_{solute} + \Delta H_{hydration}$ where $\Delta H_{solute} = -\Delta H_{lattice}$ so $\Delta H_{hydration} = \Delta H_{soln} + \Delta H_{lattice}$
        $\Delta H_{hydration} = 22.6$ kJ/mol $- 820.$ kJ/mol $= -797$ kJ/mol

        Check: The units (kJ/mol) are correct. The magnitude of the answer (-800 kJ/mol) makes physical sense because the
        lattice energy is so negative; thus, it dominates the calculation.

12.10   **Given:** LiCl: lattice energy $= -834$ kJ/mol, $\Delta H_{soln} = -37.0$ kJ/mol; NaCl: lattice energy $= -769$ kJ/mol,
        $\Delta H_{soln} = +3.88$ kJ/mol   **Find:** $\Delta H_{hydration}$ and which has stronger ion–dipole interactions
        Conceptual Plan: lattice energy, $\Delta H_{soln} \rightarrow \Delta H_{hydration}$ then compare values

$$\Delta H_{soln} = \Delta H_{solute} + \Delta H_{hydration} \text{ where } \Delta H_{solute} = -\Delta H_{lattice}$$

        Solution: $\Delta H_{soln} = \Delta H_{solute} + \Delta H_{hydration}$ where $\Delta H_{solute} = -\Delta H_{lattice}$ so $\Delta H_{hydration} = \Delta H_{soln} + \Delta H_{lattice}$
        LiCl: $\Delta H_{hydration} = -37.0$ kJ/mol $- 834$ kJ/mol $= -871$ kJ/mol
        NaCl: $\Delta H_{hydration} = +3.88$ kJ/mol $- 769$ kJ/mol $= -765$ kJ/mol
        Because $\Delta H_{hydration}$ of LiCl is more negative than for NaCl, LiCl has the stronger ion–dipole interactions.

        Check: The units (kJ/mol) are correct. The magnitude of the answers (-900 and -800 kJ/mol) makes physical sense
        because the lattice energies are so negative; thus, they dominate the calculation. We expect stronger interactions with
        lithium because the Li^+ ion is smaller than the Na^+ ion. Its charge density is higher, and it will interact more strongly
        with the dipoles of the water molecules.

12.11   **Given:** LiI: lattice energy $= -7.3 \times 10^2$ kJ/mol, $\Delta H_{hydration} = -793$ kJ/mol; 15.0 g LiI
        Find: ΔH_{soln} and heat evolved
        Conceptual Plan: lattice energy, $\Delta H_{hydration} \rightarrow \Delta H_{soln}$ and g $\rightarrow$ mol then mol, $\Delta H_{soln} \rightarrow q$

$$\Delta H_{soln} = \Delta H_{solute} + \Delta H_{hydration} \text{ where } \Delta H_{solute} = -\Delta H_{lattice} \qquad \frac{1 \text{ mol}}{133.84 \text{ g}} \qquad q = n\Delta H_{soln}$$

        Solution: $\Delta H_{soln} = \Delta H_{solute} + \Delta H_{hydration}$ where $\Delta H_{solute} = -\Delta H_{lattice}$ so $\Delta H_{soln} = \Delta H_{hydration} - \Delta H_{lattice}$
        $\Delta H_{soln} = -793$ kJ/mol $- (-7\underline{3}0$ kJ/mol$) = -\underline{6}3$ kJ/mol $= -6 \times 10^1$ kJ/mol and

$$15.0 \text{ g} \times \frac{1 \text{ mol}}{133.84 \text{ g}} = 0.112074 \text{ mol then}$$

$$q = n\Delta H_{soln} = 0.112074 \text{ mol} \times -\underline{6}.3 \times 10^1 \frac{\text{kJ}}{\text{mol}} = -7 \text{ kJ or } 7 \text{ kJ released}$$

        Check: The units (kJ/mol and kJ) are correct. The magnitude of the answer (-60 kJ/mol) makes physical sense
        because the lattice energy and the heat of hydration are about the same. The magnitude of the heat (7 kJ) makes physi-
        cal sense because 15 g is much less than a mole; thus, the amount of heat released is going to be small.

12.12   **Given:** KNO_3: lattice energy $= -163.8$ kcal/mol, $\Delta H_{hydration} = -155.5$ kcal/mol; 1.00×10^2 kJ absorbed
         Find: ΔH_{soln} and m (KNO_3)
         Conceptual Plan: lattice energy, $\Delta H_{hydration} \rightarrow \Delta H_{soln}$ (kcal) $\rightarrow \Delta H_{soln}$ (kJ) then

$$\Delta H_{soln} = \Delta H_{solute} + \Delta H_{hydration} \text{ where } \Delta H_{solute} = -\Delta H_{lattice}$$

         mol, $q \rightarrow \Delta H_{soln}$ then mol $\rightarrow$ g

$$q = n\Delta H_{soln} \qquad \frac{101.11 \text{ g}}{1 \text{ mol}}$$

         Solution: $\Delta H_{soln} = \Delta H_{solute} + \Delta H_{hydration}$ where $\Delta H_{solute} = -\Delta H_{lattice}$ so $\Delta H_{soln} = \Delta H_{hydration} - \Delta H_{lattice}$

         $\Delta H_{soln} = [-155.5 \text{ kcal/mol} - (-163.8 \text{ kcal/mol})](4.184 \text{ kJ/kcal}) = 3\underline{4}.7 \text{ kJ/mol}$ then $q = n\Delta H_{soln}$

         Rearrange to solve for n. $n = \dfrac{q}{\Delta H_{soln}} = \dfrac{1.00 \times 10^2 \text{ kJ}}{34.7 \dfrac{\text{kJ}}{\text{mol}}} = 2.\underline{8}818 \text{ mol}$ then $2.\underline{8}818 \text{ mol} \times \dfrac{101.11 \text{ g}}{1 \text{ mol}} = 2.9 \times 10^2 \text{ g}$

         Check: The units (kJ/mol and g) are correct. The magnitude of the answer ($+35$ kJ/mol) makes physical sense because the lattice energy and the heat of hydration are about the same, with the lattice energy dominating; therefore, the answer is positive. The problem hints at a positive heat of solution by saying that heat is absorbed. The magnitude of the mass (290) makes physical sense because 100 kJ will require over 2 moles of salt.

Solution Equilibrium and Factors Affecting Solubility

12.13   The solution is unsaturated because we are dissolving 25 g of NaCl per 100 g of water and the solubility from the figure is ~ 35 g NaCl per 100 g of water at 25 °C.

12.14   The solution is almost saturated because we are dissolving 32 g of KNO_3 per 100 g of water and the solubility from the figure is ~ 36 g KNO_3 per 100 g of water at 25 °C.

12.15   At 40 °C, the solution has 45 g of KNO_3 per 100 g of water, and it can contain up to 63 g of KNO_3 per 100 g of water. At 0 °C, the solubility from the figure is ~ 14 g KNO_3 per 100 g of water, so ~ 31 g KNO_3 per 100 g of water will precipitate out of solution.

12.16   At 60 °C, the solution has 42 g of KCl per 100 g of water, and it can contain up to 45 g of KCl per 100 g of water. At 0 °C, the solubility from the figure is ~ 26 g KCl per 100 g of water, so ~ 16 g KCl per 100 g of water will precipitate out of solution.

12.17   Because the solubility of gases decreases as the temperature increases, boiling will cause dissolved oxygen to be removed from the solution.

12.18   Because the solubility of gases decreases as the temperature increases, dissolved oxygen was removed from the solution and there was no oxygen in the water for the fish to breathe.

12.19   Henry's law says that as pressure increases, nitrogen will more easily dissolve in blood. To reverse this process, divers should ascend to lower pressures.

12.20   Henry's law says that as pressure increases, oxygen will more easily dissolve in blood. To reverse this process, divers should ascend to lower pressures or breathe special gas mixtures with lower oxygen levels.

12.21   **Given:** room temperature, 80.0 L aquarium, $P_{Total} = 1.0$ atm; $\chi_{N_2} = 0.78$ **Find:** m (N_2)
         Other: $k_H(N_2) = 6.1 \times 10^{-4}$ M/atm at 25 °C
         Conceptual Plan: $P_{Total}, \chi_{N_2} \rightarrow P_{N_2}$ then $P_{N_2}, k_H(N_2) \rightarrow S_{N_2}$ then $L \rightarrow$ mol $\rightarrow$ g

$$P_{N_2} = \chi_{N_2} P_{Total} \qquad S_{N_2} = k_H(N_2) P_{N_2} \qquad M = \frac{\text{amount solute (moles)}}{\text{volume solution (L)}} \frac{28.02 \text{ g } N_2}{1 \text{ mol } N_2}$$

         Solution: $P_{N_2} = \chi_{N_2} P_{Total} = 0.78 \times 1.0$ atm $= 0.78$ atm then

         $S_{N_2} = k_H(N_2) P_{N_2} = 6.1 \times 10^{-4} \dfrac{\text{M}}{\text{atm}} \times 0.78 \text{ atm} = 4.\underline{7}58 \times 10^{-4} \text{ M}$ then

         $80.0 \text{ L} \times 4.\underline{7}58 \times 10^{-4} \dfrac{\text{mol}}{\text{L}} \times \dfrac{28.02 \text{ g}}{1 \text{ mol}} = 1.1 \text{ g}$

Check: The units (g) are correct. The magnitude of the answer (1 g) seems reasonable because we have 80 L of water and expect much less than a mole of nitrogen.

12.22   **Given:** helium, 25 °C, $P_{He} = 1.0$ atm   **Find:** S_{He} (M)   **Other:** $k_H(He) = 3.7 \times 10^{-4}$ M/atm at 25 °C
Conceptual Plan: $P_{He}, k_H(He) \rightarrow S_{He}$

$$S_{He} = k_H(He)P_{He}$$

Solution: $S_{He} = k_H(He)P_{He} = 3.7 \times 10^{-4} \dfrac{M}{\text{atm}} \times 1.0 \,\text{atm} = 3.7 \times 10^{-4}\,M$

Check: The units (M) are correct. The magnitude of the answer (10^{-4} M) seems reasonable because this is the value of k_H.

Concentrations of Solutions

12.23   **Given:** NaCl and water; 145 g NaCl in 1.00 L solution   **Find:** M, m, and mass percent
Other: $d = 1.08$ g/mL
Conceptual Plan: $g_{NaCl} \rightarrow$ mol and L $\rightarrow$ mL $\rightarrow g_{soln}$ and g_{soln} $g_{NaCl} \rightarrow g_{H_2O} \rightarrow kg_{H_2O}$ then

$$\frac{1 \text{ mol NaCl}}{58.44 \text{ g NaCl}} \qquad \frac{1000 \text{ mL}}{1 \text{ L}} \quad \frac{1.08 \text{ g}}{1 \text{ mL}} \qquad g_{H_2O} = g_{soln} - g_{NaCl} \quad \frac{1 \text{ kg}}{1000 \text{ g}}$$

mol, $V \rightarrow$ M and mol, $kg_{H_2O} \rightarrow m$ and g_{soln} $g_{NaCl} \rightarrow$ mass percent

$$M = \frac{\text{amount solute (moles)}}{\text{volume solution (L)}} \quad m = \frac{\text{amount solute (moles)}}{\text{mass solvent (kg)}} \quad \text{mass percent} = \frac{\text{mass solute}}{\text{mass solution}} \times 100\%$$

Solution: $145 \text{ g NaCl} \times \dfrac{1 \text{ mol NaCl}}{58.44 \text{ g NaCl}} = 2.4\underline{8}1177$ mol NaCl and

$1.00 \text{ L} \times \dfrac{1000 \text{ mL}}{1 \text{ L}} \times \dfrac{1.08 \text{ g}}{1 \text{ mL}} = 10\underline{8}0$ g soln and

$g_{H_2O} = g_{soln} - g_{NaCl} = 10\underline{8}0 \text{ g} - 145 \text{ g} = 9\underline{3}5 \text{ g H}_2\text{O} \times \dfrac{1 \text{ kg}}{1000 \text{ g}} = 0.9\underline{3}5 \text{ kg H}_2\text{O}$ then

$M = \dfrac{\text{amount solute (moles)}}{\text{volume solution (L)}} = \dfrac{2.4\underline{8}1177 \text{ mol NaCl}}{1.00 \text{ L soln}} = 2.48$ M and

$m = \dfrac{\text{amount solute (moles)}}{\text{mass solvent (kg)}} = \dfrac{2.4\underline{8}1177 \text{ mol NaCl}}{0.9\underline{3}5 \text{ kg H}_2\text{O}} = 2.7 \, m$ and

$\text{mass percent} = \dfrac{\text{mass solute}}{\text{mass solution}} \times 100\% = \dfrac{145 \text{ g NaCl}}{10\underline{8}0 \text{ g soln}} \times 100\% = 13.4\%$ by mass

Check: The units (M, m, and percent by mass) are correct. The magnitude of the answer (2.5 M) seems reasonable because we have 145 g NaCl, which is a couple of moles, and we have 1 L. The magnitude of the answer (2.7 m) seems reasonable because it is a little higher than the molarity, which we expect because we only use the solvent weight in the denominator. The magnitude of the answer (10%) seems reasonable because we have 145 g NaCl and just under 1000 g of solution.

12.24   **Given:** KNO_3 and water; 72.3 g KNO_3 in 1.50 L solution   **Find:** M, m, and mass percent
Other: $d = 1.05$ g/mL
Conceptual Plan: $g_{KNO_3} \rightarrow$ mol and L $\rightarrow$ mL $\rightarrow g_{soln}$ and g_{soln} $g_{KNO_3} \rightarrow g_{H_2O} \rightarrow kg_{H_2O}$ then

$$\frac{1 \text{ mol } KNO_3}{101.11 \text{ g } KNO_3} \qquad \frac{1000 \text{ mL}}{1 \text{ L}} \quad \frac{1.05 \text{ g}}{1 \text{ mL}} \qquad g_{H_2O} = g_{soln} - g_{KNO_3} \quad \frac{1 \text{ kg}}{1000 \text{ g}}$$

mol, $V \rightarrow$ M and mol, $kg_{H_2O} \rightarrow m$ and g_{soln} $g_{KNO_3} \rightarrow$ mass percent

$$M = \frac{\text{amount solute (moles)}}{\text{volume solution (L)}} \quad m = \frac{\text{amount solute (moles)}}{\text{mass solvent (kg)}} \quad \text{mass percent} = \frac{\text{mass solute}}{\text{mass solution}} \times 100\%$$

Solution: $72.3 \text{ g } KNO_3 \times \dfrac{1 \text{ mol } KNO_3}{101.11 \text{ g } KNO_3} = 0.71\underline{5}0628$ mol KNO_3 and

$1.50 \text{ L} \times \dfrac{1000 \text{ mL}}{1 \text{ L}} \times \dfrac{1.05 \text{ g}}{1 \text{ mL}} = 15\underline{7}5$ g soln and

$g_{H_2O} = g_{soln} - g_{KNO_3} = 15\underline{7}5 \text{ g} - 72.3 \text{ g} = 150\underline{2}.7 \text{ g H}_2\text{O} \times \dfrac{1 \text{ kg}}{1000 \text{ g}} = 1.50\underline{2}7 \text{ kg H}_2\text{O}$ then

$$M = \frac{\text{amount solute (moles)}}{\text{volume solution (L)}} = \frac{0.71\underline{5}0628 \text{ mol KNO}_3}{1.50 \text{ L soln}} = 0.477 \text{ M and}$$

$$m = \frac{\text{amount solute (moles)}}{\text{mass solvent (kg)}} = \frac{0.71\underline{5}0628 \text{ mol KNO}_3}{1.5\underline{0}27 \text{ kg H}_2\text{O}} = 0.476 \text{ } m \text{ and}$$

$$\text{mass percent} = \frac{\text{mass solute}}{\text{mass solution}} \times 100\% = \frac{72.3 \text{ g KNO}_3}{15\underline{7}5 \text{ g soln}} \times 100\% = 4.59\% \text{ by mass}$$

Check: The units (M, m, and percent by mass) are correct. The magnitude of the answer (0.477 M) seems reasonable because we have 72.3 g KNO_3, which is less than a mole, and we have 1.5 L. The magnitude of the answer (0.476 m) seems reasonable because it is a little higher than the molarity, which we expect because we only use the solvent weight in the denominator. The magnitude of the answer (4.59%) seems reasonable because we have 72.3 g KNO_3 and ~1600 g of solution.

12.25 **Given:** initial solution: 50.0 mL of 5.00 M KI; final solution contains 3.25 g KI in 25.0 mL
Find: final volume to dilute initial solution to
Conceptual Plan: final solution: $g_{KI} \rightarrow$ **mol and** mL $\rightarrow$ L **then mol,** $V \rightarrow M_2$ **then** $M_1, V_1, M_2 \rightarrow V_2$

$$\frac{1 \text{ mol KI}}{166.00 \text{ g KI}} \qquad \frac{1 \text{ L}}{1000 \text{ mL}} \qquad M = \frac{\text{amount solute (moles)}}{\text{volume solution (L)}} \qquad M_1 V_1 = M_2 V_2$$

Solution: $3.25 \text{ g KI} \times \dfrac{1 \text{ mol KI}}{166.00 \text{ g KI}} = 0.019\underline{5}783 \text{ mol KI}$ and $25.0 \text{ mL} \times \dfrac{1 \text{ L}}{1000 \text{ mL}} = 0.0250 \text{ L}$

then $M = \dfrac{\text{amount solute (moles)}}{\text{volume solution (L)}} = \dfrac{0.019\underline{5}783 \text{ mol KI}}{0.0250 \text{ L soln}} = 0.78\underline{3}132 \text{ M then } M_1 V_1 = M_2 V_2$

Rearrange to solve for V_2. $V_2 = \dfrac{M_1}{M_2} \times V_1 = \dfrac{5.00 \text{ M}}{0.78\underline{3}132 \text{ M}} \times 50.0 \text{ mL} = 319. \text{ mL diluted volume}$

Check: The units (mL) are correct. The magnitude of the answer (320 mL) seems reasonable because we are starting with a concentration of 5 M and ending with a concentration of less than 1 M.

12.26 **Given:** initial solution: 125 mL of 8.00 M $CuCl_2$; final solution contains 5.9 g $CuCl_2$ in 50.0 mL
Find: final volume to dilute initial solution to
Conceptual Plan: final solution: $g_{CuCl_2} \rightarrow$ **mol and** mL $\rightarrow$ L **then mol,** $V \rightarrow M_2$ **then** $M_1, V_1, M_2 \rightarrow V_2$

$$\frac{1 \text{ mol CuCl}_2}{134.45 \text{ g CuCl}_2} \qquad \frac{1 \text{ L}}{1000 \text{ mL}} \qquad M = \frac{\text{amount solute (moles)}}{\text{volume solution (L)}} \qquad M_1 V_1 = M_2 V_2$$

Solution: $5.9 \text{ g CuCl}_2 \times \dfrac{1 \text{ mol CuCl}_2}{134.45 \text{ g CuCl}_2} = 0.04\underline{3}8825 \text{ mol CuCl}_2$ and $50.0 \text{ mL} \times \dfrac{1 \text{ L}}{1000 \text{ mL}} = 0.0500 \text{ L}$

then $M = \dfrac{\text{amount solute (moles)}}{\text{volume solution (L)}} = \dfrac{0.04\underline{3}8825 \text{ mol CuCl}_2}{0.0500 \text{ L soln}} = 0.8\underline{7}765 \text{ M then } M_1 V_1 = M_2 V_2$

Rearrange to solve for V_2.

$V_2 = \dfrac{M_1}{M_2} \times V_1 = \dfrac{8.00 \text{ M}}{0.8\underline{7}765 \text{ M}} \times 125 \text{ mL} = 1100 \text{ mL diluted volume}$

Check: The units (mL) are correct. The magnitude of the answer (1100 mL) seems reasonable because we are starting with a concentration of 8 M and ending with a concentration of less than 1 M.

12.27 **Given:** $AgNO_3$ and water; 3.4% Ag by mass, 4.8 L solution   **Find:** m (Ag) **Other:** $d = 1.01$ g/mL
Conceptual Plan: L $\rightarrow$ mL $\rightarrow$ g_{soln} $\rightarrow$ g_{Ag}

$$\frac{1000 \text{ mL}}{1 \text{ L}} \qquad \frac{1.01 \text{ g}}{1 \text{ mL}} \qquad \frac{3.4 \text{ g Ag}}{100 \text{ g soln}}$$

Solution: $4.8 \text{ L} \times \dfrac{1000 \text{ mL}}{1 \text{ L}} \times \dfrac{1.01 \text{ g}}{1 \text{ mL}} = 4\underline{8}48 \text{ g soln then}$

$4\underline{8}48 \text{ g soln} \times \dfrac{3.4 \text{ g Ag}}{100 \text{ g soln}} = 160 \text{ g Ag} = 1.6 \times 10^2 \text{ g Ag}$

Check: The units (g) are correct. The magnitude of the answer (160 g) seems reasonable because we have almost 5000 g of solution.

12.28   **Given:** dioxin and water; 0.085% dioxin by mass, 2.5 L solution   **Find:** m (dioxin) **Other:** $d = 1.00$ g/mL
         Conceptual Plan: $\text{L} \rightarrow \text{mL} \rightarrow \text{g}_{soln} \rightarrow \text{g}_{dioxin}$

$$\frac{1000 \text{ mL}}{1 \text{ L}} \quad \frac{1.01 \text{ g}}{1 \text{ mL}} \quad \frac{0.085 \text{ g dioxin}}{100 \text{ g soln}}$$

Solution: $2.5 \text{ L} \times \dfrac{1000 \text{ mL}}{1 \text{ L}} \times \dfrac{1.00 \text{ g}}{1 \text{ mL}} = 2\underline{5}00 \text{ g soln}$ then $2\underline{5}00 \text{ g soln} \times \dfrac{0.085 \text{ g dioxin}}{100 \text{ g soln}} = 2.1 \text{ g dioxin}$

Check: The units (g) are correct. The magnitude of the answer (2 g) seems reasonable because we have 2500 g of solution and a low concentration.

12.29   **Given:** Ca^{2+} and water; 0.0085% Ca^{2+} by mass, 1.2 g Ca   **Find:** m (water)
         Conceptual Plan: $\text{g}_{Ca} \rightarrow \text{g}_{soln} \rightarrow \text{g}_{H_2O}$

$$\frac{100 \text{ g soln}}{0.0085 \text{ g Ca}} \quad \text{g}_{H_2O} = \text{g}_{soln} - \text{g}_{Ca}$$

Solution: $1.2 \text{ g Ca} \times \dfrac{100 \text{ g soln}}{0.0085 \text{ g Ca}} = 1\underline{4}118 \text{ g soln}$ then

$\text{g}_{H_2O} = \text{g}_{soln} - \text{g}_{Ca} = 1\underline{4}118 \text{ g} - 1.2 \text{ g} = 1.4 \times 10^4 \text{ g water}$

Check: The units (g) are correct. The magnitude of the answer (10^4 g) seems reasonable because we have such a low concentration of Ca.

12.30   **Given:** Pb and water; 0.0011% Pb by mass, 150 mg Pb   **Find:** V (mL) **Other:** $d = 1.00$ g/mL
         Conceptual Plan: $\text{mg}_{Pb} \rightarrow \text{g}_{Pb} \rightarrow \text{g}_{soln} \rightarrow \text{mL}$

$$\frac{1000 \text{ g}}{1 \text{ mg}} \quad \frac{100 \text{ g soln}}{0.0011 \text{ g Pb}} \quad \frac{1 \text{ mL}}{1.00 \text{ g}}$$

Solution: $150 \text{ mg Pb} \times \dfrac{1 \text{ g Pb}}{1000 \text{ mg Pb}} \times \dfrac{100 \text{ g soln}}{0.0011 \text{ g Pb}} \times \dfrac{1 \text{ mL}}{1.00 \text{ g}} = 1.4 \times 10^4 \text{ mL}$

Check: The units (mL) are correct. The magnitude of the answer (10^4 g) seems reasonable because we have such a low concentration of Pb.

12.31   **Given:** concentrated HNO_3: 70.3% HNO_3 by mass, $d = 1.41$ g/mL; final solution: 1.15 L of 0.100 M HNO_3
         Find: describe final solution preparation
         Conceptual Plan: $M_2, V_2 \rightarrow \text{mol}_{HNO_3} \rightarrow \text{g}_{HNO_3} \rightarrow \text{g}_{conc \; acid} \rightarrow \text{mL}_{conc \; acid}$ **then describe method**

$$mol = MV \quad \frac{63.02 \text{ g HNO}_3}{1 \text{ mol HNO}_3} \quad \frac{100 \text{ g conc acid}}{70.3 \text{ g HNO}_3} \quad \frac{1 \text{ mL}}{1.41 \text{ g}}$$

Solution: $mol = MV = 0.100 \dfrac{\text{mol HNO}_3}{1 \text{ L soln}} \times 1.15 \text{ L soln} = 0.115 \text{ mol HNO}_3$ then

$0.115 \text{ mol HNO}_3 \times \dfrac{63.02 \text{ g HNO}_3}{1 \text{ mol HNO}_3} \times \dfrac{100 \text{ g conc acid}}{70.3 \text{ g HNO}_3} \times \dfrac{1 \text{ mL conc acid}}{1.41 \text{ g conc acid}} = 7.31 \text{ mL conc acid}$

Prepare the solution by putting about 1.00 L of distilled water in a container. Carefully pour in the 7.31 mL of the concentrated acid, mix the solution, and allow it to cool. Finally, add enough water to generate the total volume of solution (1.15 L). It is important to add acid to water, not the reverse, because such a large amount of heat is released upon mixing.

Check: The units (mL) are correct. The magnitude of the answer (7 mL) seems reasonable because we are starting with such a concentrated solution and diluting it to a low concentration.

12.32   **Given:** concentrated HCl: 37.0% HCl by mass, $d = 1.20$ g/mL; final solution: 2.85 L of 0.500 M HCl
         Find: describe final solution preparation
         Conceptual Plan: $M_2, V_2 \rightarrow \text{mol}_{HCl} \rightarrow \text{g}_{HCl} \rightarrow \text{g}_{conc \; acid} \rightarrow \text{mL}_{conc \; acid}$ **then describe method**

$$mol = MV \quad \frac{36.46 \text{ g HCl}}{1 \text{ mol HCl}} \quad \frac{100 \text{ g conc acid}}{37.0 \text{ g HCl}} \quad \frac{1 \text{ mL}}{1.20 \text{ g}}$$

Solution: $mol = MV = 0.500 \dfrac{\text{mol HCl}}{1 \text{ L soln}} \times 2.85 \text{ L soln} = 1.4\underline{2}5 \text{ mol HCl}$ then

$1.4\underline{2}5 \text{ mol HCl} \times \dfrac{36.46 \text{ g HCl}}{1 \text{ mol HCl}} \times \dfrac{100 \text{ g conc acid}}{37.0 \text{ g HCl}} \times \dfrac{1 \text{ mL conc acid}}{1.20 \text{ g conc acid}} = 117 \text{ mL conc acid}$

Prepare the solution by putting about 2.5 L of distilled water in a container. Carefully pour in the 117 mL of the concentrated acid, mix the solution, and allow it to cool. Finally, add enough water to generate the total volume of solution required. It is important to add acid to water, not the reverse, because such a large amount of heat is released upon mixing.

Check: The units (mL) are correct. The magnitude of the answer (117 mL) seems reasonable because we are starting with such a concentrated solution and diluting it to a low concentration.

12.33   (a)   **Given:** 1.00×10^2 mL of 0.500 M KCl   **Find:** describe final solution preparation
Conceptual Plan: mL $\rightarrow$ L then $M, V \rightarrow$ mol$_{KCl} \rightarrow$ g$_{KCl}$ then describe method

$$\frac{1 \text{ L}}{1000 \text{ mL}} \qquad mol = MV \qquad \frac{74.55 \text{ g KCl}}{1 \text{ mol KCl}}$$

Solution: $1.00 \times 10^2 \text{ mL} \times \dfrac{1 \text{ L}}{1000 \text{ mL}} = 0.100 \text{ L}$

$mol = MV = 0.500 \dfrac{\text{mol KCl}}{1 \text{ L soln}} \times 0.100 \text{ L soln} = 0.0500 \text{ mol KCl}$

then $0.0500 \text{ mol KCl} \times \dfrac{74.55 \text{ g KCl}}{1 \text{ mol KCl}} = 3.73 \text{ g KCl}$

Prepare the solution by carefully adding 3.73 g KCl to a 100 mL volumetric flask. Add ~75 mL of distilled water and agitate the solution until the salt dissolves completely. Finally, add enough water to generate a total volume of solution (add water to the mark on the flask).

Check: The units (g) are correct. The magnitude of the answer (4 g) seems reasonable because we are making a small volume of solution and the formula weight of KCl is ~75 g/mol.

   (b)   **Given:** 1.00×10^2 g of 0.500 m KCl   **Find:** describe final solution preparation
Conceptual Plan:

$m \rightarrow$ mol$_{KCl}$/1 kg solvent $\rightarrow$ g$_{KCl}$/1 kg solvent then g$_{KCl}$/1 kg solvent, g$_{soln}$ $\rightarrow$ g$_{KCl}$, g$_{H_2O}$

$$m = \frac{\text{amount solute (moles)}}{\text{mass solvent (kg)}} \qquad \frac{74.55 \text{ g KCl}}{1 \text{ mol KCl}} \qquad\qquad g_{soln} = g_{KCl} + g_{H_2O}$$

then describe method

Solution: $m = \dfrac{\text{amount solute (moles)}}{\text{mass solvent (kg)}}$ so $0.500 \; m = \dfrac{0.500 \text{ mol KCl}}{1 \text{ kg H}_2\text{O}}$ so

$\dfrac{0.500 \text{ mol KCl}}{1 \text{ kg H}_2\text{O}} \times \dfrac{74.55 \text{ g KCl}}{1 \text{ mol KCl}} = \dfrac{37.28 \text{ g KCl}}{1000 \text{ g H}_2\text{O}}$; $g_{soln} = g_{KCl} + g_{H_2O}$ so $g_{soln} - g_{KCl} = g_{H_2O}$

substitute into ratio $\dfrac{37.28 \text{ g KCl}}{1037.28 \text{ g solution}} = \dfrac{x \text{ g KCl}}{100 \text{ g solution}}$.

$100 \text{ g solution} \times \dfrac{37.28 \text{ g KCl}}{1037.28 \text{ g solution}} = \dfrac{x \text{ g KCl}}{100 \text{ g solution}} \times 100 \text{ g solution}$

$x \text{ g KCl} = \dfrac{3728 \text{ g KCl}}{1037.28}$; $x \text{ g KCl} = 3.594015 \text{ g KCl}$

$g_{H_2O} = g_{soln} - g_{KCl} = 100. \text{ g} - 3.59 \text{ g} = 96.41 \text{ g H}_2\text{O}$

Prepare the solution by carefully adding 3.59 g KCl to a container with 96.41 g of distilled water and agitate the solution until the salt dissolves completely.

Check: The units (g) are correct. The magnitude of the answer (3.6 g) seems reasonable because we are making a small volume of solution and the formula weight of KCl is ~75 g/mol.

   (c)   **Given:** 1.00×10^2 g of 5.0% KCl by mass   **Find:** describe final solution preparation
Conceptual Plan: g$_{soln} \rightarrow$ g$_{KCl}$ then g$_{KCl}$, g$_{soln} \rightarrow$ g$_{H_2O}$

$$\frac{5.0 \text{ g KCl}}{100 \text{ g soln}} \qquad\qquad g_{soln} = g_{KCl} + g_{H_2O}$$

then describe method

Solution: $1.00 \times 10^2 \text{ g soln} \times \dfrac{5.0 \text{ g KCl}}{100 \text{ g soln}} = 5.0 \text{ g KCl}$ then $g_{soln} = g_{KCl} + g_{H_2O}$

So $g_{H_2O} = g_{soln} - g_{KCl} = 100. \text{ g} - 5.0 \text{ g} = 95 \text{ g H}_2\text{O}$

Prepare the solution by carefully adding 5.0 g KCl to a container with 95 g of distilled water and agitate the solution until the salt dissolves completely.

Check: The units (g) are correct. The magnitude of the answer (5 g) seems reasonable because we are making a small volume of solution and the solution is 5% by mass KCl.

12.34   (a)   **Given:** 125 mL of 0.100 M $NaNO_3$ **Find:** describe final solution preparation

Conceptual Plan: mL $\rightarrow$ L then $M, V \rightarrow$ mol$_{NaNO_3} \rightarrow$ g$_{NaNO_3}$then describe method

$$\frac{1 \text{ L}}{1000 \text{ mL}} \qquad mol = MV \qquad \frac{85.00 \text{ g NaNO}_3}{1 \text{ mol NaNO}_3}$$

Solution: $125 \text{ mL} \times \dfrac{1 \text{ L}}{1000 \text{ mL}} = 0.125 \text{ L}$

$mol = MV = 0.100 \, \dfrac{\text{mol NaNO}_3}{1 \text{ L soln}} \times 0.125 \text{ L soln} = 0.0125 \text{ mol NaNO}_3$ then

$0.0125 \text{ mol NaNO}_3 \times \dfrac{85.00 \text{ g NaNO}_3}{1 \text{ mol NaNO}_3} = 1.06 \text{ g NaNO}_3$

Prepare the solution by carefully adding 1.06 g $NaNO_3$ to a container. Add ~ 100 mL of distilled water and agitate the solution until the salt dissolves completely. Finally, add enough water to generate a total volume of solution (125 mL).

Check: The units (g) are correct. The magnitude of the answer (1 g) seems reasonable because we are making a small volume of solution and the formula weight of $NaNO_3$ is ~ 85 g/mol.

(b)   **Given:** 125 g of 0.100 m $NaNO_3$ **Find:** describe final solution preparation

Conceptual Plan: $m \rightarrow$ mol$_{NaNO_3}$/1 kg solvent $\rightarrow$ g$_{NaNO_3}$/1 kg solvent then

$$m = \frac{\text{amount solute (moles)}}{\text{mass solvent (kg)}} \qquad \frac{85.00 \text{ g NaNO}_3}{1 \text{ mol NaNO}_3}$$

g$_{NaNO_3}$/1 kg solvent, g$_{soln} \rightarrow$ g$_{NaNO_3}$, g$_{H_2O}$ then describe method

$$g_{soln} = g_{NaNO_3} + g_{H_2O}$$

Solution: $m = \dfrac{\text{amount solute (moles)}}{\text{mass solvent (kg)}}$ so $0.100 \, m = \dfrac{0.500 \text{ mol NaNO}_3}{1 \text{ kg H}_2\text{O}}$ so

$\dfrac{0.100 \text{ mol NaNO}_3}{1 \text{ kg H}_2\text{O}} \times \dfrac{85.00 \text{ g NaNO}_3}{1 \text{ mol NaNO}_3} = \dfrac{8.50 \text{ g NaNO}_3}{1000 \text{ g H}_2\text{O}}$ then $g_{soln} = g_{NaNO_3} + g_{H_2O}$ so

substitute into ratio $\dfrac{8.50 \text{ g NaNO}_3}{1008.50 \text{ g solution}} = \dfrac{x \text{ g NaNO}_3}{125 \text{ g solution}}$

$125 \text{ g solution} \times \dfrac{8.50 \text{ g NaNO}_3}{1008.50 \text{ g solution}} = \dfrac{x \text{ g NaNO}_3}{125 \text{ g solution}} \times 125 \text{ g solution}; \; x \text{ g NaNO}_3 = \dfrac{1062.5 \text{ g NaNO}_3}{1008.50}$

$x \text{ g NaNO}_3 = 1.053545 \text{ g NaNO}_3$ then $g_{H_2O} = g_{soln} - g_{NaNO_3} = 125 \text{ g} - 1.05 \text{ g} = 124 \text{ g H}_2\text{O}$

Prepare the solution by carefully adding 1.05 g $NaNO_3$ to a container with 124 g of distilled water and agitate the solution until the salt dissolves completely.

Check: The units (g) are correct. The magnitude of the answer (1 g) seems reasonable because we are making a small volume of solution and the formula weight of $NaNO_3$ is 85 g/mol.

(c)   **Given:** 125 g of 1.0% $NaNO_3$ by mass   **Find:** describe final solution preparation

Conceptual Plan: g$_{soln} \rightarrow$ g$_{NaNO_3}$ then g$_{NaNO_3}$, g$_{soln} \rightarrow$ g$_{H_2O}$

$$\frac{1.0 \text{ g NaNO}_3}{100 \text{ g soln}} \qquad\qquad g_{soln} = g_{NaNO_3} + g_{H_2O}$$

then describe method

Solution: $125 \text{ g soln} \times \dfrac{1.0 \text{ g NaNO}_3}{100 \text{ g soln}} = 1.25 \text{ g NaNO}_3$ then $g_{soln} = g_{NaNO_3} + g_{H_2O}$

So $g_{H_2O} = g_{soln} - g_{NaNO_3} = 125 \text{ g} - 1.25 \text{ g} = 124 \text{ g H}_2\text{O}$

Prepare the solution by carefully adding 1.3 g $NaNO_3$ to a container with 124 g of distilled water and agitate the solution until the salt dissolves completely.

Check: The units (g) are correct. The magnitude of the answer (1 g) seems reasonable because we are making a small volume of solution and the solution is 1% by mass $NaNO_3$.

12.35 (a) **Given:** 28.4 g of glucose ($C_6H_{12}O_6$) in 355 g water; final volume = 378 mL   **Find:** molarity
Conceptual Plan: $mL \rightarrow L$ and $g_{C_6H_{12}O_6} \rightarrow mol_{C_6H_{12}O_6}$ then $mol_{C_6H_{12}O_6}, V \rightarrow M$

$$\frac{1\ L}{1000\ mL} \qquad \frac{1\ mol\ C_6H_{12}O_6}{180.16\ g\ C_6H_{12}O_6} \qquad M = \frac{\text{amount solute (moles)}}{\text{volume solution (L)}}$$

Solution: $378\ mL \times \dfrac{1\ L}{1000\ mL} = 0.378\ L$ and

$$28.4\ g\ C_6H_{12}O_6 \times \frac{1\ mol\ C_6H_{12}O_6}{180.16\ g\ C_6H_{12}O_6} = 0.15\underline{7}638\ mol\ C_6H_{12}O_6$$

$$M = \frac{\text{amount solute (moles)}}{\text{volume solution (L)}} = \frac{0.15\underline{7}638\ mol\ C_6H_{12}O_6}{0.378\ L} = 0.417\ M$$

Check: The units (M) are correct. The magnitude of the answer (0.4 M) seems reasonable because we have 1/8 mole in about 1/3 L.

(b) **Given:** 28.4 g of glucose ($C_6H_{12}O_6$) in 355 g water; final volume = 378 mL   **Find:** molality
Conceptual Plan: $g_{H_2O} \rightarrow kg_{H_2O}$ and $g_{C_6H_{12}O_6} \rightarrow mol_{C_6H_{12}O_6}$ then $mol_{C_6H_{12}O_6}, kg_{H_2O} \rightarrow m$

$$\frac{1\ kg}{1000\ g} \qquad \frac{1\ mol\ C_6H_{12}O_6}{180.16\ g\ C_6H_{12}O_6} \qquad m = \frac{\text{amount solute (moles)}}{\text{mass solvent (kg)}}$$

Solution: $355\ g \times \dfrac{1\ kg}{1000\ g} = 0.355\ kg$ and

$$28.4\ g\ C_6H_{12}O_6 \times \frac{1\ mol\ C_6H_{12}O_6}{180.16\ g\ C_6H_{12}O_6} = 0.15\underline{7}638\ mol\ C_6H_{12}O_6$$

$$m = \frac{\text{amount solute (moles)}}{\text{mass solvent (kg)}} = \frac{0.15\underline{7}638\ mol\ C_6H_{12}O_6}{0.355\ kg} = 0.444\ m$$

Check: The units (m) are correct. The magnitude of the answer (0.4 m) seems reasonable because we have 1/8 mole in about 1/3 kg.

(c) **Given:** 28.4 g of glucose ($C_6H_{12}O_6$) in 355 g water; final volume = 378 mL   **Find:** percent by mass
Conceptual Plan: $g_{C_6H_{12}O_6}, g_{H_2O} \rightarrow g_{soln}$ then $g_{C_6H_{12}O_6}, g_{soln} \rightarrow$ **percent by mass**

$$g_{soln} = g_{C_6H_{12}O_6} + g_{H_2O} \qquad \text{mass percent} = \frac{\text{mass solute}}{\text{mass solution}} \times 100\%$$

Solution: $g_{soln} = g_{C_6H_{12}O_6} + g_{H_2O} = 28.4\ g + 355\ g = 38\underline{3}.4\ g\ soln$ then

$$\text{mass percent} = \frac{\text{mass solute}}{\text{mass solution}} \times 100\% = \frac{28.4\ g\ C_6H_{12}O_6}{38\underline{3}.4\ g\ soln} \times 100\% = 7.41\%\ \text{by mass}$$

Check: The units (percent by mass) are correct. The magnitude of the answer (7%) seems reasonable because we are dissolving 28 g in 355 g.

(d) **Given:** 28.4 g of glucose ($C_6H_{12}O_6$) in 355 g water; final volume = 378 mL   **Find:** mole fraction
Conceptual Plan: $g_{C_6H_{12}O_6} \rightarrow mol_{C_6H_{12}O_6}$ and $g_{H_2O} \rightarrow mol_{H_2O}$ then $mol_{C_6H_{12}O_6}, mol_{H_2O} \rightarrow \chi_{C_6H_{12}O_6}$

$$\frac{1\ mol\ C_6H_{12}O_6}{180.16\ g\ C_6H_{12}O_6} \qquad \frac{1\ mol\ H_2O}{18.02\ g\ H_2O} \qquad \chi = \frac{\text{amount solute (in moles)}}{\text{total amount of solute and solvent (in moles)}}$$

Solution: $28.4\ g\ C_6H_{12}O_6 \times \dfrac{1\ mol\ C_6H_{12}O_6}{180.16\ g\ C_6H_{12}O_6} = 0.15\underline{7}638\ mol\ C_6H_{12}O_6$ and

$$355\ g\ H_2O \times \frac{1\ mol\ H_2O}{18.02\ g\ H_2O} = 19.\underline{7}003\ mol\ H_2O\ \text{then}$$

$$\chi = \frac{\text{amount solute (in moles)}}{\text{total amount of solute and solvent (in moles)}} = \frac{0.15\underline{7}638\ mol}{0.15\underline{7}638\ mol + 19.\underline{7}003\ mol} = 0.00794$$

Check: The units (none) are correct. The magnitude of the answer (0.008) seems reasonable because we have many more grams of water and water has a much lower molecular weight.

(e) **Given:** 28.4 g of glucose ($C_6H_{12}O_6$) in 355 g water; final volume = 378 mL   **Find:** mole percent
Conceptual Plan: use answer from part (d) then $\chi_{C_6H_{12}O_6} \rightarrow$ **mole percent**
$$\chi \times 100\%$$

Solution: mole percent = $\chi \times 100\% = 0.00794 \times 100\% = 0.794$ mole percent

Check: The units (%) are correct. The magnitude of the answer (0.8) seems reasonable because we have many more grams of water, water has a much lower molecular weight than glucose, and we are increasing the answer from part (d) by a factor of 100.

12.36 (a) **Given:** 20.2 mL of methanol (CH_3OH) in 100.0 mL water; final volume = 118 mL   **Find:** molarity
Other: d (CH_3OH) = 0.782 g/mL; d (H_2O) = 1.00 g/mL
Conceptual Plan: mL $\rightarrow$ L and mL$_{CH_3OH}$ $\rightarrow$ g$_{CH_3OH}$ $\rightarrow$ mol$_{CH_3OH}$ then mol$_{CH_3OH}$, $V \rightarrow$ M
$$\frac{1\ L}{1000\ mL} \qquad \frac{0.782\ g}{1\ mL} \qquad \frac{1\ mol\ CH_3OH}{32.04\ g\ CH_3OH} \qquad M = \frac{\text{amount solute (moles)}}{\text{volume solution (L)}}$$

Solution: $118\ mL \times \dfrac{1\ L}{1000\ mL} = 0.118$ L and

$$20.2\ mL\ CH_3OH \times \frac{0.782\ g\ CH_3OH}{1\ mL\ CH_3OH} \times \frac{1\ mol\ CH_3OH}{32.04\ g\ CH_3OH} = 0.49\underline{3}021\ mol\ CH_3OH$$

$$M = \frac{\text{amount solute (moles)}}{\text{volume solution (L)}} = \frac{0.49\underline{3}021\ mol\ CH_3OH}{0.118\ L} = 4.18\ M$$

Check: The units (M) are correct. The magnitude of the answer (4 M) seems reasonable because we have 1/2 mole in about 1/8 L.

(b) **Given:** 20.2 mL of methanol (CH_3OH) in 100.0 mL water; final volume = 118 mL   **Find:** molality
Other: $d(CH_3OH)$ = 0.782 g/mL; $d(H_2O)$ = 1.00 g/mL
Conceptual Plan:
mL$_{CH_3OH}$ $\rightarrow$ g$_{CH_3OH}$ $\rightarrow$ mol$_{CH_3OH}$ and mL$_{H_2O}$ $\rightarrow$ g$_{H_2O}$ $\rightarrow$ kg$_{H_2O}$ then mol$_{CH_3OH}$, kg$_{H_2O}$ $\rightarrow$ m
$$\frac{0.782\ g}{1\ mL} \quad \frac{1\ mol\ CH_3OH}{32.04\ g\ CH_3OH} \qquad \frac{1.00\ g}{1\ mL} \quad \frac{1\ kg}{1000\ g} \qquad m = \frac{\text{amount solute (moles)}}{\text{mass solvent (kg)}}$$

Solution: $20.2\ mL\ CH_3OH \times \dfrac{0.782\ g\ CH_3OH}{1\ mL\ CH_3OH} \times \dfrac{1\ mol\ CH_3OH}{32.04\ g\ CH_3OH} = 0.49\underline{3}021\ mol\ CH_3OH$ and

$$100.0\ mL \times \frac{1.00\ g}{1\ mL} \times \frac{1\ kg}{1000\ g} = 0.1000\ kg\ \text{then}$$

$$m = \frac{\text{amount solute (moles)}}{\text{mass solvent (kg)}} = \frac{0.49\underline{3}021\ mol\ CH_3OH}{0.1000\ kg} = 4.93\ m$$

Check: The units (m) are correct. The magnitude of the answer (5 m) seems reasonable because we have 1/2 mole in 1/10 kg.

(c) **Given:** 20.2 mL of methanol (CH_3OH) in 100.0 mL water; final volume = 118 mL   **Find:** percent by mass
Other: d (CH_3OH) = 0.782 g/mL; d (H_2O) = 1.00 g/mL
Conceptual Plan: mL$_{CH_3OH}$ $\rightarrow$ g$_{CH_3OH}$ and mL$_{H_2O}$ $\rightarrow$ g$_{H_2O}$ then g$_{CH_3OH}$, g$_{H_2O}$ $\rightarrow$ g$_{soln}$ then
$$\frac{0.782\ g}{1\ mL} \qquad \frac{1.00\ g}{1\ mL} \qquad g_{soln} = g_{CH_3OH} + g_{H_2O}$$

g$_{CH_3OH}$, g$_{soln}$ $\rightarrow$ percent by mass
$$\text{mass percent} = \frac{\text{mass solute}}{\text{mass solution}} \times 100\%$$

Solution: $20.2\ mL\ CH_3OH \times \dfrac{0.782\ g\ CH_3OH}{1\ mL\ CH_3OH} = 15.\underline{7}964\ g\ CH_3OH$

$100.0\ mL \times \dfrac{1.00\ g}{1\ mL} = 100.0$ g. $g_{soln} = g_{CH_3OH} + g_{H_2O} = 15.\underline{7}964\ g + 100.0\ g = 115.\underline{7}964\ g_{soln}$ then

$$\text{mass percent} = \frac{\text{mass solute}}{\text{mass solution}} \times 100\% = \frac{15.\underline{7}964\ g\ CH_3OH}{115.\underline{7}964\ g\ soln} \times 100\% = 13.6\%\ \text{by mass}$$

Check: The units (percent by mass) are correct. The magnitude of the answer (14%) seems reasonable because we are dissolving 16 g in 100 g.

(d)   **Given:** 20.2 mL of methanol (CH_3OH) in 100.0 mL water; final volume = 118 mL   **Find:** mole fraction
Other: d (CH_3OH) = 0.782 g/mL; d (H_2O) = 1.00 g/mL
Conceptual Plan: $mL_{CH_3OH} \rightarrow g_{CH_3OH} \rightarrow mol_{CH_3OH}$ and $mL_{H_2O} \rightarrow g_{H_2O} \rightarrow mol_{H_2O}$ then

$$\frac{0.782 \text{ g}}{1 \text{ mL}} \quad \frac{1 \text{ mol } CH_3OH}{32.04 \text{ g } CH_3OH} \qquad \frac{1.00 \text{ g}}{1 \text{ mL}} \quad \frac{1 \text{ mol } H_2O}{18.02 \text{ g } H_2O}$$

$mol_{CH_3OH}, mol_{H_2O} \rightarrow \chi_{CH_3OH}$

$$\chi = \frac{\text{amount solute (in moles)}}{\text{total amount of solute and solvent (in moles)}}$$

Solution: $20.2 \text{ mL } CH_3OH \times \dfrac{0.782 \text{ g } CH_3OH}{1 \text{ mL } CH_3OH} \times \dfrac{1 \text{ mol } CH_3OH}{32.04 \text{ g } CH_3OH} = 0.49\underline{3}021 \text{ mol } CH_3OH$ and

$100.0 \text{ mL} \times \dfrac{1.00 \text{ g}}{1 \text{ mL}} \times \dfrac{1 \text{ mol } H_2O}{18.02 \text{ g } H_2O} = 5.54\underline{9}390 \text{ mol } H_2O$ then

$$\chi = \frac{\text{amount solute (in moles)}}{\text{total amount of solute and solvent (in moles)}} = \frac{0.49\underline{3}021 \text{ mol}}{0.49\underline{3}021 \text{ mol} + 5.54\underline{9}390 \text{ mol}} = 0.0816$$

Check: The units (none) are correct. The magnitude of the answer (0.08) seems reasonable because we have many more grams of water and water has a lower molecular weight than methanol.

(e)   **Given:** 20.2 mL of methanol (CH_3OH) in 100.0 mL water; final volume = 118 mL   **Find:** mole percent
Other: d (CH_3OH) = 0.782 g/mL; d (H_2O) = 1.00 g/mL
Conceptual Plan: use answer from part (d) then $\chi_{CH_3OH} \rightarrow$ **mole percent**

$$\chi \times 100\%$$

Solution: mole percent = $\chi \times 100\% = 0.0816 \times 100\% = 8.16$ mole percent

Check: The units (%) are correct. The magnitude of the answer (8) seems reasonable because we have many more grams of water, water has a lower molecular weight than methanol, and we are increasing the answer from part (d) by a factor of 100.

12.37   **Given:** 3.0% H_2O_2 by mass, d = 1.01 g/mL   **Find:** molarity
Conceptual Plan:
Assume exactly 100 g of solution; $g_{solution} \rightarrow g_{H_2O_2} \rightarrow mol_{H_2O_2}$ and $g_{solution} \rightarrow mL_{solution} \rightarrow L_{solution}$

$$\frac{3.0 \text{ g } H_2O_2}{100 \text{ g solution}} \quad \frac{1 \text{ mol } H_2O_2}{34.02 \text{ g } H_2O_2} \qquad \frac{1 \text{ mL}}{1.01 \text{ g}} \quad \frac{1 \text{ L}}{1000 \text{ mL}}$$

then $mol_{H_2O_2}, L_{solution} \rightarrow$ **M**

$$M = \frac{\text{amount solute (moles)}}{\text{volume solution (L)}}$$

Solution: $100 \text{ g solution} \times \dfrac{3.0 \text{ g } H_2O_2}{100 \text{ g solution}} \times \dfrac{1 \text{ mol } H_2O_2}{34.02 \text{ g } H_2O_2} = 0.08\underline{8}1834 \text{ mol } H_2O_2$ and

$100 \text{ g solution} \times \dfrac{1 \text{ mL solution}}{1.01 \text{ g solution}} \times \dfrac{1 \text{ L solution}}{1000 \text{ mL solution}} = 0.0990\underline{0}99 \text{ L solution}$ then

$M = \dfrac{\text{amount solute (moles)}}{\text{volume solution (L)}} = \dfrac{0.08\underline{8}1834 \text{ mol } H_2O_2}{0.0990\underline{0}99 \text{ L solution}} = 0.89 \text{ M } H_2O_2.$

Check: The units (M) are correct. The magnitude of the answer (1) seems reasonable because we are starting with a low concentration solution and pure water is ~55.5 M.

12.38   **Given:** 4.55% NaOCl by mass, d = 1.02 g/mL   **Find:** molarity
Conceptual Plan: Assume exactly 100 g of solution; $g_{solution} \rightarrow g_{NaOCl} \rightarrow mol_{NaOCl}$ **and** $g_{solution} \rightarrow$

$$\frac{4.55 \text{ g NaOCl}}{100 \text{ g solution}} \quad \frac{1 \text{ mol NaOCl}}{74.44 \text{ g NaOCl}} \qquad \frac{1 \text{ mL}}{1.02 \text{ g}}$$

$mL_{solution} \rightarrow L_{solution}$ **then** $mol_{NaOCl}, L_{solution} \rightarrow$ **M**

$$\frac{1 \text{ L}}{1000 \text{ mL}} \qquad M = \frac{\text{amount solute (moles)}}{\text{volume solution (L)}}$$

Solution: $100 \text{ g solution} \times \dfrac{4.55 \text{ g NaOCl}}{100 \text{ g solution}} \times \dfrac{1 \text{ mol NaOCl}}{74.44 \text{ g NaOCl}} = 0.061\underline{1}2305 \text{ mol NaOCl}$ and

$100 \text{ g solution} \times \dfrac{1 \text{ mL solution}}{1.02 \text{ g solution}} \times \dfrac{1 \text{ L solution}}{1000 \text{ mL solution}} = 0.098\underline{0}392 \text{ L solution}$ then

$$M = \frac{\text{amount solute (moles)}}{\text{volume solution (L)}} = \frac{0.06\underline{1}12305 \text{ mol NaOCl}}{0.0980392 \text{ L solution}} = 0.623 \text{ M NaOCl}$$

Check: The units (M) are correct. The magnitude of the answer (1) seems reasonable because we are starting with a low concentration solution and pure water is ~ 55.5 M.

12.39   **Given:** 36% HCl by mass   **Find:** molality and mole fraction

Conceptual Plan: Assume exactly 100 g of solution; $g_{\text{solution}} \rightarrow g_{\text{HCl}} \rightarrow \text{mol}_{\text{HCl}}$ **and** $g_{\text{HCl}}, g_{\text{solution}} \rightarrow$

$$\frac{36 \text{ g HCl}}{100 \text{ g solution}} \quad \frac{1 \text{ mol HCl}}{36.46 \text{ g HCl}} \qquad g_{\text{soln}} = g_{\text{HCl}} + g_{\text{H}_2\text{O}}$$

$g_{\text{solvent}} \rightarrow \text{kg}_{\text{solvent}}$ **then** $\text{mol}_{\text{HCl}}, \text{kg}_{\text{solvent}} \rightarrow m$ **and** $g_{\text{solvent}} \rightarrow \text{mol}_{\text{solvent}}$ **then** $\text{mol}_{\text{HCl}}, \text{mol}_{\text{solvent}} \rightarrow \chi_{\text{HCl}}$

$$\frac{1 \text{ kg}}{1000 \text{ g}} \qquad m = \frac{\text{amount solute (moles)}}{\text{mass solvent (kg)}} \quad \frac{1 \text{ mol H}_2\text{O}}{18.02 \text{ g H}_2\text{O}} \qquad \chi = \frac{\text{amount solute (in moles)}}{\text{total amount of solute and solvent (in moles)}}$$

Solution: $100 \text{ g solution} \times \dfrac{36 \text{ g HCl}}{100 \text{ g solution}} = 36 \text{ g HCl} \times \dfrac{1 \text{ mol HCl}}{36.46 \text{ g HCl}} = 0.9\underline{8}7383 \text{ mol HCl and}$

$g_{\text{soln}} = g_{\text{HCl}} + g_{\text{H}_2\text{O}}$. Rearrange to solve for g_{solvent}. $g_{\text{H}_2\text{O}} = g_{\text{soln}} - g_{\text{HCl}} = 100 \text{ g} - 36 \text{ g} = 64 \text{ g H}_2\text{O}$

$$64 \text{ g H}_2\text{O} \times \frac{1 \text{ kg H}_2\text{O}}{1000 \text{ g H}_2\text{O}} = 0.064 \text{ kg H}_2\text{O} \text{ then}$$

$$m = \frac{\text{amount solute (moles)}}{\text{mass solvent (kg)}} = \frac{0.9\underline{8}7383 \text{ mol HCl}}{0.064 \text{ kg}} = 15 \, m \text{ HCl and}$$

$$64 \text{ g H}_2\text{O} \times \frac{1 \text{ mol H}_2\text{O}}{18.02 \text{ g H}_2\text{O}} = 3.\underline{5}5161 \text{ mol H}_2\text{O} \text{ then}$$

$$\chi = \frac{\text{amount solute (in moles)}}{\text{total amount of solute and solvent (in moles)}} = \frac{0.9\underline{8}7383 \text{ mol}}{0.9\underline{8}7383 \text{ mol} + 3.\underline{5}5161 \text{ mol}} = 0.22$$

Check: The units (m and unitless) are correct. The magnitude of the answers (15 and 0.2) seems reasonable because we are starting with a high concentration solution and the molar mass of water is much less than that of HCl.

12.40   **Given:** 5.0% NaCl by mass   **Find:** molality and mole fraction

Conceptual Plan: Assume exactly 100 g of solution; $g_{\text{solution}} \rightarrow g_{\text{NaCl}} \rightarrow \text{mol}_{\text{NaCl}}$ **and** $g_{\text{NaCl}}, g_{\text{solution}} \rightarrow$

$$\frac{5.0 \text{ g NaCl}}{100 \text{ g solution}} \quad \frac{1 \text{ mol NaCl}}{58.44 \text{ g NaCl}} \qquad g_{\text{soln}} = g_{\text{NaCl}} + g_{\text{H}_2\text{O}}$$

$g_{\text{solvent}} \rightarrow \text{kg}_{\text{solvent}}$ **then** $\text{mol}_{\text{NaCl}}, \text{kg}_{\text{solvent}} \rightarrow m$ **and** $g_{\text{solvent}} \rightarrow \text{mol}_{\text{solvent}}$ **then** $\text{mol}_{\text{NaCl}}, \text{mol}_{\text{solvent}} \rightarrow \chi_{\text{NaCl}}$

$$\frac{1 \text{ kg}}{1000 \text{ g}} \qquad m = \frac{\text{amount solute (moles)}}{\text{mass solvent (kg)}} \quad \frac{1 \text{ mol H}_2\text{O}}{18.02 \text{ g H}_2\text{O}} \qquad \chi = \frac{\text{amount solute (in moles)}}{\text{total amount of solute and solvent (in moles)}}$$

Solution: $100 \text{ g solution} \times \dfrac{5.0 \text{ g NaCl}}{100 \text{ g solution}} = 5.0 \text{ g NaCl} \times \dfrac{1 \text{ mol NaCl}}{58.44 \text{ g NaCl}} = 0.08\underline{5}5578 \text{ mol NaCl and}$

$g_{\text{soln}} = g_{\text{NaCl}} + g_{\text{H}_2\text{O}}$. Rearrange to solve for g_{solvent}. $g_{\text{H}_2\text{O}} = g_{\text{soln}} - g_{\text{NaCl}} = 100.0 \text{ g} - 5.0 \text{ g} = 95.0 \text{ g H}_2\text{O}$

$$95.0 \text{ g H}_2\text{O} \times \frac{1 \text{ kg H}_2\text{O}}{1000 \text{ g H}_2\text{O}} = 0.0950 \text{ kg H}_2\text{O} \text{ then}$$

$$m = \frac{\text{amount solute (moles)}}{\text{mass solvent (kg)}} = \frac{0.08\underline{5}5578 \text{ mol NaCl}}{0.0950 \text{ kg}} = 0.901 \, m \text{ NaCl and}$$

$$95.0 \text{ g H}_2\text{O} \times \frac{1 \text{ mol H}_2\text{O}}{18.02 \text{ g H}_2\text{O}} = 5.\underline{2}7192 \text{ mol H}_2\text{O} \text{ then}$$

$$\chi = \frac{\text{amount solute (in moles)}}{\text{total amount of solute and solvent (in moles)}} = \frac{0.08\underline{5}5578 \text{ mol}}{0.08\underline{5}5578 \text{ mol} + 5.\underline{2}7192 \text{ mol}} = 0.016$$

Check: The units (m and unitless) are correct. The magnitude of the answers (1 and 0.02) seems reasonable because we are starting with a low-concentration solution and the molar mass of water is much less than that of NaCl.

Vapor Pressure of Solutions

12.41   The level has decreased more in the beaker filled with pure water. The dissolved salt in the seawater decreases the vapor pressure and subsequently lowers the rate of vaporization.

12.42   (b) Assume that the solutions obey Raoult's law ($P_{\text{solution}} = \chi_{\text{solvent}} P^{\circ}_{\text{solvent}}$). Each of the solutions has the same amount of solvent, so we need to compare the number of moles of particles in the solvent. Without doing any calculations, we can see that (b) will have a lower number of particles than (a) because (b) has the higher molecular weight. Potassium acetate will generate ~2 moles of particles per mole of the salt, so it will generate more than the other two. So solution (b) will have the highest vapor pressure.

12.43   **Given:** 28.5 g of glycerin ($C_3H_8O_3$) in 125 mL water at 30 °C; $P^{\circ}_{H_2O} = 31.8$ torr   **Find:** P_{H_2O}

Other: $d(H_2O) = 1.00$ g/mL; glycerin is not ionic solid

Conceptual Plan: $g_{C_3H_8O_3} \rightarrow \text{mol}_{C_3H_8O_3}$ and $\text{mL}_{H_2O} \rightarrow g_{H_2O} \rightarrow \text{mol}_{H_2O}$ then $\text{mol}_{C_3H_8O_3}, \text{mol}_{H_2O} \rightarrow \chi_{H_2O}$

$$\frac{1 \text{ mol } C_3H_8O_3}{92.09 \text{ g } C_3H_8O_3} \qquad\qquad \frac{1.00 \text{ g}}{1 \text{ mL}} \quad \frac{1 \text{ mol } H_2O}{18.02 \text{ g } H_2O} \qquad\qquad \chi = \frac{\text{amount solute (in moles)}}{\text{total amount of solute and solvent (in moles)}}$$

then $\chi_{H_2O}, P^{\circ}_{H_2O} \rightarrow P_{H_2O}$

$$P_{\text{solution}} = \chi_{\text{solvent}} P^{\circ}_{\text{solvent}}$$

Solution: $28.5 \text{ g } C_3H_8O_3 \times \dfrac{1 \text{ mol } C_3H_8O_3}{92.09 \text{ g } C_3H_8O_3} = 0.30\underline{9}4799 \text{ mol } C_3H_8O_3$ and

$125 \text{ mL} \times \dfrac{1.00 \text{ g}}{1 \text{ mL}} \times \dfrac{1 \text{ mol } H_2O}{18.02 \text{ g } H_2O} = 6.9\underline{3}6737 \text{ mol } H_2O$ then

$\chi = \dfrac{\text{amount solute (in moles)}}{\text{total amount of solute and solvent (in moles)}} = \dfrac{6.9\underline{3}6737 \text{ mol}}{0.30\underline{9}4799 \text{ mol} + 6.9\underline{3}6737 \text{ mol}} = 0.957\underline{2}91$ then

$P_{\text{solution}} = \chi_{\text{solvent}} P^{\circ}_{\text{solvent}} = 0.957\underline{2}91 \times 31.8 \text{ torr} = 30.4 \text{ torr}$

Check: The units (torr) are correct. The magnitude of the answer (30 torr) seems reasonable because it is a drop from the pure vapor pressure. Very few moles of glycerin are added, so the pressure will not drop much.

12.44   **Given:** 10.85% naphthalene ($C_{10}H_8$) by mass in hexane (C_6H_{14}) at 25 °C; $P^{\circ}_{C_6H_{14}} = 151$ torr   **Find:** $P_{C_6H_{14}}$

Conceptual Plan: % naphthalene ($C_{10}H_8$) by mass $\rightarrow g_{C_{10}H_8}$, $g_{C_6H_{14}}$ then $g_{C_{10}H_8} \rightarrow \text{mol}_{C_{10}H_8}$ and

$$\frac{10.85 \text{ g } C_{10}H_8}{100 \text{ g } (C_{10}H_8 + C_6H_{14})} \qquad\qquad \frac{1 \text{ mol } C_{10}H_8}{128.16 \text{ g } C_{10}H_8}$$

$g_{C_6H_{14}} \rightarrow \text{mol}_{C_6H_{14}}$ then $\text{mol}_{C_{10}H_8}, \text{mol}_{C_6H_{14}} \rightarrow \chi_{C_6H_{14}}$ then $\chi_{C_6H_{14}}, P^{\circ}_{C_6H_{14}} \rightarrow P_{C_6H_{14}}$

$$\frac{1 \text{ mol } C_6H_{14}}{86.17 \text{ g } C_6H_{14}} \qquad \chi = \frac{\text{amount solute (in moles)}}{\text{total amount of solute and solvent (in moles)}} \qquad P_{\text{solution}} = \chi_{\text{solvent}} P^{\circ}_{\text{solvent}}$$

Solution: $\dfrac{10.85 \text{ g } C_{10}H_8}{100 \text{ g } (C_{10}H_8 + C_6H_{14})}$ means 10.85 g $C_{10}H_8$ and $(100 \text{ g} - 10.85 \text{ g}) = 89.15 \text{ g} C_6H_{14}$ then

$10.85 \text{ g } C_{10}H_8 \times \dfrac{1 \text{ mol } C_{10}H_8}{128.16 \text{ g } C_{10}H_8} = 0.0846\underline{5}980 \text{ mol } C_{10}H_8$ and

$89.15 \text{ g } C_6H_{14} \times \dfrac{1 \text{ mol } C_6H_{14}}{86.17 \text{ g } C_6H_{14}} = 1.03\underline{4}583 \text{ mol } C_6H_{14}$ then

$\chi = \dfrac{\text{amount solute (in moles)}}{\text{total amount of solute and solvent (in moles)}} = \dfrac{1.034583 \text{ mol}}{0.0846\underline{5}980 \text{ mol} + 1.03\underline{4}583 \text{ mol}} = 0.924\underline{3}598$ then

$P_{\text{solution}} = \chi_{\text{solvent}} P^{\circ}_{\text{solvent}} = 0.924\underline{3}598 \times 151 \text{ torr} = 140. \text{ torr } C_6H_{14}$

Check: The units (torr) are correct. The magnitude of the answer (140 torr) seems reasonable because it is a drop from the pure vapor pressure. Only a fraction of a mole of naphthalene is added, so the pressure will not drop much.

12.45   (a)   **Given:** 50.0 g of heptane (C_7H_{16}) and 50.0 g of octane (C_8H_{18}) at 25 °C; $P^{\circ}_{C_7H_{16}} = 45.8$ torr; $P^{\circ}_{C_8H_{18}} = 10.9$ torr

Find: $P_{C_7H_{16}}, P_{C_8H_{18}}$

Conceptual Plan: $g_{C_7H_{16}} \rightarrow \text{mol}_{C_7H_{16}}$ and $g_{C_8H_{18}} \rightarrow \text{mol}_{C_8H_{18}}$ then $\text{mol}_{C_7H_{16}}$,

$$\frac{1 \text{ mol } C_7H_{16}}{100.20 \text{ g } C_7H_{16}} \quad \frac{1 \text{ mol } C_8H_{18}}{114.22 \text{ g } C_8H_{18}} \quad \chi_{C_7H_{16}} = \frac{\text{amount } C_7H_{16} \text{ (in moles)}}{\text{total amount (in moles)}}$$

$\text{mol}_{C_8H_{18}} \rightarrow \chi_{C_7H_{16}}, \chi_{C_8H_{18}}$ then $\chi_{C_7H_{16}}, P^{\circ}_{C_7H_{16}} \rightarrow P_{C_7H_{16}}$ and $\chi_{C_8H_{18}}, P^{\circ}_{C_8H_{18}} \rightarrow P_{C_8H_{18}}$

$$\chi_{C_8H_{18}} = 1 - \chi_{C_7H_{16}} \qquad\qquad P_{C_7H_{16}} = \chi_{C_7H_{16}} P^{\circ}_{C_7H_{16}} \qquad\qquad P_{C_8H_{18}} = \chi_{C_8H_{18}} P^{\circ}_{C_8H_{18}}$$

Solution: $50.0 \text{ g } C_7H_{16} \times \dfrac{1 \text{ mol } C_7H_{16}}{100.20 \text{ g } C_7H_{16}} = 0.499\underline{0}02 \text{ mol } C_7H_{16}$ and

$50.0 \text{ g } C_8H_{18} \times \dfrac{1 \text{ mol } C_8H_{18}}{114.22 \text{ g } C_8H_{18}} = 0.43\underline{7}752 \text{ mol } C_8H_{18}$ then

$$\chi_{C_7H_{16}} = \frac{\text{amount C}_7\text{H}_{16} \text{ (in moles)}}{\text{total amount (in moles)}} = \frac{0.499002 \text{ mol}}{0.499002 \text{ mol} + 0.437752 \text{ mol}} = 0.532693 \text{ and}$$

$$\chi_{C_8H_{18}} = 1 - \chi_{C_7H_{16}} = 1 - 0.532693 = 0.467307 \text{ then}$$

$$P_{C_7H_{16}} = \chi_{C_7H_{16}} P^\circ_{C_7H_{16}} = 0.532693 \times 45.8 \text{ torr} = 24.4 \text{ torr and}$$

$$P_{C_8H_{18}} = \chi_{C_8H_{18}} P^\circ_{C_8H_{18}} = 0.467307 \times 10.9 \text{ torr} = 5.09 \text{ torr}$$

Check: The units (torr) are correct. The magnitude of the answers (24 and 5 torr) seems reasonable because we expect a drop in half from the pure vapor pressures because we have roughly a 50:50 mole ratio of the two components.

(b) **Find:** P_{Total}

Conceptual Plan: $P_{C_7H_{16}}, P_{C_8H_{18}} \rightarrow P_{\text{Total}}$

$$P_{\text{Total}} = P_{C_7H_{16}} + P_{C_8H_{18}}$$

Solution: $P_{\text{Total}} = P_{C_7H_{16}} + P_{C_8H_{18}} = 24.4 \text{ torr} + 5.09 \text{ torr} = 29.5 \text{ torr}$

Check: The units (torr) are correct. The magnitude of the answer (30 torr) seems reasonable considering the two pressures.

(c) **Find:** mass percent composition of the gas phase

Conceptual Plan: because $n \propto P$ and we are calculating a mass percent, which is a ratio of masses, we can simply convert 1 torr to 1 mole so

$$P_{C_7H_{16}}, P_{C_8H_{18}} \rightarrow n_{C_7H_{16}}, n_{C_8H_{18}} \text{ then } \text{mol}_{C_7H_{16}} \rightarrow g_{C_7H_{16}} \text{ and } \text{mol}_{C_8H_{18}} \rightarrow g_{C_8H_{18}}$$

$$\frac{100.20 \text{ g C}_7\text{H}_{16}}{1 \text{ mol C}_7\text{H}_{16}} \qquad \frac{114.22 \text{ g C}_8\text{H}_{18}}{1 \text{ mol C}_8\text{H}_{18}}$$

then $g_{C_7H_{16}}, g_{C_8H_{18}} \rightarrow$ **mass percents**

$$\text{mass percent} = \frac{\text{mass solute}}{\text{mass solution}} \times 100\%$$

Solution: so $n_{C_7H_{16}} = 24.4 \text{ mol}$ and $n_{C_8H_{18}} = 5.09 \text{ mol}$ then

$$24.4 \text{ mol C}_7\text{H}_{16} \times \frac{100.20 \text{ g C}_7\text{H}_{16}}{1 \text{ mol C}_7\text{H}_{16}} = 2444.88 \text{ g C}_7\text{H}_{16} \text{ and}$$

$$5.09 \text{ mol C}_8\text{H}_{18} \times \frac{114.22 \text{ g C}_8\text{H}_{18}}{1 \text{ mol C}_8\text{H}_{18}} = 581.380 \text{ g C}_8\text{H}_{18} \text{ then}$$

$$\text{mass percent} = \frac{\text{mass solute}}{\text{mass solution}} \times 100\% = \frac{2444.88 \text{ g C}_7\text{H}_{16}}{2444.88 \text{ g C}_7\text{H}_{16} + 581.380 \text{ g C}_8\text{H}_{18}} \times 100\%$$

$$= 80.8\% \text{ by mass C}_7\text{H}_{16}$$

then $100\% - 80.8\% = 19.2\%$ by mass C_8H_{18}

Check: The units (%) are correct. The magnitude of the answers (81% and 19%) seems reasonable considering the two pressures.

The two mass percents are different because the vapor is richer in the more volatile component (the lighter molecule).

12.46 **Given:** pentane (C_5H_{12}) and hexane (C_6H_{14}) $P_{\text{Total}} = 258 \text{ torr}; P^\circ_{C_5H_{12}} = 425 \text{ torr}; P^\circ_{C_6H_{14}} = 151 \text{ torr at } 25 \text{ °C}$

Find: $\chi_{C_5H_{12}}, \chi_{C_6H_{14}}$

Conceptual Plan: $P_{\text{Total}} = P_{C_5H_{12}} + P_{C_6H_{14}}$ where $P_{C_5H_{12}} = \chi_{C_5H_{12}} P^\circ_{C_5H_{12}}$ and $P_{C_6H_{14}} = \chi_{C_6H_{14}} P^\circ_{C_6H_{14}}$ but

$\chi_{C_6H_{14}} = 1 - \chi_{C_5H_{12}}$ so $P_{\text{Total}} = \chi_{C_5H_{12}} P^\circ_{C_5H_{12}} + (1 - \chi_{C_5H_{12}}) P^\circ_{C_6H_{14}}$ **substitute in values and solve for**

$\chi_{C_5H_{12}}, \chi_{C_6H_{14}}$

Solution: $P_{\text{Total}} = \chi_{C_5H_{12}} P^\circ_{C_5H_{12}} + (1 - \chi_{C_5H_{12}}) P^\circ_{C_6H_{14}}$ so

$258 \text{ torr} = \chi_{C_5H_{12}} 425 \text{ torr} + (1 - \chi_{C_5H_{12}}) 151 \text{ torr} \rightarrow 258 - 151 = \chi_{C_5H_{12}}(425 - 151) \rightarrow$

$$\chi_{C_5H_{12}} = \frac{107}{274} = 0.391 \text{ and } \chi_{C_6H_{14}} = 1 - \chi_{C_5H_{12}} = 1 - 0.391 = 0.609$$

Check: The units (none) are correct. The magnitude of the answers (0.4 and 0.6) seems reasonable because the total vapor pressure is closer to the vapor pressure of hexane, so we expect more hexane in the liquid.

12.47   **Given:** 5.50% NaCl by mass   **Find:** P_{H_2O}
         Other: $P^{\circ}_{H_2O} = 23.78$ torr at 25 °C
         Conceptual Plan: Assume exactly 100 g of solution;

         $g_{Solution} \rightarrow g_{NaCl}, \rightarrow mol_{NaCl} \rightarrow mol_{ions}$ **and** $g_{NaCl}, \; g_{Solution} \rightarrow g_{H_2O} \rightarrow mol_{H_2O}$

         $\dfrac{5.50 \text{ g NaCl}}{100 \text{ g solution}} \quad \dfrac{1 \text{ mol NaCl}}{58.44 \text{ g NaCl}} \quad \dfrac{2 \text{ mol ions}}{1 \text{ mol NaCl}}$ $g_{Solution} = g_{NaCl} + g_{H_2O} \quad \dfrac{1 \text{ mol H}_2\text{O}}{18.02 \text{ g H}_2\text{O}}$

         then $mol_{ions}, \; mol_{H_2O} \rightarrow \chi_{H_2O}$ **then** $\chi_{H_2O}, P^{\circ}_{H_2O} \rightarrow P_{H_2O}$

         $\chi = \dfrac{\text{amount solute (in moles)}}{\text{total amount of solute and solvent (in moles)}}$ $P_{\text{solution}} = \chi_{\text{solvent}} P^{\circ}_{\text{solvent}}$

         Solution:

         $100 \text{ g solution} \times \dfrac{5.50 \text{ g NaCl}}{100 \text{ g solution}} = 5.50 \text{ g HCl} \times \dfrac{1 \text{ mol NaCl}}{58.44 \text{ g NaCl}} \times \dfrac{2 \text{ mol ions}}{1 \text{ mol NaCl}} = 0.18\underline{8}22724 \text{ mol ions and}$

         $g_{\text{solution}} = g_{NaCl} + g_{H_2O}$ Rearrange to solve for g_{H_2O}.

         $g_{H_2O} = g_{\text{solution}} - g_{NaCl} = 100.00 \text{ g} - 5.50 \text{ g} = 94.50 \text{ g}_{H_2O}$

         then $94.50 \text{ g H}_2\text{O} \times \dfrac{1 \text{ mol H}_2\text{O}}{18.02 \text{ g H}_2\text{O}} = 5.24\underline{4}173 \text{ mol H}_2\text{O}$ then

         $\chi = \dfrac{\text{amount solute (in moles)}}{\text{total amount of solute and solvent (in moles)}} = \dfrac{5.24\underline{4}173 \text{ mol}}{0.18\underline{8}22724 \text{ mol} + 5.24\underline{4}173 \text{ mol}} = 0.9653\underline{5}10$

         $P_{\text{solution}} = \chi_{\text{solvent}} P^{\circ}_{\text{solvent}} = 0.9653\underline{5}10 \times 23.78 \text{ torr} = 22.96 \text{ torr}$

         Check: The units (torr) are correct. The magnitude of the answer (23 torr) seems reasonable because we have a dilute solution, so the vapor decreases only a small amount.

12.48   **Given:** $P_{\text{solution}} = 81.6$ mmHg at 50 °C   **Find:** $CaCl_2$% by mass
         Other: $P^{\circ}_{H_2O} = 92.6$ torr at 50 °C
         Conceptual Plan: $P_{\text{solution}} \rightarrow \chi_{H_2O}$ **then assume exactly 1 mole of water (18.02 g water)**

         $P_{\text{solution}} = \chi_{\text{solvent}} P^{\circ}_{\text{solvent}}$

         $\chi_{H_2O} \rightarrow mol_{ions} \rightarrow mol_{CaCl_2} \rightarrow g_{CaCl_2}$ **then** $g_{CaCl_2}, \; g_{H_2O} \rightarrow CaCl_2$% **by mass**

         $\chi = \dfrac{\text{amount solute (in moles)}}{\text{total amount of solute and solvent (in moles)}} \quad \dfrac{1 \text{ mol CaCl}_2}{3 \text{ mol ions}} \quad \dfrac{110.98 \text{ g CaCl}_2}{1 \text{ mol CaCl}_2}$ % by mass $= \dfrac{\text{grams solute}}{\text{grams solute} + \text{grams solvent}} \times 100\%$

         Solution: $P_{\text{solution}} = \chi_{H_2O} P^{\circ}_{H_2O}$ Rearrange to solve for χ_{H_2O}. $\chi_{H_2O} = \dfrac{P_{\text{solution}}}{P^{\circ}_{H_2O}} = \dfrac{81.6 \text{ mmHg}}{92.6 \text{ mmHg}} = 0.88\underline{1}2095$

         Assume exactly 1 mole of water. $\chi = \dfrac{\text{moles of water}}{\text{moles of ions} + \text{moles water}}$ Rearrange to solve for the moles of ions.

         moles of ions $= \dfrac{\text{moles of water}}{\chi} - \text{moles water} = \dfrac{1}{0.88\underline{1}2095} - 1 = 0.13\underline{4}803$ mol ions then

         $0.13\underline{4}803 \text{ mol ions} \times \dfrac{1 \text{ mol CaCl}_2}{3 \text{ mol ions}} \times \dfrac{110.98 \text{ g CaCl}_2}{1 \text{ mol CaCl}_2} = 4.9\underline{8}685 \text{ g CaCl}_2$ then

         % by mass $= \dfrac{\text{grams solute}}{\text{grams solute} + \text{grams solvent}} \times 100\% = \dfrac{4.9\underline{8}685 \text{ g}}{4.9\underline{8}685 \text{ g} + 18.02 \text{ g}} \times 100\% = 21.\underline{6}755\% = 22\%$

         $CaCl_2$ by mass

         Check: The units (% by mass) are correct. The magnitude of the answer (22%) seems reasonable because there is a significant drop from the pure vapor pressure.

Freezing Point Depression, Boiling Point Elevation, and Osmosis

12.49   **Given:** 55.8 g of glucose ($C_6H_{12}O_6$) in 455 g water   **Find:** T_f and T_b **Other:** $K_f = 1.86$ °C/m; $K_b = 0.512$ °C/m;
         Conceptual Plan: $g_{H_2O} \rightarrow kg_{H_2O}$ **and** $g_{C_6H_{12}O_6} \rightarrow mol_{C_6H_{12}O_6}$ **then** $mol_{C_6H_{12}O_6}, \; kg_{H_2O} \rightarrow m$

         $\dfrac{1 \text{ kg}}{1000 \text{ g}}$ $\dfrac{1 \text{ mol C}_6\text{H}_{12}\text{O}_6}{180.16 \text{ g C}_6\text{H}_{12}\text{O}_6}$ $m = \dfrac{\text{amount solute (moles)}}{\text{mass solvent (kg)}}$

         $m, K_f \rightarrow \Delta T_f \rightarrow T_f$ **and** $m, K_b \rightarrow \Delta T_b \rightarrow T_b$

         $\Delta T_f = K_f \times m \quad T_f = T^{\circ}_f - \Delta T_f \quad\quad \Delta T_b = K_b \times m \quad \Delta T_b = T_b - T^{\circ}_b$

Solution: $455 \ \cancel{g} \times \dfrac{1 \ \text{kg}}{1000 \ \cancel{g}} = 0.455 \ \text{kg}$ and $55.8 \ \cancel{\text{g C}_6\text{H}_{12}\text{O}_6} \times \dfrac{1 \ \text{mol C}_6\text{H}_{12}\text{O}_6}{180.16 \ \cancel{\text{g C}_6\text{H}_{12}\text{O}_6}} = 0.30\underline{9}725 \ \text{mol C}_6\text{H}_{12}\text{O}_6$ then

$m = \dfrac{\text{amount solute (moles)}}{\text{mass solvent (kg)}} = \dfrac{0.30\underline{9}725 \ \text{mol C}_6\text{H}_{12}\text{O}_6}{0.455 \ \text{kg}} = 0.68\underline{0}714 \ m$ then

$\Delta T_f = K_f \times m = 1.86 \ \dfrac{°\text{C}}{\cancel{m}} \times 0.68\underline{0}714 \ \cancel{m} = 1.27 \ °\text{C}$ then $T_f = T_f° - \Delta T_f = 0.00 \ °\text{C} - 1.27 \ °\text{C} = -1.27 \ °\text{C}$ and

$\Delta T_b = K_b \times m = 0.512 \ \dfrac{°\text{C}}{\cancel{m}} \times 0.68\underline{0}714 \ \cancel{m} = 0.349 \ °\text{C}$ and $\Delta T_b = T_b - T_b°$ so

$T_b = T_b° + \Delta T_b = 100.000 \ °\text{C} + 0.349 \ °\text{C} = 100.349 \ °\text{C}$

Check: The units (°C) are correct. The magnitude of the answers seems reasonable because the molality is ~2/3. The shift in boiling point is less than the shift in freezing point because the constant for boiling is smaller than the constant for freezing.

12.50   **Given:** 21.2 g of ethylene glycol ($C_2H_6O_2$) in 85.4 g water   **Find:** T_f and T_b
      Other: $K_f = 1.86 \ °\text{C}/m$; $K_b = 0.512 \ °\text{C}/m$;
      Conceptual Plan: $g_{H_2O} \rightarrow kg_{H_2O}$ and $g_{C_2H_6O_2} \rightarrow mol_{C_2H_6O_2}$ then $mol_{C_6H_{12}O_6}, kg_{H_2O} \rightarrow m$

$$\dfrac{1 \ \text{kg}}{1000 \ \text{g}} \qquad\qquad \dfrac{1 \ \text{mol C}_2\text{H}_6\text{O}_2}{62.07 \ \text{g C}_2\text{H}_6\text{O}_2} \qquad\qquad m = \dfrac{\text{amount solute (moles)}}{\text{mass solvent (kg)}}$$

      $m, K_f \rightarrow \Delta T_f \rightarrow T_f$ and $m, K_b \rightarrow \Delta T_b \rightarrow T_b$
      $\Delta T_f = K_f \times m \quad T_f = T_f° - \Delta T_f \qquad \Delta T_b = K_b \times m \quad \Delta T_b = T_b - T_b°$

      Solution: $85.4 \ \cancel{g} \times \dfrac{1 \ \text{kg}}{1000 \ \cancel{g}} = 0.0854 \ \text{kg}$ and $21.2 \ \cancel{\text{g C}_2\text{H}_6\text{O}_2} \times \dfrac{1 \ \text{mol C}_2\text{H}_6\text{O}_2}{62.07 \ \cancel{\text{g C}_2\text{H}_6\text{O}_2}} = 0.34\underline{1}550 \ \text{mol C}_2\text{H}_6\text{O}_2$ then

$m = \dfrac{\text{amount solute (moles)}}{\text{mass solvent (kg)}} = \dfrac{0.34\underline{1}550 \ \text{mol C}_2\text{H}_6\text{O}_2}{0.0854 \ \text{kg}} = 3.9\underline{9}941 \ m$ then

$\Delta T_f = K_f \times m = 1.86 \ \dfrac{°\text{C}}{\cancel{m}} \times 3.9\underline{9}941 \ \cancel{m} = 7.44 \ °\text{C}$ then $T_f = T_f° - \Delta T_f = 0.00 \ °\text{C} - 7.44 \ °\text{C} = -7.44 \ °\text{C}$ and

$\Delta T_b = K_b \times m = 0.512 \ \dfrac{°\text{C}}{\cancel{m}} \times 3.9\underline{9}941 \ \cancel{m} = 2.05 \ °\text{C}$ and $\Delta T_b = T_b - T_b°$ so

$T_b = T_b° + \Delta T_b = 100.00 \ °\text{C} + 2.05 \ °\text{C} = 102.05 \ °\text{C}$

      Check: The units (°C) are correct. The magnitude of the answers seems reasonable because the molality is ~4. The shift in boiling point is less than the shift in freezing point because the constant for boiling is smaller than the constant for freezing.

12.51   **Given:** 10.0 g of naphthalene ($C_{10}H_8$) in 100.0 mL benzene (C_6H_6)   **Find:** T_f and T_b
      Other: $d(\text{benzene}) = 0.877 \ \text{g/cm}^3$; $K_f = 5.12 \ °\text{C}/m$; $K_b = 2.53 \ °\text{C}/m$; $T_f° = 5.5 \ °\text{C}$; $T_b° = 80.1 \ °\text{C}$
      Conceptual Plan: $mL_{C_6H_6} \rightarrow g_{C_6H_6} \rightarrow kg_{C_6H_6}$ and $g_{C_{10}H_8} \rightarrow mol_{C_{10}H_8}$ then $mol_{C_{10}H_8}, kg_{C_6H_6} \rightarrow m$

$$\dfrac{0.877 \ \text{g}}{1 \ \text{cm}^3} \quad \dfrac{1 \ \text{kg}}{1000 \ \text{g}} \qquad\qquad \dfrac{1 \ \text{mol C}_{10}\text{H}_8}{128.2 \ \text{g C}_{10}\text{H}_8} \qquad\qquad m = \dfrac{\text{amount solute (moles)}}{\text{mass solvent (kg)}}$$

      $m, K_f \rightarrow \Delta T_f \rightarrow T_f$ and $m, K_b \rightarrow \Delta T_b \rightarrow T_b$
      $\Delta T_f = K_f \times m \quad T_f = T_f° - \Delta T_f \qquad \Delta T_b = K_b \times m \quad \Delta T_b = T_b - T_b°$

      Solution: $100.0 \ \cancel{\text{cm}^3} \times \dfrac{0.877 \ \cancel{g}}{1 \ \cancel{\text{cm}^3}} \times \dfrac{1 \ \text{kg}}{1000 \ \cancel{g}} = 0.0877 \ \text{kg}$ and

$10.0 \ \cancel{\text{g C}_{10}\text{H}_8} \times \dfrac{1 \ \text{mol C}_{10}\text{H}_8}{128.2 \ \cancel{\text{g C}_{10}\text{H}_8}} = 0.078\underline{0}0312 \ \text{mol C}_{10}\text{H}_8$ then

$m = \dfrac{\text{amount solute (moles)}}{\text{mass solvent (kg)}} = \dfrac{0.078\underline{0}0312 \ \text{mol C}_{10}\text{H}_8}{0.0877 \ \text{kg}} = 0.88\underline{9}4312 \ m$ then

$\Delta T_f = K_f \times m = 5.12 \ \dfrac{°\text{C}}{\cancel{m}} \times 0.88\underline{9}4312 \ \cancel{m} = 4.55 \ °\text{C}$ then $T_f = T_f° - \Delta T_f = 5.5 \ °\text{C} - 4.55 \ °\text{C} = 0.\underline{9}5 \ °\text{C} = 1 \ °\text{C}$

and $\Delta T_b = K_b \times m = 2.53 \ \dfrac{°\text{C}}{\cancel{m}} \times 0.88\underline{9}4312 \ \cancel{m} = 2.25 \ °\text{C}$ and $\Delta T_b = T_b - T_b°$ so

$T_b = T_b° + \Delta T_b = 80.1 \ °\text{C} + 2.25 \ °\text{C} = 82.\underline{3}5 \ °\text{C} = 82.4 \ °\text{C}$

Check: The units (°C) are correct. The magnitude of the answers seems reasonable because the molality is almost 1. Because the constants are larger for benzene than for water, we expect larger temperature shifts. The shift in boiling point is less than the shift in freezing point because the constant is smaller for freezing.

12.52 **Given:** 7.55 g of ethylene glycol ($C_2H_6O_2$) in 85.7 mL ethanol (C_2H_6O) **Find:** T_f and T_b
Other: d(ethanol) = 0.789 g/cm³; $K_f = 1.99$ °C/m; $K_b = 1.22$ °C/m; $T_f^\circ = -114.1$ °C; $T_b^\circ = 78.3$ °C
Conceptual Plan: $mL_{C_2H_6O} \rightarrow g_{C_2H_6O} \rightarrow kg_{C_2H_6O}$ and $g_{C_2H_6O_2} \rightarrow mol_{C_2H_6O_2}$ then

$$\frac{0.789 \text{ g}}{1 \text{ cm}^3} \qquad \frac{1 \text{ kg}}{1000 \text{ g}} \qquad\qquad \frac{1 \text{ mol } C_2H_6O_2}{62.07 \text{ g } C_2H_6O_2}$$

$mol_{C_2H_6O_2}, kg_{C_2H_6O_2} \rightarrow m$ then $m, K_f \rightarrow \Delta T_f \rightarrow T_f$ and $m, K_b \rightarrow \Delta T_b \rightarrow T_b$

$$m = \frac{\text{amount solute (moles)}}{\text{mass solvent (kg)}} \quad \Delta T_f = K_f \times m \quad T_f = T_f^\circ - \Delta T_f \quad \Delta T_b = K_b \times m \quad \Delta T_b = T_b - T_b^\circ$$

Solution: $85.7 \text{ cm}^3 \times \dfrac{0.789 \text{ g}}{1 \text{ cm}^3} \times \dfrac{1 \text{ kg}}{1000 \text{ g}} = 0.0676173$ kg and

$7.55 \text{ g } C_2H_6O_2 \times \dfrac{1 \text{ mol } C_2H_6O_2}{62.07 \text{ g } C_2H_6O_2} = 0.1216369 \text{ mol } C_2H_6O_2$ then

$m = \dfrac{\text{amount solute (moles)}}{\text{mass solvent (kg)}} = \dfrac{0.1216369 \text{ mol } C_2H_6O_2}{0.0676173 \text{ kg}} = 1.798902 \ m$ then

$\Delta T_f = K_f \times m = 1.99\dfrac{°C}{m} \times 1.798902 \ m = 3.58$ °C then

$T_f = T_f^\circ - \Delta T_f = -114.1$ °C $- 3.58$ °C $= -117.68$ °C $= -117.7$ °C and

$\Delta T_b = K_b \times m = 1.22\dfrac{°C}{m} \times 1.798902 \ m = 2.19$ °C and $\Delta T_b = T_b - T_b^\circ$ so

$T_b = T_b^\circ + \Delta T_b = 78.3$ °C $+ 2.19$ °C $= 80.49$ °C $= 80.5$ °C

Check: The units (°C) are correct. The magnitude of the answers seems reasonable because the molality is almost 2. Because the constants are larger for ethanol than for water, we expect larger temperature shifts. The shift in boiling point is less than the shift in freezing point because the constant is smaller for freezing.

12.53 **Given:** 17.5 g of unknown nonelectrolyte in 100.0 g water, $T_f = -1.8$ °C **Find:** $\mathcal{M}$
Other: $K_f = 1.86$ °C/m
Conceptual Plan: $g_{H_2O} \rightarrow kg_{H_2O}$ and $T_f \rightarrow \Delta T_f$ then $\Delta T_f, K_f \rightarrow m$ then $m, kg_{H_2O} \rightarrow mol_{Unk}$

$$\frac{1 \text{ kg}}{1000 \text{ g}} \qquad T_f = T_f^\circ - \Delta T_f \qquad \Delta T_f = K_f \times m \qquad m = \frac{\text{amount solute (moles)}}{\text{mass solvent (kg)}}$$

then $g_{Unk}, mol_{Unk} \rightarrow \mathcal{M}$

$$\mathcal{M} = \frac{g_{Unk}}{mol_{Unk}}$$

Solution: $100.0 \text{ g} \times \dfrac{1 \text{ kg}}{1000 \text{ g}} = 0.1000$ kg and $T_f = T_f^\circ - \Delta T_f$ so

$\Delta T_f = T_f^\circ - T_f = 0.00$ °C $- (-1.8$ °C$) = +1.8$ °C $\Delta T_f = K_f \times m$. Rearrange to solve for m.

$m = \dfrac{\Delta T_f}{K_f} = \dfrac{1.8 \ °C}{1.86 \ \frac{°C}{m}} = 0.96774 \ m$ then $m = \dfrac{\text{amount solute (moles)}}{\text{mass solvent (kg)}}$ so

$mol_{Unk} = m_{Unk} \times kg_{H_2O} = 0.96774 \ \dfrac{\text{mol Unk}}{\text{kg}} \times 0.1000 \text{ kg} = 0.096774$ mol Unk then

$\mathcal{M} = \dfrac{g_{Unk}}{mol_{Unk}} = \dfrac{17.5 \text{ g}}{0.096774 \text{ mol}} = 180 \ \dfrac{\text{g}}{\text{mol}} = 1.8 \times 10^2 \ \dfrac{\text{g}}{\text{mol}}$

Check: The units (g/mol) are correct. The magnitude of the answer (180 g/mol) seems reasonable because the molality is ~0.1 and we have ~18 g. It is a reasonable molecular weight for a solid or liquid.

12.54 **Given:** 35.9 g of unknown nonelectrolyte in 150.0 g water, $T_f = -1.3$ °C **Find:** $\mathcal{M}$
Other: $K_f = 1.86$ °C/m
Conceptual Plan: $g_{H_2O} \rightarrow kg_{H_2O}$ and $T_f \rightarrow \Delta T_f$ then $\Delta T_f, K_f \rightarrow m$ then $m, kg_{H_2O} \rightarrow mol_{Unk}$

$$\frac{1 \text{ kg}}{1000 \text{ g}} \qquad T_f = T_f^\circ - \Delta T_f \qquad \Delta T_f = K_f \times m \qquad m = \frac{\text{amount solute (moles)}}{\text{mass solvent (kg)}}$$

then $g_{Unk}, mol_{Unk} \rightarrow \mathcal{M}$

$$\mathcal{M} = \frac{g_{Unk}}{mol_{Unk}}$$

Solution: $150.0 \text{ g} \times \frac{1 \text{ kg}}{1000 \text{ g}} = 0.1500 \text{ kg}$ and $T_f = T_f^\circ - \Delta T_f$ so

$\Delta T_f = T_f^\circ - T_f = 0.00 \text{ °C} - (-1.3 \text{ °C}) = +1.3 \text{ °C}$; $\Delta T_f = K_f \times m$. Rearrange to solve for m.

$m = \frac{\Delta T_f}{K_f} = \frac{1.3 \text{ °C}}{1.86 \frac{\text{°C}}{m}} = 0.69892 \, m$ then $m = \frac{\text{amount solute (moles)}}{\text{mass solvent (kg)}}$ so

$mol_{Unk} = m_{Unk} \times kg_{H_2O} = 0.69892 \frac{mol_{Unk}}{kg} \times 0.1500 \text{ kg} = 0.104838 \, mol_{Unk}$ then

$\mathcal{M} = \frac{g_{Unk}}{mol_{Unk}} = \frac{35.9 \text{ g}}{0.104838 \text{ mol}} = 340 \frac{\text{g}}{\text{mol}}$

Check: The units (g/mol) are correct. The magnitude of the answer (340 g/mol) seems reasonable because the molality is ~ 0.7 and we have ~ 36 g. It is a reasonable molecular weight for a solid or liquid.

12.55 **Given:** 24.6 g of glycerin ($C_3H_8O_3$) in 250.0 mL of solution at 298 K **Find:** Π

Conceptual Plan: $mL_{soln} \rightarrow L_{soln}$ and $g_{C_3H_8O_3} \rightarrow mol_{C_3H_8O_3}$ then $mol_{C_3H_8O_3}, L_{soln} \rightarrow M$ then

$$\frac{1 \text{ L}}{1000 \text{ mL}} \qquad \frac{1 \text{ mol } C_3H_8O_3}{92.09 \text{ g } C_3H_8O_3} \qquad M = \frac{\text{amount solute (moles)}}{\text{volume solution (L)}}$$

$M, T \rightarrow \Pi$

$$\Pi = MRT$$

Solution:

$250.0 \text{ mL} \times \frac{1 \text{ L}}{1000 \text{ mL}} = 0.2500 \text{ L}$ and $24.6 \text{ g } C_3H_8O_3 \times \frac{1 \text{ mol } C_3H_8O_3}{92.09 \text{ g } C_3H_8O_3} = 0.267130 \text{ mol } C_3H_8O_3$ then

$M = \frac{\text{amount solute (moles)}}{\text{volume solution (L)}} = \frac{0.267130 \text{ mol } C_3H_8O_3}{0.2500 \text{ L}} = 1.06852 \text{ M}$ then

$\Pi = MRT = 1.06852 \frac{mol}{L} \times 0.08206 \frac{L \cdot atm}{K \cdot mol} \times 298 \text{ K} = 26.1 \text{ atm}$

Check: The units (atm) are correct. The magnitude of the answer (26 atm) seems reasonable because the molarity is ~ 1.

12.56 **Given:** sucrose ($C_{12}H_{22}O_{11}$) in 5.00×10^2 g water; $\Pi = 8.55$ atm at 298 K **Find:** m ($C_{12}H_{22}O_{11}$)

Other: $d = 1.0$ g/mL

Conceptual Plan: $\Pi, T \rightarrow M$ then $g_{H_2O}, d, \mathcal{M} \rightarrow g_{C_{12}H_{22}O_{11}}$

$$\Pi = MRT \quad M = \frac{\text{amount solute (moles)}}{\text{volume solution (L)}} \text{ with } \frac{1 \text{ L}}{1000 \text{ mL}}, \frac{342.30 \text{ g } C_{12}H_{22}O_{11}}{1 \text{ mol } C_{12}H_{22}O_{11}}, \text{ and } \frac{1.0 \text{ mL}}{1.0 \text{ g}}$$

Solution: $\Pi = MRT$ for M. $M = \frac{\Pi}{RT} = \frac{8.55 \text{ atm}}{0.08206 \frac{L \cdot atm}{K \cdot mol} \times 298 \text{ K}} = 0.349638 \frac{mol}{L}$

Substitute quantities into the definition of M.

$$M = \frac{\text{amount solute (moles)}}{\text{volume solution (L)}} = \frac{(x \text{ g } C_{12}H_{22}O_{11})\left(\frac{1 \text{ mol } C_{12}H_{22}O_{11}}{342.30 \text{ g } C_{12}H_{22}O_{11}}\right)}{(5.00 \times 10^2 \text{ g } H_2O + x \text{ g } C_{12}H_{22}O_{11}) \times \frac{1.0 \text{ mL}}{1.0 \text{ g}} \times \frac{1 \text{ L}}{1000 \text{ mL}}} = 0.349638 \frac{mol}{L}$$

Rearrange to solve for x g $C_{12}H_{22}O_{11}$. x g $C_{12}H_{22}O_{11} = 0.119681 \times (5.00 \times 10^2 \text{ g } H_2O + x \text{ g } C_{12}H_{22}O_{11}) \rightarrow$

$0.880312 \times (x \text{ g } C_{12}H_{22}O_{11}) = 59.8405 \rightarrow x \text{ g } C_{12}H_{22}O_{11} = \frac{59.8405}{0.880312} = 68.0 \text{ g } C_{12}H_{22}O_{11}$

Check: The units (g) are correct. The magnitude of the answer (68 g) seems reasonable because the molarity is $\sim 1/3$ and we have 0.5 L of water.

12.57   **Given:** 27.55 mg unknown protein in 25.0 mL solution; $\Pi = 3.22$ torr at 25 °C   **Find:** $\mathcal{M}_{\text{unknown protein}}$
Conceptual Plan: °C $\rightarrow$ K and torr $\rightarrow$ atm then $\Pi, T \rightarrow$ M then $\text{mL}_{\text{soln}} \rightarrow \text{L}_{\text{soln}}$ then

$$K = °C + 273.15 \qquad \frac{1 \text{ atm}}{760 \text{ torr}} \qquad \Pi = MRT \qquad \frac{1 \text{ L}}{1000 \text{ mL}}$$

$\text{L}_{\text{soln}}, \text{M} \rightarrow \text{mol}_{\text{unknown protein}}$ and mg $\rightarrow$ g then $g_{\text{unknown protein}}, \text{mol}_{\text{unknown protein}} \rightarrow \mathcal{M}_{\text{unknown protein}}$

$$M = \frac{\text{amount solute (moles)}}{\text{volume solution (L)}} \qquad \frac{1 \text{ g}}{1000 \text{ mg}} \qquad \mathcal{M} = \frac{g_{\text{unknown protein}}}{\text{mol}_{\text{unknown protein}}}$$

Solution: 25 °C + 273.15 = 298 K and $3.22 \text{ torr} \times \dfrac{1 \text{ atm}}{760 \text{ torr}} = 0.00423\underline{6}84 \text{ atm}$ $\Pi = MRT$ for M

$$M = \frac{\Pi}{RT} = \frac{0.00423\underline{6}84 \text{ atm}}{0.08206 \dfrac{\text{L} \cdot \text{atm}}{\text{K} \cdot \text{mol}} \times 298 \text{ K}} = 1.7\underline{3}258 \times 10^{-4} \frac{\text{mol}}{\text{L}} \text{ then } 25.0 \text{ mL} \times \frac{1 \text{ L}}{1000 \text{ mL}} = 0.0250 \text{ L then}$$

$M = \dfrac{\text{amount solute (moles)}}{\text{volume solution (L)}}$. Rearrange to solve for $\text{mol}_{\text{unknown protein}}$.

$$\text{mol}_{\text{unknown protein}} = \text{M} \times \text{L} = 1.7\underline{3}258 \times 10^{-4} \frac{\text{mol}}{\text{L}} \times 0.0250 \text{ L} = 4.3\underline{3}146 \times 10^{-6} \text{ mol and}$$

$$27.55 \text{ mg} \times \frac{1 \text{ g}}{1000 \text{ mg}} = 0.02755 \text{ g then } \mathcal{M} = \frac{g_{\text{unknown protein}}}{\text{mol}_{\text{unknown protein}}} = \frac{0.02755 \text{ g}}{4.3\underline{3}146 \times 10^{-6} \text{ mol}} = 6.36 \times 10^3 \frac{\text{g}}{\text{mol}}$$

Check: The units (g/mol) are correct. The magnitude of the answer (6400 g/mol) seems reasonable for a large biological molecule. A small amount of material is put into 0.025 L; so the concentration is very small, and the molecular weight is large.

12.58   **Given:** 18.75 mg of hemoglobin in 15.0 mL of solution at 25 °C, $\mathcal{M}_{\text{hemoglobin}} = 6.5 \times 10^4$ g/mol   **Find:** Π
Conceptual Plan: $\text{mL}_{\text{soln}} \rightarrow \text{L}_{\text{soln}}$ and $\text{mg}_{\text{H}} \rightarrow g_{\text{H}} \rightarrow \text{mol}_{\text{H}}$ then $\text{mol}_{\text{H}}, \text{L}_{\text{soln}} \rightarrow$ M then

$$\frac{1 \text{ L}}{1000 \text{ mL}} \qquad \frac{1 \text{ g}}{1000 \text{ mg}} \quad \frac{1 \text{ mol H}}{6.5 \times 10^4 \text{ g H}} \qquad M = \frac{\text{amount solute (moles)}}{\text{volume solution (L)}}$$

$\text{M}, T \rightarrow \Pi$

$$\Pi = MRT$$

Solution:

$$15.0 \text{ mL} \times \frac{1 \text{ L}}{1000 \text{ mL}} = 0.0150 \text{ L and } 18.75 \text{ mg H} \times \frac{1 \text{ g}}{1000 \text{ mg}} \times \frac{1 \text{ mol H}}{6.5 \times 10^4 \text{ g H}} = 2.\underline{8}8462 \times 10^{-7} \text{ mol H then}$$

$$M = \frac{\text{amount solute (moles)}}{\text{volume solution (L)}} = \frac{2.\underline{8}8462 \times 10^{-7} \text{ mol H}}{0.0150 \text{ L}} = 1.\underline{9}231 \times 10^{-5} \text{ M then}$$

$$\Pi = MRT = 1.\underline{9}231 \times 10^{-5} \frac{\text{mol}}{\text{L}} \times 0.08206 \frac{\text{L} \cdot \text{atm}}{\text{K} \cdot \text{mol}} \times 298 \text{ K} = 4.7 \times 10^{-4} \text{ atm} = 0.36 \text{ torr}$$

Check: The units (atm) are correct. The magnitude of the answer (10^{-4} atm) seems reasonable because the molarity is so small.

12.59   **(a)**   **Given:** 0.100 m of K_2S, completely dissociated   **Find:** T_f, T_b
Other: $K_f = 1.86$ °C/m; $K_b = 0.512$ °C/m
Conceptual Plan: $m, i, K_f \rightarrow \Delta T_f$ then $\Delta T_f \rightarrow T_f$ and $m, i, K_b \rightarrow \Delta T_b$ then $\Delta T_b \rightarrow T_b$

$$\Delta T_f = K_f \times i \times m_{i=3} \qquad T_f = T_f° - \Delta T_f \qquad \Delta T_b = K_b \times i \times m_{i=3} \qquad T_b = T_b° + \Delta T_b$$

Solution: $\Delta T_f = K_f \times i \times m = 1.86 \dfrac{°C}{m} \times 3 \times 0.100 \, m = 0.558$ °C then

$T_f = T_f° - \Delta T_f = 0.000$ °C $- 0.558$ °C $= -0.558$ °C and

$\Delta T_b = K_b \times i \times m = 0.512 \dfrac{°C}{m} \times 3 \times 0.100 \, m = 0.154$ °C then

$T_b = T_b° - \Delta T_b = 100.000$ °C $+ 0.154$ °C $= 100.154$ °C

Check: The units (°C) are correct. The magnitude of the answers (-0.6 °C and 100.2 °C) seems reasonable because the molality of the particles is 0.3. The shift in boiling point is less than the shift in freezing point because the constant for boiling is larger than the constant for freezing.

(b)   **Given:** 21.5 g $CuCl_2$ in 4.50×10^2 g water, completely dissociated   **Find:** T_f, T_b
Other: $K_f = 1.86\ °C/m$; $K_b = 0.512\ °C/m$
Conceptual Plan: $g_{H_2O} \rightarrow kg_{H_2O}$ and $g_{CuCl_2} \rightarrow mol_{CuCl_2}$ then $mol_{CuCl_2}, kg_{H_2O} \rightarrow m$

$$\frac{1\ kg}{1000\ g} \qquad \frac{1\ mol\ CuCl_2}{134.45\ g\ CuCl_2} \qquad m = \frac{amount\ solute\ (moles)}{mass\ solvent\ (kg)}$$

$m, i, K_f \rightarrow \Delta T_f \rightarrow T_f$ and $m, i, K_b \rightarrow \Delta T_b \rightarrow T_b$

$$\Delta T_f = K_f \times i \times m_{i=3} \quad T_f = T_f° - \Delta T_f \quad \Delta T_b = K_b \times i \times m_{i=3} \quad T_b = T_b° + \Delta T_b$$

Solution:

$$4.5 \times 10^2\ g \times \frac{1\ kg}{1000\ g} = 0.450\ kg \text{ and } 21.5\ g\ CuCl_2 \times \frac{1\ mol\ CuCl_2}{134.45\ g\ CuCl_2} = 0.159911\ mol\ CuCl_2 \text{ then}$$

$$m = \frac{amount\ solute\ (moles)}{mass\ solvent\ (kg)} = \frac{0.159911\ mol\ CuCl_2}{0.450\ kg} = 0.355358\ m \text{ then}$$

$$\Delta T_f = K_f \times i \times m = 1.86\ \frac{°C}{m} \times 3 \times 0.355358\ m = 1.98\ °C \text{ then}$$

$$T_f = T_f° - \Delta T_f = 0.000\ °C - 1.98\ °C = -1.98\ °C \text{ and}$$

$$\Delta T_b = K_b \times i \times m = 0.512\ \frac{°C}{m} \times 3 \times 0.355358\ m = 0.546\ °C \text{ then}$$

$$T_b = T_b° - \Delta T_b = 100.000\ °C + 0.546\ °C = 100.546\ °C$$

Check: The units (°C) are correct. The magnitude of the answers (−2 °C and 100.5 °C) seems reasonable because the molality of the particles is ~1. The shift in boiling point is less than the shift in freezing point because the constant for boiling is larger than the constant for freezing.

(c)   **Given:** 5.5% by mass $NaNO_3$, completely dissociated   **Find:** T_f, T_b
Other: $K_f = 1.86\ °C/m$; $K_b = 0.512\ °C/m$
Conceptual Plan: percent by mass $\rightarrow g_{NaNO_3}, g_{H_2O}$ then $g_{H_2O} \rightarrow kg_{H_2O}$ and $g_{NaNO_3} \rightarrow mol_{NaNO_3}$

$$mass\ percent = \frac{mass\ solute}{mass\ solution} \times 100\% \qquad \frac{1\ kg}{1000\ g} \qquad \frac{1\ mol\ NaNO_3}{85.00\ g\ NaNO_3}$$

then $mol_{NaNO_3}, kg_{H_2O} \rightarrow m$ then $m, i, K_f \rightarrow \Delta T_f \rightarrow T_f$ and $m, i, K_b \rightarrow \Delta T_b \rightarrow T_b$

$$m = \frac{amount\ solute\ (moles)}{mass\ solvent\ (kg)} \quad \Delta T_f = K_f \times i \times m_{i=2} \quad T_f = T_f° - \Delta T_f \quad \Delta T_b = K_b \times i \times m_{i=2} \quad T_b = T_b° + \Delta T_b$$

Solution: $mass\ percent = \dfrac{mass\ solute}{mass\ solution} \times 100\%$, so 5.5% by mass $NaNO_3$ means 5.5 g $NaNO_3$ and

$$100.0\ g - 5.5\ g = 94.5\ g\ water. \text{ Then } 94.5\ g \times \frac{1\ kg}{1000\ g} = 0.0945\ kg \text{ and}$$

$$5.5\ g\ NaNO_3 \times \frac{1\ mol\ NaNO_3}{85.00\ g\ NaNO_3} = 0.064706\ mol\ NaNO_3 \text{ then}$$

$$m = \frac{amount\ solute\ (moles)}{mass\ solvent\ (kg)} = \frac{0.064706\ mol\ NaNO_3}{0.0945\ kg} = 0.68472\ m \text{ then}$$

$$\Delta T_f = K_f \times i \times m = 1.86\ \frac{°C}{m} \times 2 \times 0.68472\ m = 2.5\ °C \text{ then}$$

$$T_f = T_f° - \Delta T_f = 0.000\ °C - 2.5\ °C = -2.5\ °C \text{ and}$$

$$\Delta T_b = K_b \times i \times m = 0.512\ \frac{°C}{m} \times 2 \times 0.68472\ m = 0.70\ °C \text{ then}$$

$$T_b = T_b° - \Delta T_b = 100.000\ °C + 0.70\ °C = 100.70\ °C$$

Check: The units (°C) are correct. The magnitude of the answers (−2.5 °C and 100.7 °C) seems reasonable because the molality of the particles is ~1. The shift in boiling point is less than the shift in freezing point because the constant for boiling is larger than the constant for freezing.

12.60   (a)   **Given:** 10.5 g $FeCl_3$ in 1.50×10^2 g water, completely dissociated   **Find:** T_f, T_b
Other: $K_f = 1.86\ °C/m$; $K_b = 0.512\ °C/m$
Conceptual Plan: $g_{H_2O} \rightarrow kg_{H_2O}$ and $g_{FeCl_3} \rightarrow mol_{FeCl_3}$ then $mol\ _{FeCl_3}, kg_{H_2O} \rightarrow m$

$$\frac{1\ kg}{1000\ g} \qquad \frac{1\ mol\ FeCl_3}{162.20\ g\ FeCl_3} \qquad m = \frac{amount\ solute\ (moles)}{mass\ solvent\ (kg)}$$

$$m, i, K_f \rightarrow \Delta T_f \rightarrow T_f \text{ and } m, i, K_b \rightarrow \Delta T_b \rightarrow T_b$$

$$\Delta T_f = K_f \times i \times m_{i=4} \quad T_f = T_f^\circ - \Delta T_f \quad \Delta T_b = K_b \times i \times m_{i=4} \quad T_b = T_b^\circ + \Delta T_b$$

Solution: $4.5 \times 10^2 \text{ g} \times \dfrac{1 \text{ kg}}{1000 \text{ g}} = 0.450 \text{ kg}$ and

$$10.5 \text{ g FeCl}_3 \times \dfrac{1 \text{ mol FeCl}_3}{162.20 \text{ g FeCl}_3} = 0.064\underline{7}349 \text{ mol FeCl}_3 \text{ then}$$

$$m = \dfrac{\text{amount solute (moles)}}{\text{mass solvent (kg)}} = \dfrac{0.064\underline{7}349 \text{ mol FeCl}_3}{0.150 \text{ kg}} = 0.431\underline{5}66 \, m \text{ then}$$

$$\Delta T_f = K_f \times i \times m = 1.86 \, \dfrac{^\circ\text{C}}{m} \times 4 \times 0.431\underline{5}66 \, m = 3.21 \, ^\circ\text{C then}$$

$$T_f = T_f^\circ - \Delta T_f = 0.000 \, ^\circ\text{C} - 3.21 \, ^\circ\text{C} = -3.21 \, ^\circ\text{C and}$$

$$\Delta T_b = K_b \times i \times m = 0.512 \, \dfrac{^\circ\text{C}}{m} \times 4 \times 0.431\underline{5}66 \, m = 0.884 \, ^\circ\text{C then}$$

$$T_b = T_b^\circ - \Delta T_b = 100.000 \, ^\circ\text{C} + 0.884 \, ^\circ\text{C} = 100.884 \, ^\circ\text{C}$$

Check: The units ($^\circ$C) are correct. The magnitude of the answers ($-3 \, ^\circ$C and 100.9 $^\circ$C) seems reasonable because the molality of the particles is ~ 2. The shift in boiling point is less than the shift in freezing point because the constant for boiling is smaller than the constant for freezing.

(b) **Given:** 3.5% by mass KCl, completely dissociated   **Find:** T_f, T_b
Other: $K_f = 1.86 \, ^\circ$C/m; $K_b = 0.512 \, ^\circ$C/m
Conceptual Plan: percent by mass $\rightarrow$ g_{KCl}, $g_{\text{H}_2\text{O}}$ then $g_{\text{H}_2\text{O}} \rightarrow$ kg$_{\text{H}_2\text{O}}$ and $g_{\text{KCl}} \rightarrow$ mol$_{\text{KCl}}$ then

$$\text{mass percent} = \dfrac{\text{mass solute}}{\text{mass solution}} \times 100\% \qquad \dfrac{1 \text{ kg}}{1000 \text{ g}} \qquad \dfrac{1 \text{ mol KCl}}{74.55 \text{ g KCl}}$$

$$\text{mol}_{\text{NaNO}_3}, \text{kg}_{\text{H}_2\text{O}} \rightarrow m \text{ then } m, i, K_f \rightarrow \Delta T_f \rightarrow T_f \text{ and } m, i, K_b \rightarrow \Delta T_b \rightarrow T_b$$

$$m = \dfrac{\text{amount solute (moles)}}{\text{mass solvent (kg)}} \quad \Delta T_f = K_f \times i \times m_{i=2} \quad T_f = T_f^\circ - \Delta T_f \quad \Delta T_b = K_b \times i \times m_{i=2} \quad T_b = T_b^\circ + \Delta T_b$$

Solution: mass percent $= \dfrac{\text{mass solute}}{\text{mass solution}} \times 100\%$ so 3.5% by mass KCl means

3.5 g KCl and 100.0 g $-$ 3.5 g $=$ 96.5 g water. Then $96.5 \text{ g} \times \dfrac{1 \text{ kg}}{1000 \text{ g}} = 0.0965 \text{ kg}$ and

$$3.5 \text{ g KCl} \times \dfrac{1 \text{ mol KCl}}{74.55 \text{ g KCl}} = 0.04\underline{6}948 \text{ mol KCl then}$$

$$m = \dfrac{\text{amount solute (moles)}}{\text{mass solvent (kg)}} = \dfrac{0.04\underline{6}948 \text{ mol KCl}}{0.0965 \text{ kg}} = 0.4\underline{8}651 \, m \text{ then}$$

$$\Delta T_f = K_f \times i \times m = 1.86 \, \dfrac{^\circ\text{C}}{m} \times 2 \times 0.4\underline{8}651 \, m = 1.8 \, ^\circ\text{C then}$$

$$T_f = T_f^\circ - \Delta T_f = 0.000 \, ^\circ\text{C} - 1.8 \, ^\circ\text{C} = -1.8 \, ^\circ\text{C and}$$

$$\Delta T_b = K_b \times i \times m = 0.512 \, \dfrac{^\circ\text{C}}{m} \times 2 \times 0.4\underline{8}651 \, m = 0.50 \, ^\circ\text{C then}$$

$$T_b = T_b^\circ - \Delta T_b = 100.000 \, ^\circ\text{C} + 0.50 \, ^\circ\text{C} = 100.50 \, ^\circ\text{C}$$

Check: The units ($^\circ$C) are correct. The magnitude of the answers ($-2 \, ^\circ$C and 100.5 $^\circ$C) seems reasonable because the molality of the particles is ~ 1. The shift in boiling point is less than the shift in freezing point because the constant for boiling is smaller than the constant for freezing.

(c) **Given:** 0.150 m of MgF$_2$, completely dissociated   **Find:** T_f, T_b
Other: $K_f = 1.86 \, ^\circ$C/m; $K_b = 0.512 \, ^\circ$C/m
Conceptual Plan: $m, i, K_f \rightarrow \Delta T_f$ then $\Delta T_f \rightarrow T_f$ and $m, i, K_b \rightarrow \Delta T_b$ then $\Delta T_b \rightarrow T_b$

$$\Delta T_f = K_f \times i \times m_{i=3} \qquad T_f = T_f^\circ - \Delta T_f \qquad \Delta T_b = K_b \times i \times m_{i=3} \qquad T_b = T_b^\circ + \Delta T_b$$

Solution: $\Delta T_f = K_f \times i \times m = 1.86 \, \dfrac{^\circ\text{C}}{m} \times 3 \times 0.150 \, m = 0.837 \, ^\circ\text{C then}$

$$T_f = T_f^\circ - \Delta T_f = 0.000 \, ^\circ\text{C} - 0.837 \, ^\circ\text{C} = -0.837 \, ^\circ\text{C and}$$

$$\Delta T_b = K_b \times i \times m = 0.512 \, \frac{°C}{m} \times 3 \times 0.150 \, m = 0.230 \, °C \text{ then}$$

$$T_b = T_b° - \Delta T_b = 100.000 \, °C + 0.230 \, °C = 100.230 \, °C$$

Check: The units (°C) are correct. The magnitude of the answers (–0.8 °C and 100.2 °C) seems reasonable because the molality of the particles is 0.5. The shift in boiling point is less than the shift in freezing point because the constant for boiling is smaller than the constant for freezing.

12.61　**Given:** NaCl complete dissociation; 1.0 L water and $T_f = -10.0 \, °C$　　**Find:** mass of NaCl

Other: $K_f = 1.86 \, °C/m$; d(water) = 1.0 g/mL

Conceptual Plan:

$T_f \rightarrow \Delta T_f \text{ then } \Delta T_f, \, i, K_f \rightarrow m \text{ then } L_{H_2O} \rightarrow mL_{H_2O} \rightarrow g_{H_2O} \rightarrow kg_{H_2O} \text{ then } m, kg_{H_2O} \rightarrow mol_{NaCl}$

$T_f = T_f° - \Delta T_f \qquad \Delta T_f = K_f \times i \times m \qquad \frac{1000 \, mL}{1 \, L} \quad \frac{1.0 \, g}{1 \, mL} \quad \frac{1 \, kg}{1000 \, g} \qquad m = \frac{\text{amount solute (moles)}}{\text{mass solvent (kg)}}$

then $mol_{NaCl} \rightarrow g_{NaCl}$

$\frac{58.44 \ g \ NaCl}{1 \ mol \ NaCl}$

Solution: $T_f = T_f° - \Delta T_f$ so $\Delta T_f = T_f° - T_f = 0.0 \, °C - 10.0 \, °C = -10.0 \, °C$ then $\Delta T_f = K_f \times i \times m$

Rearrange to solve for m. Because the salt completely dissolves, $i = 2$.

$$m = \frac{\Delta T_f}{K_f \times i} = \frac{10.0 \, °C}{1.86 \, \frac{°C}{m} \times 2} = 2.6\underline{8}8172 \, m \text{ NaCl then } 1.0 \, L \times \frac{1000 \, mL}{1 \, L} \times \frac{1.0 \, g}{1 \, mL} \times \frac{1 \, kg}{1000 \, g} = 1.0 \, kg \text{ then}$$

$$m = \frac{\text{amount solute (moles)}}{\text{mass solvent (kg)}} \text{ so } mol_{NaCl} = m \times kg_{H_2O} = 2.6\underline{8}8172 \frac{mol \ NaCl}{kg_{H_2O}} \times 1.0 \, kg_{H_2O} = 2.6\underline{8}8172 \, mol \text{ NaCl}$$

$$\text{then } 2.6\underline{8}8172 \, mol \ NaCl \times \frac{58.44 \, g \ NaCl}{1 \, mol \ NaCl} = 1\underline{5}7.097 \, g \text{ NaCl} = 160 \, g \text{ NaCl}$$

Check: The units (g) are correct. The magnitude of the answer (160 g) seems reasonable because the temperature change is moderate and NaCl has a low formula mass.

12.62　**Given:** ethylene glycol ($C_2H_6O_2$) in water and $T_b = 104.0 \, °C$　　**Find:** ethylene glycol % by mass

Other: $K_b = 0.512 \, °C/m$; d(water) = 1.0 g/mL

Conceptual Plan: $T_b \rightarrow \Delta T_b \text{ then } \Delta T_b, K_b \rightarrow m \text{ then assume exactly 1 kg of water}$

$\Delta T_b = T_b - T_b° \qquad \Delta T_b = K_b \times m$

then $m, kg_{H_2O} \rightarrow mol_{C_2H_6O_2} \rightarrow g_{C_2H_6O_2} \text{ and } kg_{H_2O} \rightarrow g_{H_2O} \text{ then } g_{C_2H_6O_2}, g_{H_2O} \rightarrow C_2H_6O_2\% \text{ by mass}$

$m = \frac{\text{amount solute (moles)}}{\text{mass solvent (kg)}} \quad \frac{62.07 \ g \ C_2H_6O_2}{1 \ mol \ C_2H_6O_2} \qquad \frac{1000 \ g}{1 \ kg} \qquad \% \text{ by mass} = \frac{\text{grams solute}}{\text{grams solute + grams solvent}} \times 100\%$

Solution: $\Delta T_b = T_b - T_b° = 104.0 \, °C - 100.0 \, °C = 4.0 \, °C$ then $\Delta T_b = K_b \times m$

Rearrange to solve for m. $m = \frac{\Delta T_b}{K_b} = \frac{4.0 \, °C}{0.512 \, \frac{°C}{m}} = 7.\underline{8}125 \, m \, C_2H_6O_2$ then assume exactly 1 kg of water

$$m = \frac{\text{amount solute (moles)}}{\text{mass solvent (kg)}} \text{ so } mol_{C_2H_6O_2} = m \times kg_{H_2O} = 7.\underline{8}125 \, \frac{mol \ C_2H_6O_2}{kg_{H_2O}} \times 1 \, kg_{H_2O} = 7.\underline{8}125 \, mol \, C_2H_6O_2$$

$$\text{then } 7.\underline{8}125 \, mol \ C_2H_6O_2 \times \frac{62.07 \, g \ C_2H_6O_2}{1 \, mol \ C_2H_6O_2} = 4\underline{8}4.922 \, g \, C_2H_6O_2 \text{ and } 1 \, kg \times \frac{1000 \, g}{1 \, kg} = 1000 \, g \text{ (exactly)}$$

finally

$$\% \text{ by mass} = \frac{\text{grams solute}}{\text{grams solute + grams solvent}} \times 100\% = \frac{4\underline{8}4.922 \, g}{4\underline{8}4.922 \, g + 1000 \, g} \times 100\% = 3\underline{2}.65640\%$$

$= 33\% \, C_2H_6O_2$ by mass

Check: The units (% by mass) are correct. The magnitude of the answer (33) seems reasonable because the temperature change is moderate and ethylene glycol has a low formula mass.

12.63   (a)   **Given:** 0.100 m of $FeCl_3$ **Find:** T_f **Other:** $K_f = 1.86\,°C/m$; $i_{measured} = 3.4$
       Conceptual Plan: $m, i, K_f \rightarrow \Delta T_f$ then $\Delta T_f \rightarrow T_f$

$$\Delta T_f = K_f \times i \times m \qquad\qquad T_f = T_f^\circ - \Delta T_f$$

       Solution: $\Delta T_f = K_f \times i \times m = 1.86\,\dfrac{°C}{m} \times 3.4 \times 0.100\,m = 0.632\,°C$ then

$$T_f = T_f^\circ - \Delta T_f = 0.000\,°C - 0.632\,°C = -0.632\,°C$$

       Check: The units (°C) are correct. The magnitude of the answer (−0.6 °C) seems reasonable because the theoretical molality of the particles is 0.4.

   (b)   **Given:** 0.085 M of K_2SO_4 at 298 K   **Find:** Π **Other:** $i_{measured} = 2.6$
       Conceptual Plan: $M, i, T \rightarrow \Pi$

$$\Pi = i \times MRT$$

       Solution: $\Pi = i \times MRT = 2.6 \times 0.085\,\dfrac{mol}{L} \times 0.08206\,\dfrac{L \cdot atm}{K \cdot mol} \times 298\,K = 5.4\,atm$

       Check: The units (atm) are correct. The magnitude of the answer (5 atm) seems reasonable because the molarity of particles is $\sim 0.2\,m$.

   (c)   **Given:** 1.22% by mass $MgCl_2$ **Find:** T_b **Other:** $K_b = 0.512\,°C/m$; $i_{measured} = 2.7$
       Conceptual Plan: percent by mass $\rightarrow$ g_{MgCl_2}, g_{H_2O} **then** $g_{H_2O} \rightarrow kg_{H_2O}$ **and** $g_{MgCl_2} \rightarrow mol_{MgCl_2}$ **then**

$$\text{mass percent} = \dfrac{\text{mass solute}}{\text{mass solution}} \times 100\% \qquad \dfrac{1\,kg}{1000\,g} \qquad \dfrac{1\,mol\,MgCl_2}{95.21\,g\,MgCl_2}$$

       $mol_{MgCl_2}, kg_{H_2O} \rightarrow m$ **then** $m, i, K_b \rightarrow \Delta T_b \rightarrow T_b$

$$m = \dfrac{\text{amount solute (moles)}}{\text{mass solvent (kg)}} \qquad \Delta T_b = K_b \times i \times m \quad T_b = T_b^\circ + \Delta T_b$$

       Solution: $\text{mass percent} = \dfrac{\text{mass solute}}{\text{mass solution}} \times 100\%$, so 1.22% by mass $MgCl_2$ means 1.22 g $MgCl_2$ and

       $100.00\,g - 1.22\,g = 98.78\,g$ water. Then $98.78\,g \times \dfrac{1\,kg}{1000\,g} = 0.09878\,kg$ and

       $1.22\,g\,MgCl_2 \times \dfrac{1\,mol\,MgCl_2}{95.21\,g\,MgCl_2} = 0.0128138\,mol\,MgCl_2$ then

       $m = \dfrac{\text{amount solute (moles)}}{\text{mass solvent (kg)}} = \dfrac{0.0128138\,mol\,MgCl_2}{0.09878\,kg} = 0.129721\,m$ then

       $\Delta T_b = K_b \times i \times m = 0.512\,\dfrac{°C}{m} \times 2.7 \times 0.129721\,m = 0.18\,°C$ then

       $T_b = T_b^\circ - \Delta T_b = 100.000\,°C + 0.18\,°C = 100.18\,°C$

       Check: The units (°C) are correct. The magnitude of the answer (100.2 °C) seems reasonable because the molality of the particles is $\sim 1/3$.

12.64   (a)   **Given:** NaCl; 1.50×10^2 g water and $T_f = -1.0\,°C$ **Find:** $m(NaCl)$
       Other: $K_f = 1.86\,°C/m$; $i_{measured} = 1.9$
       Conceptual Plan: $T_f \rightarrow \Delta T_f$ then $\Delta T_f, i, K_f \rightarrow m$ then $g_{H_2O} \rightarrow kg_{H_2O}$ then $m, kg_{H_2O} \rightarrow mol_{NaCl}$

$$T_f = T_f^\circ - \Delta T_f \qquad\qquad \Delta T_f = K_f \times i \times m \qquad \dfrac{1\,kg}{1000\,kg} \qquad m = \dfrac{\text{amount solute (moles)}}{\text{mass solvent (kg)}}$$

       then $mol_{NaCl} \rightarrow g_{NaCl}$

$$\dfrac{58.44\,g\,NaCl}{1\,mol\,NaCl}$$

       Solution: $T_f = T_f^\circ - \Delta T_f$ so $\Delta T_f = T_f^\circ - T_f = 0.0\,°C - 1.0\,°C = -1.0\,°C$ then $\Delta T_f = K_f \times i \times m$

       Rearrange to solve for m. $m = \dfrac{\Delta T_f}{K_f \times i} = \dfrac{1.0\,°C}{1.86\,\dfrac{°C}{m} \times 1.9} = 0.28297\,m$ NaCl then

       $1.50 \times 10^2\,g \times \dfrac{1\,kg}{1000\,g} = 0.150\,kg$ then $m = \dfrac{\text{amount solute (moles)}}{\text{mass solvent (kg)}}$ so

$$\text{mol}_{\text{NaCl}} = m \times \text{kg}_{\text{H}_2\text{O}} = 0.28297 \frac{\text{mol NaCl}}{\text{kg}_{\text{H}_2\text{O}}} \times 0.150 \text{ kg}_{\text{H}_2\text{O}} = 0.042446 \text{ mol NaCl then}$$

$$0.042446 \text{ mol NaCl} \times \frac{58.44 \text{ g NaCl}}{1 \text{ mol NaCl}} = 2.5 \text{ g NaCl}$$

Check: The units (g) are correct. The magnitude of the answer (2.5 g) seems reasonable because the temperature change is moderate and NaCl has a low formula mass.

(b) **Given:** $MgSO_4$; 2.50×10^2 mL solution and $\Pi = 3.82$ atm at 298 K   **Find:** $m(MgSO_4)$
Other: $i_{\text{measured}} = 1.3$
Conceptual Plan: $i, \Pi, T \rightarrow M$ then $mL_{\text{soln}} \rightarrow L_{\text{soln}}$ then $L_{\text{soln}}, M \rightarrow \text{mol}_{MgSO_4} \rightarrow g_{MgSO_4}$

$$\Pi = i \times MRT \qquad \frac{1 \text{ L}}{1000 \text{ mL}} \qquad M = \frac{\text{amount solute (moles)}}{\text{volume solution (L)}} \qquad \frac{120.37 \text{ g MgSO}_4}{1 \text{ mol MgSO}_4}$$

Solution: $\Pi = i \times MRT$. Rearrange to solve for M.

$$M = \frac{\Pi}{i \times RT} = \frac{3.82 \text{ atm}}{1.3 \times 0.08206 \frac{\text{L} \cdot \text{atm}}{\text{K} \cdot \text{mol}} \times 298 \text{ K}} = 0.12016 \frac{\text{mol MgSO}_4}{\text{L}} \text{ then}$$

$$2.50 \times 10^2 \text{ mL} \times \frac{1 \text{ L}}{1000 \text{ mL}} = 0.250 \text{ L then } M = \frac{\text{amount solute (moles)}}{\text{volume solution (L)}} \text{ so}$$

$$\text{mol}_{MgSO_4} = M \times L_{\text{soln}} = 0.12016 \frac{\text{mol MgSO}_4}{\text{L}} \times 0.250 \text{ L} = 0.030040 \text{ mol MgSO}_4 \text{ finally}$$

$$0.030040 \text{ mol MgSO}_4 \times \frac{120.37 \text{ g MgSO}_4}{1 \text{ mol MgSO}_4} = 3.6 \text{ g MgSO}_4$$

Check: The units (g) are correct. The magnitude of the answer (4 g) seems reasonable because the pressure is moderate and $MgSO_4$ has a low formula mass.

(c) **Given:** $FeCl_3$; 2.50×10^2 g water and $T_b = 102 \,°C$ **Find:** $m(FeCl_3)$ **Other:**
$K_b = 0.512 \,°C/m$; $i_{\text{measured}} = 3.4$
Conceptual Plan: $T_b \rightarrow \Delta T_b$ then $\Delta T_b, i, K_b \rightarrow m$ then $g_{\text{H}_2\text{O}} \rightarrow \text{kg}_{\text{H}_2\text{O}}$ then $m, \text{kg}_{\text{H}_2\text{O}} \rightarrow \text{mol}_{FeCl_3}$

$$T_b = T_b^\circ + \Delta T_b \qquad \Delta T_b = K_b \times i \times m \qquad \frac{1 \text{ kg}}{1000 \text{ g}} \qquad m = \frac{\text{amount solute (moles)}}{\text{mass solvent (kg)}}$$

then $\text{mol}_{FeCl_3} \rightarrow g_{FeCl_3}$

$$\frac{162.20 \text{ g FeCl}_3}{1 \text{ mol FeCl}_3}$$

Solution: $T_b = T_b^\circ + \Delta T_b$ so $\Delta T_b = T_b - T_b^\circ = 102 \,°C - 100 \,°C = 2 \,°C$ then $\Delta T_b = K_b \times i \times m$

Rearrange to solve for m. $m = \dfrac{\Delta T_b}{K_b \times i} = \dfrac{2 \,°C}{0.512 \frac{°C}{m} \times 3.4} = 1.149 \, m \text{ FeCl}_3$ then

$$2.50 \times 10^2 \text{ g} \times \frac{1 \text{ kg}}{1000 \text{ g}} = 0.250 \text{ kg then } m = \frac{\text{amount solute (moles)}}{\text{mass solvent (kg)}} \text{ so}$$

$$\text{mol}_{FeCl_3} = m \times \text{kg}_{\text{H}_2\text{O}} = 1.149 \frac{\text{mol FeCl}_3}{\text{kg}_{\text{H}_2\text{O}}} \times 0.250 \text{ kg}_{\text{H}_2\text{O}} = 0.2873 \text{ mol FeCl}_3 \text{ then}$$

$$0.2873 \text{ mol FeCl}_3 \times \frac{162.20 \text{ g FeCl}_3}{1 \text{ mol FeCl}_3} = 47 \text{ g FeCl}_3 = 50 \text{ g FeCl}_3$$

Check: The units (g) are correct. The magnitude of the answer (50 g) seems reasonable because the temperature change is significant and we are making 0.25 L of solution.

12.65 **Given:** $1.2 \, m \, MX_2$ in water and $T_b = 101.4 \,°C$ **Find:** i
Other: $K_b = 0.512 \,°C/m$
Conceptual Plan: $T_b \rightarrow \Delta T_b$ then $m, \Delta T_b, K_b \rightarrow i$

$$\Delta T_b = T_b - T_b^\circ \qquad \Delta T_b = K_b \times i \times m$$

Solution: $\Delta T_b = T_b - T_b^\circ = 101.4 \,°C - 100.0 \,°C = 1.4 \,°C$ then $\Delta T_b = K_b \times i \times m$

Rearrange to solve for i. $i = \dfrac{\Delta T_b}{K_b \times m} = \dfrac{1.4\,°\!\!\!\!C}{0.512\,\dfrac{°\!\!\!\!C}{m\!\!/} \times 1.2\,m\!\!/} = 2.2\underline{7}865 = 2.3$

Check: The units (none) are correct. The magnitude of the answer (2.3) seems reasonable because the formula of the salt is MX_2, where $i = 3$ if it completely dissociated.

12.66   **Given:** 0.95 m MX in water and $T_f = -3.0\,°C$ **Find:** i
          Other: $K_f = 1.86\,°C/m$
          Conceptual Plan: $T_f \rightarrow \Delta T_f$ then $m, \Delta T_f, K_f \rightarrow i$
          $$T_f = T_f° - \Delta T_f \qquad\qquad \Delta T_f = K_f \times i \times m.$$
          Solution: $T_f = T_f° - \Delta T_f$ so $\Delta T_f = T_f° - T_f = 0.0\,°C - 3.0\,°C = -3.0\,°C$ then $\Delta T_f = K_f \times i \times m$

Rearrange to solve for i. $i = \dfrac{\Delta T_f}{K_f \times m} = \dfrac{3.0\,°\!\!\!\!C}{1.86\,\dfrac{°\!\!\!\!C}{m\!\!/} \times 0.95\,m\!\!/} = 1.\underline{6}9779 = 1.7$

Check: The units (none) are correct. The magnitude of the answer (1.7) seems reasonable because the formula of the salt is MX, where $i = 2$ if it completely dissociated.

12.67   **Given:** 0.100 M of ionic solution, $\Pi = 8.3$ atm at 25 °C   **Find:** $i_{measured}$
          Conceptual Plan: $°C \rightarrow K$ then $\Pi, M, T \rightarrow i$
          $$K = °C + 273.15 \qquad\qquad \Pi = i \times MRT$$
          Solution: $25\,°C + 273.15 = 298\,K$ then $\Pi = i \times MRT$. Rearrange to solve for i.

$i = \dfrac{\Pi}{MRT} = \dfrac{8.3\,atm\!\!\!\!/}{0.100\,\dfrac{mol\!\!\!/}{L\!\!/} \times 0.08206\,\dfrac{L\!\!/ \cdot atm\!\!\!\!/}{K\!\!/ \cdot mol\!\!\!/} \times 298\,K\!\!/} = 3.4$

Check: The units (none) are correct. The magnitude of the answer (3) seems reasonable for an ionic solution with a high osmotic pressure.

12.68   **Given:** 8.92 g of KBr in 500.0 mL solution, $\Pi = 6.97$ atm at 25 °C   **Find:** $i_{measured}$
          Conceptual Plan: $°C \rightarrow K$ and $mL_{soln} \rightarrow L_{soln}$ and $g_{KBr} \rightarrow mol_{KBr}$ then $mol_{KBr}, L_{soln} \rightarrow M$ then
          $$K = °C + 273.15 \qquad \dfrac{1\,L}{1000\,ml} \qquad \dfrac{1\,mol\,KBr}{119.00\,g\,KBr} \qquad M = \dfrac{amount\,solute\,(moles)}{volume\,solution\,(L)}$$

$\Pi, M, T \rightarrow i$
$$\Pi = i \times MRT$$

Solution: $25\,°C + 273.15 = 298\,K$ and $500.0\,m\!L\!\!/ \times \dfrac{1\,L}{1000\,m\!L\!\!/} = 0.5000\,L$ and

$8.92\,g\text{-}KBr\!\!\!\!/ \times \dfrac{1\,mol\,KBr}{119.00\,g\text{-}KBr\!\!\!\!/} = 0.074\underline{9}580\,mol\,KBr$ then

$M = \dfrac{amount\,solute\,(moles)}{volume\,solution\,(L)} = \dfrac{0.074\underline{9}580\,mol\,KBr}{0.5000\,L} = 0.149916\,\dfrac{mol\,KBr}{L}$ then $\Pi = i \times MRT$

Rearrange to solve for i. $i = \dfrac{\Pi}{MRT} = \dfrac{6.97\,atm\!\!\!\!/}{0.149916\,\dfrac{mol\!\!\!/}{L\!\!/} \times 0.08206\,\dfrac{L\!\!/ \cdot atm\!\!\!\!/}{K\!\!/ \cdot mol\!\!\!/} \times 298\,K\!\!/} = 1.90$

Check: The units (none) are correct. The magnitude of the answer (1.9) seems reasonable for KBr because we expect i to be 2 if it completely dissociates. Because both ions are large and have only one charge each, we expect i to be close to the theoretical value.

Cumulative Problems

12.69   Chloroform is polar and has stronger solute–solvent interactions than does nonpolar carbon tetrachloride.

12.70   Each molecule has one —OH group that is capable of hydrogen bonding. Because phenol is a smaller molecule than naphthol, the —OH group has a bigger impact on the overall polarity of the phenol molecule.

12.71   **Given:** $KClO_4$: lattice energy $= -599$ kJ/mol, $\Delta H_{hydration} = -548$ kJ/mol; 10.0 g $KClO_4$ in 100.00 mL solution
Find: ΔH_{soln} and ΔT **Other:** $C_s = 4.05$ J/g °C; $d = 1.05$ g/mL
Conceptual Plan: lattice energy, $\Delta H_{hydration} \rightarrow \Delta H_{soln}$ and g $\rightarrow$ mol then mol, $\Delta H_{soln} \rightarrow q(kJ) \rightarrow q(J)$

$$\Delta H_{soln} = \Delta H_{solute} + \Delta H_{hydration} \text{ where } \Delta H_{solute} = -\Delta H_{lattice} \quad \frac{1 \text{ mol}}{138.55 \text{ g}} \qquad q = n\,\Delta H_{soln} \quad \frac{1000 \text{ J}}{1 \text{ kJ}}$$

then $mL_{soln} \rightarrow g_{soln}$ then $q, g_{soln}, C_s \rightarrow \Delta T$

$$\frac{1.05 \text{ g}}{1 \text{ mL}} \qquad\qquad q = mC_s\,\Delta T$$

Solution: $\Delta H_{soln} = \Delta H_{solute} + \Delta H_{hydration}$ where $\Delta H_{solute} = -\Delta H_{lattice}$ so $\Delta H_{soln} = \Delta H_{hydration} - \Delta H_{lattice}$

$\Delta H_{soln} = -548$ kJ/mol $- (-599$ kJ/mol$) = +51$ kJ/mol and $10.0 \text{ g} \times \dfrac{1 \text{ mol}}{138.55 \text{ g}} = 0.072\underline{1}761$ mol then

$q = n\,\Delta H_{soln} = 0.072\underline{1}761 \text{ mol} \times 51 \dfrac{\text{kJ}}{\text{mol}} = +3.6\underline{8}10 \text{ kJ} \times \dfrac{1000 \text{ J}}{1 \text{ kJ}} = +3\underline{6}81.0$ J absorbed then

$100.0 \text{ mL} \times \dfrac{1.05 \text{ g}}{1 \text{ mL}} = 105$ g. Because heat is absorbed when $KClO_4$ dissolves, the temperature will drop or

$q = -3\underline{6}81.0$ J and $q = mC_s\Delta T$. Rearrange to solve for ΔT.

$\Delta T = \dfrac{q}{mC_s} = \dfrac{-3\underline{6}81.0 \text{ J}}{105 \text{ g} \times 4.05 \dfrac{\text{J}}{\text{g} \cdot {}^\circ\text{C}}} = -8.7\,{}^\circ\text{C}$

Check: The units (kJ/mol and °C) are correct. The magnitude of the answer (51 kJ/mol) makes physical sense because the lattice energy is larger than the heat of hydration. The magnitude of the temperature change (-9 °C) makes physical sense because heat is absorbed and the heat of solution is fairly small.

12.72   **Given:** NaOH: lattice energy $= -887$ kJ/mol, $\Delta H_{hydration} = -932$ kJ/mol; 25.0 g NaOH in solution, $T_i = 25.0$ °C; $T_f = 100.0$ °C   **Find:** ΔH_{soln} and m (solution) **Other:** $C_s = 4.0$ J/g °C; $d = 1.05$ g/mL
Conceptual Plan: lattice energy, $\Delta H_{hydration} \rightarrow \Delta H_{soln}$ and g $\rightarrow$ mol then mol, $\Delta H_{soln} \rightarrow q(kJ) \rightarrow q(J)$

$$\Delta H_{soln} = \Delta H_{solute} + \Delta H_{hydration} \text{ where } \Delta H_{solute} = -\Delta H_{lattice} \quad \frac{1 \text{ mol}}{40.00 \text{ g}} \qquad q = n\,\Delta H_{soln} \quad \frac{1000 \text{ J}}{1 \text{ kJ}}$$

and $T_i, T_f \rightarrow \Delta T$ then $q, \Delta T, C_s \rightarrow g_{soln}$ then $g_{soln} \rightarrow mL_{soln}$

$$\Delta T = T_f - T_i \qquad q = mC_s\,\Delta T \qquad \frac{1 \text{ mL}}{1.05 \text{ g}}$$

Solution: $\Delta H_{soln} = \Delta H_{solute} + \Delta H_{hydration}$ where $\Delta H_{solute} = -\Delta H_{lattice}$ so $\Delta H_{soln} = \Delta H_{hydration} - \Delta H_{lattice}$

$\Delta H_{soln} = -932$ kJ/mol $- (-887$ kJ/mol$) = -45$ kJ/mol and $25.0 \text{ g} \times \dfrac{1 \text{ mol}}{40.00 \text{ g}} = 0.625$ mol then

$q = n\,\Delta H_{soln} = 0.625 \text{ mol} \times \left(-45 \dfrac{\text{kJ}}{\text{mol}}\right) = -28.125 \text{ kJ} \times \dfrac{1000 \text{ J}}{1 \text{ kJ}} = -2\underline{8}125$ J released then

$\Delta T = T_f - T_i = 100.0$ °C $- 25.0$ °C $= 75.0$ °C. Because heat is released when NaOH dissolves, the temperature will rise or $q = +2\underline{8}125$ J and $q = mC_s\Delta T$. Rearrange to solve for m.

$m = \dfrac{q}{C_s\Delta T} = \dfrac{+2\underline{8}125 \text{ J}}{4.0 \dfrac{\text{J}}{\text{g} \cdot {}^\circ\text{C}} \times 75.0\,{}^\circ\text{C}} = 9\underline{3}.750$ g soln then $9\underline{3}.750 \text{ g} \times \dfrac{1 \text{ mL}}{1.05 \text{ g}} = 89$ mL soln

Check: The units (kJ/mol and mL) are correct. The magnitude of the answer (-45 kJ/mol) makes physical sense because the lattice energy is smaller than the heat of hydration. The magnitude of the solution volume (90 mL) makes physical sense because we have 2/3 mole of NaOH and a large temperature change. NaOH is a strong base, so we expect heat to be released and need to take precautions in the lab.

12.73   **Given:** Argon, 0.0537 L; 25 °C, $P_{Ar} = 1.0$ atm to make 1.0 L saturated solution   **Find:** $k_H(Ar)$
Conceptual Plan: °C $\rightarrow$ K and $P_{Ar}, V, T \rightarrow mol_{Ar}$ then $mol_{Ar}, V_{soln}, P_{Ar} \rightarrow k_H(Ar)$

$$K = {}^\circ\text{C} + 273.15 \qquad PV = nRT \qquad S_{Ar} = k_H(Ar)P_{Ar} \text{ with } S_{Ar} = \frac{mol_{Ar}}{L_{soln}}$$

Solution: 25 °C $+ 273.15 = 298$ K and $PV = nRT$. Rearrange to solve for n.

$$n = \frac{PV}{RT} = \frac{1.0 \text{ atm} \times 0.0537 \text{ L}}{0.08206 \dfrac{\text{L} \cdot \text{atm}}{\text{K} \cdot \text{mol}} \times 298 \text{ K}} = 0.0021\underline{9}597 \text{ mol then } S_{Ar} = k_H(Ar)P_{Ar} \text{ with } S_{Ar} = \frac{\text{mol}_{Ar}}{\text{L}_{soln}}$$

Substitute in values and rearrange to solve for k_H.

$$k_H(Ar) = \frac{\text{mol}_{Ar}}{\text{L}_{soln} P_{Ar}} = \frac{0.0021\underline{9}597 \text{ mol}}{1.0 \text{ L}_{soln} \times 1.0 \text{ atm}} = 2.2 \times 10^{-3} \frac{\text{M}}{\text{atm}}$$

Check: The units (M/atm) are correct. The magnitude of the answer (10^{-3}) seems reasonable because it is consistent with other values in the text.

12.74 **Given:** gas: 1.65 L; 25 °C, $P = 725$ torr; and $k_H = 0.112$ M/atm   **Find:** volume of saturated solution
Conceptual Plan: °C → K and torr → atm P, V, T → mol$_{gas}$ then mol$_{gas}, k_H, P$ → V_{soln}

$$K = °C + 273.15 \qquad \frac{1 \text{ atm}}{760 \text{ torr}} \qquad PV = nRT \qquad S_{gas} = k_H(gas)P_{gas} \text{ with } S_{gas} = \frac{\text{mol}_{gas}}{\text{L}_{soln}}$$

Solution: $25 \text{ °C} + 273.15 = 298 \text{ K}$ and $725 \text{ torr} \times \dfrac{1 \text{ atm}}{760 \text{ torr}} = 0.953\underline{9}47 \text{ atm}$ then $PV = nRT$. Rearrange to solve for

n. $$n = \frac{PV}{RT} = \frac{0.953\underline{9}47 \text{ atm} \times 1.65 \text{ L}}{0.08206 \dfrac{\text{L} \cdot \text{atm}}{\text{K} \cdot \text{mol}} \times 298 \text{ K}} = 0.0643\underline{6}66 \text{ mol then } S_{gas} = k_H(gas)P_{gas}$$

with $S_{gas} = \dfrac{\text{mol}_{gas}}{\text{L}_{soln}}$. Substitute values and rearrange to solve for V_{soln}.

$$L_{soln} = \frac{\text{mol}_{gas}}{k_H(gas)P_{gas}} = \frac{0.0643\underline{6}66 \text{ mol}}{0.112 \dfrac{\text{mol}}{\text{L} \cdot \text{atm}} \times 0.953\underline{9}47 \text{ atm}} = 0.602 \text{ L soln}$$

Check: The units (L) are correct. The magnitude of the answer (0.6 L) seems reasonable because the Henry's law constant is so large.

12.75 **Given:** 0.0020 ppm by mass Hg = legal limit; 0.0040 ppm by mass Hg = contaminated water; 50.0 mg Hg ingested
Find: volume of contaminated water
Conceptual Plan: mg$_{Hg}$ → g$_{Hg}$ → g$_{H_2O}$ → mL$_{H_2O}$ → L$_{H_2O}$

$$\frac{1 \text{ g}}{1000 \text{ mg}} \qquad \frac{10^6 \text{ g water}}{0.0040 \text{ g Hg}} \qquad \frac{1 \text{ mL}}{1.00 \text{ g}} \qquad \frac{1 \text{ L}}{1000 \text{ mL}}$$

Solution: $50.0 \text{ mg Hg} \times \dfrac{1 \text{ g Hg}}{1000 \text{ mg Hg}} \times \dfrac{10^6 \text{ g water}}{0.0040 \text{ g Hg}} \times \dfrac{1 \text{ mL water}}{1.00 \text{ g water}} \times \dfrac{1 \text{ L water}}{1000 \text{ mL water}} = 1.3 \times 10^4 \text{ L water}$

Check: The units (L) are correct. The magnitude of the answer (10^4 L) seems reasonable because the concentration is so low.

12.76 **Given:** 2.4 g Na ingested/day; 0.050% Na by mass in water; $d = 1.0$ g/mL   **Find:** volume of water
Conceptual Plan: g$_{Na}$ → g$_{H_2O}$ → mL$_{H_2O}$ → L$_{H_2O}$

$$\frac{100.000 \text{ g water}}{0.050 \text{ g Na}} \qquad \frac{1 \text{ mL}}{1.0 \text{ g}} \qquad \frac{1 \text{ L}}{1000 \text{ mL}}$$

Solution: $2.4 \text{ g Na} \times \dfrac{100.000 \text{ g solution}}{0.050 \text{ g Na}} \times \dfrac{1 \text{ mL water}}{1.0 \text{ g solution}} \times \dfrac{1 \text{ L water}}{1000 \text{ mL water}} = 4.8 \text{ L water}$

Check: The units (L) are correct. The magnitude of the answer (5 L) seems reasonable because the concentration is low but not extremely low.

12.77 **Given:** 12.5% NaCl by mass in water at 55 °C; 2.5 L vapor   **Find:** g$_{H_2O}$ in vapor
Other: $P°_{H_2O} = 118$ torr, $i_{NaCl} = 2.0$ (complete dissociation)
Conceptual Plan: % NaCl by mass → g$_{NaCl}$, g$_{H_2O}$ then g$_{NaCl}$ → mol$_{NaCl}$ and g$_{H_2O}$ → mol$_{H_2O}$

$$\frac{12.5 \text{ g NaCl}}{100 \text{ g (NaCl + H}_2\text{O)}} \qquad \frac{1 \text{ mol NaCl}}{58.44 \text{ g NaCl}} \qquad \frac{1 \text{ mol H}_2\text{O}}{18.02 \text{ g H}_2\text{O}}$$

then mol$_{NaCl}$, mol$_{H_2O}$ → χ_{NaCl} → χ_{H_2O} then $\chi_{H_2O}, P°_{H_2O}$ → P_{H_2O}

$$\chi = \frac{\text{amount solute (in moles)}}{\text{total amount of solute and solvent (in moles)}} \qquad \chi_{H_2O} = 1 - i_{NaCl}\chi_{NaCl} \qquad P_{solution} = \chi_{solvent}P°_{solvent}$$

then torr $\rightarrow$ atm and °C $\rightarrow$ K $P, V, T \rightarrow$ mol$_{H_2O} \rightarrow$ g$_{H_2O}$

$$\frac{1\ atm}{760\ torr} \qquad K = °C + 273.15 \qquad PV = nRT \qquad \frac{18.02\ g\ H_2O}{1\ mol\ H_2O}$$

Solution: $\dfrac{12.5\ g\ NaCl}{100\ g\ (NaCl + H_2O)}$ means 12.5 g NaCl and $(100\ g - 12.5\ g) = 87.5\ g\ H_2O$ then

$12.5\ g\ NaCl \times \dfrac{1\ mol\ NaCl}{58.44\ g\ NaCl} = 0.213895\ mol\ NaCl$ and $87.5\ g\ H_2O \times \dfrac{1\ mol\ H_2O}{18.02\ g\ H_2O} = 4.85572\ mol\ H_2O$

then $\chi = \dfrac{\text{amount solute (in moles)}}{\text{total amount of solute and solvent (in moles)}} = \dfrac{0.213895\ mol}{0.213895\ mol + 4.85572\ mol} = 0.0421916$

then $\chi_{H_2O} = 1 - i_{NaCl}\chi_{NaCl} = 1 - (2.0 \times 0.0421916) = 0.915617$

then $P_{solution} = \chi_{solvent} P°_{solvent} = 0.915617 \times 118\ torr = 108.043\ torr\ H_2O$ then

$108.043\ torr\ H_2O \times \dfrac{1\ atm}{760\ torr} = 0.142162\ atm$

and $55\ °C + 273.15 = 328\ K$ then $PV = nRT$. Rearrange to solve for n.

$n = \dfrac{PV}{RT} = \dfrac{0.142162\ atm \times 2.5\ L}{0.08206\ \dfrac{L \cdot atm}{K \cdot mol} \times 328\ K} = 0.013204\ mol$ then

$0.013204\ mol\ H_2O \times \dfrac{18.02\ g\ H_2O}{1\ mol\ H_2O} = 0.24\ g\ H_2O$

Check: The units (g) are correct. The magnitude of the answer (0.2 g) seems reasonable because there is very little mass in a vapor.

12.78 **Given:** 19.5 mg water in 1 L vapor at 25 °C **Find:** mole percent solute in solution **Other:** $P°_{H_2O} = 23.78$ torr

Conceptual Plan: mg$_{H_2O} \rightarrow$ g$_{H_2O} \rightarrow$ mol$_{H_2O}$ and °C $\rightarrow$ K then V, mol$_{H_2O}$, $T \rightarrow P_{H_2O}$

$$\frac{1\ g}{1000\ mg} \qquad \frac{1\ mol\ H_2O}{18.02\ g\ H_2O} \qquad\qquad K = °C + 273.15 \qquad\qquad PV = nRT$$

then atm $\rightarrow$ torr then $P_{H_2O}, P°_{H_2O} \rightarrow \chi_{H_2O} \rightarrow \chi_{solute} \rightarrow$ **mole percent solute**

$$\frac{760\ torr}{1\ atm} \qquad\qquad P_{H_2O} = \chi_{H_2O} P°_{H_2O} \quad \chi_{Solute} = 1 - \chi_{H_2O} \quad \text{mole percent solute} = \chi_{Solute} \times 100\%$$

Solution: $19.5\ mg\ H_2O \times \dfrac{1\ g\ H_2O}{1000\ mg\ H_2O} \times \dfrac{1\ mol\ H_2O}{18.02\ g\ H_2O} = 0.00108213\ mol\ H_2O$ and

$25\ °C + 273.15 = 298\ K$ then $PV = nRT$. Rearrange to solve for P.

$P = \dfrac{nRT}{V} = \dfrac{0.00108213\ mol \times 0.08206\ \dfrac{L \cdot atm}{K \cdot mol} \times 298\ K}{1.00\ L} = 0.02646228\ atm$

$0.02646228\ atm \times \dfrac{760\ torr}{1\ atm} = 20.11133\ torr$ and $P_{H_2O} = \chi_{H_2O} P°_{H_2O}$. Rearrange to solve for χ_{H_2O}.

$\chi_{H_2O} = \dfrac{P_{H_2O}}{P°_{H_2O}} = \dfrac{20.11133\ torr}{23.78\ torr} = 0.845725$ then $\chi_{solute} = 1 - \chi_{H_2O} = 1 - 0.845725 = 0.15428$ then

mole percent solute $= \chi_{solute} \times 100\% = 0.15428 \times 100\% = 15.4$ mole percent

Check: The units (mole percent) are correct. The magnitude of the answer (15 mole percent) seems reasonable because we expect more water than solute.

12.79 **Given:** $T_b = 106.5\ °C$ aqueous solution **Find:** T_f **Other:** $K_f = 1.86\ °C/m$; $K_b = 0.512\ °C/m$

Conceptual Plan: $T_b \rightarrow \Delta T_b$ then $\Delta T_b, K_b \rightarrow m$ then $m, K_f \rightarrow \Delta T_f \rightarrow T_f$

$$T_b = T°_b + \Delta T_b \qquad\qquad \Delta T_b = K_b \times m \quad \Delta T_f = K_f \times m \qquad T_f = T°_f - \Delta T_f$$

Solution: $T_b = T°_b + \Delta T_b$ so $\Delta T_b = T_b - T°_b = 106.5\ °C - 100.0\ °C = 6.5\ °C$ then $\Delta T_b = K_b \times m$

Rearrange to solve for m. $m = \dfrac{\Delta T_b}{K_b} = \dfrac{6.5\ °C}{0.512\ \dfrac{°C}{m}} = 12.695\ m$ then

$$\Delta T_f = K_f \times m = 1.86 \frac{°C}{m} \times 12.695\ \cancel{m} = 23.6\ °C \text{ then } T_f = T_f° - \Delta T_f = 0.000\ °C - 23.6\ °C = -24\ °C$$

Check: The units (°C) are correct. The magnitude of the answer (−24 °C) seems reasonable because the shift in boiling point is less than the shift in freezing point because the constant for boiling is smaller than the constant for freezing.

12.80   **Given:** $P_{H_2O} = 20.5$ torr at 25 °C aqueous solution   **Find:** T_b **Other:** $P_{H_2O}° = 23.78$ torr; $K_b = 0.512\ °C/m$
Conceptual Plan: $P_{H_2O}, P_{H_2O}° \rightarrow \chi_{H_2O}$ assume 1 kg water $kg_{H_2O} \rightarrow mol_{H_2O}$ then

$$P_{H_2O} = \chi_{H_2O} P_{H_2O}° \qquad \frac{1\ mol\ H_2O}{18.02\ g\ H_2O}$$

$mol_{H_2O}, \chi_{H_2O} \rightarrow mol_{solute}$ then $mol_{solute}, kg_{H_2O} \rightarrow m_{solute}$ then $m, K_b \rightarrow \Delta T_b \rightarrow T_b$

$$\chi_{H_2O} = \frac{moles\ H_2O}{moles\ H_2O + moles\ solute} \qquad m = \frac{amount\ solute\ (moles)}{mass\ solvent\ (kg)} \qquad \Delta T_b = K_b \times m \quad T_b = T_b° + \Delta T_b$$

Solution: $P_{H_2O} = \chi_{H_2O} P_{H_2O}°$. Rearrange to solve for χ_{H_2O}. $\chi_{H_2O} = \dfrac{P_{H_2O}}{P_{H_2O}°} = \dfrac{20.5\ \cancel{torr}}{23.78\ \cancel{torr}} = 0.862069$ then

$$1000\ \cancel{g\ H_2O} \times \frac{1\ mol\ H_2O}{18.02\ \cancel{g\ H_2O}} = 55.49390\ mol\ H_2O \text{ then}$$

$$\chi_{H_2O} = \frac{moles\ H_2O}{moles\ H_2O + moles\ solute} = \frac{55.49390\ \cancel{mol}}{55.49390\ \cancel{mol} + x\ \cancel{mol}} = 0.862069. \text{ Solve for } x \text{ moles of solute.}$$

$$55.49390\ mol = 0.862069\ (55.49390\ mol + x\ mol) \rightarrow x = \frac{(55.49390 - 47.8396)\ mol}{0.862069} = 8.87899\ mol \text{ then}$$

$$m = \frac{amount\ solute\ (moles)}{mass\ solvent\ (kg)} = \frac{8.87899\ mol}{1\ kg} = 8.87899\ m \text{ then } \Delta T_b = K_b \times m = 0.512\ \frac{°C}{m} \times 8.87899\ \cancel{m} = 4.5\ °C$$

then $T_b = T_b° + \Delta T_b = 100.0\ °C + 4.5\ °C = 104.5\ °C$

Check: The units (°C) are correct. The magnitude of the answer (4.5 °C) seems reasonable because there is a significant lowering of the vapor pressure.

12.81   (a)   **Given:** 0.90% NaCl by mass per volume; isotonic aqueous solution at 25 °C; KCl; $i = 1.9$
Find: % KCl by mass per volume
Conceptual Plan: Isotonic solutions will have the same number of particles. Because i is the same,

$$\frac{1\ mol\ KCl}{1\ mol\ NaCl}$$

the new % mass per volume will be the mass ratio of the two salts.

$$\text{percent by mass per volume} = \frac{mass\ solute}{V} \times 100\% \qquad \frac{1\ mol\ NaCl}{58.44\ g\ NaCl} \text{ and } \frac{74.55\ g\ KCl}{1\ mol\ KCl}$$

Solution: percent by mass per volume $= \dfrac{mass\ solute}{V} \times 100\%$

$$= \frac{0.0090\ g\ \cancel{NaCl}}{V} \times \frac{1\ \cancel{mol\ NaCl}}{58.44\ g\ \cancel{NaCl}} \times \frac{1\ \cancel{mol\ KCl}}{1\ \cancel{mol\ NaCl}} \times \frac{74.55\ g\ KCl}{1\ \cancel{mol\ KCl}} \times 100\%$$

$= 1.1\%$ KCl by mass per volume

Check: The units (% KCl by mass per volume) are correct. The magnitude of the answer (1.1%) seems reasonable because the molar mass of KCl is larger than the molar mass of NaCl.

(b)   **Given:** 0.90% NaCl by mass per volume; isotonic aqueous solution at 25 °C; NaBr; $i = 1.9$
Find: % NaBr by mass per volume
Conceptual Plan: Isotonic solutions will have the same number of particles. Because i is the same,

$$\frac{1\ mol\ NaBr}{1\ mol\ NaCl}$$

the new % mass per volume will be the mass ratio of the two salts.

$$\text{percent by mass per volume} = \frac{mass\ solute}{V} \times 100\% \qquad \frac{1\ mol\ NaCl}{58.44\ g\ NaCl} \text{ and } \frac{102.89\ g\ NaBr}{1\ mol\ NaBr}$$

Solution: percent by mass per volume $= \dfrac{\text{mass solute}}{V} \times 100\%$

$$= \dfrac{0.0090 \text{ g NaCl}}{V} \times \dfrac{1 \text{ mol NaCl}}{58.44 \text{ g NaCl}} \times \dfrac{1 \text{ mol NaBr}}{1 \text{ mol NaCl}} \times \dfrac{102.89 \text{ g NaBr}}{1 \text{ mol NaBr}} \times 100\%$$

$= 1.6\%$ NaBr by mass per volume

Check: The units (% NaBr by mass per volume) are correct. The magnitude of the answer (1.6%) seems reasonable because the molar mass of NaBr is larger than the molar mass of NaCl.

(c)　**Given:** 0.90% NaCl by mass per volume; isotonic aqueous solution at 25 °C; glucose ($C_6H_{12}O_6$); $i = 1.9$
Find: % glucose by mass per volume
Conceptual Plan: Isotonic solutions will have the same number of particles. Because glucose is a nonelectrolyte, the i is not the same; then use the mass ratio of the two compounds.

$$\dfrac{1.9 \text{ mol } C_6H_{12}O_6}{1 \text{ mol NaCl}} \qquad \text{percent by mass per volume} = \dfrac{\text{mass solute}}{V} \times 100\% \qquad \dfrac{1 \text{ mol NaCl}}{58.44 \text{ g NaCl}} \text{ and } \dfrac{180.16 \text{ g } C_6H_{12}O_6}{1 \text{ mol } C_6H_{12}O_6}$$

Solution: percent by mass per volume $= \dfrac{\text{mass solute}}{V} \times 100\%$

$$= \dfrac{0.0090 \text{ g NaCl}}{V} \times \dfrac{1 \text{ mol NaCl}}{58.44 \text{ g NaCl}} \times \dfrac{1.9 \text{ mol } C_6H_{12}O_6}{1 \text{ mol NaCl}} \times \dfrac{180.16 \text{ g } C_6H_{12}O_6}{1 \text{ mol } C_6H_{12}O_6} \times 100\%$$

$= 5.3\%$ $C_6H_{12}O_6$ by mass per volume

Check: The units (% $C_6H_{12}O_6$ by mass per volume) are correct. The magnitude of the answer (5.3%) seems reasonable because the molar mass of $C_6H_{12}O_6$ is larger than the molar mass of NaCl and we need more moles of $C_6H_{12}O_6$ because it is a nonelectrolyte.

12.82　**Given:** 28.5 g of magnesium citrate ($Mg_3(C_6H_5O_7)_2$) in 235 mL of solution at 37 °C, complete dissociation
Find: Π
Conceptual Plan: $mL_{soln} \rightarrow L_{soln}$ and $g_{Mg_3(C_6H_5O_7)_2} \rightarrow mol_{Mg_3(C_6H_5O_7)_2}$ then $mol_{Mg_3(C_6H_5O_7)_2}, L_{soln} \rightarrow M$

$$\dfrac{1 \text{ L}}{1000 \text{ mL}} \qquad\qquad \dfrac{1 \text{ mol } Mg_3(C_6H_5O_7)_2}{451.13 \text{ g } Mg_3(C_6H_5O_7)_2} \qquad\qquad M = \dfrac{\text{amount solute (moles)}}{\text{volume solution (L)}}$$

then $M, i, T \rightarrow \Pi$

$$\Pi = i \times MRT \text{ where } i = 5$$

Solution: $235 \text{ mL} \times \dfrac{1 \text{ L}}{1000 \text{ mL}} = 0.235 \text{ L}$ and

$$28.5 \text{ g } Mg_3(C_6H_5O_7)_2 \times \dfrac{1 \text{ mol } Mg_3(C_6H_5O_7)_2}{451.13 \text{ g } Mg_3(C_6H_5O_7)_2} = 0.063\underline{1}747 \text{ mol } Mg_3(C_6H_5O_7)_2 \text{ then}$$

$$M = \dfrac{\text{amount solute (moles)}}{\text{volume solution (L)}} = \dfrac{0.063\underline{1}747 \text{ mol } Mg_3(C_6H_5O_7)_2}{0.235 \text{ L}} = 0.268828 \text{ M then}$$

$$\Pi = i \times MRT = 5 \times 0.268\underline{8}28 \dfrac{\text{mol}}{L} \times 0.08206 \dfrac{L \cdot \text{atm}}{K \cdot \text{mol}} \times 310. \text{ K} = 34.2 \text{ atm}$$

Check: The units (atm) are correct. The magnitude of the answer (34 atm) seems reasonable because the molarity is ~1.5.

12.83　**Given:** 4.5701 g of $MgCl_2$ and 43.238 g water, $P_{soln} = 0.3624$ atm, $P^\circ_{soln} = 0.3804$ atm at 348.0 K
Find: $i_{measured}$
Conceptual Plan: $g_{MgCl_2} \rightarrow mol_{MgCl_2}$ and $g_{H_2O} \rightarrow mol_{H_2O}$ then $P_{soln}, P^\circ_{soln}, \rightarrow \chi_{MgCl_2}$

$$\dfrac{1 \text{ mol } MgCl_2}{95.21 \text{ g } MgCl_2} \qquad\qquad \dfrac{1 \text{ mol } H_2O}{18.02 \text{ g } H_2O} \qquad\qquad P_{soln} = (1 - \chi_{MgCl_2})P^\circ_{H_2O}$$

then $mol_{MgCl_2}, mol_{H_2O}, \chi_{MgCl_2} \rightarrow i$

$$\chi_{MgCl_2} = \dfrac{i(\text{moles } MgCl_2)}{\text{moles } H_2O + i(\text{moles } MgCl_2)}$$

Solution: $4.5701 \text{ g } MgCl_2 \times \dfrac{1 \text{ mol } MgCl_2}{95.21 \text{ g } MgCl_2} = 0.0480\underline{0}021 \text{ mol } MgCl_2 \text{ and}$

$$43.238 \text{ g } H_2O \times \frac{1 \text{ mol } H_2O}{18.02 \text{ g } H_2O} = 2.39944506 \text{ mol } H_2O \text{ then } P_{\text{soln}} = (1 - \chi_{MgCl_2})P^{\circ}_{H_2O} \text{ so}$$

$$\chi_{MgCl_2} = 1 - \frac{P_{\text{soln}}}{P^{\circ}_{H_2O}} = 1 - \frac{0.3624 \text{ atm}}{0.3804 \text{ atm}} = 0.04731861. \text{ Solve for } i.$$

$$i(0.04800021) = 0.04731861(2.39944506 + i(0.04800021)) \rightarrow$$

$$i(0.04800021 - 0.002271303) = 0.1135384 \rightarrow i = \frac{0.1135384}{0.04572891} = 2.483$$

Check: The units (none) are correct. The magnitude of the answer (2.5) seems reasonable for $MgCl_2$ because we expect i to be 3 if it completely dissociates. Because Mg is small and doubly charged, we expect a significant drop from 3.

12.84   **Given:** 7.050 g of HNO_2 and 1.000 kg of water, $T_f = -0.2929 \,^{\circ}C$ **Find:** fraction dissociated
Other: $K_f = 1.86 \,^{\circ}C/m$
Conceptual Plan: $g_{HNO_2} \rightarrow mol_{HNO_2}$ then mol_{HNO_2}, $kg_{H_2O} \rightarrow m$ then m, $\Delta T_{f\text{actual}}$, $K_f \rightarrow i_{\text{actual}}$ then

$$\frac{1 \text{ mol } HNO_2}{47.02 \text{ g } HNO_2} \qquad\qquad m = \frac{\text{amount solute (moles)}}{\text{mass solvent (kg)}} \qquad\qquad \Delta T_{f\text{actual}} = i_{\text{actual}} \times m \times K_f$$

$i_{\text{actual}} \rightarrow$ **fraction dissociated**

$$\text{fraction dissociated} = i_{\text{actual}} - 1$$

Solution: $7.050 \text{ g } HNO_2 \times \dfrac{1 \text{ mol } HNO_2}{47.02 \text{ g } HNO_2} = 0.1499362 \text{ mol } HNO_2$ then

$$m = \frac{\text{amount solute (moles)}}{\text{mass solvent (kg)}} = \frac{0.1499362 \text{ mol } HNO_2}{1.000 \text{ kg}} = 0.1499362 \; m \text{ then } \Delta T_{f\text{actual}} = i_{\text{actual}} \times m \times K_f \rightarrow$$

$$0.2929 = i(0.1499362 \; m)\left(\frac{1.86 \,^{\circ}C}{m}\right) \rightarrow i = 1.0503 \text{ then fraction dissociated} = i_{\text{actual}} - 1 = 1.0503 - 1 = 0.050$$

Check: The units (none) are correct. The magnitude of the answer (0.05) seems reasonable because weak acids do not fully dissociate.

12.85   **Given:** $T_b = 375.3 \text{ K}$ aqueous solution   **Find:** P_{H_2O} **Other:** $P^{\circ}_{H_2O} = 0.2467 \text{ atm}$; $K_b = 0.512 \,^{\circ}C/m$
Conceptual Plan: $T_b \rightarrow \Delta T_b$ then ΔT_b, $K_b \rightarrow m$ assume 1 kg water $kg_{H_2O} \rightarrow mol_{H_2O}$ then

$$T_b = T^{\circ}_b + \Delta T_b \qquad\qquad \Delta T_b = K_b \times m \qquad\qquad \frac{1 \text{ mol } H_2O}{18.02 \text{ g } H_2O}$$

$m \rightarrow mol_{\text{solute}}$ then mol_{H_2O}, $mol_{\text{solute}} \rightarrow \chi_{H_2O}$ then χ_{H_2O}, $P^{\circ}_{H_2O} \rightarrow P_{H_2O}$

$$m = \frac{\text{amount solute (moles)}}{\text{mass solvent (kg)}} \qquad \chi_{H_2O} = \frac{\text{moles } H_2O}{\text{moles } H_2O + \text{moles solute}} \qquad P_{H_2O} = \chi_{H_2O} P^{\circ}_{H_2O}$$

Solution: $T_b = T^{\circ}_b + \Delta T_b$ so $\Delta T_b = T_b - T^{\circ}_b = 375.3 \text{ K} - 373.15 \text{ K} = 2.2 \text{ K} = 2.2 \,^{\circ}C$ then

$$\Delta T_b = K_b \times m. \text{ Rearrange to solve for } m. \; m = \frac{\Delta T_b}{K_b} = \frac{2.2 \,^{\circ}C}{0.512 \dfrac{^{\circ}C}{m}} = 4.296875 \; m \text{ then}$$

$$1000 \text{ g } H_2O \times \frac{1 \text{ mol } H_2O}{18.02 \text{ g } H_2O} = 55.49390 \text{ mol } H_2O \text{ then}$$

$$m = \frac{\text{amount solute (moles)}}{\text{mass solvent (kg)}} = \frac{x \text{ mol}}{1 \text{ kg}} = 4.296875 \; m \text{ so } x = 4.296875 \text{ mol then}$$

$$\chi_{H_2O} = \frac{\text{moles } H_2O}{\text{moles } H_2O + \text{ moles solute}} = \frac{55.49390 \text{ mol}}{55.49390 \text{ mol} + 4.296875 \text{ mol}} = 0.9281348 \text{ then}$$

$$P_{H_2O} = \chi_{H_2O} P^{\circ}_{H_2O} = 0.9281348 \times 0.2467 \text{ atm} = 0.229 \text{ atm}$$

Check: The units (atm) are correct. The magnitude of the answer (0.229 atm) seems reasonable because the mole fraction is lowered by ~7%.

12.86   **Given:** 0.438 M K_2CrO_4 aqueous solution; $d = 1.063$ g/mL at 298 K; complete dissociation   **Find:** P_{soln}
Other: $P^{\circ}_{H_2O} = 0.0313 \text{ atm}$

Conceptual Plan: assume 1 L solution; so we have $0.438 \text{ mol}_{K_2CrO_4} \rightarrow g_{K_2CrO_4}$ then $mL_{soln} \rightarrow g_{soln}$ then

$$\frac{194.20 \text{ g } K_2CrO_4}{1 \text{ mol } K_2CrO_4} \qquad\qquad \frac{1.063 \text{ g}}{1 \text{ mL}}$$

$g_{K_2CrO_4}, g_{soln} \rightarrow g_{H_2O} \rightarrow \text{mol}_{H_2O}$ then $\text{mol}_{H_2O}, \text{mol}_{solute} \rightarrow \chi_{H_2O}$ then $\chi_{H_2O}, P^{\circ}_{H_2O} \rightarrow P_{H_2O}$

$$g_{H_2O} = g \text{ soln} - g \ K_2CrO_4 \quad \frac{1 \text{ mol } H_2O}{18.02 \text{ g } H_2O} \qquad \chi_{H_2O} = \frac{\text{moles } H_2O}{\text{moles } H_2O + \text{moles solute}} \qquad P_{soln} = (1 - i\chi_{K_2CrO_4})P^{\circ}_{H_2O} \ i = 3$$

Solution: $0.438 \ \cancel{\text{mol } K_2CrO_4} \times \dfrac{194.20 \text{ g } K_2CrO_4}{1 \ \cancel{\text{mol } K_2CrO_4}} = 85.\underline{0}596 \text{ g } K_2CrO_4$ then

$1000 \ \cancel{\text{mL}} \times \dfrac{1.063 \text{ g}}{1 \ \cancel{\text{mL}}} = 1063 \text{ g soln}$ then

$g \ H_2O = g \text{ soln} - g \ K_2CrO_4 = 1063 \text{ g soln} - 85.\underline{0}596 \text{ g } K_2CrO_4 = 977.\underline{9}404 \text{ g } H_2O$ then

$977.9404 \ \cancel{\text{g } H_2O} \times \dfrac{1 \text{ mol } H_2O}{18.02 \ \cancel{\text{g } H_2O}} = 54.\underline{2}697 \text{ mol } H_2O$ then

$\chi_{K_2CrO_4} = \dfrac{\text{moles } K_2CrO_4}{\text{moles } H_2O + \text{moles } K_2CrO_4} = \dfrac{0.438 \ \cancel{\text{mol}}}{54.2697 \ \cancel{\text{mol}} + 0.438 \ \cancel{\text{mol}}} = 0.00800\underline{6}19$ then

$P_{soln} = (1 - i\chi_{K_2CrO_4})P^{\circ}_{H_2O} = (1 - 3 \times 0.00800619)0.0313 \text{ atm} = 0.0305 \text{ atm}$

Check: The units (atm) are correct. The magnitude of the answer (0.03 atm) seems reasonable because the mole fraction is lowered by $< 1\%$.

12.87   **Given:** equal masses of carbon tetrachloride (CCl_4) and chloroform ($CHCl_3$) at 316 K; $P^{\circ}_{CCl_4} = 0.354$ atm; $P^{\circ}_{CHCl_3} = 0.526$ atm   **Find:** χ_{CCl_4}, χ_{CHCl_3} in vapor and P_{CHCl_3} in flask of condensed vapor

Conceptual Plan: assume 100 grams of each $g_{CCl_4} \rightarrow \text{mol}_{CCl_4}$ and $g_{CHCl_3} \rightarrow \text{mol}_{CHCl_3}$ then

$$\frac{1 \text{ mol } CCl_4}{153.81 \text{ g } CCl_4} \qquad\qquad \frac{1 \text{ mol } CHCl_3}{119.37 \text{ g } CHCl_3}$$

$\text{mol}_{CCl_4}, \text{mol}_{CHCl_3} \rightarrow \chi_{CCl_4}, \chi_{CHCl_3}$ then $\chi_{CCl_4}, P^{\circ}_{CCl_4} \rightarrow P_{CCl_4}$ and $\chi_{CHCl_3}, P^{\circ}_{CHCl_3} \rightarrow P_{CHCl_3}$ then

$$\chi_{CCl_4} = \frac{\text{amount } CCl_4 \text{ (in moles)}}{\text{total amount (in moles)}} \quad \chi_{CHCl_3} = 1 - \chi_{CCl_4} \qquad P_{CCl_4} = \chi_{CCl_4} P^{\circ}_{CCl_4} \qquad\qquad P_{CHCl_3} = \chi_{CHCl_3} P^{\circ}_{CHCl_3}$$

$P^{\circ}_{CCl_4}, P_{CHCl_3} \rightarrow P_{Total}$ then because $n \ \alpha \ P$ and we are calculating a mass percent, which is a ratio of masses,

$$P_{Total} = P_{CCl_4} + P_{CHCl_3}$$

we can simply convert 1 atm to 1 mole so $P_{CCl_4}, P_{CHCl_3} \rightarrow n_{CHCl_4}, n_{CHCl_3}$ then

$$\chi_{CCl_4} = \frac{\text{amount } CCl_4 \text{ (in moles)}}{\text{total amount (in moles)}}$$

$\text{mol}_{CCl_4}, \text{mol}_{CHCl_3} \rightarrow \chi_{CCl_4}, \chi_{CHCl_3}$ then for the second vapor $\chi_{CHCl_3}, P^{\circ}_{CHCl_3} \rightarrow P_{CHCl_3}$

$$\chi_{CHCl_3} = 1 - \chi_{CCl_4} \qquad\qquad P_{CHCl_3} = \chi_{CHCl_3} P^{\circ}_{CHCl_3}$$

Solution: $100.00 \ \cancel{\text{g } CCl_4} \times \dfrac{1 \text{ mol } CCl_4}{153.81 \ \cancel{\text{g } CCl_4}} = 0.65015\underline{2}79 \text{ mol } CCl_4$ and

$100.00 \ \cancel{\text{g } CHCl_3} \times \dfrac{1 \text{ mol } CHCl_3}{119.37 \ \cancel{\text{g } CHCl_3}} = 0.83773\underline{1}42 \text{ mol } CHCl_3$ then

$\chi_{CCl_4} = \dfrac{\text{amount } CCl_4 \text{ (in moles)}}{\text{total amount (in moles)}} = \dfrac{0.65015279 \ \cancel{\text{mol}}}{0.65015279 \ \cancel{\text{mol}} + 0.83773142 \ \cancel{\text{mol}}} = 0.4369\underline{6}464$ and

$\chi_{CHCl_3} = 1 - \chi_{CCl_4} = 1 - 0.43696464 = 0.5630\underline{3}536$ then

$P_{CCl_4} = \chi_{CCl_4} P^{\circ}_{CCl_4} = 0.43696464 \times 0.354 \text{ atm} = 0.154\underline{6}85 \text{ atm}$ and

$P_{CHCl_3} = \chi_{CHCl_3} P^{\circ}_{CHCl_3} = 0.56303536 \times 0.526 \text{ atm} = 0.296\underline{1}57 \text{ atm}$ then

$P_{Total} = P_{CCl_4} + P_{CHCl_3} = 0.154\underline{6}85 \text{ atm} + 0.296\underline{1}57 \text{ atm} = 0.450\underline{8}42 \text{ atm}$ then

$\text{mol}_{CCl_4} = 0.154\underline{6}85 \text{ mol}$ and $\text{mol}_{CHCl_3} = 0.296\underline{1}57 \text{ mol}$ then

$\chi_{CCl_4} = \dfrac{\text{amount } CCl_4 \text{ (in moles)}}{\text{total amount (in moles)}} = \dfrac{0.154\underline{6}85 \ \cancel{\text{mol}}}{0.154\underline{6}85 \ \cancel{\text{mol}} + 0.296\underline{1}57 \ \cancel{\text{mol}}} = 0.343\underline{1}02 = 0.343$ in the first vapor and

$\chi_{CHCl_3} = 1 - \chi_{CCl_4} = 1 - 0.343\underline{1}02 = 0.656\underline{8}98 = 0.657$ in the first vapor; then in the second vapor

$P_{CHCl_3} = \chi_{CHCl_3} P^{\circ}_{CHCl_3} = 0.656\underline{8}98 \times 0.526 \text{ atm} = 0.345\underline{5}28 \text{ atm} = 0.346 \text{ atm}$

Check: The units (none and atm) are correct. The magnitude of the answers seems reasonable because we expect the lighter component to be found preferentially in the vapor phase. This effect is magnified in the second vapor.

12.88 In the previous problem, we saw that the original liquid has the $\chi_{CHCl_3} = 0.563$, and when the second vapor is condensed, it rose to 0.657. Continue the preceding calculation scheme from Problem 87.

$P_{CCl_4} = \chi_{CCl_4} P°_{CCl_4} = 0.34\underline{3}102 \times 0.354$ atm $= 0.12\underline{1}458$ atm converting to moles; $mol_{CCl_4} = 0.121458$ mol and

$mol_{CHCl_3} = 0.34\underline{5}528$ mol then

$$\chi_{CCl_4} = \frac{amount\ CCl_4\ (in\ moles)}{total\ amount\ (in\ moles)} = \frac{0.12\underline{1}458\ mol}{0.12\underline{1}458\ mol + 0.34\underline{5}528\ mol} = 0.26\underline{0}089 = 0.260\ in\ the\ second\ vapor\ and$$

$\chi_{CHCl_3} = 1 - \chi_{CCl_4} = 1 - 0.26\underline{0}089 = 0.73\underline{9}911 = 0.740$ in the second vapor then in the third vapor

$P_{CHCl_3} = \chi_{CHCl_3} P°_{CHCl_3} = 0.73\underline{9}911 \times 0.526$ atm $= 0.38\underline{9}193$ atm and

$P_{CCl_4} = \chi_{CCl_4} P°_{CCl_4} = 0.26\underline{0}089 \times 0.354$ atm $= 0.09\underline{2}0715$ atm converting to moles

$mol_{CCl_4} = 0.09\underline{2}0715$ mol and $mol_{CHCl_3} = 0.389193$ mol then

$$\chi_{CCl_4} = \frac{amount\ CCl_4\ (in\ moles)}{total\ amount\ (in\ moles)} = \frac{0.09\underline{2}0715\ mol}{0.09\underline{2}0715\ mol + 0.389193\ mol} = 0.19\underline{1}312 = 0.191\ in\ the\ third\ vapor\ and$$

$\chi_{CHCl_3} = 1 - \chi_{CCl_4} = 1 - 0.19\underline{1}312 = 0.80\underline{8}688 = 0.809$ in the third vapor then in the fourth vapor

$P_{CHCl_3} = \chi_{CHCl_3} P°_{CHCl_3} = 0.80\underline{8}688 \times 0.526$ atm $= 0.42\underline{5}370$ atm and

$P_{CCl_4} = \chi_{CCl_4} P°_{CCl_4} = 0.19\underline{1}312 \times 0.354$ atm $= 0.06\underline{7}7244$ atm converting to moles

$mol_{CCl_4} = 0.06\underline{7}7244$ mol and $mol_{CHCl_3} = 0.425370$ mol then

$$\chi_{CCl_4} = \frac{amount\ CCl_4\ (in\ moles)}{total\ amount\ (in\ moles)} = \frac{0.06\underline{7}7244\ mol}{0.06\underline{7}7244\ mol + 0.42\underline{5}370\ mol} = 0.13\underline{7}346 = 0.137\ in\ the\ fourth\ vapor\ and$$

$\chi_{CHCl_3} = 1 - \chi_{CCl_4} = 1 - 0.13\underline{7}346 = 0.86\underline{2}654 = 0.863$ in the fourth vapor. The concentration of the lighter component (chloroform) in the gas phase increases with each step.

12.89 **Given:** 49.0% H_2SO_4 by mass, $d = 1.39$ g/cm^3, 25.0 mL diluted to 99.8 cm^3 **Find:** molarity

Conceptual Plan: initial mL$_{solution}$ → g$_{solution}$ → g$_{H_2SO_4}$ → mol$_{H_2SO_4}$ and final mL$_{solution}$ → L$_{solution}$

$$\frac{1.39\ g}{1\ mL} \qquad \frac{49.0\ g\ H_2SO_4}{100\ g\ solution} \qquad \frac{1\ mol\ H_2SO_4}{98.08\ g\ H_2SO_4} \qquad\qquad\qquad \frac{1\ L}{1000\ mL}$$

then mol$_{H_2SO_4}$, L$_{solution}$ → **M**

$$M = \frac{amount\ solute\ (moles)}{volume\ solution\ (L)}$$

Solution:

$$25.0\ mL\ solution \times \frac{1.39\ g\ solution}{1\ mL\ solution} \times \frac{49.0\ g\ H_2SO_4}{100\ g\ solution} \times \frac{1\ mol\ H_2SO_4}{98.08\ g\ H_2SO_4} = 0.17\underline{3}6803\ mol\ H_2SO_4\ and$$

$$99.8\ mL\ solution \times \frac{1\ L\ solution}{1000\ mL\ solution} = 0.0998\ L\ solution\ then$$

$$M = \frac{amount\ solute\ (moles)}{volume\ solution\ (L)} = \frac{0.17\underline{3}6803\ mol\ H_2SO_4}{0.0998\ L\ solution} = 1.74\ M\ H_2SO_4$$

Check: The units (M) are correct. The magnitude of the answer (1.74 M) seems reasonable because the solution is ~1/6 surfuric acid.

12.90 **Given:** 50.0 g of solution in water, $\chi_{CH_4N_2O} = 0.0770$ **Find:** mass CH_4N_2O

Conceptual Plan: Set up equations for mass and moles

$$g_{CH_4N_2O} + g_{H_2O} = 50.0\ g \qquad \chi_{CH_4N_2O} = \frac{mol\ CH_4N_2O}{mol\ CH_4N_2O + mol\ H_2O} \qquad \frac{1\ mol\ H_2O}{18.02\ g\ H_2O}\ and\ \frac{1\ mol\ CH_4N_2O}{60.06\ g\ CH_4N_2O}$$

Combine relationships and solve for g$_{CH_4N_2O}$

Solution: $g_{CH_4N_2O} + g_{H_2O} = 50.0\ g$, $\chi_{CH_4N_2O} = \dfrac{mol\ CH_4N_2O}{mol\ CH_4N_2O + mol\ H_2O}$, $\dfrac{1\ mol\ H_2O}{18.02\ g\ H_2O}$, and

$\dfrac{1\ mol\ CH_4N_2O}{60.06\ g\ CH_4N_2O}$. Combine relationships and solve for $g_{CH_4N_2O}$. Start with $g_{H_2O} = 50.0\ g - g_{CH_4N_2O}$ and substitute into $\chi_{CH_4N_2O}$.

$$\chi_{CH_4N_2O} = 0.0770 = \cfrac{g\ CH_4N_2O \times \cfrac{1\ mol\ CH_4N_2O}{60.06\ g\ CH_4N_2O}}{g\ CH_4N_2O \times \cfrac{1\ mol\ CH_4N_2O}{60.06\ g\ CH_4N_2O} + (50.0\ g - g\ CH_4N_2O) \times \cfrac{1\ mol\ H_2O}{18.02\ g\ H_2O}} \text{ and}$$

solve for $g_{CH_4N_2O}$. $0.0770 \left(g\ CH_4N_2O \times \cfrac{1\ mol\ CH_4N_2O}{60.06\ g\ CH_4N_2O} + (50.0\ g - g\ CH_4N_2O) \times \cfrac{1\ mol\ H_2O}{18.02\ g\ H_2O} \right)$

$$= g\ CH_4N_2O \times \frac{1\ mol\ CH_4N_2O}{60.06\ g\ CH_4N_2O}$$

$\rightarrow$ g CH_4N_2O (0.001282051) + 0.21365150 g $-$ g CH_4N_2O (0.0042730300) = g CH_4N_2O(0.01665002)

$\rightarrow$ 0.21365150 g = g CH_4N_2O(0.01964100) $\rightarrow$

$$g\ CH_4N_2O = \frac{0.21365150\ g}{0.01964100} = 10.877832\ g\ CH_4N_2O = 10.9\ g\ CH_4N_2O$$

Check: The units (g) are correct. The magnitude of the answer (11 g) seems reasonable because the molar mass of urea is over three times the molar mass of water and the mole fraction is almost 0.1.

12.91　**Given:** 10.05 g of unknown compound in 50.0 g water, $T_f = -3.16\ °C$, mass percent composition of the compound is 60.97% C and 11.94% H; the rest is O　**Find:** molecular formula

Other: $K_f = 1.86\ °C/m$; $d = 1.00\ g/mL$

Conceptual Plan: $g_{H_2O} \rightarrow kg_{H_2O}$ and $T_f \rightarrow \Delta T_f$ then $\Delta T_f, K_f \rightarrow m$ then $m, kg_{H_2O} \rightarrow mol_{Unk}$

$$\frac{1\ kg}{1000\ g} \qquad T_f = T_f^° - \Delta T_f \qquad \Delta T_f = K_f \times m \qquad m = \frac{amount\ solute\ (moles)}{mass\ solvent\ (kg)}$$

then $g_{Unk}, mol_{Unk} \rightarrow \mathcal{M} \rightarrow g_C, g_H, g_O \rightarrow mol_C, mol_H, mol_O \rightarrow$ **molecular formula**

$$\mathcal{M} = \frac{g_{Unk}}{mol_{Unk}} \quad \text{mass percents} \quad \frac{1\ mol\ C}{12.01\ g\ C} \qquad \frac{1\ mol\ H}{1.008\ g\ H} \qquad \frac{1\ mol\ O}{16.00\ g\ O}$$

Solution: $50.0\ g \times \dfrac{1\ kg}{1000\ g} = 0.0500\ kg$ and $T_f = T_f^° - \Delta T_f$ so

$\Delta T_f = T_f^° - T_f = 0.00\ °C - (-3.16\ °C) = +3.16\ °C$　$\Delta T_f = K_f \times m$. Rearrange to solve for m.

$$m = \frac{\Delta T_f}{K_f} = \frac{3.16\ °C}{1.86\ \dfrac{°C}{m}} = 1.69892\ m \text{ then } m = \frac{amount\ solute\ (moles)}{mass\ solvent\ (kg)} \text{ so}$$

$$mol_{Unk} = m_{Unk} \times kg_{H_2O} = 1.69892\ \frac{mol\ Unk}{kg} \times 0.0500\ kg = 0.08494600\ mol\ Unk \text{ then}$$

$$\mathcal{M} = \frac{g_{Unk}}{mol_{Unk}} = \frac{10.05\ g}{0.08494600\ mol} = 118.3105\ \frac{g}{mol} \text{ then}$$

$$\frac{118.3105\ g\ Unk}{1\ mol\ Unk} \times \frac{60.97\ g\ C}{100\ g\ Unk} \times \frac{1\ mol\ C}{12.01\ g\ C} = \frac{6.01\ mol\ C}{1\ mol\ Unk}$$

$$\frac{118.3105\ g\ Unk}{1\ mol\ Unk} \times \frac{11.94\ g\ H}{100\ g\ Unk} \times \frac{1\ mol\ H}{1.008\ g\ H} = \frac{14.0\ mol\ H}{1\ mol\ Unk} \text{ and}$$

$$\frac{118.3105\ g\ Unk}{1\ mol\ Unk} \times \frac{(100 - (60.97 + 11.94))\ g\ O}{100\ g\ Unk} \times \frac{1\ mol\ O}{16.00\ g\ O} = \frac{2.00\ mol\ O}{1\ mol\ Unk}$$

So the molecular formula is $C_6H_{12}O_2$.

Check: The units (formula) are correct. The magnitude of the answer (formula with ~118 g/mol) seems reasonable because the molality is ~1.7 and we have ~10 g. It is a reasonable molecular weight for a solid or liquid. The formula does have the correct molar mass.

12.92　**Given:** 1.05 g unknown compound in 175.0 mL solution; $\Pi = 1.93\ atm$ at 25 °C; combustion of 24.02 g of the unknown compound produced 28.16 g CO_2 and 8.64 g H_2O　**Find:** molecular formula

Conceptual Plan: °C $\rightarrow$ K then $\Pi, T \rightarrow$ M then $mL_{soln} \rightarrow L_{soln}$ then $L_{soln}, M \rightarrow mol_{unknown}$

$$K = °C + 273.15 \qquad \Pi = MRT \qquad \frac{1\ L}{1000\ mL} \qquad M = \frac{amount\ solute\ (moles)}{volume\ solution\ (L)}$$

then g $_{\text{unknown}}$, mol$_{\text{unknown}}$ $\rightarrow$ $\mathcal{M}_{\text{unknown}}$ then g$_{CO_2}$ $\rightarrow$ mol$_C$ and g$_{H_2O}$ $\rightarrow$ mol$_H$

$$\mathcal{M} = \frac{g_{\text{unknown}}}{\text{mol}_{\text{unknown}}} \qquad \frac{1 \text{ mol } CO_2}{44.01 \text{ g } CO_2} \qquad \frac{1 \text{ mol } H_2O}{18.02 \text{ g } H_2O} \text{ and } \frac{2 \text{ mol H}}{1 \text{ mol H}}$$

then g $_{\text{unknown}}$, mol$_C$, mol$_H$ $\rightarrow$ mol$_O$ then mol$_C$, mol$_H$, mol$_O$, $\mathcal{M}_{\text{unknown}}$ $\rightarrow$ **molecular formula**

$$\frac{12.01 \text{ g C}}{1 \text{ mol C}} \quad \frac{1.008 \text{ g H}}{1 \text{ mol H}} \qquad\qquad g \, O = g \, \text{Total} - g \, C - g \, H \frac{1 \text{ mol O}}{16.00 \text{ g O}}$$

Solution: $25 \,°C + 273.15 = 298$ K and $\Pi = MRT$ for M.

$$M = \frac{\Pi}{RT} = \frac{1.93 \text{ atm}}{0.08206 \dfrac{L \cdot \text{atm}}{K \cdot \text{mol}} \times 298 \text{ K}} = 0.07\underline{8}92408 \, \frac{\text{mol}}{L} \text{ then } 175.0 \text{ mL} \times \frac{1 \text{ L}}{1000 \text{ mL}} = 0.1750 \text{ L then}$$

$$M = \frac{\text{amount solute (moles)}}{\text{volume solution (L)}}. \text{ Rearrange to solve for mol}_{\text{unknown}}.$$

$$\text{mol}_{\text{unknown}} = M \times L = 0.07\underline{8}92408 \, \frac{\text{mol}}{L} \times 0.1750 \, L = 0.013\underline{8}11714 \text{ mol then}$$

$$\mathcal{M} = \frac{g_{\text{unknown}}}{\text{mol}_{\text{unknown}}} = \frac{1.05 \text{ g}}{0.013\underline{8}11714 \text{ mol}} = 76.0\underline{2}2425 \, \frac{g}{\text{mol}} \text{ then using the combustion data}$$

$$28.16 \text{ g } CO_2 \times \frac{1 \text{ mol } CO_2}{44.01 \text{ g } CO_2} \times \frac{1 \text{ mol C}}{1 \text{ mol } CO_2} = 0.639\underline{8}54578 \text{ mol C}$$

$$8.64 \text{ g } H_2O \times \frac{1 \text{ mol } H_2O}{18.02 \text{ g } H_2O} \times \frac{2 \text{ mol H}}{1 \text{ mol } H_2O} = 0.95\underline{8}93452 \text{ mol H then } g \, O = g \, \text{Total} - g \, C - g \, H =$$

$$24.02 \text{ g Total} - \left(0.639\underline{8}54578 \text{ mol C} \times \frac{12.01 \text{ g C}}{1 \text{ mol C}} + 0.95\underline{8}93452 \text{ mol H} \times \frac{1.008 \text{ g H}}{1 \text{ mol H}}\right) = 15.3\underline{6}87381 \text{ g O then}$$

$$15.3\underline{6}87381 \text{ g O} \times \frac{1 \text{ mol O}}{16.00 \text{ g O}} = 0.960\underline{5}4613 \text{ mol O. Finally, use the molar mass and the moles of each element to get}$$

the molecular formula. $\dfrac{76.0\underline{2}2425 \text{ g Unk}}{1 \text{ mol Unk}} \times \dfrac{0.639\underline{8}54578 \text{ mol C}}{24.02 \text{ g Unk}} = \dfrac{2.02 \text{ mol C}}{1 \text{ mol Unk}}$

$$\frac{76.0\underline{2}2381 \text{ g Unk}}{1 \text{ mol Unk}} \times \frac{0.95\underline{8}93452 \text{ mol H}}{24.02 \text{ g Unk}} = \frac{3.03 \text{ mol H}}{1 \text{ mol Unk}}$$

and $\dfrac{76.0\underline{2}2381 \text{ g Unk}}{1 \text{ mol Unk}} \times \dfrac{0.960\underline{5}4613 \text{ mol O}}{24.02 \text{ g Unk}} = \dfrac{3.04 \text{ mol O}}{1 \text{ mol Unk}}$

So the molecular formula is $C_2H_3O_3$.

Check: The units (formula) are correct. The magnitude of the answer (formula with ~152 g/mol) seems reasonable because the molarity is ~0.08 and we have ~2 g. It is a reasonable molecular weight for a solid or liquid. The formula does have the correct molar mass.

12.93 **Given:** 100.0 mL solution 13.5% by mass NaCl, $d = 1.12$ g/mL; $T_b = 104.4 \,°C$ **Find:** gNaCl or water to add
Other: $K_b = 0.512 \,°C/m$; $i_{\text{measured}} = 1.8$
Conceptual Plan: $T_b \rightarrow \Delta T_b$ then $\Delta T_b, i, K_b \rightarrow m$ then mL$_{\text{solution}} \rightarrow$ g$_{\text{solution}} \rightarrow$ g$_{\text{NaCl}} \rightarrow$ mol$_{\text{NaCl}}$ then

$$\Delta T_b = T_b - T_b° \qquad\qquad \Delta T_b = K_b \times i \times m \qquad\qquad \frac{1.12 \text{ g solution}}{1 \text{ mL solution}} \quad \frac{13.5 \text{ g NaCl}}{100 \text{ g solution}} \quad \frac{1 \text{ mol NaCl}}{58.44 \text{ g NaCl}}$$

m, mol$_{\text{NaCl}} \rightarrow$ kg$_{H_2O} \rightarrow$ g$_{H_2O}$ and g$_{\text{solution}}$, g$_{\text{NaCl}} \rightarrow$ g$_{H_2O}$ then compare the initial and final g$_{H_2O}$ then

$$m = \frac{\text{amount solute (moles)}}{\text{mass solvent (kg)}} \quad \frac{1000 \text{ g}}{1 \text{ kg}} \qquad\qquad g_{\text{solution}} = g_{\text{NaCl}} + g_{H_2O}$$

Calculate the total NaCl in final solution by scaling up the amount from the initial solution. Then calculate the difference between the needed and starting amounts of NaCl.

Solution: $\Delta T_b = T_b - T_b° = 104.4 \,°C - 100.0 \,°C = 4.4 \,°C$ then $\Delta T_b = K_b \times i \times m$

Rearrange to solve for m. $m = \dfrac{\Delta T_b}{K_b \, i} = \dfrac{4.4 \,°C}{0.512 \dfrac{°C}{m} \times 1.8} = 4.\underline{7}74306 \, m$ NaCl then

$$\text{mass of solution} = 10.0 \ \cancel{\text{mL solution}} \times \frac{1.12 \ \text{g solution}}{1 \ \cancel{\text{mL solution}}} = 112 \ \text{g solution}$$

$$\text{mass of NaCl} = 112 \ \cancel{\text{g solution}} \times \frac{13.5 \ \text{g NaCl}}{100 \ \cancel{\text{g solution}}} = 15.\underline{1}2 \ \text{g NaCl}$$

$$\text{mol NaCl} = 15.12 \ \cancel{\text{g NaCl}} \times \frac{1 \ \text{mol NaCl}}{58.44 \ \cancel{\text{g NaCl}}} = 0.25\underline{8}7269 \ \text{mol NaCl}$$

then $m = \dfrac{\text{amount solute (moles)}}{\text{mass solvent (kg)}}$. Rearrange to solve for kg_{H_2O}.

$$\text{kg}_{H_2O} = \frac{\text{mol}_{NaCl}}{m} = \frac{0.25\underline{8}7269 \ \cancel{\text{mol NaCl}}}{\dfrac{4.\underline{7}74306 \ \cancel{\text{mol NaCl}}}{1 \ \text{kg}_{H_2O}}} = 0.05\underline{4}1915 \ \cancel{\text{kg}_{H_2O}} \times \frac{1000 \ \text{g}_{H_2O}}{1 \ \cancel{\text{kg}_{H_2O}}} = 54.\underline{1}915 \ \text{g}_{H_2O} \text{ in final solution then}$$

$\text{g}_{\text{solution}} = \text{g}_{NaCl} + \text{g}_{H_2O} = 112 \ \text{g solution} - 15.\underline{1}2 \ \text{g NaCl} = 96.\underline{8}8 \ \text{g } H_2O$ in initial solution. Comparing the initial and final solutions, we find that there is a lot more water in the initial solution; so NaCl needs to be added.

In the solution with a boiling point of 104.4 °C, $\dfrac{15.\underline{1}2 \ \text{g NaCl}}{54.\underline{1}915 \ \text{g } H_2O} = \dfrac{x \ \text{g NaCl}}{96.\underline{8}8 \ \text{g } H_2O}$. Solve for x g NaCl.

$$x \ \text{g NaCl} = \frac{15.\underline{1}2 \ \text{g NaCl}}{54.\underline{1}915 \ \cancel{\text{g } H_2O}} \times 96.\underline{8}8 \ \cancel{\text{g } H_2O} = 27.\underline{0}31 \ \text{g NaCl; so the amount to be added is}$$

$27.\underline{0}31 \ \text{g NaCl} - 15.\underline{1}2 \ \text{g NaCl} = 11.\underline{9}11 \ \text{g NaCl} = 12 \ \text{g NaCl}$

Check: The units (g) are correct. The magnitude of the answer (12 g) seems reasonable because there is approximately twice as much water as is desired in the initial solution; so the NaCl amount needs to be approximately doubled.

12.94   **Given:** 50.0 mL solution 1.55% by mass $MgCl_2$, $d = 1.05$ g/mL; add 1.35 g $MgCl_2$ **Find:** T_f
Other: $K_b = 1.86$ °C/m; $i_{\text{measured}} = 2.5$
Conceptual Plan: $\text{mL}_{\text{solution}} \to \text{g}_{\text{solution}} \to \text{g}_{MgCl_2}$ then calculate the final mass of $MgCl_2 \ \text{g}_{MgCl_2} \to \text{mol}_{MgCl_2}$ and

$$\frac{1.05 \ \text{g solution}}{1 \ \text{mL solution}} \qquad \frac{1.55 \ \text{g } MgCl_2}{100 \ \text{g solution}} \qquad\qquad \text{add 1.35 g } MgCl_2 \qquad\qquad \frac{1 \ \text{mol } MgCl_2}{95.21 \ \text{g } MgCl_2}$$

$\text{g}_{\text{solution}}, \text{g}_{MgCl} \to \text{g}_{H_2O} \to \text{kg}_{H_2O}$ then $\text{g}_{H_2O}, \text{mol}_{MgCl_2} \to m$ then $m, i, K_f \to \Delta T_f \to T_f$

$$\text{g}_{\text{solution}} = \text{g}_{MgCl_2} + \text{g}_{H_2O} \frac{1 \ \text{kg}}{1000 \ \text{g}} \qquad m = \frac{\text{amount solute (moles)}}{\text{mass solvent (kg)}} \qquad \Delta T_f = K_f \times i \times m \qquad T_f = T_f^\circ - \Delta T_f$$

Solution:

$$50.0 \ \cancel{\text{mL solution}} \times \frac{1.05 \ \text{g solution}}{1 \ \cancel{\text{mL solution}}} = 52.5 \ \text{g solution then } 52.5 \ \cancel{\text{g solution}} \times \frac{1.55 \ \text{g } MgCl_2}{100 \ \cancel{\text{g solution}}} = 0.\underline{8}1375 \ \text{g } MgCl_2$$

$$(0.\underline{8}1375 + 1.35) \ \cancel{\text{g } MgCl_2} \times \frac{1 \ \text{mol } MgCl_2}{95.21 \ \cancel{\text{g } MgCl_2}} = 0.022\underline{7}261 \ \text{mol } MgCl_2 \text{ and } \text{g}_{\text{solution}} = \text{g}_{MgCl_2} + \text{g}_{H_2O} \text{ so}$$

$\text{g}_{H_2O} = \text{g}_{\text{solution}} - \text{g}_{MgCl_2} = 52.5 \ \text{g solution} - 0.\underline{8}1375 \ \text{g } MgCl_2 = 51.\underline{6}863 \ \text{g } H_2O$ and

$$51.\underline{6}863 \ \cancel{\text{g } H_2O} \times \frac{1 \ \text{kg } H_2O}{1000 \ \cancel{\text{g } H_2O}} = 0.051\underline{6}863 \ \text{kg } H_2O \text{ then } m = \frac{\text{amount solute (moles)}}{\text{mass solvent (kg)}}$$

$$m = \frac{0.022\underline{7}261 \ \text{mol } MgCl_2}{0.051\underline{6}863 \ \text{kg } H_2O} = 0.43\underline{9}693 \ m \text{ then } \Delta T_f = K_f \times i \times m = 1.86 \ \frac{°C}{\cancel{m}} \times 2.5 \times 0.43\underline{9}693 \ \cancel{m} = 2.\underline{0}446 \ °C$$

then $T_f = T_f^\circ - \Delta T_f = 0.00 \ °C - 2.\underline{0}446 \ °C = -2.0 \ °C$

Check: The units (°C) are correct. The magnitude of the answer (−2 °C) seems reasonable because the freezing point drops and almost three particles are generated for each $MgCl_2$.

Challenge Problems

12.95   **Given:** N_2: $k_H(N_2) = 6.1 \times 10^{-4}$ M/atm at 25 °C; 14.6 mg/L at 50 °C and 1.00 atm; $P_{N_2} = 0.78$ atm;
O_2: $k_H(O_2) = 1.3 \times 10^{-3}$ M/atm at 25 °C; 27.8 mg/L at 50 °C and 1.00 atm; $P_{O_2} = 0.21$ atm; and 1.5 L water
Find: $V(N_2)$ and $V(O_2)$
Conceptual Plan: at 25 °C: $P_{\text{Total}}, \chi_{N_2} \to P_{N_2}$ then $P_{N_2}, k_H(N_2) \to S_{N_2}$ then L $\to$ mol

$$P_{N_2} = \chi_{N_2} P_{\text{Total}} \qquad\qquad S_{N_2} = k_H(N_2) P_{N_2} \qquad\qquad S_{N_2}$$

at 50 °C: $L \rightarrow mL \rightarrow mg \rightarrow g \rightarrow mol$ then $mol_{25\,°C}, mol_{25\,°C} \rightarrow mol_{removed}$ then $°C \rightarrow K$

$$\frac{1000\ mL}{1\ L} \quad \frac{14.6\ mg}{1\ L} \quad \frac{1\ g}{1000\ mg} \quad \frac{1\ mol}{28.02\ g} \qquad\qquad mol_{removed} = mol_{25\,°C} - mol_{50\,°C} \qquad K = °C + 273.15$$

then $P, n, T \rightarrow V$

$$PV = nRT$$

at 25 °C: $P_{Total}, \chi_{O_2} \rightarrow P_{O_2}$ then $P_{O_2}, k_H(O_2) \rightarrow S_{O_2}$ then $L \rightarrow mol$

$$P_{O_2} = \chi_{O_2} P_{Total} \qquad\qquad S_{O_2} = k_H(O_2) P_{O_2} \qquad\qquad S_{O_2}$$

at 50 °C: $L \rightarrow mL \rightarrow mg \rightarrow g \rightarrow mol$ then $mol_{25\,°C}, mol_{25\,°C} \rightarrow mol_{removed}$ then $°C \rightarrow K$

$$\frac{1000\ mL}{1\ L} \quad \frac{27.8\ mg}{1\ L} \quad \frac{1\ g}{1000\ mg} \quad \frac{1\ mol}{32.00\ g} \qquad\qquad mol_{removed} = mol_{25\,°C} - mol_{50\,°C} \qquad K = °C + 273.15$$

then $P, n, T \rightarrow V$

$$PV = nRT$$

Solution: at 25 °C: $P_{N_2} = \chi_{N_2} P_{Total} = 0.78 \times 1.0\ atm = 0.78\ atm$ then

$$S_{N_2} = k_H(N_2) P_{N_2} = 6.1 \times 10^{-4} \frac{M}{atm} \times 0.78\ atm = 4.\underline{7}58 \times 10^{-4}\ M \text{ then}$$

$$1.5\ L \times 4.\underline{7}58 \times 10^{-4} \frac{mol}{L} = 0.00071370\ mol$$

at 50 °C: $1.5\ L \times \dfrac{14.6\ mg}{1\ L \cdot atm} \times 0.78\ atm \times \dfrac{1\ g}{1000\ mg} \times \dfrac{1\ mol}{28.02\ g} = 0.00060964\ mol$ then

$mol_{removed} = mol_{25\,°C} - mol_{50\,°C} = 0.00071370\ mol - 0.00060964\ mol = 1.\underline{0}39 \times 10^{-4}\ mol\ N_2$

then $50\ °C + 273.15 = 323\ K$ then $PV = nRT$. Rearrange to solve for V.

$$V = \frac{nRT}{P} = \frac{1.\underline{0}39 \times 10^{-4}\ mol \times 0.08206 \dfrac{L \cdot atm}{K \cdot mol} \times 323\ K}{1.00\ atm} = 0.002\underline{7}539\ L\ N_2$$

at 25 °C: $P_{O_2} = \chi_{O_2} P_{Total} = 0.21 \times 1.0\ atm = 0.21\ atm$ then

$$S_{O_2} = k_H(O_2) P_{O_2} = 1.3 \times 10^{-3} \frac{M}{atm} \times 0.21\ atm = 2.\underline{7}3 \times 10^{-4}\ M \text{ then}$$

$$1.5\ L \times 2.\underline{7}3 \times 10^{-4} \frac{mol}{L} = 0.0004\underline{0}95\ mol$$

at 50 °C: $1.5\ L \times \dfrac{27.8\ mg}{1\ L \cdot atm} \times 0.21\ atm \times \dfrac{1\ g}{1000\ mg} \times \dfrac{1\ mol}{32.00\ g} = 0.00027366\ mol$ then

$mol_{removed} = mol_{25\,°C} - mol_{50\,°C} = 0.0004\underline{0}95\ mol - 0.00027366\ mol = 1.\underline{3}58 \times 10^{-4}\ mol\ O_2$

then $50\ °C + 273.15 = 323\ K$ then $PV = nRT$. Rearrange to solve for V.

$$V = \frac{nRT}{P} = \frac{1.\underline{3}58 \times 10^{-4}\ mol \times 0.08206 \dfrac{L \cdot atm}{K \cdot mol} \times 323\ K}{1.00\ atm} = 0.003\underline{5}994\ L\ O_2 \text{ finally}$$

$V_{Total} = V_{N_2} + V_{O_2} = 0.002\underline{7}526\ L + 0.003\underline{5}994\ L = 0.0064\ L$

Check: The units (L) are correct. The magnitude of the answer (0.006 L) seems reasonable because we have so little dissolved gas at room temperature and most is still soluble at 50 °C.

12.96   **Given:** pentane (C_5H_{12}) and hexane (C_6H_{14}): 35.5% by mass C_5H_{12} in vapor at 25 °C; $P°_{C_5H_{12}} = 425$ torr; $P°_{C_6H_{14}} = 151$ torr   **Find:** percent by mass C_5H_{12} and percent by mass C_6H_{14} in solution

Conceptual Plan: mass percents $\rightarrow g_{C_5H_{12}}, g_{C_6H_{14}}$, then $g_{C_5H_{12}} \rightarrow mol_{C_5H_{12}}$ and $g_{C_6H_{14}} \rightarrow mol_{C_6H_{14}}$then

$$\text{mass percent} = \frac{\text{mass solute}}{\text{mass solution}} \times 100\% \qquad\qquad \frac{1\ mol\ C_5H_{12}}{72.15\ g\ C_5H_{12}} \qquad\qquad \frac{1\ mol\ C_6H_{14}}{86.17\ g\ C_6H_{14}}$$

$mol_{C_5H_{12}}, mol_{C_6H_{14}} \rightarrow \chi_{C_5H_{12}vapor}$ then $\chi_{C_5H_{12}vapor}, P°_{C_5H_{12}}, P°_{C_6H_{14}} \rightarrow \chi_{C_5H_{12}soln}$ then assume

$$\chi_{C_5H_{12}} = \frac{\text{amount }C_5H_{12}\ (\text{in moles})}{\text{total amount (in moles)}} \qquad\qquad \chi_{C_5H_{12}vapor} = \frac{P_{C_5H_{12}}}{P_{Total}} = \frac{\chi_{C_5H_{12}soln}P°_{C_5H_{12}}}{\chi_{C_5H_{12}soln}P°_{C_5H_{12}} + (1 - \chi_{C_5H_{12}soln})P°_{C_6H_{14}}}$$

1 total mole of solution $\rightarrow mol_{C_5H_{12}}, mol_{C_6H_{14}}$ then $mol_{C_5H_{12}} \rightarrow g_{C_5H_{12}}$ and $mol_{C_6H_{14}} \rightarrow g_{C_6H_{14}}$

$$\chi_{C_6H_{14}so\ ln} = 1 - \chi_{C_5H_{12}so\ ln} \qquad\qquad \frac{72.15\ g\ C_5H_{12}}{1\ mol\ C_5H_{12}} \qquad\qquad \frac{86.17\ g\ C_6H_{14}}{1\ mol\ C_6H_{14}}$$

finally $g_{C_5H_{12}}$, $g_{C_6H_{14}}$ → **mass percents**

$$\text{mass percent} = \frac{\text{mass solute}}{\text{mass solution}} \times 100\%$$

Solution: mass percent $= \dfrac{\text{mass solute}}{\text{mass solution}} \times 100\%$ means that 35.5 g C_5H_{12} and 100.0 g $- 35.5$ g $= 64.5$ g C_6H_{14}

then 35.5 g $C_5H_{12} \times \dfrac{1 \text{ mol } C_5H_{12}}{72.15 \text{ g } C_5H_{12}} = 0.49\underline{2}030$ mol C_5H_{12} and

64.5 g $C_6H_{14} \times \dfrac{1 \text{ mol } C_6H_{14}}{86.17 \text{ g } C_6H_{14}} = 0.74\underline{8}520$ mol C_6H_{14} then

$\chi_{C_5H_{12}} = \dfrac{\text{amount } C_5H_{12} \text{ (in moles)}}{\text{total amount (in moles)}} = \dfrac{0.49\underline{2}030 \text{ mol}}{0.49\underline{2}030 \text{ mol} + 0.74\underline{8}520 \text{ mol}} = 0.396622$ then

$\chi_{C_5H_{12}\text{vapor}} = \dfrac{P_{C_5H_{12}}}{P_{\text{Total}}} = \dfrac{\chi_{C_5H_{12}\text{soln}} P^\circ_{C_5H_{12}}}{\chi_{C_5H_{12}\text{soln}} P^\circ_{C_5H_{12}} + (1 - \chi_{C_5H_{12}\text{soln}}) P^\circ_{C_6H_{14}}}$.

Substitute in values and solve for $\chi_{C_5H_{12}\text{ soln}}$.

$0.396622 = \dfrac{\chi_{C_5H_{12}\text{soln}} \times 425 \text{ torr}}{\chi_{C_5H_{12}\text{soln}} \times 425 \text{ torr} + (1 - \chi_{C_5H_{12}\text{soln}}) \times 151 \text{ torr}} \rightarrow$

$0.396622(425 \chi_{C_5H_{12}\text{soln}} + 151(1 - \chi_{C_5H_{12}\text{soln}})) = 425 \chi_{C_5H_{12}\text{soln}} \rightarrow$

$16\underline{8}.564 \chi_{C_5H_{12}\text{soln}} + 59.\underline{8}900 - 59.\underline{8}900 \chi_{C_5H_{12}\text{soln}} = 425 \chi_{C_5H_{12}\text{soln}} \rightarrow 31\underline{6}.326 \chi_{C_5H_{12}\text{soln}} = 59.\underline{8}900 \rightarrow$

$\chi_{C_5H_{12}\text{soln}} = \dfrac{59.\underline{8}900}{31\underline{6}.326} = 0.18\underline{9}330$ then $\chi_{C_6H_{14}\text{soln}} = 1 - \chi_{C_5H_{12}\text{soln}} = 1 - 0.189330 = 0.81\underline{0}670$ so

$\text{mol}_{C_5H_{12}} = 0.189330$ mol and $\text{mol}_{C_6H_{14}} = 0.81\underline{0}670$ mol then

0.189330 mol $C_5H_{12} \times \dfrac{72.15 \text{ g } C_5H_{12}}{1 \text{ mol } C_5H_{12}} = 13.\underline{6}602$ g C_5H_{12} and

0.810670 mol $C_6H_{14} \times \dfrac{86.17 \text{ g } C_6H_{14}}{1 \text{ mol } C_6H_{14}} = 69.\underline{8}554$ g C_6H_{14} finally

mass percent $= \dfrac{\text{mass solute}}{\text{mass solution}} \times 100\% = \dfrac{13.\underline{6}602 \text{ g } C_5H_{12}}{13.\underline{6}602 \text{ g } C_5H_{12} + 69.\underline{8}554 \text{ g } C_6H_{14}} \times 100\%$

$= 16.4\%$ by mass C_5H_{12}

and $100.0 - 16.4 = 83.6$ mass percent C_6H_{14}

Check: The units (mass percent) are correct. We expect the mass percent of C_6H_{14} to be much higher than the mass percent of C_5H_{12} because the vapor is richer in this component and it is the less volatile phase.

12.97 **Given:** 1.10 g glucose ($C_6H_{12}O_6$) and sucrose ($C_{12}H_{22}O_{11}$) mixture in 25.0 mL solution and $\Pi = 3.78$ atm at 298 K
Find: percent composition of mixture
Conceptual Plan: $\Pi, T \rightarrow M$ then $\text{mL}_{\text{soln}} \rightarrow \text{L}_{\text{soln}}$ then $\text{L}_{\text{soln}}, M \rightarrow \text{mol}_{\text{mixture}}$ then

$\Pi = MRT \qquad\qquad \dfrac{1 \text{ L}}{1000 \text{ mL}} \qquad\qquad M = \dfrac{\text{amount solute (moles)}}{\text{volume solution (L)}}$

$\text{mol}_{\text{mixture}}, g_{\text{mixture}} \rightarrow \text{mol}_{C_6H_{12}O_6}, \text{mol}_{C_{12}H_{22}O_{11}}$ then

$g_{\text{mixture}} = \text{mol } C_6H_{12}O_6 \times \dfrac{180.16 \text{ g } C_6H_{12}O_6}{1 \text{ mol } C_6H_{12}O_6} + \text{mol } C_{12}H_{22}O_{11} \times \dfrac{342.30 \text{ g } C_{12}H_{22}O_{11}}{1 \text{ mol } C_{12}H_{22}O_{11}}$ *with* $\text{mol}_{\text{mixture}} = \text{mol}_{C_6H_{12}O_6} + \text{mol}_{C_{12}H_{22}O_{11}}$

$\text{mol}_{C_6H_{12}O_6} \rightarrow g_{C_6H_{12}O_6}$ and $\text{mol}_{C_{12}H_{22}O_{11}} \rightarrow g_{C_{12}H_{22}O_{11}}$ and $g_{C_6H_{12}O_6}, g_{C_{12}H_{22}O_{11}} \rightarrow$ **mass percents**

$\dfrac{180.16 \text{ g } C_6H_{12}O_6}{1 \text{ mol } C_6H_{12}O_6} \qquad\qquad \dfrac{342.30 \text{ g } C_{12}H_{22}O_{11}}{1 \text{ mol } C_{12}H_{22}O_{11}} \qquad\qquad \text{mass percent} = \dfrac{\text{mass solute}}{\text{mass solution}} \times 100\%$

Solution: $\Pi = MRT$. Rearrange to solve for M.

$M = \dfrac{\Pi}{RT} = \dfrac{3.78 \text{ atm}}{0.08206 \dfrac{L \cdot \text{atm}}{K \cdot \text{mol}} \times 298 \text{ K}} = 0.15\underline{4}577 \dfrac{\text{mol mixture}}{L}$ then 25.0 mL $\times \dfrac{1 \text{ L}}{1000 \text{ mL}} = 0.0250$ L then

$M = \dfrac{\text{amount solute (moles)}}{\text{volume solution (L)}}$ so

$\text{mol}_{\text{mixture}} = M \times L_{\text{soln}} = 0.15\underline{4}577 \dfrac{\text{mol mixture}}{L} \times 0.0250 \text{ L} = 0.0038\underline{6}442$ mol mixture then

$$g_{\text{mixture}} = \text{mol } \cancel{C_6H_{12}O_6} \times \frac{180.16 \text{ g } C_6H_{12}O_6}{1 \text{ mol } \cancel{C_6H_{12}O_6}} + \text{mol } \cancel{C_{12}H_{22}O_{11}} \times \frac{342.30 \text{ g } C_{12}H_{22}O_{11}}{1 \text{ mol } \cancel{C_{12}H_{22}O_{11}}} \text{ with}$$

$$\text{mol}_{\text{mixture}} = \text{mol}_{C_6H_{12}O_6} + \text{mol}_{C_{12}H_{22}O_{11}} \text{ so}$$

$$1.10 \text{ g} = \text{mol } C_6H_{12}O_6 \times \frac{180.16 \text{ g } C_6H_{12}O_6}{1 \text{ mol } C_6H_{12}O_6} + (0.00386442 \text{ mol} - \text{mol } C_6H_{12}O_6) \times \frac{342.30 \text{ g } C_{12}H_{22}O_{11}}{1 \text{ mol } C_{12}H_{22}O_{11}} \rightarrow$$

$$1.10 = 180.16 \times \text{mol } C_6H_{12}O_6 + 1.32\underline{2}79 - 342.30 \times \text{mol } C_6H_{12}O_6 \rightarrow 162.14 \, x \text{ mol } C_6H_{12}O_6 = 0.22\underline{2}79 \rightarrow$$

$$x \text{ mol } C_6H_{12}O_6 = \frac{0.22\underline{2}79}{162.14} = 0.0013\underline{7}406 \text{ mol } C_6H_{12}O_6 \text{ then}$$

$$\text{mol}_{C_{12}H_{22}O_{11}} = \text{mol}_{\text{mixture}} - \text{mol}_{C_6H_{12}O_6} = 0.00386442 \text{ mol} - 0.0013\underline{7}406 \text{ mol}$$

$$= 0.0024\underline{9}04 \text{ mol } C_{12}H_{22}O_{11} \text{ then}$$

$$0.0013\underline{7}406 \text{ mol } \cancel{C_6H_{12}O_6} \times \frac{180.16 \text{ g } C_6H_{12}O_6}{1 \text{ mol } \cancel{C_6H_{12}O_6}} = 0.2\underline{4}755 \text{ g } C_6H_{12}O_6 \text{ and}$$

$$0.0024\underline{9}04 \text{ mol } \cancel{C_{12}H_{22}O_{11}} \times \frac{342.30 \text{ g } C_{12}H_{22}O_{11}}{1 \text{ mol } \cancel{C_{12}H_{22}O_{11}}} = 0.8\underline{5}245 \text{ g } C_{12}H_{22}O_{11} \text{ finally}$$

$$\text{mass percent} = \frac{\text{mass solute}}{\text{mass solution}} \times 100\% = \frac{0.2\underline{4}755 \text{ g } \cancel{C_6H_{12}O_6}}{0.2\underline{4}755 \text{ g } \cancel{C_6H_{12}O_6} + 0.8\underline{5}245 \text{ g } \cancel{C_{12}H_{22}O_{11}}} \times 100\%$$

$$= 22.50\% \, C_6H_{12}O_6 \text{ by mass and } 100.00\% - 22.50\% = 77.50\% \, C_{12}H_{22}O_{11} \text{ by mass}$$

Check: The units (% by mass) are correct. We expect the percent by $C_{12}H_{22}O_{11}$ to be larger than that for $C_6H_{12}O_6$ because the $g_{\text{mixture}}/\text{mol}_{\text{mixture}} = 285$ g/mol, which is closer to $C_{12}H_{22}O_{11}$ than $C_6H_{12}O_6$ and the molar mass of $C_{12}H_{22}O_{11}$ is larger than the molar mass of $C_6H_{12}O_6$. In addition, and most definitively, the masses obtained for sucrose and glucose sum to 1.1 g, the initial amount of solid dissolved.

12.98 **Given:** 631 mL methanol (CH_3OH) and 501 mL water; solution = 14.29 M CH_3OH, $d(CH_3OH) = 0.792$ g/mL
Find: volume change on mixing
Conceptual Plan: $V_{CH_3OH}, V_{H_2O} \rightarrow V_{\text{before mixing}}$ then $\text{mL}_{CH_3OH} \rightarrow \text{g}_{CH_3OH} \rightarrow \text{mol}_{CH_3OH}$ then

$$V_{\text{before mixing}} = V_{CH_3OH} + V_{H_2O} \qquad \frac{0.792 \text{ g}}{1 \text{ mL}} \quad \frac{1 \text{ mol } CH_3OH}{32.04 \text{ g } CH_3OH}$$

$\text{mol}_{CH_3OH}, M \rightarrow L_{\text{soln}} \rightarrow \text{mL}_{\text{soln}}$ then $V_{\text{before mixing}}, L_{\text{soln}} \rightarrow \Delta V_{\text{mixing}}$

$$M = \frac{\text{amount solute (moles)}}{\text{volume solution (L)}} \quad \frac{1000 \text{ mL}}{1 \text{ L}} \qquad \qquad \Delta V_{\text{mixing}} = V_{\text{before mixing}} - V_{\text{soln}}$$

Solution: $V_{\text{before mixing}} = V_{CH_3OH} + V_{H_2O} = 631 \text{ mL} + 501 \text{ mL} = 1132 \text{ mL}$ then

$$631 \text{ mL} \times \frac{0.792 \text{ g}}{1 \text{ mL}} \times \frac{1 \text{ mol } CH_3OH}{32.04 \text{ g } CH_3OH} = 15.\underline{5}798 \text{ mol } CH_3OH \text{ then } M = \frac{\text{amount solute (moles)}}{\text{volume solution (L)}} \text{ so}$$

$$L_{\text{soln}} = \frac{\text{mol}_{CH_3OH}}{M} = \frac{15.\underline{5}798 \text{ mol } CH_3OH}{14.29 \dfrac{\text{mol } CH_3OH}{L}} = 1.0\underline{9}152 \text{ L then } 1.0\underline{9}152 \text{ L} \times \frac{1000 \text{ mL}}{1 \text{ L}} = 10\underline{9}1.52 \text{ mL then}$$

$$\Delta V_{\text{mixing}} = V_{\text{before mixing}} - V_{\text{soln}} = 1132 \text{ mL} - 10\underline{9}1.52 \text{ mL} = \underline{4}0.48 \text{ mL} = 4 \times 10^1 \text{ mL}$$

Check: The units (mL) are correct. Because the intermolecular forces between a methanol molecule and a water molecule are different than between two water molecules or between two methanol molecules, the spacing between molecules changes and thus the volume changes. The amount of the change ($\sim 4\%$) is reasonable.

12.99 **Given:** isopropyl alcohol (($CH_3)_2CHOH$) and propyl alcohol ($CH_3CH_2CH_2OH$) at 313 K; solution 2/3 by mass isopropyl alcohol $P_{2/3} = 0.110$ atm; solution 1/3 by mass isopropyl alcohol $P_{1/3} = 0.089$ atm
Find: P_{iso}° and P_{pro}° and explain why they are different
Conceptual Plan: Because these are isomers, they have the same molar mass and so the fraction by mass is the same as the mole fraction, so mole fractions, P_{soln}s $\rightarrow P^\circ$s

$$\chi_{\text{iso}} = \frac{\text{amount iso (in moles)}}{\text{total amount (in moles)}} \quad \chi_{\text{pro}} = 1 - \chi_{\text{iso}} \quad P_{\text{iso}} = \chi_{\text{iso}} P_{\text{iso}}^\circ \quad P_{\text{pro}} = \chi_{\text{pro}} P_{\text{pro}}^\circ \text{ and } P_{\text{soln}} = P_{\text{iso}} + P_{\text{pro}}$$

Solution:

Solution 1: $\chi_{iso} = 2/3$ and $\chi_{iso} = 1/3$ $P_{soln} = P_{iso} + P_{pro}$ so $0.110 \text{ atm} = 2/3 P_{iso}^\circ + 1/3 P_{pro}^\circ$

Solution 2: $\chi_{iso} = 1/3$ and $\chi_{iso} = 2/3$ $P_{soln} = P_{iso} + P_{pro}$ so $0.089 \text{ atm} = 1/3 P_{iso}^\circ + 2/3 P_{pro}^\circ$. We now have two equations and two unknowns and a number of ways to solve this. One way is to rearrange the first equation for P_{iso}° and substitute into the other equation. Thus, $P_{iso}^\circ = 3/2(0.110 \text{ atm} - 1/3 P_{pro}^\circ)$ and

$$0.089 \text{ atm} = \frac{1}{\cancel{3}} \frac{\cancel{3}}{2}(0.110 \text{ atm} - 1/3\,P_{pro}^\circ) + \frac{2}{3}P_{pro}^\circ \rightarrow 0.089 \text{ atm} = 0.0550 \text{ atm} - \frac{1}{6}P_{pro}^\circ + \frac{2}{3}P_{pro}^\circ \rightarrow$$

$$\frac{1}{2}P_{pro}^\circ = 0.03\underline{4}0 \text{ atm} \rightarrow P_{pro}^\circ = 0.06\underline{8}0 \text{ atm} = 0.068 \text{ atm} \text{ and then}$$

$$P_{iso}^\circ = 3/2(0.110 \text{ atm} - 1/3P_{pro}^\circ) = 3/2(0.110 \text{ atm} - 1/3(0.06\underline{8}0 \text{ atm})) = 0.131 \text{ atm}$$

The major intermolecular attractions are between the OH groups. The OH group at the end of the chain in propyl alcohol is more accessible than the one in the middle of the chain in isopropyl alcohol. In addition, the molecular shape of propyl alcohol is a straight chain of carbon atoms, while that of isopropyl alcohol has a branched chain and is more like a ball. The contact area between two ball-like objects is smaller than that of two chain-like objects. The smaller contact area in isopropyl alcohol means that the molecules do not attract each other as strongly as do those of propyl alcohol. As a result of both of these factors, the vapor pressure of isopropyl alcohol is higher.

Check: The units (atm) are correct. The magnitude of the answers seems reasonable because both solution partial pressures are ~ 0.1 atm.

12.100   **Given:** metal, M, of atomic weight 96 forms MF_x salt; 9.18 g of MF_x completely dissociates in 100.0 g water, $T_b = 374.38$ K   **Find:** x and formula unit **Other:** $K_b = 0.512\,°C/m$

Conceptual Plan: $g_{H_2O} \rightarrow kg_{H_2O}$ and $T_b \rightarrow \Delta T_b$ then $\Delta T_f, i, K_f \rightarrow m$ then $m, kg_{H_2O} \rightarrow mol_{Unk}$

$$\frac{1 \text{ kg}}{1000 \text{ g}} \qquad T_b = T_b^\circ + \Delta T_b \qquad \Delta T_b = K_b \times i \times m \text{ where } i = 1 + x \quad m = \frac{\text{amount solute (moles)}}{\text{mass solvent (kg)}}$$

then $g_{MFx}, mol_{MFx} \rightarrow \mathcal{M} \rightarrow x$

$$\mathcal{M} = \frac{g_{MF_x}}{mol_{MF_x}} \quad \frac{1 \text{ mol } MF_x}{(96 + 19x)\text{g } MF_x}$$

Solution: $100.0 \text{ g} \times \dfrac{1 \text{ kg}}{1000 \text{ g}} = 0.1000 \text{ kg}$ and $T_b = T_b^\circ + \Delta T_b$ so

$\Delta T_b = T_b - T_b^\circ = 374.38 \text{ K} - 373.15 \text{ K} = +1.23 \text{ K} = +1.23\,°C$ then $\Delta T_b = K_b \times i \times m$ where $i = 1 + x$ so

$\Delta T_b = K_b(1 + x)m$. Rearrange to solve for m. $m = \dfrac{\Delta T_b}{K_b(1 + x)} = \dfrac{1.23\,°C}{0.512\,\frac{°C}{m}(1 + x)} = \dfrac{2.40\underline{2}34}{(1 + x)} m$ then

$m = \dfrac{\text{amount solute (moles)}}{\text{mass solvent (kg)}}$ so

$mol_{MF_x} = m_{MF_x} \times kg_{H_2O} = \dfrac{2.40\underline{2}34 \text{ mol } MF_x}{(1 + x) \text{ kg}} \times 0.1000 \text{ kg} = \dfrac{0.240\underline{2}34}{(1 + x)} \text{ mol } MF_x$ then

$\mathcal{M} = \dfrac{g_{MF_x}}{mol_{MF_x}} = \dfrac{9.18 \text{ g}}{\dfrac{0.240\underline{2}34}{(1 + x)} \text{ mol } MF_x} = \dfrac{(96 + 19x) \text{ g } MF_x}{1 \text{ mol } MF_x}$. Rearrange and solve for x.

$(9.18 \text{ g})(1 \text{ mol } MF_x) = (96 + 19x)(\text{g } MF_x)\left(\dfrac{0.240\underline{2}34}{(1 + x)} \text{ mol } MF_x\right) \rightarrow 9.18(1 + x) = 0.240\underline{2}34(96 + 19x)$

$\rightarrow 9.18x - 4.\underline{5}645x = 2\underline{3}.062 - 9.18 \rightarrow 4.\underline{6}155x = 1\underline{3}.882 \rightarrow x = \dfrac{13.882}{4.\underline{6}155} = 3.0$; so the salt is MF_3.

Because molybdenum has an atomic mass ~ 96 amu, the salt is MoF_3.

Check: The units (none) are correct. The answer (3.0) seems reasonable because it is a small integer.

12.101   **Given:** 75.0 g of benzene (C_6H_6) and 75.0 g of toluene (C_7H_8) at 303 K $P_{Total}^\circ = 80.9$ mmHg; 100.0 g of benzene (C_6H_6) and 50.0 g of toluene (C_7H_8) at 303 K $P_{Total}^\circ = 93.9$ mmHg   **Find:** $P_{C_6H_6}^\circ, P_{C_8H_8}^\circ$

Conceptual Plan: for each solution,

$g_{C_6H_6} \rightarrow mol_{C_7H_8}$ and $g_{C_7H_8} \rightarrow mol_{C_7H_8}$ then $mol_{C_6H_6}, mol_{C_7H_8} \rightarrow \chi_{C_6H_6}, \chi_{C_7H_8}$ then

$$\frac{1 \text{ mol } C_6H_6}{78.11 \text{ g } C_6H_6} \qquad \frac{1 \text{ mol } C_7H_8}{92.13 \text{ g } C_7H_8} \qquad \chi_{C_6H_6} = \frac{\text{amount } C_6H_6 \text{ (in moles)}}{\text{total amount (in moles)}} \qquad \chi_{C_7H_8} = 1 - \chi_{C_6H_6}$$

write expressions relating $\chi_{C_6H_6}, P^{\circ}_{C_6H_6} \rightarrow P_{C_6H_6}$ and $\chi_{C_7H_8}, P^{\circ}_{C_7H_8} \rightarrow P_{C_8H_{18}}$ and $P_{C_6H_6}, P_{C_7H_8} \rightarrow P_{Total}$

$$P_{C_6H_6} = \chi_{C_6H_6} P^{\circ}_{C_6H_6} \qquad P_{C_7H_8} = \chi_{C_7H_8} P^{\circ}_{C_7H_8} \qquad P_{Total} = P_{C_6H_6} + P_{C_7H_8}$$

then solve the two simultaneous equations for $P^{\circ}_{C_6H_6}$ and $P^{\circ}_{C_7H_8}$

Solution: For the first solution: $75.0 \text{ g } C_6H_6 \times \dfrac{1 \text{ mol } C_6H_6}{78.11 \text{ g } C_6H_6} = 0.96\underline{0}18436 \text{ mol } C_6H_6$ and

$75.0 \text{ g } C_7H_8 \times \dfrac{1 \text{ mol } C_7H_8}{92.13 \text{ g } C_7H_8} = 0.81\underline{4}06708 \text{ mol } C_7H_8$ then

$\chi_{C_6H_6} = \dfrac{\text{amount } C_6H_6 \text{ (in moles)}}{\text{total amount (in moles)}} = \dfrac{0.96\underline{0}18436 \text{ mol}}{0.96\underline{0}18436 \text{ mol} + 0.81\underline{4}06708 \text{ mol}} = 0.54\underline{1}17716$ and

$\chi_{C_7H_8} = 1 - \chi_{C_6H_6} = 1 - 0.54\underline{1}17716 = 0.45\underline{8}82284$ then

$P_{Total} = P_{C_6H_6} + P_{C_7H_8} = \chi_{C_6H_6} P^{\circ}_{C_6H_6} + \chi_{C_7H_8} P^{\circ}_{C_7H_8}$

$= 0.54\underline{1}17716 P^{\circ}_{C_6H_6} + 0.45\underline{8}82284 P^{\circ}_{C_7H_8} = 80.9 \text{ mmHg}$

For the second solution: $100.0 \text{ g } C_6H_6 \times \dfrac{1 \text{ mol } C_6H_6}{78.11 \text{ g } C_6H_6} = 1.28\underline{0}24581 \text{ mol } C_6H_6$ and

$50.0 \text{ g } C_7H_8 \times \dfrac{1 \text{ mol } C_7H_8}{92.13 \text{ g } C_7H_8} = 0.54\underline{2}71139 \text{ mol } C_7H_8$ then

$\chi_{C_6H_6} = \dfrac{\text{amount } C_6H_6 \text{ (in moles)}}{\text{total amount (in moles)}} = \dfrac{1.28\underline{0}24581 \text{ mol}}{1.28\underline{0}24581 \text{ mol} + 0.54\underline{2}71139 \text{ mol}} = 0.702\underline{2}90657$ and

$\chi_{C_7H_8} = 1 - \chi_{C_6H_6} = 1 - 0.702\underline{2}90657 = 0.297\underline{7}09343$ then

$P_{Total} = P_{C_6H_6} + P_{C_7H_8} = P_{C_7H_{16}} = \chi_{C_6H_6} P^{\circ}_{C_6H_6} + \chi_{C_7H_8} P_{C_7H_8}$

$= 0.702\underline{2}90657 P^{\circ}_{C_6H_6} + 0.297\underline{7}09343 P^{\circ}_{C_7H_8} = 93.9 \text{ mmHg}$

Solve the two simultaneous equations for $P^{\circ}_{C_6H_6}$ and $P^{\circ}_{C_7H_8}$.

$P^{\circ}_{C_6H_6} = \dfrac{80.9 \text{ mmHg} - 0.45\underline{8}82284 P^{\circ}_{C_7H_8}}{0.54\underline{1}17716} = 149.\underline{4}8894 \text{ mmHg} - 0.84\underline{7}82373 \, P^{\circ}_{C_7H_8}$ then

$0.702\underline{2}90657(149.\underline{4}8894 \text{ mmHg} - 0.84\underline{7}82373 P^{\circ}_{C_7H_8}) + 0.297\underline{7}09343 P^{\circ}_{C_7H_8} = 93.9 \text{ mmHg} \rightarrow$

$104.\underline{9}8468 \text{ mmHg} - 0.59\underline{5}41868 P^{\circ}_{C_7H_8} + 0.297\underline{7}09343 P^{\circ}_{C_7H_8} = 93.9 \text{ mmHg} \rightarrow$

$11.\underline{0}8469 \text{ mmHg} = 0.29\underline{7}70935 P^{\circ}_{C_7H_8} \rightarrow$

$P^{\circ}_{C_7H_8} = \dfrac{11.\underline{0}8469 \text{ mmHg}}{0.29\underline{7}70935} = 37.\underline{2}33261 \text{ mmHg} = 37.2 \text{ mmHg}$ then

$P^{\circ}_{C_6H_6} = 149.\underline{4}8894 \text{ mmHg} - 0.84\underline{7}82373 P^{\circ}_{C_7H_8}$

$= 149.\underline{4}8894 \text{ mmHg} - 0.84\underline{7}82373 \times 37.\underline{2}33261 \text{ mmHg} = 117.\underline{9}217 \text{ mmHg} = 118 \text{ mmHg}$

Check: The units (mmHg and mmHg) are correct. The magnitude of the answers (118 mmHg and 37.2 mmHg) seems reasonable because we expect toluene to have a lower vapor pressure than benzene (based on molar mass).

12.102   **Given:** $Na_2CO_3 + NaHCO_3 = 11.60 \text{ g}$ in 1.00 L; treat 300.0 cm^3 of solution with HNO_3 and collect 0.940 L CO_2 at 298 K and 0.972 atm   **Find:** $M(Na_2CO_3)$ and $M(NaHCO_3)$

Conceptual Plan: $P, V, T \rightarrow n$ in 300.0 cm^3 then n in 300.0 cm^3 $\rightarrow n$ in 1.00 L then

$$PV = nRT \qquad\qquad\qquad\qquad\qquad \text{take ratio of volumes}$$

set up equations for the total mass and the total moles and solve. Then calculate concentrations.

$$g_{Na_2CO_3} + g_{NaHCO_3} = 11.60 \text{ g} \quad \dfrac{1 \text{ mol } Na_2CO_3}{105.99 \text{ g } Na_2CO_3} \quad \dfrac{1 \text{ mol } NaHCO_3}{84.01 \text{ g } NaHCO_3} \quad n_{Na_2CO_3} + n_{NaHCO_3} = n$$

Solution: $PV = nRT$. Rearrange to solve for n. $n = \dfrac{PV}{RT}$

$n_{CO_2} = \dfrac{0.972 \text{ atm} \times 0.940 \text{ L}}{0.08206 \dfrac{\text{L} \cdot \text{atm}}{\text{mol} \cdot \text{K}} \times 298 \text{ K}} = 0.037\underline{3}6340 \text{ mol } CO_2$ in 300.0 cm^3 then take ratio of moles to volume to get the

moles in 1.00 L

$$\frac{0.03736340 \text{ mol } CO_2}{300.0 \text{ cm}^3} \times 1000 \text{ cm}^3 = 0.1245447 \text{ mol } CO_2 \text{ in } 1.00 \text{ L}$$ because one mole of CO_2 is generated for each

mole of carbonate. So $n = n_{Na_2CO_3} + n_{NaHCO_3} = 0.1245447$ mol and $g_{Na_2CO_3} + g_{NaHCO_3} = 11.60$ g or

$g_{Na_2CO_3} = 11.60 \text{ g} - g_{NaHCO_3}$ using molar masses and substituting

$$n_{Na_2CO_3} + n_{NaHCO_3} = 0.1245447 \text{ mol} = g_{Na_2CO_3} \times \frac{1 \text{ mol } Na_2CO_3}{105.99 \text{ g } Na_2CO_3} + g_{NaHCO_3} \times \frac{1 \text{ mol } NaHCO_3}{84.01 \text{ g } NaHCO_3} =$$

$$(11.60 \text{ g} - g_{NaHCO_3}) \times \frac{1 \text{ mol } Na_2CO_3}{105.99 \text{ g } Na_2CO_3} + g_{NaHCO_3} \times \frac{1 \text{ mol } NaHCO_3}{84.01 \text{ g } NaHCO_3}$$

$$\rightarrow 0.1245447 \text{ mol} = 0.10944429 \text{ mol} - g_{NaHCO_3} \times 0.009434852 \frac{\text{mol}}{\text{g}} + g_{NaHCO_3} \, 0.011903345 \frac{\text{mol}}{\text{g}}$$

$$\rightarrow 0.01510041 \text{ mol} = g_{NaHCO_3} \times 0.002468493 \frac{\text{mol}}{\text{g}} \rightarrow$$

$$g_{NaHCO_3} = \frac{0.01510041 \text{ mol}}{0.002468493 \frac{\text{mol}}{\text{g}}} = 6.117259 \text{ g } NaHCO_3 = 6.1 \text{ g } NaHCO_3 \text{ and then } g_{Na_2CO_3} =$$

$11.60 \text{ g} - g_{NaHCO_3} = 11.60 \text{ g} - 6.117259 \text{ g } NaHCO_3 = 5.48274 \text{ g } Na_2CO_3 = 5.5 \text{ g } Na_2CO_3$ then M = mol/L

$$\frac{6.117259 \text{ g } NaHCO_3 \times \frac{1 \text{ mol } NaHCO_3}{84.01 \text{ g } NaHCO_3}}{1.00 \text{ L}} = 0.073 \text{ M } NaHCO_3 \text{ and}$$

$$\frac{5.48274 \text{ g } Na_2CO_3 \times \frac{1 \text{ mol } Na_2CO_3}{105.99 \text{ g } Na_2CO_3}}{1.00 \text{ L}} = 0.052 \text{ M } Na_2CO_3$$

Check: The units (M and M) are correct. The magnitude of the answers (0.052 M and 0.073 M) makes sense because the number of moles of CO_2 is small (0.12 M). The balance of the two components makes sense because if it were all Na_2CO_3, the number of moles would have been 0.109 moles (11.6/105.99) and if it were all $NaHCO_3$, the number of moles would have been 0.138 moles (11.6/84.01)—the actual number of moles is roughly in the middle of these two values.

Conceptual Problems

12.103　(a)　The two substances mix because the intermolecular forces among all of the species are roughly equal and there is a pervasive tendency to increase randomness, which happens when the two substances mix.

　　　　(b)　$\Delta H_{\text{soln}} \approx 0$ because the intermolecular forces between themselves are roughly equal to the forces between each other.

　　　　(c)　ΔH_{solute} and $\Delta H_{\text{solvent}}$ are positive, and ΔH_{mix} is negative and equals the sum of ΔH_{solute} and $\Delta H_{\text{solvent}}$.

12.104　The warm coolant water should not be put directly in the river without being cooled because it will raise the temperature of the water. When water is warmed, there is less dissolved oxygen in the water; this will be detrimental to aquatic life, which depends on the dissolved oxygen.

12.105　(d) More solute particles are found in an ionic solution because the solute breaks apart into its ions. The vapor pressure is lowered due to fewer solvent particles in the vapor phase as more solute particles are present.

12.106　(e) NaCl. If all of the substances have the same cost per kilogram, we need to determine which substance will generate the largest number of particles per kilogram (or gram). $HOCH_2CH_2OH$ generates 1 mol particle/62.07 g, NaCl generates 2 mol particles/58.44 g, KCl generates 2 mol particles/74.56 g, $MgCl_2$ generates 3 mol particles/95.22 g, and $SrCl_2$ generates 3 particles/158.53 g. So NaCl will generate 1 mole of particles for each 29 g.

12.107　The balloon not only loses He, it also takes in N_2 and O_2 from the air surrounding the balloon (due to the tendency for mixing), increasing the density of the gas inside the balloon, thus increasing the density of the balloon.

Questions for Group Work

12.108 1-propanol contains three carbon atoms and an alcohol functional group (—OH). The end with the carbon chain is nonpolar and so is soluble in nonpolar solvents, like hexane. The alcohol group exhibits hydrogen bonding, and so it can interact well with water. Since hexane is nonpolar, it cannot interact very well with water (a very polar molecular with strong hydrogen bonding), so hexane has little solubility in water.

12.109 The lattice energy, $\Delta H_{lattice}$, is the enthalpy change during the formation of the crystalline solid from the gaseous ions.

The energy required to separate solute particles is called ΔH_{solute} and is always endothermic. For ionic compounds, ΔH_{solute}, the energy required to separate the solute into its constituent particles, is simply the negative of the solute's lattice energy ($\Delta H_{solute} = -\Delta H_{lattice}$), discussed in Section 9.4.

The energy required to separate solvent particles is called $\Delta H_{solvent}$ and is always endothermic.

The energy of mixing solute particles and solvent particles is called ΔH_{mix} and is always exothermic.

The heat of hydration is simply the enthalpy change that occurs when 1 mol of the gaseous solute ions is dissolved in water. In aqueous solutions, $\Delta H_{solvent}$ and ΔH_{mix} can be combined into a single term called the heat of hydration ($\Delta H_{hydration}$) so, $\Delta H_{hydration} = \Delta H_{solvent} + \Delta H_{mix}$. Because the ion–dipole interactions that occur between a dissolved ion and the surrounding water molecules are much stronger than the hydrogen bonds in water, $\Delta H_{hydration}$ is always largely negative (exothermic) for ionic compounds.

The overall enthalpy change upon solution formation is called the enthalpy of solution (ΔH_{soln}). Using the heat of hydration, we can write the enthalpy of solution as a sum of just two terms, one endothermic and one exothermic: $\Delta H_{soln} = \Delta H_{solute} + \Delta H_{solvent} + \Delta H_{mix} = \Delta H_{solute} + \Delta H_{hydration} = $ endothermic(+) term + exothermic(−) term.

For ionic aqueous solutions, then, the overall enthalpy of solution depends on the relative magnitudes of ΔH_{solute} and $\Delta H_{hydration}$, with three possible scenarios (in each case we refer to the magnitude or absolute value of ΔH): (1) If $\Delta H_{solute} < \Delta H_{hydration}$, the amount of energy required to separate the solute into its constituent ions is less than the energy given off when the ions are hydrated. ΔH_{soln} is therefore negative, the solution process is exothermic, and the solution feels warm to the touch. (2) If $\Delta H_{solute} > \Delta H_{hydration}$, the amount of energy required to separate the solute into its constituent ions is greater than the energy given off when the ions are hydrated. ΔH_{soln} is therefore positive and the solution process is endothermic (if a solution forms at all), and the resulting solution feels cool to the touch. (3) If $\Delta H_{solute} \approx \Delta H_{hydration}$, the amount of energy required to separate the solute into its constituent ions is about equal to the energy given off when the ions are hydrated. ΔH_{soln} is therefore approximately zero, and the solution process is neither appreciably exothermic nor appreciably endothermic and there is no noticeable change in temperature.

12.110

	Increasing Temperature	**Increasing Pressure**
Solubility of gas in water	Decreases	Increases
Solubility of a solid in water	Generally increases	No effect

12.111 (a) **Given:** 13.62 g of sucrose ($C_{12}H_{22}O_{11}$) in 241.5 mL water; d (water) = 0.997 g/mL **Find:** percent by mass
Conceptual Plan: $d, V \rightarrow g_{H_2O}$ then $g_{C_{12}H_{22}O_{11}}, g_{H_2O} \rightarrow g_{soln}$ then $g_{C_{12}H_{22}O_{11}}, g_{soln} \rightarrow$ **percent by mass**

$$d = \frac{m}{V} \qquad g_{soln} = g_{C_6H_{12}O_6} + g_{H_2O} \qquad \text{mass percent} = \frac{\text{mass solute}}{\text{mass solution}} \times 100\%$$

Solution: $d = \dfrac{m}{V}$ so $241.5 \; \cancel{mL} \times \dfrac{0.997 \text{ g}}{1 \cancel{mL}} = 240.7755$ g

$g_{soln} = g_{C_6H_{12}O_6} + g_{H_2O} = 13.62 \text{ g} + 240.7755 \text{ g} = 254.3955$ g soln then

$$\text{mass percent} = \frac{\text{mass solute}}{\text{mass solution}} \times 100\% = \frac{13.62 \text{ g } C_{12}H_{22}O_{11}}{254.3955 \text{ g soln}} \times 100\% = 5.35 \text{ percent by mass}$$

Check: The units (percent by mass) are correct. The magnitude of the answer (5%) seems reasonable since we are dissolving 14 g in 241 g.

(b) **Given:** 13.62 g of sucrose ($C_{12}H_{22}O_{11}$) in 241.5 mL water; final volume = 250.0 mL **Find:** molarity
Conceptual Plan: $mL \rightarrow L$ and $g_{C_{12}H_{22}O_{11}} \rightarrow mol_{C_{12}H_{22}O_{11}}$ then $mol_{C_{12}H_{22}O_{11}}, V \rightarrow M$

$$\frac{1 \text{ L}}{1000 \text{ mL}} \qquad \frac{1 \text{ mol } C_{12}H_{22}O_{11}}{342.30 \text{ g } C_{12}H_{22}O_{11}} \qquad M = \frac{\text{amount solute (moles)}}{\text{volume solution (L)}}$$

Solution: $250.0 \text{ mL} \times \dfrac{1 \text{ L}}{1000 \text{ mL}} = 0.2500 \text{ L}$ and

$$13.62 \text{ g } C_{12}H_{22}O_{11} \times \dfrac{1 \text{ mol } C_{12}H_{22}O_{11}}{342.30 \text{ g } C_{12}H_{22}O_{11}} = 0.03978966 \text{ mol } C_{12}H_{22}O_{11}$$

$$M = \dfrac{\text{amount solute (moles)}}{\text{volume solution (L)}} = \dfrac{0.03978966 \text{ mol } C_{12}H_{22}O_{11}}{0.2500 \text{ L}} = 0.1592 \text{ M}$$

Check: The units (M) are correct. The magnitude of the answer (0.2 M) seems reasonable since we have 1/25 mole in 1/4 L.

(c)   **Given:** 13.62 g of sucrose ($C_{12}H_{22}O_{11}$) in 241.5 mL water; d (water) = 0.997 g/mL   **Find:** molality

Conceptual Plan: $g_{H_2O} \rightarrow kg_{H_2O}$ and $g_{C_6H_{12}O_6} \rightarrow mol_{C_6H_{12}O_6}$ then $mol_{C_6H_{12}O_6}, kg_{H_2O} \rightarrow m$

$$\dfrac{1 \text{ kg}}{1000 \text{ g}} \qquad \dfrac{1 \text{ mol } C_{12}H_{22}O_{11}}{342.30 \text{ g } C_{12}H_{22}O_{11}} \qquad m = \dfrac{\text{amount solute (moles)}}{\text{mass solvent (kg)}}$$

Solution: $g_{H_2O} = 240.7755 \text{ g}$ from part (a); $240.7755 \text{ g} \times \dfrac{1 \text{ kg}}{1000 \text{ g}} = 0.2407755 \text{ kg}$ and

$mol_{C_6H_{12}O_6} = 0.03978966 \text{ mol } C_{12}H_{22}O_{11}$ from part (a);

$$m = \dfrac{\text{amount solute (moles)}}{\text{mass solvent (kg)}} = \dfrac{0.03978966 \text{ mol } C_{12}H_{22}O_{11}}{0.2407755 \text{ kg}} = 0.165 \, m$$

Check: The units (m) are correct. The magnitude of the answer (0.2 m) seems reasonable since we have 1/25 mole in about 1/4 kg.

12.112   **Given:** 0.165 m sucrose **Other:** $K_f = 1.86 \,°C/m$; $K_b = 0.512 \,°C/m$ **Find:** T_f and T_b

Conceptual Plan: $m, K_f \rightarrow \Delta T_f \rightarrow T_f$ and $m, K_b \rightarrow \Delta T_b \rightarrow T_b$

$$\Delta T_f = K_f m \quad T_f = T_f^\circ - \Delta T_f \qquad \Delta T_b = K_b m \quad \Delta T_b = T_b - T_b^\circ$$

Solution: $\Delta T_f = K_f m = 1.86 \dfrac{°C}{m} \times 0.165 \, m = 0.307 \,°C$ then $T_f = T_f^\circ - \Delta T_f = 0.000 \,°C - 0.307 \,°C = -0.307 \,°C$

and $\Delta T_b = K_b m = 0.512 \dfrac{°C}{m} \times 0.165 \, m = 0.0845 \,°C$ and $\Delta T_b = T_b - T_b^\circ$ so

$T_b = T_b^\circ + \Delta T_b = 100.000 \,°C + 0.0845 \,°C = 100.0845 \,°C$

Check: The units (°C) are correct. The magnitudes of the answers seem reasonable since the molality is $\sim 0.2 \, m$. The shift in boiling point is less than the shift in freezing point because the constant is smaller for freezing.

In order to boil this sucrose solution, the solution needs to be raised to a slightly higher temperature than for pure water. In addition, the heat capacity of a sucrose solution is slightly higher than pure water. This results in a slightly increased time to boil the sucrose solution.

The syrup will freeze in a typical freezer because the freezing point has been dropped by less than 1 °C.

13 Chemical Kinetics

Reaction Rates

13.1   (a) $\text{Rate} = -\dfrac{1}{2}\dfrac{\Delta[\text{HBr}]}{\Delta t} = \dfrac{\Delta[\text{H}_2]}{\Delta t} = \dfrac{\Delta[\text{Br}_2]}{\Delta t}$

       (b)   **Given:** first 15.0 s; 0.500 M to 0.455 M   **Find:** average rate
           Conceptual Plan: $t_1, t_2, [\text{HBr}]_1, [\text{HBr}]_2 \rightarrow$ **average rate**

$$\text{Rate} = -\dfrac{1}{2}\dfrac{\Delta[\text{HBr}]}{\Delta t}$$

           Solution: $\text{Rate} = -\dfrac{1}{2}\dfrac{[\text{HBr}]_{t_2} - [\text{HBr}]_{t_1}}{t_2 - t_1} = -\dfrac{1}{2}\dfrac{0.455\ \text{M} - 0.500\ \text{M}}{15.0\ \text{s} - 0.0\ \text{s}} = 1.5 \times 10^{-3}\ \text{M} \cdot \text{s}^{-1}$

           Check: The units $(\text{M} \cdot \text{s}^{-1})$ are correct. The magnitude of the answer $(10^{-3}\ \text{M} \cdot \text{s}^{-1})$ makes physical sense because rates are always positive and we are not changing the concentration much in 15 s.

       (c)   **Given:** 0.500 L vessel, first 15.0 s of reaction, and part (b) data   **Find:** mol_{Br_2} formed
           Conceptual Plan: average rate, $t_1, t_2, \rightarrow \Delta[\text{Br}_2]$ **then** $\Delta[\text{Br}_2], \text{L} \rightarrow \text{mol}_{\text{Br}_2}$ **formed**

$$\text{Rate} = \dfrac{\Delta[\text{Br}_2]}{\Delta t} \qquad\qquad M = \dfrac{\text{mol}_{\text{Br}_2}}{\text{L}}$$

           Solution: $\text{Rate} = 1.5 \times 10^{-3}\ \text{M} \cdot \text{s}^{-1} = \dfrac{\Delta[\text{Br}_2]}{\Delta t} = \dfrac{\Delta[\text{Br}_2]}{15.0\ \text{s} - 0.0\ \text{s}}$. Rearrange to solve for $\Delta[\text{Br}_2]$.

           $\Delta[\text{Br}_2] = 1.5 \times 10^{-3}\dfrac{\text{M}}{\text{s}} \times 15.0\ \text{s} = 0.0225\ \text{M}$ then $M = \dfrac{\text{mol}_{\text{Br}_2}}{\text{L}}$. Rearrange to solve for

           mol_{Br_2}. $0.0225\dfrac{\text{mol Br}_2}{\text{L}} \times 0.500\ \text{L} = 0.011\ \text{mol Br}_2$

           Check: The units (mol) are correct. The magnitude of the answer (0.01 mol) makes physical sense because of the stoichiometric coefficient difference and the volume of the vessel, respectively.

13.2   (a) $\text{Rate} = -\dfrac{1}{2}\dfrac{\Delta[\text{N}_2\text{O}]}{\Delta t} = \dfrac{1}{2}\dfrac{\Delta[\text{N}_2]}{\Delta t} = \dfrac{\Delta[\text{O}_2]}{\Delta t}$

       (b)   **Given:** first 10.0 s; 0.018 mol O_2 in 0.250 L   **Find:** average rate
           Conceptual Plan: $\text{mol}_{\text{O}_2}, \text{L} \rightarrow M$ **then** $t_1, t_2, [\text{O}_2]_1, [\text{O}_2]_2 \rightarrow$ **average rate**

$$M = \dfrac{\text{mol}_{\text{O}_2}}{\text{L}} \qquad\qquad \text{Rate} = \dfrac{\Delta[\text{O}_2]}{\Delta t}$$

           Solution: At $t_1 = 0$ s, we have no O_2. $M = \dfrac{\text{mol}_{\text{O}_2}}{\text{L}} = \dfrac{0.018\ \text{mol O}_2}{0.250\ \text{L}} = 0.072\ \text{M}$ then

           $\text{Rate} = \dfrac{[\text{O}_2]_{t_2} - [\text{O}_2]_{t_1}}{t_2 - t_1} = \dfrac{0.072\ \text{M} - 0.000\ \text{M}}{10.0\ \text{s} - 0.0\ \text{s}} = 7.2 \times 10^{-3}\ \text{M} \cdot \text{s}^{-1}$

           Check: The units $(\text{M} \cdot \text{s}^{-1})$ are correct. The magnitude of the answer $(7 \times 10^{-3}\ \text{M} \cdot \text{s}^{-1})$ makes physical sense because rates are always positive and we are not changing the concentration much in 10 s.

(c)   **Given:** part (b) data   **Find:** $\dfrac{\Delta[N_2O]}{\Delta t}$

Conceptual Plan: average rate $\rightarrow \dfrac{\Delta[N_2O]}{\Delta t}$

$$\text{Rate} = -\frac{1}{2}\frac{\Delta[N_2O]}{\Delta t} = \frac{\Delta[O_2]}{\Delta t}$$

Solution: Rate $= -\dfrac{1}{2}\dfrac{\Delta[N_2O]}{\Delta t} = \dfrac{\Delta[O_2]}{\Delta t}$. Rearrange to solve for $\dfrac{\Delta[N_2O]}{\Delta t}$.

$$\frac{\Delta[N_2O]}{\Delta t} = -2\,\frac{\Delta[O_2]}{\Delta t} = -2 \times 7.2 \times 10^{-3}\,\text{M}\cdot\text{s}^{-1} = -0.014\,\text{M}\cdot\text{s}^{-1}$$

Check: The units ($\text{M}\cdot\text{s}^{-1}$) are correct. The magnitude of the answer ($-0.014\,\text{M}\cdot\text{s}^{-1}$) makes physical sense because we multiply by 2 because of the different stoichiometric coefficients. The change in concentration with time is negative because this is a reactant.

13.3   (a)   Rate $= -\dfrac{1}{2}\dfrac{\Delta[A]}{\Delta t} = -\dfrac{\Delta[B]}{\Delta t} = \dfrac{1}{3}\dfrac{\Delta[C]}{\Delta t}$

(b)   **Given:** $\dfrac{\Delta[A]}{\Delta t} = -0.100\,\text{M/s}$ **Find:** $\dfrac{\Delta[B]}{\Delta t}$ and $\dfrac{\Delta[C]}{\Delta t}$

Conceptual Plan: $\dfrac{\Delta[A]}{\Delta t} \rightarrow \dfrac{\Delta[B]}{\Delta t}$ and $\dfrac{\Delta[C]}{\Delta t}$

$$\text{Rate} = -\frac{1}{2}\frac{\Delta[A]}{\Delta t} = -\frac{\Delta[B]}{\Delta t} = \frac{1}{3}\frac{\Delta[C]}{\Delta t}$$

Solution: Rate $= -\dfrac{1}{2}\dfrac{\Delta[A]}{\Delta t} = -\dfrac{\Delta[B]}{\Delta t} = \dfrac{1}{3}\dfrac{\Delta[C]}{\Delta t}$. Substitute value and solve for the two desired values.

$$-\frac{1}{2}\frac{-0.100\,\text{M}}{\text{s}} = -\frac{\Delta[B]}{\Delta t}\ \text{ so }\ \frac{\Delta[B]}{\Delta t} = -0.0500\,\text{M}\cdot\text{s}^{-1}\ \text{ and }\ -\frac{1}{2}\frac{-0.100\,\text{M}}{\text{s}} = \frac{1}{3}\frac{\Delta[C]}{\Delta t}\ \text{ so}$$

$$\frac{\Delta[C]}{\Delta t} = 0.150\,\text{M}\cdot\text{s}^{-1}$$

Check: The units ($\text{M}\cdot\text{s}^{-1}$) are correct. The magnitude of the answer ($-0.05\,\text{M}\cdot\text{s}^{-1}$) makes physical sense because fewer moles of B are reacting for every mole of A and the change in concentration with time is negative because this is a reactant. The magnitude of the answer ($0.15\,\text{M}\cdot\text{s}^{-1}$) makes physical sense because more moles of C are being formed for every mole of A reacting and the change in concentration with time is positive because this is a product.

13.4   (a)   Rate $= -\dfrac{\Delta[A]}{\Delta t} = -2\,\dfrac{\Delta[B]}{\Delta t} = \dfrac{1}{2}\dfrac{\Delta[C]}{\Delta t}$

(b)   **Given:** $\dfrac{\Delta[C]}{\Delta t} = 0.025\,\text{M/s}$ **Find:** $\dfrac{\Delta[B]}{\Delta t}$ and $\dfrac{\Delta[A]}{\Delta t}$

Conceptual Plan: $\dfrac{\Delta[C]}{\Delta t} \rightarrow \dfrac{\Delta[B]}{\Delta t}$ and $\dfrac{\Delta[A]}{\Delta t}$

$$\text{Rate} = -\frac{\Delta[A]}{\Delta t} = -2\frac{\Delta[B]}{\Delta t} = \frac{1}{2}\frac{\Delta[C]}{\Delta t}$$

Solution: Rate $= -\dfrac{\Delta[A]}{\Delta t} = -2\,\dfrac{\Delta[B]}{\Delta t} = \dfrac{1}{2}\dfrac{\Delta[C]}{\Delta t}$. Substitute value and solve for the two desired values.

$$-2\frac{\Delta[B]}{\Delta t} = \frac{1}{2}\frac{0.025\,\text{M}}{\text{s}}\ \text{ so }\ \frac{\Delta[B]}{\Delta t} = -0.0063\,\text{M}\cdot\text{s}^{-1}\ \text{ and }\ -\frac{\Delta[A]}{\Delta t} = \frac{1}{2}\frac{0.025\,\text{M}}{\text{s}}\ \text{ so }\ \frac{\Delta[A]}{\Delta t} = -0.013\,\text{M}\cdot\text{s}^{-1}$$

Check: The units ($\text{M}\cdot\text{s}^{-1}$) are correct. The magnitude of the answer ($-0.006\,\text{M}\cdot\text{s}^{-1}$) makes physical sense because fewer moles of B are reacting for every mole of C being formed and the change in concentration with time is negative because this is a reactant. The magnitude of the answer ($-0.01\,\text{M}\cdot\text{s}^{-1}$) makes physical sense because fewer moles of A are reacting for every mole of C being formed and the change in concentration with time is negative because this is a reactant. B has the smallest stoichiometric coefficient, so its rate of change has the smallest magnitude.

13.5 **Given:** $Cl_2(g) + 3 F_2(g) \rightarrow 2 ClF_3(g)$; $\Delta[Cl_2]/\Delta t = -0.012$ M/s **Find:** $\Delta[F_2]/\Delta t$; $\Delta[ClF_3]/\Delta t$; and Rate

Conceptual Plan: Write the expression for the rate with respect to each species then

$$\text{Rate} = -\frac{\Delta[Cl_2]}{\Delta t} = -\frac{1}{3}\frac{\Delta[F_2]}{\Delta t} = \frac{1}{2}\frac{\Delta[ClF_3]}{\Delta t}$$

rate expression, $\dfrac{\Delta[Cl_2]}{\Delta t} \rightarrow \dfrac{\Delta[F_2]}{\Delta t}$; $\dfrac{\Delta[ClF_3]}{\Delta t}$; **Rate**

$$\text{Rate} = -\frac{\Delta[Cl_2]}{\Delta t} = -\frac{1}{3}\frac{\Delta[F_2]}{\Delta t} = \frac{1}{2}\frac{\Delta[ClF_3]}{\Delta t}$$

Solution: Rate $= -\dfrac{\Delta[Cl_2]}{\Delta t} = -\dfrac{1}{3}\dfrac{\Delta[F_2]}{\Delta t} = \dfrac{1}{2}\dfrac{\Delta[ClF_3]}{\Delta t}$ so $-\dfrac{\Delta[Cl_2]}{\Delta t} = -\dfrac{1}{3}\dfrac{\Delta[F_2]}{\Delta t}$

Rearrange to solve for $\dfrac{\Delta[F_2]}{\Delta t}$. $\dfrac{\Delta[F_2]}{\Delta t} = 3\dfrac{\Delta[Cl_2]}{\Delta t} = 3(-0.012 \text{ M} \cdot \text{s}^{-1}) = -0.036 \text{ M} \cdot \text{s}^{-1}$ and

$-\dfrac{\Delta[Cl_2]}{\Delta t} = \dfrac{1}{2}\dfrac{\Delta[ClF_3]}{\Delta t}$ Rearrange to solve for $\dfrac{\Delta[ClF_3]}{\Delta t}$.

$\dfrac{\Delta[ClF_3]}{\Delta t} = -2\dfrac{\Delta[Cl_2]}{\Delta t} = -2(-0.012 \text{ M} \cdot \text{s}^{-1}) = 0.024 \text{ M} \cdot \text{s}^{-1}$

Check: The units ($M \cdot s^{-1}$) are correct. The magnitude of the answers ($-0.036 \text{ M} \cdot \text{s}^{-1}$ and $0.024 \text{ M} \cdot \text{s}^{-1}$) makes physical sense because F_2 is being used at three times the rate of Cl_2, ClF_3 is being formed at two times the rate of Cl_2 disappearance, and Cl_2 has a stoichiometric coefficient of 1.

13.6 **Given:** $8 H_2S(g) + 4 O_2(g) \rightarrow 8 H_2O(g) + S_8(g)$; $\Delta[H_2S]/\Delta t = -0.080$ M/s
Find: $\Delta[O_2]/\Delta t$; $\Delta[H_2O]/\Delta t$; $\Delta[S_8]/\Delta t$; and Rate
Conceptual Plan: Write the expression for the rate with respect to each species then

$$\text{Rate} = -\frac{1}{8}\frac{\Delta[H_2S]}{\Delta t} = -\frac{1}{4}\frac{\Delta[O_2]}{\Delta t} = \frac{1}{8}\frac{\Delta[H_2O]}{\Delta t} = \frac{\Delta[S_8]}{\Delta t}$$

rate expression, $\dfrac{\Delta[H_2S]}{\Delta t} \rightarrow \dfrac{\Delta[O_2]}{\Delta t}$; $\dfrac{\Delta[H_2O]}{\Delta t}$; $\dfrac{\Delta[S_8]}{\Delta t}$; **Rate**

$$\text{Rate} = -\frac{1}{8}\frac{\Delta[H_2S]}{\Delta t} = -\frac{1}{4}\frac{\Delta[O_2]}{\Delta t} = \frac{1}{8}\frac{\Delta[H_2O]}{\Delta t} = \frac{\Delta[S_8]}{\Delta t}$$

Solution: Rate $= -\dfrac{1}{8}\dfrac{\Delta[H_2S]}{\Delta t} = -\dfrac{1}{4}\dfrac{\Delta[O_2]}{\Delta t} = \dfrac{1}{8}\dfrac{\Delta[H_2O]}{\Delta t} = \dfrac{\Delta[S_8]}{\Delta t}$ so

$-\dfrac{1}{8}\dfrac{\Delta[H_2S]}{\Delta t} = -\dfrac{1}{4}\dfrac{\Delta[O_2]}{\Delta t}$ Rearrange to solve for $\dfrac{\Delta[O_2]}{\Delta t}$.

$\dfrac{\Delta[O_2]}{\Delta t} = \dfrac{4}{8}\dfrac{\Delta[H_2S]}{\Delta t} = \dfrac{1}{2}(-0.080 \text{ M} \cdot \text{s}^{-1}) = -0.040 \text{ M} \cdot \text{s}^{-1}$

and $-\dfrac{1}{8}\dfrac{\Delta[H_2S]}{\Delta t} = \dfrac{1}{8}\dfrac{\Delta[H_2O]}{\Delta t}$ Rearrange to solve for $\dfrac{\Delta[H_2O]}{\Delta t}$.

$\dfrac{\Delta[H_2O]}{\Delta t} = -\dfrac{8}{8}\dfrac{\Delta[H_2S]}{\Delta t} = -(-0.080 \text{ M} \cdot \text{s}^{-1}) = 0.080 \text{ M} \cdot \text{s}^{-1}$

and $\dfrac{\Delta[S_8]}{\Delta t} = -\dfrac{1}{8}\dfrac{\Delta[H_2S]}{\Delta t} = -\dfrac{1}{8}(-0.080 \text{ M} \cdot \text{s}^{-1}) = 0.010 \text{ M} \cdot \text{s}^{-1}$

Check: The units ($M \cdot s^{-1}$) are correct. The magnitude of the answers ($-0.040 \text{ M} \cdot \text{s}^{-1}$, $-0.080 \text{ M} \cdot \text{s}^{-1}$, and $0.010 \text{ M} \cdot \text{s}^{-1}$) makes physical sense because O_2 is being used at one-half times the rate of H_2S, H_2O is being formed at a rate equal to the rate of H_2S disappearance, S_8 is being formed at one-eighth times the rate of H_2S disappearance, and S_8 has a stoichiometric coefficient of 1.

13.7 **(a)** **Given:** $[C_4H_8]$ versus time data **Find:** average rate between 0 and 10 s and between 40 and 50 s
Conceptual Plan: $t_1, t_2, [C_4H_8]_1, [C_4H_8]_2 \rightarrow$ **average rate**

$$\text{Rate} = -\frac{\Delta[C_4H_8]}{\Delta t}$$

Solution: For 0 to 10 s, Rate $= -\dfrac{[C_4H_8]_{t_2} - [C_4H_8]_{t_1}}{t_2 - t_1} = -\dfrac{0.913 \text{ M} - 1.000 \text{ M}}{10.\text{ s} - 0.\text{ s}} = 8.7 \times 10^{-3} \text{ M} \cdot \text{s}^{-1}$ and

for 40 to 50 s, Rate $= -\dfrac{[C_4H_8]_{t_2} - [C_4H_8]_{t_1}}{t_2 - t_1} = -\dfrac{0.637 \text{ M} - 0.697 \text{ M}}{50.\text{ s} - 40.\text{ s}} = 6.0 \times 10^{-3} \text{ M} \cdot \text{s}^{-1}$

Check: The units ($M \cdot s^{-1}$) are correct. The magnitude of the answers ($10^{-3} M \cdot s^{-1}$) makes physical sense because rates are always positive and we are not changing the concentration much in 10 s. Also, reactions slow as they proceed because the concentration of the reactants is decreasing.

(b) **Given:** $[C_4H_8]$ versus time data   **Find:** $\dfrac{\Delta[C_2H_4]}{\Delta t}$ between 20 and 30 s

Conceptual Plan: $t_1, t_2, [C_4H_8]_1, [C_4H_8]_2 \rightarrow \dfrac{\Delta[C_2H_4]}{\Delta t}$

$$\text{Rate} = -\dfrac{\Delta[C_4H_8]}{\Delta t} = \dfrac{1}{2}\dfrac{\Delta[C_2H_4]}{\Delta t}$$

Solution: $\text{Rate} = -\dfrac{[C_4H_8]_{t_2} - [C_4H_8]_{t_1}}{t_2 - t_1} = -\dfrac{0.763\,M - 0.835\,M}{30.\,s - 20.\,s} = 7.2 \times 10^{-3}\,M \cdot s^{-1} = \dfrac{1}{2}\dfrac{\Delta[C_2H_4]}{\Delta t}$

Rearrange to solve for $\dfrac{\Delta[C_2H_4]}{\Delta t}$. So $\dfrac{\Delta[C_2H_4]}{\Delta t} = 2(7.2 \times 10^{-3}\,M \cdot s^{-1}) = 1.4 \times 10^{-2}\,M \cdot s^{-1}$

Check: The units ($M \cdot s^{-1}$) are correct. The magnitude of the answer ($10^{-2} M \cdot s^{-1}$) makes physical sense because the rate of product formation is always positive and we are not changing the concentration much in 10 s. The rate of change of the product is faster than the decline of the reactant because of the stoichiometric coefficients.

13.8 (a) **Given:** $[NO_2]$ versus time data   **Find:** average rate between 10 and 20 s and between 50 and 60 s
Conceptual Plan: $t_1, t_2, [NO_2]_1, [NO_2]_2 \rightarrow$ **average rate**

$$\text{Rate} = -\dfrac{\Delta[NO_2]}{\Delta t}$$

Solution: For 10 to 20 s, $\text{Rate} = -\dfrac{[NO_2]_{t_2} - [NO_2]_{t_1}}{t_2 - t_1} = -\dfrac{0.904\,M - 0.951\,M}{20.\,s - 10.\,s} = 4.7 \times 10^{-3}\,M \cdot s^{-1}$ and

for 50 to 60 s, $\text{Rate} = -\dfrac{[NO_2]_{t_2} - [NO_2]_{t_1}}{t_2 - t_1} = -\dfrac{0.740\,M - 0.778\,M}{60.\,s - 50.\,s} = 3.8 \times 10^{-3}\,M \cdot s^{-1}$

Check: The units ($M \cdot s^{-1}$) are correct. The magnitude of the answer ($10^{-3} M \cdot s^{-1}$) makes physical sense because rates are always positive and we are not changing the concentration much in 10 s. Also, reactions slow as they proceed because the concentration of the reactants is decreasing.

(b) **Given:** $[NO_2]$ versus time data   **Find:** $\dfrac{\Delta[O_2]}{\Delta t}$ between 50 and 60 s

Conceptual Plan: **average rate from part (a)** $\rightarrow \dfrac{\Delta[O_2]}{\Delta t}$

$$\text{Rate} = -\dfrac{\Delta[NO_2]}{\Delta t} = 2\dfrac{\Delta[O_2]}{\Delta t}$$

Solution: $\text{Rate} = -\dfrac{\Delta[NO_2]}{\Delta t} = 2\dfrac{\Delta[O_2]}{\Delta t}$. Substitute value and solve for the desired value.

$3.8 \times 10^{-3}\,M \cdot s^{-1} = 2\dfrac{\Delta[O_2]}{\Delta t}$ so $\dfrac{\Delta[O_2]}{\Delta t} = 1.9 \times 10^{-3}\,M \cdot s^{-1}$

Check: The units ($M \cdot s^{-1}$) are correct. The magnitude of the answer ($10^{-3} M \cdot s^{-1}$) makes physical sense because the rate of product formation is always positive and we are not changing the concentration much in 10 s. The rate of change of the product is slower than the decline of the reactant because of the stoichiometric coefficients.

13.9 (a) **Given:** $[Br_2]$ versus time plot
Find: (i) average rate between 0 and 25 s; (ii) instantaneous rate at 25 s; (iii) instantaneous rate of HBr formation at 50 s
Conceptual Plan: (i) $t_1, t_2, [Br_2]_1, [Br_2]_2 \rightarrow$ **average rate** then

$$\text{Rate} = -\dfrac{\Delta[Br_2]}{\Delta t}$$

(ii) draw tangent at 25 s and determine slope $\rightarrow$ instantaneous rate then

$$\text{Rate} = -\dfrac{\Delta[Br_2]}{\Delta t}$$

(iii) draw tangent at 50 s and determine slope → instantaneous rate → $\dfrac{\Delta[\text{HBr}]}{\Delta t}$

$$\text{Rate} = -\dfrac{\Delta[\text{Br}_2]}{\Delta t} \qquad \text{Rate} = \dfrac{1}{2}\dfrac{\Delta[\text{HBr}]}{\Delta t}$$

Solution:

(i) Rate $= -\dfrac{[\text{Br}_2]_{t_2} - [\text{Br}_2]_{t_1}}{t_2 - t_1} = -\dfrac{0.75\ \text{M} - 1.00\ \text{M}}{25\ \text{s} - 0.\ \text{s}} = 1.0 \times 10^{-2}\ \text{M}\cdot\text{s}^{-1}$

and (ii) at 25 s:

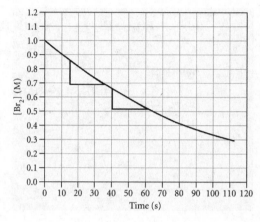

Slope $= \dfrac{\Delta y}{\Delta x} = \dfrac{0.68\ \text{M} - 0.85\ \text{M}}{35\ \text{s} - 15\ \text{s}} = -8.5 \times 10^{-3}\ \text{M}\cdot\text{s}^{-1}$

because the slope $= \dfrac{\Delta[\text{Br}_2]}{\Delta t}$ and Rate $= -\dfrac{\Delta[\text{Br}_2]}{\Delta t}$,

then Rate $= -(-8.5 \times 10^{-3}\ \text{M}\cdot\text{s}^{-1}) = 8.5 \times 10^{-3}\ \text{M}\cdot\text{s}^{-1}$

(iii) at 50 s:

Slope $= \dfrac{\Delta y}{\Delta x} = \dfrac{0.53\ \text{M} - 0.66\ \text{M}}{60.\ \text{s} - 40.\ \text{s}} = -6.5 \times 10^{-3}\ \text{M}\cdot\text{s}^{-1}$

because the slope $= \dfrac{\Delta[\text{Br}_2]}{\Delta t}$ and

Rate $= -\dfrac{\Delta[\text{Br}_2]}{\Delta t} = \dfrac{1}{2}\dfrac{\Delta[\text{HBr}]}{\Delta t}$, then

$\dfrac{\Delta[\text{HBr}]}{\Delta t} = -2\dfrac{\Delta[\text{Br}_2]}{\Delta t} = -2(-6.5 \times 10^{-3}\ \text{M}\cdot\text{s}^{-1}) = 1.3 \times 10^{-2}\ \text{M}\cdot\text{s}^{-1}$

Check: The units ($\text{M}\cdot\text{s}^{-1}$) are correct. The magnitude of the first answer is larger than the second answer because the rate is slowing down and the first answer includes the initial portion of the data. The magnitude of the answers ($10^{-3}\ \text{M}\cdot\text{s}^{-1}$) makes physical sense because rates are always positive and we are not changing the concentration much.

(b) **Given:** $[\text{Br}_2]$ versus time data and $[\text{HBr}]_0 = 0\ \text{M}$ **Find:** plot $[\text{HBr}]$ with time

Conceptual Plan: Because Rate $= -\dfrac{\Delta[\text{Br}_2]}{\Delta t} = \dfrac{1}{2}\dfrac{\Delta[\text{HBr}]}{\Delta t}$. **The rate of change of $[\text{HBr}]$ will be twice that of $[\text{Br}_2]$. The plot will start at the origin.**

Solution:

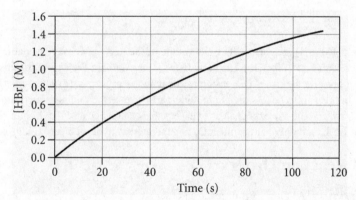

Check: The units (M versus s) are correct. The plot makes sense because the plot has the same general shape of the original plot, except that we are increasing instead of decreasing our concentration axis by a factor of two (to account for the difference in stoichiometric coefficients).

13.10   **Given:** $[\text{H}_2\text{O}_2]$ versus time plot and 1.5 L H_2O_2 initially

Find: (a) average rate between 10 and 20 s; (b) instantaneous rate at 30 s; (c) instantaneous rate of O_2 formation at 50 s; (d) mol_{O_2} formed in first 50 s

Conceptual Plan: (a) t_1, t_2, $[H_2O_2]_1$, $[H_2O_2]_2 \rightarrow$ average rate then

$$\text{Rate} = -\frac{1}{2}\frac{\Delta[H_2O_2]}{\Delta t}$$

(b) draw tangent at 30 s and determine slope → instantaneous rate then

$$\text{Rate} = -\frac{1}{2}\frac{\Delta[H_2O_2]}{\Delta t}$$

(c) draw tangent at 50 s and determine slope → instantaneous rate → $\dfrac{\Delta[O_2]}{\Delta t}$

$$\text{Rate} = -\frac{1}{2}\frac{\Delta[H_2O_2]}{\Delta t} \qquad \text{Rate} = \frac{\Delta[O_2]}{\Delta t}$$

(d) $[H_2O_2]_{0\,s}$, $[H_2O_2]_{50\,s} \rightarrow \Delta\,[H_2O_2] \rightarrow \Delta\,[O_2]$ then $\Delta\,[O_2]$, $V \rightarrow \text{mol}_{O_2}$

$$\Delta[H_2O_2] = [H_2O_2]_{50\,s} - [H_2O_2]_{0\,s} \qquad \text{Rate} = -\frac{1}{2}\frac{\Delta[H_2O_2]}{\Delta t} = \frac{\Delta[O_2]}{\Delta t} \qquad M = \frac{\text{mol}_{O_2}}{L}$$

Solution:

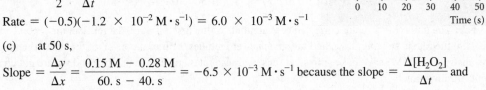

(a) $\quad \text{Rate} = -\dfrac{1}{2}\dfrac{[H_2O_2]_{t_2} - [H_2O_2]_{t_1}}{t_2 - t_1}$

$$= -\frac{1}{2}\frac{0.55\ M - 0.75\ M}{20.\ s - 10.\ s}$$

$$= 1.0 \times 10^{-2}\ M \cdot s^{-1}\ \text{and}$$

(b) at 30 s, $\text{Slope} = \dfrac{\Delta y}{\Delta x} = \dfrac{0.28\ M - 0.52\ M}{40.\ s - 20.\ s}$

$= -1.2 \times 10^{-2}\ M \cdot s^{-1}$ because the slope $= \dfrac{\Delta[H_2O_2]}{\Delta t}$ and

$\text{Rate} = -\dfrac{1}{2}\dfrac{\Delta[H_2O_2]}{\Delta t}$ then

$\text{Rate} = (-0.5)(-1.2 \times 10^{-2}\ M \cdot s^{-1}) = 6.0 \times 10^{-3}\ M \cdot s^{-1}$

(c) at 50 s,

$\text{Slope} = \dfrac{\Delta y}{\Delta x} = \dfrac{0.15\ M - 0.28\ M}{60.\ s - 40.\ s} = -6.5 \times 10^{-3}\ M \cdot s^{-1}$ because the slope $= \dfrac{\Delta[H_2O_2]}{\Delta t}$ and

$\text{Rate} = -\dfrac{1}{2}\dfrac{\Delta[H_2O_2]}{\Delta t} = \dfrac{\Delta[O_2]}{\Delta t}$ then $\dfrac{\Delta[O_2]}{\Delta t} = (-0.5)(-6.5 \times 10^{-3}\ M \cdot s^{-1}) = 3.3 \times 10^{-3}\ M \cdot s^{-1}$

(d) $\Delta[H_2O_2] = [H_2O_2]_{50\,s} - [H_2O_2]_{0\,s} = 0.23\ M - 1.00\ M = 0.77\ M$ because

$\Delta[O_2] = -\dfrac{1}{2}\Delta[H_2O_2] = (-0.5)(0.77\ M) = 0.38\underline{5}\ M$ then $M = \dfrac{\text{mol}_{O_2}}{L}$ so

$\text{mol}_{O_2} = M \cdot L = 0.38\underline{5}\dfrac{\text{mol}_{O_2}}{L} \times 1.5\ L = 0.58\ \text{mol}_{O_2}$

Check: (a) The units $(M \cdot s^{-1})$ are correct. The magnitude of the first answer is reasonable considering the concentrations and times involved (1 M/100 s). **(b)** The units $(M \cdot s^{-1})$ are correct. We expect the answer in this part to be less than in the first part because the rate is decreasing as the reaction proceeds. **(c)** The units $(M \cdot s^{-1})$ are correct. We expect the answer in this part to be less than in the first part because the rate is decreasing as the reaction proceeds. **(d)** The units (mol) are correct. We expect an answer less than 1 mol because the drop in reactant concentration is less than 1 M, we have 1.5 L, and only half as much O_2 is generated as hydrogen peroxide is consumed.

The Rate Law and Reaction Orders

13.11 **(a)** **Given:** Rate versus [A] plot **Find:** reaction order
Conceptual Plan: Look at shape of plot and match to possibilities.
Solution: The plot is a linear plot, so Rate $\propto$ [A] or the reaction is first order.

Check: The order of the reaction is a common reaction order.

(b) **Given:** part (a) **Find:** sketch plot of [A] versus time
Conceptual Plan: Using the result from part (a), shape plot of [A] versus time should be curved with [A]
decreasing. Use 1.0 M as initial concentration.

Solution:

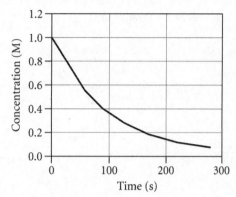

Check: The plot has a shape that matches the one in the text for first-order plots.

(c) **Given:** part (a) **Find:** write a rate law and estimate k

Conceptual Plan: Using result from part (a), the slope of the plot is the rate constant.

Solution: Slope $= \dfrac{\Delta y}{\Delta x} = \dfrac{0.010 \, \dfrac{M}{s} - 0.00 \, \dfrac{M}{s}}{1.0 \, M - 0.0 \, M} = 0.010 \, s^{-1}$ so Rate $= k \, [A]^1$ or Rate $= k \, [A]$ or

Rate $= 0.010 \, s^{-1} \, [A]$

Check: The units (s^{-1}) are correct. The magnitude of the answer $(10^{-2} \, s^{-1})$ makes physical sense because of the rate and concentration data. Remember that concentration is in units of M, so plugging the rate constant into the equation has the units of the rate as $M \cdot s^{-1}$, which is correct.

13.12   (a) **Given:** Rate versus [A] plot **Find:** reaction order

Conceptual Plan: Look at shape of plot and match to possibilities.

Solution: The plot is a linear plot that is horizontal, so rate is independent of [A] or the reaction is zero order with respect to A.

Check: The order of the reaction is a common reaction order.

(b) **Given:** part (a) **Find:** sketch plot of [A] versus time

Conceptual Plan: Using the result from part (a), shape plot of [A] versus time should be a straight line with [A] decreasing. Use 1.0 M as initial concentration.

Solution:

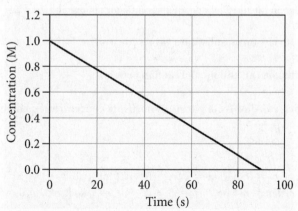

Check: The plot has a shape that matches the one in the text for zero-order plots.

(c) **Given:** part (a) **Find:** write a rate law and estimate k

Conceptual Plan: Using result from part (a), the rate is equal to the rate constant.

Solution: Rate $= k \, [A]^0$ or Rate $= k$ or Rate $= 0.011 \, M \cdot s^{-1}$

Check: The units $(M \cdot s^{-1})$ are correct. The magnitude of the answer $(10^{-2} \, M \cdot s^{-1})$ makes physical sense because of the rate and concentration data. Plugging the rate constant into the equation, the rate has the units of $M \cdot s^{-1}$, which is correct.

13.13   **Given:** reaction order: (a) first order, (b) second order, and (c) zero order   **Find:** units of k
                Conceptual Plan: Using rate law, rearrange to solve for k.

$$\text{Rate} = k\,[\text{A}]^n, \text{ where } n = \text{reaction order}$$

Solution: For all cases, rate has units of $\text{M} \cdot \text{s}^{-1}$ and [A] has units of M.

(a) $\text{Rate} = k\,[\text{A}]^1 = k\,[\text{A}]$ so $k = \dfrac{\text{Rate}}{[\text{A}]} = \dfrac{\frac{\text{M}}{\text{s}}}{\text{M}} = \text{s}^{-1}$

(b) $\text{Rate} = k\,[\text{A}]^2$ so $k = \dfrac{\text{Rate}}{[\text{A}]^2} = \dfrac{\frac{\text{M}}{\text{s}}}{\text{M} \cdot \text{M}} = \text{M}^{-1} \cdot \text{s}^{-1}$

(c) $\text{Rate} = k\,[\text{A}]^0 = k = \text{M} \cdot \text{s}^{-1}$

Check: The units $(\text{s}^{-1}, \text{M}^{-1} \cdot \text{s}^{-1}, \text{ and } \text{M} \cdot \text{s}^{-1})$ are correct. The units for k change with the reaction order so that the units on the rate remain as $\text{M} \cdot \text{s}^{-1}$.

13.14   **Given:** $k = 0.053/\text{s}$ and $[\text{N}_2\text{O}_5] = 0.055$ M; reaction order: (a) first order, (b) second order, and zero order (change units on k as necessary)   **Find:** rate
                Conceptual Plan: Using rate law, substitute in values to solve for Rate.

$$\text{Rate} = k\,[\text{N}_2\text{O}_5]^n, \text{ where } n = \text{reaction order}$$

Solution: For all cases, Rate has units of $\text{M} \cdot \text{s}^{-1}$ and [A] has units of M. Use the results from Problem 13.35 to choose the appropriate units for k.

(a) $\text{Rate} = k\,[\text{N}_2\text{O}_5]^1 = k\,[\text{N}_2\text{O}_5] = \dfrac{0.053}{\text{s}} \times 0.055 \text{ M} = 2.9 \times 10^{-3} \dfrac{\text{M}}{\text{s}}$

(b) $\text{Rate} = k\,[\text{N}_2\text{O}_5]^2 = k\,[\text{N}_2\text{O}_5]^2 = \dfrac{0.053}{\text{M s}} \times (0.055 \text{ M})^2 = 1.6 \times 10^{-4} \dfrac{\text{M}}{\text{s}}$

        $\text{Rate} = k\,[\text{N}_2\text{O}_5]^0 = k = 5.3 \times 10^{-2} \dfrac{\text{M}}{\text{s}}$

Check: The units $(\text{M} \cdot \text{s}^{-1})$ are correct. The magnitude of the rate changes as the order of the reaction changes because we are multiplying by the concentration a different number of times in each case. The higher the order, the lower the rate because the concentration is less than 1 M.

13.15   **Given:** A, B, and C react to form products. Reaction is first order in A, second order in B, and zero order in C
           Find: (a) rate law; (b) overall order of reaction; (c) factor change in rate if [A] doubled; (d) factor change in rate if [B] doubled; (e) factor change in rate if [C] doubled; and (f) factor change in rate if [A], [B], and [C] doubled
           Conceptual Plan:
           (a)   **Using general rate law form, substitute values for orders.**

$$\text{Rate} = k\,[\text{A}]^m\,[\text{B}]^n\,[\text{C}]^p, \text{ where } m, n, \text{ and } p = \text{reaction orders}$$

           (b)   **Using rate law in part (a), add up all reaction orders.**

$$\text{overall reaction order} = m + n + p$$

           (c)   **Through (f), using rate law from part (a), substitute concentration changes.**

$$\frac{\text{Rate 2}}{\text{Rate 1}} = \frac{k\,[\text{A}]_2^1\,[\text{B}]_2^2}{k\,[\text{A}]_1^1\,[\text{B}]_1^2}$$

Solution:

(a) $m = 1, n = 2,$ and $p = 0$ so $\text{Rate} = k\,[\text{A}]^1\,[\text{B}]^2\,[\text{C}]^0$ or $\text{Rate} = k\,[\text{A}][\text{B}]^2$

(b)   *overall reaction order* $= m + n + p = 1 + 2 + 0 = 3,$ so it is a third-order reaction overall.

(c) $\dfrac{\text{Rate 2}}{\text{Rate 1}} = \dfrac{k\,[\text{A}]_2^1\,[\text{B}]_2^2}{k\,[\text{A}]_1^1\,[\text{B}]_1^2}$ and $[\text{A}]_2 = 2\,[\text{A}]_1, [\text{B}]_2 = [\text{B}]_1, [\text{C}]_2 = [\text{C}]_1,$ so $\dfrac{\text{Rate 2}}{\text{Rate 1}} = \dfrac{k\,(2[\text{A}]_1)^1\,[\text{B}]_1^2}{k\,[\text{A}]_1^1\,[\text{B}]_1^2} = 2$

        so the reaction rate doubles (factor of 2)

(d) $\dfrac{\text{Rate 2}}{\text{Rate 1}} = \dfrac{k\,[\text{A}]_2^1\,[\text{B}]_2^2}{k\,[\text{A}]_1^1\,[\text{B}]_1^2}$ and $[\text{A}]_2 = [\text{A}]_1, [\text{B}]_2 = 2[\text{B}]_1, [\text{C}]_2 = [\text{C}]_1,$ so $\dfrac{\text{Rate 2}}{\text{Rate 1}} = \dfrac{k\,[\text{A}]_1(2\,[\text{B}]_1)^2}{k\,[\text{A}]_1^1\,[\text{B}]_1^2} = 2^2 = 4$

        so the reaction rate quadruples (factor of 4)

(e) $\dfrac{\text{Rate 2}}{\text{Rate 1}} = \dfrac{k\,[A]_2^1\,[B]_2^2}{k\,[A]_1^1\,[B]_1^2}$ and $[A]_2 = [A]_1$, $[B]_2 = [B]_1$, $[C]_2 = 2\,[C]_1$, so $\dfrac{\text{Rate 2}}{\text{Rate 1}} = \dfrac{k\,\cancel{[A]_1^1}\,\cancel{[B]_1^2}}{k\,\cancel{[A]_1^1}\,\cancel{[B]_1^2}} = 1$

so the reaction rate is unchanged (factor of 1)

(f) $\dfrac{\text{Rate 2}}{\text{Rate 1}} = \dfrac{k\,[A]_2^1\,[B]_2^2}{k\,[A]_1^1\,[B]_1^2}$ and $[A]_2 = 2[A]_1$, $[B]_2 = 2[B]_1$, $[C]_2 = 2\,[C]_1$, so

$\dfrac{\text{Rate 2}}{\text{Rate 1}} = \dfrac{k(2\cancel{[A]_1})^1\,(2\cancel{[B]_1})^2}{k\,\cancel{[A]_1^1}\,\cancel{[B]_1^2}} = 2 \times 2^2 = 8$, so the reaction rate goes up by a factor of 8.

Check: The units (none) are correct. The rate law is consistent with the orders given, and the overall order is larger than any of the individual orders. The factors are consistent with the reaction orders. The larger the order, the larger the factor. When all concentrations are changed, the rate changes the most. If a reactant is not in the rate law, then changing its concentration has no effect on the reaction rate.

13.16   **Given:** A, B, and C react to form products. Reaction is zero order in A, one-half order in B, and second order in C. **Find:** (a) rate law; (b) overall order of reaction; (c) factor change in rate if [A] doubled; (d) factor change in rate if [B] doubled; (e) factor change in rate if [C] doubled; and (f) factor change in rate if [A], [B], and [C] doubled

Conceptual Plan:

(a)   **Using general rate law form, substitute values for orders.**

$$\text{Rate} = k\,[A]^m\,[B]^n\,[C]^p, \text{ where } m, n, \text{ and } p = \text{reaction orders}$$

(b)   **Using rate law in part (a), add up all reaction orders.**

$$\textit{overall reaction order} = m + n + p$$

(c)   **Through (f), using rate law from part (a), substitute concentration changes.**

$$\frac{\text{Rate 2}}{\text{Rate 1}} = \frac{k\,[B]_2^{1/2}\,[C]_2^2}{k\,[B]_1^{1/2}\,[C]_1^2}$$

Solution:

(a) $m = 0$, $n = 1/2$, and $p = 2$ so Rate $= k\,[A]^0[B]^{1/2}[C]^2$ or Rate $= k\,[B]^{1/2}[C]^2$.

(b) $\textit{overall reaction order} = m + n + p = 0 + 1/2 + 2 = 5/2 = 2.5$, so it is a two-and-a-half-order reaction overall.

(c) $\dfrac{\text{Rate 2}}{\text{Rate 1}} = \dfrac{k\,[B]_2^{1/2}\,[C]_2^2}{k\,[B]_1^{1/2}\,[C]_1^2}$ and $[A]_2 = 2[A]_1$, $[B]_2 = [B]_1$, $[C]_2 = [C]_1$, so $\dfrac{\text{Rate 2}}{\text{Rate 1}} = \dfrac{k\,\cancel{[B]_1^{1/2}}\,\cancel{[C]_1^2}}{k\,\cancel{[B]_1^{1/2}}\,\cancel{[C]_1^2}} = 1$

so the reaction rate is unchanged (factor of 1).

(d) $\dfrac{\text{Rate 2}}{\text{Rate 1}} = \dfrac{k\,[B]_2^{1/2}\,[C]_2^2}{k\,[B]_1^{1/2}\,[C]_1^2}$ and $[A]_2 = [A]_1$, $[B]_2 = 2[B]_1$, $[C]_2 = [C]_1$, so $\dfrac{\text{Rate 2}}{\text{Rate 1}} = \dfrac{k\,(2\cancel{[B]_1})^{1/2}\,\cancel{[C]_1^2}}{k\,\cancel{[B]_1^{1/2}}\,\cancel{[C]_1^2}} = 2^{1/2}$

so the reaction rate increases by a factor of $2^{1/2}$ or $\sqrt{2}$ or 1.414.

(e) $\dfrac{\text{Rate 2}}{\text{Rate 1}} = \dfrac{k\,[B]_2^{1/2}\,[C]_2^2}{k\,[B]_1^{1/2}\,[C]_1^2}$ and $[A]_2 = [A]_1$, $[B]_2 = [B]_1$, $[C]_2 = 2[C]_1$, so

$\dfrac{\text{Rate 2}}{\text{Rate 1}} = \dfrac{k\,\cancel{[B]_1^{1/2}}\,(2\cancel{[C]_1})^2}{k\,\cancel{[B]_1^{1/2}}\,\cancel{[C]_1^2}} = 2^2 = 4$, so the reaction rate quadruples (factor of 4).

(f) $\dfrac{\text{Rate 2}}{\text{Rate 1}} = \dfrac{k\,[B]_2^{1/2}\,[C]_2^2}{k\,[B]_1^{1/2}\,[C]_1^2}$ and $[A]_2 = 2[A]_1$, $[B]_2 = 2[B]_1$, $[C]_2 = 2[C]_1$, so

$\dfrac{\text{Rate 2}}{\text{Rate 1}} = \dfrac{k\,(2\cancel{[B]_1})^{1/2}\,(2\cancel{[C]_1})^2}{k\,\cancel{[B]_1^{1/2}}\,\cancel{[C]_1^2}} = 2^{1/2} \times 2^2 = 2^{5/2}$, so the reaction rate goes up by a factor of $2^{5/2}$

or $4\sqrt{2}$ or 5.66.

Check: The units (none) are correct. The rate law is consistent with the orders given, and the overall order is larger than any of the individual orders. The factors are consistent with the reaction orders. The larger the order, the larger the factor. When all concentrations are changed, the rate changes the most. If a reactant is not in the rate law, then changing its concentration has no effect on the reaction rate.

13.17   **Given:** table of [A] versus initial rate   **Find:** rate law and k

Conceptual Plan: Using general rate law form, compare rate ratios to determine reaction order.

$$\frac{\text{Rate 2}}{\text{Rate 1}} = \frac{k\,[A]_2^n}{k\,[A]_1^n}$$

Then use one of the concentration/initial rate pairs to determine k.

$$\text{Rate} = k[A]^n$$

Solution: $\dfrac{\text{Rate } 2}{\text{Rate } 1} = \dfrac{k \, [A]_2^n}{k \, [A]_1^n}$ Comparing the first two sets of data $\dfrac{0.210 \, M\!/s}{0.053 \, M\!/s} = \dfrac{k \, (0.200 \, M)^n}{k \, (0.100 \, M)^n}$ and $3.\underline{9}623 = 2^n$,

so $n = 2$. If we compare the first and the last data sets, $\dfrac{0.473 \, M\!/s}{0.053 \, M\!/s} = \dfrac{k \, (0.300 \, M)^n}{k \, (0.100 \, M)^n}$ and $8.\underline{9}245 = 3^n$, so $n = 2$.

This second comparison is not necessary, but it increases our confidence in the reaction order. So Rate $= k \, [A]^2$. Selecting the second data set and rearranging the rate equation,

$$k = \frac{\text{Rate}}{[A]^2} = \frac{0.210 \, \dfrac{M}{s}}{(0.200 \, M)^2} = 5.25 \, M^{-1} \cdot s^{-1}, \text{ so Rate} = 5.25 \, M^{-1} \cdot s^{-1}[A]^2.$$

Check: The units (none and $M^{-1} \cdot s^{-1}$) are correct. The rate law is a common form. The rate is changing more rapidly than the concentration, so second order is consistent. The rate constant is consistent with the units necessary to get rate as M/s, and the magnitude is reasonable because we have a second-order reaction.

13.18   **Given:** table of [A] versus initial rate   **Find:** rate law and k
Conceptual Plan: Using general rate law form, compare rate ratios to determine reaction order.

$$\frac{\text{Rate } 2}{\text{Rate } 1} = \frac{k \, [A]_2^n}{k \, [A]_1^n}$$

Then use one of the concentration/initial rate pairs to determine k.

$$\text{Rate} = k \, [A]^n$$

Solution: $\dfrac{\text{Rate } 2}{\text{Rate } 1} = \dfrac{k \, [A]_2^n}{k \, [A]_1^n}$ Comparing the first two sets of data, $\dfrac{0.016 \, M\!/s}{0.008 \, M\!/s} = \dfrac{k \, (0.30 \, M)^n}{k \, (0.15 \, M)^n}$ and $2 = 2^n$,

so $n = 1$. If we compare the first and the last data sets, $\dfrac{0.032 \, M\!/s}{0.008 \, M\!/s} = \dfrac{k \, (0.032 \, M)^n}{k \, (0.008 \, M)^n}$ and $4 = 4^n$, so $n = 1$.

This second comparison is not necessary, but it increases our confidence in the reaction order. So Rate $= k \, [A]$.

Selecting the second data set and rearranging the rate equation, $k = \dfrac{\text{Rate}}{[A]} = \dfrac{0.016 \, \dfrac{M}{s}}{0.30 \, M} = 5.3 \times 10^{-2} \, s^{-1}$,

so Rate $= 5.3 \times 10^{-2} \, s^{-1}[A]$.

Check: The units (none and s^{-1}) are correct. The rate law is a common form. The rate is changing as rapidly as the concentration is consistent with first order. The rate constant is consistent with the units necessary to get rate as M/s, and the magnitude is reasonable because we have a first-order reaction.

13.19   **Given:** table of [A] versus initial rate   **Find:** rate law and k
Conceptual Plan: Using general rate law form, compare rate ratios to determine reaction order.

$$\frac{\text{Rate } 2}{\text{Rate } 1} = \frac{k \, [A]_2^n}{k \, [A]_1^n}$$

Then use one of the concentration/initial rate pairs to determine k.

Solution: $\dfrac{\text{Rate } 2}{\text{Rate } 1} = \dfrac{k \, [A]_2^n}{k \, [A]_1^n}$ Comparing the first two sets of data: $\dfrac{0.16 \, M\!/s}{0.12 \, M\!/s} = \dfrac{k \, (0.0104 \, M)^n}{k \, (0.0078 \, M)^n}$ and $1.3333 = 1.\underline{3}333^n$

so $n = 1$. If we compare the first and the last data sets: $\dfrac{0.20 \, M\!/s}{0.12 \, M\!/s} = \dfrac{k \, (0.0130 \, M)^n}{k \, (0.0078 \, M)^n}$ and $1.6667 = 1.\underline{6}667^n$ so $n = 1$.

This second comparison is not necessary, but it increases our confidence in the reaction order. So Rate $= k \, [A]$.

Selecting the second data set and rearranging the rate equation $k = \dfrac{\text{Rate}}{[A]} = \dfrac{0.0104 \, \dfrac{M}{s}}{0.16 \, M} = 0.065 \, s^{-1}$

so Rate $= 0.065 \, s^{-1} \, [A]$

Check: The units (none and s^{-1}) are correct. The rate law is a common form. The rate is changing proportionately to the concentration, so first order is consistent. The rate constant is consistent with the units necessary to get rate as M/s and the magnitude is reasonable since we have a first-order reaction.

13.20   **Given:** table of [A] versus initial rate   **Find:** rate law and k
Conceptual Plan: Using general rate law form, compare rate ratios to determine reaction order.

$$\frac{\text{Rate 2}}{\text{Rate 1}} = \frac{k\,[A]_2^n}{k\,[A]_1^n}$$

Then use one of the concentration/initial rate pairs to determine k.

$$\text{Rate} = k\,[A]^n$$

Solution: $\dfrac{\text{Rate 2}}{\text{Rate 1}} = \dfrac{k\,[A]_2^n}{k\,[A]_1^n}$ Comparing the first two sets of data: $\dfrac{0.18\ \cancel{M/s}}{0.12\ \cancel{M/s}} = \dfrac{\cancel{k}\,(0.000875\ \text{M})^n}{\cancel{k}\,(0.000389\ \text{M})^n}$ and $1.5 = \sqrt{2.24936}$

$= 1.4998; 2.24936^2 = 5.0596$ so $n = 1/2$. If we compare the first and the last data sets: $\dfrac{0.28\ \cancel{M/s}}{0.12\ \cancel{M/s}} = \dfrac{\cancel{k}\,(0.00212\ \text{M})^n}{\cancel{k}\,(0.000389\ \text{M})^n}$

and $2.\underline{3}333 = 5.44987^n$ so $n = 1/2$. This second comparison is not necessary, but it increases our confidence in the reaction order. So Rate $= k\,[A]^{1/2}$. Selecting the second data set and rearranging the rate equation

$$k = \frac{\text{Rate}}{[A]^{1/2}} = \frac{0.000875\ \dfrac{\text{M}}{\text{s}}}{(0.18\ \text{M})^{1/2}} = 0.27\ \text{M}^{-1}\text{s}^{-1} \text{ so Rate} = 0.27\ \text{M}^{1/2}\text{s}^{-1}\,[A]^{1/2}$$

Check: The units (none and $\text{M}^{1/2}\text{s}^{-1}$) are correct. The rate law is a common form. The rate is changing less rapidly than the concentration, so one-half order is consistent. The rate constant is consistent with the units necessary to get rate as M/s, and the magnitude is reasonable since we have a one-half order reaction.

13.21   **Given:** table of [NO$_2$] and [F$_2$] versus initial rate   **Find:** rate law, k, and overall order
Conceptual Plan: Using general rate law form, compare rate ratios to determine reaction order of each reactant. Be sure to choose data that changes only one concentration at a time.

$$\frac{\text{Rate 2}}{\text{Rate 1}} = \frac{k\,[NO_2]_2^m\,[F_2]_2^n}{k\,[NO_2]_1^m\,[F_2]_1^n}$$

Then use one of the concentration/initial rate pairs to determine k.

$$\text{Rate} = k[NO_2]^m\,[F_2]^n$$

Solution: $\dfrac{\text{Rate 2}}{\text{Rate 1}} = \dfrac{k\,[NO_2]_2^m\,[F_2]_2^n}{k\,[NO_2]_1^m\,[F_2]_1^n}$ Comparing the first two sets of data,

$\dfrac{0.051\ \cancel{M/s}}{0.026\ \cancel{M/s}} = \dfrac{\cancel{k}\,(0.200\ \text{M})^m\,(\cancel{0.100\ \text{M}})^n}{\cancel{k}\,(0.100\ \text{M})^m\,(\cancel{0.100\ \text{M}})^n}$ and $1.\underline{9}615 = 2^m$, so $m = 1$. If we compare the second and third data sets,

$\dfrac{0.103\ \cancel{M/s}}{0.051\ \cancel{M/s}} = \dfrac{\cancel{k}\,(\cancel{0.200\ \text{M}})^m\,(0.200\ \text{M})^n}{\cancel{k}\,(\cancel{0.200\ \text{M}})^m\,(0.100\ \text{M})^n}$ and $2.\underline{0}196 = 2^n$, so $n = 1$. Other comparisons can be made, but they are not necessary. They should reinforce these values of the reaction orders. So Rate $= k\,[NO_2][F_2]$. Selecting the

last data set and rearranging the rate equation, $k = \dfrac{\text{Rate}}{[NO_2][F_2]} = \dfrac{0.411\dfrac{\text{M}}{\text{s}}}{(0.400\ \cancel{M})(0.400\ \text{M})} = 2.57\ \text{M}^{-1}\cdot\text{s}^{-1}$,

so Rate $= 2.57\ \text{M}^{-1}\cdot\text{s}^{-1}\,[NO_2][F_2]$ and the reaction is second order overall.

Check: The units (none and $\text{M}^{-1}\cdot\text{s}^{-1}$) are correct. The rate law is a common form. The rate is changing as rapidly as each concentration is changing, which is consistent with first order in each reactant. The rate constant is consistent with the units necessary to get rate as M/s, and the magnitude is reasonable because we have a second-order reaction.

13.22   **Given:** table of [CH$_3$Cl] and [Cl$_2$] versus initial rate   **Find:** rate law, k, and overall order
Conceptual Plan: Using general rate law form, compare rate ratios to determine reaction order of each reactant. Be sure to choose data that changes only one concentration at a time.

$$\frac{\text{Rate 2}}{\text{Rate 1}} = \frac{k\,[CH_3Cl]_2^m\,[Cl_2]_2^n}{k\,[CH_3Cl]_1^m\,[Cl_2]_1^n}$$

Then use one of the concentration/initial rate pairs to determine k.

$$\text{Rate} = k\,[CH_3Cl]^m\,[Cl_2]^n$$

Solution: $\dfrac{\text{Rate 2}}{\text{Rate 1}} = \dfrac{k\,[CH_3Cl]_2^m\,[Cl_2]_2^n}{k\,[CH_3Cl]_1^m\,[Cl_2]_1^n}$. Comparing the first two sets of data,

$\dfrac{0.029\ \cancel{M/s}}{0.014\ \cancel{M/s}} = \dfrac{\cancel{k}\,(0.100\ \text{M})^m\,(\cancel{0.050\ \text{M}})^n}{\cancel{k}\,(0.050\ \text{M})^m\,(\cancel{0.050\ \text{M}})^n}$ and $2.\underline{0}714 = 2^m$, so $m = 1$. If we compare the second and third data sets,

$$\frac{0.041 \ \cancel{M/s}}{0.029 \ \cancel{M/s}} = \frac{k \ (\cancel{0.100 \ M})^m \ (0.100 \ M)^n}{k \ (\cancel{0.100 \ M})^m \ (0.050 \ M)^n} \text{ and } 1.\underline{4}14 = 2^n; \text{ so } n = 1/2. \text{ Other comparisons can be made, but they}$$

are not necessary. They should reinforce these values of the reaction orders. So Rate $= k \ [CH_3Cl] \ [Cl_2]^{1/2}$. Selecting the last data set and rearranging the rate equation,

$$k = \frac{\text{Rate}}{[CH_3Cl] \ [Cl_2]^{1/2}} = \frac{0.115 \ \dfrac{M}{s}}{(0.200 \ M)(0.200 \ M)^{1/2}} = 1.29 \ M^{-1/2} \cdot s^{-1}, \text{ so Rate } = 1.29 \ M^{-1/2} \cdot s^{-1} [CH_3Cl] \ [Cl_2]^{1/2}$$

and the reaction is one-and-a-half-order overall.

Check: The units (none and $M^{-1/2} \cdot s^{-1}$) are correct. The rate law is not as common as others, but it is reasonable. The rate is changing as rapidly as the CH_3Cl concentration is changing, which is consistent with first order in this reactant. The rate is changing a bit more slowly than the Cl_2 concentration, which is consistent with half order in this reactant. The rate constant is consistent with the units necessary to get rate as M/s, and the magnitude is reasonable because we have a one-and-a-half-order reaction.

The Integrated Rate Law and Half-Life

13.23   (a)   The reaction is zero order. Because the slope of the plot is independent of the concentration, there is no dependence on the concentration of the reactant in the rate law.

       (b)   The reaction is first order. The expression for the half-life of a first-order reaction is $t_{1/2} = \dfrac{0.693}{k}$, which is independent of the reactant concentration.

       (c)   The reaction is second order. The integrated rate expression for a second-order reaction is $\dfrac{1}{[A]_t} = kt + \dfrac{1}{[A]_0}$, which is linear when the inverse of the concentration is plotted versus time.

13.24   (a)   The reaction is second order. The expression for the half-life of a second-order reaction, $t_{1/2} = \dfrac{1}{k[A]_0}$, shows that the half-life decreases as concentration increases.

       (b)   The reaction is first order. The integrated rate expression for a first-order reaction is $\ln[A]_t = -kt + \ln[A]_0$, which is linear when the natural log of the concentration is plotted versus time.

       (c)   The reaction is zero order. The expression for the half-life of a zero-order reaction, $t_{1/2} = \dfrac{[A]_0}{2k}$, shows that the half-life increases as concentration increases.

13.25   **Given:** table of [AB] versus time   **Find:** reaction order, k, and [AB] at 25 s

       Conceptual Plan: Look at the data and see if any common reaction orders can be eliminated. If the data does not show an equal concentration drop with time, zero order can be eliminated. Look for changes in the half-life (compare time for concentration to drop to one-half of any value). If the half-life is not constant, the first order can be eliminated. If the half-life is getting longer as the concentration drops, this might suggest second order. Plot the data as indicated by the appropriate rate law. Determine k from the slope of the plot. Finally, calculate the [AB] at 25 s by using the appropriate integrated rate expression.

       Solution: By the preceding logic, we can eliminate both the zero-order and the first-order reactions. (Alternatively, you could make all three plots and only one should be linear.) This suggests that we should have a second-order reaction. Plot 1/[AB] versus time.

       Because $\dfrac{1}{[AB]_t} = kt + \dfrac{1}{[AB]_0}$, the slope will be the rate constant. The slope can be determined by measuring $\Delta y / \Delta x$ on the plot or by using functions such as "add trendline" in Excel. Thus, the rate constant is 0.0225 $M^{-1} \cdot s^{-1}$, and the rate law is Rate $= 0.0225 \ M^{-1} \cdot s^{-1} [AB]^2$.

       Finally, use $\dfrac{1}{[AB]_t} = kt + \dfrac{1}{[AB]_0}$; substitute the values of $[AB]_0$, 25 s, and k; and rearrange to solve for [AB] at 25 s.

$$[AB]_t = \frac{1}{kt + \dfrac{1}{[AB]_0}} = \frac{1}{(0.0225 \ M^{-1} \cdot \cancel{s^{-1}})(25 \ \cancel{s}) + \left(\dfrac{1}{0.950 \ M}\right)} = 0.619 \ M.$$

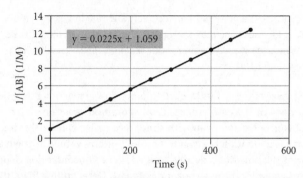

Check: The units (none, $M^{-1} \cdot s^{-1}$, and M) are correct. The rate law is a common form. The plot was extremely linear, confirming second-order kinetics. The rate constant is consistent with the units necessary to get rate as M/s, and the magnitude is reasonable because we have a second-order reaction. The [AB] at 25 s is between the values at 0 s and 50 s.

13.26 **Given:** table of $[N_2O_5]$ versus time **Find:** reaction order, k, and $[N_2O_5]$ at 250 s
Conceptual Plan: Look at the data and see if any common reaction orders can be eliminated. If the data does not show an equal concentration drop with time, zero order can be eliminated. Look for changes in the half-life (compare time for concentration to drop to one-half of any value). If the half-life is not constant, the first order can be eliminated. If the half-life is getting longer as the concentration drops, this might suggest second order. Plot the data as indicated by the appropriate rate law. Determine k from the slope of the plot. Finally, calculate the $[N_2O_5]$ at 250 s by using the appropriate integrated rate expression.

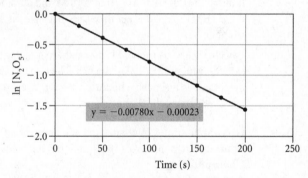

Solution: By the preceding logic, we can see that the reaction is most likely first order. It takes just under 75 s for the concentration to be cut in half for any concentration. Plot $\ln [N_2O_5]$ versus time. Because $\ln[A]_t = -kt + \ln[A]_0$, the negative of the slope will be the rate constant. The slope can be determined by measuring $\Delta y/\Delta x$ on the plot or by using functions such as "add trendline" in Excel. Thus, the rate constant is $0.00780\ s^{-1}$, and the rate law is Rate $= 0.00780\ s^{-1}\ [N_2O_5]$. Finally, use $\ln[N_2O_5]_t = -kt + \ln[N_2O_5]_0$; substitute the values of $[N_2O_5]_0$, 250 s, and k; and rearrange to solve for $[N_2O_5]$ at 250 s. $\ln[N_2O_5]_{250\,s} = -(0.00780\ s^{-1})(250\ s) + \ln[1.000]_0$; then $[N_2O_5]_{250\,s} = e^{-1.95} = 0.142$ M.

Check: The units (none, s^{-1}, and M) are correct. The rate law is a common form. The plot was extremely linear, confirming first-order kinetics. The rate constant is consistent with the units necessary to get rate as M/s, and the magnitude is reasonable because we have a first-order reaction. The $[N_2O_5]$ at 250 s is less than the value at 200 s.

13.27 **Given:** table of $[C_4H_8]$ versus time **Find:** reaction order, k, and reaction rate when $[C_4H_8] = 0.25$ M
Conceptual Plan: Look at the data and see if any common reaction orders can be eliminated. If the data does not show an equal concentration drop with time, zero order can be eliminated. Look for changes in half-life (compare time for concentration to drop to one-half of any value). If the half-life is not constant, the first order can be eliminated. If the half-life is getting longer as the concentration drops, this might suggest second order. Plot the data as indicated by the appropriate rate law. Determine k from the slope of the plot. Finally, calculate the reaction rate when $[C_4H_8] = 0.25$ M by using the rate law.

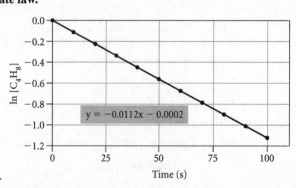

Solution: By the preceding logic, we can see that the reaction is most likely first order. It takes about 60 s for the concentration to be cut in half for any concentration. Plot $\ln [C_4H_8]$ versus time. Because $\ln[A]_t = -kt + \ln[A]_0$, the negative of the slope will be the rate constant. The slope can be determined by measuring $\Delta y/\Delta x$ on the plot or by using functions such as "add trendline" in Excel. Thus, the rate constant is $0.0112\ s^{-1}$, and the rate law is Rate $= 0.0112\ s^{-1}[C_4H_8]$. Finally, use Rate $= 0.0112\ s^{-1}[C_4H_8]$ and substitute the values of $[C_4H_8]$: Rate $= 0.0112\ s^{-1}[0.25\ M] = 2.8 \times 10^{-3}\ M \cdot s^{-1}$.

Check: The units (none, s^{-1}, and $M \cdot s^{-1}$) are correct. The rate law is a common form. The plot was extremely linear, confirming first-order kinetics. The rate constant is consistent with the units necessary to get rate as M/s, and the magnitude is reasonable because we have a first-order reaction. The rate when $[C_4H_8] = 0.25$ M is consistent with the average rate using 90 s and 100 s.

13.28   **Given:** table of [A] versus time   **Find:** reaction order, k, and reaction rate when $[A] = 0.10$ M
Conceptual Plan: Look at the data and see if any common reaction orders can be eliminated. If the data does not show an equal concentration drop with time, zero order can be eliminated. Look for changes in half-life (compare time for concentration to drop to one-half of any value). If the half-life is not constant, the first order can be eliminated. If the half-life is getting longer as the concentration drops, this might suggest second order. Plot the data as indicated by the appropriate rate law. Determine k from the slope of the plot. Finally, calculate the reaction rate when [A] = 0.10 M by using the rate law.

Solution: By the preceding logic, we can see that the reaction is most likely zero order. There is a difference of about 0.085 M between each data point, so the rate is independent of the [A]. Plot [A] versus time. Because $[A]_t = -kt + [A]_0$, the negative of the slope will be the rate constant. The slope can be determined by measuring $\Delta y/\Delta x$ on the plot or by using functions such as "add trendline" in Excel. Thus, the rate constant is 3.41×10^{-3} M $\cdot$ s^{-1}, and the rate law is Rate $= 3.41 \times 10^{-3}$ M $\cdot$ s^{-1}. Finally, because the rate is independent of concentration, Rate $= 3.41 \times 10^{-3}$ M $\cdot$ s^{-1} at 0.10 M and all other concentrations. NOTE: A plot is not necessary because the kinetics are so simple.

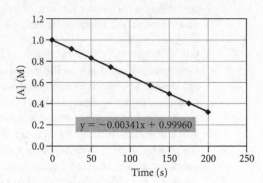

Check: The units (none, M $\cdot$ s^{-1}, and M $\cdot$ s^{-1}) are correct. The rate law is a common form. The plot was extremely linear, confirming zero-order kinetics. The rate constant is consistent with the units necessary to get rate as M/s, and the magnitude is reasonable because we have a zero-order reaction. The rate is the same as any average rate that can be calculated using the data.

13.29   **Given:** plot of ln [A] versus time has slope $= -0.0045$/s; $[A]_0 = 0.250$ M
Find: (a) k, (b) rate law, (c) $t_{1/2}$, and (d) [A] after 225 s
Conceptual Plan:
(a)   **A plot of ln [A] versus time is linear for a first-order reaction. Using $\ln[A]_t = -kt + \ln[A]_0$, the rate constant is the negative of the slope.**
(b)   **Rate law is first order. Add rate constant from part (a).**
(c)   **For a first-order reaction, $t_{1/2} = \dfrac{0.693}{k}$. Substitute k from part (a).**
(d)   **Use the integrated rate law, $\ln[A]_t = -kt + \ln[A]_0$, and substitute k and the initial concentration.**
Solution:
(a)   Because the rate constant is the negative of the slope, $k = 4.5 \times 10^{-3}$ s^{-1}.
(b)   Because the reaction is first order, Rate $= 4.5 \times 10^{-3}$ s^{-1} [A].
(c) $t_{1/2} = \dfrac{0.693}{k} = \dfrac{0.693}{0.0045/\text{s}} = 1.5 \times 10^2$ s
(d) $\ln[A]_t = -kt + \ln[A]_0$ and substitute k and the initial concentration. So
        $\ln[A]_t = -(0.0045/\text{s})(225\ \text{s}) + \ln 0.250\ \text{M} = -2.39879$ and $[A]_{250\ \text{s}} = e^{-2.39879} = 0.0908$ M

Check: The units (s^{-1}, none, s, and M) are correct. The rate law is a common form. The rate constant is consistent with value of the slope. The half-life is consistent with a small value of k. The concentration at 225 s is consistent with being between one and two half-lives.

13.30   **Given:** plot of 1/[AB] versus time has slope $= 0.055/$M s
Find: (a) k, (b) rate law, (c) $t_{1/2}$ when $[AB]_0 = 0.55$ M, and (d) [A] and [B] after 75 s when $[AB]_0 = 0.250$ M
Conceptual Plan:
(a)   **A plot of 1/[AB] versus time is linear for a second-order reaction. Using $\dfrac{1}{[AB]_t} = kt + \dfrac{1}{[AB]_0}$, the rate constant is the slope.**

(b) Rate law is second order. Add rate constant from part (a).

(c) For a second-order reaction, $t_{1/2} = \dfrac{1}{k[AB]_0}$. Substitute k from part (a).

(d) Use the integrated rate law, $\dfrac{1}{[AB]_t} = kt + \dfrac{1}{[AB]_0}$, and substitute k, t, and the initial concentration to get the $[AB]$. Then $[AB]_0, [AB] \rightarrow [A], [B]$.

$$\Delta[AB] = [AB]_{0\,s} - [AB]_{75\,s} \text{ with } \frac{1 \text{ mol A}}{1 \text{ mol AB}} \text{ and } \frac{1 \text{ mol B}}{1 \text{ mol AB}}$$

Solution:

(a) Because the rate constant is the slope, $k = 5.5 \times 10^{-2}\,M^{-1} \cdot s^{-1}$.

(b) Because the reaction is second order, Rate $= 5.5 \times 10^{-2}\,M^{-1} \cdot s^{-1}\,[AB]^2$.

(c) $t_{1/2} = \dfrac{1}{k\,[AB]_0}$ so $t_{1/2} = \dfrac{1}{(5.5 \times 10^{-2}\,M^{-1} \cdot s^{-1})(0.550\,M)} = 33\,s$

(d) $\dfrac{1}{[AB]_t} = kt + \dfrac{1}{[AB]_0}$ so $[AB]_t = \dfrac{1}{kt + \dfrac{1}{[AB]_0}} = \dfrac{1}{(5.5 \times 10^{-2}\,M^{-1} \cdot s^{-1})\,(75\,s) + \left(\dfrac{1}{0.250\,M}\right)} = 0.12308\,M$

then $\Delta[AB] = [AB]_{0\,s} - [AB]_{75\,s} = 0.250\,M - 0.12308\,M = 0.12692\,M\,AB$

so $0.12692\,\dfrac{\text{mol AB}}{L} \times \dfrac{1 \text{ mol A}}{1 \text{ mol AB}} = 0.13\,M\,A$ and $0.12692\,\dfrac{\text{mol AB}}{L} \times \dfrac{1 \text{ mol B}}{1 \text{ mol AB}} = 0.13\,M\,B$

Check: The units ($M^{-1} \cdot s^{-1}$, none, s, and M) are correct. The rate law is a common form. The rate constant is consistent with value of the slope. The half-life is consistent with a small value of k. The concentration at 75 s is consistent with being about one half-life.

13.31 **Given:** decomposition of SO_2Cl_2, for order; $k = 1.42 \times 10^{-4}\,s^{-1}$
Find: (a) $t_{1/2}$, (b) t to decrease to 25% of $[SO_2Cl_2]_0$, (c) t to 0.78 M when $[SO_2Cl_2]_0 = 1.00\,M$, and (d) $[SO_2Cl_2]$ after $2.00 \times 10^2\,s$ and $5.00 \times 10^2\,s$ when $[SO_2Cl_2]_0 = 0.150\,M$
Conceptual Plan:

(a) $k \rightarrow t_{1/2}$

$t_{1/2} = \dfrac{0.693}{k}$

(b) $[SO_2Cl_2]_0, 25\% \text{ of } [SO_2Cl_2]_0, k \rightarrow t$

$\ln[A]_t = -kt + \ln[A]_0$

(c) $[SO_2Cl_2]_0, [SO_2Cl_2]_t, k \rightarrow t$

$\ln[A]_t = -kt + \ln[A]_0$

(d) $[SO_2Cl_2]_0, t, k \rightarrow [SO_2Cl_2]_t$

$\ln[A]_t = -kt + \ln[A]_0$

Solution:

(a) $t_{1/2} = \dfrac{0.693}{k} = \dfrac{0.693}{1.42 \times 10^{-4}\,s^{-1}} = 4.88 \times 10^3\,s$

(b) $[SO_2Cl_2]_t = 0.25\,[SO_2Cl_2]_0$. Because $\ln[SO_2Cl_2]_t = -kt + \ln[SO_2Cl_2]_0$, rearrange to solve for t.

$t = -\dfrac{1}{k}\ln\dfrac{[SO_2Cl_2]_t}{[SO_2Cl_2]_0} = -\dfrac{1}{1.42 \times 10^{-4}\,s^{-1}}\ln\dfrac{0.25\,[SO_2Cl_2]_0}{[SO_2Cl_2]_0} = 9.8 \times 10^3\,s$

(c) $[SO_2Cl_2]_t = 0.78\,M$; $[SO_2Cl_2]_0 = 1.00\,M$. Because $\ln[SO_2Cl_2]_t = -kt + \ln[SO_2Cl_2]_0$, rearrange to solve for t. $t = -\dfrac{1}{k}\ln\dfrac{[SO_2Cl_2]_t}{[SO_2Cl_2]_0} = -\dfrac{1}{1.42 \times 10^{-4}\,s^{-1}}\ln\dfrac{0.78\,M}{1.00\,M} = 1.7 \times 10^3\,s$

(d) $[SO_2Cl_2]_0 = 0.150\,M$ and $2.00 \times 10^2\,s$ in
$\ln[SO_2Cl_2]_t = -(1.42 \times 10^{-4}\,s^{-1})(2.00 \times 10^2\,s) + \ln 0.150\,M = -1.92552 \rightarrow$
$[SO_2Cl_2]_t = e^{-1.92552} = 0.146\,M$
$[SO_2Cl_2]_0 = 0.150\,M$ and $5.00 \times 10^2\,s$ in
$\ln[SO_2Cl_2]_t = -(1.42 \times 10^{-4}\,s^{-1})(5.00 \times 10^2\,s) + \ln 0.150\,M = -1.96812 \rightarrow$
$[SO_2Cl_2]_t = e^{-1.96812} = 0.140\,M$

Check: The units (s, s, s, and M) are correct. The rate law is a common form. The half-life is consistent with a small value of k. The time to 25% is consistent with two half-lives. The time to 0.78 M is consistent with being less than one half-life. The final concentrations are consistent with the time being less than one half-life.

13.32 **Given:** decomposition of XY, second order in XY; $k = 7.02 \times 10^{-3} \, M^{-1} \cdot s^{-1}$
Find: (a) $t_{1/2}$ when $[XY]_0 = 0.100$ M, (b) t to decrease to 12.5% of $[XY]_0 = 0.100$ M and 0.200 M, (c) t to 0.062 M when $[XY]_0 = 0.150$ M, and (d) $[XY]$ after 5.0×10^1 s and 5.50×10^2 s when $[XY]_0 = 0.050$ M
Conceptual Plan:
(a) $[XY]_0, k \rightarrow t_{1/2}$

$$t_{1/2} = \frac{1}{k[A]_0}$$

(b) $[XY]_0, 12.5\%$ of $[XY]_0, k \rightarrow t$

$$\frac{1}{[A]_t} = kt + \frac{1}{[A]_0}$$

(c) $[XY]_0, [XY]_t, k \rightarrow t$

$$\frac{1}{[A]_t} = kt + \frac{1}{[A]_0}$$

(d) $[XY]_0, t, k \rightarrow [XY]_t$

$$\frac{1}{[A]_t} = kt + \frac{1}{[A]_0}$$

Solution:

(a) $t_{1/2} = \dfrac{1}{k\,[XY]_0} = \dfrac{1}{(7.02 \times 10^{-3} \, M^{-1}s^{-1})(0.100 \, M)} = 1.42 \times 10^3$ s

(b) $[XY]_t = 0.125 \, [XY]_0 = 0.125 \times 0.100$ M $= 0.0125$ M. Because $\dfrac{1}{[XY]_t} = kt + \dfrac{1}{[XY]_0}$ rearrange to solve

for t. $t = \dfrac{1}{k}\left(\dfrac{1}{[XY]_t} - \dfrac{1}{[XY]_0}\right) = \dfrac{1}{(7.02 \times 10^{-3} \, M^{-1} \cdot s^{-1})}\left(\dfrac{1}{0.0125 \, M} - \dfrac{1}{0.100 \, M}\right) = 9.97 \times 10^3$ s and

$[XY]_t = 0.125 \, [XY]_0 = 0.125 \times 0.200$ M $= 0.0250$ M. Because $\dfrac{1}{[XY]_t} = kt + \dfrac{1}{[XY]_0}$, rearrange to solve

for t. $t = \dfrac{1}{k}\left(\dfrac{1}{[XY]_t} - \dfrac{1}{[XY]_0}\right) = \dfrac{1}{(7.02 \times 10^{-3} \, M^{-1} \cdot s^{-1})}\left(\dfrac{1}{0.0250 \, M} - \dfrac{1}{0.200 \, M}\right) = 4.99 \times 10^3$ s

(c) $[XY]_t = 0.062$; $[XY]_0 = 0.150$ M. Because $\dfrac{1}{[XY]_t} = kt + \dfrac{1}{[XY]_0}$ rearrange to solve for t.

$t = \dfrac{1}{k}\left(\dfrac{1}{[XY]_t} - \dfrac{1}{[XY]_0}\right) = \dfrac{1}{(7.02 \times 10^{-3} \, M^{-1} \cdot s^{-1})}\left(\dfrac{1}{0.062 \, M} - \dfrac{1}{0.150 \, M}\right) = 1.3 \times 10^3$ s

(d) $[XY]_0 = 0.050$ M and 5.0×10^1 s in $\dfrac{1}{[XY]_t} = kt + \dfrac{1}{[XY]_0} \rightarrow$

$\dfrac{1}{[XY]_t} = (7.02 \times 10^{-3} \, M^{-1} \cdot s^{-1})(5.0 \times 10^1 \, s) + \dfrac{1}{0.050 \, M} = \dfrac{20.351}{M}$ so $[XY] = 0.049$ M and

$[XY]_0 = 0.050$ M and 5.50×10^2 s in $\dfrac{1}{[XY]_t} = (7.02 \times 10^{-3} \, M^{-1} \cdot s^{-1})(5.50 \times 10^2 \, s) + \dfrac{1}{0.050 \, M} = \dfrac{23.861}{M}$

so $[XY] = 0.042$ M

Check: The units (s, s, s, s, M, and M) are correct. The rate law is a common form. The half-life is consistent with a small value of k. The time to 12.5% is consistent with three half-lives, where the half-life time is increasing. The next time (5000 s) is shorter because the initial concentration is higher. The last time is the shortest because it is less than a half-life with an intermediate concentration. The final concentrations are consistent with the time being much less than one half-life.

13.33 **Given:** $t_{1/2}$ for radioactive decay of U-238 = 4.5 billion years and independent of $[\text{U-238}]_0$
Find: t to decrease by 10%; number U-238 atoms today, when 1.5×10^{18} atoms formed 13.8 billion years ago

Conceptual Plan: $t_{1/2}$ independent of concentration implies first-order kinetics, $t_{1/2} \rightarrow k$ then

$$t_{1/2} = \frac{0.693}{k}$$

90% of [U-238]$_0$, $k \rightarrow t$ and [U-238]$_0$, t, $k \rightarrow$ [U-238]$_t$

$$\ln[A]_t = -kt + \ln[A]_0 \qquad \ln[A]_t = -kt + \ln[A]_0$$

Solution: $t_{1/2} = \dfrac{0.693}{k}$ Rearrange to solve for k. $k = \dfrac{0.693}{t_{1/2}} = \dfrac{0.693}{4.5 \times 10^9 \text{ yr}} = 1.5\underline{4} \times 10^{-10} \text{ yr}^{-1}$ then

[U-238]$_t$ = 0.90 [U-238]$_0$. Because $\ln[\text{U-238}]_t = -kt + \ln[\text{U-238}]_0$, rearrange to solve for t.

$$t = -\frac{1}{k} \ln \frac{[\text{U-238}]_t}{[\text{U-238}]_0} = -\frac{1}{1.5\underline{4} \times 10^{-10} \text{ yr}^{-1}} \ln \frac{0.90 \, \cancel{[\text{U-238}]_0}}{\cancel{[\text{U-238}]_0}} = 6.8 \times 10^8 \text{ yr}$$

and [U-238]$_0$ = 1.5×10^{18} atoms; $t = 13.8 \times 10^9$ yr

$$\ln[\text{U-238}]_t = -kt + \ln[\text{U-238}]_0 = -(1.5\underline{4} \times 10^{-10} \, \cancel{\text{yr}^{-1}})(13.8 \times 10^9 \, \cancel{\text{yr}})$$

$$+\ln(1.5 \times 10^{18} \text{ atoms}) = 39.7\underline{2}6797 \rightarrow$$

$$[\text{U-238}]_t = e^{39.7\underline{2}6797} = 1.8 \times 10^{17} \text{atoms}$$

Check: The units (yr and atoms) are correct. The time to 10% decay is consistent with less than one half-life. The final concentration is consistent with the time being about three half-lives.

13.34 **Given:** $t_{1/2}$ for radioactive decay of C-14 = 5730 years
 Find: t to decrease by 25%; mmol C-14 atoms left, after 2255 yr in sample initially contains 1.5 mmol C-14
 Conceptual Plan: radioactive decay implies first-order kinetics, $t_{1/2} \rightarrow k$ then

$$t_{1/2} = \frac{0.693}{k}$$

75% of [C-14]$_0$, $k \rightarrow t$ and [C-14]$_0$, t, $k \rightarrow$ [C-14]$_t$

$$\ln[A]_t = -kt + \ln[A]_0 \qquad \ln[A]_t = -kt + \ln[A]_0$$

Solution: $t_{1/2} = \dfrac{0.693}{k}$ Rearrange to solve for k. $k = \dfrac{0.693}{t_{1/2}} = \dfrac{0.693}{5730 \text{ yr}} = 1.2\underline{0}942 \times 10^{-4} \text{ yr}^{-1}$ then

[C-14]$_t$ = 0.75 [C-14]$_0$. Because $\ln[\text{C-14}]_t = -kt + \ln[\text{C-14}]_0$, rearrange to solve for t.

$$t = -\frac{1}{k} \ln \frac{[\text{C-14}]_t}{[\text{C-14}]_0} = -\frac{1}{1.2\underline{0}942 \times 10^{-4} \text{ yr}^{-1}} \ln \frac{0.75 \, \cancel{[\text{C-14}]_0}}{\cancel{[\text{C-14}]_0}} = 2.4 \times 10^3 \text{ yr and } [\text{C-14}]_0 = 1.5 \text{ mmol}$$

$$t = 2255 \text{ yr}$$

$$\ln[\text{C-14}]_t = -kt + \ln[\text{C-14}]_0 = -(1.2\underline{0}942 \times 10^{-4} \, \cancel{\text{yr}^{-1}})(2255 \, \cancel{\text{yr}}) + \ln(1.5 \text{ mmol}) = 0.13\underline{2}741 \rightarrow$$

$$[\text{C-14}]_t = e^{0.13\underline{2}741} = 1.1 \text{ mmol}$$

Check: The units (yr and mmol) are correct. The time to 25% decay is consistent with less than one half-life. The final concentration is consistent with the time being less than one half-life.

The Effect of Temperature and the Collision Model

13.35

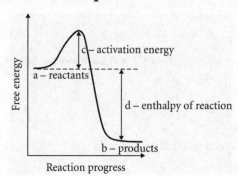

13.36

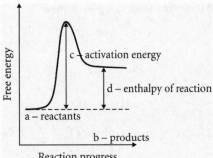

13.37   **Given:** activation energy $= 56.8$ kJ/mol, frequency factor $= 1.5 \times 10^{11}$/s, 25 °C   **Find:** rate constant
Conceptual Plan: °C $\rightarrow$ K and kJ/mol $\rightarrow$ J/mol then $E_a, T, A \rightarrow k$

$$K = °C + 273.15 \qquad \frac{1000 \text{ J}}{1 \text{ kJ}} \qquad k = Ae^{-E_a/RT}$$

Solution: $T = 25$ °C $+ 273.15 = 298$ K and $\dfrac{56.8 \text{ kJ}}{\text{mol}} \times \dfrac{1000 \text{ J}}{1 \text{ kJ}} = 5.68 \times 10^4 \dfrac{\text{J}}{\text{mol}}$ then

$$k = Ae^{-E_a/RT} = (1.5 \times 10^{11} \text{ s}^{-1})e^{\dfrac{-5.68 \times 10^4 \frac{\text{J}}{\text{mol}}}{\left(8.314 \frac{\text{J}}{\text{K} \cdot \text{mol}}\right)298 \text{ K}}} = 17 \text{ s}^{-1}$$

Check: The units (s^{-1}) are correct. The rate constant is consistent with a large activation energy and a large frequency factor.

13.38   **Given:** 32 °C, rate constant $= 0.055$/s, and frequency factor $= 1.5 \times 10^{13}$/s   **Find:** activation energy
Conceptual Plan: °C $\rightarrow$ K then $E_a, T, A \rightarrow k$ then J/mol $\rightarrow$ kJ/mol

$$K = °C + 273.15 \qquad k = A e^{-E_a/RT} \qquad \frac{1 \text{ kJ}}{1000 \text{ J}}$$

Solution: $T = 32$ °C $+ 273.15 = 305$ K then $k = A e^{-E_a/RT}$. Rearrange to solve for E_a.

$$E_a = -RT \ln\left(\frac{k}{A}\right) = -8.314 \frac{\text{J}}{\text{K} \cdot \text{mol}} \times 305 \text{ K} \times \ln\left(\frac{0.055 \text{ s}^{-1}}{1.2 \times 10^{13} \text{ s}^{-1}}\right) = 8.37 \times 10^4 \frac{\text{J}}{\text{mol}} \times \frac{1 \text{ kJ}}{1000 \text{ J}} = 83.7 \frac{\text{kJ}}{\text{mol}}$$

Check: The units (kJ/mol) are correct. The activation energy is consistent with a modest rate constant and a large frequency factor.

13.39   **Given:** plot of $\ln k$ versus $1/T$ (in K) is linear with a slope of -7445 K   **Find:** E_a
Conceptual Plan: Because $\ln k = \dfrac{-E_a}{R}\left(\dfrac{1}{T}\right) + \ln A$ plot of $\ln k$ versus $1/T$ will have a slope $= -E_a/R$.

Solution: Because the slope $= -7445$ K $= -E_a/R$, then

$$E_a = -(\text{slope})R = -(-7445 \text{ K})\left(8.314 \frac{\text{J}}{\text{K} \cdot \text{mol}}\right)\left(\frac{1 \text{ kJ}}{1000 \text{ J}}\right) = 61.90 \frac{\text{kJ}}{\text{mol}}$$

Check: The units (kJ/mol) are correct. The activation energy is typical for many reactions.

13.40   **Given:** Plot of $\ln k$ versus $1/T$ (in K) is linear with a slope of -1.01×10^4 K.   **Find:** E_a
Conceptual Plan: Because $\ln k = \dfrac{-E_a}{R}\left(\dfrac{1}{T}\right) + \ln A$, a plot of $\ln k$ versus $1/T$ will have a slope $= -E_a/R$.

Solution: Because the slope $= -1.01 \times 10^4$ K $= -E_a/R$, then

$$E_a = -(\text{slope})R = -(-1.01 \times 10^4 \text{ K})\left(8.314 \frac{\text{J}}{\text{K} \cdot \text{mol}}\right)\left(\frac{1 \text{ kJ}}{1000 \text{ J}}\right) = 84.0 \frac{\text{kJ}}{\text{mol}}.$$

Check: The units (kJ/mol) are correct. The activation energy is typical for many reactions.

13.41   **Given:** table of rate constant versus T **Find:** E_a and A

Conceptual Plan: Because $\ln k = \dfrac{-E_a}{R}\left(\dfrac{1}{T}\right) + \ln A$, a plot of $\ln k$ versus $1/T$ will have a slope $= -E_a/R$ and an intercept $= \ln A$.

Solution: The slope can be determined by measuring $\Delta y/\Delta x$ on the plot or by using functions such as "add trendline" in Excel. Because the slope $= -30189$ K $= -E_a/R$, then
$E_a = -(\text{slope})R$

$= -(-30189 \text{ K})\left(8.314 \dfrac{J}{K \cdot mol}\right)\left(\dfrac{1 \text{ kJ}}{1000 \text{ J}}\right)$

$= 251 \dfrac{kJ}{mol}$ and intercept $= 27.399 = \ln A$ then

$A = e^{\text{intercept}} = e^{27.399} = 7.93 \times 10^{11} \text{s}^{-1}$.

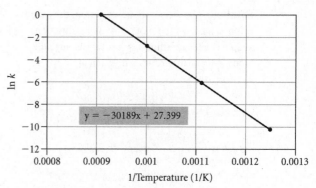

Check: The units (kJ/mol and s^{-1}) are correct. The plot was extremely linear, confirming Arrhenius behavior. The activation energy and frequency factor are typical for many reactions.

13.42   **Given:** table of rate constant versus T **Find:** E_a and A

Conceptual Plan: Because ln $k = \dfrac{-E_a}{R}\left(\dfrac{1}{T}\right) + \ln A$, a plot of ln k versus 1/T will have a slope $= -E_a/R$ and an intercept $= \ln A$.

Solution: The slope can be determined by measuring $\Delta y/\Delta x$ on the plot or by using functions such as "add trendline" in Excel. Because the slope $= -10283$ K $= -E_a/R$, then
$E_a = -(\text{slope})R$

$= -(-10283 \text{ K})\left(8.314 \dfrac{J}{K \cdot mol}\right)\left(\dfrac{1 \text{ kJ}}{1000 \text{ J}}\right)$ and

$= 85.5 \dfrac{kJ}{mol}$ and intercept $= 29.967 = \ln A$ then

$A = e^{\text{intercept}} = e^{29.967} = 1.03 \times 10^{13} \text{ s}^{-1}$.

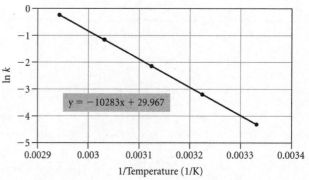

Check: The units (kJ/mol and s^{-1}) are correct. The plot was extremely linear, confirming Arrhenius behavior. The activation energy and frequency factor are typical for many reactions.

13.43   **Given:** table of rate constant versus T **Find:** E_a and A

Conceptual Plan: Because ln $k = \dfrac{-E_a}{R}\left(\dfrac{1}{T}\right) + \ln A$, a plot of ln k versus 1/T will have a slope $= -E_a/R$ and an intercept $= \ln A$.

Solution: The slope can be determined by measuring $\Delta y/\Delta x$ on the plot or by using functions such as "add trendline" in Excel. Because the slope $= -2767.2$ K $= -E_a/R$, then
$E_a = -(\text{slope})R$

$= -(-2767.2 \text{ K})\left(8.314 \dfrac{J}{K \cdot mol}\right)\left(\dfrac{1 \text{ kJ}}{1000 \text{ J}}\right)$

$= 23.0 \dfrac{kJ}{mol}$ and intercept $= 25.112 = \ln A$ then

$A = e^{\text{intercept}} = e^{25.112} = 8.05 \times 10^{10} \text{ s}^{-1}$.

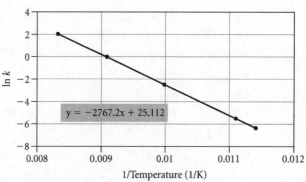

Check: The units (kJ/mol and s^{-1}) are correct. The plot was extremely linear, confirming Arrhenius behavior. The activation energy and frequency factor are typical for many reactions.

13.44   **Given:** table of rate constant versus T **Find:** E_a and A

Conceptual Plan: Because ln $k = \dfrac{-E_a}{R}\left(\dfrac{1}{T}\right) + \ln A$, a plot of ln k versus 1/T will have a slope $= -E_a/R$ and an intercept $= \ln A$.

Solution: The slope can be determined by measuring $\Delta y/\Delta x$ on the plot or by using functions such as "add trendline" in Excel. Because the slope $= -11\underline{6}24$ K $= -E_a/R$, then

$$E_a = -(\text{slope})R$$

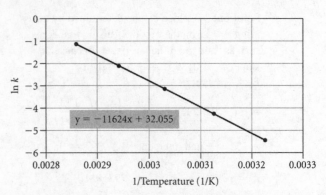

y = −11624x + 32.055

$$= -(-11\underline{6}24 \text{ K})\left(8.314 \frac{\text{J}}{\text{K}\cdot\text{mol}}\right)\left(\frac{1 \text{ kJ}}{1000 \text{ J}}\right)$$

$$= 96.6 \frac{\text{kJ}}{\text{mol}} \text{ and intercept} = 32.0\underline{5}5 = \ln A \text{ then}$$

$$A = e^{\text{intercept}} = e^{32.0\underline{5}5} = 8.34 \times 10^{13} \text{ s}^{-1}.$$

Check: The units (kJ/mol and s^{-1}) are correct. The plot was extremely linear, confirming Arrhenius behavior. The activation energy and frequency factor are typical for many reactions.

13.45   **Given:** rate constant $= 0.0117$/s at 400.0 K and 0.689/s at 450.0 K   **Find:** (a) E_a and (b) rate constant at 425 K
Conceptual Plan:

(a) $k_1, T_1, k_2, T_2, \rightarrow E_a$ then **J/mol $\rightarrow$ kJ/mol**

$$\ln\left(\frac{k_2}{k_1}\right) = \frac{E_a}{R}\left(\frac{1}{T_1} - \frac{1}{T_2}\right) \qquad \frac{1 \text{ kJ}}{1000 \text{ J}}$$

(b) $E_a, k_1, T_1, T_2 \rightarrow k_2$

$$\ln\left(\frac{k_2}{k_1}\right) = \frac{E_a}{R}\left(\frac{1}{T_1} - \frac{1}{T_2}\right)$$

Solution:

(a) $\ln\left(\dfrac{k_2}{k_1}\right) = \dfrac{E_a}{R}\left(\dfrac{1}{T_1} - \dfrac{1}{T_2}\right)$. Rearrange to solve for E_a.

$$E_a = \frac{R\ln\left(\dfrac{k_2}{k_1}\right)}{\left(\dfrac{1}{T_1} - \dfrac{1}{T_2}\right)} = \frac{8.314 \dfrac{\text{J}}{\text{K}\cdot\text{mol}} \ln\left(\dfrac{0.689 \text{ s}^{-1}}{0.0117 \text{ s}^{-1}}\right)}{\left(\dfrac{1}{400.0 \text{ K}} - \dfrac{1}{450.0 \text{ K}}\right)} = 1.22 \times 10^5 \frac{\text{J}}{\text{mol}} \times \frac{1 \text{ kJ}}{1000 \text{ J}} = 122 \frac{\text{kJ}}{\text{mol}}$$

(b) $\ln\left(\dfrac{k_2}{k_1}\right) = \dfrac{E_a}{R}\left(\dfrac{1}{T_1} - \dfrac{1}{T_2}\right)$ with $k_1 = 0.0117$/s, $T_1 = 400.0$ K, $T_2 = 425$ K. Rearrange to solve for k_2.

$$\ln k_2 = \frac{E_a}{R}\left(\frac{1}{T_1} - \frac{1}{T_2}\right) + \ln k_1 = \frac{1.22 \times 10^5 \dfrac{\text{J}}{\text{mol}}}{8.314 \dfrac{\text{J}}{\text{K}\cdot\text{mol}}}\left(\frac{1}{400.0 \text{ K}} - \frac{1}{425.0 \text{ K}}\right) + \ln 0.0117 \text{ s}^{-1} = -2.29\underline{0}2 \rightarrow$$

$$k_2 = e^{-2.29\underline{0}2} = 0.101 \text{ s}^{-1}$$

Check: The units (kJ/mol and s^{-1}) are correct. The activation energy is typical for a reaction. The rate constant at 425 K is between the values given at 400 K and 450 K.

13.46   **Given:** rate constant $= 0.000122$/s at 27 °C and 0.228/s at 77 °C   **Find:** (a) E_a and (b) rate constant at 17 °C
Conceptual Plan:

(a)   °C $\rightarrow$ K then $k_1, T_1, k_2, T_2 \rightarrow E_a$ then **J/mol $\rightarrow$ kJ/mol**

$$K = \text{°C} + 273.15 \qquad \ln\left(\frac{k_2}{k_1}\right) = \frac{E_a}{R}\left(\frac{1}{T_1} - \frac{1}{T_2}\right) \qquad \frac{1 \text{ kJ}}{1000 \text{ J}}$$

(b)   °C $\rightarrow$ K then $E_a, k_1, T_1, T_2 \rightarrow k_2$

$$K = \text{°C} + 273.15 \qquad \ln\left(\frac{k_2}{k_1}\right) = \frac{E_a}{R}\left(\frac{1}{T_1} - \frac{1}{T_2}\right)$$

Solution: $T_1 = 27$ °C $+ 273.15 = 300.$ K and $T_2 = 77$ °C $+ 273.15 = 350.$ K then $\ln\left(\dfrac{k_2}{k_1}\right) = \dfrac{E_a}{R}\left(\dfrac{1}{T_1} - \dfrac{1}{T_2}\right)$

(a)   Rearrange to solve for E_a.

$$E_a = \frac{R\ln\left(\dfrac{k_2}{k_1}\right)}{\left(\dfrac{1}{T_1} - \dfrac{1}{T_2}\right)} = \frac{8.314 \dfrac{\text{J}}{\text{K}\cdot\text{mol}} \ln\left(\dfrac{0.228 \text{ s}^{-1}}{0.000122 \text{ s}^{-1}}\right)}{\left(\dfrac{1}{300.\text{ K}} - \dfrac{1}{350.\text{ K}}\right)} = 1.32 \times 10^5 \frac{\text{J}}{\text{mol}} \times \frac{1 \text{ kJ}}{1000 \text{ J}} = 132 \frac{\text{kJ}}{\text{mol}}$$

(b) $\ln\left(\dfrac{k_2}{k_1}\right) = \dfrac{E_a}{R}\left(\dfrac{1}{T_1} - \dfrac{1}{T_2}\right)$ with $k_1 = 0.000122/s$, $T_1 = 300.\ K$, $T_2 = 17\ ^\circ C + 273.15 = 290\ K$

Rearrange to solve for k_2.

$$\ln k_2 = \frac{E_a}{R}\left(\frac{1}{T_1} - \frac{1}{T_2}\right) + \ln k_1 = \frac{1.32 \times 10^5\ \dfrac{J}{mol}}{8.314\ \dfrac{J}{K \cdot mol}}\left(\frac{1}{300.\ K} - \frac{1}{290.\ K}\right) + \ln 0.000122\ s^{-1} = -10.8\underline{3}64 \rightarrow$$

$$k_2 = e^{-10.8\underline{3}64} = 0.0000197\ s^{-1} = 1.97 \times 10^{-5}\ s^{-1}$$

Check: The units (kJ/mol and s^{-1}) are correct. The activation energy is typical for a reaction. The rate constant at 17 °C is smaller than the values given at 27 °C.

13.47   **Given:** rate constant doubles from 10.0 °C to 20.0 °C   **Find:** E_a
Conceptual Plan: °C → K then $k_1, T_1, k_2, T_2 \rightarrow E_a$ then J/mol → kJ/mol

$$K = {}^\circ C + 273.15 \qquad \ln\left(\frac{k_2}{k_1}\right) = \frac{E_a}{R}\left(\frac{1}{T_1} - \frac{1}{T_2}\right) \qquad \frac{1\ kJ}{1000\ J}$$

Solution: $T_1 = 10.0\ ^\circ C + 273.15 = 283.2\ K$ and $T_2 = 20.0\ ^\circ C + 273.15 = 293.2\ K$ and $k_2 = 2\ k_1$ then

$\ln\left(\dfrac{k_2}{k_1}\right) = \dfrac{E_a}{R}\left(\dfrac{1}{T_1} - \dfrac{1}{T_2}\right)$. Rearrange to solve for E_a.

$$E_a = \frac{R\ln\left(\dfrac{k_2}{k_1}\right)}{\left(\dfrac{1}{T_1} - \dfrac{1}{T_2}\right)} = \frac{8.314\ \dfrac{J}{K \cdot mol}\ \ln\left(\dfrac{2\ k_1}{k_1}\right)}{\left(\dfrac{1}{283.2\ K} - \dfrac{1}{293.2\ K}\right)} = 4.7\underline{8}51 \times 10^4\ \frac{J}{mol} \times \frac{1\ kJ}{1000\ J} = 47.85\ \frac{kJ}{mol}$$

Check: The units (kJ/mol) are correct. The activation energy is typical for a reaction.

13.48   **Given:** rate constant triples from 20.0 °C to 35.0 °C   **Find:** E_a
Conceptual Plan: °C → K then $k_1, T_1, k_2, T_2 \rightarrow E_a$ then J/mol → kJ/mol

$$K = {}^\circ C + 273.15 \qquad \ln\left(\frac{k_2}{k_1}\right) = \frac{E_a}{R}\left(\frac{1}{T_1} - \frac{1}{T_2}\right) \qquad \frac{1\ kJ}{1000\ J}$$

Solution: $T_1 = 20.0\ ^\circ C + 273.15 = 293.2\ K$ and $T_2 = 35.0\ ^\circ C + 273.15 = 308.2\ K$ and $k_2 = 3\ k_1$ then

$\ln\left(\dfrac{k_2}{k_1}\right) = \dfrac{E_a}{R}\left(\dfrac{1}{T_1} - \dfrac{1}{T_2}\right)$. Rearrange to solve for E_a.

$$E_a = \frac{R\ln\left(\dfrac{k_2}{k_1}\right)}{\left(\dfrac{1}{T_1} - \dfrac{1}{T_2}\right)} = \frac{8.314\ \dfrac{J}{K \cdot mol}\ \ln\left(\dfrac{3\ k_1}{k_1}\right)}{\left(\dfrac{1}{293.2\ K} - \dfrac{1}{308.2\ K}\right)} = 5.502 \times 10^4\ \frac{J}{mol} \times \frac{1\ kJ}{1000\ J} = 55.02\ \frac{kJ}{mol}$$

Check: The units (kJ/mol) are correct. The activation energy is typical for a reaction.

13.49   Reaction a would have the faster rate because the orientation factor p would be larger for this reaction because the reactants are symmetrical.

13.50   Reaction b would have the smaller orientation factor because we are reacting an asymmetric molecule with a homonuclear diatomic molecule (symmetrical); so the orientation is important. In reaction a, both reacting species are symmetrical; so orientation is unimportant.

Reaction Mechanisms

13.51   Because the first reaction is the slow step, it is the rate-determining step. Using this first step to determine the rate law, Rate $= k_1\,[AB]^2$. Because this is the observed rate law, this mechanism is consistent with the experimental data.

13.52   (a)   The reaction cannot occur in a single step in which X and Y collide because the rate law would be Rate $= k[X][Y]$. This is not consistent with the stated rate law of Rate $= k[X]^2[Y]$.

(b)   Because the second step is the rate-determining step, Rate $= k_3$ [X$_2$] [Y]. X$_2$ is an intermediate; so its concentration cannot appear in the rate law. Using the fast equilibrium in the first step, we

see that k_1[X]$^2 = k_2$ [X$_2$] or [X$_2$] $= \dfrac{k_1}{k_2}$ [X]^2. Substituting this into the first rate expression, we get

Rate $= \dfrac{k_3 k_1}{k_2}$ [X]^2[Y]. Simplifying this expression, we see that Rate $= k$ [X]^2[Y], which is consistent

with the experimentally derived rate law.

13.53   (a)   The overall reaction is the sum of the steps in the mechanism:

$$Cl_2(g) \underset{k_2}{\overset{k_1}{\rightleftharpoons}} 2\,\cancel{Cl(g)}$$

$$\cancel{Cl(g)} + CHCl_3(g) \underset{k_3}{\rightarrow} HCl(g) + \cancel{CCl_3(g)}$$

$$\cancel{Cl(g)} + \cancel{CCl_3(g)} \underset{k_4}{\rightarrow} CCl_4(g)$$

$$\overline{Cl_2(g) + CHCl_3(g) \rightarrow HCl(g) + CCl_4(g)}$$

(b)   The intermediates are the species that are generated by one step and consumed by other steps. These are Cl(g) and CCl$_3$(g).

(c)   Because the second step is the rate-determining step, Rate $= k_3$ [Cl] [CHCl$_3$]. Because Cl is an intermediate, its concentration cannot appear in the rate law. Using the fast equilibrium in the first step, we

see that k_1[Cl$_2$] $= k_2$[Cl]^2 or [Cl] $= \sqrt{\dfrac{k_1}{k_2}}$ [Cl$_2$]. Substituting this into the first rate expression, we get

Rate $= k_3 \sqrt{\dfrac{k_1}{k_2}}$ [Cl$_2$]$^{1/2}$[CHCl$_3$]. Simplifying this expression, we see that Rate $= k$[Cl$_2$]$^{1/2}$ [CHCl$_3$].

13.54   (a)   The overall reaction is the sum of the steps in the mechanism:

$$NO_2(g) + Cl_2(g) \underset{k_1}{\rightarrow} ClNO_2(g) + \cancel{Cl(g)}$$

$$NO_2(g) + \cancel{Cl(g)} \underset{k_2}{\rightarrow} ClNO_2(g)$$

$$\overline{2\,NO_2(g) + Cl_2(g) \rightarrow 2\,ClNO_2(g)}$$

(b)   The intermediates are the species that are generated by one step and consumed by other steps. This is Cl(g).

(c)   Because the first step is the rate-determining step, Rate $= k_1$[NO$_2$] [Cl$_2$]. Because both of these species are reactants, this is the predicted rate law.

Catalysis

13.55   Heterogeneous catalysts require a large surface area because catalysis can only happen at the active sites on the surface. A greater surface area means greater opportunity for the substrate to react, which results in a speedier reaction.

13.56   The initial and final energies (reactants and products) remain the same. The activation energy drops from 75 kJ/mol to a smaller value, for example, 30 kJ/mol. There are usually more steps in the reaction progress diagram.

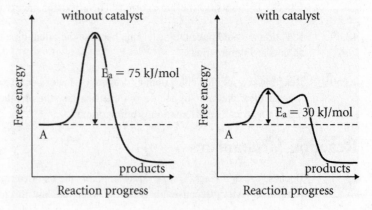

13.57   Assume rate ratio $\propto k$ ratio (because concentration terms will cancel each other) and $k = A\,e^{-E_a/RT}$. $T = 25\,°C + 273.15 = 298$ K, $E_{a_1} = 1.25 \times 10^5$ J/mol, and $E_{a_2} = 5.5 \times 10^4$ J/mol. Ratio of rates will be

$$\frac{k_2}{k_1} = \frac{\cancel{A}\,e^{-E_{a_2}/RT}}{\cancel{A}\,e^{-E_{a_1}/RT}} = \frac{e^{\dfrac{-5.5\times10^4\frac{\cancel{J}}{\cancel{mol}}}{\left(8.314\frac{\cancel{J}}{\cancel{K}\cdot\cancel{mol}}\right)298\,\cancel{K}}}}{e^{\dfrac{-1.25\times10^5\frac{\cancel{J}}{\cancel{mol}}}{\left(8.314\frac{\cancel{J}}{\cancel{K}\cdot\cancel{mol}}\right)298\,\cancel{K}}}} = \frac{e^{-22.199}}{e^{-50.\underline{4}53}} = 10^{12}$$

13.58   Assume rate ratio $\propto k$ ratio (because concentration terms will cancel each other) and $k = A\,e^{-E_a/RT}$.
$T = 25\,°C + 273.15 = 298\,K$ and $E_{a_1} = 1.08 \times 10^5$ J/mol. Ratio of rates will be

$$\frac{k_2}{k_1} = 10^6 = \frac{\cancel{A}\,e^{-E_{a_2}/RT}}{\cancel{A}\,e^{-E_{a_1}/RT}} = \frac{e^{\dfrac{-E_{a_2}}{\left(8.314\frac{J}{\cancel{K}\cdot mol}\right)298\,\cancel{K}}}}{e^{\dfrac{-1.08\times10^5\frac{\cancel{J}}{\cancel{mol}}}{\left(8.314\frac{\cancel{J}}{\cancel{K}\cdot\cancel{mol}}\right)298\,\cancel{K}}}} = \frac{e^{\dfrac{-E_{a_2}}{2.4\underline{7}756\times10^3\frac{J}{mol}}}}{1.17\times10^{-19}} \rightarrow \frac{e^{-E_{a_2}}}{e^{2.4\underline{7}756\times10^3\frac{J}{mol}}} = 1.17\times10^{-13} \rightarrow$$

$$\frac{-E_{a_2}}{2.4\underline{7}756\times10^3\,\dfrac{J}{mol}} = \ln(1.17\times10^{-13}) = -29.\underline{7}766 \rightarrow E_{a_2} = 7.38\times10^4\,\frac{J}{mol} = 73.8\,\frac{kJ}{mol}$$

Cumulative Problems

13.59   **Given:** table of [CH$_3$CN] versus time   **Find:** (a) reaction order, k; (b) $t_{1/2}$; and (c) t for 90% conversion
Conceptual Plan: (a) and (b) Look at the data and see if any common reaction orders can be eliminated. If the data does not show an equal concentration drop with time, zero order can be eliminated. Look for changes in the half-life (compare time for concentration to drop to one-half of any value). If the half-life is not constant, the first order can be eliminated. If the half-life is getting longer as the concentration drops, this might suggest second order. Plot the data as indicated by the appropriate rate law, or if it is first order and there is an obvious half-life in the data, a plot is not necessary. Determine k from the slope of the plot (or using the half-life equation for first order). (c) Finally, calculate the time to 90% conversion using the appropriate integrated rate equation.
Solution: (a) and (b) By the preceding logic, we can see that the reaction is first order. It takes 15.0 h for the concentration to be cut in half for any concentration (1.000 M to 0.501 M, 0.794 M to 0.398 M, and 0.631 M to 0.316 M), so

$t_{1/2} = 15.0$ h. Then use $t_{1/2} = \dfrac{0.693}{k}$ and rearrange to solve for k.

$k = \dfrac{0.693}{t_{1/2}} = \dfrac{0.693}{15.0\,h} = 0.0462\,h^{-1}$

(c) [CH$_3$CN]$_t$ = 0.10 [CH$_3$CN]$_0$. Because $\ln$[CH$_3$CN]$_t = -kt + \ln$[CH$_3$CN]$_0$, rearrange to solve for t.

$t = -\dfrac{1}{k}\ln\dfrac{[CH_3CN]_t}{[CH_3CN]_0} = -\dfrac{1}{0.0462\,h^{-1}}\ln\dfrac{0.10\,\cancel{[CH_3CN]_0}}{\cancel{[CH_3CN]_0}} = 49.8\,h$

Check: The units (none, h^{-1}, h, and h) are correct. The rate law is a common form. The data showed a constant half-life very clearly. The rate constant is consistent with the units necessary to get rate as M/s, and the magnitude is reasonable because we have a first-order reaction. The time to 90% conversion is consistent with a time between three and four half-lives.

13.60   **Given:** table of [X$_2$Y] versus time
Find: (a) reaction order, k; (b) $t_{1/2}$ at initial concentration; and (c) [X] at 10.0 h
Conceptual Plan: (a) Look at the data and see if any common reaction orders can be eliminated. If the data does not show an equal concentration drop with time, zero order can be eliminated. Look for changes in the half-life (compare time for concentration to drop to one-half of any value). If the half-life is not constant, the first order

can be eliminated. **If the half-life is getting longer as the concentration drops, this might suggest second order. Plot the data as indicated by the appropriate rate law. Determine k from the slope of the plot. (b) Calculate the half-life with the appropriate equation. (c) Finally, calculate the $[X_2Y]$ at 10.0 h using the appropriate integrated rate expression and convert this to a change in $[X_2Y]$ and then to $[X]$ using the reaction stoichiometry.**
Solution:

(a)   By the preceding logic, we can eliminate both the zero-order and first-order reactions. (Alternatively, you could make all three plots, and only one should be linear.) This suggests that we should have a second-order reaction. Plot $1/[X_2Y]$ versus time.

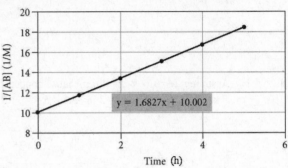

Because $\dfrac{1}{[X_2Y]_t} = kt + \dfrac{1}{[X_2Y]_0}$, the slope will be the rate constant. The slope can be determined by measuring $\Delta y/\Delta x$ on the plot or by using functions such as "add trendline" in Excel. Thus, the rate constant is $1.6\underline{8}27\ M^{-1}\cdot h^{-1}$, and the rate law is Rate $= 1.68\ M^{-1}\cdot h^{-1}[X_2Y]^2$.

(b) $t_{1/2} = \dfrac{1}{k[X_2Y]_0}$ so $t_{1/2} = \dfrac{1}{(1.6\underline{8}27\ M^{-1}\cdot h^{-1})(0.100\ M)} = 5.94\ h$

(c)   Finally, use $\dfrac{1}{[X_2Y]_t} = kt + \dfrac{1}{[X_2Y]_0}$; substitute the values of $[X_2Y]_0$, 10.0 h, and k; and rearrange to solve for $[X_2Y]$ at 10.0 h.

$[X_2Y]_t = \dfrac{1}{kt + \dfrac{1}{[X_2Y]_0}} = \dfrac{1}{(1.6\underline{8}27\ M^{-1}\cdot h^{-1})(10.0\ h) + \left(\dfrac{1}{0.100\ M}\right)} = 0.037\underline{2}759\ M$ then

$\Delta[X_2Y] = [X_2Y]_0 - [X_2Y]_{10.0\ h} = 0.100\ M - 0.037\underline{2}759\ M = 0.06\underline{2}724\ M$ then

$\dfrac{0.06\underline{2}724\ \text{mol } X_2Y}{L} \times \dfrac{2\ \text{mol } X}{1\ \text{mol } X_2Y} = 0.13\ M\ X$

Check: The units (none, $M^{-1}\cdot h^{-1}$, h, and M) are correct. The rate law is a common form. The plot was extremely linear, confirming second-order kinetics. The rate constant is consistent with the units necessary to get rate as M/s, and the magnitude is reasonable since we have a second-order reaction. The half-life is consistent with the data table, which indicates that the half-life is a little over 5 h. The $[X]$ at 10 h s is consistent with the changes that we see in the data table through 5 h.

13.61   **Given:** Rate $= k\dfrac{[A][C]^2}{[B]^{1/2}} = 0.0115$ M/s at certain initial concentrations of A, B, and C; double A and C concentration and triple B concentration   **Find:** reaction rate
Conceptual Plan: $[A]_1, [B]_1, [C]_1,$ Rate 1, $[A]_2, [B]_2, [C]_2 \rightarrow$ **Rate 2**

$$\dfrac{\text{Rate 2}}{\text{Rate 1}} = \dfrac{k\dfrac{[A]_2[C]_2^2}{[B]_2^{1/2}}}{k\dfrac{[A]_1[C]_1^2}{[B]_1^{1/2}}}$$

Solution: $\dfrac{\text{Rate 2}}{\text{Rate 1}} = \dfrac{k\dfrac{[A]_2[C]_2^2}{[B]_2^{1/2}}}{k\dfrac{[A]_1[C]_1^2}{[B]_1^{1/2}}}$. Rearrange to solve for Rate 2. Rate 2 $= \dfrac{k\dfrac{[A]_2[C]_2^2}{[B]_2^{1/2}}}{k\dfrac{[A]_1[C]_1^2}{[B]_1^{1/2}}}$,

Rate 1 $[A]_2 = 2[A]_1$, $[B]_2 = 3[B]_1$, $[C]_2 = 2[C]_1$, and Rate 1 $= 0.0115$ M/s so

Rate 2 $= \dfrac{k\dfrac{2\,[A]_1(2\,[C]_1)^2}{(3\,[B]_1)^{1/2}}}{k\dfrac{[A]_1[C]_1^2}{[B]_1^{1/2}}}\ 0.0115\ \dfrac{M}{s} = \dfrac{2^3}{3^{1/2}}\ 0.0115\ \dfrac{M}{s} = 0.0531\ \dfrac{M}{s}$

Check: The units $(M \cdot s^{-1})$ are correct. They should increase because we have a factor of eight (2^3) divided by the square root of three (1.73).

13.62   **Given:** Rate $= k \dfrac{[O_3]^2}{[O_2]}$; initially, 1.0 mol O_3 and 1.0 mol O_2 in 1.0 L

Find: fraction O_3 reacted when reaction rate is cut in half

Conceptual Plan:

mol, L → M then $[O_3]_1$, $[O_2]_1$, Rate 1, Rate 2 → $[O_3]_2$ then $[O_3]_1$, $[O_3]_2$ → O_3 fraction reacted

$$M = \frac{mol}{L} \qquad \frac{\text{Rate 2}}{\text{Rate 1}} = \frac{k\frac{[O_3]_2^2}{[O_2]_2}}{k\frac{[O_3]_1^2}{[O_2]_1}} \qquad O_3 \text{ fraction reacted} = \frac{[O_3]_1 - [O_3]_2}{[O_3]_1}$$

Solution: $M = \dfrac{mol}{L}$ so $[O_3]_1 = \dfrac{1.0 \text{ mol}}{1.0 \text{ L}} = 1.0$ M and $[O_2]_1 = \dfrac{1.0 \text{ mol}}{1.0 \text{ L}} = 1.0$ M. Rate 1 = 2 Rate 2.

Let $x = \Delta[O_3]$ so $[O_3]_2 = [O_3]_{1-x}$ and $[O_2]_2 = [O_2]_{1+3/2x}$. Substitute values into $\dfrac{\text{Rate 2}}{\text{Rate 1}} = \dfrac{k\frac{[O_3]_2^2}{[O_2]_2}}{k\frac{[O_3]_1^2}{[O_2]_1}}$ and

rearrange to solve for x. $\dfrac{\cancel{\text{Rate 2}}}{2\,\cancel{\text{Rate 2}}} = \dfrac{k\dfrac{(1.0 \text{ M} - x)^2}{(1.0 \text{ M} + 3/2x)}}{k\dfrac{(1.0 \text{ M})^{\cancel{2}}}{\cancel{(1.0 \text{ M})}}} \rightarrow 0.50 \text{ M } (1.0 \text{ M} + 3/2x) = (1.0 \text{ M} - x)^2 \rightarrow$

$0.50 + 0.75x = 1.0 - 2.0x + x^2 \rightarrow 0 = x^2 - 2.\underline{7}5x + 0.\underline{5}0$ solve with quadratic equation

$\left(x = \dfrac{-b \pm \sqrt{b^2 - 4\,ac}}{2a}\right)$. So

$x = \dfrac{2.\underline{7}5 \pm \sqrt{(-2.\underline{7}5)^2 - (4)(1.0)(0.50)}}{2(1.0)} = \dfrac{2.\underline{7}5 \pm \sqrt{5.\underline{5}625}}{2.0} = \dfrac{2.\underline{7}5 \pm 2.3585}{2.0} = 0.\underline{1}9575$ M or 2.\underline{5}5 M

The answer must be 0.\underline{1}9575 M because the other answer is larger than our initial concentration (and is, therefore, impossible).

$$O_3 \text{ fraction reacted} = \frac{[O_3]_1 - [O_3]_2}{[O_3]_1} = \frac{x}{[O_3]_1} = \frac{0.\underline{1}9575 \cancel{M}}{1.0 \cancel{M}} = 0.2$$

Check: The units (unitless) are correct. The concentration is reasonable because two forces are slowing down the reaction: (1) the decrease in the reactant and (2) the increase of the product (which appears in the rate law). The calculation can be double-checked by substituting the value of x; the resulting rate $= 0.5 \, k$.

13.63   **Given:** table of P_{Total} versus time   **Find:** rate law, k, and P_{Total} at 2.00×10^4 s
Conceptual Plan: Because two moles of gas are generated for each mole of CH_3CHO decomposed, $P_{CH_3CHO} = P^\circ_{Total} - (P_{Total} - P^\circ_{Total})$. Look at the data and see if any common reaction orders can be eliminated. If the data does not show an equal P_{Total} rise (or P_{CH_3CHO} drop) with time, zero order can be eliminated. It does appear that the half-life is getting longer, so the first order can be eliminated. Plot the data as indicated by the appropriate rate law. Determine k from the slope of the plot. Finally, calculate the P_{CH_3CHO} at 2.00×10^4 s using the appropriate integrated rate expression and convert this to P_{Total} using the reaction stoichiometry.
Solution: Calculate $P_{CH_3CHO} = P^\circ_{Total} - (P_{Total} - P^\circ_{Total})$.

Time (s)	P_{Total} (atm)	P_{CH_3CHO} (atm)
0	0.22	0.22
1000	0.24	0.20
3000	0.27	0.17
7000	0.31	0.13

By the preceding logic, we can eliminate both the zero-order and the first-order reactions. (Alternatively, you could make all three plots, and only one should be linear.) This suggests that we should have a second-order reaction. Plot $1/P_{CH_3CHO}$ versus time. Because $\dfrac{1}{P_{CH_3CHO}} = kt + \dfrac{1}{P^\circ_{CH_3CHO}}$, the slope will be the rate constant. The slope can be determined by measuring $\Delta y / \Delta x$ on the plot or by using functions such as "add trendline" in Excel. Thus, the rate constant is 4.5×10^{-4} atm$^{-1} \cdot$ s^{-1}, and the rate law is Rate $= 4.5 \times 10^{-4}$ atm$^{-1} \cdot$ s$^{-1} P_{CH_3CHO}$.

Finally, use $\dfrac{1}{P_{CH_3CHO}} = kt + \dfrac{1}{P^{\circ}_{CH_3CHO}}$; substitute the

values of $P^{\circ}_{CH_3CHO}$, 2.00×10^4 s, and k and rearrange to solve for $P^{\circ}_{CH_3CHO}$ at 2.00×10^4 s.

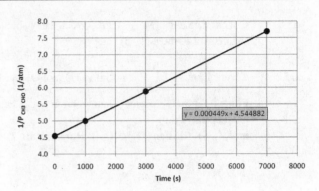

$$P_{CH_3CHO} = \cfrac{1}{kt + \cfrac{1}{P^{\circ}_{CH_3CHO}}} =$$

$$\cfrac{1}{(4.5 \times 10^{-4}\text{ atm}^{-1} \cdot \text{s}^{-1})(2.00 \times 10^4\text{ s}) + \left(\cfrac{1}{0.22\text{ atm}}\right)} = 0.07\underline{3}8255\text{ atm} = 0.074\text{ atm}$$

Finally, from the first equation in the solution, $P_{Total} = 2P^{\circ}_{Total} - P_{CH_3CHO} = 2(0.22\text{ atm}) - 0.0738255\text{ atm} = 0.3\underline{6}6175\text{ atm} = 0.37\text{ atm}$.

Check: The units (none, atm$^{-1} \cdot$ s^{-1}, and atm) are correct. The rate law is a common form. The plot was extremely linear, confirming second-order kinetics. The rate constant is consistent with the units necessary to get rate as atm/s, and the magnitude is reasonable because we have a second-order reaction. The P_{Total} at 2.00×10^4 s is consistent with the changes we see in the data table through 7000 s.

13.64   **Given:** table of $P^{\circ}_{H_2C_2O_4}$ versus P_{Total} at 20,000 s   **Find:** rate law and k
Conceptual Plan: Because two moles of gas are generated for each mole of $H_2C_2O_4$ decomposed, this $P_{H_2C_2O_4} = P^{\circ}_{H_2C_2O_4} - (P_{Total} - P^{\circ}_{H_2C_2O_4})$ and the Rate $= -(P^{\circ}_{H_2C_2O_4} - P_{Total})/20,000$ s. Using general rate law form, compare rate ratios to determine reaction order.

$$\frac{\text{Rate 2}}{\text{Rate 1}} = \frac{k[A]^n_2}{k[A]^n_1}$$

Then use one of the concentration/initial rate pairs to determine k.

$$\text{Rate} = k[A]^n$$

Solution: Calculate Rate $= -(P^{\circ}_{H_2C_2O_4} - P_{Total})/20,000$ s.

	Experiment 1	**Experiment 2**	**Experiment 3**
$P^{\circ}_{H_2C_2O_4}$ (mmHg)	65.8	92.1	111
P_{Total} at 20,000 s (mmHg)	94.6	132	160
Rate (mmHg/s)	0.0014$\underline{4}$	0.001$\underline{9}$95	0.002$\underline{4}$5

$\dfrac{\text{Rate 2}}{\text{Rate 1}} = \dfrac{k[A]^n_2}{k[A]^n_1}$. Comparing the first two sets of data,

$\dfrac{0.001\underline{9}95\text{ mmHg/s}}{0.00144\text{ mmHg/s}} = \dfrac{k(92.1\text{ mmHg})^n}{k(65.8\text{ mmHg})^n}$ and $1.\underline{3}854 = 1.3\underline{9}97^n$; so $n = 1$. If we compare the first and third data sets,

$\dfrac{0.002\underline{4}5\text{ mmHg/s}}{0.00144\text{ mmHg/s}} = \dfrac{k(111\text{ mmHg})^n}{k(65.8\text{ mmHg})^n}$ and $1.\underline{7}0139 = 1.\underline{6}8693^n$; so $n = 1$. This second comparison is not necessary,

but it increases our confidence in the reaction order. So Rate $= k P^{\circ}_{H_2C_2O_4}$. Selecting the first data set and rearranging

the rate equation, $k = \dfrac{\text{Rate}}{P^{\circ}_{H_2C_2O_4}} = \dfrac{0.00144\,\dfrac{\text{mmHg}}{\text{s}}}{65.8\text{ mmHg}} = 2.19 \times 10^{-5}\text{s}^{-1}$; so Rate $= 2.19 \times 10^{-5}\text{s}^{-1} P^{\circ}_{H_2C_2O_4}$.

Check: The units (none and s^{-1}) are correct. The rate law is a common form. The rate is changing proportionately with the initial pressure, so first order is consistent. The rate constant is consistent with the units necessary to get rate as mmHg/s, and the magnitude is reasonable because we have a first-order reaction.

13.65 **Given:** N_2O_5 decomposes to NO_2 and O_2, first order in $[N_2O_5]$; $t_{1/2} = 2.81$ h at 25 °C; $V = 1.5$ L, $P^\circ_{N_2O_5} = 745$ torr
Find: P_{O_2} after 215 minutes
Conceptual Plan: Write a balanced reaction. Then $t_{1/2} \rightarrow k$ **then** °C $\rightarrow$ K **and torr** $\rightarrow$ **atm then**

$$N_2O_5 \rightarrow 2\,NO_2 + \tfrac{1}{2}O_2 \qquad t_{1/2} = \frac{0.693}{k} \qquad K = °C + 273.15 \qquad \frac{1\ \text{atm}}{760\ \text{torr}}$$

$P^\circ_{N_2O_5}, V, T \rightarrow n/V$ **then min** $\rightarrow$ **h then** $[N_2O_5]_0, t, k \rightarrow [N_2O_5]_t$ **then** $[N_2O_5]_0, [N_2O_5]_t \rightarrow [O_2]_t$

$$PV = nRT \qquad \frac{1\ \text{h}}{60\ \text{min}} \qquad \ln[A]_t = -kt + \ln[A]_0 \qquad [O_2]_t = ([N_2O_5]_0 - [N_2O_5]_t) \times \frac{1/2\ \text{mol}\ O_2}{1\ \text{mol}\ N_2O_5}$$

then $[O_2]_t, V, T \rightarrow P^\circ_{O_2}$ **and finally atm** $\rightarrow$ **torr**

$$PV = nRT \qquad \frac{760\ \text{torr}}{1\ \text{atm}}$$

Solution: $t_{1/2} = \dfrac{0.693}{k}$ and rearrange to solve for k. $k = \dfrac{0.693}{t_{1/2}} = \dfrac{0.693}{2.81\ \text{h}} = 0.24\underline{6}619\ \text{h}^{-1}$. Then

$T = 25\ °C + 273.15 = 298$ K. $745\ \text{torr} \times \dfrac{1\ \text{atm}}{760\ \text{torr}} = 0.98\underline{0}263$ atm then $PV = nRT$. Rearrange to solve for n/V.

$\dfrac{n}{V} = \dfrac{P}{RT} = \dfrac{0.98\underline{0}263\ \text{atm}}{0.08206\dfrac{\text{L} \cdot \text{atm}}{\text{K} \cdot \text{mol}} \times 298\ \text{K}} = 0.040\underline{0}862$ M then $215\ \text{min} \times \dfrac{1\ \text{h}}{60\ \text{min}} = 3.5\underline{8}333$ h

Because $\ln[N_2O_5]_t = -kt + \ln[N_2O_5]_0 = -(0.24\underline{6}619\ \text{h}^{-1})(3.5\underline{8}333\ \text{h}) + \ln(0.040\underline{0}862\ \text{M}) = -4.1\underline{0}044 \rightarrow$
$[N_2O_5]_t = e^{-4.10044} = 0.016\underline{5}654$ M then

$$[O_2]_t = ([N_2O_5]_0 - [N_2O_5]_t) \times \frac{1/2\ \text{mol}\ O_2}{1\ \text{mol}\ N_2O_5} = \left(0.040\underline{0}862\ \frac{\text{mol}\ N_2O_5}{\text{L}} - 0.016\underline{5}654\ \frac{\text{mol}\ N_2O_5}{\text{L}}\right) \times \frac{1/2\ \text{mol}\ O_2}{1\ \text{mol}\ N_2O_5}$$
$= 0.011\underline{7}604$ M O_2
then finally $PV = nRT$ and rearrange to solve for P.

$$P = \frac{n}{V}RT = 0.011\underline{7}604\ \frac{\text{mol}}{\text{L}} \times 0.08206\ \frac{\text{L atm}}{\text{K} \cdot \text{mol}} \times 298\ \text{K} = 0.287587\ \text{atm} \times \frac{760\ \text{torr}}{1\ \text{atm}} = 219\ \text{torr}$$

Check: The units (torr) are correct. The pressure is reasonable because it must be less than one-half of the original pressure.

13.66 **Given:** Cyclopropane (C_3H_6) reacts, first order in $[C_3H_6]$; $k = 5.87 \times 10^{-4}$/s at 485 °C; $V = 2.5$ L, $P^\circ_{C_3H_6} = 722$ torr
Find: t to $P_{C_3H_6} = 100.0$ torr
Conceptual Plan: Because $P \propto M$, **we do not need to convert** P **to** M. $P^\circ_{C_3H_6}, P_{C_3H_6}, k \rightarrow t$

$$\ln[A]_t = -kt + \ln[A]_0$$

Solution: $\ln[C_3H_6]_t = -kt + \ln[C_3H_6]_0$. Rearrange to solve for t.

$$t = -\frac{1}{k}\ln\frac{[C_3H_6]_t}{[C_3H_6]_0} = -\frac{1}{k}\ln\frac{P_{C_3H_6}}{P^\circ_{C_3H_6}} = -\frac{1}{5.87 \times 10^{-4}\ \text{s}^{-1}}\ln\frac{100.\ \text{torr}}{722\ \text{torr}} = 3.37 \times 10^3\ \text{s} = 56.1\ \text{min}$$

Check: The units (s or min) are correct. The time is reasonable because it is about three half-lives (pressure dropped to 14% of original pressure).

13.67 **Given:** I_2 formation from I atoms, second order in I; $k = 1.5 \times 10^{10}\ \text{M}^{-1} \cdot \text{s}^{-1}$, $[I]_0 = 0.0100$ M
Find: t to decrease by 95%
Conceptual Plan: $[I]_0, [I]_t, k \rightarrow t$

$$\frac{1}{[A]_t} = kt + \frac{1}{[A]_0}$$

Solution: $[I]_t = 0.05\,[I]_0 = 0.05 \times 0.0100$ M $= 0.0005$ M. Because $\dfrac{1}{[I]_t} = kt + \dfrac{1}{[I]_0}$. Rearrange to solve for t.

$$t = \frac{1}{k}\left(\frac{1}{[I]_t} - \frac{1}{[I]_0}\right) = \frac{1}{(1.5 \times 10^{10}\ \text{M}^{-1} \cdot \text{s}^{-1})}\left(\frac{1}{0.0005\ \text{M}} - \frac{1}{0.0100\ \text{M}}\right) = 1.\underline{2}67 \times 10^{-7}\ \text{s} = 1 \times 10^{-7}\ \text{s}$$

Check: The units (s) are correct. We expect the time to be extremely small because the rate constant is so large.

13.68 **Given:** sucrose hydrolysis, first order in $[C_{12}H_{22}O_{11}]$; $k = 1.8 \times 10^{-4}\ \text{s}^{-1}$ at 25 °C; $V = 2.55$ L,
$[C_{12}H_{22}O_{11}]_0 = 0.150$ M, and 195 min **Find:** $m(C_{12}H_{22}O_{11})$ hydrolyzed

Conceptual Plan: min $\rightarrow$ s then $[C_{12}H_{22}O_{11}]_0, t, k \rightarrow [C_{12}H_{22}O_{11}]_t$ then

$$\frac{60\ s}{1\ min} \qquad\qquad \ln[A]_t = -kt + \ln[A]_0$$

$V, [C_{12}H_{22}O_{11}]_0, [C_{12}H_{22}O_{11}]_t \rightarrow$ mol $C_{12}H_{22}O_{11}$ hydrolyzed $\rightarrow$ g $C_{12}H_{22}O_{11}$ hydrolyzed

$$\text{mol } C_{12}H_{22}O_{11} = ([C_{12}H_{22}O_{11}]_0 - [C_{12}H_{22}O_{11}]_t) \times V \qquad \frac{342.30\ g\ C_{12}H_{22}O_{11}}{1\ mol\ C_{12}H_{22}O_{11}}$$

Solution: $195\ \cancel{min} \times \dfrac{60\ sec}{1\ \cancel{min}} = 11\underline{7}00$ s. Because

$\ln[C_{12}H_{22}O_{11}]_t = -kt + \ln[C_{12}H_{22}O_{11}]_0 = -(1.8 \times 10^{-4}\ \cancel{s^{-1}})(11\underline{7}00\ \cancel{s}) + \ln(0.150\ M) = -4.0\underline{0}312 \rightarrow$

$[C_{12}H_{22}O_{11}]_t = e^{-4.0\underline{0}312} = 0.018\underline{2}586$ M, then

mol $C_{12}H_{22}O_{11} = ([C_{12}H_{22}O_{11}]_0 - [C_{12}H_{22}O_{11}]_t) \times V =$

$\left(0.150\ \dfrac{\text{mol } C_{12}H_{22}O_{11}}{\cancel{L}} - 0.018\underline{2}586\ \dfrac{\text{mol } C_{12}H_{22}O_{11}}{\cancel{L}} \right) \times 2.55\ \cancel{L} = 0.33\underline{5}941$ mol $C_{12}H_{22}O_{11}$

$0.33\underline{5}941\ \cancel{\text{mol } C_{12}H_{22}O_{11}} \times \dfrac{342.30\ g\ C_{12}H_{22}O_{11}}{1\ \cancel{\text{mol } C_{12}H_{22}O_{11}}} = 115$ g $C_{12}H_{22}O_{11}$

Check: The units (g) are correct. The mass is reasonable because it must be less than the original amount in solution (131 g). The amount is close to the original amount in solution because the final sucrose concentration is so low because we have gone over three half-lives.

13.69   **Given:** $AB(aq) \rightarrow A(g) + B(g)$; $k = 0.0118\ M^{-1} \cdot s^{-1}$; 250.0 mL of 0.100 M AB; collect gas over water $T = 25.0\ ^\circ C$, $P_{Total} = 755.1$ mmHg, and $V = 200.0$ mL; $P^\circ_{H_2O} = 23.8$ mmHg   **Find:** t

       Conceptual Plan: $P_{Total}, P_{H_2O} \rightarrow P_A + P_B$ then mmHg $\rightarrow$ atm and mL $\rightarrow$ L

$$P_{Total} = P_{H_2O} + P_A + P_B \qquad \frac{1\ atm}{760\ mmHg} \qquad \frac{1\ L}{1000\ mL}$$

       and $^\circ C \rightarrow K$ $P, V, T \rightarrow n_{A+B} \rightarrow \Delta n_{AB}$ then $[AB]_0, V_{AB}, \Delta n_{AB} \rightarrow [AB]$ then $k, [AB] \rightarrow t$

$$K = {}^\circ C + 273.15 \quad PV = nRT \quad \Delta n_{AB} = \tfrac{1}{2}n_{A+B} \qquad [AB] = [AB]_0 - \frac{\Delta n_{AB}}{V_{AB} \times \frac{1\ L}{1000\ mL}} \qquad \frac{1}{[AB]_t} = kt + \frac{1}{[AB]_0}$$

       Solution: $P_{Total} = P_{H_2O} + P_A + P_B$. Rearrange to solve for $P_A + P_B$. $P_A + P_B = P_{Total} - P_{H_2O} = 755.1$ mmHg $- 23.8$ mmHg $= 731.3$ mmHg

$P_A + P_B = 731.3\ \cancel{mmHg} \times \dfrac{1\ atm}{760\ \cancel{mmHg}} = 0.962\underline{2}3684$ atm $V = 200.0\ \cancel{mL} \times \dfrac{1\ L}{1000\ \cancel{mL}} = 0.2000$ L,

$T = 25.0\ ^\circ C + 273.15 = 298.2$ K, $PV = nRT$. Rearrange to solve for n. $n = \dfrac{PV}{RT}$

$n_{A+B} = \dfrac{0.962\underline{2}3684\ \cancel{atm} \times 0.2000\ \cancel{L}}{0.08206\ \dfrac{\cancel{L} \cdot \cancel{atm}}{mol \cdot \cancel{K}} \times 298.2\ \cancel{K}} = 0.00786\underline{4}5309$ mol A $+$ B. Because one mole each of A and B are

generated for each mole of AB reacting, $\Delta n_{AB} = \tfrac{1}{2}n_{A+B} = \tfrac{1}{2}(0.00786\underline{4}5309\ \text{mol A} + \text{B}) = 0.00393\underline{2}2655$ mol AB

then $[AB] = [AB]_0 - \dfrac{\Delta n_{AB}}{V_{AB} \times \dfrac{1\ L}{1000\ mL}} = 0.100\ M - \dfrac{0.00393\underline{2}2655\ \text{mol AB}}{250.0\ \cancel{mL} \times \dfrac{1\ L}{1000\ \cancel{mL}}} = 0.100\ M - 0.01572\underline{9}062\ M$

$= 0.084\underline{2}709$ M.

Because $\dfrac{1}{[AB]_t} = kt + \dfrac{1}{[AB]_0}$, rearrange to solve for t.

$t = \dfrac{1}{k}\left(\dfrac{1}{[AB]_t} - \dfrac{1}{[AB]_0} \right) = \dfrac{1}{(0.0118\ M^{-1} \cdot s^{-1})}\left(\dfrac{1}{0.084\underline{2}709\ M} - \dfrac{1}{0.100\ M} \right) = 15\underline{8}.1773$ s $= 160$ s

       Check: The units (s) are correct. The magnitude of the answer (160 s) makes sense because the rate constant is $0.0118\ M^{-1}s^{-1}$ and a small volume of gas is generated.

13.70   **Given:** $2\ H_2O_2(aq) \rightarrow 2\ H_2O(l) + O_2(g)$; $k = 0.00752\ s^{-1}$; 150.0 mL of 30.0% H_2O_2 by mass, $d = 1.11$ g/mL; collect gas over water $T = 20.0\ ^\circ C$, $P_{Total} = 742.5$ mmHg, and $t = 85.0$ s; $P^\circ_{H_2O} = 17.5$ mmHg   **Find:** V_{O_2}

Conceptual Plan: $mL_{solution} \rightarrow g_{solution} \rightarrow g_{H_2O_2} \rightarrow mol_{H_2O_2}$ and $mL_{solution} \rightarrow L_{solution}$

$$\frac{1.11\ g}{1\ mL} \qquad \frac{30.0\ g\ H_2O_2}{100\ g\ solution} \quad \frac{1\ mol\ H_2O_2}{34.02\ g\ H_2O_2} \qquad\qquad \frac{1\ L}{1000\ mL}$$

then $mol_{H_2O_2}, L_{solution} \rightarrow M\ H_2O_2$ **then** $k, [H_2O_2]_0, t \rightarrow [H_2O_2]_t$ **then**

$$M = \frac{amount\ solute\ (moles)}{volume\ solution\ (L)} \qquad\qquad \ln[A]_t = -kt + \ln[A]_0$$

$[H_2O_2]_0, [H_2O_2]_t, L_{solution} \rightarrow \Delta n_{H_2O_2} \rightarrow n_{O_2}$ **then** $P_{Total}, P_{H_2O} \rightarrow P_{O_2}$ **then** mmHg $\rightarrow$ atm

$$\Delta n_{H_2O_2} = ([H_2O_2]_0 - [H_2O_2]) \times V_{H_2O_2} \quad \Delta n_{H_2O_2} = 1/2\ n_{O_2} \qquad P_{Total} = P_{H_2O} + P_{O_2} \qquad \frac{1\ atm}{760\ mmHg}$$

and $mL \rightarrow L$ **and** $°C \rightarrow K$ **then** $P, n, T \rightarrow V_{O_2}$

$$\frac{1\ L}{1000\ mL} \qquad K = °C + 273.15 \qquad PV = nRT$$

Solution: $150.0\ \cancel{mL\ solution} \times \dfrac{1.11\ g\ \cancel{solution}}{1\ \cancel{mL\ solution}} \times \dfrac{30.0\ g\ \cancel{H_2O_2}}{100\ g\ \cancel{solution}} \times \dfrac{1\ mol\ H_2O_2}{34.02\ g\ \cancel{H_2O_2}} = 1.4\underline{6}8254\ mol\ H_2O_2$ and

$150.0\ \cancel{mL\ solution} \times \dfrac{1\ L\ solution}{1000\ \cancel{mL\ solution}} = 0.1500\ L\ solution$ then

$M = \dfrac{amount\ solute\ (moles)}{volume\ solution\ (L)} = \dfrac{1.4\underline{6}8254\ mol\ H_2O_2}{0.1500\ L\ solution} = 9.7\underline{8}8360\ M\ H_2O_2$

Because $\ln[H_2O_2]_t = -kt + \ln[H_2O_2]_0 = -(0.00752\ \cancel{s^{-1}})(85.0\ \cancel{s}) + \ln(9.7\underline{8}8360\ M) = 1.6\underline{4}1994 \rightarrow$

$[H_2O_2]_t = e^{1.6\underline{4}1994} = 5.1\underline{6}5459\ M$, then $\Delta n_{H_2O_2} = ([H_2O_2]_0 - [H_2O_2]) \times V_{H_2O_2} \times \dfrac{1\ L}{1000\ mL}$

$\Delta n_{H_2O_2} = (9.7\underline{8}8360\ M - 5.1\underline{6}5459\ M) \times (0.1500\ L) = 0.69\underline{3}4352\ mol\ H_2O_2$ then

$\Delta n_{H_2O_2} = 0.5 n_{O_2} = 0.34672\ mol\ O_2$ then $P_{Total} = P_{H_2O} + P_{O_2}$. Rearrange to solve for P_{O_2}.

$P_{O_2} = P_{Total} - P_{H_2O} = 742.5\ mmHg - 17.5\ mmHg = 725.0\ mmHg$

$P_{O_2} = 725.0\ \cancel{mmHg} \times \dfrac{1\ atm}{760\ \cancel{mmHg}} = 0.953\underline{9}4737\ atm,\ T = 20.0\ °C + 273.15 = 293.2\ K,\ PV = nRT.$

Rearrange to solve for V. $V = \dfrac{nRT}{P}$ and

$$V_{O_2} = \frac{0.34672\ \cancel{mol\ O_2} \times 0.08206\ \dfrac{L \cdot \cancel{atm}}{\cancel{mol} \cdot \cancel{K}} \times 293.2\ \cancel{K}}{0.953\underline{9}4737\ \cancel{atm}} = 8.74480\ L\ O_2 = 8.75\ L\ O_2$$

Check: The units (L) are correct. The magnitude of the answer (9 L) makes sense because about 0.4 mole of gas is generated (22.4 L = 1 mole gas at STP).

13.71   (a)   There are two elementary steps in the reaction mechanism because there are two peaks in the reaction progress diagram.

(b)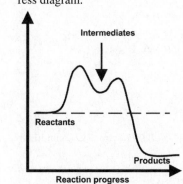

(c)   The first step is the rate-limiting step because it has the higher activation energy.

(d)   The overall reaction is exothermic because the products are at a lower energy than the reactants.

13.72   (a)   The first step is the rate-limiting step because it has the higher activation energy.

(b)   Because the first step is the rate-determining step, Rate $= k_1[HCl][H_2C = CH_2]$. The reaction will be second order overall.

(c)   The overall reaction is exothermic because the products are at a lower energy than the reactants.

13.73   **Given:** *n*-butane desorption from single crystal aluminum oxide, first order; $k = 0.128 \text{ s}^{-1}$ at 150 K; initially completely covered

Find: (a) $t_{1/2}$; (b) t for 25% and for 50% to desorb; (c) fraction remaining after 10 s and 20 s

Conceptual Plan: (a) $k \rightarrow t_{1/2}$ (b) $[C_4H_{10}]_0, [C_4H_{10}]_t, k \rightarrow t$ (c) $[C_4H_{10}]_0, t, k \rightarrow [C_4H_{10}]_t$

$$t_{1/2} = \frac{0.693}{k} \qquad\qquad \ln[A]_t = -kt + \ln[A]_0 \qquad \ln[A]_t = -kt + \ln[A]_0$$

Solution:

(a) $t_{1/2} = \dfrac{0.693}{k} = \dfrac{0.693}{0.128 \text{ s}^{-1}} = 5.41 \text{ s}$

(b) $\ln[C_4H_{10}]_t = -kt + \ln[C_4H_{10}]_0$. Rearrange to solve for t. For 25% desorbed, $[C_4H_{10}]_t = 0.75\,[C_4H_{10}]_0$

and $t = -\dfrac{1}{k} \ln \dfrac{[C_4H_{10}]_t}{[C_4H_{10}]_0} = -\dfrac{1}{0.128 \text{ s}^{-1}} \ln \dfrac{0.75\,[C_4H_{10}]_0}{[C_4H_{10}]_0} = 2.2 \text{ s}$. For 50% desorbed,

$[C_4H_{10}]_t = 0.50\,[C_4H_{10}]_0$ and $t = -\dfrac{1}{k} \ln \dfrac{[C_4H_{10}]_t}{[C_4H_{10}]_0} = -\dfrac{1}{0.128 \text{ s}^{-1}} \ln \dfrac{0.50\,[C_4H_{10}]_0}{[C_4H_{10}]_0} = 5.4 \text{ s}$.

(c)   For 10 s, $\ln[C_4H_{10}]_t = -kt + \ln[C_4H_{10}]_0 = -(0.128 \text{ s}^{-1})(10 \text{ s}) + \ln(1.00) = -1.28 \rightarrow$

$[C_4H_{10}]_t = e^{-1.28} = 0.28 =$ fraction covered.

For 20 s, $\ln[C_4H_{10}]_t = -kt + \ln[C_4H_{10}]_0 = -(0.128 \text{ s}^{-1})(20 \text{ s}) + \ln(1.00) = -2.56 \rightarrow$

$[C_4H_{10}]_t = e^{-2.56} = 0.077 =$ fraction covered.

Check: The units (s, s, s, none, and none) are correct. The half-life is reasonable considering the size of the rate constant. The time to 25% desorbed is less than one half-life. The time to 50% desorbed is the half-life. The fraction at 10 s is consistent with about two half-lives. The fraction covered at 20 s is consistent with about four half-lives.

13.74   **Given:** 120 nm film *n*-pentane evaporation from single crystal aluminum oxide, zero order; $k = 1.92 \times 10^{13}$ molecules/cm^2 s at 120 K; initially, coverage $= 8.9 \times 10^{16}$ molecules/cm^2

Find: (a) $t_{1/2}$; (b) fraction remaining after 10 s

Conceptual Plan:

(a) $[C_5H_{12}]_0, k \rightarrow t_{1/2}$

$$t_{1/2} = \frac{[A]_0}{2k}$$

(b) $[C_5H_{12}]_0, t, k \rightarrow [C_5H_{12}]_t$ then $[C_5H_{12}]_0, [C_5H_{12}]_t \rightarrow$ **fraction remaining**

$$[A]_t = -kt + [A]_0 \qquad\qquad \text{fraction remaining} = \frac{[C_5H_{12}]_t}{[C_5H_{12}]_0}$$

Solution:

(a) $t_{1/2} = \dfrac{[C_5H_{12}]_0}{2k} = \dfrac{8.9 \times 10^{16} \dfrac{\text{molecules}}{\text{cm}^2}}{2 \times 1.92 \times 10^{13} \dfrac{\text{molecules}}{\text{cm}^2 \cdot \text{s}}} = 2.3 \times 10^3 \text{ s}$

(b) $[C_5H_{12}]_t = -kt + [C_5H_{12}]_0 = -\left(1.92 \times 10^{13} \dfrac{\text{molecules}}{\text{cm}^2 \cdot \text{s}}\right)(10 \cdot \text{s}) + 8.9 \times 10^{16} \dfrac{\text{molecules}}{\text{cm}^2}$

$= 8.8808 \times 10^{16} \dfrac{\text{molecules}}{\text{cm}^2}$

$\text{fraction remaining} = \dfrac{[C_5H_{12}]_t}{[C_5H_{12}]_0} = \dfrac{8.8808 \times 10^{16} \dfrac{\text{molecules}}{\text{cm}^2}}{8.9 \times 10^{16} \dfrac{\text{molecules}}{\text{cm}^2}} = 0.99784 = 1.0$; so within experimental error,

all are remaining on the surface.

Check: The units (s and none) are correct. The half-life is reasonable considering the size of the rate constant. The fraction at 10 s is reasonable given the fact that the time is very, very small compared to the half-life.

13.75   (a)   **Given:** table of rate constant versus T **Find:** E_a and A

Conceptual Plan: First, convert temperature data into kelvin (°C + 273.15 = K). Because

$$\ln k = \frac{-E_a}{R}\left(\frac{1}{T}\right) + \ln A \text{ a plot of } \ln k \text{ versus } 1/T \text{ will have a slope } = -E_a/R \text{ and an intercept } = \ln A.$$

Solution: The slope can be determined by measuring $\Delta y/\Delta x$ on the plot or by using functions such as "add trendline" in Excel. Because the slope $= -10759$ K $= -E_a/R$, then

$E_a = -(\text{slope})R$

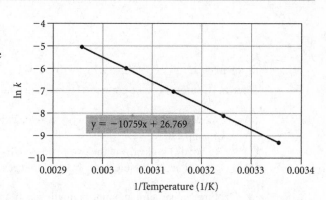

$$= -(-10759 \text{ K})\left(8.314 \frac{J}{K \cdot mol}\right)\left(\frac{1 \text{ kJ}}{1000 \text{ J}}\right)$$

$$= 89.5 \frac{kJ}{mol}$$

and intercept $= 26.769 = \ln A$ then

$A = e^{\text{intercept}} = e^{26.769} = 4.22 \times 10^{11} \text{s}^{-1}$.

Check: The units (kJ/mol and s^{-1}) are correct. The plot was extremely linear, confirming Arrhenius behavior. The activation and frequency factor are typical for many reactions.

(b) **Given:** part (a) results   **Find:** k at 15 °C
   Conceptual Plan: °C $\rightarrow$ K then $T, E_a, A \rightarrow k$

$$°C + 273.15 = K \qquad \ln k = \frac{-E_a}{R}\left(\frac{1}{T}\right) + \ln A$$

Solution: 15 °C + 273.15 = 288 K then

$$\ln k = \frac{-E_a}{R}\left(\frac{1}{T}\right) + \ln A = \frac{-89.5 \frac{kJ}{mol} \times \frac{1000 \text{ J}}{1 \text{ kJ}}}{8.314 \frac{J}{K \cdot mol}}\left(\frac{1}{288 \text{ K}}\right) + \ln(4.22 \times 10^{11} \text{ s}^{-1}) = -10.610 \rightarrow$$

$k = e^{-10.610} = 2.5 \times 10^{-5} M^{-1} \cdot s^{-1}$

Check: The units ($M^{-1} \cdot s^{-1}$) are correct. The value of the rate constant is less than the value at 25 °C.

(c) **Given:** part (a) results, 0.155 M C_2H_5Br and 0.250 M OH^- at 75 °C   **Find:** initial reaction rate
   Conceptual Plan: °C $\rightarrow$ K then $T, E_a, A \rightarrow k$ then k, $[C_2H_5Br]$, $[OH^-] \rightarrow$ initial reaction rate

$$°C + 273.15 = K \qquad \ln k = \frac{-E_a}{R}\left(\frac{1}{T}\right) + \ln A \qquad\qquad \text{Rate} = k[C_2H_5Br][OH^-]$$

Solution: 75 °C + 273.15 = 348 K then

$$\ln k = \frac{-E_a}{R}\left(\frac{1}{T}\right) + \ln A = \frac{-89.5 \frac{kJ}{mol} \times \frac{1000 \text{ J}}{1 \text{ kJ}}}{8.314 \frac{J}{K \cdot mol}}\left(\frac{1}{348 \text{ K}}\right) + \ln(4.22 \times 10^{11} \text{ s}^{-1}) = -4.1656 \rightarrow$$

$k = e^{-4.1656} = 1.5521 \times 10^{-2} M^{-1} \cdot s^{-1}$

Rate $= k[C_2H_5Br][OH^-] = (1.5521 \times 10^{-2} M^{-1} \cdot s^{-1})(0.155 \text{ M})(0.250 \text{ M}) = 6.0 \times 10^{-4} \text{ M} \cdot s^{-1}$

Check: The units ($M \cdot s^{-1}$) are correct. The value of the rate is reasonable considering the value of the rate constant (larger than in the table) and the fact that the concentrations are less than 1 M.

13.76 **Given:** $k = 2.35 \times 10^{-4} s^{-1}$ at 293 K and $k = 9.15 \times 10^{-4} s^{-1}$ at 303 K   **Find:** A
   Conceptual Plan: $k_1, T_1, k_2, T_2 \rightarrow E_a$ then $k_2, T_2, E_a \rightarrow A$

$$\ln k = \frac{-E_a}{R}\left(\frac{1}{T}\right) + \ln A \qquad\qquad k = A e^{-E_a/RT}$$

Solution: $T_1 = 293$ K and $k_1 = 2.35 \times 10^{-4} s^{-1}$; $T_2 = 303$ K and $k_2 = 9.15 \times 10^{-4} s^{-1}$ then

$\ln\left(\dfrac{k_2}{k_1}\right) = \dfrac{E_a}{R}\left(\dfrac{1}{T_1} - \dfrac{1}{T_2}\right)$. Rearrange to solve for E_a.

$$E_a = \frac{R \ln\left(\dfrac{k_2}{k_1}\right)}{\left(\dfrac{1}{T_1} - \dfrac{1}{T_2}\right)} = \frac{8.314 \dfrac{J}{K \cdot mol} \ln\left(\dfrac{9.15 \times 10^{-4} s^{-1}}{2.35 \times 10^{-4} s^{-1}}\right)}{\left(\dfrac{1}{293 \text{ K}} - \dfrac{1}{303 \text{ K}}\right)} = 1.00334 \times 10^5 \frac{J}{mol}. \text{ Because } k = Ae^{-E_a/RT}, \text{ rearrange}$$

$$\frac{1.00334 \times 10^5 \frac{J}{mol}}{\left(8.314 \frac{J}{K \cdot mol}\right) 303 K}$$

to solve for A. $A = ke^{E_a/RT} = 9.15 \times 10^{-4} \text{ s}^{-1} e \qquad = 1.8 \times 10^{14} \text{ s}^{-1}$

Check: The units (s^{-1}) are correct. The frequency factor is typical for a reaction.

13.77 (a) No, because the activation energy is zero. This means that the rate constant ($k = Ae^{-E_a/RT}$) will be independent of temperature.

   (b) No bond is broken, and the two radicals (CH_3) attract each other.

   (c) Formation of diatomic gases from atomic gases

13.78 (a) Nitrogen has a triple bond, so it will take more energy to break the $N\equiv N$ bond than the $H-H$ bond.

   (b) **Given:** $E_a = 315$ kJ/mol for reaction 1 and $E_a = 23$ kJ/mol for reaction 2, frequency factor similar, and 25 °C   **Find:** ratio of rate constants
   Conceptual Plan: °C $\rightarrow$ K then $T, E_{a1}, E_{a2}, A \rightarrow k_1/k_2$

   $$°C + 273.15 = K \qquad \frac{k_1}{k_2} = \frac{Ae^{-E_{a_1}/RT}}{Ae^{-E_{a_2}/RT}}$$

   Solution: $T = 25$ °C $+ 273.15 = 298$ K. $E_{a_1} = 315$ kJ/mol and $E_{a_2} = 23$ kJ/mol. Ratio of rate constants

   will be $\dfrac{k_1}{k_2} = \dfrac{\cancel{A}e^{-E_{a_1}/RT}}{\cancel{A}e^{-E_{a_2}/RT}} = \dfrac{e^{\frac{-315\frac{k\cancel{J}}{mol} \times \frac{1000\cancel{J}}{1\,k\cancel{J}}}{\left(8.314\frac{\cancel{J}}{K\cdot mol}\right)298\,K}}}{e^{\frac{-23\frac{k\cancel{J}}{mol} \times \frac{1000\cancel{J}}{1\,k\cancel{J}}}{\left(8.314\frac{\cancel{J}}{K\cdot mol}\right)298\,K}}} = 6.5 \times 10^{-52}$.

   Check: The units (none) are correct. Because there is a large difference between the activation energies, we expect a large difference in the rate constants.

13.79 **Given:** $t_{1/2}$ for radioactive decay of C-14 $= 5730$ years; bone has 19.5% C-14 in living bone
   Find: age of bone
   Conceptual Plan: Radioactive decay implies first-order kinetics, $t_{1/2} \rightarrow k$ then 19.5% of $[C\text{-}14]_0, k \rightarrow t$

   $$t_{1/2} = \frac{0.693}{k} \qquad \ln[A]_t = -kt + \ln[A]_0$$

   Solution: $t_{1/2} = \dfrac{0.693}{k}$. Rearrange to solve for k. $k = \dfrac{0.693}{t_{1/2}} = \dfrac{0.693}{5730 \text{ yr}} = 1.2\underline{0}942 \times 10^{-4} \text{ yr}^{-1}$ then

   $[C\text{-}14]_t = 0.195[C\text{-}14]_0$. Because $\ln[C\text{-}14]_t = -kt + \ln[C\text{-}14]_0$, rearrange to solve for t.

   $t = -\dfrac{1}{k} \ln \dfrac{[C\text{-}14]_t}{[C\text{-}14]_0} = -\dfrac{1}{1.2\underline{0}942 \times 10^{-4} \text{ yr}^{-1}} \ln \dfrac{0.195\cancel{[C\text{-}14]_0}}{\cancel{[C\text{-}14]_0}} = 1.35 \times 10^4 \text{ yr}$

   Check: The units (yr) are correct. The time to 19.5% decay is consistent with the time being between two and three half-lives.

13.80 **Given:** $t_{1/2}$ for radioactive decay of U-238 $= 4.5$ billion years; rock has 83.2% of original U-238
   Find: age of rock
   Conceptual Plan: Radioactive decay implies first-order kinetics, $t_{1/2} \rightarrow k$ then 82.3% of $[U\text{-}238]_0, k \rightarrow t$

   $$t_{1/2} = \frac{0.693}{k} \qquad \ln[A]_t = -kt + \ln[A]_0$$

   Solution: $t_{1/2} = \dfrac{0.693}{k}$. Rearrange to solve for k. $k = \dfrac{0.693}{t_{1/2}} = \dfrac{0.693}{4.5 \times 10^9 \text{ yr}} = 1.54 \times 10^{-10} \text{ yr}^{-1}$ then

   $[U\text{-}238]_t = 0.823[U\text{-}238]_0$. Because $\ln[U\text{-}238]_t = -kt + \ln[U\text{-}238]_0$, rearrange to solve for t.

   $t = -\dfrac{1}{k} \ln \dfrac{[U\text{-}238]_t}{[U\text{-}238]_0} = -\dfrac{1}{1.54 \times 10^{-10} \text{ yr}^{-1}} \ln \dfrac{0.832\cancel{[U\text{-}238]_0}}{[U\text{-}238]_0} = 1.19 \times 10^9 \text{ yr}$

   Check: The units (yr) are correct. The time to 82.3% decay is consistent with the time being less than one half-life.

13.81 (a) For each, check that all steps sum to overall reaction and that the predicted rate law is consistent with experimental data (Rate $= k[H_2][I_2]$).

For the first mechanism, the single step is the overall reaction. The rate law is determined by the stoichiometry, so Rate $= k[H_2][I_2]$, and the mechanism is valid.

For the second mechanism, the overall reaction is the sum of the steps in the mechanism:

$$I_2(g) \underset{k_2}{\overset{k_1}{\rightleftharpoons}} 2\,\cancel{I(g)}$$

$$H_2(g) + 2\,\cancel{I(g)} \xrightarrow{k_3} 2\,HI(g) \quad \text{So the sum matches the overall reaction.}$$

$$\overline{H_2(g) + I_2(g) \rightarrow 2\,HI(g)}$$

Because the second step is the rate-determining step, Rate $= k_3[H_2][I]^2$. Because I is an intermediate, its concentration cannot appear in the rate law. Using the fast equilibrium in the first step, we see that

$k_1[I_2] = k_2[I]^2$ or $[I]^2 = \dfrac{k_1}{k_2}[I_2]$. Substituting this into the first rate expression, we get Rate $= k_3\dfrac{k_1}{k_2}[H_2][I_2]$,

and the mechanism is valid.

(b) To distinguish between mechanisms, you could look for the buildup of $I(g)$, the intermediate in the second mechanism.

13.82 (a) The overall reaction is the sum of the steps in the mechanism:

$$NH_3(aq) + OCl^-(aq) \underset{k_2}{\overset{k_1}{\rightleftharpoons}} \cancel{NH_2Cl(aq)} + \cancel{OH^-(aq)}$$

$$\cancel{NH_2Cl(aq)} + NH_3(aq) \xrightarrow{k_3} \cancel{N_2H_5^+(aq)} + Cl^-(aq)$$

$$\cancel{N_2H_5^+(aq)} + \cancel{OH^-(aq)} \xrightarrow{k_4} N_2H_4(aq) + H_2O(l)$$

$$\overline{2\,NH_3(aq) + OCl^-(aq) \rightarrow N_2H_4(aq) + H_2O(l) + Cl^-(aq)}$$

So the sum matches the overall reaction.

(b) Because the second step is the rate-determining step, Rate $= k_3[NH_2Cl][NH_3]$. Because NH_2Cl is an intermediate, its concentration cannot appear in the rate law. Using the fast equilibrium in the first step, we see

that $k_1[NH_3][OCl^-] = k_2[NH_2Cl][OH^-]$ or $[NH_2Cl] = \dfrac{k_1}{k_2}\dfrac{[NH_3][OCl^-]}{[OH^-]}$. Substituting this into the first rate

expression, we get Rate $= k_3\dfrac{k_1}{k_2}\dfrac{[NH_3][OCl^-]}{[OH^-]}[NH_3]$ or Rate $= k_3\dfrac{k_1}{k_2}\dfrac{[NH_3]^2[OCl^-]}{[OH^-]}$. In a pH-neutral

solution, $[OH^-] = 10^{-7}$ (see Chapter 15), so that the rate law can be approximated as Rate $= k[NH_3]^2[OCl^-]$.

13.83 (a) For a zero-order reaction, the rate is independent of the concentration. If the first half goes in the first 100 minutes, the second half will go in the second 100 minutes. This means that none or 0% will be left at 200 minutes.

(b) For a first-order reaction, the half-life is independent of concentration. This means that if half of the reactant decomposes in the first 100 minutes, half of this (or another 25% of the original amount) will decompose in the second 100 minutes. This means that at 200 minutes, 50% + 25% = 75% has decomposed or 25% remains.

(c) For a second-order reaction, $t_{1/2} = \dfrac{1}{k[A]_0} = 100$ min, and the integrated rate expression is $\dfrac{1}{[A]_t} = kt + \dfrac{1}{[A]_0}$.

We can rearrange the first expression to solve for k as $k = \dfrac{1}{100\text{ min }[A]_0}$. Substituting this and 200 minutes

into the integrated rate expression, we get $\dfrac{1}{[A]_t} = \dfrac{200\cancel{\text{ min}}}{100\cancel{\text{ min }}[A]_0} + \dfrac{1}{[A]_0} \rightarrow \dfrac{1}{[A]_t} = \dfrac{3}{[A]_0} \rightarrow \dfrac{[A]_t}{[A]_0} = \dfrac{1}{3}$ or

33% remains.

13.84 **Given:** $t_{1/2}$ for radioactive decay of Pu-239 $= 24{,}000$ years; 1 mole initially to 1 atom   **Find:** t

Conceptual Plan: Radioactive decay implies first-order kinetics, $t_{1/2} \rightarrow k$ then $[\text{Pu-239}]_0, [\text{Pu-239}]_t, k \rightarrow t$

$$t_{1/2} = \frac{0.693}{k} \qquad\qquad\qquad \ln[A]_t = -kt + \ln[A]_0$$

Solution: $t_{1/2} = \dfrac{0.693}{k}$. Rearrange to solve for k. $k = \dfrac{0.693}{t_{1/2}} = \dfrac{0.693}{24000 \text{ yr}} = 2.\underline{8}875 \times 10^{-5} \text{ yr}^{-1}$ then

$[\text{Pu-239}]_t = 1$ and $[\text{Pu-239}]_0 = 6.022 \times 10^{23}$. Because $\ln[\text{Pu-239}]_t = -kt + \ln[\text{Pu-239}]_0$, rearrange to solve for t.

$$t = -\frac{1}{k} \ln \frac{[\text{Pu-239}]_t}{[\text{Pu-239}]_0} = -\frac{1}{2.\underline{8}875 \times 10^{-5} \text{ yr}^{-1}} \ln \frac{1 \text{ atom Pu-239}}{6.022 \times 10^{23} \text{ atom Pu-239}} = 1.9 \times 10^6 \text{ yr}$$

Check: The units (yr) are correct. The time to decay to 1 atom is consistent with the time being 79 half-lives, which makes sense because $2^{79} = 6.09 \times 10^{23}$.

13.85   Using the energy diagram shown and using Hess's law, we can see that the activation energy for the decomposition is equal to the activation energy for the formation reaction plus the heat of formation of 2 moles of HI, or $E_{a \text{ formation}} = E_{a \text{ decomposition}} + 2\Delta H_f^\circ(\text{HI})$. So $E_{a \text{ formation}} = 185 \text{ kJ} + 2 \text{ mol}(-5.65 \text{ kJ/mol}) = 174 \text{ kJ}$.

Check: Because the reaction is endothermic, we expect the activation energy in the reverse direction to be less than that in the forward direction.

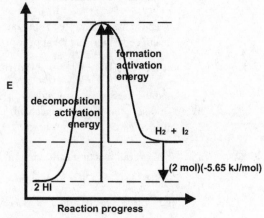

Note: energy axis is not to scale.

13.86   **Given:** first-order reaction, $E_a = 249 \text{ kJ/mol}$, $A = 1.6 \times 10^{14} \text{ s}^{-1}$, and 710 K
     Find: k, fraction decomposed in 15 min and T for double the reaction rate
     Conceptual Plan: $T, A, E_a \rightarrow k$ then min $\rightarrow$ s then $k, t \rightarrow$ fraction decomposed then $k_2/k_1, T_1, E_a \rightarrow T_2$

$$k = Ae^{-E_a/RT} \qquad \frac{60 \text{ s}}{1 \text{ min}} \qquad \ln[A]_t = -kt + \ln[A]_0 \qquad \ln\left(\frac{k_2}{k_1}\right) = \frac{E_a}{R}\left(\frac{1}{T_1} - \frac{1}{T_2}\right)$$

Solution: Because $k = Ae^{-E_a/RT} = 1.6 \times 10^{14} \text{ s}^{-1}\, e^{\dfrac{-249\frac{\text{kJ}}{\text{mol}} \times \frac{1000\text{ J}}{1\text{ kJ}}}{\left(8.314\frac{\text{J}}{\text{K}\cdot\text{mol}}\right)710 \text{ K}}} = 7.\underline{6}657 \times 10^{-5} \text{ s}^{-1} = 7.7 \times 10^{-5} \text{ s}^{-1}$, then

$15 \text{ min} \times \dfrac{60 \text{ s}}{1 \text{ min}} = 9\underline{0}0 \text{ s}$ in $\ln[\text{C}_2\text{H}_5\text{Cl}]_t = -kt + \ln[\text{C}_2\text{H}_5\text{Cl}]_0$. Rearrange to solve for

fraction remaining $\rightarrow \dfrac{[\text{C}_2\text{H}_5\text{Cl}]_t}{[\text{C}_2\text{H}_5\text{Cl}]_0} = e^{-kt} = e^{-(7.\underline{6}657 \times 10^{-5} \text{ s}^{-1})(9\underline{0}0 \text{ s})} = 0.9\underline{3}333$; thus, fraction decomposed $=$

$1 - 0.9\underline{3}333 = 0.0\underline{6}667 = 0.07$. $T_1 = 710 \text{ K}$, $k_2/k_1 = 2$ and $\ln\left(\dfrac{k_2}{k_1}\right) = \dfrac{E_a}{R}\left(\dfrac{1}{T_1} - \dfrac{1}{T_2}\right)$. Rearrange to solve for T_2.

$$T_2 = \frac{\dfrac{E_a}{R}}{\dfrac{E_a}{RT_1} - \ln\left(\dfrac{k_2}{k_1}\right)} = \frac{\dfrac{249\frac{\text{kJ}}{\text{mol}} \times \frac{1000\text{ J}}{1\text{ kJ}}}{8.314\frac{\text{J}}{\text{K}\cdot\text{mol}}}}{\left(\dfrac{249\frac{\text{kJ}}{\text{mol}} \times \frac{1000\text{ J}}{1\text{ kJ}}}{8.314\frac{\text{J}}{\text{K}\cdot\text{mol}} \times 710 \text{ K}}\right) - \ln(2)} = 7\underline{2}1.86 \text{ K} = 720 \text{ K}$$

Check: The units (s^{-1}, none, and K) are correct. The rate constant is reasonable considering the frequency factor, the activation energy, and T. The fraction decomposed is reasonable because 900 s is a small fraction of the half-life. The temperature is reasonable because many reactions double their rate with an increase in temperature of 10 K.

Challenge Problems

13.87   (a)   Because the rate-determining step involves the collision of two molecules, the expected reaction order would be second order.

(b)   The proposed mechanism is

$$CH_3NC + \cancel{CH_3NC} \underset{k_2}{\overset{k_1}{\rightleftharpoons}} CH_3NC^* + \cancel{CH_3NC} \qquad \text{(fast)}$$

$$\cancel{CH_3NC^*} \overset{k_3}{\rightarrow} CH_3CN \qquad\qquad\qquad \text{(slow)}$$

$$\overline{CH_3NC \rightarrow CH_3CN} \qquad\qquad\qquad \text{So the sum matches the overall reaction.}$$

CH_3NC^* is the activated molecule. Because the second step is the rate-determining step, Rate $= k_3[CH_3NC^*]$. Because CH_3NC^* is an intermediate, its concentration cannot appear in the rate law. Using the fast equilibrium in the first step, we see that $k_1[CH_3NC]^2 = k_2[CH_3NC^*][CH_3NC]$ or $[CH_3NC^*] = \dfrac{k_1}{k_2}[CH_3NC]$. Substituting this into the first rate expression, we get Rate $= k_3 \dfrac{k_1}{k_2}[CH_3NC]$, which simplifies to Rate $= k[CH_3NC]$.

This matches the experimental observation of first order, and the mechanism is valid.

13.88   (a)   Rate $= k[A]^{1/2}$ and Rate $= -\dfrac{d[A]}{dt}$, so $\dfrac{d[A]}{dt} = -k[A]^{1/2}$. Moving the A terms to the left and the t and constants to the right, we have $\dfrac{d[A]}{[A]^{1/2}} = -kdt$. Integrating, we get $\displaystyle\int_{[A]_0}^{[A]} \dfrac{d[A]}{[A]^{1/2}} = -\int_0^t kdt$. When we evaluate this integral, $2[A]^{1/2}\Big|_{[A]_0}^{[A]} = -kt\Big|_0^t \rightarrow 2[A]_t^{1/2} - 2[A]_0^{1/2} = -kt \rightarrow 2[A]_t^{1/2} = -kt + 2[A]_0^{1/2}$, which is the desired integrated rate law.

       (b)   To derive the half-life, set $[A]_t = 1/2[A]_0$. Substituting this into $2[A]_t^{1/2} = -kt + 2[A]_0^{1/2}$, we get

$$2(1/2[A]_0)^{1/2} = -kt_{1/2} + 2[A]_0^{1/2} \rightarrow t_{1/2} = \frac{2[A]_0^{1/2} - 2(1/2[A]_0)^{1/2}}{k} \rightarrow t_{1/2} = \frac{(2 - 2\sqrt{2})[A]_0^{1/2}}{k}.$$

13.89   Rate $= k[A]^2$ and Rate $= -\dfrac{d[A]}{dt}$, so $\dfrac{d[A]}{dt} = -k[A]^2$. Moving the A terms to the left and the t and constants to the right, we have $\dfrac{d[A]}{[A]^2} = -kdt$. Integrating, we get $\displaystyle\int_{[A]_0}^{[A]} \dfrac{d[A]}{[A]^2} = -\int_0^t kdt$. When we evaluate this integral, $-[A]^{-1}\Big|_{[A]_0}^{[A]} = -kt\Big|_0^t \rightarrow -[A]_t^{-1} - (-[A]_0^{-1}) = -kt \rightarrow [A]_t^{-1} = kt + [A]_0^{-1}$ or $\dfrac{1}{[A]_t} = kt + \dfrac{1}{[A]_0}$, which is the desired integrated rate law.

13.90   (a)   **Given:** N_2O_5 decomposes to NO_2 and O_2, first order in $[N_2O_5]$; $k = 7.48 \times 10^{-3}$ s^{-1}; $P^\circ_{N_2O_5} = 0.100$ atm

         Find: t to $P_{Total} = 0.145$ atm

         Conceptual Plan: Write a balanced reaction. Then

$$N_2O_5 \rightarrow 2\,NO_2 + \frac{1}{2}O_2$$

         Then write the expression for P_{Total} in terms of amount reacted then x, $P^\circ_{N_2O_5}, k \rightarrow t$

         let $x = P_{N_2O_5 \text{ reacted}}$ $P_{Total} = P_{N_2O_5} + P_{NO_2} + P_{O_2}$ $\ln[A]_t = -kt + \ln[A]_0$

         Solution: $P_{Total} = P_{N_2O_5} + P_{NO_2} + P_{O_2} = (0.100 \text{ atm} - x) + (2x) + (1/2x) = 0.100 \text{ atm} + 1.5\,x$

         Set $P_{Total} = 0.145$ atm $= 0.100$ atm $+ 1.5\,x$ and solve for x. Note that for every one mole of reactant decomposing, 2.5 moles of product are generated; so the pressure increases by a factor of 1.5.

$$x = \frac{0.145 \text{ atm} - 0.100 \text{ atm}}{1.5} = 0.030 \text{ atm}$$

         then $P_{N_2O_5} = 0.100$ atm $- x = 0.100$ atm $- 0.030$ atm $= 0.070$ atm. Because $P \propto n/V$ or M,

         $\ln[N_2O_5]_t = -kt + \ln[N_2O_5]_0$. Rearrange to solve for t.

$$t = -\frac{\ln\dfrac{[N_2O_5]_t}{[N_2O_5]_0}}{k} = -\frac{\ln\left(\dfrac{0.070 \cancel{\text{ atm}}}{0.100 \cancel{\text{ atm}}}\right)}{7.48 \times 10^{-3} \text{ s}^{-1}} = 47.684 \text{ s} = 48 \text{ s}$$

         Check: The units (s) are correct. The time is reasonable because it is less than one half-life and the amount decomposing is less than 50%.

(b) **Given:** N_2O_5 decomposes to NO_2 and O_2, first order $[N_2O_5]$; $k = 7.48 \times 10^{-3} \text{ s}^{-1}$; $P^\circ_{N_2O_5} = 0.100$ atm
Find: t to $P_{Total} = 0.200$ atm
Conceptual Plan: Write a balanced reaction.

$$N_2O_5 \rightarrow 2\,NO_2 + \frac{1}{2}O_2$$

Then write the expression for P_{Total} in terms of amount reacted then x, $P^\circ_{N_2O_5}$, $k \rightarrow t$

let $x = P_{N_2O_5 \text{ reacted}}$ $P_{Total} = P_{N_2O_5} + P_{NO_2} + P_{O_2}$ $\ln[A]_t = -kt + \ln[A]_0$

Solution: $P_{Total} = P_{N_2O_5} + P_{NO_2} + P_{O_2} = (0.100 \text{ atm} - x) + (2x) + (1/2x) = 0.100 \text{ atm} + 1.5x$

$P_{Total} = 0.200 \text{ atm} = 0.100 \text{ atm} + 1.5x$. Solve for x. $x = \dfrac{0.200 \text{ atm} - 0.100 \text{ atm}}{1.5} = 0.066667$ atm

then $P_{N_2O_5} = 0.100 \text{ atm} - x = 0.100 \text{ atm} - 0.066667 \text{ atm} = 0.033333$ atm. Because $P \propto n/V$ or M,
$\ln[N_2O_5]_t = -kt + \ln[N_2O_5]_0$. Rearrange to solve for t.

$$t = -\dfrac{\ln \dfrac{[N_2O_5]_t}{[N_2O_5]_0}}{k} = -\dfrac{\ln \left(\dfrac{0.033333 \text{ atm}}{0.100 \text{ atm}} \right)}{7.48 \times 10^{-3} \text{ s}^{-1}} = 146.875 \text{ s} = 150 \text{ s} = 1.5 \times 10^2 \text{ s}$$

Check: The units (s) are correct. The time is reasonable because it is between one and two half-lives and the amount decomposing is 67%.

(c) **Given:** N_2O_5 decomposes to NO_2 and O_2, first order in $[N_2O_5]$; $k = 7.48 \times 10^{-3} \text{ s}^{-1}$; $P^\circ_{N_2O_5} = 0.100$ atm
Find: P_{Total} after 100 s
Conceptual Plan: $P^\circ_{N_2O_5}, k, t \rightarrow P^\circ_{N_2O_5}$ **then write a balanced reaction. Then** $P^\circ_{N_2O_5}, P_{N_2O_5} \rightarrow x$ **then**

$\ln[A]_t = -kt + \ln[A]_0$. $N_2O_5 \rightarrow 2\,NO_2 + \frac{1}{2}O_2$ $x = P^\circ_{N_2O_5} - P_{N_2O_5}$

write the expression for P_{Total} in terms of amount reacted

let $x = P_{N_2O_5 \text{ reacted}}$ $P_{Total} = P_{N_2O_5} + P_{NO_2} + P_{O_2}$

Solution: Because $P \propto n/V$ or M,
$\ln[N_2O_5]_t = -kt + \ln[N_2O_5]_0 = -(7.48 \times 10^{-3} \text{ s}^{-1})(100 \text{ s}) + \ln(0.100 \text{ atm}) = -3.05059$
$P_{N_2O_5} = e^{-3.05059} = 0.0473310$ atm so
$x = P^\circ_{N_2O_5} - P_{N_2O_5} = 0.100 \text{ atm} - 0.0473310 \text{ atm} = 0.052669$ atm
finally $P_{Total} = P_{N_2O_5} + P_{NO_2} + P_{O_2} = (0.100 \text{ atm} - x) + (2x) + (1/2x) = 0.100 \text{ atm} + 1.5x = 0.100 \text{ atm} + 1.5(0.052669 \text{ atm}) = 0.179$ atm

Check: The units (atm) are correct. The pressure is reasonable because the time is between those for parts (a) and (b).

13.91 For this mechanism, the overall reaction is the sum of the steps in the mechanism:

$$Cl_2(g) \underset{k_2}{\overset{k_1}{\rightleftharpoons}} 2\,Cl(g)$$

$$\cancel{Cl(g)} + CO(g) \underset{k_4}{\overset{k_3}{\rightleftharpoons}} \cancel{ClCO(g)}$$

$$\underline{\cancel{ClCO(g)} + Cl_2(g) \overset{k_5}{\rightarrow} Cl_2CO(g) + Cl(g)}$$

$$CO(g) + 2\,Cl_2(g) \rightarrow Cl_2CO(g) + 2\,Cl(g)$$

No overall reaction is given. Because the third step is the rate-determining step, Rate $= k_5 [ClCO][Cl_2]$. Because ClCO is an intermediate, its concentration cannot appear in the rate law. Using the fast equilibrium in the second step, we see that $k_3[Cl][CO] = k_4[ClCO]$ or $[ClCO] = \dfrac{k_3}{k_4}[Cl][CO]$. Substituting this expression into the first rate expression, we get Rate $= k_5 \dfrac{k_3}{k_4}[Cl][CO][Cl_2]$. Because Cl is an intermediate, its concentration cannot appear in the rate law. Using the fast equilibrium in the first step, we see that $k_1[Cl_2] = k_2[Cl]^2$ or $[Cl] = \sqrt{\dfrac{k_1}{k_2}}[Cl_2]$. Substituting this expression into the last first rate expression, we get Rate $= k_5 \dfrac{k_3}{k_4}\sqrt{\dfrac{k_1}{k_2}}[Cl_2][CO][Cl_2] = k_5 \dfrac{k_3}{k_4}\sqrt{\dfrac{k_1}{k_2}}[CO][Cl_2]^{3/2}$.

Simplifying this expression, we see Rate $= k[CO][Cl_2]^{3/2}$.

13.92   **Given:** N_2O_3 decomposes to NO_2 and NO, first order in $[N_2O_3]$, table of $[NO_2]$ versus time, at 50,000 s = $[N_2O_3]$ = 0   **Find:** k

       Conceptual Plan: Write a balanced reaction. Then write the expression for $[NO_2]$ in terms $[N_2O_3]$, then

$$N_2O_3 \rightarrow NO_2 + NO \qquad\qquad [N_2O_3] = 0.784\ M - [NO_2]$$

       plot $\ln[N_2O_3]$ versus time. Because $\ln[A]_t = -kt + \ln[A]_0$, the negative of the slope will be the rate constant.

       Solution: $[N_2O_3] = 0.784\ M - [NO_2]$

       Plot $\ln[N_2O_3]$ versus time. Because $\ln[A]_t = -kt + \ln[A]_0$, the negative of the slope will be the rate constant. The slope can be determined by measuring $\Delta y/\Delta x$ on the plot or by using functions such as "add trendline" in Excel. The last point (50,000 s) cannot be plotted because the concentration is 0 and the ln 0 is undefined. Thus, the rate constant is $3.20 \times 10^{-4}\ \text{s}^{-1}$, and the rate law is Rate = $3.20 \times 10^{-4}\ \text{s}^{-1}[N_2O_3]$.

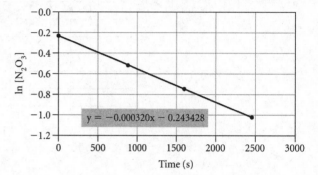

       Check: The units (s^{-1}) are correct. The rate constant is typical for a reaction.

13.93   For the elementary reaction $2\ NOCl(g) \underset{k_{-1}}{\overset{k_1}{\rightleftharpoons}} 2\ NO(g) + Cl_2(g)$, we see that $k_1[NOCl]^2 = k_{-1}[NO]^2[Cl_2]$.

       For each mole of NOCl that reacts, one mole of NO and one-half mole of Cl_2 are generated. Because before any reaction only NOCl is present, $[NO] = 2[Cl_2]$. Substituting this into the first expression, we get $k_1[NOCl]^2 = k_{-1}(2[Cl_2])^2[Cl_2] \rightarrow k_1[NOCl]^2 = 4k_{-1}[Cl_2]^3$. Rearranging and substituting the specific values into this expression, we get

$$[Cl_2] = \sqrt[3]{\frac{k_1}{4k_{-1}}}\,[NOCl]^{2/3} = \sqrt[3]{\frac{7.8 \times 10^{-2}\,\frac{L^2}{mol^2 \cdot s}}{4\left(4.7 \times 10^2\,\frac{L^2}{mol \cdot s}\right)}}\left(0.12\,\frac{mol}{L}\right)^{2/3} = 0.008\underline{4}2235\,\frac{mol}{L}\,Cl_2$$

$$= 0.0084\ M\ Cl_2\ \text{and}\ [NO] = 2[Cl_2] = 2\left(0.008\underline{4}2235\,\frac{mol}{L}\right) = 0.016\underline{8}445\,\frac{mol}{L}\,NO = 0.017\ M\ NO$$

Conceptual Problems

13.94   Because Rate = $k\,[CHCl_3][Cl_2]^{1/2}$, Rate a = $k(3)(3)^{1/2}$ = 5.2 k, Rate b = $k(4)(2)^{1/2}$ = 5.7 k, and Rate c = $k(2)(4)^{1/2}$ = 4k. So b has the fastest rate.

13.95   Reactant concentrations drop more quickly for first-order reactions than for second-order reactions, so reaction A must be second order. A plot of $1/[A]$ versus time will be linear $\left(\dfrac{1}{[A]_t} = kt + \dfrac{1}{[A]_0}\right)$. Reaction B is first order. A plot of $\ln[A]$ versus time will be linear ($\ln[A]_t = -kt + \ln[A]_0$).

13.96   A reaction that slows down as the reaction proceeds and has a half-life that is dependent on the concentration is a second-order reaction. Statement (a) is false because it describes a first-order reaction. Statement (b) is true because it describes a second-order reaction. Statements (c) and (d) are false because they describe a zero-order reaction.

Questions for Group Work

13.97   It is very tempting to think that the same descriptor that relates the concentration change to the rate change is the order of the reaction. This statement is incorrect, because the reaction order is first order. For a first-order reaction, Rate = $k[A]^1$, so doubling the concentration of A doubles the reaction rate. For a second-order reaction, Rate = $k[A]^2$, so doubling the concentration of A quadruples the reaction rate ($2^2 = 4$).

13.98   For [A] versus t:

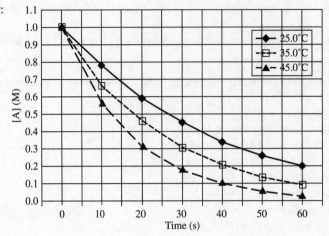

For ln[A] versus t:

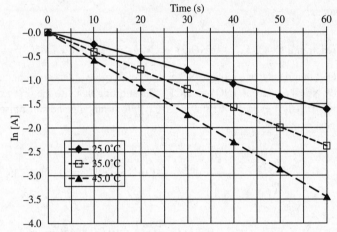

For 1/[A] versus t:

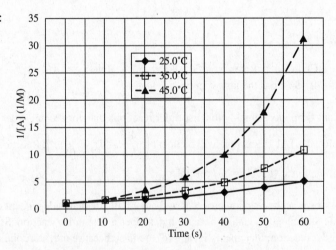

Since the plot of ln[A] versus t is the only linear plot, the reaction is first order.

13.99   Using Excel, the slope is the negative of the rate constant ($\ln[A]_t = -kt + \ln[A]_0$). The rate constants are 0.2711 s^{-1}, 0.3959 s^{-1}, and 0.5728 s^{-1}, for 25.0 °C, 35.0 °C, and 45.0 °C, respectively.

13.100   Since $\ln k = \dfrac{-E_a}{R}\left(\dfrac{1}{T}\right) + \ln A$ a plot of $\ln k$ versus $1/T$ will have a slope $= -E_a/R$ and an intercept $= \ln A$.

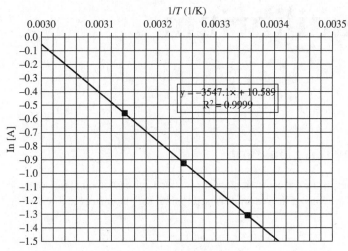

Since the slope $= -3547.1 \ K = -E_a/R$ then

$$E_a = -(-3547.1 \ K)\left(8.314 \ \dfrac{J}{K \cdot mol}\right)\left(\dfrac{1 \ kJ}{1000 \ J}\right) = 29.5 \ \dfrac{kJ}{mol}$$

13.101   A catalyst will speed up a reaction by reducing the activation energy. The reaction is still first order, as seen by the linear plots of ln[A] versus t.

Using Excel, the slope is the negative of the rate constant ($\ln[A]_t = -kt + \ln[A]_0$). The rate constants are 3.246 s^{-1}, 4.215 s^{-1}, and 5.269 s^{-1}, for 25.0 °C, 35.0 °C, and 45.0 °C, respectively.

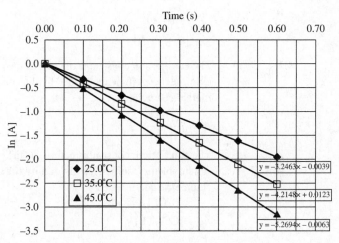

Since $\ln k = \dfrac{-E_a}{R}\left(\dfrac{1}{T}\right) + \ln A$ a plot of $\ln k$ versus $1/T$ will have a slope $= -E_a/R$ and an intercept $= \ln A$.

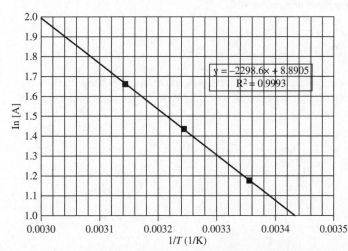

Since the slope $= -2298.6 \ K = -E_a/R$ then

$$E_a = -(-2298.6 \ K)\left(8.314 \ \dfrac{J}{K \cdot mol}\right)\left(\dfrac{1 \ kJ}{1000 \ J}\right)$$

$$= 19.1 \ \dfrac{kJ}{mol}$$

The activation energy has been cut by about a third by adding a catalyst.

14 Chemical Equilibrium

Problems by Topic

Equilibrium and the Equilibrium Constant

14.1 The equilibrium constant is defined as the concentrations of the products raised to their stoichiometric coefficients divided by the concentrations of the reactants raised to their stoichiometric coefficients.

(a) $K = \dfrac{[SbCl_3][Cl_2]}{[SbCl_5]}$

(b) $K = \dfrac{[NO]^2[Br_2]}{[BrNO]^2}$

(c) $K = \dfrac{[CS_2][H_2]^4}{[CH_4][H_2S]^2}$

(d) $K = \dfrac{[CO_2]^2}{[CO]^2[O_2]}$

14.2 (a) The equilibrium constant is defined as the concentrations of the products **raised to their stoichiometric coefficients** divided by the concentrations of the reactants **raised to their stoichiometric coefficients**.

$K = \dfrac{[H_2]^2[S_2]}{[H_2S]^2}$

(b) The equilibrium constant is defined as the **concentrations of the products** raised to their stoichiometric coefficients **divided by the concentrations of the reactants** raised to their stoichiometric coefficients.

$K = \dfrac{[COCl_2]}{[CO][Cl_2]}$

14.3 With an equilibrium constant of 1.4×10^{-5}, the value of the equilibrium constant is small; therefore, the concentration of reactants will be greater than the concentration of products. This is independent of the initial concentration of the reactants and products.

14.4 Figure a at equilibrium has 8 $C_2H_4Cl_2$, 2 Cl_2, and 2 C_2H_4.
Figure b at equilibrium has 6 $C_2H_4Br_2$, 4 Br_2, and 4 C_2H_4.
Figure c at equilibrium has 3 $C_2H_4I_2$, 7 I_2, and 7 C_2H_4.
Because the equilibrium constant is concentration of products/concentration of reactants, the equilibrium situation that has the largest concentration of products will have the largest equilibrium constant. Therefore, $K_{Cl_2} > K_{Br_2} > K_{I_2}$.

14.5 (i) has 10 H_2 and 10 I_2
(ii) has 7 H_2 and 7 I_2 and 6 HI
(iii) has 5 H_2 and 5 I_2 and 10 HI
(iv) has 4 H_2 and 4 I_2 and 12 HI
(v) has 3 H_2 and 3 I_2 and 14 HI
(vi) has 3 H_2 and 3 I_2 and 14 HI

(a) Concentrations of (v) and (vi) are the same, so the system reached equilibrium at (v).

(b) If a catalyst was added to the system, the system would reach the conditions at (v) sooner because a catalyst speeds up the reaction but does not change the equilibrium conditions.

(c) The final figure (vi) would have the same amount of reactants and products because a catalyst speeds up the reaction but does not change the equilibrium concentrations.

14.6 The equilibrium constant gives us the ratio of products to reactants at equilibrium; it does not say how long it takes to reach equilibrium. So after 15 minutes, if the smaller equilibrium constant has more products, the kinetics of that reaction are faster.

14.7 (a) If you reverse the reaction, invert the equilibrium constant. So $K' = \dfrac{1}{K_p} = \dfrac{1}{2.26 \times 10^4} = 4.42 \times 10^{-5}$.

The reactants will be favored.

(b) If you multiply the coefficients in the equation by a factor, raise the equilibrium constant to the same factor. So $K' = (K_p)^{1/2} = (2.26 \times 10^4)^{1/2} = 1.50 \times 10^2$. The products will be favored.

(c) Begin with the reverse of the reaction and invert the equilibrium constant.

$$K_{reverse} = \frac{1}{K_p} = \frac{1}{2.26 \times 10^4} = 4.42 \times 10^{-5}$$

Then multiply the reaction by 2 and raise the value of $K_{reverse}$ to the second power.
$K' = (K_{reverse})^2 = (4.42 \times 10^{-5})^2 = 1.95 \times 10^{-9}$. The reactants will be favored.

14.8 (a) The reaction is multiplied by 1/2, so raise the value of the equilibrium constant to 1/2.
$K' = (K_p)^{1/2} = (2.2 \times 10^6)^{1/2} = 1.5 \times 10^3$. The products will be favored.

(b) The reaction is multiplied by 3, so raise the value of the equilibrium constant to 3.
$K' = (K_p)^3 = (2.2 \times 10^6)^3 = 1.1 \times 10^{19}$. The products will be favored.

(c) Begin with the reverse of the reaction and invert the equilibrium constant.

$$K_{reverse} = \frac{1}{K_p} = \frac{1}{2.2 \times 10^6} = 4.5 \times 10^{-7}$$

Then multiply the reaction by 2 and raise the value of $K_{reverse}$ to the second power.
$K' = (K_{reverse})^2 = (4.5 \times 10^{-7})^2 = 2.0 \times 10^{-13}$. The reactants will be favored.

14.9 To find the equilibrium constant for reaction 3, you need to combine reactions 1 and 2 to get reaction 3. Begin by reversing reaction 2; then multiply reaction 1 by 2 and add the two new reactions. When you add reactions, you multiply the values of K.

$N_2(g) + O_2(g) \rightleftharpoons 2\,\cancel{NO}(g)$ $\qquad K_1 = \dfrac{1}{K_p} = \dfrac{1}{2.1 \times 10^{30}} = 4.\underline{7}6 \times 10^{-31}$

$2\,\cancel{NO}(g) + Br_2(g) \rightleftharpoons 2\,NOBr(g)$ $\qquad K_2 = (K_p)^2 = (5.3)^2 = 28.\underline{0}9$

$N_2(g) + O_2(g) + Br_2(g) \rightleftharpoons 2\,NOBr(g)$ $\qquad K_3 = K_1 K_2 = (4.\underline{7}6 \times 10^{-31})(28.\underline{0}9) = 1.3 \times 10^{-29}$

14.10 To find the equilibrium constant for reaction 3, you need to combine reactions 1 and 2 to get reaction 3. Begin by multiplying reaction 1 by 2; then reverse reaction 2 and add the two new reactions. When you add reactions, you multiply the values of K.

$2\,A(s) \rightleftharpoons B(g) + 2\,\cancel{C}(g)$ $\qquad K_1 = (K_p)^2 = (0.0334)^2 = 1.1 \times 10^{-3}$

$B(g) + 2\,\cancel{C}(g) \rightleftharpoons 3\,D(g)$ $\qquad K_2 = \dfrac{1}{K_p} = \dfrac{1}{2.35} = 0.426$

$2\,A(s) \rightleftharpoons 3D(g)$ $\qquad K' = K_1 K_2 = (1.1 \times 10^{-3})(0.426) = 4.69 \times 10^{-4}$

K_p, K_c, and Heterogeneous Equilibria

14.11 (a) **Given:** $K_p = 6.26 \times 10^{-22}$ $\quad T = 298$ K $\quad$ **Find:** K_c

Conceptual Plan: $K_p \rightarrow K_c$
$$K_p = K_c(RT)^{\Delta n}$$

Solution: $\Delta n = $ mol product gas $-$ mol reactant gas $= 2 - 1 = 1$

$$K_c = \frac{K_p}{(RT)^{\Delta n}} = \frac{6.26 \times 10^{-22}}{\left(0.08206 \ \frac{L \cdot atm}{mol \cdot K} \times 298 \ K\right)^1} = 2.56 \times 10^{-23}$$

Check: Substitute into the equation and confirm that you get the original value of K_p.

$$K_p = K_c(RT)^{\Delta n} = (2.56 \times 10^{-23})\left(0.08206 \ \frac{L \cdot atm}{mol \cdot K} \times 298 \ K\right)^1 = 6.26 \times 10^{-22}$$

(b) **Given:** $K_p = 7.7 \times 10^{24}$ $T = 298 \ K$ **Find:** K_c
   Conceptual Plan: $K_p \rightarrow K_c$

$$K_p = K_c(RT)^{\Delta n}$$

   Solution: $\Delta n = $ mol product gas $-$ mol reactant gas $= 4 - 2 = 2$

$$K_c = \frac{K_p}{(RT)^{\Delta n}} = \frac{7.7 \times 10^{24}}{\left(0.08206 \ \frac{L \cdot atm}{mol \cdot K} \times 298 \ K\right)^2} = 1.3 \times 10^{22}$$

   Check: Substitute into the equation and confirm that you get the original value of K_p.

$$K_p = K_c(RT)^{\Delta n} = (1.3 \times 10^{22})\left(0.08206 \ \frac{L \cdot atm}{mol \cdot K} \times 298 \ K\right)^2 = 7.7 \times 10^{24}$$

(c) **Given:** $K_p = 81.9$ $T = 298 \ K$ **Find:** K_c
   Conceptual Plan: $K_p \rightarrow K_c$

$$K_p = K_c(RT)^{\Delta n}$$

   Solution: $\Delta n = $ mol product gas $-$ mol reactant gas $= 2 - 2 = 0$

$$K_c = \frac{K_p}{(RT)^{\Delta n}} = \frac{81.9}{\left(0.08206 \ \frac{L \cdot atm}{mol \cdot K} \times 298 \ K\right)^0} = 81.9$$

   Check: Substitute into the equation and confirm that you get the original value of K_p.

$$K_p = K_c(RT)^{\Delta n} = (81.9)\left(0.08206 \ \frac{L \cdot atm}{mol \cdot K} \times 298 \ K\right)^0 = 81.9$$

14.12 (a) **Given:** $K_c = 5.9 \times 10^{-3}$ $T = 298 \ K$ **Find:** K_p
   Conceptual Plan: $K_p \rightarrow K_c$

$$K_p = K_c(RT)^{\Delta n}$$

   Solution: $\Delta n = $ mol product gas $-$ mol reactant gas $= 2 - 1 = 1$

$$K_p = K_c(RT)^{\Delta n} = 5.9 \times 10^{-3}\left(0.08206 \ \frac{L \cdot atm}{mol \cdot K} \times 298 \ K\right)^1 = 1.4 \times 10^{-1}$$

   Check: Substitute into the equation and confirm that you get the original value of K_p.

$$K_c = \frac{K_p}{(RT)^{\Delta n}} = \frac{1.4 \times 10^{-1}}{\left(0.08206 \ \frac{L \cdot atm}{mol \cdot K} \times 298 \ K\right)^1} = 0.0059$$

(b) **Given:** $K_c = 3.7 \times 10^8$ $T = 298 \ K$ **Find:** K_p
   Conceptual Plan: $K_p \rightarrow K_c$

$$K_p = K_c(RT)^{\Delta n}$$

   Solution: $\Delta n = $ mol product gas $-$ mol reactant gas $= 2 - 4 = -2$

$$K_p = K_c(RT)^{\Delta n} = 3.7 \times 10^8\left(0.08206 \ \frac{L \cdot atm}{mol \cdot K} \times 298 \ K\right)^{-2} = 6.2 \times 10^5$$

   Check: Substitute into the equation and confirm that you get the original value of K_p.

$$K_c = \frac{K_p}{(RT)^{\Delta n}} = \frac{6.2 \times 10^5}{\left(0.08206 \ \frac{L \cdot atm}{mol \cdot K} \times 298 \ K\right)^{-2}} = 3.7 \times 10^8$$

(c) **Given:** $K_c = 4.10 \times 10^{-31}$ $T = 298$ K   **Find:** K_p

Conceptual Plan: $K_p \rightarrow K_c$

$$K_p = K_c(RT)^{\Delta n}$$

Solution: $\Delta n = $ mol product gas $-$ mol reactant gas $= 2 - 2 = 0$

$$K_p = K_c(RT)^{\Delta n} = 4.10 \times 10^{-31}\left(0.08206 \frac{L \cdot atm}{mol \cdot K} \times 298 \, K\right)^0 = 4.10 \times 10^{-31}$$

Check: Substitute into the equation and confirm that you get the original value of K_p.

$$K_c = \frac{K_p}{(RT)^{\Delta n}} = \frac{4.10 \times 10^{-31}}{\left(0.08206 \dfrac{L \cdot atm}{mol \cdot K} \times 298 \, K\right)^0} = 4.10 \times 10^{-31}$$

14.13   (a)   Because H_2O is a liquid, it is omitted from the equilibrium expression. $K_{eq} = \dfrac{[HCO_3^-][OH^-]}{[CO_3^{2-}]}$

(b)   Because $KClO_3$ and KCl are both solids, they are omitted from the equilibrium expression. $K_{eq} = [O_2]^3$

(c)   Because H_2O is a liquid, it is omitted from the equilibrium expression. $K_{eq} = \dfrac{[H_3O^+][F^-]}{[HF]}$

(d)   Because H_2O is a liquid, it is omitted from the equilibrium expression. $K_{eq} = \dfrac{[NH_4^+][OH^-]}{[NH_3]}$

14.14   Because PCl_3 is a liquid, it is omitted from the equilibrium expression. $K_{eq} = \dfrac{[Cl_2]}{[PCl_5]}$

Relating the Equilibrium Constant to Equilibrium Concentrations and Equilibrium Partial Pressures

14.15   **Given:** at equilibrium: $[CO] = 0.105$ M, $[H_2] = 0.114$ M, $[CH_3OH] = 0.185$ M   **Find:** K_c

Conceptual Plan: Balanced reaction $\rightarrow$ equilibrium expression $\rightarrow$ K_c

Solution: $K_c = \dfrac{[CH_3OH]}{[CO][H_2]^2} = \dfrac{(0.185)}{(0.105)(0.114)^2} = 136$

Check: The answer is reasonable because the concentration of products is greater than the concentration of reactants and the equilibrium constant should be greater than 1.

14.16   **Given:** at equilibrium: $[NH_3] = 0.278$ M, $[H_2S] = 0.355$ M   **Find:** K_c

Conceptual Plan: Balanced reaction $\rightarrow$ equilibrium expression $\rightarrow$ K_c

Solution: Because NH_4HS is a solid, it is omitted from the equilibrium expression.

$K_c = [NH_3][H_2S] = (0.278)(0.355) = 0.0987$

Check: The answer is reasonable because the concentration of products is less than 1 M and the equilibrium constant is less than 1.

14.17   At 500 K: **Given:** at equilibrium: $[N_2] = 0.115$ M, $[H_2] = 0.105$ M, and $[NH_3] = 0.439$ M   **Find:** K_c

Conceptual Plan: Balanced reaction $\rightarrow$ equilibrium expression $\rightarrow$ K_c

Solution: $K_c = \dfrac{[NH_3]^2}{[N_2][H_2]^3} = \dfrac{(0.439)^2}{(0.115)(0.105)^3} = 1.45 \times 10^3$

Check: The value is reasonable because the concentration of products is greater than the concentration of reactants.

At 575 K: **Given:** at equilibrium: $[N_2] = 0.110$ M, $[NH_3] = 0.128$ M, $K_c = 9.6$ **Find:** $[H_2]$

Conceptual Plan: Balanced reaction $\rightarrow$ equilibrium expression $\rightarrow$ $[H_2]$

Solution: $K_c = \dfrac{[NH_3]^2}{[N_2][H_2]^3}$ $9.6 = \dfrac{(0.128)^2}{(0.110)(x)^3}$ $x = 0.249$ M

Check: Plug the value for x back into the equilibrium expression and check the value.

$$9.6 = \frac{(0.128)^2}{(0.110)(0.249)^3}$$

At 775 K: Given: at equilibrium: $[N_2] = 0.120$ M, $[H_2] = 0.140$ M, $K_c = 0.0584$ **Find:** $[NH_3]$
Conceptual Plan: Balanced reaction → equilibrium expression → $[NH_3]$

Solution: $K_c = \dfrac{[NH_3]^2}{[N_2][H_2]^3}$ $0.0584 = \dfrac{(x)^2}{(0.120)(0.140)^3}$ $x = 0.00439$ M

Check: Plug the value for x back into the equilibrium expression and check the value.

$$0.0584 = \frac{(0.00439)^2}{(0.120)(0.140)^3}$$

14.18   **At 25 °C: Given:** at equilibrium: $[H_2] = 0.0355$ M, $[I_2] = 0.0388$ M, and $[HI] = 0.922$ M   **Find:** K_c
Conceptual Plan: Balanced reaction → equilibrium expression → K_c

Solution: $K_c = \dfrac{[HI]^2}{[H_2][I_2]} = \dfrac{(0.922)^2}{(0.0355)(0.0388)} = 617$

Check: The value is reasonable because the concentration of products is greater than the concentration of reactants.

At 340 °C: Given: at equilibrium: $[I_2] = 0.0455$ M, $[HI] = 0.387$ M, $K_c = 9.6$ **Find:** $[H_2]$
Conceptual Plan: Balanced reaction → equilibrium expression → $[H_2]$

Solution: $K_c = \dfrac{[HI]^2}{[H_2][I_2]}$ $9.6 = \dfrac{(0.387)^2}{(x)(0.0455)}$ $x = 0.343$ M

Check: Plug the value for x back into the equilibrium expression and check the value.

$$9.6 = \frac{(0.387)^2}{(0.343)(0.0455)}$$

At 445 °C: Given: at equilibrium: $[H_2] = 0.0485$ M, $[I_2] = 0.0468$ M, $K_c = 50.2$ **Find:** $[HI]$
Conceptual Plan: Balanced reaction → equilibrium expression → $[HI]$

Solution: $K_c = \dfrac{[HI]^2}{[H_2][I_2]}$ $50.2 = \dfrac{(x)^2}{(0.0485)(0.0468)}$ $x = 0.338$ M

Check: Plug the value for x back into the equilibrium expression and check the value.

$$50.2 = \frac{(0.338)^2}{(0.0485)(0.0468)}$$

14.19   **Given:** $P_{NO} = 118$ torr; $P_{Br_2} = 176$ torr, $K_p = 28.4$ **Find:** P_{NOBr}
Conceptual Plan: torr → atm and then balanced reaction → equilibrium expression → P_{NOBr}

$$\frac{1 \text{ atm}}{760 \text{ torr}}$$

Solution: $P_{NO} = 118 \text{ torr} \times \dfrac{1 \text{ atm}}{760 \text{ torr}} = 0.155\underline{3}$ atm $P_{Br_2} = 176 \text{ torr} \times \dfrac{1 \text{ atm}}{760 \text{ torr}} = 0.231\underline{6}$ atm

$K_p = \dfrac{P_{NOBr}^2}{P_{NO}^2 P_{Br_2}}$ $28.4 = \dfrac{x^2}{(0.155\underline{3})^2(0.231\underline{6})}$ $x = 0.398 \text{ atm} = 303$ torr

Check: Plug the value for x back into the equilibrium expression and check the value.

$$28.4 = \frac{(0.398)^2}{(0.155\underline{3})^2(0.231\underline{6})}$$

14.20   **Given:** $P_{SO_2} = 117$ torr; $P_{Cl_2} = 255$ torr, $K_p = 2.91 \times 10^3$ **Find:** $P_{SO_2Cl_2}$
Conceptual Plan: torr → atm and then balanced reaction → equilibrium expression → $P_{SO_2Cl_2}$

$$\frac{1 \text{ atm}}{760 \text{ torr}}$$

Solution: $P_{SO_2} = 117 \text{ torr} \times \dfrac{1 \text{ atm}}{760 \text{ torr}} = 0.15\underline{3}9 \text{ atm}$ $P_{Cl_2} = 255 \text{ torr} \times \dfrac{1 \text{ atm}}{760 \text{ torr}} = 0.23\underline{1}6 \text{ atm}$

$$K_p = \frac{P_{SO_2} P_{Cl_2}}{P_{SO_2Cl_2}} \qquad 2.91 \times 10^3 = \frac{(0.15\underline{3}9)(0.33\underline{5}5)}{(x)} \qquad x = 1.77 \times 10^{-5} \text{ atm} = 0.0135 \text{ torr}$$

Check: Plug the value for x back into the equilibrium expression and check the value.

$$2.92 \times 10^3 = \frac{(0.15\underline{3}9)(0.33\underline{5}5)}{(1.77 \times 10^{-5})}$$

14.21   **Given:** $P_{A, \text{ initial}} = 1.32 \text{ atm}$; $P_{A, \text{ eq}} = 0.25 \text{ atm}$ **Find:** K_p

       Conceptual Plan: **1. Prepare Initial, Change, and Equil (ICE) table.**
                                2. Calculate pressure change for known value.
                                3. Calculate pressure changes for other reactants/products.
                                4. Determine equilibrium pressures.
                                5. Write the equilibrium expression and determine K_p.

       Solution: $A(g) \rightleftharpoons 2B(g)$

	P_A	P_B
Initial	1.32 atm	0.00
Change	$-x$	$+2x$
Equil	0.25 atm	$2x$

$$x = 1.32 - 0.25 = 1.07 \text{ atm}$$
$$2x = 2(1.07 \text{ atm}) = 2.14 \text{ atm} = P_B$$
$$K_p = \frac{P_B^2}{P_A} = \frac{(2.14)^2}{(0.25)} = 1\underline{8}.32 = 18$$

14.22   By definition, K_p must be based on partial pressures in atm, not mmHg, and the different units result in different values for K_p. Change the work as shown below:

       Conceptual Plan: **1. Convert partial pressures in torr $\rightarrow$ atm.**
                                2. Prepare Initial, Change, and Equil (ICE) table.
                                3. Calculate pressure change for known value.
                                4. Calculate pressure changes for other reactant/products.
                                5. Determine equilibrium pressures.
                                6. Write the equilibrium expression and determine K_p.

       Solution: $P_A = 255 \text{ mmHg} \times \dfrac{1 \text{ atm}}{760 \text{ mmHg}} = 0.33\underline{5}5 \text{ atm}$

$$P_{A,\text{eq}} = 55 \text{ mmHg} \times \frac{1 \text{ atm}}{760 \text{ mmHg}} = 0.072\underline{3}7 \text{ atm}$$

$$2 A(g) \rightarrow B(g) + 2 C(g)$$

	P_A	P_B	P_C
Initial	0.336 atm	0.00	0.00
Change	$-2x$	$+x$	$+2x$
Equil	0.0724 atm	x	$2x$

$$2x = 0.336 - 0.0724 = 0.26\underline{3}6 \text{ atm} = P_C; \quad x = 0.13\underline{1}8 \text{ atm} = P_B$$

$$K_P = \frac{(0.13\underline{1}8)(0.26\underline{3}6)^2}{(0.0724)^2} = 1.7\underline{4}7 = 1.75$$

14.23   **Given:** $[Fe^{3+}]_{\text{initial}} = 1.0 \times 10^{-3} \text{ M}$; $[SCN^-]_{\text{initial}} = 8.0 \times 10^{-4} \text{ M}$; $[FeSCN^{2+}]_{\text{eq}} = 1.7 \times 10^{-4} \text{ M}$ **Find:** K_c

       Conceptual Plan: **1. Prepare Initial, Change, and Equil (ICE) table.**
                                2. Calculate concentration change for known value.
                                3. Calculate concentration changes for other reactants/products.
                                4. Determine equilibrium concentration.
                                5. Write the equilibrium expression and determine K_c.

Solution: $Fe^{3+}(aq) + SCN^-(aq) \rightleftharpoons FeSCN^{3+}(aq)$

	$[Fe^{3+}]$	$[SCN^-]$	$[FeSCN^{3+}]$
Initial	1.0×10^{-3}	8.0×10^{-4}	0.00
Change	-1.7×10^{-4}	-1.7×10^{-4}	$+1.7 \times 10^{-4}$
Equil	8.3×10^{-4}	6.3×10^{-4}	1.7×10^{-4}

$$K_c = \frac{[FeSCN^{2+}]}{[Fe^{3+}][SCN^-]} = \frac{(1.7 \times 10^{-4})}{(8.3 \times 10^{-4})(6.3 \times 10^{-4})} = 3.3 \times 10^2$$

14.24   **Given:** $[SO_2Cl_2]_{initial} = 0.020$ M; $[Cl_2]_{eq} = 1.2 \times 10^{-2}$ M   **Find:** K_c
Conceptual Plan: 1. **Prepare Initial, Change, and Equil (ICE) table.**
2. **Calculate concentration change for known value.**
3. **Calculate concentration changes for other reactants/products.**
4. **Determine equilibrium concentration.**
5. **Write the equilibrium expression and determine K_c.**

Solution: $SO_2Cl_2(g) \rightleftharpoons SO_2(g) + Cl_2(g)$

	$[SO_2Cl_2]$	$[SO_2]$	$[Cl_2]$
Initial	0.020	0.00	0.00
Change	-1.2×10^{-2}	$+1.2 \times 10^{-2}$	$+1.2 \times 10^{-2}$
Equil	0.0080	1.2×10^{-2}	1.2×10^{-2}

$$K_c = \frac{[SO_2][Cl_2]}{[SO_2Cl_2]} = \frac{(1.2 \times 10^{-2})(1.2 \times 10^{-2})}{(0.0080)} = 0.018$$

14.25   **Given**: 3.67 L flask, 0.763 g H_2 initial, 96.9 g I_2 initial, 90.4 g HI equilibrium   **Find:** K_c
Conceptual Plan: g → mol → M and then

$$n = \frac{g}{\text{molar mass}} \quad M = \frac{n}{V}$$

1. **Prepare Initial, Change, and Equil (ICE) table.**
2. **Calculate concentration change for known value.**
3. **Calculate concentration changes for other reactants/products.**
4. **Determine equilibrium concentration.**
5. **Write the equilibrium expression and determine K_c.**

Solution: $0.763 \text{ g } H_2 \times \dfrac{1 \text{ mol } H_2}{2.016 \text{ g } H_2} = 0.37\underline{8}5 \text{ mol } H_2$ $\dfrac{0.37\underline{8}5 \text{ mol } H_2}{3.67 \text{ L}} = 0.103$ M. This is an initial concentration.

$96.9 \text{ g } I_2 \times \dfrac{1 \text{ mol } I_2}{253.8 \text{ g } I_2} = 0.38\underline{1}8 \text{ mol } I_2$ $\dfrac{0.38\underline{1}8 \text{ mol } I_2}{3.67 \text{ L}} = 0.104$ M. This is an initial concentration.

$90.4 \text{ g } HI \times \dfrac{1 \text{ mol } HI}{127.9 \text{ g } HI} = 0.70\underline{6}8 \text{ mol } HI$ $\dfrac{0.70\underline{6}8 \text{ mol } HI}{3.67 \text{ L}} = 0.193$ M. This is an equilibrium concentration.

$$H_2(g) + I_2(g) \rightleftharpoons 2\,HI(g)$$

	$[H_2]$	$[I_2]$	$[HI]$
Initial	0.103	0.104	0.00
Change	-0.0965	-0.0965	$+0.193$
Equil	0.0065	0.0075	0.193

Because HI gained 0.193 M, H_2 and I_2 had to lose $0.193/2$ $= 0.0965$ M from the stoichiometry of the balanced reaction.

$$K_c = \frac{[HI]^2}{[H_2][I_2]} = \frac{(0.193)^2}{(0.0065)(0.0075)} = 764$$

14.26 **Given:** 5.19 L flask, 26.9 g CO initial, 2.34 g H_2 initial, 8.65 g CH_3OH equilibrium **Find:** K_c

Conceptual Plan: g → mol → M and then

$$n = \frac{g}{\text{molar mass}} \quad M = \frac{n}{V}$$

1. **Prepare Initial, Change, and Equil (ICE) table.**
2. **Calculate concentration change for known value.**
3. **Calculate concentration changes for other reactants/products.**
4. **Determine equilibrium concentration.**
5. **Write the equilibrium expression and determine K_c.**

Solution: $26.9 \text{ g CO} \times \dfrac{1 \text{ mol CO}}{28.01 \text{ g CO}} = 0.96\underline{0}4 \text{ mol CO}$ $\dfrac{0.96\underline{0}4 \text{ mol CO}}{5.19 \text{ L}} = 0.185 \text{ M}$

$2.34 \text{ g H}_2 \times \dfrac{1 \text{ mol H}_2}{2.016 \text{ g H}_2} = 1.1\underline{6}1 \text{ mol H}_2$ $\dfrac{1.1\underline{6}1 \text{ mol H}_2}{5.19 \text{ L}} = 0.224 \text{ M}$

$8.65 \text{ g CH}_3\text{OH} \times \dfrac{1 \text{ mol CH}_3\text{OH}}{32.04 \text{ g CH}_3\text{OH}} = 0.27\underline{0}0 \text{ mol CH}_3\text{OH}$ $\dfrac{0.27\underline{0}0 \text{ mol CH}_3\text{OH}}{5.19 \text{ L}} = 0.0520 \text{ M}$

$$CO(g) + 2 H_2(g) \rightleftharpoons CH_3OH(g)$$

	[CO]	[H₂]	[CH₃OH]
Initial	0.185	0.224	0.00
Change	−0.0520	−0.104	+0.0520
Equil	0.133	0.120	0.0520

Because CH_3OH gained 0.0520 M, CO had to lose 0.0520 M.
Because the stoichiometry is 1:2, H_2 had to lose 0.104 M.

$$K_c = \frac{[CH_3OH]}{[CO][H_2]^2} = \frac{(0.0520)}{(0.133)(0.120)^2} = 27.2$$

The Reaction Quotient and Reaction Direction

14.27 **Given:** $K_c = 8.5 \times 10^{-3}$; $[NH_3] = 0.166$ M; $[H_2S] = 0.166$ M **Find:** Will solid form or decompose?

Conceptual Plan: Calculate Q → compare Q → and K_c

Solution: $Q = [NH_3][H_2S] = (0.166)(0.166) = 0.0276$

$Q = 0.0276$ and $K_c = 8.5 \times 10^{-3}$ so $Q > K_c$ and the reaction will shift to the left; so more solid will form.

14.28 **Given:** $K_p = 2.4 \times 10^{-4}$; $P_{H_2} = 0.112$ atm; $P_{S_2} = 0.055$ atm; $P_{H_2S} = 0.445$ atm **Find:** Is the reaction at equilibrium?

Conceptual Plan: Calculate Q → compare Q and K_p

Solution: $Q = \dfrac{P_{H_2}^2 P_{S_2}}{P_{H_2S}^2} = \dfrac{(0.112)^2(0.055)}{(0.445)^2} = 3.48 \times 10^{-3}$ $Q = 3.48 \times 10^{-3}$ and $K_p = 2.4 \times 10^{-4}$

$Q > K_p$, so the system is not at equilibrium, and the reaction will shift to the left.

14.29 **Given:** 6.55 g Ag_2SO_4, 1.5 L solution, $K_c = 1.1 \times 10^{-5}$ **Find:** Will more solid dissolve?

Conceptual Plan: g Ag_2SO_4 → mol Ag_2SO_4 → [Ag_2SO_4] → [Ag^+], [SO_4^{2-}] → calculate Q and compare to K_c

$$\frac{1 \text{ mol Ag}_2\text{SO}_4}{311.81 \text{ g}} \qquad [] = \frac{\text{mol Ag}_2\text{SO}_4}{\text{vol solution}} \qquad Q = [Ag^+]^2[SO_4^{2-}]$$

Solution: $6.55 \text{ g Ag}_2\text{SO}_4 \left(\dfrac{1 \text{ mol Ag}_2\text{SO}_4}{311.81 \text{ g Ag}_2\text{SO}_4} \right) = 0.0210 \text{ mol Ag}_2\text{SO}_4$

$\dfrac{0.0210 \text{ mol Ag}_2\text{SO}_4}{1.5 \text{ L solution}} = 0.01\underline{4}0 \text{ M Ag}_2\text{SO}_4$

$[Ag^+] = 2[Ag_2SO_4] = 2(0.01\underline{4}0 \text{ M}) = 0.02\underline{8}0 \text{ M}$ $[SO_4^{2-}] = [Ag_2SO_4] = 0.01\underline{4}0 \text{ M}$

$Q = [Ag^+]^2[SO_4^{2-}] = (0.02\underline{8}0)^2(0.01\underline{4}0) = 1.1 \times 10^{-5}$

$Q = K_c$, so the system is at equilibrium and is a saturated solution. Therefore, if more solid is added, it will not dissolve.

14.30   **Given:** $K_p = 6.7$ at 298 K; 2.25 L flask; $NO_2 = 0.055$ mol; $N_2O_4 = 0.082$ mol   **Find:** Is the reaction at equilibrium?

Conceptual Plan: $K_p \rightarrow K_c$ and mol $\rightarrow$ M and then calculate Q and compare to K_c

$$K_p = K_c(RT)^{\Delta n} \qquad M = \frac{mol}{V}$$

Solution: $K_c = \dfrac{K_p}{(RT)^{\Delta n}} = \dfrac{(6.7)}{\left[\left(0.08206 \dfrac{L \cdot atm}{mol \cdot K}\right)(298 \text{ K})\right]^{-1}} = 16\underline{4}$

$$Q = \frac{[N_2O_4]}{[NO]^2} = \frac{\left(\dfrac{0.082 \text{ mol}}{2.25 \text{ L}}\right)}{\left(\dfrac{0.055 \text{ mol}}{2.25 \text{ L}}\right)^2} = 61$$

$Q < K_c$, so the reaction is not at equilibrium and will shift to the right.

Finding Equilibrium Concentrations from Initial Concentrations and the Equilibrium Constant

14.31   (a)   **Given:** [A] = 1.0 M, [B] = 0.0 M; $K_c = 2.0$; $a = 1, b = 1$ **Find:** [A], [B] at equilibrium

Conceptual Plan: Prepare an ICE table, calculate Q, compare Q and K_c, predict the direction of the reaction, represent the change with x, sum the table, determine the equilibrium values, put the equilibrium values in the equilibrium expression, and solve for x. Determine [A] and [B].

Solution: $A(g) \rightleftharpoons B(g)$

	[A]	[B]
Initial	1.0	0.00
Change	$-x$	x
Equil	$1 - x$	x

$Q = \dfrac{[B]}{[A]} = \dfrac{0}{1} = 0$ $Q < K$ Therefore, the reaction will proceed to the right by x.

$K_c = \dfrac{[B]}{[A]} = \dfrac{(x)}{(1 - x)} = 2.0$ $x = 0.67$

[A] = $1 - 0.67 = 0.33$ M   [B] = 0.67 M

Check: Plug the values into the equilibrium expression: $K_c = \dfrac{0.67}{0.33} = 2.0$.

(b)   **Given:** [A] = 1.0 M, [B] = 0.0 M; $K_c = 2.0$; $a = 2, b = 2$ **Find:** [A], [B] at equilibrium

Conceptual Plan: Prepare an ICE table, calculate Q, compare Q and K_c, predict the direction of the reaction, represent the change with x, sum the table, determine the equilibrium values, put the equilibrium values in the equilibrium expression, and solve for x. Determine [A] and [B].

Solution: $2 A(g) \rightleftharpoons 2 B(g)$

	[A]	[B]
Initial	1.0	0.00
Change	$-2x$	$2x$
Equil	$1 - 2x$	$2x$

$Q = \dfrac{[B]^2}{[A]^2} = \dfrac{0}{1} = 0$ $Q < K$ Therefore, the reaction will proceed to the right by x.

$K_c = \dfrac{[B]^2}{[A]^2} = \dfrac{(2x)^2}{(1 - 2x)^2} = 2.0$ $x = 0.29\underline{3}$

[A] = $1 - 2(0.29\underline{3}) = 0.41\underline{4} = 0.41$ M   [B] = $2(0.29\underline{3}) = 0.58\underline{6} = 0.59$ M

Check: Plug the values into the equilibrium expression: $K_c = \dfrac{(0.59)^2}{(0.41)^2} = 2.1$.

(c) **Given:** [A] = 1.0 M, [B] = 0.0 M; K_c = 2.0; a = 1, b = 2 **Find:** [A], [B] at equilibrium
Conceptual Plan: Prepare an ICE table, calculate Q, compare Q and K_c, predict the direction of the reaction, represent the change with x, sum the table, determine the equilibrium values, put the equilibrium values in the equilibrium expression, and solve for x. Determine [A] and [B].
Solution: $A(g) \rightleftharpoons 2\,B(g)$

	[A]	**[B]**
Initial	1.0	0.00
Change	$-x$	$2x$
Equil	$1 - x$	$2x$

$$Q = \frac{[B]^2}{[A]} = \frac{0}{1} = 0 \qquad\qquad Q < K \text{ Therefore, the reaction will proceed to the right by } x.$$

$$K_c = \frac{[B]^2}{[A]} = \frac{(2x)^2}{(1 - x)} = 2.0 \quad 4x^2 + 2x - 2 = 0 \qquad \text{Solve using the quadratic equation, Appendix I.}$$

$x = -1$ or $x = 0.50$; therefore, $x = 0.50$.

[A] = $1 - 0.50 = 0.50$ M   [B] = $2x = 2(0.50) = 1.\underline{0}$ M = 1.0 M

Check: Plug the values into the equilibrium expression: $K_c = \dfrac{(1.0)^2}{0.50} = 2.0$.

14.32 (a) **Given:** [A] = 1.0 M, [B] = 1.0 M, [C] = 0.0 M; K_c = 4.0; a = 1, b = 1, c = 2 **Find:** [A], [B], [C] at equilibrium
Conceptual Plan: Prepare an ICE table, calculate Q, compare Q and K_c, predict the direction of the reaction, represent the change with x, sum the table, determine the equilibrium values, put the equilibrium values in the equilibrium expression, and solve for x. Determine [A], [B], and [C].
Solution: $A(g) + B(g) \rightleftharpoons 2\,C(g)$

	[A]	**[B]**	**[C]**
Initial	1.0	1.0	0.0
Change	$-x$	$-x$	$2x$
Equil	$1-x$	$1-x$	$2x$

$$Q = \frac{[C]^2}{[A][B]} = \frac{0}{(1)(1)} = 0 \qquad\qquad Q < K \text{ Therefore, the reaction will proceed to the right by } x.$$

$$K_c = \frac{[C]^2}{[A][B]} = \frac{(2x)^2}{(1 - x)(1 - x)} = 4.0 \quad x = 0.50. \text{ Solve by taking the square root of both sides.}$$

[A] = [B] = $1 - 0.50 = 0.50$ M   [C] = $2x = 1.00$ M = 1.0 M

Check: Plug the values into the equilibrium expression: $K_c = \dfrac{(1.0)^2}{(0.50)(0.50)} = 4.0$.

(b) **Given:** [A] = 1.0 M, [B] = 1.0 M, [C] = 0.0 M; K_c = 4.0; a = 1, b = 1, c = 1 **Find:** [A], [B], [C] at equilibrium
Conceptual Plan: Prepare an ICE table, calculate Q, compare Q and K_c, predict the direction of the reaction, represent the change with x, sum the table, determine the equilibrium values, put the equilibrium values in the equilibrium expression, and solve for x. Determine [A], [B], and [C].
Solution: $A(g) + B(g) \rightleftharpoons C(g)$

	[A]	**[B]**	**[C]**
Initial	1.0	1.0	0.0
Change	$-x$	$-x$	x
Equil	$1 - x$	$1 - x$	x

$$Q = \frac{[C]}{[A][B]} = \frac{0}{(1)(1)} = 0 \qquad\qquad Q < K \text{ Therefore, the reaction will proceed to the right by } x.$$

$$K_c = \frac{[C]}{[A][B]} = \frac{(x)}{(1-x)(1-x)} = 4.0; \quad 4x^2 - 9x + 4 = 0 \quad \text{Solve by using the quadratic equation.}$$

$x = 1.64$ or $x = 0.61$ Therefore, $x = 0.61$.
$[A] = [B] = 1 - 0.61 = 0.39$ M $[C] = x = 0.61$ M

Check: Plug the values into the equilibrium expression: $K_c = \dfrac{(0.61)}{(0.39)(0.39)} = 4.0$.

(c)   **Given:** $[A] = 1.0$ M, $[B] = 1.0$ M, $[C] = 0.0$ M; $K_c = 4.0$; $a = 2, b = 1, c = 1$ **Find:** $[A]$, $[B]$, $[C]$ at equilibrium
Conceptual Plan: Prepare an ICE table, calculate Q, compare Q and K_c, predict the direction of the reaction, represent the change with x, sum the table, determine the equilibrium values, put the equilibrium values in the equilibrium expression, and solve for x. Determine $[A]$, $[B]$, and $[C]$.
Solution: $2 A(g) + B(g) \rightleftharpoons C(g)$

	[A]	**[B]**	**[C]**
Initial	1.0	1.0	0.0
Change	$-2x$	$-x$	x
Equil	$1 - 2x$	$1 - x$	x

$$Q = \frac{[C]}{[A]^2[B]} = \frac{0}{(1)(1)} = 0 \quad Q < K \quad \text{Therefore, the reaction will proceed to the right by } x.$$

$$K_c = \frac{[C]}{[A]^2[B]} = \frac{(x)}{(1-2x)^2(1-x)} = 4.0$$

$-16x^3 + 32x^2 - 21x + 4 = 0$. Solve by using successive approximations or a cubic equation calculator found on the Internet.
$x = 0.3261 = 0.33$
$[A] = 1 - 2x = 0.34$ M, $[B] = 1 - x = 0.67$ M, $[C] = x = 0.33$ M

Check: Plug the values into the equilibrium expression: $K_c = \dfrac{(0.33)}{(0.34)^2(0.67)} = 4.3$.

14.33   **Given:** $[N_2O_4] = 0.0;500$ M, $[NO_2] = 0.0$ M; $K_c = 0.513$ **Find:** $[N_2O_4]$, $[NO_2]$ at equilibrium
Conceptual Plan: Prepare an ICE table, calculate Q, compare Q and K_c, predict the direction of the reaction, represent the change with x, sum the table, determine the equilibrium values, put the equilibrium values in the equilibrium expression, and solve for x. Determine $[N_2O_4]$ and $[NO_2]$.
Solution: $N_2O_4(g) \rightleftharpoons 2 NO_2(g)$

	[N₂O₄]	**[NO₂]**
Initial	0.0500	0.00
Change	$-x$	$2x$
Equil	$0.0500 - x$	$2x$

$$Q = \frac{[NO_2]^2}{[N_2O_4]} = \frac{0}{0.0500} = 0 \quad Q < K \quad \text{Therefore, the reaction will proceed to the right by } x.$$

$$K_c = \frac{[NO_2]^2}{[N_2O_4]} = \frac{(2x)^2}{(0.0500 - x)} = 0.513 \quad 4x^2 + 0.513x - 0.02565 = 0$$

$$\frac{-b \pm \sqrt{b^2 - 4ac}}{2a} = \frac{-0.513 \pm \sqrt{(0.513)^2 - 4(4)(-0.02565)}}{2(4)} = \frac{-0.513 \pm \sqrt{0.6735}}{2(4)}$$

$x = -0.1667$ or $x = 0.0385$ Therefore, $x = 0.0385$.
$[N_2O_4] = 0.0500 - 0.0385 = 0.0115$ M $[NO_2] = 2x = 2(0.0385) = 0.0770$ M

Check: Plug the values into the equilibrium expression: $K_c = \dfrac{(0.0770)^2}{0.0115} = 0.516$.

14.34 **Given:** $[CO] = 0.1500$ M, $[Cl_2] = 0.175$ M, $[COCl_2] = 0.0$ M; $K_c = 255$ **Find:** $[CO]$, $[Cl_2]$, $[COCl_2]$ at equilibrium

Conceptual Plan: Prepare an ICE table, calculate Q, compare Q and K_c, predict the direction of the reaction, represent the change with x, sum the table, determine the equilibrium values, put the equilibrium values in the equilibrium expression, and solve for x. Determine $[CO]$, $[Cl_2]$, and $[COCl_2]$.

Solution: $CO(g) + Cl_2(g) \rightleftharpoons COCl_2(g)$

	$[CO]$	$[Cl_2]$	$[COCl_2]$
Initial	0.1500	0.175	0.0
Change	$-x$	$-x$	x
Equil	$0.1500 - x$	$0.175 - x$	x

$$Q = \frac{[COCl_2]}{[CO][Cl_2]} = \frac{0}{(0.1500)(0.175)} = 0 \quad Q < K \text{ Therefore, the reaction will proceed to the right by } x.$$

$$K_c = \frac{[COCl_2]}{[CO][Cl_2]} = \frac{x}{(0.1500 - x)(0.175 - x)} = 255 \quad 255x^2 - 83.875x + 6.69375 = 0$$

$$\frac{-b \pm \sqrt{b^2 - 4ac}}{2a} = \frac{-(-83.875) \pm \sqrt{(-83.875)^2 - 4(255)(6.69375)}}{2(255)}$$

$x = 0.192\underline{7}$ or $x = 0.136\underline{2}2$ Therefore, $x = 0.136\underline{2}2$.

$[CO] = 0.1500 - 0.136\underline{2}2 = 0.013\underline{7}8$ M

$[Cl_2] = 0.175 - 0.136\underline{2}2 = 0.038\underline{7}8$ M

$[COCl_2] = x = 0.136\underline{2}2$ M

Check: Plug the values into the equilibrium expression: $K_c = \dfrac{(0.136\underline{2}2)}{(0.013\underline{7}8)(0.038\underline{7}8)} = 2.5 \times 10^2$.

14.35 **Given:** $[CO] = 0.10$ M, $[CO_2] = 0.0$ M; $K_c = 4.0 \times 10^3$ **Find:** $[CO_2]$ at equilibrium

Conceptual Plan: Prepare an ICE table, calculate Q, compare Q and K_c, predict the direction of the reaction, represent the change with x, sum the table, determine the equilibrium values, put the equilibrium values in the equilibrium expression, and solve for x. Determine $[CO]$ and $[CO_2]$.

Solution: $NiO(s) + CO(g) \rightleftharpoons Ni(s) + CO_2(g)$

	$[CO]$	$[CO_2]$
Initial	0.10	0.0
Change	$-x$	x
Equil	$0.10 - x$	x

$$Q = \frac{[CO_2]}{[CO]} = \frac{0}{(0.10)} = 0 \quad Q < K \text{ Therefore, the reaction will proceed to the right by } x.$$

$$K_c = \frac{[CO_2]}{[CO]} = \frac{x}{(0.10 - x)} = 4.0 \times 10^3 \quad 4.0 \times 10^3(0.10 - x) = x$$

$x = 0.099\underline{9}8$

$[CO_2] = 0.099\underline{9}8$ M $= 0.100$ M

Check: Because the equilibrium constant is so large, the reaction goes essentially to completion; therefore, it is reasonable that the concentration of the product is 0.099\underline{9} M.

14.36 **Given:** $[CO] = 0.125$ M, $[H_2O] = 0.125$ M, $[CO_2] = 0.0$; $[H_2] = 0.0$; $K_c = 102$ **Find:** $[CO]$, $[H_2O]$, $[CO_2]$, $[H_2]$ at equilibrium

Conceptual Plan: Prepare an ICE table, calculate Q, compare Q and K_c, predict the direction of the reaction, represent the change with x, sum the table, determine the equilibrium values, put the equilibrium values in the equilibrium expression, and solve for x. Determine $[CO]$, $[H_2O]$, $[CO_2]$ and $[H_2]$.

Solution:

$$CO(g) + H_2O(g) \rightleftharpoons CO_2(g) + H_2(g)$$

	[CO]	[H$_2$O]	[CO$_2$]	[H$_2$]
Initial	0.125	0.125	0.0	0.0
Change	$-x$	$-x$	x	x
Equil	$0.125 - x$	$0.125 - x$	x	x

$Q = \dfrac{[CO_2][H_2]}{[CO][H_2O]} = \dfrac{0}{(0.125)(0.125)} = 0$ $Q < K$ Therefore, the reaction will proceed to the right by x.

$K_c = \dfrac{[CO_2][H_2]}{[CO][H_2O]} = \dfrac{(x)(x)}{(0.125 - x)(0.125 - x)} = 102$

$\sqrt{\dfrac{(x)(x)}{(0.125 - x)(0.125 - x)}} = \sqrt{102}$

$\dfrac{x}{0.125 - x} = \pm 10.0995$

$\pm 10.0995(0.125 - x) = x$

$x = 0.1137$ or $x = 7.208$ Therefore, $x = 0.1137 = 0.114$.

$[CO] = [H_2O] = 0.125 - 0.1137 = 0.0113 = 0.011$ M

$[H_2] = [CO_2] = x = 0.1137 = 0.114$ M

Check: Plug the values into the equilibrium expression: $K_c = \dfrac{(0.114)(0.114)}{(0.011)(0.011)} = 107.4 = 107$, which is close to the

true value; so the answers are valid.

14.37   **Given:** $[HC_2H_3O_2] = 0.210$ M, $[H_3O^+] = 0.0$, $[C_2H_3O_2^-] = 0.0$, $K_c = 1.8 \times 10^{-5}$
Find: $[HC_2H_3O_2]$, $[H_3O^+]$, $[C_2H_3O_2^-]$ at equilibrium
Conceptual Plan: Prepare an ICE table, calculate Q, compare Q and K_c, predict the direction of the reaction, represent the change with x, sum the table, determine the equilibrium values, put the equilibrium values in the equilibrium expression, and solve for x. Determine $[HC_2H_3O_2]$, $[H_3O^+]$, and $[C_2H_3O_2^-]$.
Solution: $HC_2H_3O_2(aq) + H_2O(l) \rightleftharpoons H_3O^+(aq) + C_2H_3O_2^-(aq)$

	[HC$_2$H$_3$O$_2$]	[H$_3$O$^+$]	[C$_2$H$_3$O$_2{}^-$]
Initial	0.210	0.0	0.0
Change	$-x$	x	x
Equil	$0.210 - x$	x	x

$Q = \dfrac{[H_3O^+][C_2H_3O_2^-]}{[HC_2H_3O_2]} = \dfrac{0}{(0.210)} = 0$ $Q < K$ Therefore, the reaction will proceed to the right by x.

$K_c = \dfrac{[H_3O^+][C_2H_3O_2^-]}{[HC_2H_3O_2]} = \dfrac{(x)(x)}{(0.210 - x)} = 1.8 \times 10^{-5}$

Assume that x is small compared to 0.210.

$x^2 = 0.210(1.8 \times 10^{-5})$

$x = 0.00194$ Check assumption: $\dfrac{0.00194}{0.210} \times 100 = 0.92\%$; assumption is valid.

$[H_3O^+] = [C_2H_3O_2^-] = 0.00194$ M

$[HC_2H_3O_2] = 0.210 - 0.00194 = 0.2081 = 0.208$ M

Check: Plug the values into the equilibrium expression: $K_c = \dfrac{(0.00194)(0.00194)}{(0.208)} = 1.81 \times 10^{-5}$.

The answer is the same to two significant figures with the true value, so the answers are valid.

14.38   **Given:** $[SO_2Cl_2] = 0.175$ M, $[SO_2] = 0.0$ M, $[Cl_2] = 0.0$ M; $K_c = 2.99 \times 10^{-7}$
Find: $[SO_2Cl_2]$, $[SO_2]$, $[Cl_2]$ at equilibrium
Conceptual Plan: Prepare an ICE table, calculate Q, compare Q and K_c, predict the direction of the reaction, represent the change with x, sum the table, determine the equilibrium values, put the equilibrium values in the equilibrium expression, and solve for x. Determine $[SO_2Cl_2]$, $[SO_2]$, and $[Cl_2]$.

Solution: $SO_2Cl_2(g) \rightleftharpoons SO_2(g) + Cl_2(g)$

	$[SO_2Cl_2]$	$[SO_2]$	$[Cl_2]$
Initial	0.175	0.0	0.0
Change	$-x$	x	x
Equil	$0.175 - x$	x	x

$Q = \dfrac{[SO_2][Cl_2]}{[SO_2Cl_2]} = \dfrac{0}{(0.175)} = 0$ $Q < K$ Therefore, the reaction will proceed to the right by x.

$K_c = \dfrac{[SO_2][Cl_2]}{[SO_2Cl_2]} = \dfrac{(x)(x)}{(0.175 - x)} = 2.99 \times 10^{-7}$

Assume that x is small compared to 0.175.

$x^2 = 2.99 \times 10^{-7}(0.175)$

$x = 2.2\underline{8}7 \times 10^{-4}$ Check assumption: $\dfrac{2.2\underline{8}7 \times 10^{-4}}{0.175} \times 100 = 0.13\%$; assumption is valid.

$[SO_2] = [Cl_2] = x = 2.2\underline{8}7 \times 10^{-4} = 2.29 \times 10^{-4}$ M
$[SO_2Cl_2] = 0.175 - 2.2\underline{8}7 \times 10^{-4} = 0.17\underline{4}8 = 0.175$ M

Check: Plug the values into the equilibrium expression:

$K_c = \dfrac{(2.2\underline{8}7 \times 10^{-4})(2.2\underline{8}7 \times 10^{-4})}{(0.175)} = 2.9\underline{8}9 \times 10^{-7} = 2.99 \times 10^{-7}$

14.39 **Given:** $P_{Br_2} = 755$ torr, $P_{Cl_2} = 735$ torr, $P_{BrCl} = 0.0$, $K_p = 1.11 \times 10^{-4}$ **Find:** P_{BrCl} at equilibrium
Conceptual Plan: Torr $\rightarrow$ atm and then prepare an ICE table, calculate Q, compare Q and K_c, predict the direction of the reaction, represent the change with x, sum the table, determine the equilibrium values, put the equilibrium values in the equilibrium expression, and solve for x. Determine P_{BrCl}.
Solution:

$P_{Br_2} = 755 \text{ torr} \times \dfrac{1 \text{ atm}}{760 \text{ torr}} = 0.99\underline{3}4$ atm $P_{Cl_2} = 735 \text{ torr} \times \dfrac{1 \text{ atm}}{760 \text{ torr}} = 0.96\underline{7}1$ atm

$Br_2(g) + Cl_2(g) \rightleftharpoons 2\,BrCl(g)$

	P_{Br_2}	P_{Cl_2}	P_{BrCl}
Initial	0.9934	0.9671	0.0
Change	$-x$	$-x$	$2x$
Equil	$0.9934 - x$	$0.9671 - x$	$2x$

$Q = \dfrac{P_{BrCl}^2}{P_{Br_2}P_{Cl_2}} = \dfrac{0}{(0.9934)(0.9671)} = 0$ $Q < K$ Therefore, the reaction will proceed to the right by x.

$K_p = \dfrac{P_{BrCl}^2}{P_{Br_2}P_{Cl_2}} = \dfrac{(2x)^2}{(0.99\underline{3}4 - x)(0.96\underline{7}1 - x)} = 1.11 \times 10^{-4}$

Assume that x is small compared to 0.9934 and 0.9671.

$\dfrac{(2x)^2}{(0.99\underline{3}4)(0.96\underline{7}1)} = 1.11 \times 10^{-4}$ $4x^2 = 1.0\underline{6}6 \times 10^{-4}$

$x = 0.00516$ atm $= 3.92$ torr
$P_{BrCl} = 2x = 2(3.92 \text{ torr}) = 7.84$ torr

Check: Plug the values into the equilibrium expression:

$K_c = \dfrac{(2(0.00516))^2}{(0.99\underline{3}4 - 0.00516)(0.96\underline{7}1 - 0.00516)} = 1.1\underline{2}0 \times 10^{-4} = 1.12 \times 10^{-4}.$

This is within 0.01×10^{-4} of the true value; therefore, the answers are valid.

14.40 **Given:** $P_{CO} = 1344$ torr, $P_{H_2O} = 1766$ torr, $P_{CO_2} = 0.0$, $P_{H_2} = 0.0$, $K_p = 0.0611$ **Find:** P_{CO_2}, P_{H_2} at equilibrium
Conceptual Plan: Torr $\rightarrow$ atm and then prepare an ICE table, calculate Q, compare Q and K_c, predict the direction of the reaction, represent the change with x, sum the table, determine the equilibrium values, put the equilibrium values in the equilibrium expression, and solve for x. Determine P_{CO_2} and P_{H_2}.

Solution: $P_{CO} = 1344 \text{ torr} \times \dfrac{1 \text{ atm}}{760 \text{ torr}} = 1.76\underline{8}4 \text{ atm}$ $P_{H_2O} = 1766 \text{ torr} \times \dfrac{1 \text{ atm}}{760 \text{ torr}} = 2.32\underline{3}7 \text{ atm}$

$$CO(g) + H_2O(g) \rightleftharpoons CO_2(g) + H_2(g)$$

	P_{CO}	P_{H_2O}	P_{CO_2}	P_{H_2}
Initial	1.76\underline{8}4	2.3237	0.0	0.0
Change	$-x$	$-x$	x	x
Equil	$1.7684 - x$	$2.3237 - x$	x	x

$Q = \dfrac{P_{CO_2}P_{H_2}}{P_{CO}P_{H_2O}} = \dfrac{0}{(1.7684)(2.3237)} = 0$ $Q < K$ Therefore, the reaction will proceed to the right by x.

$K_p = \dfrac{P_{CO_2}P_{H_2}}{P_{CO}P_{H_2O}} = \dfrac{(x)(x)}{(1.7684 - x)(2.3237 - x)} = 0.0611$

$x^2 = (0.0611)(4.1092 - 4.0921x + x^2)$
$x^2 = (0.25107 - 0.2500\,x + 0.0611\,x^2)$
$0.9389x^2 + 0.2500x - 0.25107 = 0$

$\dfrac{-b \pm \sqrt{b^2 - 4ac}}{2a} = \dfrac{-0.2500 \pm \sqrt{(0.2500)^2 - 4(0.9389)(-0.25107)}}{2(0.9389)}$

$x = 0.4008$ or -0.6671 so $x = 0.4008$
$P_{CO_2} = P_{H_2} = x = 0.4008 \text{ atm} = 305 \text{ torr}$

Check: Plug the values into the equilibrium expression:

$K_p = \dfrac{(0.4008)^2}{(1.7684 - 0.4008)(2.3237 - 0.4008)} = 0.06109 = 0.061.$

The answers are the same to two significant figures with the true value; therefore, the answers are valid.

14.41　(a)　**Given:** $[A] = 1.0 \text{ M}$, $[B] = [C] = 0.0$, $K_c = 1.0$　**Find:** [A], [B], [C] at equilibrium
Conceptual Plan: Prepare an ICE table, calculate Q, compare Q and K_c, predict the direction of the reaction, represent the change with x, sum the table, determine the equilibrium values, put the equilibrium values in the equilibrium expression, and solve for x. Determine [A], [B], and [C].
Solution:　　　$A(g) \rightleftharpoons B(g) + C(g)$

	[A]	[B]	[C]
Initial	1.0	0.0	0.0
Change	$-x$	x	x
Equil	$1.0 - x$	x	x

$Q = \dfrac{[B][C]}{[A]} = \dfrac{0}{(1.0)} = 0$ $Q < K$ Therefore, the reaction will proceed to the right by x.

$K_c = \dfrac{[B][C]}{[A]} = \dfrac{(x)(x)}{(1.0 - x)} = 1.0$

$x^2 = 1.0(1.0 - x)$
$x^2 + x - 1 = 0$

$\dfrac{-b \pm \sqrt{b^2 - 4ac}}{2a} = \dfrac{-1 \pm \sqrt{1^2 - 4(1)(-1)}}{2(1)}$

$x = 0.6\underline{1}8$ or $x = -1.618$ Therefore, $x = 0.6\underline{1}8$.
$[B] = [C] = x = 0.6\underline{1}8 = 0.62 \text{ M}$
$[A] = 1.0 - 0.6\underline{1}8 = 0.3\underline{8}2 = 0.38 \text{ M}$

Check: Plug the values into the equilibrium expression:

$K_c = \dfrac{(0.62)(0.62)}{(0.38)} = 1.01 = 1.0$, which is the equilibrium constant; so the values are correct.

(b) **Given:** [A] = 1.0 M, [B] = [C] = 0.0, K_c = 0.010 **Find:** [A], [B], [C] at equilibrium

Conceptual Plan: Prepare an ICE table, calculate Q, compare Q and K_c, predict the direction of the reaction, represent the change with x, sum the table, determine the equilibrium values, put the equilibrium values in the equilibrium expression, and solve for x. Determine [A], [B], and [C].

Solution:

$$A(g) \rightleftharpoons B(g) + C(g)$$

	[A]	[B]	[C]
Initial	1.0	0.0	0.0
Change	$-x$	x	x
Equil	$1.0 - x$	x	x

$Q = \dfrac{[B][C]}{[A]} = \dfrac{0}{(1.0)} = 0$ $Q < K$ Therefore, the reaction will proceed to the right by x.

$K_c = \dfrac{[B][C]}{[A]} = \dfrac{(x)(x)}{(1.0 - x)} = 0.010$

$x^2 = 0.010(1.0 - x)$

$x^2 + 0.010x - 0.010 = 0$

$\dfrac{-b \pm \sqrt{b^2 - 4ac}}{2a} = \dfrac{-(0.010) \pm \sqrt{(0.010)^2 - 4(1)(-0.010)}}{2(1)}$

$x = 0.09\underline{5}12$ or $x = -0.1051$ Therefore, $x = 0.09\underline{5}12$.

[B] = [C] = x = 0.09512 = 0.095 M

[A] = 1.0 − 0.09512 = 0.9\underline{0}488 = 0.9 M

Check: Plug the values into the equilibrium expression:

$K_c = \dfrac{(0.095)(0.095)}{(0.90)} = 0.0\underline{1}003 = 0.01$, which is the equilibrium constant; so the values are correct.

(c) **Given:** [A] = 1.0 M, [B] = [C] = 0.0, K_c = 1.0×10^{-5} **Find:** [A], [B], [C] at equilibrium

Conceptual Plan: Prepare an ICE table, calculate Q, compare Q and K_c, predict the direction of the reaction, represent the change with x, sum the table, determine the equilibrium values, put the equilibrium values in the equilibrium expression, and solve for x. Determine [A], [B], and [C].

Solution:

$$A(g) \rightleftharpoons B(g) + C(g)$$

	[A]	[B]	[C]
Initial	1.0	0.0	0.0
Change	$-x$	x	x
Equil	$1.0 - x$	x	x

$Q = \dfrac{[B][C]}{[A]} = \dfrac{0}{(1.0)} = 0$ $Q < K$ Therefore, the reaction will proceed to the right by x.

$K_c = \dfrac{[B][C]}{[A]} = \dfrac{(x)(x)}{(1.0 - x)} = 1.0 \times 10^{-5}$

Assume that x is small compared to 1.0.

$x^2 = 1.0(1.0 \times 10^{-5})$

$x = 0.003\underline{1}6$ Check assumption: $\dfrac{0.003\underline{1}6}{1.0} \times 100 = 0.32\%$; assumption is valid.

[B] = [C] = x = 0.003\underline{1}6 = 0.0032 M

[A] = 1.0 − 0.003\underline{1}6 = 0.9968 = 1.0 M

Check: Plug the values into the equilibrium expression:

$K_c = \dfrac{(0.0032)(0.0032)}{(1.0)} = 1.\underline{0}24 \times 10^{-5} = 1.0 \times 10^{-5}$,

which is the equilibrium constant; so the values are correct.

14.42   (a)   **Given:** $P_B = 1.0$ atm, $P_A = 0.0$ atm, $K_p = 1.0$ **Find:** P_B, P_A at equilibrium

Conceptual Plan: Prepare an ICE table, calculate Q, compare Q and K_p, predict the direction of the reaction, represent the change with x, sum the table, determine the equilibrium values, put the equilibrium values in the equilibrium expression, and solve for x. Determine P_A and P_B.

Solution:

$$A(g) \rightleftharpoons 2\,B(g)$$

	P_A	P_B
Initial	0.0	1.0
Change	x	$-2x$
Equil	x	$1.0 - 2x$

$Q = \dfrac{P_B^2}{P_A} = \dfrac{(1.0)^2}{0}$ Because there is no A, the reaction shifts to the left.

$K_p = \dfrac{P_B^2}{P_A} = \dfrac{(1.0 - 2x)^2}{(x)} = 1.0$

$1.0 - 4x + 4x^2 = 1.0x$

$4x^2 - 5x + 1.0 = 0$

$\dfrac{-b \pm \sqrt{b^2 - 4ac}}{2a} = \dfrac{-(-5) \pm \sqrt{(-5)^2 - 4(4)(1)}}{2(4)}$

$x = 0.25$ or $x = 1.0$ Therefore, $x = 0.25$.

$P_A = x = 0.25$ atm; $P_B = 1.0 - 2x = 1.0 - 0.50 = 0.50$ atm

Check: Plug the values into the equilibrium expression:

$K_p = \dfrac{(0.50)^2}{(0.25)} = 1.0$, which is the equilibrium constant.

(b)   **Given:** $P_B = 1.0$ atm, $P_A = 0.0$ atm, $K_p = 1.0 \times 10^{-4}$ **Find:** P_B, P_A at equilibrium

Conceptual Plan: Prepare an ICE table, calculate Q, compare Q and K_p, predict the direction of the reaction, represent the change with x, sum the table, determine the equilibrium values, put the equilibrium values in the equilibrium expression, and solve for x. Determine P_A and P_B.

Solution:

$$A(g) \rightleftharpoons 2\,B(g)$$

	P_A	P_B
Initial	0.0	1.0
Change	x	$-2x$
Equil	x	$1.0 - 2x$

$Q = \dfrac{P_B^2}{P_A} = \dfrac{(1.0)^2}{0}$ Because there is no A, the reaction shifts to the left.

$K_p = \dfrac{P_B^2}{P_A} = \dfrac{(1.0 - 2x)^2}{(x)} = 1.0 \times 10^{-4}$

$1.0 - 4x + 4x^2 = (1.0 \times 10^{-4})x$

$4x^2 - 4.0001x + 1.0 = 0$

$\dfrac{-b \pm \sqrt{b^2 - 4ac}}{2a} = \dfrac{-(-4.0001) \pm \sqrt{(-4.0001)^2 - 4(4)(1)}}{2(4)} = \dfrac{-(-4.0001) \pm \sqrt{8.0 \times 10^{-4}}}{2(4)}$

$x = 0.5\underline{0}35$ or $x = 0.4\underline{9}65$ Therefore, $x = 0.4\underline{9}65$.

$P_A = x = 0.4\underline{9}65 = 0.50$ atm; $P_B = 1.0 - 2x = 1.0 - 2(0.4\underline{9}65) = 0.007$ atm

Check: Plug the values into the equilibrium expression:

$K_p = \dfrac{(0.007)^2}{(0.4\underline{9}65)} = 9.\underline{8}69 \times 10^{-5} = 1.0 \times 10^{-4}$, which is the equilibrium constant.

(c)   **Given:** $P_B = 1.0$ atm, $P_A = 0.0$ atm, $K_p = 1.0 \times 10^5$ **Find:** P_B, P_A at equilibrium
Conceptual Plan: Prepare an ICE table, calculate Q, compare Q and K_p, predict the direction of the reaction, represent the change with x, sum the table, determine the equilibrium values, put the equilibrium values in the equilibrium expression, and solve for x. Determine P_A and P_B.
Solution:

$A(g) \rightleftharpoons 2\, B(g)$

	P_A	P_B
Initial	0.0	1.0
Change	x	$-2x$
Equil	x	$1.0 - 2x$

$Q = \dfrac{P_B^2}{P_A} = \dfrac{(1.0)^2}{0}$ Because there is no A, the reaction shifts to the left.

$K_p = \dfrac{P_B^2}{P_A} = \dfrac{(1.0 - 2x)^2}{(x)} = 1.0 \times 10^5$

Assume that $2x$ is small compared to 1.0.

$\dfrac{1.0}{x} = 1.0 \times 10^5$

$x = 1.0 \times 10^{-5}$ Check assumption: $\dfrac{2(1.0 \times 10^{-5})}{1.0} \times 100\% = 0.002\%$; assumption is valid.

$P_A = x = 1.0 \times 10^{-5}$ atm; $P_B = 1.0 - 2x = 1.0 - 2(1.0 \times 10^{-5}) = 0.99998$ atm

Check: Plug the values into the equilibrium expression:

$K_p = \dfrac{(0.99998)^2}{(1.0 \times 10^{-5})} = 9.9996 \times 10^4 = 1.0 \times 10^5$, which is the equilibrium constant.

Le Châtelier's Principle

14.43   **Given:** $CO(g) + Cl_2(g) \rightleftharpoons COCl_2(g)$ at equilibrium   **Find:** What is the effect of each of the following?
(a) $COCl_2$ is added to the reaction mixture: Adding $COCl_2$ increases the concentration of $COCl_2$ and causes the reaction to shift to the left.
(b) Cl_2 is added to the reaction mixture: Adding Cl_2 increases the concentration of Cl_2 and causes the reaction to shift to the right.
(c) $COCl_2$ is removed from the reaction mixture: Removing the $COCl_2$ decreases the concentration of $COCl_2$ and causes the reaction to shift to the right.

14.44   **Given:** $2\, BrNO(g) \rightleftharpoons 2\, NO(g) + Br_2(g)$ at equilibrium   **Find:** What is the effect of each of the following?
(a)   NO is added to the reaction mixture: Adding NO increases the concentration of NO and causes the reaction to shift to the left.
(b)   BrNO is added to the reaction mixture: Adding BrNO increases the concentration of BrNO and causes the reaction to shift to the right.
(c) Br_2 is removed from the reaction mixture: Removing Br_2 decreases the concentration of Br_2 and causes the reaction to shift to the right.

14.45   **Given:** $2\, KClO_3(s) \rightleftharpoons 2\, KCl(s) + 3\, O_2(g)$ at equilibrium   **Find:** What is the effect of each of the following?
(a) O_2 is removed from the reaction mixture: Removing the O_2 decreases the concentration of O_2 and causes the reaction to shift to the right.
(b)   KCl is added to the reaction mixture: Adding KCl does not cause any change in the reaction. KCl is a solid, and the concentration remains constant; so the addition of more solid does not change the equilibrium concentration.
(c) $KClO_3$ is added to the reaction mixture: Adding $KClO_3$ does not cause any change in the reaction. $KClO_3$ is a solid, and the concentration remains constant; so the addition of more solid does not change the equilibrium concentration.
(d) O_2 is added to the reaction mixture: Adding O_2 increases the concentration of O_2 and causes the reaction to shift to the left.

14.46   **Given:** $C(s) + H_2O(g) \rightleftharpoons CO(g) + H_2(g)$ **Find:** What is the effect of each of the following?

(a)   C is added to the reaction mixture: Adding C does not cause any change in the reaction. C is a solid, and the concentration remains constant; so the addition of more solid does not change the equilibrium concentration.

(b) H_2O is condensed and removed from the reaction mixture: Removing the H_2O decreases the concentration of H_2O and causes the reaction to shift to the left.

(c)   CO is added to the reaction mixture: Adding CO increases the concentration of CO and causes the reaction to shift to the left.

(d) H_2 is removed from the reaction mixture: Removing the H_2 decreases the concentration of H_2 and causes the reaction to shift to the right.

14.47   (a)   **Given:** $I_2(g) \rightleftharpoons 2I(g)$ at equilibrium   **Find:** the effect of increasing the volume.
The chemical equation has 2 moles of gas on the right and 1 mole of gas on the left. Increasing the volume of the reaction mixture decreases the pressure and causes the reaction to shift to the right (toward the side with more moles of gas particles).

(b)   **Given:** $2H_2S(g) \rightleftharpoons 2H_2(g) + S_2(g)$ **Find:** the effect of decreasing the volume.
The chemical equation has 3 moles of gas on the right and 2 moles of gas on the left. Decreasing the volume of the reaction mixture increases the pressure and causes the reaction to shift to the left (toward the side with fewer moles of gas particles).

(c)   **Given:** $I_2(g) + Cl_2(g) \rightleftharpoons 2ICl(g)$ **Find:** the effect of decreasing the volume.
The chemical equation has 2 moles of gas on the right and 2 moles of gas on the left. Decreasing the volume of the reaction mixture increases the pressure but causes no shift in the reaction because the moles are equal on both sides.

14.48   (a)   **Given:** $CO(g) + H_2O(g) \rightleftharpoons CO_2(g) + H_2(g)$ **Find:** the effect of decreasing the volume.
The chemical equation has 2 moles of gas on the right and 2 moles of gas on the left. Decreasing the volume of the reaction mixture increases the pressure but causes no shift in the reaction because the moles are equal on both sides.

(b)   **Given:** $PCl_3(g) + Cl_2(g) \rightleftharpoons PCl_5(g)$ **Find:** the effect of increasing the volume.
The chemical equation has 2 moles of gas on the left and 1 mole of gas on the right. Increasing the volume of the reaction mixture decreases the pressure and causes the reaction to shift to the left (toward the side with more moles of gas particles).

(c)   **Given:** $CaCO_3(s) \rightleftharpoons CaO(s) + CO_2(g)$ **Find:** the effect of increasing the volume.
The chemical equation has 1 mole of gas on the right and 0 mole of gas on the left. Increasing the volume of the reaction mixture decreases the pressure and causes the reaction to shift to the right (toward the side with more moles of gas particles).

14.49   **Given:** $C(s) + CO_2(g) \rightleftharpoons 2CO(g)$ is endothermic.   **Find:** the effect of increasing the temperature.
Because the reaction is endothermic, we can think of the heat as a reactant: Increasing the temperature is equivalent to adding a reactant, causing the reaction to shift to the right. This will cause an increase in the concentration of products and a decrease in the concentration of reactant; therefore, the value of K will increase.
Find: the effect of decreasing the temperature
Because the reaction is endothermic, we can think of the heat as a reactant: Decreasing the temperature is equivalent to removing a reactant, causing the reaction to shift to the left. This will cause a decrease in the concentration of products and an increase in the concentration of reactants; therefore, the value of K will decrease.

14.50   **Given:** $C_6H_{12}O_6(s) + 6 O_2(g) \rightleftharpoons 6CO_2(g) + 6 H_2O(g)$ is exothermic.
Find: the effect of increasing the temperature
Because the reaction is exothermic, we can think of the heat as a product: Increasing the temperature is equivalent to adding a product, causing the reaction to shift to the left. This will cause a decrease in the concentration of products and an increase in the concentration of reactant; therefore, the value of K will decrease.
Find: the effect of decreasing the temperature

Because the reaction is exothermic, we can think of the heat as a product: Decreasing the temperature is equivalent to removing a product, causing the reaction to shift to the right. This will cause an increase in the concentration of products and a decrease in the concentration of reactants; therefore, the value of K will increase.

14.51   **Given:** $C(s) + 2 H_2(g) \rightleftharpoons CH_4(g)$ is exothermic.   **Find:** Determine which will favor CH_4.
(a) Adding more C to the reaction mixture does *not* favor CH_4. Adding C does not cause any change in the reaction. C is a solid, and the concentration remains constant; so the addition of more solid does not change the equilibrium concentration.
(b) Adding more H_2 to the reaction mixture favors CH_4. Adding H_2 increases the concentration of H_2, causing the reaction to shift to the right.
(c) Raising the temperature of the reaction mixture does *not* favor CH_4. Because the reaction is exothermic, we can think of heat as a product. Raising the temperature is equivalent to adding a product, causing the reaction to shift to the left.
(d) Lowering the volume of the reaction mixture favors CH_4. The chemical equation has 1 mole of gas on the right and 2 moles of gas on the left. Decreasing the volume of the reaction mixture increases the pressure and causes the reaction to shift to the right (toward the side with fewer moles of gas particles).
(e) Adding a catalyst to the reaction mixture does *not* favor CH_4. A catalyst added to the reaction mixture only speeds up the reaction; it does not change the equilibrium concentration.
(f) Adding neon gas to the reaction mixture does *not* favor CH_4. Adding an inert gas to a reaction mixture at a fixed volume has no effect on the equilibrium.

14.52   **Given:** $C(s) + H_2O(g) \rightleftharpoons CO(g) + H_2(g)$ is endothermic.   **Find:** Determine which will favor H_2.
(a) Adding more C to the reaction mixture has no effect on the quantity of H_2. Adding C does not cause any change in the reaction. C is a solid, and the concentration remains constant; so the addition of more solid does not change the equilibrium concentration.
(b) Adding more H_2O to the reaction mixture results in the formation of additional H_2. Adding H_2O increases the concentration and causes the reaction to shift to the right.
(c) Raising the temperature of the reaction mixture results in the formation of additional H_2. Because the reaction is endothermic, we can think of heat as a reactant: Raising the temperature is equivalent to adding a reactant, causing the reaction to shift to the right.
(d) Increasing the volume of the reaction mixture results in the formation of additional H_2. The chemical equation has 2 moles of gas on the right and 1 mole of gas on the left. Increasing the volume of the reaction mixture decreases the pressure and causes the reaction to shift to the right (toward the side with more moles of gas particles).
(e) Adding a catalyst to the reaction mixture has no effect on the quantity of H_2. A catalyst added to the reaction mixture only speeds up the reaction; it does not change the equilibrium concentration.
(f) Adding an inert gas to the reaction mixture has no effect on the quantity of H_2. Adding an inert gas to a reaction mixture at a fixed volume has no effect on the equilibrium.

Cumulative Problems

14.53   (a) To find the value of K for the new equation, combine the two given equations to yield the new equation. Reverse equation 1 and use $1/K_1$, then add to equation 2. To find K for equation 3, use $(1/K_1)(K_2)$.

$HbO_2(aq)$ $\rightleftharpoons$ $\cancel{Hb(aq)} + O_2(aq)$ $K_1 = 1/1.8$
$\cancel{Hb(aq)} + CO(aq)$ $\rightleftharpoons$ $HbCO(aq)$ $K_2 = 306$
$\overline{}$
$HbO_2(aq) + CO(aq) \rightleftharpoons HbCO(aq) + O_2(aq)$ $K_3 = K_1K_2 = (1/1.8)(306) = 170$

(b) **Given:** $O_2 = 20\%, CO = 0.10\%$ **Find:** The ratio $\dfrac{[HbCO]}{[HbO_2]}$

Conceptual Plan: Determine the equilibrium expression and then determine $\dfrac{[HbCO]}{[HbO_2]}$.

Solution: $K = \dfrac{[HbCO][O_2]}{[HbO_2][CO]}$ $170 = \dfrac{[HbCO](20.0)}{[HbO_2](0.10)}$ $\dfrac{[HbCO]}{[HbO_2]} = 170\left(\dfrac{0.10}{20.0}\right) = \dfrac{0.85}{1.0}$

Because the ratio is almost 1:1, 0.10% CO will replace about 50% of the O_2 in the blood. The CO blocks the uptake of O_2 by the blood and is therefore highly toxic.

14.54   **Given:** $P = 1$ atm, $T = 298$ K, $N_2 = 78\%$, $O_2 = 21\%$, $K_p = 4.1 \times 10^{-31}$ **Find:** [NO] in molecules/cm³

Conceptual Plan:

%vol → n → M and then K_p → K_c and then prepare an ICE table, represent the change with x,

$$PV = nRT \quad \frac{n}{1 \text{ L air}} \qquad\qquad K_p = K_c(RT)^{\Delta n}$$

sum the table, determine the equilibrium values, put the equilibrium values in the equilibrium expression, and solve for x. Determine [NO] in mol/L → molecules/cm³.

$$\frac{6.022 \times 10^{23} \text{ molecules}}{\text{mole}} \qquad \frac{1 \text{ L}}{1000 \text{ mL}} \qquad \frac{\text{mL}}{\text{cm}^3}$$

Solution: Assume 1 L of air.

$$n_{N_2} = \frac{(1 \text{ atm})(0.78 \text{ L})}{\left(0.08206 \dfrac{\text{L} \cdot \text{atm}}{\text{mol} \cdot \text{K}}\right)(298 \text{ K})} = 0.03190 \text{ mol} \qquad n_{O_2} = \frac{(1 \text{ atm})(0.21 \text{ L})}{\left(0.08206 \dfrac{\text{L} \cdot \text{atm}}{\text{mol} \cdot \text{K}}\right)(298 \text{ K})} = 0.00859 \text{ mol}$$

$[N_2] = 0.03190 \text{ mol/L} \qquad [O_2] = 0.00859 \text{ mol/L}$

$$K_p = K_c(RT)^{\Delta n} \quad K_c = \frac{K_p}{(RT)^{\Delta n}} = \frac{4.1 \times 10^{-31}}{\left((0.08206 \dfrac{\text{L} \cdot \text{atm}}{\text{mol} \cdot \text{K}})(298 \text{ K})\right)^0} = 4.1 \times 10^{-31}$$

$$N_2(g) \quad + \quad O_2(g) \quad \rightleftharpoons \quad 2 \text{ NO}(g)$$

	[N₂]	[O₂]	[NO]
Initial	0.0319	0.00859	0.0
Change	$-x$	$-x$	$2x$
Equil	$0.0319 - x$	$0.00859 - x$	$2x$

The reaction will proceed to the right by x.

$$K_c = \frac{[NO]^2}{[N_2][O_2]} = \frac{(2x)^2}{(0.0319 - x)(0.00859 - x)} = 4.1 \times 10^{-31}$$

Assume that x is small compared to 0.00859 and to 0.0319.

$x = 5.30 \times 10^{-18}$ Check assumption: $\dfrac{5.30 \times 10^{-18}}{0.00858} \times 100\% = 6.2 \times 10^{-14}\%$

$[NO] = 2x = 2(5.30 \times 10^{-18}) = 1.06 \times 10^{-17}$ M

$$1.06 \times 10^{-17} \frac{\text{mol}}{\text{L}} \times \frac{6.022 \times 10^{23} \text{ molecules}}{\text{mol}} \times \frac{\text{L}}{1000 \text{ mL}} \times \frac{\text{mL}}{\text{cm}^3} = 6.38 \times 10^3 \frac{\text{molecules}}{\text{cm}^3}$$

$$= 6.4 \times 10^3 \frac{\text{molecules}}{\text{cm}^3}$$

Check: The answer is reasonable because the reaction has a small equilibrium constant, so you would not expect to produce much product.

The reaction to produce NO is endothermic, so we can think of heat as a reactant. Therefore, raising the temperature (as in an automobile engine) shifts the reaction to the right, producing more NO.

14.55   (a)   **Given:** 4.45 g CO₂, 10.0 L, 1200 K, 2.00 g C, $K_p = 5.78$ **Find:** total pressure

Conceptual Plan: g CO₂ → mol CO₂ and g C → mol C and then determine limiting reactant

$$\frac{1 \text{ mol CO}_2}{44.01 \text{ g CO}_2} \qquad\qquad \frac{1 \text{ mol C}}{12.01 \text{ g C}}$$

and then mol CO₂ → P_{CO_2}. Prepare an ICE table, represent the change with x, sum the table,

$$PV = nRT$$

determine the equilibrium values, put the equilibrium values in the equilibrium expression, and solve for x.

Solution: $CO_2(g) + C(s) \rightleftharpoons 2 CO(g)$

$$4.45 \text{ g CO}_2 \times \frac{1 \text{ mol}}{44.01 \text{ g CO}_2} = 0.1011 \text{ mol CO}_2 \quad 2.00 \text{ g C} \times \frac{1 \text{ mol}}{12.01 \text{ g C}} = 0.1665 \text{ mol C}$$

Because the stoichiometry is 1:1, the CO_2 is the limiting reactant.

$$P_{CO_2} = \frac{(0.1011 \text{ mol})\left(\dfrac{0.08206 \text{ L atm}}{\text{mol K}}\right)(1200 \text{ K})}{10.0 \text{ L}} = 0.9956 \text{ atm}$$

$$CO_2(g) \ + \ C(s) \rightleftharpoons 2 \, CO\,(g)$$

	P_{CO_2}	P_{CO}
Initial	0.996	0.0
Change	$-x$	$2x$
Equil	$0.996 - x$	$2x$

The reaction will proceed to the right by x.

$$K_p = \frac{P_{CO}^2}{P_{CO_2}} = \frac{(2x)^2}{(0.996 - x)} = 5.78. \text{ Solve using the quadratic equation, found in Appendix I.}$$

$x = 0.678 \text{ atm}$

$P_{CO_2} = 0.996 \text{ atm} - 0.678 \text{ atm} = 0.318 \text{ atm} \quad P_{CO} = 2(0.678 \text{ atm}) = 1.356 \text{ atm}$

$P \text{ total} = 1.67 \text{ atm}$

Check: Plug the values for the partial pressure into the equilibrium expression. $\dfrac{(1.356)^2}{0.318} = 5.78$, which is the value of the equilibrium constant.

(b)   **Given:** 4.45 g CO_2, 10.0 L, 1200 K, 0.50 g C, $K_p = 5.78$ **Find:** total pressure
Conceptual Plan: g CO_2 → mol CO_2 and g C → mol C and then determine limiting reactant

$$\frac{1 \text{ mol } CO_2}{44.01 \text{ g } CO_2} \qquad\qquad \frac{1 \text{ mol C}}{12.01 \text{ g C}}$$

and then mol CO_2 → P_{CO_2} and mol C → mol CO → P_{CO}

$$PV = nRT \qquad\qquad PV = nRT$$

Solution: $CO_2(g) + C(s) \rightleftharpoons 2 \, CO(g)$

$$4.45 \text{ g } CO_2 \times \frac{1 \text{ mol}}{44.01 \text{ g } CO_2} = 0.1011 \text{ mol } CO_2 \qquad 0.50 \text{ g C} \times \frac{1 \text{ mol}}{12.01 \text{ g C}} = 0.0416 \text{ mol C}$$

Because the stoichiometry is 1:1, the C is the limiting reactant; therefore, the moles of CO formed will be determined from the reaction, not the equilibrium.

$$0.0416 \text{ mol C} \times \frac{2 \text{ mol CO}}{1 \text{ mol C}} = 0.0.832 \text{ mol CO}$$

$$CO_2(g) \ + \ C(s) \rightleftharpoons 2 \, CO(g)$$

Initial	0.1011	0.0416	0.0
Change	-0.0416	-0.0416	$2(0.0416)$
Equil	0.0595	0	0.0832

$$P_{CO_2} = \frac{(0.0595 \text{ mol})\left(\dfrac{0.08206 \text{ L atm}}{\text{mol K}}\right)(1200 \text{ K})}{10.0 \text{ L}} = 0.586 \text{ atm}$$

$$P_{CO} = \frac{(0.0832 \text{ mol})\left(\dfrac{0.08206 \text{ L atm}}{\text{mol K}}\right)(1200 \text{ K})}{10.0 \text{ L}} = 0.819 \text{ atm}$$

$P_{total} = 0.586 + 0.819 = 1.405 = 1.41 \text{ atm}$

Check: The pressure is less than the equilibrium pressure, which is reasonable because the C was the limiting reactant.

14.56   **Given:** at equilibrium: 0.13 mol H_2, 0.13 mol CO, 0.43 mol H_2O, then react all H_2O.
Find: CO at new equilibrium

Conceptual Plan: equilibrium values → K_c, and then new value of H_2O. Prepare an ICE table, represent the change with x, sum the table, determine the equilibrium values, put the equilibrium values in the equilibrium expression, and solve for x.

Solution: $H_2O(g) + C(s) \rightleftharpoons H_2(g) + CO(g)$

E 0.43   0.13   0.13 $K_c = \dfrac{[H_2][CO]}{[H_2O]} = \dfrac{(0.13)(0.13)}{(0.43)} = 0.039\underline{3}$

$2 H_2(g) + O_2(g) \rightarrow 2 H_2O(g)$ So, 0.13 mol H_2 produces 0.13 mol H_2O, giving new initial conditions of 0.56 mol H_2O (0.13 + 0.43), 0 mol H_2 (reacts completely), and 0.13 mol CO (unaffected).

$$H_2O(g) + C(s) \rightleftharpoons H_2(g) + CO(g)$$

	$[H_2O]$	$[H_2]$	$[CO]$
Initial	0.56	0	0.13
Change	$-x$	$+x$	$+x$
Equil	$0.56 - x$	x	$0.13 + x$

$K_c = \dfrac{[H_2][CO]}{[H_2O]} = \dfrac{(x)(0.13 + x)}{(0.56 - x)} = 0.039\underline{3}$ so, $x^2 + 0.1693x - 0.0220 = 0$. Solve using quadratic equation,

Appendix I. $x = 0.086$

$[CO] = 0.13 + 0.086 = 0.216 = 0.22$ therefore, 0.22 mol CO.

Check: Determine equilibrium concentration and plug into the equilibrium expression.

$K_c = \dfrac{[H_2][CO]}{[H_2O]} = \dfrac{(0.086)(0.22)}{(0.47)} = 0.040$. This is within 0.001 of the equilibrium value, so the answer is reasonable.

14.57   **Given:** $V = 10.0$ L, $T = 650$ K, 1.0 g MgO, $P_{CO_2} = 0.026$ atm, $K_p = 0.0260$
Find: mass $MgCO_3$ when volume is 0.100 L

Conceptual Plan: $P(10.0$ L$) \rightarrow P(0.100$ L$)$. Prepare an ICE table, represent the change with x, sum the table, determine the equilibrium value, put the equilibrium values in the equilibrium expression, and solve for x. Then determine moles CO_2, the limiting reactant, and the mass of $MgCO_3$ formed.

$P_1V_1 = P_2V_2 \quad PV = nRT$

$P_1V_1 = P_2V_2 \quad (0.0260 \text{ atm})(10.0 \text{ L}) = (x)(0.100 \text{ L}) \quad x = 2.60$ atm

$$MgCO_3(s) \rightleftharpoons MgO_3(s) + CO_2(g)$$

		P_{CO_2}
Initial		2.60
Change		$-x$
Equil		$2.60 - x$

$K_p = P_{CO_2} = 0.026 = 2.60 - x \qquad x = 2.5\underline{7}9$ atm

$n_{CO_2} = \dfrac{(2.5\underline{7}9 \text{ atm})10.0 \text{ L}}{\left(\dfrac{0.08206 \text{ L atm}}{\text{mol K}}\right)(650 \text{ K})} = 0.48\underline{3}5$ mol CO_2 $1.0 \text{ g MgO} \times \dfrac{1 \text{ mol}}{40.30 \text{ g MgO}} = 0.024\underline{8}$ mol MgO

Therefore, MgO is the limiting reactant and produces 0.0248 mol $MgCO_3$.

$0.0248 \text{ mol MgCO}_3 \times \dfrac{84.31 \text{ g MgCO}_3}{1 \text{ mol MgCO}_3} = 2.09 \text{ g MgCO}_3$

14.58   **Given:** at equilibrium: $P_{I_2} = 0.21$ atm, $P_I = 0.23$ atm
Find: P of each gas when the volume is compressed to half the initial volume
Conceptual Plan: P at equilibrium to equilibrium constant, determine P at new volume, prepare an ICE

$P_1V_1 = P_2V_2$

table, represent the change with x, sum the table, determine the equilibrium value, put the equilibrium values in the equilibrium expression, and solve for x.

Solution: $I_2(g) \rightleftharpoons 2\,I(g)$ $\quad K_p = \dfrac{P_I^2}{P_{I_2}} = \dfrac{(0.23)^2}{(0.21)} = 0.2\underline{5}2$

$P_1V_1 = P_2V_2$ $\qquad$ For I_2: $(0.21\text{ atm})(1) = (x\text{ atm})(0.5)$ $x = 0.42$ atm
$\qquad\qquad\qquad\qquad$ For I: $(0.23\text{ atm})(1) = (y\text{ atm})(0.5)$ $y = 0.46$ atm

$$I_2(g) \rightleftharpoons 2\,I(g)$$

	$[I_2]$	$[I]$
Initial	0.42	0.46
Change	$+x$	$-2x$
Equil	$0.42 + x$	$0.46 - 2x$

$Q = \dfrac{(0.46)^2}{(0.42)} = 0.50$ $\qquad Q > K$, so the reaction shifts to the left.

$K_p = \dfrac{(0.46 - 2x)^2}{(0.42 + x)} = 0.2\underline{5}2$ $\quad x = 0.05\underline{6}7$ Solve using the quadratic equation, found in Appendix I.

$P_{(I_2)} = 0.42 + 0.057 = 0.477 = 0.48$ atm
$P_{(I)} = 0.46 - 2(0.057) = 0.346 = 0.35$ atm

Check: Plug the equilibrium values into the equilibrium expression: $K_p = \dfrac{(0.35)^2}{(0.48)} = 0.2\underline{5}5 = 0.26.$

The value is within 1 significant figure of the original K_p, so the answer is reasonable.

14.59 **Given:** $C_2H_4(g) + Cl_2(g) \rightleftharpoons C_2H_4Cl_2(g)$ is exothermic $\quad$ **Find:** Which of the following will maximize $C_2H_4Cl_2$?
(a) Increasing the reaction volume will not maximize $C_2H_4Cl_2$. The chemical equation has 1 mole of gas on the right and 2 moles of gas on the left. Increasing the volume of the reaction mixture decreases the pressure and causes the reaction to shift to the left (toward the side with more moles of gas particles).
(b) Removing $C_2H_4Cl_2$ as it forms will maximize $C_2H_4Cl_2$. Removing the $C_2H_4Cl_2$ will decrease the concentration of $C_2H_4Cl_2$ and will cause the reaction to shift to the right, producing more $C_2H_4Cl_2$.
(c) Lowering the reaction temperature will maximize $C_2H_4Cl_2$. The reaction is exothermic, so we can think of heat as a product. Lowering the temperature will cause the reaction to shift to the right, producing more $C_2H_4Cl_2$.
(d) Adding Cl_2 will maximize $C_2H_4Cl_2$. Adding Cl_2 increases the concentration of Cl_2, so the reaction shifts to the right, which will produce more $C_2H_4Cl_2$.

14.60 **Given:** $C_2H_4(g) + I_2(g) \rightleftharpoons C_2H_4I_2(g)$ is endothermic $\quad$ **Find:** Which of the following will maximize $C_2H_4I_2$?
(a) Decreasing the reaction volume will maximize $C_2H_4I_2$. The chemical equation has 1 mole of gas on the right and 2 moles of gas on the left. Decreasing the volume of the reaction mixture increases the pressure and causes the reaction to shift to the right (toward the side with fewer moles of gas particles).
(b) Removing I_2 from the reaction mixture will not maximize $C_2H_4I_2$. Removing I_2 decreases the concentration of I_2, and the reaction will shift to the left to produce more I_2.
(c) Raising the temperature of the reaction will maximize $C_2H_4I_2$. The reaction is endothermic, so we can think of heat as a reactant. Raising the temperature will cause the reaction to shift to the right, producing more $C_2H_4I_2$.
(d) Adding C_2H_4 to the reaction mixture will maximize $C_2H_4I_2$. Adding C_2H_4 will increase the concentration of C_2H_4 and cause the reaction to shift to the right to produce more $C_2H_4I_2$.

14.61 **Given:** reaction 1 at equilibrium: $P_{H_2} = 0.958$ atm, $P_{I_2} = 0.877$ atm, $P_{HI} = 0.020$ atm; reaction 2: $P_{H_2} = P_{I_2} = 0.621$ atm, $P_{HI} = 0.101$ atm $\quad$ **Find:** Is reaction 2 at equilibrium? If not, what is the P_{HI} at equilibrium?
Conceptual Plan: Use equilibrium partial pressures to determine K_p. Use K_p to determine whether reaction 2 is at equilibrium. Prepare an ICE table, calculate Q, compare Q and K_p, predict the direction of the reaction, represent the change with x, sum the table, determine the equilibrium values, put the equilibrium values in the equilibrium expression, and solve for x. Determine P_{HI}.
Solution: $\qquad H_2(g) + I_2(g) \rightleftharpoons 2HI(g)$

	P_{H_2}	P_{I_2}	P_{HI}
Reaction 1:	0.958	0.877	0.020

$K_p = \dfrac{P_{HI}^2}{P_{H_2}P_{I_2}} = \dfrac{(0.020)^2}{(0.958)(0.877)} = 4.7\underline{6}10 \times 10^{-4}$

$$Q = \frac{P_{HI}^2}{P_{H_2}P_{I_2}} = \frac{(0.101)^2}{(0.621)(0.621)} = 0.0264 \; Q > K, \text{ so the reaction shifts to the left.}$$

$$H_2(g) \quad + \quad I_2(g) \quad \rightleftharpoons \quad 2\,HI(g)$$

Reaction 2:	P_{H_2}	P_{I_2}	P_{HI}
Initial	0.621	0.621	0.101
Change	x	x	$-2x$
Equil	$0.621 + x$	$0.621 + x$	$0.101 - 2x$

$$K_p = \frac{P_{HI}^2}{P_{H_2}P_{I_2}} = \frac{(0.101 - 2x)^2}{(0.621 + x)(0.621 + x)} = 4.7\underline{6}10 \times 10^{-4}$$

$$\sqrt{\frac{(0.101 - 2x)^2}{(0.621 + x)(0.621 + x)}} = \sqrt{4.7\underline{6}10 \times 10^{-4}}$$

$$\frac{(0.101 - 2x)}{(0.621 + x)} = 2.1\underline{8}2 \times 10^{-2}$$

$x = 0.04325 = 0.0433$
$P_{H_2} = P_{I_2} = 0.621 + x = 0.621 + 0.0433 = 0.664 \text{ atm}$
$P_{HI} = 0.101 - 2x = 0.101 - 2(0.0433) = 0.0144 \text{ atm}$

Check: Plug the values into the equilibrium expression:

$$K_p = \frac{(0.0144)^2}{(0.664)^2} = 4.703 \times 10^{-4} = 4.70 \times 10^{-4}; \text{ this value is close to the original equilbirium constant.}$$

14.62　**Given:** reaction 1 initial: $H_2S = 0.500$ M, $SO_2 = 0.500$ M, H_2O at equilibrium $= 0.0011$ M; reaction 2: H_2S $= 0.250$ M, $SO_2 = 0.325$ M　**Find:** $[H_2O]$ at equilibrium in reaction 2
Conceptual Plan: Prepare an ICE table. Determine the equilibrium concentrations in reaction 1 and determine K_c. Use K_c to determine the equilibrium concentrations for reaction 2. Prepare an ICE table, calculate Q, compare Q and K_c, predict the direction of the reaction, represent the change with x, sum the table, determine the equilibrium values, put the equilibrium values in the equilibrium expression, and solve for x. Determine $[H_2O]$.
Solution: 　　$2\,H_2S(g) \quad + \quad SO_2(g) \quad \rightleftharpoons \quad 3\,S(s) \quad + \quad 2\,H_2O(g)$

Reaction 1:	$[H_2S]$	$[SO_2]$	$[S]$	$[H_2O]$
Initial	0.500	0.500	constant	0
Change	$-2x$	$-x$		$2x$
Equil	$0.500 - 2x$	$0.500 - x$		0.0011

$2x = 0.0011, x = 5.5 \times 10^{-4}$
$[H_2S] = 0.500 - 0.0011 = 0.4989 \qquad [SO_2] = 0.500 - 5.5 \times 10^{-4} = 0.49945$

$$K_c = \frac{[H_2O]^2}{[H_2S]^2[SO_2]} = \frac{(0.0011)^2}{(0.4989)^2(0.49945)} = 9.7\underline{3}3 \times 10^{-6}$$

$$2\,H_2S(g) \quad + \quad SO_2(g) \quad \rightleftharpoons \quad 3\,S(s) \quad + \quad 2\,H_2O(g)$$

Reaction 2:	$[H_2S]$	$[SO_2]$	$[S]$	$[H_2O]$
Initial	0.250	0.325	constant	
Change	$-2x$	$-x$		$2x$
Equil	$0.250 - 2x$	$0.325 - x$		$2x$

Reaction shifts to the right.

$$K_c = \frac{[H_2O]^2}{[H_2S]^2[SO_2]} = \frac{(2x)^2}{(0.250 - 2x)^2(0.325 - x)} = 9.7\underline{3}3 \times 10^{-6}$$

Assume that $2x$ and x are small, respectively, compared to 0.250 and 0.325.
$4x^2 = 1.9\underline{7}70 \times 10^{-7}$
$x^2 = 4.9\underline{4}25 \times 10^{-8}$

$x = 2.2\underline{2}3 \times 10^{-4}$ Check assumption: $\dfrac{2.22 \times 10^{-4}}{0.250} = 8.88 \times 10^{-4} \times 100\% = 0.089\%$; assumption is valid.

$[H_2O] = 2x = 2(2.22 \times 10^{-4}) = 4.44 \times 10^{-4}$ M

$[H_2S] = 0.250 - 2(2.22 \times 10^{-4}) = 0.250$ M

$[SO_2] = 0.325 - 2.22 \times 10^{-4} = 0.325$ M

Check: Plug the values into the equilibrium expression:

$K_c = \dfrac{(4.44 \times 10^{-4})^2}{(0.250)^2(0.325)} = 9.71 \times 10^{-6}$; this value is close to the original equilibrium constant.

14.63 **Given:** 200.0 L container; 1.27 kg N_2; 0.310 kg H_2; 725 K; $K_p = 5.3 \times 10^{-5}$ **Find:** mass in g of NH_3 and % yield

Conceptual Plan: $K_p \rightarrow K_c$ and then $kg \rightarrow g \rightarrow mol \rightarrow M$ and then prepare an ICE table. Represent

$$K_p = K_c(RT)^{\Delta n} \qquad \frac{1000\ g}{kg} \quad \frac{g}{molar\ mass} \quad \frac{mol}{vol}$$

the change with x, sum the table, determine the equilibrium values, put the equilibrium values in the equilibrium expression, and solve for x. Determine $[NH_3]$. Then $M \rightarrow mol \rightarrow g$ and then determine

$$M \times vol \quad mol \times molar\ mass$$

theoretical yield $NH_3 \rightarrow$ % yield.

$$determine\ limiting\ reactant\ \frac{actual\ yield}{theoretical\ yield}$$

Solution: $K_p = K_c(RT)^{\Delta n}$ $K_c = \dfrac{K_p}{(RT)^{\Delta n}} = \dfrac{5.3 \times 10^{-5}}{\left(\left(0.08206\ \dfrac{L \cdot atm}{mol \cdot K}\right)(725K)\right)^{-2}} = 0.18\underline{7}6$

$n_{N_2} = 1.27\ kg\ \cancel{N_2} \times \dfrac{1000\ \cancel{g}}{kg} \times \dfrac{1\ mol\ N_2}{28.02\ \cancel{g\ N_2}} = 45.\underline{3}25\ mol\ N_2$ $[N_2] = \dfrac{45.\underline{3}25\ mol}{200.0\ L} = 0.22\underline{6}63$ M

$n_{H_2} = 0.310\ kg\ \cancel{H_2} \times \dfrac{1000\ \cancel{g}}{kg} \times \dfrac{1\ mol\ H_2}{2.016\ \cancel{g\ H_2}} = 153.\underline{7}7\ mol\ H_2$ $[H_2] = \dfrac{153.\underline{7}7\ mol}{200.0\ L} = 0.76\underline{8}85$ M

$$N_2(g) \ + \ 3\ H_2(g) \ \rightleftharpoons \ 2\ NH_3(g)$$

Reaction 1:	$[N_2]$	$[H_2]$	$[NH_3]$
Initial	0.2266	0.7689	0.0
Change	$-x$	$-3x$	$2x$
Equil	$0.2266 - x$	$0.7689 - 3x$	$2x$

Reaction shifts to the right.

$K_c = \dfrac{[NH_3]^2}{[N_2][H_2]^3} = \dfrac{(2x)^2}{(0.2266 - x)(0.7689 - 3x)^3} = 0.1876$

Assume that x is small compared to 0.2268 and $3x$ is small compared to 0.7689.

$\dfrac{(2x)^2}{(0.2266)(0.7689)^3} = 0.1877$ $x = 0.06951$

Check assumptions: $\dfrac{0.06951}{0.2268} \times 100\% = 30.6$, which is not valid, and $\dfrac{3(0.06951)}{0.7689} \times 100\% = 27.1\%$

Use method of successive substitution to solve for x. This yields $x = 0.0460$.

$[NH_3] = 2x = 2(0.0460) = 0.0920$ M

Check: Plug the values into the equilibrium expression:

$K_c = \dfrac{(0.0920)^2}{(0.2266 - 0.0460)((0.7689 - 3(0.0460))^3} = 0.1866$;

this value is close to the original equilibrium constant.

Determine grams NH_3: $\dfrac{0.0920\ mol\ \cancel{NH_3}}{\cancel{L}} \times 200.0\ \cancel{L} \times \dfrac{17.03\ g\ NH_3}{\cancel{mol\ NH_3}} = 31\underline{3}.4\ g = 3.1 \times 10^2$ g

Determine the theoretical yield: Determine the limiting reactant:

$1.27\ kg\ \cancel{N_2} \times \dfrac{1000\ \cancel{g}}{kg} \times \dfrac{1\ \cancel{mol\ N_2}}{28.02\ \cancel{g\ N_2}} \times \dfrac{2\ \cancel{mol\ NH_3}}{1\ \cancel{mol\ N_2}} \times \dfrac{17.03\ g\ NH_3}{\cancel{mol\ NH_3}} = 15\underline{4}4\ g\ NH_3$

$$0.310 \text{ kg } \cancel{H_2} \times \frac{1000 \cancel{g}}{\cancel{kg}} \times \frac{1 \text{ mol } \cancel{H_2}}{2.016 \text{ g } \cancel{H_2}} \times \frac{2 \text{ mol } \cancel{NH_3}}{3 \text{ mol } \cancel{H_2}} \times \frac{17.03 \text{ g } NH_3}{\text{mol } \cancel{NH_3}} = 1746 \text{ g } NH_3$$

N_2 produces the least amount of NH_3; therefore, it is the limiting reactant, and the theoretical yield is 1.54×10^3 g NH_3.

$$\% \text{ yield} = \frac{3.1 \times 10^2 \cancel{g}}{1.54 \times 10^3 \cancel{g}} \times 100 = 20.\%$$

14.64 **Given:** $V = 85.0$ L, 22.3 kg CH_4, 55.4 kg CO_2, $T = 825$ K, $K_p = 4.5 \times 10^2$ **Find:** g H_2 at equilibrium

Conceptual Plan: kg → g → mol → P and then prepare an ICE table. Represent the change

$$\frac{1000 \text{ g}}{\text{kg}} \quad \frac{\text{g}}{\text{molar mass}} \quad PV = nRT$$

with x, sum the table, determine the equilibrium values, put the equilibrium values in the equilibrium expression, and solve for x. Determine P_{H_2}. Then P → mol → g and then determine

$$PV = nRT \quad \text{mol} \times \text{molar mass}$$

theoretical yield H_2 → % yield.

$$\text{determine limiting reactant } \frac{\text{actual yield}}{\text{theoretical yield}}$$

Solution:

$$n_{CH_4} = 22.3 \text{ kg} \times \frac{1000 \cancel{g}}{\cancel{kg}} \times \frac{1 \text{ mol}}{16.04 \cancel{g}} = 139\underline{0}.3 \text{ mol}$$

$$P_{CH_4} = \frac{nRT}{V} = \frac{(139\underline{0} \text{ mol})\left(0.08206 \dfrac{\cancel{L} \cdot \text{atm}}{\text{mol} \cdot \cancel{K}}\right)(825 \cancel{K})}{85.0 \cancel{L}} = 110\underline{7} \text{ atm}$$

$$n_{CO_2} = 55.4 \text{ kg} \times \frac{1000 \cancel{g}}{\cancel{kg}} \times \frac{1 \text{ mol}}{44.01 \cancel{g}} = 125\underline{9} \text{ mol}$$

$$P_{CO_2} = \frac{nRT}{V} = \frac{(125\underline{9} \text{ mol})\left(0.08206 \dfrac{\cancel{L} \cdot \text{atm}}{\text{mol} \cdot \cancel{K}}\right)(825 \cancel{K})}{85.0 \cancel{L}} = 100\underline{3} \text{ atm}$$

$$CH_4(g) + CO_2(g) \rightleftharpoons 2 CO(g) + 2 H_2(g)$$

	P_{CH_4}	P_{CO_2}	P_{CO}	P_{H_2}
Initial	1107	1003	0.00	0.00
Change	$-x$	$-x$	$2x$	$2x$
Equil	$1107 - x$	$1003 - x$	$2x$	$2x$

$$K_p = \frac{P_{CO}^2 P^2}{P_{CH_2} P_{CO_2}} = \frac{(2x)^2 (2x)^2}{(1107 - x)(1003 - x)} = 4.5 \times 10^2$$

Assume that x is small compared to 1003 and 1110.

$$x^4 = 3.13 \times 10^7 \quad x = 74.8$$

Check assumptions: $\dfrac{74.8}{1003} \times 100\% = 7.46\%$ and $\dfrac{74.8}{1107} \times 100\% = 6.75\%$; assumptions are not valid.

Use method of successive substitutions, which yields

$$x = 72.1.$$

Check: Plug into equilibrium expression:

$$K_p = \frac{P_{CO}^2 P_{H_2}}{P_{CH_2} P_{CO_2}} = \frac{(2(72.1))^2 (2(72.1))^2}{(1107 - 72.1)(1003 - 72.1)} = 4.49 \times 10^2 = 4.5 \times 10^2, \text{ which is the equilibrium constant.}$$

Determine grams of H_2.

$$P_{H_2} = 2(72.1) = 144 \text{ atm} \qquad n_{H_2} = \frac{PV}{RT} = \frac{(144 \cancel{\text{atm}})(85.0 \cancel{L})}{\left(0.08206 \dfrac{\cancel{L} \cdot \text{atm}}{\text{mol} \cdot \cancel{K}}\right)(825 \cancel{K})} = 18\underline{0}.8 \text{ mol}$$

$$180.8 \ \cancel{mol} \times \frac{2.016 \ \text{g H}_2}{\cancel{mol}} = 364.5 \ \text{g} = 365 \ \text{g H}_2$$

Determine % yield.

$$1390 \ \text{mol CH}_4 \times \frac{2 \ \text{mol H}_2}{\text{mol CH}_4} = 2780 \ \text{mol H}_2$$

$$1259 \ \text{mol CO}_2 \times \frac{2 \ \text{mol H}_2}{\text{mol CO}_2} = 2518 \ \text{mol H}_2$$

CO_2 is the limiting reactant.

$$\frac{180.8 \ \cancel{\text{mol H}_2}}{2518 \ \cancel{\text{mol H}_2}} \times 100 = 7.18\% \ \text{yield}$$

14.65 **Given:** at equilibrium: $P_{CO} = 0.30$ atm; $P_{Cl_2} = 0.10$ atm; $P_{COCl_2} = 0.60$ atm, add 0.40 atm Cl_2
Find: P_{CO} when system returns to equilibrium
Conceptual Plan: Use equilibrium partial pressures to determine K_p. For the new conditions, prepare an ICE table, represent the change with x, sum the table, determine the equilibrium values, put the equilibrium values in the equilibrium expression, and solve for x. Determine P_{CO}.
Solution: $CO(g) + Cl_2(g) \rightleftharpoons COCl_2(g)$

Condition 1:	P_{CO}	P_{Cl_2}	P_{COCl_2}
	0.30	0.10	0.60

$$K_p = \frac{P_{COCl_2}}{P_{CO}P_{Cl_2}} = \frac{(0.60)}{(0.30)(0.10)} = 20$$

$$CO(g) + Cl_2(g) \rightleftharpoons COCl_2(g)$$

Condition 2:	P_{CO}	P_{Cl_2}	P_{COCl_2}
Initial	0.30	0.10 + 0.40	0.60
Change	$-x$	$-x$	$+x$
Equil	0.30 − x	0.50 − x	0.60 + x

Reaction shifts to the right because the concentration of Cl_2 was increased.

$$K_p = \frac{P_{COCl_2}}{P_{CO}P_{Cl_2}} = \frac{(0.60 + x)}{(0.30 - x)(0.50 - x)} = 20$$

$$20x^2 - 17x + 2.4 = 0$$

$$\frac{-b \pm \sqrt{b^2 - 4ac}}{2a} = \frac{-(-17) \pm \sqrt{(-17)^2 - 4(20)(2.4)}}{2(20)}$$

$x = 0.67$ or 0.18 so, $x = 0.18$

$P_{CO} = 0.30 - 0.18 = 0.12$ atm; $P_{Cl_2} = 0.50 - 0.18 = 0.32$; $P_{COCl_2} = 0.60 + 0.18 = 0.78$ atm

Check: Plug the values into the equilibrium expression:

$$K_p = \frac{(0.78)}{(0.12)(0.32)} = 20.3 = 20; \text{ this is the same as the original equilibrium constant.}$$

14.66 **Given:** $P_{SO_2} = 3.00$ atm; $P_{O_2} = 1.00$ atm; at equilibrium, $P_{total} = 3.75$ atm, $T = 27 \ °C$ **Find:** K_c
Conceptual Plan: Prepare an ICE table, represent the change with x, sum the table, determine the equilibrium values, use the total pressure, and solve for x. Determine partial pressure of each at equilibrium. Determine $K_p \rightarrow K_c$.
$K_p = K_c(RT)^{\Delta n}$

Solution: $2 \ SO_2(g) + O_2(g) \rightleftharpoons 2 \ SO_3(g)$

	P_{SO_2}	P_{O_2}	P_{SO_3}
Initial	3.00	1.00	0.00
Change	$-2x$	$-x$	$+2x$
Equil	3.00 − 2x	1.00 − x	2x

$P_{Total} = P_{SO_2} + P_{O_2} + P_{SO_3}$ $3.75 = (3.00 - 2x) + (1.00 - x) + 2x$

$x = 0.25$ $P_{SO_2} = (3.00 - 2(0.25)) = 2.50$ atm; $P_{O_2} = (1.00 - 0.25)) = 0.75$ atm; $P_{SO_3} = 2(0.25) = 0.50$ atm

$$K_p = \frac{P_{SO_3}^2}{P_{SO_2}^2 P_{O_2}} = \frac{(0.50)^2}{(2.50)^2(0.75)} = 0.05\underline{3}3 = 0.053$$

Check: The value of the pressure of SO_3 is small compared to the pressures of SO_2 and O_2; therefore, you would expect K_p to be less than 1.

$$K_p = K_c(RT)^{\Delta n} \quad 0.05\underline{3}3 = K_c\left(\left(0.08206\,\frac{L\cdot atm}{mol\cdot K}\right)(27 + 273\,K)\right)^{-1}$$

$K_c = 1.\underline{3}12 = 1.3$

14.67   **Given:** $K_p = 0.76$; P_{total} at equilibrium $= 1.00$ atm   **Find:** $P_{initial}$ CCl_4
Conceptual Plan: Prepare an ICE table, represent the P_{CCl_4} with A and the change with x, sum the table, determine the equilibrium values, use the total pressure, and solve for A in terms of x. Determine partial pressure of each at equilibrium, use the equilibrium expression to determine x, and determine A.
Solution: $CCl_4(g) \rightleftharpoons C(s) + 2\,Cl_2(g)$

	P_{CCl_4}	P_C	P_{Cl_2}
Initial	A	constant	0.00
Change	$-x$		$+2x$
Equil	$A - x$		$2x$

$P_{Total} = P_{CCl_4} + P_{Cl_2}$ $1.0 = A - x + 2x$ $A = 1 - x$

$P_{CCl_4} = (A - x) = (1 - x) - x = 1 - 2x$; $P_{Cl_2} = (2x)$

$$K_p = \frac{P_{Cl_2}^2}{P_{CCl_4}} = \frac{(2x)^2}{(1 - 2x)} = 0.76$$

$4x^2 + 1.52x - 0.76 = 0$ $x = 0.285$ or -0.665 so $x = 0.2\underline{8}5$

$A = 1 - x = 1.0 - 0.285 = 0.715 = 0.72$ atm

Check: Plug the values into the equilibrium expression:

$$K_p = \frac{P_{Cl_2}^2}{P_{CCl_4}} = \frac{(2x)^2}{(A - x)} = \frac{(2(0.285))^2}{(0.715 - 0.285)} = 0.756 = 0.76;\text{ the original equilibrium is constant.}$$

14.68   **Given:** $K = 3.0$; $SO_2 = 2.4$ mol initial; $SO_3 = 1.2$ mol equilibrium   **Find:** mol NO_2 initial
Conceptual Plan: Assume 1.0 L, prepare an ICE table, represent the change with x, sum the table, determine the equilibrium values, and determine the initial values.
Solution: $SO_2(g) + NO_2(g) \rightleftharpoons SO_3(g) + NO(g)$

	$[SO_2]$	$[NO_2]$	$[SO_3]$	$[NO]$
Initial	2.4	y	0.0	0.0
Change	$-x$	$-x$	x	x
Equil	1.2	$y - 1.2$	1.2	1.2

$x = 1.2$ Fill in the table.

$$K = \frac{[SO_3][NO]}{[SO_2][NO_2]} \quad 3.0 = \frac{(1.2)(1.2)}{(1.2)(y - 1.2)} \quad y = 1.6$$

mol NO_2 initial $= 1.6$ mol

Check: The initial amount 1.6 mol is greater than the amount lost.

14.69   **Given:** $V = 0.654$ L, $T = 1000$ K, $K_p = 3.9 \times 10^{-2}$ **Find:** mass CaO at equilibrium
Conceptual Plan: $K_p \rightarrow P_{CO_2} \rightarrow n_{(CO_2)} \rightarrow n_{(CaO)} \rightarrow g$
$\quad\quad\quad\quad\quad\quad$ $PV = nRT$ stoichiometry $g = n$(molar mass)

Solution: Because $CaCO_3$ and CaO are solids, they are not included in the equilibrium expression.

$$K_p = P_{CO_2} = 3.9 \times 10^{-2} \quad n = \frac{PV}{RT} = \frac{(3.9 \times 10^{-2} \text{ atm})(0.654 \text{ L})}{\left(0.08206 \dfrac{\text{L} \cdot \text{atm}}{\text{mol} \cdot \text{K}}\right)(1000 \text{ K})} = 3.\underline{1}08 \times 10^{-4} \text{ mol } CO_2$$

$$3.\underline{1}08 \times 10^{-4} \text{ mol } CO_2 \times \frac{1 \text{ mol CaO}}{1 \text{ mol CO}_2} \times \frac{56.1 \text{ g CaO}}{1 \text{ mol CaO}} = 0.0174 \text{ g} = 0.0174 \text{ g CaO}$$

Check: The small value of K would give a small amount of products, so we would not expect to have a large mass of CaO formed.

14.70   **Given:** at equilibrium: N_2O_4, $P = 0.28$ atm, NO_2, $P = 1.1$ atm; $T = 350$ K
Find: equilibrium pressures when volume doubles
Conceptual Plan: $P_{(N_2O_4)}, P_{(NO_2)} \rightarrow K_p$ **and then P when volume doubles. Then prepare an ICE table, represent the change with x, sum the table, and determine the equilibrium values.**

Solution: $K_p = \dfrac{P_{NO_2}^2}{P_{N_2O_4}} = \dfrac{(1.1)^2}{0.28} = 4.\underline{3}21$

When the volume is doubled, the partial pressure of each gas decreases by half.

$$N_2O_2(g) \rightleftharpoons 2\,NO_2(g)$$

	$P_{N_2O_4}$	P_{NO_2}
Initial	0.28/2	1.1/2
Change	$-x$	$+2x$
Equil	$0.14 - x$	$0.55 + 2x$

The reaction shifts to the side with more moles—to the right.

$$K_p = \frac{P_{NO_2}^2}{P_{N_2O_4}} = \frac{(0.55 + 2x)^2}{(0.14 - x)} = 4.\underline{3}21$$

$$4x^2 + 6.521x - 0.3024 = 0$$

$$\frac{-b \pm \sqrt{b^2 - 4ac}}{2a} = \frac{-(6.521) \pm \sqrt{(6.521)^2 - 4(4)(-0.3024)}}{2(4)}$$

$x = 0.0451$ or -1.675 so $x = 0.0451$

$P_{N_2O_4} = 0.14 - 0.0451 = 0.0949$ atm $= 0.095$ atm; $P_{NO_2} = 0.55 + 2(0.0451) = 0.6402 = 0.64$ atm

Check: Plug the values into the equilibrium expression:

$$K_p = \frac{(0.6402)^2}{(0.0949)} = 4.32 = 4.3; \text{ this is the same as the original equilibrium constant.}$$

14.71   **Given:** $K_p = 3.10$, initial $P_{CO} = 215$ torr, $P_{Cl_2} = 245$ torr   **Find:** mole fraction $COCl_2$
Conceptual Plan: P **in torr** $\rightarrow$ P **in atm. Prepare an ICE table, represent the change with x, sum the table,**

$$\frac{1 \text{ atm}}{760 \text{ torr}}$$

determine the equilibrium values, use the total pressure, and solve for mole fraction.

$$\frac{P_{COCl_2}}{P_{Total}}$$

Solution: $P_{CO} = (215 \text{ torr})\left(\dfrac{1 \text{ atm}}{760 \text{ torr}}\right) = 0.28\underline{2}9$ atm $P_{Cl_2} = (245 \text{ torr})\left(\dfrac{1 \text{ atm}}{760 \text{ torr}}\right) = 0.32\underline{2}4$ atm

$$CO(g) \quad + \quad Cl_2(g) \rightleftharpoons COCl_2(g)$$

Initial	0.28$\underline{2}$9	0.32$\underline{2}$4	0
Change	$-x$	$-x$	$+x$
Equil	0.28$\underline{2}$9 $- x$	0.32$\underline{2}$4 $- x$	x

$Q < K$, so the reaction shifts to the right.

$$K_p = \frac{P_{COCl_2}}{P_{CO}P_{Cl_2}} = \frac{x}{(0.28\underline{2}9 - x)(0.32\underline{2}4 - x)} = 3.10 \text{ so, } 3.10x^2 - 2.87643x + 0.2827 = 0$$

Solve using quadratic expression in Appendix I.

$x = 0.8161$ or 0.1117 so $x = 0.1117$

$P_{CO} = 0.2829 - 0.1117 = 0.1712$ $P_{Cl_2} = 0.3224 - 0.1117 = 0.2107$ $P_{COCl_2} = 0.1117$

mole fraction $COCl_2 = \dfrac{P_{COCl_2}}{P_{CO} + P_{Cl_2} + P_{COCl_2}} = \dfrac{0.1117}{0.1712 + 0.2107 + 0.1117} = 0.2263 = 0.226$

Check: Plug the equilibrium pressures into the equilibrium expression:

$K_p = \dfrac{0.1117}{(0.1712)(0.2107)} = 3.0966 = 3.10$, which is the equilibrium constant; so the answer is reasonable.

14.72   **Given:** $K_p = 1.60 \times 10^{-3}$, $T = 700$ K, 1.55 L, $P_{H_2O} = 145$ torr   **Find:** % mass H_2 at equilibrium
          Conceptual Plan: $P(\text{torr}) \rightarrow P(\text{atm})$. **Prepare an ICE table, represent the change with x, sum the table,**

$$\dfrac{1 \text{ atm}}{760 \text{ torr}}$$

and determine the equilibrium values. $P \rightarrow n \rightarrow$ **mass for each** $\rightarrow$ **mass %**

$$PV = nRT \quad \dfrac{28.01 \text{ g CO}}{1 \text{ mol CO}} \quad \dfrac{2.016 \text{ g } H_2}{1 \text{ mol } H_2} \quad \dfrac{18.02 \text{ g } H_2O}{1 \text{ mol } H_2O} \quad \dfrac{\text{mass } H_2}{\text{total mass}} \times 100\%$$

Solution: $P_{H_2O} = (145 \text{ torr})\left(\dfrac{1 \text{ atm}}{760 \text{ torr}}\right) = 0.1908 \text{ atm}$

$$H_2O(g) + C(s) \rightleftharpoons CO(g) + H_2(g)$$

Initial	0.1908	0	0
Change	$-x$	$+x$	$+x$
Equil	$0.1908 - x$	x	x

$Q < K$ reaction shifts to the right.

$K_p = \dfrac{P_{CO}P_{H_2}}{P_{H_2O}} = \dfrac{(x)(x)}{(0.1908 - x)} = 1.60 \times 10^{-3}$ $x = 0.01668$ or -0.01828 so $x = 0.01668$

$P_{CO} = P_{H_2} = 0.01668 \text{ atm}$ $P_{H_2O} = 0.1908 - 0.01668 = 0.1741 \text{ atm}$

$n_{CO} = n_{H_2} = \dfrac{(0.01668 \text{ atm})(1.55 \text{ L})}{\left(\dfrac{0.08206 \text{ L atm}}{\text{mol K}}\right)(700.0 \text{ K})} = 4.501 \times 10^{-4} \text{ mol}$

$n_{H_2O} = \dfrac{(0.1741 \text{ atm})(1.55 \text{ L})}{\left(\dfrac{0.08206 \text{ L atm}}{\text{mol K}}\right)(700.0 \text{ K})} = 4.698 \times 10^{-3} \text{ mol}$

$(4.501 \times 10^{-4} \text{ mol CO}) \dfrac{28.01 \text{ g CO}}{1 \text{ mol CO}} = 0.01261 \text{ g CO}$ $(4.501 \times 10^{-4} \text{ mol } H_2) \dfrac{2.016 \text{ g } H_2}{1 \text{ mol } H_2} = 9.074 \times 10^{-4} \text{ g } H_2$

$(4.698 \times 10^{-3} \text{ mol } H_2O) \dfrac{18.02 \text{ g } H_2O}{1 \text{ mol } H_2O} = 0.08466 \text{ g } H_2O$

$$\dfrac{9.074 \times 10^{-4} \text{ g } H_2}{(0.01261 \text{ g} + 9.074 \times 10^{-4} \text{ g} + 0.08466 \text{ g})} \times 100 = \dfrac{9.074 \times 10^{-4} \text{ g } H_2}{(0.0981774 \text{ g})} \times 100 = 0.9242\% = 0.924\% \text{ } H_2$$

Check: Plug the equilibrium values into the equilibrium expression:

$K_p = \dfrac{(0.01668)(0.01668)}{(0.1741)} = 1.60 \times 10^{-3}$, which is the equilibrium constant. Thus, the answer is reasonable.

Challenge Problems

14.73   (a)   **Given:** $P_{NO} = 522$ torr, $P_{O_2} = 421$ torr; at equilibrium, $P_{total} = 748$ torr   **Find:** K_p
                  Conceptual Plan: **Prepare an ICE table, represent the change with x, sum the table, determine the equi-**
                  librium values, use the total pressure, and solve for x. torr $\rightarrow$ atm $\rightarrow$ K_p

Solution: $2 NO(g) + O_2(g) \rightleftharpoons 2 NO_2(g)$

	P_{NO}	P_{O_2}	P_{NO_2}
Initial	522 torr	421 torr	0.00
Change	$-2x$	$-x$	$+2x$
Equil	$522 - 2x$	$421 - x$	$2x$

$P_{Total} = P_{NO} + P_{O_2} + P_{NO_2}$ $748 = 522 - 2x + (421 - x) + 2x$

$x = 195$ torr $P_{NO} = (522 - 2(195)) = 132$ torr;

$P_{O_2} = (421 - 195) = 226$ torr; $P_{NO_2} = 2(195) = 390$ torr

$P_{NO} = 132 \text{ torr} \times \dfrac{1 \text{ atm}}{760 \text{ torr}} = 0.17\underline{3}7$ atm; $P_{O_2} = 226 \text{ torr} \times \dfrac{1 \text{ atm}}{760 \text{ torr}} = 0.29\underline{7}4$ atm;

$P_{NO_2} = 390 \text{ torr} \times \dfrac{1 \text{ atm}}{760 \text{ torr}} = 0.51\underline{3}2$ atm

$K_p = \dfrac{P_{NO_2}^2}{P_{NO}^2 P_{O_2}} = \dfrac{(0.51\underline{3}2)^2}{(0.17\underline{3}7)^2(0.29\underline{7}4)} = 29.35 = 29.3$

(b)   **Given:** $= P_{NO} = 255$ torr, $P_{O_2} = 185$ torr, $K_p = 29.3$ **Find:** equilibrium P_{NO_2}

Conceptual Plan:

torr $\rightarrow$ atm and then prepare an ICE table. Represent the change with x, sum the table,

$$\dfrac{\text{atm}}{760 \text{ torr}}$$

determine the equilibrium values, put the equilibrium values in the equilibrium expression, and solve

for x. Determine P_{NO_2}.

Solution: $P_{NO} = 255 \text{ torr} \times \dfrac{1 \text{ atm}}{760 \text{ torr}} = 0.33\underline{5}5$ atm $P_{O_2} = 185 \text{ torr} \times \dfrac{1 \text{ atm}}{760 \text{ torr}} = 0.24\underline{3}4$ atm

$2 NO(g) + O_2(g) \rightleftharpoons 2 NO_2(g)$

	P_{NO}	P_{O_2}	P_{NO_2}
Initial	0.3355	0.2434	0.00
Change	$-2x$	$-x$	$+2x$
Equil	$0.3355 - 2x$	$0.2434 - x$	$2x$

$K_p = \dfrac{P_{NO_2}^2}{P_{NO}^2 P_{O_2}} = \dfrac{(2x)^2}{(0.3355 - 2x)^2(0.2434 - x)} = 29.3$

$-117.2x^3 + 63.847x^2 - 12.867x + 0.80282 = 0$. Solve using successive approximations or a cubic equation calculator found on the Internet.

$x = 0.11\underline{1}3$ $P_{NO_2} = 2x = 2(0.11\underline{1}3) = 0.22\underline{2}6$ atm

$P_{NO} = (0.3355 - 2(0.1113)) = 0.1129$ $P_{O_2} = (0.2434 - 0.1113) = 0.1321$

$0.22\underline{2}6 \text{ atm} \times \dfrac{760 \text{ torr}}{1 \text{ atm}} = 169.2 \text{ torr} = 169$ torr

Check: Plug the values into the equilibrium expression:

$K_p = \dfrac{(0.22\underline{2}6)^2}{(0.1129)^2(0.1321)} = 29.428 = 29.4$; this is within 0.1 of the original equilibrium constant.

14.74   **Given:** 2.75 L, 950 K, 0.100 mol SO_2, 0.100 mol O_2; $K_p = 0.355$ **Find:** P_{total} at equilibrium

Conceptual Plan: $n \rightarrow P$ and then prepare an ICE table. Represent the change with x, sum the table,

$$PV = nRT$$

determine the equilibrium values, put the equilibrium values in the equilibrium expression, solve for x, and

then determine P for each reactant and product $\rightarrow P_{total}$.

$$P_{total} = P_{SO_2} + P_{O_2} + P_{SO_3}$$

Solution: $P = \dfrac{nRT}{V}$ $P_{O_2} = P_{SO_2} = \dfrac{(0.100\ \text{mol})\left(0.08206\ \dfrac{L \cdot atm}{mol \cdot K}\right)(950\ K)}{2.75\ L} = 2.8\underline{3}5\ \text{atm}$

$$2\,SO_2(g) + O_2(g) \rightleftharpoons 2\,SO_3(g)$$

	P_{SO_2}	P_{O_2}	P_{SO_3}
Initial	2.835	2.835	0.00
Change	$-2x$	$-x$	$+2x$
Equil	$2.835 - 2x$	$2.835 - x$	$2x$

$$K_p = \frac{P_{SO_3}^2}{P_{SO_2}^2 P_{O_2}} = \frac{(2x)^2}{(2.835 - 2x)^2(2.835 - x)} = 0.355$$

$-1.42x^3 + 4.051x^2 - 14.266x + 8.089 = 0$. Solve using successive approximations or a cubic equation calculator found on the Internet.

$x = 0.6628 = 0.663$ and the other two roots are imaginary numbers.

$P_{SO_3} = 2x = 2(0.663) = 1.3\underline{2}6 = 1.33\ \text{atm}$

$P_{SO_2} = (2.836 - 2x) = (2.836 - 2(0.663)) = 1.5\underline{1}0 = 1.51\ \text{atm}$

$P_{O_2} = (2.836 - x) = (2.836 - 0.663) = 2.1\underline{7}3 = 2.17\ \text{atm}$

$P_{Total} = 1.33 + 1.51 + 2.17 = 5.01\ \text{atm}$

Check: Plug the values into the equilibrium expression:

$$K_p = \frac{P_{SO_3}^2}{P_{SO_2}^2 P_{O_2}} = \frac{(1.33)^2}{(1.51)^2(2.17)} = 0.3575$$

This is within 99% of the significant figures of the original equilibrium constant.

14.75   **Given:** P_{NOCl} at equilibrium $= 115$ torr; $K_p = 0.27$, $T = 700$ K   **Find:** initial pressure NO, Cl_2

Conceptual Plan: torr $\rightarrow$ atm and then prepare an ICE table. Represent the change with x, sum the table,

$$\frac{atm}{760\ torr}$$

determine the equilibrium values, put the equilibrium values in the equilibrium expression, and determine initial pressure.

Solution: $115\ \text{torr} \times \dfrac{1\ \text{atm}}{760\ \text{torr}} = 0.15\underline{1}3\ \text{atm}$

$$2\,NO(g) + Cl_2(g) \rightleftharpoons 2\,NOCl(g)$$

	P_{NO}	P_{Cl_2}	P_{NOCl}
Initial	A	A	0.00
Change	$-2x$	$-x$	$+2x$
Equil	$A - 2x$	$A - x$	0.151
	$A - 0.151$	$A - 0.0756$	

Let $A =$ initial pressure of NO and Cl_2.

$2x = 0.151\ \ x = 0.0756$

$$K_p = \frac{P_{NOCl}^2}{P_{NO}^2\, P_{Cl_2}} = \frac{(0.151)^2}{(A - 0.151)^2(A - 0.0756)} = 0.27$$

$0.27A^3 - 0.1019A^2 + 0.01231A - 0.023266 = 0$. Solve using successive approximations or a cubic equation calculator found on the Internet.

$A = 0.566$

$P_{NO} = P_{Cl_2} = A = 0.566\ \text{atm} = 430\ \text{torr}$

Check: Plug the values into the equilibrium expression:

$$K_p = \frac{P_{NOCl}^2}{P_{NO}^2\, P_{Cl_2}} = \frac{(0.151)^2}{(0.566 - 0.151)^2(0.566 - 0.0756)} = 0.2699 = 0.27$$

This is the same as the original equilibrium constant.

14.76   **Given:** $P_{N_2O_4} = 1$ atm, K_p reaction $1 = 1 \times 10^4$, K_p reaction $2 = 0.10$ **Find:** Which component will have $P > 0.2$ atm?
Conceptual Plan: Use reaction 2 to determine P_{NO_2}. Then prepare an ICE table, represent the change with x, sum the table, determine the equilibrium values, put the equilibrium values in the equilibrium expression, and solve for x.

Solution: $2\ NO(g) \rightleftharpoons N_2O_4(g)$

	P_{NO}	$P_{N_2O_4}$
Initial	0.00	1.00
Change	$+2x$	$-x$
Equil	$+2x$	$1.00 - x$

$$K_p = \frac{P_{N_2O_4}}{P_{NO}^2} = \frac{(1.00 - x)}{(2x)^2} = 0.10$$

$$0.40x^2 + x - 1.00 = 0$$

$$\frac{-b \pm \sqrt{b^2 - 4ac}}{2a} = \frac{-1 \pm \sqrt{1^2 - 4(0.40)(-1.00)}}{2(0.40)}$$

$$x = 0.7655 = 0.77$$

$$P_{NO_2} = 2x = 1.54$$

Because K_p for reaction 1 is so large, essentially all of the materials are products; so the P_{NO} and P_{O_2} in reaction 1 will be negligible.

14.77   **Given:** $P = 0.750$ atm, density $= 0.520$ g/L, $T = 337\ °C$ **Find:** K_c
Conceptual Plan: Prepare an ICE table, represent the P_{NO_2} with A and the change with x, sum the table, determine the equilibrium values, use the total pressure, and solve for A in terms of x. Determine partial pressure of each at equilibrium in terms of x, use the density to determine the apparent molar mass, and use

$$d = \frac{PM}{RT}$$

the mole fraction (in terms of P) and the molar mass of each

$$\chi_A = \frac{P_A}{P_{Total}}$$

gas to determine x.

Solution: $2\ NO_2(g) \rightleftharpoons 2\ NO(g) + O_2(g)$

	P_{NO_2}	P_{NO}	P_{O_2}
Initial	A	0.00	0.00
Change	$-2x$	$+2x$	$+x$
Equil	$A - 2x$	$2x$	x

$P_{Total} = P_{NO_2} + P_{NO} + P_{O_2}$ $0.750 = A - 2x + 2x + x$ $A = 0.750 - x$

$P_{NO_2} = (A - 2x) = (0.750 - x) - 2x = (0.750 - 3x)$; $P_{NO} = 2x$; $P_{O_2} = x$

$$d = \frac{PM}{RT} \quad M = \frac{dRT}{P} = \frac{\left(0.520\ \frac{g}{L}\right)\left(0.08206\ \frac{L \cdot atm}{mol \cdot K}\right)(610\ K)}{0.750\ atm} = 34.\underline{7}1\ \text{g/mol}$$

$$M = \chi_{NO_2}M_{NO_2} + \chi_{NO}M_{NO} + \chi_{O_2}M_{O_2} = \frac{P_{NO_2}}{P_{total}}M_{NO_2} + \frac{P_{NO}}{P_{total}}M_{NO} + \frac{P_{O_2}}{P_{total}}M_{O_2}$$

$$P_{Total}M = P_{NO_2}M_{NO_2} + P_{NO}M_{NO} + P_{O_2}M_{O_2}$$

$$(0.750)(34.7) = (0.750 - 3x)(46.0) + 2x(30.0) + x(32.0)$$

$$x = 0.184$$

$$K_p = \frac{P_{NO}^2 P_{O_2}}{P_{NO_2}^2} = \frac{(2x)^2(x)}{(0.750 - 3x)^2} = \frac{(2(0.184))^2(0.184)}{(0.750 - 3(0.184))^2} = 0.63\underline{5}6$$

$$K_p = K_c(RT)^{\Delta n} \quad 0.63\underline{5}6 = K_c\left(\left(0.08206\frac{L \cdot atm}{mol \cdot K}\right)(610\ K)\right)^1$$

$$K_c = 1.27 \times 10^{-2}$$

14.78   **Given:** reaction 1: $K_c = 7.75$; reaction 2: $K_c = 4.00$, $[N_2O_5]_{initial} = 4.00$ M, $[O_2]_{equil} = 4.50$ M
Find: concentration of other species at equilibrium
Conceptual Plan: Combine reaction 1 and reaction 2 to get the overall reaction; then prepare an ICE table. Represent the change with x, sum the table, determine the equilibrium values, use the total pressure, and solve for x. Use x to determine equilibrium concentration.
Solution:

$$N_2O_5(g) \rightleftharpoons \cancel{N_2O_3(g)} + O_2(g) \qquad K_1 = 7.75$$
$$\cancel{N_2O_3(g)} \rightleftharpoons N_2O(g) + O_2(g) \qquad K_2 = 4.00$$
$$\overline{N_2O_5(g) \rightleftharpoons N_2O(g) + 2\,O_2(g) \qquad K = K_1 K_2 = 31.0}$$

	$[N_2O_5]$	$[N_2O]$	$[O_2]$
Initial	4.00	0.00	0.00
Change	$-x$	x	$2x$
Equil	$4.00 - x$	x	4.50

$$K_c = \frac{[N_2O][O_2]^2}{[N_2O_5]} = 31.0 = \frac{(x)(4.50)^2}{(4.00 - x)}$$

$x = 2.42$

$[N_2O_5] = 4.00 - x = 4.00 - 2.42 = 1.58$ M

$[N_2O] = x = 2.42$ M

$[O_2] = 4.50$ M

Use reaction 1 or reaction 2 and solve for $[N_2O_3]$ represented as y.

$$K_c = \frac{[N_2O_3][O_2]}{[N_2O_5]} = 7.75 = \frac{(y)(4.50)}{(1.58)}$$

$y = 2.72 \quad [N_2O_3] = y = 2.72$ M

Check: Plug the values into any of the equilibrium expressions: For example, for the overall reaction:

$$K_c = \frac{[N_2O][O_2]^2}{[N_2O_5]} = \frac{(2.42)(4.50)^2}{(1.58)} = 31.0; \text{ the equilibrium constant.}$$

For example, for reaction 2:

$$K_c = \frac{[N_2O][O_2]}{[N_2O_3]} = \frac{(2.42)(4.50)}{(2.72)} = 4.00$$

14.79   **Given:** $P_{total} = 3.0$ atm, mole fraction $O_2 = 0.12$, $T = 600$ K   **Find:** K_p
Conceptual Plan: mole fraction $\rightarrow P_{O_2} \rightarrow P_{SO_2} \rightarrow P_{SO_3} \rightarrow K_p$

$$\text{mol fraction} = \frac{P_{O_2}}{P_{Total}} \qquad \frac{2P_{SO_2}}{P_{O_2}} \qquad P_{SO_3} = P_{Total} - P_{SO_2} - P_{O_2} \qquad K_p = \frac{P_{SO_2}^2 P_{O_2}}{P_{SO_3}^2}$$

Solution: $P_{O_2} = (0.12)(3.0) = 0.36$ atm $P_{SO_2} = 2P_{O_2} = 2(0.36 \text{ atm}) = 0.72$ atm

$$P_{SO_3} = 3.0 - 0.36 - 0.72 = 1.\underline{9}2 \quad K_p = \frac{P_{SO_2}^2 P_{O_2}}{P_{SO_3}^2} = \frac{(0.72)^2(0.36)}{(1.\underline{9}2)^2} = 0.050\underline{6} = 5.1 \times 10^{-2}$$

Conceptual Problems

14.80   The equilibrium constant is very small; therefore, at equilibrium the concentration of products will be small compared to the concentration of reactants. In reaction mixture c, the initial concentration of reactants is large and there are no products. Since only a small amount of products will be formed, the x is small approximation will most likely apply. In reaction mixture b, there is initially no reactant and only products. To reach equilibrium, most of the product would have to go to reactants and the x is small approximation would not apply. In reaction mixture a, there is a smaller amount of reactants than in reaction mixture c. Since there are fewer initial reactants, the percentage needed to reach equilibrium is higher and the x is small approximation is less likely to apply.

14.81   Yes, the direction will depend on the volume. If the initial moles of A and B are equal, the initial concentrations of

A and B are equal regardless of the volume. Because $K_c = \dfrac{[B]^2}{[A]} = 1$, if the volume is such that the $[A] = [B] < 1.0$,

then $Q < K$ and the reaction goes to the right to reach equilibrium. However, if the volume is such that the $[A] = [B] > 1.0$, then $Q > K$ and the reaction goes to the left to reach equilibrium.

14.82 $K_p = 0.50$ means that $P(\text{products}) < P(\text{reactants})$. If the reactants and products are in their standard states, then P of each reactant and product $= 1.0$; so $Q > K$. To reach equilibrium, the reaction will have to shift to the left.

14.83   An examination of the data shows that when $P_A = 1.0$, then $P_B = 1.0$; therefore, $K_p = \dfrac{P_B^b}{P_A^a} = \dfrac{(1.0)^b}{(1.0)^a} = 1.0$.

Therefore, the value of the numerator and denominator must be equal. We see from the data that $P_B = \sqrt{P_A}$, so $P_B^2 = P_A$. Because the stoichiometric coefficients become exponents in the equilibrium expression, $a = 1$ and $b = 2$.

14.84   When the concentration of A is increased, the rate of the reaction in the forward direction is increased. This will increase the amount of product, B. The rate of reaction in the reverse direction will increase slightly as the concentration of product increases, but not to the same extent as the forward reaction. According to Le Châtelier's Principle, increasing the amount of reactant will increase both the reactant and product at equilibrium. This is consistent with the rate of reaction increasing to a greater extent in the forward direction than in the reverse direction.

14.85   Looking at the plot, at equilibrium $[A] = 0.59$ M and $[B] = 0.78$ M.

Since $A(g) \rightleftharpoons 2\,B(g)$, $K = \dfrac{[B]^2}{[A]} = \dfrac{(0.78)^2}{0.59} = 1.0$. This value is reasonable, since the concentrations of the reactant and product are similar.

Questions for Group Work

14.86   To find the value of K for the new equation, combine the three given equations to yield the new equation. Use equation a as is, reverse and halve equation b, and reverse and halve equation c. To find K for new reaction use $K_a / (K_b K_c)^{1/2}$.

$$C(s) + O_2(g) \rightleftharpoons CO_2(g) \qquad\qquad K = 1.363 \times 10^{69}$$

$$H_2O(g) \rightleftharpoons H_2(g) + \tfrac{1}{2}O_2(g) \qquad K = \sqrt{\dfrac{1}{K_b}} = \sqrt{\dfrac{1}{1.389 \times 10^{80}}} = 8.48\underline{4}942 \times 10^{-41}$$

$$CO_2(g) \rightleftharpoons CO(g) + \tfrac{1}{2}O_2(g) \qquad K = \sqrt{\dfrac{1}{K_c}} = \sqrt{\dfrac{1}{1.477 \times 10^{90}}} = 8.22\underline{8}293 \times 10^{-46}$$

$$\overline{C(s) + H_2O(g) \rightleftharpoons CO(g) + H_2(g)} \qquad K = (1.363 \times 10^{69}) \times (8.48\underline{4}942 \times 10^{-41}) \times (8.22\underline{8}293 \times 10^{-46})$$
$$= 9.516 \times 10^{-17}$$

14.87   (a) $K = \dfrac{[NH_3]^2}{[N_2][H_2]^3}$

    (b)   Adding H_2 will increase the denominator and not change the numerator.

    (c)   Since the denominator is larger, Q will be less than K.

    (d)   Since $Q < K$, the denominator needs to be decreased—so the reaction will shift to the right or in the forward direction.

    (e)   Yes, the reaction will shift to return Q to K.

14.88   For the first reaction, $A \rightleftharpoons B$, $K = \dfrac{[B]}{[A]}$. For the second reaction, $C \rightleftharpoons 2\,D$, $K = \dfrac{[D]^2}{[C]} \neq \dfrac{[D]}{[C]}$. Since K is the

same as the ratio of products to reactants for the first reaction, it is independent of the starting concentrations. Since K is not the same as the ratio of products to reactants for the second reaction, the ratio of products to reactants is dependent on the starting concentrations. The equilibrium constant value is independent of the starting concentrations.

14.89   (a) $x^2/(0.2 - x) = 1.3 \times 10^4 \rightarrow x^2 = 1.3 \times 10^4(0.2 - x) \rightarrow x^2 = 2.6 \times 10^3 - 1.3 \times 10^4 x$
                    $\rightarrow x^2 + 1.3 \times 10^4 x - 2.6 \times 10^3 = 0$

$$x = \frac{-b \pm \sqrt{b^2 - 4ac}}{2a} = \frac{-1.3 \times 10^4 \pm \sqrt{(1.3 \times 10^4)^2 - (4)(1)(-2.6 \times 10^3)}}{(2)(1)} = -13{,}000.2 \text{ or } 0.199997.$$

The x is small approximation is not valid.

(b) $x^2/(0.2 - x) = 1.3 \rightarrow x^2 = 1.3\,(0.2 - x) \rightarrow x^2 = 0.26 - 1.3x \rightarrow x^2 + 1.3x - 0.26 = 0$

$$x = \frac{-b \pm \sqrt{b^2 - 4ac}}{2a} = \frac{-1.3 \pm \sqrt{(1.3)^2 - (4)(1)(-0.26)}}{(2)(1)} = -1.47614 \text{ or } 0.176136.$$

The x is small approximation is not valid.

(c) $x^2/(0.2 - x) = 1.3 \times 10^{-4} \rightarrow x^2 = 1.3 \times 10^{-4}(0.2 - x) \rightarrow x^2 = 2.6 \times 10^{-5} - 1.3 \times 10^{-4} x$
                    $\rightarrow x^2 + 1.3 \times 10^{-4} x - 2.6 \times 10^{-5} = 0$

$$x = \frac{-b \pm \sqrt{b^2 - 4ac}}{2a} = \frac{-1.3 \times 10^{-4} \pm \sqrt{(1.3 \times 10^{-4})^2 - (4)(1)(-2.6 \times 10^{-5})}}{(2)(1)}$$
$$= -0.00516443 \text{ or } 0.00503443.$$

The x is small approximation is valid.

(d) $x^2/(0.01 - x) = 1.3 \times 10^{-4} \rightarrow x^2 = 1.3 \times 10^{-4}(0.01 - x) \rightarrow x^2 = 1.3 \times 10^{-6} - 1.3 \times 10^{-4} x$
                    $\rightarrow x^2 + 1.3 \times 10^{-4} x - 1.3 \times 10^{-6} = 0$

$$x = \frac{-b \pm \sqrt{b^2 - 4ac}}{2a} = \frac{-1.3 \times 10^{-4} \pm \sqrt{(1.3 \times 10^{-4})^2 - (4)(1)(-1.3 \times 10^{-6})}}{(2)(1)}$$
$$= -0.00120703 \text{ or } 0.00107703.$$

The x is small approximation is not valid.

In order for the x is small approximation to be valid in the expression $x^2/(y - x) = z$, $y/z > {\sim}1000$. So y needs to be much larger than z.

14.90   (a)   When a concentration of a reactant is increased, the denominator of Q increases and the reaction must shift to the right.

(b)   When a solid product is added, the value of Q will not change (as long as the volume is not changed) because solids do not appear in the equilibrium expression.

(c)   When the volume is decreased, the reaction will shift to the side of the reaction that has the fewer number of moles of gas. If the number of moles of gas is the same on both sides of the reaction, the reaction will not shift as the volume is changed.

(d)   Heat can be considered a reactant in an endothermic reaction and a product in an exothermic reaction. As the temperature is increased, an endothermic reaction will shift to the right. As the temperature is increased, an exothermic reaction will shift to the left.

15 Acids and Bases

Problems by Topic

The Nature and Definitions of Acids and Bases

15.1   (a)   acid $HNO_3(aq) \rightarrow H^+(aq) + NO_3^-(aq)$

         (b)   acid $NH_4^+(aq) \rightarrow H^+(aq) + NH_3(aq)$

         (c)   base $KOH(aq) \rightarrow K^+(aq) + OH^-(aq)$

         (d)   acid $HC_2H_3O_2(aq) \rightarrow H^+(aq) + C_2H_3O_2^-(aq)$

15.2   (a)   base $NaOH(aq) \rightarrow Na^+(aq) + OH^-(aq)$

         (b)   acid $H_2SO_4(aq) \rightarrow 2\,H^+(aq) + SO_4^{2-}(aq)$

         (c)   acid $HBr(aq) \rightarrow H^+(aq) + Br^-(aq)$

         (d)   base $Sr(OH)_2(aq) \rightarrow Sr^{2+}(aq) + 2\,OH^-(aq)$

15.3   (a)   Because H_2CO_3 donates a proton to H_2O, it is the acid. After H_2CO_3 donates the proton, it becomes HCO_3^-, the conjugate base. Because H_2O accepts a proton, it is the base. After H_2O accepts the proton, it becomes H_3O^+, the conjugate acid.

         (b)   Because H_2O donates a proton to NH_3, it is the acid. After H_2O donates the proton, it becomes OH^-, the conjugate base. Because NH_3 accepts a proton, it is the base. After NH_3 accepts the proton, it becomes NH_4^+, the conjugate acid.

         (c)   Because HNO_3 donates a proton to H_2O, it is the acid. After HNO_3 donates the proton, it becomes NO_3^-, the conjugate base. Because H_2O accepts a proton, it is the base. After H_2O accepts the proton, it becomes H_3O^+, the conjugate acid.

         (d)   Because H_2O donates a proton to C_5H_5N, it is the acid. After H_2O donates the proton, it becomes OH^-, the conjugate base. Because C_5H_5N accepts a proton, it is the base. After C_5H_5N accepts the proton, it becomes $C_5H_5NH^+$, the conjugate acid.

15.4   (a)   Because HI donates a proton to H_2O, it is the acid. After HI donates the proton, it becomes I^-, the conjugate base. Because H_2O accepts a proton, it is the base. After H_2O accepts the proton, it becomes H_3O^+, the conjugate acid.

         (b)   Because H_2O donates a proton to CH_3NH_2, it is the acid. After H_2O donates the proton, it becomes OH^-, the conjugate base. Because CH_3NH_2 accepts a proton, it is the base. After CH_3NH_2 accepts the proton, it becomes $CH_3NH_3^+$, the conjugate acid.

         (c)   Because H_2O donates a proton to CO_3^{2-}, it is the acid. After H_2O donates the proton, it becomes OH^-, the conjugate base. Because CO_3^{2-} accepts a proton, it is the base. After CO_3^{2-} accepts the proton, it becomes HCO_3^-, the conjugate acid.

         (d)   Because HBr donates a proton to H_2O, it is the acid. After HBr donates the proton, it becomes Br^-, the conjugate base. Because H_2O accepts a proton, it is the base. After H_2O accepts the proton, it becomes H_3O^+, the conjugate acid.

15.5   (a) Cl^- $HCl(aq) + H_2O(l) \rightarrow H_3O^+(aq) + Cl^-(aq)$

         (b) HSO_3^- $H_2SO_3(aq) + H_2O(l) \rightleftharpoons H_3O^+(aq) + HSO_3^-(aq)$

         (c) CHO_2^- $HCHO_2(aq) + H_2O(l) \rightleftharpoons H_3O^+(aq) + CHO_2^-(aq)$

         (d) F^- $HF(aq) + H_2O(l) \rightleftharpoons H_3O^+(aq) + F^-(aq)$

15.6   (a) NH_4^+ $NH_3(aq) + H_2O(l) \rightleftharpoons NH_4^+(aq) + OH^-(aq)$
        (b) $HClO_4$ $HClO_4(aq) + H_2O(l) \rightarrow H_3O^+(aq) + ClO_4^-(aq)$
        (c) H_2SO_4 $H_2SO_4(aq) + H_2O(l) \rightarrow H_3O^+(aq) + HSO_4^-(aq)$
        (d) HCO_3^- $HCO_3^-(aq) + H_2O(l) \rightleftharpoons H_3O^+(aq) + CO_3^{2-}(aq)$

15.7 $H_2PO_4^-(aq) + H_2O(l) \rightleftharpoons H_3O^+(aq) + HPO_4^{2-}(aq)$
        $H_2PO_4^-(aq) + H_2O(l) \rightleftharpoons H_3PO_4(aq) + OH^-(aq)$

15.8 $HCO_3^-(aq) + H_2O(l) \rightleftharpoons H_3O^+(aq) + CO_3^{2-}(aq)$
        $HCO_3^-(aq) + H_2O(l) \rightleftharpoons H_2CO_3(aq) + OH^-(aq)$

Acid Strength and K_a

15.9   (a) HNO_3 is a strong acid.
        (b)   HCl is a strong acid.
        (c)   HBr is a strong acid.
        (d) H_2SO_3 is a weak acid. $H_2SO_3(aq) + H_2O(l) \rightleftharpoons H_3O^+(aq) + HSO_3^-(aq)$

        $K_{a_1} = \dfrac{[H_3O^+][HSO_3^-]}{[H_2SO_3]}$

15.10   (a)   HF is a weak acid. $HF(aq) + H_2O(l) \rightleftharpoons H_3O^+(aq) + F^-(aq)$

        $K_a = \dfrac{[H_3O^+][F^-]}{[HF]}$

        (b) $HCHO_2$ is a weak acid. $HCHO_2(aq) + H_2O(l) \rightleftharpoons H_3O^+(aq) + CHO_2^-(aq)$

        $K_a = \dfrac{[H_3O^+][CHO_2^-]}{[HCHO_2]}$

        (c) H_2SO_4 is a strong acid.
        (d) H_2CO_3 is a weak acid. $H_2CO_3(aq) + H_2O(l) \rightleftharpoons H_3O^+(aq) + HCO_3^-(aq)$

        $K_{a_1} = \dfrac{[H_3O^+][HCO_3^-]}{[H_2CO_3]}$

15.11   (a)   contains no HA, 10 H^+, and 10 A^-
        (b)   contains 3 HA, 3 H^+, and 7 A^-
        (c)   contains 9 HA, 1 H^+, and 1 A^-
        So solution a > solution b > solution c.

15.12   HCl is a strong acid, $K_a(HF) = 3.5 \times 10^{-4}$, $K_a(HClO) = 2.9 \times 10^{-8}$, $K_a(HC_6H_5O) = 1.3 \times 10^{-10}$.
        The larger the value of K_a, the stronger the acid and the greater the $[H_3O^+]$.
        The order of decreasing $[H_3O^+]$ is HCl > HF > HClO > HC_6H_5O.

15.13   (a) F^- is a stronger base than is Cl^-.
               F^- is the conjugate base of HF (a weak acid); Cl^- is the conjugate base of HCl (a strong acid); the weaker the
               acid, the stronger the conjugate base.
        (b) NO_2^- is a stronger base than is NO_3^-.
               NO_2^- is the conjugate base of HNO_2 (a weak acid); NO_3^- is the conjugate base of HNO_3 (a strong acid); the
               weaker the acid, the stronger the conjugate base.
        (c) ClO^- is a stronger base than is F^-.
               F^- is the conjugate base of HF ($K_a = 3.5 \times 10^{-4}$); ClO^- is the conjugate base of HClO ($K_a = 2.9 \times 10^{-8}$);
               HClO is the weaker acid; the weaker the acid, the stronger the conjugate base.

15.14   (a) ClO_2^- is a stronger base than is ClO_4^-.
               ClO_2^- is the conjugate base of $HClO_2$ (a weak acid); ClO_4^- is the conjugate base of $HClO_4$ (a strong acid); the
               weaker the acid, the stronger the conjugate base.

    (b) H_2O is a stronger base than is Cl^-.

        H_2O is the conjugate base of H_3O^+; Cl^- is the conjugate base of HCl (a strong acid); the weaker the acid, the stronger the conjugate base.

    (c) CN^- is stronger base than is ClO^-.

        CN^- is the conjugate base of HCN ($K_a = 4.9 \times 10^{-10}$); ClO^- is the conjugate base of $HClO$ ($K_a = 2.9 \times 10^{-8}$); the weaker the acid, the stronger the conjugate base.

Autoionization of Water and pH

15.15   (a)   **Given:** $K_w = 1.0 \times 10^{-14}$, $[H_3O^+] = 9.7 \times 10^{-9}$ M   **Find:** $[OH^-]$

        Conceptual Plan: $[H_3O^+] \rightarrow [OH^-]$

            $K_w = 1.0 \times 10^{-14} = [H_3O^+][OH^-]$

        Solution:

        $K_w = 1.0 \times 10^{-14} = (9.7 \times 10^{-9})[OH^-]$

        $[OH^-] = 1.0 \times 10^{-6}$ M

        $[OH^-] > [H_3O^+]$ so the solution is basic.

    (b)   **Given:** $K_w = 1.0 \times 10^{-14}$, $[H_3O^+] = 2.2 \times 10^{-6}$ M   **Find:** $[OH^-]$

        Conceptual Plan: $[H_3O^+] \rightarrow [OH^-]$

            $K_w = 1.0 \times 10^{-14} = [H_3O^+][OH^-]$

        Solution:

        $K_w = 1.0 \times 10^{-14} = (2.2 \times 10^{-6})[OH^-]$

        $[OH^-] = 4.5 \times 10^{-9}$ M

        $[H_3O^+] > [OH^-]$ so the solution is acidic.

    (c)   **Given:** $K_w = 1.0 \times 10^{-14}$, $[H_3O^+] = 1.2 \times 10^{-9}$ M   **Find:** $[OH^-]$

        Conceptual Plan: $[H_3O^+] \rightarrow [OH^-]$

            $K_w = 1.0 \times 10^{-14} = [H_3O^+][OH^-]$

        Solution:

        $K_w = 1.0 \times 10^{-14} = (1.2 \times 10^{-9})[OH^-]$

        $[OH^-] = 8.3 \times 10^{-6}$ M

        $[OH^-] > [H_3O^+]$ so the solution is basic.

15.16   (a)   **Given:** $K_w = 1.0 \times 10^{-14}$, $[OH^-] = 5.1 \times 10^{-4}$ M   **Find:** $[H_3O^+]$

        Conceptual Plan: $[OH^-] \rightarrow [H_3O^+]$

            $K_w = 1.0 \times 10^{-14} = [H_3O^+][OH^-]$

        Solution:

        $K_w = 1.0 \times 10^{-14} = [H_3O^+](5.1 \times 10^{-4})$

        $[H_3O^+] = 2.0 \times 10^{-11}$ M

        $[OH^-] > [H_3O^+]$ so the solution is basic.

    (b)   **Given:** $K_w = 1.0 \times 10^{-14}$, $[OH^-] = 1.7 \times 10^{-12}$ M   **Find:** $[H_3O^+]$

        Conceptual Plan: $[OH^-] \rightarrow [H_3O^+]$

            $K_w = 1.0 \times 10^{-14} = [H_3O^+][OH^-]$

        Solution:

        $K_w = 1.0 \times 10^{-14} = [H_3O^+](1.7 \times 10^{-12})$

        $[H_3O^+] = 5.9 \times 10^{-3}$ M

        $[H_3O^+] > [OH^-]$ so the solution is acidic.

    (c)   **Given:** $K_w = 1.0 \times 10^{-14}$, $[OH^-] = 2.8 \times 10^{-2}$ M   **Find:** $[H_3O^+]$

        Conceptual Plan: $[OH^-] \rightarrow [H_3O^+]$

            $K_w = 1.0 \times 10^{-14} = [H_3O^+][OH^-]$

        Solution:

        $K_w = 1.0 \times 10^{-14} = [H_3O^+](2.8 \times 10^{-2})$

        $[H_3O^+] = 3.6 \times 10^{-13}$ M

        $[OH^-] > [H_3O^+]$ so the solution is basic.

15.17   (a)   **Given:** $[H_3O^+] = 1.7 \times 10^{-8}$ M   **Find:** pH and pOH

            Conceptual Plan: $[H_3O^+] \rightarrow pH \rightarrow pOH$

                                     $pH = -\log[H_3O^+]$ $pH + pOH = 14$

            Solution: $pH = -\log(1.7 \times 10^{-8}) = 7.77$ $pOH = 14.00 - 7.77 = 6.23$

            $pH > 7$ so the solution is basic.

  (b)   **Given:** $[H_3O^+] = 1.0 \times 10^{-7}$ M   **Find:** pH and pOH

            Conceptual Plan: $[H_3O^+] \rightarrow pH \rightarrow pOH$

                                       $pH = -\log[H_3O^+]$ $pH + pOH = 14$

            Solution: $pH = -\log(1.0 \times 10^{-7}) = 7.00$ $pOH = 14.00 - 7.00 = 7.00$

            $pH = 7$ so the solution is neutral.

  (c)   **Given:** $[H_3O^+] = 2.2 \times 10^{-6}$ M   **Find:** pH and pOH

            Conceptual Plan: $[H_3O^+] \rightarrow pH \rightarrow pOH$

                                       $pH = -\log[H_3O^+]$ $pH + pOH = 14$

            Solution: $pH = -\log(2.2 \times 10^{-6}) = 5.66$ $pOH = 14.00 - 5.66 = 8.34$

            $pH < 7$ so the solution is acidic.

15.18   (a)   **Given:** $pH = 8.55$ **Find:** $[H_3O^+]$, $[OH^-]$

            Conceptual Plan: $pH \rightarrow [H_3O^+] \rightarrow [OH^-]$

                            $pH = -\log[H_3O^+]$ $K_w = 1.0 \times 10^{-14} = [H_3O^+][OH^-]$

            Solution: $pH = -\log[H_3O^+]$ $8.55 = -\log[H_3O^+]$

                    $-8.55 = \log[H_3O^+]$ $10^{-8.55} = 10^{\log[H_3O^+]}$

                $10^{-8.55} = [H_3O^+]$ $[H_3O^+] = 2.8 \times 10^{-9}$

                $K_w = 1 \times 10^{-14} = (2.8 \times 10^{-9})[OH^-]$

                $[OH^-] = 3.6 \times 10^{-6}$ M

  (b)   **Given:** $pH = 11.23$ **Find:** $[H_3O^+]$, $[OH^-]$

            Conceptual Plan: $pH \rightarrow [H_3O^+] \rightarrow [OH^-]$

                              $pH = -\log[H_3O^+]$ $K_w = 1.0 \times 10^{-14} = [H_3O^+][OH^-]$

            Solution: $pH = -\log[H_3O^+]$ $11.23 = -\log[H_3O^+]$

                    $-11.23 = \log[H_3O^+]$ $10^{-11.23} = 10^{\log[H_3O^+]}$

                $10^{-11.23} = [H_3O^+]$ $[H_3O^+] = 5.9 \times 10^{-12}$

                $K_w = 1 \times 10^{-14} = (5.9 \times 10^{-12})[OH^-]$

                $[OH^-] = 1.7 \times 10^{-3}$ M

  (c)   **Given:** $pH = 2.87$ **Find:** $[H_3O^+]$, $[OH^-]$

            Conceptual Plan: $pH \rightarrow [H_3O^+] \rightarrow [OH^-]$

                              $pH = -\log[H_3O^+]$ $K_w = 1.0 \times 10^{-14} = [H_3O^+][OH^-]$

            Solution: $pH = -\log[H_3O^+]$ $2.87 = -\log[H_3O^+]$

                    $-2.87 = \log[H_3O^+]$ $10^{-2.87} = 10^{\log[H_3O^+]}$

                $10^{-2.87} = [H_3O^+]$ $[H_3O^+] = 1.3 \times 10^{-3}$

                $K_w = 1 \times 10^{-14} = (1.3 \times 10^{-3})[OH^-]$

                $[OH^-] = 7.7 \times 10^{-12}$ M

15.19 $pH = -\log[H_3O^+]$ $K_w = 1.0 \times 10^{-14} = [H_3O^+][OH^-]$

$[H_3O^+]$	$[OH^-]$	pH	Acidic or basic
7.1×10^{-4}	1.4×10^{-11}	**3.15**	acidic
3.7×10^{-9}	2.7×10^{-6}	8.43	basic
8×10^{-12}	1×10^{-3}	**11.1**	basic
6.3×10^{-4}	**1.6×10^{-11}**	3.20	acidic

$$[H_3O^+] = 10^{-3.15} = 7.1 \times 10^{-4} \qquad [OH^-] = \frac{1.0 \times 10^{-14}}{7.1 \times 10^{-4}} = 1.4 \times 10^{-11}$$

$$[OH^-] = \frac{1.0 \times 10^{-14}}{3.7 \times 10^{-9}} = 2.7 \times 10^{-6} \qquad pH = -\log(3.7 \times 10^{-9}) = 8.43$$

$$[H_3O^+] = 10^{-11.1} = 8 \times 10^{-12} \qquad [OH^-] = \frac{1.0 \times 10^{-14}}{8 \times 10^{-12}} = 1 \times 10^{-3}$$

$$[H_3O^+] = \frac{1.0 \times 10^{-14}}{1.6 \times 10^{-11}} = 6.3 \times 10^{-4} \qquad pH = -\log(6.3 \times 10^{-4}) = 3.20$$

15.20 $pH = -\log[H_3O^+] \quad K_w = 1.0 \times 10^{-14} = [H_3O^+][OH^-]$

$[H_3O^+]$	$[OH^-]$	pH	Acidic or basic
3.5 × 10⁻³	2.9 × 10⁻¹²	2.46	acidic
2.6 × 10⁻⁸	**3.8 × 10⁻⁷**	7.58	basic
1.8 × 10⁻⁹	5.6 × 10⁻⁶	8.74	basic
7.1 × 10⁻⁸	1.4 × 10⁻⁷	**7.15**	basic

$$[OH^-] = \frac{1.0 \times 10^{-14}}{3.5 \times 10^{-3}} = 2.9 \times 10^{-12} \qquad pH = -\log(3.5 \times 10^{-3}) = 2.46$$

$$[H_3O^+] = \frac{1.0 \times 10^{-14}}{3.8 \times 10^{-7}} = 2.6 \times 10^{-8} \qquad pH = -\log(2.6 \times 10^{-8}) = 7.58$$

$$[OH^-] = \frac{1.0 \times 10^{-14}}{1.8 \times 10^{-9}} = 5.6 \times 10^{-6} \qquad pH = -\log(1.8 \times 10^{-9}) = 8.74$$

$$[H_3O^+] = 10^{-7.15} = 7.1 \times 10^{-8} \qquad [OH^-] = \frac{1.0 \times 10^{-14}}{7.1 \times 10^{-8}} = 1.4 \times 10^{-7}$$

15.21   **Given:** $K_w = 2.4 \times 10^{-14}$ at 37°C   **Find:** $[H_3O^+]$, pH
Conceptual Plan: $K_w \rightarrow [H_3O^+] \rightarrow pH$
$$K_w = [H_3O^+][OH^-] \quad pH = -\log[H_3O^+]$$
Solution: $H_2O(l) + H_2O(l) \rightleftharpoons H_3O^+(aq) + OH^-(aq)$
$$K_w = [H_3O^+][OH^-]$$
$$[H_3O^+] = [OH^-] = \sqrt{K_w} = \sqrt{2.4 \times 10^{-14}} = 1.5 \times 10^{-7}$$
$$pH = -\log[H_3O^+] = -\log(1.5 \times 10^{-7}) = 6.82$$

Check: The value of K_w increased, indicating more products formed; so the $[H_3O^+]$ increases and the pH decreases from the values at 25 °C.

15.22   The increasing value of K_w indicates that more products are formed as the temperature increases. According to Le Châtelier, this means that the heat is a reactant. Therefore, the autoionization of water is endothermic.

15.23   (a)   **Given:** $[H_3O^+] = 0.044$ M   **Find:** pH
Conceptual Plan: $[H_3O^+] \rightarrow pH$
$$pH = -\log[H_3O^+]$$
Solution: $pH = -\log(0.044) = 1.3\underline{5}7 = 1.36$

(b)   **Given:** $[H_3O^+] = 0.045$ M   **Find:** pH
Conceptual Plan: $[H_3O^+] \rightarrow pH$
$$pH = -\log[H_3O^+]$$
Solution: $pH = -\log(0.045) = 1.3\underline{4}7 = 1.35$

(c)   **Given:** $[H_3O^+] = 0.046$ M   **Find:** pH
Conceptual Plan: $[H_3O^+] \rightarrow pH$
$$pH = -\log[H_3O^+]$$

Solution: pH $= -\log(0.046) = 1.3\underline{3}7 = 1.34$

If the pH of the solution did not carry as many decimal places as the significant digits to the right of the decimal point, you would not be able to distinguish a difference in the pH of solutions b and c. Also, solution a would have a pH that was too high.

15.24   (a)   **Given:** pH $= 2.50$ **Find:** $[H_3O^+]$
              Conceptual Plan: pH $\rightarrow$ $[H_3O^+]$
                         $pH = -\log[H_3O^+]$

              Solution: pH $= -\log[H_3O^+]$ $2.50 = -\log[H_3O^+]$
                       $-2.50 = \log[H_3O^+]$ $10^{-2.50} = 10^{\log[H_3O^+]}$
                         $10^{-2.50} = [H_3O^+]$ $[H_3O^+] = 3.16 \times 10^{-3} = 3.2 \times 10^{-3}$ M

     (b)   **Given:** pH $= 2.51$ **Find:** $[H_3O^+]$
              Conceptual Plan: pH $\rightarrow$ $[H_3O^+]$
                         $pH = -\log[H_3O^+]$

              Solution: pH $= -\log[H_3O^+]$ $2.51 = -\log[H_3O^+]$
                       $-2.51 = \log[H_3O^+]$ $10^{-2.51} = 10^{\log[H_3O^+]}$
                       $10^{-2.51} = [H_3O^+]$ $[H_3O^+] = 3.09 \times 10^{-3} = 3.1 \times 10^{-3}$ M

     (c)   **Given:** pH $= 2.52$ **Find:** $[H_3O^+]$
              Conceptual Plan: pH $\rightarrow$ $[H_3O^+]$
                         $pH = -\log[H_3O^+]$

              Solution: pH $= -\log[H_3O^+]$ $2.52 = -\log[H_3O^+]$
                       $-2.52 = \log[H_3O^+]$ $10^{-2.52} = 10^{\log[H_3O^+]}$
                       $10^{-2.52} = [H_3O^+]$ $[H_3O^+] = 3.02 \times 10^{-3} = 3.0 \times 10^{-3}$ M

The pH values have two digits to the right of the decimal point. This gives two significant figures in the concentration of H_3O^+. If you do not carry out the concentration to two significant figures, all of the concentrations will appear to be the same.

Acid Solutions

15.25   (a)   **Given:** 0.15 M HCl (strong acid)   **Find:** $[H_3O^+]$, $[OH^-]$, pH
              Conceptual Plan: [HCl] $\rightarrow$ $[H_3O^+]$ $\rightarrow$ pH and then $[H_3O^+]$ $\rightarrow$ $[OH^-]$
                           $[HCl] \rightarrow [H_3O^+]$ $pH = -\log[H_3O^+]$ $[H_3O^+][OH^-] = 1.0 \times 10^{-14}$

              Solution: 0.15 M HCl $=$ 0.15 M H_3O^+ pH $= -\log(0.15) = 0.82$
                    $[OH^-] = 1.0 \times 10^{-14}/0.15$ M $= 6.7 \times 10^{-14}$

              Check: HCl is a strong acid with a relatively high concentration, so we expect the pH to be low and the $[OH^-]$ to be small.

     (b)   **Given:** 0.025 M HNO_3 (strong acid)   **Find:** $[H_3O^+]$, $[OH^-]$, pH
              Conceptual Plan: $[HNO_3]$ $\rightarrow$ $[H_3O^+]$ $\rightarrow$ pH and then $[H_3O^+]$ $\rightarrow$ $[OH^-]$
                         $[HNO_3] \rightarrow [H_3O^+]$ $pH = -\log[H_3O^+]$ $[H_3O^+][OH^-] = 1.0 \times 10^{-14}$

              Solution: 0.025 M HNO_3 $=$ 0.025 M H_3O^+ pH $= -\log(0.025) = 1.60$
                    $[OH^-] = 1.0 \times 10^{-14}/0.025$ M $= 4.0 \times 10^{-13}$

              Check: HNO_3 is a strong acid, so we expect the pH to be low and the $[OH^-]$ to be small.

     (c)   **Given:** 0.072 M HBr and 0.015 M HNO_3 (strong acids)   **Find:** $[H_3O^+]$, $[OH^-]$, pH
              Conceptual Plan: [HBr] $+$ $[HNO_3]$ $\rightarrow$ $[H_3O^+]$ $\rightarrow$ pH and then $[H_3O^+]$ $\rightarrow$ $[OH^-]$
                         $[HBr] + [HNO_3] \rightarrow [H_3O^+]$ $pH = -\log[H_3O^+]$ $[H_3O^+][OH^-] = 1.0 \times 10^{-14}$

              Solution: 0.072 M HBr $=$ 0.072 M H_3O^+ and 0.015 M HNO_3 $=$ 0.015 M H_3O^+
                  Total H_3O^+ $=$ 0.072 M $+$ 0.015 M $=$ 0.087 M   pH $= -\log(0.087) = 1.06$
                  $[OH^-] = 1.0 \times 10^{-14}/0.087$ M $= 1.1 \times 10^{-13}$

Check: HBr and HNO_3 are both strong acids that completely dissociate. This gives a relatively high concentration, so we expect the pH to be low and the $[OH^-]$ to be small.

(d) **Given:** $HNO_3 = 0.855\%$ by mass, $d_{solution} = 1.01$ g/mL   **Find:** $[H_3O^+]$, $[OH^-]$, pH
Conceptual Plan:

% mass HNO_3 → g HNO_3 → mol HNO_3 and then g soln → mL soln → L soln → M HNO_3

$$\frac{\%}{100} \qquad \frac{mol\ HNO_3}{63.018\ g\ HNO_3} \qquad\qquad \frac{1.01\ g\ soln}{mL\ soln} \quad \frac{1000\ mL\ soln}{L\ soln} \quad \frac{mol\ HNO_3}{L\ soln}$$

M HNO_3 → M H_3O^+ → pH and then $[H_3O^+]$ → $[OH^-]$

$$[HNO_3] \rightarrow [H_3O^+] \quad pH = -\log[H_3O^+] \qquad [H_3O^+][OH^-] = 1.0 \times 10^{-14}$$

Solution: $\dfrac{0.855\ \cancel{g\ HNO_3}}{100\ \cancel{g\ soln}} \times \dfrac{1\ mol\ HNO_3}{63.018\ \cancel{g\ HNO_3}} \times \dfrac{1.01\ \cancel{g\ soln}}{\cancel{mL\ soln}} \times \dfrac{1000\ \cancel{mL\ soln}}{L\ soln} = 0.137$ M HNO_3

0.137 M $HNO_3 = 0.137$ M H_3O^+ pH $= -\log(0.137) = 0.863$

$[OH^-] = 1.00 \times 10^{-14}/0.137$ M $= 7.30 \times 10^{-14}$

Check: HNO_3 is a strong acid that completely dissociates. This gives a relatively high concentration, so we expect the pH to be low and the $[OH^-]$ to be small.

15.26 (a) **Given:** 0.028 M HI (strong acid)   **Find:** $[H_3O^+]$, $[OH^-]$, pH
Conceptual Plan: **[HI] → $[H_3O^+]$ → pH and then $[H_3O^+]$ → $[OH^-]$**

$$[HI] \rightarrow [H_3O^+] \quad pH = -\log[H_3O^+] \qquad [H_3O^+][OH^-] = 1.0 \times 10^{-14}$$

Solution: 0.028 M HI = 0.028 M H_3O^+ pH $= -\log(0.028) = 1.55$

$[OH^-] = 1.0 \times 10^{-14}/0.028$ M $= 3.6 \times 10^{-13}$

Check: HI is a strong acid with a relatively high concentration, so we expect the pH to be low and the $[OH^-]$ to be small.

(b) **Given:** 0.115 M $HClO_4$ (strong acid)   **Find:** $[H_3O^+]$, $[OH^-]$, pH
Conceptual Plan: **$[HClO_4]$ → $[H_3O^+]$ → pH and then $[H_3O^+]$ → $[OH^-]$**

$$[HClO_4] \rightarrow [H_3O^+] \quad pH = -\log[H_3O^+] \qquad [H_3O^+][OH^-] = 1.0 \times 10^{-14}$$

Solution: 0.115 M $HClO_4$ = 0.115 M H_3O^+ pH $= -\log(0.115) = 0.939$

$[OH^-] = 1.00 \times 10^{-14}/0.115$ M $= 8.70 \times 10^{-14}$

Check: $HClO_4$ is a strong acid, so we expect the pH to be low and the $[OH^-]$ to be small.

(c) **Given:** 0.055 M $HClO_4$ and 0.028 M HCl (strong acids)   **Find:** $[H_3O^+]$, $[OH^-]$, pH
Conceptual Plan: **[HCl] + $[HClO_4]$ → $[H_3O^+]$ → pH and then $[H_3O^+]$ → $[OH^-]$**

$$[HCl] + [HClO_4] \rightarrow [H_3O^+] \quad pH = -\log[H_3O^+] \qquad [H_3O^+][OH^-] = 1.0 \times 10^{-14}$$

Solution: 0.055 M $HClO_4$ = 0.055 M H_3O^+ and 0.028 M HCl = 0.028 M H_3O^+

Total $H_3O^+ = 0.055$ M $+ 0.028$ M $= 0.083$ M   pH $= -\log(0.083) = 1.08$

$[OH^-] = 1.0 \times 10^{-14}/0.083$ M $= 1.2 \times 10^{-13}$

Check: $HClO_4$ and HCl are both strong acids that completely dissociate. This gives a relatively high concentration, so we expect the pH to be low and the $[OH^-]$ to be small.

(d) **Given:** HCl $= 1.85\%$ by mass, $d_{solution} = 1.01$ g/mL   **Find:** $[H_3O^+]$, $[OH^-]$, pH
Conceptual Plan:

% mass HCl → g HCl → mol HCl and then g soln → mL soln → L soln → M HCl

$$\frac{\%}{100} \qquad \frac{1\ mol\ HCl}{36.46\ g\ HCl} \qquad\qquad \frac{1.01\ g\ soln}{mL\ soln} \quad \frac{1000\ mL\ soln}{1\ L\ soln} \quad \frac{mol\ HCl}{L\ soln}$$

M HCl → M H_3O^+ → pH and then $[H_3O^+]$ → $[OH^-]$

$$[HCl] \rightarrow [H_3O^+] \quad pH = -\log[H_3O^+] \qquad [H_3O^+][OH^-] = 1.0 \times 10^{-14}$$

Solution: $\dfrac{1.85 \text{ g HCl}}{100 \text{ g soln}} \times \dfrac{1 \text{ mol HCl}}{36.46 \text{ g HCl}} \times \dfrac{1.01 \text{ g soln}}{\text{mL soln}} \times \dfrac{1000 \text{ mL soln}}{1 \text{ L soln}} = 0.5125 \text{ M} = 0.513 \text{ M HCl}$

$0.513 \text{ M HCl} = 0.513 \text{ M H}_3\text{O}^+ \quad \text{pH} = -\log(0.513) = 0.290$

$[\text{OH}^-] = 1.00 \times 10^{-14}/0.513 \text{ M} = 1.95 \times 10^{-14}$

Check: HCl is a strong acid that completely dissociates. This gives a relatively high concentration, so we expect the pH to be low and the $[\text{OH}^-]$ to be small.

15.27   (a)   **Given:** pH = 1.25, 0.250 L   **Find:** g HI
Conceptual Plan: pH → [H₃O⁺] → [HI] → mol HI → g HI

$$\text{pH} = -\log[\text{H}_3\text{O}^+] \quad [\text{H}_3\text{O}^+] \rightarrow [\text{HI}] \quad \text{mol} = MV \quad \dfrac{127.9 \text{ g HI}}{1 \text{ mol HI}}$$

Solution: $[\text{H}_3\text{O}^+] = 10^{-1.25} = 0.056 \text{ M} = [\text{HI}]$ $\dfrac{0.056 \text{ mol HI}}{L} \times 0.250 \text{ L} \times \dfrac{127.9 \text{ g HI}}{1 \text{ mol HI}} = 1.8 \text{ g HI}$

(b)   **Given:** pH = 1.75, 0.250 L   **Find:** g HI
Conceptual Plan: pH → [H₃O⁺] → [HI] → mol HI → g HI

$$\text{pH} = -\log[\text{H}_3\text{O}^+] \quad [\text{H}_3\text{O}^+] \rightarrow [\text{HI}] \quad \text{mol} = MV \quad \dfrac{127.9 \text{ g HI}}{1 \text{ mol HI}}$$

Solution: $[\text{H}_3\text{O}^+] = 10^{-1.75} = 0.017\underline{8} \text{ M} = [\text{HI}]$ $\dfrac{0.017\underline{8} \text{ mol HI}}{L} \times 0.250 \text{ L} \times \dfrac{127.9 \text{ g HI}}{1 \text{ mol HI}} = 0.57 \text{ g HI}$

(c)   **Given:** pH = 2.85, 0.250 L   **Find:** g HI
Conceptual Plan: pH → [H₃O⁺] → [HI] → mol HI → g HI

$$\text{pH} = -\log[\text{H}_3\text{O}^+] \quad [\text{H}_3\text{O}^+] \rightarrow [\text{HI}] \quad \text{mol} = MV \quad \dfrac{127.9 \text{ g HI}}{1 \text{ mol HI}}$$

Solution: $[\text{H}_3\text{O}^+] = 10^{-2.85} = 0.0014 \text{ M} = [\text{HI}]$ $\dfrac{0.0014 \text{ mol HI}}{L} \times 0.250 \text{ L} \times \dfrac{127.9 \text{ g HI}}{1 \text{ mol HI}} = 0.045 \text{ g HI}$

15.28   (a)   **Given:** pH = 2.50, 0.500 L   **Find:** g HClO₄
Conceptual Plan: pH → [H₃O⁺] → [HClO₄] → mol HClO₄ → g HClO₄

$$\text{pH} = -\log[\text{H}_3\text{O}^+] \quad [\text{H}_3\text{O}^+] \rightarrow [\text{HClO}_4] \quad \text{mol} = MV \quad \dfrac{100.46 \text{ g HClO}_4}{1 \text{ mol HClO}_4}$$

Solution:

$$[\text{H}_3\text{O}^+] = 10^{-2.50} = 0.003\underline{16} \text{ M} = [\text{HClO}_4]$$

$$\dfrac{0.003\underline{16} \text{ mol HClO}_4}{L} \times 0.500 \text{ L} \times \dfrac{100.46 \text{ g HClO}_4}{1 \text{ mol HClO}_4} = 0.16 \text{ g HClO}_4$$

(b)   **Given:** pH = 1.50, 0.500 L   **Find:** g HClO₄
Conceptual Plan: pH → [H₃O⁺] → [HClO₄] → mol HClO₄ → g HClO₄

$$\text{pH} = -\log[\text{H}_3\text{O}^+] \quad [\text{H}_3\text{O}^+] \rightarrow [\text{HClO}_4] \quad \text{mol} = MV \quad \dfrac{100.46 \text{ g HClO}_4}{1 \text{ mol HClO}_4}$$

Solution:

$$[\text{H}_3\text{O}^+] = 10^{-1.50} = 0.03\underline{16} \text{ M} = [\text{HClO}_4]$$

$$\dfrac{0.03\underline{16} \text{ mol HClO}_4}{L} \times 0.500 \text{ L} \times \dfrac{100.46 \text{ g HClO}_4}{1 \text{ mol HClO}_4} = 1.6 \text{ g HClO}_4$$

(c)   **Given:** pH = 0.50, 0.500 L   **Find:** g HClO₄
Conceptual Plan: pH → [H₃O⁺] → [HClO₄] → mol HClO₄ → g HClO₄

$$\text{pH} = -\log[\text{H}_3\text{O}^+] \quad [\text{H}_3\text{O}^+] \rightarrow [\text{HClO}_4] \quad \text{mol} = MV \quad \dfrac{100.46 \text{ g HClO}_4}{1 \text{ mol HClO}_4}$$

Solution:

$$[\text{H}_3\text{O}^+] = 10^{-0.50} = 0.3\underline{16} \text{ M} = [\text{HClO}_4]$$

$$\dfrac{0.3\underline{16} \text{ mol HClO}_4^-}{L} \times 0.500 \text{ L} \times \dfrac{100.46 \text{ g HClO}_4}{1 \text{ mol HClO}_4^-} = 16 \text{ g HClO}_4$$

15.29   **Given:** 224 mL HCl, 27.2 °C, 1.02 atm, 1.5 L solution   **Find:** pH

          Conceptual Plan: vol HCl → mol HCl → [HCl] → [H$_3$O$^+$] → pH

$$PV = nRT \qquad M = \frac{\text{mol HCl}}{\text{vol soln}} \qquad [HCl] = [H_3O^+] \qquad pH = -\log[H_3O^+]$$

          Solution: $n = \dfrac{(1.02\ \text{atm})(224\ \text{mL})\left(\dfrac{1\ L}{1000\ \text{mL}}\right)}{\left(\dfrac{0.08206\ L\ \text{atm}}{\text{mol}\ K}\right)((27.2 + 273.15)\ K)} = 0.00927\ \text{mol}$

          $[HCl] = \dfrac{0.00927\ \text{mol}}{1.5\ L} = 0.0061\underline{8}\ M = [H_3O^+] \quad pH = -\log(0.0061\underline{8}) = 2.21$

15.30   **Given:** 36.0% HCl, $d_{\text{soln}} = 1.179$ g/mL; 5.00 L, pH 1.8   **Find:** vol soln

          Conceptual Plan: % mass HCl → g HCl → mol HCl and then g soln → mL soln → L soln → M HCl

$$\frac{\%}{100} \qquad \frac{\text{mol HCl}}{36.46\ \text{g HCl}} \qquad\qquad \frac{1.179\ \text{g soln}}{\text{mL soln}} \qquad \frac{1000\ \text{L soln}}{1\ \text{L soln}} \qquad \frac{\text{mol HCl}}{\text{L soln}}$$

          M HCl → M H$_3$O$^+$ and then pH → [H$_3$O$^+$] and the V_1M_1 → V_2M_2

$$[HCl] \rightarrow [H_3O^+] \qquad\qquad [H_3O^+] = 10^{-pH} \qquad\qquad V_1M_1 = V_2M_2$$

          Solution: $\dfrac{36.0\ \text{g HCl}}{100\ \text{g soln}} \times \dfrac{1\ \text{mol HCl}}{36.46\ \text{g HCl}} \times \dfrac{1.179\ \text{g soln}}{\text{mL soln}} \times \dfrac{1000\ \text{mL soln}}{1\ \text{L soln}} = 11.\underline{6}4\ \text{M HCl}$

          $[H_3O^+] = 10^{-1.8} = 0.0158\ M$

          $V_1M_1 = V_2M_2 \quad V_1(11.\underline{6}4\ M) = (5.00\ L)(0.0158\ M) \quad V_1 = 0.00678\underline{7}\ L = 6.79\ \text{mL}$

15.31   **Given:** 0.100 M benzoic acid, $K_a = 6.5 \times 10^{-5}$ **Find:** [H$_3$O$^+$], pH

          Conceptual Plan: Write a balanced reaction. Prepare an ICE (Initial, Change, Equil) table, represent the change with x, sum the table, determine the equilibrium values, put the equilibrium values in the equilibrium expression, and solve for x. Determine [H$_3$O$^+$] and pH.

          Solution: $HC_7H_5O_2(aq) + H_2O(l) \rightleftharpoons H_3O^+(aq) + C_7H_5O_2{}^-(aq)$

	[HC$_7$H$_5$O$_2$]	**[H$_3$O$^.$]**	**[C$_7$H$_5$O$_2$$^.$]**
Initial	0.100 M	0.0	0.0
Change	$-x$	x	x
Equil	$0.100 - x$	x	x

          $K_a = \dfrac{[H_3O^+][C_7H_5O_2{}^-]}{[HC_7H_5O_2]} = \dfrac{(x)(x)}{(0.100 - x)} = 6.5 \times 10^{-5}$

          Assume that x is small compared to 0.100.

          $x^2 = (6.5 \times 10^{-5})(0.100) \qquad x = 2.5 \times 10^{-3}\ M = [H_3O^+]$

          Check assumption: $\dfrac{2.5 \times 10^{-3}}{0.100} \times 100\% = 2.5\%$; assumption is valid.

          $pH = -\log(2.5 \times 10^{-3}) = 2.60$

15.32   **Given:** 0.200 M formic acid, $K_a = 1.8 \times 10^{-4}$ **Find:** [H$_3$O$^+$], pH

          Conceptual Plan: Write a balanced reaction. Prepare an ICE table, represent the change with x, sum the table, determine the equilibrium values, put the equilibrium values in the equilibrium expression, and solve for x. Determine [H$_3$O$^+$] and pH.

          Solution: $HCHO_2(aq) + H_2O(l) \rightleftharpoons H_3O^+(aq) + CHO_2{}^-(aq)$

	[HCHO$_2$]	**[H$_3$O$^.$]**	**[CHO$_2$$^.$]**
Initial	0.200 M	0.0	0.0
Change	$-x$	x	x
Equil	$0.200 - x$	x	x

$$K_a = \frac{[H_3O^+][CHO_2^-]}{[HCHO_2]} = \frac{(x)(x)}{(0.200 - x)} = 1.8 \times 10^{-4}$$

Assume that x is small compared to 0.200.

$$x^2 = (1.8 \times 10^{-4})(0.200) \qquad x = 6.0 \times 10^{-3} \text{ M} = [H_3O^+]$$

Check assumption: $\dfrac{6.0 \times 10^{-3}}{0.200} \times 100\% = 3.0\%$; assumption is valid.

$$pH = -\log(6.0 \times 10^{-3}) = 2.22$$

15.33   (a)   **Given:** 0.500 M HNO$_2$, $K_a = 4.6 \times 10^{-4}$ **Find:** pH

        Conceptual Plan: Write a balanced reaction. Prepare an ICE table, represent the change with x, sum the table, determine the equilibrium values, put the equilibrium values in the equilibrium expression, and solve for x. Determine [H$_3$O$^+$] and pH.

        Solution: $HNO_2(aq) + H_2O(l) \rightleftharpoons H_3O^+(aq) + NO_2^-(aq)$

	[HNO$_2$]	**[H$_3$O$^+$]**	**[NO$_2^-$]**
Initial	0.500 M	0.0	0.0
Change	$-x$	x	x
Equil	$0.500 - x$	x	x

$$K_a = \frac{[H_3O^+][NO_2^-]}{[HNO_2]} = \frac{(x)(x)}{(0.500 - x)} = 4.6 \times 10^{-4}$$

Assume that x is small compared to 0.500.

$$x^2 = (4.6 \times 10^{-4})(0.500) \qquad x = 0.015 \text{ M} = [H_3O^+]$$

Check assumption: $\dfrac{0.015}{0.500} \times 100\% = 3.0\%$; assumption is valid.

$$pH = -\log(0.015) = 1.82$$

   (b)   **Given:** 0.100 M HNO$_2$, $K_a = 4.6 \times 10^{-4}$ **Find:** pH

        Conceptual Plan: Write a balanced reaction. Prepare an ICE table, represent the change with x, sum the table, determine the equilibrium values, put the equilibrium values in the equilibrium expression, and solve for x. Determine [H$_3$O$^+$] and pH.

        Solution: $HNO_2(aq) + H_2O(l) \rightleftharpoons H_3O^+(aq) + NO_2^-(aq)$

	[HNO$_2$]	**[H$_3$O$^+$]**	**[NO$_2^-$]**
Initial	0.100 M	0.0	0.0
Change	$-x$	x	x
Equil	$0.100 - x$	x	x

$$K_a = \frac{[H_3O^+][NO_2^-]}{[HNO_2]} = \frac{(x)(x)}{(0.100 - x)} = 4.6 \times 10^{-4}$$

Assume that x is small compared to 0.100.

$$x^2 = (4.6 \times 10^{-4})(0.100) \qquad x = 0.0068 \text{ M} = [H_3O^+]$$

Check assumption: $\dfrac{0.0068}{0.100} \times 100\% = 6.8\%$; assumption is not valid; solve using the quadratic equation.

$$x^2 = (4.6 \times 10^{-4})(0.100 - x) \qquad x^2 + 4.6 \times 10^{-4}x - 4.6 \times 10^{-5} = 0$$

$$x = 0.00656$$

$$pH = -\log(0.00656) = 2.18$$

   (c)   **Given:** 0.0100 M HNO$_2$, $K_a = 4.6 \times 10^{-4}$ **Find:** pH

        Conceptual Plan: Write a balanced reaction. Prepare an ICE table, represent the change with x, sum the table, determine the equilibrium values, put the equilibrium values in the equilibrium expression, and solve for x. Determine [H$_3$O$^+$] and pH.

Solution: $HNO_2(aq) + H_2O(l) \rightleftharpoons H_3O^+(aq) + NO_2^-(aq)$

	[HNO₂]	[H₃O]	[NO₂]
Initial	0.0100 M	0.0	0.0
Change	−x	x	x
Equil	0.0100 − x	x	x

$$K_a = \frac{[H_3O^+][NO_2^-]}{[HNO_2]} = \frac{(x)(x)}{(0.0100 - x)} = 4.6 \times 10^{-4}$$

Assume that x is small compared to 0.100.

$$x^2 = (4.6 \times 10^{-4})(0.0100) \qquad x = 0.0021 \text{ M} = [H_3O^+]$$

Check assumption: $\dfrac{0.0021}{0.0100} \times 100\% = 21\%$; assumption is not valid; solve with the quadratic equation.

$$x^2 = (4.6 \times 10^{-4})(0.0100 - x) \qquad x^2 + 4.6 \times 10^{-4}x - 4.6 \times 10^{-6} = 0$$

$$x = 0.0019$$

$$pH = -\log(0.0019) = 2.72$$

15.34   (a)   **Given:** 0.250 M HF, $K_a = 3.5 \times 10^{-4}$ **Find:** pH

Conceptual Plan: Write a balanced reaction. Prepare an ICE table, represent the change with x, sum the table, determine the equilibrium values, put the equilibrium values in the equilibrium expression, and solve for x. Determine [H₃O⁺] and pH.

Solution: $HF(aq) + H_2O(l) \rightleftharpoons H_3O^+(aq) + F^-(aq)$

	[HF]	[H₃O]	[F]
Initial	0.250 M	0.0	0.0
Change	−x	x	x
Equil	0.250 − x	x	x

$$K_a = \frac{[H_3O^+][F^-]}{[HF]} = \frac{(x)(x)}{(0.250 - x)} = 3.5 \times 10^{-4}$$

Assume that x is small compared to 0.250.

$$x^2 = (3.5 \times 10^{-4})(0.250) \qquad x = 0.00935 \text{ M} = [H_3O^+]$$

Check assumption: $\dfrac{0.00935}{0.250} \times 100\% = 3.7\%$; assumption is valid.

$$pH = -\log(0.00935) = 2.03$$

(b)   **Given:** 0.0500 M HF, $K_a = 3.5 \times 10^{-4}$ **Find:** pH

Conceptual Plan: Write a balanced reaction. Prepare an ICE table, represent the change with x, sum the table, determine the equilibrium values, put the equilibrium values in the equilibrium expression, and solve for x. Determine [H₃O⁺] and pH.

Solution: $HF(aq) + H_2O(l) \rightleftharpoons H_3O^+(aq) + F^-(aq)$

	[HF]	[H₃O]	[F]
Initial	0.0500 M	0.0	0.0
Change	−x	x	x
Equil	0.0500 − x	x	x

$$K_a = \frac{[H_3O^+][F^-]}{[HF]} = \frac{(x)(x)}{(0.0500 - x)} = 3.5 \times 10^{-4}$$

Assume that x is small compared to 0.0500.

$$x^2 = (3.5 \times 10^{-4})(0.0500) \qquad x = 0.00418 \text{ M} = [H_3O^+]$$

Check assumption: $\dfrac{0.00418}{0.050} \times 100\% = 8.4\%$; assumption is not valid; solve with the quadratic equation.

$$x^2 + 3.5 \times 10^{-4}x - 1.75 \times 10^{-5} = 0 \qquad x = 0.0040 = [H_3O^+]$$

$$pH = -\log(0.0040) = 2.40$$

(c)   **Given:** 0.0250 M HF, $K_a = 3.5 \times 10^{-4}$ **Find:** pH

Conceptual Plan: Write a balanced reaction. Prepare an ICE table, represent the change with x, sum the table, determine the equilibrium values, put the equilibrium values in the equilibrium expression, and solve for x. Determine $[H_3O^+]$ and pH.

Solution: $HF(aq) + H_2O(l) \rightleftharpoons H_3O^+(aq) + F^-(aq)$

	[HF]	[H₃O⁺]	[F⁻]
Initial	0.0250 M	0.0	0.0
Change	$-x$	x	x
Equil	$0.0250 - x$	x	x

$$K_a = \frac{[H_3O^+][F^-]}{[HF]} = \frac{(x)(x)}{(0.0250 - x)} = 3.5 \times 10^{-4}$$

Assume that x is small compared to 0.0250.

$x^2 = (3.5 \times 10^{-4})(0.0250)$ $x = 0.00296 \, M = [H_3O^+]$

Check assumption: $\dfrac{0.00296}{0.0250} \times 100\% = 11.8\%$; assumption is not valid; solve with the quadratic equation.

$x^2 + 3.5 \times 10^{-4}x - 8.75 \times 10^{-6} = 0$ $x = 0.00279 = [H_3O^+]$

$pH = -\log(0.00279) = 2.55$

15.35   **Given:** 15.0 mL glacial acetic, $d = 1.05$ g/mL, dilute to 1.50 L, $K_a = 1.8 \times 10^{-5}$ **Find:** pH

Conceptual Plan: mL acetic acid $\rightarrow$ g acetic acid $\rightarrow$ mol acetic acid $\rightarrow$ M and then write a balanced reaction.

$$\frac{1.05 \text{ g}}{\text{mL}} \qquad \frac{\text{mol acetic acid}}{60.05 \text{ g}} \qquad M = \frac{\text{mol}}{\text{L}}$$

Prepare an ICE table, represent the change with x, sum the table, determine the equilibrium values, put the equilibrium values in the equilibrium expression, and solve for x. Determine $[H_3O^+]$ and pH.

Solution: $15.0 \text{ mL} \times \dfrac{1.05 \text{ g}}{\text{mL}} \times \dfrac{1 \text{ mol}}{60.05 \text{ g}} \times \dfrac{1}{1.50 \text{ L}} = 0.1749 \, M$

$$HC_2H_3O_2(aq) + H_2O(l) \rightleftharpoons H_3O^+(aq) + C_2H_3O_2^-(aq)$$

	[HC₂H₃O₂]	[H₃O⁺]	[C₂H₃O₂⁻]
Initial	0.1749 M	0.0	0.0
Change	$-x$	x	x
Equil	$0.1749 - x$	x	x

$$K_a = \frac{[H_3O^+][C_2H_3O_2^-]}{[HC_2H_3O_2]} = \frac{(x)(x)}{(0.1749 - x)} = 1.8 \times 10^{-5}$$

Assume that x is small compared to 0.1749.

$x^2 = (1.8 \times 10^{-5})(0.1749)$ $x = 0.00177 \, M = [H_3O^+]$

Check assumption: $\dfrac{0.00177}{0.1749} \times 100\% = 1.0\%$; assumption is valid.

$pH = -\log(0.00177) = 2.75$

15.36   **Given:** 1.35% formic acid, $d = 1.01$ g/mL, $K_a = 1.8 \times 10^{-4}$ **Find:** pH

Conceptual Plan: % formic acid $\rightarrow$ g formic acid $\rightarrow$ mol and g soln $\rightarrow$ mL soln $\rightarrow$ L soln and then M

$$\frac{\text{mol}}{46.03 \text{ g}} \qquad \frac{1.01 \text{ g soln}}{\text{mL soln}} \qquad \frac{1000 \text{ mL}}{\text{L soln}}$$

Write a balanced reaction. Prepare an ICE table, represent the change with x, sum the table, determine the equilibrium values, put the equilibrium values in the equilibrium expression, and solve for x. Determine $[H_3O^+]$ and pH.

Solution: $\dfrac{1.35 \text{ g } HCHO_2}{100 \text{ g soln}} \times \dfrac{\text{mol } HCHO_2}{46.03 \text{ g}} \times \dfrac{1.01 \text{ g soln}}{\text{mL soln}} \times \dfrac{1000 \text{ mL soln}}{\text{L soln}} = 0.2962 \, M$

$$HCHO_2(aq) + H_2O(l) \rightleftharpoons H_3O^+(aq) + CHO_2^-(aq)$$

	[HCHO$_2$]	[H$_3$O$^+$]	[CHO$_2^-$]
Initial	0.2962 M	0.0	0.0
Change	$-x$	x	x
Equil	$0.2962 - x$	x	x

$$K_a = \frac{[H_3O^+][CHO_2^-]}{[HCHO_2]} = \frac{(x)(x)}{(0.2962 - x)} = 1.8 \times 10^{-4}$$

Assume that x is small compared to 0.2962.

$$x^2 = (1.8 \times 10^{-4})(0.2962) \qquad x = 0.00730 \text{ M} = [H_3O^+]$$

Check assumption: $\dfrac{0.00730}{0.2962} \times 100\% = 2.5\%$; assumption is valid.

$$pH = -\log(0.00730) = 2.14$$

15.37   **Given:** 0.185 M HA, pH = 2.95   **Find:** K_a
Conceptual Plan: pH → [H$_3$O$^+$] and then write a balanced reaction. Prepare an ICE table, calculate equilibrium concentrations, and plug into the equilibrium expression to solve for K_a.
Solution: $[H_3O^+] = 10^{-2.95} = 0.00112$ M $= [A^-]$

$$HA(aq) + H_2O(l) \rightleftharpoons H_3O^+(aq) + A^-(aq)$$

	[HA]	[H$_3$O$^+$]	[A$^-$]
Initial	0.185 M	0.0	0.0
Change	$-x$	x	x
Equil	$0.185 - 0.00112$	0.00112	0.00112

$$K_a = \frac{[H_3O^+][A^-]}{[HA]} = \frac{(0.00112)(0.00112)}{(0.185 - 0.00112)} = 6.82 \times 10^{-6}$$

15.38   **Given:** 0.115 M HA, pH = 3.29   **Find:** K_a
Conceptual Plan: pH → [H$_3$O$^+$] and then write a balanced reaction. Prepare an ICE table, calculate equilibrium concentrations, and plug into the equilibrium expression to solve for K_a.
Solution: $[H_3O^+] = 10^{-3.29} = 5.13 \times 10^{-4}$ M $= [A^-]$

$$HA(aq) + H_2O(l) \rightleftharpoons H_3O^+(aq) + A^-(aq)$$

	[HA]	[H$_3$O$^+$]	[A$^-$]
Initial	0.115 M	0.0	0.0
Change	$-x$	x	x
Equil	$0.115 - 5.13 \times 10^{-4}$	5.13×10^{-4}	5.13×10^{-4}

$$K_a = \frac{[H_3O^+][A^-]}{[HA]} = \frac{(5.13 \times 10^{-4})(5.13 \times 10^{-4})}{(0.115 - 5.13 \times 10^{-4})} = 2.30 \times 10^{-6}$$

15.39   **Given:** 0.125 M HCN, $K_a = 4.9 \times 10^{-10}$ **Find:** % ionization
Conceptual Plan: Write a balanced reaction. Prepare an ICE table, represent the change with x, sum the table, determine the equilibrium values, put the equilibrium values in the equilibrium expression, solve for x, and then x → % ionization.

$$\% \text{ ionization} = \frac{x}{[HCN]_{original}} \times 100\%$$

Solution: $$HCN(aq) + H_2O(l) \rightleftharpoons H_3O^+(aq) + CN^-(aq)$$

	[HCN]	[H$_3$O$^+$]	[CN$^-$]
Initial	0.125 M	0.0	0.0
Change	$-x$	x	x
Equil	$0.125 - x$	x	x

$$K_a = \frac{[H_3O^+][CN^-]}{[HCN]} = \frac{(x)(x)}{(0.125 - x)} = 4.9 \times 10^{-10}$$

Assume that x is small compared to 0.125.

$$x^2 = (4.9 \times 10^{-10})(0.125) \qquad x = 7.\underline{8}3 \times 10^{-6}$$

$$\% \text{ ionization} = \frac{7.\underline{8}3 \times 10^{-6}}{0.125} \times 100\% = 0.0063\% \text{ ionized}$$

15.40   **Given:** 0.225 M $HC_7H_5O_2$, $K_a = 6.5 \times 10^{-5}$ **Find:** % ionization

Conceptual Plan: Write a balanced reaction. Prepare an ICE table, represent the change with x, sum the table, determine the equilibrium values, put the equilibrium values in the equilibrium expression, solve for x, and then $x \rightarrow$ % ionization.

$$\% \text{ ionization} = \frac{x}{[HC_7H_5O_2]_{original}} \times 100\%$$

Solution: $HC_7H_5O_2(aq) + H_2O(l) \rightleftharpoons H_3O^+(aq) + C_7H_5O_2^-(aq)$

	$[HC_7H_5O_2]$	$[H_3O^+]$	$[C_7H_5O_2^-]$
Initial	0.225 M	0.0	0.0
Change	$-x$	x	x
Equil	$0.225 - x$	x	x

$$K_a = \frac{[H_3O^+][C_7H_5O_2^-]}{[HC_7H_5O_2]} = \frac{(x)(x)}{(0.225 - x)} = 6.5 \times 10^{-5}$$

Assume that x is small compared to 0.225.

$$x^2 = (6.5 \times 10^{-5})(0.225) \qquad x = 0.003\underline{8}2$$

$$\% \text{ ionization} = \frac{0.003\underline{8}2}{0.225} \times 100\% = 1.7\% \text{ ionized}$$

15.41   (a)   **Given:** 1.00 M $HC_2H_3O_2$, $K_a = 1.8 \times 10^{-5}$ **Find:** % ionization

Conceptual Plan: Write a balanced reaction. Prepare an ICE table, represent the change with x, sum the table, determine the equilibrium values, put the equilibrium values in the equilibrium expression, solve for x, and then $x \rightarrow$ % ionization.

$$\% \text{ ionization} = \frac{x}{[HC_2H_3O_2]_{original}} \times 100\%$$

Solution: $HC_2H_3O_2(aq) + H_2O(l) \rightleftharpoons H_3O^+(aq) + C_2H_3O_2^-(aq)$

	$[HC_2H_3O_2]$	$[H_3O^+]$	$[C_2H_3O_2^-]$
Initial	1.00 M	0.0	0.0
Change	$-x$	x	x
Equil	$1.00 - x$	x	x

$$K_a = \frac{[H_3O^+][C_2H_3O_2^-]}{[HC_2H_3O_2]} = \frac{(x)(x)}{(1.00 - x)} = 1.8 \times 10^{-5}$$

Assume that x is small compared to 1.00.

$$x^2 = (1.8 \times 10^{-5})(1.00) \qquad x = 0.004\underline{2}4$$

$$\% \text{ ionization} = \frac{0.004\underline{2}4}{1.00} \times 100\% = 0.42\% \text{ ionized}$$

(b)   **Given:** 0.500 M $HC_2H_3O_2$, $K_a = 1.8 \times 10^{-5}$ **Find:** % ionization

Conceptual Plan: Write a balanced reaction. Prepare an ICE table, represent the change with x, sum the table, determine the equilibrium values, put the equilibrium values in the equilibrium expression, solve for x, and then $x \rightarrow$ % ionization.

$$\% \text{ ionization} = \frac{x}{[HC_2H_3O_2]_{original}} \times 100\%$$

Solution: $HC_2H_3O_2(aq) + H_2O(l) \rightleftharpoons H_3O^+(aq) + C_2H_3O_2{}^-(aq)$

	$[HC_2H_3O_2]$	$[H_3O^+]$	$[C_2H_3O_2{}^-]$
Initial	0.500 M	0.0	0.0
Change	$-x$	x	x
Equil	$0.500 - x$	x	x

$$K_a = \frac{[H_3O^+][C_2H_3O_2{}^-]}{[HC_2H_3O_2]} = \frac{(x)(x)}{(0.500 - x)} = 1.8 \times 10^{-5}$$

Assume that x is small compared to 0.500.

$x^2 = (1.8 \times 10^{-5})(0.500)$ $x = 0.00300$

$\%\ \text{ionization} = \dfrac{0.00300}{0.500} \times 100\% = 0.60\%$ ionized

(c) **Given:** 0.100 M $HC_2H_3O_2$, $K_a = 1.8 \times 10^{-5}$ **Find:** % ionization
Conceptual Plan: Write a balanced reaction. Prepare an ICE table, represent the change with x, sum the table, determine the equilibrium values, put the equilibrium values in the equilibrium expression, solve for x, and then $x \rightarrow$ % ionization.

$$\%\ \text{ionization} = \frac{x}{[HC_2H_3O_2]_{\text{original}}} \times 100\%$$

Solution: $HC_2H_3O_2(aq) + H_2O(l) \rightleftharpoons H_3O^+(aq) + C_2H_3O_2{}^-(aq)$

	$[HC_2H_3O_2]$	$[H_3O^+]$	$[C_2H_3O_2{}^-]$
Initial	0.100 M	0.0	0.0
Change	$-x$	x	x
Equil	$0.100 - x$	x	x

$$K_a = \frac{[H_3O^+][C_2H_3O_2{}^-]}{[HC_2H_3O_2]} = \frac{(x)(x)}{(0.100 - x)} = 1.8 \times 10^{-5}$$

Assume that x is small compared to 0.100.

$x^2 = (1.8 \times 10^{-5})(0.100)$ $x = 0.00134$

$\%\ \text{ionization} = \dfrac{0.00134}{0.100} \times 100\% = 1.3\%$ ionized

(d) **Given:** 0.0500 M $HC_2H_3O_2$, $K_a = 1.8 \times 10^{-5}$ **Find:** % ionization
Conceptual Plan: Write a balanced reaction. Prepare an ICE table, represent the change with x, sum the table, determine the equilibrium values, put the equilibrium values in the equilibrium expression, solve for x, and then $x \rightarrow$ % ionization.

$$\%\ \text{ionization} = \frac{x}{[HC_2H_3O_2]_{\text{original}}} \times 100\%$$

Solution: $HC_2H_3O_2(aq) + H_2O(l) \rightleftharpoons H_3O^+(aq) + C_2H_3O_2{}^-(aq)$

	$[HC_2H_3O_2]$	$[H_3O^+]$	$[C_2H_3O_2{}^-]$
Initial	0.0500 M	0.0	0.0
Change	$-x$	x	x
Equil	$0.0500 - x$	x	x

$$K_a = \frac{[H_3O^+][C_2H_3O_2{}^-]}{[HC_2H_3O_2]} = \frac{(x)(x)}{(0.0500 - x)} = 1.8 \times 10^{-5}$$

Assume that x is small compared to 0.0500.

$x^2 = (1.8 \times 10^{-5})(0.0500)$ $x = 9.49 \times 10^{-4}$

$\%\ \text{ionization} = \dfrac{9.49 \times 10^{-4}}{0.0500} \times 100\% = 1.9\%$ ionized

15.42   (a)   **Given:** 1.00 M $HCHO_2$, $K_a = 1.8 \times 10^{-4}$ **Find:** % ionization

Conceptual Plan: Write a balanced reaction. Prepare an ICE table, represent the change with x, sum the table, determine the equilibrium values, put the equilibrium values in the equilibrium expression, solve for x, and then $x \rightarrow$ % ionization.

$$\% \text{ ionization} = \frac{x}{[HCHO_2]_{original}} \times 100\%$$

Solution: $HCHO_2(aq) + H_2O(l) \rightleftharpoons H_3O^+(aq) + CHO_2^-(aq)$

	[HCHO₂]	[H₃O⁺]	[CHO₂⁻]
Initial	1.00 M	0.0	0.0
Change	$-x$	x	x
Equil	$1.00 - x$	x	x

$$K_a = \frac{[H_3O^+][CHO_2^-]}{[HCHO_2]} = \frac{(x)(x)}{(1.00 - x)} = 1.8 \times 10^{-4}$$

Assume that x is small compared to 1.00.

$x^2 = (1.8 \times 10^{-4})(1.00)$ $x = 0.0134$

$$\% \text{ ionization} = \frac{0.0134}{1.00} \times 100\% = 1.3\% \text{ ionized}$$

(b)   **Given:** 0.500 M $HCHO_2$, $K_a = 1.8 \times 10^{-4}$ **Find:** % ionization

Conceptual Plan: Write a balanced reaction. Prepare an ICE table, represent the change with x, sum the table, determine the equilibrium values, put the equilibrium values in the equilibrium expression, solve for x, and then $x \rightarrow$ % ionization.

$$\% \text{ ionization} = \frac{x}{[HCHO_2]_{original}} \times 100\%$$

Solution: $HCHO_2(aq) + H_2O(l) \rightleftharpoons H_3O^+(aq) + CHO_2^-(aq)$

	[HCHO₂]	[H₃O⁺]	[CHO₂⁻]
Initial	0.500 M	0.0	0.0
Change	$-x$	x	x
Equil	$0.500 - x$	x	x

$$K_a = \frac{[H_3O^+][CHO_2^-]}{[HCHO_2]} = \frac{(x)(x)}{(0.500 - x)} = 1.8 \times 10^{-4}$$

Assume that x is small compared to 1.00.

$x^2 = (1.8 \times 10^{-4})(0.500)$ $x = 0.00949$

$$\% \text{ ionization} = \frac{0.00949}{0.500} \times 100\% = 1.9\% \text{ ionized}$$

(c)   **Given:** 0.100 M $HCHO_2$, $K_a = 1.8 \times 10^{-4}$ **Find:** % ionization

Conceptual Plan: Write a balanced reaction. Prepare an ICE table, represent the change with x, sum the table, determine the equilibrium values, put the equilibrium values in the equilibrium expression, solve for x, and then $x \rightarrow$ % ionization.

$$\% \text{ ionization} = \frac{x}{[HCHO_2]_{original}} \times 100\%$$

Solution: $HCHO_2(aq) + H_2O(l) \rightleftharpoons H_3O^+(aq) + CHO_2^-(aq)$

	[HCHO₂]	[H₃O⁺]	[CHO₂⁻]
Initial	0.100 M	0.0	0.0
Change	$-x$	x	x
Equil	$0.100 - x$	x	x

$$K_a = \frac{[H_3O^+][CHO_2^-]}{[HCHO_2]} = \frac{(x)(x)}{(0.100 - x)} = 1.8 \times 10^{-4}$$

Assume that x is small compared to 0.100.

$x^2 = (1.8 \times 10^{-4})(0.100)$ $x = 0.00424$

$$\% \text{ ionization} = \frac{0.00424}{0.100} \times 100\% = 4.2\% \text{ ionized}$$

(d)   **Given:** 0.0500 M HCHO$_2$, $K_a = 1.8 \times 10^{-4}$ **Find:** % ionization

Conceptual Plan: Write a balanced reaction. Prepare an ICE table, represent the change with x, sum the table, determine the equilibrium values, put the equilibrium values in the equilibrium expression, solve for x, and then $x \rightarrow$ % ionization.

$$\% \text{ ionization} = \frac{x}{[\text{HCHO}_2]_{\text{original}}} \times 100\%$$

Solution: $HCHO_2(aq) + H_2O(l) \rightleftharpoons H_3O^+(aq) + CHO_2^-(aq)$

	[HCHO$_2$]	**[H$_3$O$^+$]**	**[CHO$_2^-$]**
Initial	0.0500 M	0.0	0.0
Change	$-x$	x	x
Equil	$0.0500 - x$	x	x

$$K_a = \frac{[H_3O^+][CHO_2^-]}{[HCHO_2]} = \frac{(x)(x)}{(0.0500 - x)} = 1.8 \times 10^{-4}$$

Assume that x is small compared to 0.0500.

$$x^2 = (1.8 \times 10^{-4})(0.0500) \qquad x = 0.00300$$

$$\% \text{ ionization} = \frac{0.00300}{0.0500} \times 100\% = 6.0\% \text{ ionized}$$

x is small assumption is invalid because 6.0% is greater than the 5.0% limit.

$$x^2 + 1.8 \times 10^{-4}x - 9.0 \times 10^{-6} = 0$$

Solve for x using the quadratic equation. $x = 0.00291$

$$\% \text{ ionization} = \frac{0.00291}{0.0500} \times 100\% = 5.8\%$$

15.43   **Given:** 0.148 M HA, 1.55% dissociation   **Find:** K_a

Conceptual Plan: M $\rightarrow$ [H$_3$O$^+$] $\rightarrow$ K_a and then write a balanced reaction, determine equilibrium concentration, and plug into the equilibrium expression.

Solution: (0.148 M HA)(0.0155) = 0.002294   [H$_3$O$^+$] = [A$^-$]

$$HA(aq) + H_2O(l) \rightleftharpoons H_3O^+(aq) + A^-(aq)$$

	[HA]	**[H$_3$O$^+$]**	**[A$^-$]**
Initial	0.148 M	0.0	0.0
Change	$-x$	x	x
Equil	$0.148 - 0.002294$	0.002294	0.002294

$$K_a = \frac{[H_3O^+][A^-]}{[HA]} = \frac{(0.002294)(0.002294)}{(0.148 - 0.002294)} = 3.61 \times 10^{-5}$$

15.44   **Given:** 0.085 M HA, 0.59% dissociation   **Find:** K_a

Conceptual Plan: M $\rightarrow$ [H$_3$O$^+$] $\rightarrow$ K_a and then write a balanced reaction, determine equilibrium concentration, and plug into the equilibrium expression.

Solution: (0.085 M HA)(0.0059) = 5.02×10^{-4} [H$_3$O$^+$] = [A$^-$]

$$HA(aq) + H_2O(l) \rightleftharpoons H_3O^+(aq) + A^-(aq)$$

	[HA]	**[H$_3$O$^+$]**	**[A$^-$]**
Initial	0.085 M	0.0	0.0
Change	$-x$	x	x
Equil	$0.085 - 5.02 \times 10^{-4}$	5.02×10^{-4}	5.02×10^{-4}

$$K_a = \frac{[H_3O^+][A^-]}{[HA]} = \frac{(5.02 \times 10^{-4})(5.02 \times 10^{-4})}{(0.085 - 5.02 \times 10^{-4})} = 3.0 \times 10^{-6}$$

15.45   (a)   **Given:** 0.250 M HF, $K_a = 3.5 \times 10^{-4}$ **Find:** pH, % dissociation
Conceptual Plan: Write a balanced reaction. Prepare an ICE table, represent the change with x, sum the table, determine the equilibrium values, put the equilibrium values in the equilibrium expression, solve for x, and then $x \rightarrow$ % ionization.

$$\% \text{ ionization} = \frac{x}{[\text{HF}]_{\text{original}}} \times 100\%$$

Solution: $HF(aq) + H_2O(l) \rightleftharpoons H_3O^+(aq) + F^-(aq)$

	[HF]	[H₃O⁺]	[F⁻]
Initial	0.250 M	0.0	0.0
Change	$-x$	x	x
Equil	$0.250 - x$	x	x

$$K_a = \frac{[H_3O^+][F^-]}{[HF]} = \frac{(x)(x)}{(0.250 - x)} = 3.5 \times 10^{-4}$$

Assume that x is small compared to 0.250.

$x^2 = (3.5 \times 10^{-4})(0.250)$ $x = 0.00935 \text{ M} = [H_3O^+]$

$$\frac{0.00935}{0.250} \times 100\% = 3.7\%$$

$pH = -\log(0.00935) = 2.03$

(b)   **Given:** 0.100 M HF, $K_a = 3.5 \times 10^{-4}$ **Find:** pH, % dissociation
Conceptual Plan: Write a balanced reaction. Prepare an ICE table, represent the change with x, sum the table, determine the equilibrium values, put the equilibrium values in the equilibrium expression, solve for x, and then $x \rightarrow$ % ionization.

$$\% \text{ ionization} = \frac{x}{[\text{HF}]_{\text{original}}} \times 100\%$$

Solution: $HF(aq) + H_2O(l) \rightleftharpoons H_3O^+(aq) + F^-(aq)$

	[HF]	[H₃O⁺]	[F⁻]
Initial	0.1000 M	0.0	0.0
Change	$-x$	x	x
Equil	$0.100 - x$	x	x

$$K_a = \frac{[H_3O^+][F^-]}{[HF]} = \frac{(x)(x)}{(0.100 - x)} = 3.5 \times 10^{-4}$$

Assume that x is small compared to 0.100.

$x^2 = (3.5 \times 10^{-4})(0.100)$ $x = 0.00592 \text{ M} = [H_3O^+]$

$$\frac{0.00592}{0.100} \times 100\% = 5.9\%$$

$x > 5.0\%$ Therefore, assumption is invalid; solve using the quadratic equation.

$x^2 + 3.5 \times 10^{-4}x - 3.5 \times 10^{-5} = 0$

$x = 0.00574$ or -0.00609

$pH = -\log(0.00574) = 2.24$

$$\% \text{ dissociation} = \frac{0.00574}{0.100} \times 100\% = 5.7\%$$

(c)   **Given:** 0.050 M HF, $K_a = 3.5 \times 10^{-4}$ **Find:** pH, % dissociation
Conceptual Plan: Write a balanced reaction. Prepare an ICE table, represent the change with x, sum the table, determine the equilibrium values, put the equilibrium values in the equilibrium expression, solve for x, and then $x \rightarrow$ % ionization.

$$\% \text{ ionization} = \frac{x}{[\text{HF}]_{\text{original}}} \times 100\%$$

Solution: $HF(aq) + H_2O(l) \rightleftharpoons H_3O^+(aq) + F^-(aq)$

	[HF]	**[H₃O⁺]**	**[F⁻]**
Initial	0.050 M	0.0	0.0
Change	$-x$	x	x
Equil	$0.050 - x$	x	x

$$K_a = \frac{[H_3O^+][F^-]}{[HF]} = \frac{(x)(x)}{(0.050 - x)} = 3.5 \times 10^{-4}$$

Assume that x is small compared to 0.050.

$$x^2 = (3.5 \times 10^{-4})(0.050) \qquad x = 0.00418 \text{ M} = [H_3O^+]$$

$$\frac{0.00418}{0.050} \times 100\% = 8.4\%$$

Assumption is invalid; solve using the quadratic equation.

$$x^2 + 3.5 \times 10^{-4}x - 1.75 \times 10^{-5} = 0$$

$$x = 0.00401 \text{ or } -0.00436$$

$$pH = -\log(0.00401) = 2.40$$

$$\% \text{ dissociation} = \frac{0.00401}{0.050} \times 100\% = 8.0\%$$

15.46   (a)   **Given:** 0.100 M HA, $K_a = 1.0 \times 10^{-5}$ **Find:** pH, % dissociation

Conceptual Plan: Write a balanced reaction. Prepare an ICE table, represent the change with x, sum the table, determine the equilibrium values, put the equilibrium values in the equilibrium expression, solve for x, and then $x \rightarrow$ % ionization.

$$\% \text{ ionization} = \frac{x}{[HA]_{original}} \times 100\%$$

Solution: $HA(aq) + H_2O(l) \rightleftharpoons H_3O^+(aq) + A^-(aq)$

	[HA]	**[H₃O⁺]**	**[A⁻]**
Initial	0.100 M	0.0	0.0
Change	$-x$	x	x
Equil	$0.100 - x$	x	x

$$K_a = \frac{[H_3O^+][A^-]}{[HA]} = \frac{(x)(x)}{(0.100 - x)} = 1.0 \times 10^{-5}$$

Assume that x is small compared to 0.100.

$$x^2 = (1.0 \times 10^{-5})(0.100) \qquad x = 0.00100 \text{ M} = [H_3O^+]$$

$$\frac{0.00100}{0.100} \times 100\% = 1.0\%$$

$$pH = -\log(0.00100) = 3.00$$

(b)   **Given:** 0.100 M HA, $K_a = 1.0 \times 10^{-3}$ **Find:** pH, % dissociation

Conceptual Plan: Write a balanced reaction. Prepare an ICE table, represent the change with x, sum the table, determine the equilibrium values, put the equilibrium values in the equilibrium expression, solve for x, and then $x \rightarrow$ % ionization.

$$\% \text{ ionization} = \frac{x}{[HA]_{original}} \times 100\%$$

Solution: $HA(aq) + H_2O(l) \rightleftharpoons H_3O^+(aq) + A^-(aq)$

	[HA]	**[H₃O⁺]**	**[A⁻]**
Initial	0.100 M	0.0	0.0
Change	$-x$	x	x
Equil	$0.100 - x$	x	x

$$K_a = \frac{[H_3O^+][A^-]}{[HA]} = \frac{(x)(x)}{(0.100 - x)} = 1.0 \times 10^{-3} \text{ Solve using the quadratic equation.}$$

$$x^2 = (1.0 \times 10^{-3} - x)(0.100) \qquad x^2 + 1 \times 10^{-3}x - 1 \times 10^{-4} = 0$$

$$x = 0.009\underline{5} = [H_3O^+]$$

$$\frac{0.009\underline{5}}{0.100} \times 100\% = 9.5\%$$

$$pH = -\log(0.009\underline{5}) = 2.02$$

(c) **Given:** 0.100 M HA, $K_a = 1.0 \times 10^{-1}$ **Find:** pH, % dissociation

Conceptual Plan: Write a balanced reaction. Prepare an ICE table, represent the change with x, sum the table, determine the equilibrium values, put the equilibrium values in the equilibrium expression, solve for x, and then $x \rightarrow$ % ionization.

$$\% \text{ ionization} = \frac{x}{[HA]_{original}} \times 100\%$$

Solution: $\quad HA(aq) + H_2O(l) \rightleftharpoons H_3O^+(aq) + A^-(aq)$

	[HA]	**[H₃O⁺]**	**[A⁻]**
Initial	0.100 M	0.0	0.0
Change	$-x$	x	x
Equil	$0.100 - x$	x	x

$$K_a = \frac{[H_3O^+][A^-]}{[HA]} = \frac{(x)(x)}{(0.100 - x)} = 1.0 \times 10^{-1}$$

$$x^2 = (1.0 \times 10^{-1} - x)(0.100) \quad x^2 + 0.10x - 0.01 = 0 \text{ Solve using the quadratic equation.}$$

$$x = 0.061\underline{8} = [H_3O^+]$$

$$\frac{0.061\underline{8}}{0.100} \times 100\% = 61.8\%$$

$$pH = -\log(0.061\underline{8}) = 1.21$$

15.47 $\quad H_3PO_4(aq) + H_2O(l) \rightleftharpoons H_3O^+(aq) + H_2PO_4^-(aq) \qquad K_{a_1} = \dfrac{[H_3O^+][H_2PO_4^-]}{[H_3PO_4]}$

$\quad H_2PO_4^-(aq) + H_2O(l) \rightleftharpoons H_3O^+(aq) + HPO_4^{2-}(aq) \qquad K_{a_2} = \dfrac{[H_3O^+][HPO_4^{2-}]}{[H_2PO_4^-]}$

$\quad HPO_4^{2-}(aq) + H_2O(l) \rightleftharpoons H_3O^+(aq) + PO_4^{3-}(aq) \qquad K_{a_3} = \dfrac{[H_3O^+][PO_4^{3-}]}{[HPO_4^{2-}]}$

15.48 $\quad H_2CO_3(aq) + H_2O(l) \rightleftharpoons H_3O^+(aq) + HCO_3^-(aq) \qquad K_{a_1} = \dfrac{[H_3O^+][HCO_3^-]}{[H_2CO_3]}$

$\quad HCO_3^-(aq) + H_2O(l) \rightleftharpoons H_3O^+(aq) + CO_3^{2-}(aq) \qquad K_{a_2} = \dfrac{[H_3O^+][CO_3^{2-}]}{[HCO_3^-]}$

15.49 (a) **Given:** 0.350 M H_3PO_4, $K_{a_1} = 7.5 \times 10^{-3}$, $K_{a_2} = 6.2 \times 10^{-8}$ **Find:** $[H_3O^+]$, pH

Conceptual Plan: K_{a_1} is much larger than K_{a_2}, so use K_{a_1} to calculate $[H_3O^+]$. Write a balanced reaction. Prepare an ICE table, represent the change with x, sum the table, determine the equilibrium values, put the equilibrium values in the equilibrium expression, and solve for x.

Solution: $\quad H_3PO_4(aq) + H_2O(l) \rightleftharpoons H_3O^+(aq) + H_2PO_4^-(aq)$

	[H₃PO₄]	**[H₃O⁺]**	**[H₂PO₄⁻]**
Initial	0.350 M	0.0	0.0
Change	$-x$	x	x
Equil	$0.350 - x$	x	x

$$K_a = \frac{[H_3O^+][H_2PO_4^-]}{[H_3PO_4]} = \frac{(x)(x)}{(0.350 - x)} = 7.5 \times 10^{-3}$$

Assume that x is small compared to 0.350.

$$x^2 = (7.5 \times 10^{-3})(0.350) \qquad x = 0.0512 \text{ M} = [H_3O^+]$$

Check assumption: $\frac{0.0512}{0.350} \times 100\% = 14.6\%$; assumption is not valid.

$$x^2 + 7.5 \times 10^{-3}x - 0.002625 = 0 \qquad x = 0.04\underline{7}62 = [H_3O^+]$$

$$pH = -\log(0.04\underline{7}62) = 1.32$$

(b)   **Given:** 0.350 M $H_2C_2O_4$, $K_{a_1} = 6.0 \times 10^{-2}$, $K_{a_2} = 6.0 \times 10^{-5}$ **Find:** $[H_3O^+]$, pH

Conceptual Plan: K_{a_1} is much larger than K_{a_2}, so use K_{a_1} to calculate $[H_3O^+]$. Write a balanced reaction. Prepare an ICE table, represent the change with x, sum the table, determine the equilibrium values, put the equilibrium values in the equilibrium expression, and solve for x.

Solution: $H_2C_2O_4(aq) + H_2O(l) \rightleftharpoons H_3O^+(aq) + HC_2O_4^-(aq)$

	$[H_2C_2O_4]$	$[H_3O^+]$	$[HC_2O_4^-]$
Initial	0.350 M	0.0	0.0
Change	$-x$	x	x
Equil	$0.350 - x$	x	x

$$K_{a_1} = \frac{[H_3O^+][HC_2O_4^-]}{[H_2C_2O_4]} = \frac{(x)(x)}{(0.350 - x)} = 6.0 \times 10^{-2}$$

$$x^2 + 6.0 \times 10^{-2}x - 0.021 = 0 \qquad x = 0.1\underline{1}80 = 0.12 \text{ M } [H_3O^+]$$

$$pH = -\log(0.1\underline{1}80) = 0.93$$

15.50   (a)   **Given:** 0.125 M H_2CO_3, $K_{a_1} = 4.3 \times 10^{-7}$, $K_{a_2} = 5.6 \times 10^{-11}$ **Find:** $[H_3O^+]$, pH

Conceptual Plan: K_{a_1} is much larger than K_{a_2}, so use K_{a_1} to calculate $[H_3O^+]$. Write a balanced reaction. Prepare an ICE table, represent the change with x, sum the table, determine the equilibrium values, put the equilibrium values in the equilibrium expression, and solve for x.

Solution: $H_2CO_3(aq) + H_2O(l) \rightleftharpoons H_3O^+(aq) + HCO_3^-(aq)$

	$[H_2CO_3]$	$[H_3O^+]$	$[HCO_3^-]$
Initial	0.125 M	0.0	0.0
Change	$-x$	x	x
Equil	$0.125 - x$	x	x

$$K_{a_1} = \frac{[H_3O^+][HCO_3^-]}{[H_2CO_3]} = \frac{(x)(x)}{(0.125 - x)} = 4.3 \times 10^{-7}$$

Assume that x is small.

$$x^2 = (4.3 \times 10^{-7})(0.125) \qquad x = 2.\underline{3}2 \times 10^{-4} = [H_3O^+]$$

$$\frac{2.\underline{3}2 \times 10^{-4}}{0.125} \times 100\% = 0.19\%; \text{ assumption is valid.}$$

$$pH = -\log(2.\underline{3}2 \times 10^{-4}) = 3.63$$

(b)   **Given:** 0.125 M $H_3C_6H_5O_3$, $K_{a_1} = 7.4 \times 10^{-4}$, $K_{a_2} = 1.7 \times 10^{-5}$, $K_{a_3} = 4.0 \times 10^{-7}$ **Find:** $[H_3O^+]$, pH

Conceptual Plan: K_{a_1} and K_{a_2} are only 10^{-1} apart, so use both to calculate $[H_3O^+]$. Write a balanced reaction. Prepare an ICE table, represent the change with x, sum the table, determine the equilibrium values, put the equilibrium values in the equilibrium expression, and solve for x.

Solution: $H_3C_6H_5O_3(aq) + H_2O(l) \rightleftharpoons H_3O^+(aq) + H_2C_6H_5O_3^-(aq)$

	$[H_3C_6H_5O_3]$	$[H_3O^+]$	$[H_2C_6H_5O_3^-]$
Initial	0.125 M	0.0	0.0
Change	$-x$	x	x
Equil	$0.125 - x$	x	x

$$K_{a_1} = \frac{[H_3O^+][H_2C_6H_5O_3^-]}{[H_3C_6H_5O_3]} = \frac{(x)(x)}{(0.125 - x)} = 7.4 \times 10^{-4}$$

Assume that x is small.

$$x^2 = (7.4 \times 10^{-4})(0.125) \qquad x = 9.\underline{6}2 \times 10^{-3} = [H_3O^+]$$

$$\frac{9.\underline{6}2 \times 10^{-3}}{0.125} \times 100\% = 7.7\%; \text{ assumption is not valid.}$$

$$x^2 + 7.4 \times 10^{-4}x - 9.25 \times 10^{-5} = 0 \qquad x = 0.009\underline{2}55 = [H_3O^+] = [H_2C_6H_5O_3^-]$$

and then

$$H_2C_6H_5O_3^-(aq) + H_2O(l) \rightleftharpoons H_3O^+(aq) + HC_6H_5O_3^{2-}(aq)$$

	[H₂C₆H₅O₃⁻]	**[H₃O⁺]**	**[HC₆H₅O₃²⁻]**
Initial	0.009255 M	0.009255	0.0
Change	−y	y	y
Equil	0.009255 − y	0.009255 + y	y

$$K_{a_2} = \frac{[H_3O^+][HC_6H_5O_3^{2-}]}{[H_2C_6H_5O_3^-]} = \frac{(0.009255 + y)(y)}{(0.009255 - y)} = 1.7 \times 10^{-5}$$

Assume that y is small. Then $y = 1.7 \times 10^{-5}$

$$\frac{1.7 \times 10^{-5}}{0.009255} \times 100\% = 1.8\%; \text{ assumption is valid.}$$

$[H_3O^+] = 1.7 \times 10^{-5}$ (from second ionization)

$[H_3O^+] = 0.009\underline{2}55 + 1.7 \times 10^{-5} = 0.009\underline{2}7 \text{ M} \qquad pH = -\log(0.00927) = 2.03$

Base Solutions

15.51   (a)   **Given:** 0.15 M NaOH   **Find:** [OH⁻], [H₃O⁺], pH, pOH

Conceptual Plan: [NaOH] → [OH⁻] → [H₃O⁺] → pH → pOH

     $K_w = [H_3O^+][OH^-]$ $pH = -\log[H_3O^+]$ $pH + pOH = 14$

Solution: $[OH^-] = [NaOH] = 0.15$ M

$$[H_3O^+] = \frac{K_w}{[OH^-]} = \frac{1.0 \times 10^{-14}}{0.15 \text{ M}} = 6.7 \times 10^{-14} \text{ M}$$

$$pH = -\log(6.7 \times 10^{-14}) = 13.17$$

$$pOH = 14.00 - 13.17 = 0.83$$

(b)   **Given:** 1.5×10^{-3} M Ca(OH)₂   **Find:** [OH⁻], [H₃O⁺], pH, pOH

Conceptual Plan: [Ca(OH)₂] → [OH⁻] → [H₃O⁺] → pH → pOH

     $K_w = [H_3O^+][OH^-]$ $pH = -\log[H_3O^+]$ $pH + pOH = 14$

Solution: $[OH^-] = 2[Ca(OH)_2] = 2(1.5 \times 10^{-3}) = 0.0030$ M

$$[H_3O^+] = \frac{K_w}{[OH^-]} = \frac{1.0 \times 10^{-14}}{0.0030 \text{ M}} = 3.\underline{3}3 \times 10^{-12} \text{ M}$$

$$pH = -\log(3.\underline{3}3 \times 10^{-12}) = 11.48$$

$$pOH = 14.00 - 11.48 = 2.52$$

(c)   **Given:** 4.8×10^{-4} M Sr(OH)₂   **Find:** [OH⁻], [H₃O⁺], pH, pOH

Conceptual Plan: [Sr(OH)₂] → [OH⁻] → [H₃O⁺] → pH → pOH

     $K_w = [H_3O^+][OH^-]$ $pH = -\log[H_3O^+]$ $pH + pOH = 14$

Solution: $[OH^+] = [Sr(OH)_2] = 2(4.8 \times 10^{-4}) = 9.6 \times 10^{-4}$ M

$$[H_3O^-] = \frac{K_w}{[OH^-]} = \frac{1.0 \times 10^{-14}}{9.6 \times 10^{-4} \text{ M}} = 1.\underline{0}4 \times 10^{-11} \text{ M}$$

$$pH = -\log(1.\underline{0}4 \times 10^{-11}) = 10.98$$

$$pOH = 14.00 - 10.98 = 3.02$$

(d)   **Given:** 8.7×10^{-5} M KOH   **Find:** $[OH^-]$, $[H_3O^+]$, pH, pOH

       Conceptual Plan: **[KOH]** $\rightarrow$ **[OH⁻]** $\rightarrow$ **[H₃O⁺]** $\rightarrow$ **pH** $\rightarrow$ **pOH**

$$K_w = [H_3O^+][OH^-] \quad pH = -\log[H_3O^+] \quad pH + pOH = 14$$

       Solution: $[OH^-] = [KOH] = 8.7 \times 10^{-5}$ M

$$[H_3O^+] = \frac{K_w}{[OH^-]} = \frac{1.0 \times 10^{-14}}{8.7 \times 10^{-5} \text{ M}} = 1.\underline{1} \times 10^{-10} \text{ M}$$

$$pH = -\log(1.\underline{1} \times 10^{-10}) = 9.96$$

$$pOH = 14.00 - 9.96 = 4.04$$

15.52   (a)   **Given:** 8.77×10^{-3} M LiOH   **Find:** $[OH^-]$, $[H_3O^+]$, pH, pOH

       Conceptual Plan: **[LiOH]** $\rightarrow$ **[OH⁻]** $\rightarrow$ **[H₃O⁺]** $\rightarrow$ **pH** $\rightarrow$ **pOH**

$$K_w = [H_3O^+][OH^-] \quad pH = -\log[H_3O^+] \quad pH + pOH = 14$$

       Solution: $[OH^-] = [LiOH] = 8.77 \times 10^{-3}$ M

$$[H_3O^+] = \frac{K_w}{[OH^-]} = \frac{1.0 \times 10^{-14}}{8.77 \times 10^{-3} \text{ M}} = 1.1\underline{4}0 \times 10^{-12} \text{ M}$$

$$pH = -\log(1.1\underline{4}0 \times 10^{-12}) = 11.943$$

$$pOH = 14.00 - 11.943 = 2.057$$

(b)   **Given:** 0.0112 M $Ba(OH)_2$ **Find:** $[OH^-]$, $[H_3O^+]$, pH, pOH

       Conceptual Plan: **[Ba(OH)₂]** $\rightarrow$ **[OH⁻]** $\rightarrow$ **[H₃O⁺]** $\rightarrow$ **pH** $\rightarrow$ **pOH**

$$K_w = [H_3O^+][OH^-] \quad pH = -\log[H_3O^+] \quad pH + pOH = 14$$

       Solution: $[OH^-] = 2[Ba(OH)_2] = 2(0.0112) = 0.0224$ M

$$[H_3O^+] = \frac{K_w}{[OH^-]} = \frac{1.0 \times 10^{-14}}{0.0224 \text{ M}} = 4.4\underline{6}4 \times 10^{-13} \text{ M}$$

$$pH = -\log(4.4\underline{6}4 \times 10^{-13}) = 12.350$$

$$pOH = 14.000 - 12.350 = 1.650$$

(c)   **Given:** 1.9×10^{-4} M KOH   **Find:** $[OH^-]$, $[H_3O^+]$, pH, pOH

       Conceptual Plan: **[KOH]** $\rightarrow$ **[OH⁻]** $\rightarrow$ **[H₃O⁺]** $\rightarrow$ **pH** $\rightarrow$ **pOH**

$$K_w = [H_3O^+][OH^-] \quad pH = -\log[H_3O^+] \quad pH + pOH = 14$$

       Solution: $[OH^-] = [KOH] = 1.9 \times 10^{-4}$ M

$$[H_3O^+] = \frac{K_w}{[OH^-]} = \frac{1.0 \times 10^{-14}}{1.9 \times 10^{-4} \text{ M}} = 5.2\underline{6} \times 10^{-11} \text{ M}$$

$$pH = -\log(5.2\underline{6} \times 10^{-11}) = 10.28$$

$$pOH = 14.00 - 10.28 = 3.72$$

(d)   **Given:** 5.0×10^{-4} M $Ca(OH)_2$ **Find:** $[OH^-]$, $[H_3O^+]$, pH, pOH

       Conceptual Plan: **[Ca(OH)₂]** $\rightarrow$ **[OH⁻]** $\rightarrow$ **[H₃O⁺]** $\rightarrow$ **pH** $\rightarrow$ **pOH**

$$K_w = [H_3O^+][OH^-] \quad pH = -\log[H_3O^+] \quad pH + pOH = 14$$

       Solution: $[OH^-] = [Ca(OH)_2] = 2(5.0 \times 10^{-4}) = 0.0010$ M

$$[H_3O^+] = \frac{K_w}{[OH^-]} = \frac{1.0 \times 10^{-14}}{0.0010 \text{ M}} = 1.\underline{0}0 \times 10^{-11} \text{ M}$$

$$pH = -\log(1.\underline{0}0 \times 10^{-11}) = 11.00$$

$$pOH = 14.00 - 11.00 = 3.00$$

15.53   **Given:** 3.85% KOH by mass, $d = 1.01$ g/mL   **Find:** pH

   Conceptual Plan:

   % mass $\rightarrow$ **g KOH** $\rightarrow$ **mol KOH and mass soln** $\rightarrow$ **mL soln** $\rightarrow$ **L soln** $\rightarrow$ **M KOH** $\rightarrow$ **[OH⁻]**

$$\frac{1 \text{ mol KOH}}{56.11 \text{ g KOH}} \qquad \frac{1.01 \text{ g soln}}{\text{mL soln}} \quad \frac{1000 \text{ mL soln}}{1 \text{ L soln}} \quad \frac{\text{mol KOH}}{\text{L soln}}$$

   $\rightarrow$ **pOH** $\rightarrow$ **pH**

$$pOH = -\log[OH^-] \quad pH + pOH = 14$$

Solution: $\dfrac{3.85 \text{ g KOH}}{100.0 \text{ g soln}} \times \dfrac{1 \text{ mol KOH}}{56.11 \text{ g KOH}} \times \dfrac{1.01 \text{ g soln}}{\text{mL soln}} \times \dfrac{1000 \text{ mL soln}}{1 \text{ L soln}} = 0.69\underline{3}0 \text{ M KOH}$

$[OH^-] = [KOH] = 0.69\underline{3}0 \text{ M}$; $pOH = -\log(0.69\underline{3}0) = 0.159$; $pH = 14.000 - 0.159 = 13.841$

15.54   **Given:** 1.55% NaOH by mass, $d = 1.01 \text{ g/mL}$ **Find:** pH
Conceptual Plan:
% mass → g NaOH → mol NaOH and mass soln → mL soln → L soln → M NaOH → [OH⁻]

$\dfrac{1 \text{ mol NaOH}}{40.00 \text{ g NaOH}}$ $\dfrac{1.01 \text{ g soln}}{\text{mL soln}}$ $\dfrac{1000 \text{ mL soln}}{1 \text{ L soln}}$ $\dfrac{\text{mol NaOH}}{\text{L soln}}$

→ pOH → pH

$pOH = -\log[OH^-]$ $pH + pOH = 14$

Solution: $\dfrac{1.55 \text{ g NaOH}}{100.0 \text{ g soln}} \times \dfrac{1 \text{ mol NaOH}}{40.00 \text{ g NaOH}} \times \dfrac{1.01 \text{ g soln}}{\text{mL soln}} \times \dfrac{1000 \text{ mL soln}}{1 \text{ L soln}} = 0.39\underline{1}4 \text{ M NaOH}$

$[OH^-] = [NaOH] = 0.39\underline{1}4 \text{ M}$; $pOH = -\log(0.39\underline{1}4) = 0.407$; $pH = 14.000 - 0.407 = 13.593$

15.55   **Given:** 3.55 L, pH = 12.4; 0.855 M KOH   **Find:** Vol
Conceptual Plan: pH → $[H_3O^+]$ → $[OH^-]$ and then $V_1M_1 = V_2M_2$

$[H_3O^+] = 10^{-pH}$ $1.0 \times 10^{-14} = [H_3O^+][OH^-]$ $V_1M_1 = V_2M_2$

Solution: $[H_3O^+] = 10^{-12.4} = 3.98 \times 10^{-13}$ $1.0 \times 10^{-14} = 3.98 \times 10^{-13}[OH^-]$

$[OH^-] = 0.025\underline{1}3$

$V_1M_1 = V_2M_2$ $V_1(0.855 \text{ M}) = (3.55 \text{ L})(0.0251 \text{ M})$ $V_1 = 0.104 \text{ L}$

15.56   **Given:** 5.00 L, pH = 10.8; 15.0% NaOH, $d = 1.116 \text{ g/mL}$ **Find:** Vol
Conceptual Plan:
% mass → g NaOH → mol NaOH and mass soln → mL soln → L soln → M NaOH → [OH⁻]

$\dfrac{1 \text{ mol NaOH}}{40.00 \text{ g NaOH}}$ $\dfrac{1.116 \text{ g soln}}{\text{mL soln}}$ $\dfrac{1000 \text{ mL soln}}{1 \text{ L soln}}$ $\dfrac{\text{mol NaOH}}{\text{L soln}}$

and then $V_1M_1 → V_2M_2$

$V_1M_1 = V_2M_2$

Solution: $\dfrac{15.0 \text{ g NaOH}}{100.0 \text{ g soln}} \times \dfrac{1 \text{ mol NaOH}}{40.00 \text{ g NaOH}} \times \dfrac{1.116 \text{ g soln}}{\text{mL soln}} \times \dfrac{1000 \text{ mL soln}}{1 \text{ L soln}} = 4.1\underline{8}5 \text{ M NaOH}$

$[OH^-] = [NaOH] = 4.1\underline{8}5 \text{ M}$

$[H_3O^+] = 10^{-10.8} = 1.58 \times 10^{-11}$ $1.0 \times 10^{-14} = (1.58 \times 10^{-11})[OH^-]$

$[OH^-] = 6.33 \times 10^{-4} \text{ M}$

$V_1(4.19 \text{ M}) = (5.00 \text{ L})(6.33 \times 10^{-4} \text{ M})$ $V_1 = 7.55 \times 10^{-4} \text{ L} = 0.8 \text{ mL}$

15.57   (a) $NH_3(aq) + H_2O(l) \rightleftharpoons NH_4^+(aq) + OH^-(aq)$ $K_b = \dfrac{[NH_4^+][OH^-]}{[NH_3]}$

       (b) $HCO_3^-(aq) + H_2O(l) \rightleftharpoons H_2CO_3(aq) + OH^-(aq)$ $K_b = \dfrac{[H_2CO_3][OH^-]}{[HCO_3^-]}$

       (c) $CH_3NH_2(aq) + H_2O(l) \rightleftharpoons CH_3NH_3^+(aq) + OH^-(aq)$ $K_b = \dfrac{[CH_3NH_3^+][OH^-]}{[CH_3NH_2]}$

15.58   (a) $CO_3^{2-}(aq) + H_2O(l) \rightleftharpoons HCO_3^-(aq) + OH^-(aq)$ $K_b = \dfrac{[HCO_3^-][OH^-]}{[CO_3^{2-}]}$

       (b) $C_6H_5NH_2(aq) + H_2O(l) \rightleftharpoons C_6H_5NH_3^+(aq) + OH^-(aq)$ $K_b = \dfrac{[C_6H_5NH_3^+][OH^-]}{[C_6H_5NH_2]}$

       (c) $C_2H_5NH_2(aq) + H_2O(l) \rightleftharpoons C_2H_5NH_3^+(aq) + OH^-(aq)$ $K_b = \dfrac{[C_2H_5NH_3^+][OH^-]}{[C_2H_5NH_2]}$

15.59   **Given:** 0.15 M NH_3, $K_b = 1.76 \times 10^{-5}$ **Find:** $[OH^-]$, pH, pOH
Conceptual Plan: Write a balanced reaction. Prepare an ICE table, represent the change with x, sum the table, determine the equilibrium values, put the equilibrium values in the equilibrium expression, and solve for x.
$x = [OH^-] \rightarrow [pOH] \rightarrow$ **pH**
   $pOH = -\log[OH^-]$ $pH + pOH = 14$

Solution: $NH_3(aq) + H_2O(l) \rightleftharpoons NH_4^+(aq) + OH^-(aq)$

	$[NH_3]$	$[NH_4^+]$	$[OH^-]$
Initial	0.15 M	0.0	0.0
Change	$-x$	x	x
Equil	$0.15 - x$	x	x

$K_b = \dfrac{[NH_4^+][OH^-]}{[NH_3]} = \dfrac{(x)(x)}{(0.15 - x)} = 1.76 \times 10^{-5}$

Assume that x is small.

$x^2 = (1.76 \times 10^{-5})(0.15)$ $x = [OH^-] = 0.00162$ M

$pOH = -\log(0.00162) = 2.79$

$pH = 14.00 - 2.79 = 11.21$

15.60   **Given:** 0.125 M CO_3^{2-}, $K_b = 1.8 \times 10^{-4}$ **Find:** $[OH^-]$, pH, pOH
Conceptual Plan: Write a balanced reaction. Prepare an ICE table, represent the change with x, sum the table, determine the equilibrium values, put the equilibrium values in the equilibrium expression, and solve for x.
$x = [OH^-] \rightarrow [pOH] \rightarrow$ **pH**
   $pOH = -\log[OH^-]$ $pH + pOH = 14$

Solution: $CO_3^{2-}(aq) + H_2O(l) \rightleftharpoons HCO_3^-(aq) + OH^-(aq)$

	$[CO_3^{2-}]$	$[HCO_3^-]$	$[OH^-]$
Initial	0.125 M	0.0	0.0
Change	$-x$	x	x
Equil	$0.125 - x$	x	x

$K_b = \dfrac{[HCO_3^-][OH^-]}{[CO_3^{2-}]} = \dfrac{(x)(x)}{(0.125 - x)} = 1.8 \times 10^{-4}$

Assume that x is small.

$x^2 = (1.8 \times 10^{-4})(0.125)$ $x = [OH^-] = 0.00474$ M

$\dfrac{0.00474}{0.125} \times 100\% = 3.8\%$; assumption is valid.

$pOH = -\log(0.00474) = 2.32$

$pH = 14.00 - 2.32 = 11.68$

15.61   **Given:** $pK_b = 10.4$, 455 mg/L caffeine   **Find:** pH
Conceptual Plan: $pK_b \rightarrow K_b$ and then mg/L $\rightarrow$ g/L $\rightarrow$ mol/L and then write a balanced reaction. Prepare an ICE table, represent the change with x, sum the table, determine the equilibrium values, put the equilibrium values in the equilibrium expression, and solve for x.
$x = [OH^-] \rightarrow [pOH] \rightarrow$ **pH**
   $pOH = -\log[OH^-]$ $pH + pOH = 14$

Solution: $K_b = 10^{-10.4} = 3.98 \times 10^{-11}$

$\dfrac{455 \text{ mg caffeine}}{\text{L soln}} \times \dfrac{\text{g caffeine}}{1000 \text{ mg caffeine}} \times \dfrac{1 \text{ mol caffeine}}{194.20 \text{ g}} = 0.002343$ M caffeine

$$C_8H_{10}N_4O_2(aq) + H_2O(l) \rightleftharpoons HC_8H_{10}N_4O_2^+(aq) + OH^-(aq)$$

	$[C_8H_{10}N_4O_2]$	$[HC_8H_{10}N_4O_2^{\cdot}]$	$[OH^{\cdot}]$
Initial	0.002343	0.0	0.0
Change	$-x$	x	x
Equil	$0.002343 - x$	x	x

$$K_b = \frac{[HC_8H_{10}N_4O_2^+][OH^-]}{[C_8H_{10}N_4O_2]} = \frac{(x)(x)}{(0.002343 - x)} = 3.98 \times 10^{-11}$$

Assume that x is small.

$$x^2 = (3.98 \times 10^{-11})(0.002343) \quad x = [OH^-] = 3.05 \times 10^{-7} \text{ M}$$

$$\frac{3.05 \times 10^{-7} \text{ M}}{0.002343} \times 100\% = 0.013\%; \text{ assumption is valid.}$$

$$pOH = -\log(3.05 \times 10^{-7}) = 6.5$$

$$pH = 14.00 - 6.5 = 7.5$$

15.62   **Given:** $pK_b = 4.2$, 225 mg/L amphetamine   **Find:** pH
Conceptual Plan: $pK_b \rightarrow K_b$ and then mg/L $\rightarrow$ g/L $\rightarrow$ mol/L and then write a balanced reaction. Prepare an ICE table, represent the change with x, sum the table, determine the equilibrium values, put the equilibrium values in the equilibrium expression, and solve for x.
$$x = [OH^-] \rightarrow [pOH] \rightarrow pH$$
$$pOH = -\log[OH^-] \quad pH + pOH = 14$$

Solution: $K_b = 10^{-4.2} = 6.31 \times 10^{-5}$

$$\frac{225 \text{ mg amphetamine}}{\text{L soln}} \times \frac{1 \text{ g amphetamine}}{1000 \text{ mg amphetamine}} \times \frac{1 \text{ mol amphetamine}}{135.20 \text{ g}} = 0.001664 \text{ M amphetamine}$$

$$C_9H_{13}N(aq) + H_2O(l) \rightleftharpoons C_9H_{13}NH^+(aq) + OH^-(aq)$$

	$[C_9H_{13}N]$	$[C_9H_{13}NH^{\cdot}]$	$[OH^{\cdot}]$
Initial	0.001664 M	0.0	0.0
Change	$-x$	x	x
Equil	$0.001664 - x$	x	x

$$K_b = \frac{[C_9H_{13}NH^+][OH^-]}{[C_9H_{13}N]} = \frac{(x)(x)}{(0.001664 - x)} = 6.31 \times 10^{-5}$$

Assume that x is small.

$$x^2 = (6.31 \times 10^{-5})(0.001664) \quad x = [OH^-] = 3.24 \times 10^{-4} \text{ M}$$

$$\frac{3.24 \times 10^{-4}}{0.001664} \times 100\% = 19.5\%; \text{ assumption is not valid; solve with the quadratic equation.}$$

$$x^2 + 6.31 \times 10^{-5}x - 1.05 \times 10^{-7} = 0$$

$$x = [OH^-] = 2.94 \times 10^{-4} \text{ M}$$

$$pOH = -\log(2.94 \times 10^{-4}) = 3.5$$

$$pH = 14.00 - 3.5 = 10.5$$

15.63   **Given:** 0.150 M morphine, pH = 10.5   **Find:** K_b
Conceptual Plan:
pH $\rightarrow$ pOH $\rightarrow$ [OH$^-$] and then write a balanced equation, prepare an ICE table, and determine
$pH + pOH = 14 \quad pOH = -\log[OH^-]$

equilibrium concentrations $\rightarrow K_b$.

Solution: $pOH = 14.0 - 10.5 = 3.5 \quad [OH^-] = 10^{-3.5} = 3.16 \times 10^{-4} = [Hmorphine^+]$

$$\text{morphine}(aq) + H_2O(l) \rightleftharpoons \text{Hmorphine}^+ (aq) + OH^- (aq)$$

	[morphine]	[Hmorphine·]	[OH·]
Initial	0.150 M	0.0	0.0
Change	$-x$	x	x
Equil	$0.150 - x$	3.16×10^{-4}	3.16×10^{-4}

$$K_b = \frac{[\text{Hmorphine}^+][OH^-]}{[\text{morphine}]} = \frac{(3.16 \times 10^{-4})(3.16 \times 10^{-4})}{(0.150 - 3.16 \times 10^{-4})} = \underline{6}.67 \times 10^{-7} = 7 \times 10^{-7}$$

15.64   **Given:** 0.135 M base, pH=11.23   **Find:** K_b

Conceptual Plan:

pH → pOH → [OH⁻] and then write a balanced equation, prepare an ICE table, and determine

pH = pOH = 14 pOH = −log[OH⁻]

equilibrium concentrations → K_b.

Solution: pOH = 14.00 − 11.23 = 2.77 $[OH^-] = 10^{-2.77} = 1.\underline{6}98 \times 10^{-3} = [HB^+]$

$$B(aq) + H_2O(l) \rightleftharpoons HB^+ (aq) + OH^-(aq)$$

	[B]	[HB·]	[OH·]
Initial	0.135	0.0	0.0
Change	$-x$	x	x
Equil	$0.135 - x$	$1.\underline{6}98 \times 10^{-3}$	$1.\underline{6}98 \times 10^{-3}$

$$K_b = \frac{[HB^+][OH^-]}{[B]} = \frac{(1.\underline{6}98 \times 10^{-3})(1.\underline{6}98 \times 10^{-3})}{(0.135 - 1.\underline{6}98 \times 10^{-3})} = 2.\underline{1}6 \times 10^{-5} = 2.2 \times 10^{-5}$$

Acid–Base Properties of Ions and Salts

15.65   (a)   pH neutral: Br^- is the conjugate base of a strong acid; therefore, it is pH-neutral.

   (b)   weak base: ClO^- is the conjugate base of a weak acid; therefore, it is a weak base.

   $$ClO^-(aq) + H_2O(l) \rightleftharpoons HClO(aq) + OH^-(aq)$$

   (c)   weak base: CN^- is the conjugate base of a weak acid; therefore, it is a weak base.

   $$CN^-(aq) + H_2O(l) \rightleftharpoons HCN(aq) + OH^-(aq)$$

   (d)   pH neutral: Cl^- is the conjugate base of a strong acid; therefore, it is pH-neutral.

15.66   (a)   weak base: $C_7H_5O_2^-$ is the conjugate base of a weak acid; therefore, it is a weak base.

   $$C_7H_5O_2^-(aq) + H_2O(l) \rightleftharpoons HC_7H_5O_2(aq) + OH^-(aq)$$

   (b)   pH neutral: I^- is the conjugate base of a strong acid; therefore, it is pH-neutral.

   (c)   pH neutral: NO_3^- is the conjugate base of a strong acid; therefore, it is pH-neutral.

   (d)   weak base: F^- is the conjugate base of a weak acid; therefore, it is a weak base.

   $$F^-(aq) + H_2O(l) \rightleftharpoons HF(aq) + OH^-(aq)$$

15.67   **Given:** $[F^-] = 0.140$ M, $K_a(HF) = 3.5 \times 10^{-4}$ **Find :** $[OH^-]$, pOH

Conceptual Plan: Determine K_b. Write a balanced reaction. Prepare an ICE table, represent the change

$$K_b = \frac{K_w}{K_a}$$

with x, sum the table, determine the equilibrium values, put the equilibrium values in the equilibrium expression, and solve for x. Determine $[OH^-]$ → pOH → pH.

pOH = −log[OH⁻]   pH + pOH = 14

Solution: $F^-(aq) + H_2O(l) \rightleftharpoons HF (aq) + OH^-(aq)$

	[F·]	[HF]	[OH·]
Initial	0.140 M	0.0	0.0
Change	$-x$	x	x
Equil	$0.140 - x$	x	x

$$K_b = \frac{K_w}{K_a} = \frac{1 \times 10^{-14}}{3.5 \times 10^{-4}} = 2.\underline{8}6 \times 10^{-11} = \frac{(x)(x)}{(0.140 - x)}$$

Assume that x is small.

$x = 2.0 \times 10^{-6} = [OH^-]$ $pOH = -\log(2.0 \times 10^{-6}) = 5.70$

$pH = 14.00 - 5.70 = 8.30$

15.68   **Given:** $[HCO_3^-] = 0.250$ M, $K_a(H_2CO_3) = 4.3 \times 10^{-7}$ **Find:** $[OH^-]$, pOH

Conceptual Plan: Determine K_b. Write a balanced reaction. Prepare an ICE table, represent the change

$$K_b = \frac{K_w}{K_a}$$

with x, sum the table, determine the equilibrium values, put the equilibrium values in the equilibrium expression, and solve for x. Determine $[OH^-] \rightarrow pOH \rightarrow pH$.

$$pOH = -\log[OH^-] \quad pH + pOH = 14$$

Solution: $HCO_3^-(aq) + H_2O(l) \rightleftharpoons H_2CO_3(aq) + OH^-(aq)$

	$[HCO_3^-]$	$[H_2CO_3]$	$[OH^-]$
Initial	0.250	0.0	0.0
Change	$-x$	x	x
Equil	$0.250 - x$	x	x

$$K_b = \frac{K_w}{K_a} = \frac{1 \times 10^{-14}}{4.3 \times 10^{-7}} = 2.\underline{3}3 \times 10^{-8} = \frac{(x)(x)}{(0.250 - x)}$$

Assume that x is small.

$x = 7.6 \times 10^{-5} = [OH^-]$ $pOH = -\log(7.6 \times 10^{-5}) = 4.12$

$pH = 14.00 - 4.12 = 9.88$

15.69   (a)   weak acid: NH_4^+ is the conjugate acid of a weak base; therefore, it is a weak acid.

$NH_4^+(aq) + H_2O(l) \rightleftharpoons H_3O^+(aq) + NH_3(aq)$

(b)   pH-neutral: Na^+ is the counterion of a strong base; therefore, it is pH-neutral.

(c)   weak acid: The Co^{3+} cation is a small, highly charged metal cation; therefore, it is a weak acid.

$Co(H_2O)_6^{3+}(aq) + H_2O(l) \rightleftharpoons Co(H_2O)_5(OH)^{2+}(aq) + H_3O^+(aq)$

(d)   weak acid: $CH_2NH_3^+$ is the conjugate acid of a weak base; therefore, it is a weak acid.

$CH_2NH_3^+(aq) + H_2O(l) \rightleftharpoons H_3O^+(aq) + CH_2NH_2(aq)$

15.70   (a)   pH-neutral: Sr^{2+} is the counterion of a strong base; therefore, it is pH-neutral.

(b)   weak acid: The Mn^{3+} cation is a small, highly charged metal cation; therefore, it is a weak acid.

$Mn(H_2O)_6^{3+}(aq) + H_2O(l) \rightleftharpoons Mn(H_2O)_5(OH)^{2+}(aq) + H_3O^+(aq)$

(c)   weak acid: $C_5H_5NH_3^+$ is the conjugate acid of a weak base; therefore, it is a weak acid.

$C_5H_5NH_3^+(aq) + H_2O(l) \rightleftharpoons H_3O^+(aq) + C_5H_5NH_2(aq)$

(d)   pH-neutral: Li^+ is the counterion of a strong base; therefore, it is pH-neutral.

15.71   (a)   acidic: $FeCl_3$ Fe^{3+} is a small, highly charged metal cation; therefore, it is acidic. Cl^- is the conjugate base of a strong acid; therefore, it is pH-neutral.

(b)   basic: NaF Na^+ is the counterion of a strong base; therefore, it is pH-neutral. F^- is the conjugate base of a weak acid; therefore, it is basic.

(c)   pH-neutral: $CaBr_2$ Ca^{2+} is the counterion of a strong base; therefore, it is pH-neutral. Br^- is the conjugate base of a strong acid; therefore, it is pH-neutral.

(d)   acidic: NH_4Br NH_4^+ is the conjugate acid of a weak base; therefore, it is acidic. Br^- is the conjugate base of a strong acid; therefore, it is pH-neutral.

(e)   acidic: $C_6H_5NH_3NO_2$ $C_6H_5NH_3^+$ is the conjugate acid of a weak base; therefore, it is a weak acid.

NO_2^- is the conjugate base of a weak acid; therefore, it is a weak base. To determine pH, compare K values.

$$K_a(C_6H_5NH_3^+) = \frac{1.0 \times 10^{-14}}{3.9 \times 10^{-10}} = 2.6 \times 10^{-5} \quad K_b(NO_2^-) = \frac{1.0 \times 10^{-14}}{4.6 \times 10^{-4}} = 2.2 \times 10^{-11}$$

$K_a > K_b$; therefore, the solution is acidic.

15.72 (a) acidic: $Al(NO_3)_3$ Al^{3+} is a small, highly charged metal cation; therefore, it is acidic. NO_3^- is the conjugate base of a strong acid; therefore, it is pH-neutral.

(b) acidic: $C_2H_5NH_3NO_3$ $C_2H_5NH_3^+$ is the conjugate acid of a weak base; therefore, it is acidic. NO_3^- is the conjugate base of a strong acid; therefore, it is pH-neutral.

(c) basic: K_2CO_3 K^+ is the counterion of a strong base; therefore, it is pH-neutral. CO_3^{2-} is the conjugate base of a weak acid; therefore, it is basic.

(d) pH-neutral: RbI Rb^+ is the counterion of a strong base; therefore, it is pH-neutral. I^- is the conjugate base of a strong acid; therefore, it is pH-neutral.

(e) basic: NH_4ClO NH_4^+ is the conjugate acid of a weak base; therefore, it is a weak acid. ClO^- is the conjugate base of a weak acid; therefore, it is a weak base. To determine pH, compare K values.

$$K_a(NH_4^+) = \frac{1.0 \times 10^{-14}}{1.8 \times 10^{-5}} = 5.6 \times 10^{-10} \qquad K_b(ClO^-) = \frac{1.0 \times 10^{-14}}{2.9 \times 10^{-8}} = 3.4 \times 10^{-7}$$

$K_b > K_a$; therefore, the solution is basic.

15.73 **Conceptual Plan:** Identify each species and determine whether it is acidic, basic, or neutral.

NaCl pH-neutral: Na^+ is the counterion of a strong base; therefore, it is pH-neutral. Cl^- is the conjugate base of a strong acid; therefore, it is pH-neutral.

NH_4Cl acidic: NH_4^+ is the conjugate acid of a weak base; therefore, it is acidic. Cl^- is the conjugate base of a strong acid; therefore, it is pH-neutral.

$NaHCO_3$ basic: Na^+ is the counterion of a strong base; therefore, it is pH-neutral. HCO_3^- is the conjugate base of a weak acid; therefore, it is basic.

NH_4ClO_2 acidic: NH_4^+ is the conjugate acid of a weak base; therefore, it is a weak acid. ClO_2^- is the conjugate base of a weak acid; therefore, it is a weak base. $K_a(NH_4^+) = 5.6 \times 10^{-10}$ $K_b(ClO_2^-) = 9.1 \times 10^{-13}$

NaOH strong base

Increasing acidity: $NaOH < NaHCO_3 < NaCl < NH_4ClO_2 < NH_4Cl$

15.74 **Conceptual Plan:** Identify each species and determine whether it is acidic, basic, or neutral.

CH_3NH_3Br acidic: $CH_3NH_3^+$ is the conjugate acid of a weak base; therefore, it is acidic. Br^- is the conjugate base of a strong acid; therefore, it is pH-neutral.

KOH strong base

KBr pH-neutral: K^+ is the counterion of a strong base; therefore, it is pH-neutral. Br^- is the conjugate base of a strong acid; therefore, it is pH-neutral.

KCN basic: K^+ is the counterion of a strong base; therefore, it is pH-neutral. CN^- is the conjugate base of a weak acid; therefore, it is basic.

$C_5H_5NHNO_2$ acidic: $C_5H_5NH^+$ is the conjugate acid of a weak base; therefore, it is acidic. NO_2^- is the conjugate base of a weak acid; therefore, it is basic. $K_a(C_5H_5NH^+) = 5.9 \times 10^{-6}$; $K_b(NO_2^-) = 2.2 \times 10^{-11}$

Increasing basicity: $CH_3NH_3Br < C_5H_5NHNO_2 < KBr < KCN < KOH$

15.75 (a) **Given:** 0.10 M NH_4Cl **Find:** pH

Conceptual Plan: Identify each species and determine which will contribute to pH. Write a balanced reaction. Prepare an ICE table, represent the change with x, sum the table, determine the equilibrium values, put the equilibrium values in the equilibrium expression, and solve for x. Determine $[H_3O^+] \rightarrow$ pH.

Solution: NH_4^+ is the conjugate acid of a weak base; therefore, it is acidic. Cl^- is the conjugate base of a strong acid; therefore, it is pH-neutral.

$$NH_4^+(aq) + H_2O(l) \rightleftharpoons NH_3(aq) + H_3O^+(aq)$$

	$[NH_4^+]$	$[NH_3]$	$[H_3O^+]$
Initial	0.10	0.0	0.0
Change	$-x$	x	x
Equil	$0.10 - x$	x	x

$$K_a = \frac{K_w}{K_b} = \frac{1.0 \times 10^{-14}}{1.76 \times 10^{-5}} = 5.\underline{6}8 \times 10^{-10} = \frac{(x)(x)}{(0.10 - x)}$$

Assume that x is small.

$x = 7.\underline{5}4 \times 10^{-6} = [H_3O^+]$ pH $= -\log(7.\underline{5}4 \times 10^{-6}) = 5.12$

(b) **Given:** 0.10 M NaC$_2$H$_3$O$_2$ **Find:** pH

Conceptual Plan: Identify each species and determine which will contribute to pH. Write a balanced reaction. Prepare an ICE table, represent the change with x, sum the table, determine the equilibrium values, put the equilibrium values in the equilibrium expression, and solve for x. Determine [OH$^-$] → pOH → pH.

pOH = −log[OH$^-$] pH + pOH = 14

Solution: Na$^+$ is the counterion of a strong base; therefore, it is pH-neutral. C$_2$H$_3$O$_2^-$ is the conjugate base of a weak acid; therefore, it is basic.

C$_2$H$_3$O$_2^-(aq)$ + H$_2$O(l) ⇌ HC$_2$H$_3$O$_2(aq)$ + OH$^-(aq)$

	[C$_2$H$_3$O$_2^-$]	[HC$_2$H$_3$O$_2$]	[OH$^-$]
Initial	0.10	0.0	0.0
Change	−x	x	x
Equil	0.10 − x	x	x

$$K_b = \frac{K_w}{K_a} = \frac{1.0 \times 10^{-14}}{1.8 \times 10^{-5}} = 5.\underline{56} \times 10^{-10} = \frac{(x)(x)}{(0.10 - x)}$$

Assume that x is small.

$x = 7.\underline{46} \times 10^{-6}$ = [OH$^-$] pOH = −log(7.$\underline{46}$ × 10^{-6}) = 5.13

pH = 14.00 − 5.13 = 8.87

(c) **Given:** 0.10 M NaCl   **Find:** pH

Conceptual Plan: Identify each species and determine which will contribute to pH.

Solution: Na$^+$ is the counterion of a strong base; therefore, it is pH-neutral. Cl$^-$ is the conjugate base of a strong acid; therefore, it is pH-neutral.

pH = 7.0

15.76 (a) **Given:** 0.20 M KCHO$_2$ **Find:** pH

Conceptual Plan: Identify each species and determine which will contribute to pH. Write a balanced reaction. Prepare an ICE table, represent the change with x, sum the table, determine the equilibrium values, put the equilibrium values in the equilibrium expression, and solve for x. Determine [OH$^-$] → pOH → pH.

pOH = −log[OH$^-$] pH + pOH = 14

Solution: K$^+$ is the counterion of a strong base; therefore, it is pH-neutral. CHO$_2^-$ is the conjugate base of a weak acid; therefore, it is basic.

CHO$_2^-(aq)$ + H$_2$O(l) ⇌ HCHO$_2(aq)$ + OH$^-(aq)$

	[CHO$_2^-$]	[HCHO$_2$]	[OH$^-$]
Initial	0.20 M	0.0	0.0
Change	−x	x	x
Equil	0.20 − x	x	x

$$K_b = \frac{K_w}{K_a} = \frac{1.0 \times 10^{-14}}{1.8 \times 10^{-4}} = 5.\underline{56} \times 10^{-11} = \frac{(x)(x)}{(0.20 - x)}$$

Assume that x is small.

$x = 3.\underline{33} \times 10^{-6}$ = [OH$^-$] pOH = −log(3.$\underline{33}$ × 10^{-6}) = 5.48

pH = 14.00 − 5.48 = 8.52

(b) **Given:** 0.20 M CH$_3$NH$_3$I   **Find:** pH

Conceptual Plan: Identify each species and determine which will contribute to pH. Write a balanced reaction. Prepare an ICE table, represent the change with x, sum the table, determine the equilibrium values, put the equilibrium values in the equilibrium expression, and solve for x. Determine [H$_3$O$^+$] → pH.

Solution: CH$_3$NH$_3^+$ is the conjugate acid of a weak base; therefore, it is acidic. Cl$^-$ is the conjugate base of a strong acid; therefore, it is pH-neutral.

$$CH_3NH_3^+(aq) + H_2O(l) \rightleftharpoons CH_3NH_2(aq) + H_3O^+(aq)$$

	$[CH_3NH_3^-]$	$[CH_3NH_2]$	$[H_3O^-]$
Initial	0.20 M	0.0	0.0
Change	$-x$	x	x
Equil	$0.20 - x$	x	x

$$K_a = \frac{K_w}{K_b} = \frac{1.0 \times 10^{-14}}{4.4 \times 10^{-4}} = 2.\underline{2}7 \times 10^{-11} = \frac{(x)(x)}{(0.20 - x)}$$

Assume that x is small.

$$x = 2.\underline{1}3 \times 10^{-6} = [H_3O^+] \quad pH = -\log(2.\underline{1}3 \times 10^{-6}) = 5.67$$

(c) **Given:** 0.20 M KI **Find:** pH

Conceptual Plan: Identify each species and determine which will contribute to pH.

Solution: K^+ is the counterion of a strong base; therefore, it is pH-neutral. I^- is the conjugate base of a strong acid; therefore, it is pH-neutral.

pH = 7.0

15.77 **Given:** 0.15 M KF **Find:** concentration of all species

Conceptual Plan: Identify each species and determine which will contribute to pH. Write a balanced reaction. Prepare an ICE table, represent the change with x, sum the table, determine the equilibrium values, put the equilibrium values in the equilibrium expression, and solve for x. Then $[OH^-] \rightarrow [H_3O^+]$.

$$K_w = [H_3O^+][OH^-]$$

Solution: K^+ is the counterion of a strong base; therefore, it is pH-neutral. F^- is the conjugate base of a weak acid; therefore, it is basic.

$$F^-(aq) + H_2O(l) \rightleftharpoons HF(aq) + OH^-(aq)$$

	$[F^-]$	$[HF]$	$[OH^-]$
Initial	0.15 M	0.0	0.0
Change	$-x$	x	x
Equil	$0.15 - x$	x	x

$$K_b = \frac{K_w}{K_a} = \frac{1.0 \times 10^{-14}}{3.5 \times 10^{-4}} = 2.\underline{8}6 \times 10^{-11} = \frac{(x)(x)}{(0.15 - x)}$$

Assume that x is small.

$$x = 2.1 \times 10^{-6} = [OH^-] = [HF] \qquad [H_3O^+] = \frac{K_w}{[OH^-]} = \frac{1 \times 10^{-14}}{2.1 \times 10^{-6}} = 4.8 \times 10^{-9}$$

$$[K^+] = 0.15 \text{ M}$$

$$[F^-] = (0.15 - 2.1 \times 10^{-6}) = 0.15 \text{ M}$$

$$[HF] = 2.1 \times 10^{-6}$$

$$[OH^-] = 2.1 \times 10^{-6}$$

$$[H_3O^+] = 4.8 \times 10^{-9}$$

15.78 **Given:** 0.225 M $C_6H_5NH_3Cl$ **Find:** concentration of all species

Conceptual Plan: Identify each species and determine which will contribute to pH. Write a balanced reaction. Prepare an ICE table, represent the change with x, sum the table, determine the equilibrium values, put the equilibrium values in the equilibrium expression, and solve for x. Then determine $[H_3O^+] \rightarrow [OH^-]$.

$$K_w = [H_3O^+][OH^-]$$

Solution: $C_6H_5NH_3^+$ is the conjugate acid of a weak base; therefore, it is a weak acid. Cl^- is the conjugate base of a strong acid; therefore, it is pH-neutral.

$$C_6H_5NH_3^+(aq) + H_2O(l) \rightleftharpoons C_6H_5NH_2(aq) + H_3O^+(aq)$$

	$[C_6H_5NH_3^-]$	$[C_6H_5NH_2]$	$[H_3O^-]$
Initial	0.225 M	0.0	0.0
Change	$-x$	x	x
Equil	$0.225 - x$	x	x

$$K_a = \frac{K_w}{K_b} = \frac{1.0 \times 10^{-14}}{3.9 \times 10^{-10}} = 2.\underline{5}6 \times 10^{-5} = \frac{(x)(x)}{(0.225 - x)}$$

Assume that x is small.

$$x = 0.0024 = [H_3O^+] = [C_6H_5NH_2] \qquad [OH^-] = \frac{K_w}{[H_3O^+]} = \frac{1.0 \times 10^{-14}}{0.0024} = 4.2 \times 10^{-12}$$

$[C_6H_5NH_3^+] = 0.225 - 0.0024 = 0.223$ M

$[Cl^-] = 0.225$ M

$[C_6H_5NH_2] = 0.0024$ M

$[H_3O^+] = 0.0024$ M

$[OH^-] = 4.2 \times 10^{-12}$ M

Molecular Structure and Acid Strength

15.79   (a)   HCl is the stronger acid. HCl is the weaker bond; therefore, it is more acidic.

        (b)   HF is the stronger acid. F is more electronegative than is O, so the bond is more polar and more acidic.

        (c) H_2Se is the stronger acid. The H—Se bond is weaker; therefore, it is more acidic.

15.80   Increasing acid strength: $NaH < H_2S < H_2Te < HI$

        H_2Te is a stronger acid than is H_2S because the H—Te bond is weaker. HI is a stronger acid than is H_2Te because I is more electronegative than Te. NaH is not acidic because H is more electronegative than Na.

15.81   (a) H_2SO_4 is the stronger acid because it has more oxygen atoms.

        (b) $HClO_2$ is the stronger acid because it has more oxygen atoms.

        (c)   HClO is the stronger acid because Cl is more electronegative than is Br.

        (d) CCl_3COOH is the stronger acid because Cl is more electronegative than is H.

15.82   Increasing acid strength: $HIO_3 < HBrO_3 < HClO_3$

        Cl is more electronegative than is Br, which is more electronegative than is I.

15.83 S^{2-} is the stronger base. Base strength is determined from the corresponding acid. The weaker the acid, the stronger the base. H_2S is the weaker acid because it has a stronger bond.

15.84 AsO_4^{3-} is the stronger base. Base strength is determined from the corresponding acid. The weaker the acid, the stronger the base. H_3AsO_4 is the weaker acid because P is more electronegative than is As.

Lewis Acids and Bases

15.85   (a)   Lewis acid: Fe^{3+} has an empty d orbital and can accept lone pair electrons.

        (b)   Lewis acid: BH_3 has an empty p orbital to accept a lone pair of electrons.

        (c)   Lewis base: NH_3 has a lone pair of electrons to donate.

        (d)   Lewis base: F^- has lone pair electrons to donate.

15.86   (a)   Lewis acid: $BeCl_2$ has empty p orbitals to accept lone pair electrons.

        (b)   Lewis base: OH^- has lone pair electrons to donate.

        (c)   Lewis acid: $B(OH)_3$ has an empty p orbital to accept a lone pair of electrons.

        (d)   Lewis base: CN^- has lone pair electrons to donate.

15.87   (a) Fe^{3+} accepts an electron pair from H_2O; so Fe^{3+} is the Lewis acid, and H_2O is the Lewis base.

        (b) Zn^{2+} accepts an electron pair from NH_3; so Zn^{2+} is the Lewis acid, and NH_3 is the Lewis base.

        (c)   The empty p orbital on B accepts an electron pair from $(CH_3)_3N$; so BF_3 is the Lewis acid, and $(CH_3)_3N$ is the Lewis base.

15.88   (a) Ag^+ accepts an electron pair from NH_3; so Ag^+ is the Lewis acid, and NH_3 is the Lewis base.

        (b)   The empty p orbital on Al accepts an electron pair from NH_3; so $AlBr_3$ is the Lewis acid, and NH_3 is the Lewis base.

        (c)   The empty p orbital on B accepts an electron pair from F^-; so BF_3 is the Lewis acid, and F^- is the Lewis base.

Cumulative Problems

15.89   (a)   weak acid. The beaker contains 10 HF molecules, 2 H_3O^+ ions, and 2 F^- ions. Because both the molecule and the ions exist in solution, the acid is a weak acid.

      (b)   strong acid. The beaker contains 12 H_3O^+ ions and 12 L^- ions. Because the molecule is completely ionized in solution, the acid is a strong acid.

      (c)   weak acid. The beaker contains 10 $HCHO_2$ molecules, 2 H_3O^+ ions, and 2 CHO_2^- ions. Because both the molecule and the ions exist in solution, the acid is a weak acid.

      (d)   strong acid. The beaker contains 12 H_3O^+ ions and 12 NO_3^- ions. Because the molecule is completely ionized in solution, the acid is a strong acid.

15.90   (a)   weak base. The beaker contains 11 NH_3 molecules, 2 NH_4^+ ions, and 2 OH^- ions. Because both the molecule and the ions exist in solution, this is a weak base.

      (b)   strong base. The beaker contains 12 Na^+ ions and 12 OH^- ions. Because the molecule is completely ionized in solution, it is a strong base.

      (c)   weak base. The beaker contains 12 Na^+, 10 H_2CO_3 molecules, 2 HCO_3^- ions, and 2 OH^- ions. The beaker contains the HCO_3^- ion from the $NaHCO_3$ and H_2CO_3 molecules from the reaction of the salt.

      (d)   strong base. The beaker contains 12 Sr^{2+} ions and 24 OH^- ions. Because the molecule is completely ionized in solution, it is a strong base.

15.91 $HbH^+(aq) + O_2(aq) \rightleftharpoons HbO_2(aq) + H^+(aq)$

Using Le Châtelier's principle, if the $[H^+]$ increases, the reaction will shift left, and if the $[H^+]$ decreases, the reaction will shift right. So if the pH of blood is too acidic (low pH; $[H^+]$ increased), the reaction will shift to the left. This will cause less of the HbO_2 in the blood and decrease the oxygen-carrying capacity of the hemoglobin in the blood.

15.92 $CO_2(g) + H_2O(l) \rightleftharpoons H_2CO_3(aq)$

$H_2CO_3(aq) + H_2O(l) \rightleftharpoons HCO_3^-(aq) + H_3O^+(aq)$

As the concentration of CO_2 in the atmosphere increases, more will dissolve in H_2O and form H_2CO_3. The H_2CO_3 will then act as a weak acid with H_2O and form HCO_3^- and H_3O^+, causing the water (oceans) to be more acidic. If the pH of the oceans decreases, the added H_3O^+ will react with the CO_3^{2-} ion in the $CaCO_3$ of the limestone structures and decompose the $CaCO_3$.

$2\ H_3O^+(aq) + CaCO_3(s) \rightarrow Ca^{2+}(aq) + H_2CO_3(aq) + 2H_2O(l)$ $H_2CO_3(aq) \rightarrow H_2O(l) + CO_2(g)$

15.93   **Given:** 4.00×10^2 mg $Mg(OH)_2$, 2.00×10^2 mL HCl solution, pH $= 1.3$

Find: volume neutralized, % neutralized

Conceptual Plan:

mg $Mg(OH)_2$ $\rightarrow$ g $Mg(OH)_2$ $\rightarrow$ mol $Mg(OH)_2$ and then pH $\rightarrow$ $[H_3O^+]$ and then mol $Mg(OH)_2$

$$\frac{1\ g\ Mg(OH)_2}{1000\ mg} \quad\quad \frac{1\ mol\ Mg(OH)_2}{58.326\ g} \quad\quad\quad\quad pH = -\log [H_3O^+]$$

mol OH^- $\rightarrow$ mol H_3O^+ $\rightarrow$ vol H_3O^+ $\rightarrow$ % neutralized

$$\frac{2\ OH^-}{Mg(OH)_2} \quad \frac{H_3O^+}{OH^-} \quad\quad \frac{mol\ H_3O^+}{M(H_3O^+)} \quad\quad \frac{vol\ HCl\ neutralized}{total\ vol\ HCl} \times 100\%$$

Solution: $[H_3O^+] = 10^{-1.3} = 0.0\underline{5}012\ M = 0.05\ M$

$$4.00 \times 10^2\ \text{mg Mg(OH)}_2 \times \frac{\text{g Mg(OH)}_2}{1000\ \text{mg Mg(OH)}_2} \times \frac{1\ \text{mol Mg(OH)}_2}{58.3\underline{2}6\ \text{g Mg(OH)}_2} \times \frac{2\ \text{mol OH}^-}{1\ \text{mol Mg(OH)}_2}$$

$$\times \frac{1\ \text{mol H}_3\text{O}^+}{1\ \text{mol OH}^-} \times \frac{1\ \text{L}}{0.0\underline{5}01\ \text{mol H}_3\text{O}^+} \times \frac{1000\ \text{mL}}{\text{L}} = 2\underline{7}3.8\ \text{mL} = 3 \times 10^2\ \text{mL neutralized}$$

The stomach contains 2.00×10^2 mL HCl at pH $= 1.3$, and 4.00×10^2 mg will neutralize 274 mL of pH 1.3 HCl; so all of the stomach acid will be neutralized.

15.94 **Given:** 4.3 billion L, pH = 5.5 **Find:** mass in kg $CaCO_3$

Conceptual Plan:

pH → [H_3O^+] and then vol lake → mol [H_3O^+] → mol $CaCO_3$ → g $CaCO_3$ → kg $CaCO_3$

pH = −log[H_3O^+]   mol = vol × M $\frac{1\ mol\ CaCO_3}{2\ mol\ H_3O^+}$ $\frac{100.09\ g\ CaCO_3}{1\ mol\ CaCO_3}$ $\frac{1\ kg\ CaCO_3}{1000\ g\ CaCO_3}$

Solution: [H_3O^+] = $10^{-5.5}$ = $\underline{3}.16 \times 10^{-6}$ M

$$4.3 \times 10^9\ \cancel{L} \times \frac{3.16 \times 10^{-6}\ \cancel{mol\ H_3O^+}}{\cancel{L}} \times \frac{1\ \cancel{mol\ CaCO_3}}{2\ \cancel{mol\ H_3O^+}} \times \frac{100.09\ g\ \cancel{CaCO_3}}{1\ \cancel{mol\ CaCO_3}} \times \frac{1\ kg}{1000\ \cancel{g}}$$

$$= \underline{6}80.01\ kg = 7 \times 10^2\ kg\ CaCO_3$$

15.95 **Given:** pH of Great Lakes acid rain = 4.5, West Coast = 5.4

Find: [H_3O^+] and ratio of Great Lakes/West Coast

Conceptual Plan: pH → [H_3O^+] and then ratio of [H_3O^+] Great Lakes to West Coast

pH = −log[H_3O^+]

Solution: Great Lakes: [H_3O^+] = $10^{-4.5}$ = $\underline{3}.16 \times 10^{-5}$ M   West Coast: [H_3O^+] = $10^{-5.4}$ = $\underline{3}.98 \times 10^{-6}$ M

$$\frac{Great\ Lakes}{West\ Coast} = \frac{3.16 \times 10^{-5}\ M}{3.98 \times 10^{-6}\ M} = \underline{7}.94 = 8\ times\ more\ acidic$$

15.96 **Given:** pH of Sauvignon Blanc = 3.23, Cabernet Sauvignon = 3.64

Find: [H_3O^+] and ratio of Sauvignon Blanc to Cabernet Sauvignon

Conceptual Plan: pH → [H_3O^+] and then ratio of [H_3O^+] Sauvignon Blanc to Cabernet Sauvignon

pH = −log[H_3O^+]

Solution:

Sauvignon Blanc: [H_3O^+] = $10^{-3.23}$ = $5.\underline{8}88 \times 10^{-4}$ M

Cabernet Sauvignon: [H_3O^+] = $10^{-3.64}$ = $2.\underline{2}91 \times 10^{-4}$ M

$$\frac{Sauvignon\ Blanc}{Cabernet\ Sauvignon} = \frac{5.\underline{8}88 \times 10^{-4}\ M}{2.\underline{2}91 \times 10^{-4}\ M} = 2.\underline{5}70 = 2.6\ times\ more\ acidic$$

15.97 **Given:** 6.5×10^2 mg aspirin, 8 oz water, pK_a = 3.5 **Find:** pH of solution

Conceptual Plan:

mg aspirin → g aspirin → mol aspirin and ounces → quart → L and then [aspirin] and pK_a

$\frac{1\ g\ aspirin}{1000\ mg}$ $\frac{1\ mol\ aspirin}{180.15\ g}$ $\frac{1\ qt}{32\ oz}$ $\frac{1\ L}{1.0567\ qt}$ $\frac{mol\ aspirin}{L\ soln}$ $pK_a = -\log K_a$

→ K_a. Write a balanced reaction. Prepare an ICE table, represent the change with x, sum the table, determine the equilibrium values, put the equilibrium values in the equilibrium expression, and solve for x. Determine [H_3O^+] → pH.

pH = −log[H_3O^+]

Solution: $\dfrac{6.5 \times 10^2\ \cancel{mg\ aspirin}}{8\ \cancel{oz}} \times \dfrac{1\ \cancel{g\ aspirin}}{1000\ \cancel{mg\ aspirin}} \times \dfrac{1\ mol\ aspirin}{180.15\ \cancel{g}} \times \dfrac{32\ \cancel{oz}}{1\ \cancel{qt}} \times \dfrac{1.0567\ \cancel{qt}}{1\ L} = 0.01\underline{5}3$ M

$K_a = 10^{-3.5} = \underline{3}.16 \times 10^{-4}$

aspirin(aq) + H_2O(l) ⇌ H_3O^+(aq) + aspirin$^-$(aq)

	[aspirin]	[H_3O^+]	[aspirin⁻]
Initial	0.01$\underline{5}$3 M	0.0	0.0
Change	−x	x	x
Equil	0.01$\underline{5}$3 − x	x	x

$$K_a = \frac{[H_3O^+][aspirin^-]}{[aspirin]} = \frac{(x)(x)}{(0.0153 - x)} = \underline{3}.16 \times 10^{-4}$$

$x^2 + 3.16 \times 10^{-4}x - 4.83 \times 10^{-6} = 0$ $x = \underline{2}.04 \times 10^{-3}$ M = [H_3O^+]

pH = −log($\underline{2}.04 \times 10^{-3}$) = 2.69 = 2.7

15.98   **Given:** 565 mg/L ddC, $pK_b = 9.8$ **Find:** % protonated
Conceptual Plan: mg → g → mol → M and then pK_b → K_b then write a balanced reaction. Prepare an ICE table, represent the change with x, sum the table, determine the equilibrium values, put the the equilibrium values in the equilibrium expression, and solve for x.

Solution: $\dfrac{565 \text{ mg ddC}}{L} \times \dfrac{g \text{ ddC}}{1000 \text{ mg ddC}} \times \dfrac{\text{mol ddC}}{224.22 \text{ g ddC}} = 0.0025\underline{1}98 \text{ M}$

$K_b = 10^{-9.8} = \underline{1}.585 \times 10^{-10}$

$$ddC(aq) + H_2O(l) \rightleftharpoons HddC^+(aq) + OH^-(aq)$$

	[ddC]	[HddC⁺]	[OH⁻]
Initial	0.0025\underline{1}98 M	0.0	0.0
Change	$-x$	x	x
Equil	0.0025\underline{1}98 $- x$	x	x

$K_b = \dfrac{[HddC^+][OH^-]}{[ddC]} = \dfrac{(x)(x)}{(0.0025\underline{1}98 - x)} = \underline{1}.585 \times 10^{-10}$

Assume that x is small.

$x^2 = (\underline{1}.585 \times 10^{-10})(0.0025\underline{1}98) \qquad x = [OH^-] = [HddC^+] = \underline{6}.32 \times 10^{-7} \text{ M}$

$\%\text{protonated} = \dfrac{[HddC^+]_{\text{equilibrium}}}{[ddC]_{\text{original}}} \times 100\% = \dfrac{(6.32 \times 10^{-7})}{(0.0025\underline{1}98)} \times 100\% = 0.03\%$

15.99   **(a)**   **Given:** 0.0100 M $HClO_4$ **Find:** pH
Conceptual Plan: $[HClO_4] \rightarrow [H_3O^+] \rightarrow$ pH

$$[HClO_4] \rightarrow [H_3O^+] \quad pH = -\log[H_3O^+]$$

Solution: $HClO_4$ is a strong acid so: 0.0100 M $HClO_4$ = 0.0100 M H_3O^+ $pH = -\log(0.0100) = 2.000$

(b)   **Given:** 0.115 M $HClO_2$, $K_a = 1.1 \times 10^{-2}$ **Find:** pH
Conceptual Plan: Write a balanced reaction. Prepare an ICE table, represent the change with x, sum the table, determine the equilibrium values, put the equilibrium values in the equilibrium expression, and solve for x. Determine $[H_3O^+]$ and pH.

Solution: $HClO_2 (aq) + H_2O(l) \rightleftharpoons H_3O^+(aq) + ClO_2^- (aq)$

	[HClO₂]	[H₃O⁺]	[ClO₂⁻]
Initial	0.115 M	0.0	0.0
Change	$-x$	x	x
Equil	0.115 $- x$	x	x

$K_a = \dfrac{[H_3O^+][ClO_2^-]}{[HClO_2]} = \dfrac{(x)(x)}{(0.115 - x)} = 1.1 \times 10^{-2}$

Assume that x is small compared to 0.115.

$x^2 = (1.1 \times 10^{-2})(0.115) \qquad x = 0.03\underline{5}6 \text{ M} = [H_3O^+]$

Check assumption: $\dfrac{0.03\underline{5}6}{0.115} \times 100\% = 31.0\%$; assumption is not valid; solve with the quadratic equation.

$x^2 + 1.1 \times 10^{-2} x - 0.001265 = 0$

$x = 0.03\underline{0}49 \text{ or } -0.0415$

$pH = -\log(0.03\underline{0}49) = 1.52$

(c)   **Given:** 0.045 M $Sr(OH)_2$ **Find:** pH
Conceptual Plan: $[Sr(OH)_2] \rightarrow [OH^-] \rightarrow [H_3O^+] \rightarrow$ pH

$$K_w = [H_3O^+][OH^-] \quad pH = -\log[H_3O^+] \quad pH + pOH = 14$$

Solution: $Sr(OH)_2$ is a strong base so: $[OH^-] = 2[Sr(OH)_2] = 2(0.045) = 0.090 M$

$$[H_3O^+] = \frac{K_w}{[OH^-]} = \frac{1.0 \times 10^{-14}}{0.090 \text{ M}} = 1.\underline{1}1 \times 10^{-13} \text{ M}$$

$$pH = -\log(1.\underline{1}1 \times 10^{-13}) = 12.95$$

(d)   **Given:** 0.0852 KCN, K_a(HCN) $= 4.9 \times 10^{-10}$ **Find:** pH

Conceptual Plan: Identify each species and determine which will contribute to pH. Write a balanced reaction. Prepare an ICE table, represent the change with x, sum the table, determine the equilibrium values, put the equilibrium values in the equilibrium expression, and solve for x. Determine $[OH^-] \rightarrow pOH \rightarrow pH$.

$pOH = -\log[OH^-]$ $pH + pOH = 14$

Solution: K^+ is the counterion of a strong base; therefore, it is pH-neutral. CN^- is the conjugate base of a weak acid; therefore, it is basic.

$$CN^-(aq) + H_2O(l) \rightleftharpoons HCN(aq) + OH^-(aq)$$

	[CN⁻]	**[HCN]**	**[OH⁻]**
Initial	0.0852 M	0.0	0.0
Change	$-x$	x	x
Equil	$0.0852 - x$	x	x

$$K_b = \frac{K_w}{K_a} = \frac{1.0 \times 10^{-14}}{4.9 \times 10^{-10}} = 2.\underline{0}4 \times 10^{-5} = \frac{(x)(x)}{(0.0852 - x)}$$

Assume that x is small.

$x = 1.\underline{3}2 \times 10^{-3} \text{ M} = [OH^-]$ $pOH = -\log(1.\underline{3}2 \times 10^{-3}) = 2.88$

$pH = 14.00 - 2.88 = 11.12$

(e)   **Given:** 0.155 NH_4Cl, K_b (NH_3) $= 1.76 \times 10^{-5}$ **Find:** pH

Conceptual Plan: Identify each species and determine which will contribute to pH. Write a balanced reaction. Prepare an ICE table, represent the change with x, sum the table, determine the equilibrium values, put the equilibrium values in the equilibrium expression, and solve for x. Determine $[H_3O^+] \rightarrow pH$.

Solution: NH_4^+ is the conjugate acid of a weak base; therefore, it is acidic. Cl^- is the conjugate base of a strong acid; therefore, it is pH-neutral.

$$NH_4^+(aq) + H_2O(l) \rightleftharpoons NH_3(aq) + H_3O^+(aq)$$

	[NH₄⁺]	**[NH₃]**	**[H₃O⁺]**
Initial	0.155 M	0.0	0.0
Change	$-x$	x	x
Equil	$0.155 - x$	x	x

$$K_a = \frac{K_w}{K_b} = \frac{1 \times 10^{-14}}{1.76 \times 10^{-5}} = 5.6\underline{8}2 \times 10^{-10} = \frac{(x)(x)}{(0.155 - x)}$$

Assume that x is small.

$x = 9.3\underline{8}5 \times 10^{-6} \text{ M} = [H_3O^+]$ $pH = -\log(9.3\underline{8}5 \times 10^{-6}) = 5.028$

15.100   (a)   **Given:** 0.0650 M HNO_3 **Find:** pH

Conceptual Plan: $[HNO_3] \rightarrow [H_3O^+] \rightarrow pH$

$[HNO_3] \rightarrow [H_3O]$ $pH = -\log[H_3O^+]$

Solution: HNO_3 is a strong acid so: 0.0650 M HNO_3 = 0.0650 M H_3O^+ $pH = -\log(0.0650) = 1.187$

(b)   **Given:** 0.150 M HNO_2, $K_a = 4.6 \times 10^{-4}$ **Find:** pH

Conceptual Plan: Write a balanced reaction. Prepare an ICE table, represent the change with x, sum the table, determine the equilibrium values, put the equilibrium values in the equilibrium expression, and solve for x. Determine $[H_3O^+]$ and pH.

Solution: $HNO_2(aq) + H_2O(l) \rightleftharpoons H_3O^+(aq) + NO_2^-(aq)$

	[HNO$_2$]	**[H$_3$O$^+$]**	**[NO$_2^-$]**
Initial	0.150 M	0.0	0.0
Change	$-x$	x	x
Equil	$0.150 - x$	x	x

$$K_a = \frac{[H_3O^+][NO_2^-]}{[HNO_2]} = \frac{(x)(x)}{(0.150 - x)} = 4.6 \times 10^{-4}$$

Assume that x is small compared to 0.150.

$$x^2 = (4.6 \times 10^{-4})(0.150) \qquad x = 0.00831\ M = [H_3O^+]$$

Check assumption: $\dfrac{0.00831}{0.150} \times 100\% = 5.54\%$; assumption is not valid; solve with the quadratic equation.

$$x^2 + 4.6 \times 10^{-4}x - 6.9 \times 10^{-5} = 0$$
$$x = 0.00808\ M = [H_3O^+]$$
$$pH = -\log(0.00808) = 2.09$$

(c)   **Given:** 0.0195 M KOH   **Find:** pH
Conceptual Plan: [KOH] $\rightarrow$ [OH$^-$] $\rightarrow$ [H$_3$O$^+$] $\rightarrow$ pH

$$K_w = [H_3O^+][OH^-] \quad pH = -\log[H_3O^+] \quad pH + pOH = 14$$

Solution: KOH is a strong base so: $[OH^-] = [KOH] = 0.0195\ M$

$$[H_3O^+] = \frac{K_w}{[OH^-]} = \frac{1.0 \times 10^{-14}}{0.0195\ M} = 5.128 \times 10^{-13}\ M$$

$$pH = -\log(5.128 \times 10^{-13}) = 12.290$$

(d)   **Given:** 0.245 CH$_3$NH$_3$I, K_b (CH$_3$NH$_3$) = 4.4×10^{-4} **Find:** pH
Conceptual Plan: Identify each species and determine which will contribute to pH. Write a balanced reaction. Prepare an ICE table, represent the change with x, sum the table, determine the equilibrium values, put the equilibrium values in the equilibrium expression, and solve for x. Determine [H$_3$O$^+$] $\rightarrow$ pH.

Solution: CH$_3$NH$_3^+$ is the conjugate acid of a weak base; therefore, it is acidic. I$^-$ is the conjugate base of a strong acid; therefore, it is pH-neutral.

$$CH_3NH_3^+(aq) + H_2O(l) \rightleftharpoons CH_3NH_2(aq) + H_3O^+(aq)$$

	[CH$_3$NH$_3^+$]	**[CH$_3$NH$_2$]**	**[H$_3$O$^+$]**
Initial	0.245 M	0.0	0.0
Change	$-x$	x	x
Equil	$0.245 - x$	x	x

$$K_a = \frac{K_w}{K_b} = \frac{1.0 \times 10^{-14}}{4.4 \times 10^{-4}} = 2.273 \times 10^{-11} = \frac{(x)(x)}{(0.245 - x)}$$

Assume that x is small.

$$x = 2.36 \times 10^{-6} = [H_3O^+] \quad pH = -\log(2.36 \times 10^{-6}) = 5.63$$

(e)   **Given:** 0.318 KC$_6$H$_5$O, K_a (HC$_6$H$_5$O) = 1.3×10^{-10} **Find:** pH
Conceptual Plan: Identify each species and determine which will contribute to pH. Write a balanced reaction. Prepare an ICE table, represent the change with x, sum the table, determine the equilibrium values, put the equilibrium values in the equilibrium expression, and solve for x. Determine [OH$^-$] $\rightarrow$ pOH $\rightarrow$ pH.

$$pOH = -\log[OH^-] \quad pH + pOH = 14$$

Solution: K$^+$ is the counterion of a strong base; therefore, it is pH-neutral. C$_6$H$_5$O$^-$ is the conjugate base of a weak acid; therefore, it is basic.

$$C_6H_5O^-(aq) + H_2O(l) \rightleftharpoons HC_6H_5O\ (aq) + OH^-(aq)$$

	$[C_6H_5O^-]$	$[HC_6H_5O]$	$[OH^-]$
Initial	0.318 M	0.0	0.0
Change	$-x$	x	x
Equil	$0.318 - x$	x	x

$$K_b = \frac{K_w}{K_a} = \frac{1.0 \times 10^{-14}}{1.3 \times 10^{-10}} = 7.\underline{6}9 \times 10^{-5} = \frac{(x)(x)}{(0.318 - x)}$$

Assume that x is small.

$x = 4.\underline{9}5 \times 10^{-3} = [OH^-]$ $pOH = -\log(4.\underline{9}5 \times 10^{-3}) = 2.31$

$pH = 14.00 - 2.31 = 11.69$

15.101   (a)   sodium cyanide = NaCN, nitric acid = HNO_3
$$H^+(aq) + CN^-(aq) \rightleftharpoons HCN(aq)$$

(b)   ammonium chloride = NH_4Cl, sodium hydroxide = NaOH
$$NH_4^+(aq) + OH^-(aq) \rightleftharpoons NH_3(aq) + H_2O(l)$$

(c)   sodium cyanide = NaCN, ammonium bromide = NH_4Br
$$NH_4^+(aq) + CN^-(aq) \rightleftharpoons NH_3(aq) + HCN(aq)$$

(d)   potassium hydrogen sulfate = $KHSO_4$, lithium acetate = $LiC_2H_3O_2$
$$HSO_4^-(aq) + C_2H_3O_2^-(aq) \rightleftharpoons SO_4^{2-}(aq) + HC_2H_3O_2(aq)$$

(e)   sodium hypochlorite = NaClO, ammonia = NH_3
No reaction; both are bases.

15.102   **Given:** 0.682 g opium, 8.92 mL of 0.0116 M H_2SO_4 **Find:** % morphine

Conceptual Plan: vol H_2SO_4 → mol H_2SO_4 → mol H_3O^+ → mol morphine → g morphine → % morphine

$$mol = VM \qquad \frac{2\ mol\ H_3O^+}{H_2SO_4} \qquad \frac{1\ mol\ morphine}{1\ mol\ H_3O^+} \qquad \frac{285.3\ g\ morphine}{1\ mol\ morphine} \qquad \frac{g\ morphine}{g\ opium} \times 100\%$$

Solution:

$$8.92\ \cancel{mL\ H_2SO_4} \times \frac{1\ \cancel{L}}{1000\ \cancel{mL}} \times \frac{0.0116\ \cancel{mol\ H_2SO_4}}{\cancel{L}} \times \frac{2\ \cancel{mol\ H_3O^+}}{1\ \cancel{mol\ H_2SO_4}} \times \frac{1\ \cancel{mol\ morphine}}{1\ \cancel{mol\ H_3O^+}} \times \frac{285.3\ g\ morphine}{1\ \cancel{mol\ morphine}}$$

$$= 0.0590\underline{4}\ g\ morphine$$

$$\frac{0.0590\underline{4}\ g\ morphine}{0.682\ g\ opium} \times 100\% = 8.66\%$$

15.103   **Given:** 1.00 M urea, pH = 7.050   **Find:** K_a Hurea$^+$

Conceptual Plan: pH → pOH → $[OH^-]$ → K_b(urea) → K_a(Hurea$^+$). Write a balanced reaction.

$$pH + pOH = 14 \qquad pOH = -\log[OH^-]$$

Prepare an ICE table, represent the change with x, sum the table, determine the equilibrium values, put the equilibrium values in the equilibrium expression, and determine K_b.

Solution: $pOH = 14.000 - 7.050 = 6.950$ $[OH^-] = 10^{-6.950} = 1.1\underline{2}2 \times 10^{-7}$ M

$$urea(aq) + H_2O(l) \rightleftharpoons Hurea^+(aq) + OH^-(aq)$$

	[urea]	[Hurea$^-$]	$[OH^-]$
Initial	1.00	0.0	0.0
Change	$-x$	x	x
Equil	$1.00 - 1.1\underline{2}2 \times 10^{-7}$	$1.1\underline{2}2 \times 10^{-7}$	$1.1\underline{2}2 \times 10^{-7}$

$$K_b = \frac{[Hurea^+][OH^-]}{[urea]} = \frac{(1.1\underline{2}2 \times 10^{-7})(1.1\underline{2}2 \times 10^{-7})}{(1.00 - 1.1\underline{2}2 \times 10^{-7})} = 1.2\underline{5}89 \times 10^{-14}$$

$$K_a = \frac{K_w}{K_b} = \frac{1.00 \times 10^{-14}}{1.2\underline{5}89 \times 10^{-14}} = 0.79\underline{4}3 = 0.794$$

15.104 **Given:** 0.10 M $HC_2H_3O_2$, $K_a = 1.8 \times 10^{-5}$; 0.10 M NH_4Cl, $K_b = 1.76 \times 10^{-5}$ **Find:** $[NH_3]$
Conceptual Plan: Use $HC_2H_3O_2$ to determine $[H_3O^+]$; then use NH_4Cl to determine $[NH_3]$. Write a balanced reaction. Prepare an ICE table, represent the change with x, sum the table, and determine the equilibrium values.

Solution: $HC_2H_3O_2(aq) + H_2O(l) \rightleftharpoons H_3O^+(aq) + C_2H_3O_2^-(aq)$

	$[HC_2H_3O_2]$	$[H_3O^+]$	$[C_2H_3O_2^-]$
Initial	0.10 M	0.0	0.0
Change	$-x$	x	x
Equil	$0.10 - x$	x	x

$K_a = \dfrac{[H_3O^+][C_2H_3O_2^-]}{[HC_2H_3O_2]} = \dfrac{(x)(x)}{(0.10 - x)} = 1.8 \times 10^{-5}$

Assume that x is small compared to 0.10.

$x^2 = (1.8 \times 10^{-5})(0.10)$

$x = [H_3O^+] = 0.00134$ M

$NH_4^+(aq) + H_2O(l) \rightleftharpoons NH_3(aq) + H_3O^+(aq)$

	$[NH_4^+]$	$[NH_3]$	$[H_3O^+]$
Initial	0.10 M	0.0	0.00134
Change	$-y$	y	y
Equil	$0.10 - y$	y	$0.00134 + y$

$K_a = \dfrac{K_w}{K_b} = \dfrac{1.00 \times 10^{-14}}{1.76 \times 10^{-5}} = 5.\underline{6}82 \times 10^{-10} = \dfrac{(y)(0.00134 + y)}{(0.10 - y)}$

Assume that y is small compared to 0.10.

$y^2 + 0.00134y - 5.\underline{6}82 \times 10^{-11} = 0$ Solve using the quadratic equation.

$y = [NH_3] = 4.2 \times 10^{-8}$ M

15.105 **Given:** $Ca(Lact)_2$, $[Ca^{2+}] = 0.26$ M, pH $= 8.40$ **Find:** K_a lactic acid
Conceptual Plan: $[Ca^{2+}] \rightarrow [Lact^-]$; determine K_b lactate ion. Prepare an ICE table, represent the

$$\dfrac{2 \text{ mol lactate ion}}{1 \text{ mol Ca}^{2+}}$$

change with x, sum the table, and determine the equilibrium constant. $K_b \rightarrow K_a$

$$K_a = \dfrac{K_w}{K_b}$$

Solution: 0.26 M $Ca^{2+} \left(\dfrac{2 \text{ mol Lact}^-}{1 \text{ mol Ca}^{2+}} \right) = 0.52$ M $Lact^-$

$Lact^-(aq) + H_2O(l) \rightleftharpoons HLact(aq) + OH^-(aq)$

	$[Lact^-]$	$[HLact]$	$[OH^-]$
Initial	0.52 M	0	0
Change	$-x$	$+x$	$+x$
Equil	$0.52 - x$	x	x

pH $= 8.40$ $[H_3O^+] = 10^{-8.40} = 4.0 \times 10^{-9}$ $[OH^-] = \dfrac{1.0 \times 10^{-14}}{4.0 \times 10^{-9}} = 2.5 \times 10^{-6} = x$

$K_b = \dfrac{[HLact][OH^-]}{[Lact^-]} = \dfrac{(2.5 \times 10^{-6})(2.5 \times 10^{-6})}{(0.52 - 2.5 \times 10^{-6})} = 1.2 \times 10^{-11}$

$K_a = \dfrac{K_w}{K_b} = \dfrac{(1.0 \times 10^{-14})}{(1.2 \times 10^{-11})} = 8.3 \times 10^{-4}$

15.106 **Given:** 0.23 mol QHCl, 1.0 L, pH = 4.58   **Find:** K_b quinine

Conceptual Plan: mol QHCl $\rightarrow$ [QHCl] $\rightarrow$ [QH$^+$]; determine K_a QH$^+$. Prepare an ICE table, represent the

$$M = \frac{mol}{L} \qquad \frac{1 \text{ mol QH}^+}{1 \text{ mol QHCl}}$$

change with x, sum the table, and determine the equilibrium constant. $K_a \rightarrow K_b$

$$K_b = \frac{K_w}{K_a}$$

Solution: $\dfrac{0.23 \text{ mol QHCl}}{1 \text{ L}} \left(\dfrac{1 \text{ mol QH}^+}{1 \text{ mol QHCl}} \right) = 0.23 \text{ M QH}^+$

$$QH^+(aq) + H_2O(l) \rightleftharpoons Q(aq) + H_3O^+(aq)$$

	[QH$^+$]	**[Q]**	**[H$_3$O$^+$]**
Initial	0.23 M	0	0
Change	$-x$	$+x$	$+x$
Equil	$0.23 - x$	x	x

pH $= 4.58$ $[H_3O^+] = 10^{-4.58} = 2.6 \times 10^{-5} = x$

$$K_a = \frac{[Q][H_3O^+]}{[QH^+]} = \frac{(2.6 \times 10^{-5})(2.6 \times 10^{-5})}{(0.23 - 2.6 \times 10^{-5})} = 2.9 \times 10^{-9}$$

$$K_b = \frac{K_w}{K_a} = \frac{(1.0 \times 10^{-14})}{(2.9 \times 10^{-9})} = 3.4 \times 10^{-6}$$

Challenge Problems

15.107 The calculation is incorrect because it neglects the contribution from the autoionization of water. HI is a strong acid, so $[H_3O^+]$ from HI $= 1.0 \times 10^{-7}$.

$$H_2O(l) + H_2O(l) \rightleftharpoons H_3O^+(aq) + OH^-(aq)$$

	[H$_2$O]	**[H$_3$O$^+$]**	**[OH$^-$]**
Initial		1×10^{-7}	0.0
Change	$-x$	x	x
Equil		$1 \times 10^{-7} + x$	x

$K_w = [H_3O^+][OH^-] = 1.0 \times 10^{-14}$

$\qquad (1 \times 10^{-7} + x)(x) = 1.0 \times 10^{-14}$ $x^2 + 1 \times 10^{-7}x - 1.0 \times 10^{-14} = 0$

$x = 6.18 \times 10^{-8}$

$[H_3O^+] = (1 \times 10^{-7} + x) = (1 \times 10^{-7} + 6.18 \times 10^{-8}) = 1.618 \times 10^{-7}$

pH $= -\log(1.618 \times 10^{-7}) = 6.79$

15.108 **Given:** 2.55 g HA, molar mass $= 85.0$ g/mol, 250.0 g H_2O, FP $= -0.257\,°C$ **Find:** K_a

Conceptual Plan:

g HA $\rightarrow$ mol HA $\rightarrow$ m HA $\rightarrow$ i $\rightarrow$ % ionization and then mol HA $\rightarrow$ M HA. Then write a

$$\text{mol HA} = \frac{g \text{ HA}}{\text{molar mass}} \qquad \frac{\text{mol HA}}{\text{kg } H_2O} \qquad \Delta T = iK_f m$$

balanced reaction, prepare an ICE table, calculate equilibrium concentrations, and plug into the equilibrium expression to solve for K_a.

Solution: $2.55 \text{ g HA} \times \dfrac{1 \text{ mol}}{85.0 \text{ g HA}} = 0.0300 \text{ mol HA}$ $\dfrac{0.0300 \text{ mol HA}}{\left(250.0 \text{ g } H_2O \times \dfrac{1 \text{ kg}}{1000 \text{ g}} \right)} = 0.120 \, m$

$\Delta T = iK_f m$ $\Delta T = 0.000\,°C - (-0.257\,°C) = 0.257\,°C$

$(0.257\,°C) = i \left(1.86 \dfrac{°C}{m} \right)(0.120 \, m)$ $i = 1.151 =$ moles of particles in solution/mol HA

$$HA(aq) + H_2O(l) \rightleftharpoons H_3O^+(aq) + A^-(aq)$$

$$1 - y \qquad\qquad\qquad y \qquad\quad y$$

So $(1 - y) + y + y = 1.151 \qquad y = 0.151 =$ fraction of HA dissociated

$$M\ HA = \dfrac{0.0300\ \text{mol HA}}{(250.0\ \text{g} + 2.55\ \text{g})\left(\dfrac{1.00\ \text{mL}}{1.00\ \text{g}}\right)\left(\dfrac{1\ \text{L}}{1000\ \text{mL}}\right)} = 0.1188\ \text{M}$$

$(0.1188\ \text{M})(0.151) = 0.01794\ \text{M} = [H_3O^+] = [A^-]$ at equilibrium

$$HA(aq) + H_2O(l) \rightleftharpoons H_3O^+(aq) + A^-(aq)$$

	[HA]	**[H₃O']**	**[A']**
Initial	0.1188 M	0.0	0.0
Change	$-x$	x	x
Equil	$0.1188 - 0.01794$	0.01794	0.01794

$$K_a = \dfrac{[H_3O^+][A^-]}{[HA]} = \dfrac{(0.01794)(0.01794)}{(0.1188 - 0.01794)} = 0.003191 = 3.2 \times 10^{-3}$$

15.109   **Given:** 0.00115 M HCl, 0.01000 M HClO₂, $K_a = 1.1 \times 10^{-2}$ **Find:** pH

Conceptual Plan: Use HCl to determine $[H_3O^+]$. Use $[H_3O^+]$ and HClO₂ to determine dissociation of HClO₂. Write a balanced reaction, prepare an ICE table, calculate equilibrium concentrations, and plug into the equilibrium expression.

Solution: $0.00115\ \text{M HCl} = 0.00115\ \text{M}\ H_3O^+$

$$HClO_2(aq) + H_2O(l) \rightleftharpoons H_3O^+(aq) + ClO_2^-(aq)$$

	[HClO₂]	**[H₃O']**	**[ClO₂']**
Initial	0.0100 M	0.00115 M	0.0
Change	$-x$	x	x
Equil	$0.01000 - x$	$0.00115 + x$	x

$$K_a = \dfrac{[H_3O^+][ClO_2^-]}{[HClO_2]} = \dfrac{(0.00115 + x)(x)}{(0.0100 - x)} = 1.1 \times 10^{-2}$$

$x^2 + 0.01215x - 1.1 \times 10^{-4} = 0 \qquad x = 0.006045$

$[H_3O^+] = 0.00115 + 0.006045 = 0.007195$

pH $= -\log(0.007195) = 2.14$

15.110   Volume should be increased to 4 L.

$$HA(aq) + H_2O(l) \rightleftharpoons H_3O^+(aq) + A^-(aq)$$

Initial equilibrium conditions: $[HA] = A$, $[H_3O^+] = [A^-] = x$

$$K_a = \dfrac{[H_3O^+][A^-]}{[HA]} = \dfrac{(x)(x)}{(A)}$$

Second equilibrium conditions: $[HA] = A/y$, $[H_3O^+] = [A^-] = x/2$

$$K_a = \dfrac{[H_3O^+][A^-]}{[HA]} = \dfrac{(x)(x)}{(A)} = \dfrac{\left(\dfrac{x}{2}\right)\left(\dfrac{x}{2}\right)}{\left(\dfrac{A}{y}\right)}$$

$\dfrac{x^2 A}{y} = \dfrac{x^2 A}{4}$ $y = 4$; so for the concentration of H$^+$ to be halved, the [A] needs to decrease to one-fourth the original

concentration. So the volume has to increase to 4 L.

15.111   **Given:** 1.0 M HA, $K_a = 1.0 \times 10^{-8}$, $K = 4.0$ for reaction 2   **Find:** $[H^+]$, $[A^-]$, $[HA_2^-]$

Conceptual Plan: Combine reaction 1 and reaction 2; then determine the equilibrium expression and the value of K. Prepare an ICE table, calculate equilibrium concentrations, and plug into the equilibrium expression.

Solution:

$$HA(aq) \rightleftharpoons H^+(aq) + A^-(aq) \qquad K = 1.0 \times 10^{-8}$$

$$HA(aq) + A^-(aq) \rightleftharpoons HA_2^+(aq) \qquad K = 4.0$$

$$2\,HA(aq) \rightleftharpoons H^+(aq) + HA_2^+(aq) \qquad K = 4.0 \times 10^{-8}$$

	[HA]	**[H⁺]**	**[HA₂⁺]**
Initial	1.0 M	0.0	0.0
Change	$-2x$	x	x
Equil	$1.0 - 2x$	x	x

$$K = \frac{[H^+][HA_2^-]}{[HA]^2} = 4.0 \times 10^{-8} = \frac{(x)(x)}{(1.0 - 2x)^2}$$

Take the square root of both sides of the equation. $x = 1.9992 \times 10^{-4}$

$$HA(aq) \rightleftharpoons H^+(aq) + A^-(aq) \qquad K = 1.0 \times 10^{-8}$$

	[HA]	**[H⁺]**	**[A⁻]**
Initial	1.0 M	1.9992×10^{-4}	0.0
Change	$-y$	y	y
Equil	$1.0 - y$	$1.9992 \times 10^{-4} + y$	y

$$K = \frac{[H^+][A^-]}{[HA]} = 1.0 \times 10^{-8} = \frac{(1.9992 \times 10^{-4} + y)(y)}{(1.0 - y)}$$

Assume y is small compared to 1.0

$y^2 + 1.9992 \times 10^{-4}y - 1 \times 10^{-8} = 0$ $y = 4.14 \times 10^{-5}$

$[H^+] = x + y = 1.9992 \times 10^{-4} + 4.29 \times 10^{-5} = 2.4 \times 10^{-4}$

$[A^-] = y = 4.14 \times 10^{-5}$

$[HA_2^-] = x = 2.0 \times 10^{-4}$

15.112   In the gas phase, $(CH_3)_3N$ is a stronger Lewis base than is CH_3NH_2 because the $N-H$ bond is more polar than the $N-C$ bond, making the lone pair on the N less accessible to the H^+ that needs to be added. In the liquid phase, the steric hindrance from the size of the CH_3 groups becomes more pronounced; therefore, it is harder to add the H^+ ion.

15.113   **Given:** 0.200 mol NH_4CN, 1.00 L, $K_b(NH_3) = 1.76 \times 10^{-5}$, $K_a(HCN) = 4.9 \times 10^{-10}$ **Find:** pH

Conceptual Plan: $K_b\,NH_3 \rightarrow K_a\,NH_4^+$; $K_a\,HCN \rightarrow K_b\,CN^-$ Prepare an ICE table, represent the

$$K_aK_b = K_w$$

change with x, sum the table, and determine the equilibrium conditions.

Solution: $K_a(NH_4^+) = \dfrac{1.0 \times 10^{-14}}{1.76 \times 10^{-5}} = 5.68 \times 10^{-10}$ $K_b(CN^-) = \dfrac{1.0 \times 10^{-14}}{4.9 \times 10^{-10}} = 2.0 \times 10^{-5}$

0.200 M $NH_4CN = 0.200$ M NH_4^+ and 0.200 M CN^-

Because the value for K for CN^- is greater than the K for NH_4^+, the CN^- reaction will be larger and the solution will be basic.

$$CN^-(aq) + H_2O(l) \rightleftharpoons HCN(aq) + OH^-(aq)$$

	[CN⁻]	**[HCN]**	**[OH⁻]**
Initial	0.200 M	0	0
Change	$-x$	$+x$	$+x$
Equil	$0.200 - x$	x	x

$$K_b = \frac{[HCN][OH^-]}{[CN^-]} \qquad 2.0 \times 10^{-5} = \frac{(x)(x)}{(0.200 - x)} \qquad \text{Solve using the quadratic equation.}$$

$$x = 0.0020 = [OH^-]$$

$$[H_3O^+] = \frac{1.0 \times 10^{-14}}{0.0020} = 5.0 \times 10^{-12} \quad pH = -\log(5.0 \times 10^{-12}) = 11.30$$

15.114 **Given:** 1.0 L, 0.30 M $HClO_2$, 0.20 mol NaF, K_a ($HClO_2$) = 1.1×10^{-2}, K_a (HF) = 3.5×10^{-4} **Find:** [$HClO_2$]
Conceptual Plan: Determine the products of the reaction of $HClO_2$ and NaF. Prepare an ICE table, represent the change with x, sum the table, and determine the equilibrium conditions.
Solution:

$$HClO_2(aq) + NaF(aq) \rightarrow HF\ (aq) + NaClO_2(aq)$$

	[$HClO_2$]	[NaF]	[HF]	[$NaClO_2$]
Initial	0.30 M	0.20 M		
	−0.20	−0.20	+0.20	+0.20
Final	0.10	0	0.20	0.20

Because HF is the weaker acid, the reaction will proceed to the right. Because NaF is the smaller amount, NaF is the limiting reactant.

The $HClO_2$ has the largest equilibrium constant, so it will be the species that contributes to the pH to the largest extent.

$$HClO_2(aq) + H_2O(l) \rightleftharpoons ClO_2^-(aq) + H_3O^+(aq)$$

	[$HClO_2$]	[ClO_2^-]	[H_3O^+]
Initial	0.10 M	0.20	0
Change	−x	+x	+x
Equil	0.10 − x	0.20 + x	x

$$K_a = \frac{[ClO_2^-][H_3O^+]}{[HClO_2]} \qquad 1.1 \times 10^{-2} = \frac{(0.20 + x)(x)}{(0.10 - x)}$$

Solve the quadratic, $x = 0.0051$ $\qquad$ [$HClO_2$] = 0.10 − 0.0051 = 0.095 M

15.115 **Given:** mixture Na_2CO_3 and $NaHCO_3$ = 82.2 g, 1.0 L, pH = 9.95, K_a (H_2CO_3) = K_{a_1} = 4.3×10^{-7}, K_{a_2} = 5.6×10^{-11}
Find: mass $NaHCO_3$
Conceptual Plan: Let x = g $NaHCO_3$, y = g Na_2CO_3 → mol $NaHCO_3$, Na_2CO_3 → [$NaHCO_3$], [Na_2CO_3]

$$\frac{1\ \text{mol } NaHCO_3}{84.01\ \text{g}} \qquad \frac{1\ \text{mol } Na_2CO_3}{105.99\ \text{g}} \qquad\qquad M = \frac{mol}{L}$$

→ [HCO_3^-], [CO_3^{2-}], K_a (HCO_3^-) → K_b(CO_3^{2-}). Prepare an ICE table, represent the change with z,

$$\frac{1\ \text{mol } HCO_3^-}{1\ \text{mol } NaHCO_3} \quad \frac{1\ \text{mol } CO_3^{2-}}{1\ \text{mol } Na_2CO_3} \qquad K_b = \frac{K_w}{K_a}$$

sum the table, and determine the equilibrium conditions.

Solution: Let x = g $NaHCO_3$ and y = g Na_2CO_3 $\qquad$ $x + y = 82.2$, so $y = 82.2 - x$

$$\text{mol } NaHCO_3 = x\ \text{g } NaHCO_3 \left(\frac{1\ \text{mol}}{84.01\ \text{g } NaHCO_3} \right) = \frac{x}{84.01}$$

$$[HCO_3^-] = \left(\frac{\dfrac{x}{84.01}\ \text{mol } NaHCO_3}{1\ L} \right) \frac{1\ \text{mol } HCO_3^-}{1\ \text{mol } NaHCO_3} = \frac{x}{84.01}\ M\ HCO_3^-$$

$$\text{mol } Na_2CO_3 = 82.2 - x\ \text{g } Na_2CO_3 \left(\frac{1\ \text{mol}}{105.99\ \text{g } Na_2CO_3} \right) = \frac{82.2 - x}{105.99}\ Na_2CO_3$$

$$[CO_3^{2-}] = \left(\frac{\dfrac{82.2 - x}{105.99}\ \text{mol } Na_2CO_3}{1\ L} \right) \frac{1\ \text{mol } CO_3^{2-}}{1\ \text{mol } Na_2CO_3} = \frac{82.2 - x}{105.99}\ M\ CO_3^{2-}$$

Because the pH of the solution is basic, it is the hydrolysis of CO_3^{2-} that dominates in the solution.

$$K_b(CO_3^{2-}) = \frac{1.0 \times 10^{-14}}{5.6 \times 10^{-11}} = 1.79 \times 10^{-4} \text{ and } [H_3O^+] = 10^{-9.95} = 1.12 \times 10^{-10} \qquad [OH^-] = \frac{1.0 \times 10^{-14}}{1.12 \times 10^{-10}}$$

$$= 8.93 \times 10^{-5}$$

$$CO_3^{2-}(aq) + H_2O(l) \rightleftharpoons HCO_3^-(aq) + OH^-(aq)$$

	$[CO_3^{2-}]$	$[HCO_3^-]$	$[OH^-]$
Initial	$\dfrac{82.2 - x}{105.99}$	$\dfrac{x}{84.01}$	
Change	$-z$	$+z$	
Equil	$\left(\dfrac{82.2 - x}{105.99}\right) - z$	$\left(\dfrac{x}{84.01}\right) + z$	8.93×10^{-5}

$$K_b(CO_3^{2-}) = 1.79 \times 10^{-4} = \frac{[HCO_3^-][OH^-]}{[CO_3^{2-}]} = \frac{\left(\left(\dfrac{x}{84.01}\right) - z\right)(8.93 \times 10^{-5})}{\left(\dfrac{82.2 - x}{105.99}\right) - z} \quad \text{Assume that } z \text{ is small.}$$

$$\frac{1.79 \times 10^{-4}}{8.93 \times 10^{-5}} = \frac{\left(\dfrac{x}{84.01}\right)}{\left(\dfrac{82.2 - x}{105.99}\right)} \qquad x = 50.38 = 50.4 \text{ g NaHCO}_3$$

15.116 **Given:** mixture NaCN and NaHSO₄ = 0.60 mol, 1.0 L, pH = 9.9; K_a(HCN) = 4.9×10^{-10}, K_a(HSO₄⁻) = 1.2×10^{-2} **Find:** amount NaCN

Conceptual Plan: Determine $[CN^-]$ in solution after the reaction of NaCN and NaHSO₄. Then prepare an ICE table, represent the change by x, and determine the equilibrium conditions.

Solution: Because HCN is the weaker acid, we can assume complete reaction between NaCN and NaHSO₄. Also, because the solution is basic, the CN^- must be in excess. So let x = moles of NaCN.

$$NaHSO_4(aq) + NaCN(aq) \rightarrow HCN(aq) + SO_4^{2-}(aq)$$

$[NaHSO_4]$	$[NaCN]$	$[HCN]$	$[SO_4^{2-}]$
$0.60 - x$	x	0	0
$-(0.60 - x)$	$-(0.60 - x)$	$0.60 - x$	$0.60 - x$
0	$2x - 0.60$	$0.60 - x$	$0.60 - x$

$$[H_3O^+] = 10^{-9.9} = 1.26 \times 10^{-10} \qquad [OH^-] = \frac{1.0 \times 10^{-14}}{1.26 \times 10^{-10}} = 7.9 \times 10^{-5}$$

$$CN^-(aq) + H_2O(l) \rightleftharpoons HCN(aq) + OH^-(aq)$$

	$[CN^-]$	$[HCN]$	$[OH^-]$
Initial	$2x - 0.60$	$0.60 - x$	0
Change	-7.9×10^{-5}	$+7.9 \times 10^{-5}$	$+7.9 \times 10^{-5}$
Equil	$2x - 0.60 - 7.9 \times 10^{-5}$	$0.60 - x + 7.9 \times 10^{-5}$	7.9×10^{-5}

$$K_b(CN^-) = \frac{K_w}{K_a(HCN)} = \frac{1.0 \times 10^{-14}}{4.9 \times 10^{-10}} = 2.0 \times 10^{-5} = \frac{[HCN][OH^-]}{[CN^-]} = \frac{(0.60 - x)(7.9 \times 10^{-5})}{(2x - 0.60)}$$

$$x = 0.50 = \text{mol NaCN}$$

Conceptual Problems

15.117 Solution b would be most acidic.

   (a) 0.0100 M HCl (strong acid) and 0.0100 M KOH (strong base) because the concentrations are equal, the acid and base will completely neutralize each other, and the resulting solution will be pH-neutral.

(b)   0.0100 M HF (weak acid) and 0.0100 M KBr (salt). K_a (HF) $= 3.5 \times 10^{-4}$. The weak acid will produce an acidic solution. K^+ is the counterion of a strong base and is pH-neutral. Br^- is the conjugate base of a strong acid and is pH-neutral.

(c)   0.0100 M NH_4Cl (salt) and 0.0100 M CH_3NH_3Br. $K_b(NH_3) = 1.8 \times 10^{-5}$, $K_b(CH_3NH_2) = 4.4 \times 10^{-4}$. NH_4^+ is the conjugate acid of a weak base, and $CH_3NH_3^+$ is the conjugate acid of a weak base. Cl^- and Br^- are the conjugate bases of strong acids and will be pH-neutral. The solution will be acidic. However, because the K_a for the conjugate acid in this solution is smaller than the K_a for HF, the solution will be acidic, but not as acidic as HF.

(d)   0.100 M NaCN (salt) and 0.100 M $CaCl_2$. Na^+ and Ca^{2+} ions are the counterions of strong bases; therefore, they are pH-neutral. Cl^- is the conjugate base of a strong acid and is pH-neutral. CN^- is the conjugate base of a weak acid and will produce a basic solution.

15.118   Solution a would be most basic.

(a)   0.100 M NaClO (salt) and 0.100 M NaF (salt). Na^+ is the counterion of a strong base and is pH-neutral. ClO^- is the conjugate base of a weak acid (HClO, $K_a = 2.9 \times 10^{-8}$). F^- is the conjugate base of a weak acid (HF, $K_a = 3.5 \times 10^{-4}$). The solution will be basic, and ClO^- is a stronger base than is F^-.

(b)   0.0100 M KCl (salt) and 0.0100 M $KClO_2$ (salt). K^+ is the counterion of a strong base and is pH-neutral. Cl^- is the conjugate base of a strong acid and is pH-neutral. ClO_2^- is the conjugate base of a weak acid ($HClO_2$, $K_a = 1.1 \times 10^{-2}$) and will produce a basic solution. However, because the ClO_2^- is a weaker conjugate base than is ClO^-, solution a will be more basic.

(c)   0.0100 M HNO_3 (strong acid) and 0.0100 M NaOH (strong base) because the concentrations are equal, the acid and base will completely neutralize each other, and the resulting solution will be pH-neutral.

(d)   0.0100 M NH_4Cl (salt) and 0.0100 M HCN (weak acid). NH_4^+ is the conjugate acid of a weak base and will be acidic. HCN is a weak acid and will be acidic. Cl^- is the conjugate base of a strong acid and is pH-neutral.

15.119 $CH_3COOH < CH_2ClCOOH < CHCl_2COOH < CCl_3COOH$
Because Cl is more electronegative than is H, as you add Cl, you increase the number of electronegative atoms, which pulls the electron density away from the O—H group, polarizing the O—H bond, making it more acidic.

15.120   Remember that $pH = -\log[H_3O^+]$, $pOH = -\log[OH^-]$, and $pH + pOH = 14$. Since all of the values have a coefficient of 1.0, the pH or pOH is the negative of the exponent.

(a) 1.0×10^{-2} M HCl will have a pH $= 2.00$ and a pOH $= 14 - pH = 14 - 2.00 = 12.00$.

(b) 1.0×10^{-4} M HCl will have a pH $= 4.00$ and a pOH $= 14 - pH = 14 - 4.00 = 10.00$.

(c) 1.0×10^{-2} M NaOH will have a pOH $= 2.00$ and a pH $= 14 - pOH = 14 - 2.00 = 12.00$.

(d) 1.0×10^{-4} M NaOH will have a pOH $= 4.00$ and a pH $= 14 - pOH = 14 - 4.00 = 10.00$.

Ranked from most acidic to most basic: a → b → d → c

Questions for Group Work

15.121   Acids have the following general properties: a sour taste, the ability to dissolve many metals, the ability to turn blue litmus paper red, and the ability to neutralize bases.
Bases have the following general properties: a bitter taste, a slippery feel, the ability to turn red litmus paper blue, and the ability to neutralize acids.

15.122   A conjugate acid–base pair is made up of two substances related to each other by the transfer of a proton. In the reaction: $NH_3(aq) + H_2O(l) \rightleftharpoons NH_4^+(aq) + OH^-(aq)$, the acid–base conjugate pairs are: NH_4^+/NH_3 and H_2O/OH^-, with the acid listed first and the base second. Look for examples of acids and bases in Tables 15.1, 15.2, 15.3, 15.4, 15.5, 15.7, and 15.9.

15.123   (a)   A strong acid completely ionizes in solution, and the pH will equal the −log of the acid concentration. An example is HCl. A weak acid only partially ionizes in solution and the pH will be greater than the −log of the acid concentration. An example is HF. Table 15.3 lists the strong acids. If the acid is not in this table, it is a weak acid.

(b)   For a strong acid, HA, $pH = -\log[HA]$.

(c)   For a weak acid, write a balanced reaction for the ionization of the acid. Prepare an ICE table; represent the change with x; sum the table and determine the equilibrium values; put the equilibrium values in the equilibrium expression and solve for x. Finally, determine $[H_3O^+]$ and pH $(-\log[H_3O^+])$.

(d)   Since $K_a \times K_b = K_w$, $K_b = K_w/K_a$. The larger the K_a the smaller the K_b.

(e)   Since $K_w = [H_3O^+] \times [OH^-]$, $[H_3O^+] = K_w/[OH^-]$. The larger the $[OH^-]$ the smaller the $[H_3O^+]$.

15.124   **Given:** 5.3 g $NaC_2H_3O_2$ in 100.0 mL water   **Find:** pH
Other: K_a $(HC_2H_3O_2) = 1.8 \times 10^{-5}$
Conceptual Plan: g $NaC_2H_3O_2$ → **mol** $C_2H_3O_2^-$ **and mL** → **L then mol** $C_2H_3O_2^-$, **mL** → **M** $C_2H_3O_2^-$

$$NaC_2H_3O_2\,(aq) \rightarrow Na^+(aq) + C_2H_3O_2^-(aq) \quad \frac{1 \text{ mol } NaC_2H_3O_2}{82.03 \text{ g } NaC_2H_3O_2} \quad \frac{1 \text{ L}}{1000 \text{ mL}} \qquad M = \frac{\text{amount solute (moles)}}{\text{volume solution (L)}}$$

then K_a → K_b **then M** $C_2H_3O_2^-$ → $[OH^-]$ → **pOH** → **pH**
$\quad K_w = K_a \times K_b \qquad\qquad$ ICE Chart   pH $= -\log[H_3O^+]$ pH $= 14 - $pOH

Solution: Since 1 $C_2H_3O_2^-$ ion is generated for each $NaC_2H_3O_2$, $[C_2H_3O_2^-] = [NaC_2H_3O_2]$.

$$5.3 \text{ g } NaC_2H_3O_2 \times \frac{1 \text{ mol } NaC_2H_3O_2}{82.03 \text{ g } NaC_2H_3O_2} = 0.0\underline{6}46105 \text{ mol } NaC_2H_3O_2 \quad 100.0 \text{ mL} \times \frac{1 \text{ L}}{1000 \text{ mL}} = 0.1000 \text{ L}$$

$$\frac{0.0\underline{6}46105 \text{ mol } NaC_2H_3O_2}{0.1000 \text{ L}} = 0.6\underline{4}6105 \text{ M } NaC_2H_3O_2$$

Since $K_w = K_a \times K_b$, rearrange to solve for K_b. $K_b = \dfrac{K_w}{K_a} = \dfrac{1.0 \times 10^{-14}}{1.8 \times 10^{-5}} = 5.\underline{5}556 \times 10^{-10}$

$$C_2H_3O_2^-(aq) + H_2O(l) \rightleftharpoons HC_2H_3O_2(aq) + OH^-(aq)$$

	$[C_2H_3O_2^-]$	$[HC_2H_3O_2]$	$[OH^-]$
Initial	0.6$\underline{4}$6105	0.000	≈ 0.00
Change	$-x$	$+x$	$+x$
Equil	0.6$\underline{4}$6105 $- x$	$+x$	$+x$

$K_a = \dfrac{[HC_2H_3O_2]\,[OH^-]}{[C_2H_3O_2^-]} = 5.\underline{5}556 \times 10^{-10} = \dfrac{(x)(x)}{0.6\underline{4}6105 - x}$ Assume x is small ($x \ll 0.65$) so

$\dfrac{x^2}{0.6\underline{4}6105 - \cancel{x}} = 5.\underline{5}556 \times 10^{-10} = \dfrac{x^2}{0.6\underline{4}6105}$ and $x = 1.89459 \times 10^{-5}$ M $= [OH^-]$.

Confirm that assumption is valid $\dfrac{1.\underline{8}9459 \times 10^{-5}}{0.6\underline{4}6105} \times 100\% = 0.0029\%$ so assumption is valid.

Then, pOH $= -\log[OH^-] = -\log(1.\underline{8}9459 \times 10^{-5}) = 4.72$. Finally, pH $= 14 - $pOH $= 14.00 - 4.72 = 9.28$.

NOTE: Another way to do this problem is to convert $[OH^-]$ to $[H_3O^+]$ (using $K_w = [H_3O^+] \times [OH^-]$) and then calculate the pH (using pH $= -\log[H_3O^+]$).

Check: The units (none) are correct. The magnitude of the answer makes physical sense because the expected pH is greater than 7 (sodium acetate is a salt formed by a strong base and a weak acid).

15.125   An Arrhenius acid is a substance that produces H^+ in aqueous solution. An example is HCl.
A Bronsted–Lowry base is a proton (H^+) acceptor. Examples are H_2O and F^-.
A Lewis acid is an electron pair acceptor. An example is BF_3.

16 Aqueous Ionic Equilibrium

The Common Ion Effect and Buffers

16.1   The only solution in which HNO_2 will ionize less is (d) 0.10 M $NaNO_2$. It is the only solution that generates a common ion NO_2^- with nitrous acid.

16.2   Formic acid is $HCHO_2$, which dissociates to H^+ and CHO_2^-. The only solution that generates a common ion (CHO_2^-) with formic acid is (c) $NaCHO_2$.

16.3   (a)   **Given:** 0.15 M $HCHO_2$ and 0.10 M $NaCHO_2$ **Find:** pH   **Other:** $K_a(HCHO_2) = 1.8 \times 10^{-4}$
        Conceptual Plan: M $NaCHO_2 \to$ M CHO_2^- then M $HCHO_2$, M $CHO_2^- \to [H_3O^+] \to$ pH

$$NaCHO_2(aq) \to Na^+(aq) + CHO_2^-(aq) \qquad \text{ICE table} \qquad pH = -\log[H_3O^+]$$

Solution: Because one CHO_2^- ion is generated for each $NaCHO_2$, $[CHO_2^-] = 0.10$ M CHO_2^-.

$$HCHO_2(aq) + H_2O(l) \rightleftharpoons H_3O^+(aq) + CHO_2^-(aq)$$

	$[HCHO_2]$	$[H_3O^+]$	$[CHO_2^-]$
Initial	0.15	≈ 0.00	0.10
Change	$-x$	$+x$	$+x$
Equil	$0.15 - x$	$+x$	$0.10 + x$

$$K_a = \frac{[H_3O^+][CHO_2^-]}{[HCHO_2]} = 1.8 \times 10^{-4} = \frac{x(0.10 + x)}{0.15 - x} \quad \text{Assume that } x \text{ is}$$

small ($x \ll 0.10 < 0.15$), so $\dfrac{x(0.10 + \cancel{x})}{0.15 - \cancel{x}} = 1.8 \times 10^{-4} = \dfrac{x(0.10)}{0.15}$ and

$x = 2.7 \times 10^{-4}$ M $= [H_3O^+]$. Confirm that the more stringent assumption is valid.

$\dfrac{2.7 \times 10^{-4}}{0.10} \times 100\% = 0.27\%$, so the assumption is valid. Finally,

$pH = -\log[H_3O^+] = -\log(2.7 \times 10^{-4}) = 3.57$.

Check: The units (none) are correct. The magnitude of the answer makes physical sense because pH should be greater than $-\log(0.15) = 0.82$ because this is a weak acid and there is a common ion effect.

(b)   **Given:** 0.12 M NH_3 and 0.18 M NH_4Cl **Find:** pH   **Other:** $K_b(NH_3) = 1.76 \times 10^{-5}$
        Conceptual Plan: M $NH_4Cl \to$ M NH_4^+ then M NH_3, M $NH_4^+ \to [OH^-] \to [H_3O^+] \to$ pH

$$NH_4Cl(aq) \to NH_4^+(aq) + Cl^-(aq) \qquad \text{ICE table} \quad K_w = [H_3O^+][OH^-] \quad pH = -\log[H_3O^+]$$

Solution: Because one NH_4^+ ion is generated for each NH_4Cl, $[NH_4^+] = 0.18$ M NH_4^+.

$$NH_3(aq) + H_2O(l) \rightleftharpoons NH_4^+(aq) + OH^-(aq)$$

	$[NH_3]$	$[NH_4^+]$	$[OH^-]$
Initial	0.12	0.18	≈ 0.00
Change	$-x$	$+x$	$+x$
Equil	$0.12 - x$	$0.18 + x$	$+x$

$$K_b = \frac{[NH_4^-][OH^-]}{[NH_3]} = 1.76 \times 10^{-5} = \frac{(0.18 + x)x}{0.12 - x}$$

Assume that x is small ($x \ll 0.12 < 0.18$), so $\dfrac{(0.18 + \cancel{x})x}{0.12 - \cancel{x}} = 1.76 \times 10^{-5} = \dfrac{(0.18)x}{0.12}$ and

$x = 1.\underline{1}73333 \times 10^{-5}$ M $= [OH^-]$. Confirm that the more stringent assumption is valid.

$$\frac{1.173333 \times 10^{-5}}{0.12} \times 100\% = 9.8 \times 10^{-3}\%, \text{ so the assumption is valid.}$$

$K_w = [H_3O^+][OH^-]$, so $[H_3O^+] = \dfrac{K_w}{[OH^-]} = \dfrac{1.0 \times 10^{-14}}{1.\underline{1}73333 \times 10^{-5}} = 8.\underline{5}2273 \times 10^{-10}$ M.

Finally, pH $= -\log[H_3O^+] = -\log(8.\underline{5}2273 \times 10^{-10}) = 9.07$

Check: The units (none) are correct. The magnitude of the answer makes physical sense because the pH should be less than $14 + \log(0.12) = 13.1$ because this is a weak base and there is a common ion effect.

16.4   (a)   **Given:** 0.175 M $HC_2H_3O_2$ and 0.110 M $KC_2H_3O_2$ **Find:** pH
           Other: $K_a(HC_2H_3O_2) = 1.8 \times 10^{-5}$
           Conceptual Plan: M $KC_2H_3O_2$ → M $C_2H_3O_2^-$ then M $HC_2H_3O_2$, M $C_2H_3O_2^-$ → $[H_3O^+]$ → pH

                             $KC_2H_3O_2(aq) \rightarrow K^+(aq) + C_2H_3O_2^-(aq)$ ICE table   pH $= -\log[H_3O^+]$

           Solution: Because one $C_2H_3O_2^-$ ion is generated for each $KC_2H_3O_2$, $[C_2H_3O_2^-] = 0.110$ M $C_2H_3O_2^-$.

                     $HC_2H_3O_2(aq) + H_2O(l) \rightleftharpoons H_3O^+(aq) + C_2H_3O_2^-(aq)$

	$[HC_2H_3O_2]$	$[H_3O^+]$	$[C_2H_3O_2^-]$
Initial	0.175	≈ 0.00	0.110
Change	$-x$	$+x$	$+x$
Equil	$0.175 - x$	$+x$	$0.110 + x$

$K_a = \dfrac{[H_3O^+][HC_2H_3O_2^-]}{[HC_2H_3O_2]} = 1.8 \times 10^{-5} = \dfrac{x(0.110 + x)}{0.175 - x}$ Assume that x is small ($x \ll 0.125 < 0.195$), so

$\dfrac{x(0.110 + \cancel{x})}{0.175 - \cancel{x}} = 1.8 \times 10^{-5} = \dfrac{x(0.110)}{0.175}$ and $x = 2.\underline{8}636 \times 10^{-5}$ M $= [H_3O^+]$. Confirm that the more

stringent assumption is valid.

$$\frac{2.\underline{8}636 \times 10^{-5}}{0.175} \times 100\% = 0.016\%, \text{ so assumption is valid. Finally,}$$

pH $= -\log[H_3O^+] = -\log(2.\underline{8}636 \times 10^{-5}) = 4.54$.

Check: The units (none) are correct. The magnitude of the answer makes physical sense because the pH should be greater than $-\log(0.110) = 0.96$ because this is a weak acid and there is a common ion effect.

  (b)   **Given:** 0.195 M CH_3NH_2 and 0.105 M CH_3NH_3Br **Find:** pH
           Other: $K_b(CH_3NH_2) = 4.4 \times 10^{-4}$
           Conceptual Plan: M CH_3NH_3Br → M $CH_3NH_3^+$ then

                          $CH_3NH_3Br(aq) \rightarrow CH_3NH_3^+(aq) + Br^-(aq)$

           M CH_3NH_3, M $CH_3NH_3^+$ → $[OH^-]$ → $[H_3O^+]$ → pH

                   ICE table $K_w = [H_3O^+][OH^-]$ pH $= -\log[H_3O^+]$

           Solution: Because one $CH_3NH_3^+$ ion is generated for each CH_3NH_3Br, $[CH_3NH_3^+] = 0.105$ M $CH_3NH_3^+$.

                  $CH_3NH_2(aq) + H_2O(l) \rightleftharpoons CH_3NH_3^+(aq) + OH^-(aq)$

	$[CH_3NH_2]$	$[CH_3NH_3^+]$	$[OH^-]$
Initial	0.195	0.105	≈ 0.00
Change	$-x$	$+x$	$+x$
Equil	$0.195 - x$	$0.105 + x$	$+x$

$$K_b = \frac{[CH_3NH_3^+][OH^-]}{[CH_3NH_2]} = 4.4 \times 10^{-4} = \frac{(0.105 + x)x}{0.195 - x}$$

Assume that x is small ($x \ll 0.105 < 0.195$), so $\dfrac{(0.105 + \cancel{x})x}{0.195 - \cancel{x}} = 4.4 \times 10^{-4} = \dfrac{(0.105)x}{0.195}$ and

$x = 8.\underset{\text{.}}{1}714 \times 10^{-4}\,M = [OH^-]$. Confirm that the more stringent assumption is valid.

$$\frac{8.\underset{\text{.}}{1}714 \times 10^{-4}}{0.105} \times 100\% = 0.78\%, \text{ so the assumption is valid.}$$

$K_w = [H_3O^+][OH^-]$, so $[H_3O^+] = \dfrac{K_w}{[OH^-]} = \dfrac{1.0 \times 10^{-14}}{8.\underset{\text{.}}{1}714 \times 10^{-4}} = 1.\underset{\text{.}}{2}238 \times 10^{-11}\,M.$

Finally, pH $= -\log[H_3O^+] = -\log(1.\underset{\text{.}}{2}238 \times 10^{-11}) = 10.91.$

Check: The units (none) are correct. The magnitude of the answer makes physical sense because the pH should be less than $14 + \log(0.195) = 13.3$ because this is a weak base and there is a common ion effect.

16.5 **Given:** 0.15 M $HC_7H_5O_2$ in pure water and in 0.10 M $NaC_7H_5O_2$
Find: % ionization in both solutions **Other:** $K_a(HC_7H_5O_2) = 6.5 \times 10^{-5}$
Conceptual Plan: pure water: M $HC_7H_5O_2 \rightarrow [H_3O^+] \rightarrow$ % ionization then in $NaC_7H_5O_2$ solution:

$$\text{ICE table} \quad \% \text{ ionization} = \frac{[H_3O^+]_{equil}}{[HC_7H_5O_2]_0} \times 100\%$$

M $NaC_7H_5O_2 \rightarrow$ M $C_7H_5O_2^-$ then M $HC_7H_5O_2$, M $C_7H_5O_2^- \rightarrow [H_3O^+] \rightarrow$ % ionization

$NaC_7H_5O_2(aq) \rightarrow Na^+(aq) + C_7H_5O_2^-(aq)$ $\qquad$ ICE table $\quad \% \text{ ionization} = \dfrac{[H_3O^+]_{equil}}{[HC_7H_5O_2]_0} \times 100\%$

Solution: in pure water:

$$HC_7H_5O_2(aq) + H_2O(l) \rightleftharpoons H_3O^+(aq) + C_7H_5O_2^-(aq)$$

	$[HC_7H_5O_2]$	$[H_3O^+]$	$[C_7H_5O_2^-]$
Initial	0.15	≈ 0.00	0.00
Change	$-x$	$+x$	$+x$
Equil	$0.15 - x$	$+x$	$+x$

$$K_a = \frac{[H_3O^+][C_7H_5O_2^-]}{[HC_7H_5O_2]} = 6.5 \times 10^{-5} = \frac{x^2}{0.15 - x}$$

Assume that x is small ($x \ll 0.10$), so $\dfrac{x^2}{0.15 - \cancel{x}} = 6.5 \times 10^{-5} = \dfrac{x^2}{0.15}$ and $x = 3.\underset{\text{.}}{1}225 \times 10^{-3}\,M = [H_3O^+]$. Then

$\% \text{ ionization} = \dfrac{[H_3O^+]_{equil}}{[HC_7H_5O_2]_0} \times 100\% = \dfrac{3.\underset{\text{.}}{1}225 \times 10^{-3}}{0.15} \times 100\% = 2.1\%,$ which also confirms that the assumption

is valid (because it is less than 5%). In $NaC_7H_5O_2$ solution: Because one $C_7H_5O_2^-$ ion is generated for each $NaC_7H_5O_2$, $[C_7H_5O_2^-] = 0.10\,M\,C_7H_5O_2^-$.

$$HC_7H_5O_2(aq) + H_2O(l) \rightleftharpoons H_3O^+(aq) + C_7H_5O_2^-(aq)$$

	$[HC_7H_5O_2]$	$[H_3O^+]$	$[C_7H_5O_2^-]$
Initial	0.15	≈ 0.00	0.10
Change	$-x$	$+x$	$+x$
Equil	$0.15 - x$	$+x$	$0.10 + x$

$$K_a = \frac{[H_3O^+][C_7H_5O_2^-]}{[HC_7H_5O_2]} = 6.5 \times 10^{-5} = \frac{x(0.10 + x)}{0.15 - x}$$ Assume that x is small ($x \ll 0.10 < 0.15$), so

$\dfrac{x(0.10 + \cancel{x})}{0.15 - \cancel{x}} = 6.5 \times 10^{-5} = \dfrac{x(0.10)}{0.15}$ and $x = 9.\underset{\text{.}}{7}5 \times 10^{-5}\,M = [H_3O^+]$. Then

$\% \text{ ionization} = \dfrac{[H_3O^+]_{equil}}{[HC_7H_5O_2]_0} \times 100\% = \dfrac{9.\underset{\text{.}}{7}5 \times 10^{-5}}{0.15} \times 100\% = 0.065\%,$ which also confirms that the assumption is valid (because it is less than 5%). The percent ionization in the sodium benzoate solution is less than that in pure water because of the common ion effect. An increase in one of the products (benzoate ion) shifts the equilibrium to the left, so less acid dissociates.

Check: The units (%) are correct. The magnitude of the answer makes physical sense because the acid is weak, so the percent ionization is low. With a common ion present, the percent ionization decreases.

16.6 **Given:** 0.13 M $HCHO_2$ in pure water and in 0.11 M $KCHO_2$ **Find:** % ionization in both solutions
Other: $K_a(HCHO_2) = 1.8 \times 10^{-4}$
Conceptual Plan: pure water: M $HCHO_2$ → [H_3O^+] → % ionization then in $KCHO_2$ solution:

$$\text{ICE table} \quad \% \text{ ionization} = \frac{[H_3O^+]_{equil}}{[HCHO_2]_0} \times 100\%$$

M $KCHO_2$ → M CHO_2^- then M $HCHO_2$, M CHO_2^- → [H_3O^+] → % ionization

$KCHO_2(aq) \rightarrow K^+(aq) + CHO_2^-(aq)$ $\text{ICE table} \quad \% \text{ ionization} = \frac{[H_3O^+]_{equil}}{[HCHO_2]_0} \times 100\%$

Solution: in pure water:

$$HCHO_2(aq) + H_2O(l) \rightleftharpoons H_3O^+(aq) + CHO_2^-(aq)$$

	[$HCHO_2$]	[H_3O^+]	[CHO_2^-]
Initial	0.13	≈0.00	0.00
Change	$-x$	$+x$	$+x$
Equil	$0.13 - x$	$+x$	$+x$

$$K_a = \frac{[H_3O^+][CHO_2^-]}{[HCHO_2]} = 1.8 \times 10^{-4} = \frac{x^2}{0.13 - x}$$

Assume that x is small ($x \ll 0.10$), so $\dfrac{x^2}{0.13 - \cancel{x}} = 1.8 \times 10^{-4} = \dfrac{x^2}{0.13}$ and $x = 4.8374 \times 10^{-3}$ M $= [H_3O^+]$. Then

$$\% \text{ ionization} = \frac{[H_3O^+]_{equil}}{[HCHO_2]_0} \times 100\% = \frac{4.8374 \times 10^{-3}}{0.13} \times 100\% = 3.7\%, \text{ which also confirms that the assumption}$$

is valid (because it is less than 5%).
In $KCHO_2$ solution: Because one CHO_2^- ion is generated for each $KCHO_2$, [CHO_2^-] = 0.11 M CHO_2^-.

$$HCHO_2(aq) + H_2O(l) \rightleftharpoons H_3O^+(aq) + CHO_2^-(aq)$$

	[$HCHO_2$]	[H_3O^+]	[CHO_2^-]
Initial	0.13	≈0.00	0.11
Change	$-x$	$+x$	$+x$
Equil	$0.13 - x$	$+x$	$0.11 + x$

$$K_a = \frac{[H_3O^+][CHO_2^-]}{[HCHO_2]} = 1.8 \times 10^{-4} = \frac{x(0.11 + x)}{0.13 - x}$$

Assume that x is small ($x \ll 0.11 < 0.13$), so $\dfrac{x(0.11 + \cancel{x})}{0.13 - \cancel{x}} = 1.8 \times 10^{-4} = \dfrac{x(0.11)}{0.13}$ and $x = 2.1273 \times 10^{-4}$ M $= [H_3O^+]$.

Then % ionization $= \dfrac{[H_3O^+]_{equil}}{[HCHO_2]_0} \times 100\% = \dfrac{2.1273 \times 10^{-4}}{0.13} \times 100\% = 0.16\%$, which also confirms that the assumption is valid (because it is less than 5%). The percent ionization in the potassium formate solution is less than that in pure water because of the common ion effect. An increase in one of the products (formate ion) shifts the equilibrium to the left, so less acid dissociates.

Check: The units (%) are correct. The magnitude of the answer makes physical sense because the acid is weak, so the percent ionization is low. With a common ion present, the percent ionization decreases.

16.7 (a) **Given:** 0.15 M HF   **Find:** pH **Other:** $K_a(HF) = 3.5 \times 10^{-4}$
Conceptual Plan: M HF → [H_3O^+] → pH
$$\text{ICE table} \qquad pH = -\log[H_3O^+]$$

Solution:

$$HF(aq) + H_2O(l) \rightleftharpoons H_3O^+(aq) + F^-(aq)$$

	[HF]	[H₃O⁺]	[F⁻]
Initial	0.15	≈0.00	0.00
Change	−x	+x	+x
Equil	0.15 − x	+x	+x

$$K_a = \frac{[H_3O^+][F^-]}{[HF]} = 3.5 \times 10^{-4} = \frac{x^2}{0.15 - x} \text{ Assume that } x \text{ is small } (x \ll 0.15), \text{ so}$$

$$\frac{x^2}{0.15 - \cancel{x}} = 3.5 \times 10^{-4} = \frac{x^2}{0.15} \text{ and } x = 7.\underline{2}457 \times 10^{-3} \text{ M} = [H_3O^+]. \text{ Confirm that the}$$

assumption is valid. $\dfrac{7.\underline{2}457 \times 10^{-3}}{0.15} \times 100\% = 4.8\% < 5\%$, so the assumption is valid.

Finally, $pH = -\log[H_3O^+] = -\log(7.\underline{2}457 \times 10^{-3}) = 2.14$.

Check: The units (none) are correct. The magnitude of the answer makes physical sense because the pH should be greater than $-\log(0.15) = 0.82$ because this is a weak acid.

(b) **Given:** 0.15 M NaF **Find:** pH **Other:** $K_a(HF) = 3.5 \times 10^{-4}$

Conceptual Plan: M NaF → M F⁻ and K_a → K_b then M F⁻ → [OH⁻] → [H₃O⁺] → pH

$$NaF(aq) \rightarrow Na^+(aq) + F^-(aq) \qquad K_w = K_a K_b \qquad \text{ICE table} \qquad K_w = [H_3O^+][OH^-] \quad pH = -\log[H_3O^+]$$

Solution:

Because one F⁻ ion is generated for each NaF, [F⁻] = 0.15 M F⁻. Because $K_w = K_a K_b$, rearrange to solve for K_b.

$$K_b = \frac{K_w}{K_a} = \frac{1.0 \times 10^{-14}}{3.5 \times 10^{-4}} = 2.\underline{8}571 \times 10^{-11}$$

$$F^-(aq) + H_2O(l) \rightleftharpoons HF(aq) + OH^-(aq)$$

	[F⁻]	[HF]	[OH⁻]
Initial	0.15	0.00	≈0.00
Change	−x	+x	+x
Equil	0.15 − x	+x	+x

$$K_b = \frac{[HF][OH^-]}{[F^-]} = 2.\underline{8}571 \times 10^{-11} = \frac{x^2}{0.15 - x}$$

Assume that x is small $(x \ll 0.15)$, so $\dfrac{x^2}{0.15 - \cancel{x}} = 2.\underline{8}571 \times 10^{-11} = \dfrac{x^2}{0.15}$ and $x = 2.\underline{0}702 \times 10^{-6} \text{ M} = $ [OH⁻].

Confirm that the assumption is valid. $\dfrac{2.\underline{0}702 \times 10^{-6}}{0.15} \times 100\% = 0.0014\% < 5\%$, so the assumption is valid.

$$K_w = [H_3O^+][OH^-], \text{ so } [H_3O^+] = \frac{K_w}{[OH^-]} = \frac{1.0 \times 10^{-14}}{2.\underline{0}702 \times 10^{-6}} = 4.\underline{8}305 \times 10^{-9} \text{ M}.$$

Finally, $pH = -\log[H_3O^+] = -\log(4.\underline{8}305 \times 10^{-9}) = 8.32$.

Check: The units (none) are correct. The magnitude of the answer makes physical sense because the pH should be slightly basic because the fluoride ion is a very weak base.

(c) **Given:** 0.15 M HF and 0.15 M NaF **Find:** pH **Other:** $K_a(HF) = 3.5 \times 10^{-4}$

Conceptual Plan: M NaF → M F⁻ then M HF, M F⁻ → [H₃O⁺] → pH

$$NaF(aq) \rightarrow Na^+(aq) + F^-(aq) \qquad \text{ICE table} \qquad pH = -\log[H_3O^+]$$

Solution: Because one F⁻ ion is generated for each NaF, [F⁻] = 0.15 M F⁻.

$$HF(aq) + H_2O(l) \rightleftharpoons H_3O^+(aq) + F^-(aq)$$

	[HF]	**[H₃O⁺]**	**[F⁻]**
Initial	0.15	≈ 0.00	0.15
Change	$-x$	$+x$	$+x$
Equil	$0.15 - x$	$+x$	$0.15 + x$

$$K_a = \frac{[H_3O^+][F^-]}{[HF]} = 3.5 \times 10^{-4} = \frac{x(0.15 + x)}{0.15 - x}$$

Assume that x is small ($x \ll 0.15$), so

$$\frac{x(0.15 + \cancel{x})}{0.15 - \cancel{x}} = 3.5 \times 10^{-4} = \frac{x(0.15)}{0.15} \text{ and } x = 3.5 \times 10^{-4}\,M = [H_3O^+].$$

Confirm that the assumption is valid. $\dfrac{3.5 \times 10^{-4}}{0.15} \times 100\% = 0.23\% < 5\%$, so the assumption is valid.

Finally, pH $= -\log[H_3O^+] = -\log(3.5 \times 10^{-4}) = 3.46$.

Check: The units (none) are correct. The magnitude of the answer makes physical sense because the pH should be greater than that in part (a) (2.14) because of the common ion effect suppressing the dissociation of the weak acid.

16.8   (a)   **Given:** 0.18 M CH₃NH₂   **Find:** pH   **Other:** $K_b(CH_3NH_2) = 4.4 \times 10^{-4}$
Conceptual Plan: M CH₃NH₃ → [OH⁻] → [H₃O⁺] → pH

ICE table $K_w = [H_3O^+][OH^-]$ pH $= -\log[H_3O^+]$

Solution:

$$CH_3NH_2(aq) + H_2O(l) \rightleftharpoons CH_3NH_3^+(aq) + OH^-(aq)$$

	[CH₃NH₂]	**[CH₃NH₃⁺]**	**[OH⁻]**
Initial	0.18	0.00	≈ 0.00
Change	$-x$	$+x$	$+x$
Equil	$0.18 - x$	$+x$	$+x$

$$K_b = \frac{[CH_3NH_3^+][OH^-]}{[CH_3NH_2]} = 4.4 \times 10^{-4} = \frac{x^2}{0.18 - x}$$

Assume that x is small ($x \ll 0.18$), so $\dfrac{x^2}{0.18 - \cancel{x}} = 4.4 \times 10^{-4} = \dfrac{x^2}{0.18}$ and $x = 8.\underline{8}994 \times 10^{-3}\,M = [OH^-]$.

Confirm that the assumption is valid $\dfrac{8.\underline{8}994 \times 10^{-3}}{0.18} \times 100\% = 4.9\% < 5\%$, so the assumption is valid.

$$K_w = [H_3O^+][OH^-], \text{ so } [H_3O^+] = \frac{K_w}{[OH^-]} = \frac{1.0 \times 10^{-14}}{8.8994 \times 10^{-3}} = 1.\underline{1}237 \times 10^{-12}\,M.$$

Finally, pH $= -\log[H_3O^+] = -\log(1.\underline{1}237 \times 10^{-12}) = 11.95$.

Check: The units (none) are correct. The magnitude of the answer makes physical sense because the pH should be less than $14 + \log(0.18) = 13.3$ because this is a weak base.

(b)   **Given:** 0.18 M CH₃NH₃Cl   **Find:** pH   **Other:** $K_b(CH_3NH_2) = 4.4 \times 10^{-4}$
Conceptual Plan: M CH₃NH₃Cl → M CH₃NH₃⁺ and K_b → K_a then M CH₃NH₃⁺ → [H₃O⁺] → pH

$CH_3NH_3Cl(aq) \rightarrow CH_3NH_3^+(aq) + Cl^-(aq)$ $K_w = K_a K_b$ ICE table   pH $= -\log[H_3O^+]$

Solution: Because one CH₃NH₃⁺ ion is generated for each CH₃NH₃Cl, $[CH_3NH_3^+] = 0.18$ M CH₃NH₃⁺.

Because $K_w = K_a K_b$, rearrange to solve for K_a. $K_a = \dfrac{K_w}{K_b} = \dfrac{1.0 \times 10^{-14}}{4.4 \times 10^{-4}} = 2.\underline{2}727 \times 10^{-11}$

$$CH_3NH_3^+(aq) + H_2O(l) \rightleftharpoons H_3O^+(aq) + CH_3NH_2(aq)$$

	$[CH_3NH_3^+]$	$[H_3O^+]$	$[CH_3NH_2]$
Initial	0.18	≈ 0.00	0.00
Change	$-x$	$+x$	$+x$
Equil	$0.18 - x$	$+x$	$+x$

$K_a = \dfrac{[H_3O^+][CH_3NH_2]}{[CH_3NH_3^+]} = 2.\underline{2}727 \times 10^{-11} = \dfrac{x^2}{0.18 - x}$. Assume that x is small ($x \ll 0.18$), so

$\dfrac{x^2}{0.18 - \cancel{x}} = 2.\underline{2}727 \times 10^{-11} = \dfrac{x^2}{0.18}$ and $x = 2.\underline{0}226 \times 10^{-6}$ M $= [H_3O^+]$.

Confirm that the assumption is valid $\dfrac{2.\underline{0}226 \times 10^{-6}}{0.18} \times 100\% = 0.0012\% < 5\%$, so the assumption is valid.

Finally, pH $= -\log[H_3O^+] = -\log(2.\underline{0}226 \times 10^{-6}) = 5.69$.

Check: The units (none) are correct. The magnitude of the answer makes physical sense because the pH should be slightly acidic because the methylammonium cation is a very weak acid.

(c)   **Given:** 0.18 M CH_3NH_2 and 0.18 M CH_3NH_3Cl **Find:** pH **Other:** $K_b(CH_3NH_2) = 4.4 \times 10^{-4}$
Conceptual Plan: M $CH_3NH_3Cl \rightarrow$ M $CH_3NH_3^+$ then

$$CH_3NH_3Cl(aq) \rightarrow CH_3NH_3^+(aq) + Cl^-(aq)$$

M CH_3NH_2, M $CH_3NH_3^+ \rightarrow [OH^-] \rightarrow [H_3O^+] \rightarrow$ pH

ICE table $K_w = [H_3O^+][OH^-]$ pH $= -\log[H_3O^+]$

Solution: Because one $CH_3NH_3^+$ ion is generated for each CH_3NH_3Cl, $[CH_3NH_3^+] = 0.18$ M $CH_3NH_3^+$.

$$CH_3NH_2(aq) + H_2O(l) \rightleftharpoons CH_3NH_3^+(aq) + OH^-(aq)$$

	$[CH_3NH_2]$	$[CH_3NH_3^+]$	$[OH^-]$
Initial	0.18	0.18	≈ 0.00
Change	$-x$	$+x$	$+x$
Equil	$0.18 - x$	$0.18 + x$	$+x$

$K_b = \dfrac{[CH_3NH_3^+][OH^-]}{[CH_3NH_2]} = 4.4 \times 10^{-4} = \dfrac{(0.18 + x)x}{0.18 - x}$ Assume that x is small ($x \ll 0.18$), so

$\dfrac{(0.18 + \cancel{x})x}{0.18 - \cancel{x}} = 4.4 \times 10^{-4} = \dfrac{(0.18)x}{0.18}$ and $x = 4.4 \times 10^{-4}$ M $= [OH^-]$.

Confirm that the assumption is valid $\dfrac{4.4 \times 10^{-4}}{0.18} \times 100\% = 0.24\% < 5\%$, so the assumption is valid.

$K_w = [H_3O^+][OH^-]$, so $[H_3O^+] = \dfrac{K_w}{[OH^-]} = \dfrac{1.0 \times 10^{-14}}{4.4 \times 10^{-4}} = 2.\underline{2}727 \times 10^{-11}$ M.

Finally, pH $= -\log[H_3O^+] = -\log(2.\underline{2}727 \times 10^{-11}) = 10.64$.

Check: The units (none) are correct. The magnitude of the answer makes physical sense because the pH should be less than $14 + \log(0.18) = 13.3$ because this is a weak base and there is a common ion effect.

16.9   When an acid (such as HCl) is added, it will react with the conjugate base of the buffer system as follows: $HCl + NaC_2H_3O_2 \rightarrow HC_2H_3O_2 + NaCl$. When a base (such as NaOH) is added, it will react with the weak acid of the buffer system as follows: $NaOH + HC_2H_3O_2 \rightarrow H_2O + NaC_2H_3O_2$. The reaction generates the other buffer system component.

16.10   When an acid (such as HCl) is added, it will react with the conjugate base of the buffer system as follows: $HCl + NH_3 \rightarrow NH_4Cl$. When a base (such as NaOH) is added, it will react with the weak acid of the buffer system as follows: $NaOH + NH_4Cl \rightarrow H_2O + NH_3 + NaCl$. The reaction generates the other buffer system component.

16.11   (a)   **Given:** 0.15 M $HCHO_2$ and 0.10 M $NaCHO_2$ **Find:** pH   **Other:** $K_a(HCHO_2) = 1.8 \times 10^{-4}$
          Conceptual Plan: Identify acid and base components then M $NaCHO_2 \rightarrow$ M $CHO_2^- $ then

acid = $HCHO_2$ base = CHO_2^- $NaCHO_2(aq) \rightarrow Na^+(aq) + CHO_2^-(aq)$

          K_a**, M $HCHO_2$, M $CHO_2^- \rightarrow$ pH.**

$pH = pK_a + \log \dfrac{[\text{base}]}{[\text{acid}]}$

          Solution: Acid = $HCHO_2$, so [acid] = $[HCHO_2]$ = 0.15 M. Base = CHO_2^-. Because one CHO_2^- ion is generated for each $NaCHO_2$, $[CHO_2^-]$ = 0.10 M CHO_2^- = [base]. Then

$$pH = pK_a + \log \frac{[\text{base}]}{[\text{acid}]} = -\log(1.8 \times 10^{-4}) + \log \frac{0.10 \text{ M}}{0.15 \text{ M}} = 3.57.$$

          Note that to use the Henderson–Hasselbalch equation, the assumption that x is small must be valid. This was confirmed in Problem 16.3.

          Check: The units (none) are correct. The magnitude of the answer makes physical sense because the pH should be less than the pK_a of the acid because there is more acid than base. The answer agrees with Problem 16.3.

     (b)   **Given:** 0.12 M NH_3 and 0.18 M NH_4Cl **Find:** pH   **Other:** $K_b(NH_3) = 1.76 \times 10^{-5}$
          Conceptual Plan: Identify acid and base components then M $NH_4Cl \rightarrow$ M NH_4^+ and $K_b \rightarrow pK_b \rightarrow pK_a$

acid = NH_4^+ base = NH_3 $NH_4Cl(aq) \rightarrow NH_4^+(aq) + Cl^-(aq)$ $pK_b = -\log K_b$ $14 = pK_a + pK_b$

          then pK_a, M NH_3, M $NH_4^+ \rightarrow$ pH.

$pH = pK_a + \log \dfrac{[\text{base}]}{[\text{acid}]}$

          Solution: Base = NH_3, [base] = $[NH_3]$ = 0.12 M. Acid = NH_4^+. Because one NH_4^+ ion is generated for each NH_4Cl, $[NH_4^+]$ = 0.18 M NH_4^+ = [acid].
          Because $K_b(NH_3) = 1.76 \times 10^{-5}$, $pK_b = -\log K_b = -\log(1.76 \times 10^{-5}) = 4.75$. Because $14 = pK_a + pK_b$,

$$pK_a = 14 - pK_b = 14 - 4.75 = 9.25. \text{ Then } pH = pK_a + \log \frac{[\text{base}]}{[\text{acid}]} = 9.25 + \log \frac{0.12 \text{ M}}{0.18 \text{ M}} = 9.07.$$

          Note that to use the Henderson–Hasselbalch equation, the assumption that x is small must be valid. This was confirmed in Problem 16.3.

          Check: The units (none) are correct. The magnitude of the answer makes physical sense because the pH should be less than the pK_a of the acid because there is more acid than base. The answer agrees with Problem 16.3 within the error of the value.

16.12   (a)   **Given:** 0.175 M $HC_2H_3O_2$ and 0.110 M $KC_2H_3O_2$ **Find:** pH   **Other:** $K_a(HC_2H_3O_2) = 1.8 \times 10^{-5}$
          Conceptual Plan: Identify acid and base components then M $KC_2H_3O_2 \rightarrow$ M $C_2H_3O_2^-$ then

acid = $HC_2H_3O_2$ base = $C_2H_3O_2^-$ $KC_2H_3O_2(aq) \rightarrow K^+(aq) + C_2H_3O_2^-(aq)$

          M $HC_2H_3O_2$, M $C_2H_3O_2^- \rightarrow$ pH.

$pH = pK_a + \log \dfrac{[\text{base}]}{[\text{acid}]}$

          Solution: Acid = $HC_2H_3O_2$, so [acid] = $[HC_2H_3O_2]$ = 0.175 M. Base = $C_2H_3O_2^-$. Because one $C_2H_3O_2^-$ ion is generated for each $KC_2H_3O_2$, $[C_2H_3O_2^-]$ = 0.110 M $C_2H_3O_2^-$ = [base]. Then

$$pH = pK_a + \log \frac{[\text{base}]}{[\text{acid}]} = -\log(1.8 \times 10^{-5}) + \log \frac{0.110 \text{ M}}{0.175 \text{ M}} = 4.54.$$

          Note that to use the Henderson–Hasselbalch equation, the assumption that x is small must be valid. This was confirmed in Problem 16.4.

          Check: The units (none) are correct. The magnitude of the answer makes physical sense because the pH should be less than the pK_a of the acid because there is more acid than base. The answer agrees with Problem 16.4.

     (b)   **Given:** 0.195 M CH_3NH_2 and 0.105 M CH_3NH_3Br **Find:** pH   **Other:** $K_b(CH_3NH_2) = 4.4 \times 10^{-4}$
          Conceptual Plan: Identify acid and base components then M $CH_3NH_3Br \rightarrow$ M $CH_3NH_3^+$ and

acid = $CH_3NH_3^+$ base = CH_3NH_2 $CH_3NH_3Br(aq) \rightarrow CH_3NH_3^+(aq) + Br^-(aq)$

          $K_b \rightarrow pK_b \rightarrow pK_a$ **then pK_a, M NH_3, M $NH_4^+ \rightarrow$ pH.**

$pK_b = -\log K_b$ $14 = pK_a + pK_b$ $pH = pK_a + \log \dfrac{[\text{base}]}{[\text{acid}]}$

Solution: Base $= CH_3NH_2$, so $[\text{base}] = [CH_3NH_2] = 0.195$ M. Acid $= CH_3NH_3^+$. Because one $CH_3NH_3^+$ ion is generated for each CH_3NH_3Br, $[CH_3NH_3^+] = 0.105$ M $CH_3NH_3^+ = [\text{acid}]$.
Because $K_b(CH_3NH_2) = 4.4 \times 10^{-4}$, $pK_b = -\log K_b = -\log(4.4 \times 10^{-4}) = 3.36$.
Because $14 = pK_a + pK_b$, $pK_a = 14 - pK_b = 14 - 3.36 = 10.64$. Then

$$pH = pK_a + \log \frac{[\text{base}]}{[\text{acid}]} = 10.64 + \log \frac{0.195 \text{ M}}{0.105 \text{ M}} = 10.91.$$

Note that to use the Henderson–Hasselbalch equation, the assumption that x is small must be valid. This was confirmed in Problem 16.4.

Check: The units (none) are correct. The magnitude of the answer makes physical sense because the pH should be greater than the pK_a of the acid because there is more base than acid. The answer agrees with Problem 16.4.

16.13 (a) **Given:** 0.125 M HClO and 0.150 M KClO **Find:** pH **Other:** $K_a(\text{HClO}) = 2.9 \times 10^{-8}$
Conceptual Plan: Identify acid and base components then M KClO $\rightarrow$ M ClO$^-$ then

acid = HClO   base = ClO$^-$ $KClO(aq) \rightarrow K^+(aq) + ClO^-(aq)$

M HClO, M ClO$^-$ $\rightarrow$ pH.

$pH = pK_a + \log \frac{[\text{base}]}{[\text{acid}]}$

Solution: Acid $=$ HClO, so $[\text{acid}] = [\text{HClO}] = 0.125$ M. Base $=$ ClO$^-$. Because one ClO$^-$ ion is generated for each KClO, $[\text{ClO}^-] = 0.150$ M ClO$^- = [\text{base}]$. Then

$$pH = pK_a + \log \frac{[\text{base}]}{[\text{acid}]} = -\log(2.9 \times 10^{-8}) + \log \frac{0.150 \text{ M}}{0.125 \text{ M}} = 7.62.$$

Check: The units (none) are correct. The magnitude of the answer makes physical sense because the pH should be greater than the pK_a of the acid because there is more base than acid.

(b) **Given:** 0.175 M $C_2H_5NH_2$ and 0.150 M $C_2H_5NH_3Br$ **Find:** pH **Other:** $K_b(C_2H_5NH_2) = 5.6 \times 10^{-4}$
Conceptual Plan: Identify acid and base components then M $C_2H_5NH_3Br \rightarrow$ M $C_2H_5NH_3^+$ and

acid = $C_2H_5NH_3^+$ base = $C_2H_5NH_2$ $C_2H_5NH_3Br(aq) \rightarrow C_2H_5NH_3^+(aq) + Br^-(aq)$

$K_b \rightarrow pK_b \rightarrow pK_a$ **than** pK_a**, M $C_2H_5NH_2$, M $C_2H_5NH_3^+ \rightarrow$ pH.**

$pK_b = -\log K_b$ $14 = pK_a + pK_b$ $pH = pK_a + \log \frac{[\text{base}]}{[\text{acid}]}$

Solution:
Base $= C_2H_5NH_2$, so $[\text{base}] = [C_2H_5NH_2] = 0.175$ M. Acid $= C_2H_5NH_3^+$. Because one $C_2H_5NH_3^+$ ion is generated for each $C_2H_5NH_3Br$, $[C_2H_5NH_3^+] = 0.150$ M $= [\text{acid}]$.
Because $K_b(C_2H_5NH_2) = 5.6 \times 10^{-4}$, $pK_b = -\log K_b = -\log(5.6 \times 10^{-4}) = 3.25$.
Because $14 = pK_a + pK_b$, $pK_a = 14 - pK_b = 14 - 3.25 = 10.75$. Then

$$pH = pK_a + \log \frac{[\text{base}]}{[\text{acid}]} = 10.75 + \log \frac{0.175 \text{ M}}{0.150 \text{ M}} = 10.82.$$

Check: The units (none) are correct. The magnitude of the answer makes physical sense because the pH should be greater than the pK_a of the acid because there is more base than acid.

(c) **Given:** 10.0 g $HC_2H_3O_2$ and 10.0 g $NaC_2H_3O_2$ in 150.0 mL solution **Find:** pH
Other: $K_a(HC_2H_3O_2) = 1.8 \times 10^{-5}$
Conceptual Plan: Identify acid and base components then mL $\rightarrow$ L and g $HC_2H_3O_2 \rightarrow$ mol $HC_2H_3O_2$

acid = $HC_2H_3O_2$ base = $C_2H_3O_2^-$ $\frac{1 \text{ L}}{1000 \text{ mL}}$ $\frac{1 \text{ mol } HC_2H_3O_2}{60.05 \text{ g } HC_2H_3O_2}$

then mol $HC_2H_3O_2$, L $\rightarrow$ M $HC_2H_3O_2$ and g $NaC_2H_3O_2 \rightarrow$ mol $NaC_2H_3O_2$ then

$M = \frac{\text{mol}}{\text{L}}$ $\frac{1 \text{ mol } NaC_2H_3O_2}{82.03 \text{ g } NaC_2H_3O_2}$

mol $NaC_2H_3O_2$, L $\rightarrow$ M $NaC_2H_3O_2$ $\rightarrow$ M $C_2H_3O_2^-$ then M $HC_2H_3O_2$, M $C_2H_3O_2^-$ $\rightarrow$ pH.

$M = \frac{\text{mol}}{\text{L}}$ $NaC_2H_3O_2(aq) \rightarrow Na^+(aq) + C_2H_3O_2^-(aq)$ $pH = pK_a + \log \frac{[\text{base}]}{[\text{acid}]}$

Solution: $150.0 \text{ mL} \times \dfrac{1 \text{ L}}{1000 \text{ mL}} = 0.1500$ L and

$$10.0 \text{ g HC}_2\text{H}_3\text{O}_2 \times \frac{1 \text{ mol HC}_2\text{H}_3\text{O}_2}{60.05 \text{ g HC}_2\text{H}_3\text{O}_2} = 0.166528 \text{ mol HC}_2\text{H}_3\text{O}_2$$

$$\text{then M} = \frac{\text{mol}}{\text{L}} = \frac{0.166528 \text{ mol HC}_2\text{H}_3\text{O}_2}{0.1500 \text{ L}} = 1.11019 \text{ M HC}_2\text{H}_3\text{O}_2 \text{ and}$$

$$10.0 \text{ g NaC}_2\text{H}_3\text{O}_2 \times \frac{1 \text{ mol NaC}_2\text{H}_3\text{O}_2}{82.03 \text{ g NaC}_2\text{H}_3\text{O}_2} = 0.121907 \text{ mol NaC}_2\text{H}_3\text{O}_2 \text{ then}$$

$$\text{M} = \frac{\text{mol}}{\text{L}} = \frac{0.121907 \text{ mol NaC}_2\text{H}_3\text{O}_2}{0.1500 \text{ L}} = 0.812713 \text{ M NaC}_2\text{H}_3\text{O}_2. \text{ Acid} = \text{HC}_2\text{H}_3\text{O}_2, \text{ so [acid]} =$$

$[\text{HC}_2\text{H}_3\text{O}_2] = 1.11019$ M and base $= \text{C}_2\text{H}_3\text{O}_2^-$. Because one $\text{C}_2\text{H}_3\text{O}_2^-$ ion is generated for each $\text{NaC}_2\text{H}_3\text{O}_2$, $[\text{C}_2\text{H}_3\text{O}_2^-] = 0.812713$ M $\text{C}_2\text{H}_3\text{O}_2^- =$ [base]. Then

$$\text{pH} = \text{p}K_a + \log \frac{[\text{base}]}{[\text{acid}]} = -\log(1.8 \times 10^{-5}) + \log \frac{0.812713 \text{ M}}{1.11019 \text{ M}} = 4.61.$$

Check: The units (none) are correct. The magnitude of the answer makes physical sense because the pH should be less than the $\text{p}K_a$ of the acid because there is more acid than base.

16.14 (a) **Given:** 0.155 M $\text{HC}_3\text{H}_5\text{O}_2$ (propanoic acid) and 0.110 M $\text{KC}_3\text{H}_5\text{O}_2$ (potassium propanoate) **Find:** pH
Other: $K_a(\text{HC}_3\text{H}_5\text{O}_2) = 1.3 \times 10^{-5}$
Conceptual Plan: Identify acid and base components then M $\text{KC}_3\text{H}_5\text{O}_2 \to$ M $\text{C}_3\text{H}_5\text{O}_2^-$ then

$$\text{acid} = \text{HC}_3\text{H}_5\text{O}_2 \quad \text{base} = \text{C}_3\text{H}_5\text{O}_2^- \quad \text{KC}_3\text{H}_5\text{O}_2(aq) \to \text{K}^+(aq) + \text{C}_3\text{H}_5\text{O}_2^-(aq)$$

M $\text{HC}_3\text{H}_5\text{O}_2$, M $\text{C}_3\text{H}_5\text{O}_2^- \to$ pH.

$$\text{pH} = \text{p}K_a + \log \frac{[\text{base}]}{[\text{acid}]}$$

Solution: Acid $= \text{HC}_3\text{H}_5\text{O}_2$, so [acid] $= [\text{HC}_3\text{H}_5\text{O}_2] = 0.155$ M. Base $= \text{C}_3\text{H}_5\text{O}_2^-$. Because one $\text{C}_3\text{H}_5\text{O}_2^-$ ion is generated for each $\text{KC}_3\text{H}_5\text{O}_2$, $[\text{C}_3\text{H}_5\text{O}_2^-] = 0.110$ M $\text{C}_3\text{H}_5\text{O}_2^- =$ [base]. Then

$$\text{pH} = \text{p}K_a + \log \frac{[\text{base}]}{[\text{acid}]} = -\log(1.3 \times 10^{-5}) + \log \frac{0.110 \text{ M}}{0.155 \text{ M}} = 4.74.$$

Check: The units (none) are correct. The magnitude of the answer makes physical sense because the pH should be less than the $\text{p}K_a$ of the acid because there is more acid than base.

(b) **Given:** 0.15 M $\text{C}_5\text{H}_5\text{N}$ and 0.10 M $\text{C}_5\text{H}_5\text{NHCl}$ **Find:** pH **Other:** $K_b(\text{C}_5\text{H}_5\text{N}) = 1.7 \times 10^{-9}$
Conceptual Plan: Identify acid and base components then M $\text{C}_5\text{H}_5\text{NHCl} \to$ M $\text{C}_5\text{H}_5\text{NH}^+$ and

$$\text{acid} = \text{C}_5\text{H}_5\text{NH}^+ \quad \text{base} = \text{C}_5\text{H}_5\text{N} \quad \text{C}_5\text{H}_5\text{NHCl}(aq) \to \text{C}_5\text{H}_5\text{NH}^+(aq) + \text{Cl}^-(aq)$$

$K_b \to \text{p}K_b \to \text{p}K_a$ **then** $\text{p}K_a$, M $\text{C}_5\text{H}_5\text{N}$, M $\text{C}_5\text{H}_5\text{NH}^+ \to$ **pH.**

$$\text{p}K_b = -\log K_b \quad 14 = \text{p}K_a + \text{p}K_b \qquad \text{pH} = \text{p}K_a + \log \frac{[\text{base}]}{[\text{acid}]}$$

Solution: Base $= \text{C}_5\text{H}_5\text{N}$, so [base] $= [\text{C}_5\text{H}_5\text{N}] = 0.15$ M. Acid $= \text{C}_5\text{H}_5\text{NH}^+$.
Because one $\text{C}_5\text{H}_5\text{NH}^+$ ion is generated for each $\text{C}_5\text{H}_5\text{NHCl}$, $[\text{C}_5\text{H}_5\text{NH}^+] = 0.10$ M.
Because $K_b(\text{C}_5\text{H}_5\text{N}) = 1.7 \times 10^{-9}$, $\text{p}K_b = -\log K_b = -\log(1.7 \times 10^{-9}) = 8.77$. Because $14 = \text{p}K_a + \text{p}K_b$,

$$\text{p}K_a = 14 - \text{p}K_b = 14 - 8.77 = 5.23. \text{ Then pH} = \text{p}K_a + \log \frac{[\text{base}]}{[\text{acid}]} = 5.23 + \log \frac{0.15 \text{ M}}{0.10 \text{ M}} = 5.41.$$

Check: The units (none) are correct. The magnitude of the answer makes physical sense because the pH should be greater than the $\text{p}K_a$ of the acid because there is more base than acid.

(c) **Given:** 15.0 g HF and 25.0 g NaF in 125 mL solution **Find:** pH **Other:** $K_a(\text{HF}) = 3.5 \times 10^{-4}$
Conceptual Plan: Identify acid and base components then mL $\to$ L and g HF $\to$ mol HF

$$\text{acid} = \text{HF} \quad \text{base} = \text{F}^- \qquad \frac{1 \text{ L}}{1000 \text{ mL}} \qquad \frac{1 \text{ mol HF}}{20.01 \text{ g HF}}$$

then mol HF, L $\to$ M HF and g NaF $\to$ mol NaF then

$$\text{M} = \frac{\text{mol}}{\text{L}} \qquad \frac{1 \text{ mol NaF}}{41.99 \text{ g NaF}}$$

mol NaF, L $\to$ M NaF $\to$ M F^- then M HF, M F^- pH.

$$\text{M} = \frac{\text{mol}}{\text{L}} \quad \text{NaF}(aq) \to \text{Na}^+(aq) + \text{F}^-(aq) \qquad \text{pH} = \text{p}K_a + \log \frac{[\text{base}]}{[\text{acid}]}$$

Solution: $125 \text{ mL} \times \dfrac{1 \text{ L}}{1000 \text{ mL}} = 0.125 \text{ L}$ and $15.0 \text{ g HF} \times \dfrac{1 \text{ mol HF}}{20.01 \text{ g HF}} = 0.749625 \text{ mol HF}$. Then

$$M = \frac{\text{mol}}{\text{L}} = \frac{0.749625 \text{ mol HF}}{0.125 \text{ L}} = 5.997 \text{ M HF} \text{ and } 25.0 \text{ g NaF} \times \frac{1 \text{ mol NaF}}{41.99 \text{ g NaF}} = 0.595380 \text{ mol NaF}.$$

Then $M = \dfrac{\text{mol}}{\text{L}} = \dfrac{0.595380 \text{ mol NaF}}{0.125 \text{ L}} = 4.76304 \text{ M NaF}$. Acid $=$ HF, so $[\text{acid}] = [\text{HF}] = 5.997$ M

and base $= F^-$. Because one F^- ion is generated for each NaF, $[F^-] = 4.76304 \text{ M } F^- = [\text{base}]$. Then

$$pH = pK_a + \log \frac{[\text{base}]}{[\text{acid}]} = -\log(3.5 \times 10^{-4}) + \log \frac{4.76304 \text{ M}}{5.997 \text{ M}} = 3.36.$$

Check: The units (none) are correct. The magnitude of the answer makes physical sense because the pH should be less than the pK_a of the acid because there is more acid than base.

16.15   (a)   **Given:** 50.0 mL of 0.15 M $HCHO_2$ and 75.0 mL of 0.13 M $NaCHO_2$ **Find:** pH
        Other: $K_a(HCHO_2) = 1.8 \times 10^{-4}$
        Conceptual Plan: Identify acid and base components then mL $HCHO_2$, mL $NaCHO_2$ → total mL then

$$\text{acid} = HCHO_2 \qquad \text{base} = CHO_2^- \qquad\qquad \text{total mL} = \text{mL } HCHO_2 + \text{mL } NaCHO_2$$

        mL $HCHO_2$, M $HCHO_2$, total mL → buffer M $HCHO_2$ and

$$M_1 V_1 = M_2 V_2$$

        mL $NaCHO_2$, M $NaCHO_2$, total mL → buffer M $NaCHO_2$ → buffer M CHO_2^- then

$$M_1 V_1 = M_2 V_2 \qquad NaCHO_2(aq) \rightarrow Na^+(aq) + CHO_2^-(aq)$$

        K_a, M $HCHO_2$, M CHO_2^- → pH.

$$pH = pK_a + \log \frac{[\text{base}]}{[\text{acid}]}$$

        Solution: total mL $=$ mL $HCHO_2 +$ mL $NaCHO_2 = 50.0 \text{ mL} + 75.0 \text{ mL} = 125.0 \text{ mL}$. Then because $M_1 V_1 = M_2 V_2$, rearrange to solve for M_2.

$$M_2 = \frac{M_1 V_1}{V_2} = \frac{(0.15 \text{ M})(50.0 \text{ mL})}{125.0 \text{ mL}} = 0.060 \text{ M } HCHO_2 \text{ and}$$

$$M_2 = \frac{M_1 V_1}{V_2} = \frac{(0.13 \text{ M})(75.0 \text{ mL})}{125.0 \text{ mL}} = 0.078 \text{ M } NaCHO_2. \text{ Acid} = HCHO_2, \text{ so } [\text{acid}] = [HCHO_2] =$$

0.060 M. Base $= CHO_2^-$. Because one CHO_2^- ion is generated for each $NaCHO_2$, $[CHO_2^-] =$

$0.078 \text{ M } CHO_2^- = [\text{base}]$. Then $pH = pK_a + \log \dfrac{[\text{base}]}{[\text{acid}]} = -\log(1.8 \times 10^{-4}) + \log \dfrac{0.078 \text{ M}}{0.060 \text{ M}} = 3.86.$

        Check: The units (none) are correct. The magnitude of the answer makes physical sense because the pH should be greater than the pK_a of the acid because there is more base than acid.

     (b)   **Given:** 125.0 mL of 0.10 M NH_3 and 250.0 mL of 0.10 M NH_4Cl **Find:** pH
        Other: $K_b(NH_3) = 1.76 \times 10^{-5}$
        Conceptual Plan: Identify acid and base components then mL NH_3, mL NH_4Cl → total mL then

$$\text{acid} = NH_4^+ \text{ base} = NH_3 \qquad\qquad \text{total mL} = \text{mL } NH_3 + \text{mL } NH_4Cl$$

        mL NH_3, M NH_3, total mL → buffer M NH_3 and

$$M_1 V_1 = M_2 V_2$$

        mL NH_4Cl, M NH_4Cl, total mL → buffer M NH_4Cl → buffer M NH_4^+ and K_b → pK_b → pK_a then

$$M_1 V_1 = M_2 V_2 \qquad NH_4Cl(aq) \rightarrow NH_4^+(aq) + Cl^-(aq) \qquad pK_b = -\log K_b \quad 14 = pK_a + pK_b$$

        pK_a, M NH_3, M NH_4^+ → pH.

$$pH = pK_a + \log \frac{[\text{base}]}{[\text{acid}]}$$

        Solution: total mL $=$ mL $NH_3 +$ mL $NH_4Cl = 125.0 \text{ mL} + 250.0 \text{ mL} = 375.0 \text{ mL}$. Then because $M_1 V_1 = M_2 V_2$, rearrange to solve for M_2.

$$M_2 = \frac{M_1 V_1}{V_2} = \frac{(0.10 \text{ M})(125.0 \text{ mL})}{375.0 \text{ mL}} = 0.033333 \text{ M } NH_3 \text{ and}$$

$$M_2 = \frac{M_1 V_1}{V_2} = \frac{(0.10 \text{ M})(250.0 \text{ mL})}{375.0 \text{ mL}} = 0.066667 \text{ M NH}_4\text{Cl. Base} = \text{NH}_3, [\text{base}] = [\text{NH}_3] =$$

0.033333 M acid = NH_4^+. Because one NH_4^+ ion is generated for each NH_4Cl, $[\text{NH}_4^+]$ = 0.0666667 M NH_4^+ = [acid]. Because $K_b(\text{NH}_3) = 1.76 \times 10^{-5}$,

$pK_b = -\log K_b = -\log(1.76 \times 10^{-5}) = 4.75$. Because $14 = pK_a + pK_b$,

$$pK_a = 14 - pK_b = 14 - 4.75 = 9.25. \text{ Then pH} = pK_a + \log\frac{[\text{base}]}{[\text{acid}]} = 9.25 + \log\frac{0.033333 \text{ M}}{0.066667 \text{ M}} = 8.95.$$

Check: The units (none) are correct. The magnitude of the answer makes physical sense because the pH should be less than the pK_a of the acid because there is more acid than base.

16.16   (a)   **Given:** 150.0 mL of 0.25 M HF and 225.0 mL of 0.30 M NaF   **Find:** pH

           Other: $K_a(\text{HF}) = 3.5 \times 10^{-4}$

           Conceptual Plan: Identify acid and base components then mL HF, mL NaF → total mL then

                          acid = HF base = F^- total mL = mL HF + mL NaF

           mL HF, M HF, total mL → buffer M HF and

                          $M_1 V_1 = M_2 V_2$

           mL NaF, M NaF, total mL → buffer M NaF → buffer M F^-

                          $M_1 V_1 = M_2 V_2$ $\text{NaF}(aq) \rightarrow \text{Na}^+(aq) + \text{F}^-(aq)$

           then K_a, M HF, M F^- → pH.

                     $pH = pK_a + \log\frac{[\text{base}]}{[\text{acid}]}$

           Solution: total mL = mL HF + mL NaF = 150.0 mL + 225.0 mL = 375.0 mL. Then because

           $M_1 V_1 = M_2 V_2$, rearrange to solve for M_2. $M_2 = \dfrac{M_1 V_1}{V_2} = \dfrac{(0.25 \text{ M})(150.0 \text{ mL})}{375.0 \text{ mL}} = 0.10 \text{ M HF and}$

$$M_2 = \frac{M_1 V_1}{V_2} = \frac{(0.30 \text{ M})(225.0 \text{ mL})}{375.0 \text{ mL}} = 0.18 \text{ M NaF. Acid} = \text{HF, so [acid]} = [\text{HF}] = 0.10 \text{ M. Base} = \text{F}^-.$$

           Because one F^- ion is generated for each NaF, $[\text{F}^-] = 0.18 \text{ M F}^-$ = [base]. Then

$$pH = pK_a + \log\frac{[\text{base}]}{[\text{acid}]} = -\log(3.5 \times 10^{-4}) + \log\frac{0.18 \text{ M}}{0.10 \text{ M}} = 3.71.$$

           Check: The units (none) are correct. The magnitude of the answer makes physical sense because the pH should be greater than the pK_a of the acid because there is more base than acid.

     (b)   **Given:** 175.0 mL of 0.10 M $\text{C}_2\text{H}_5\text{NH}_2$ and 275.0 mL of 0.20 M $\text{C}_2\text{H}_5\text{NH}_3\text{Cl}$ **Find:** pH

           Other: $K_b(\text{C}_2\text{H}_5\text{NH}_2) = 5.6 \times 10^{-4}$

           Conceptual Plan: Identify acid and base components then mL $\text{C}_2\text{H}_5\text{NH}_2$, mL $\text{C}_2\text{H}_5\text{NH}_3\text{Cl}$ → total mL

                    acid = $\text{C}_2\text{H}_5\text{NH}_3^+$ base = $\text{C}_2\text{H}_5\text{NH}_2$ total mL = mL $\text{C}_2\text{H}_5\text{NH}_2$ + mL $\text{C}_2\text{H}_5\text{NH}_3\text{Cl}$

           then mL $\text{C}_2\text{H}_5\text{NH}_2$, M $\text{C}_2\text{H}_5\text{NH}_2$, total mL → buffer M $\text{C}_2\text{H}_5\text{NH}_2$ and

                          $M_1 V_1 = M_2 V_2$

           mL $\text{C}_2\text{H}_5\text{NH}_3\text{Cl}$, M $\text{C}_2\text{H}_5\text{NH}_3\text{Cl}$, total mL → buffer M $\text{C}_2\text{H}_5\text{NH}_3\text{Cl}$ → buffer M $\text{C}_2\text{H}_5\text{NH}_3^+$ and

                          $M_1 V_1 = M_2 V_2$ $\text{C}_2\text{H}_5\text{NH}_3\text{Cl}(aq) \rightarrow \text{C}_2\text{H}_5\text{NH}_3^+(aq) + \text{Cl}^-(aq)$

           $K_b \rightarrow pK_b \rightarrow pK_a$ then pK_a, M $\text{C}_2\text{H}_5\text{NH}_2$, M $\text{C}_2\text{H}_5\text{NH}_3^+$ → pH.

            $pK_b = -\log K_b$ $14 = pK_a + pK_b$ $pH = pK_a + \log\frac{[\text{base}]}{[\text{acid}]}$

           Solution: total mL = mL $\text{C}_2\text{H}_5\text{NH}_2$ + mL $\text{C}_2\text{H}_5\text{NH}_3\text{Cl}$ = 175.0 mL + 275.0 mL = 450.0 mL. Then because $M_1 V_1 = M_2 V_2$, rearrange to solve for M_2.

$$M_2 = \frac{M_1 V_1}{V_2} = \frac{(0.10 \text{ M})(175.0 \text{ mL})}{450.0 \text{ mL}} = 0.038889 \text{ M C}_2\text{H}_5\text{NH}_2 \text{ and}$$

$$M_2 = \frac{M_1 V_1}{V_2} = \frac{(0.20 \text{ M})(275.0 \text{ mL})}{450.0 \text{ mL}} = 0.12222 \text{ M C}_2\text{H}_5\text{NH}_3\text{Cl. Base} = \text{C}_2\text{H}_5\text{NH}_2, \text{ so}$$

[base] = [C₂H₅NH₂] = 0.038889 M. Acid = $C_2H_5NH_3^+$. Because one $C_2H_5NH_3^+$ ion is generated for each $C_2H_5NH_3Cl$, $[C_2H_5NH_3^+] = 0.12222$ M $C_2H_5NH_3^+ = $ [acid]. Because $K_b(C_2H_5NH_2) = 5.6 \times 10^{-4}$, $pK_b = -\log K_b = -\log(5.6 \times 10^{-4}) = 3.25$. Because $14 = pK_a + pK_b$, $pK_a = 14 - pK_b = 14 - 3.25 = 10.75$. Then

$$pH = pK_a + \log \frac{[base]}{[acid]} = 10.75 + \log \frac{0.038889 \text{ M}}{0.12222 \text{ M}} = 10.25.$$

Check: The units (none) are correct. The magnitude of the answer makes physical sense because the pH should be less than the pK_a of the acid because there is more acid than base.

16.17   **Given:** NaF/HF buffer at pH = 4.00   **Find:** [NaF]/[HF]   **Other:** $K_a(HF) = 3.5 \times 10^{-4}$
Conceptual Plan: Identify acid and base components then pH, K_a → [NaF]/[HF].

$$\text{acid = HF} \qquad \text{base = F}^- \qquad pH = pK_a + \log \frac{[base]}{[acid]}$$

Solution: $pH = pK_a + \log \frac{[base]}{[acid]} = -\log(3.5 \times 10^{-4}) + \log \frac{[NaF]}{[HF]} = 4.00$. Solve for [NaF]/[HF].

$$\log \frac{[NaF]}{[HF]} = 4.00 - 3.46 = 0.54 \rightarrow \frac{[NaF]}{[HF]} = 10^{0.54} = 3.5.$$

Check: The units (none) are correct. The magnitude of the answer makes physical sense because the pH is greater than the pK_a of the acid; so there needs to be more base than acid.

16.18   **Given:** CH_3NH_2/CH_3NH_3Cl buffer at pH = 10.24   **Find:** [CH₃NH₂]/[CH₃NH₃Cl]
Other: $K_b(CH_3NH_2) = 4.4 \times 10^{-4}$
Conceptual Plan: Identify acid and base components and K_b → pK_b → pK_a then

$$\text{acid = CH}_3\text{NH}_3^+ \qquad \text{base = CH}_3\text{N} \qquad pK_b = -\log K_b \qquad 14 = pK_a + pK_b$$

pH, K_a → [CH₃NH₂]/[CH₃NH₃Cl].

$$pH = pK_a + \log \frac{[base]}{[acid]}$$

Solution: Because $K_b(CH_3NH_2) = 4.4 \times 10^{-4}$, $pK_b = -\log K_b = -\log(4.4 \times 10^{-4}) = 3.36$. Because $14 = pK_a + pK_b$, $pK_a = 14 - pK_b = 14 - 3.36 = 10.64$. Then

$$pH = pK_a + \log \frac{[base]}{[acid]} = 10.64 + \log \frac{[CH_3NH_2]}{[CH_3NH_3Cl]} = 10.24. \text{ Solve for [CH}_3\text{NH}_2]/[\text{CH}_3\text{NH}_3\text{Cl}].$$

$$\log \frac{[CH_3NH_2]}{[CH_3NH_3Cl]} = 10.24 - 10.64 = -0.40 \rightarrow \frac{[CH_3NH_2]}{[CH_3NH_3Cl]} = 10^{-0.40} = 0.40.$$

Check: The units (none) are correct. The magnitude of the answer makes physical sense because the pH is less than the pK_a of the acid; so there needs to be less base than acid.

16.19   **Given:** 150.0 mL buffer of 0.15 M benzoic acid at pH = 4.25   **Find:** mass sodium benzoate
Other: $K_a(HC_7H_5O_2) = 6.5 \times 10^{-5}$
Conceptual Plan: Identify acid and base components then pH, K_a, [HC₇H₅O₂] → [NaC₇H₅O₂]

$$\text{acid = HC}_7\text{H}_5\text{O}_2 \qquad \text{base = C}_7\text{H}_5\text{O}_2^- \qquad pH = pK_a + \log \frac{[base]}{[acid]}$$

mL → L then [NaC₇H₅O₂], L → mol NaC₇H₅O₂ → g NaC₇H₅O₂.

$$\frac{1 \text{ L}}{1000 \text{ mL}} \qquad M = \frac{mol}{L} \qquad \frac{144.11 \text{ g NaC}_7\text{H}_5\text{O}_2}{1 \text{ mol NaC}_7\text{H}_5\text{O}_2}$$

Solution: $pH = pK_a + \log \frac{[base]}{[acid]} = -\log(6.5 \times 10^{-5}) + \log \frac{[NaC_7H_5O_2]}{0.15 \text{ M}} = 4.25$. Solve for [NaC₇H₅O₂].

$$\log \frac{[NaC_7H_5O_2]}{0.15 \text{ M}} = 4.25 - 4.1870866 = 0.06291 \rightarrow \frac{[NaC_7H_5O_2]}{0.15 \text{ M}} = 10^{0.06291} = 1.1559 \rightarrow$$

$[NaC_7H_5O_2] = 0.17338$ M.

Convert to moles using $M = \frac{mol}{L}$.

$$\frac{0.17338 \text{ mol NaC}_7\text{H}_5\text{O}_2}{1 \text{ L}} \times 0.150 \text{ L} = 0.026007 \text{ mol NaC}_7\text{H}_5\text{O}_2 \times \frac{144.11 \text{ g NaC}_7\text{H}_5\text{O}_2}{1 \text{ mol NaC}_7\text{H}_5\text{O}_2} = 3.7 \text{ g NaC}_7\text{H}_5\text{O}_2.$$

Check: The units (g) are correct. The magnitude of the answer makes physical sense because the volume of solution is small and the concentration is low; so much less than a mole is needed.

16.20　**Given:** 2.55 L buffer of 0.155 M NH_3 at pH $= 9.55$　**Find:** mass ammonium chloride
　　　Other: $K_b(NH_3) = 1.76 \times 10^{-5}$
　　　Conceptual Plan: Identify acid and base components then $K_b \rightarrow pK_b \rightarrow pK_a$ **then**

$$\text{acid} = NH_4^+ \qquad \text{base} = NH_3 \qquad pK_b = -\log K_b \qquad 14 = pK_a + pK_b$$

　　　pH, K_a, [NH_3] $\rightarrow$ [NH_4Cl] then [NH_4Cl], L $\rightarrow$ mol NH_4Cl $\rightarrow$ g NH_4Cl.

$$pH = pK_a + \log \frac{[\text{base}]}{[\text{acid}]} \qquad\qquad M = \frac{\text{mol}}{L} \qquad\qquad \frac{53.49 \text{ g } NH_4Cl}{1 \text{ mol } NH_4Cl}$$

　　　Solution: Because $K_b(NH_3) = 1.76 \times 10^{-5}$, $pK_b = -\log K_b = -\log(1.76 \times 10^{-5}) = 4.75$.
　　　Because $14 = pK_a + pK_b$, $pK_a = 14 - pK_b = 14 - 4.75 = 9.25$. Then

$$pH = pK_a + \log \frac{[\text{base}]}{[\text{acid}]} = 9.25 + \log \frac{0.155 \text{ M}}{[NH_4Cl]} = 9.55. \text{ Solve for } [NH_4Cl].$$

$$\log \frac{0.155 \text{ M}}{[NH_4Cl]} = 9.55 - 9.25 = 0.30 \rightarrow \frac{0.155 \text{ M}}{[NH_4Cl]} = 10^{0.30} = 1.99526 \rightarrow [NH_4Cl] = 0.0776841 \text{ M. Convert to}$$

　　　moles using $M = \dfrac{\text{mol}}{L}$.

$$\frac{0.0776841 \text{ mol } NH_4Cl}{1 \text{ L}} \times 2.55 \text{ L} = 0.198094 \text{ mol } NH_4Cl \times \frac{53.49 \text{ g } NH_4Cl}{1 \text{ mol } NH_4Cl} = 11 \text{ g } NH_4Cl.$$

　　　Check: The units (g) are correct. The magnitude of the answer makes physical sense because the volume of solution is large and the concentration is low; so less than a mole is needed.

16.21　(a)　**Given:** 250.0 mL buffer of 0.250 M $HC_2H_3O_2$ and 0.250 M $NaC_2H_3O_2$　**Find:** initial pH
　　　　　Other: $K_a(HC_2H_3O_2) = 1.8 \times 10^{-5}$
　　　　　Conceptual Plan: Identify acid and base components then M $NaC_2H_3O_2 \rightarrow$ M $C_2H_3O_2^-$ **then**

$$\text{acid} = HC_2H_3O_2 \qquad \text{base} = C_2H_3O_2^- \qquad NaC_2H_3O_2(aq) \rightarrow Na^+(aq) + C_2H_3O_2^-(aq)$$

　　　　　M $HC_2H_3O_2$, M $C_2H_3O_2^- \rightarrow$ pH.

$$pH = pK_a + \log \frac{[\text{base}]}{[\text{acid}]}$$

　　　　　Solution: Acid $= HC_2H_3O_2$, so $[\text{acid}] = [HC_2H_3O_2] = 0.250$ M. Base $= C_2H_3O_2^-$. Because one
　　　　　$C_2H_3O_2^-$ ion is generated for each $NaC_2H_3O_2$, $[C_2H_3O_2^-] = 0.250$ M $C_2H_3O_2^- = [\text{base}]$. Then

$$pH = pK_a + \log \frac{[\text{base}]}{[\text{acid}]} = -\log(1.8 \times 10^{-5}) + \log \frac{0.250 \text{ M}}{0.250 \text{ M}} = 4.74.$$

　　　　　Check: The units (none) are correct. The magnitude of the answer makes physical sense because the pH is equal to the pK_a of the acid because there are equal amounts of acid and base.

　　　(b)　**Given:** 250.0 mL buffer of 0.250 M $HC_2H_3O_2$ and 0.250 M $NaC_2H_3O_2$, add 0.0050 mol HCl　**Find:** pH
　　　　　Other: $K_a(HC_2H_3O_2) = 1.8 \times 10^{-5}$
　　　　　Conceptual Plan: Part I: Stoichiometry:
　　　　　mL $\rightarrow$ L then [$NaC_2H_3O_2$], L $\rightarrow$ mol $NaC_2H_3O_2$ and [$HC_2H_3O_2$], L $\rightarrow$ mol $HC_2H_3O_2$

$$\frac{1 \text{ L}}{1000 \text{ mL}} \qquad\qquad M = \frac{\text{mol}}{L} \qquad\qquad M = \frac{\text{mol}}{L}$$

　　　　　write balanced equation then

$$HCl + NaC_2H_3O_2 \rightarrow HC_2H_3O_2 + NaCl$$

　　　　　mol $NaC_2H_3O_2$, mol $HC_2H_3O_2$, mol HCl $\rightarrow$ mol $NaC_2H_3O_2$, mol $HC_2H_3O_2$ then

$$\text{set up stoichiometry table}$$

　　　　　Part II: Equilibrium:
　　　　　mol $NaC_2H_3O_2$, mol $HC_2H_3O_2$, L, $K_a \rightarrow$ pH

$$pH = pK_a + \log \frac{[\text{base}]}{[\text{acid}]}$$

　　　　　Solution: $250.0 \text{ mL} \times \dfrac{1 \text{ L}}{1000 \text{ mL}} = 0.2500 \text{ L then}$

$$\frac{0.250 \text{ mol } HC_2H_3O_2}{1 \text{ L}} \times 0.250 \text{ L} = 0.0625 \text{ mol } HC_2H_3O_2 \text{ and}$$

$$\frac{0.250 \text{ mol } NaC_2H_3O_2}{1 \text{ L}} \times 0.250 \text{ L} = 0.0625 \text{ mol } NaC_2H_3O_2. \text{ Set up a table to track changes:}$$

	HCl(aq) +	NaC₂H₃O₂(aq) →	HC₂H₃O₂(aq) +	NaCl(aq)
Before addition	≈0.00 mol	0.0625 mol	0.0625 mol	0.00 mol
Addition	0.0050 mol	—	—	—
After addition	≈0.00 mol	0.0575 mol	0.0675 mol	0.0050 mol

Because the amount of HCl is small, there are still significant amounts of both buffer components; so the Henderson–Hasselbalch equation can be used to calculate the new pH.

$$pH = pK_a + \log\frac{[\text{base}]}{[\text{acid}]} = -\log(1.8 \times 10^{-5}) + \log\frac{\frac{0.0575 \text{ mol}}{0.250 \text{ L}}}{\frac{0.0675 \text{ mol}}{0.250 \text{ L}}} = 4.68$$

Check: The units (none) are correct. The magnitude of the answer makes physical sense because the pH dropped slightly when acid was added.

(c) **Given:** 250.0 mL buffer of 0.250 M HC₂H₃O₂ and 0.250 M NaC₂H₃O₂, add 0.0050 mol NaOH
Find: pH   **Other:** $K_a(HC_2H_3O_2) = 1.8 \times 10^{-5}$
Conceptual Plan: Part I: Stoichiometry:
mL → L then [NaC₂H₃O₂], L → mol NaC₂H₃O₂ and [HC₂H₃O₂], L → mol HC₂H₃O₂

$$\frac{1 \text{ L}}{1000 \text{ mL}} \qquad M = \frac{\text{mol}}{\text{L}} \qquad M = \frac{\text{mol}}{\text{L}}$$

write balanced equation then

NaOH + HC₂H₃O₂ → H₂O + NaC₂H₃O₂

mol NaC₂H₃O₂, mol HC₂H₃O₂, mol NaOH → mol NaC₂H₃O₂, mol HC₂H₃O₂ then

set up stoichiometry table

Part II: Equilibrium:
mol NaC₂H₃O₂, mol HC₂H₃O₂, L, K_a → pH

$$pH = pK_a + \log\frac{[\text{base}]}{[\text{acid}]}$$

Solution: $250.0 \text{ mL} \times \frac{1 \text{ L}}{1000 \text{ mL}} = 0.2500 \text{ L then}$

$$\frac{0.250 \text{ mol } HC_2H_3O_2}{1 \text{ L}} \times 0.2500 \text{ L} = 0.0625 \text{ mol } HC_2H_3O_2 \text{ and}$$

$$\frac{0.250 \text{ mol } NaC_2H_3O_2}{1 \text{ L}} \times 0.2500 \text{ L} = 0.0625 \text{ mol } NaC_2H_3O_2. \text{ Set up a table to track changes:}$$

	NaOH(aq) +	HC₂H₃O₂(aq) →	NaC₂H₃O₂(aq) +	H₂O(l)
Before addition	≈0.00 mol	0.0625 mol	0.0625 mol	—
Addition	0.0050 mol	—	—	—
After addition	≈0.00 mol	0.0575 mol	0.0675 mol	—

Because the amount of NaOH is small, there are still significant amounts of both buffer components; so the Henderson–Hasselbalch equation can be used to calculate the new pH.

$$pH = pK_a + \log\frac{[\text{base}]}{[\text{acid}]} = -\log(1.8 \times 10^{-5}) + \log\frac{\frac{0.0675 \text{ mol}}{0.2500 \text{ L}}}{\frac{0.0575 \text{ mol}}{0.2500 \text{ L}}} = 4.81$$

Check: The units (none) are correct. The magnitude of the answer makes physical sense because the pH rose slightly when base was added.

16.22 (a) **Given:** 100.0 mL buffer of 0.175 M HClO and 0.150 M NaClO   **Find:** initial pH
Other: $K_a(HClO) = 2.9 \times 10^{-8}$

Conceptual Plan: Identify acid and base components then M NaClO → M ClO⁻ then

$$acid = HClO \qquad base = ClO^- \qquad NaClO(aq) \rightarrow Na^+(aq) + ClO^-(aq)$$

M HClO, M ClO⁻ → pH.

$$pH = pK_a + \log \frac{[base]}{[acid]}$$

Solution: Acid = HClO, so [acid] = [HClO] = 0.175 M. Base = ClO⁻. Because one ClO⁻ ion is generated for each NaClO, [ClO⁻] = 0.150 M ClO⁻ = [base].

Then $pH = pK_a + \log \dfrac{[base]}{[acid]} = -\log(2.9 \times 10^{-8}) + \log \dfrac{0.150 \text{ M}}{0.175 \text{ M}} = 7.47.$

Check: The units (none) are correct. The magnitude of the answer makes physical sense because the pH is less than the pK_a of the acid because there is more acid than base.

(b)　**Given:** 100.0 mL buffer of 0.175 M HClO and 0.150 M NaClO, add 150.0 mg HBr　**Find:** pH
Other: $K_a(\text{HClO}) = 2.9 \times 10^{-8}$
Conceptual Plan: Part I: Stoichiometry:
mL → L then [NaClO], L → mol NaClO and [HClO], L → mol HClO and

$$\frac{1 \text{ L}}{1000 \text{ mL}} \qquad\qquad M = \frac{mol}{L} \qquad\qquad M = \frac{mol}{L}$$

mg HBr → g HBr → mol HBr write balanced equation then

$$\frac{1 \text{ g HBr}}{1000 \text{ mg HBr}} \quad \frac{1 \text{ mol HBr}}{80.91 \text{ g HBr}} \qquad HBr + NaClO \rightarrow HClO + NaBr$$

mol NaClO, mol HClO, mol HBr → mol NaClO, mol HClO then

$$set\ up\ stoichiometry\ table$$

Part II: Equilibrium:
mol NaClO, mol HClO, L, K_a → pH

$$pH = pK_a + \log \frac{[base]}{[acid]}$$

Solution: $100.0 \text{ mL} \times \dfrac{1 \text{ L}}{1000 \text{ mL}} = 0.1000 \text{ L}$ then $\dfrac{0.175 \text{ mol HClO}}{1 \text{ L}} \times 0.1000 \text{ L} = 0.0175 \text{ mol HClO}$

and $\dfrac{0.150 \text{ mol NaClO}}{1 \text{ L}} \times 0.1000 \text{ L} = 0.0150 \text{ mol NaClO}$ and

$150.0 \text{ mg HBr} \times \dfrac{1 \text{ g HBr}}{1000 \text{ mg HBr}} \times \dfrac{1 \text{ mol HBr}}{80.91 \text{ g HBr}} = 0.00185\underline{3}912 \text{ mol HBr}$. Set up a table to track changes :

	HBr(aq)	+	NaClO(aq)	→	HClO(aq)	+	NaBr(aq)
Before addition	≈0.00 mol		0.0150 mol		0.0175 mol		0.00 mol
Addition	0.001853912 mol		—		—		—
After addition	≈0.00 mol		0.013146 mol		0.015646 mol		0.001853912 mol

Because the amount of HBr is small, there are still significant amounts of both buffer components; so the Henderson–Hasselbalch equation can be used to calculate the new pH.

$$pH = pK_a + \log \frac{[base]}{[acid]} = -\log(2.9 \times 10^{-8}) + \log \frac{\dfrac{0.013\underline{1}46 \text{ mol}}{0.1000 \text{ L}}}{\dfrac{0.015\underline{6}46 \text{ mol}}{0.1000 \text{ L}}} = 7.46.$$

Check: The units (none) are correct. The magnitude of the answer makes physical sense because the pH dropped slightly when acid was added. The pH is closer to the pK_a of the acid than at the start.

(c)　**Given:** 100.0 mL buffer of 0.175 M HClO and 0.150 M NaClO, add 85.0 mg NaOH　**Find:** pH
Other: $K_a(\text{HClO}) = 2.9 \times 10^{-8}$
Conceptual Plan: Part I: Stoichiometry:
mL → L then [NaClO], L → mol NaClO and [HClO], L → mol HClO and

$$\frac{1 \text{ L}}{1000 \text{ mL}} \qquad\qquad M = \frac{mol}{L} \qquad\qquad M = \frac{mol}{L}$$

mg NaOH → g NaOH → mol NaOH write balanced equation then

$$\frac{1 \text{ g NaOH}}{1000 \text{ mg NaOH}} \quad \frac{1 \text{ mol NaOH}}{40.00 \text{ g NaOH}} \qquad NaOH + HClO \rightarrow H_2O + NaClO$$

mol NaClO, mol HClO, mol NaOH → mol NaClO, mol HClO then

set up stoichiometry table

Part II: Equilibrium:
mol NaClO, mol HClO, L, K_a → pH

$$pH = pK_a + \log \frac{[\text{base}]}{[\text{acid}]}$$

Solution: $100.0 \text{ mL} \times \dfrac{1 \text{ L}}{1000 \text{ mL}} = 0.1000 \text{ L}$ then $\dfrac{0.175 \text{ mol HClO}}{1 \text{ L}} \times 0.1000 \text{ L} = 0.0175 \text{ mol HClO}$ and

$$\frac{0.150 \text{ mol NaClO}}{1 \text{ L}} \times 0.1000 \text{ L} = 0.0150 \text{ mol NaClO} \text{ and}$$

$$85.0 \text{ mg NaOH} \times \frac{1 \text{ g NaOH}}{1000 \text{ mg NaOH}} \times \frac{1 \text{ mol NaOH}}{40.00 \text{ g NaOH}} = 0.00213 \text{ mol NaOH}$$

Set up a table to track changes:

$$NaOH(aq) + HClO(aq) \rightarrow NaClO(aq) + H_2O(l)$$

	NaOH(aq)	HClO(aq)	NaClO(aq)	H₂O(l)
Before addition	≈0.00 mol	0.0175 mol	0.0150 mol	—
Addition	0.00213 mol	—	—	—
After addition	≈0.00 mol	0.0154 mol	0.0171 mol	—

Because the amount of NaOH is small, there are still significant amounts of both buffer components; so the Henderson–Hasselbalch equation can be used to calculate the new pH.

$$pH = pK_a + \log \frac{[\text{base}]}{[\text{acid}]} = -\log(2.9 \times 10^{-8}) + \log \frac{\dfrac{0.0171 \text{ mol}}{0.1000 \text{ L}}}{\dfrac{0.0154 \text{ mol}}{0.1000 \text{ L}}} = 7.58$$

Check: The units (none) are correct. The magnitude of the answer makes physical sense because the pH rose slightly when base was added.

16.23   (a)   **Given:** 500.0 mL pure water   **Find:** initial pH and after adding 0.010 mol HCl
Conceptual Plan: Pure water has a pH of 7.00 then mL → L then mol HCl, L → [H₃O⁺] → pH

$$\frac{1 \text{ L}}{1000 \text{ mL}} \qquad\qquad M = \frac{\text{mol}}{\text{L}} \qquad pH = -\log[H_3O^+]$$

Solution: Pure water has a pH of 7.00, so initial pH = 7.00, $500.0 \text{ mL} \times \dfrac{1 \text{ L}}{1000 \text{ mL}} = 0.5000 \text{ L}$, then

$$M = \frac{\text{mol}}{\text{L}} = \frac{0.010 \text{ mol HCl}}{0.5000 \text{ L}} = 0.020 \text{ M HCl}. \text{ Because HCl is a strong acid, it dissociates completely; so}$$

$pH = -\log[H_3O^+] = -\log(0.020) = 1.70$.

Check: The units (none) are correct. The magnitude of the answers makes physical sense because the pH starts neutral and then drops significantly when acid is added and no buffer is present.

(b)   **Given:** 500.0 mL buffer of 0.125 M $HC_2H_3O_2$ and 0.115 M $NaC_2H_3O_2$
Find: initial pH and after adding 0.010 mol HCl **Other:** $K_a(HC_2H_3O_2) = 1.8 \times 10^{-5}$
Conceptual Plan: initial pH:
Identify acid and base components then M $NaC_2H_3O_2$ → M $C_2H_3O_2^-$ then

$$\text{acid} = HC_2H_3O_2 \qquad \text{base} = C_2H_3O_2^- \qquad NaC_2H_3O_2(aq) \rightarrow Na^+(aq) + C_2H_3O_2^-(aq)$$

M $HC_2H_3O_2$, M $C_2H_3O_2^-$ → pH

$$pH = pK_a + \log \frac{[\text{base}]}{[\text{acid}]}$$

pH after HCl addition: Part I: Stoichiometry:
mL → L then $[NaC_2H_3O_2]$, L → mol $NaC_2H_3O_2$ and $[HC_2H_3O_2]$, L → mol $HC_2H_3O_2$

$$\frac{1 \text{ L}}{1000 \text{ mL}} \qquad\qquad M = \frac{\text{mol}}{\text{L}} \qquad\qquad M = \frac{\text{mol}}{\text{L}}$$

write balanced equation then

$$HCl + NaC_2H_3O_2 \rightarrow HC_2H_3O_2 + NaCl$$

mol NaC$_2$H$_3$O$_2$, mol HC$_2$H$_3$O$_2$, mol HCl $\rightarrow$ mol NaC$_2$H$_3$O$_2$, mol HC$_2$H$_3$O$_2$ then

set up stoichiometry table

Part II: Equilibrium:
mol NaC$_2$H$_3$O$_2$, mol HC$_2$H$_3$O$_2$, L, K_a $\rightarrow$ pH

$$pH = pK_a + \log \frac{[base]}{[acid]}$$

Solution: Initial pH: Acid = HC$_2$H$_3$O$_2$, so [acid] = [HC$_2$H$_3$O$_2$] = 0.125 M. Base = C$_2$H$_3$O$_2^-$. Because one C$_2$H$_3$O$_2^-$ ion is generated for each NaC$_2$H$_3$O$_2$, [C$_2$H$_3$O$_2^-$] = 0.115 M C$_2$H$_3$O$_2^-$ = [base]. Then

$$pH = pK_a + \log \frac{[base]}{[acid]} = -\log(1.8 \times 10^{-5}) + \log \frac{0.115 \text{ M}}{0.125 \text{ M}} = 4.71.$$

pH after HCl addition:

$$500.0 \text{ mL} \times \frac{1 \text{ L}}{1000 \text{ mL}} = 0.5000 \text{ L then } \frac{0.125 \text{ mol HC}_2\text{H}_3\text{O}_2}{1 \text{ L}} \times 0.5000 \text{ L} = 0.0625 \text{ mol HC}_2\text{H}_3\text{O}_2 \text{ and}$$

$$\frac{0.115 \text{ mol NaC}_2\text{H}_3\text{O}_2}{1 \text{ L}} \times 0.5000 \text{ L} = 0.0575 \text{ mol NaC}_2\text{H}_3\text{O}_2. \text{ Set up a table to track changes:}$$

$$HCl(aq) + NaC_2H_3O_2(aq) \rightarrow HC_2H_3O_2(aq) + NaCl(aq)$$

	$HCl(aq)$	$NaC_2H_3O_2(aq)$	$HC_2H_3O_2(aq)$	$NaCl(aq)$
Before addition	≈0.00 mol	0.0575 mol	0.0625 mol	0.00 mol
Addition	0.010 mol	—	—	—
After addition	≈0.00 mol	0.0475 mol	0.0725 mol	0.10 mol

Because the amount of HCl is small, there are still significant amounts of both buffer components; so the Henderson–Hasselbalch equation can be used to calculate the new pH.

$$pH = pK_a + \log \frac{[base]}{[acid]} = -\log(1.8 \times 10^{-5}) + \log \frac{\dfrac{0.0475 \text{ mol}}{0.5000 \text{ L}}}{\dfrac{0.0725 \text{ mol}}{0.5000 \text{ L}}} = 4.56$$

Check: The units (none) are correct. The magnitude of the answers makes physical sense because the pH started below the pK_a of the acid and it dropped slightly when acid was added.

(c) **Given:** 500.0 mL buffer of 0.155 M C$_2$H$_5$NH$_2$ and 0.145 M C$_2$H$_5$NH$_3$Cl
Find: initial pH and after adding 0.010 mol HCl **Other:** K_b(C$_2$H$_5$NH$_2$) = 5.6 × 10^{-4}
Conceptual Plan: initial pH:
Identify acid and base components then M C$_2$H$_5$NH$_3$Cl $\rightarrow$ M C$_2$H$_5$NH$_3^+$

acid = C$_2$H$_5$NH$_3^+$ base = C$_2$H$_5$NH$_2$ C$_2$H$_5$NH$_3$Cl(aq) $\rightarrow$ C$_2$H$_5$NH$_3^+$(aq) + Cl$^-$(aq)

and K_b $\rightarrow$ pK_b $\rightarrow$ pK_a then pK_a, M C$_2$H$_5$NH$_2$, M C$_2$H$_5$NH$_3^+$ $\rightarrow$ pH

pK_b = $-\log K_b$ 14 = pK_a + pK_b pH = pK_a + $\log \frac{[base]}{[acid]}$

pH after HCl addition: Part I: Stoichiometry:
mL $\rightarrow$ L then [C$_2$H$_5$NH$_2$], L $\rightarrow$ mol C$_2$H$_5$NH$_2$ and

$\frac{1 \text{ L}}{1000 \text{ mL}}$ M = $\frac{mol}{L}$

[C$_2$H$_5$NH$_3$Cl], L $\rightarrow$ mol C$_2$H$_5$NH$_3$Cl write balanced equation then

M = $\frac{mol}{L}$ HCl + C$_2$H$_5$NH$_2$ $\rightarrow$ C$_2$H$_5$NH$_3$Cl

mol C$_2$H$_5$NH$_2$, mol C$_2$H$_5$NH$_3$Cl, mol HCl $\rightarrow$ mol C$_2$H$_5$NH$_2$, mol C$_2$H$_5$NH$_3$Cl then

set up stoichiometry table

Part II: Equilibrium:
mol C$_2$H$_5$NH$_2$, mol C$_2$H$_5$NH$_3$Cl, L, K_a $\rightarrow$ pH

pH = pK_a + $\log \frac{[base]}{[acid]}$

Solution: Base = C$_2$H$_5$NH$_2$, so [base] = [C$_2$H$_5$NH$_2$] = 0.155 M. Acid = C$_2$H$_5$NH$_3^+$. Because one C$_2$H$_5$NH$_3^+$ ion is generated for each C$_2$H$_5$NH$_3$Cl, [C$_2$H$_5$NH$_3^+$] = 0.145 M C$_2$H$_5$NH$_3^+$ = [acid].

Because $K_b(C_2H_5NH_2) = 5.6 \times 10^{-4}$, $pK_b = -\log K_b = -\log(5.6 \times 10^{-4}) = 3.25$. Because $14 = pK_a + pK_b$, $pK_a = 14 - pK_b = 14 - 3.25 = 10.75$ then

$$pH = pK_a + \log \frac{[base]}{[acid]} = 10.75 + \log \frac{0.155 \text{ M}}{0.145 \text{ M}} = 10.78.$$

pH after HCl addition: $500.0 \text{ mL} \times \dfrac{1 \text{ L}}{1000 \text{ mL}} = 0.5000 \text{ L}$ then

$$\frac{0.155 \text{ mol } C_2H_5NH_2}{1 \text{ L}} \times 0.5000 \text{ L} = 0.0775 \text{ mol } C_2H_5NH_2 \text{ and}$$

$$\frac{0.145 \text{ mol } C_2H_5NH_3Cl}{1 \text{ L}} \times 0.5000 \text{ L} = 0.0725 \text{ mol } C_2H_5NH_3Cl. \text{ Set up a table to track changes:}$$

$$HCl(aq) \;+\; C_2H_5NH_2(aq) \rightarrow C_2H_5NH_3Cl(aq)$$

	HCl	C₂H₅NH₂	C₂H₅NH₃Cl
Before addition	≈ 0.00 mol	0.0775 mol	0.0725 mol
Addition	0.010 mol	—	—
After addition	≈ 0.00 mol	0.0675 mol	0.0825 mol

Because the amount of HCl is small, there are still significant amounts of both buffer components; so the Henderson–Hasselbalch equation can be used to calculate the new pH.

$$pH = pK_a + \log \frac{[base]}{[acid]} = 10.75 + \log \frac{\dfrac{0.0675 \text{ mol}}{0.5000 \text{ L}}}{\dfrac{0.0825 \text{ mol}}{0.5000 \text{ L}}} = 10.66$$

Check: The units (none) are correct. The magnitude of the answers makes physical sense because the initial pH should be greater than the pK_a of the acid because there is more base than acid and the pH drops slightly when acid is added.

16.24 (a) **Given:** 250.0 mL pure water **Find:** initial pH and after adding 0.010 mol NaOH
Conceptual Plan:
Pure water has a pH of 7.00 then mL $\rightarrow$ L then mol NaOH, L $\rightarrow$ [OH⁻] $\rightarrow$ [H₃O⁺] $\rightarrow$ pH

$$\frac{1 \text{ L}}{1000 \text{ mL}} \qquad\qquad M = \frac{mol}{L} \quad K_w = [H_3O^+][OH^-] \quad pH = -\log[H_3O^+]$$

Solution: Pure water has a pH of 7.00, so initial pH $= 7.00$, then $250.0 \text{ mL} \times \dfrac{1 \text{ L}}{1000 \text{ mL}} = 0.2500 \text{ L}$, then

$M = \dfrac{mol}{L} = \dfrac{0.010 \text{ mol NaOH}}{0.2500 \text{ L}} = 0.040 \text{ M NaOH}$. Because NaOH is a strong base, it dissociates

completely; so $[OH^-] = 0.040$ M. $K_w = [H_3O^+][OH^-]$, so

$$[H_3O^-] = \frac{K_w}{[OH^-]} = \frac{1.0 \times 10^{-14}}{0.040} = 2.5 \times 10^{-13} \text{ M and}$$

$$pH = -\log[H_3O^+] = -\log(2.5 \times 10^{-13}) = 12.60.$$

Check: The units (none) are correct. The magnitude of the answers make physical sense because the pH started neutral and then rose significantly when base was added and no buffer is present.

(b) **Given:** 250.0 mL buffer of 0.195 M HCHO₂ and 0.275 M KCHO₂
Find: initial pH and after adding 0.010 mol NaOH **Other:** $K_a(HCHO_2) = 1.8 \times 10^{-4}$
Conceptual Plan: initial pH:
Identify acid and base components then M KCHO₂ $\rightarrow$ M CHO₂⁻ then

$$\text{acid} = HCHO_2 \qquad \text{base} = CHO_2^- \qquad KCHO_2(aq) \rightarrow K^+(aq) + CHO_2^-(aq)$$

M HCHO₂, M CHO₂⁻ $\rightarrow$ pH

$$pH = pK_a + \log \frac{[base]}{[acid]}$$

pH after NaOH addition: Part I: Stoichiometry:
mL $\rightarrow$ L then [KCHO₂], L $\rightarrow$ mol KCHO₂ and [HCHO₂], L $\rightarrow$ mol HCHO₂

$$\frac{1 \text{ L}}{1000 \text{ mL}} \qquad\qquad M = \frac{mol}{L} \qquad\qquad M = \frac{mol}{L}$$

write balanced equation then

$NaOH + HCHO_2 \rightarrow NaCHO_2 + H_2O$

mol CHO_2^-, mol $HCHO_2$, mol $NaOH$ $\rightarrow$ mol $NaCHO_2$, mol $HCHO_2$ then

set up stoichiometry table

Part II: Equilibrium:

mol $NaC_2H_3O_2$, mol $HC_2H_3O_2$, L, K_a $\rightarrow$ pH

$$pH = pK_a + \log \frac{[base]}{[acid]}$$

Solution: Initial pH: Acid = $HCHO_2$, so [acid] = $[HCHO_2]$ = 0.195 M. Base = CHO_2^-. Because one CHO_2^- ion is generated for each $KCHO_2$, $[CHO_2^-]$ = 0.275 M CHO_2^- = [base]. Then

$$pH = pK_a + \log \frac{[base]}{[acid]} = -\log(1.8 \times 10^{-4}) + \log \frac{0.275 \text{ M}}{0.195 \text{ M}} = 3.89.$$

pH after NaOH addition: $250.0 \text{ mL} \times \dfrac{1 \text{ L}}{1000 \text{ mL}} = 0.2500 \text{ L}$ then

$$\frac{0.195 \text{ mol } HCHO_2}{1 \text{ L}} \times 0.2500 \text{ L} = 0.04875 \text{ mol } HCHO_2 \text{ and}$$

$$\frac{0.275 \text{ mol } KCHO_2}{1 \text{ L}} \times 0.2500 \text{ L} = 0.06875 \text{ mol } KCHO_2$$

Set up a table to track changes:

$$NaOH(aq) + HCHO_2(aq) \rightarrow NaCHO_2(aq) + H_2O(l)$$

	$NaOH(aq)$	$HCHO_2(aq)$	$NaCHO_2(aq)$	$H_2O(l)$
Before addition	≈ 0.00 mol	0.04875 mol	0.06875 mol	—
Addition	0.010 mol	—	—	—
After addition	≈ 0.00 mol	0.03875 mol	0.07875 mol	—

Because the amount of NaOH is small, there are still significant amounts of both buffer components; so the Henderson–Hasselbalch equation can be used to calculate the new pH.

$$pH = pK_a + \log \frac{[base]}{[acid]} = -\log(1.8 \times 10^{-4}) + \log \frac{\dfrac{0.07875 \text{ mol}}{0.2500 \text{ L}}}{\dfrac{0.03875 \text{ mol}}{0.2500 \text{ L}}} = 4.05$$

Check: The units (none) are correct. The magnitude of the answers makes physical sense because the pH started above the pK_a of the acid and it rose slightly when base was added.

(c) **Given:** 250.0 mL buffer of 0.255 M $C_2H_5NH_2$ and 0.235 M $C_2H_5NH_3Cl$
Find: initial pH and after adding 0.010 mol NaOH   **Other:** $K_b(C_2H_5NH_2) = 5.6 \times 10^{-4}$
Conceptual Plan: initial pH:
Identify acid and base components then M $C_2H_5NH_3Cl$ $\rightarrow$ M $C_2H_5NH_3^+$

acid = $C_2H_5NH_3^+$ base = $C_2H_5NH_2$ $C_2H_5NH_3Cl(aq) \rightarrow C_2H_5NH_3^+(aq) + Cl^-(aq)$

and K_b $\rightarrow$ pK_b $\rightarrow$ pK_a then pK_a, M $C_2H_5NH_2$, M $C_2H_5NH_3^+$ $\rightarrow$ pH

$pK_b = -\log K_b$ $14 = pK_a + pK_b$ $pH = pK_a + \log \dfrac{[base]}{[acid]}$

pH after NaOH addition: Part I: Stoichiometry:
mL $\rightarrow$ L then $[C_2H_5NH_2]$, L $\rightarrow$ mol $C_2H_5NH_2$ and

$\dfrac{1 \text{ L}}{1000 \text{ mL}}$ $M = \dfrac{mol}{L}$

$[C_2H_5NH_3Cl]$, L $\rightarrow$ mol $C_2H_5NH_3Cl$

$M = \dfrac{mol}{L}$

write balanced equation then

$NaOH + C_2H_5NH_3Cl \rightarrow C_2H_5NH_2 + NaCl + H_2O$

mol $C_2H_5NH_2$, mol $C_2H_5NH_3Cl$, mol NaOH $\rightarrow$ mol $C_2H_5NH_2$, mol $C_2H_5NH_3Cl$

set up stoichiometry table

Part II: Equilibrium:
mol $C_2H_5NH_2$, mol $C_2H_5NH_3Cl$, L, K_a → pH

$$pH = pK_a + \log \frac{[base]}{[acid]}$$

Solution: Base = $C_2H_5NH_2$, so [base] = $[C_2H_5NH_2]$ = 0.255 M. Acid = $C_2H_5NH_3^+$. Because one $C_2H_5NH_3^+$ ion is generated for each $C_2H_5NH_3Cl$, $[C_2H_5NH_3^+]$ = 0.235 M $C_2H_5NH_3^+$ = [acid]. Because $K_b(C_2H_5NH_2) = 5.6 \times 10^{-4}$, $pK_b = -\log K_b = -\log(5.6 \times 10^{-4}) = 3.25$. Because $14 = pK_a + pK_b$, $pK_a = 14 - pK_b = 14 - 3.25 = 10.75$. Then

$$pH = pK_a + \log \frac{[base]}{[acid]} = 10.75 + \log \frac{0.255 \text{ M}}{0.235 \text{ M}} = 10.78.$$

pH after HCl addition: $250.0 \text{ mL} \times \dfrac{1 \text{ L}}{1000 \text{ mL}} = 0.2500 \text{ L}$ then

$$\frac{0.255 \text{ mol } C_2H_5NH_2}{1 \text{ L}} \times 0.2500 \text{ L} = 0.06375 \text{ mol } C_2H_5NH_2 \text{ and}$$

$$\frac{0.235 \text{ mol } C_2H_5NH_3Cl}{1 \text{ L}} \times 0.2500 \text{ L} = 0.05875 \text{ mol } C_2H_5NH_3Cl. \text{ Set up a table to track changes:}$$

$$NaOH(aq) + C_2H_5NH_3Cl(aq) \rightarrow C_2H_5NH_2(aq) + NaCl(aq) + H_2O(aq)$$

	NaOH	$C_2H_5NH_3Cl$	$C_2H_5NH_2$	NaCl	
Before addition	≈0.00 mol	0.05875 mol	0.06375 mol	0.00 mol	—
Addition	0.010 mol	—	—	—	—
After addition	≈0.00 mol	0.04875 mol	0.07375 mol	—	—

Because the amount of NaOH is small, there are still significant amounts of both buffer components; so the Henderson–Hasselbalch equation can be used to calculate the new pH.

$$pH = pK_a + \log \frac{[base]}{[acid]} = 10.75 + \log \frac{\dfrac{0.07375 \text{ mol}}{0.2500 \text{ L}}}{\dfrac{0.04875 \text{ mol}}{0.2500 \text{ L}}} = 10.93$$

Check: The units (none) are correct. The magnitude of the answers makes physical sense because the initial pH should be greater than the pK_a of the acid because there is more base than acid and the pH rises slightly when base is added.

16.25 **Given:** 350.00 mL 0.150 M HF and 0.150 M NaF buffer
Find: mass NaOH to raise pH to 4.00 and mass NaOH to raise pH to 4.00 with buffer concentrations raised to 0.350 M
Other: $K_a(HF) = 3.5 \times 10^{-4}$
Conceptual Plan: Identify acid and base components. Because [NaF] = [HF], then initial pH = pK_a

$$acid = HF \qquad base = F^- \qquad pH = pK_a$$

final pH, pK_a → [NaF]/[HF] and mL → L then [HF], L → mol HF and [NaF], L → mol NaF

$$pH = pK_a + \log \frac{[base]}{[acid]} \qquad \frac{1 \text{ L}}{1000 \text{ mL}} \qquad M = \frac{mol}{L} \qquad M = \frac{mol}{L}$$

then write balanced equation then

$$NaOH + HF \rightarrow NaF + H_2O$$

mol HF, mol NaF, [NaF]/[HF] → mol NaOH → g NaOH.

$$set \text{ up stoichiometry table} \qquad \frac{40.00 \text{ g NaOH}}{1 \text{ mol NaOH}}$$

Finally, when the buffer concentrations are raised to 0.350 M, simply multiply the g NaOH by the ratio of concentrations (0.350 M/0.150 M).

Solution: initial pH = $pK_a = -\log(3.5 \times 10^{-4}) = 3.46$ then

$$pH = pK_a + \log \frac{[base]}{[acid]} = -\log(3.5 \times 10^{-4}) + \log \frac{[NaF]}{[HF]} = 4.00. \text{ Solve for [NaF]/[HF].}$$

$$\log \frac{[NaF]}{[HF]} = 4.00 - 3.46 = 0.54 \rightarrow \frac{[NaF]}{[HF]} = 10^{0.54} = 3.5. \quad 350.0 \text{ mL} \times \frac{1 \text{ L}}{1000 \text{ mL}} = 0.3500 \text{ L then}$$

$$\frac{0.150 \text{ mol HF}}{1 \text{ L}} \times 0.3500 \text{ L} = 0.0525 \text{ mol HF and} \quad \frac{0.150 \text{ mol NaF}}{1 \text{ L}} \times 0.3500 \text{ L} = 0.0525 \text{ mol NaF}$$

Set up a table to track changes:

	NaOH(aq)	+	HF(aq)	→	NaF(aq)	+	H$_2$O(aq)
Before addition	≈0.00 mol		0.0525 mol		0.0525 mol		—
Addition	x		—		—		—
After addition	≈0.00 mol		(0.0525 − x) mol		(0.0525 + x) mol		—

Because $\frac{[NaF]}{[HF]} = 3.5 = \frac{(0.0525 + x)\ \text{mol}}{(0.0525 - x)\ \text{mol}}$, solve for x. Note that the ratio of moles is the same as the ratio of

concentrations because the volume for both terms is the same. $3.5(0.0525 - x) = (0.0525 + x) \rightarrow$
$0.18375 - 3.5x = 0.0525 + x \rightarrow 0.13125 = 4.5x \rightarrow x = 0.029167$ mol NaOH then

$0.029167\ \text{mol NaOH} \times \frac{40.00\ \text{g NaOH}}{1\ \text{mol NaOH}} = 1.1667\ \text{g NaOH} = 1.2\ \text{g NaOH}.$

To scale the amount of NaOH up to a 0.350 M HF and NaF solution, multiply the NaOH mass by the ratio of concen-

trations. $1.1667\ \text{g NaOH} \times \frac{0.350\ \text{M}}{0.150\ \text{M}} = 2.7\ \text{g NaOH}$

Check: The units (g) are correct. The magnitude of the answers makes physical sense because there is much less than a mole of each of the buffer components; so there must be much less than a mole of NaOH. The higher the buffer concentrations, the higher the buffer capacity and the mass of NaOH it can neutralize.

16.26   **Given:** 100.00 mL of 0.100 M NH$_3$ and 0.125 M NH$_4$Br buffer
Find: mass HCl to lower pH to 9.00 and mass HCl to lower pH to 9.00 with buffer concentrations raised to 0.250 M NH$_3$ and 0.400 M NH$_4$Br
Other: $K_b(NH_3) = 1.76 \times 10^{-5}$
Conceptual Plan: Identify acid and base components then $K_b \rightarrow pK_b \rightarrow pK_a$ **then**

acid = NH$_4^+$ base = NH$_3$ $pK_b = -\log K_b$ $14 = pK_a + pK_b$

final pH, pK_a $\rightarrow$ **[NH$_3$]/[NH$_4^+$] and mL $\rightarrow$ L then [NH$_3$], L $\rightarrow$ mol NH$_3$ and**

$pH = pK_a + \log \frac{[base]}{[acid]}$ $\frac{1\ L}{1000\ mL}$ $M = \frac{mol}{L}$

[NH$_4^+$], L $\rightarrow$ mol NH$_4^+$ then write balanced equation then

$M = \frac{mol}{L}$ $H^+ + NH_3 \rightarrow NH_4^+$

mol NH$_3$, mol NH$_4^+$, [NH$_3$]/[NH$_4^+$] $\rightarrow$ mol HCl $\rightarrow$ g HCl.

set up stoichiometry table $\frac{36.46\ \text{g HCl}}{1\ \text{mol HCl}}$

Solution: Because $K_b(NH_3) = 1.76 \times 10^{-5}$, $pK_b = -\log K_b = -\log(1.76 \times 10^{-5}) = 4.75$.
Because $14 = pK_a + pK_b$, $pK_a = 14 - pK_b = 14 - 4.75 = 9.25$, then

$pH = pK_a + \log \frac{[base]}{[acid]} = 9.25 + \log \frac{[NH_3]}{[NH_4^+]} = 9.00.$

Solve for [NH$_4$Br]. $\log \frac{[NH_3]}{[NH_4^+]} = 9.00 - 9.25 = -0.25 \rightarrow \frac{[NH_3]}{[NH_4^+]} = 10^{-0.25} = 0.562341.$

$100.0\ \text{mL} \times \frac{1\ L}{1000\ \text{mL}} = 0.1000\ L$ then $\frac{0.100\ \text{mol NH}_3}{1\ L} \times 0.1000\ L = 0.0100\ \text{mol NH}_3$ and

$\frac{0.125\ \text{mol NH}_4\text{Br}}{1\ L} \times 0.1000\ L = 0.0125\ \text{mol NH}_4\text{Br} = 0.0125\ \text{mol NH}_4^+$. Because HCl is a strong acid,

[HCl] = [H$^+$], and set up a table to track changes:

	H$^+$(aq)	+	NH$_3$(aq)	→	NH$_4^+$(aq)
Before addition	≈0.00 mol		0.0100 mol		0.0125 mol
Addition	x		—		—
After addition	≈0.00 mol		(0.0100 − x) mol		(0.0125 + x) mol

Because $\dfrac{[\text{NH}_3]}{[\text{NH}_4{}^+]} = 0.562341 = \dfrac{(0.0100 - x)\ \text{mol}}{(0.0125 + x)\ \text{mol}}$, solve for x. Note that the ratio of moles is the same as the ratio

of concentrations because the volume for both terms is the same. $0.562341(0.0125 + x) = (0.0100 - x) \rightarrow$
$0.00702926 + 0.562341x = 0.0100 - x \rightarrow 1.562341x = 0.0029707 \rightarrow x = 0.0019015$ mol HCl, then

$$0.0019015\ \text{mol HCl} \times \dfrac{36.46\ \text{g HCl}}{1\ \text{mol HCl}} = 0.06933\ \text{g HCl} = 0.07\ \text{g HCl}.$$ For the higher concentration

buffer, repeat part of the previous calculations. $\dfrac{0.250\ \text{mol NH}_3}{1\ L} \times 0.1000\ L = 0.0250$ mol NH_3 and

$\dfrac{0.400\ \text{mol NH}_4\text{Br}}{1\ L} \times 0.1000\ L = 0.0400$ mol $\text{NH}_4\text{Br} = 0.0400$ mol $\text{NH}_4{}^+$.

Because HCl is a strong acid, [HCl] = [H$^+$], and set up a table to track changes:

	$\text{H}^+(aq)$	+	$\text{NH}_3(aq)$	$\rightarrow$	$\text{NH}_4{}^+(aq)$
Before addition	≈ 0.00 mol		0.0250 mol		0.0400 mol
Addition	x		—		—
After addition	≈ 0.00 mol		$(0.0250 - x)$ mol		$(0.0400 + x)$ mol

Because $\dfrac{[\text{NH}_3]}{[\text{NH}_4{}^+]} = 0.562341 = \dfrac{(0.0250 - x)\ \text{mol}}{(0.0400 + x)\ \text{mol}}$, solve for x. Note that the ratio of moles is the same as the

ratio of concentrations because the volume for both terms is the same. $0.562341(0.0400 + x) = (0.0250 - x) \rightarrow$
$0.0224936 + 0.562341x = 0.0250 - x \rightarrow 1.562341x = 0.00250636 \rightarrow x = 0.0016042$ mol HCl then

$$0.0016042\ \text{mol HCl} \times \dfrac{36.46\ \text{g HCl}}{1\ \text{mol HCl}} = 0.058489\ \text{g HCl} = 0.06\ \text{g HCl}$$

Check: The units (g) are correct. The magnitude of the answers makes physical sense because there is much less than a mole of each of the buffer components; so there must be much less than a mole of HCl. Also, the pH of the initial buffer is less than the pK_a of the acid, so even less acid is necessary to drop the pH below 9.00. The higher concentration buffer solution requires about the same amount of acid because the initial pH of this buffer is closer to 9.00 than is the low concentration buffer.

16.27   (a)   Yes, this will be a buffer because NH_3 is a weak base and $\text{NH}_4{}^+$ is its conjugate acid. The ratio of base to acid is $0.10/0.15 = 0.67$, so the pH will be within 1 pH unit of the pK_a.

      (b)   No, this will not be a buffer solution because HCl is a strong acid and NaOH is a strong base.

      (c)   Yes, this will be a buffer because HF is a weak acid and the NaOH will convert $20.0/50.0 = 40\%$ of the acid to its conjugate base.

      (d)   No, this will not be a buffer solution because both components are bases.

      (e)   No, this will not be a buffer solution because both components are bases.

16.28   (a)   Yes, this will be a buffer because HF is a weak acid and F$^-$ is its conjugate base. The ratio of base to acid is $(55.0 \times 0.15)/(75.0 \times 0.10) = 1.1$, so the pH will be within 1 pH unit of the pK_a.

      (b)   No, this will not be a buffer solution because both components are acids.

      (c)   Yes, this will be a buffer because HF is a weak acid and the KOH will convert $(135.0 \times 0.050)/(165.0 \times 0.10) = 41\%$ of the acid to its conjugate base.

      (d)   Yes, this will be a buffer because CH_3NH_2 is a weak base and $\text{CH}_3\text{NH}_3{}^+$ is its conjugate acid. The ratio of base to acid is $(125.0 \times 0.15)/(120.0 \times 0.25) = 0.63$, so the pH will be within 1 pH unit of the pK_a.

      (e)   Yes, this will be a buffer because CH_3NH_2 is a weak base and the HCl will convert $(95.0 \times 0.10)/(105.0 \times 0.15) = 60\%$ of the base to its conjugate acid.

16.29   (a)   **Given:** blood buffer 0.024 M $\text{HCO}_3{}^-$ and 0.0012 M H_2CO_3, p$K_a = 6.1$ **Find:** initial pH

       Conceptual Plan: Identify acid and base components then M $\text{HCO}_3{}^-$, M $\text{H}_2\text{CO}_3 \rightarrow$ pH.

$$\text{acid} = \text{H}_2\text{CO}_3 \qquad\qquad \text{base} = \text{HCO}_3{}^- \qquad\qquad \text{pH} = \text{p}K_a + \log\dfrac{[\text{base}]}{[\text{acid}]}$$

       Solution: Acid = H_2CO_3, so [acid] = $[\text{H}_2\text{CO}_3] = 0.0012$ M. Base = $\text{HCO}_3{}^-$, so [base] = $[\text{HCO}_3{}^-] =$

       0.024 M $\text{HCO}_3{}^-$. Then $\text{pH} = \text{p}K_a + \log\dfrac{[\text{base}]}{[\text{acid}]} = 6.1 + \log\dfrac{0.024\ M}{0.0012\ M} = 7.4$.

Check: The units (none) are correct. The magnitude of the answer makes physical sense because the pH is greater than the pK_a of the acid because there is more base than acid.

(b)   **Given:** 5.0 L of blood buffer   **Find:** mass HCl to lower pH to 7.0

Conceptual Plan: final pH, pK_a → $[HCO_3^-]/[H_2CO_3]$ then $[HCO_3^-]$, L → mol HCO_3^- and

$$pH = pK_a + \log \frac{[base]}{[acid]}$$ $$M = \frac{mol}{L}$$

$[H_2CO_3]$, L → mol H_2CO_3 then write balanced equation then

$$M = \frac{mol}{L}$$ $$H^+ + HCO_3^- \rightarrow H_2CO_3$$

mol HCO_3^-, mol H_2CO_3, $[HCO_3^-]/[H_2CO_3]$ → mol HCl → g HCl

set up stoichiometry table $$\frac{36.46 \text{ g HCl}}{1 \text{ mol HCl}}$$

Solution: $pH = pK_a + \log \frac{[base]}{[acid]} = 6.1 + \log \frac{[HCO_3^-]}{[H_2CO_3]} = 7.0$. Solve for $[HCO_3^-]/[H_2CO_3]$.

$$\log \frac{[HCO_3^-]}{[H_2CO_3]} = 7.0 - 6.1 = 0.9 \rightarrow \frac{[HCO_3^-]}{[H_2CO_3]} = 10^{0.9} = 7.9433. \text{ Then}$$

$$\frac{0.024 \text{ mol } HCO_3^-}{1 \text{ L}} \times 5.0 \text{ L} = 0.12 \text{ mol } HCO_3^- \text{ and } \frac{0.0012 \text{ mol } H_2CO_3}{1 \text{ L}} \times 5.0 \text{ L} = 0.0060 \text{ mol } H_2CO_3.$$

Because HCl is a strong acid, $[HCl] = [H^+]$, and set up a table to track changes:

$$H^+(aq) + HCO_3^-(aq) \rightarrow H_2CO_3(aq)$$

	$H^+(aq)$	$HCO_3^-(aq)$	$H_2CO_3(aq)$
Before addition	≈ 0.00 mol	0.12 mol	0.0060 mol
Addition	x	—	—
After addition	≈ 0.00 mol	$(0.12 - x)$ mol	$(0.0060 + x)$ mol

Because $\dfrac{[HCO_3^-]}{[H_2CO_3]} = 7.9433 = \dfrac{(0.12 - x) \text{ mol}}{(0.0060 + x) \text{ mol}}$, solve for x. Note that the ratio of moles is the same as the ratio of concentrations because the volume for both terms is the same.

$7.9433(0.0060 + x) = (0.12 - x) \rightarrow 0.0476598 + 7.9433x = 0.12 - x \rightarrow 8.9433x = 0.07234 \rightarrow$

$x = 0.0080888 \text{ mol HCl then } 0.0080888 \text{ mol HCl} \times \dfrac{36.46 \text{ g HCl}}{1 \text{ mol HCl}} = 0.29492 \text{ g HCl} = 0.3 \text{ g HCl}$

Check: The units (g) are correct. The amount of acid needed is small because the concentrations of the buffer components are very low and the buffer starts only 0.4 pH unit above the final pH.

(c)   **Given:** 5.0 L of blood buffer   **Find:** mass NaOH to raise pH to 7.8

Conceptual Plan: final pH, pK_a → $[HCO_3^-]/[H_2CO_3]$ then $[HCO_3^-]$, L → mol HCO_3^- and

$$pH = pK_a + \log \frac{[base]}{[acid]}$$ $$M = \frac{mol}{L}$$

$[H_2CO_3]$, L → mol H_2CO_3 then write balanced equation then

$$M = \frac{mol}{L}$$ $$OH^- + H_2CO_3 \rightarrow HCO_3^- + H_2O$$

mol HCO_3^-, mol H_2CO_3, $[HCO_3^-]/[H_2CO_3]$ → mol NaOH → g NaOH

set up stoichiometry table $$\frac{40.00 \text{ g NaOH}}{1 \text{ mol NaOH}}$$

Solution: $pH = pK_a + \log \frac{[base]}{[acid]} = 6.1 + \log \frac{[HCO_3^-]}{[H_2CO_3]} = 7.8$

Solve for $[HCO_3^-]/[H_2CO_3]$. $\log \dfrac{[HCO_3^-]}{[H_2CO_3]} = 7.8 - 6.1 = 1.7 \rightarrow \dfrac{[HCO_3^-]}{[H_2CO_3]} = 10^{1.7} = 50.11872.$ Then

$$\frac{0.024 \text{ mol } HCO_3^-}{1 \text{ L}} \times 5.0 \text{ L} = 0.12 \text{ mol } HCO_3^- \text{ and } \frac{0.0012 \text{ mol } H_2CO_3}{1 \text{ L}} \times 5.0 \text{ L} = 0.0060 \text{ mol } H_2CO_3.$$

Because NaOH is a strong base, [NaOH] = [OH$^-$], and set up a table to track changes:

$$OH^-(aq) \ + \ H_2CO_3(aq) \ \rightarrow \ HCO_3^-(aq) + H_2O(l)$$

Before addition	≈ 0.00 mol	0.0060 mol	0.12 mol	—
Addition	x	—	—	—
After addition	≈ 0.00 mol	(0.0060 − x) mol	(0.12 + x) mol	—

Because $\dfrac{[HCO_3^-]}{[H_2CO_3]} = 50.11872 = \dfrac{(0.12 + x) \text{ mol}}{(0.0060 - x) \text{ mol}}$, solve for x. Note that the ratio of moles is the same as the ratio of concentrations because the volume for both terms is the same.

$50.11872(0.0060 - x) = (0.12 + x) \rightarrow 0.30071 - 50.11872x = 0.12 + x \rightarrow 51.11872x = 0.18071$
$\rightarrow x = 0.0035351$ mol NaOH then

$$0.0035351 \text{ mol NaOH} \times \frac{40.00 \text{ g NaOH}}{1 \text{ mol NaOH}} = 0.14140 \text{ g NaOH} = 0.14 \text{ g NaOH}$$

Check: The units (g) are correct. The amount of base needed is small because the concentrations of the buffer components are very low.

16.30   (a)   **Given:** HPO$_4^{2-}$/H$_2$PO$_4^-$ buffer at pH = 7.1   **Find:** [HPO$_4^{2-}$]/[H$_2$PO$_4^-$]
           Other: K_{a_2}(H$_3$PO$_4$) = 6.2 × 10^{-8}
           Conceptual Plan: Identify acid and base components then pH, K_{a_2} → [HPO$_4^{2-}$]/[H$_2$PO$_4^-$].

$$\text{acid} = H_2PO_4^- \qquad \text{base} = HPO_4^{2-} \qquad pH = pK_a + \log \frac{[\text{base}]}{[\text{acid}]}$$

           Solution: $pH = pK_a + \log \dfrac{[\text{base}]}{[\text{acid}]} = -\log(6.2 \times 10^{-8}) + \log \dfrac{[HPO_4^{2-}]}{[H_2PO_4^-]} = 7.1$

           Solve for [HPO$_4^{2-}$]/[H$_2$PO$_4^-$].

$$\log \frac{[HPO_4^{2-}]}{[H_2PO_4^-]} = 7.1 - 7.2 = -0.1 \rightarrow \frac{[HPO_4^{2-}]}{[H_2PO_4^-]} = 10^{-0.1} = 0.79433 = 0.8$$

           Check: The units (none) are correct. The magnitude of the answer makes physical sense because the pH is very close but less than the pK$_a$ of the acid.

       (b)   No, H$_3$PO$_4$ and H$_2$PO$_4^-$ cannot be used as a buffer in the cell because the K_{a_1}(H$_3$PO$_4$) = 7.5 × 10^{-3}; so the pK$_{a_1}$ = 2.1. To have an effective buffer, the pK$_a$ should be within 1 pH unit of the desired pH (not 5.0 pH unit).

16.31   **Given:** HC$_2$H$_3$O$_2$/KC$_2$H$_3$O$_2$, HClO$_2$/KClO$_2$, NH$_3$/NH$_4$Cl, and HClO/KClO potential buffer systems to create buffer at pH = 7.20   **Find:** best buffer system and ratio of component masses
       Other: K_a(HC$_2$H$_3$O$_2$) = 1.8 × 10^{-5}, K_a(HClO$_2$) = 1.1 × 10^{-2}, K_b(NH$_3$) = 1.76 × 10^{-5}, K_a(HClO) = 2.9 × 10^{-8}
       Conceptual Plan: Calculate pK$_a$ of all potential buffer acids for the base K_b → pK_b → pK$_a$ and

$$pK_a = -\log K_a \qquad\qquad\qquad pK_b = -\log K_b \quad 14 = pK_a + pK_b$$

       choose the pK$_a$ that is closest to 7.20. Then pH, K_a → [base]/[acid] → mass base/mass acid.

$$pH = pK_a + \log \frac{[\text{base}]}{[\text{acid}]} \qquad \frac{\mathcal{M}(\text{base})}{\mathcal{M}(\text{acid})}$$

       Solution: for HC$_2$H$_3$O$_2$/KC$_2$H$_3$O$_2$:pK$_a$ = $-\log K_a = -\log(1.8 \times 10^{-5}) = 4.74$;
       for HClO$_2$/KClO$_2$:pK$_a$ = $-\log K_a = -\log(1.1 \times 10^{-2}) = 1.96$;
       for NH$_3$/NH$_4$Cl :pK$_b$ = $-\log K_b = -\log(1.76 \times 10^{-5}) = 4.75$
       Because $14 = pK_a + pK_b$, pK$_a$ = $14 - pK_b = 14 - 4.75 = 9.25$;
       and for HClO/KClO :pK$_a$ = $-\log K_a = -\log(2.9 \times 10^{-8}) = 7.54$. So the HClO/KClO buffer system has the pK$_a$

       that is closest to 7.20. So $pH = pK_a + \log \dfrac{[\text{base}]}{[\text{acid}]} = 7.54 + \log \dfrac{[KClO]}{[HClO]} = 7.20$. Solve for [KClO]/[HClO].

$$\log \frac{[KClO]}{[HClO]} = 7.20 - 7.54 = -0.34 \rightarrow \frac{[KClO]}{[HClO]} = 10^{-0.34} = 0.457088. \text{ Then convert to mass ratio using}$$

$$\frac{\mathcal{M}(\text{base})}{\mathcal{M}(\text{acid})}, \ 0.457088 \ \frac{\dfrac{\text{KClO mol}}{L}}{\dfrac{\text{HClO mol}}{L}} \times \frac{90.55 \text{ g KClO}}{\text{mol KClO}} \Bigg/ \frac{}{52.46 \text{ g HClO}} = 0.79 \frac{\text{g KClO}}{\text{g HClO}}.$$

Check: The units (none and g base/g acid) are correct. The buffer system with the K_a closest to 10^{-7} is the best choice. The magnitude of the answer makes physical sense because the buffer needs more acid than base (and this fact is not overcome by the heavier molar mass of the base).

16.32   **Given:** HF/KF, HNO_2/KNO_2, NH_3/NH_4Cl, and HClO/KClO potential buffer systems to create buffer at pH = 9.00
Find: best buffer system and ratio of component masses
Other: $K_a(HF) = 3.5 \times 10^{-4}$, $K_a(HNO_2) = 4.6 \times 10^{-4}$, $K_b(NH_3) = 1.76 \times 10^{-5}$, $K_a(HClO) = 2.9 \times 10^{-8}$
Conceptual Plan: Calculate pK_a of all potential buffer acids for the base $K_b \rightarrow$ p$K_b \rightarrow$ pK_a and

$$pK_a = -\log K_a \qquad\qquad pK_b = -\log K_b, \quad 14 = pK_a + pK_b$$

choose the pK_a that is closest to 9.00. Then pH, $K_a \rightarrow$ [base]/[acid] $\rightarrow$ mass base/mass acid.

$$pH = pK_a + \log \frac{[base]}{[acid]} \qquad \frac{\mathcal{M}\,(base)}{\mathcal{M}\,(acid)}$$

Solution: for HF/KF: p$K_a = -\log K_a = -\log(3.5 \times 10^{-4}) = 3.46$;
for HNO_2/KNO_2 :p$K_a = -\log K_a = -\log(4.6 \times 10^{-4}) = 3.34$;
for NH_3/NH_4Cl :p$K_b = -\log K_b = -\log(1.76 \times 10^{-5}) = 4.75$.
Because $14 = pK_a + pK_b$, $pK_a = 14 - pK_b = 14 - 4.75 = 9.25$;
and for HClO/KClO: p$K_a = -\log K_a = -\log(2.9 \times 10^{-8}) = 7.54$.
So the NH_3/NH_4Cl buffer system has the pK_a that is closest to 9.00.

So pH $= pK_a + \log \dfrac{[base]}{[acid]} = 9.25 + \log \dfrac{[NH_3]}{[NH_4Cl]} = 9.00$. Solve for $[NH_3]$/$[NH_4Cl]$.

$\log \dfrac{[NH_3]}{[NH_4Cl]} = 9.00 - 9.25 = -0.25 \rightarrow \dfrac{[NH_3]}{[NH_4Cl]} = 10^{-0.25} = 0.562341$. Then convert to mass ratio using

$$\frac{\mathcal{M}(base)}{\mathcal{M}(acid)}, \ 0.562341 \frac{\dfrac{\cancel{NH_3}\ \cancel{mol}}{\cancel{L}}}{\dfrac{\cancel{NH_4Cl}\ \cancel{mol}}{\cancel{L}}} \times \frac{\dfrac{17.03 \text{ g } NH_3}{\cancel{mol\ NH_3}}}{\dfrac{53.49 \text{ g } NH_4Cl}{\cancel{mol\ NH_4Cl}}} = 0.18 \frac{\text{g } NH_3}{\text{g } NH_4Cl}.$$

Check: The units (none and g base/g acid) are correct. The buffer system with the K_a closest to 10^{-9} is the best choice. The magnitude of the answer makes physical sense because the buffer needs more acid than base and the acid component has a heavier molar mass, so the mass ratio is small.

16.33   **Given:** 500.0 mL of 0.100 M HNO_2/0.150 M KNO_2 buffer and (a) 250 mg NaOH, (b) 350 mg KOH, (c) 1.25 g HBr and (d) 1.35 g HI   **Find:** whether buffer capacity is exceeded
Conceptual Plan: mL $\rightarrow$ L then [HNO_2], L $\rightarrow$ mol HNO_2 and [KNO_2], L $\rightarrow$ mol KNO_2

$$\frac{1\text{ L}}{1000\text{ mL}} \qquad\qquad M = \frac{\text{mol}}{\text{L}} \qquad\qquad M = \frac{\text{mol}}{\text{L}}$$

then calculate moles of acid or base to be added to the buffer mg $\rightarrow$ g $\rightarrow$ mol then

$$\frac{1\text{ g}}{1000\text{ mg}} \quad \mathcal{M}$$

compare the added amount to the buffer amount of the opposite component. Ratio of base/acid must be between 0.1 and 10 to maintain the buffer integrity.

Solution: $500.00 \text{ mL} \times \dfrac{1\text{ L}}{1000 \text{ mL}} = 0.5000$ L then $\dfrac{0.100 \text{ mol } HNO_2}{1 \text{ L}} \times 0.5000 \text{ L} = 0.0500$ mol HNO_2 and

$\dfrac{0.150 \text{ mol } KNO_2}{1 \text{ L}} \times 0.5000 \text{ L} = 0.0750$ mol KNO_2.

(a)   For NaOH: $250 \text{ mg NaOH} \times \dfrac{1 \text{ g NaOH}}{1000 \text{ mg NaOH}} \times \dfrac{1 \text{ mol NaOH}}{40.00 \text{ g NaOH}} = 0.00625$ mol NaOH. Because the buffer

contains 0.0500 mol acid, the amount of acid is reduced by 0.00625/0.0500 = 12.5% and the ratio of base/acid is still between 0.1 and 10. The buffer capacity is not exceeded.

(b)   For KOH: $350 \text{ mg KOH} \times \dfrac{1 \text{ g KOH}}{1000 \text{ mg KOH}} \times \dfrac{1 \text{ mol KOH}}{56.11 \text{ g KOH}} = 0.00624$ mol KOH. Because the buffer

contains 0.0500 mol acid, the amount of acid is reduced by 0.00624/0.0500 = 12.5% and the ratio of base/acid is still between 0.1 and 10. The buffer capacity is not exceeded.

(c) For HBr: $1.25 \text{ g HBr} \times \dfrac{1 \text{ mol HBr}}{80.91 \text{ g HBr}} = 0.015\underline{4}493$ mol HBr. Because the buffer contains 0.0750 mol base, the amount of acid is reduced by $0.0154/0.0750 = 20.6\%$ and the ratio of base/acid is still between 0.1 and 10. The buffer capacity is not exceeded.

(d) For HI: $1.35 \text{ g HI} \times \dfrac{1 \text{ mol HI}}{127.91 \text{ g HI}} = 0.010\underline{5}543$ mol HI. Because the buffer contains 0.0750 mol base, the amount of acid is reduced by $0.0106/0.0750 = 14.1\%$ and the ratio of base/acid is still between 0.1 and 10. The buffer capacity is not exceeded.

16.34 **Given:** 1.0 L of 0.125 M HNO_2/0.145 M $NaNO_2$ buffer and (a) 1.5 g HCl, (b) 1.5 g NaOH, (c) 1.5 g HI
Find: $[HNO_2]$ and $[NaNO_2]$ after addition **Other:** $K_a(HNO_2) = 4.6 \times 10^{-4}$
Conceptual Plan: $[HNO_2], L \rightarrow$ mol HNO_2 and $[NaNO_2], L \rightarrow$ mol $NaNO_2 (=$ mol $NO_2^{-})$

$$M = \frac{\text{mol}}{L} \qquad\qquad M = \frac{\text{mol}}{L}$$

then calculate moles of acid or base to be added to the buffer $g \rightarrow$ **mol**

$$\mathcal{M}$$

then write balanced equation then mol HNO_2, mol NO_2^{-}, mol added species $\rightarrow$ mol HNO_2, mol NO_2^{-}

$$H^{+} + NO_2^{-} \rightarrow HNO_2 \qquad\qquad \text{set up stoichiometry table}$$
$$OH^{-} + HNO_2 \rightarrow NO_2^{-} + H_2O$$

mol HNO_2, L $\rightarrow [HNO_2]$ and mol $NO_2^{-} (=$ mol $NaNO_2$), L $\rightarrow [NaNO_2]$

$$M = \frac{\text{mol}}{L} \qquad\qquad M = \frac{\text{mol}}{L}$$

Solution: $\dfrac{0.125 \text{ mol } HNO_2}{1 \text{ L}} \times 1.0 \text{ L} = 0.1\underline{2}5$ mol HNO_2 and $\dfrac{0.145 \text{ mol } KNO_2}{1 \text{ L}} \times 1.0 \text{ L} = 0.1\underline{4}5$ mol KNO_2

(a) For HCl: $1.5 \text{ g HCl} \times \dfrac{1 \text{ mol HCl}}{36.46 \text{ g HCl}} = 0.041\underline{1}41$ mol HCl. Because HCl is a strong acid, $[HCl] = [H^{+}]$, and set up a table to track changes:

	$H^{+}(aq)$ +	$NO_2^{-}(aq) \rightarrow$	$HNO_2(aq)$
Before addition	≈ 0.00 mol	0.1$\underline{4}$5 mol	0.1$\underline{2}$5 mol
Addition	0.041$\underline{1}$41 mol	—	—
After addition	≈ 0.00 mol	0.104 mol	0.166 mol

Because the concentrations of the acid and base components have not changed much, the buffer is still able to do its job. Finally, because there is 1.0 L of solution, $[HNO_2] = 0.17$ M and $[NaNO_2] = 0.10$ M.

(b) For NaOH: $1.5 \text{ g NaOH} \times \dfrac{1 \text{ mol NaOH}}{40.00 \text{ g NaOH}} = 0.037\underline{5}$ mol NaOH. Because NaOH is a strong base, $[NaOH] = [OH^{-}]$, and set up a table to track changes:

	$OH^{-}(aq)$ +	$HNO_2(aq) \rightarrow$	$NO_2^{-}(aq)$ +	$H_2O(l)$
Before addition	≈ 0.00 mol	0.1$\underline{2}$5 mol	0.1$\underline{4}$5 mol	—
Addition	0.037$\underline{5}$ mol	—	—	—
After addition	≈ 0.00 mol	0.08$\underline{7}$5 mol	0.1$\underline{8}$25 mol	—

Because the concentrations of the acid and base components have not changed much, the buffer is still able to do its job. Finally, because there is 1.0 L of solution, $[HNO_2] = 0.09$ M and $[NaNO_2] = 0.18$ M.

(c) For HI: $1.5 \text{ g HI} \times \dfrac{1 \text{ mol HI}}{127.91 \text{ g HI}} = 0.011\underline{7}27$ mol HI. Because HI is a strong acid, $[HI] = [H^{+}]$, and set up a table to track changes:

	$H^{+}(aq)$ +	$NO_2^{-}(aq) \rightarrow$	$HNO_2(aq)$
Before addition	≈ 0.00 mol	0.1$\underline{4}$5 mol	0.1$\underline{2}$5 mol
Addition	0.011$\underline{7}$27 mol	—	—
After addition	≈ 0.00 mol	0.133 mol	0.137 mol

Because the concentrations of the acid and base components have not changed much, the buffer is still able to do its job. Finally, because there is 1.0 L of solution, $[HNO_2] = 0.14$ M and $[NaNO_2] = 0.13$ M.

Check: The units (M) are correct. Because the number of moles added is small compared to the buffer components, the buffer still remains active. Adding acid increases the amount of the conjugate base. Adding base increases the amount of the weak acid.

Titrations, pH Curves, and Indicators

16.35   (i)   The equivalence point of a titration is where the pH rises sharply as base is added. The pH at the equivalence point is the midpoint of the sharp rise at ~50 mL added base. For (a), the pH = ~8, and for (b), the pH = ~7.

       (ii)   Graph (a) represents a weak acid, and graph (b) represents a strong acid. A strong acid titration starts at a lower pH, has a flatter initial region, and has a sharper rise at the equivalence point than does a weak acid. The pH at the equivalence point of a strong acid is neutral, while the pH at the equivalence point of a weak acid is basic.

16.36   **Given:** 25.0 mL 0.100 M HCl and 0.100 M HF titrated with 0.200 M KOH

       (a)   **Find:** volume of base to reach equivalence point

           Conceptual Plan: The answer for both titrations will be the same because the initial concentration and volumes of the acids are the same and both acids are monoprotic. Write balanced equation

$$HCl + KOH \rightarrow KCl + H_2O \text{ and } HF + KOH \rightarrow KF + H_2O$$

           then mL $\rightarrow$ L then [acid], L $\rightarrow$ mol acid then set mol acid = mol base and

$$\frac{1\text{ L}}{1000\text{ mL}} \qquad\qquad M = \frac{mol}{L} \qquad\qquad \text{balanced equation has 1 : 1 stoichiometry}$$

           [KOH], mol KOH $\rightarrow$ L KOH $\rightarrow$ mL KOH.

$$M = \frac{mol}{L} \qquad\qquad \frac{1000\text{ mL}}{1\text{ L}}$$

           Solution: $25.0 \text{ mL acid} \times \dfrac{1\text{ L}}{1000\text{ mL}} = 0.0250$ L acid then

$$\frac{0.100\text{ mol acid}}{1\text{ L}} \times 0.0250\text{ L} = 0.00250 \text{ mol acid. So mol acid} = 0.00250 \text{ mol} = \text{mol KOH then}$$

$$0.00250 \text{ mol KOH} \times \frac{1\text{ L KOH}}{0.200\text{ mol KOH}} = 0.0125 \text{ L KOH} \times \frac{1000\text{ mL}}{1\text{ L}} = 12.5 \text{ mL KOH for both titrations.}$$

           Check: The units (mL) are correct. The volume of base is half the volume of acids because the concentration of the base is twice that of the acids. The answer for both titrations is the same because the stoichiometry is the same for both titration reactions.

       (b)   The pH at the equivalence point will be neutral for HCl (because it is a strong acid), and it will be basic for HF (because it is a weak acid and will produce a conjugate base when titrated).

       (c)   The initial pH will be lower for HCl (because it is a strong acid), so it dissociates completely. The HF (because it is a weak acid) will only partially dissociate and not drop the pH as low as HCl at the same acid concentration.

       (d)   The titration curves will look like the following:

HCl:

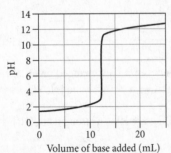

HF:

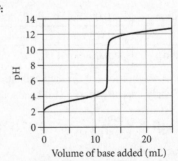

Important features to include are low initial pH (if strong acid pH is 1 and is higher for a weak acid), flat initial region (very flat for strong acid, not as flat for weak acid where pH halfway to equivalence point is the pK_a of the acid), sharp rise at equivalence point, pH at equivalence point (neutral for strong acid and higher for weak acid), and then flattening out at high pH.

16.37   **Given:** 20.0 mL 0.200 M KOH and 0.200 M CH_3NH_2 titrated with 0.100 M HI

(a)   **Find:** volume of base to reach equivalence point

Conceptual Plan: The answer for both titrations will be the same because the initial concentration and volumes of the bases are the same. Write balanced equation then mL → L then

$$HI + KOH \rightarrow KI + H_2O \text{ and } HI + KOH \rightarrow CH_3NH_3I \qquad \frac{1 \text{ L}}{1000 \text{ mL}}$$

[base], L → mol base then set mol base = mol acid and [HI], mol HI → L HI → mL HI.

$$M = \frac{mol}{L} \qquad\qquad \text{balanced equation has 1 : 1 stoichiometry} \qquad\qquad M = \frac{mol}{L} \qquad \frac{1000 \text{ mL}}{1 \text{ L}}$$

Solution: $20.0 \text{ mL base} \times \dfrac{1 \text{ L}}{1000 \text{ mL}} = 0.0200 \text{ L base}$ then

$\dfrac{0.200 \text{ mol base}}{1 \text{ L}} \times 0.0200 \text{ L} = 0.00400 \text{ mol base}$. So mol base = 0.00400 mol = mol HI then

$0.00400 \text{ mol HI} \times \dfrac{1 \text{ L HI}}{0.100 \text{ mol HI}} = 0.0400 \text{ L HI} \times \dfrac{1000 \text{ mL}}{1 \text{ L}} = 40.0 \text{ mL HI for both titrations.}$

Check: The units (mL) are correct. The volume of acid is twice the volume of bases because the concentration of the base is twice that of the acid in each case. The answer for both titrations is the same because the stoichiometry is the same for both titration reactions.

(b)   The pH at the equivalence point will be neutral for KOH (because it is a strong base), and it will be acidic for CH_3NH_2 (because it is a weak base and will produce a conjugate acid when titrated).

(c)   The initial pH will be lower for CH_3NH_2 (because it is a weak base and will only partially dissociate) and not raise the pH as high as KOH will (because it is a strong base and so dissociates completely) at the same base concentration.

(d)   The titration curves will look like the following:

KOH:

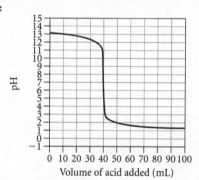

CH_3NH_2:

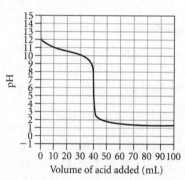

Important features to include are a high initial pH (if strong base pH is over 13 and is lower for a weak base), flat initial region (very flat for strong base, not as flat for weak base where pH halfway to equivalence point is the pK_b of the base), sharp drop at equivalence point, pH at equivalence point (neutral for strong base and lower for weak base), and then a flattening out at low pH.

16.38   (i)   The equivalence point of a titration is where the pH drops sharply as acid is added. The pH at the equivalence point is the midpoint of the sharp drop at ~25 mL added acid. For (a), the pH = ~7, and for (b), the pH = ~5.

(ii)   Graph (a) represents a strong base, and graph (b) represents a weak base. A strong base titration starts at a higher pH, has a flatter initial region and a sharper drop at the equivalence point than does a weak base. The pH at the equivalence point of a strong base is neutral, while the pH at the equivalence point of a weak base is acidic.

16.39   (a)   The equivalence point of a titration is where the pH rises sharply as base is added. The volume at the equivalence point is ~30 mL. The pH at the equivalence point is the midpoint of the sharp rise at ~30 mL added base, which is a pH = ~9.

(b)   At 0 mL, the pH is calculated by doing an equilibrium calculation of a weak acid in water (as done in Chapter 15).

(c)   The pH halfway to the equivalence point is equal to the pK_a of the acid, or ~15 mL.

(d)   The pH at the equivalence point, or ~30 mL, is calculated by doing an equilibrium problem with the K_b of the acid. At the equivalence point, all of the acid has been converted to its conjugate base.

(e)   Beyond the equivalence point (30 mL), there is excess base. All of the acid has been converted to its conjugate base, so the pH is calculated by focusing on this excess base concentration.

16.40   (a)   The equivalence point of a titration is where the pH drops sharply as acid is added. The volume at the equivalence point is ~ 25 mL. The pH at the equivalence point is the midpoint of the sharp drop at ~ 25 mL added acid, which is a pH $= \sim 6$.

(b)   At 0 mL, the pH is calculated by doing an equilibrium calculation of a weak base in water (as done in Chapter 15).

(c)   The pH halfway to the equivalence point is equal to the $14 - pK_b = pK_a$ of the base, or ~ 12 mL.

(d)   The pH at the equivalence point, or ~ 25 mL, is calculated by doing an equilibrium problem with the K_a of the base. At the equivalence point, all of the base has been converted to its conjugate acid.

(e)   Beyond the equivalence point (25 mL), there is excess acid. All of the base has been converted to its conjugate acid, so the pH is calculated by focusing on this excess acid concentration.

16.41   **Given:** 35.0 mL of 0.175 M HBr titrated with 0.200 M KOH

(a)   **Find:** initial pH

Conceptual Plan: Because HBr is a strong acid, it will dissociate completely; so initial pH $= -\log[H_3O^+] = -\log[HBr]$.

Solution: pH $= -\log[HBr] = -\log 0.175 = 0.757$

Check: The units (none) are correct. The pH is reasonable because the concentration is greater than 0.1 M, and when the acid dissociates completely, the pH becomes less than 1.

(b)   **Find:** volume of base to reach equivalence point

Conceptual Plan: Write balanced equation then mL $\rightarrow$ L then [HBr], L $\rightarrow$ mol HBr then

$$HBr + KOH \rightarrow KBr + H_2O \qquad \frac{1\,L}{1000\,mL} \qquad M = \frac{mol}{L}$$

set mol acid (HBr) $=$ mol base (KOH) and [KOH], mol KOH $\rightarrow$ L KOH $\rightarrow$ mL KOH.

$$\text{balanced equation has 1:1 stoichiometry} \qquad M = \frac{mol}{L} \qquad \frac{1000\,mL}{1\,L}$$

Solution: $35.0 \; \text{mL HBr} \times \dfrac{1\,L}{1000\,mL} = 0.0350\,L\,\text{HBr}$ then

$\dfrac{0.175\,\text{mol HBr}}{1\,L} \times 0.0350\,L = 0.006125\,\text{mol HBr}$ then

So mol acid $=$ mol HBr $= 0.006125$ mol $=$ mol KOH then

$0.006125\;\text{mol KOH} \times \dfrac{1\,L}{0.200\;\text{mol KOH}} = 0.030625\;\text{L KOH} \times \dfrac{1000\,mL}{1\,L} = 30.6\,\text{mL KOH}$

Check: The units (mL) are correct. The volume of base is a little less than the volume of acid because the concentration of the base is a little greater than that of the acid.

(c)   **Find:** pH after adding 10.0 mL of base

Conceptual Plan: Use calculations from part (b). Then mL $\rightarrow$ L then [KOH], L $\rightarrow$ mol KOH then

$$\frac{1\,L}{1000\,mL} \qquad M = \frac{mol}{L}$$

mol HBr, mol KOH $\rightarrow$ mol excess HBr and L HBr, L KOH $\rightarrow$ total L then

$$\text{set up stoichiometry table} \qquad L\,HBr + L\,KOH = \text{total L}$$

mol excess HBr, L $\rightarrow$ [HBr] $\rightarrow$ pH.

$$M = \frac{mol}{L} \qquad pH = -\log[HBr]$$

Solution: $10.0 \; \text{mL KOH} \times \dfrac{1\,L}{1000\,mL} = 0.0100\,L\,\text{KOH}$ then

$\dfrac{0.200\,\text{mol KOH}}{1\,L} \times 0.0100\,L = 0.00200\,\text{mol KOH}$

Because KOH is a strong base, [KOH] $=$ [OH$^-$], and set up a table to track changes:

	KOH(aq) $+$	HBr(aq) $\rightarrow$	KBr(aq) $+$	H$_2$O(l)
Before addition	≈ 0.00 mol	0.006125 mol	0.00 mol	—
Addition	0.00200 mol	—	—	—
After addition	≈ 0.00 mol	0.004125 mol	0.00200 mol	—

Then 0.0350 L HBr + 0.0100 L KOH = 0.0450 L total volume.

So mol excess acid = mol HBr = 0.004125 mol in 0.0450 L so

$$[HBr] = \frac{0.004125 \text{ mol HBr}}{0.0450 \text{ L}} = 0.0916667 \text{ M and}$$

pH = −log[HBr] = −log 0.0916667 = 1.038

Check: The units (none) are correct. The pH is a little higher than the initial pH, which is expected because this is a strong acid.

(d) **Find:** pH at equivalence point
Solution: Because this is a strong acid–strong base titration, the pH at the equivalence point is neutral, or 7.

(e) **Find:** pH after adding 5.0 mL of base beyond the equivalence point
Conceptual Plan: Use calculations from parts (b) and (c). Then the pH is only dependent on the amount of excess base and the total solution volumes.
mL excess → L excess then [KOH], L excess → mol KOH excess

$$\frac{1 \text{ L}}{1000 \text{ mL}} \qquad\qquad M = \frac{mol}{L}$$

then L HBr, L KOH to equivalence point, L KOH excess → total L then

$$L \text{ HBr} + L \text{ KOH to equivalence point} + L \text{ KOH excess} = \text{total L}$$

mol excess KOH, total L → [KOH] = [OH⁻] → [H₃O⁺] → pH

$$M = \frac{mol}{L} \qquad K_w = [H_3O^+][OH^-] \qquad pH = -\log[H_3O^+]$$

Solution: $5.0 \text{ mL KOH} \times \dfrac{1 \text{ L}}{1000 \text{ mL}} = 0.0050 \text{ L KOH excess then}$

$$\frac{0.200 \text{ mol KOH}}{1 \text{ L}} \times 0.0050 \text{ L} = 0.0010 \text{ mol KOH excess. Then } 0.0350 \text{ L HBr} + 0.0306 \text{ L KOH} + 0.0050 \text{ L}$$

KOH = 0.0706 L total volume. $[KOH \text{ excess}] = \dfrac{0.0010 \text{ mol KOH excess}}{0.0706 \text{ L}} = 0.014164 \text{ M KOH excess.}$

Because KOH is a strong base, [KOH] excess = [OH⁻]. $K_w = [H_3O^+][OH^-]$, so

$$[H_3O^+] = \frac{K_w}{[OH^-]} = \frac{1.0 \times 10^{-14}}{0.014164} = 7.06 \times 10^{-13} \text{ M.}$$

Finally, pH = −log[H₃O⁺] = −log(7.06 × 10⁻¹³) = 12.15.

Check: The units (none) are correct. The pH is rising sharply at the equivalence point, so the pH after 5 mL past the equivalence point should be quite basic.

16.42 **Given:** 20.0 mL of 0.125 M HNO₃ titrated with 0.150 M NaOH
Find: pH at five different points and plot titration curve
Conceptual Plan: Choose points to calculate (a) initial pH, (b) pH after 5.0 mL, (c) pH after 10.0 mL, (d) pH at equivalence point, and (e) pH at 25.0 mL. Points should be on both sides of the equivalence point.
(a) **Because HNO₃ is a strong acid, it will dissociate completely, so initial pH = −log[H₃O⁺] = −log[HNO₃].**
Solution: pH = −log[HNO₃] = −log 0.125 = 0.903

Check: The units (none) are correct. The pH is reasonable because the concentration is greater than 0.1 M, and when the acid dissociates completely, the pH becomes less than 1.

(b) **Find:** pH after adding 5.0 mL of base
Conceptual Plan: Write balanced equation then mL → L then [HNO₃], L → mol HNO₃ then

$$HNO_3 + NaOH \rightarrow NaNO_3 + H_2O \qquad \frac{1 \text{ L}}{1000 \text{ mL}} \qquad M = \frac{mol}{L}$$

mL → L then [NaOH], L → mol NaOH then mol HNO₃, mol NaOH → mol excess HNO₃

$$\frac{1 \text{ L}}{1000 \text{ mL}} \qquad M = \frac{mol}{L} \qquad\qquad \text{set up stoichiometry table}$$

and L HNO₃, L NaOH → total L then mol excess HNO₃, L → [HNO₃] → pH.

$$L \text{ HNO}_3 + L \text{ NaOH} = \text{total L} \qquad M = \frac{mol}{L} \qquad pH = -\log[HNO_3]$$

Solution: 20.0 mL HNO$_3$ × $\dfrac{1\,L}{1000\,mL}$ = 0.0200 L HNO$_3$ then

$\dfrac{0.125\,mol\,HNO_3}{1\,L}$ × 0.0200 L = 0.00250 mol HNO$_3$ and 5.0 mL NaOH × $\dfrac{1\,L}{1000\,mL}$ = 0.0050 L NaOH

then $\dfrac{0.150\,mol\,NaOH}{1\,L}$ × 0.0050 L = 0.00075 mol NaOH

This is a strong acid–strong base titration, so set up a table to track changes:

$$NaOH(aq) + HNO_3(aq) \rightarrow NaNO_3(aq) + H_2O(l)$$

	NaOH	HNO$_3$	NaNO$_3$	H$_2$O
Before addition	0.00 mol	0.00250 mol	0.00 mol	—
Addition	0.00075 mol	—	—	—
After addition	≈0.00 mol	0.00175 mol	0.00075 mol	—

Then 0.0200 L HNO$_3$ + 0.0050 L NaOH = 0.0250 L total volume. So mol excess acid = mol HNO$_3$ =

0.00175 mol in 0.0250 L, so [HNO$_3$] = $\dfrac{0.00175\,mol\,HNO_3}{0.0250\,L}$ = 0.0700 M and

pH = −log[HNO$_3$] = −log 0.0700 = 1.155.

Check: The units (none) are correct. The pH remains very low in a strong acid–strong base titration before the equivalence point.

(c) **Find:** pH after adding 10.0 mL of base
  Conceptual Plan: Use calculations for point (b) then mL → L then [NaOH], L → mol NaOH then

$\dfrac{1\,L}{1000\,mL}$ $M = \dfrac{mol}{L}$

  mol HNO$_3$, mol NaOH → mol excess HNO$_3$ and L HNO$_3$, L NaOH → total L then

  set up stoichiometry table   L HNO$_3$ + L NaOH = total L

  mol excess HNO$_3$, L → [HNO$_3$] → pH.

  $M = \dfrac{mol}{L}$ pH = −log[HNO$_3$]

Solution: 10.0 mL NaOH × $\dfrac{1\,L}{1000\,mL}$ = 0.0100 L NaOH then

$\dfrac{0.150\,mol\,NaOH}{1\,L}$ × 0.0100 L = 0.00150 mol NaOH. Set up a table to track changes:

$$NaOH(aq) + HNO_3(aq) \rightarrow NaNO_3(aq) + H_2O(l)$$

	NaOH	HNO$_3$	NaNO$_3$	H$_2$O
Before addition	0.00 mol	0.00250 mol	0.00 mol	—
Addition	0.00150 mol	—	—	—
After addition	≈0.00 mol	0.00100 mol	0.00150 mol	—

Then 0.0200 L HNO$_3$ + 0.0100 L NaOH = 0.0300 L total volume. So mol excess acid = mol HNO$_3$ =

0.00100 mol in 0.0300 L, so [HNO$_3$] = $\dfrac{0.00100\,mol\,HNO_3}{0.0300\,L}$ = 0.0333333 M and

pH = −log[HNO$_3$] = −log 0.0333333 = 1.477.

Check: The units (none) are correct. The pH remains very low in a strong acid–strong base titration before the equivalence point.

(d) **Find:** pH at equivalence point and volume of base to reach equivalence point
  Conceptual Plan: Because this is a strong acid–strong base titration, the pH at the equivalence point is neutral, or 7. Use calculations for point (b) then set mol acid (HNO$_3$) = mol base (NaOH) and

  balanced equation has 1:1 stoichiometry

  [NaOH], mol NaOH → L NaOH → mL NaOH.

  $M = \dfrac{mol}{L}$ $\dfrac{1000\,mL}{1\,L}$

Solution: Because this is a strong acid–strong base titration, the pH at the equivalence point is neutral, or 7. So mol acid = mol HNO$_3$ = 0.00250 mol = mol NaOH then

$$0.00250 \ \text{mol NaOH} \times \frac{1 \ \text{L}}{0.150 \ \text{mol NaOH}} = 0.0166667 \ \text{L NaOH} \times \frac{1000 \ \text{mL}}{1 \ \text{L}} = 16.7 \ \text{mL NaOH}.$$

Check: The units (none and mL) are correct. The equivalence point pH of a strong acid–strong base titration is neutral. The volume of base is a little less than the volume of acid because the concentration of the base is a little greater than that of the acid.

(e)   **Find:** pH after adding 25.0 mL of base

Conceptual Plan: Use calculations for point (b) then mL → L then [NaOH], L → mol NaOH then

$$\frac{1 \ \text{L}}{1000 \ \text{mL}} \qquad\qquad M = \frac{\text{mol}}{\text{L}}$$

mol HNO_3, mol NaOH → mol excess HNO_3 and L HNO_3, L NaOH → total L then

set up stoichiometry table   L HNO_3 + L NaOH = total L

mol excess NaOH, total L → [NaOH] = [OH^-] → [H_3O^+] → pH.

$$M = \frac{\text{mol}}{\text{L}} \qquad\qquad K_w = [H_3O^+][OH^-] \quad pH = -\log[H_3O^+]$$

Solution: $25.0 \ \text{mL NaOH} \times \dfrac{1 \ \text{L}}{1000 \ \text{mL}} = 0.0250 \ \text{L NaOH}$ then

$\dfrac{0.150 \ \text{mol NaOH}}{1 \ \text{L}} \times 0.0250 \ \text{L} = 0.00375 \ \text{mol NaOH}.$ Set up a table to track changes:

$$NaOH(aq) \ + \ HNO_3(aq) \ \rightarrow \ NaNO_3(aq) \ + \ H_2O(l)$$

Before addition	0.00 mol	0.00250 mol	0.00 mol	—
Addition	0.00375 mol	—	—	—
After addition	0.00125 mol	≈0.00 mol	0.00275 mol	—

Then $0.0200 \ \text{L} \ HNO_3 + 0.0250 \ \text{L NaOH} = 0.0450 \ \text{L}$ total volume. So mol excess acid = mol NaOH =

0.00125 mol in 0.0450 L, so $[\text{NaOH excess}] = \dfrac{0.00125 \ \text{mol NaOH excess}}{0.0450 \ \text{L}} = 0.0277778 \ \text{M NaOH excess}.$

Because NaOH is a strong base, [NaOH] excess = [OH^-]. $K_w = [H_3O^+][OH^-]$, so

$$[H_3O^+] = \frac{K_w}{[OH^-]} = \frac{1.0 \times 10^{-14}}{0.0277778} = 3.6 \times 10^{-13} \ \text{M}.$$

Finally, $pH = -\log[H_3O^+] = -\log(3.6 \times 10^{-13}) = 12.44.$

Check: The units (none) are correct. The pH is rising sharply at the equivalence point, so the pH over 5 mL past the equivalence point should be quite basic. Finally, after plotting these five points, the titration curve looks like the following:

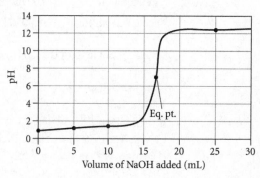

16.43   **Given:** 25.0 mL of 0.115 M RbOH titrated with 0.100 M HCl

(a)   **Find:** initial pH

Conceptual Plan: Because RbOH is a strong base, it will dissociate completely, so
[RbOH] = [OH^-] → [H_3O^+] → pH.

$$K_w = [H_3O^+][OH^-] \quad pH = -\log[H_3O^+]$$

Solution: Because RbOH is a strong base, [RbOH] excess = [OH^-]. $K_w = [H_3O^+][OH^-]$, so

$$[H_3O^+] = \frac{K_w}{[OH^-]} = \frac{1.0 \times 10^{-14}}{0.115} = 8.69565 \times 10^{-14} \ \text{M and}$$

$pH = -\log[H_3O^+] = -\log(8.69565 \times 10^{-14}) = 13.06.$

Check: The units (none) are correct. The pH is reasonable because the concentration is greater than 0.1 M, and when the base dissociates completely, the pH becomes greater than 13.

(b) **Find:** volume of acid to reach equivalence point
Conceptual Plan: Write balanced equation then mL → L then [RbOH], L → mol RbOH then

$$HCl + RbOH \rightarrow RbCl + H_2O \qquad \frac{1\ L}{1000\ mL} \qquad M = \frac{mol}{L}$$

set mol base (RbOH) = mol acid (HCl) and [HCl], mol HCl → L HCl → mL HCl.

$$\text{balanced equation has 1:1 stoichiometry} \qquad M = \frac{mol}{L} \qquad \frac{1000\ mL}{1\ L}$$

Solution: $25.0\ mL\ RbOH \times \dfrac{1\ L}{1000\ mL} = 0.0250\ L\ RbOH$ then

$\dfrac{0.115\ mol\ RbOH}{1\ L} \times 0.0250\ L = 0.002875\ mol\ RbOH.$ So mol base = mol RbOH = 0.002875 mol = mol

HCl then $0.002875\ mol\ HCl \times \dfrac{1\ L}{0.100\ mol\ HCl} = 0.02875\ L\ HCl \times \dfrac{1000\ mL}{1\ L} = 28.8\ mL\ HCl.$

Check: The units (mL) are correct. The volume of acid is greater than the volume of base because the concentration of the base is a little greater than that of the acid.

(c) **Find:** pH after adding 5.0 mL of acid
Conceptual Plan: Use calculations from part (b). Then mL → L then [HCl], L → mol HCl then

$$\frac{1\ L}{1000\ mL} \qquad M = \frac{mol}{L}$$

mol RbOH, mol HCl → mol excess RbOH and L RbOH, L HCl → total L then

$$\text{set up stoichiometry table} \qquad L\ RbOH + L\ HCl = total\ L$$

mol excess RbOH, L → [RbOH] = [OH⁻] → [H₃O⁺] → pH.

$$M = \frac{mol}{L} \qquad K_w = [H_3O^+][OH^-] \quad pH = -\log[H_3O^+]$$

Solution: $5.0\ mL\ HCl \times \dfrac{1\ L}{1000\ mL} = 0.0050\ L\ HCl$ then $\dfrac{0.100\ mol\ HCl}{1\ L} \times 0.0050\ L = 0.00050\ mol\ HCl$

Because HCl is a strong acid, $[HCl] = [H_3O^+]$. Set up a table to track changes:

	HCl(aq)	+ RbOH(aq)	→ RbCl(aq)	+ H₂O(l)
Before addition	0.00 mol	0.002875 mol	0.00 mol	—
Addition	0.00050 mol	—	—	—
After addition	≈0.00 mol	0.002375 mol	0.00050 mol	—

Then $0.0250\ L\ RbOH + 0.0050\ L\ HCl = 0.0300\ L$ total volume. So mol excess base = mol RbOH =

0.002375 mol in 0.0300 L, so $[RbOH] = \dfrac{0.002375\ mol\ RbOH}{0.0300\ L} = 0.0791667\ M.$ Because RbOH is a strong

base, $[RbOH]$ excess = $[OH^-]$. $K_w = [H_3O^+][OH^-]$ so $[H_3O^+] = \dfrac{K_w}{[OH^-]} = \dfrac{1.0 \times 10^{-14}}{0.0791667}$

$= 1.26316 \times 10^{-13}\ M$ and $pH = -\log[H_3O^+] = -\log(1.26316 \times 10^{-13}) = 12.90$

Check: The units (none) are correct. The pH is a little lower than the initial pH, which is expected because this is a strong base.

(d) **Find:** pH at equivalence point
Solution: Because this is a strong acid–strong base titration, the pH at the equivalence point is neutral, or 7.

(e) **Find:** pH after adding 5.0 mL of acid beyond the equivalence point
Conceptual Plan: Use calculations from parts (b) and (c). Then the pH is only dependent on the amount of excess acid and the total solution volumes. Then
mL excess → L excess then [HCl], L excess → mol HCl excess

$$\frac{1\ L}{1000\ mL} \qquad M = \frac{mol}{L}$$

then L RbOH, L HCl to equivalence point, L HCl excess → total L then

$$L\ RbOH + L\ HCl\ to\ equivalence\ point + L\ HCl\ excess = total\ L$$

mol excess HCl, total L → [HCl] = [H₃O⁺] → pH

$$M = \frac{mol}{L} \qquad\qquad pH = -\log[H_3O^+]$$

Solution: $5.0 \text{ mL HCl} \times \dfrac{1 \text{ L}}{1000 \text{ mL}} = 0.0050 \text{ L HCl excess then}$

$\dfrac{0.100 \text{ mol HCl}}{1 \text{ L}} \times 0.0050 \text{ L} = 0.00050 \text{ mol HCl excess. Then } 0.0250 \text{ L RbOH} + 0.0288 \text{ L HCl} + 0.0050 \text{ L}$

$\text{HCl} = 0.0588 \text{ L total volume. [HCl excess]} = \dfrac{0.00050 \text{ mol HCl excess}}{0.0588 \text{ L}} = 0.008\underline{5}034 \text{ M HCl excess}$

Because HCl is a strong acid, [HCl] excess = $[H_3O^+]$.

Finally, $pH = -\log[H_3O^+] = -\log(0.008\underline{5}034) = 2.07$.

Check: The units (none) are correct. The pH is dropping sharply at the equivalence point, so the pH after 5 mL past the equivalence point should be quite acidic.

16.44   **Given:** 15.0 mL of 0.100 M Ba(OH)₂ titrated with 0.125 M HCl

Find: pH at five different points and plot titration curve

Conceptual Plan: Choose points to calculate (a) initial pH, (b) pH after 10.0 mL, (c) pH after 20.0 mL, (d) pH at equivalence point, and (e) pH at 30.0 mL. Points should be on both sides of the equivalence point.

(a)   **Find:** initial pH

Conceptual Plan: Because Ba(OH)₂ is a strong base, it will dissociate completely. Keep in mind that Ba(OH)₂ → Ba²⁺ + 2 OH⁻, so two hydroxide ions are generated for each barium hydroxide and 2 [Ba(OH)₂] = [OH⁻] → [H₃O⁺] → pH.

$$K_w = [H_3O^+][OH^-] \qquad pH = -\log[H_3O^+]$$

Solution: Because Ba(OH)₂ is a strong base, $2\,[Ba(OH)_2] = [OH^-] = 2 \times 0.100 \text{ M} = 0.200 \text{ M}$.

$K_w = [H_3O^+][OH^-]$, so $[H_3O^+] = \dfrac{K_w}{[OH^-]} = \dfrac{1.0 \times 10^{-14}}{0.200} = 5.0 \times 10^{-14} \text{ M and}$

$pH = -\log[H_3O^+] = -\log(5.0 \times 10^{-14}) = 13.30$

Check: The units (none) are correct. The pH is reasonable because the concentration is greater than 0.1 M, and when the base dissociates completely, the pH is greater than 13.

(b)   **Find:** pH after adding 10.0 mL of acid

Conceptual Plan: Write a balanced equation then mL → L then [Ba(OH)₂], L → mol Ba(OH)₂ then

$$2\,HCl + Ba(OH)_2 \rightarrow BaCl_2 + 2\,H_2O \qquad \frac{1 \text{ L}}{1000 \text{ mL}} \qquad M = \frac{mol}{L}$$

mL → L then [HCl], L → mol HCl then mol Ba(OH)₂, mol HCl → mol excess Ba(OH)₂ and

$$\frac{1 \text{ L}}{1000 \text{ mL}} \qquad M = \frac{mol}{L} \qquad\qquad\qquad \text{set up stoichiometry table}$$

L Ba(OH)₂, L HCl → total L then

$$M = \frac{mol}{L}$$

mol excess Ba(OH)₂, L → 2[(Ba(OH)₂] = [OH⁻] → [H₃O⁺] → pH.

$$\text{L Ba(OH)}_2 + \text{L HCl} = \text{total L} \qquad K_w = [H_3O^+][OH^-] \qquad pH = -\log[H_3O^+]$$

Solution: $15.0 \text{ mL Ba(OH)}_2 \times \dfrac{1 \text{ L}}{1000 \text{ mL}} = 0.0150 \text{ L Ba(OH)}_2 \text{ then}$

$\dfrac{0.100 \text{ mol Ba(OH)}_2}{1 \text{ L}} \times 0.0150 \text{ L} = 0.00150 \text{ mol Ba(OH)}_2 \text{ and } 10.0 \text{ mL HCl} \times \dfrac{1 \text{ L}}{1000 \text{ mL}} = 0.0100 \text{ L HCl}$

then $\dfrac{0.125 \text{ mol HCl}}{1 \text{ L}} \times 0.0100 \text{ L} = 0.00125 \text{ mol HCl. Because HCl is a strong acid, [HCl]} = [H_3O^+], \text{ and}$

set up a table to track changes:

	2 HCl(aq)	+ Ba(OH)₂(aq)	→ BaCl₂(aq)	+ 2 H₂O(l)
Before addition	0.00 mol	0.00150 mol	0.00 mol	—
Addition	0.00125 mol	—	—	—
After addition	≈0.00 mol	0.000875 mol	0.000625 mol	—

Then 0.0150 L Ba(OH)$_2$ + 0.0100 L HCl = 0.0250 L total volume. So mol excess base = mol Ba(OH)$_2$ = 0.000875 mol in 0.0250 L, so [Ba(OH)$_2$] = $\dfrac{0.000875 \text{ mol Ba(OH)}_2}{0.0250 \text{ L}}$ = 0.035 M. Because Ba(OH)$_2$ is a strong base, 2 [Ba(OH)$_2$] = [OH$^-$] = 2 × 0.035 M = 0.070 M. K_w = [H$_3$O$^+$][OH$^-$], so

[H$_3$O$^+$] = $\dfrac{K_w}{\text{[OH}^-]}$ = $\dfrac{1.0 \times 10^{-14}}{0.070}$ = 1.4286 × 10^{-13} M and

pH = $-$log[H$_3$O$^+$] = $-$log(1.4286 × 10^{-13}) = 12.85.

Check: The units (none) are correct. The pH is a little lower than the initial pH, which is expected because this is a strong base.

(c)   **Find:** pH after adding 20.0 mL of acid
Conceptual Plan: Use calculations from part (b) then mL → L then [HCl], L → mol HCl then

$$\frac{1 \text{ L}}{1000 \text{ mL}} \qquad\qquad M = \frac{\text{mol}}{\text{L}}$$

mol Ba(OH)$_2$, mol HCl → mol excess Ba(OH)$_2$ and L Ba(OH)$_2$, L HCl → total L then

set up stoichiometry table   L Ba(OH)$_2$ + L HCl = total L

mol excess Ba(OH)$_2$, L → 2 [Ba(OH)$_2$] = [OH$^-$] → [H$_3$O$^+$] → pH.

$$M = \frac{\text{mol}}{\text{L}} \qquad\qquad K_w = \text{[H}_3\text{O}^+]\text{[OH}^-] \quad pH = -\log\text{[H}_3\text{O}^+]$$

Solution: 20.0 mL HCl × $\dfrac{1 \text{ L}}{1000 \text{ mL}}$ = 0.0200 L HCl then $\dfrac{0.125 \text{ mol HCl}}{1 \text{ L}}$ × 0.0200 L = 0.00250 mol HCl

Because HCl is a strong acid, [HCl] = [H$_3$O$^+$], and set up a table to track changes:

$$2 \text{ HCl}(aq) + \text{Ba(OH)}_2(aq) \rightarrow \text{BaCl}_2(aq) + 2 \text{ H}_2\text{O}(l)$$

	2 HCl(aq)	Ba(OH)$_2$(aq)	BaCl$_2$(aq)	H$_2$O(l)
Before addition	0.00 mol	0.00150 mol	0.00 mol	—
Addition	0.00250 mol	—	—	—
After addition	≈0.00 mol	0.00025 mol	0.00125 mol	—

Then 0.0150 L Ba(OH)$_2$ + 0.0200 L HCl = 0.0350 L total volume. So mol excess base = mol Ba(OH)$_2$ = 0.00025 mol in 0.0350 L, so [Ba(OH)$_2$] = $\dfrac{0.00025 \text{ mol Ba(OH)}_2}{0.0350 \text{ L}}$ = 0.0071429 M. Because Ba(OH)$_2$ is a strong base, 2 [Ba(OH)$_2$] = [OH$^-$] = 2 × 0.0071429 M = 0.014286 M. K_w = [H$_3$O$^+$][OH$^-$], so

[H$_3$O$^+$] = $\dfrac{K_w}{\text{[OH}^-]}$ = $\dfrac{1.0 \times 10^{-14}}{0.014286}$ = 6.99986 × 10^{-13} M and

pH = $-$log[H$_3$O$^+$] = $-$log(6.99986 × 10^{-13}) = 12.15.

Check: The units (none) are correct. The pH is a little lower than the initial pH, which is expected because this is a strong base.

(d)   **Find:** pH at equivalence point and volume of acid to reach equivalence point
Solution: Because this is a strong acid–strong base titration, the pH at the equivalence point is neutral, or 7.
Conceptual Plan: Use calculations from part (b) then set 2 mol base (Ba(OH)$_2$) = mol acid (HCl) and

balanced equation has 1:2 stoichiometry

[HCl], mol HCl → L HCl → mL HCl.

$$M = \frac{\text{mol}}{\text{L}} \qquad \frac{1000 \text{ mL}}{1 \text{ L}}$$

Solution: 0.00150 mol Ba(OH)$_2$ × $\dfrac{2 \text{ mol HCl}}{1 \text{ mol Ba(OH)}_2}$ = 0.00300 mol HCl then

0.00300 mol HCl × $\dfrac{1 \text{ L}}{0.125 \text{ mol HCl}}$ = 0.0240 L HCl × $\dfrac{1000 \text{ mL}}{1 \text{ L}}$ = 24.0 mL HCl

Check: The units (mL) are correct. The volume of acid is greater than the volume of base because two moles of acid are needed for each mole of base.

(e) **Find:** pH after adding 30.0 mL of acid

Conceptual Plan: Use calculations from earlier parts. Then the pH is only dependent on the amount of excess acid and the total solution volumes.

mL added, mL at equiv. pt. → mL excess → L excess then

$$\text{mL excess} = \text{mL added} - \text{mL at equiv. pt.} \quad \frac{1 \text{ L}}{1000 \text{ mL}}$$

[HCl], L excess → mol HCl excess then L Ba(OH)$_2$, L HCl → total L then

$$M = \frac{\text{mol}}{\text{L}} \qquad\qquad \text{L Ba(OH)}_2 + \text{L HCl} = \text{total L}$$

mol excess HCl, total L → [HCl] = [H$_3$O$^+$] → pH

$$M = \frac{\text{mol}}{\text{L}} \qquad \text{pH} = -\log[\text{H}_3\text{O}^+]$$

Solution: mL HCl excess = mL added − mL to equiv. pt. = 30.0 mL − 24.0 mL = 6.0 mL.

$$6.0 \text{ mL HCl} \times \frac{1 \text{ L}}{1000 \text{ mL}} = 0.0060 \text{ L HCl excess then}$$

$$\frac{0.125 \text{ mol HCl}}{1 \text{ L}} \times 0.0060 \text{ L} = 0.00075 \text{ mol HCl excess. Then } 0.0150 \text{ L Ba(OH)}_2 + 0.0300 \text{ L HCl} =$$

$$0.0450 \text{ L total volume. [HCl excess]} = \frac{0.00075 \text{ mol HCl excess}}{0.0450 \text{ L}} = 0.016667 \text{ M HCl excess. Because}$$

HCl is a strong acid, [HCl] excess = [H$_3$O$^+$]. Finally, pH = −log[H$_3$O$^+$] = −log(0.016667) = 1.78.

Check: The units (none) are correct. The pH is dropping sharply at the equivalence point, so the pH after 6 mL past the equivalence point should be quite acidic. Finally, after plotting these five points, the titration curve looks like the following:

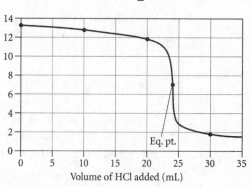

16.45 **Given:** 20.0 mL of 0.105 M HC$_2$H$_3$O$_2$ titrated with 0.125 M NaOH **Other:** K_a(HC$_2$H$_3$O$_2$) = 1.8 × 10^{-5}

(a) **Find:** initial pH

Conceptual Plan: Because HC$_2$H$_3$O$_2$ is a weak acid, set up an equilibrium problem using the initial concentration.

So M HC$_2$H$_3$O$_2$ → [H$_3$O$^+$] → pH

$$\text{ICE table} \qquad \text{pH} = -\log[\text{H}_3\text{O}^+]$$

Solution:

$$\text{HC}_2\text{H}_3\text{O}_2(aq) + \text{H}_2\text{O}(l) \rightleftharpoons \text{H}_3\text{O}^+(aq) + \text{C}_2\text{H}_3\text{O}_2^-(aq)$$

	[HC$_2$H$_3$O$_2$]	[H$_3$O$^+$]	[C$_2$H$_3$O$_2^-$]
Initial	0.105	≈ 0.00	0.00
Change	−x	+x	+x
Equil	0.105 − x	+x	+x

$$K_a = \frac{[\text{H}_3\text{O}^+][\text{C}_2\text{H}_3\text{O}_2^-]}{[\text{HC}_2\text{H}_3\text{O}_2]} = 1.8 \times 10^{-5} = \frac{x^2}{0.105 - x}. \text{ Assume that } x \text{ is small } (x \ll 0.105), \text{ so}$$

$$\frac{x^2}{0.105 - x} = 1.8 \times 10^{-5} = \frac{x^2}{0.105} \text{ and } x = 1.3748 \times 10^{-3} \text{ M} = [\text{H}_3\text{O}^+]. \text{ Confirm that the assumption is}$$

valid. $\dfrac{1.3748 \times 10^{-3}}{0.105} \times 100\% = 1.3\% < 5\%$, so the assumption is valid. Finally,

pH = −log[H$_3$O$^+$] = −log(1.3748 × 10^{-3}) = 2.86.

Check: The units (none) are correct. The magnitude of the answer makes physical sense because the pH should be greater than $-\log(0.105) = 0.98$ because this is a weak acid.

(b) **Find:** volume of base to reach equivalence point

Conceptual Plan: Write a balanced equation then mL $\rightarrow$ **L then [HC$_2$H$_3$O$_2$], L** $\rightarrow$ **mol HC$_2$H$_3$O$_2$ then**

$$HC_2H_3O_2 + NaOH \rightarrow NaC_2H_3O_2 + H_2O \qquad \frac{1\ L}{1000\ mL} \qquad\qquad M = \frac{mol}{L}$$

set mol acid(HC$_2$H$_3$O$_2$) = mol base(NaOH) and [NaOH], mol NaOH $\rightarrow$ **L NaOH** $\rightarrow$ **mL NaOH.**

$$\text{balanced equation has 1:1 stoichiometry} \qquad\qquad M = \frac{mol}{L} \qquad \frac{1000\ mL}{1\ L}$$

Solution: $20.0\ \text{mL HC}_2\text{H}_3\text{O}_2 \times \dfrac{1\ L}{1000\ mL} = 0.0200\ \text{L HC}_2\text{H}_3\text{O}_2$

then $\dfrac{0.105\ \text{mol HC}_2\text{H}_3\text{O}_2}{1\ L} \times 0.0200\ L = 0.00210\ \text{mol HC}_2\text{H}_3\text{O}_2$

So mol acid $=$ mol HC$_2$H$_3$O$_2$ $= 0.00210$ mol $=$ mol NaOH then

$0.00210\ \text{mol NaOH} \times \dfrac{1\ L}{0.125\ \text{mol NaOH}} = 0.0168\ \text{L NaOH} \times \dfrac{1000\ mL}{1\ L} = 16.8\ \text{mL NaOH}$

Check: The units (mL) are correct. The volume of base is a little less than the volume of acid because the concentration of the base is a little greater than that of the acid.

(c) **Find:** pH after adding 5.0 mL of base

Conceptual Plan: Use calculations from part (b). Then mL $\rightarrow$ **L then [NaOH], L** $\rightarrow$ **mol NaOH then**

$$\frac{1\ L}{1000\ mL} \qquad\qquad M = \frac{mol}{L}$$

mol HC$_2$H$_3$O$_2$, mol NaOH $\rightarrow$ **mol excess HC$_2$H$_3$O$_2$, mol C$_2$H$_3$O$_2^-$ and**

set up stoichiometry table

L HC$_2$H$_3$O$_2$, L NaOH $\rightarrow$ **total L then**

L HC$_2$H$_3$O$_2$ + L NaOH = total L

mol excess HC$_2$H$_3$O$_2$, L $\rightarrow$ **[HC$_2$H$_3$O$_2$] and mol excess C$_2$H$_3$O$_2^-$, L** $\rightarrow$ **[C$_2$H$_3$O$_2^-$] then**

$$M = \frac{mol}{L} \qquad\qquad\qquad M = \frac{mol}{L}$$

M HC$_2$H$_3$O$_2$, M C$_2$H$_3$O$_2^-$ $\rightarrow$ **[H$_3$O$^+$]** $\rightarrow$ **pH.**

ICE table $\qquad$ pH $= -\log[\text{H}_3\text{O}^+]$

Solution: $5.0\ \text{mL NaOH} \times \dfrac{1\ L}{1000\ mL} = 0.0050\ \text{L NaOH}$ then

$\dfrac{0.125\ \text{mol NaOH}}{1\ L} \times 0.0050\ L = 0.000625\ \text{mol NaOH}$. Set up a table to track changes:

	NaOH(aq) +	HC$_2$H$_3$O$_2$(aq) $\rightarrow$	NaC$_2$H$_3$O$_2$(aq) +	H$_2$O(l)
Before addition	0.00 mol	0.00210 mol	0.00 mol	—
Addition	0.000625 mol	—	—	—
After addition	≈0.00 mol	0.001475 mol	0.000625 mol	—

Then $0.0200\ \text{L HC}_2\text{H}_3\text{O}_2 + 0.0050\ \text{L NaOH} = 0.0250\ \text{L total volume.}$ Then

$[\text{HC}_2\text{H}_3\text{O}_2] = \dfrac{0.001475\ \text{mol HC}_2\text{H}_3\text{O}_2}{0.0250\ L} = 0.0590\ M$ and $[\text{NaC}_2\text{H}_3\text{O}_2] = \dfrac{0.000625\ \text{mol C}_2\text{H}_3\text{O}_2^-}{0.0250\ L} = 0.025\ M.$

Because one C$_2$H$_3$O$_2^-$ ion is generated for each NaC$_2$H$_3$O$_2$, [C$_2$H$_3$O$_2^-$] = 0.025 M C$_2$H$_3$O$_2^-$.

$$\text{HC}_2\text{H}_3\text{O}_2(aq) + \text{H}_2\text{O}(l) \rightleftharpoons \text{H}_3\text{O}^+(aq) + \text{C}_2\text{H}_3\text{O}_2^-(aq)$$

	[HC$_2$H$_3$O$_2$]	[H$_3$O$^+$]	[C$_2$H$_3$O$_2^-$]
Initial	0.0590	≈0.00	0.025
Change	$-x$	$+x$	$+x$
Equil	$0.0590 - x$	$+x$	$0.025 + x$

$$K_a = \frac{[H_3O^+]\,[C_2H_3O_2^-]}{[HC_2H_3O_2]} = 1.8 \times 10^{-5} = \frac{x(0.025 + x)}{0.0590 - x}$$ Assume that x is small ($x \ll 0.025 < 0.0590$), so

$$\frac{x(0.025 + \cancel{x})}{0.0590 - \cancel{x}} = 1.8 \times 10^{-5} = \frac{x(0.025)}{0.0590}$$ and $x = 4.\underline{2}48 \times 10^{-5}$ M = $[H_3O^+]$. Confirm that the assumption is valid.

$$\frac{4.\underline{2}48 \times 10^{-5}}{0.025} \times 100\% = 0.17\% < 5\%,$$ so the assumption is valid.

Finally, pH = $-\log[H_3O^+] = -\log(4.\underline{2}48 \times 10^{-5}) = 4.37$.

Check: The units (none) are correct. The pH is a little higher than the initial pH, which is expected because some of the acid has been neutralized.

(d) **Find:** pH at one-half the equivalence point
Conceptual Plan: Because this is a weak acid–strong base titration, the pH at one-half the equivalence point is the pK_a of the weak acid.
Solution: pH = pK_a = $-\log K_a = -\log(1.8 \times 10^{-5}) = 4.74$.

Check: The units (none) are correct. Because this is a weak acid–strong base titration, the pH at one-half the equivalence point is the pK_a of the weak acid; so it should be a little below 5.

(e) **Find:** pH at equivalence point
Conceptual Plan: Use calculations from part (b). Then because all of the weak acid has been converted to its conjugate base, the pH is only dependent on the hydrolysis reaction of the conjugate base. The mol $C_2H_3O_2^-$ = initial mol $HC_2H_3O_2$ and L $HC_2H_3O_2$, L NaOH to equivalence point $\rightarrow$ total L then

$$\text{L } HC_2H_3O_2 + \text{L NaOH} = \text{total L}$$

mol excess $C_2H_3O_2^-$, L $\rightarrow$ $[C_2H_3O_2^-]$ and K_a $\rightarrow$ K_b then do an equilibrium calculation:

$$M = \frac{\text{mol}}{L} \qquad\qquad K_w = K_a K_b$$

$[C_2H_3O_2^-]$, K_b $\rightarrow$ $[OH^-]$ $\rightarrow$ $[H_3O^+]$ $\rightarrow$ pH.

set up ICE table $K_w = [H_3O^+]\,[OH^-]$ pH = $-\log[H_3O^+]$

Solution: mol $C_2H_3O_2^-$ = initial mol $HC_2H_3O_2$ = 0.00210 mol and total volume = L $HC_2H_3O_2$ + L NaOH = 0.020 L + 0.0168 L = 0.0368 L then

$$[C_2H_3O_2^-] = \frac{0.00210 \text{ mol } C_2H_3O_2^-}{0.0368 \text{ L}} = 0.057\underline{0}652 \text{ M}$$ and $K_w = K_a K_b$. Rearrange to solve for K_b.

$$K_b = \frac{K_w}{K_a} = \frac{1.0 \times 10^{-14}}{1.8 \times 10^{-5}} = 5.\underline{5}556 \times 10^{-10}.$$ Set up an ICE table:

$$C_2H_3O_2^-(aq) + H_2O(l) \rightleftharpoons HC_2H_3O_2(aq) + OH^-(aq)$$

	$[C_2H_3O_2^-]$	$[HC_2H_3O_2]$	$[OH^-]$
Initial	0.057$\underline{0}$652	≈ 0.00	≈ 0.00
Change	$-x$	$+x$	$+x$
Equil	0.057$\underline{0}$652 $- x$	$+x$	$+x$

$$K_b = \frac{[HC_2H_3O_2]\,[OH^-]}{[C_2H_3O_2^-]} = 5.\underline{5}556 \times 10^{-10} = \frac{x^2}{0.057\underline{0}652 - x}.$$ Assume that x is small ($x \ll 0.057$), so

$$\frac{x^2}{0.057\underline{0}652 - \cancel{x}} = 5.\underline{5}556 \times 10^{-10} = \frac{x^2}{0.057\underline{0}652}$$ and $x = 5.\underline{6}306 \times 10^{-6}$ M = $[OH^-]$. Confirm that the

assumption is valid. $\dfrac{5.\underline{6}306 \times 10^{-6}}{0.057\underline{0}652} \times 100\% = 0.0099\% < 5\%,$ so the assumption is valid.

$$K_w = [H_3O^+]\,[OH^-], \text{ so } [H_3O^+] = \frac{K_w}{[OH^-]} = \frac{1.0 \times 10^{-14}}{5.\underline{6}305 \times 10^{-6}} = 1.\underline{7}760 \times 10^{-9} \text{ M}.$$

Finally, pH = $-\log[H_3O^+] = -\log(1.\underline{7}760 \times 10^{-9}) = 8.75$.

Check: The units (none) are correct. Because this is a weak acid–strong base titration, the pH at the equivalence point is basic.

(f)   **Find:** pH after adding 5.0 mL of base beyond the equivalence point

Conceptual Plan: Use calculations from parts (b) and (c). Then the pH is only dependent on the amount of excess base and the total solution volumes.

mL excess → L excess then [NaOH], L excess → mol NaOH excess

$$\frac{1\ L}{1000\ mL} \qquad\qquad M = \frac{mol}{L}$$

then L HC$_2$H$_3$O$_2$, L NaOH to equivalence point, L NaOH excess → total L then

$$\text{L HC}_2\text{H}_3\text{O}_2 + \text{L NaOH to equivalence point} + \text{L NaOH excess} = \text{total L}$$

mol excess NaOH, total L → [NaOH] = [OH$^-$] → [H$_3$O$^+$] → pH

$$M = \frac{mol}{L} \qquad\qquad K_w = [\text{H}_3\text{O}^+]\,[\text{OH}^-] \quad \text{pH} = -\log[\text{H}_3\text{O}^+]$$

Solution: $5.0\ \text{mL NaOH} \times \dfrac{1\ L}{1000\ \text{mL}} = 0.0050$ L NaOH excess then

$\dfrac{0.125\ \text{mol NaOH}}{1\ L} \times 0.0050\ L = 0.000625$ mol NaOH excess. Then 0.0200 L HC$_2$H$_3$O$_2$ + 0.0168 L NaOH

+ 0.0050 L NaOH = 0.0418 L total volume.

$$[\text{NaOH excess}] = \frac{0.000625\ \text{mol NaOH excess}}{0.0418\ L} = 0.0149522\ \text{M NaOH excess. Because NaOH is a strong}$$

base, [NaOH] excess = [OH$^-$]. The strong base overwhelms the weak base, which becomes insignificant in the

calculation. $K_w = [\text{H}_3\text{O}^+]\,[\text{OH}^-]$, so $[\text{H}_3\text{O}^+] = \dfrac{K_w}{[\text{OH}^-]} = \dfrac{1.0 \times 10^{-14}}{0.0149522} = 6.\underline{6}88 \times 10^{-13}$ M.

Finally, pH $= -\log[\text{H}_3\text{O}^+] = -\log(6.\underline{6}88 \times 10^{-13}) = 12.17$.

Check: The units (none) are correct. The pH is rising sharply at the equivalence point, so the pH after 5 mL past the equivalence point should be quite basic.

16.46   **Given:** 30.0 mL of 0.165 M HC$_3$H$_5$O$_2$ titrated with 0.300 M KOH **Other:** $K_a(\text{HC}_3\text{H}_5\text{O}_2) = 1.3 \times 10^{-5}$

Find: initial pH

Conceptual Plan: Because HC$_3$H$_5$O$_2$ is a weak acid, set up an equilibrium problem using the initial concentration. So M HC$_3$H$_5$O$_2$ → [H$_3$O$^+$] → pH.

$$\text{ICE table} \qquad \text{pH} = -\log[\text{H}_3\text{O}^+]$$

Solution:

$$\text{HC}_3\text{H}_5\text{O}_2(aq) + \text{H}_2\text{O}(l) \rightleftharpoons \text{H}_3\text{O}^+(aq) + \text{C}_3\text{H}_5\text{O}_2^-(aq)$$

	[HC$_3$H$_5$O$_2$]	[H$_3$O$^+$]	[C$_3$H$_5$O$_2^-$]
Initial	0.165	≈ 0.00	≈ 0.00
Change	$-x$	$+x$	$+x$
Equil	$0.165 - x$	$+x$	$+x$

$K_a = \dfrac{[\text{H}_3\text{O}^+]\,[\text{C}_3\text{H}_5\text{O}_2^-]}{[\text{HC}_3\text{H}_5\text{O}_2]} = 1.3 \times 10^{-5} = \dfrac{x^2}{0.165 - x}$. Assume that x is small ($x \ll 0.165$), so

$\dfrac{x^2}{0.165 - x} = 1.3 \times 10^{-5} = \dfrac{x^2}{0.165}$ and $x = 1.\underline{4}646 \times 10^{-3}$ M = [H$_3$O$^+$]. Confirm that the assumption is valid.

$\dfrac{1.\underline{4}646 \times 10^{-3}}{0.165} \times 100\% = 0.89\% < 5\%$, so the assumption is valid. Finally,

pH $= -\log[\text{H}_3\text{O}^+] = -\log(1.\underline{4}646 \times 10^{-3}) = 2.83$.

Check: The units (none) are correct. The magnitude of the answer makes physical sense because the pH should be greater than $-\log(0.165) = 0.78$ because this is a weak acid.

Find: pH after adding 5.0 mL of base

Conceptual Plan: Write a balanced equation then mL → L then [HC₃H₅O₂], L → mol HC₃H₅O₂ then

$$HC_3H_5O_2 + KOH \rightarrow KC_3H_5O_2 + H_2O \qquad \frac{1\ L}{1000\ mL} \qquad M = \frac{mol}{L}$$

mL → L then [KOH], L → mol KOH then

$$\frac{1\ L}{1000\ mL} \qquad M = \frac{mol}{L}$$

mol HC₃H₅O₂, mol KOH → mol excess HC₃H₅O₂, mol C₃H₅O₂⁻.

set up stoichiometry table

Because there are significant concentrations of both the acid and the conjugate base species, this is a buffer solution; so the Henderson–Hasselbalch equation $\left(pH = pK_a + \log \dfrac{[base]}{[acid]} \right)$ **can be used. Also note that the ratio of concentrations is the same as the ratio of moles because the volume is the same for both species.**

Solution: $30.0\ \text{mL HC}_3\text{H}_5\text{O}_2 \times \dfrac{1\ L}{1000\ mL} = 0.0300\ L\ HC_3H_5O_2$ then

$\dfrac{0.165\ mol\ HC_3H_5O_2}{1\ L} \times 0.0300\ L = 0.00495\ mol\ HC_3H_5O_2$ and $5.0\ \text{mL KOH} \times \dfrac{1\ L}{1000\ mL} = 0.0050\ L\ KOH$ then

$\dfrac{0.300\ mol\ KOH}{1\ L} \times 0.0050\ L = 0.0015\ mol\ KOH.$ Set up a table to track changes:

$$KOH(aq) \ + \ HC_3H_5O_2(aq) \rightarrow KC_3H_5O_2(aq) \ + \ H_2O(l)$$

	KOH(aq)	HC₃H₅O₂(aq)	KC₃H₅O₂(aq)	H₂O(l)
Before addition	0.00 mol	0.00495 mol	0.00 mol	—
Addition	0.0015 mol	—	—	—
After addition	≈0.00 mol	0.00345 mol	0.0015 mol	—

Then use the Henderson–Hasselbalch equation because the solution is a buffer.

$$pH = pK_a + \log \frac{[base]}{[acid]} = -\log(1.3 \times 10^{-5}) + \log \frac{0.0015}{0.00345} = 4.52$$

Check: The units (none) are correct. The pH is a little higher than the initial pH, which is expected because some of the acid has been neutralized.

Find: pH after adding 10.0 mL of base

Conceptual Plan: Use previous calculations, then mL → L then [KOH], L → mol KOH then

$$\frac{1\ L}{1000\ mL} \qquad M = \frac{mol}{L}$$

mol HC₃H₅O₂, mol KOH → mol excess HC₃H₅O₂, mol C₃H₅O₂⁻.

set up stoichiometry table

Because there are significant concentrations of both the acid and the conjugate base species, this is a buffer solution; so the Henderson–Hasselbalch equation $\left(pH = pK_a + \log \dfrac{[base]}{[acid]} \right)$ **can be used. Also note that the ratio of concentrations is the same as the ratio of moles because the volume is the same for both species.**

Solution: $10.0\ \text{mL KOH} \times \dfrac{1\ L}{1000\ mL} = 0.0100\ L\ KOH$ then $\dfrac{0.300\ mol\ KOH}{1\ L} \times 0.0100\ L = 0.0030\ mol\ KOH.$
Set up a table to track changes:

$$KOH(aq) \ + \ HC_3H_5O_2(aq) \rightarrow KC_3H_5O_2(aq) \ + \ H_2O(l)$$

	KOH(aq)	HC₃H₅O₂(aq)	KC₃H₅O₂(aq)	H₂O(l)
Before addition	0.00 mol	0.00495 mol	0.00 mol	—
Addition	0.0030 mol	—	—	—
After addition	≈0.00 mol	0.00195 mol	0.0030 mol	—

Then use the Henderson–Hasselbalch equation because the solution is a buffer.

$$pH = pK_a + \log \frac{[base]}{[acid]} = -\log(1.3 \times 10^{-5}) + \log \frac{0.0030}{0.00195} = 5.07$$

Check: The units (none) are correct. The pH is a little higher than the last pH, which is expected because some of the acid has been neutralized.

Find: pH at equivalence point

Conceptual Plan: Use previous calculations, then set mol acid ($HC_3H_5O_2$) = mol base KOH

balanced equation has 1:1 stoichiometry

and [KOH], mol KOH → L KOH then because all of the weak acid has been converted to its

$$M = \frac{mol}{L}$$

conjugate base, the pH is only dependent on the hydrolysis reaction of the conjugate base. The mol $C_3H_5O_2^-$ = initial mol $HC_3H_5O_2$ and L $HC_3H_5O_2$, L KOH to equivalence point → total L

L $HC_3H_5O_2$ + L KOH = total L

then mol $C_2H_3O_2^-$, L → [$C_2H_3O_2^-$] and K_a → K_b.

$$M = \frac{mol}{L} \qquad\qquad K_w = K_a K_b$$

Then do an equilibrium calculation: [$C_2H_3O_2^-$], K_b → [OH⁻] → [H_3O^+] → pH.

set up ICE table $K_w = [H_3O^+][OH^-]$ pH $= -\log[H_3O^+]$

Solution: mol acid = mol $HC_3H_5O_2$ = 0.00495 mol = mol KOH then

$$0.00495 \ \cancel{\text{mol KOH}} \times \frac{1 \ L}{0.300 \ \cancel{\text{mol KOH}}} = 0.0165 \ L \ KOH. \text{ Then total volume} = L \ HC_3H_5O_2 + L \ KOH =$$

$$0.0300 \ L + 0.0165 \ L = 0.0465 \text{ then } [C_3H_5O_2^-] = \frac{0.00495 \ mol \ C_3H_5O_2^-}{0.0465 \ L} = 0.10\underline{6}452 \ M \text{ and } K_w = K_a K_b.$$

Rearrange to solve for K_b. $K_b = \dfrac{K_w}{K_a} = \dfrac{1.0 \times 10^{-14}}{1.3 \times 10^{-5}} = 7.6\underline{9}23 \times 10^{-10} \ M.$ Set up an ICE table:

$C_3H_5O_2^- \ (aq) + H_2O(l) \rightleftharpoons HC_3H_5O_2 \ (aq) + OH^- (aq)$

	[$C_3H_5O_2^-$]	[$HC_3H_5O_2$]	[OH⁻]
Initial	0.10$\underline{6}$452	≈0.00	0.00
Change	−x	+x	+x
Equil	0.10$\underline{6}$452 − x	+x	+x

$$K_b = \frac{[HC_3H_5O_2][OH^-]}{[C_3H_5O_2^-]} = 7.6\underline{9}23 \times 10^{-10} = \frac{x^2}{0.10\underline{6}452 - x}. \text{ Assume that } x \text{ is small } (x \ll 0.106), \text{ so}$$

$$\frac{x^2}{0.10\underline{6}452 - \cancel{x}} = 7.6\underline{9}23 \times 10^{-10} = \frac{x^2}{0.10\underline{6}452} \text{ and } x = 9.0\underline{4}91 \times 10^{-6} \ M = [OH^-].$$

Confirm that the assumption is valid. $\dfrac{9.0\underline{4}91 \times 10^{-6}}{0.10\underline{6}452} \times 100\% = 0.0085\% < 5\%$, so the assumption is valid.

$$K_w = [H_3O^+][OH^-], \text{ so } [H_3O^+] = \frac{K_w}{[OH^-]} = \frac{1.0 \times 10^{-14}}{9.0\underline{4}91 \times 10^{-6}} = 1.\underline{1}051 \times 10^{-9} \ M.$$

Finally, pH $= -\log[H_3O^+] = -\log(1.\underline{1}051 \times 10^{-9}) = 8.96.$

Check: The units (none) are correct. Because this is a weak acid–strong base titration, the pH at the equivalence point is basic.

Find: pH at one-half the equivalence point

Conceptual Plan: Because this is a weak acid–strong base titration, the pH at one-half the equivalence point is the pK_a of the weak acid.

Solution: pH = pK_a = $-\log K_a$ = $-\log(1.3 \times 10^{-5})$ = 4.89, and the volume of added base is 0.5×16.5 mL = 8.3 mL.

Check: The units (none) are correct. Because this is a weak acid–strong base titration, the pH at one-half the equivalence point is the pK_a of the weak acid; so it should be a little below 5.

Find: pH after adding 20.0 mL of base

Conceptual Plan: Use previous calculations. Then the pH is only dependent on the amount of excess base and the total solution volumes. mL added, mL at equiv. pt. → mL excess → L excess

$$\text{mL excess} = \text{mL added} - \text{mL at equiv. pt.} \quad \frac{1\ \text{L}}{1000\ \text{mL}}$$

then mL excess → L excess then [KOH], L excess → mol KOH excess

$$\frac{1\ \text{L}}{1000\ \text{mL}} \qquad\qquad M = \frac{\text{mol}}{\text{L}}$$

then L HC$_3$H$_5$O$_2$, L KOH to equivalence point, L KOH excess → total L then

$$\text{L HC}_2\text{H}_3\text{O}_2 + \text{L KOH to equivalence point} + \text{L KOH excess} = \text{total L}$$

mol excess KOH, total L → [KOH] = [OH$^-$] → [H$_3$O$^+$] → pH

$$M = \frac{\text{mol}}{\text{L}} \qquad K_w = [\text{H}_3\text{O}^+][\text{OH}^-] \quad \text{pH} = -\log[\text{H}_3\text{O}^+]$$

Solution: mL KOH excess = mL added − mL to equiv. pt. = 20.0 mL − 16.5 mL = 3.5 mL

$$3.5\ \text{mL KOH} \times \frac{1\ \text{L}}{1000\ \text{mL}} = 0.0035\ \text{L KOH excess then}$$

$$\frac{0.300\ \text{mol KOH}}{1\ \text{L}} \times 0.0035\ \text{L} = 0.00105\ \text{mol KOH excess. Then } 0.0300\ \text{L HC}_3\text{H}_5\text{O}_2 + 0.0165\ \text{L KOH } +$$

$$0.0035\ \text{L KOH} = 0.0500\ \text{L total volume. [KOH excess]} = \frac{0.00105\ \text{mol KOH excess}}{0.0500\ \text{L}} = 0.021\ \text{M KOH excess.}$$

Because KOH is a strong base, [KOH] excess = [OH$^-$]. The strong base overwhelms the weak base, which becomes

insignificant in the calculation. $K_w = [\text{H}_3\text{O}^+][\text{OH}^-]$, so $[\text{H}_3\text{O}^+] = \dfrac{K_w}{[\text{OH}^-]} = \dfrac{1.0 \times 10^{-14}}{0.021} = 4.7619 \times 10^{-13}$ M.

Finally, pH $= -\log[\text{H}_3\text{O}^+] = -\log(4.7619 \times 10^{-13}) = 12.32$.

Check: The units (none) are correct. The pH is rising sharply at the equivalence point, so the pH after 5 mL past the equivalence point should be quite basic.

Find: pH after adding 25.0 mL of base

Conceptual Plan: Use previous calculations. Then the pH is only dependent on the amount of excess base and the total solution volumes. mL added, mL at equiv. pt. → mL excess → L excess

$$\text{mL excess} = \text{mL added} - \text{mL at equiv. pt.} \quad \frac{1\ \text{L}}{1000\ \text{mL}}$$

then mL excess → L excess then [KOH], L excess → mol KOH excess

$$\frac{1\ \text{L}}{1000\ \text{mL}} \qquad\qquad M = \frac{\text{mol}}{\text{L}}$$

then L HC$_3$H$_5$O$_2$, L KOH to equivalence point, L KOH excess → total L then

$$\text{L HC}_2\text{H}_3\text{O}_2 + \text{L KOH to equivalence point} + \text{L KOH excess} = \text{total L}$$

mol excess KOH, total L → [KOH] = [OH$^-$] → [H$_3$O$^+$] → pH

$$M = \frac{\text{mol}}{\text{L}} \qquad K_w = [\text{H}_3\text{O}^+][\text{OH}^-] \quad \text{pH} = -\log[\text{H}_3\text{O}^+]$$

Solution: mL KOH excess = mL added − mL to equiv. pt. = 25.0 mL − 16.5 mL = 8.5 mL

$$8.5\ \text{mL KOH} \times \frac{1\ \text{L}}{1000\ \text{mL}} = 0.0085\ \text{L KOH excess then}$$

$$\frac{0.300\ \text{mol KOH}}{1\ \text{L}} \times 0.0085\ \text{L} = 0.00255\ \text{mol KOH excess. Then } 0.0300\ \text{L HC}_3\text{H}_5\text{O}_2 + 0.0165\ \text{L KOH } +$$

$$0.0085\ \text{L KOH} = 0.0550\ \text{L total volume. [KOH excess]} = \frac{0.00255\ \text{mol KOH excess}}{0.0550\ \text{L}} = 0.046364\ \text{M KOH excess.}$$

Because KOH is a strong base, [KOH] excess = [OH$^-$]. The strong base overwhelms the weak base, which becomes

insignificant in the calculation. $K_w = [\text{H}_3\text{O}^+][\text{OH}^-]$, so $[\text{H}_3\text{O}^+] = \dfrac{K_w}{[\text{OH}^-]} = \dfrac{1.0 \times 10^{-14}}{0.046364} = 2.1568 \times 10^{-13}$ M.

Finally, pH $= -\log[\text{H}_3\text{O}^+] = -\log(2.1568 \times 10^{-13}) = 12.67$.

Check: The units (none) are correct. The pH is rising sharply at the equivalence point, so the pH after 5 mL past the equivalence point should be quite basic. This pH is higher than the last pH. Plotting these data points is shown as follows:

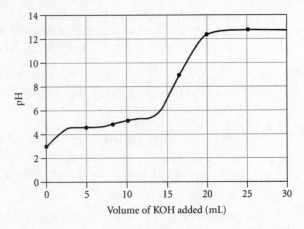

16.47   **Given:** 25.0 mL of 0.175 M CH_3NH_2 titrated with 0.150 M HBr **Other:** $K_b(CH_3NH_2) = 4.4 \times 10^{-4}$

(a)   **Find:** initial pH

Conceptual Plan: Because CH_3NH_2 is a weak base, set up an equilibrium problem using the initial concentration, so M $CH_3NH_2 \rightarrow [OH^-] \rightarrow [H_3O^+] \rightarrow$ pH.

ICE table $K_w = [H_3O^+][OH^-]$ pH $= -\log[H_3O^+]$

Solution:

$$CH_3NH_2(aq) + H_2O(l) \rightleftharpoons CH_3NH_3^+(aq) + OH^-(aq)$$

	$[CH_3NH_2]$	$[CH_3NH_3^+]$	$[OH^-]$
Initial	0.175	0.00	≈ 0.00
Change	$-x$	$+x$	$+x$
Equil	$0.175 - x$	$+x$	$+x$

$$K_b = \frac{[CH_3NH_3^+][OH^-]}{[CH_3NH_2]} = 4.4 \times 10^{-4} = \frac{x^2}{0.175 - x}$$

Assume that x is small

$(x \ll 0.175)$, so $\dfrac{x^2}{0.175 - \cancel{x}} = 4.4 \times 10^{-4} = \dfrac{x^2}{0.175}$ and $x = 8.\underline{7}750 \times 10^{-3}$ M $= [OH^-]$.

Confirm that the assumption is valid. $\dfrac{8.7750 \times 10^{-3}}{0.175} \times 100\% = 5.0\%$, so the assumption is valid.

$K_w = [H_3O^+][OH^-]$, so $[H_3O^+] = \dfrac{K_w}{[OH^-]} = \dfrac{1.0 \times 10^{-14}}{8.\underline{7}750 \times 10^{-3}} = 1.\underline{1}396 \times 10^{-12}$ M.

Finally, pH $= -\log[H_3O^+] = -\log(1.\underline{1}396 \times 10^{-12}) = 11.94$.

Check: The units (none) are correct. The magnitude of the answer makes physical sense because the pH should be less than $14 + \log(0.175) = 13.2$ because this is a weak base.

(b)   **Find:** volume of acid to reach equivalence point

Conceptual Plan: Write a balanced equation, then mL $\rightarrow$ L then $[CH_3NH_2]$, L $\rightarrow$ mol CH_3NH_2

$HBr + CH_3NH_2 \rightarrow CH_3NH_3Br + H_2O$ $\dfrac{1\,L}{1000\,mL}$ $M = \dfrac{mol}{L}$

then set mol base $[CH_3NH_2] =$ mol acid (HBr) and [HBr], mol HBr $\rightarrow$ L HBr $\rightarrow$ mL HBr.

balanced equation has 1:1 stoichiometry $M = \dfrac{mol}{L}$ $\dfrac{1000\,mL}{1\,L}$

Solution: $25.0 \ \cancel{mL \ CH_3NH_2} \times \dfrac{1\,L}{1000 \ \cancel{mL}} = 0.0250$ L CH_3NH_2 then

$\dfrac{0.175 \ mol \ CH_3NH_2}{1 \ \cancel{L}} \times 0.0250 \ \cancel{L} = 0.004\underline{3}75$ mol CH_3NH_2. So mol base $=$ mol $CH_3NH_2 = 0.004375$ mol

$=$ mol HBr then $0.004\underline{3}75 \ \cancel{mol \ HBr} \times \dfrac{1\,L}{0.150 \ \cancel{mol \ HBr}} = 0.029\underline{1}667 \ \cancel{L \ HBr} \times \dfrac{1000\,mL}{1 \ \cancel{L}} = 29.2$ mL HBr.

Check: The units (mL) are correct. The volume of acid is greater than the volume of base because the concentration of the base is a little greater than that of the acid.

(c) **Find:** pH after adding 5.0 mL of acid
Conceptual Plan: Use calculations from part (b). Then mL → L then [HBr], L → mol HBr

$$\frac{1\,L}{1000\,mL} \qquad\qquad M = \frac{mol}{L}$$

then mol CH_3NH_2, mol HBr → mol excess CH_3NH_2 and L CH_3NH_2, L HBr → total L.

set up stoichiometry table $\qquad\qquad$ L CH_3NH_2 + L HBr = total L

Because there are significant concentrations of both the acid and the conjugate base species, this is a buffer solution; so the Henderson–Hasselbalch equation $\left(pH = pK_a + \log \dfrac{[base]}{[acid]} \right)$ can be used.

Convert K_b to K_a using $K_w = K_aK_b$. Also note that the ratio of concentrations is the same as the ratio of moles because the volume is the same for both species.

Solution: $5.0\ \cancel{mL\ HBr} \times \dfrac{1\,L}{1000\ \cancel{mL}} = 0.0050\ L\ HBr$ then $\dfrac{0.150\ mol\ HBr}{1\ \cancel{L}} \times 0.0050\ \cancel{L} = 0.00075\ mol\ HBr$

Set up a table to track changes:

$$HBr(aq) \quad + \quad CH_3NH_2(aq) \quad \rightarrow \quad CH_3NH_3Br(aq)$$

	$HBr(aq)$	$CH_3NH_2(aq)$	$CH_3NH_3Br(aq)$
Before addition	0.00 mol	0.004375 mol	0.00 mol
Addition	0.00075 mol	—	—
After addition	≈0.00 mol	0.003625 mol	0.000750 mol

then $K_w = K_aK_b$ so

$K_a = \dfrac{K_w}{K_b} = \dfrac{1.0 \times 10^{-14}}{4.4 \times 10^{-4}} = 2.\underline{2}727 \times 10^{-11}$ M. Then use the Henderson–Hasselbalch equation because the

solution is a buffer. $pH = pK_a + \log \dfrac{[base]}{[acid]} = -\log(2.\underline{2}727 \times 10^{-11}) + \log \dfrac{0.003625}{0.000750} = 11.33$

Check: The units (none) are correct. The pH is a little lower than the last pH, which is expected because some of the base has been neutralized.

(d) **Find:** pH at one-half the equivalence point
Conceptual Plan: Because this is a weak base–strong acid titration, the pH at one-half the equivalence point is the pK_a of the conjugate acid of weak base.
Solution: $pH = pK_a = -\log K_a = -\log(2.\underline{2}727 \times 10^{-11}) = 10.64$

Check: The units (none) are correct. Because this is a weak acid–strong base titration, the pH at one-half the equivalence point is the pK_a of the conjugate acid of the weak base; so it should be a little below 11.

(e) **Find:** pH at equivalence point
Conceptual Plan: Use previous calculations. Because all of the weak base has been converted to its conjugate acid, the pH is only dependent on the hydrolysis reaction of the conjugate acid. The mol $CH_3NH_3^+$ = initial mol CH_3NH_2 and
L CH_3NH_2, L HBr to equivalence point → total L then mol $CH_3NH_3^+$, L → [$CH_3NH_3^+$]

L CH_3NH_2 + L HBr = total L $\qquad\qquad M = \dfrac{mol}{L}$

then do an equilibrium calculation: [$CH_3NH_3^+$], K_a → [H_3O^+] → pH.

set up ICE table $\quad$ pH $= -\log[H_3O^+]$

Solution: mol base = mol acid = mol $CH_3NH_3^+$ = 0.004375 mol. Then total volume = L $CH_3NH_3^+$

L HBr = 0.0250 L + 0.0292 L = 0.0542 then $[CH_3NH_3^+] = \dfrac{0.004375\ mol\ CH_3NH_3^+}{0.0542\ L} = 0.080\underline{7}196$ M.

Set up an ICE table:

$$CH_3NH_3^+(aq) + H_2O\ (l) \rightleftharpoons CH_3NH_2(aq) + H_3O^+(aq)$$

	$[CH_3NH_3^+]$	$[CH_3NH_2]$	$[H_3O^+]$
Initial	0.0807196	≈ 0.00	≈ 0.00
Change	$-x$	$+x$	$+x$
Equil	$0.0807196 - x$	$+x$	$+x$

$$K_a = \frac{[CH_3NH_2]\,[H_3O^+]}{[CH_3NH_3^+]} = 2.2727 \times 10^{-11} = \frac{x^2}{0.0807196 - x}. \text{ Assume that } x \text{ is small } (x \ll 0.0807), \text{ so}$$

$$\frac{x^2}{0.0807196 - \cancel{x}} = 2.2727 \times 10^{-11} = \frac{x^2}{0.0807196} \text{ and } x = 1.3544 \times 10^{-6} = [H_3O^+].$$

Confirm that the assumption is valid. $\dfrac{1.3544 \times 10^{-6}}{0.0807106} \times 100\% = 0.0017\% < 5\%,$ so the assumption is valid.

Finally, pH $= -\log[H_3O^+] = -\log(1.3544 \times 10^{-6}) = 5.87.$

Check: The units (none) are correct. Because this is a weak base–strong acid titration, the pH at the equivalence point is acidic.

(f)   **Find:** pH after adding 5.0 mL of acid beyond the equivalence point

Conceptual Plan: Use calculations from parts (b) and (c). Then the pH is only dependent on the amount of excess acid and the total solution volumes.

mL excess → L excess then [HBr], L excess → mol HBr excess

$$\frac{1\ L}{1000\ mL} \qquad\qquad M = \frac{mol}{L}$$

then L CH_3NH_2, L HBr to equivalence point, L HBr excess → total L then

$$L\ CH_3NH_2 + L\ HBr\ \text{to equivalence point} + L\ HBr\ \text{excess} = \text{total L}$$

mol excess HBr, total L → [HBr] = $[H_3O^+]$ → pH

$$M = \frac{mol}{L} \qquad\qquad pH = -\log[H_3O^+]$$

Solution: $5.0\ \cancel{mL\ HBr} \times \dfrac{1\ L}{1000\ \cancel{mL}} = 0.0050\ L\ HBr\ \text{excess then}$

$\dfrac{0.150\ mol\ HBr}{1\ \cancel{L}} \times 0.0050\ \cancel{L} = 0.00075\ mol\ HBr\ \text{excess. Then } 0.0250\ L\ CH_3NH_2 + 0.0292\ L\ HBr + $

$0.0050\ L\ HBr = 0.0592\ L\ \text{total volume.}$

$$[HBr\ \text{excess}] = \frac{0.00075\ mol\ HBr\ \text{excess}}{0.0592\ L} = 0.012669\ M\ HBr\ \text{excess}$$

Because HBr is a strong acid, [HBr] excess $= [H_3O^+]$. The strong acid overwhelms the weak acid, which becomes insignificant in the calculation. Finally, pH $= -\log[H_3O^+] = -\log(0.012669) = 1.90.$

Check: The units (none) are correct. The pH is dropping sharply at the equivalence point, so the pH after 5 mL past the equivalence point should be quite acidic.

16.48   **Given:** 25.0 mL of 0.125 M pyridine (C_5H_5N) titrated with 0.100 M HCl **Other:** K_b (C_5H_5N) $= 1.7 \times 10^{-9}$
Find: initial pH
Conceptual Plan: Because C_5H_5N is a weak base, set up an equilibrium problem using the initial concentration, so M C_5H_5N → $[OH^-]$ → $[H_3O^+]$ → pH.

$$\text{ICE table} \quad K_w = [H_3O^+]\,[OH^-] \quad pH = -\log[H_3O^+]$$

Solution:

$$C_5H_5N(aq) + H_2O(l) \rightleftharpoons C_5H_5NH^+(aq) + OH^-(aq)$$

	$[C_5H_5N]$	$[C_5H_5NH^+]$	$[OH^-]$
Initial	0.125	0.00	≈ 0.00
Change	$-x$	$+x$	$+x$
Equil	$0.125 - x$	$+x$	$+x$

$$K_b = \frac{[C_5H_5NH^+][OH^-]}{[C_5H_5N]} = 1.7 \times 10^{-9} = \frac{x^2}{0.125 - x}$$

Assume that x is small ($x \ll 0.125$), so $\dfrac{x^2}{0.125 - \cancel{x}} = 1.7 \times 10^{-9} = \dfrac{x^2}{0.125}$ and $x = 1.4577 \times 10^{-5} = [OH^-]$.

Confirm that the assumption is valid. $\dfrac{1.4577 \times 10^{-5}}{0.125} \times 100\% = 0.012\% < 5.0\%$, so the assumption is valid.

$K_w = [H_3O^+][OH^-]$ so $[H_3O^+] = \dfrac{K_w}{[OH^-]} = \dfrac{1.0 \times 10^{-14}}{1.4577 \times 10^{-5}} = 6.8601 \times 10^{-10}$ M.

Finally, $pH = -\log[H_3O^+] = -\log(6.8601 \times 10^{-10}) = 9.16$.

Check: The units (none) are correct. The magnitude of the answer makes physical sense because the pH should be less than $14 + \log(0.125) = 13.1$ because this is a weak base.

Find: pH after adding 10.0 mL of acid

Conceptual Plan: Write balanced equation then mL → L then [C₅H₅N], L → mol C₅H₅N then

$$HCl + C_5H_5N \rightarrow C_5H_5NHCl \qquad \frac{1\ L}{1000\ mL} \qquad M = \frac{mol}{L}$$

mL → L then [HCl], L → mol HCl then mol C₅H₅N, mol HCl → mol excess C₅H₅N and

$$\frac{1\ L}{1000\ mL} \qquad M = \frac{mol}{L} \qquad \text{set up stoichiometry table}$$

L C₅H₅N, L HCl → total L then because there are significant concentrations of both the acid and

$$L\ C_5H_5N + L\ HCl = total\ L$$

the conjugate base species, this is a buffer solution; so the Henderson–Hasselbalch equation

$$\left(pH = pK_a + \log \frac{[base]}{[acid]} \right)$$ **can be used. Convert K_b to K_a using $K_w = K_a K_b$. Also note that the ratio of**

concentrations is the same as the ratio of moles because the volume is the same for both species.

Solution: $25.0\ \cancel{mL\ C_5H_5N} \times \dfrac{1\ L}{1000\ \cancel{mL}} = 0.0250\ L\ C_5H_5N$ then

$\dfrac{0.125\ mol\ C_5H_5N}{1\ \cancel{L}} \times 0.0250\ \cancel{L} = 0.003125\ mol\ C_5H_5N$ and $10.0\ \cancel{mL\ HCl} \times \dfrac{1\ L}{1000\ \cancel{mL}} = 0.0100\ L\ HCl$ then

$10.0\ mL\ HCl \times \dfrac{1\ L}{1000\ mL} = 0.0100\ L\ HCl$ then

$\dfrac{0.100\ mol\ HCl}{1\ \cancel{L}} \times 0.0100\ \cancel{L} = 0.00100\ mol\ HCl.$ Set up a table to track changes:

	HCl(aq)	+ C₅H₅N(aq)	→ C₅H₅NHCl(aq)
Before addition	0.00 mol	0.003125 mol	0.00 mol
Addition	0.00100 mol	—	—
After addition	≈0.00 mol	0.002125 mol	0.00100 mol

Then $K_w = K_a K_b$, so $K_a = \dfrac{K_w}{K_b} = \dfrac{1.0 \times 10^{-14}}{1.7 \times 10^{-9}} = 5.8824 \times 10^{-6}$ M. Then use the Henderson–Hasselbalch equation

because the solution is a buffer.

$pH = pK_a + \log \dfrac{[base]}{[acid]} = -\log(5.8824 \times 10^{-6}) + \log \dfrac{0.002125}{0.00100} = 5.56$

Check: The units (none) are correct. The pH is lower than the last pH, which is expected because some of the base has been neutralized.

Find: pH after adding 20.0 mL of acid

Conceptual Plan: Use previous calculations. Then mL → L then [HCl], L → mol HCl

$$\frac{1\ L}{1000\ mL} \qquad M = \frac{mol}{L}$$

then mol C₅H₅N, mol HCl → mol excess C₅H₅N and L C₅H₅N, L HCl → total L.

$$\text{set up stoichiometry table} \qquad L\ C_5H_5N + L\ HCl = total\ L$$

Because there are significant concentrations of both the acid and the conjugate base species, this is a buffer solution; so the Henderson–Hasselbalch equation $\left(\text{pH} = \text{p}K_a + \log \dfrac{[\text{base}]}{[\text{acid}]} \right)$ can be used. Convert K_b to K_a using $K_w = K_a K_b$. Also note that the ratio of concentrations is the same as the ratio of moles because the volume is the same for both species.

Solution: $20.0 \ \cancel{\text{mL HCl}} \times \dfrac{1 \ \text{L}}{1000 \ \cancel{\text{mL}}} = 0.0200 \ \text{L HCl}$ then $\dfrac{0.100 \ \text{mol HCl}}{1 \ \cancel{L}} \times 0.0200 \ \cancel{L} = 0.00200 \ \text{mol HCl}$

Set up a table to track changes:

$$\text{HCl}(aq) \ + \ \text{C}_5\text{H}_5\text{N}(aq) \ \rightarrow \ \text{C}_5\text{H}_5\text{NHCl}(aq)$$

	HCl	C$_5$H$_5$N	C$_5$H$_5$NHCl
Before addition	0.00 mol	0.003125 mol	0.00 mol
Addition	0.00200 mol	—	—
After addition	≈0.00 mol	0.001125 mol	0.00200 mol

Then use the Henderson–Hasselbalch equation because the solution is a buffer.

$$\text{pH} = \text{p}K_a + \log \dfrac{[\text{base}]}{[\text{acid}]} = -\log(5.8824 \times 10^{-6}) + \log \dfrac{0.001125}{0.00200} = 4.98$$

Check: The units (none) are correct. The pH is lower than the last pH, which is expected because some of the base has been neutralized.

Find: pH at equivalence point

Conceptual Plan: Use previous calculations. Because all of the weak base has been converted to its conjugate acid, the pH is only dependent on the hydrolysis reaction of the conjugate acid. The mol $\text{C}_5\text{H}_5\text{NH}^+ =$ initial mol $\text{C}_5\text{H}_5\text{N}$ then set mol base $(\text{C}_5\text{H}_5\text{N}) =$ mol acid (HCl) and [HCl], mol HCl $\rightarrow$ L HCl then

$$\text{balanced equation has 1:1 stoichiometry} \qquad\qquad M = \dfrac{\text{mol}}{\text{L}}$$

L $\text{C}_5\text{H}_5\text{N}$, L HCl to equivalence point $\rightarrow$ total L then mol $\text{C}_5\text{H}_5\text{NH}^+$, L $\rightarrow$ [$\text{C}_5\text{H}_5\text{NH}^+$]

$$\text{L C}_5\text{H}_5\text{N} + \text{L HCl} = \text{total L} \qquad\qquad M = \dfrac{\text{mol}}{\text{L}}$$

then do an equilibrium calculation: [$\text{C}_5\text{H}_5\text{NH}^+$], K_a $\rightarrow$ [H_3O^+] $\rightarrow$ pH.

$$\text{set up ICE table} \qquad \text{pH} = -\log[\text{H}_3\text{O}^+]$$

Solution: mol base = mol acid = mol $\text{C}_5\text{H}_5\text{NH}^+$ = 0.003125 mol. Then

$$0.003125 \ \cancel{\text{mol HCl}} \times \dfrac{1 \ \text{L}}{0.100 \ \cancel{\text{mol HCl}}} = 0.03125 \ \cancel{\text{L HCl}} \times \dfrac{1000 \ \text{mL}}{1 \ \cancel{L}} = 31.3 \ \text{mL HCl} \text{ then}$$

total volume = L $\text{C}_5\text{H}_5\text{N}$ + L HCl = 0.0250 L + 0.0313 L = 0.0563 L then

$$[\text{C}_5\text{H}_5\text{NH}^+] = \dfrac{0.003125 \ \text{mol C}_5\text{H}_5\text{NH}^+}{0.0563 \ \text{L}} = 0.0555062 \ \text{M. Set up an ICE table:}$$

$$\text{C}_5\text{H}_5\text{NH}^+(aq) \ + \ \text{H}_2\text{O}(l) \rightleftharpoons \text{C}_5\text{H}_5\text{N}(aq) \ + \ \text{H}_3\text{O}^+(aq)$$

	[C$_5$H$_5$NH$^+$]	[C$_5$H$_5$N]	[H$_3$O$^+$]
Initial	0.0555062	≈0.00	≈0.00
Change	$-x$	$+x$	$+x$
Equil	$0.0555062 - x$	$+x$	$+x$

$K_a = \dfrac{[\text{C}_5\text{H}_5\text{N}][\text{H}_3\text{O}^+]}{[\text{C}_5\text{H}_5\text{NH}^+]} = 5.8824 \times 10^{-6} = \dfrac{x^2}{0.0555062 - x}$. Assume that x is small ($x \ll 0.0556$), so

$\dfrac{x^2}{0.0555062 - \cancel{x}} = 5.8824 \times 10^{-6} = \dfrac{x^2}{0.0555062}$ and $x = 5.7141 \times 10^{-4} \ \text{M} = [\text{H}_3\text{O}^+]$. Confirm that the

assumption is valid. $\dfrac{5.7141 \times 10^{-4}}{0.0555062} \times 100\% = 1.0\% < 5\%$, so the assumption is valid.

Finally, pH $= -\log[\text{H}_3\text{O}^+] = -\log(5.7141 \times 10^{-4}) = 3.24.$

Check: The units (none) are correct. Because this is a weak base–strong acid titration, the pH at the equivalence point is acidic.

Find: pH at one-half the equivalence point
Conceptual Plan: Because this is a weak base–strong acid titration, the pH at one-half the equivalence point is the pK_a of the conjugate acid of weak base.
Solution: pH = pK_a = $-\log K_a$ = $-\log(5.8824 \times 10^{-6})$ = 5.23, and the volume is 0.5 × 31.3 mL = 15.7 mL.

Check: The units (none) are correct. Because this is a weak base–strong acid titration, the pH at one-half the equivalence point is the pK_a of the conjugate acid of the weak base; so it should be a little below 6.

Find: pH after adding 40.0 mL of acid
Conceptual Plan: Use previous calculations. Then the pH is only dependent on the amount of excess acid and the total solution volumes.
mL added, mL at equiv. pt. → mL excess → L excess then

$$\text{mL excess} = \text{mL added} - \text{mL at equiv. pt.} \quad \frac{1\,\text{L}}{1000\,\text{mL}}$$

mL excess → L excess then [HCl], L excess → mol HCl excess

$$\frac{1\,\text{L}}{1000\,\text{mL}} \qquad\qquad M = \frac{\text{mol}}{\text{L}}$$

then L C_5H_5N, L HCl to equivalence point, L HCl excess → total L then

$$\text{L } C_5H_5N + \text{L HCl to equivalence point} + \text{L HCl excess} = \text{total L}$$

mol excess HCl, total L → [HCl] = [H_3O^+] → pH

$$M = \frac{\text{mol}}{\text{L}} \qquad\qquad \text{pH} = -\log[H_3O^+]$$

Solution: mL excess = mL added − mL at equiv. pt. = 40.0 mL − 31.3 mL = 8.7 mL

$$8.7\ \cancel{\text{mL HCl}} \times \frac{1\,\text{L}}{1000\ \cancel{\text{mL}}} = 0.0087 \text{ L HCl excess then } \frac{0.100\text{ mol HCl}}{1\ \cancel{\text{L}}} \times 0.0087\ \cancel{\text{L}} = 0.00087 \text{ mol HCl excess}$$

Then 0.0250 L C_5H_5N + 0.0313 L HCl + 0.0087 L HCl = 0.0650 L total volume

$$[\text{HCl excess}] = \frac{0.00087 \text{ mol HCl excess}}{0.0650\,\text{L}} = 0.013385 \text{ M HCl excess}$$

Because HCl is a strong acid, [HCl] excess = [H_3O^+]. The strong acid overwhelms the weak acid, which becomes insignificant in the calculation. Finally, pH = $-\log[H_3O^+]$ = $-\log(0.013385)$ = 1.87.

Check: The units (none) are correct. The pH is dropping sharply at the equivalence point, so the pH after 5 mL past the equivalence point should be quite acidic.

Find: pH after adding 50.0 mL of acid
Conceptual Plan: Use previous calculations. Then the pH is only dependent on the amount of excess acid and the total solution volumes. mL added, mL at equiv. pt. → mL excess → L excess then

$$\text{mL excess} = \text{mL added} - \text{mL at equiv. pt.} \quad \frac{1\,\text{L}}{1000\,\text{mL}}$$

mL excess → L excess then [HCl], L excess → mol HCl excess

$$\frac{1\,\text{L}}{1000\,\text{mL}} \qquad\qquad M = \frac{\text{mol}}{\text{L}}$$

then L C_5H_5N, L HCl to equivalence point, L HCl excess → total L then

$$\text{L } C_5H_5N + \text{L HCl to equivalence point} + \text{L HCl excess} = \text{total L}$$

mol excess HCl, total L → [HCl] = [H_3O^+] → pH

$$M = \frac{\text{mol}}{\text{L}} \qquad\qquad \text{pH} = -\log[H_3O^+]$$

Solution: mL excess = mL added − mL at equiv. pt. = 50.0 mL − 31.3 mL = 18.7 mL

$$18.7\ \cancel{\text{mL HCl}} \times \frac{1\,\text{L}}{1000\ \cancel{\text{mL}}} = 0.0187 \text{ L HCl excess then}$$

$$\frac{0.100\text{ mol HCl}}{1\ \cancel{\text{L}}} \times 0.0187\ \cancel{\text{L}} = 0.00187 \text{ mol HCl excess. Then } 0.0250 \text{ L } C_5H_5N + 0.0313 \text{ L HCl} + 0.0187 \text{ L HBr}$$

$$= 0.0750 \text{ L total volume. } [\text{HCl excess}] = \frac{0.00187 \text{ mol HCl excess}}{0.0750\,\text{L}} = 0.024933 \text{ M HCl excess}$$

Because HCl is a strong acid, [HCl] excess = [H_3O^+]. The strong acid overwhelms the weak acid and is insignificant in the calculation. Finally, pH = $-\log[H_3O^+]$ = $-\log(0.024933)$ = 1.60.

Check: The units (none) are correct. The pH is dropping sharply at the equivalence point, so the pH after 5 mL past the equivalence point should be quite acidic. The pH is lower than at the last point. Plotting these points gives the following:

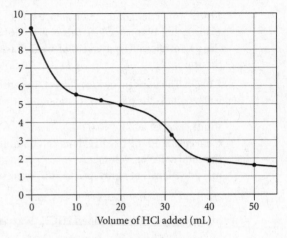

16.49   (i)   Acid a is more concentrated because the equivalence point (where sharp pH rise occurs) is at a higher volume of added base.

(ii)   Acid b has the larger K_a because the pH at a volume of added base equal to half the equivalence point volume is lower.

16.50   (i)   Base b is more concentrated because the equivalence point (where sharp pH drop occurs) is at a higher volume of added acid.

(ii)   Base b has the larger K_b because the pH at a volume of added base equal to half the equivalence point volume is higher.

16.51   **Given:** 0.229 g unknown monoprotic acid titrated with 0.112 M NaOH and curve
Find: molar mass and pK_a of acid
Conceptual Plan: The equivalence point is where sharp pH rise occurs. The pK_a is the pH at a volume of added base equal to half the equivalence point volume. Then mL NaOH → L NaOH

$$\frac{1\ L}{1000\ mL}$$

then [NaOH], L NaOH → mol NaOH = mol acid then mol NaOH, g acid → molar mass.

$$M = \frac{mol}{L} \qquad\qquad \frac{g\ acid}{mol\ acid}$$

Solution: The equivalence point is at 25 mL NaOH. The pH at 0.5 × 25 mL = 13 mL is ~3 = pK_a. Then

$$25\ \text{mL NaOH} \times \frac{1\ L}{1000\ mL} = 0.025\ L\ NaOH \text{ then}$$

$$\frac{0.112\ mol\ NaOH}{1\ L} \times 0.025\ L = 0.0028\ mol\ NaOH = 0.0028\ mol\ acid \text{ then}$$

$$\text{molar mass} = \frac{0.229\ g\ acid}{0.0028\ mol\ acid} = 82\ g/mol.$$

Check: The units (none and g/mol) are correct. The pK_a is consistent with a weak acid. The molar mass is reasonable for an acid (> 1 g/mol).

16.52   **Given:** 0.446 g unknown monoprotic acid titrated with 0.105 M KOH and curve
Find: molar mass and pK_a of acid
Conceptual Plan: The equivalence point is where sharp pH rise occurs. The pK_a is the pH at a volume of added base equal to half the equivalence point volume. Then mL KOH → L KOH then

$$\frac{1\ L}{1000\ mL}$$

[KOH], L KOH → mol KOH = mol acid then mol KOH, g acid → molar mass.

$$M = \frac{mol}{L} \qquad\qquad \frac{g\ acid}{mol\ acid}$$

Solution: The equivalence point is at 35 mL NaOH. The pH at 0.5×35 mL $= 18$ mL is $\sim 4.5 = pK_a$. Then

$$35 \text{ mL KOH} \times \frac{1 \text{ L}}{1000 \text{ mL}} = 0.035 \text{ L KOH then}$$

$$\frac{0.105 \text{ mol KOH}}{1 \text{ L}} \times 0.035 \text{ L} = 0.003\underline{6}75 \text{ mol KOH} = 0.003\underline{6}75 \text{ mol acid then}$$

$$\text{molar mass} = \frac{0.446 \text{ g acid}}{0.003\underline{6}75 \text{ mol acid}} = 120 \text{ g/mol}.$$

Check: The units (none and g/mol) are correct. The pK_a is consistent with a weak acid. The molar mass is reasonable for an acid (> 1 g/mol).

16.53 **Given:** 20.0 mL of 0.115 M sulfurous acid (H_2SO_3) titrated with 0.1014 M KOH   **Find:** volume of base added
Conceptual Plan: Because this is a diprotic acid, each proton is titrated sequentially. Write balanced equations.

$$H_2SO_3 + OH^- \rightarrow HSO_3^- + H_2O \text{ and } HSO_3^- + OH^- \rightarrow SO_3^{2-} + H_2O$$

Then mL $\rightarrow$ L then [H_2SO_3], L $\rightarrow$ mol H_2SO_3 then set mol base (H_2SO_3) $=$ mol acid (KOH) and

$$\frac{1 \text{ L}}{1000 \text{ mL}} \qquad\qquad M = \frac{\text{mol}}{\text{L}} \qquad\qquad \textit{balanced equation has 1:1 stoichiometry (1 st equivalence point)}$$

[KOH], mol KOH $\rightarrow$ L KOH $\rightarrow$ mL KOH the volume to the second equivalence point will be

$$M = \frac{\text{mol}}{\text{L}} \qquad \frac{1000 \text{ mL}}{1 \text{ L}}$$

double the volume to the first equivalence point.

Solution: $20.0 \text{ mL } H_2SO_3 \times \dfrac{1 \text{ L}}{1000 \text{ mL}} = 0.0200 \text{ L } H_2SO_3$ then $\dfrac{0.115 \text{ mol } H_2SO_3}{1 \text{ L}} \times 0.0200 \text{ L} = 0.00230$

mol H_2SO_3. So mol base $=$ mol $H_2SO_3 = 0.00230$ mol $=$ mol KOH then

$$0.00230 \text{ mol KOH} \times \frac{1 \text{ L}}{0.1014 \text{ mol KOH}} = 0.0226\underline{8}245 \text{ L KOH} \times \frac{1000 \text{ ml}}{1 \text{ L}} = 22.7 \text{ mL KOH}$$

to the first equivalence point. The volume to the second equivalence point is simply twice this amount, or 45.4 mL, to the second equivalence point.

Check: The units (mL) are correct. The volume of base is greater than the volume of acid because the concentration of the acid is a little greater than that of the base. The volume to the second equivalence point is twice the volume to the first equivalence point.

16.54 **Given:** 20.0 mL of 0.125 M diprotic acid (H_2A) titrated with 0.1019 M KOH   **Find:** volume of base added
Conceptual Plan: Because this is a diprotic acid, each proton is titrated sequentially. Write balanced equations.

$$H_2A + OH^- \rightarrow HA^- + H_2O \text{ and } HA^- + OH^- \rightarrow A^{2-} + H_2O$$

Then mL $\rightarrow$ L then [H_2A], L $\rightarrow$ mol H_2A then set mol base (H_2A) $=$ mol acid (KOH) and

$$\frac{1 \text{ L}}{1000 \text{ mL}} \qquad\qquad M = \frac{\text{mol}}{\text{L}} \qquad\qquad \textit{balanced equation has 1:1 stoichiometry}$$

[KOH], mol KOH $\rightarrow$ L KOH $\rightarrow$ mL KOH the volume to the second equivalence point will be

$$M = \frac{\text{mol}}{\text{L}} \qquad \frac{1000 \text{ mL}}{1 \text{ L}}$$

double the volume to the first equivalence point.

Solution: $20.0 \text{ mL } H_2A \times \dfrac{1 \text{ L}}{1000 \text{ mL}} = 0.0200 \text{ L } H_2A$ then $\dfrac{0.125 \text{ mol } H_2A}{1 \text{ L}} \times 0.0200 \text{ L} = 0.00250 \text{ mol } H_2A$

So mol base $=$ mol $H_2A = 0.00250$ mol $=$ mol KOH then

$$0.00250 \text{ mol KOH} \times \frac{1 \text{ L}}{0.1019 \text{ mol KOH}} = 0.024\underline{5}339 \text{ L KOH} \times \frac{1000 \text{ mL}}{1 \text{ L}} = 24.5 \text{ mL KOH to first equivalence}$$

point. The volume to the second equivalence point is simply twice this amount, or 49.0 mL, to the second equivalence point.

Check: The units (mL) are correct. The volume of base is less than the volume of acid because the concentration of the acid is a little greater than that of the base. The volume to the second equivalence point is twice the volume to the first equivalence point.

16.55   Because the exact conditions of the titration are not given, a rough calculation will suffice. Recall that at the equivalence point the moles of acid and base are equal. If it is assumed that the concentrations of the acid and the base are equal, then the total volume of the solution will have doubled. Assuming an acid and base concentration of 0.1 M, then the conjugate base formed must have a concentration of ~0.05 M. From earlier calculations, it can be seen that

the $K_b = \dfrac{K_w}{K_a} = \dfrac{[OH^-]^2}{0.05}$; thus, $[OH^-] = \sqrt{\dfrac{0.05\, K_w}{K_a}} = \sqrt{\dfrac{5 \times 10^{-16}}{K_a}}$ and the pH $= 14 + \log \sqrt{\dfrac{5 \times 10^{-16}}{K_a}}$.

(a)   For HF, the $K_a = 3.5 \times 10^{-4}$; so the above equation approximates the pH at the equivalence point of ~8.0. Looking at Table 16.1, phenol red or *m*-nitrophenol will change at the appropriate pH range.

(b)   For HCl, the pH at the equivalence point is 7 because HCl is a strong acid. Looking at Table 16.1, alizarin, bromthymol blue, *m*-nitrophenol or phenol red will change at the appropriate pH range.

(c)   For HCN, the $K_a = 4.9 \times 10^{-10}$; so the preceding equation approximates the pH at the equivalence point of ~11.0. Looking at Table 16.1, alizarin yellow R will change at the appropriate pH range.

16.56   Because the exact conditions of the titration are not given, a rough calculation will suffice. Looking at the pattern of earlier problems, the pH at the equivalence point of a titration of a weak base and a strong acid is the hydrolysis of the conjugate acid of the weak base that has been diluted by a factor of roughly 2 with acid. If it is assumed that the initial concentration of the weak base is ~0.1 M, the conjugate acid concentration will be ~0.05 M. From earlier

calculations, it can be seen that the $K_a = \dfrac{K_w}{K_b} = \dfrac{[H_3O^+]^2}{0.05}$; thus, $[H_3O^+] = \sqrt{\dfrac{0.05\, K_w}{K_b}} = \sqrt{\dfrac{5 \times 10^{-16}}{K_b}}$ and the

pH $= -\log \sqrt{\dfrac{5 \times 10^{-16}}{K_b}}$.

(a)   For CH_3NH_2, the $K_b = 4.4 \times 10^{-4}$; so the above equation approximates the pH at the equivalence point of ~6.0. Looking at Table 16.1, methyl red, Eriochrome Black T, bromocresol purple, or alizarin or bromthymol blue will change at the appropriate pH range.

(b)   For NaOH, the pH at the equivalence point is 7 because NaOH is a strong base. Looking at Table 16.1, alizarin, bromthymol blue, or phenol red will change at the appropriate pH range.

(c)   For $C_6H_5NH_2$, the $K_b = 3.9 \times 10^{-10}$; so the above equation approximates the pH at the equivalence point of ~2.9. Looking at Table 16.1, erythrosin B or 2,4-dinitrophenol will change at the appropriate pH range.

Solubility Equilibria

16.57   For the dissolution reaction, start with the ionic compound as a solid and put it in equilibrium with the appropriate cation and anion, making sure to include the appropriate stoichiometric coefficients. The K_{sp} expression is the product of the concentrations of the cation and anion concentrations raised to their stoichiometric coefficients.

(a) $BaSO_4(s) \rightleftharpoons Ba^{2+}(aq) + SO_4^{2-}(aq)$ and $K_{sp} = [Ba^{2+}][SO_4^{2-}]$

(b) $PbBr_2(s) \rightleftharpoons Pb^{2+}(aq) + 2\, Br^-(aq)$ and $K_{sp} = [Pb^{2+}][Br^-]^2$

(c) $Ag_2CrO_4(s) \rightleftharpoons 2\, Ag^+(aq) + CrO_4^{2-}(aq)$ and $K_{sp} = [Ag^+]^2[CrO_4^{2-}]$

16.58   For the dissolution reaction, start with the ionic compound as a solid and put it in equilibrium with the appropriate cation and anion, making sure to include the appropriate stoichiometric coefficients. The K_{sp} expression is the product of the concentrations of the cation and anion concentrations raised to their stoichiometric coefficients.

(a) $CaCO_3(s) \rightleftharpoons Ca^{2+}(aq) + CO_3^{2-}(aq)$ and $K_{sp} = [Ca^{2+}][CO_3^{2-}]$

(b) $PbCl_2(s) \rightleftharpoons Pb^{2+}(aq) + 2\, Cl^-(aq)$ and $K_{sp} = [Pb^{2+}][Cl^-]^2$

(c) $AgI(s) \rightleftharpoons Ag^+(aq) + I^-(aq)$ and $K_{sp} = [Ag^+][I^-]$

16.59   **Given:** ionic compound formula and Table 16.2 of K_{sp} values   **Find:** molar solubility (*S*)
Conceptual Plan: Since the balanced chemical equation for the dissolution of A_mX_n is $A_mX_n(s) \rightleftharpoons mA^{n+}(aq) + nX^{m-}(aq)$, the expression of the solubility product constant of A_mX_n is $K_{sp} = [A^{n+}]^m[X^{m-}]^n$. The molar solubility of a compound, A_mX_n, can be computed directly from K_{sp} by solving for *S* in the expression $K_{sp} = (mS)^m(nS)^n = m^m n^n S^{m+n}$.

Solution:

(a) For AgBr, $K_{sp} = 5.35 \times 10^{-13}$, $A = Ag^+$, $m = 1$, $X = Br^-$, and $n = 1$; so $K_{sp} = 5.35 \times 10^{-13} = S^2$.

Rearrange to solve for S. $S = \sqrt{5.35 \times 10^{-13}} = 7.31 \times 10^{-7}$ M.

(b) For $Mg(OH)_2$, $K_{sp} = 2.06 \times 10^{-13}$, $A = Mg^{2+}$, $m = 1$, $X = OH^-$, and $n = 2$; so $K_{sp} = 2.06 \times 10^{-13} = 2^2 S^3$.

Rearrange to solve for S. $S = \sqrt[3]{\dfrac{2.06 \times 10^{-13}}{4}} = 3.72 \times 10^{-5}$ M.

(c) For CaF_2, $K_{sp} = 1.46 \times 10^{-10}$, $A = Ca^{2+}$, $m = 1$, $X = F^-$, and $n = 2$; so $K_{sp} = 1.46 \times 10^{-10} = 2^2 S^3$.

Rearrange to solve for S. $S = \sqrt[3]{\dfrac{1.46 \times 10^{-10}}{4}} = 3.32 \times 10^{-4}$ M.

Check: The units (M) are correct. The molar solubilities are much less than 1 and dependent not only on the value of the K_{sp}, but also on the stoichiometry of the ionic compound. The more ions generated, the greater the molar solubility for the same value of the K_{sp}.

16.60 **Given:** ionic compound formula and Table 16.2 of K_{sp} values **Find:** molar solubility (S)

Conceptual Plan: Since the balanced chemical equation for the dissolution of A_mX_n is $A_mX_n(s) \rightleftharpoons$ $mA^{n+}(aq) + nX^{m-}(aq)$, the expression of the solubility product constant of A_mX_n is $K_{sp} = [A^{n+}]^m[X^{m-}]^n$. The molar solubility of a compound, A_mX_n, can be computed directly from K_{sp} by solving for S in the expression $K_{sp} = (mS)^m(nS)^n = m^m n^n S^{m+n}$.

Solution:

(a) For MX, $K_{sp} = 1.27 \times 10^{-36}$, $A = M^+$, $m = 1$, $X = X^-$, and $n = 1$; so $K_{sp} = 1.27 \times 10^{-36} = S^2$.

Rearrange to solve for S. $S = \sqrt{1.27 \times 10^{-36}} = 1.13 \times 10^{-18}$ M.

(b) For Ag_2CrO_4, $K_{sp} = 1.12 \times 10^{-12}$, $A = Ag^+$, $m = 2$, $X = CrO_4^{2-}$, and $n = 1$; so $K_{sp} = 1.12 \times 10^{-12} = 2^2 S^3$.

Rearrange to solve for S. $S = \sqrt[3]{\dfrac{1.12 \times 10^{-12}}{4}} = 6.54 \times 10^{-5}$ M.

(c) For $Ca(OH)_2$, $K_{sp} = 4.68 \times 10^{-6}$, $A = Ca^{2+}$, $m = 1$, $X = OH^-$, and $n = 2$; so $K_{sp} = 4.68 \times 10^{-6} = 2^2 S^3$.

Rearrange to solve for S. $S = \sqrt[3]{\dfrac{4.68 \times 10^{-6}}{4}} = 1.05 \times 10^{-2}$ M.

Check: The units (M) are correct. The molar solubilities are much less than 1 and dependent not only on the value of the K_{sp}, but also on the stoichiometry of the ionic compound. The more ions generated, the greater the molar solubility for the same value of the K_{sp}.

16.61 **Given:** ionic compound formula and molar solubility (S) **Find:** K_{sp}

Conceptual Plan: The expression of the solubility product constant of A_mX_n is $K_{sp} = [A^{n+}]^m[X^{m-}]^n$. The molar solubility of a compound, A_mX_n, can be computed directly from K_{sp} by solving for S in the expression $K_{sp} = (mS)^m(nS)^n = m^m n^n S^{m+n}$.

Solution:

(a) For MX, $S = 3.27 \times 10^{-11}$ M, $A = M^+$, $m = 1$, $X = X^-$, and $n = 1$; so $K_{sp} = S^2 = (3.27 \times 10^{-11})^2 = 1.07 \times 10^{-21}$.

(b) For PbF_2, $S = 5.63 \times 10^{-3}$ M, $A = Pb^{2+}$, $m = 1$, $X = F^-$, and $n = 2$; so $K_{sp} = 2^2 S^3 = 2^2(5.63 \times 10^{-3})^3 = 7.14 \times 10^{-7}$.

(c) For MgF_2, $S = 2.65 \times 10^{-4}$ M, $A = Mg^{2+}$, $m = 1$, $X = F^-$, and $n = 2$; so $K_{sp} = 2^2 S^3 = 2^2(2.65 \times 10^{-4})^3 = 7.44 \times 10^{-11}$.

Check: The units (none) are correct. The K_{sp} values are much less than 1 and dependent not only on the value of the solubility, but also on the stoichiometry of the ionic compound. The more ions generated, the smaller the K_{sp} for the same value of the S.

16.62 **Given:** ionic compound formula and molar solubility (S) **Find:** K_{sp}

Conceptual Plan: The expression of the solubility product constant of A_mX_n is $K_{sp} = [A^{n+}]^m[X^{m-}]^n$. The molar solubility of a compound, A_mX_n, can be computed directly from K_{sp} by solving for S in the expression $K_{sp} = (mS)^m(nS)^n = m^m n^n S^{m+n}$.

Solution:

(a)   For $BaCrO_4$, $S = 1.08 \times 10^{-5}$ M, A = Ba^{2+}, $m = 1$, X = CrO_4^{2-}, and $n = 1$; so $K_{sp} = S^2 = (1.08 \times 10^{-5})^2 = 1.17 \times 10^{-10}$.

(b)   For Ag_2SO_3, $S = 1.55 \times 10^{-5}$ M, A = Ag^+, $m = 2$, X = SO_3^{2-}, and $n = 1$; so $K_{sp} = 2^2 S^3 = 2^2(1.55 \times 10^{-5})^3 = 1.49 \times 10^{-14}$.

(c)   For $Pd(SCN)_2$, $S = 2.22 \times 10^{-8}$ M, A = Pd^{2+}, $m = 1$, X = SCN^-, and $n = 2$; so $K_{sp} = 2^2 S^3 = 2^2(2.22 \times 10^{-8})^3 = 4.38 \times 10^{-23}$.

Check: The units (none) are correct. The K_{sp} values are much less than 1 and dependent not only on the value of the solubility, but also on the stoichiometry of the ionic compound. The more ions generated, the smaller the K_{sp} for the same value of the S.

16.63   **Given:** ionic compound formulas AX and AX_2 and $K_{sp} = 1.5 \times 10^{-5}$ **Find:** higher molar solubility (S)
Conceptual Plan: The expression of the solubility product constant of A_mX_n is $K_{sp} = [A^{n+}]^m[X^{m-}]^n$. The molar solubility of a compound, A_mX_n, can be computed directly from K_{sp} by solving for S in the expression $K_{sp} = (mS)^m(nS)^n = m^m n^n S^{m+n}$.
Solution: For AX, $K_{sp} = 1.5 \times 10^{-5}$, $m = 1$, and $n = 1$; so $K_{sp} = 1.5 \times 10^{-5} = S^2$. Rearrange to solve for S.
$S = \sqrt{1.5 \times 10^{-5}} = 3.9 \times 10^{-3}$ M. For AX_2, $K_{sp} = 1.5 \times 10^{-5}$, $m = 1$, and $n = 2$; so $K_{sp} = 1.5 \times 10^{-5} = 2^2 S^3$.

Rearrange to solve for S. $S = \sqrt[3]{\dfrac{1.5 \times 10^{-5}}{4}} = 1.6 \times 10^{-2}$ M. Because 10^{-2} M $> 10^{-3}$ M, AX_2 has a higher molar solubility.

Check: The units (M) are correct. The more ions generated, the greater the molar solubility for the same value of the K_{sp}.

16.64   **Given:** ionic compound formula and molar solubility (S)   **Find:** K_{sp}
Conceptual Plan: The expression of the solubility product constant of A_mX_n is $K_{sp} = [A^{n+}]^m[X^{m-}]^n$. The molar solubility of a compound, A_mX_n, can be computed directly from K_{sp} by solving for S in the expression $K_{sp} = (mS)^m(nS)^n = m^m n^n S^{m+n}$.
Solution: For AX, $S = 1.35 \times 10^{-4}$ M, $m = 1$, and $n = 1$; so $K_{sp} = S^2 = (1.35 \times 10^{-4})^2 = 1.82 \times 10^{-8}$.
For AX_2, $S = 2.25 \times 10^{-4}$ M, $m = 1$, and $n = 2$; so $K_{sp} = 2^2 S^3 = 2^2(2.25 \times 10^{-4})^3 = 4.56 \times 10^{-11}$.
For A_2X, $S = 1.75 \times 10^{-4}$ M, $m = 2$, and $n = 1$; so $K_{sp} = 2^2 S^3 = 2^2(1.75 \times 10^{-4})^3 = 2.14 \times 10^{-11}$. So A_2X has the lowest K_{sp} because it has a lower S than for AX_2.

Check: The units (none) are correct. The K_{sp} values are much less than 1 and dependent not only on the value of the solubility, but also on the stoichiometry of the ionic compound. The more ions generated, the smaller the K_{sp} for the same value of the S.

16.65   **Given:** $Fe(OH)_2$ in 100.0 mL solution   **Find:** grams of $Fe(OH)_2$ **Other:** $K_{sp} = 4.87 \times 10^{-17}$
Conceptual Plan: The expression of the solubility product constant of A_mX_n is $K_{sp} = [A^{n+}]^m[X^{m-}]^n$. The molar solubility of a compound, A_mX_n, can be computed directly from K_{sp} by solving for S in the expression $K_{sp} = (mS)^m(nS)^n = m^m n^n S^{m+n}$. Then solve for S, then mL $\rightarrow$ L then

$$\frac{1\,L}{1000\,mL}$$

$S, L \rightarrow$ mol $Fe(OH)_2$ $\rightarrow$ g $Fe(OH)_2$.

$$M = \frac{mol}{L} \qquad \frac{89.87 \text{ g } Fe(OH)_2}{1 \text{ mol } Fe(OH)_2}$$

Solution:
For $Fe(OH)_2$, $K_{sp} = 4.87 \times 10^{-17}$, A = Fe^{2+}, $m = 1$, X = OH^-, and $n = 2$; so $K_{sp} = 4.87 \times 10^{-17} = 2^2 S^3$.

Rearrange to solve for S. $S = \sqrt[3]{\dfrac{4.87 \times 10^{-17}}{4}} = 2.30050 \times 10^{-6}$ M. Then $100.0 \text{ mL} \times \dfrac{1 \text{ L}}{1000 \text{ mL}} = 0.1000$ L

then $\dfrac{2.30050 \times 10^{-6} \text{ mol } Fe(OH)_2}{1 \text{ L}} \times 0.1000 \text{ L} = 2.30050 \times 10^{-7}$ mol $Fe(OH)_2$

and mass $Fe(OH)_2 = 2.30050 \times 10^{-7} \text{ mol } Fe(OH)_2 \times \dfrac{89.87 \text{ g } Fe(OH)_2}{1 \text{ mol } Fe(OH)_2} = 2.07 \times 10^{-5}$ g $Fe(OH)_2$

Check: The units (g) are correct. The solubility rules from Chapter 4 (most hydroxides are insoluble) suggest that very little $Fe(OH)_2$ will dissolve; so the magnitude of the answer is not surprising.

16.66   **Given:** 3.91 mg CuCl in 100.0 mL solution   **Find:** K_{sp}
Conceptual Plan: mL → L then mg CuCl → g CuCl → mol CuCl then L, mol CuCl → S

$$\frac{1\ L}{1000\ mL} \qquad \frac{1\ g\ CuCl}{1000\ mg\ CuCl} \quad \frac{1\ mol\ CuCl}{99.00\ g\ CuCl} \qquad M = \frac{mol}{L}$$

The expression of the solubility product constant of A_mX_n is $K_{sp} = [A^{n+}]^m[X^{m-}]^n$. The molar solubility of a compound, A_mX_n, can be computed directly from K_{sp} by solving for S in the expression $K_{sp} = (mS)^m(nS)^n = m^m n^n S^{m+n}$.

Solution: $100.0\ \text{mL} \times \dfrac{1\ L}{1000\ \text{mL}} = 0.1000\ L$ then

$$3.91\ \text{mg CuCl} \times \frac{1\ \text{g CuCl}}{1000\ \text{mg CuCl}} \times \frac{1\ mol\ CuCl}{99.00\ \text{g CuCl}} = 3.9\underline{4}950 \times 10^{-5}\ mol\ CuCl\ then$$

$$\frac{3.9\underline{4}950 \times 10^{-5}\ mol\ CuCl}{0.1000\ L} = 3.9\underline{4}950 \times 10^{-4}\ M\ CuCl = S\ then\ for\ CuCl,\ A = Cu^+, m = 1, X = Cl^-,\ and\ n = 1;\ so$$

$K_{sp} = S^2 = (3.9\underline{4}950 \times 10^{-4})^2 = 1.56 \times 10^{-7}$.

Check: The units (none) are correct. The value of $K_{sp} \ll 1$ because only mg dissolve in a liter of solution. The K_{sp} is not too low because CuCl dissociates into only two ions and S is 10^{-4}.

16.67   (a)   **Given:** BaF_2 **Find:** molar solubility (S) in pure water **Other:** $K_{sp}(BaF_2) = 2.45 \times 10^{-5}$
Conceptual Plan: The expression of the solubility product constant of A_mX_n is $K_{sp} = [A^{n+}]^m[X^{m-}]^n$. The molar solubility of a compound, A_mX_n, can be computed directly from K_{sp} by solving for S in the expression $K_{sp} = (mS)^m(nS)^n = m^m n^n S^{m+n}$.
Solution: For BaF_2, $K_{sp} = 2.45 \times 10^{-5}$, $A = Ba^{2+}$, $m = 1$, $X = F^-$, and $n = 2$; so $K_{sp} = 2.45 \times 10^{-5} = 2^2 S^3$.

Rearrange to solve for S. $S = \sqrt[3]{\dfrac{2.45 \times 10^{-5}}{4}} = 1.83 \times 10^{-2}\ M$.

(b)   **Given:** BaF_2 **Find:** molar solubility (S) in 0.10 M $Ba(NO_3)_2$ **Other:** $K_{sp}(BaF_2) = 2.45 \times 10^{-5}$
Conceptual Plan: M $Ba(NO_3)_2$ → M Ba^{2+} then M Ba^{2+}, K_{sp} → S

$$Ba(NO_3)_2(s) \rightarrow Ba^{2+}(aq) + 2\ NO_3^-(aq) \qquad \text{ICE table}$$

Solution: Because one Ba^{2+} ion is generated for each $Ba(NO_3)_2$, $[Ba^{2+}] = 0.10\ M$.

$BaF_2(s) \rightleftharpoons Ba^{2-}(aq) + 2\ F^-(aq)$

Initial	0.10	0.00
Change	S	2S
Equil	0.10 + S	2S

$K_{sp}(BaF_2) = [Ba^{2+}][F^-]^2 = 2.45 \times 10^{-5} = (0.10 + S)(2S)^2$

Assume that $S \ll 0.10$, $2.45 \times 10^{-5} = (0.10)(2S)^2$, and $S = 7.83 \times 10^{-3}\ M$. Confirm that the assumption is valid. $\dfrac{7.83 \times 10^{-3}}{0.10} \times 100\% = 7.8\% > 5\%$, so the assumption is not valid. Because expanding the expression will give a third-order polynomial, that is not easily solved directly, solve by successive approximations. Substitute $S = 7.83 \times 10^{-3}\ M$ for the S term that is part of a sum (i.e., the one in (0.10 + S)). Thus, $2.45 \times 10^{-5} = (0.10 + 7.83 \times 10^{-3})(2S)^2$ and $S = 7.53 \times 10^{-3}\ M$. Substitute this new S value again. Thus, $2.45 \times 10^{-5} = (0.10 + 7.53 \times 10^{-3})(2S)^2$ and $S = 7.55 \times 10^{-3}\ M$. Substitute this new S value again. Thus, $2.45 \times 10^{-5} = (0.10 + 7.55 \times 10^{-3})(2S)^2$ and $S = 7.55 \times 10^{-3}\ M$. So the solution has converged and $S = 7.55 \times 10^{-3}\ M$.

(c)   **Given:** BaF_2 **Find:** molar solubility (S) in 0.15 M NaF   **Other:** $K_{sp}(BaF_2) = 2.45 \times 10^{-5}$
Conceptual Plan: M NaF → M F^- then M F^-, K_{sp} → S

$$NaF(S) \rightarrow Na^+(aq) + F^-(aq) \qquad \text{ICE table}$$

Solution: Because one F^- ion is generated for each NaF, $[F^-] = 0.15$ M.

$$BaF_2(s) \rightleftharpoons Ba^{2-}(aq) + 2\,F^-(aq)$$

Initial	0.00	0.15
Change	S	$2S$
Equil	S	$0.15 + 2S$

$$K_{sp}(BaF_2) = [Ba^{2+}][F^-]^2 = 2.45 \times 10^{-5} = (S)(0.15 + 2S)^2$$

Because $2S \ll 0.15$, $2.45 \times 10^{-5} = (S)(0.15)^2$ and $S = 1.09 \times 10^{-3}$ M. Confirm that the assumption is

valid. $\dfrac{2\,(1.09 \times 10^{-3})}{0.15} \times 100\% = 1.5\% < 5\%$, so the assumption is valid.

Check: The units (M) are correct. The solubility of the BaF_2 decreases in the presence of a common ion. The effect of the anion is greater because the K_{sp} expression has the anion concentration squared.

16.68 (a) **Given:** MX   **Find:** molar solubility (S) in pure water   **Other:** $K_{sp}(MX) = 1.27 \times 10^{-36}$
Conceptual Plan: The expression of the solubility product constant of A_mX_n is $K_{sp} = [A^{n+}]^m[X^{m-}]^n$. The molar solubility of a compound, A_mX_n, can be computed directly from K_{sp} by solving for S in the expression $K_{sp} = (mS)^m(nS)^n = m^m n^n S^{m+n}$.

Solution: For MX, $K_{sp} = 1.27 \times 10^{-36}$, $A = M^{2+}$, $m = 1$, $X = X^{2-}$, and $n = 1$. There is a 1:1 ratio of the cation:anion, so $K_{sp} = 1.27 \times 10^{-36} = S^2$. Rearrange to solve for S. $S = 1.13 \times 10^{-18}$ M.

(b) **Given:** MX   **Find:** molar solubility (S) in 0.25 M MCl_2 **Other:** K_{sp} (MX) $= 1.27 \times 10^{-36}$
Conceptual Plan: M MCl_2 $\rightarrow$ M M^{2+} then M M^{2+}, K_{sp} $\rightarrow$ S

$$MCl_2(S) \rightarrow M^{2+}(aq) + 2\,Cl^-(aq) \qquad \text{ICE table}$$

Solution: Because one M^{2+} ion is generated for each MCl_2, $[M^{2+}] = 0.25$ M.

$$MX(s) \rightleftharpoons M^{2+}(aq) + X^{2-}(aq)$$

Initial	0.25	0.00
Change	S	S
Equil	$0.25 + S$	S

$$K_{sp}(MX) = [M^{2+}][X^{2-}] = 1.27 \times 10^{-36} = (0.25 + S)S$$

Assume that $S \ll 0.25$, $1.27 \times 10^{-36} = (0.25)S$, and $S = 5.08 \times 10^{-36}$ M. Confirm that the assumption is

valid. $\dfrac{5.08 \times 10^{-36}}{0.25} \times 100\% = 2.0 \times 10^{-33}\% \ll 5\%$, so the assumption is valid.

(c) **Given:** MX   **Find:** molar solubility (S) in 0.20 M Na_2S **Other:** $K_{sp}(MX) = 1.27 \times 10^{-36}$
Conceptual Plan: M Na_2X $\rightarrow$ M X^{2-} then M X^{2-}, K_{sp} $\rightarrow$ S

$$Na_2X(s) \rightarrow 2\,Na^+(aq) + X^{2-}(aq) \qquad \text{ICE table}$$

Solution: Because one X^{2-} ion is generated for each Na_2X, $[X^{2-}] = 0.20$ M.

$$MX(s) \rightleftharpoons M^{2+}(aq) + X^{2-}(aq)$$

Initial	0.00	0.20
Change	S	S
Equil	S	$0.20 + S$

$$K_{sp}(MX) = [M^{2+}][X^{2-}] = 1.27 \times 10^{-36} = (S)(0.20 + S).$$

Assume that $S \ll 0.20$, $1.27 \times 10^{-36} = (S)(0.20)$, and $S = 6.35 \times 10^{-36}$ M. Confirm that the assumption is

valid. $\dfrac{6.35 \times 10^{-36}}{0.20} \times 100\% = 3.2 \times 10^{-33}\% \ll 5\%$, so the assumption is valid.

Check: The units (M) are correct. The solubility of the MX decreases in the presence of a common ion.

16.69 **Given:** $Ca(OH)_2$ **Find:** molar solubility (S) in buffers at (a) pH $= 4$, (b) pH $= 7$, and (c) pH $= 9$
Other: K_{sp} ($Ca(OH)_2$) $= 4.68 \times 10^{-6}$
Conceptual Plan: pH $\rightarrow$ $[H_3O^+]$ $\rightarrow$ $[OH^-]$ then M OH^-, K_{sp} $\rightarrow$ S

$$[H_3O^+] = 10^{-pH} \qquad K_w = [H_3O^+][OH^-] \qquad \text{set up ICE table}$$

Solution:

(a) $pH = 4$, so $[H_3O^+] = 10^{-pH} = 10^{-4} = 1 \times 10^{-4}$ M then $K_w = [H_3O^+][OH^-]$ so

$$[OH^-] = \frac{K_w}{[H_3O^+]} = \frac{1.0 \times 10^{-14}}{1 \times 10^{-4}} = 1 \times 10^{-10} \text{ M then}$$

$$Ca(OH)_2(s) \rightleftharpoons Ca^{2+}(aq) + 2\,OH^-(aq)$$

Initial	0.00	1×10^{-10}
Change	S	—
Equil	S	1×10^{-10}

$K_{sp}(Ca(OH)_2) = [Ca^{2+}][OH^-]^2 = 4.68 \times 10^{-6} = S(1 \times 10^{-10})^2$ and $S = 5 \times 10^{14}$ M

(b) $pH = 7$, so $[H_3O^+] = 10^{-pH} = 10^{-7} = 1 \times 10^{-7}$ M then $K_w = [H_3O^+][OH^-]$ so

$$[OH^-] = \frac{K_w}{[H_3O^+]} = \frac{1.0 \times 10^{-14}}{1 \times 10^{-7}} = 1 \times 10^{-7} \text{ M then}$$

$$Ca(OH)_2(s) \rightleftharpoons Ca^{2+}(aq) + 2\,OH^-(aq)$$

Initial	0.00	1×10^{-7}
Change	S	—
Equil	S	1×10^{-7}

$K_{sp}(Ca(OH)_2) = [Ca^{2+}][OH^-]^2 = 4.68 \times 10^{-6} = S(1 \times 10^{-7})^2$ and $S = 5 \times 10^8$ M

(c) $pH = 9$, so $[H_3O^+] = 10^{-pH} = 10^{-9} = 1 \times 10^{-9}$ M then $K_w = [H_3O^+][OH^-]$ so

$$[OH^-] = \frac{K_w}{[H_3O^+]} = \frac{1.0 \times 10^{-14}}{1 \times 10^{-9}} = 1 \times 10^{-5} \text{ M then}$$

$$Ca(OH)_2(s) \rightleftharpoons Ca^{2+}(aq) + 2\,OH^-(aq)$$

Initial	0.00	1×10^{-5}
Change	S	—
Equil	S	1×10^{-5}

$K_{sp}(Ca(OH)_2) = [Ca^{2+}][OH^-]^2 = 4.68 \times 10^{-6} = S(1 \times 10^{-5})^2$ and $S = 5 \times 10^4$ M

Check: The units (M) are correct. The solubility of the $Ca(OH)_2$ decreases as the pH increases (and the hydroxide ion concentration increases). These molar solubilities are not achievable because the saturation point of pure $Ca(OH)_2$ is ~ 30 M. The bottom line is that as long as the hydroxide concentration can be controlled with a buffer, the $Ca(OH)_2$ will be very soluble.

16.70 **Given:** $Mg(OH)_2$ in 1.00×10^2 mL solution **Find:** grams of $Mg(OH)_2$ in pure water and buffer at $pH = 10$
Other: $K_{sp}(Mg(OH)_2) = 2.06 \times 10^{-13}$
Conceptual Plan: For pure water:
The expression of the solubility product constant of A_mX_n is $K_{sp} = [A^{n+}]^m[X^{m-}]^n$. The molar solubility of a compound, A_mX_n, can be computed directly from K_{sp} by solving for S in the expression $K_{sp} = (mS)^m(nS)^n = m^m n^n S^{m+n}$. Then mL $\rightarrow$ L then S, L $\rightarrow$ mol $Mg(OH)_2$ $\rightarrow$ g $Mg(OH)_2$.

$$\frac{1\text{ L}}{1000\text{ mL}} \qquad M = \frac{\text{mol}}{\text{L}} \qquad \frac{58.33\text{ g } Mg(OH)_2}{1\text{ mol } Mg(OH)_2}$$

For buffer solution: pH $\rightarrow$ $[H_3O^+]$ $\rightarrow$ $[OH^-]$ then

$$[H_3O^+] = 10^{-pH} \qquad K_w = [H_3O^+][OH^-]$$

M OH^-, K_{sp} $\rightarrow$ S then S, L $\rightarrow$ mol $Mg(OH)_2$ $\rightarrow$ g $Mg(OH)_2$.

$$\text{set up ICE table} \qquad M = \frac{\text{mol}}{\text{L}} \qquad \frac{58.33\text{ g } Mg(OH)_2}{1\text{ mol } Mg(OH)_2}$$

Solution: For pure water, $K_{sp} = 2.06 \times 10^{-13}$, $A = Mg^{2+}$, $m = 1$, $X = OH^-$, and $n = 2$; so $K_{sp} = 2.06 \times 10^{-13} = 2^2 S^3$.

Rearrange to solve for S. $S = \sqrt[3]{\dfrac{2.06 \times 10^{-13}}{4}} = 3.72051 \times 10^{-5}$ M. Then

$$1.00 \times 10^2 \ \cancel{mL} \times \frac{1 \ L}{1000 \ \cancel{mL}} = 0.100 \ L \ \text{then}$$

$$\frac{3.7\underline{2}051 \times 10^{-5} \ \text{mol Mg(OH)}_2}{1 \ \cancel{L}} \times 0.100 \ \cancel{L} = 3.7\underline{2}051 \times 10^{-6} \ \text{mol Mg(OH)}_2$$

$$3.7\underline{2}051 \times 10^{-6} \ \cancel{\text{mol Mg(OH)}_2} \times \frac{58.33 \ \text{g Mg(OH)}_2}{1 \ \cancel{\text{mol Mg(OH)}_2}} = 2.17 \times 10^{-4} \ \text{g Mg(OH)}_2$$

pH = 10, so $[H_3O^+] = 10^{-pH} = 10^{-10} = 1 \times 10^{-10} \ M$ then $K_w = [H_3O^+][OH^-]$ so

$$[OH^-] = \frac{K_w}{[H_3O^+]} = \frac{1.0 \times 10^{-14}}{1 \times 10^{-10}} = 1 \times 10^{-4} \ M \ \text{then}$$

$$Mg(OH)_2(s) \rightleftharpoons Mg^{2+}(aq) + OH^-(aq)$$

Initial	0.00	1×10^{-4}
Change	S	—
Equil	S	1×10^{-4}

$K_{sp}(Mg(OH)_2) = [Mg^{2+}][OH^-]^2 = 2.06 \times 10^{-13} = S(1 \times 10^{-4})^2$ and $\underline{2}.06 \times 10^{-5}$ M. Then

$$\frac{2.06 \times 10^{-5} \ \text{mol Mg(OH)}_2}{1 \ \cancel{L}} \times 0.100 \ \cancel{L} = \underline{2}.06 \times 10^{-6} \ \text{mol Mg(OH)}_2$$

$$\underline{2}.06 \times 10^{-6} \ \cancel{\text{mol Mg(OH)}_2} \times \frac{58.33 \ \text{g Mg(OH)}_2}{1 \ \cancel{\text{mol Mg(OH)}_2}} = 1 \times 10^{-4} \ \text{g Mg(OH)}_2$$

Check: The units (M) are correct. The solubility of the $Mg(OH)_2$ decreases as the pH increases (and the hydroxide ion concentration increases).

16.71 (a) $BaCO_3$ will be more soluble in acidic solutions because CO_3^{2-} is basic. In acidic solutions, it can be converted to HCO_3^- and H_2CO_3. These species are not CO_3^{2-}, so they do not appear in the K_{sp} expression.

(b) CuS will be more soluble in acidic solutions because S^{2-} is basic. In acidic solutions, it can be converted to HS^- and H_2S. These species are not S^{2-}, so they do not appear in the K_{sp} expression.

(c) $AgCl$ will not be more soluble in acidic solutions because Cl^- will not react with acidic solutions because HCl is a strong acid.

(d) PbI_2 will not be more soluble in acidic solutions because I^- will not react with acidic solutions because HI is a strong acid.

16.72 (a) Hg_2Br_2 will not be more soluble in acidic solutions because Br^- will not react with acidic solutions because HBr is a strong acid.

(b) $Mg(OH)_2$ will be more soluble in acidic solutions because OH^- is basic. In acidic solutions, it can be converted to H_2O. This species is not OH^-, so it does not appear in the K_{sp} expression.

(c) $CaCO_3$ will be more soluble in acidic solutions because CO_3^{2-} is basic. In acidic solutions, it can be converted to HCO_3^- and H_2CO_3. These species are not CO_3^{2-}, so they do not appear in the K_{sp} expression.

(d) AgI will not be more soluble in acidic solutions because I^- will not react with acidic solutions because HI is a strong acid.

16.73 **Given:** 0.015 M NaF and 0.010 M $Ca(NO_3)_2$ **Find:** Will a precipitate form? If so, identify it.
Other: $K_{sp}(CaF_2) = 1.46 \times 10^{-10}$
Conceptual Plan: Look at all possible combinations and consider the solubility rules from Chapter 4. Salts of alkali metals (Na) are very soluble, so NaF and $NaNO_3$ will be very soluble. Nitrate compounds are very soluble, so $NaNO_3$ will be very soluble. The only possibility for a precipitate is CaF_2. Determine whether a precipitate will form by determining the concentration of the Ca^{2+} and F^- in solution. Then compute the reaction quotient, Q. If $Q > K_{sp}$, a precipitate will form.
Solution: Because the only possible precipitate is CaF_2, calculate the concentrations of Ca^{2+} and F^-. NaF(s) $\rightarrow$ $Na^+(aq) + F^-(aq)$. Because one F^- ion is generated for each NaF, $[F^-] = 0.015$ M.
$Ca(NO_3)_2(s) \rightarrow Ca^{2+}(aq) + 2 NO_3^-(aq)$. Because one Ca^{2+} ion is generated for each $Ca(NO_3)_2$, $[Ca^{2+}] = 0.010$ M. Then calculate Q (CaF_2), A = Ca^{2+}, $m = 1$, X = F^-, and $n = 2$. Because $Q = [A^{n+}]^m [X^{m-}]^n$,
$Q(CaF_2) = [Ca^{2+}][F^-]^2 = (0.010)(0.015)^2 = 2.3 \times 10^{-6} > 1.46 \times 10^{-10} = K_{sp}(CaF_2)$; so a precipitate will form.

Check: The units (none) are correct. The solubility of the CaF_2 is low, and the concentrations of ions are extremely large compared to the K_{sp}; so a precipitate will form.

16.74   **Given:** 0.013 M KBr and 0.0035 M Pb($C_2H_3O_2$)$_2$ **Find:** Will a precipitate form? If so, identify it.
Other: K_{sp}(PbBr$_2$) = 4.67×10^{-6}
Conceptual Plan: Look at all possible combinations and consider the solubility rules from Chapter 4. Salts of alkali metals (K) are very soluble, so KBr and KC$_2$H$_3$O$_2$ will be very soluble. Acetate compounds are very soluble, so Pb(C$_2$H$_3$O$_2$)$_2$ and KC$_2$H$_3$O$_2$ will be very soluble. The only possibility for a precipitate is PbBr$_2$. Determine whether a precipitate will form by determining the concentration of the Pb^{2+} and Br$^-$ in solution. Then compute the reaction quotient, Q. If $Q > K_{sp}$, a precipitate will form.
Solution: Because the only possible precipitate is PbBr$_2$, calculate the concentrations of Pb^{2+} and Br$^-$.
KBr(s) $\rightarrow$ K$^+$(aq) + Br$^-$(aq). Because one Br$^-$ ion is generated for each KBr, [Br$^-$] = 0.013 M. Pb(C$_2$H$_3$O$_2$)$_2$(s) $\rightarrow$ Pb^{2+}(aq) + 2 C$_2$H$_3$O$_2^-$(aq). Because one Pb^{2+} ion is generated for each Pb(C$_2$H$_3$O$_2$)$_2$, [Pb$^+$] = 0.0035 M.
Then calculate Q(PbBr$_2$), A = Pb^{2+}, m = 1, X = Br$^-$, and n = 2. Because $Q = [A^{n+}]^m [X^{m-}]^n$, Q(PbBr$_2$) = [Pb^{2+}] [Br$^-$]^2 = (0.0035) (0.013)^2 = $6.0 \times 10^{-7} < 4.67 \times 10^{-6} = K_{sp}$(PbBr$_2$); so a precipitate will not form.

Check: The units (none) are correct. The K_{sp} of the PbBr$_2$ is not too low compared to the solution ion concentrations, so a precipitate will not form.

16.75   **Given:** 75.0 mL of NaOH with pOH = 2.58 and 125.0 mL of 0.018 M MgCl$_2$ **Find:** Will a precipitate form? If so, identify it. **Other:** K_{sp}(Mg(OH)$_2$) = 2.06×10^{-13}
Conceptual Plan: Look at all possible combinations and consider the solubility rules from Chapter 4. Salts of alkali metals (Na) are very soluble, so NaOH and NaCl will be very soluble. Chloride compounds are generally very soluble, so MgCl$_2$ and NaCl will be very soluble. The only possibility for a precipitate is Mg(OH)$_2$. Determine whether a precipitate will form by determining the concentration of the Mg^{2+} and OH$^-$ in solution. Because pH, not NaOH concentration, is given, pOH $\rightarrow$ [OH$^-$] then

$$[OH^-] = 10^{-pOH}$$

mix solutions and calculate diluted concentrations mL NaOH, mL MgCl$_2$ $\rightarrow$ mL total then

$$\text{mL NaOH + mL MgCl}_2 = \text{total mL}$$

mL, initial M $\rightarrow$ final M then compute the reaction quotient, Q.

$$M_1V_1 = M_2V_2$$

If $Q > K_{sp}$, a precipitate will form.
Solution: Because the only possible precipitate is Mg(OH)$_2$, calculate the concentrations of Mg^{2+} and OH$^-$.
For NaOH at pOH = 2.58, so [OH$^-$] = 10^{-pOH} = $10^{-2.58}$ = 2.63027×10^{-3} M and
MgCl$_2$(s) $\rightarrow$ Mg^{2+}(aq) + 2 Cl$^-$(aq). Because one Mg^{2+} ion is generated for each MgCl$_2$, [Mg^{2+}] = 0.018 M.
Then total mL = mL NaOH + mL MgCl$_2$ = 75.0 mL + 125.0 mL = 200.0 mL. Then $M_1 V_1 = M_2 V_2$;

rearrange to solve for M_2. $M_2 = M_1 \dfrac{V_1}{V_2}$ = 2.63027×10^{-3} M OH$^-$ $\times \dfrac{75.0 \text{ mL}}{200.0 \text{ mL}}$ = 9.8635×10^{-4} M OH$^-$ and

$M_2 = M_1 \dfrac{V_1}{V_2}$ = 0.018 M Mg^{2+} $\times \dfrac{125.0 \text{ mL}}{200.0 \text{ mL}}$ = 1.125×10^{-2} M Mg^{2+}. Calculate Q(Mg(OH)$_2$), A = Mg^{2+},

m = 1, X = OH$^-$, and n = 2. Because $Q = [A^{n+}]^m [X^{m-}]^n$, Q(Mg(OH)$_2$) = [Mg^{2+}] [OH$^-$]^2 = (1.125×10^{-2})(9.8635×10^{-4})^2 = $1.1 \times 10^{-8} > 2.06 \times 10^{-13} = K_{sp}$(Mg(OH)$_2$); so a precipitate will form.

Check: The units (none) are correct. The solubility of the Mg(OH)$_2$ is low, and the NaOH (a base) is high enough that the product of the concentration of ions is large compared to the K_{sp}; so a precipitate will form.

16.76   **Given:** 175.0 mL of 0.0055 M KCl and 145.0 mL of 0.0015 M AgNO$_3$
Find: Will a precipitate form? If so, identify it. **Other:** K_{sp}(AgCl) = 1.77×10^{-10}
Conceptual Plan: Look at all possible combinations and consider the solubility rules from Chapter 4. Salts of alkali metals (K) are very soluble, so KCl and KNO$_3$ will be very soluble. Nitrate compounds are very soluble, so KNO$_3$ and AgNO$_3$ will be very soluble. The only possibility for a precipitate is AgCl. Determine whether a precipitate will form by determining the concentration of the Ag$^+$ and Cl$^-$ in solution. Mix solutions and calculate diluted concentrations mL KCl, mL AgNO$_3$ $\rightarrow$ mL total then

$$\text{mL KCl + mL AgNO}_3 = \text{total mL}$$

mL, initial M $\rightarrow$ final M then compute the reaction quotient, Q. If $Q > K_{sp}$, a precipitate will form.

$$M_1 V_1 = M_2 V_2$$

Solution: Because the only possible precipitate is AgCl, calculate the concentrations of Ag$^+$ and Cl$^-$.
KCl(s) $\rightarrow$ K$^+$(aq) + Cl$^-$(aq). Because one Cl$^-$ ion is generated for each AgCl, [Cl$^-$] = 0.0055 M and

$AgNO_3(s) \rightarrow Ag^+(aq) + NO_3^-(aq)$. Because one Ag^+ ion is generated for each $AgNO_3$, $[Ag^+] = 0.0015$ M. Then total mL = mL KCl + mL $AgNO_3$ = 175.0 mL + 145.0 mL = 320.0. Then $M_1V_1 = M_2V_2$; rearrange to solve for M_2.

$$M_2 = M_1 \frac{V_1}{V_2} = 0.0055 \text{ M Cl}^- \times \frac{175.0 \text{ mL}}{320.0 \text{ mL}} = 0.00300\underline{7}81 \text{ M Cl}^- \text{ and}$$

$$M_2 = M_1 \frac{V_1}{V_2} = 0.0015 \text{ M Ag}^+ \times \frac{145.0 \text{ mL}}{320.0 \text{ mL}} = 0.000\underline{6}7969 \text{ M Ag}^+. \text{ Calculate } Q(AgCl), A = Ag^+, m = 1,$$

X = Cl$^-$, and $n = 1$. Because $Q = [A^{n+}]^m [X^{m-}]^n$, $Q(AgCl) = [Ag^+][Cl^-] = (0.000\underline{6}7969)(0.00300\underline{7}81) = 2.0 \times 10^{-6} > 1.77 \times 10^{-10} = K_{sp}(AgCl)$; so a precipitate will form.

Check: The units (none) are correct. The solubility of the AgCl is low, and the concentrations of the ions are high enough that the product of the concentration of ions is very large compared to the K_{sp}; so a precipitate will form.

16.77 **Given:** KOH as precipitation agent in (a) 0.015 M $CaCl_2$, (b) 0.0025 M $Fe(NO_3)_2$, and (c) 0.0018 M $MgBr_2$
Find: concentration of KOH necessary to form a precipitate
Other: $K_{sp}(Ca(OH)_2) = 4.68 \times 10^{-6}$, $K_{sp}(Fe(OH)_2) = 4.87 \times 10^{-17}$, $K_{sp}(Mg(OH)_2) = 2.06 \times 10^{-13}$
Conceptual Plan: The solubility rules from Chapter 4 state that most hydroxides are insoluble, so all precipitates will be hydroxides. Determine the concentration of the cation in solution. Because all metals have an

oxidation state of $+2$ and $[OH^-] = [KOH]$, all of the K_{sp} = [cation] [KOH]^2; so $[KOH] = \sqrt{\dfrac{K_{sp}}{[\text{cation}]}}$.

Solution:

(a) $CaCl_2(s) \rightarrow Ca^{2+}(aq) + 2 Cl^-(aq)$. Because one Ca^{2+} ion is generated for each $CaCl_2$, $[Ca^{2+}] = 0.015$ M.

Then $[KOH] = \sqrt{\dfrac{K_{sp}}{[\text{cation}]}} = \sqrt{\dfrac{4.68 \times 10^{-6}}{0.015}} = 0.018$ M KOH.

(b) $Fe(NO_3)_2(s) \rightarrow Fe^{2+}(aq) + 2 NO_3^-(aq)$. Because one Fe^{2+} ion is generated for each $Fe(NO_3)_2$, $[Fe^{2+}] = 0.0025$ M.

Then $[KOH] = \sqrt{\dfrac{K_{sp}}{[\text{cation}]}} = \sqrt{\dfrac{4.87 \times 10^{-17}}{0.0025}} = 1.4 \times 10^{-7}$ M KOH.

(c) $MgBr_2(s) \rightarrow Mg^{2+}(aq) + 2 Br^-(aq)$. Because one Mg^{2+} ion is generated for each $MgBr_2$, $[Mg^{2+}] = 0.0018$ M.

Then $[KOH] = \sqrt{\dfrac{K_{sp}}{[\text{cation}]}} = \sqrt{\dfrac{2.06 \times 10^{-13}}{0.0018}} = 1.1 \times 10^{-5}$ M KOH.

Check: The units (none) are correct. Because all cations have an oxidation state of +2, it can be seen that the [KOH] needed to precipitate the hydroxide is lower the smaller the K_{sp}.

16.78 **Given:** solution and precipitation agent pairs (a) 0.035 M $Ba(NO_3)_2$: NaF, (b) 0.086 M CaI_2: K_2SO_4, and (c) 0.0018 M $AgNO_3$: RbCl   **Find:** concentration of precipitation agent necessary to form a precipitate
Other: $K_{sp}(BaF_2) = 2.45 \times 10^{-5}$, $K_{sp}(CaSO_4) = 7.10 \times 10^{-5}$, $K_{sp}(AgCl) = 1.77 \times 10^{-10}$
Conceptual Plan: Determine the concentration of the cation in solution. The solubility product constant (K_{sp}) is the equilibrium expression for a chemical equation representing the dissolution of an ionic compound. The expression of the solubility product constant of A_mX_n is $K_{sp} = [A^{n+}]^m [X^{m-}]^n$. Substitute concentration of cation and solve for concentration of anion.
Solution:

(a) The precipitate is BaF_2. $Ba(NO_3)_2(s) \rightarrow Ba^{2+}(aq) + 2 NO_3^-(aq)$. Because one Ba^{2+} ion is generated for each $Ba(NO_3)_2$, $[Ba^{2+}] = 0.035$ M. Then derive expression for $K_{sp}(BaF_2)$, $A = Ba^{2+}$, $m = 1$, $X = F^-$, and $n = 2$. Because $K_{sp} = [Ba^{2+}][F^-]^2$, $K_{sp}(BaF_2) = 2.45 \times 10^{-5} = 0.035 [F^-]^2$. Solve for $[F^-]$. $[F^-] = 0.026$ M F^-. Because $NaF(s) \rightarrow Na^+(aq) + F^-(aq)$, one F^- ion is generated for each NaF, [NaF]=0.026 M NaF.

(b) The precipitate is $CaSO_4$. $CaI_2(s) \rightarrow Ca^{2+}(aq) + 2 I^-(aq)$. Because one Ca^{2+} ion is generated for each CaI_2, $[Ca^{2+}] = 0.086$ M. Then derive expression for $K_{sp}(CaSO_4)$, $A = Ca^{2+}$, $m = 1$, $X = SO_4^{2-}$, and $n = 1$. Because $K_{sp} = [Ca^{2+}][SO_4^{2-}]$, $K_{sp}(CaSO_4) = 7.10 \times 10^{-5} = 0.086 [SO_4^{2-}]$. Solve for $[SO_4^{2-}]$. $[SO_4^{2-}] = 0.00083$ M SO_4^{2-}. Because $K_2SO_4(s) \rightarrow 2 K^+(aq) + SO_4^{2-}(aq)$, one SO_4^{2-} ion is generated for each K_2SO_4, $[K_2SO_4] = 0.00083$ M K_2SO_4.

(c) The precipitate is AgCl. Then $AgNO_3(s) \rightarrow Ag^+(aq) + NO_3^-(aq)$. Because one Ag^+ ion is generated for each $AgNO_3$, $[Ag^+] = 0.0018$ M. Then derive expression for K_{sp} (AgCl), $A = Ag^+$, $m = 1$, $X = Cl^-$, and $n = 1$. Because $K_{sp} = [Ag^+][Cl^-]$, $K_{sp}(AgCl) = 1.77 \times 10^{-10} = 0.0018 \, [Cl^-]$. Solve for $[Cl^-]$. $[Cl^-] = 9.8 \times 10^{-8}$ M Cl^-. Because $RbCl(s) \rightarrow Rb^+(aq) + Cl^-(aq)$, one Cl^- ion is generated for each RbCl, $[RbCl] = 9.8 \times 10^{-8}$ M RbCl.

Check: The units (M) are correct. Comparing part (a) and part (b), the effect of the stoichiometry of the precipitate is seen and the concentration of the precipitation agent is much lower. Looking at part (c), the concentration of the precipitation agent is so low because the K_{sp} is so small.

Complex Ion Equilbria

16.79 **Given:** solution with 1.1×10^{-3} M $Zn(NO_3)_2$ and 0.150 M NH_3 　　**Find:** $[Zn^{2+}]$ at equilibrium
Other: $K_f(Zn(NH_3)_4{}^{2+}) = 2.8 \times 10^9$
Conceptual Plan: Write a balanced equation and expression for K_f. Use initial concentrations to set up an ICE table. Because the K_f is so large, assume that reaction essentially goes to completion. Solve for $[Zn^{2+}]$ at equilibrium.
Solution: $Zn(NO_3)_2(s) \rightarrow Zn^{2+}(aq) + 2 NO_3^-(aq)$. Because one Zn^{2+} ion is generated for each $Zn(NO_3)_2$, $[Zn^{2+}] = 1.1 \times 10^{-3}$ M. Balanced equation is:

$$Zn^{2+}(aq) \quad + \quad 4 NH_3(aq) \quad \rightleftharpoons \quad Zn(NH_3)_4^{2+}(aq)$$

	$[Zn^{2+}]$	$[NH_3]$	$[Zn(NH_3)_4{}^{2+}]$
Initial	1.1×10^{-3}	0.150	0.00
Change	$\approx 1.1 \times 10^{-3}$	$\approx -4(1.1 \times 10^{-3})$	$\approx 1.1 \times 10^{-3}$
Equil	x	0.14$\underline{5}$6	1.1×10^{-3}

Set up an ICE table with initial concentrations. Because K_f is so large and because initially $[NH_3] > 4[Zn^{2+}]$, the reaction essentially goes to completion; then write equilibrium expression and solve for x.

$K_f = \dfrac{[Zn(NH_3)_4{}^{2+}]}{[Zn^{2+}][NH_3]^4} = 2.8 \times 10^9 = \dfrac{1.1 \times 10^{-3}}{x \, (0.14\underline{5}6)^4}$. So $x = 8.7 \times 10^{-10}$ M Zn^{2+}. Because x is insignificant compared to the initial concentration, the assumption is valid.

Check: The units (M) are correct. Because K_f is so large, the reaction essentially goes to completion and $[Zn^{2+}]$ is extremely small.

16.80 **Given:** 120.0 mL of 2.8×10^{-3} M $AgNO_3$ mixed with 225.0 mL of 0.10 M NaCN 　　**Find:** $[Ag^+]$ at equilibrium
Other: $K_f(Ag(CN)_2{}^-) = 1 \times 10^{21}$
Conceptual Plan: Mix solutions and calculate diluted concentrations mL $AgNO_3$, mL NaCN $\rightarrow$ mL total

　　　　　　　　　　　　　　　　　　　　　　mL $AgNO_3$ + mL NaCN = total mL

then mL, initial M $\rightarrow$ final M then write balanced equation and expression for K_f.

　　　　　　　　$M_1 V_1 = M_2 V_2$

Use initial concentrations to set up an ICE table. Because the K_f is so large, assume that reaction essentially goes to completion. Solve for $[Ag^+]$ at equilibrium.
Solution: $AgNO_3(s) \rightarrow Ag^+(aq) + NO_3^-(aq)$. Because one Ag^+ ion is generated for each $AgNO_3$, $[Ag^+] = 2.8 \times 10^{-3}$ M and $NaCN(s) \rightarrow Na^+(aq) + CN^-(aq)$. Because one CN^- ion is generated for each NaCN, $[CN^-] = 0.10$ M. Then total mL = mL $AgNO_3$ + mL NaCN = 120.0 mL + 225.0 mL = 345.0 mL. Then $M_1 V_1 = M_2 V_2$. Rearrange to solve for M_2. $M_2 = M_1 \dfrac{V_1}{V_2} = 2.8 \times 10^{-3}$ M $Ag^+ \times \dfrac{120.0 \text{ mL}}{345.0 \text{ mL}} = 0.0009\underline{7}391$ M Ag^+ and

$M_2 = M_1 \dfrac{V_1}{V_2} = 0.10$ M $CN^- \times \dfrac{225.0 \text{ mL}}{345.0 \text{ mL}} = 0.065\underline{2}17$ M CN^-. The balanced equation is as follows:

$$Ag^+(aq) \quad + \quad CN^-(aq) \quad \rightleftharpoons \quad Ag(CN)_2^-(aq)$$

	$[Ag^+]$	$[CN^-]$	$[Ag(CN)_2{}^-]$
Initial	0.0009$\underline{7}$391	0.065$\underline{2}$17	0.00
Change	$\approx 0.0009\underline{7}391$	$\approx -2(0.0009\underline{7}391)$	$\approx 0.0009\underline{7}391$
Equil	x	0.063$\underline{2}$69	0.0009$\underline{7}$391

Set up an ICE table with initial concentrations. Because K_f is so large and because initially $[CN^-] > 2\,[Ag^+]$, the reaction essentially goes to completion; then write equilibrium expression and solve for x.

$$K_f = \frac{[Ag(CN)_2^-]}{[Ag^+][CN^-]^2} = 1 \times 10^{21} = \frac{0.00097391}{x\,(0.063269)^2}.$$ So $x = 2 \times 10^{-22}$ M Ag^+. Because x is insignificant compared to the initial concentration, the assumption is valid.

Check: The units (M) are correct. Because K_f is so large, the reaction essentially goes to completion and $[Ag^+]$ is extremely small.

Cumulative Problems

16.81   **Given:** 150.0 mL solution of 2.05 g sodium benzoate and 2.47 g benzoic acid   **Find:** pH
Other: $K_a(HC_7H_5O_2) = 6.5 \times 10^{-5}$
Conceptual Plan: g $NaC_7H_5O_2 \rightarrow$ mol $NaC_7H_5O_2$ and g $HC_7H_5O_2 \rightarrow$ mol $HC_7H_5O_2$

$$\frac{1\ \text{mol } NaC_7H_5O_2}{144.10\ \text{g } NaC_7H_5O_2} \qquad\qquad \frac{1\ \text{mol } HC_7H_5O_2}{122.12\ \text{g } HC_7H_5O_2}$$

Because the two components are in the same solution, the ratio of [base]/[acid] = (mol base)/(mol acid). Then K_a**, mol** $NaC_7H_5O_2$**, mol** $HC_7H_5O_2 \rightarrow$ **pH.**

$$pH = pK_a + \log\frac{[\text{base}]}{[\text{acid}]}$$

Solution: $2.05\ \text{g } NaC_7H_5O_2 \times \dfrac{1\ \text{mol } NaC_7H_5O_2}{144.10\ \text{g } NaC_7H_5O_2} = 0.0142262\ \text{mol } NaC_7H_5O_2$ and

$2.47\ \text{g } HC_7H_5O_2 \times \dfrac{1\ \text{mol } HC_7H_5O_2}{122.12\ \text{g } HC_7H_5O_2} = 0.0202260\ \text{mol } HC_7H_5O_2$ then

$$pH = pK_a + \log\frac{[\text{base}]}{[\text{acid}]} = pK_a + \log\frac{\text{mol base}}{\text{mol acid}} = -\log(6.5 \times 10^{-5}) + \log\frac{0.0142262\ \text{mol}}{0.0202260\ \text{mol}} = 4.03$$

Check: The units (none) are correct. The magnitude of the answer makes physical sense because the pH is a little lower than the pK_a of the acid because there is more acid than base in the buffer solution.

16.82   **Given:** 10.0 mL of 17.5 M acetic acid and 5.54 g sodium acetate diluted to 1.50 L   **Find:** pH
Other: $K_a(HC_2H_3O_2) = 1.8 \times 10^{-5}$
Conceptual Plan: mL $\rightarrow$ L then L, initial $HC_2H_3O_2$ M $\rightarrow$ mol $HC_2H_3O_2$ then

$$\frac{1\ \text{L}}{1000\ \text{mL}} \qquad\qquad\qquad\qquad M = \frac{\text{mol}}{\text{L}}$$

g $NaC_2H_3O_2 \rightarrow$ mol $NaC_2H_3O_2$ then because the two components are in the same solution,

$$\frac{1\ \text{mol } NaC_2H_3O_2}{82.03\ \text{g } NaC_2H_3O_2}$$

the ratio of [base]/[acid] = (mol base)/(mol acid). Then K_a**, mol** $NaC_2H_3O_2$ **mol** $HC_2H_3O_2 \rightarrow$ **pH.**

$$pH = pK_a + \log\frac{[\text{base}]}{[\text{acid}]}$$

Solution: $10.0\ \text{mL} \times \dfrac{1\ \text{L}}{1000\ \text{mL}} = 0.0100\ \text{L}$ then

$0.0100\ \text{L } HC_2H_3O_2 \times \dfrac{17.5\ \text{mol } HC_2H_3O_2}{1\ \text{L } HC_2H_3O_2} = 0.175\ \text{mol } HC_2H_3O_2$ then

$5.54\ \text{g } NaC_2H_3O_2 \times \dfrac{1\ \text{mol } NaC_2H_3O_2}{82.03\ \text{g } NaC_2H_3O_2} = 0.06753627\ \text{mol } NaC_2H_3O_2$ then

$$pH = pK_a + \log\frac{[\text{base}]}{[\text{acid}]} = pK_a + \log\frac{\text{mol base}}{\text{mol acid}} = -\log(1.8 \times 10^{-5}) + \log\frac{0.06753627\ \text{mol}}{0.175\ \text{mol}} = 4.33$$

Check: The units (none) are correct. The magnitude of the answer makes physical sense because the pH is a little lower than the pK_a of the acid because there is more acid than base in the buffer solution.

16.83   **Given:** 150.0 mL of 0.25 M $HCHO_2$ and 75.0 ml of 0.20 M NaOH   **Find:** pH **Other:** $K_a(HCHO_2) = 1.8 \times 10^{-4}$
Conceptual Plan: In this buffer, the base is generated by converting some of the formic acid to the formate ion.
Part I: Stoichiometry:
mL $\rightarrow$ L then L, initial $HCHO_2$ M $\rightarrow$ mol $HCHO_2$ then mL $\rightarrow$ L then

$$\frac{1\,L}{1000\,mL} \qquad\qquad M = \frac{mol}{L} \qquad\qquad \frac{1\,L}{1000\,mL}$$

L, initial NaOH M $\rightarrow$ mol NaOH then write a balanced equation then

$$M = \frac{mol}{L} \qquad NaOH + HCHO_2 \rightarrow H_2O + NaCHO_2$$

mol $HCHO_2$, mol NaOH $\rightarrow$ mol $NaCHO_2$, mol $HCHO_2$ then

set up stoichiometry table

Part II: Equilibrium:
Because the two components are in the same solution, the ratio of [base]/[acid] = (mol base)/(mol acid). Then
K_a, **mol $NaCHO_2$, mol $HCHO_2$ $\rightarrow$ pH.**

$$pH = pK_a + \log \frac{[base]}{[acid]}$$

Solution: $150.0\ \text{mL} \times \dfrac{1\,L}{1000\ \text{mL}} = 0.1500\ L$ then

$$0.1500\ \text{L HCHO}_2 \times \frac{0.25\ mol\ HCHO_2}{1\ \text{L HCHO}_2} = 0.0375\ mol\ HCHO_2$$

Then $75.0\ \text{mL} \times \dfrac{1\,L}{1000\ \text{mL}} = 0.0750\ L$ then $0.0750\ \text{L NaOH} \times \dfrac{0.20\ mol\ NaOH}{1\ \text{L NaOH}} = 0.015\ mol\ NaOH$ then set up a

table to track changes:

$$NaOH(aq) + HCHO_2(aq) \rightarrow NaCHO_2(aq) + H_2O(l)$$

Before addition	0.00 mol	0.0375 mol	0.00 mol	—
Addition	0.015 mol	—	—	—
After addition	≈0.00 mol	0.0225 mol	0.015 mol	—

Because the amount of NaOH is small, there are significant amounts of both buffer components; so the Henderson–
Hasselbalch equation can be used to calculate the pH.

$$pH = pK_a + \log \frac{[base]}{[acid]} = pK_a + \log \frac{mol\ base}{mol\ acid} = -\log(1.8 \times 10^{-4}) + \log \frac{0.015\ mol}{0.0225\ mol} = 3.57$$

Check: The units (none) are correct. The magnitude of the answer makes physical sense because the pH is a little
lower than the pK_a of the acid because there is more acid than base in the buffer solution.

16.84   **Given:** 750.0 mL solution of 3.55 g NH_3 and 4.78 g HCl   **Find:** pH   **Other:** $K_b(NH_3) = 1.76 \times 10^{-5}$
**Conceptual Plan: In this buffer, the acid is generated by converting some of the ammonia to the ammonium
ion. Part I: Stoichiometry:**
g NH_3 $\rightarrow$ mol NH_3 and g HCl $\rightarrow$ mol HCl write a balanced equation then

$$\frac{1\ mol\ NH_3}{17.03\ g\ NH_3} \qquad\qquad \frac{1\ mol\ HCl}{36.46\ g\ HCl} \qquad NH_3 + HCl \rightarrow NH_4Cl$$

mol NH_3, mol HCl $\rightarrow$ mol NH_3, mol NH_4Cl then

set up stoichiometry table

Part II: Equilibrium:
$K_b \rightarrow pK_b \rightarrow pK_a$ **then because the two components are in the same solution,**

$pK_b = -\log K_b \quad 14 = pK_a + pK_b$

the ratio of [base]/[acid] = (mol base)/(mol acid). Then pK_a, mol NH_3, mol NH_4Cl $\rightarrow$ pH.

$$pH = pK_a + \log \frac{[base]}{[acid]}$$

Solution: $3.55\ \text{g NH}_3 \times \dfrac{1\ mol\ NH_3}{17.03\ \text{g NH}_3} = 0.208456\ mol\ NH_3$ and

$$4.78\ \text{g HCl} \times \frac{1\ mol\ HCl}{36.46\ \text{g HCl}} = 0.131103\ mol\ HCl.$$

Set up a table to track changes:

	HCl(aq) +	NH$_3$(aq) →	NH$_4$Cl(aq)
Before addition	0.00 mol	0.208456 mol	0.00 mol
Addition	0.131103 mol	—	—
After addition	≈0.00 mol	0.077353 mol	0.131103 mol

Because the amount of HCl is small, there are significant amounts of both buffer components; so the Henderson–Hasselbalch equation can be used to calculate the pH.

Because $K_b(NH_3) = 1.76 \times 10^{-5}$, $pK_b = -\log K_b = -\log(1.76 \times 10^{-5}) = 4.75$. Because $14 = pK_a + pK_b$, $pK_a = 14 - pK_b = 14 - 4.75 = 9.25$ then

$$pH = pK_a + \log \frac{[\text{base}]}{[\text{acid}]} = pK_a + \log \frac{\text{mol base}}{\text{mol acid}} = 9.25 + \log \frac{0.077353 \text{ mol}}{0.131103 \text{ mol}} = 9.02$$

Check: The units (none) are correct. The magnitude of the answer makes physical sense because the pH is a little lower than the pK_a of the acid because there is more acid than base in the buffer solution.

16.85 **Given:** 1.0 L of buffer of 0.25 mol NH$_3$ and 0.25 mol NH$_4$Cl; adjust to pH = 8.75
Find: mass NaOH or HCl **Other:** $K_b(NH_3) = 1.76 \times 10^{-5}$
Conceptual Plan: To decide which reagent needs to be added to adjust pH, calculate the initial pH. Because the mol NH$_3$ = mol NH$_4$Cl, the pH = pK_a so $K_b \rightarrow pK_b \rightarrow pK_a$ then

acid = NH$_4^+$ base = NH$_3$ $pK_b = -\log K_b$ $14 = pK_a + pK_b$

final pH, $pK_a \rightarrow$ [NH$_3$]/[NH$_4^+$] then [NH$_3$], L $\rightarrow$ mol [NH$_3$] and [NH$_4^+$], L $\rightarrow$ mol [NH$_4^+$]

$pH = pK_a + \log \frac{[\text{base}]}{[\text{acid}]}$ $M = \frac{\text{mol}}{L}$ $M = \frac{\text{mol}}{L}$

then write a balanced equation then

H$^+$ + NH$_3 \rightarrow$ NH$_4^+$

mol NH$_3$, mol NH$_4^+$, [NH$_3$]/[NH$_4^+$] $\rightarrow$ mol HCl $\rightarrow$ g HCl.

set up stoichiometry table $\frac{36.46 \text{ g HCl}}{1 \text{ mol HCl}}$

Solution: Because $K_b(NH_3) = 1.76 \times 10^{-5}$, $pK_b = -\log K_b = -\log(1.76 \times 10^{-5}) = 4.75$. Because $14 = pK_a + pK_b$, $pK_a = 14 - pK_b = 14 - 4.75 = 9.25$. Because the desired pH is lower (8.75), HCl (a strong acid) needs to be

added. Then $pH = pK_a + \log \frac{[\text{base}]}{[\text{acid}]} = 9.25 + \log \frac{[NH_3]}{[NH_4^+]} = 8.75$. Solve for $\frac{[NH_3]}{[NH_4^+]}$.

$\log \frac{[NH_3]}{[NH_4^+]} = 8.75 - 9.25 = -0.50 \rightarrow \frac{[NH_3]}{[NH_4^+]} = 10^{-0.50} = 0.31623$. Then

$\frac{0.25 \text{ mol NH}_3}{1 \text{ L}} \times 1.0 \text{ L} = 0.25 \text{ mol NH}_3$ and

$\frac{0.25 \text{ mol NH}_4\text{Cl}}{1 \text{ L}} \times 1.0 \text{ L} = 0.25 \text{ mol NH}_4\text{Cl} = 0.25 \text{ mol NH}_4^+$. Because HCl is a strong acid, [HCl] = [H$^+$], and

set up a table to track changes:

	H$^+$(aq) +	NH$_3$(aq) →	NH$_4^+$(aq)
Before addition	≈0.00 mol	0.25 mol	0.25 mol
Addition	x	—	—
After addition	≈0.00 mol	$(0.25 - x)$ mol	$(0.25 + x)$ mol

Because $\frac{[NH_3]}{[NH_4^+]} = 0.31623 = \frac{(0.25 - x) \text{ mol}}{(0.25 + x) \text{ mol}}$, solve for x. Note that the ratio of moles is the same as the ratio of concentrations, because the volume for both terms is the same. $0.31623(0.25 + x) = (0.25 - x) \rightarrow 0.0790575 + 0.31623x = 0.25 - x \rightarrow 1.31623x = 0.17094 \rightarrow x = 0.12987 \text{ mol HCl}$ then

$0.12987 \text{ mol HCl} \times \frac{36.46 \text{ g HCl}}{1 \text{ mol HCl}} = 4.7 \text{ g HCl}$

Check: The units (g) are correct. The magnitude of the answer makes physical sense because there is much less than a mole of each of the buffer components; so there must be much less than a mole of HCl.

16.86 **Given:** 250.0 mL of buffer of 0.025 mol $HCHO_2$ and 0.025 mol $NaCHO_2$; adjust to pH $= 4.10$
Find: mass NaOH or HCl **Other:** $K_a(HCHO_2) = 1.8 \times 10^{-4}$
Conceptual Plan: To decide which reagent needs to be added to adjust pH, calculate the initial pH. Because the mol $HCHO_2$ $=$ mol $NaCHO_2$, the pH $=$ pK_a then final pH, pK_a $\rightarrow$ [NaCHO$_2$]/[HCHO$_2$]

acid $=$ $HCHO_2$ base $=$ CHO_2^- p$K_a = -\log K_a$ $pH = pK_a + \log \dfrac{[base]}{[acid]}$

then mL $\rightarrow$ L then write a balanced equation then

$\dfrac{1\,L}{1000\,mL}$ $NaOH + HCHO_2 \rightarrow NaCHO_2 + H_2O$

mol NaCHO$_2$, mol HCHO$_2$, [NaCHO$_2$]/[HCHO$_2$] $\rightarrow$ mol NaOH $\rightarrow$ g NaOH.

set up stoichiometry table $\cdot \dfrac{40.00\text{ g NaOH}}{1\text{ mol NaOH}}$

Solution: Because $K_a(HCHO_2) = 1.8 \times 10^{-4}$, p$K_a = -\log K_a = -\log(1.8 \times 10^{-4}) = 3.74$. Because the desired pH (4.10) is higher, NaOH (a strong base) needs to be added. Then

$pH = pK_a + \log \dfrac{[base]}{[acid]} = 3.74 + \log \dfrac{[NaCHO_2]}{[HCHO_2]} = 4.10$. Solve for $\dfrac{[NaCHO_2]}{[HCHO_2]}$.

$\log \dfrac{[NaCHO_2]}{[HCHO_2]} = 4.10 - 3.74 = 0.36 \rightarrow \dfrac{[NaCHO_2]}{[HCHO_2]} = 10^{+0.36} = 2.29087$. Then because NaOH is a strong base,

[NaOH] $=$ [OH$^-$], and set up a table to track changes:

	NaOH(aq) $+$	HCHO$_2$(aq)	$\rightarrow$ NaCHO$_2$(aq)	$+$ H$_2$O(l)
Before addition	≈ 0.00 mol	0.025 mol	0.025 mol	—
Addition	x	$-x$	$+x$	—
After addition	≈ 0.00 mol	$(0.025 - x)$ mol	$(0.025 + x)$ mol	—

Because $pH = pK_a + \log \dfrac{[A^-]}{[HA]}$ we get $4.10 = 3.74 + \log \dfrac{0.025\text{ mol} + x}{0.025\text{ mol} - x}$. Solve for x. Note that the ratio of moles is the same as the ratio of concentrations because the volume for both terms is the same.

$0.360 = \log \dfrac{0.025\text{ mol} + x}{0.025\text{ mol} - x} \rightarrow 2.29 = \dfrac{0.025\text{ mol} + x}{0.025\text{ mol} - x} \rightarrow 0.0573 - 2.29x = 0.025 + x \rightarrow 3.29x = 0.0323 \rightarrow$

$x = 0.00981$ mol then $0.00981 \text{ mol NaOH} \times \dfrac{40.00\text{ g NaOH}}{1\text{ mol NaOH}} = 0.39$ g NaOH

Check: The units (g) are correct. The magnitude of the answer makes physical sense because there is much less than a mole of each of the buffer components; so there must be much less than a mole of NaOH.

16.87 (a) **Given:** potassium hydrogen phthalate $=$ KHP $=$ KHC$_8$H$_4$O$_4$ titration with NaOH
Find: balanced equation
Conceptual Plan: The reaction will be a titration of the acid proton, leaving the phthalate ion intact.
Solution: $NaOH(aq) + KHC_8H_4O_4(aq) \rightarrow Na^+(aq) + K^+(aq) + C_8H_4O_4^{2-}(aq) + H_2O(l)$

Check: An acid–base reaction generates a salt (soluble here) and water. There is only one acidic proton in KHP.

(b) **Given:** 0.5527 g KHP titrated with 25.87 mL of NaOH solution   **Find:** [NaOH]
Conceptual Plan:
g KHP $\rightarrow$ mol KHP $\rightarrow$ mol NaOH and mL $\rightarrow$ L then mol NaOH and mL $\rightarrow$ M NaOH

$\dfrac{1\text{ mol KHP}}{204.22\text{ g KHP}}$ 1:1 from balanced equation $\dfrac{1\,L}{1000\,mL}$ $M = \dfrac{mol}{L}$

Solution: $0.5527 \text{ g KHP} \times \dfrac{1\text{ mol KHP}}{204.22\text{ g KHP}} = 0.002706395$ mol KHP; mol KHP $=$ mol acid $=$ mol base $=$

0.002706395 mol NaOH then $25.87 \text{ mL} \times \dfrac{1\,L}{1000\,mL} = 0.02587$ L then

$[NaOH] = \dfrac{0.002706395\text{ mol NaOH}}{0.02587\text{ L}} = 0.1046$ M NaOH

Check: The units (M) are correct. The magnitude of the answer makes physical sense because there is much less than a mole of acid. The magnitude of the moles of acid and base is smaller than the volume of base in liters.

16.88 **Given:** 0.5224 g monoprotic acid titrated with 23.82 mL of 0.0998 M NaOH solution
Find: molar mass of acid
Conceptual Plan: mL $\rightarrow$ L then M NaOH, L $\rightarrow$ mol NaOH $\rightarrow$ mol acid then mol acid, g acid $\rightarrow$ $\mathcal{M}$

$$\frac{1 \text{ L}}{1000 \text{ mL}} \qquad M = \frac{mol}{L} \qquad \text{1:1 for monoprotic acid} \qquad \mathcal{M} = \frac{g \text{ acid}}{mol \text{ acid}}$$

Solution: $23.82 \text{ mL} \times \dfrac{1 \text{ L}}{1000 \text{ mL}} = 0.02382 \text{ L}$ then

$0.02382 \text{ L NaOH} \times \dfrac{0.0998 \text{ mol NaOH}}{1 \text{ L NaOH}} = 0.00237\underline{7}24 \text{ mol NaOH};\ 0.00237\underline{7}24 \text{ mol NaOH} = \text{mol base} = \text{mol acid} =$

$0.00237\underline{7}24 \text{ mol acid then } M = \dfrac{g \text{ acid}}{mol \text{ acid}} = \dfrac{0.5224 \text{ g acid}}{0.00237\underline{7}24 \text{ mol acid}} = 220. \text{ g/mol}$

Check: The units (g/mol) are correct. The magnitude of the answer makes physical sense because there is much less than a mole of acid and about half a gram of acid; so the molar mass will be high. The number is reasonable for an acid (must be > 20 g/mol—lightest acid is HF).

16.89 **Given:** 0.25 mol weak acid with 10.0 mL of 3.00 M KOH diluted to 1.500 L has pH = 3.85 **Find:** pK_a of acid
Conceptual Plan: mL $\rightarrow$ L then M KOH, L $\rightarrow$ mol KOH then write a balanced reaction

$$\frac{1 \text{ L}}{1000 \text{ mL}} \qquad M = \frac{mol}{L} \qquad KOH + HA \rightarrow NaA + H_2O$$

added mol KOH, initial mol acid $\rightarrow$ equil. mol KOH, equil. mol acid then

set up stoichiometry table

equil. mol KOH, equil. mol acid, pH $\rightarrow$ pK_a

$$pH = pK_a + \log \frac{[base]}{[acid]}$$

Solution: $10.00 \text{ mL} \times \dfrac{1 \text{ L}}{1000 \text{ mL}} = 0.01000 \text{ L}$ then $0.01000 \text{ L KOH} \times \dfrac{3.00 \text{ mol KOH}}{1 \text{ L KOH}} = 0.0300 \text{ mol KOH}$

Because KOH is a strong base, [KOH] = [OH⁻], and set up a table to track changes:

	KOH(aq)	+ HA(aq)	$\rightarrow$ KA(aq)	+ H₂O(l)
Before addition	≈ 0.00 mol	0.25 mol	0.00 mol	—
Addition	0.0300 mol	—	—	—
After addition	≈ 0.00 mol	0.22 mol	0.0300 mol	—

Because the ratio of base to acid is between 0.1 and 10, it is a buffer solution. Note that the ratio of moles is the same as the ratio of concentrations because the volume for both terms is the same.

$$pH = pK_a + \log \frac{[base]}{[acid]} = pK_a + \log \frac{0.0300 \text{ mol}}{0.22 \text{ mol}} = 3.85. \text{ Solve for } pK_a.$$

$$pK_a = 3.85 - \log \frac{0.0300 \text{ mol}}{0.22 \text{ mol}} = 4.72$$

Check: The units (none) are correct. The magnitude of the answer makes physical sense because there is more acid than base at equilibrium; so the pK_a is higher than the pH of the solution.

16.90 **Given:** 5.55 g weak acid with $K_a = 1.3 \times 10^{-4}$ with 5.00 mL of 6.00 M NaOH diluted to 750 mL has pH = 4.25
Find: molar mass of acid
Conceptual Plan: mL $\rightarrow$ L then M NaOH, L $\rightarrow$ mol NaOH then write a balanced reaction

$$\frac{1 \text{ L}}{1000 \text{ mL}} \qquad M = \frac{mol}{L} \qquad NaOH + HA \rightarrow NaA + H_2O$$

added mol NaOH, initial mol acid $\rightarrow$ equil. mol NaOH, equil. mol acid then

set up stoichiometry table

added mol NaOH, equil. mol acid, pH, pK_a $\rightarrow$ equil. mol NaOH, equil. mol acid then

$$pH = pK_a + \log \frac{[base]}{[acid]}$$

mol acid, g acid → $\mathcal{M}$

$$\mathcal{M} = \frac{\text{g acid}}{\text{mol acid}}$$

Solution: $5.00 \text{ mL} \times \dfrac{1 \text{ L}}{1000 \text{ mL}} = 0.00500 \text{ L}$ then $0.00500 \text{ L NaOH} \times \dfrac{6.00 \text{ mol NaOH}}{1 \text{ L NaOH}} = 0.0300 \text{ mol NaOH}$

Because NaOH is a strong base, $[\text{NaOH}] = [\text{OH}^-]$, and set up a table to track changes:

$$\text{NaOH}(aq) \quad + \quad \text{HA}(aq) \quad \rightarrow \quad \text{NaA}(aq) + \text{H}_2\text{O}(l)$$

Before addition	≈0.00 mol	x mol	0.00 mol	—
Addition	0.0300 mol	—	—	—
After addition	≈0.00 mol	$x - 0.0300$ mol	0.0300 mol	—

Because the pH is within 1 unit of the pK_a, it is a buffer solution. Note that the ratio of moles is the same as the ratio of concentrations because the volume for both terms is the same.

$$\text{pH} = pK_a + \log \frac{[\text{base}]}{[\text{acid}]} = -\log(1.3 \times 10^{-4}) + \log \frac{0.0300 \text{ mol}}{(x - 0.0300) \text{ mol}} = 4.25$$

Solve for x. $\log 0.0300 - \log(x - 0.0300) = 4.25 - 3.89 \rightarrow -\log(x - 0.0300) = 1.88288 \rightarrow$
$x - 0.0300 = 10^{-1.88288} = 0.0130954 \rightarrow x = 0.0430854$ mol. Finally,

$$\mathcal{M} = \frac{\text{g acid}}{\text{mol acid}} = \frac{5.55 \text{ g acid}}{0.0430854 \text{ mol acid}} = 129 \text{ g/mol}$$

Check: The units (g/mol) are correct. The magnitude of the answer makes physical sense because there is much less than a mole of acid and about 6 grams of acid; so the molar mass will be high. The number is reasonable for an acid (must be >20 g/mol—lightest acid is HF).

16.91 **Given:** 0.867 g diprotic acid titrated with 32.2 mL of 0.182 M Ba(OH)$_2$ solution **Find:** molar mass of acid
Conceptual Plan: Write a balanced reaction then mL → L then M Ba(OH)$_2$, L → mol Ba(OH)$_2$ → mol acid

$$\text{H}_2\text{A} + \text{Ba(OH)}_2 \rightarrow \text{BaA} + 2\text{H}_2\text{O} \qquad \frac{1 \text{ L}}{1000 \text{ ml}} \qquad M = \frac{\text{mol}}{\text{L}} \qquad 1{:}1$$

then mol acid, g acid → $\mathcal{M}$.

$$\mathcal{M} = \frac{\text{g acid}}{\text{mol acid}}$$

Solution: $32.2 \text{ mL} \times \dfrac{1 \text{ L}}{1000 \text{ mL}} = 0.0322 \text{ L}$ then

$0.0322 \text{ L Ba(OH)}_2 \times \dfrac{0.182 \text{ mol Ba(OH)}_2}{1 \text{ L Ba(OH)}_2} = 0.0058604 \text{ mol Ba(OH)}_2 \times \dfrac{1 \text{ mol H}_2\text{A}}{1 \text{ mol Ba(OH)}_2} = 0.0058604 \text{ mol H}_2\text{A}$

then $\mathcal{M} = \dfrac{\text{g acid}}{\text{mol acid}} = \dfrac{0.867 \text{ g H}_2\text{A}}{0.0058604 \text{ mol H}_2\text{A}} = 148 \text{ g/mol}$

Check: The units (g/mol) are correct. The magnitude of the answer makes physical sense because there is much less than a mole of acid and about half a gram of acid, so the molar mass will be high. The number is reasonable for an acid (must be >20 g/mol—lightest acid is HF).

16.92 **Given:** 25.0 mL of NaOH titrated with 19.6 mL of 0.189 M HCl solution; 10.0 mL of H$_3$PO$_4$ titrated with 34.9 mL NaOH **Find:** concentration of H$_3$PO$_4$ solution
Conceptual Plan: Write the first balanced reaction then mL → L then M HCl, L → mol HCl → mol NaOH

$$\text{HCl} + \text{NaOH} \rightarrow \text{NaCl} + \text{H}_2\text{O} \qquad \frac{1 \text{ L}}{1000 \text{ mL}} \qquad M = \frac{\text{mol}}{\text{L}} \qquad 1{:}1$$

then mL → L then mol NaOH, L → M NaOH then write second balanced reaction then mL → L

$$\frac{1 \text{ L}}{1000 \text{ mL}} \qquad \text{H}_3\text{PO}_4 + 3 \text{ NaOH} \rightarrow \text{Na}_3\text{PO}_4 + 3 \text{ H}_2\text{O} \qquad \frac{1 \text{ L}}{1000 \text{ mL}}$$

then M NaOH, L → mol NaOH → mol H$_3$PO$_4$ then mL → L then mol H$_3$PO$_4$, L → M H$_3$PO$_4$.

$$M = \frac{\text{mol}}{\text{L}} \qquad 3{:}1 \qquad \frac{1 \text{ L}}{1000 \text{ mL}} \qquad M = \frac{\text{mol}}{\text{L}}$$

Solution: In the first titration, $19.6 \text{ mL} \times \dfrac{1 \text{ L}}{1000 \text{ mL}} = 0.0196 \text{ L}$ then

$$0.0196 \text{ L HCl} \times \frac{0.189 \text{ mol HCl}}{1 \text{ L HCl}} = 0.0037044 \text{ mol HCl} \times \frac{1 \text{ mol NaOH}}{1 \text{ mol HCl}} = 0.0037044 \text{ mol NaOH then}$$

$$25.0 \text{ mL} \times \frac{1 \text{ L}}{1000 \text{ mL}} = 0.0250 \text{ L than } \frac{0.0037044 \text{ mol NaOH}}{0.0250 \text{ L NaOH}} = 0.148176 \text{ M NaOH}$$

In the second titration, $34.9 \text{ mL} \times \frac{1 \text{ L}}{1000 \text{ mL}} = 0.0349 \text{ L then}$

$$0.0349 \text{ L NaOH} \times \frac{0.148176 \text{ mol NaOH}}{1 \text{ L NaOH}} = 0.00517134 \text{ mol NaOH} \times \frac{1 \text{ mol H}_3\text{PO}_4}{3 \text{ mol NaOH}} = 0.00172378 \text{ mol H}_3\text{PO}_4$$

then $10.0 \text{ mL} \times \frac{1 \text{ L}}{1000 \text{ mL}} = 0.0100 \text{ L then } \frac{0.00172378 \text{ mol H}_3\text{PO}_4}{0.0100 \text{ L H}_3\text{PO}_4} = 0.172 \text{ M H}_3\text{PO}_4$

Check: The units (M) are correct. The magnitude of the answer makes physical sense because the concentration of NaOH is a little lower than the HCl (because the volume of NaOH is greater than HCl) and the concentration of H_3PO_4 is more than the NaOH (because the ratio of the volume of NaOH to volume of H_3PO_4 is just over 3 and H_3PO_4 is a triprotic acid).

16.93 **Given:** saturated $CaCO_3$ solution; precipitate 1.00×10^2 mg $CaCO_3$ **Find:** volume of solution evaporated
Other: $K_{sp}(CaCO_3) = 4.96 \times 10^{-9}$
Conceptual Plan: mg $CaCO_3 \rightarrow$ g $CaCO_3 \rightarrow$ mol $CaCO_3$

$$\frac{1 \text{ g CaCO}_3}{1000 \text{ mg CaCO}_3} \qquad \frac{1 \text{ mol CaCO}_3}{100.09 \text{ g CaCO}_3}$$

The expression of the solubility product constant of A_mX_n is $K_{sp} = [A^{n+}]^m [X^{m-}]^n$. The molar solubility of a compound, A_mX_n, can be computed directly from K_{sp} by solving for S in the expression $K_{sp} = (mS)^m (nS)^n = m^n n^n S^{m+n}$. Then mol $CaCO_3$, $S \rightarrow$ L.

$$M = \frac{\text{mol}}{\text{L}}$$

Solution: $1.00 \times 10^2 \text{ mg CaCO}_3 \times \frac{1 \text{ g CaCO}_3}{1000 \text{ mg CaCO}_3} \times \frac{1 \text{ mol CaCO}_3}{100.09 \text{ g CaCO}_3} = 9.99101 \times 10^{-4} \text{ mol CaCO}_3$ then

$K_{sp} = 4.96 \times 10^{-9}$, $A = Ca^{2+}$, $m = 1$, $X = CO_3^{2-}$, and $n = 1$; so $K_{sp} = 4.96 \times 10^{-9} = S^2$.
Rearrange to solve for S. $S = \sqrt{4.96 \times 10^{-9}} = 7.04273 \times 10^{-5}$ M. Finally,

$$9.99101 \times 10^{-4} \text{ mol CaCO}_3 \times \frac{1 \text{ L}}{7.04273 \times 10^{-5} \text{ mol CaCO}_3} = 14.2 \text{ L.}$$

Check: The units (L) are correct. The volume should be large because the solubility is low.

16.94 **Given:** $[Na^+] = 0.140$ M and $K_{sp}(NaC_5H_3N_4) = 5.76 \times 10^{-8}$ **Find:** $[C_5H_3N_4^-]$ to form precipitate
Conceptual Plan: Write a balanced equation and expression for K_{sp}. Then $[Na^+]$, $K_{sp} \rightarrow [C_5H_3N_4^-]$.
Solution: $NaC_5H_3N_4(s) \rightarrow Na^+(aq) + C_5H_3N_4^-(aq)$. So $K_{sp} = [Na^+][C_5H_3N_4^-] = 5.76 \times 10^{-8} = (0.140)[C_5H_3N_4^-]$. Solve for $[C_5H_3N_4^-]$ then $[C_5H_3N_4^-] = 4.11 \times 10^{-7}$ M.

Check: The units (M) are correct. Because K_{sp} is so small and the sodium concentration is fairly high, the urate concentration required is at a very low level.

16.95 **Given:** $[Ca^{2+}] = 9.2$ mg/dL and $K_{sp}(Ca_2P_2O_7) = 8.64 \times 10^{-13}$ **Find:** $[P_2O_7^{4-}]$ to form precipitate
Conceptual Plan: mg Ca^{2+}/dL $\rightarrow$ g Ca^{2+}/dL $\rightarrow$ mol Ca^{2+}/dL $\rightarrow$ mol Ca^{2+}/L then

$$\frac{1 \text{ g Ca}^{2+}}{1000 \text{ mg Ca}^{2+}} \qquad \frac{1 \text{ mol Ca}^{2+}}{40.08 \text{ g Ca}^{2+}} \qquad \frac{10 \text{ dL}}{1 \text{ L}}$$

write a balanced equation and expression for K_{sp}. Then $[Ca^{2+}]$, $K_{sp} \rightarrow [P_2O_7^{4-}]$.

Solution: $9.2 \dfrac{\text{mg Ca}^{2+}}{\text{dL}} \times \dfrac{1 \text{ g Ca}^{2+}}{1000 \text{ mg Ca}^{2+}} \times \dfrac{1 \text{ mol Ca}^{2+}}{40.08 \text{ g Ca}^{2+}} \times \dfrac{10 \text{ dL}}{1 \text{ L}} = 2.29541 \times 10^{-3} \text{ M Ca}^{2+}$ then write

equation $Ca_2P_2O_7(s) \rightarrow 2 Ca^{2+}(aq) + P_2O_7^{4-}(aq)$. So $K_{sp} = [Ca^{2+}]^2 [P_2O_7^{4-}] = 8.64 \times 10^{-13} = (2.29541 \times 10^{-3})^2 [P_2O_7^{4-}]$. Solve for $[P_2O_7^{4-}]$ then $[P_2O_7^{4-}] = 1.6 \times 10^{-7}$ M.

Check: The units (M) are correct. Because K_{sp} is so small and the calcium concentration is relatively high, the diphosphate concentration required is at a very low level.

16.96   **Given:** AgCl in 0.100 M NH_3 **Find:** molar solubility (S)
Other: $K_f(Ag(NH_3)_2^+) = 1.7 \times 10^7$, $K_{sp}(AgCl) = 1.77 \times 10^{-10}$
Conceptual Plan: Identify the appropriate solid and complex ion. Write balanced equations for dissolving the solid and forming the complex ion. Add these two reactions to get the desired overall reaction. Using the rules from Chapter 14, multiply the individual reaction Ks to get the overall K for the sum of these reactions. Then M NH_3, $K \rightarrow S$.

ICE table

Solution: Identify the solid as AgCl and the complex ion as $Ag(NH_3)_2^+$. Write the individual reactions and add them together.

$AgCl(s) \rightleftharpoons Ag^+(aq) + Cl^-(aq)$ $K_{sp} = 1.77 \times 10^{-10}$

$Ag^+(aq) + 2\,NH_3(aq) \rightleftharpoons Ag(NH_3)_2^+(aq)$ $K_f = 1.7 \times 10^7$

$AgCl(s) + 2\,NH_3(aq) \rightleftharpoons Ag(NH_3)_2^+(aq) + Cl^-(aq)$

Because the overall reaction is the simple sum of the two reactions, the overall reaction $K = K_f K_{sp} = (1.7 \times 10^7) \times (1.77 \times 10^{-10}) = 3.\underline{0}09 \times 10^{-3}$. Then set up an ICE table:

$$AgCl(s) + 2\,NH_3(aq) \rightleftharpoons Ag(NH_3)_2^+(aq) + Cl^-(aq)$$

	$[NH_3]$	$[Ag(NH_3)_2^+]$	$[Cl^-]$
Initial	0.100	0.00	0.00
Change	$-2S$	$+S$	$+S$
Equil	$0.100 - 2S$	$+S$	$+S$

$K = \dfrac{[Ag(NH_3)_2^+][Cl^-]}{[NH_3]^2} = 3.\underline{0}09 \times 10^{-3} = \dfrac{S^2}{(0.100 - 2S)^2}$. Simplify by taking the square root of the expression.

$\sqrt{3.\underline{0}09 \times 10^{-3}} = 5.4854 \times 10^{-2} = \dfrac{S}{(0.100 - 2S)}$. Solve for S. $(5.\underline{4}854 \times 10^{-2})(0.100 - 2S) = S \rightarrow$

$5.\underline{4}854 \times 10^{-3} = (1.1\underline{0}971)S \rightarrow S = 4.\underline{9}431 \times 10^{-3} = 4.9 \times 10^{-3}$ M.

Check: The units (M) are correct. Because K_f is large, the overall K is larger than the original K_{sp} and the solubility of AgCl increases over that of pure water ($\sqrt{1.77 \times 10^{-10}} = 1.33 \times 10^{-5}$ M).

16.97   **Given:** CuX in 0.150 M NaCN   **Find:** molar solubility (S)
Other: $K_f(Cu(CN)_4^{2-}) = 1.0 \times 10^{25}$, $K_{sp}(CuX) = [Cu^{2+}][X^{2-}] = 1.27 \times 10^{-36}$
Conceptual Plan: Identify the appropriate solid and complex ion. Write balanced equations for dissolving the solid and forming the complex ion. Add these two reactions to get the desired overall reaction. Using the rules from Chapter 14, multiply the individual reaction Ks to get the overall K for the sum of these reactions. Then M NaCN, $K \rightarrow S$.

ICE table

Solution: Identify the solid as MX and the complex ion as $M(CN)_4^{2-}$. Write the individual reactions and add them together.

$CuX(s) \rightleftharpoons Cu^+(aq) + X^{2-}(aq)$ $K_{sp} = 1.27 \times 10^{-36}$

$Cu^{2+}(aq) + 4\,CN^-(aq) \rightleftharpoons Cu(CN)_4^{2-}(aq)$ $K_f = 1.0 \times 10^{25}$

$Cu(s) + 4\,CN^-(aq) \rightleftharpoons Cu(CN)_4^{2-}(aq) + X^{2-}(aq)$

Because the overall reaction is the simple sum of the two reactions, the overall reaction $K = K_f K_{sp} = (1.0 \times 10^{25}) \times (1.27 \times 10^{-36}) = 1.27 \times 10^{-11}$. $NaCN(s) \rightarrow Na^+(aq) + CN^-(aq)$. Because one CN^- ion is generated for each NaCN, $[CN^-] = 0.1\underline{5}0$ M. Set up an ICE table:

$$Cu(s) + 4\,CN^-(aq) \rightleftharpoons Cu(CN)_4^{2-}(aq) + X^{2-}(aq)$$

	$[CN^-]$	$[Cu(CN)_4^{2-}]$	$[X^{2-}]$
Initial	0.150	0.00	0.00
Change	$-4S$	$+S$	$+S$
Equil	$0.150 - 4S$	$+S$	$+S$

$$K = \frac{[Cu(CN)_4{}^{2-}]\,[X^{2-}]}{[CN^-]^4} = 1.\underline{2}7 \times 10^{-11} = \frac{S^2}{(0.150 - 4S)^4}$$

Assume that S is small ($4S \ll 0.150$); so $\dfrac{S^2}{(0.150 - \cancel{4S})^4} = 1.\underline{2}7 \times 10^{-11} = \dfrac{S^2}{(0.150)^4}$ and $S = 8.\underline{0}183 \times 10^{-8} =$

8.0×10^{-8} M. Confirm that the assumption is valid. $\dfrac{4(8.\underline{0}183 \times 10^{-8})}{0.150} \times 100\% = 0.00021\% \ll 5\%$, so the

assumption is valid.

Check: The units (M) are correct. Because K_f is large, the overall K is larger than the original K_{sp} and the solubility of MX increases over that of pure water ($\sqrt{1.27 \times 10^{-36}} = 1.13 \times 10^{-18}$ M).

16.98 **Given:** 0.10 M ϕNH_2, keep $[\phi NH_3{}^+] < 1.0 \times 10^{-9}$ and $K_b(\phi NH_2) = 4.3 \times 10^{-10}$ **Find:** [NaOH]

Conceptual Plan: M ϕNH_2, maximum M ϕNH_3^+ $\rightarrow$ $[OH^-] = [NaOH]$

ICE table $K_w = [H_3O^+]\,[OH^-]$ $pH = -\log[H_3O^+]$

Solution: Set up an ICE table. Because the amount of the conjugate acid is set so small, the concentration of the weak base does not significantly change.

$\phi NH_2(aq) + H_2O(l) \rightleftharpoons \phi NH_3{}^+(aq) + OH^-(aq)$

	$[\phi NH_2]$	$[\phi NH_3{}^+]$	$[OH^-]$
Initial	0.10	0.00	≈ 0.00
Change	—	—	$+x$
Equil	≈ 0.10	1.0×10^{-9}	$+x$

$$K_b = \frac{[\phi NH_3{}^+]\,[OH^-]}{[\phi NH_2]} = 4.3 \times 10^{-10} = \frac{(1.0 \times 10^{-9})x}{\approx 0.10}$$

Solve for x. So $x = 0.043$ M $= [OH^-]$. NaOH$(aq) \rightarrow$ Na$^+(aq) +$ OH$^-(aq)$. Because one OH$^-$ ion is generated for each NaOH, [NaOH] $= 0.043$ M NaOH.

Check: The units (M) are correct. The magnitude of the answer makes physical sense because $[OH^-]$ needs to be about one order of magnitude lower than the aniline concentration (comparing K_b with maximum conjugate acid concentrations).

16.99 **Given:** 100.0 mL of 0.36 M NH$_2$OH and 50.0 mL of 0.26 M HCl and $K_b(NH_2OH) = 1.10 \times 10^{-8}$ **Find:** pH

Conceptual Plan: Identify acid and base components mL $\rightarrow$ L then [NH$_2$OH], L $\rightarrow$ mol NH$_2$OH

acid = NH$_3$OH$^+$ base = NH$_2$OH $\dfrac{1\,L}{1000\,mL}$ $M = \dfrac{mol}{L}$

then mL $\rightarrow$ L then [HCl], L $\rightarrow$ mol HCl then write balanced equation then

$\dfrac{1\,L}{1000\,mL}$ $M = \dfrac{mol}{L}$ HCl + NH$_2$OH $\rightarrow$ NH$_3$OHCl

mol NH$_2$OH, mol HCl $\rightarrow$ mol excess NH$_2$OH, mol NH$_3$OH$^+$.

set up stoichiometry table

Because there are significant amounts of both the acid and the conjugate base species, this is a buffer solution;

so the Henderson–Hasselbalch equation $\left(pH = pK_a + \log \dfrac{[base]}{[acid]} \right)$ can be used. Convert K_b to K_a using

$K_w = K_a K_b$. **Also note that the ratio of concentrations is the same as the ratio of moles because the volume is the same for both species.**

Solution: $100 \text{ mL NH}_2\text{OH} \times \dfrac{1\,L}{1000\,mL} = 0.1000$ L NH$_2$OH then

$\dfrac{0.36 \text{ mol NH}_2\text{OH}}{1\,L} \times 0.1000\,L = 0.036$ mol NH$_2$OH. $50.0 \text{ mL HCl} \times \dfrac{1\,L}{1000\,mL} = 0.0500$ L HCl then

$\dfrac{0.26 \text{ mol HCl}}{1\,L} \times 0.0500\,L = 0.013$ mol HCl.

Set up a table to track changes:

$$HCl(aq) \ + \ NH_2OH(aq) \rightarrow NH_3OHCl(aq)$$

Before addition	0.00 mol	0.036 mol	0.00 mol
Addition	0.013 mol	—	—
After addition	$\approx$0.00 mol	0.023 mol	0.013 mol

Then $K_w = K_a K_b$, so $K_a = \dfrac{K_w}{K_b} = \dfrac{1.0 \times 10^{-14}}{1.10 \times 10^{-8}} = 9.\underline{0}909 \times 10^{-7}$ M.

Then use the Henderson–Hasselbalch equation because the solution is a buffer. Note that the ratio of moles is the same as the ratio of concentrations because the volume for both terms is the same.

$$pH = pK_a + \log \frac{[base]}{[acid]} = -\log(9.\underline{0}909 \times 10^{-7}) + \log \frac{0.023 \text{ mol}}{0.013 \text{ mol}} = 6.\underline{2}8918 = 6.29.$$

Check: The units (none) are correct. The magnitude of the answer makes physical sense because the pH should be more than the pK_a of the acid because there is more base than acid.

16.100 **Given:** 250.0 cm^3 of 1.4 M HCOOH; adjust to pH $= 3.36$ **Find:** mass NaCOOH
Other: K_a(HCOOH) $= 1.8 \times 10^{-4}$
Conceptual Plan: cm$^3 \rightarrow$ L and $K_a \rightarrow pK_a$ then [HCOOH], pH, $pK_a \rightarrow$ [NaCOOH]

$$\frac{1 \text{ L}}{1000 \text{ mL}} \qquad pK_a = -\log K_a \qquad \text{acid} = \text{HCOOH} \qquad \text{base} = \text{NaCOOH} \qquad pH = pK_a + \log \frac{[base]}{[acid]}$$

then [NaCOOH], L $\rightarrow$ mol NaCOOH $\rightarrow$ g NaCOOH

$$M = \frac{mol}{L} \qquad \frac{68.01 \text{ g NaCOOH}}{1 \text{ mol NaCOOH}}$$

Solution: 250.0 mL $\times \dfrac{1 \text{ L}}{1000 \text{ mL}} = 0.2500$ L because K_a(HCOOH) $= 1.8 \times 10^{-4}$,

$pK_a = -\log K_a = -\log(1.8 \times 10^{-4}) = 3.74$. Because acid = HCOOH, base = NaCOOH

$$pH = pK_a + \log \frac{[base]}{[acid]} = 3.74 + \log \frac{[NaCOOH]}{1.4 \text{ M}} = 3.36. \text{ Solve for [NaCOOH]}.$$

$$\log \frac{[NaCOOH]}{1.4 \text{ M}} = 3.36 - 3.74 = -0.38 \rightarrow \frac{[NaCOOH]}{1.4 \text{ M}} = 10^{-0.38} = 0.416869 \rightarrow$$

[NaCOOH] $= 0.416869 \times 1.4$ M $= 0.5\underline{8}3617$ M NaCOOH. Then

$$\frac{0.5\underline{8}3617 \text{ mol NaCOOH}}{1 \text{ L}} \times 0.2500 \text{ L} = 0.1\underline{4}590 \text{ mol NaCOOH} \times \frac{68.01 \text{ g NaCOOH}}{1 \text{ mol NaCOOH}} = 9.\underline{9}227 \text{ g NaCOOH}$$

$= 9.9$ g NaCOOH.

Check: The units (g) are correct. The magnitude of the answer makes physical sense because there is more acid than base in the buffer (pH $<$ pK_a) and there is less than a mole of acid in the buffer; so there must be less than a mole of NaCOOH.

16.101 **Given:** $(CH_3)_2NH/(CH_3)_2NH_2Cl$ buffer at pH $= 10.43$ **Find:** relative masses of $(CH_3)_2NH$ and $(CH_3)_2NH_2Cl$
Other: $K_b((CH_3)_2NH) = 5.4 \times 10^{-4}$
Conceptual Plan: $K_b \rightarrow pK_b \rightarrow pK_a$ then pH, $pK_a \rightarrow [(CH_3)_2NH] / [(CH_3)_2NH_2{}^+]$ then

$$pK_b = -\log K_b \qquad 14 = pK_a + pK_b \qquad \text{acid} = (CH_3)_2NH_2{}^+ \qquad \text{base} = (CH_3)_2NH \qquad pH = pK_a + \log \frac{[base]}{[acid]}$$

$[(CH_3)_2NH] / [(CH_3)_2NH_2{}^+] \rightarrow g(CH_3)_2NH / g(CH_3)_2NH_2{}^+$

$$\frac{45.09 \text{ g}(CH_3)_2NH}{1 \text{ mol }(CH_3)_2NH} \qquad \frac{1 \text{ mol }(CH_3)_2NH_2Cl}{81.54 \text{ g }(CH_3)_2NH_2Cl}$$

Solution: Because $K_b((CH_3)_2NH) = 5.4 \times 10^{-4}$, $pK_b = -\log K_b = -\log(5.4 \times 10^{-4}) = 3.27$. Because $14 = pK_a + pK_b$, $pK_a = 14 - pK_b = 14 - 3.27 = 10.73$. Because [acid] $= [(CH_3)_2NH_2{}^+] = [(CH_3)_2NH_2Cl]$

and [base] $= [(CH_3)_2NH]$, then $pH = pK_a + \log \dfrac{[base]}{[acid]} = 10.73 + \log \dfrac{[(CH_3)_2NH]}{[(CH_3)_2NH_2Cl]} = 10.43$. Solve for

$$\frac{[(CH_3)_2NH]}{[(CH_3)_2NH_2Cl]} \cdot \log \frac{[(CH_3)_2NH]}{[(CH_3)_2NH_2Cl]} = 10.43 - 10.73 = -0.30 \rightarrow \frac{[(CH_3)_2NH]}{[(CH_3)_2NH_2Cl]} = 10^{-0.30} = 0.5\underline{0}1187.$$

Then $\dfrac{0.501187 \text{ mol(CH}_3)_2\text{NH}}{1 \text{ mol(CH}_3)_2\text{NH}_2\text{Cl}} \times \dfrac{45.09 \text{ g(CH}_3)_2\text{NH}}{1 \text{ mol(CH}_3)_2\text{NH}} \times \dfrac{1 \text{ mol(CH}_3)_2\text{NH}_2\text{Cl}}{81.54 \text{ g(CH}_3)_2\text{NH}_2\text{Cl}} = \dfrac{0.277146 \text{ g(CH}_3)_2\text{NH}}{\text{g(CH}_3)_2\text{NH}_2\text{Cl}}$

$= \dfrac{0.28 \text{ g (CH}_3)_2\text{NH}}{\text{g (CH}_3)_2\text{NH}_2\text{Cl}}$ or $\dfrac{3.6 \text{ g (CH}_3)_2\text{NH}_2\text{Cl}}{\text{g (CH}_3)_2\text{NH}}$.

Check: The units (g/g) are correct. The magnitude of the answer makes physical sense because there are more moles of acid than base in the buffer (pH $<$ pK_a) and the molar mass of the acid is greater than the molar mass of the base. Thus, the ratio of the mass of the base to the mass of the acid is expected to be less than 1.

16.102 **Given:** 2.0 L HCN/NaCN buffer at pH $= 9.8$, complete dissociation of NaCN; osmotic pressure $= 1.35$ atm at 298 K **Find:** masses of HCN and NaCN **Other:** $K_a(\text{HCN}) = 4.9 \times 10^{-10}$

Conceptual Plan: $K_a \rightarrow$ pK_a then pH, p$K_a \rightarrow$ [CN$^-$] / [HCN] then $\Pi, T \rightarrow$ M then

$$\text{p}K_a = -\log K_a \qquad \text{acid} = \text{HCN} \qquad \text{base} = \text{CN}^- \qquad \text{pH} = \text{p}K_a + \log \frac{[\text{base}]}{[\text{acid}]} \qquad \Pi = MRT$$

assume that HCN does not dissociate and NaCN completely dissociates, then M = [HCN] + 2[NaCN]. Use [NaCN] / [HCN] and M = [HCN] + 2[NaCN] to solve for [HCN] and [NaCN]. Then [HCN], L → g HCN and [HCN], L → g HCN.

$$M = \frac{\text{amount solute (moles)}}{\text{volume solution (L)}} \qquad \frac{27.03 \text{ g HCN}}{1 \text{ mol HCN}} \qquad \frac{49.01 \text{ g NaCN}}{1 \text{ mol NaCN}}$$

Solution: Because $K_a(\text{HCN}) = 4.9 \times 10^{-10}$, p$K_a = -\log K_a = -\log (4.9 \times 10^{-10}) = 9.31$. Because

$[\text{acid}] = [\text{HCN}]$ and $[\text{base}] = [\text{CN}^-] = [\text{NaCN}]$, then pH $= \text{p}K_a + \log \dfrac{[\text{base}]}{[\text{acid}]} = 9.31 + \log \dfrac{[\text{NaCN}]}{[\text{HCN}]} = 9.8$.

Solve for $\dfrac{[\text{NaCN}]}{[\text{HCN}]}$. $\log \dfrac{[\text{NaCN}]}{[\text{HCN}]} = 9.8 - 9.31 = 0.49 \rightarrow \dfrac{[\text{NaCN}]}{[\text{HCN}]} = 10^{0.49} = 3.09030$

Then $\Pi = MRT$. Rearrange to solve for M.

$$M = \frac{\Pi}{RT} = \frac{1.35 \text{ atm}}{0.08206 \dfrac{\text{L} \cdot \text{atm}}{\text{K} \cdot \text{mol}} \times 298 \text{ K}} = 0.05520596 \frac{\text{mol particles}}{\text{L}}$$

Assume that HCN does not dissociate and that NaCN completely dissociates; then M = [HCN] + 2[NaCN]. Use [NaCN]/[HCN] $= 3.09030$ and M = [HCN] + 2[NaCN] to solve for [HCN] and [NaCN]. So [NaCN] $=$

$3.09030 \, [\text{HCN}] \rightarrow \text{M} = 0.05520596 \dfrac{\text{mol particles}}{\text{L}} = [\text{HCN}] + 2(3.09030[\text{HCN}]) \rightarrow$

$0.05520596 \dfrac{\text{mol particles}}{\text{L}} = 7.18060 \, [\text{HCN}] \rightarrow [\text{HCN}] = 0.00768821 \text{ M}$ and

$[\text{NaCN}] = 3.09030 \, [\text{HCN}] = 3.09030 \times 0.00768821 \text{ M} = 0.0237589 \text{ M}$. Finally,

$\dfrac{0.00768821 \text{ mol HCN}}{\text{L solution}} \times 2.0 \text{ L solution} \times \dfrac{27.03 \text{ g HCN}}{1 \text{ mol HCN}} = 0.41562 \text{ g HCN} = 0.42 \text{ g HCN}$ and

$\dfrac{0.0237589 \text{ mol NaCN}}{\text{L solution}} \times 2.0 \text{ L solution} \times \dfrac{49.01 \text{ g NaCN}}{1 \text{ mol NaCN}} = 2.3288 \text{ g NaCN} = 2.3 \text{ g NaCN}$.

Check: The units (g and g) are correct. The magnitude of the answer makes physical sense because there are more moles of base than acid in the buffer (pH $>$ pK_a) and the molar mass of the base is greater than the molar mass of the acid.

16.103 **Given:** $\text{HC}_7\text{H}_5\text{O}_2/\text{C}_7\text{H}_5\text{O}_2\text{Na}$ buffer at pH $= 4.55$, complete dissociation of $\text{C}_7\text{H}_5\text{O}_2\text{Na}$, $d = 1.01$ g/mL; $T_f = -2.0 \,^\circ\text{C}$ **Find:** $[\text{HC}_7\text{H}_5\text{O}_2]$ and $[\text{C}_7\text{H}_5\text{O}_2\text{Na}]$ **Other:** $K_a(\text{HC}_7\text{H}_5\text{O}_2) = 6.5 \times 10^{-5}$, $K_f = 1.86 \,^\circ\text{C}/m$

Conceptual Plan: $K_a \rightarrow$ pK_a then pH, p$K_a \rightarrow$ [C$_7$H$_5$O$_2$Na] / [HC$_7$H$_5$O$_2$] and $T_f \rightarrow \Delta T_f$ then

$$\text{p}K_a = -\log K_a \qquad \text{acid} = \text{HC}_7\text{H}_5\text{O}_2 \qquad \text{base} = \text{C}_7\text{H}_5\text{O}_2^- \qquad \text{pH} = \text{p}K_a + \log \frac{[\text{base}]}{[\text{acid}]} \qquad T_f = T_f^\circ - \Delta T_f$$

$\Delta T_f, i, K_f \rightarrow m$ then **assume 1 kg water (or 1000 g water)**

$$\Delta T_f = K_f \times m \qquad m = \frac{\text{amount solute (moles)}}{\text{mass solvent (kg)}}$$

Assume that $HC_7H_5O_2$ does not dissociate and that $C_7H_5O_2Na$ completely dissociates, then mol particles $=$ mol $HC_7H_5O_2$ $+$ 2(mol $C_7H_5O_2Na$). Use $[C_7H_5O_2Na] / [HC_7H_5O_2]$ and total mol particles $=$ mol $[HC_7H_5O_2]$ $+$ 2(mol $C_7H_5O_2Na$) to solve for mol $HC_7H_5O_2$ and mol $C_7H_5O_2Na$. Then

mol $HC_7H_5O_2$ $\rightarrow$ g mol $HC_7H_5O_2$ and mol $C_7H_5O_2Na$ $\rightarrow$ g $C_7H_5O_2Na$ then

$$\frac{122.12 \text{ g } HC_7H_5O_2}{1 \text{ mol } HC_7H_5O_2} \qquad \frac{144.10 \text{ g } C_7H_5O_2Na}{1 \text{ mol } C_7H_5O_2Na}$$

g mol $HC_7H_5O_2$, g $C_7H_5O_2Na$, g water $\rightarrow$ g solution $\rightarrow$ mL solution $\rightarrow$ L solution then

$$\text{g mol } HC_7H_5O_2 + \text{g } C_7H_5O_2Na + \text{g water} = \text{g solution} \qquad d = \frac{1 \text{ mL}}{1.01 \text{ g}} \qquad \frac{1 \text{ L}}{1000 \text{ mL}}$$

mol $HC_7H_5O_2$, L $\rightarrow$ M $HC_7H_5O_2$ and mol $C_7H_5O_2Na$, L $\rightarrow$ M $C_7H_5O_2Na$.

$$M = \frac{\text{mol}}{L} \qquad\qquad M = \frac{\text{mol}}{L}$$

Solution: Because $K_a(HC_7H_5O_2) = 6.5 \times 10^{-5}$, $pK_a = -\log K_a = -\log(6.5 \times 10^{-5}) = 4.19$. Because [acid] $=$ $[HC_7H_5O_2]$ and [base] $= [C_7H_5O_2^-] = [C_7H_5O_2Na]$, then

$$pH = pK_a + \log \frac{[\text{base}]}{[\text{acid}]} = 4.19 + \log \frac{[C_7H_5O_2Na]}{[HC_7H_5O_2]} = 4.55. \text{ Solve for } \frac{[C_7H_5O_2Na]}{[HC_7H_5O_2]}.$$

$$\log \frac{[C_7H_5O_2Na]}{[HC_7H_5O_2]} = 4.55 - 4.19 = 0.36 \rightarrow \frac{[C_7H_5O_2Na]}{[HC_7H_5O_2]} = 10^{0.36} = 2.29087. \text{ Then } T_f = T_f^\circ - \Delta T_f, \text{ so}$$

$$\Delta T_f = T_f^\circ - T_f = 0.0 \text{ °C} - (-2.0 \text{ °C}) = 2.0 \text{ °C then } \Delta T_f = K_f \times m. \text{ Rearrange to solve for } m.$$

$$m = \frac{\Delta T_f}{K_f} = \frac{2.0 \text{ °C}}{1.86 \dfrac{\text{°C}}{m}} = 1.07527 \frac{\text{mol particles}}{\text{kg solvent}}. \text{ Assume that 1 kg water, so we have } 1.07527 \text{ mol particles.}$$

Assume that $HC_7H_5O_2$ does not dissociate and that $C_7H_5O_2Na$ completely dissociates; then 1.07527 mol particles $=$ mol $HC_7H_5O_2$ $+$ 2(mol $C_7H_5O_2Na$). Use $[C_7H_5O_2Na]/[HC_7H_5O_2] = 2.29087$ and 1.07527 mol particles $=$ mol $[HC_7H_5O_2]$ $+$ 2(mol $C_7H_5O_2Na$) to solve for mol $HC_7H_5O_2$ and mol $C_7H_5O_2Na$. So mol $C_7H_5O_2Na =$ $2.29087(\text{mol } HC_7H_5O_2) \rightarrow 1.07527$ mol particles $=$ mol $HC_7H_5O_2$ $+$ 2(2.29087 mol $HC_7H_5O_2$) $\rightarrow$ 1.07527 mol particles $= 5.58174$ mol $HC_7H_5O_2$ $\rightarrow$ mol $HC_7H_5O_2 = 0.192641$ mol and mol $C_7H_5O_2Na = 2.29087 \times \text{mol } HC_7H_5O_2 = 2.29087 \times 0.192641 \text{ mol } HC_7H_5O_2 = 0.441315 \text{ mol } C_7H_5O_2Na$

$$0.192641 \text{ mol } HC_7H_5O_2 \times \frac{122.12 \text{ g } HC_7H_5O_2}{1 \text{ mol } HC_7H_5O_2} = 23.5253 \text{ g } HC_7H_5O_2 \text{ and}$$

$$0.441315 \text{ mol } C_7H_5O_2Na \times \frac{144.10 \text{ g } C_7H_5O_2Na}{1 \text{ mol } C_7H_5O_2Na} = 63.5935 \text{ g } C_7H_5O_2Na \text{ then}$$

23.5253 g mol $HC_7H_5O_2$ $+$ 63.5935 g $C_7H_5O_2Na$ $+$ 1000 g water $= 1087.119$ g solution then

$$1087.119 \text{ g solution} \times \frac{1 \text{ mL}}{1.01 \text{ g}} \times \frac{1 \text{ L}}{1000 \text{ mL}} = 1.076355 \text{ L. Finally,}$$

$$\frac{0.192641 \text{ mol } HC_7H_5O_2}{1.076355 \text{ L}} = 0.178975 \text{ M } HC_7H_5O_2 = 0.18 \text{ M } HC_7H_5O_2 \text{ and}$$

$$\frac{0.441315 \text{ mol } C_7H_5O_2Na}{1.076355 \text{ L}} = 0.410009 \text{ M } C_7H_5O_2Na = 0.41 \text{ M } C_7H_5O_2Na.$$

Check: The units (M and M) are correct. The magnitude of the answer makes physical sense because there are more moles of base than acid in the buffer (pH $>$ pK_a).

Challenge Problems

16.104 $\qquad$ The Henderson–Hasselbalch equation is $pH = pK_a + \log \dfrac{[\text{base}]}{[\text{acid}]}$. Remember that $14 = pH + pOH$ and that

$14 = pK_a + pK_b$. Substituting these into the Henderson–Hasselbalch equation:

$14 - pOH = 14 - pK_b + \log \dfrac{[\text{base}]}{[\text{acid}]}$. Simplifying the expression gives $pOH = pK_b - \log \dfrac{[\text{base}]}{[\text{acid}]}$.

16.105   **Given:** 10.0 L of 75 ppm $CaCO_3$ and 55 ppm $MgCO_3$ (by mass)
Find: mass Na_2CO_3 to precipitate 90.0% of ions
Other: $K_{sp}(CaCO_3) = 4.96 \times 10^{-9}$ and $K_{sp}(MgCO_3) = 6.82 \times 10^{-6}$
Conceptual Plan: Assume that the density of water is 1.00 g/mL, L water $\rightarrow$ mL water $\rightarrow$ g water then

$$\frac{1000 \text{ mL}}{1 \text{ L}} \qquad \frac{1.00 \text{ g water}}{1 \text{ mL}}$$

g water $\rightarrow$ g $CaCO_3$ $\rightarrow$ mol $CaCO_3$ $\rightarrow$ mol Ca^{2+} and g water $\rightarrow$ g $MgCO_3$ $\rightarrow$ mol $MgCO_3$ then

$$\frac{75 \text{ g } CaCO_3}{10^6 \text{ g water}} \quad \frac{1 \text{ mol } CaCO_3}{100.09 \text{ g } CaCO_3} \quad \frac{1 \text{ mol } Ca^{2+}}{1 \text{ mol } CaCO_3} \qquad \frac{55 \text{ g } MgCO_3}{10^6 \text{ g water}} \quad \frac{1 \text{ mol } MgCO_3}{84.32 \text{ g } MgCO_3}$$

mol $MgCO_3$ $\rightarrow$ mol Mg^{2+} then comparing the two K_{sp} values, essentially all of the Ca^{2+} will

$$\frac{1 \text{ mol } Mg^{2+}}{1 \text{ mol } MgCO_3}$$

**precipitate before the Mg^{2+} will begin to precipitate. Because 90.0% of the ions are to be precipitates, 10.0% of
the ions will be left in solution (all will be Mg^{2+}).**

$$(0.100)(\text{mol } Ca^{2+} + \text{mol } Mg^{2+})$$

Calculate the moles of ions remaining in solution. Then mol Mg^{2+}, L $\rightarrow$ M Mg^{2+}.

$$M = \frac{mol}{L}$$

The solubility product constant (K_{sp}) is the equilibrium expression for a chemical equation representing
the dissolution of an ionic compound. The expression of the solubility product constant of $A_m X_n$ is $K_{sp} = [A^{n+}]^m [X^{m-}]^n$. Use this equation to M Mg^{2+}, K_{sp} $\rightarrow$ M CO_3^{2-} then M CO_3^{2-}, L $\rightarrow$ mol CO_3^{2-}

$$\text{for ionic compound, } A_m X_n, K_{sp} = [A^{n+}]^m [X^{m-}]^n \qquad\qquad M = \frac{mol}{L}$$

then mol CO_3^{2-} $\rightarrow$ mol Na_2CO_3 $\rightarrow$ g Na_2CO_3.

$$\frac{1 \text{ mol } CO_3^{2-}}{1 \text{ mol } Na_2CO_3} \qquad \frac{105.99 \text{ g } Na_2CO_3}{1 \text{ mol } Na_2CO_3}$$

Solution: $10.0 \text{ L} \times \dfrac{1000 \text{ mL}}{1 \text{ L}} \times \dfrac{1.00 \text{ g water}}{1 \text{ mL}} = 1.00 \times 10^4$ g water then

$1.00 \times 10^4 \text{ g water} \times \dfrac{75 \text{ g } CaCO_3}{10^6 \text{ g water}} \times \dfrac{1 \text{ mol } CaCO_3}{100.09 \text{ g } CaCO_3} \times \dfrac{1 \text{ mol } Ca^{2+}}{1 \text{ mol } CaCO_3} = 0.0074933$ mol Ca^{2+} and

$1.00 \times 10^4 \text{ g water} \times \dfrac{55 \text{ g } MgCO_3}{10^6 \text{ g water}} \times \dfrac{1 \text{ mol } MgCO_3}{84.32 \text{ g } MgCO_3} \times \dfrac{1 \text{ mol } Mg^{2+}}{1 \text{ mol } MgCO_3} = 0.0065228$ mol Mg^{2+} so the ions

remaining in solution after 90.0% precipitate out = $(0.100)(\text{mol } Ca^{2+} + \text{mol } Mg^{2+})$

$= (0.100)(0.0074933 \text{ mol } Ca^{2+} + 0.0065228 \text{ mol } Mg^{2+}) = 0.00140161$ mol ions

so $\dfrac{0.00140161 \text{ mol } Mg^{2+}}{10.0 \text{ L}} = 0.000140161$ M Mg^{2+}. Then $K_{sp} = 6.82 \times 10^{-6}$, A = Mg^{2+}, $m = 1$, X = CO_3^{2-}, and

$n = 1$; so $K_{sp} = 6.82 \times 10^{-6} = [Mg^{2+}][CO_3^{2-}] = (0.00140161)[CO_3^{2-}]$. Rearrange to solve for $[CO_3^{2-}]$.

So $[CO_3^{2-}] = 0.0486583$ M. Then

$\dfrac{0.0486583 \text{ mol } CO_3^{2-}}{1 \text{ L}} \times 10.0 \text{ L} \times \dfrac{1 \text{ mol } Na_2CO_3}{1 \text{ mol } CO_3^{2-}} \times \dfrac{105.99 \text{ g } Na_2CO_3}{1 \text{ mol } Na_2CO_3} = 51.6$ g Na_2CO_3.

Check: The units (g) are correct. The mass is reasonable to put in a washing machine load.

16.106   **Given:** excess $Mg(OH)_2$ in 1.00 L of 1.0 M NH_4Cl has pH = 9.00   **Find:** $K_{sp}(Mg(OH)_2)$
Other: $K_b(NH_3) = 1.76 \times 10^{-5}$
Conceptual Plan: M NH_4Cl $\rightarrow$ M NH_4^+ and $K_b \rightarrow K_a$ then final pH $\rightarrow [H_3O^+]$ then

$$NH_4Cl \, (aq) \rightarrow NH_4^+(aq) + Cl^-(aq) \qquad K_w = K_a K_b \qquad [H_3O^+] = 10^{-pH}$$

M NH_4^+, M H_3O^+, K_a $\rightarrow$ x. **Because x is significant compared to initial M NH_4^+, this is a buffer solution.**

ICE table

The NH_4^+ is neutralized with $Mg(OH)_2$. Because $Mg(OH)_2(s) \rightleftharpoons Mg^{2+}(aq) + 2 \, OH^-(aq)$, there are two moles
of OH^- generated for each mole of $Mg(OH)_2$ dissolved. Thus, $\frac{1}{2}(x \text{ mol } OH^-)$ = mol $Mg(OH)_2$ was dissolved in
1.00 L of solution. Because there is 1.00 L solution, mol $Mg(OH)_2$ = $[Mg^{2+}]$ and $[H_3O^+] \rightarrow [OH^-]$.

$$K_w = [H_3O^+][OH^-]$$

Finally, write an expression for $K_{sp}(Mg(OH)_2)$ and substitute values for $[Mg^{2+}]$ and $[OH^-]$.

Solution: Because one NH_4^+ ion is generated for each NH_4Cl, $[NH_4^+] = 1.0$ M NH_4^+. Because $K_w = K_aK_b$,

rearrange to solve for K_a. $K_a = \dfrac{K_w}{K_b} = \dfrac{1.0 \times 10^{-14}}{1.76 \times 10^{-5}} = 5.\underline{6}818 \times 10^{-10}$. Final pH = 9.00, so

$[H_3O^+] = 10^{-pH} = 10^{-9.00} = 1.0 \times 10^{-9}$ M. Set up an ICE table:

$$NH_4^+(aq) + H_2O(l) \rightleftharpoons H_3O^+(aq) + NH_3(aq)$$

	$[NH_4^+]$	$[H_3O^+]$	$[NH_3]$
Initial	1.0	≈ 0.00	0.00
Change	$-x$	$+x$	$+x$
Equil	$1.0 - x$	1×10^{-9}	x

$K_a = \dfrac{[H_3O^+][NH_3]}{[NH_4^+]} = 5.\underline{6}818 \times 10^{-10} = \dfrac{(1.0 \times 10^{-9})x}{1.0 - x}$

Solve for x. $5.\underline{6}818 \times 10^{-10}(1.0 - x) = (1.0 \times 10^{-9})x \rightarrow 5.\underline{6}818 \times 10^{-10} = (1.0 \times 10^{-9} + 5.\underline{6}818 \times 10^{-10})x \rightarrow$
$x = 0.3\underline{6}2318$, so this is a buffer solution. Because there is 1.00 L of solution, 0.362318 mol of NH_4^+ is neutralized with $Mg(OH)_2$. Because $Mg(OH)_2(s) \rightleftharpoons Mg^{2+}(aq) + 2\,OH^-(aq)$, there are two moles of OH^- generated for each mole of $Mg(OH)_2$ dissolved. Thus, $\frac{1}{2}(0.362318$ mol $OH^-) = 0.181159$ mol $Mg(OH)_2$ was dissolved in 1.00 L of solution. Thus, the $[Mg^{2+}] = 0.1\underline{8}1159$ M. Because $K_w = [H_3O^+][OH^-]$,

$[OH^-] = \dfrac{K_w}{[H_3O^+]} = \dfrac{1.0 \times 10^{-14}}{1.0 \times 10^{-9}} = 1.0 \times 10^{-5}$ M then

$K_{sp}(Mg(OH)_2) = [Mg^{2+}][OH^-]^2 = (0.1\underline{8}1159)(1.0 \times 10^{-5})^2 = 1.8 \times 10^{-11}$.

Check: The units (none) are correct. The magnitude of the answer makes physical sense because the concentration of NH_4Cl is high; so it took a significant amount of $Mg(OH)_2$ to raise the pH to 9.00. Note that this number disagrees with the accepted value for the $K_{sp}(Mg(OH)_2)$. This is most likely due to errors in the measurements in this experiment.

16.107 **Given:** 1.00 L of 0.100 M $Mg(NO_3)_2$ **Find:** volume of 0.100 M Na_2CO_3 to precipitate 99% of Mg^{2+} ions
Other: $K_{sp}(MgCO_3) = 6.82 \times 10^{-6}$
Conceptual Plan:
Because 99% of the Mg^{2+} ions are to be precipitated, 1% of the ions will be left in solution.

$$(0.01)(0.100\ M\ Mg^{2+})$$

Let x = required volume (in L). Calculate the amount of CO_3^{2-} added and the amount of Mg^{2+} that does not precipitate and remains in solution. Use these to calculate the $[Mg^{2+}]$ and $[CO_3^{2-}]$. The solubility product constant (K_{sp}) is the equilibrium expression for a chemical equation representing the dissolution of an ionic compound. The expression of the solubility product constant of A_mX_n is $K_{sp} = [A^{n+}]^m[X^{m-}]^n$. Substitute these expressions in this equation to $[Mg^{2+}], [CO_3^{2-}], K_{sp} \rightarrow x$.

$$\text{for ionic compound, } A_mX_n, K_{sp} = [A^{n+}]^m[X^{m-}]^n$$

Solution: Because 99% of the Mg^{2+} ions are to be precipitated, 1% of the ions will be left in solution, or $(0.01)(0.100$ M $Mg^{2+}) = 0.001$ M Mg^{2+}. Let x = required volume (in L). The volume of the solution after precipitation is $(1.00 + x)$. The amount of CO_3^{2-} added = $(0.100$ M$)(x$ L$) = 0.100x$ mol CO_3^{2-}. The amount of Mg^{2+} that does not precipitate and remains in solution is $(0.100$ M$)(1.00$ L$)(0.001) = 1.00 \times 10^{-3}$ mol, and the amount that precipitates = 0.099 mol, which is also equal to the amount of CO_3^{2-} used. The amount of CO_3^{2-} remaining in solution is $(0.10x - 0.099)$. Thus, $[Mg^{2+}] = 1.00 \times 10^{-3}$mol/$(1.00 + x)$ L and $[CO_3^{2-}] = (0.10x - 0.099)$ mol/$(1.00 + x)$ L. Then $K_{sp} = 6.82 \times 10^{-6}$, $A = Mg^{2+}, m = 1, X = CO_3^{2-}$, and

$n = 1$; so $K_{sp} = 6.82 \times 10^{-6} = [Mg^{2+}][CO_3^{2-}] = \dfrac{(1.00 \times 10^{-3})(0.10x - 0.099)}{(1.00 + x)^2}$. Rearrange to solve for x.

$1.00 + 2.00x + x^2 = \dfrac{1.0 \times 10^{-4}x - 9.9 \times 10^{-5}}{6.82 \times 10^{-6}} \rightarrow 0 = x^2 - 1\underline{2}.6628x + 1\underline{5}.5161$. Using quadratic equation,
$x = 1.\underline{3}75$ L = 1.4 L.

Check: The units (L) are correct. The necessary concentration is very low, so the volume is fairly large.

16.108 **Given:** solution with 0.40 M HCN **Find:** solubility of CuI
Other: $K_{sp}(CuI) = 1.1 \times 10^{-12}$, $K_f(Cu(CN)_2^-) = 1 \times 10^{24}$
Conceptual Plan: Write balanced equations for the solubility of CuI and reaction with CN^- and expressions for K_{sp} and K_f. Use initial concentrations to set up an ICE table. Because the K is so large, assume that reaction essentially goes to completion. Solve for $[I^-]$ at equilibrium.
Solution: Write two reactions and combine.

$CuI(s) \rightleftharpoons \cancel{Cu^+}(aq) + I^-(aq)$ with $K_{sp} = [Cu^+][I^-] = 1.1 \times 10^{-12}$

$\cancel{Cu^+}(aq) + 2\,CN^-(aq) \rightleftharpoons Cu(CN)_2^-(aq)$ with $K_f = \dfrac{[Cu(CN)_2^-]}{[Cu^+][CN^-]^2} = 1 \times 10^{24}$

$\overline{CuI(s) + 2\,CN^-(aq) \rightleftharpoons Cu(CN)_2^-(aq) + I^-(aq)}$

with $K = K_{sp}K_f = \cancel{[Cu^+]}[I^-]\dfrac{[Cu(CN)_2^-]}{\cancel{[Cu^+]}[CN^-]^2} = (1.1 \times 10^{-12})(1 \times 10^{24})$

$K = \dfrac{[Cu(CN)_2^-][I^-]}{[CN^-]^2} = 1.1 \times 10^{12}$

Because $K_{sp} = [Cu^-][I^-] = 1.1 \times 10^{-12}$ without HCN present, $[Cu^+] = [I^-] = \sqrt{1.1 \times 10^{-12}} = 1.049 \times 10^{-6}$ M. Set up an ICE table with initial concentrations. Because K is so large and because initially $[CN^-] > [I^-]$, the reaction essentially goes to completion; then write equilibrium expression and solve for x.

$$CuI(s) + 2\,CN^-(aq) \rightleftharpoons Cu(CN)_2^-(aq) + I^-(aq)$$

	$[CN^-]$	$[Cu(CN)_2^-]$	$[I^-]$
Initial	0.40	0.00	1.049×10^{-6}
Change	≈ -0.40	$\approx 1/2\,(0.40)$	$\approx 1/2\,(0.40)$
Equil	$0.40 - 2x$	x	$1.049 \times 10^{-6} + x$

$K = \dfrac{[Cu(CN)_2^-][I^-]}{[CN^-]^2} = \dfrac{(x)(1.049 \times 10^{-6} + x)}{(0.40 - 2x)^2} = 1.1 \times 10^{12}$. Assume that $x >\ > 1.049 \times 10^{-6}$ M, so

$\dfrac{(x)(x)}{(0.40 - 2x)^2} = 1.1 \times 10^{12} = \dfrac{(x)^2}{(0.40 - 2x)^2} \rightarrow \sqrt{1.1 \times 10^{12}} = \dfrac{x}{0.40 - 2x} = 1.049 \times 10^6 \rightarrow$

$x = 0.19995$. So $[I^-] = x = 0.19995$ M $= 0.2$ M I^-. Because 1.048×10^{-6} M is insignificant compared to x, the assumption is valid. The solubility of CuI is 0.2 M, or one-half the initial concentration of HCN.

Check: The units (M) are correct. Because K is so large, the reaction essentially goes to completion and the solubility of CuI is dramatically increased.

16.109 **Given:** 1.0 L solution with 0.10 M $Ba(OH)_2$ and excess $Zn(OH)_2$ **Find:** pH
Other: $K_{sp}(Zn(OH)_2) = 3 \times 10^{-15}$, $K_f(Zn(OH)_4^{2-}) = 2 \times 10^{15}$
Conceptual Plan: Because $[Ba(OH)_2] = 0.10$ M, $[OH^-] = 0.20$ M. Write balanced equations for the solubility of $Zn(OH)_2$ and reaction with excess OH^- and expressions for K_{sp} and K_f. Use initial concentrations to set up an ICE table. Solve for $[OH^-]$ at equilibrium. Then $[OH^-] \rightarrow [H_3O^+] \rightarrow$ pH.

$$K_w = [H_3O^+][OH^-] \quad pH = -\log\,[H_3O^+]$$

Solution: Write two reactions and combine.

$Zn(OH)_2(s) \rightleftharpoons Zn^{2+}(aq) + 2\,OH^-(aq)$ with $K_{sp} = [Zn^{2+}][OH^-]^2 = 3 \times 10^{-15}$

$Zn^{2+}(aq) + \overset{2}{\cancel{4}}\,OH^-(aq) \rightleftharpoons Zn(OH)_4^{2-}(aq)$ with $K_f = \dfrac{[Zn(OH)_4^{2-}]}{[Zn^{2+}][OH^-]^4} = 2 \times 10^{15}$

$\overline{Zn(OH)_2(s) + 2\,OH^-(aq) \rightleftharpoons Zn(OH)_4^{2-}(aq)}$

with $K = K_{sp}K_f = \cancel{[Zn^{2+}]}\cancel{[OH^-]^2}\dfrac{[Zn(OH)_4^{2-}]}{\cancel{[Zn^{2+}]}\cancel{[OH^-]^4}} = (3 \times 10^{-15})(2 \times 10^{15})$

$K = \dfrac{[Zn(OH)_4^{2-}]}{[OH^-]^2} = 6$. Set up an ICE table with initial concentration and solve for x.

$$Zn(OH)_2(s) + 2\,OH^-(aq) \rightleftharpoons Zn(OH)_4^{2-}(aq)$$

	$[OH^-]$	$[Zn(OH)_4^{2-}]$
Initial	0.20	0.00
Change	$-2x$	x
Equil	$0.20 - 2x$	x

$$K = \frac{[Zn(OH)_4^{2-}]}{[OH^-]^2} = \frac{x}{(0.20 - 2x)^2} = 6$$

$x = 6(0.20 - 2x)^2 \rightarrow x = 6(4x^2 - 0.80x + 0.040) \rightarrow x = 24x^2 - 4.8x + 0.24 \rightarrow$
$0 = 24x^2 - 5.8x + 0.24$. Using quadratic equation, $x = 0.0530049 \rightarrow$
$[OH^-] = 0.20 - 2x = 0.20 - 2(0.0530049) = 0.093990$ M OH$^-$. Then $K_w = [H_3O^+][OH^-]$, so

$$[H_3O^+] = \frac{K_w}{[OH^-]} = \frac{1.0 \times 10^{-14}}{0.093990} = 1.06394 \times 10^{-13}\,M\text{ . Finally,}$$

$$pH = -\log[H_3O^+] = -\log(1.06394 \times 10^{-13}) = 12.97.$$

Check: The units (none) are correct. Because the pH of the solution before the addition of the $Zn(OH)_2$ is 13.30, the reaction decreases the $[OH^-]$ and the pH drops.

16.110   **Given:** 1.00 L of 2.0 M $HC_2H_3O_2$ and 1.0 M $C_2H_3O_2^-$ **Find:** amount of HCl to pH = 4.00
Other: $K_a(HC_2H_3O_2) = 1.8 \times 10^{-5}$
Conceptual Plan: Identify acid and base components then final pH, $pK_a \rightarrow [C_2H_3O_2^-]/[HC_2H_3O_2]$ then

$$\text{acid} = HC_2H_3O_2 \qquad \text{base} = C_2H_3O_2^- \qquad pH = pK_a + \log\frac{[\text{base}]}{[\text{acid}]}$$

$[C_2H_3O_2^-]$, L $\rightarrow$ mol $C_2H_3O_2^-$ and $[HC_2H_3O_2]$, L $\rightarrow$ mol $HC_2H_3O_2$ then write balanced equation then

$$M = \frac{mol}{L} \qquad\qquad M = \frac{mol}{L} \qquad HCl + C_2H_3O_2^- \rightarrow HC_2H_3O_2 + Cl^-$$

initial mol $NaC_2H_3O_2$, initial mol $HC_2H_3O_2$, final $[C_2H_3O_2^-]/[HC_2H_3O_2] \rightarrow$ mol HCl $\rightarrow$ g HCl.

$$\text{set up stoichiometry table} \qquad \frac{36.46 \text{ g HCl}}{1 \text{ mol HCl}}$$

Solution: Because $K_a(HC_2H_3O_2) = 1.8 \times 10^{-5}$, $pK_a = -\log K_a = -\log(1.8 \times 10^{-5}) = 4.74$.

Then $pH = pK_a + \log\dfrac{[\text{base}]}{[\text{acid}]} = 4.74 + \log\dfrac{[C_2H_3O_2^-]}{[HC_2H_3O_2]} = 4.00$. Solve for $\dfrac{[C_2H_3O_2^-]}{[HC_2H_3O_2]}$.

$$\log\frac{[C_2H_3O_2^-]}{[HC_2H_3O_2]} = 4.00 - 4.74 = -0.74 \rightarrow \frac{[C_2H_3O_2^-]}{[HC_2H_3O_2]} = 10^{-0.74} = 0.181970.$$

Then $\dfrac{2.0 \text{ mol } HC_2H_3O_2}{1\,L} \times 1.00\,L = 2.0$ mol $HC_2H_3O_2$ and

$\dfrac{1.0 \text{ mol } C_2H_3O_2^-}{1\,L} \times 1.00\,L = 1.0$ mol $C_2H_3O_2^-$. Set up a table to track changes:

$$HCl(aq) + C_2H_3O_2^-(aq) \rightarrow HC_2H_3O_2(aq) + Cl^-(aq)$$

Before addition	0.0 mol	1.0 mol	2.0 mol	0.0 mol
Addition	$-x$ mol	$-x$ mol	x mol	x mol
After addition	≈ 0.00 mol	$(1.0 - x)$ mol	$(2.0 + x)$ mol	x mol

Combine the final line of table with $\dfrac{[C_2H_3O_2^-]}{[HC_2H_3O_2]} = 0.181970.$

So $\dfrac{[C_2H_3O_2^-]}{[HC_2H_3O_2]} = 0.181970 = \dfrac{(1.0 - x)}{(2.0 + x)}$. Solve for x. $0.181970(2.0 + x) = 1.0 - x \rightarrow$

$x + 0.181970x = 1.0 - 0.36394 \rightarrow 1.181970x = 0.63606 \rightarrow x = 0.538135$ mol HCl = 0.54 mol HCl then

$0.538135 \text{ mol HCl} \times \dfrac{36.46 \text{ g HCl}}{1 \text{ mol HCl}} = 19.6204$ g HCl = 20. g HCl.

Check: The units (mol and g) are correct. The magnitude of the answer makes physical sense because the initial $[C_2H_3O_2^-]/[HC_2H_3O_2] = 0.50$ and is reduced to ~0.18 and the starting number of moles of base = 1.0 mol, so much less than a mole of HCl must be added.

Conceptual Problems

16.111   If the concentration of the acid is greater than the concentration of the base, then the pH will be less than the pK_a. If the concentration of the acid is equal to the concentration of the base, then the pH will be equal to the pK_a. If the concentration of the acid is less than the concentration of the base, then the pH will be greater than the pK_a.

    (a) $pH < pK_a$

    (b) $pH > pK_a$

    (c) $pH = pK_a$, the OH^- will convert half of the acid to base

    (d) $pH > pK_a$, the OH^- will convert more than half of the acid to base

16.112   As long as the [base]/[acid] is between 0.1 and 10, the buffer will be active and the buffer capacity will not have been exceeded.

    (a)   No, the buffer capacity is not exceeded because [base]/[acid] = 0.22/0.08.

    (b)   No, the buffer capacity is not exceeded because [base]/[acid] = 0.18/0.12.

    (c)   Yes, the buffer capacity will be exceeded because all of the acid is converted to base.

    (d)   No, the buffer capacity is not exceeded because [base]/[acid] = 0.19/0.11.

16.113   Only (a) is the same for all three solutions. The volume to the first equivalence point will be the same because the number of moles of acid is the same. The pH profiles of the three titrations will be different.

16.114   Only (c) is correct. If the volume of base is twice as high, then the acid concentration is twice as high and the weaker acid has the higher pH at the equivalence point.

16.115   (a)   The solubility will be unchanged because the pH is constant and no common ions are added.

    (b)   The solubility will be less because extra fluoride ions are added, suppressing the solubility of the fluoride ionic compound.

    (c)   The solubility will increase because some of the fluoride ion will be converted to HF; so more of the ionic compound can be dissolved.

16.116   At the equivalence point, the acid has all been converted into its conjugate base, resulting in a weakly basic solution.

Questions for Group Work

16.117   In each case, you must add the conjugate acid to a weak base or the conjugate base to a weak acid. (Additionally, you can make a buffer by adding a little strong acid to a weak base or a little strong base to a weak acid. The product of the neutralization is the conjugate you need.)

    (a)   an acetate salt, such as sodium acetate, potassium acetate, rubidium acetate, ... (The cation may vary.)

    (b)   nitrous acid

    (c)   an ammonium salt, such as ammonium chloride, ammonium bromide, ammonium iodide, ammonium nitrate, ... (The anion may vary.)

    (d)   formic acid

    (e)   a phosphate salt or a dihydrogen phosphate salt, such as Na_3PO_4 or NaH_2PO_4, Li_3PO_4 or LiH_2PO_4, K_3PO_4 or KH_2PO_4, ... (The cations may vary.)

16.118   Start with the balanced equation for the ionization of a weak acid: $HA\,(aq) + H_2O\,(l) \rightleftharpoons H_3O^+\,(aq) + A^-(aq)$

Write the expression for the equilibrium constant: $K_a = \dfrac{[H_3O^+]\,[A^-]}{[HA]}$.

Rearrange this expression to solve for $[H_3O^+]$: $[H_3O^+] = K_a\dfrac{[HA]}{[A^-]}$

Take the negative logarithm of this equation: $-\log[H_3O^+] = -\log\left(K_a\dfrac{[HA]}{[A^-]}\right)$

Since the $-\log(AB) = -\log A - \log B$, rearrange the equation: $-\log[H_3O^+] = -\log K_a - \log\dfrac{[HA]}{[A^-]}$

Since $pH = -\log[H_3O^+]$ and $pK_a = -\log K_a$, substituting into the equation: $pH = pK_a - \log\dfrac{[HA]}{[A^-]}$

Since the $-\log(A/B) = \log B/A$, rearrange the equation: $pH = pK_a + \log\dfrac{[A^-]}{[HA]}$

16.119   Students will take roles of H^+, $C_2H_3O_2^-$, Na^+, and Cl^-. As HCl (H^+ and Cl^-) is added, the H^+ will pair with $C_2H_3O_2^-$, neutralizing the acetate ion and becoming acetic acid. Since acetic acid is a weak acid, it will remain primarily undissociated and the amount of H^+ ions in solution will not significantly change.

16.120   (a)   Since this is a solubility equilibrium, the equilibrium constant will be $K_{sp} = 4.96 \times 10^{-9}$.

      (b) $K_{sp} = 4.96 \times 10^{-9} = [Ca^{2+}][CO_3^{2-}] = S^2$ and so $S = 7.04 \times 10^{-5}$ M.

      (c) $200.\ mL \times \dfrac{1\ L}{1000\ mL} \times \dfrac{7.04 \times 10^{-5}\ mol\ CaCO_3}{1\ L} \times \dfrac{100.09\ g\ CaCO_3}{1\ mol\ CaCO_3} \times \dfrac{1000\ mg\ CaCO_3}{1\ g\ CaCO_3} = 1.41\ mg\ CaCO_3$

      (d)   Acidic. Calcium carbonate is more soluble in acidic solution because the carbonate ion is a weak base and will react with the acid in the cleaning solution.

16.121   The molar solubility, S, is simply the solubility in units of moles per liter (mol/L). The molar solubility of a compound, A_mX_n, can be computed directly from K_{sp} by solving for S in the expression: $K_{sp} = (mS)^m (nS)^n = m^m n^n S^{m+n}$. As an example, for $Ca(OH)_2$, $K_{sp} = 4.68 \times 10^{-6}$, $A = Ca^{2+}$, $m = 1$, $X = OH^-$, and $n = 2$ so $K_{sp} = 4.68 \times 10^{-6} = 2^2 S^3$. Rearrange to solve for S. $S = \sqrt[3]{\dfrac{4.68 \times 10^{-6}}{4}} = 1.05 \times 10^{-2}$ M. The solubility rules in Chapter 4 predict that hydroxides are not very soluble, which agrees with the calculated value of S.

17 Free Energy and Thermodynamics

Entropy, the Second Law of Thermodynamics, and the Direction of Spontaneous Change

17.1   a and c are spontaneous processes.

17.2   a and c are nonspontaneous processes. Nonspontaneous processes are not impossible. Work of some form must be added to make the process proceed.

17.3   System B has the greatest entropy. There is only one energetically equivalent arrangement for System A. However, the particles of System B may exchange positions for a second energetically equivalent arrangement.

17.4   There is only one energetically equivalent arrangement for System A. There are 3! or 6 energetically equivalent arrangements for System B. System B has the greatest entropy because there are more energetically equivalent arrangements for System B.

17.5   (a) $\Delta S > 0$ because a gas is being generated.
        (b) $\Delta S < 0$ because 2 moles of gas are being converted to 1 mole of gas.
        (c) $\Delta S < 0$ because a gas is being converted to a solid.
        (d) $\Delta S < 0$ because 4 moles of gas are being converted to 2 moles of gas.

17.6   (a) $\Delta S < 0$ because a gas is being converted to a solid.
        (b) $\Delta S < 0$ because 5 moles of gas are being converted to 4 moles of gas.
        (c) $\Delta S > 0$ because 2 moles of gas are being converted to 3 moles of gas.
        (d) $\Delta S < 0$ because 2 moles of gas are being converted to a solid.

17.7   (a) $\Delta S_{sys} > 0$ because 6 moles of gas are being converted to 7 moles of gas. Because $\Delta H < 0$ and $\Delta S_{surr} > 0$, the reaction is spontaneous at all temperatures.
        (b) $\Delta S_{sys} < 0$ because 2 moles of different gases are being converted to 2 moles of one gas. Because $\Delta H > 0$ and $\Delta S_{surr} < 0$, the reaction is nonspontaneous at all temperatures.
        (c) $\Delta S_{sys} < 0$ because 3 moles of gas are being converted to 2 moles of gas. Because $\Delta H > 0$ and $\Delta S_{surr} < 0$, the reaction is nonspontaneous at all temperatures.
        (d) $\Delta S_{sys} > 0$ because 9 moles of gas are being converted to 10 moles of gas. Because $\Delta H < 0$ and $\Delta S_{surr} > 0$, the reaction is spontaneous at all temperatures.

17.8   (a) $\Delta S_{sys} < 0$ because 3 moles of gas are being converted to 2 moles of gas. Because $\Delta H < 0$ and $\Delta S_{surr} > 0$, the reaction is spontaneous at low temperatures.
        (b) $\Delta S_{sys} > 0$ because 2 moles of gas are being converted to 3 moles of gas. Because $\Delta H > 0$ and $\Delta S_{surr} < 0$, the reaction is spontaneous at high temperatures.
        (c) $\Delta S_{sys} < 0$ because 3 moles of gas are being converted to 2 moles of gas. Because $\Delta H < 0$ and $\Delta S_{surr} > 0$, the reaction is spontaneous at low temperatures.
        (d) $\Delta S_{sys} < 0$ because 1 mole of a complicated gas is being converted to 1 mole of gas and a solid. Because $\Delta H > 0$ and $\Delta S_{surr} > 0$, the reaction is nonspontaneous at all temperatures.

17.9   (a)   **Given:** $\Delta H^{\circ}_{rxn} = -287$ kJ, $T = 298$ K   **Find:** ΔS_{surr}
            Conceptual Plan: kJ $\rightarrow$ J then $\Delta H^{\circ}_{rxn}, T \rightarrow \Delta S_{surr}$

$$\frac{1000 \text{ J}}{1 \text{ kJ}} \qquad\qquad \Delta S_{surr} = \frac{-\Delta H_{sys}}{T}$$

            Solution: $-287 \text{ kJ} \times \dfrac{1000 \text{ J}}{1 \text{ kJ}} = -287,000$ J then

$$\Delta S_{surr} = \frac{-\Delta H_{sys}}{T} = \frac{-(-287,000 \text{ J})}{298 \text{ K}} = 963 \text{ J/K}$$

            Check: The units (J/K) are correct. The magnitude of the answer (10^3 J/K) makes sense because the kJ and the temperature started with similar values and then a factor of 10^3 was applied.

    (b)   **Given:** $\Delta H^{\circ}_{rxn} = -287$ kJ, $T = 77$ K   **Find:** ΔS_{surr}
            Conceptual Plan: kJ $\rightarrow$ J then $\Delta H^{\circ}_{rxn}, T \rightarrow \Delta S_{surr}$

$$\frac{1000 \text{ J}}{1 \text{ kJ}} \qquad\qquad \Delta S_{surr} = \frac{-\Delta H_{sys}}{T}$$

            Solution: $-287 \text{ kJ} \times \dfrac{1000 \text{ J}}{1 \text{ kJ}} = -287,000$ J then $\Delta S_{surr} = \dfrac{-\Delta H_{sys}}{T} = \dfrac{-(-287,000 \text{ J})}{77 \text{ K}} = 3.73 \times 10^3 \text{ J/K}$

            Check: The units (J/K) are correct. The magnitude of the answer (4×10^3 J/K) makes sense because the temperature is much lower than in part (a); so the answer should increase.

    (c)   **Given:** $\Delta H^{\circ}_{rxn} = +127$ kJ, $T = 298$ K   **Find:** ΔS_{surr}
            Conceptual Plan: kJ $\rightarrow$ J then $\Delta H^{\circ}_{rxn}, T \rightarrow \Delta S_{surr}$

$$\frac{1000 \text{ J}}{1 \text{ kJ}} \qquad\qquad \Delta S_{surr} = \frac{-\Delta H_{sys}}{T}$$

            Solution: $+127 \text{ kJ} \times \dfrac{1000 \text{ J}}{1 \text{ kJ}} = +127,000$ J then $\Delta S_{surr} = \dfrac{-\Delta H_{sys}}{T} = \dfrac{-127,000 \text{ J}}{298 \text{ K}} = -426 \text{ J/K}$

            Check: The units (J/K) are correct. The magnitude of the answer (-400 J/K) makes sense because the kJ are less and of the opposite sign than in part (a); so the answer should decrease.

    (d)   **Given:** $\Delta H^{\circ}_{rxn} = +127$ kJ, $T = 77$ K   **Find:** ΔS_{surr}
            Conceptual Plan: kJ $\rightarrow$ J then $\Delta H^{\circ}_{rxn}, T \rightarrow \Delta S_{surr}$

$$\frac{1000 \text{ J}}{1 \text{ kJ}} \qquad\qquad \Delta S_{surr} = \frac{-\Delta H_{sys}}{T}$$

            Solution: $+127 \text{ kJ} \times \dfrac{1000 \text{ J}}{1 \text{ kJ}} = +127,000$ J then

$$\Delta S_{surr} = \frac{-\Delta H_{sys}}{T} = \frac{-127,000 \text{ J}}{77 \text{ K}} = -1650 \frac{\text{J}}{\text{K}} = -1.65 \times 10^3 \text{ J/K}$$

            Check: The units (J/K) are correct. The magnitude of the answer (-2×10^3 J/K) makes sense because the temperature is much lower than in part (c); so the answer should increase.

17.10   **Given:** $\Delta H^{\circ}_{rxn} = -127$ kJ, $\Delta S^{\circ}_{rxn} = 314$ J/K   **Find:** T when $\Delta S^{\circ}_{rxn} = \Delta S_{surr}$
         Conceptual Plan: kJ $\rightarrow$ J then set $\Delta S^{\circ}_{rxn} = \Delta S_{surr}$ then $\Delta H^{\circ}_{rxn}, \Delta S_{surr} \rightarrow T$

$$\frac{1000 \text{ J}}{1 \text{ kJ}} \qquad\qquad\qquad\qquad\qquad\qquad \Delta S_{surr} = \frac{-\Delta H_{sys}}{T}$$

         Solution: $-127 \text{ kJ} \times \dfrac{1000 \text{ J}}{1 \text{ kJ}} = -127,000$ J then set $\Delta S^{\circ}_{rxn} = 314 \text{ J/K} = \Delta S_{surr}$ then

$$T = \frac{-\Delta H_{sys}}{\Delta S_{surr}} = \frac{-(-127,000 \text{ J})}{314 \dfrac{\text{J}}{\text{K}}} = +404 \text{ K}$$

         Check: The units (K) are correct. The magnitude of the answer (400 K) makes sense because there is almost a factor of 400 between the enthalpy and the entropy.

17.11   (a)   **Given:** $\Delta H^{\circ}_{rxn} = -125$ kJ, $\Delta S^{\circ}_{rxn} = +253$ J/K, $T = 298$ K   **Find:** ΔS_{univ} and spontaneity
Conceptual Plan: kJ → J then $\Delta H^{\circ}_{rxn}, T \rightarrow \Delta S_{surr}$ then $\Delta S_{rxn}, \Delta S_{surr} \rightarrow \Delta S_{univ}$

$$\frac{1000 \text{ J}}{1 \text{ kJ}} \qquad \Delta S_{surr} = \frac{-\Delta H_{sys}}{T} \qquad \Delta S_{univ} = \Delta S_{sys} + \Delta S_{surr}$$

Solution: $-125 \text{ kJ} \times \dfrac{1000 \text{ J}}{1 \text{ kJ}} = -125{,}000 \text{ J}$ then $\Delta S_{surr} = \dfrac{-\Delta H_{sys}}{T} = \dfrac{-(-125{,}000 \text{ J})}{298 \text{ K}} = 419.4631$ J/K then

$\Delta S_{univ} = \Delta S_{sys} + \Delta S_{surr} = +253$ J/K $= +419.4631$ J/K $= +672$ J/K; so the reaction is spontaneous.

Check: The units (J/K) are correct. The magnitude of the answer (+670 J/K) makes sense because both terms are positive; so the reaction is spontaneous.

(b)   **Given:** $\Delta H^{\circ}_{rxn} = +125$ kJ, $\Delta S^{\circ}_{rxn} = -253$ J/K, $T = 298$ K   **Find:** ΔS_{univ} and spontaneity
Conceptual Plan: kJ → J then $\Delta H^{\circ}_{rxn}, T \rightarrow \Delta S_{surr}$ then $\Delta S_{rxn}, \Delta S_{surr} \rightarrow \Delta S_{univ}$

$$\frac{1000 \text{ J}}{1 \text{ kJ}} \qquad \Delta S_{surr} = \frac{-\Delta H_{sys}}{T} \qquad \Delta S_{univ} = \Delta S_{sys} + \Delta S_{surr}$$

Solution: $+125 \text{ kJ} \times \dfrac{1000 \text{ J}}{1 \text{ kJ}} = +125{,}000 \text{ J}$ then $\Delta S_{surr} = \dfrac{-\Delta H_{sys}}{T} = \dfrac{-(+125{,}000 \text{ J})}{298 \text{ K}} = -419.4631$ J/K then

$\Delta S_{univ} = \Delta S_{sys} + \Delta S_{surr} = -253$ J/K $- 419.4631$ J/K $= -672$ J/K; so the reaction is nonspontaneous.

Check: The units (J/K) are correct. The magnitude of the answer (-670 J/K) makes sense because both terms are negative; so the reaction is nonspontaneous.

(c)   **Given:** $\Delta H^{\circ}_{rxn} = -125$ kJ, $\Delta S^{\circ}_{rxn} = -253$ J/K, $T = 298$ K   **Find:** ΔS_{univ} and spontaneity
Conceptual Plan: kJ → J then $\Delta H^{\circ}_{rxn}, T \rightarrow \Delta S_{surr}$ then $\Delta S_{rxn}, \Delta S_{surr} \rightarrow \Delta S_{univ}$

$$\frac{1000 \text{ J}}{1 \text{ kJ}} \qquad \Delta S_{surr} = \frac{-\Delta H_{sys}}{T} \qquad \Delta S_{univ} = \Delta S_{sys} + \Delta S_{surr}$$

Solution: $-125 \text{ kJ} \times \dfrac{1000 \text{ J}}{1 \text{ kJ}} = -125{,}000 \text{ J}$ then $\Delta S_{surr} = \dfrac{-\Delta H_{sys}}{T} = \dfrac{-(-125{,}000 \text{ J})}{298 \text{ K}} = +419.4631$ J/K

then $\Delta S_{univ} = \Delta S_{sys} + \Delta S_{surr} = -253$ J/K $+ 419.4631$ J/K $= +166$ J/K; so the reaction is spontaneous.

Check: The units (J/K) are correct. The magnitude of the answer (170 J/K) makes sense because the larger term is positive; so the reaction is spontaneous.

(d)   **Given:** $\Delta H^{\circ}_{rxn} = -125$ kJ, $\Delta S^{\circ}_{rxn} = -253$ J/K, $T = 555$ K   **Find:** ΔS_{univ} and spontaneity
Conceptual Plan: kJ → J then $\Delta H^{\circ}_{rxn}, T \rightarrow \Delta S_{surr}$ then $\Delta S_{rxn}, \Delta S_{surr} \rightarrow \Delta S_{univ}$

$$\frac{1000 \text{ J}}{1 \text{ kJ}} \qquad \Delta S_{surr} = \frac{-\Delta H_{sys}}{T} \qquad \Delta S_{univ} = \Delta S_{sys} + \Delta S_{surr}$$

Solution: $-125 \text{ kJ} \times \dfrac{1000 \text{ J}}{1 \text{ kJ}} = -125{,}000 \text{ J}$ then $\Delta S_{surr} = \dfrac{-\Delta H_{sys}}{T} = \dfrac{-(-125{,}000 \text{ J})}{555 \text{ K}} = +225.225$ J/K

then $\Delta S_{univ} = \Delta S_{sys} + \Delta S_{surr} = -253$ J/K $+ 225.225$ J/K $= -28$ J/K; so the reaction is nonspontaneous.

Check: The units (J/K) are correct. The magnitude of the answer (-30 J/K) makes sense because the larger term is negative; so the reaction is nonspontaneous.

17.12   (a)   **Given:** $\Delta H^{\circ}_{rxn} = +85$ kJ, $\Delta S^{\circ}_{rxn} = +147$ J/K, $T = 298$ K   **Find:** ΔS_{univ} and spontaneity
Conceptual Plan: kJ → J then $\Delta H^{\circ}_{rxn}, T \rightarrow \Delta S_{surr}$ then $\Delta S_{rxn}, \Delta S_{surr} \rightarrow \Delta S_{univ}$

$$\frac{1000 \text{ J}}{1 \text{ kJ}} \qquad \Delta S_{surr} = \frac{-\Delta H_{sys}}{T} \qquad \Delta S_{univ} = \Delta S_{sys} + \Delta S_{surr}$$

Solution: $+85 \text{ kJ} \times \dfrac{1000 \text{ J}}{1 \text{ kJ}} = +85{,}000 \text{ J}$ then $\Delta S_{surr} = \dfrac{-\Delta H_{sys}}{T} = \dfrac{-(+85{,}000 \text{ J})}{298 \text{ K}} = -285.235$ J/K then

$\Delta S_{univ} = \Delta S_{sys} + \Delta S_{surr} = +147$ J/K $- 285.235$ J/K $= -138$ J/K $= -1.4 \times 10^2$ J/K; so the reaction is nonspontaneous.

Check: The units (J/K) are correct. The magnitude of the answer (-140 J/K) makes sense because the surroundings lose more entropy than the system gains; so the reaction is nonspontaneous.

(b) **Given:** $\Delta H^\circ_{rxn} = +85$ kJ, $\Delta S_{rxn} = +147$ J/K, $T = 755$ K **Find:** ΔS_{univ} and spontaneity

Conceptual Plan: kJ $\rightarrow$ J then $\Delta H^\circ_{rxn}, T \rightarrow \Delta S_{surr}$ then $\Delta S_{rxn}, \Delta S_{surr} \rightarrow \Delta S_{univ}$

$$\frac{1000 \text{ J}}{1 \text{ kJ}} \qquad \Delta S_{surr} = \frac{-\Delta H_{sys}}{T} \qquad \Delta S_{univ} = \Delta S_{sys} + \Delta S_{surr}$$

Solution: $+85 \text{ kJ} \times \dfrac{1000 \text{ J}}{1 \text{ kJ}} = +85{,}000 \text{ J}$ then $\Delta S_{surr} = \dfrac{-\Delta H_{sys}}{T} = \dfrac{-(85{,}000 \text{ J})}{755 \text{ K}} = -1\underline{1}2.583 \text{ J/K}$ then

$\Delta S_{univ} = \Delta S_{sys} + \Delta S_{surr} = +147 \text{ J/K} - 112.583 \text{ J/K} = \underline{3}4 \text{ J/K} = +3 \times 10^1 \text{ J/K}$; so the reaction is spontaneous.

Check: The units (J/K) are correct. The magnitude of the answer ($+30$ J/K) makes sense because at a higher temperature, the entropy of the surroundings is reduced so that the entropy of the system dominates and the reaction is spontaneous.

(c) **Given:** $\Delta H^\circ_{rxn} = +85$ kJ, $\Delta S_{rxn} = -147$ J/K, $T = 298$ K **Find:** ΔS_{univ} and spontaneity

Conceptual Plan: kJ $\rightarrow$ J then $\Delta H^\circ_{rxn}, T \rightarrow \Delta S_{surr}$ then $\Delta S_{rxn}, \Delta S_{surr} \rightarrow \Delta S_{univ}$

$$\frac{1000 \text{ J}}{1 \text{ kJ}} \qquad \Delta S_{surr} = \frac{-\Delta H_{sys}}{T} \qquad \Delta S_{univ} = \Delta S_{sys} + \Delta S_{surr}$$

Solution: $+85 \text{ kJ} \times \dfrac{1000 \text{ J}}{1 \text{ kJ}} = +85{,}000 \text{ J}$ then $\Delta S_{surr} = \dfrac{-\Delta H_{sys}}{T} = \dfrac{-85{,}000 \text{ J}}{298 \text{ K}} = -2\underline{8}5.235 \text{ J/K}$ then

$\Delta S_{univ} = \Delta S_{sys} + \Delta S_{surr} = -147 \text{ J/K} - 285.235 \text{ J/K} = -4\underline{3}2 \text{ J/K} = -4.3 \times 10^2 \text{ J/K}$; so the reaction non-spontaneous.

Check: The units (J/K) are correct. The magnitude of the answer (-430 J/K) makes sense because both terms are negative; so the sum is negative and the reaction is nonspontaneous.

(d) **Given:** $\Delta H^\circ_{rxn} = -85$ kJ, $\Delta S_{rxn} = +147$ J/K, $T = 398$ K **Find:** ΔS_{univ} and spontaneity

Conceptual Plan: kJ $\rightarrow$ J then $\Delta H^\circ_{rxn}, T \rightarrow \Delta S_{surr}$ then $\Delta S_{rxn}, \Delta S_{surr} \rightarrow \Delta S_{univ}$

$$\frac{1000 \text{ J}}{1 \text{ kJ}} \qquad \Delta S_{surr} = \frac{-\Delta H_{sys}}{T} \qquad \Delta S_{univ} = \Delta S_{sys} + \Delta S_{surr}$$

Solution: $-85 \text{ kJ} \times \dfrac{1000 \text{ J}}{1 \text{ kJ}} = -85{,}000 \text{ J}$ then $\Delta S_{surr} = \dfrac{-\Delta H_{sys}}{T} = \dfrac{-(-85{,}000 \text{ J})}{398 \text{ K}} = +2\underline{1}3.568 \text{ J/K}$

then $\Delta S_{univ} = \Delta S_{sys} + \Delta S_{surr} = +147 \text{ J/K} + 21\underline{3}.568 \text{ J/K} = +3\underline{6}1 \text{ J/K} = +3.6 \times 10^2 \text{ J/K}$; so the reaction is spontaneous.

Check: The units (J/K) are correct. The magnitude of the answer (360 J/K) makes sense because both terms are positive; so the sum is positive and the reaction is spontaneous.

Standard Entropy Changes and Gibbs Free Energy

17.13 (a) **Given:** $\Delta H^\circ_{rxn} = -125$ kJ, $\Delta S_{rxn} = +253$ J/K, $T = 298$ K **Find:** ΔG and spontaneity

Conceptual Plan: J/K $\rightarrow$ kJ/K then $\Delta H^\circ_{rxn}, \Delta S_{rxn}, T \rightarrow \Delta G$

$$\frac{1 \text{ kJ}}{1000 \text{ J}} \qquad \Delta G = \Delta H_{rxn} - T\Delta S_{rxn}$$

Solution: $+253 \dfrac{\text{J}}{\text{K}} \times \dfrac{1 \text{ kJ}}{1000 \text{ J}} = +0.253 \text{ kJ/K}$ then

$\Delta G = \Delta H_{rxn} - T\Delta S_{rxn} = -125 \text{ kJ} - (298 \text{ K})\left(0.253 \dfrac{\text{kJ}}{\text{K}}\right) = -2.00 \times 10^2 \text{ kJ} = -2.00 \times 10^5 \text{ J}$; so the reaction is spontaneous.

Check: The units (kJ) are correct. The magnitude of the answer (-200 kJ) makes sense because both terms are negative; so the reaction is spontaneous.

(b) **Given:** $\Delta H^\circ_{rxn} = +125$ kJ, $\Delta S_{rxn} = -253$ J/K, $T = 298$ K **Find:** ΔG and spontaneity

Conceptual Plan: J/K $\rightarrow$ kJ/K then $\Delta H^\circ_{rxn}, \Delta S_{rxn}, T \rightarrow \Delta G$

$$\frac{1 \text{ kJ}}{1000 \text{ J}} \qquad \Delta G = \Delta H_{rxn} - T\Delta S_{rxn}$$

Solution: $-253 \dfrac{\text{J}}{\text{K}} \times \dfrac{1 \text{ kJ}}{1000 \text{ J}} = -0.253 \text{ kJ/K}$ then

$$\Delta G = \Delta H_{rxn} - T\Delta S_{rxn} = +125 \text{ kJ} - (298 \text{ K})\left(-0.253 \frac{\text{kJ}}{\text{K}}\right) = +200. \text{ kJ} = +2.00 \times 10^2 \text{ kJ} = +2.00 \times 10^5 \text{ J};$$

so the reaction is nonspontaneous.

Check: The units (kJ) are correct. The magnitude of the answer (+200 kJ) makes sense because both terms are positive; so the reaction is nonspontaneous.

(c) **Given:** $\Delta H_{rxn}^\circ = -125 \text{ kJ}$, $\Delta S_{rxn} = -253 \text{ J/K}$, $T = 298 \text{ K}$ **Find:** ΔG and spontaneity
Conceptual Plan: J/K → kJ/K then $\Delta H_{rxn}^\circ, \Delta S_{rxn}, T \rightarrow \Delta G$

$$\frac{1 \text{ kJ}}{1000 \text{ J}} \qquad\qquad \Delta G = \Delta H_{rxn} - T\Delta S_{rxn}$$

Solution: $-253 \dfrac{\text{J}}{\text{K}} \times \dfrac{1 \text{ kJ}}{1000 \text{ J}} = -0.253 \text{ kJ/K}$ then

$$\Delta G = \Delta H_{rxn} - T\Delta S_{rxn} = -125 \text{ kJ} - (298 \text{ K})\left(-0.253 \frac{\text{kJ}}{\text{K}}\right) = -49.606 \text{ kJ} = -5.0 \times 10^1 \text{ kJ} = -5.0 \times 10^4 \text{ J};$$

so the reaction is spontaneous.

Check: The units (kJ) are correct. The magnitude of the answer (−50 kJ) makes sense because the larger term is negative; so the reaction is spontaneous.

(d) **Given:** $\Delta H_{rxn}^\circ = -125 \text{ kJ}$, $\Delta S_{rxn} = -253 \text{ J/K}$, $T = 555 \text{ K}$ **Find:** ΔG and spontaneity
Conceptual Plan: J/K → kJ/K then $\Delta H_{rxn}^\circ, \Delta S_{rxn}, T \rightarrow \Delta G$

$$\frac{1 \text{ kJ}}{1000 \text{ J}} \qquad\qquad \Delta G = \Delta H_{rxn} - T\Delta S_{rxn}$$

Solution: $-253 \dfrac{\text{J}}{\text{K}} \times \dfrac{1 \text{ kJ}}{1000 \text{ J}} = -0.253 \text{ kJ/K}$ then

$$\Delta G = \Delta H_{rxn} - T\Delta S_{rxn} = -125 \text{ kJ} - (555 \text{ K})\left(-0.253 \frac{\text{kJ}}{\text{K}}\right) = +15 \text{ kJ} = +1.5 \times 10^4 \text{ J};$$

so the reaction is nonspontaneous.

Check: The units (J/K) are correct. The magnitude of the answer (+15 kJ) makes sense because the larger term is positive; so the reaction is nonspontaneous.

17.14 (a) **Given:** $\Delta H_{rxn}^\circ = +85 \text{ kJ}$, $\Delta S_{rxn} = +147 \text{ J/K}$, $T = 298 \text{ K}$ **Find:** ΔG and spontaneity
Conceptual Plan: J/K → kJ/K then $\Delta H_{rxn}^\circ, \Delta S_{rxn}, T \rightarrow \Delta G$

$$\frac{1 \text{ kJ}}{1000 \text{ J}} \qquad\qquad \Delta G = \Delta H_{rxn} - T\Delta S_{rxn}$$

Solution: $+147 \dfrac{\text{J}}{\text{K}} \times \dfrac{1 \text{ kJ}}{1000 \text{ J}} = +0.147 \text{ kJ/K}$ then

$$\Delta G = \Delta H_{rxn} - T\Delta S_{rxn} = +85 \text{ kJ} - (298 \text{ K})\left(+0.147 \frac{\text{kJ}}{\text{K}}\right) = +41 \text{ kJ}; \text{ so the reaction is nonspontaneous.}$$

Check: The units (kJ) are correct. The magnitude of the answer (+41 kJ) makes sense because the positive enthalpy dominates over the entropy term; so the reaction is nonspontaneous.

(b) **Given:** $\Delta H_{rxn}^\circ = +85 \text{ kJ}$, $\Delta S_{rxn} = +147 \text{ J/K}$, $T = 755 \text{ K}$ **Find:** ΔG and spontaneity
Conceptual Plan: J/K → kJ/K then $\Delta H_{rxn}^\circ, \Delta S_{rxn}, T \rightarrow \Delta G$

$$\frac{1 \text{ kJ}}{1000 \text{ J}} \qquad\qquad \Delta G = \Delta H_{rxn} - T\Delta S_{rxn}$$

Solution: $+147 \dfrac{\text{J}}{\text{K}} \times \dfrac{1 \text{ kJ}}{1000 \text{ J}} = +0.147 \text{ kJ/K}$ then

$$\Delta G = \Delta H_{rxn} - T\Delta S_{rxn} = +85 \text{ kJ} - (755 \text{ K})\left(+0.147 \frac{\text{kJ}}{\text{K}}\right) = -26 \text{ kJ}; \text{ so the reaction is spontaneous.}$$

Check: The units (kJ) are correct. The magnitude of the answer (−30 kJ) makes sense because at a higher temperature, the entropy term dominates and the reaction is spontaneous.

(c)   **Given:** $\Delta H^\circ_{rxn} = +85$ kJ, $\Delta S_{rxn} = -147$ J/K, $T = 298$ K   **Find:** ΔG and spontaneity
Conceptual Plan: J/K → kJ/K then ΔH°_{rxn}, ΔS_{rxn}, T **→** ΔG

$$\frac{1 \text{ kJ}}{1000 \text{ J}} \qquad\qquad \Delta G = \Delta H_{rxn} - T\Delta S_{rxn}$$

Solution: $-147 \dfrac{\text{J}}{\text{K}} \times \dfrac{1 \text{ kJ}}{1000 \text{ J}} = -0.147$ kJ/K then

$$\Delta G = \Delta H_{rxn} - T\Delta S_{rxn} = +85 \text{ kJ} - (298 \text{ K})\left(-0.147 \frac{\text{kJ}}{\text{K}}\right) = +129 \text{ kJ; so the reaction is nonspontaneous.}$$

Check: The units (kJ) are correct. The magnitude of the answer ($+130$ kJ) makes sense because both terms are positive; so the sum is positive and the reaction is nonspontaneous.

(d)   **Given:** $\Delta H^\circ_{rxn} = -85$ kJ, $\Delta S_{rxn} = +147$ J/K, $T = 398$ K   **Find:** ΔG and spontaneity
Conceptual Plan: J/K → kJ/K then ΔH°_{rxn}, ΔS_{rxn}, T **→** ΔG

$$\frac{1 \text{ kJ}}{1000 \text{ J}} \qquad\qquad \Delta G = \Delta H_{rxn} - T\Delta S_{rxn}$$

Solution: $+147 \dfrac{\text{J}}{\text{K}} \times \dfrac{1 \text{ kJ}}{1000 \text{ J}} = +0.147$ kJ/K then

$$\Delta G = \Delta H_{rxn} - T\Delta S_{rxn} = -85 \text{ kJ} - (398 \text{ K})\left(0.147 \frac{\text{kJ}}{\text{K}}\right) = -144 \text{ kJ; so the reaction is spontaneous.}$$

Check: The units (kJ) are correct. The magnitude of the answer (-140 kJ) makes sense because both terms are negative; so the sum is negative and the reaction is spontaneous.

17.15   **Given:** $\Delta H^\circ_{rxn} = -2217$ kJ, $\Delta S^\circ_{rxn} = +101.1$ J/K, $T = 25\ ^\circ$C   **Find:** ΔG and spontaneity
Conceptual Plan: °C → K then J/K → kJ/K then ΔH°_{rxn}, ΔS_{rxn}, T **→** ΔG

$$\text{K} = 273.15 + \ ^\circ\text{C} \qquad \frac{1 \text{ kJ}}{1000 \text{ J}} \qquad\qquad \Delta G = \Delta H_{rxn} - T\Delta S_{rxn}$$

Solution: $T = 273.15 + 25\ ^\circ\text{C} = 298$ K then $+101.1 \dfrac{\text{J}}{\text{K}} \times \dfrac{1 \text{ kJ}}{1000 \text{ J}} = +0.1011 \dfrac{\text{kJ}}{\text{K}}$ then

$$\Delta G = \Delta H_{rxn} - T\Delta S_{rxn} = -2217 \text{ kJ} - (298 \text{ K})\left(0.1011 \frac{\text{kJ}}{\text{K}}\right) = -2247 \text{ kJ} = -2.247 \times 10^6 \text{ J; so the reaction is}$$
spontaneous.

Check: The units (kJ) are correct. The magnitude of the answer (-2250 kJ) makes sense because both terms are negative; so the reaction is spontaneous.

17.16   **Given:** $\Delta H^\circ_{rxn} = -1269.8$ kJ, $\Delta S^\circ_{rxn} = -364.6$ J/K, $T = 25\ ^\circ$C   **Find:** ΔG and spontaneity
Conceptual Plan: °C → K then J/K → kJ/K then ΔH°_{rxn}, ΔS_{rxn}, T **→** ΔG

$$\text{K} = 273.15 + \ ^\circ\text{C} \qquad \frac{1 \text{ kJ}}{1000 \text{ J}} \qquad\qquad \Delta G = \Delta H_{rxn} - T\Delta S_{rxn}$$

Solution: $T = 273.15 + 25\ ^\circ\text{C} = 298$ K then $-364.6 \dfrac{\text{J}}{\text{K}} \times \dfrac{1 \text{ kJ}}{1000 \text{ J}} = -0.3646 \dfrac{\text{kJ}}{\text{K}}$ then

$$\Delta G = \Delta H_{rxn} - T\Delta S_{rxn} = -1269.8 \text{ kJ} - (298 \text{ K})\left(-0.3646 \frac{\text{kJ}}{\text{K}}\right) = -1161.1 \text{ kJ} = -1.161 \times 10^6 \text{ J; so the reaction}$$
is spontaneous.

Check: The units (kJ) are correct. The magnitude of the answer (-1200 kJ) makes sense because the negative enthalpy term dominates over the positive entropy term; so the reaction is spontaneous.

17.17

ΔH	ΔS	ΔG	Low Temp.	High Temp.
−	+	−	**Spontaneous**	Spontaneous
−	−	**Temp. dependent**	Spontaneous	Nonspontaneous
+	+	Temp. dependent	Nonspontaneous	**Spontaneous**
+	−	+	**Nonspontaneous**	**Nonspontaneous**

17.18 (a) ΔH_{rxn}° for a condensation is negative, and ΔS_{rxn} is negative; so the reaction will be spontaneous at low temperatures (< 100 °C).

(b) ΔH_{rxn}° for a sublimation is positive, and ΔS_{rxn} is positive; so the reaction will be spontaneous at high temperatures (> −78.5 °C).

(c) ΔH_{rxn}° for a bond breaking is positive, and ΔS_{rxn} is positive; so the reaction will be spontaneous at high temperatures.

(d) ΔH_{rxn}° is positive, and ΔS_{rxn} is positive; so the reaction will be spontaneous at high temperatures.

17.19 The molar entropy of a substance increases with increasing temperatures. The kinetic energy and the molecular motion increase. The substance will have access to an increased number of energy levels.

17.20 The third law of thermodynamics states that the entropy of a perfect crystal at absolute zero (0 K) is zero. For enthalpy, we defined a standard state so that we could define a "zero" for the scale. This is not necessary for entropy because there is an absolute zero for the entropy scale.

17.21 (a) $CO_2(g)$ because it has greater molar mass/complexity.

(b) $CH_3OH(g)$ because it is in the gas phase.

(c) $CO_2(g)$ because it has greater molar mass/complexity.

(d) $SiH_4(g)$ because it has greater molar mass.

(e) $CH_3CH_2CH_3(g)$ because it has greater molar mass/complexity.

(f) $NaBr(aq)$ because a solution has more entropy than a solid crystal.

17.22 (a) $NaNO_3(aq)$ because a solution has more entropy than does a solid crystal.

(b) $CH_3CH_3(g)$ because it has greater molar mass/complexity.

(c) $Br_2(g)$ because it is in the gas phase.

(d) $Br_2(g)$ because it has greater molar mass.

(e) $PCl_5(g)$ because it has greater molar mass/complexity.

(f) $CH_3CH_2CH_2CH_3(g)$ because it has greater complexity.

17.23 (a) $He(g) < Ne(g) < SO_2(g) < NH_3(g) < CH_3CH_2OH(g)$. All are in the gas phase. From He to Ne, there is an increase in molar mass; beyond that, the molecules increase in complexity.

(b) $H_2O(s) < H_2O(l) < H_2O(g)$. Entropy increases as we go from a solid to a liquid to a gas.

(c) $CH_4(g) < CF_4(g) < CCl_4(g)$. Entropy increases as the molar mass increases.

17.24 (a) $F_2(g) < Cl_2(g) < Br_2(g) < I_2(g)$. All are in the gas phase. Entropy increases as the molar mass increases.

(b) $H_2O(g) < H_2S(g) < H_2O_2(g)$. Entropy increases as the molar mass and the complexity of the molecules increase.

(c) $C(s, diamond) < C(s, graphite) < C(s, amorphous)$. Entropy increases as the complexity increases. The diamond structure is ordered in all three dimensions. Graphite has ordered sheets that can slide with respect to each other. The amorphous carbon has no long-range order.

17.25 (a) **Given:** $C_2H_4(g) + H_2(g) \rightarrow C_2H_6(g)$ **Find:** ΔS_{rxn}°
Conceptual Plan: $\Delta S_{rxn}^{\circ} = \sum n_p S^{\circ}(\text{products}) - \sum n_r S^{\circ}(\text{reactants})$
Solution:

Reactant/Product	S°(J/mol · K from Appendix IIB)
$C_2H_4(g)$	219.3
$H_2(g)$	130.7
$C_2H_6(g)$	229.2

Be sure to pull data for the correct formula and phase.

$$\Delta S_{rxn}^{\circ} = \sum n_p S^{\circ}(\text{products}) - \sum n_r S^{\circ}(\text{reactants})$$
$$= [1(S^{\circ}(C_2H_6(g)))] - [1(S^{\circ}(C_2H_4(g))) + 1(S^{\circ}(H_2(g)))]$$
$$= [1(229.2 \text{ J/K})] - [1(219.3 \text{ J/K}) + 1(130.7 \text{ J/K})]$$
$$= [229.2 \text{ J/K}] - [350.0 \text{ J/K}]$$
$$= -120.8 \text{ J/K} \quad \text{The moles of gas are decreasing.}$$

Check: The units (J/K) are correct. The answer is negative, which is consistent with 2 moles of gas going to 1 mole of gas.

(b)   **Given:** $C(s) + H_2O(g) \rightarrow CO(g) + H_2(g)$ **Find:** $\Delta S°_{rxn}$
Conceptual Plan: $\Delta S°_{rxn} = \sum n_p S°(\text{products}) - \sum n_r S°(\text{reactants})$
Solution:

Reactant/Product	$S°(\text{J/mol} \cdot \text{K from Appendix IIB})$
$C(s)$	5.7
$H_2O(g)$	188.8
$CO(g)$	197.7
$H_2(g)$	130.7

Be sure to pull data for the correct formula and phase.

$\Delta S°_{rxn} = \sum n_p S°(\text{products}) - \sum n_r S°(\text{reactants})$
$= [1(S°(CO(g))) + 1(S°(H_2(g)))] - [1(S°(C(s))) + 1(S°(H_2O(g)))]$
$= [1(197.7 \text{ J/K}) + 1(130.7 \text{ J/K})] - [1(5.7 \text{ J/K}) + 1(188.8 \text{ J/K})]$
$= [328.4 \text{ J/K}] - [194.5 \text{ J/K}]$
$= +133.9 \text{ J/K}$ The moles of gas are increasing.

Check: The units (J/K) are correct. The answer is positive, which is consistent with 1 mole of gas going to 2 moles of gas.

(c)   **Given:** $CO(g) + H_2O(g) \rightarrow H_2(g) + CO_2(g)$ **Find:** $\Delta S°_{rxn}$
Conceptual Plan: $\Delta S°_{rxn} = \sum n_p S°(\text{products}) - \sum n_r S°(\text{reactants})$
Solution:

Reactant/Product	$S°(\text{J/mol} \cdot \text{K from Appendix IIB})$
$CO(g)$	197.7
$H_2O(g)$	188.8
$H_2(g)$	130.7
$CO_2(g)$	213.8

Be sure to pull data for the correct formula and phase.

$\Delta S°_{rxn} = \sum n_p S°(\text{products}) - \sum n_r S°(\text{reactants})$
$= [1(S°(H_2(g))) + 1(S°(CO_2(g)))] - [1(S°(CO(g))) + 1(S°(H_2O(g)))]$
$= [1(130.7 \text{ J/K}) + 1(213.8 \text{ J/K})] - [1(197.7 \text{ J/K}) + 1(188.8 \text{ J/K})]$
$= [344.5 \text{ J/K}] - [386.5 \text{ J/K}]$
$= -42.0 \text{ J/K}$

The change is small because the number of moles of gas is constant.

Check: The units (J/K) are correct. The answer is small and negative, which is consistent with a constant number of moles of gas. Water molecules are bent, and carbon dioxide molecules are linear; so the water has more complexity. Also, carbon monoxide is more complex than is hydrogen gas.

(d)   **Given:** $2 H_2S(g) + 3 O_2(g) \rightarrow 2 H_2O(l) + 2 SO_2(g)$ **Find:** $\Delta S°_{rxn}$
Conceptual Plan: $\Delta S°_{rxn} = \sum n_p S°(\text{products}) - \sum n_r S°(\text{reactants})$
Solution:

Reactant/Product	$S°(\text{J/mol} \cdot \text{K from Appendix IIB})$
$H_2S(g)$	205.8
$O_2(g)$	205.2
$H_2O(l)$	70.0
$SO_2(g)$	248.2

Be sure to pull data for the correct formula and phase.

$$\Delta S^\circ_{rxn} = \sum n_p S^\circ(\text{products}) - \sum n_r S^\circ(\text{reactants})$$
$$= [2(S^\circ(H_2O(l))) + 2(S^\circ(SO_2(g)))] - [2(S^\circ(H_2S(g))) + 3(S^\circ(O_2(g)))]$$
$$= [2(70.0 \text{ J/K}) + 2(248.2 \text{ J/K})] - [2(205.8 \text{ J/K}) + 3(205.2 \text{ J/K})]$$
$$= [636.4 \text{ J/K}] - [1027.2 \text{ J/K}]$$
$$= -390.8 \text{ J/K}$$

The number of moles of gas is decreasing.

Check: The units (J/K) are correct. The answer is negative, which is consistent with a decrease in the number of moles of gas.

17.26 **(a)** **Given:** $3 NO_2(g) + H_2O(l) \rightarrow 2 HNO_3(aq) + NO(g)$ **Find:** ΔS°_{rxn}
Conceptual Plan: $\Delta S^\circ_{rxn} = \sum n_p S^\circ(\text{products}) - \sum n_r S^\circ(\text{reactants})$
Solution:

Reactant/Product	S°(J/mol · K from Appendix IIB)
$NO_2(g)$	240.1
$H_2O(l)$	70.0
$HNO_3(aq)$	146
$NO(g)$	210.8

Be sure to pull data for the correct formula and phase.

$$\Delta S^\circ_{rxn} = \sum n_p S^\circ(\text{products}) - \sum n_r S^\circ(\text{reactants})$$
$$= [2(S^\circ(HNO_3(aq))) + 1(S^\circ(NO(g)))] - [3(S^\circ(NO_2(g))) + 1(S^\circ(H_2O(l)))]$$
$$= [2(146 \text{ J/K}) + 1(210.8 \text{ J/K})] - [3(240.1 \text{ J/K}) + 1(70.0 \text{ J/K})]$$
$$= [502.8 \text{ J/K}] - [790.3 \text{ J/K}]$$
$$= -288 \text{ J/K}$$

The number of moles of gas is decreasing.

Check: The units (J/K) are correct. The answer is negative, which is consistent with a decrease in the number of moles of gas.

(b) **Given:** $Cr_2O_3(s) + 3 CO(g) \rightarrow 2 Cr(s) + 3 CO_2(g)$ **Find:** ΔS°_{rxn}
Conceptual Plan: $\Delta S^\circ_{rxn} = \sum n_p S^\circ(\text{products}) - \sum n_r S^\circ(\text{reactants})$
Solution:

Reactant/Product	S°(J/mol · K from Appendix IIB)
$Cr_2O_3(s)$	81.2
$CO(g)$	197.7
$Cr(s)$	23.8
$CO_2(g)$	213.8

Be sure to pull data for the correct formula and phase.

$$\Delta S^\circ_{rxn} = \sum n_p S^\circ(\text{products}) - \sum n_r S^\circ(\text{reactants})$$
$$= [2(S^\circ(Cr(s))) + 3(S^\circ(CO_2(g)))] - [1(S^\circ(Cr_2O_3(s))) + 3(S^\circ(CO(g)))]$$
$$= [2(23.8 \text{ J/K}) + 3(213.8 \text{ J/K})] - [1(81.2 \text{ J/K}) + 3(197.7 \text{ J/K})]$$
$$= [689.0 \text{ J/K}] - [674.3 \text{ J/K}]$$
$$= +14.7 \text{ J/K}$$

The change is small because the number of moles of gas is constant.

Check: The units (J/K) are correct. The answer is small and positive, which is consistent with a constant number of moles of gas. Carbon dioxide molecules have more complexity than do carbon monoxide molecules, but the chromium oxide is more complex than is chromium metal.

(c) **Given:** $SO_2(g) + \frac{1}{2} O_2(g) \rightarrow SO_3(g)$ **Find:** ΔS°_{rxn}
Conceptual Plan: $\Delta S^\circ_{rxn} = \sum n_p S^\circ(\text{products}) - \sum n_r S^\circ(\text{reactants})$

Solution:

Reactant/Product	$S°$(J/mol · K from Appendix IIB)
$SO_2(g)$	248.2
$O_2(g)$	205.2
$SO_3(g)$	256.8

Be sure to pull data for the correct formula and phase.

$$\Delta S°_{rxn} = \sum n_p S°(products) - \sum n_r S°(reactants)$$
$$= [1(S°(SO_3(g)))] - [1(S°(SO_2(g))) + 1/2(S°(O_2(g)))]$$
$$= [1(256.8 \text{ J/K})] - [1(248.2 \text{ J/K}) + 1/2(205.2 \text{ J/K})]$$
$$= [256.8 \text{ J/K}] - [350.8 \text{ J/K}]$$
$$= -94.0 \text{ J/K}$$

The number of moles of gas is decreasing.

Check: The units (J/K) are correct. The answer is negative, which is consistent with a decrease in the number of moles of gas.

(d)   **Given:** $N_2O_4(g) + 4 H_2(g) \rightarrow N_2(g) + 4 H_2O(g)$ **Find:** $\Delta S°_{rxn}$
Conceptual Plan: $\Delta S°_{rxn} = \sum n_p S°(products) - \sum n_r S°(reactants)$
Solution:

Reactant/Product	$S°$(J/mol · K from Appendix IIB)
$N_2O_4(g)$	304.4
$H_2(g)$	130.7
$N_2(g)$	191.6
$H_2O(g)$	188.8

Be sure to pull data for the correct formula and phase.

$$\Delta S°_{rxn} = \sum n_p S°(products) - \sum n_r S°(reactants)$$
$$= [1(S°(N_2(g))) + 4(S°(H_2O(g)))] - [1(S°(N_2O_4(g))) + 4(S°(H_2(g)))]$$
$$= [1(191.6 \text{ J/K}) + 4(188.8 \text{ J/K})] - [1(304.4 \text{ J/K}) + 4(130.7 \text{ J/K})]$$
$$= [946.8 \text{ J/K}] - [827.2 \text{ J/K}]$$
$$= +119.6 \text{ J/K}$$

The change is small because the number of moles of gas is constant.

Check: The units (J/K) are correct. The answer is positive, which is consistent with 1 mole of a complex gas and 4 moles of a simple gas going to 1 mole of a simple gas and 4 moles of a complex gas, respectively.

17.27   **Given:** $CH_2Cl_2(g)$ formed from elements in standard states   **Find:** $\Delta S°$ and rationalize sign
Conceptual Plan: Write a balanced reaction, then $\Delta S°_{rxn} = \sum n_p S°(products) - \sum n_r S°(reactants)$
Solution: $C(s) + H_2(g) + Cl_2(g) \rightarrow CH_2Cl_2(g)$

Reactant/Product	$S°$(J/mol · K from Appendix IIB)
$C(s)$	5.7
$H_2(g)$	130.7
$Cl_2(g)$	223.1
$CH_2Cl_2(g)$	270.2

Be sure to pull data for the correct formula and phase.

$$\Delta S°_{rxn} = \sum n_p S°(products) - \sum n_r S°(reactants)$$
$$= [1(S°(CH_2Cl_2(g)))] - [1(S°(C(s))) + 1(S°(H_2(g))) + 1(S°(Cl_2(g)))]$$
$$= [1(270.2 \text{ J/K})] - [1(5.7 \text{ J/K}) + 1(130.7 \text{ J/K}) + 1(223.1 \text{ J/K})]$$
$$= [270.2 \text{ J/K}] - [359.5 \text{ J/K}]$$
$$= -89.3 \text{ J/K}$$

The moles of gas are decreasing.

Check: The units (J/K) are correct. The answer is negative, which is consistent with 2 moles of gas going to 1 mole of gas.

17.28   **Given:** $NF_3(g)$ formed from elements in standard states   **Find:** $\Delta S°$ and rationalize sign

Conceptual Plan: Write balanced reaction, then $\Delta S°_{rxn} = \sum n_p S°(\text{products}) - \sum n_r S°(\text{reactants})$.

Solution: $\frac{1}{2}N_2(g) + \frac{3}{2}F_2(g) \longrightarrow NF_3(g)$

Reactant/Product	$S°$(J/mol · K from Appendix IIB)
$N_2(g)$	191.6
$F_2(g)$	202.79
$NF_3(g)$	260.8

Be sure to pull data for the correct formula and phase.

$$\Delta S°_{rxn} = \sum n_p S°(\text{products}) - \sum n_r S°(\text{reactants})$$
$$= [1(S°(NF_3(g)))] - [1/2(S°(N_2(g))) + 3/2(S°(F_2(g)))]$$
$$= [1(260.8 \text{ J/K})] - [1/2(191.6 \text{ J/K}) + 3/2(202.79 \text{ J/K})]$$
$$= [260.8 \text{ J/K}] - [399.\underline{9}85 \text{ J/K}]$$
$$= -139.2 \text{ J/K} \quad \text{The moles of gas are decreasing.}$$

Check: The units (J/K) are correct. The answer is negative, which is consistent with 2 moles of simple gases going to 1 mole of a complex gas.

17.29   **Given:** methanol (CH_3OH) combustion at 25 °C   **Find:** $\Delta H°_{rxn}$, $\Delta S°_{rxn}$, $\Delta G°_{rxn}$, and spontaneity

Conceptual Plan: Write a balanced reaction then $\Delta H°_{rxn} = \sum n_p H°_f(\text{products}) - \sum n_r H°_f(\text{reactants})$ **then**

$\Delta S°_{rxn} = \sum n_p S°(\text{products}) - \sum n_r S°(\text{reactants})$ **then** °C → K **then** J/K → kJ/K **then**

$$K = 273.15 + °C \qquad \frac{1 \text{ kJ}}{1000 \text{ J}}$$

$\Delta H°_{rxn}, \Delta S°_{rxn}, T \rightarrow \Delta G°.$

$$\Delta G = \Delta H_{rxn} - T\Delta S_{rxn}$$

Solution: Combustion is combined with oxygen to form carbon dioxide and water.

$2 \, CH_3OH(l) + 3 \, O_2(g) \longrightarrow 2 \, CO_2(g) + 4 \, H_2O(g)$

Reactant/Product	$\Delta H°_f$ (kJ · mol from Appendix IIB)
$CH_3OH(l)$	−238.6
$O_2(g)$	0.0
$CO_2(g)$	−393.5
$H_2O(g)$	−241.8

Be sure to pull data for the correct formula and phase.

$$\Delta H°_{rxn} = \sum n_p \Delta H°_f(\text{products}) - \sum n_r \Delta H°_f(\text{reactants})$$
$$= [2(\Delta H°_f(CO_2(g))) + 4(\Delta H°_f(H_2O(g)))] - [2(\Delta H°_f(CH_3OH(l))) + 3(\Delta H°_f(O_2(g)))]$$
$$= [2(-393.5 \text{ kJ}) + 4(-241.8 \text{ kJ})] - [2(-238.6 \text{ kJ}) + 3(0.0 \text{ kJ})]$$
$$= [-1754.2 \text{ kJ}] - [-477.2 \text{ kJ}]$$
$$= -1277.0 \text{ kJ} \text{ then}$$

Reactant/Product	$S°$(J/mol · K from Appendix IIB)
$CH_3OH(l)$	126.8
$O_2(g)$	205.2
$CO_2(g)$	213.8
$H_2O(g)$	188.8

Be sure to pull data for the correct formula and phase.

$$\Delta S°_{rxn} = \sum n_p S°(\text{products}) - \sum n_r S°(\text{reactants})$$
$$= [2(S°(CO_2(g))) + 4(S°(H_2O(g)))] - [2(S°(CH_3OH(l))) + 3(S°(O_2(g)))]$$
$$= [2(213.8 \text{ J/K}) + 4(188.8 \text{ J/K})] - [2(126.8 \text{ J/K}) + 3(205.2 \text{ J/K})]$$
$$= [1182.8 \text{ J/K}] - [869.2 \text{ J/K}]$$
$$= 313.6 \text{ J/K}$$

then $T = 273.15 + 25 \text{ °C} = 298 \text{ K}$ then $+313.6 \, \dfrac{J}{K} \times \dfrac{1 \text{ kJ}}{1000 \, J} = +0.3136 \text{ kJ/K}$ then

$\Delta G = \Delta H_{rxn} - T\Delta S_{rxn} = -1277.0 \text{ kJ} - (298 \text{ K})\left(+0.3136 \frac{\text{kJ}}{\text{K}}\right) = -1370.5 \text{ kJ} = -1.3705 \times 10^6 \text{ J}$; so the reaction is spontaneous.

Check: The units (kJ, J/K, and kJ) are correct. Combustion reactions are exothermic, and we see a large negative enthalpy. We expect a large positive entropy because we have an increase in the number of moles of gas. The free energy is the sum of two negative terms; so we expect a large negative free energy, and the reaction is spontaneous.

17.30   **Given:** form glucose ($C_6H_{12}O_6$) and oxygen from sunlight, carbon dioxide, and water at 25 °C
Find: $\Delta H°_{rxn}$, $\Delta S°_{rxn}$, $\Delta G°_{rxn}$, and spontaneity
Conceptual Plan: Write a balanced reaction then $\Delta H°_{rxn} = \sum n_p H°_f \text{ (products)} - \sum n_r H°_f \text{ (reactants) then}$
$\Delta S°_{rxn} = \sum n_p S° \text{(products)} - \sum n_r S°\text{(reactants) then } °C \rightarrow K \text{ then } J/K \rightarrow kJ/K \text{ then } \Delta H°_{rxn}, \Delta S°_{rxn}, T \rightarrow \Delta G°.$

$$K = 273.15 + °C \qquad \frac{1 \text{ kJ}}{1000 \text{ J}} \qquad \Delta G = \Delta H_{rxn} - T\Delta S_{rxn}$$

Solution: $6 CO_2(g) + 6 H_2O(l) \rightarrow C_6H_{12}O_6(s) + 6 O_2(g)$

Reactant/Product	$\Delta H°_f$ (kJ/mol from Appendix IIB)
$CO_2(g)$	−393.5
$H_2O(l)$	−285.8
$C_6H_{12}O_6(s)$	−1273.3
$O_2(g)$	0.0

Be sure to pull data for the correct formula and phase.
$\Delta H°_{rxn} = \sum n_p \Delta H°_f \text{(products)} - \sum n_r \Delta H°_f \text{(reactants)}$
$\quad = [1(\Delta H°_f(C_6H_{12}O_6(s))) + 6(\Delta H°_f(O_2(g)))] - [6(\Delta H°_f(CO_2(g))) + 6(\Delta H°_f(H_2O(l)))]$
$\quad = [1(-1273.3 \text{ kJ}) + 6(0.0 \text{ kJ})] - [6(-393.5 \text{ kJ}) + 6(-285.8 \text{ kJ})]$
$\quad = [-1273.3 \text{ kJ}] - [-4075.8 \text{ kJ}]$
$\quad = +2802.5 \text{ kJ then}$

Reactant/Product	$S°$(J/mol · K from Appendix IIB)
$CO_2(g)$	213.8
$H_2O(l)$	70.0
$C_6H_{12}O_6(s)$	212.1
$O_2(g)$	205.2

Be sure to pull data for the correct formula and phase.
$\Delta S°_{rxn} = \sum n_p S°\text{(products)} - \sum n_r S°\text{(reactants)}$
$\quad = [1(S°(C_6H_{12}O_6(s))) + 6(S°(O_2(g)))] - [6(S°(CO_2(g))) + 6(S°(H_2O(l)))]$
$\quad = [1(212.1 \text{ J/K}) + 6(205.2 \text{ J/K})] - [6(213.8 \text{ J/K}) + 6(70.0 \text{ J/K})]$
$\quad = [1443.3 \text{ J/K}] - [1702.8 \text{ J/K}]$
$\quad = -259.5 \text{ J/K}$

then $T = 273.15 + 25 °C = 298 \text{ K}$ then $-259.5 \dfrac{\text{J}}{\text{K}} \times \dfrac{1 \text{ kJ}}{1000 \text{ J}} = -0.2595 \text{ kJ/K}$ then

$\Delta G = \Delta H_{rxn} - T\Delta S_{rxn} = +2802.5 \text{ kJ} - (298 \text{ K})\left(-0.2595\dfrac{\text{kJ}}{\text{K}}\right) = +2879.8 \text{ kJ} = +2.8798 \times 10^6 \text{ J}$;

so the reaction is nonspontaneous.

Check: The units (kJ, J/K, and kJ) are correct. The reaction requires the input of light energy, so we expect that this will be an endothermic reaction. We expect a negative entropy change because we are going from 6 moles of a gas and 6 moles of a liquid to 6 moles of a gas and 1 mole of a solid, respectively. The free energy is the sum of two positive terms; so we expect a large positive free energy, and the reaction is nonspontaneous. Photosynthesis does not happen on its own; light energy must be added to make the process move forward.

17.31   (a)   **Given:** $N_2O_4(g) \rightarrow 2 NO_2(g)$ at 25 °C
Find: $\Delta H°_{rxn}$, $\Delta S°_{rxn}$, $\Delta G°_{rxn}$, and spontaneity. Can temperature be changed to make it spontaneous?
Conceptual Plan: $\Delta H°_{rxn} = \sum n_p H°_f \text{ (products)} - \sum n_r H°_f \text{ (reactants) then}$

$\Delta S^\circ_{rxn} = \sum n_p S^\circ(\text{products}) - \sum n_r S^\circ(\text{reactants})$ then °C → K then J/K → kJ/K then

$K = 273.15 + °C \qquad \frac{1\ kJ}{1000\ J}$

$\Delta H^\circ_{rxn}, \Delta S^\circ_{rxn}, T \to \Delta G^\circ$

$\Delta G = \Delta H_{rxn} - T\Delta S_{rxn}$

Solution:

Reactant/Product	ΔH°_f (kJ/mol from Appendix IIB)
$N_2O_4(g)$	9.16
$NO_2(g)$	33.2

Be sure to pull data for the correct formula and phase.

$\Delta H^\circ_{rxn} = \sum n_p \Delta H^\circ_f(\text{products}) - \sum n_r \Delta H^\circ_f(\text{reactants})$
$= [2(\Delta H^\circ_f(NO_2(g)))] - [1(\Delta H^\circ_f(N_2O_4(g)))]$
$= [2(33.2\ kJ)] - [1(9.16\ kJ)]$
$= [66.4\ kJ] - [9.16\ kJ)]$
$= +57.2\ kJ$ then

Reactant/Product	S°(J/mol · K from Appendix IIB)
$N_2O_4(g)$	304.4
$NO_2(g)$	240.1

Be sure to pull data for the correct formula and phase.

$\Delta S^\circ_{rxn} = \sum n_p S^\circ(\text{products}) - \sum n_r S^\circ(\text{reactants})$
$= [2(S^\circ(NO_2(g)))] - [1(S^\circ(N_2O_4(g)))]$
$= [2(240.1\ J/K)] - [1(304.4\ J/K)]$
$= [480.2\ J/K] - [304.4\ J/K]$
$= +175.8\ J/K$ then $T = 273.15 + 25\ °C = 298\ K$ then

$+175.8\ \frac{J}{K} \times \frac{1\ kJ}{1000\ J} = +0.1758\ kJ$ then

$\Delta G^\circ = \Delta H^\circ_{rxn} - T\Delta S^\circ_{rxn} = +57.2\ kJ - (298\ K)\left(+0.1758\ \frac{kJ}{K}\right) = +4.8\ kJ = +4.8 \times 10^3\ J$; so the reaction is nonspontaneous. It can be made spontaneous by raising the temperature.

Check: The units (kJ, J/K, and kJ) are correct. The reaction requires the breaking of a bond, so we expect that this will be an endothermic reaction. We expect a positive entropy change because we are increasing the number of moles of gas. Because the positive enthalpy term dominates at room temperature, the reaction is nonspontaneous. The second term can dominate if we raise the temperature high enough.

(b) **Given:** $NH_4Cl(s) \to HCl(g) + NH_3(g)$ at 25 °C
Find: $\Delta H^\circ_{rxn}, \Delta S^\circ_{rxn}, \Delta G^\circ_{rxn}$, and spontaneity. Can temperature be changed to make it spontaneous?
Conceptual Plan: $\Delta H^\circ_{rxn} = \sum n_p H^\circ_f(\text{products}) - \sum n_r H^\circ_f(\text{reactants})$ then

$\Delta S^\circ_{rxn} = \sum n_p S^\circ(\text{products}) - \sum n_r S^\circ(\text{reactants})$ then °C → K then J/K → kJ/K then

$K = 273.15 + °C \qquad \frac{1\ kJ}{1000\ J}$

$\Delta H^\circ_{rxn}, \Delta S^\circ_{rxn}, T \to \Delta G^\circ$

$\Delta G = \Delta H_{rxn} - T\Delta S_{rxn}$

Solution:

Reactant/Product	ΔH°_f (kJ/mol from Appendix IIB)
$NH_4Cl(s)$	−314.4
$HCl(g)$	−92.3
$NH_3(g)$	−45.9

Be sure to pull data for the correct formula and phase.

$$\Delta H^{\circ}_{rxn} = \sum n_p \Delta H^{\circ}_f \text{(products)} - \sum n_r \Delta H^{\circ}_f \text{(reactants)}$$
$$= [1(\Delta H^{\circ}_f (\text{HCl}(g))) + 1(\Delta H^{\circ}_f (\text{NH}_3(g)))] - [1(\Delta H^{\circ}_f (\text{NH}_4\text{Cl}(g)))]$$
$$= [1(-92.3 \text{ kJ}) + 1(-45.9 \text{ kJ})] - [1(-314.4 \text{ kJ})]$$
$$= [-138.2 \text{ kJ}] - [-314.4 \text{ kJ}]$$
$$= +176.2 \text{ kJ then}$$

Reactant/Product	$S°$(J/mol · K from Appendix IIB)
NH$_4$Cl(s)	94.6
HCl(g)	186.9
NH$_3$(g)	192.8

Be sure to pull data for the correct formula and phase.

$$\Delta S^{\circ}_{rxn} = \sum n_p S^{\circ}\text{(products)} - \sum n_r S^{\circ}\text{(reactants)}$$
$$= [1(S^{\circ}(\text{HCl}(g))) + 1(S^{\circ}(\text{NH}_3(g)))] - [1(S^{\circ}(\text{NH}_4\text{Cl}(g)))]$$
$$= [1(186.9 \text{ J/K}) + 1(192.8 \text{ J/K})] - [1(94.6 \text{ J/K})]$$
$$= [379.7 \text{ J/K}] - [94.6 \text{ J/K}]$$
$$= +285.1 \text{ J/K}$$

then $T = 273.15 + 25\,°C = 298$ K then $+285.1 \dfrac{J}{K} \times \dfrac{1 \text{ kJ}}{1000 \text{ J}} = +0.2851$ kJ/K then

$$\Delta G° = \Delta H^{\circ}_{rxn} - T\Delta S^{\circ}_{rxn} = +176.2 \text{ kJ} - (298 \text{ K})\left(+0.2851 \dfrac{\text{kJ}}{\text{K}} \right) = +91.2 \text{ kJ} = +9.12 \times 10^4 \text{ J};$$

so the reaction is nonspontaneous. It can be made spontaneous by raising the temperature.

Check: The units (kJ, J/K, and kJ) are correct. The reaction requires the breaking of a bond, so we expect that this will be an endothermic reaction. We expect a positive entropy change because we are increasing the number of moles of gas. Because the positive enthalpy term dominates at room temperature, the reaction is non-spontaneous. The second term can dominate if we raise the temperature high enough.

(c) **Given:** $3\,\text{H}_2(g) + \text{Fe}_2\text{O}_3(s) \rightarrow 2\,\text{Fe}(s) + 3\,\text{H}_2\text{O}(g)$ at 25 °C **Find:** ΔH°_{rnx}, ΔS°_{rxn}, ΔG°_{rxn}, and spontaneity. Can temperature be changed to make it spontaneous?
Conceptual Plan: $\Delta H^{\circ}_{rxn} = \sum n_p H^{\circ}_f \text{(products)} - \sum n_r H^{\circ}_f \text{(reactants)}$ then

$\Delta S^{\circ}_{rxn} = \sum n_p S^{\circ}\text{(products)} - \sum n_r S^{\circ}\text{(reactants)}$ then °C $\rightarrow$ K then J/K $\rightarrow$ kJ/K then

$$K = 273.15 + °C \qquad \dfrac{1 \text{ kJ}}{1000 \text{ J}}$$

$\Delta H^{\circ}_{rxn}, \Delta S^{\circ}_{rxn}, T \rightarrow \Delta G°$

$$\Delta G = \Delta H_{rxn} - T\Delta S_{rxn}$$

Solution:

Reactant/Product	ΔH°_f (kJ/mol from Appendix IIB)
H$_2$(g)	0.0
Fe$_2$O$_3$(s)	−824.2
Fe(s)	0.0
H$_2$O(g)	−241.8

Be sure to pull data for the correct formula and phase.

$$\Delta H^{\circ}_{rxn} = \sum n_p \Delta H^{\circ}_f \text{(products)} - \sum n_r \Delta H^{\circ}_f \text{(reactants)}$$
$$= [2(\Delta H^{\circ}_f (\text{Fe}(s))) + 3(\Delta H^{\circ}_f (\text{H}_2\text{O}(g)))] - [3(\Delta H^{\circ}_f (\text{H}_2(g))) + 1(\Delta H^{\circ}_f (\text{Fe}_2\text{O}_3(s)))]$$
$$= [2(0.0 \text{ kJ}) + 3(-241.8 \text{ kJ})] - [3(0.0 \text{ kJ}) + 1(-824.2 \text{ kJ})]$$
$$= [-725.4 \text{ kJ}] - [-824.2 \text{ kJ}]$$
$$= +98.8 \text{ kJ then}$$

Reactant/Product	$S°$(J/mol · K from Appendix IIB)
H$_2$(g)	130.7
Fe$_2$O$_3$(s)	87.4
Fe(s)	27.3
H$_2$O(g)	188.8

Be sure to pull data for the correct formula and phase.

$$\Delta S^\circ_{rxn} = \sum n_p S^\circ(\text{products}) - \sum n_r S^\circ(\text{reactants})$$

$$= [2(S^\circ(\text{Fe}(s))) + 3(S^\circ(\text{H}_2\text{O}(g)))] - [3(S^\circ(\text{H}_2(g))) + 1(S^\circ(\text{Fe}_2\text{O}_3(s)))]$$

$$= [2(27.3 \text{ J/K}) + 3(188.8 \text{ J/K})] - [3(130.7 \text{ J/K}) + 1(87.4 \text{ J/K})]$$

$$= [621.0 \text{ J/K}] - [479.5 \text{ J/K}]$$

$$= +141.5 \text{ J/K}$$

then $T = 273.15 + 25\,^\circ\text{C} = 298$ K then $+141.5\,\dfrac{J}{K} \times \dfrac{1 \text{ kJ}}{1000 \text{ J}} = +0.1415$ kJ/K then

$$\Delta G^\circ = \Delta H^\circ_{rxn} - T\Delta S^\circ_{rxn} = +98.8 \text{ kJ} - (298 \text{ K})\left(+0.1415\,\frac{kJ}{K}\right) = +56.6 \text{ kJ} = +5.66 \times 10^4 \text{ J};$$

so the reaction is nonspontaneous. It can be made spontaneous by raising the temperature.

Check: The units (kJ, J/K, and kJ) are correct. The reaction requires the breaking of a bond, so we expect that this will be an endothermic reaction. We expect a positive entropy change because there is no change in the number of moles of gas, but the product gas is more complex. Because the positive enthalpy term dominates at room temperature, the reaction is nonspontaneous. The second term can dominate if we raise the temperature high enough. This process is the opposite of rusting, so we are not surprised that it is nonspontaneous.

(d)   **Given:** $N_2(g) + 3 H_2(g) \rightarrow 2 NH_3(g)$ at 25 °C

Find: $\Delta H^\circ_{rxn}, \Delta S^\circ_{rxn}, \Delta G^\circ_{rxn}$, and spontaneity. Can temperature be changed to make it spontaneous?

Conceptual Plan: $\Delta H^\circ_{rxn} = \sum n_p H^\circ_f(\text{products}) - \sum n_r H^\circ_f(\text{reactants})$ then

$\Delta S^\circ_{rxn} = \sum n_p S^\circ(\text{products}) - \sum n_r S^\circ(\text{reactants})$ then °C → K then J/K → kJ/K then

$$K = 273.15 + {}^\circ\text{C} \qquad \frac{1 \text{ kJ}}{1000 \text{ J}}$$

$\Delta H^\circ_{rxn}, \Delta S^\circ_{rxn}, T \rightarrow \Delta G^\circ$

$$\Delta G = \Delta H_{rxn} - T\Delta S_{rxn}$$

Solution:

Reactant/Product	ΔH°_f (kJ · mol from Appendix IIB)
$N_2(g)$	0.0
$H_2(g)$	0.0
$NH_3(g)$	−45.9

Be sure to pull data for the correct formula and phase.

$$\Delta H^\circ_{rxn} = \sum n_p \Delta H^\circ_f(\text{products}) - \sum n_r \Delta H^\circ_f(\text{reactants})$$

$$= [2(\Delta H^\circ_f(\text{NH}_3(g)))] - [1(\Delta H^\circ_f(\text{N}_2(g))) + 3(\Delta H^\circ_f(\text{H}_2(g)))]$$

$$= [2(-45.9 \text{ kJ})] - [1(0.0 \text{ kJ}) + 3(0.0 \text{ kJ})]$$

$$= [-91.8 \text{ kJ}] - [0.0 \text{ kJ}]$$

$$= -91.8 \text{ kJ then}$$

Reactant/Product	S° (J/mol · K from Appendix IIB)
$N_2(g)$	191.6
$H_2(g)$	130.7
$NH_3(g)$	192.8

Be sure to pull data for the correct formula and phase.

$$\Delta S^\circ_{rxn} = \sum n_p S^\circ(\text{products}) - \sum n_r S^\circ(\text{reactants})$$

$$= [2(S^\circ(\text{NH}_3(g)))] - [1(S^\circ(\text{N}_2(g))) + 3(S^\circ(\text{H}_2(g)))]$$

$$= [2(192.8 \text{ J/K})] - [1(191.6 \text{ J/K}) + 3(130.7 \text{ J/K})]$$

$$= [385.6 \text{ J/K}] - [583.7 \text{ J/K}]$$

$$= -198.1 \text{ J/K}$$

then $T = 273.15 + 25\,^\circ\text{C} = 298$ K then $-198.1\,\dfrac{J}{K} \times \dfrac{1 \text{ kJ}}{1000 \text{ J}} = -0.1981$ kJ/K then

$$\Delta G^\circ = \Delta H^\circ_{rxn} - T\Delta S^\circ_{rxn} = -91.8 \text{ kJ} - (298 \text{ K})\left(-0.1981\,\frac{kJ}{K}\right) = -32.8 \text{ kJ} = -3.28 \times 10^4 \text{ J};$$

so the reaction is spontaneous.

Check: The units (kJ, J/K, and kJ) are correct. The reaction forms more bonds than it breaks, so we expect that this will be an exothermic reaction. We expect a negative entropy change because we are decreasing the number of moles of gas. Because the negative enthalpy term dominates at room temperature, the reaction is spontaneous. The second term can dominate if we raise the temperature high enough.

17.32   (a)   **Given:** $2\,CH_4(g) \rightarrow C_2H_6(g) + H_2(g)$ at 25 °C   **Find:** ΔH°_{rxn}, ΔS°_{rxn}, ΔG°_{rxn}, and spontaneity. Can temperature be changed to make it spontaneous?

Conceptual Plan: $\Delta H^\circ_{rxn} = \sum n_p H^\circ_f(\text{products}) - \sum n_r H^\circ_f(\text{reactants})$ then

$\Delta S^\circ_{rxn} = \sum n_p S^\circ(\text{products}) - \sum n_r S^\circ(\text{reactants})$ then °C → K then J/K → kJ/K then

$$K = 273.15 + °C \qquad \frac{1\,kJ}{1000\,J}$$

$\Delta H^\circ_{rxn}, \Delta S^\circ_{rxn}, T \rightarrow \Delta G^\circ$

$$\Delta G = \Delta H_{rxn} - T\Delta S_{rxn}$$

Solution:

Reactant/Product	ΔH°_f (kJ · mol from Appendix IIB)
$CH_4(g)$	−74.6
$C_2H_6(g)$	−84.6
$H_2(g)$	0.0

Be sure to pull data for the correct formula and phase.

$\Delta H^\circ_{rxn} = \sum n_p \Delta H^\circ_f(\text{products}) - \sum n_r \Delta H^\circ_f(\text{reactants})$

$= [1(\Delta H^\circ_f(C_2H_6(g))) + 1(\Delta H^\circ_f(H_2(g)))] - [2(\Delta H^\circ_f(CH_4(g)))]$

$= [1(-84.6\,kJ) + 1(0.0\,kJ)] - [2(-74.6\,kJ)]$

$= [-84.6\,kJ] - [-149.2\,kJ]$

$= +64.6\,kJ$ then

Reactant/Product	S° (J/mol · K from Appendix IIB)
$CH_4(g)$	186.3
$C_2H_6(g)$	229.2
$H_2(g)$	130.7

Be sure to pull data for the correct formula and phase.

$\Delta S^\circ_{rxn} = \sum n_p S^\circ(\text{products}) - \sum n_r S^\circ(\text{reactants})$

$= [1(S^\circ(C_2H_6(g))) + 1(S^\circ(H_2(g)))] - [2(S^\circ(CH_4(g)))]$

$= [1(229.2\,J/K) + 1(130.7\,J/K)] - [2(186.3\,J/K)]$

$= [359.9\,J/K] - [372.6\,J/K]$

$= -12.7\,J/K$

then $T = 273.15 + 25\,°C = 298\,K$ then $-12.7\,\dfrac{J}{K} \times \dfrac{1\,kJ}{1000\,J} = -0.0127\,kJ/K$ then

$$\Delta G^\circ = \Delta H^\circ_{rxn} - T\Delta S^\circ_{rxn} = +64.6\,kJ - (298\,K)\left(-0.0127\,\frac{kJ}{K}\right) = +68.4\,kJ = +6.84 \times 10^4\,J;$$

so the reaction is nonspontaneous. Because enthalpy is positive and entropy is negative, this reaction cannot be spontaneous at any temperature.

Check: The units (kJ, J/K, and kJ) are correct. The 2 moles of methane have a lower enthalpy than does 1 mole of ethane, so we expect that this will be an endothermic reaction. We expect a very small entropy change because the number of moles of gas is unchanged. Because enthalpy is positive and entropy is negative, the reaction is nonspontaneous and cannot be spontaneous at any temperature.

   (b)   **Given:** $2\,NH_3(g) \rightarrow N_2H_4(g) + H_2(g)$ at 25 °C

Find: ΔH°_{rxn}, ΔS°_{rxn}, ΔG°_{rxn}, and spontaneity. Can temperature be changed to make it spontaneous?

Conceptual Plan: $\Delta H^\circ_{rxn} = \sum n_p H^\circ_f(\text{products}) - \sum n_r H^\circ_f(\text{reactants})$ then

$\Delta S^\circ_{rxn} = \sum n_p S^\circ(\text{products}) - \sum n_r S^\circ(\text{reactants})$ then °C → K then J/K → kJ/K then

$$K = 273.15 + °C \qquad \frac{1\,kJ}{1000\,J}$$

$\Delta H^\circ_{rxn}, \Delta S^\circ_{rxn}, T \rightarrow \Delta G^\circ$

$$\Delta G = \Delta H_{rxn} - T\Delta S_{rxn}$$

Solution:

Reactant/Product	ΔH°_f (kJ/mol from Appendix IIB)
$NH_3(g)$	-45.9
$N_2H_4(g)$	95.4
$H_2(g)$	0.0

Be sure to pull data for the correct formula and phase.

$$\begin{aligned}
\Delta H^\circ_{rxn} &= \sum n_p \Delta H^\circ_f \text{ (products)} - \sum n_r \Delta H^\circ_f \text{ (reactants)}\\
&= [1(\Delta H^\circ_f (N_2H_4(g))) + 1(\Delta H^\circ_f (H_2(g)))] - [2(\Delta H^\circ_f (NH_3(g)))]\\
&= [1(95.4 \text{ kJ}) + 1(0.0 \text{ kJ})] - [2(-45.9 \text{ kJ})]\\
&= [95.4 \text{ kJ}] - [-91.8 \text{ kJ}]\\
&= +187.2 \text{ kJ then}
\end{aligned}$$

Reactant/Product	S°(J/mol · K from Appendix IIB)
$NH_3(g)$	192.8
$N_2H_4(g)$	238.5
$H_2(g)$	130.7

Be sure to pull data for the correct formula and phase.

$$\begin{aligned}
\Delta S^\circ_{rxn} &= \sum n_p S^\circ \text{(products)} + \sum n_r S^\circ \text{(reactants)}\\
&= [1(S^\circ(N_2H_4(g))) + 1(S^\circ(H_2(g)))] - [2(S^\circ(NH_3(g)))]\\
&= [1(238.5 \text{ J/K}) + 1(130.7 \text{ J/K}) - [2(192.8 \text{ J/K})]\\
&= [369.2 \text{ J/K}] - [385.6 \text{ J/K}]\\
&= -16.4 \text{ J/K then}
\end{aligned}$$

$T = 273.15 + 25 \,^\circ\text{C} = 298 \text{ K then } -16.4 \dfrac{J}{K} \times \dfrac{1 \text{ kJ}}{1000 \text{ J}} = -0.0164 \text{ kJ/K then}$

$\Delta G^\circ = \Delta H^\circ_{rxn} - T\Delta S^\circ_{rxn} = +187.2 \text{ kJ} - (298 \text{ K})\left(-0.0164 \dfrac{kJ}{K}\right) = +192.1 \text{ kJ} = +1.921 \times 10^5 \text{ J; so the}$

reaction is nonspontaneous. Because enthalpy is positive and entropy is negative, the reaction is not spontaneous at any temperature.

Check: The units (kJ, J/K, and kJ) are correct. N_2H_4 has such a high enthalpy of formation compared to ammonia that we expect this to be an endothermic reaction. We expect a very small entropy change because the number of moles of gas is unchanged. Because enthalpy is positive and entropy is negative, the reaction is nonspontaneous and cannot be spontaneous at any temperature.

(c)   **Given:** $N_2(g) + O_2(g) \rightarrow 2 NO(g)$ at 25 °C

Find: $\Delta H^\circ_{rxn}, \Delta S^\circ_{rxn}, \Delta G^\circ_{rxn}$, and spontaneity. Can temperature be changed to make it spontaneous?

Conceptual Plan: $\Delta H^\circ_{rxn} = \sum n_p H^\circ_f \text{ (products)} - \sum n_r H^\circ_f \text{ (reactants) then}$

$\Delta S^\circ_{rxn} = \sum n_p S^\circ \text{(products)} - \sum n_r S^\circ \text{(reactants) then } °C \rightarrow K \text{ then J/K} \rightarrow \text{kJ/K then}$

$$K = 273.15 + °C \qquad \dfrac{1 \text{ kJ}}{1000 \text{ J}}$$

$\Delta H^\circ_{rxn}, \Delta S^\circ_{rxn}, T \rightarrow \Delta G^\circ$

$$\Delta G = \Delta H_{rxn} - T\Delta S_{rxn}$$

Solution:

Reactant/Product	ΔH°_f (kJ/mol from Appendix IIB)
$N_2(g)$	0.0
$O_2(g)$	0.0
$NO(g)$	91.3

Be sure to pull data for the correct formula and phase.

$$\Delta H^{\circ}_{\text{rxn}} = \sum n_p \Delta H^{\circ}_f \text{ (products)} - \sum n_r \Delta H^{\circ}_f \text{ (reactants)}$$

$$= [2(\Delta H^{\circ}_f (\text{NO}(g)))] - [1(\Delta H^{\circ}_f (\text{N}_2(g))) + 1(\Delta H^{\circ}_f (\text{O}_2(g)))]$$

$$= [2(91.3 \text{ kJ})] - [1(0.0 \text{ kJ}) + 1(0.0 \text{ kJ})]$$

$$= [182.6 \text{ kJ}] - [0.0 \text{ kJ}]$$

$$= +182.6 \text{ kJ then}$$

Reactant/Product	S°(J/mol · K from Appendix IIB)
N$_2$(g)	191.6
O$_2$(g)	205.2
NO(g)	210.8

Be sure to pull data for the correct formula and phase.

$$\Delta S^{\circ}_{\text{rxn}} = \sum n_p S^{\circ} \text{(products)} - \sum n_r S^{\circ} \text{(reactants)}$$

$$= [2(S^{\circ}(\text{NO}(g)))] - [1(S^{\circ}(\text{N}_2(g))) + 1(S^{\circ}(\text{O}_2(g)))]$$

$$= [2(210.8 \text{ J/K})] - [1(191.6 \text{ J/K}) + 1(205.2 \text{ J/K})]$$

$$= [421.6 \text{ J/K}] - [396.8 \text{ J/K}]$$

$$= +24.8 \text{ J/K}$$

then $T = 273.15 + 25 \,°\text{C} = 298 \text{ K}$ then $+24.8 \dfrac{J}{K} \times \dfrac{1 \text{ kJ}}{1000 \, J} = +0.0248 \text{ kJ/K}$ then

$$\Delta G^{\circ} = \Delta H^{\circ}_{\text{rxn}} - T\Delta S^{\circ}_{\text{rxn}} = +182.6 \text{ kJ} - (298 \text{ K})\left(0.0248 \dfrac{kJ}{K}\right) = +175.2 \text{ kJ} = +1.752 \times 10^5 \text{ J; so the}$$

reaction is nonspontaneous. It can be spontaneous at high temperatures.

Check: The units (kJ, J/K, and kJ) are correct. The enthalpy is twice the enthalpy of formation of NO. We expect a very small entropy change because the number of moles of gas is unchanged. Because the positive enthalpy term dominates at room temperature, the reaction is nonspontaneous. The second term can dominate if we raise the temperature high enough.

(d) **Given:** 2 KClO$_3$(s) $\rightarrow$ 2 KCl(s) + 3 O$_2$(g) at 25 °C
Find: $\Delta H^{\circ}_{\text{rxn}}$, $\Delta S^{\circ}_{\text{rxn}}$, $\Delta G^{\circ}_{\text{rxn}}$, and spontaneity. Can temperature be changed to make it spontaneous?
Conceptual Plan: $\Delta H^{\circ}_{\text{rxn}} = \sum n_p H^{\circ}_f \text{ (products)} - \sum n_r H^{\circ}_f \text{ (reactants)}$ then

$\Delta S^{\circ}_{\text{rxn}} = \sum n_p S^{\circ} \text{ (products)} - \sum n_r S^{\circ} \text{ (reactants)}$ then °C $\rightarrow$ K then J/K $\rightarrow$ kJ/K then

$$K = 273.15 + °C \qquad \dfrac{1 \text{ kJ}}{1000 \text{ J}}$$

$\Delta H^{\circ}_{\text{rxn}}, \Delta S^{\circ}_{\text{rxn}}, T \rightarrow \Delta G^{\circ}$

$$\Delta G = \Delta H_{\text{rxn}} - T\Delta S_{\text{rxn}}$$

Solution:

Reactant/Product	ΔH°_f (kJ/mol from Appendix IIB)
KClO$_3$(s)	−397.7
KCl(s)	−436.5
O$_2$(g)	0.0

Be sure to pull data for the correct formula and phase.

$$\Delta H^{\circ}_{\text{rxn}} = \sum n_p \Delta H^{\circ}_f \text{ (products)} - \sum n_r \Delta H^{\circ}_f \text{ (reactants)}$$

$$= [2(\Delta H^{\circ}_f (\text{KCl}(s))) + 3(\Delta H^{\circ}_f (\text{O}_2(g)))] - [2(\Delta H^{\circ}_f (\text{KClO}_3(s)))]$$

$$= [2(-436.5 \text{ kJ}) + 3(0.0 \text{ kJ})] - [2(-397.7 \text{ kJ})]$$

$$= [-873.0 \text{ kJ}] - [-795.4 \text{ kJ}]$$

$$= -77.6 \text{ kJ then}$$

Reactant/Product	S°(J/mol · K from Appendix IIB)
KClO$_3$(s)	143.1
KCl(s)	82.6
O$_2$(g)	205.2

Be sure to pull data for the correct formula and phase.

$$\Delta S^{\circ}_{rxn} = \sum n_p S^{\circ}(products) - \sum n_r S^{\circ}(reactants)$$
$$= [2(S^{\circ}(KCl(s))) + 3(S^{\circ}(O_2(g)))] - [2(S^{\circ}(KClO_3(s)))]$$
$$= [2(82.6 \text{ J/K}) + 3(205.2 \text{ J/K})] - [2(143.1 \text{ J/K})]$$
$$= [780.8 \text{ J/K}] - [286.2 \text{ J/K}]$$
$$= +494.6 \text{ J/K then}$$

$$T = 273.15 + 25\,^{\circ}\text{C} = 298 \text{ K then} +494.6 \frac{J}{K} \times \frac{1 \text{ kJ}}{1000 \text{ J}} = +0.4946 \text{ kJ/K then}$$

$$\Delta G^{\circ} = \Delta H^{\circ}_{rxn} - T\Delta S^{\circ}_{rxn} = -77.6 \text{ kJ} - (298 \text{ K})\left(0.4946 \frac{kJ}{K}\right) = -225.0 \text{ kJ} = -2.250 \times 10^6 \text{ J; so the}$$

reaction is spontaneous. Because enthalpy is negative and entropy is positive, the reaction is spontaneous at all temperatures.

Check: The units (kJ, J/K, and kJ) are correct. The reaction is exothermic because the enthalpy of formation of KCl is less than that for KClO₃. We expect a positive entropy change because the number of moles of gas is increasing. Because enthalpy is negative and entropy is positive, the reaction is spontaneous at all temperatures.

17.33   (a)   **Given:** $N_2O_4(g) \rightarrow 2 NO_2(g)$ at 25 °C   **Find:** ΔG°_{rxn} and spontaneity and compare to Problem 17.31 Determine which method would show how free energy changes with temperature.
Conceptual Plan: $\Delta G^{\circ}_{rxn} = \sum n_p \Delta G^{\circ}_f (products) - \sum n_r \Delta G^{\circ}_f (reactants)$ **then compare to Problem 17.31**
Solution:

Reactant/Product	ΔG°_f (kJ/mol from Appendix IIB)
$N_2O_4(g)$	99.8
$NO_2(g)$	51.3

Be sure to pull data for the correct formula and phase.
$$\Delta G^{\circ}_{rxn} = \sum n_p \Delta G^{\circ}_f (products) - \sum n_r \Delta G^{\circ}_f (reactants)$$
$$= [2(\Delta G^{\circ}_f (NO_2(g)))] - [1(\Delta G^{\circ}_f (N_2O_4(g)))]$$
$$= [2(51.3 \text{ kJ})] - [1(99.8 \text{ kJ})]$$
$$= [102.6 \text{ kJ}] - [99.8 \text{ kJ}]$$
$$= +2.8 \text{ kJ}$$

So the reaction is nonspontaneous. The value is similar to Problem 17.31.

Check: The units (kJ) are correct. The free energy of the products is greater than that of the reactants; so the answer is positive, and the reaction is nonspontaneous. The answer is the same as in Problem 17.31 within the error of the calculation.

   (b)   **Given:** $NH_4Cl(s) \rightarrow HCl(g) + NH_3(g)$ at 25 °C
Find: ΔG°_{rxn} and spontaneity and compare to Problem 17.31
Conceptual Plan: $\Delta G^{\circ}_{rxn} = \sum n_p \Delta G^{\circ}_f (products) - \sum n_r \Delta G^{\circ}_f (reactants)$ **then compare to Problem 17.31**
Solution:

Reactant/Product	ΔG°_f (kJ/mol from Appendix IIB)
$NH_4Cl(s)$	−202.9
$HCl(g)$	−95.3
$NH_3(g)$	−16.4

Be sure to pull data for the correct formula and phase.
$$\Delta G^{\circ}_{rxn} = \sum n_p \Delta G^{\circ}_f (products) - \sum n_r \Delta G^{\circ}_f (reactants)$$
$$= [1(\Delta G^{\circ}_f (HCl(g))) + 1(\Delta G^{\circ}_f (NH_3(g)))] - [1(\Delta G^{\circ}_f (NH_4Cl(g)))]$$
$$= [1(-95.3 \text{ kJ}) + 1(-16.4 \text{ kJ})] - [1(-202.9 \text{ kJ})]$$
$$= [-111.7 \text{ kJ}] - [-202.9 \text{ kJ}]$$
$$= +91.2 \text{ kJ}$$

So the reaction is nonspontaneous. The result is the same as in Problem 17.31.

Check: The units (kJ) are correct. The answer matches the one in Problem 17.31.

   (c)   **Given:** $3 H_2(g) + Fe_2O_3(s) \rightarrow 2 Fe(s) + 3 H_2O(g)$ at 25 °C
Find: ΔG°_{rxn} and spontaneity and compare to Problem 17.31

Conceptual Plan: $\Delta G_{rxn}^{\circ} = \sum n_p \Delta G_f^{\circ} \text{(products)} - \sum n_r \Delta G_f^{\circ} \text{(reactants)}$ then compare to Problem 17.31
Solution:

Reactant/Product	ΔG_f° (kJ/mol from Appendix IIB)
$H_2(g)$	0.0
$Fe_2O_3(s)$	−742.2
$Fe(s)$	0.0
$H_2O(g)$	−228.6

Be sure to pull data for the correct formula and phase.

$$\Delta G_{rxn}^{\circ} = \sum n_p \Delta G_f^{\circ} \text{(products)} - \sum n_r \Delta G_f^{\circ} \text{(reactants)}$$
$$= [2(\Delta G_f^{\circ}(Fe(s))) + 3(\Delta G_f^{\circ}(H_2O(g)))] - [3(\Delta G_f^{\circ}(H_2(g))) + 1(\Delta G_f^{\circ}(Fe_2O_3(s)))]$$
$$= [2(0.0 \text{ kJ}) + 3(-228.6 \text{ kJ})] - [3(0.0 \text{ kJ}) + 1(-742.2 \text{ kJ})]$$
$$= [-685.8 \text{ kJ}] - [-742.2 \text{ kJ}]$$
$$= +56.4 \text{ kJ}$$

So the reaction is nonspontaneous. The value is similar to that in Problem 17.31.

Check: The units (kJ) are correct. The answer is the same as in Problem 17.31 within the error of the calculation.

(d) **Given:** $N_2(g) + 3 H_2(g) \rightarrow 2 NH_3(g)$ at 25 °C
Find: ΔG_{rxn}° and spontaneity and compare to Problem 17.31
Conceptual Plan: $\Delta G_{rxn}^{\circ} = \sum n_p \Delta G_f^{\circ} \text{(products)} - \sum n_r \Delta G_f^{\circ} \text{(reactants)}$ then compare to Problem 17.31
Solution:

Reactant/Product	ΔG_f° (kJ/mol from Appendix IIB)
$N_2(g)$	0.0
$H_2(g)$	0.0
$NH_3(g)$	−16.4

Be sure to pull data for the correct formula and phase.

$$\Delta G_{rxn}^{\circ} = \sum n_p \Delta G_f^{\circ} \text{(products)} - \sum n_r \Delta G_f^{\circ} \text{(reactants)}$$
$$= [2(\Delta G_f^{\circ}(NH_3(g)))] - [1(\Delta G_f^{\circ}(N_2(g))) + 3(\Delta G_f^{\circ}(H_2(g)))]$$
$$= [2(-16.4 \text{ kJ})] - [1(0.0 \text{ kJ}) + 3(0.0 \text{ kJ})]$$
$$= [-32.8 \text{ kJ}] - [0.0 \text{ kJ}]$$
$$= -32.8 \text{ kJ}$$

So the reaction is spontaneous. The result is the same as in Problem 17.31.

Check: The units (kJ) are correct. The answer matches the one in Problem 17.31.
Values calculated by the two methods are comparable. The method using ΔH° and ΔS° is longer, but it can be used to determine how ΔG° changes with temperature.

17.34 (a) **Given:** $2 CH_4(g) \rightarrow C_2H_6(g) + H_2(g)$ at 25 °C   **Find:** ΔG_{rxn}° and spontaneity and compare to Problem 17.32
Determine which method would show how free energy changes with temperature.
Conceptual Plan: $\Delta G_{rxn}^{\circ} = \sum n_p \Delta G_f^{\circ} \text{(products)} - \sum n_r \Delta G_f^{\circ} \text{(reactants)}$ then compare to Problem 17.32
Solution:

Reactant/Product	ΔG_f° (kJ/mol from Appendix IIB)
$CH_4(g)$	−50.5
$C_2H_6(g)$	−32.0
$H_2(g)$	0.0

Be sure to pull data for the correct formula and phase.

$$\Delta G_{rxn}^{\circ} = \sum n_p \Delta G_f^{\circ} \text{(products)} - \sum n_r \Delta G_f^{\circ} \text{(reactants)}$$
$$= [1(\Delta G_f^{\circ}(C_2H_6(g))) + 1(\Delta G_f^{\circ}(H_2(g)))] - [2(\Delta G_f^{\circ}(CH_4(g)))]$$
$$= [1(-32.0 \text{ kJ}) + 1(0.0 \text{ kJ})] - [2(-50.5 \text{ kJ})]$$
$$= [-32.0 \text{ kJ}] - [-101.0 \text{ kJ}]$$
$$= +69.0 \text{ kJ}$$

So the reaction is spontaneous. The value is similar to that in Problem 17.32.

Check: The units (kJ) are correct. The answer is the same as in Problem 17.32 within the error of the calculation.

(b) **Given:** $2 NH_3(g) \rightarrow N_2H_4(g) + H_2(g)$ at 25 °C

Find: ΔG°_{rxn}, spontaneity and compare to Problem 17.32

Conceptual Plan: $\Delta G^{\circ}_{rxn} = \sum n_p \Delta G^{\circ}_f (\text{products}) - \sum n_r \Delta G^{\circ}_f (\text{reactants})$ **then compare to Problem 17.32**

Solution:

Reactant/Product	ΔG°_f (kJ/mol from Appendix IIB)
$NH_3(g)$	−16.4
$N_2H_4(g)$	159.4
$H_2(g)$	0.0

Be sure to pull data for the correct formula and phase.

$$\Delta G^{\circ}_{rxn} = \sum n_p \Delta G^{\circ}_f (\text{products}) - \sum n_r \Delta G^{\circ}_f (\text{reactants})$$
$$= [1(\Delta G^{\circ}_f (N_2H_4(g))) + 1(\Delta G^{\circ}_f (H_2(g)))] - [2(\Delta G^{\circ}_f (NH_3(g)))]$$
$$= [1(159.4 \text{ kJ}) + 1(0.0 \text{ kJ})] - [2(-16.4 \text{ kJ})]$$
$$= [159.4 \text{ kJ}] - [-32.8 \text{ kJ}]$$
$$= +192.2 \text{ kJ}$$

So the reaction is nonspontaneous. The value is similar to that in Problem 17.32.

Check: The units (kJ) are correct. The answer is the same as in Problem 17.32 within the error of the calculation.

(c) **Given:** $N_2(g) + O_2(g) \rightarrow 2 NO(g)$ at 25 °C

Find: ΔG°_{rxn} and spontaneity and compare to Problem 17.32

Conceptual Plan: $\Delta G^{\circ}_{rxn} = \sum n_p \Delta G^{\circ}_f (\text{products}) - \sum n_r \Delta G^{\circ}_f (\text{reactants})$ **then compare to Problem 17.32**

Solution:

Reactant/Product	ΔG°_f (kJ/mol from Appendix IIB)
$N_2(g)$	0.0
$O_2(g)$	0.0
$NO(g)$	87.6

Be sure to pull data for the correct formula and phase.

$$\Delta G^{\circ}_{rxn} = \sum n_p \Delta G^{\circ}_f (\text{products}) - \sum n_r \Delta G^{\circ}_f (\text{reactants})$$
$$= [2(\Delta G^{\circ}_f (NO(g)))] - [1(\Delta G^{\circ}_f (N_2(g))) + 1(\Delta G^{\circ}_f (O_2(g)))]$$
$$= [2(87.6 \text{ kJ})] - [1(0.0 \text{ kJ}) + 1(0.0 \text{ kJ})]$$
$$= [175.2 \text{ kJ}] - [0.0 \text{ kJ}]$$
$$= +175.2 \text{ kJ}$$

So the reaction is nonspontaneous. The result is the same as in Problem 17.32.

Check: The units (kJ) are correct. The answer matches the one in Problem 17.32.

(d) **Given:** $2 KClO_3(s) \rightarrow 2 KCl(s) + 3 O_2(g)$ at 25 °C

Find: ΔG°_{rxn} and spontaneity and compare to Problem 17.32

Conceptual Plan: $\Delta G^{\circ}_{rxn} = \sum n_p \Delta G^{\circ}_f (\text{products}) - \sum n_r \Delta G^{\circ}_f (\text{reactants})$ **then compare to Problem 17.32**

Solution:

Reactant/Product	ΔG°_f (kJ/mol from Appendix IIB)
$KClO_3(s)$	−296.3
$KCl(s)$	−408.5
$O_2(g)$	0.0

Be sure to pull data for the correct formula and phase.

$$\Delta G^{\circ}_{rxn} = \sum n_p \Delta G^{\circ}_f (\text{products}) - \sum n_r \Delta G^{\circ}_f (\text{reactants})$$
$$= [2(\Delta G^{\circ}_f (KCl(s))) + 1(\Delta G^{\circ}_f (O_2(g)))] - [2(\Delta G^{\circ}_f (KClO_3(s)))]$$
$$= [2(-408.5 \text{ kJ}) + 3(0.0 \text{ kJ})] - [2(-296.3 \text{ kJ})]$$
$$= [-817.0 \text{ kJ}] - [-592.6 \text{ kJ}]$$
$$= -224.4 \text{ kJ}$$

So the reaction is spontaneous. The value is similar to that in Problem 17.32.

Check: The units (kJ) are correct. The answer is the same as in Problem 17.32 within the error of the calculation.

Values calculated by the two methods are comparable. The method using $\Delta H°$ and $\Delta S°$ is longer, but it can be used to determine how $\Delta G°$ changes with temperature.

17.35   **Given:** $2 \, NO(g) + O_2(g) \rightarrow 2 \, NO_2(g)$ **Find:** $\Delta G°_{rxn}$ and spontaneity at (a) 298 K, (b) 715 K, and (c) 855 K
Conceptual Plan: $\Delta H°_{rxn} = \sum n_p H°_f \text{(products)} - \sum n_r H°_f \text{(reactants)}$ then
$\Delta S°_{rxn} = \sum n_p S° \text{(products)} - \sum n_r S° \text{(reactants)}$ then J/K → kJ/K then $\Delta H°_{rxn}, \Delta S°_{rxn}, T \rightarrow \Delta G°$

$$\frac{1 \text{ kJ}}{1000 \text{ J}} \qquad \Delta G = \Delta H_{rxn} - T\Delta S_{rxn}$$

Solution:

Reactant/Product	$\Delta G°_f$ (kJ/mol from Appendix IIB)
$NO(g)$	91.3
$O_2(g)$	0.0
$NO_2(g)$	33.2

Be sure to pull data for the correct formula and phase.

$\Delta H°_{rxn} = \sum n_p \Delta H°_f \text{(products)} - \sum n_r \Delta H°_f \text{(reactants)}$

$= [2(\Delta H°_f (NO_2(g)))] - [2(\Delta H°_f (NO \, (g))) + 1(\Delta H°_f (O_2(g)))]$

$= [2(33.2 \text{ kJ})] - [2(91.3 \text{ kJ}) + 1(0.0 \text{ kJ})]$

$= [66.4 \text{ kJ}] - [182.6 \text{ kJ}]$

$= -116.2 \text{ kJ}$ then

Reactant/Product	$S°$(J/mol · K from Appendix IIB)
$NO(g)$	210.8
$O_2(g)$	205.2
$NO_2(g)$	240.1

Be sure to pull data for the correct formula and phase.

$\Delta S°_{rxn} = \sum n_p S° \text{(products)} - \sum n_r S° \text{(reactants)}$

$= [2(S°(NO_2(g)))] - [2(S°(NO \, (g))) + 1(S°(O_2(g)))]$

$= [2(240.1 \text{ J/K})] - [2(210.8 \text{ J/K}) + 1(205.2 \text{ J/K})]$

$= [480.2 \text{ J/K}] - [626.8 \text{ J/K}]$

$= -146.6 \text{ J/K}$ then $-146.6 \dfrac{J}{K} \times \dfrac{1 \text{ kJ}}{1000 \, J} = -0.1466$ kJ/K

(a) $\Delta G° = \Delta H°_{rxn} - T\Delta S°_{rxn} = -116.2 \text{ kJ} - (298 \, K)\left(-0.1466 \dfrac{kJ}{K}\right) = -72.5 \text{ kJ} = -7.25 \times 10^4$ J; so the reaction is spontaneous.

(b) $\Delta G° = \Delta H°_{rxn} - T\Delta S°_{rxn} = -116.2 \text{ kJ} - (715 \, K)\left(-0.1466 \dfrac{kJ}{K}\right) = -11.4 \text{ kJ} = -1.14 \times 10^4$ J; so the reaction is spontaneous.

(c) $\Delta G° = \Delta H°_{rxn} - T\Delta S°_{rxn} = -116.2 \text{ kJ} - (855 \, K)\left(-0.1466 \dfrac{kJ}{K}\right) = +9.1 \text{ kJ} = +9.1 \times 10^3$ J; so the reaction is nonspontaneous.

Check: The units (kJ) are correct. The enthalpy term dominates at low temperatures, making the reaction spontaneous. As the temperature increases, the decrease in entropy starts to dominate and in the last case the reaction is nonspontaneous.

17.36   **Given:** $CaCO_3(s) \rightarrow CaO(s) + CO_2(g)$ **Find:** $\Delta G°_{rxn}$ and spontaneity at (a) 298 K, (b) 1055 K, and (c) 1455 K
Conceptual Plan: $\Delta H°_{rxn} = \sum n_p H°_f \text{(products)} - \sum n_r H°_f \text{(reactants)}$ then
$\Delta S°_{rxn} = \sum n_p S° \text{(products)} - \sum n_r S° \text{(reactants)}$ then J/K → kJ/K then $\Delta H°_{rxn}, \Delta S°_{rxn}, T \rightarrow \Delta G°$

$$\frac{1 \text{ kJ}}{1000 \text{ J}} \qquad \Delta G = \Delta H_{rxn} - T\Delta S_{rxn}$$

Solution:

Reactant/Product	ΔH_f° (kJ/mol from Appendix IIB)
$CaCO_3(s)$	-1207.6
$CaO(s)$	-634.9
$CO_2(g)$	-393.5

Be sure to pull data for the correct formula and phase.

$$\Delta H_{rxn}^\circ = \sum n_p \Delta H_f^\circ (\text{products}) - \sum n_r \Delta H_f^\circ (\text{reactants})$$
$$= [1(\Delta H_f^\circ(CaO(g))) + 1(\Delta H_f^\circ(CO_2(g)))] - [1(\Delta H_f^\circ(CaCO_2(g)))]$$
$$= [1(-634.9 \text{ kJ}) + 1(-393.5 \text{ kJ})] - [1(-1207.6 \text{ kJ})]$$
$$= [-1028.4 \text{ kJ}] - [-1207.6 \text{ kJ}]$$
$$= +179.2 \text{ kJ then}$$

Reactant/Product	S°(J/mol · K from Appendix IIB)
$CaCO_3(s)$	91.7
$CaO(s)$	38.1
$CO_2(g)$	213.8

Be sure to pull data for the correct formula and phase.

$$\Delta S_{rxn}^\circ = \sum n_p S^\circ(\text{products}) - \sum n_r S^\circ(\text{reactants})$$
$$= [1(S^\circ(CaO(g))) + 1(S^\circ(CO_2(g)))] - [1(S^\circ(CaCO_2(g)))]$$
$$= [1(38.1 \text{ J/K}) + 1(213.8 \text{ J/K})] - [1(91.7 \text{ J/K})]$$
$$= [251.9 \text{ J/K}] - [91.7 \text{ J/K}]$$
$$= +160.2 \text{ J/K then } 160.2 \frac{J}{K} \times \frac{1 \text{ kJ}}{1000 \text{ J}} = +0.1602 \text{ kJ/K}$$

(a)　$\Delta G^\circ = \Delta H_{rxn}^\circ - T\Delta S_{rxn}^\circ = +179.2 \text{ kJ} - (298 \text{ K})\left(+0.1602 \frac{\text{kJ}}{\text{K}}\right) = +131.5 \text{ kJ} = +1.315 \times 10^5 \text{ J}$; so the reaction is nonspontaneous.

(b)　$\Delta G^\circ = \Delta H_{rxn}^\circ - T\Delta S_{rxn}^\circ = +179.2 \text{ kJ} - (1055 \text{ K})\left(+0.1602 \frac{\text{kJ}}{\text{K}}\right) = +10.2 \text{ kJ} = +1.02 \times 10^4 \text{ J}$; so the reaction is nonspontaneous.

(c)　$\Delta G^\circ = \Delta H_{rxn}^\circ - T\Delta S_{rxn}^\circ = +179.2 \text{ kJ} - (1455 \text{ K})\left(+0.1602 \frac{\text{kJ}}{\text{K}}\right) = -53.9 \text{ kJ} = -5.39 \times 10^4 \text{ J}$; so the reaction is spontaneous.

Check: The units (kJ) are correct. The enthalpy term dominates at low temperatures, making the reaction nonspontaneous. As the temperature increases, the increase in entropy starts to dominate and in the last case the reaction is spontaneous.

17.37　Because the first reaction has Fe_2O_3 as a product and the reaction of interest has it as a reactant, we need to reverse the first reaction. When the reaction direction is reversed, the sign of ΔG changes.

$Fe_2O_3(s) \rightarrow 2 Fe(s) + 3/2 O_2(g)$　　　　　　$\Delta G^\circ = +742.2 \text{ kJ}$

Because the second reaction has 1 mole of CO as a reactant and the reaction of interest has 3 moles of CO as a reactant, we need to multiply the second reaction and the ΔG by 3.

$3[CO(g) + 1/2 O_2(g) \rightarrow CO_2(g)]$　　　　　　$\Delta G^\circ = 3(-257.2 \text{ kJ}) = -771.6 \text{ kJ}$

Hess's law states the ΔG of the net reaction is the sum of the ΔG of the steps. The rewritten reactions are:

$Fe_2O_3(s) \rightarrow 2 Fe(s) + 3/2\ \cancel{O_2(g)}$	$\Delta G^\circ = +742.2 \text{ kJ}$
$3 CO(g) + 3/2\ \cancel{O_2(g)} \rightarrow 3 CO_2(g)$	$\Delta G^\circ = -771.6 \text{ kJ}$
$Fe_2O_3(s) \rightarrow 3 CO(g) \rightarrow 2 Fe(s) + 3 CO_2(g)$	$\Delta G_{rxn}^\circ = -29.4 \text{ kJ}$

17.38　Because the first reaction has $CaCO_3$ as a product and the reaction of interest has it as a reactant, we need to reverse the first reaction. When the reaction direction is reversed, the sign of ΔG changes.

$CaCO_3(s) \rightarrow Ca(s) + CO_2(g) + 1/2 O_2(g)$　　　　$\Delta G^\circ = +734.4 \text{ kJ}$

Because the second reaction has 2 moles of CaO as a product and the reaction of interest has 1 mole of CaO as a product, we need to multiply it by $\frac{1}{2}$. The ΔG of the second reaction is multiplied by $\frac{1}{2}$.

$$1/2[2\,\text{Ca}(s) + O_2(g) \rightarrow 2\,\text{CaO}(s)] \qquad \Delta G° = 1/2(-1206.6\,\text{kJ}) = -603.3\,\text{kJ}$$

Hess's law states the ΔH of the net reaction is the sum of the ΔH of the steps. The rewritten reactions are:

$$\text{CaCO}_3(s) \rightarrow \cancel{\text{Ca}(s)} + CO_2(g) + \cancel{1/2\,O_2(g)} \quad \Delta G° = +734.4\,\text{kJ}$$
$$\underline{1/2[2\,\cancel{\text{Ca}(s)} + \cancel{O_2(g)} \rightarrow 2\,\text{CaO}(s)]} \quad \Delta G° = -603.3\,\text{kJ}$$
$$\text{CaCO}_3(s) \rightarrow \text{CaO}(s) + CO_2(g) \quad \Delta G°_{\text{rxn}} = +131.1\,\text{kJ}$$

Free Energy Changes, Nonstandard Conditions, and the Equilibrium Constant

17.39   (a)   **Given:** $I_2(s) \rightarrow I_2(g)$ at 25.0 °C   **Find:** $\Delta G°_{\text{rxn}}$

     Conceptual Plan: $\Delta G°_{\text{rxn}} = \sum n_p \Delta G°_f \text{(products)} - \sum n_r \Delta G°_f \text{(reactants)}$

     Solution:

Reactant/Product	$\Delta G°_f$ (kJ/mol from Appendix IIB)
$I_2(s)$	0.0
$I_2(g)$	19.3

     Be sure to pull data for the correct formula and phase.

$$\Delta G°_{\text{rxn}} = \sum n_p \Delta G°_f \text{(products)} - \sum n_r \Delta G°_f \text{(products)}$$
$$= [1(\Delta G°_f(I_2(g)))] - [1(\Delta G°_f(I_2(s)))]$$
$$= [1(19.3\,\text{kJ})] - [1(0.0\,\text{kJ})]$$
$$= +19.3\,\text{kJ; so the reaction is nonspontaneous.}$$

     Check: The units (kJ) are correct. The answer is positive because gases have higher free energy than do solids and the free energy change of the reaction is the same as free energy of formation of gaseous iodine.

   (b)   **Given:** $I_2(s) \rightarrow I_2(g)$ at 25.0 °C (i) $P_{I_2} = 1.00$ mmHg; (ii) $P_{I_2} = 0.100$ mmHg   **Find:** ΔG_{rxn}

     Conceptual Plan: °C → K and mmHg → atm then $\Delta G°_{\text{rxn}}, P_{I_2}, T \rightarrow \Delta G_{\text{rxn}}$

$$K = 273.15 + °C \qquad \frac{1\,\text{atm}}{760\,\text{mmHg}} \qquad \Delta G_{\text{rxn}} = \Delta G°_{\text{rxn}} + RT \ln Q \text{ where } Q = P_{I_2}$$

     Solution: $T = 273.15 + 25.0\,°C = 298.2\,\text{K}$ and (i) $1.00\,\cancel{\text{mmHg}} \times \dfrac{1\,\text{atm}}{760\,\cancel{\text{mmHg}}} = 0.00131\underline{5}79\,\text{atm}$

     then $\Delta G_{\text{rxn}} = \Delta G°_{\text{rxn}} + RT \ln Q = \Delta G°_{\text{rxn}} + RT \ln P_{I_2} =$

$$+19.3\,\text{kJ} + \left(8.314\,\frac{\cancel{J}}{\cancel{K}\cdot\text{mol}}\right)\left(\frac{1\,\text{kJ}}{1000\,\cancel{J}}\right)(298.2\,\cancel{K})\ln(0.00131\underline{5}79) = +2.9\,\text{kJ; so the reaction is}$$

     nonspontaneous.

     Then (ii) $0.100\,\cancel{\text{mmHg}} \times \dfrac{1\,\text{atm}}{760\,\cancel{\text{mmHg}}} = 0.000131\underline{5}79\,\text{atm}$ then

$$\Delta G_{\text{rxn}} = \Delta G°_{\text{rxn}} + RT \ln Q = \Delta G°_{\text{rxn}} + RT \ln P_{I_2} =$$

$$+19.3\,\text{kJ} + \left(8.314\,\frac{\cancel{J}}{\cancel{K}\cdot\text{mol}}\right)\left(\frac{1\,\text{kJ}}{1000\,\cancel{J}}\right)(298.2\,\cancel{K})\ln(0.000131\underline{5}79) = -2.9\,\text{kJ; so the reaction is}$$

     spontaneous.

     Check: The units (kJ) are correct. The answer is positive at higher pressure because the pressure is higher than the vapor pressure of iodine. Once the desired pressure is below the vapor pressure (0.31 mmHg at 25.0 °C), the reaction becomes spontaneous.

   (c)   Iodine sublimes at room temperature because there is an equilibrium between the solid and the gas phases. The vapor pressure is low (0.31 mmHg at 25.0 °C), so a small amount of iodine can remain in the gas phase, which is consistent with the free energy values.

17.40   (a)   **Given:** $\text{CH}_3\text{OH}(l) \rightarrow \text{CH}_3\text{OH}(g)$ at 25.0 °C   **Find:** $\Delta G°_{\text{rxn}}$

     Conceptual Plan: $\Delta G°_{\text{rxn}} = \sum n_p \Delta G°_f \text{(products)} - \sum n_r \Delta G°_f \text{(reactants)}$

Solution:

Reactant/Product	ΔG_f° (kJ/mol from Appendix IIB)
$CH_3OH(l)$	-166.6
$CH_3OH(g)$	-162.3

Be sure to pull data for the correct formula and phase.

$$\Delta G_{rxn}^\circ = \sum n_p \Delta G_f^\circ \text{ (products)} - \sum n_r \Delta G_f^\circ \text{ (reactants)}$$
$$= [1(\Delta G_f^\circ (CH_3OH(g)))] - [1(\Delta G_f^\circ (CH_3OH(l)))]$$
$$= [1(-162.3 \text{ kJ})] - [1(-166.6 \text{ kJ})]$$
$$= +4.3 \text{ kJ; so the reaction is nonspontaneous.}$$

Check: The units (kJ) are correct. The answer is positive because gases have higher free energy than do liquids.

(b) **Given:** $CH_3OH(l) \rightarrow CH_3OH(g)$ at 25.0 °C (i) $P_{CH_3OH} = 150.0$ mmHg; (ii) $P_{CH_3OH} = 100.0$ mmHg; (iii) $P_{CH_3OH} = 10.0$ mmHg **Find:** ΔG_{rxn}

Conceptual Plan: °C $\rightarrow$ K and mmHg $\rightarrow$ atm then $\Delta G_{rxn}^\circ, P_{CH_3OH}, T \rightarrow \Delta G_{rxn}$

$$K = 273.15 + °C \qquad \frac{1 \text{ atm}}{760 \text{ mmHg}} \qquad \Delta G_{rxn} = \Delta G_{rxn}^\circ + RT \ln Q \text{ where } Q = P_{CH_3OH}$$

Solution: $T = 273.15 + 25.0\,°C = 298.2$ K and (i) $150.0 \text{ mmHg} \times \dfrac{1 \text{ atm}}{760 \text{ mmHg}} = 0.197\underline{3}684$ atm then

$$\Delta G_{rxn} = \Delta G_{rxn}^\circ + RT \ln Q = \Delta G_{rxn}^\circ + RT \ln P_{CH_3OH} =$$

$$+4.3 \text{ kJ} + \left(8.314 \frac{J}{K \cdot mol}\right)\left(\frac{1 \text{ kJ}}{1000 \text{ J}}\right)(298.2 \text{ K}) \ln (0.197\underline{3}684) = +0.3 \text{ kJ; so the reaction is nonspontaneous.}$$

Then (ii) $100.0 \text{ mmHg} \times \dfrac{1 \text{ atm}}{760 \text{ mmHg}} = 0.131\underline{5}79$ atm then

$$\Delta G_{rxn} = \Delta G_{rxn}^\circ + RT \ln Q = \Delta G_{rxn}^\circ + RT \ln P_{CH_3OH} =$$

$$+4.3 \text{ kJ} + \left(8.314 \frac{J}{K \cdot mol}\right)\left(\frac{1 \text{ kJ}}{1000 \text{ J}}\right)(298.2 \text{ K}) \ln (0.131\underline{5}79) = -0.7 \text{ kJ; so the reaction is spontaneous.}$$

Then (iii) $10.0 \text{ mmHg} \times \dfrac{1 \text{ atm}}{760 \text{ mmHg}} = 0.0131\underline{5}79$ atm then

$$\Delta G_{rxn} = \Delta G_{rxn}^\circ + RT \ln Q = \Delta G_{rxn}^\circ + RT \ln P_{CH_3OH} =$$

$$+4.3 \text{ kJ} + \left(8.314 \frac{J}{K \cdot mol}\right)\left(\frac{1 \text{ kJ}}{1000 \text{ J}}\right)(298.2 \text{ K}) \ln (0.0131\underline{5}79) = -6.4 \text{ kJ; so the reaction is spontaneous.}$$

Check: The units (kJ) are correct. The answer is positive at high pressures because the pressure is higher than the vapor pressure of methanol. Once the desired pressure is below the vapor pressure (143 mmHg at 25.0 °C), the reaction becomes spontaneous.

(c) Methanol evaporates at room temperature because there is an equilibrium between the liquid and the gas phases. The vapor pressure is moderate (143 mmHg at 25.0 °C), so a moderate amount of methanol can remain in the gas phase, which is consistent with the free energy values.

17.41 **Given:** $CH_3OH(g) \rightleftharpoons CO(g) + 2\,H_2(g)$ at 25.0 °C, $P_{CH_3OH} = 0.855$ atm, $P_{CO} = 0.125$ atm, $P_{H_2} = 0.183$ atm
Find: ΔG

Conceptual Plan:

$$\Delta G_{rxn}^\circ = \sum n_p \Delta G_f^\circ \text{ (products)} - \sum n_r \Delta G_f^\circ \text{ (reactants)} \text{ then °C} \rightarrow \text{K then } \Delta G_{rxn}^\circ, P_{CH_3OH}, P_{CO}, P_{H_2}, T \rightarrow \Delta G$$

$$K = 273.15 + °C \qquad \Delta G_{rxn} = \Delta G_{rxn}^\circ + RT \ln Q \quad \text{where } Q = \frac{P_{CO} P_{H_2}^2}{P_{CH_3OH}}$$

Solution:

Reactant/Product	ΔG_f° (kJ/mol from Appendix IIB)
$CH_3OH(g)$	-162.3
$CO(g)$	-137.2
$H_2(g)$	0.0

Be sure to pull data for the correct formula and phase.

$$\Delta G^\circ_{rxn} = \sum n_p \Delta G^\circ_f (\text{products}) - \sum n_r \Delta G^\circ_f (\text{reactants})$$
$$= [1(\Delta G^\circ_f (\text{CO}(g))) + 2(\Delta G^\circ_f (\text{H}_2(g)))] - [1(\Delta G^\circ_f (\text{CH}_3\text{OH}(g)))]$$
$$= [1(-137.2 \text{ kJ}) + 2(0.0 \text{ kJ})] - [1(-162.3 \text{ kJ})]$$
$$= [-137.2 \text{ kJ}] - [-162.3 \text{ kJ}]$$
$$= +25.1 \text{ kJ}$$

$T = 273.15 + 25.0 °C = 298.2 \text{ K}$ then $Q = \dfrac{P_{CO}P^2_{H_2}}{P_{CH_3OH}} = \dfrac{(0.125)(0.183)^2}{0.855} = 0.00489605$ then

$$\Delta G_{rxn} = \Delta G^\circ_{rxn} + RT \ln Q = +25.1 \text{ kJ} + \left(8.314 \frac{J}{K \cdot mol}\right)\left(\frac{1 \text{ kJ}}{1000 J}\right)(298.2 \text{ K}) \ln (0.00489605) = +11.9 \text{ kJ}$$

So the reaction is nonspontaneous.

Check: The units (kJ) are correct. The standard free energy for the reaction was positive and the fact that Q was less than 1 made the free energy smaller, but the reaction at these conditions is still not spontaneous.

17.42   **Given:** $CO_2(g) + CCl_4(g) \rightleftharpoons 2 \, COCl_2(g)$ at 25.0 °C, $P_{CO_2} = 0.112$ atm, $P_{CCl_4} = 0.174$ atm, $P_{COCl_2} = 0.744$ atm
        Find: ΔG
        Conceptual Plan:
$$\Delta G^\circ_{rxn} = \sum n_p \Delta G^\circ_f (\text{products}) - \sum n_r \Delta G^\circ_f (\text{reactants}) \text{ then } °C \rightarrow K \text{ then } \Delta G^\circ_{rxn}, P_{CO_2}, P_{CCl_4}, P_{COCl_2}, T \rightarrow \Delta G$$

                      $K = 273.15 + °C$ $\Delta G_{rxn} = \Delta G^\circ_{rxn} + RT \ln Q$ where $Q = \dfrac{P^2_{COCl_2}}{P_{CO_2}P_{CCl_4}}$

Solution:

Reactant/Product	ΔG°_f (kJ/mol from Appendix IIB)
$CO_2(g)$	−394.4
$CCl_4(g)$	−62.3
$COCl_2(g)$	−204.9

Be sure to pull data for the correct formula and phase.

$$\Delta G^\circ_{rxn} = \sum n_p \Delta G^\circ_f (\text{products}) - \sum n_r \Delta G^\circ_f (\text{reactants})$$
$$= [2(\Delta G^\circ_f (\text{COCl}_2(g)))] - [1(\Delta G^\circ_f (\text{CO}_2(g))) + 1(\Delta G^\circ_f (\text{CCl}_4(g)))]$$
$$= [2(-204.9 \text{ kJ})] - [1(-394.4 \text{ kJ}) + 1(-62.3 \text{ kJ})]$$
$$= [-409.8 \text{ kJ}] - [-456.7 \text{ kJ}]$$
$$= +46.9 \text{ kJ}$$

$T = 273.15 + 25.0 °C = 298.2 \text{ K}$ then $Q = \dfrac{P^2_{COCl_2}}{P_{CO_2}P_{CCl_4}} = \dfrac{(0.744)^2}{(0.112)(0.174)} = 28.4039$ then

$$\Delta G_{rxn} = \Delta G^\circ_{rxn} + RT \ln Q = +46.9 \text{ kJ} + \left(8.314 \frac{J}{K \cdot mol}\right)\left(\frac{1 \text{ kJ}}{1000 J}\right)(298.2 \text{ K}) \ln (28.4039) = +55.2 \text{ kJ}$$

So the reaction is nonspontaneous.

Check: The units (kJ) are correct. The standard free energy for the reaction was positive, and the fact that Q was greater than 1 made the free energy larger; so the reaction is less spontaneous in the forward direction at these conditions than at standard conditions.

17.43   (a)   **Given:** $2 \, CO(g) + O_2(g) \rightleftharpoons 2 \, CO_2(g)$ at 25.0 °C   **Find:** K
              Conceptual Plan:
$$\Delta G^\circ_{rxn} = \sum n_p \Delta G^\circ_f (\text{products}) - \sum n_r \Delta G^\circ_f (\text{reactants}) \text{ then } °C \rightarrow K \text{ then } \Delta G^\circ_{rxn}, T \rightarrow K$$

                         $K = 273.15 + °C$ $\Delta G^\circ_{rxn} = -RT \ln K$

Solution:

Reactant/Product	ΔG°_f (kJ/mol from Appendix IIB)
$CO(g)$	−137.2
$O_2(g)$	0.0
$CO_2(g)$	−394.4

Be sure to pull data for the correct formula and phase.

$$\Delta G_{rxn}^\circ = \sum n_p \Delta G_f^\circ \text{(products)} - \sum n_r \Delta G_f^\circ \text{(reactants)}$$
$$= [2(\Delta G_f^\circ (CO_2(g)))] - [2(\Delta G_f^\circ (CO(g))) + 1(\Delta G_f^\circ (O_2(g)))]$$
$$= [2(-394.4 \text{ kJ})] - [2(-137.2 \text{ kJ}) + 1(0.0 \text{ kJ})]$$
$$= [-788.8 \text{ kJ}] - [-274.4 \text{ kJ}]$$
$$= -514.4 \text{ kJ} \qquad\qquad\qquad T = 273.15 + 25.0\,^\circ\text{C} = 298.2 \text{ K then}$$

$\Delta G_{rxn}^\circ = -RT \ln K$ Rearrange to solve for K.

$$K = e^{\frac{-\Delta G_{rxn}^\circ}{RT}} = e^{\frac{-(-514.4\ \cancel{kJ}) \times \frac{1000\ J}{1\ \cancel{kJ}}}{\left(8.314 \frac{J}{K \cdot mol}\right)(298.2\ \cancel{K})}} = e^{207.483} = 1.28 \times 10^{90}$$

Check: The units (none) are correct. The standard free energy for the reaction was very negative, so we expect a very large K. The reaction is spontaneous, so mostly products are present at equilibrium.

(b)   **Given:** $2\,H_2S(g) \rightleftharpoons 2\,H_2(g) + S_2(g)$ at 25.0 °C   **Find:** K
Conceptual Plan:
$$\mathbf{\Delta G_{rxn}^\circ = \sum n_p \Delta G_f^\circ (\textbf{products}) - \sum n_r \Delta G_f^\circ (\textbf{reactants}) \textbf{ then }^\circ C \rightarrow K \textbf{ then } \Delta G_{rxn}^\circ, T \rightarrow K}$$
$$\qquad\qquad\qquad\qquad\qquad\qquad\qquad\qquad K = 273.15 + {}^\circ C \qquad\quad \Delta G_{rxn}^\circ = -RT \ln K$$

Solution:

Reactant/Product	ΔG_f° (kJ/mol from Appendix IIB)
$H_2S(g)$	-33.4
$H_2(g)$	0.0
$S_2(g)$	79.7

Be sure to pull data for the correct formula and phase.
$$\Delta G_{rxn}^\circ = \sum n_p \Delta G_f^\circ \text{(products)} - \sum n_r \Delta G_f^\circ \text{(reactants)}$$
$$= [2(\Delta G_f^\circ (H_2(g))) + 1(\Delta G_f^\circ (S_2(g)))] - [2(\Delta G_f^\circ (H_2S(g)))]$$
$$= [2(0.0 \text{ kJ})] + 1(79.7 \text{ kJ})] - [2(-33.4 \text{ kJ})]$$
$$= [79.7 \text{ kJ}] - [-66.8 \text{ kJ}]$$
$$= +146.5 \text{ kJ} \qquad\qquad\qquad T = 273.15 + 25.0\,^\circ\text{C} = 298.2 \text{ K then}$$

$\Delta G_{rxn}^\circ = -RT \ln K$ Rearrange to solve for K.

$$K = e^{\frac{-\Delta G_{rxn}^\circ}{RT}} = e^{\frac{-146.5\ \cancel{kJ} \times \frac{1000\ J}{1\ \cancel{kJ}}}{\left(8.314 \frac{J}{K \cdot mol}\right)(298.2\ \cancel{K})}} = e^{-59.0908} = 2.17 \times 10^{-26}$$

Check: The units (none) are correct. The standard free energy for the reaction was positive, so we expect a small K. The reaction is nonspontaneous, so mostly reactants are present at equilibrium.

17.44   (a)   **Given:** $2\,NO_2(g) \rightleftharpoons N_2O_4(g)$ at 25 °C   **Find:** K
Conceptual Plan:
$$\mathbf{\Delta G_{rxn}^\circ = \sum n_p \Delta G_f^\circ (\textbf{products}) - \sum n_r \Delta G_f^\circ (\textbf{reactants}) \textbf{ then }^\circ C \rightarrow K \textbf{ then } \Delta G_{rxn}^\circ, T \rightarrow K}$$
$$\qquad\qquad\qquad\qquad\qquad\qquad\qquad\qquad K = 273.15 + {}^\circ C \qquad\quad \Delta G_{rxn}^\circ = -RT \ln K$$

Solution:

Reactant/Product	ΔG_f° (kJ/mol from Appendix IIB)
$NO_2(g)$	51.3
$N_2O_4(g)$	99.8

Be sure to pull data for the correct formula and phase.
$$\Delta G_{rxn}^\circ = \sum n_p \Delta G_f^\circ \text{(products)} - \sum n_r \Delta G_f^\circ \text{(reactants)}$$
$$= [1(\Delta G_f^\circ (N_2O_4(g)))] - [2(\Delta G_f^\circ (NO_2(g)))]$$
$$= [1(99.8 \text{ kJ})] - [2(51.3 \text{ kJ})]$$
$$= [99.8 \text{ kJ}] - [102.6 \text{ kJ}]$$
$$= -2.8 \text{ kJ} \qquad\qquad\qquad T = 273.15 + 25.0\,^\circ\text{C} = 298.2 \text{ K then}$$

$\Delta G_{rxn}^\circ = -RT \ln K$ Rearrange to solve for K.

$$K = e^{\frac{-\Delta G°_{rxn}}{RT}} = e^{\frac{-(-2.8 \text{ kJ}) \times \frac{1000 \text{ J}}{1 \text{ kJ}}}{\left(8.314 \frac{\text{J}}{\text{K} \cdot \text{mol}}\right)(298 \text{ K})}} = e^{1.1301} = 3.1$$

Check: The units (none) are correct. The standard free energy for the reaction was very slightly negative, so we expect a K just over 1. The reaction is spontaneous, so mostly products are present at equilibrium.

(b) **Given:** $Br_2(g) + Cl_2(g) \rightleftharpoons 2 \, BrCl(g)$ at 25 °C   **Find:** K
Conceptual Plan:
$$\Delta G°_{rxn} = \sum n_p \Delta G°_f (\text{products}) - \sum n_r \Delta G°_f (\text{reactants}) \text{ then } °C \rightarrow K \text{ then } \Delta G°_{rxn}, T \rightarrow K$$
$$K = 273.15 + °C \qquad \Delta G°_{rxn} = -RT \ln K$$

Solution:

Reactant/Product	$\Delta G°_f$ (kJ/mol from Appendix IIB)
$Br_2(g)$	3.1
$Cl_2(g)$	0.0
$BrCl(g)$	−1.0

Be sure to pull data for the correct formula and phase.
$$\begin{aligned}\Delta G°_{rxn} &= \sum n_p \Delta G°_f (\text{products}) - \sum n_r \Delta G°_f (\text{reactants}) \\ &= [2(\Delta G°_f (BrCl(g)))] - [1(\Delta G°_f (Br_2(g))) + 1(\Delta G°_f (Cl_2(g)))] \\ &= [2(-1.0 \text{ kJ})] - [1(3.1 \text{ kJ}) + 1(0.0 \text{ kJ})] \\ &= [-2.0 \text{ kJ}] - [3.1 \text{ kJ}] \\ &= -5.1 \text{ kJ} \end{aligned}$$
$T = 273.15 + 25 \, °C = 298 \text{ K}$ then $\Delta G°_{rxn} = -RT \ln K$

Rearrange to solve for K. $K = e^{\frac{-\Delta G°_{rxn}}{RT}} = e^{\frac{-(-5.1 \text{ kJ}) \times \frac{1000 \text{ J}}{1 \text{ kJ}}}{\left(8.314 \frac{\text{J}}{\text{K} \cdot \text{mol}}\right)(298 \text{ K})}} = e^{2.0585} = 7.8$

Check: The units (none) are correct. The standard free energy for the reaction was very slightly negative, so we expect a K just over 1. The reaction is spontaneous.

17.45   **Given:** $CO(g) + 2 \, H_2(g) \rightleftharpoons CH_3OH(g)$ $K_p = 2.26 \times 10^4$ at 25 °C
Find: $\Delta G°_{rxn}$ at (a) standard conditions; (b) at equilibrium; and (c) $P_{CH_3OH} = 1.0$ atm, $P_{CO} = P_{H_2} = 0.010$ atm
Conceptual Plan: $°C \rightarrow K$ then (a) $K, T \rightarrow \Delta G°_{rxn}$ then (b) at equilibrium $\Delta G_{rxn} = 0$ then
$$K = 273.15 + °C \qquad \Delta G°_{rxn} = -RT \ln K$$
(c) $\Delta G°_{rxn}, P_{CH_3OH}, P_{CO}, P_{H_2}, T \rightarrow \Delta G$
$$\Delta G_{rxn} = \Delta G°_{rxn} + RT \ln Q \quad \text{where } Q = \frac{P_{CH_3OH}}{P_{CO} P_{H_2}^2}$$

Solution: $T = 273.15 + 25 \, °C = 298 \text{ K}$ then

(a) $\Delta G°_{rxn} = -RT \ln K = -\left(8.314 \dfrac{\text{J}}{\text{K} \cdot \text{mol}}\right)\left(\dfrac{1 \text{ kJ}}{1000 \text{ J}}\right)(298 \text{ K}) \ln(2.26 \times 10^4) = -24.8 \text{ kJ}$

(b) at equilibrium, $\Delta G_{rxn} = 0$

(c) $Q = \dfrac{P_{CH_3OH}}{P_{CO} P_{H_2}^2} = \dfrac{1.0}{(0.010)(0.010)^2} = 1.0 \times 10^6$ then

$\Delta G_{rxn} = \Delta G°_{rxn} + RT \ln Q = -24.8 \text{ kJ} + \left(8.314 \dfrac{\text{J}}{\text{K} \cdot \text{mol}}\right)\left(\dfrac{1 \text{ kJ}}{1000 \text{ J}}\right)(298 \text{ K}) \ln(1.0 \times 10^6) = +9.4 \text{ kJ}$

Check: The units (kJ) are correct. The K was greater than 1, so we expect a negative standard free energy for the reaction. At equilibrium, by definition, the free energy change is zero. Because the conditions give a $Q > K$, the reaction needs to proceed in the reverse direction, which means that the reaction is spontaneous in the reverse direction.

17.46   **Given:** $I_2(g) + Cl_2(g) \rightleftharpoons 2 \, ICl(g)$ $K_p = 81.9$ at 25 °C   **Find:** $\Delta G°_{rxn}$ at (a) standard conditions; (b) at equilibrium; and (c) $P_{ICl} = 2.55$ atm, $P_{I_2} = 0.325$ atm, $P_{Cl_2} = 0.221$ atm

Conceptual Plan: °C → K then (a) K, T → ΔG°_{rxn} then (b) at equilibrium $\Delta G_{rxn} = 0$ then

$$K = 273.15 + °C \qquad \Delta G^\circ_{rxn} = -RT \ln K$$

(c) $\Delta G^\circ_{rxn}, P_{ICl}, P_{I_2}, P_{Cl_2}, T$ → ΔG

$$\Delta G_{rxn} = \Delta G^\circ_{rxn} + RT \ln Q \quad \text{where } Q = \frac{P^2_{ICl}}{P_{I_2}P_{Cl_2}}$$

Solution: $T = 273.15 + 25\ °C = 298\ K$ then

(a) $\Delta G^\circ_{rxn} = -RT \ln K = -\left(8.314\ \dfrac{J}{K \cdot mol}\right)\left(\dfrac{1\ kJ}{1000\ J}\right)(298\ K)\ln(81.9) = -10.9\ kJ$

(b) at equilibrium, $\Delta G_{rxn} = 0$

(c) $Q = \dfrac{P^2_{ICl}}{P_{I_2}P_{Cl_2}} = \dfrac{(2.55)^2}{(0.325)(0.221)} = 90.\underline{5}325$ then

$$\Delta G_{rxn} = \Delta G^\circ_{rxn} + RT \ln Q = -10.9\ kJ + \left(8.314\ \dfrac{J}{K \cdot mol}\right)\left(\dfrac{1\ kJ}{1000\ J}\right)(298\ K)\ln(90.\underline{5}325) = +0.3\ kJ$$

Check: The units (kJ) are correct. The K was greater than 1, so we expect a negative standard free energy for the reaction. At equilibrium, by definition, the free energy change is zero. Because the conditions give a Q just greater than K, the reaction needs to proceed in the reverse direction, which means that the reverse reaction is slightly spontaneous.

17.47 (a) **Given:** $2\ CO(g) + O_2(g) \rightleftharpoons 2\ CO_2(g)$ at 25.0 °C   **Find:** K at 525 K

Conceptual Plan: $\Delta H^\circ_{rxn} = \sum n_p H^\circ_f \text{(products)} - \sum n_r H^\circ_f \text{(reactants)}$ then

$\Delta S^\circ_{rxn} = \sum n_p S^\circ \text{(products)} - \sum n_r S^\circ \text{(reactants)}$ then J/K → kJ/K then $\Delta H^\circ_{rxn}, \Delta S_{rxn}, T$ → ΔG

$$\dfrac{1\ kJ}{1000\ J} \qquad \Delta G = \Delta H_{rxn} - T\Delta S_{rxn}$$

then $\Delta G^\circ_{rxn}, T$ → K

$$\Delta G^\circ_{rxn} = -RT \ln K$$

Solution:

Reactant/Product	ΔH°_f (kJ/mol from Appendix IIB)
CO(g)	−110.5
O$_2$(g)	0.0
CO$_2$(g)	−393.5

Be sure to pull data for the correct formula and phase.

$$\begin{aligned}
\Delta H^\circ_{rxn} &= \sum n_p \Delta H^\circ_f \text{(products)} - \sum n_r \Delta H^\circ_f \text{(reactants)} \\
&= [2(\Delta H^\circ_f(CO_2(g)))] - [2(\Delta H^\circ_f(CO(g))) + 1(\Delta H^\circ_f(O_2(g)))] \\
&= [2(-393.5\ kJ)] - [2(-110.5\ kJ) + 1(0.0\ kJ)]\ \text{then} \\
&= [-787.0\ kJ] - [-221.0\ kJ] \\
&= -566.0\ kJ
\end{aligned}$$

Reactant/Product	S°(J/mol · K from Appendix IIB)
CO(g)	197.7
O$_2$(g)	205.2
CO$_2$(g)	213.8

Be sure to pull data for the correct formula and phase.

$$\begin{aligned}
\Delta S^\circ_{rxn} &= \sum n_p S^\circ \text{(products)} - \sum n_r S^\circ \text{(reactants)} \\
&= [2(S^\circ(CO_2(g)))] - [2(S^\circ(CO(g))) + 1(S^\circ(O_2(g)))] \\
&= [2(213.8\ J/K)] - [2(197.7\ J/K) + 1(205.2\ J/K)] \\
&= [427.6\ J/K] - [600.6\ J/K]\ \text{then} \\
&= -173.0\ J/K
\end{aligned}$$

$$-173.0\ \dfrac{J}{K} \times \dfrac{1\ kJ}{1000\ J} = -0.1730\ kJ/K\ \text{then}$$

$$\Delta G^\circ = \Delta H^\circ_{rxn} - T\Delta S^\circ_{rxn} = -566.0\ kJ - (525\ K)\left(-0.1730\ \dfrac{kJ}{K}\right) = -475.2\ kJ = -4.752 \times 10^5\ J\ \text{then}$$

$\Delta G^\circ_{\text{rxn}} = -RT \ln K$ Rearrange to solve for K.

$$K = e^{\frac{-\Delta G^\circ_{\text{rxn}}}{RT}} = e^{\frac{-(-4.752 \times 10^5 \, J)}{\left(8.314 \frac{J}{K \cdot \text{mol}}\right)(525 \, K)}} = e^{108.870} = 1.91 \times 10^{47}$$

Check: The units (none) are correct. The free energy change was very negative, indicating a spontaneous reaction. This results in a very large K.

(b) **Given:** $2 \, H_2S(g) \rightleftharpoons 2 \, H_2(g) + S_2(g)$ at 25.0 °C **Find:** K at 525 K

Conceptual Plan: $\Delta H^\circ_{\text{rxn}} = \sum n_p H^\circ_f \text{(products)} - \sum n_r H^\circ_f \text{(reactants)}$ then

$\Delta S^\circ_{\text{rxn}} = \sum n_p S^\circ \text{(products)} - \sum n_r S^\circ \text{(reactants)}$ then J/K → kJ/K then $\Delta H^\circ_{\text{rxn}}, \Delta S_{\text{rxn}}, T \rightarrow \Delta G$

$$\frac{1 \, \text{kJ}}{1000 \, \text{J}} \qquad\qquad \Delta G = \Delta H_{\text{rxn}} - T\Delta S_{\text{rxn}}$$

then $\Delta G^\circ_{\text{rxn}}, T \rightarrow K$

$$\Delta G^\circ_{\text{rxn}} = -RT \ln K$$

Solution:

Reactant/Product	ΔH°_f (kJ/mol from Appendix IIB)
$H_2S(g)$	−20.6
$H_2(g)$	0.0
$S_2(g)$	128.6

Be sure to pull data for the correct formula and phase.

$$\begin{aligned}
\Delta H^\circ_{\text{rxn}} &= \sum n_p \Delta H^\circ_f \text{(products)} - \sum n_r \Delta H^\circ_f \text{(reactants)} \\
&= [2(\Delta H^\circ_f(H_2(g))) + 1(\Delta H^\circ_f(S_2(g)))] - [2(\Delta H^\circ_f(H_2S(g)))] \\
&= [2(0.0 \, \text{kJ}) + 1(128.6 \, \text{kJ})] - [2(-20.6 \, \text{kJ})] \\
&= [128.6 \, \text{kJ}] - [-41.2 \, \text{kJ}] \\
&= +169.8 \, \text{kJ}
\end{aligned}$$

Reactant/Product	S° (J/mol · K from Appendix IIB)
$H_2S(g)$	205.8
$H_2(g)$	130.7
$S_2(g)$	228.2

Be sure to pull data for the correct formula and phase.

$$\begin{aligned}
\Delta S^\circ_{\text{rxn}} &= \sum n_p S^\circ \text{(products)} - \sum n_r S^\circ \text{(reactants)} \\
&= [2(S^\circ(H_2(g))) + 1(S^\circ(S_2(g)))] - [2(S^\circ(H_2S(g)))] \\
&= [2(130.7 \, \text{J/K}) + 1(228.2 \, \text{J/K})] - [2(205.8 \, \text{J/K})] \\
&= [489.6 \, \text{J/K}] - [411.6 \, \text{J/K}] \\
&= +78.0 \, \text{J/K}
\end{aligned}$$

then $+78.0 \, \dfrac{J}{K} \times \dfrac{1 \, \text{kJ}}{1000 \, J} = +0.0780 \, \text{kJ/K}$ then

$$\Delta G^\circ = \Delta H^\circ_{\text{rxn}} - T\Delta S^\circ_{\text{rxn}} = +169.8 \, \text{kJ} - (525 \, K)\left(+0.0780 \, \frac{\text{kJ}}{K}\right) = +128.\underline{85} \, \text{kJ} = +1.28\underline{85} \times 10^5 \, \text{J then}$$

$\Delta G^\circ_{\text{rxn}} = -RT \ln K$ Rearrange to solve for K.

$$K = e^{\frac{-\Delta G^\circ_{\text{rxn}}}{RT}} = e^{\frac{-1.28\underline{85} \times 10^5 \, J}{\left(8.314 \frac{J}{K \cdot \text{mol}}\right)(525 \, K)}} = e^{-29.\underline{5}199} = 1.51 \times 10^{-13}$$

Check: The units (none) are correct. The free energy change is positive, indicating a nonspontaneous reaction. This results in a very small K.

17.48 (a) **Given:** $2 \, NO_2(g) \rightleftharpoons N_2O_4(g)$ at 25 °C **Find:** K at 655 K

Conceptual Plan: $\Delta H^\circ_{\text{rxn}} = \sum n_p H^\circ_f \text{(products)} - \sum n_r H^\circ_f \text{(reactants)}$ then

$\Delta S^\circ_{\text{rxn}} = \sum n_p S^\circ \text{(products)} - \sum n_r S^\circ \text{(reactants)}$ then J/K → kJ/K then $\Delta H^\circ_{\text{rxn}}, \Delta S_{\text{rxn}}, T \rightarrow \Delta G$

$$\frac{1 \, \text{kJ}}{1000 \, \text{J}} \qquad\qquad \Delta G = \Delta H_{\text{rxn}} - T\Delta S_{\text{rxn}}$$

then ΔG°_{rxn}, $T \rightarrow K$

$\Delta G^\circ_{rxn} = -RT \ln K$

Solution:

Reactant/Product	**ΔH°_f (kJ/mol from Appendix IIB)**
$NO_2(g)$	33.2
$N_2O_4(g)$	9.16

Be sure to pull data for the correct formula and phase.

$$\begin{aligned}\Delta H^\circ_{rxn} &= \sum n_p \Delta H^\circ_f(\text{products}) - \sum n_r \Delta H^\circ_f(\text{reactants})\\ &= [1(\Delta H^\circ_f(N_2O_4(g)))] - [2(\Delta H^\circ_f(NO_2(g)))]\\ &= [1(9.16\text{ kJ})] - [2(33.2\text{ kJ})]\\ &= [9.16\text{ kJ}] - [66.4\text{ kJ}]\\ &= -57.2\text{ kJ then}\end{aligned}$$

Reactant/Product	**S°(J/mol · K from Appendix IIB)**
$NO_2(g)$	240.1
$N_2O_4(g)$	304.4

Be sure to pull data for the correct formula and phase.

$$\begin{aligned}\Delta S^\circ_{rxn} &= \sum n_p S^\circ(\text{products}) - \sum n_r S^\circ(\text{reactants})\\ &= [1(S^\circ(N_2O_4(g)))] - [2(S^\circ(NO_2(g)))]\\ &= [1(304.4\text{ J/K})] - [2(240.1\text{ J/K})]\\ &= [304.4\text{ K/J}] - [480.2\text{ J/K}]\\ &= -175.8\text{ J/K}\end{aligned}$$

then $-175.8 \frac{\cancel{J}}{K} \times \frac{1\text{ kJ}}{1000\ \cancel{J}} = -0.1758$ kJ/K then

$$\Delta G^\circ = \Delta H^\circ_{rxn} - T\Delta S^\circ_{rxn} = -57.2\text{ kJ} - (655\ \cancel{K})\left(-0.1758\frac{\text{kJ}}{\cancel{K}}\right) = +57.\underline{9}\text{ kJ} = +5.7\underline{9}49 \times 10^4\text{ J then}$$

$\Delta G^\circ_{rxn} = -RT \ln K$ Rearrange to solve for K.

$$K = e^{\frac{-\Delta G^\circ_{rxn}}{RT}} = e^{\frac{-5.7\underline{9}49 \times 10^4\ \cancel{J}}{\left(8.314\frac{\cancel{J}}{\cancel{K}\cdot\text{mol}}\right)(655\ \cancel{K})}} = e^{-10.\underline{6}413} = 2.39 \times 10^{-5}$$

Check: The units (none) are correct. The free energy change is positive, indicating a nonspontaneous reaction. This results in a very small K.

(b) **Given:** $Br_2(g) + Cl_2(g) \rightleftharpoons 2\ BrCl(g)$ at 25 °C **Find:** K at 655 K

Conceptual Plan: $\Delta H^\circ_{rxn} = \sum n_p H^\circ_f(\text{products}) - \sum n_r H^\circ_f(\text{reactants})$ then
$\Delta S^\circ_{rxn} = \sum n_p S^\circ(\text{products}) - \sum n_r S^\circ(\text{reactants})$ then J/K → kJ/K then ΔH°_{rxn}, ΔS_{rxn}, $T \rightarrow \Delta G$

$\frac{1\text{ kJ}}{1000\text{ J}}$ $\qquad \Delta G = \Delta H_{rxn} - T\Delta S_{rxn}$

then ΔG°_{rxn}, $T \rightarrow K$

$\Delta G^\circ_{rxn} = -RT \ln K$

Solution:

Reactant/Product	**ΔH°_f (kJ/mol from Appendix IIB)**
$Br_2(g)$	30.9
$Cl_2(g)$	0.0
$BrCl(g)$	14.6

Be sure to pull data for the correct formula and phase.

$$\begin{aligned}\Delta H^\circ_{rxn} &= \sum n_p \Delta H^\circ_f(\text{products}) - \sum n_r \Delta H^\circ_f(\text{reactants})\\ &= [2(\Delta H^\circ_f(BrCl(g)))] - [1(\Delta H^\circ_f(Br_2(g))) + 1(\Delta H^\circ_f(Cl_2(g)))]\\ &= [2(14.6\text{ kJ})] - [1(30.9\text{ kJ}) + 1(0.0\text{ kJ})]\\ &= [29.2\text{ kJ}] - [30.9\text{ kJ}]\\ &= -1.7\text{ kJ then}\end{aligned}$$

Reactant/Product	$S°(\text{J/mol} \cdot \text{K from Appendix IIB})$
$Br_2(g)$	245.5
$Cl_2(g)$	223.1
$BrCl(g)$	240.0

Be sure to pull data for the correct formula and phase.

$$\Delta S°_{rxn} = \sum n_p S°(\text{products}) - \sum n_r S°(\text{reactants})$$
$$= [2(S°(BrCl(g)))] - [1(S°(Br_2(g))) + 1(S°(Cl_2(g)))]$$
$$= [2(240.0 \text{ J/K}) - [1(245.5 \text{ J/K}) + 1(223.1 \text{ J/K})]$$
$$= [480.0 \text{ J/K}] - [468.6 \text{ J/K}]$$
$$= +11.4 \text{ J/K}$$

then $+11.4 \dfrac{J}{K} \times \dfrac{1 \text{ kJ}}{1000 \text{ J}} = +0.0114 \text{ kJ/K}$ then

$$\Delta G° = \Delta H°_{rxn} - T\Delta S°_{rxn} = -1.7 \text{ kJ} - (655 \text{ K})\left(+0.0114 \dfrac{kJ}{K}\right) = -9.\underline{1}67 \text{ kJ} = -9.\underline{1}67 \times 10^3 \text{ J}$$ then

$$\Delta G°_{rxn} = -RT \ln K \text{ Rearrange to solve for } K.$$

$$K = e^{\frac{-\Delta G°_{rxn}}{RT}} = e^{\frac{-(-9.167 \times 10^3 \text{ J})}{\left(8.314 \frac{J}{K \cdot mol}\right)(655 \text{ K})}} = e^{1.\underline{6}834} = 5.38$$

Check: The units (none) are correct. The free energy change is positive, indicating a nonspontaneous reaction. This results in a small K.

Cumulative Problems

17.49 (a) + because vapors have higher entropy than do liquids.

(b) − because solids have less entropy than do liquids.

(c) − because there is only one microstate for the final macrostate and there are six microstates for the initial macrostate.

17.50 (a) + because vapors have higher entropy than do solids.

(b) − because liquids have less entropy than do vapors.

(c) + because there are 20 microstates for the final macrostate and there are only 6 microstates for the initial macrostate.

17.51 (a) **Given:** $N_2(g) + O_2(g) \rightarrow 2 NO(g)$ **Find:** $\Delta G°_{rxn}$ and K_p at 298 K

Conceptual Plan: $\Delta H°_{rxn} = \sum n_p H°_f (\text{products}) - \sum n_r H°_f (\text{reactants})$ then

$\Delta S°_{rxn} = \sum n_p S°(\text{products}) - \sum n_r S°(\text{reactants})$ then °C → K then J/K → kJ/K then

$$K = 273.15 + °C \qquad \dfrac{1 \text{ kJ}}{1000 \text{ J}}$$

$\Delta H°_{rxn}, \Delta S°_{rxn}, T \rightarrow \Delta G$ then $\Delta G°_{rxn}, T \rightarrow K$

$$\Delta G = \Delta H_{rxn} - T\Delta S_{rxn} \qquad \Delta G°_{rxn} = -RT \ln K$$

Solution:

Reactant/Product	$\Delta H°_f (\text{kJ/mol from Appendix IIB})$
$N_2(g)$	0.0
$O_2(g)$	0.0
$NO(g)$	91.3

Be sure to pull data for the correct formula and phase.

$$\Delta H°_{rxn} = \sum n_p \Delta H°_f (\text{products}) - \sum n_r \Delta H°_f (\text{reactants})$$
$$= [2(\Delta H°_f (NO(g)))] - [1(\Delta H°_f (N_2(g))) + 1(\Delta H°_f (O_2(g)))]$$
$$= [2(91.3 \text{ kJ})] - [1(0.0 \text{ kJ}) + 1(0.0 \text{ kJ})]$$
$$= [182.6 \text{ kJ}] - [0.0 \text{ kJ}]$$
$$= +182.6 \text{ kJ}$$ then

Reactant/Product	$S°$(J/mol · K from Appendix IIB)
$N_2(g)$	191.6
$O_2(g)$	205.2
$NO(g)$	210.8

Be sure to pull data for the correct formula and phase.

$$\Delta S°_{rxn} = \sum n_p S°\text{(products)} - \sum n_r S°\text{(reactants)}$$
$$= [2(S°(NO(g)))] - [1(S°(N_2(g))) + 1(S°(O_2(g)))]$$
$$= [2(210.8 \text{ J/K})] - [1(191.6 \text{ J/K}) + 1(205.2 \text{ J/K})]$$
$$= [421.6 \text{ J/K}] - [396.8 \text{ JK}]$$
$$= +24.8 \text{ J/K}$$

then $+24.8 \dfrac{J}{K} \times \dfrac{1 \text{ kJ}}{1000 \, J} = +0.0248$ kJ/K then

$$\Delta G° = \Delta H°_{rxn} - T\Delta S°_{rxn} = +182.6 \text{ kJ} - (298 \text{ K})\left(0.0248 \frac{kJ}{K}\right) = +175.2 \text{ kJ} = +1.752 \times 10^5 \text{ J}$$

then $\Delta G°_{rxn} = -RT \ln K$ Rearrange to solve for K.

$$K = e^{\frac{-\Delta G°_{rxn}}{RT}} = e^{\frac{-1.752 \times 10^5 \, J}{\left(8.314 \frac{J}{K \cdot mol}\right)(298 \text{ K})}} = e^{-70.7144} = 1.95 \times 10^{-31}; \text{ so the reaction is nonspontaneous, and at}$$

equilibrium, mostly reactants are present.

Check: The units (kJ and none) are correct. The enthalpy is twice the enthalpy of formation of NO. We expect a very small entropy change because the number of moles of gas is unchanged. Because the positive enthalpy term dominates at room temperature, the free energy change is very positive and the reaction in the forward direction is nonspontaneous. This results in a very small K.

(b)   **Given:** $N_2(g) + O_2(g) \rightarrow 2 \text{ NO}(g)$ **Find:** $\Delta G°_{rxn}$ at 2000 K
    Conceptual Plan: Use results from part (a) $\Delta H°_{rxn}, \Delta S_{rxn}, T \rightarrow \Delta G$ **then** $\Delta G°_{rxn}, T \rightarrow K$
    $$\Delta G = \Delta H_{rxn} - T\Delta S_{rxn} \qquad\qquad \Delta G°_{rxn} = -RT \ln K$$

    Solution: $\Delta G = \Delta H_{rxn} - T\Delta S_{rxn} = +182.6 \text{ kJ} - (2000 \text{ K})\left(0.0248 \frac{kJ}{K}\right) = +133.0 \text{ kJ} = +1.330 \times 10^5 \text{ J}$

    then $\Delta G°_{rxn} = -RT \ln K$ Rearrange to solve for K.

$$K = e^{\frac{-\Delta G°_{rxn}}{RT}} = e^{\frac{-1.330 \times 10^5 \, J}{\left(8.314 \frac{J}{K \cdot mol}\right)(2000 \text{ K})}} = e^{-7.998557} = 3.36 \times 10^{-4}; \text{ so the forward reaction is becoming more}$$

    spontaneous.

    Check: The units (kJ and none) are correct. As the temperature rises, the entropy term becomes more significant. The free energy change is reduced, and the K increases. The reaction is still nonspontaneous.

17.52   **Given:** $3 \text{ NO}_2(g) + H_2O(l) \rightarrow 2 \text{ HNO}_3(aq) + NO(g)$ **Find:** $\Delta G°_{rxn}$ and K_p at 25 °C
    Conceptual Plan: $\Delta G°_{rxn} = \sum n_p \Delta G°_f\text{(products)} - \sum n_r \Delta G°_f\text{(reactants)}$ **then** $\Delta G°_{rxn}, T \rightarrow K$
    $$\Delta G°_{rxn} = -RT \ln K$$

Solution:

Reactant/Product	$\Delta G°_f$ (kJ/mol from Appendix IIB)
$NO_2(g)$	51.3
$H_2O(l)$	−237.1
$HNO_3(aq)$	−110.9
$NO(g)$	87.6

Be sure to pull data for the correct formula and phase.

$$\Delta G°_{rxn} = \sum n_p \Delta G°_f \text{(products)} - \sum n_r \Delta G°_f \text{(reactants)}$$
$$= [2(\Delta G°_f(HNO_3(g))) + 1(\Delta G°_f(NO(g)))] - [3(\Delta G°_f(NO_2(g))) + 1(\Delta G°_f(H_2O(l)))]$$
$$= [2(-110.9 \text{ kJ}) + 1(87.6 \text{ kJ})] - [3(51.3 \text{ kJ}) + 1(-237.1 \text{ kJ})]$$
$$= [-134.2 \text{ kJ}] - [-83.2 \text{ kJ}]$$
$$= -51.0 \text{ kJ} = -5.10 \times 10^4 \text{ J}$$

then $\Delta G^{\circ}_{\text{rxn}} = -RT \ln K$

Rearrange to solve for K. $K = e^{\frac{-\Delta G^{\circ}_{\text{rxn}}}{RT}} = e^{\frac{-(-5.10 \times 10^4 \,\text{J})}{\left(8.314 \frac{\text{J}}{\text{K} \cdot \text{mol}}\right)(298 \,\text{K})}} = e^{20.\underline{5}847} = 8.71 \times 10^8$; so the reaction is spontaneous.

Check: The units (kJ and none) are correct. The free energy change is negative, and the reaction is spontaneous. This results in a large K.

17.53   **Given:** $C_2H_4(g) + X_2(g) \rightarrow C_2H_4X_2(g)$ where X = Cl, Br, and I
Find: $\Delta H^{\circ}_{\text{rxn}}$, $\Delta S^{\circ}_{\text{rxn}}$, $\Delta G^{\circ}_{\text{rxn}}$ and K at 25 °C and spontaneity trends with X and temperature
Conceptual Plan: $\Delta H^{\circ}_{\text{rxn}} = \sum n_p H^{\circ}_f \text{(products)} - \sum n_r H^{\circ}_f \text{(reactants)}$ then
$\Delta S^{\circ}_{\text{rxn}} = \sum n_p S^{\circ} \text{(products)} - \sum n_r S^{\circ} \text{(reactants)}$ then °C → K then J/K → kJ/K then

$$K = 273.15 + °C \qquad \frac{1 \,\text{kJ}}{1000 \,\text{J}}$$

$\Delta H^{\circ}_{\text{rxn}}, \Delta S^{\circ}_{\text{rxn}}, T \rightarrow \Delta G$ then $\Delta G^{\circ}_{\text{rxn}}, T \rightarrow K$

$$\Delta G = \Delta H_{\text{rxn}} - T\Delta S_{\text{rxn}} \qquad \Delta G^{\circ}_{\text{rxn}} = -RT \ln K$$

Solution:

Reactant/Product	ΔH°_f (kJ/mol from Appendix IIB)
$C_2H_4(g)$	52.4
$Cl_2(g)$	0.0
$C_2H_4Cl_2(g)$	−129.7

Be sure to pull data for the correct formula and phase.

$\Delta H^{\circ}_{\text{rxn}} = \sum n_p \Delta H^{\circ}_f \text{(products)} - \sum n_r \Delta H^{\circ}_f \text{(reactants)}$
$= [1\Delta H^{\circ}_f (C_2H_4Cl_2)(g))] - [1(\Delta H^{\circ}_f (C_2H_4(g)) + 1(\Delta H^{\circ}_f (Cl_2(g))]$
$= [1(-129.7 \,\text{kJ})] - [1(52.4 \,\text{kJ}) + 1(0.0 \,\text{kJ})]$
$= [-129.7 \,\text{kJ}] - [52.4 \,\text{kJ}]$
$= -182.1 \,\text{kJ}$ then

Reactant/Product	S° (J/mol · K from Appendix IIB)
$C_2H_4(g)$	219.3
$Cl_2(g)$	223.1
$C_2H_4Cl_2(g)$	308.0

Be sure to pull data for the correct formula and phase.

$\Delta S^{\circ}_{\text{rxn}} = \sum n_p S^{\circ} \text{(products)} - \sum n_r S^{\circ} \text{(reactants)}$
$= [1(S^{\circ}(C_2H_4Cl_2(g))] - [1(S^{\circ}(C_2H_4(g)) + 1(S^{\circ}(Cl_2(g))]$
$= [1(308.0 \,\text{J/K})] - [1(219.3 \,\text{J/K}) + 1(223.1 \,\text{J/K})]$
$= [308.0 \,\text{J/K}] - [442.4 \,\text{J/K}]$
$= -134.4 \,\text{J/K}$

then $T = 273.15 + 25 °C = 298 \,\text{K}$ then $-134.4 \frac{\text{J}}{\text{K}} \times \frac{1 \,\text{kJ}}{1000 \,\text{J}} = -0.1344 \,\text{kJ/K}$ then

$\Delta G^{\circ} = \Delta H^{\circ}_{\text{rxn}} - T\Delta S^{\circ}_{\text{rxn}} = -182.1 \,\text{kJ} - (298 \,\text{K})\left(-0.1344 \frac{\text{kJ}}{\text{K}}\right) = -142.0 \,\text{kJ} = -1.420 \times 10^5 \,\text{J}$ then

$\Delta G^{\circ}_{\text{rxn}} = -RT \ln K$ Rearrange to solve for K.

$K = e^{\frac{-\Delta G^{\circ}_{\text{rxn}}}{RT}} = e^{\frac{-(-1.420 \times 10^5 \,\text{J})}{\left(8.314 \frac{\text{J}}{\text{K} \cdot \text{mol}}\right)(298 \,\text{K})}} = e^{57.\underline{3}14} = 7.78 \times 10^{24}$; so the reaction is spontaneous.

Reactant/Product	ΔH°_f (kJ/mol from Appendix IIB)
$C_2H_4(g)$	52.4
$Br_2(g)$	30.9
$C_2H_4Br_2(g)$	−38.3

Be sure to pull data for the correct formula and phase.

$$\Delta H^\circ_{rxn} = \sum n_p \Delta H^\circ_f \, (products) - \sum n_r \Delta H^\circ_f \, (reactants)$$
$$= [1(\Delta H^\circ_f \, (C_2H_4Br_2(g)))] - [1\Delta H^\circ_f \, (C_2H_4(g))) + 1(\Delta H^\circ_f \, (Br_2(g)))]$$
$$= [1(-38.3 \text{ kJ})] - [1(52.4 \text{ kJ}) + 1(30.9 \text{ kJ})]$$
$$= [-38.3 \text{ kJ}] - [83.3 \text{ kJ}]$$
$$= -121.6 \text{ kJ then}$$

Reactant/Product	S°(kJ/mol · K from Appendix IIB)
$C_2H_4(g)$	219.3
$Br_2(g)$	245.5
$C_2H_4Br_2(g)$	330.6

Be sure to pull data for the correct formula and phase.

$$\Delta S^\circ_{rxn} = \sum n_p S^\circ(produts) - \sum n_r S^\circ(reactants)$$
$$= [1(S^\circ(C_2H_4Br_2(g)))] - [1(S^\circ(C_2H_4(g))) + 1(S^\circ(Br_2(g)))]$$
$$= [1(330.6 \text{ J/K})] - [1(219.3 \text{ J/K})] + 1(245.5 \text{ J/K})]$$
$$= [330.6 \text{ J/K}] - [464.8 \text{ J/K}]$$
$$= -134.2 \text{ J/K}$$

then $-134.2 \dfrac{J}{K} \times \dfrac{1 \text{ kJ}}{1000 \text{ J}} = -0.1342 \text{ kJ/K}$

then $\Delta G^\circ = \Delta H^\circ_{rxn} - T\Delta S^\circ_{rxn} = -121.6 \text{ kJ} - (298 \text{ K})\left(-0.1342 \dfrac{\text{kJ}}{\text{K}}\right) = -81.\underline{6}08 \text{ kJ} = -8.1\underline{6}08 \times 10^4 \text{ J}$

then $\Delta G^\circ_{rxn} = -RT \ln K$

Rearrange to solve for K. $K = e^{\frac{-\Delta G^\circ_{rxn}}{RT}} = e^{\dfrac{-(-8.1608 \times 10^4 \text{ J})}{\left(8.314\frac{J}{K \cdot mol}\right)(298 \text{ K})}} = e^{32.\underline{9}387} = 2.02 \times 10^{14}$; so the reaction is spontaneous.

Reactant/Product	ΔH°_f (kJ/mol from Appendix IIB)
$C_2H_4(g)$	52.4
$I_2(g)$	62.42
$C_2H_4I_2(g)$	66.5

Be sure to pull data for the correct formula and phase.

$$\Delta H^\circ_{rxn} = \sum n_p \Delta H^\circ_f \, (products) - \sum n_r \Delta H^\circ_f \, (reactants)$$
$$= [1(\Delta H^\circ_f \, (C_2H_4I_2(g))) - [1\Delta H^\circ_f \, (C_2H_4(g))) + 1(\Delta H^\circ_f \, (I_2(g)))]$$
$$= [1(66.5 \text{ kJ})] - [1(52.4 \text{ kJ}) + 1(62.42 \text{ kJ})]$$
$$= [66.5 \text{ kJ}] - [114.\underline{8}2 \text{ kJ}]$$
$$= -48.\underline{3}2 \text{ kJ then}$$

Reactant/Product	S°(kJ/mol · K from Appendix IIB)
$C_2H_4(g)$	219.3
$I_2(g)$	260.69
$C_2H_4I_2(g)$	347.8

Be sure to pull data for the correct formula and phase.

$$\Delta S^\circ_{rxn} = \sum n_p S^\circ(products) - \sum n_r S^\circ(reactants)$$
$$= [1(S^\circ(C_2H_4I_2(g)))] - [1(S^\circ(C_2H_4(g))) + 1(S^\circ(I_2(g)))]$$
$$= [1(347.8 \text{ J/K})] - [1(219.3 \text{ J/K}) + 1(260.69 \text{ J/K})]$$
$$= [347.8 \text{ J/K}] - [479.\underline{9}9 \text{ J/K}]$$
$$= -132.2 \text{ J/K}$$

then $-132.2\dfrac{J}{K} \times \dfrac{1 \text{ kJ}}{1000 \text{ J}} = -0.1322 \text{ kJ/K}$

then $\Delta G^\circ = \Delta H^\circ_{rxn} - T\Delta S^\circ_{rxn} = -48.\underline{3}2 \text{ kJ} - (298 \text{ K})\left(-0.1322 \dfrac{\text{kJ}}{\text{K}}\right) = -8.\underline{9}244 \text{ kJ} = -8.\underline{9}244 \times 10^3 \text{ J}$

then $\Delta G^\circ_{rxn} = -RT \ln K$ Rearrange to solve for K.

$$K = e^{\frac{-\Delta G^\circ_{rxn}}{RT}} = e^{\frac{-(-8.9244 \times 10^3\,J)}{\left(8.314\frac{J}{K\cdot mol}\right)(298\,K)}} = e^{3.6021} = 37 \text{ and the reaction is spontaneous.}$$

Cl_2 is the most spontaneous in the forward direction; I_2 is the least. The entropy change in the reactions is very constant. The spontaneity is determined by the standard enthalpy of formation of the dihalogenated ethane. Higher temperatures make the forward reactions less spontaneous.

Check: The units (kJ and none) are correct. The enthalpy change becomes less negative as we move to larger halogens. The enthalpy term dominates at room temperature, and the free energy change is the same sign as the enthalpy change. The more negative the free energy change, the larger the K.

17.54   **Given:** $H_2(g) + X_2(g) \rightarrow 2\,HX(g)$ where $X = Cl$, Br, and I
Find: ΔH°_{rxn}, ΔS°_{rxn}, ΔG°_{rxn}, and K at 25 °C and spontaneity trends with X and temperature
Conceptual Plan: $\Delta H^\circ_{rxn} = \sum n_p H^\circ_f \text{(products)} - \sum n_r H^\circ_f \text{(reactants)}$ then

$\Delta S^\circ_{rxn} = \sum n_p S^\circ \text{(products)} - \sum n_r S^\circ \text{(reactants)}$ then °C $\rightarrow$ K then J/K $\rightarrow$ kJ/K then

$$K = 273.15 + \text{°C} \qquad \frac{1\,kJ}{1000\,J}$$

$\Delta H^\circ_{rxn}, \Delta S^\circ_{rxn}, T \rightarrow \Delta G$
$$\Delta G = \Delta H_{rxn} - T\Delta S_{rxn}$$

Solution:

Reactant/Product	ΔH°_f (kJ/mol from Appendix IIB)
$H_2(g)$	0.0
$Cl_2(g)$	0.0
$HCl(g)$	−92.3

Be sure to pull data for the correct formula and phase.

$\Delta H^\circ_{rxn} = \sum n_p \Delta H^\circ_f \text{(produts)} - \sum n_r \Delta H^\circ_f \text{(reactants)}$
$\phantom{\Delta H^\circ_{rxn}} = [2(\Delta H^\circ_f (HCl(g)))] - [1(\Delta H^\circ_f (H_2(g))) + 1(\Delta H^\circ_f (Cl_2(g)))]$
$\phantom{\Delta H^\circ_{rxn}} = [2(-92.3\,kJ)] - [1(0.0\,kJ) + 1(0.0\,kJ)]$
$\phantom{\Delta H^\circ_{rxn}} = [-184.6\,kJ] - [0.0]$
$\phantom{\Delta H^\circ_{rxn}} = -184.6\,kJ$ then

Reactant/Product	S° (kJ/mol from Appendix IIB)
$H_2(g)$	130.7
$Cl_2(g)$	223.1
$HCl(g)$	186.9

Be sure to pull data for the correct formula and phase.

$\Delta S^\circ_{rxn} = \sum n_p S^\circ \text{(produts)} - \sum n_r S^\circ \text{(reactants)}$
$\phantom{\Delta S^\circ_{rxn}} = [2(S^\circ (HCl(g)))] - [1(S^\circ (H_2(g))) + 1(S^\circ (Cl_2(g)))]$
$\phantom{\Delta S^\circ_{rxn}} = [2(186.9\,J/K)] - [1(130.7\,J/K) + 1(223.1\,J/K)]$
$\phantom{\Delta S^\circ_{rxn}} = [373.8\,J/K] - [353.8\,J/K]$
$\phantom{\Delta S^\circ_{rxn}} = +20.0\,J/K$

then $T = 273.15 + 25\,°C = 298\,K$ then $+20.0\,\dfrac{J}{K} \times \dfrac{1\,kJ}{1000\,J} = +0.0200\,kJ/K$ then

$$\Delta G^\circ = \Delta H^\circ_{rxn} - T\Delta S^\circ_{rxn} = -184.6\,kJ - (298\,K)\left(+0.0200\,\frac{kJ}{K}\right) = -190.6\,kJ = -1.906 \times 10^5\,J \text{ then}$$

$\Delta G^\circ_{rxn} = -RT \ln K$ Rearrange to solve for K.

$$K = e^{\frac{-\Delta G^\circ_{rxn}}{RT}} = e^{\left(\frac{-(-1.906 \times 10^5\,J)}{\left(8.314\frac{J}{K\cdot mol}\right)(298\,K)}\right)} = e^{76.9302} = 2.57 \times 10^{33}; \text{ so the reaction is spontaneous.}$$

Reactant/Product	ΔH_f° (kJ/mol from Appendix IIB)
$H_2(g)$	0.0
$Br_2(g)$	30.9
$HBr(g)$	−36.3

Be sure to pull data for the correct formula and phase.

$$\Delta H_{rxn}^\circ = \sum n_p \Delta H_f^\circ (\text{produts}) - \sum n_r \Delta H_f^\circ (\text{reactants})$$
$$= [2(\Delta H_f^\circ (HBr(g)))] - [1(\Delta H_f^\circ (H_2(g))) + 1(\Delta H_f^\circ (Br_2(g)))]$$
$$= [2(-36.3 \text{ kJ})] - [1(0.0 \text{ kJ}) + 1(30.9 \text{ kJ})]$$
$$= [-72.6 \text{ kJ}] - [30.9 \text{ kJ}]$$
$$= -103.5 \text{ kJ then}$$

Reactant/Product	S° (kJ/mol · K from Appendix IIB)
$H_2(g)$	130.7
$Br_2(g)$	245.5
$HBr(g)$	198.7

Be sure to pull data for the correct formula and phase.

$$\Delta S_{rxn}^\circ = \sum n_p S^\circ (\text{products}) - \sum n_r S^\circ (\text{reactants})$$
$$= [2(S^\circ (HBr(g)))] - [1(S^\circ (H_2(g))) + 1(S^\circ (Br_2(g)))]$$
$$= [2(198.7 \text{ J/K})] - [1(130.7 \text{ J/K}) + 1(245.5 \text{ J/K})]$$
$$= [397.4 \text{ J/K}] - [376.2 \text{ J/K}]$$
$$= +21.2 \text{ J/K}$$

then $+21.2 \dfrac{J}{K} \times \dfrac{1 \text{ kJ}}{1000 \text{ J}} = +0.0212 \text{ kJ/K}$

then $\Delta G^\circ = \Delta H_{rxn}^\circ - T\Delta S_{rxn}^\circ = -103.5 \text{ kJ} - (298 \text{ K})\left(+0.0212 \dfrac{kJ}{K}\right) = -109.\underline{8}176 \text{ kJ} = -1.09\underline{8}176 \times 10^5 \text{ J}$

then $\Delta G_{rxn}^\circ = -RT \ln K$ Rearrange to solve for K.

$$K = e^{\frac{-\Delta G_{rxn}^\circ}{RT}} = e^{\frac{-(-1.09\underline{8}176 \times 10^5 \text{ J})}{\left(8.314 \frac{J}{K \cdot mol}\right)(298 \text{ K})}} = e^{44.\underline{3}247} = 1.78 \times 10^{19}; \text{ so the reaction is spontaneous.}$$

Reactant/Product	ΔH_f° (kJ/mol from Appendix IIB)
$H_2(g)$	0.0
$I_2(g)$	62.42
$HI(g)$	26.5

Be sure to pull data for the correct formula and phase.

$$\Delta H_{rxn}^\circ = \sum n_p \Delta H_f^\circ (\text{produts}) - \sum n_r \Delta H_f^\circ (\text{reactants})$$
$$= [2(\Delta H_f^\circ (HI(g)))] - [1(\Delta H_f^\circ (H_2(g))) + 1(\Delta H_f^\circ (I_2(g)))]$$
$$= [2(26.5 \text{ kJ})] - [1(0.0 \text{ kJ}) + 1(62.42 \text{ kJ})]$$
$$= [53.0 \text{ kJ}] - [62.42 \text{ kJ}]$$
$$= -9.\underline{4}2 \text{ kJ then}$$

Reactant/Product	S° (kJ/mol · K from Appendix IIB)
$H_2(g)$	130.7
$I_2(g)$	260.69
$HI(g)$	206.6

Be sure to pull data for the correct formula and phase.

$$\Delta S_{rxn}^\circ = \sum n_p S^\circ (\text{products}) - \sum n_r S^\circ (\text{reactants})$$
$$= [2(S^\circ (HI(g)))] - [1(S^\circ (H_2(g))) + 1(S^\circ (I_2(g)))]$$
$$= [2(206.6 \text{ J/K})] - [1(130.7 \text{ J/K}) + 1(260.69 \text{ J/K})]$$
$$= [413.2 \text{ J/K}] - [391.39 \text{ J/K}]$$
$$= +21.8 \text{ J/K}$$

then $21.8 \dfrac{J}{K} \times \dfrac{1 \text{ kJ}}{1000 \text{ J}} = +0.0218 \text{ kJ/K}$

then $\Delta G° = \Delta H°_{rxn} - T\Delta S°_{rxn} = -9.\underline{4}2 \text{ kJ} - (298 \text{ K})\left(+0.0218 \dfrac{\text{kJ}}{\text{K}}\right) = -15.\underline{9}164 \text{ kJ} = -1.5\underline{9}164 \times 10^4 \text{ J}$

then $\Delta G°_{rxn} = -RT \ln K$ Rearrange to solve for K.

$$K = e^{\frac{-\Delta G°_{rxn}}{RT}} = e^{\frac{-(-1.5\underline{9}164 \times 10^4 \text{ J})}{\left(8.314 \frac{J}{K \cdot mol}\right)(298 \text{ K})}} = e^{6.4\underline{2}419} = 6.17 \times 10^2 = 617; \text{ so the reaction is spontaneous.}$$

Cl_2 is the most spontaneous; I_2 is the least. The entropy change in the reactions is very constant. The spontaneity is determined by the standard enthalpy of formation of the acid. Higher temperatures make the reactions more spontaneous.

Check: The units (kJ and none) are correct. The enthalpy is twice the enthalpy of formation of the acid. We expect a very small entropy change because the number of moles of gas is unchanged. Because both terms are negative, the free energy change is negative and the reaction is spontaneous. The more negative the free energy change, the larger the K.

17.55   (a)   **Given:** $N_2O(g) + NO_2(g) \rightleftharpoons 3 NO(g)$ at 298 K   **Find:** $\Delta G°_{rxn}$
            Conceptual Plan: $\Delta G°_{rxn} = \sum n_p \Delta G°_f \text{(products)} - \sum n_r \Delta G°_f \text{(reactants)}$
            Solution:

Reactant/Product	$\Delta G°_f$ (kJ/mol from Appendix IIB)
$N_2O(g)$	103.7
$NO_2(g)$	51.3
$NO(g)$	87.6

Be sure to pull data for the correct formula and phase.

$\Delta G°_{rxn} = \sum n_p \Delta G°_f \text{(produts)} - \sum n_r \Delta G°_f \text{(reactants)}$
$\qquad = [3(\Delta G°_f (NO(g)))] - [1(\Delta G°_f (N_2O(g))) + 1(\Delta G°_f (NO_2(g)))]$
$\qquad = [3(87.6 \text{ kJ})] - [1(103.7 \text{ kJ}) + 1(51.3 \text{ kJ})]$
$\qquad = [262.8 \text{ kJ}] - [155.0 \text{ kJ}]$
$\qquad = +107.8 \text{ kJ}$

The reaction is nonspontaneous.

Check: The units (kJ) are correct. The standard free energy for the reaction was positive, so the reaction is nonspontaneous.

   (b)   **Given:** $P_{N_2O} = P_{NO_2} = 1.0$ atm initially   **Find:** P_{NO} when reaction ceases to be spontaneous
            Conceptual Plan: Reaction will no longer be spontaneous when $Q = K$, **so** $\Delta G°_{rxn}, T \rightarrow K$.

$$\Delta G°_{rxn} = -RT \ln K$$

            Then solve the equilibrium problem to get gas pressures. Because $K \ll 1$, **the amount of NO generated will be very, very small compared to 1.0 atm; within experimental error,** $P_{N_2O} = P_{NO_2} = 1.0$ atm. **Simply solve for** P_{NO}.

$$K = \frac{P_{NO}^3}{P_{N_2O}P_{NO_2}}$$

Solution: $\Delta G°_{rxn} = -RT \ln K$ Rearrange to solve for K.

$$K = e^{\frac{-\Delta G°_{rxn}}{RT}} = e^{\frac{-(+107.8 \text{ kJ}) \times \frac{1000 \text{ J}}{1 \text{ kJ}}}{\left(8.314 \frac{J}{K \cdot mol}\right)(298 \text{ K})}} = e^{-43.\underline{5}103} = 1.27 \times 10^{-19} \text{ Because } K = \frac{P_{NO}^3}{P_{N_2O}P_{NO_2}}, \text{ rearrange to}$$

solve for P_{NO}. $P_{NO}^3 = \sqrt[3]{K P_{N_2O}P_{NO_2}} = \sqrt[3]{(1.27 \times 10^{-19})(1.0)(1.0)} = 5.0 \times 10^{-7}$ atm

Note that the assumption that P_{NO} was very, very small was valid.

Check: The units (atm) are correct. Because the free energy change was positive, the K was very small. This leads us to expect that very little NO will be formed.

(c)   **Given:** $N_2O(g) + NO_2(g) \rightleftharpoons 3\,NO(g)$ **Find:** temperature for spontaneity
Conceptual Plan: $\Delta H^\circ_{rxn} = \sum n_p H^\circ_f \text{ (products)} - \sum n_r H^\circ_f \text{ (reactants)}$ then

$\Delta S^\circ_{rxn} = \sum n_p S^\circ \text{(products)} - \sum n_r S^\circ \text{(reactants)}$ then J/K $\rightarrow$ kJ/K then $\Delta H^\circ_{rxn}, \Delta S_{rxn} \rightarrow T$

$$\frac{1\text{ kJ}}{1000\text{ J}} \qquad\qquad \Delta G = \Delta H_{rxn} - T\Delta S_{rxn}$$

Solution:

Reactant/Product	ΔH°_f (kJ/mol from Appendix IIB)
$N_2O(g)$	81.6
$NO_2(g)$	33.2
$NO(g)$	91.3

Be sure to pull data for the correct formula and phase.

$$\begin{aligned}
\Delta H^\circ_{rxn} &= \sum n_p \Delta H^\circ_f \text{ (products)} - \sum n_r \Delta H^\circ_f \text{ (reactants)} \\
&= [3(\Delta H^\circ_f (NO(g)))] - [1(\Delta H^\circ_f (N_2O(g))) + 1(\Delta H^\circ_f (NO_2(g)))] \\
&= [3(91.3\text{ kJ})] - [1(81.6\text{ kJ}) + 1(33.2\text{ kJ})] \\
&= [273.9\text{ kJ}] - [114.8\text{ kJ}] \\
&= +159.1\text{ kJ then}
\end{aligned}$$

Reactant/Product	S°(J/mol · K from Appendix IIB)
$N_2O(g)$	220.0
$NO_2(g)$	240.1
$NO(g)$	210.8

Be sure to pull data for the correct formula and phase.

$$\begin{aligned}
\Delta S^\circ_{rxn} &= \sum n_p S^\circ \text{(products)} - \sum n_r S^\circ \text{(reactants)} \\
&= [3(S^\circ(NO(g)))] - [1(S^\circ(N_2O(g))) + 1(S^\circ(NO_2(g)))] \\
&= [3(210.8\text{ J/K})] - [1(220.0\text{ J/K}) + 1(240.1\text{ J/K})] \\
&= [632.4\text{ J/K}] - [460.1\text{ J/K}] \\
&= +172.3\text{ J/K}
\end{aligned}$$

then $+172.3\,\dfrac{J}{K} \times \dfrac{1\text{ kJ}}{1000\text{ J}} = +0.1723$ kJ/K. Because $\Delta G = \Delta H_{rxn} - T\Delta S_{rxn}$, set $\Delta G = 0$ and rearrange to solve

for T. $T = \dfrac{\Delta H_{rxn}}{\Delta S_{rxn}} = \dfrac{+159.1\text{ kJ}}{0.1723\,\frac{kJ}{K}} = +923.4$ K

Check: The units (K) are correct. The reaction can be made more spontaneous by raising the temperature because the entropy change is positive (increase in the number of moles of gas).

17.56   (a)   **Given:** $BaCO_3(s) \rightleftharpoons BaO(s) + CO_2(g)$ at 298 K   **Find:** ΔG°_{rxn}
Conceptual Plan: $\Delta G^\circ_{rxn} = \sum n_p \Delta G^\circ_f \text{ (products)} - \sum n_r \Delta G^\circ_f \text{ (reactants)}$
Solution:

Reactant/Product	ΔG°_f (kJ/mol from Appendix IIB)
$BaCO_3(s)$	−1134.4
$BaO(s)$	−520.3
$CO_2(g)$	−394.4

Be sure to pull data for the correct formula and phase.

$$\begin{aligned}
\Delta G^\circ_{rxn} &= \sum n_p \Delta G^\circ_f \text{ (products)} - \sum n_r \Delta G^\circ_f \text{ (reactants)} \\
&= [1(\Delta G^\circ_f (BaO(s))) + 1(\Delta G^\circ_f (CO_2(g)))] - [1(\Delta G^\circ_f (BaCO_3(s)))] \\
&= [1(-520.3\text{ kJ}) + 1(-394.4\text{ kJ})] - [1(-1134.4\text{ kJ})] \\
&= [-914.7\text{ kJ}] - [-1134.4\text{ kJ}] \\
&= +219.7\text{ kJ}
\end{aligned}$$

The reaction is nonspontaneous.

Check: The units (kJ) are correct. The standard free energy for the reaction was positive, so the reaction is nonspontaneous.

(b)   **Given:** $BaCO_3(s)$ initially in container   **Find:** P_{CO_2} at equilibrium

Conceptual Plan: Reaction will be at equilibrium when $Q = K$, so $\Delta G°_{rxn}, T \rightarrow K \rightarrow P_{CO_2}$.

$$\Delta G°_{rxn} = -RT \ln K \qquad K = P_{CO_2}$$

Solution: $\Delta G°_{rxn} = -RT \ln K$ Rearrange to solve for K.

$$K = e^{\frac{-\Delta G°_{rxn}}{RT}} = e^{\frac{-(+219.7 \text{ kJ}) \times \frac{1000 \text{ J}}{1 \text{ kJ}}}{\left(8.314 \frac{\text{J}}{\text{K} \cdot \text{mol}}\right)(298 \text{ K})}} = e^{-88.\underline{6}755} = 3.08 \times 10^{-39}. \text{ So } P_{CO_2} = 3.08 \times 10^{-39} \text{ atm.}$$

Check: The units (atm) are correct. Because the free energy change was very positive, the K was very, very small. This leads us to expect that very little carbon dioxide will be formed.

(c)   **Given:** $BaCO_3(s) \rightleftharpoons BaO(s) + CO_2(g)$ **Find:** temperature for $P_{CO_2} = 1.0$ atm

Conceptual Plan: $\Delta H°_{rxn} = \sum n_p H°_f \text{ (products)} - \sum n_r H°_f \text{ (reactants)}$ **then**

$\Delta S°_{rxn} = \sum n_p S° \text{(products)} - \sum n_r S° \text{(reactants)}$ **then J/K $\rightarrow$ kJ/K then $\Delta H°_{rxn}, \Delta S_{rxn} \rightarrow T$**

$$\frac{1 \text{ kJ}}{1000 \text{ J}} \qquad\qquad \Delta G = \Delta H_{rxn} - T\Delta S_{rxn}$$

Solution:

Reactant/Product	$\Delta H°_f$ (kJ/mol from Appendix IIB)
$BaCO_3(s)$	−1213.0
$BaO(s)$	−548.0
$CO_2(g)$	−393.5

Be sure to pull data for the correct formula and phase.

$$\begin{aligned}
\Delta H°_{rxn} &= \sum n_p \Delta H°_f \text{ (products)} - \sum n_r \Delta H°_f \text{ (reactants)}\\
&= [1(\Delta H°_f (BaO(s))) + 1(\Delta H°_f (CO_2(g)))] - [1(\Delta H°_f (BaCO_3(s)))]\\
&= [1(-548.0 \text{ kJ}) + 1(-393.5 \text{ kJ})] - [1(-1213.0 \text{ kJ})]\\
&= [-941.5 \text{ kJ}] - [-1213.0 \text{ kJ}]\\
&= +271.5 \text{ kJ then}
\end{aligned}$$

Reactant/Product	$S°$(J/mol · K from Appendix IIB)
$BaCO_3(s)$	112.1
$BaO(s)$	72.1
$CO_2(g)$	213.8

Be sure to pull data for the correct formula and phase.

$$\begin{aligned}
\Delta S°_{rxn} &= \sum n_p S° \text{(products)} - \sum n_r S° \text{(reactants)}\\
&= [1(S°(BaO(s))) + 1(S°(CO_2(g)))] - [1(S°(BaCO_3(s)))]\\
&= [1(72.1 \text{ J/K}) + 1(213.8 \text{ J/K})] - [1(112.1 \text{ J/K})]\\
&= [285.9 \text{ J/K}] - [112.1 \text{ J/K}]\\
&= +173.8 \text{ J/K then}
\end{aligned}$$

$+173.8 \dfrac{\text{J}}{\text{K}} \times \dfrac{1 \text{ kJ}}{1000 \text{ J}} = +0.1738$ kJ/K. Because $\Delta G = \Delta H_{rxn} - T\Delta S_{rxn}$, set $\Delta G = 0$ and rearrange to

solve for T. $T = \dfrac{\Delta H_{rxn}}{\Delta S_{rxn}} = \dfrac{+271.5 \text{ kJ}}{0.1738 \dfrac{\text{kJ}}{\text{K}}} = +1562$ K. When $\Delta G = 0$ and $K = 1$, at 1562 K, $P_{CO_2} = 1.0$ atm.

Check: The units (K) are correct. The reaction can be made more spontaneous by raising the temperature because the entropy change is positive (increase in the number of moles of gas). We expect a high temperature because the enthalpy change is so positive.

17.57   (a)   **Given:** $ATP(aq) + H_2O(l) \rightarrow ADP(aq) + P_i(aq) \ \Delta G°_{rxn} = -30.5$ kJ at 298 K   **Find:** K

Conceptual Plan: $\Delta G°_{rxn}, T \rightarrow K$

$$\Delta G°_{rxn} = -RT \ln K$$

Solution: $\Delta G°_{rxn} = -RT \ln K$ Rearrange to solve for K.

$$K = e^{\frac{-\Delta G_{rxn}^{\circ}}{RT}} = e^{\frac{-(-30.5 \text{ kJ}) \times \frac{1000 \text{ J}}{1 \text{ kJ}}}{\left(8.314 \frac{J}{K \cdot mol}\right)(298 \text{ K})}} = e^{12.3104} = 2.22 \times 10^5$$

Check: The units (none) are correct. The free energy change is negative, and the reaction is spontaneous. This results in a large K.

(b)   **Given:** oxidation of glucose drives reforming of ATP   **Find:** ΔG_{rxn}° of oxidation of glucose and moles ATP formed per mole of glucose

Conceptual Plan: Write a balanced reaction for glucose oxidation then

$$\Delta G_{rxn}^{\circ} = \sum n_p \Delta G_f^{\circ} \text{ (products)} - \sum n_r \Delta G_f^{\circ} \text{ (reactants) then } \Delta G_{rxn}^{\circ}\text{s} \rightarrow \textbf{moles ATP/mole glucose.}$$

$$\frac{\Delta G_{rxn}^{\circ} \text{ glucose oxidation}}{\Delta G_{rxn}^{\circ} \text{ ATP hydrolysis}}$$

Solution: $C_6H_{12}O_6(s) + 6 O_2(g) \rightarrow 6 CO_2(g) + 6 H_2O(l)$

Reactant/Product	ΔG_f° (kJ/mol from Appendix IIB)
$C_6H_{12}O_6(s)$	−910.4
$O_2(g)$	0.0
$CO_2(g)$	−394.4
$H_2O(l)$	−237.1

Be sure to pull data for the correct formula and phase.

$$\begin{aligned}\Delta G_{rxn}^{\circ} &= \sum n_p \Delta G_f^{\circ} \text{ (products)} - \sum n_r \Delta G_f^{\circ} \text{ (reactants)} \\ &= [6(\Delta G_f^{\circ}(CO_2(g))) + 6(\Delta G_f^{\circ}(H_2O(l)))] - [1(\Delta G_f^{\circ}(C_6H_{12}O_6(s))) + 6(\Delta G_f^{\circ}(O_2(g)))] \\ &= [6(-394.4 \text{ kJ}) + 6(-237.1 \text{ kJ})] - [1(-910.4 \text{ kJ}) + 6(0.0 \text{ kJ})] \\ &= [-3789.0 \text{ kJ}] - [-910.4 \text{ kJ}] \\ &= -2878.6 \text{ kJ}\end{aligned}$$

So the reaction is very spontaneous. $\dfrac{2878.6 \dfrac{\text{kJ generated}}{\text{mole glucose oxidized}}}{30.5 \dfrac{\text{kJ needed}}{\text{mole ATP reformed}}} = 94.4 \dfrac{\text{mole ATP reformed}}{\text{mole glucose oxidized}}$

Check: The units (mol) are correct. The free energy change for the glucose oxidation is large compared to the ATP hydrolysis, so we expect to reform many moles of ATP.

17.58   **Given:** $ATP(aq) + H_2O(l) \rightarrow ADP(aq) + P_i(aq)$ $\Delta G_{rxn}^{\circ} = -30.5 \text{ kJ at } 298 \text{ K}$
Find: ΔG_{rxn} when [ATP] = 0.0031 M, [ADP] = 0.0014 M and [P$_i$] = 0.0048 M
Conceptual Plan: ΔG_{rxn}°, [ATP], [ADP], [P$_i$], $T \rightarrow \Delta G$

$$\Delta G_{rxn} = \Delta G_{rxn}^{\circ} + RT \ln Q \text{ where } Q = \frac{[ADP][P_i]}{[ATP]}$$

Solution: $Q = \dfrac{[ADP][P_i]}{[ATP]} = \dfrac{(0.0014)(0.0048)}{0.0031} = 0.00216774$ then

$$\Delta G_{rxn} = \Delta G_{rxn}^{\circ} + RT \ln Q = -30.5 \text{ kJ} + \left(8.314 \frac{J}{K \cdot mol}\right)\left(\frac{1 \text{ kJ}}{1000 \text{ J}}\right)(298 \text{ K}) \ln (0.00216774) = -45.7 \text{ kJ}$$

Check: The units (kJ) are correct. The Q is less than one so we expect a free energy more negative than at standard conditions.

17.59   (a)   **Given:** $2 CO(g) + 2 NO(g) \rightarrow N_2(g) + 2 CO_2(g)$ **Find:** ΔG_{rxn}° and effect of increasing T on ΔG
Conceptual Plan: $\Delta G_{rxn}^{\circ} = \sum n_p \Delta G_f^{\circ} \text{ (products)} - \sum n_r \Delta G_f^{\circ} \text{ (reactants)}$
Solution:

Reactant/Product	ΔG_f° (kJ/mol from Appendix IIB)
$CO(g)$	−137.2
$NO(g)$	87.6
$N_2(g)$	0.0
$CO_2(g)$	−394.4

Be sure to pull data for the correct formula and phase.

$$\Delta G^\circ_{rxn} = \sum n_p \Delta G^\circ_f \text{(products)} - \sum n_r \Delta G^\circ_f \text{(reactants)}$$

$$= [1(\Delta G^\circ_f (N_2(g))) + 2(\Delta G^\circ_f (CO_2(g)))] - [2(\Delta G^\circ_f (CO(g))) + 2(\Delta G^\circ_f (NO(g)))]$$

$$= [1(0.0 \text{ kJ}) + 2(-394.4 \text{ kJ})] - [2(-137.2 \text{ kJ}) + 2(87.6 \text{ kJ})]$$

$$= [-788.8 \text{ kJ}] - [-99.2 \text{ kJ}]$$

$$= -689.6 \text{ kJ}$$

Because the number of moles of gas is decreasing, the entropy change is negative; ΔG will become less negative with increasing temperature.

Check: The units (kJ) are correct. The free energy change is negative because the carbon dioxide has such a low free energy of formation.

(b)   **Given:** $5 H_2(g) + 2 NO(g) \rightarrow 2 NH_3(g) + 2 H_2O(g)$ **Find:** ΔG°_{rxn} and effect of increasing T on ΔG
   Conceptual Plan: $\Delta G^\circ_{rxn} = \sum n_p \Delta G^\circ_f \text{(products)} - \sum n_r \Delta G^\circ_f \text{(reactants)}$
   Solution:

Reactant/Product	ΔG°_f (kJ/mol from Appendix IIB)
$H_2(g)$	0.0
$NO(g)$	87.6
$NH_3(g)$	−16.4
$H_2O(g)$	−228.6

Be sure to pull data for the correct formula and phase.

$$\Delta G^\circ_{rxn} = \sum n_p \Delta G^\circ_f \text{(products)} - \sum n_r \Delta G^\circ_f \text{(reactants)}$$

$$= [2(\Delta G^\circ_f (NH_3(g))) + 2(\Delta G^\circ_f (H_2O(g)))] - [5(\Delta G^\circ_f (H_2(g))) + 2(\Delta G^\circ_f (NO(g)))]$$

$$= [2(-16.4 \text{ kJ}) + 2(-228.6 \text{ kJ})] - [5(0.0 \text{ kJ}) + 2(87.6 \text{ kJ})]$$

$$= [-490.0 \text{ kJ}] - [175.2 \text{ kJ}]$$

$$= -665.2 \text{ kJ}$$

Because the number of moles of gas is decreasing, the entropy change is negative; so ΔG will become less negative with increasing temperature.

Check: The units (kJ) are correct. The free energy change is negative because ammonia and water have such a low free energy of formation.

(c)   **Given:** $2 H_2(g) + 2 NO(g) \rightarrow N_2(g) + 2 H_2O(g)$ **Find:** ΔG°_{rxn} and effect of increasing T on ΔG
   Conceptual Plan: $\Delta G^\circ_{rxn} = \sum n_p \Delta G^\circ_f \text{(products)} - \sum n_r \Delta G^\circ_f \text{(reactants)}$
   Solution:

Reactant/Product	ΔG°_f (kJ/mol from Appendix IIB)
$H_2(g)$	0.0
$NO(g)$	87.6
$N_2(g)$	0.0
$H_2O(g)$	−228.6

Be sure to pull data for the correct formula and phase.

$$\Delta G^\circ_{rxn} = \sum n_p \Delta G^\circ_f \text{(products)} - \sum n_r \Delta G^\circ_f \text{(reactants)}$$

$$= [1(\Delta G^\circ_f (N_2(g))) + 2(\Delta G^\circ_f (H_2O(g)))] - [2(\Delta G^\circ_f (H_2(g))) + 2(\Delta G^\circ_f (NO(g)))]$$

$$= [1(0.0 \text{ kJ}) + 2(-228.6 \text{ kJ})] - [2(0.0 \text{ kJ}) + 2(87.6 \text{ kJ})]$$

$$= [-457.2 \text{ kJ}] - [175.2 \text{ kJ}]$$

$$= -632.4 \text{ kJ}$$

Because the number of moles of gas is decreasing, the entropy change is negative; so ΔG will become less negative with increasing temperature.

Check: The units (kJ) are correct. The free energy change is negative because water has such a low free energy of formation.

(d)   **Given:** $2 NH_3(g) + 2 O_2(g) \rightarrow N_2O(g) + 3 H_2O(g)$ **Find:** ΔG°_{rxn} and effect of increasing T on ΔG
   Conceptual Plan: $\Delta G^\circ_{rxn} = \sum n_p \Delta G^\circ_f \text{(products)} - \sum n_r \Delta G^\circ_f \text{(reactants)}$

Solution:

Reactant/Product	ΔG_f° (kJ/mol from Appendix IIB)
$NH_3(g)$	-16.4
$O_2(g)$	0.0
$N_2O(g)$	103.7
$H_2O(g)$	-228.6

Be sure to pull data for the correct formula and phase.

$\Delta G_{rxn}^\circ = \sum n_p \Delta G_f^\circ \text{(products)} - \sum n_r \Delta G_f^\circ \text{(reactants)}$

$= [1(\Delta G_f^\circ(N_2O(g))) + 3(\Delta G_f^\circ(H_2O(g)))] - [2(\Delta G_f^\circ(NH_3(g))) + 2(\Delta G_f^\circ(O_2(g)))]$

$= [1(103.7 \text{ kJ}) + 3(-228.6 \text{ kJ})] - [2(-16.4 \text{ kJ}) + 2(0.0 \text{ kJ})]$

$= [-582.1 \text{ kJ}] - [-32.8 \text{ kJ}]$

$= -549.3 \text{ kJ}$

Because the number of moles of gas is constant, the entropy change will be small and slightly negative; so the magnitude of ΔG will decrease with increasing temperature.

Check: The units (kJ) are correct. The free energy change is negative because water has such a low free energy of formation. The entropy change is negative once the S° values are reviewed ($\Delta S_{rxn} = -9.6$ J/K).

17.60   (a)   **Given:** $NH_3(g) + HBr(g) \rightarrow NH_4Br(s)$ **Find:** ΔG_{rxn}° effect of decreasing T on ΔG
Conceptual Plan: $\Delta G_{rxn}^\circ = \sum n_p \Delta G_f^\circ \text{(products)} - \sum n_r \Delta G_f^\circ \text{(reactants)}$
Solution:

Reactant/Product	ΔG_f° (kJ/mol from Appendix IIB)
$NH_3(g)$	-16.4
$HBr(g)$	-53.4
$NH_4Br(s)$	-175.2

Be sure to pull data for the correct formula and phase.

$\Delta G_{rxn}^\circ = \sum n_p \Delta G_f^\circ \text{(products)} - \sum n_p \Delta G_f^\circ \text{(reactants)}$

$= [1(\Delta G_f^\circ(NH_4Br(s)))] - [1(\Delta G_f^\circ(NH_3(g))) + 1(\Delta G_f^\circ(HBr(g)))]$

$= [1(-175.2 \text{ kJ})] - [1(-16.4 \text{ kJ}) + 1(-53.4 \text{ kJ})]$

$= [-175.2 \text{ kJ}] - [-69.8 \text{ kJ}]$

$= -105.4 \text{ kJ}$

Because the number of moles of gas decreases, the entropy change will be negative and ΔG will become more negative with decreasing temperature.

Check: The units (kJ) are correct. The free energy change is negative because ammonium bromide has such a low free energy of formation.

(b)   **Given:** $CaCO_3(s) \rightarrow CaO(s) + CO_2(g)$ **Find:** ΔG_{rxn}° effect of decreasing T on ΔG
Conceptual Plan: $\Delta G_{rxn}^\circ = \sum n_p \Delta G_f^\circ \text{(products)} - \sum n_r \Delta G_f^\circ \text{(reactants)}$
Solution:

Reactant/Product	ΔG_f° (kJ/mol from Appendix IIB)
$CaCO_3(s)$	-1129.1
$CaO(s)$	-603.3
$CO_2(g)$	-394.4

Be sure to pull data for the correct formula and phase.

$\Delta G_{rxn}^\circ = \sum n_p \Delta G_f^\circ \text{(products)} - \sum n_r \Delta G_f^\circ \text{(reactants)}$

$= [1(\Delta G_f^\circ(CaO(s))) + 1(\Delta G_f^\circ(CO_2(g)))] - [1(\Delta G_f^\circ(CaCO_3(s)))]$

$= [1(-603.3 \text{ kJ}) + 1(-394.4 \text{ kJ})] - [1(-1129.1 \text{ kJ})]$

$= [-997.7 \text{ kJ}] - [-1129.1 \text{ kJ}]$

$= +131.4 \text{ kJ}$

Because the number of moles of gas increases, the entropy change will be positive and ΔG will become more positive with decreasing temperature.

Check: The units (kJ) are correct. The free energy change is positive because calcium carbonate has such a large free energy of formation.

(c) **Given:** $CH_4(g) + 3 Cl_2(g) \rightarrow CHCl_3(g) + 3 HCl(g)$ **Find:** $\Delta G°_{rxn}$ effect of decreasing T on ΔG
Conceptual Plan: $\Delta G°_{rxn} = \sum n_p \Delta G°_f \text{(products)} - \sum n_r \Delta G°_f \text{(reactants)}$
Solution:

Reactant/Product	$\Delta G°_f$ (kJ/mol from Appendix IIB)
$CH_4(g)$	−50.5
$Cl_2(g)$	0.0
$CHCl_3(g)$	−70.4
$HCl(g)$	−95.3

Be sure to pull data for the correct formula and phase.

$$\Delta G°_{rxn} = \sum n_p \Delta G°_f \text{(products)} - \sum n_r G°_f \text{(reactants)}$$
$$= [1(\Delta G°_f (CHCl_3(g))) + 3(\Delta G°_f (HCl(g)))] - [1(\Delta G°_f (CH_4(g))) + 3(\Delta G°_f (Cl_2(g)))]$$
$$= [1(-70.4 \text{ kJ}) + 3(-95.3 \text{ kJ})] - [1(-50.5 \text{ kJ}) + 3(0.0 \text{ kJ})]$$
$$= [-356.3 \text{ kJ}] - [-50.5 \text{ kJ}]$$
$$= -305.8 \text{ kJ}$$

Because the number of moles of gas is constant, the entropy change will be small. The entropy change is so small that the magnitude of ΔG will remain constant with decreasing temperature.

Check: The units (kJ) are correct. The free energy change is negative because chloroform and hydrogen chloride have such low free energies of formation. The entropy change is slightly positive once the $S°$ values are reviewed ($\Delta S_{rxn} = +0.7$ J/K).

17.61 With one exception, the formation of any oxide of nitrogen at 298 K requires more moles of gas as reactants than are formed as products. For example, 1 mole of N_2O requires 0.5 mole of O_2 and 1 mole of N_2. 1 mole of N_2O_3 requires 1 mole of N_2 and 1.5 moles of O_2, and so on. The exception is NO, where 1 mole of NO requires 0.5 mole of O_2 and 0.5 mole of N_2: $\frac{1}{2} N_2(g) + \frac{1}{2} O_2(g) \rightarrow NO(g)$. This reaction has a positive ΔS because what is essentially mixing of the N and O has taken place in the product.

17.62 $\Delta G°_f$ becomes less negative as the atomic number increases because the bond length increases and the bond strength decreases. There is less chemical energy stored in the longer bonds. The $\Delta S°_f$ increases as the atomic number increases because of the halides in the hydrogen halides. This is because the hydrogen halide has a low entropy component (hydrogen) and a high entropy component (the halide, which increases as the atomic number of the halide increases).

Challenge Problems

17.63 (a) **Given:** glutamate(aq) + $NH_3(aq) \rightarrow$ glutamine(aq) + $H_2O(l)$ $\Delta G°_{rxn} = 14.2$ kJ at 298 K   **Find:** K
Conceptual Plan: $\Delta G°_{rxn}, T \rightarrow K$

$$\Delta G°_{rxn} = -RT \ln K$$

Solution: $\Delta G°_{rxn} = -RT \ln K$ Rearrange to solve for K.

$$K = e^{\frac{-\Delta G°_{rxn}}{RT}} = e^{\frac{-(+14.2 \text{ kJ}) \times \frac{1000 \text{ J}}{1 \text{ kJ}}}{\left(8.314 \frac{J}{K \cdot mol}\right)(298 \text{ K})}} = e^{-5.73142} = 3.24 \times 10^{-3}$$

Check: The units (none) are correct. The free energy change is positive, and the reaction is nonspontaneous. This results in a small K.

(b) **Given:** pair ATP hydrolysis with glutamate/NH_3 reaction   **Find:** show coupled reactions, $\Delta G°_{rxn}$ and K
Conceptual Plan: Use the reaction mechanism shown, where $A = NH_3$ and $B =$ glutamate $(C_5H_8O_4N^-)$, then calculate $\Delta G°_{rxn}$ by adding free energies of reactions then $\Delta G°_{rxn}, T \rightarrow K$.

$$\Delta G°_{rxn} = -RT \ln K$$

Solution:

$$NH_3(aq) + ATP(aq) + H_2O(l) \rightarrow NH_3\text{—}P_i(aq) + ADP(aq) \qquad \Delta G°_{rxn} = -30.5 \text{ kJ}$$

$$NH_3\text{—}P_i(aq) + C_5H_8O_4N^-(aq) \rightarrow C_5H_9O_3N_2^-(aq) + H_2O(l) + P_i(aq) \qquad \Delta G°_{rxn} = +14.2 \text{ kJ}$$

$$\overline{NH_3(aq) + C_5H_8O_4N^-(aq) + ATP(aq) \rightarrow C_5H_9O_3N_2^-(aq) + ADP(aq) + P_i(aq) \quad \Delta G°_{rxn} = -16.3 \text{ kJ}}$$

then $\Delta G°_{rxn} = -RT \ln K$ Rearrange to solve for K.

$$K = e^{\frac{-\Delta G°_{rxn}}{RT}} = e^{\frac{-(-16.3 \text{ kJ}) \times \frac{1000 \text{ J}}{1 \text{ kJ}}}{\left(8.314 \frac{J}{K \cdot mol}\right)(298 \text{ K})}} = e^{6.57902} = 7.20 \times 10^2$$

Check: The units (none) are correct. The free energy change is negative, and the reaction is spontaneous. This results in a large K.

17.64   **Given:** flask configurations   **Find:** entropy and rank as increasing entropy

     Conceptual Plan: Calculate the number of possible states then $W \rightarrow S$ then rank.

$$W = \frac{n!}{(n-r)! \, r!} \text{ where } n = \text{\# particles and } r = \text{\# particle in one flask} \qquad S = k \ln W$$

Solution:

(a) $W = \dfrac{n!}{(n-r)! r!} = \dfrac{5!}{(0)! \, 5!} = 1$ then $S = k \ln W = \left(1.38 \times 10^{-23} \dfrac{J}{K}\right) \ln 1 = 0$

(b) $W = \dfrac{n!}{(n-r)! \, r!} = \dfrac{5!}{(2)! 3!} = 10$ then $S = k \ln W = \left(1.38 \times 10^{-23} \dfrac{J}{K}\right) \ln 10 = 3.18 \times 10^{-23} \text{ J/K}$

(c) $W = \dfrac{n!}{(n-r)! r!} = \dfrac{5!}{(1)! \, 4!} = 5$ then $S = k \ln W = \left(1.38 \times 10^{-23} \dfrac{J}{K}\right) \ln 5 = 2.22 \times 10^{-23} \text{ J/K}$

So (a) < (c) < (b).

Check: The units (J/K) are correct. The more possibilities for rearranging particles, the higher the entropy.

17.65   (a)   **Given:** $\frac{1}{2} H_2(g) + \frac{1}{2} Cl_2(g) \rightarrow HCl(g)$, define standard state as 2 atm   **Find:** $\Delta G°_f$

         Conceptual Plan: $\Delta G°_f, P_{H_2}, P_{Cl_2}, P_{HCl}, T \rightarrow$ **new $\Delta G°_f$**

$$\Delta G_{rxn} = \Delta G°_{rxn} + RT \ln Q \text{ where } Q = \frac{P_{HCl}}{P_{H_2}^{1/2} P_{Cl_2}^{1/2}}$$

         Solution: $\Delta G°_{rxn} = -95.3 \text{ kJ/mol}$ and $Q = \dfrac{P_{HCl}}{P_{H_2}^{1/2} P_{Cl_2}^{1/2}} = \dfrac{2}{2^{1/2} \, 2^{1/2}} = 1$ then

$$\Delta G_{rxn} = \Delta G°_{rxn} + RT \ln Q = -95.3 \frac{kJ}{mol} + \left(8.314 \frac{J}{K \cdot mol}\right)\left(\frac{1 \text{ kJ}}{1000 \text{ J}}\right)(298 \text{ K}) \ln(1) =$$

         $-95.3 \text{ kJ/mol} = -95{,}300 \text{ J/mol}$

         Because the number of moles of reactants and products are the same, the decrease in volume affects the entropy of both equally; so there is no change in $\Delta G°_f$.

         Check: The units (kJ) are correct. The Q is 1, so $\Delta G°_f$ is unchanged under the new standard conditions.

   (b)   **Given:** $N_2(g) + \frac{1}{2} O_2(g) \rightarrow N_2O(g)$, define standard state as 2 atm   **Find:** $\Delta G°_f$

         Conceptual Plan: $\Delta G°_f, P_{N_2}, P_{O_2}, P_{N_2O}, T \rightarrow$ **new $\Delta G°_f$**

$$\Delta G_{rxn} = \Delta G°_{rxn} + RT \ln Q \text{ where } Q = \frac{P_{N_2O}}{P_{N_2} P_{O_2}^{1/2}}$$

         Solution: $\Delta G°_f = +103.7 \text{ kJ/mol}$ and $Q = \dfrac{P_{N_2O}}{P_{N_2} P_{O_2}^{1/2}} = \dfrac{2}{2 \, 2^{1/2}} = \dfrac{1}{\sqrt{2}}$ then

$$\Delta G_{rxn} = \Delta G°_{rxn} + RT \ln Q = 103.7 \frac{kJ}{mol} + \left(8.314 \frac{J}{K \cdot mol}\right)\left(\frac{1 \text{ kJ}}{1000 \text{ J}}\right)(298 \text{ K}) \ln\left(\frac{1}{\sqrt{2}}\right) =$$

         $+102.8 \text{ kJ/mol} = +102{,}800 \text{ J/mol}$

         The entropy of the reactants (1.5 mol) is decreased more than the entropy of the product (1 mol). Because the product is relatively more favored at lower volume, $\Delta G°_f$ is less positive.

         Check: The units (kJ) are correct. The Q is less than 1, so $\Delta G°_f$ is reduced under the new standard conditions.

(c) **Given:** $1/2\ H_2(g) \rightarrow H(g)$, define standard state as 2 atm   **Find:** ΔG_f°
Conceptual Plan: $\Delta G_f^\circ, P_{H_2}, P_H, T \rightarrow$ **new** ΔG_f°

$$\Delta G_{rxn} = \Delta G_{rxn}^\circ + RT \ln Q \text{ where } Q = \frac{P_H}{P_{H_2}^{1/2}}$$

Solution: $\Delta G_f^\circ = +203.3$ kJ/mol and $Q = \dfrac{P_H}{P_{H_2}^{1/2}} = \dfrac{2}{2^{1/2}} = \sqrt{2}$ then

$$\Delta G_{rxn} = \Delta G_{rxn}^\circ + RT \ln Q = +203.3\frac{\text{kJ}}{\text{mol}} + \left(8.314\ \frac{\cancel{\text{J}}}{\text{K} \cdot \text{mol}}\right)\left(\frac{1 \text{ kJ}}{1000\ \cancel{\text{J}}}\right)(298\ \cancel{\text{K}})\ln(\sqrt{2}) =$$

$+204.2$ kJ/mol $= +204,200$ J/mol

The entropy of the product (1 mol) is decreased more than the entropy of the reactant (1/2 mol). Because the product is relatively less favored, ΔG_f° is more positive.

Check: The units (kJ) are correct. The Q is greater than 1, so ΔG_f° is increased under the new standard conditions.

17.66   **Given:** $H_2O(l) \rightarrow H_2O(s)$ at $-10\ ^\circ\text{C}$ $\Delta G_{freezing} = -210$ J/mol, $\Delta H_{fusion} = +5610$ J/mol   **Find:** ΔS_{univ} at $-10\ ^\circ\text{C}$
Conceptual Plan: $^\circ\text{C} \rightarrow \text{K}$ then $\Delta G_{freezing}, \Delta H_{fus}, T \rightarrow \Delta S_{univ}$

$$\text{K} = 273.15 + {}^\circ\text{C} \qquad \Delta G = \Delta H_{rxn} - T\Delta S_{rxn} \qquad \Delta S_{univ} = \Delta S_{sys} + \Delta S_{surr}$$

Solution: $T = -10\ ^\circ\text{C} + 273.15 = 263$ K, $\Delta H_{freezing} = -5610$ J/mol $= -\Delta H_{fusion}$ then $\Delta G = \Delta H_{rxn} - T\Delta S_{rxn}$

Rearrange to solve for ΔS $\Delta S_{freezing} = \dfrac{\Delta H_{freezing} - \Delta G_{freezing}}{T} = \Delta S_{sys}$ then

$$\Delta S_{univ} = \Delta S_{sys} + \Delta S_{surr} = \frac{\Delta H_{freezing} - \Delta G_{freezing}}{T} - \frac{\Delta H_{freezing}}{T} = -\frac{\Delta G_{freezing}}{T} = \frac{-(-210\ \text{J})}{263\ \text{K}}$$

$= +0.798$ J/K

Check: The units (J/K) are correct. The entropy for freezing should be negative because the solid has a more ordered structure.

17.67   (a) **Given:** $NH_4NO_3(s) \rightarrow HNO_3(g) + NH_3(g)$ **Find:** ΔG_{rxn}°
Conceptual Plan: $\Delta G_{rxn}^\circ = \sum n_p \Delta G_f^\circ \text{(products)} - \sum n_r \Delta G_f^\circ \text{(reactants)}$
Solution:

Reactant/Product	ΔG_f° (kJ/mol from Appendix IIB)
$NH_4NO_3(s)$	-183.9
$HNO_3(g)$	-73.5
$NH_3(g)$	-16.4

Be sure to pull data for the correct formula and phase.
$\Delta G_{rxn}^\circ = \sum n_p \Delta G_f^\circ \text{(products)} - \sum n_r \Delta G_f^\circ \text{(reactants)}$
$\quad = [1(\Delta G_f^\circ (HNO_3(g))) + 1(\Delta G_f^\circ (NH_3(g)))] - [1(\Delta G_f^\circ (NH_4NO_3(s)))]$
$\quad = [1(-73.5 \text{ kJ}) + 1(-16.4 \text{ kJ})] - [1(-183.9 \text{ kJ})]$
$\quad = [-89.9 \text{ kJ}] - [-183.9 \text{ kJ}]$
$\quad = +94.0 \text{ kJ}$

Check: The units (kJ) are correct. The free energy change is positive because ammonium nitrate has such a low free energy of formation.

(b) **Given:** $NH_4NO_3(s) \rightarrow N_2O(g) + 2\ H_2O(g)$ **Find:** ΔG_{rxn}°
Conceptual Plan: $\Delta G_{rxn}^\circ = \sum n_p \Delta G_f^\circ \text{(products)} - \sum n_r \Delta G_f^\circ \text{(reactants)}$
Solution:

Reactant/Product	ΔG_f° (kJ/mol from Appendix IIB)
$NH_4NO_3(s)$	-183.9
$N_2O(g)$	103.7
$H_2O(g)$	-228.6

Be sure to pull data for the correct formula and phase.

$$\Delta G^{\circ}_{\text{rxn}} = \sum n_p \Delta G^{\circ}_f \text{(products)} - \sum n_r \Delta G^{\circ}_f \text{(reactants)}$$
$$= [1(\Delta G^{\circ}_f (N_2O(g))) + 2(\Delta G^{\circ}_f (H_2O(g)))] - [1(\Delta G^{\circ}_f (NH_4NO_3(s)))]$$
$$= [1(103.7 \text{ kJ}) + 2(-228.6 \text{ kJ})] - [1(-183.9 \text{ kJ})]$$
$$= [-353.5 \text{ kJ}] - [-183.9 \text{ kJ}]$$
$$= -169.6 \text{ kJ}$$

Check: The units (kJ) are correct. The free energy change is negative because water has such a low free energy of formation.

(c)   **Given:** $NH_4NO_3(s) \rightarrow N_2(g) + \frac{1}{2}O_2(g) + 2\,H_2O(g)$ **Find:** $\Delta G^{\circ}_{\text{rxn}}$
Conceptual Plan: $\Delta G^{\circ}_{\text{rxn}} = \sum n_p \Delta G^{\circ}_f \text{(products)} - \sum n_r \Delta G^{\circ}_f \text{(reactants)}$
Solution:

Reactant/Product	ΔG°_f (kJ/mol from Appendix IIB)
$NH_4NO_3(s)$	−183.9
$N_2(g)$	0.0
$O_2(g)$	0.0
$H_2O(g)$	−228.6

Be sure to pull data for the correct formula and phase.

$$\Delta G^{\circ}_{\text{rxn}} = \sum n_p \Delta G^{\circ}_f \text{(products)} - \sum n_p \Delta G^{\circ}_f \text{(reactants)}$$
$$= [1(\Delta G^{\circ}_f (N_2(g))) + 1/2(\Delta G^{\circ}_f (O_2(g))) + 2(\Delta G^{\circ}_f (H_2O(g)))] - [1(\Delta G^{\circ}_f (NH_4NO_3(s)))]$$
$$= [1(0.0 \text{ kJ}) + 1/2(0.0 \text{ kJ}) + 2(-228.6 \text{ kJ})] - [1(-183.9 \text{ kJ})]$$
$$= [-457.2 \text{ kJ}] - [-183.9 \text{ kJ}]$$
$$= -273.3 \text{ kJ}$$

Check: The units (kJ) are correct. The free energy change is negative because water has such a low free energy of formation.

The second and third reactions are spontaneous, so we would expect decomposition products of N_2O, N_2, O_2, and H_2O in the gas phase. It is still possible for ammonium nitrate to remain as a solid because the thermodynamics of the reaction say nothing of the kinetics of the reaction (reaction can be extremely slow). Because all of the products are gases, the decomposition of ammonium nitrate will result in a large increase in volume (explosion). Some of the products aid in combustion, which could facilitate the combustion of materials near the ammonium nitrate. Also, N_2O is known as laughing gas, which has anesthetic and toxic effects on humans. The solid should not be kept in tightly sealed containers.

17.68   At equilibrium, ($P_{H_2O} = 18.3$ mmHg), $\Delta G_{\text{rxn}} = 0$.

$$Q = P^6_{H_2O} = \left(\frac{18.3 \text{ mmHg}}{\dfrac{760 \text{ mmHg}}{1 \text{ atm}}}\right)^6 = (0.02407894 \text{ atm})^6 = 1.949059 \times 10^{-10} \text{ and}$$

$\Delta G_{\text{rxn}} = \Delta G^{\circ}_{\text{rxn}} + RT \ln Q = 0$ Rearrange to solve for $\Delta G^{\circ}_{\text{rxn}}$ (at $P_{H_2O} = 760$ mmHg = standard conditions).

$$\Delta G^{\circ}_{\text{rxn}} = \Delta G_{\text{rxn}} - RT \ln Q = 0 - \left(8.314 \frac{J}{K \cdot mol}\right)\left(\frac{1 \text{ kJ}}{1000 \text{ J}}\right)(298 \text{ K}) \ln(1.949059 \times 10^{-10}) = 55.3948 \frac{kJ}{mol}$$

$$= 55.4 \frac{kJ}{mol}$$

17.69   **Given:** $\Delta H^{\circ}_{\text{vap}}$ table   **Find:** ΔS_{vap}; then compare values
Conceptual Plan: °C $\rightarrow$ K then $\Delta H^{\circ}_{\text{vap}}, T \rightarrow \Delta S_{\text{vap}}$

$$K = 273.15 + \text{°C} \qquad \Delta S_{\text{vap}} = \frac{-\Delta H_{\text{vap}}}{T}$$

Solution:

Diethyl ether: $T = 273.15 + 34.6 = 307.8$ K then $\Delta S_{\text{vap}} = \dfrac{\Delta H_{\text{vap}}}{T} = \dfrac{26.5 \text{ kJ}}{307.8 \text{ K}} = 0.0861$ kJ/K = 86.1 J/K

Acetone: $T = 273.15 + 56.1 = 329.3$ K then $\Delta S_{vap} = \dfrac{\Delta H_{vap}}{T} = \dfrac{29.1 \text{ kJ}}{329.3 \text{ K}} = 0.0884$ kJ/K $= 88.4$ J/K

Benzene: $T = 273.15 + 79.8 = 353.0$ K then $\Delta S_{vap} = \dfrac{\Delta H_{vap}}{T} = \dfrac{30.8 \text{ kJ}}{353.0 \text{ K}} = 0.0873$ kJ/K $= 87.3$ J/K

Chloroform: $T = 273.15 + 60.8 = 334.0$ K then $\Delta S_{vap} = \dfrac{\Delta H_{vap}}{T} = \dfrac{29.4 \text{ kJ}}{334.0 \text{ K}} = 0.0880$ kJ/K $= 88.0$ J/K

Ethanol: $T = 273.15 + 77.8 = 351.0$ K then $\Delta S_{vap} = \dfrac{\Delta H_{vap}}{T} = \dfrac{38.6 \text{ kJ}}{351.0 \text{ K}} = 0.110$ kJ/K $= 110.$ J/K

Water: $T = 273.15 + 100 = 373.15$ K then $\Delta S_{vap} = \dfrac{\Delta H_{vap}}{T} = \dfrac{40.7 \text{ kJ}}{373.15 \text{ K}} = 0.109$ kJ/K $= 109$ J/K

The first four values are very similar because they have similar intermolecular forces between molecules (dispersion forces and/or dipole–dipole interactions). The values for ethanol and water are higher because the intermolecular forces between molecules are stronger due to hydrogen bonding. Because of this, more energy is dispersed when these interactions are broken.

Conceptual Problems

17.70   A butane lighter is more efficient than an electric lighter because the butane lighter process is accomplished in one step. When you use an electric lighter, fuel is burned to generate electricity. This electricity is transmitted to the lighter through wires. Once the electricity reaches the lighter, it needs to be converted to heat. Each step must pay a heat tax. Using a butane lighter has fewer steps, so it pays a much lower tax.

17.71   (c) The spontaneity of a reaction says nothing about the speed of a reaction. It only states which direction the reaction will go as it approaches equilibrium.

17.72   Both (a) and (c) increase the entropy of the surroundings because they are exothermic reactions (adding thermal energy to the surroundings).

17.73   (b) has the largest decrease in the number of microstates from the initial to the final state. In (a), there are initially $\dfrac{9!}{4!\,4!\,1!} = 90$ microstates and $\dfrac{9!}{3!\,3!\,3!} = 1680$ microstates at the end; so $\Delta S > 0$. In (b), there are initially $\dfrac{9!}{4!\,2!\,3!} = 1260$ microstates and $\dfrac{9!}{6!\,3!\,0!} = 84$ microstates at the end; so $\Delta S < 0$. In (c), there are initially $\dfrac{9!}{3!\,4!\,2!} = 1260$ microstates and $\dfrac{9!}{3!\,4!\,2!} = 1260$ microstates at the end; so $\Delta S = 0$. Also, the final state in (b) has the least entropy.

17.74   (c) If the entropy of a system is increasing, the enthalpy of a reaction can be overcome (if necessary) by the entropy change as long as the temperature is high enough. If the entropy change of the system is decreasing, the reaction must be exothermic to be spontaneous because the entropy is working against spontaneity.

17.75   (c) Because the vapor pressure of water at 298 K is 23.78 mmHg or 0.03129 atm. As long as the desired pressure (0.010 atm) is less than the equilibrium vapor pressure of water, the reaction will be spontaneous.

17.76   Both (a) and (b) are true. Because $\Delta G_{rxn} = \Delta G^{\circ}_{rxn} + RT \ln Q$ and $\Delta G^{\circ}_{rxn} = -42.5$ kJ, in order for $\Delta G_{rxn} = 0$ the second term must be positive. This necessitates that $Q > 1$ or that we have more product than reactant. Any reaction at equilibrium has $\Delta G_{rxn} = 0$.

17.77   (c) The relationship between ΔG°_{rxn} and K is $\Delta G^{\circ}_{rxn} = -RT \ln K$. When $K > 1$, then the natural log of K is positive and $\Delta G^{\circ}_{rxn} < 0$. When $Q = 336$, the second term in $\Delta G_{rxn} = \Delta G^{\circ}_{rxn} + RT \ln Q$ is positive, and so at high temperature this term can dominate and make $\Delta G_{rxn} > 0$.

Questions for Group Work

17.78   For a sum of 2, there is only one possible combination: 1 and 1. For a sum of 12, there is only one possible combination: 6 and 6. For a sum of 7, there are three possible combinations: 1 and 6; 2 and 5; 3 and 4. Since a sum of 7 has the great number of combination, it has the greatest entropy.

17.79   The average of all of the dice will be 3.5 (one-sixth will be 1; one-sixth will be 2, one-sixth will be 3, …) or

$$\frac{\left(\frac{1}{6} \times 1 \times 10^6\right) + \left(\frac{1}{6} \times 2 \times 10^6\right) + \left(\frac{1}{6} \times 3 \times 10^6\right) + \left(\frac{1}{6} \times 4 \times 10^6\right) + \left(\frac{1}{6} \times 5 \times 10^6\right) + \left(\frac{1}{6} \times 6 \times 10^6\right)}{10^6} =$$

$$\frac{1}{6}(1 + 2 + 3 + 4 + 5 + 6) = \frac{1}{6}(21) = 3.5$$

It is very unlikely $\left(\left(\frac{1}{6}\right)^{10^6}\right)$ that the sum would be one million after the earthquake because they would all have to be 1s. It is just as unlikely that the sum would be six million after the earthquake because they would all have to be 6s. The total would be close to 3.5 million (1 million times the average); this illustrates the second law because the numbers on the dice are maximizing their dispersal.

17.80   The second law refers to the total entropy of the universe. If the entropy of the surroundings is dropping more than the entropy of the system is increasing, the process will not be spontaneous. For example, ice doesn't melt at $-10\ °C$, even though the entropy of the water increases in the process.

17.81 $3\ O_2(g) + 6\ H_2(g) + 6\ C(s, graphite) \longrightarrow C_6H_{12}O_6(s, glucose)$

	$\Delta H_f°(kJ/mol)$	$S°(J/K \cdot mol)$
$O_2(g)$	0	205.2
$H_2(g)$	0	130.7
$C(s, graphite)$	0	5.7
$C_6H_{12}O_6(s, glucose)$	-1273.3	212.1

$\Delta H°_{rxn} = \sum n_P \Delta H_f° \text{(products)} - \sum n_R \Delta H_f° \text{(reactants)}$
$= [1(\Delta H_f°(C_6H_{12}O_6(s, glucose)))] - [3(\Delta H_f°(O_2(g)) + 6(\Delta H_f°(H_2(g)) + 6(\Delta H_f°(C(s, graphite))]$
$= [1(-1273.3\ kJ)] - [3(0.0\ kJ) + 6(0.0\ kJ) + 6(0.0\ kJ)]$
$= [-1273.3\ kJ] - [0.0\ kJ]$
$= -1273.3\ kJ = \Delta H_f°(C_6H_{12}O_6\ (s, glucose)$

$\Delta S°_{rxn} = \sum n_P S°\text{(products)} - \sum n_R S°\text{(reactants)}$
$= [1(S°(C_6H_{12}O_6(s, glucose)))] - [3(S°(O_2(g)) + 6(S°(H_2(g)) + 6(S°(C(s, graphite))]$
$= [1(212.1\ J/K)] - [3(205.2\ J/K) + 6(130.7\ J/K) + 6(5.7\ J/K)]$
$= [-212.1\ J/K] - [1434.0\ J/K]$
$= -1221.9\ kJ$

$\Delta H_f°$ is zero for an element in its standard state at 25 °C. $S°$ is zero only for a perfect crystal at 0 K.

17.82 $\Delta G = \Delta H°_{rxn} - T\Delta S°_{rxn} = -1273.3\ kJ - (298\ K)\left(-1.2219\ \frac{kJ}{K}\right) = -909.2\ kJ.$ The reaction will be spontaneous under standard conditions because $\Delta G_f° < 0$. The determining factor is the energy: $\Delta H_f°$ is more negative than $-T\Delta S°$ is positive.

18 Electrochemistry

Balancing Redox Reactions

18.1   **Conceptual Plan: Separate the overall reaction into two half-reactions: one for oxidation and one for reduction. → Balance each half-reaction with respect to mass in the following order: (1) Balance all elements other than H and O, (2) balance O by adding H_2O, and (3) balance H by adding H^+. → Balance each half-reaction with respect to charge by adding electrons. (The sum of the charges on both sides of the equation should be made equal by adding electrons as necessary.) → Make the number of electrons in both half-reactions equal by multiplying one or both half-reactions by a small whole number. → Add the two half-reactions together, canceling electrons and other species as necessary. → Verify that the reaction is balanced with respect to both mass and charge.**

Solution:

(a)   Separate: $K(s) \rightarrow K^+(aq)$ and $Cr^{3+}(aq) \rightarrow Cr(s)$

Balance elements: $K(s) \rightarrow K^+(aq)$ and $Cr^{3+}(aq) \rightarrow Cr(s)$

Add electrons: $K(s) \rightarrow K^+(aq) + e^-$ and $Cr^{3+}(aq) + 3\,e^- \rightarrow Cr(s)$

Equalize electrons: $3\,K(s) \rightarrow 3\,K^+(aq) + 3\,e^-$ and $Cr^{3+}(aq) + 3\,e^- \rightarrow Cr(s)$

Add half-reactions: $3\,K(s) + Cr^{3+}(aq) + 3e^- \rightarrow 3\,K^+(aq) + 3e^- + Cr(s)$

Cancel electrons: $3\,K(s) + Cr^{3+}(aq) \rightarrow 3\,K^+(aq) + Cr(s)$

Check:

Reactants	Products
3 K atoms	3 K atoms
1 Cr atom	1 Cr atom
+3 charge	+3 charge

(b)   Separate: $Al(s) \rightarrow Al^{3+}(aq)$ and $Fe^{2+}(aq) \rightarrow Fe(s)$

Balance elements: $Al(s) \rightarrow Al^{3+}(aq)$ and $Fe^{2+}(aq) \rightarrow Fe(s)$

Add electrons: $Al(s) \rightarrow Al^{3+}(aq) + 3\,e^-$ and $Fe^{2+}(aq) + 2\,e^- \rightarrow Fe(s)$

Equalize electrons: $2\,Al(s) \rightarrow 2\,Al^{3+}(aq) + 6\,e^-$ and $3\,Fe^{2+}(aq) + 6\,e^- \rightarrow 3\,Fe(s)$

Add half-reactions: $2\,Al(s) + 3\,Fe^{2+}(aq) + 6e^- \rightarrow 2\,Al^{3+}(aq) + 6e^- + 3\,Fe(s)$

Cancel electrons: $2\,Al(s) + 3\,Fe^{2+}(aq) \rightarrow 2\,Al^{3+}(aq) + 3\,Fe(s)$

Check:

Reactants	Products
2 Al atoms	2 Al atoms
3 Fe atom	3 Fe atom
+6 charge	+6 charge

(c)   Separate: $BrO_3^-(aq) \rightarrow Br^-(aq)$ and $N_2H_4(g) \rightarrow N_2(g)$

Balance non-H & O elements: $BrO_3^-(aq) \rightarrow Br^-(aq)$ and $N_2H_4(g) \rightarrow N_2(g)$

Balance O with H_2O: $BrO_3^-(aq) \rightarrow Br^-(aq) + 3\,H_2O(l)$ and $N_2H_4(g) \rightarrow N_2(g)$

Balance H with H^+: $BrO_3^-(aq) + 6\,H^+(aq) \rightarrow Br^-(aq) + 3\,H_2O(l)$ and

$N_2H_4(g) \rightarrow N_2(g) + 4\,H^+(aq)$

Add electrons:

$BrO_3^-(aq) + 6\,H^+(aq) + 6\,e^- \rightarrow Br^-(aq) + 3\,H_2O(l)$ and $N_2H_4(g) \rightarrow N_2(g) + 4\,H^+(aq) + 4\,e^-$

Equalize electrons:
$2 \, BrO_3^-(aq) + 12 \, H^+(aq) + 12 \, e^- \rightarrow 2 \, Br^-(aq) + 6 \, H_2O(l)$ and $3 \, N_2H_4(g) \rightarrow 3 \, N_2(g) + 12 \, H^+(aq) + 12 \, e^-$

Add half-reactions: $2 \, BrO_3^-(aq) + \cancel{12 \, H^+(aq)} + 3 \, N_2H_4(g) + \cancel{12 \, e^-} \rightarrow 2 \, Br^-(aq) + 6 \, H_2O \, (l) + 3 \, N_2(g)$
$+ \cancel{12 \, H^+(aq)} + \cancel{12 \, e^-}$

Cancel electrons & others: $2 \, BrO_3^-(aq) + 3 \, N_2H_4(g) \rightarrow 2 \, Br^-(aq) + 6 \, H_2O \, (l) + 3 \, N_2(g)$

Check:

Reactants	Products
2 Br atoms	2 Br atoms
6 O atoms	6 O atoms
12 H atoms	12 H atoms
6 N atoms	6 N atoms
−2 charge	−2 charge

18.2   **Conceptual Plan: Separate the overall reaction into two half-reactions: one for oxidation and one for reduction.** → **Balance each half-reaction with respect to mass in the following order: (1) Balance all elements other than H and O, (2) balance O by adding H_2O, and (3) balance H by adding H^+.** → **Balance each half-reaction with respect to charge by adding electrons. (The sum of the charges on both sides of the equation should be made equal by adding electrons as necessary.)** → **Make the number of electrons in both half-reactions equal by multiplying one or both half-reactions by a small whole number.** → **Add the two half-reactions together, canceling electrons and other species as necessary.** → **Verify that the reaction is balanced with respect to both mass and charge.**

Solution:

(a)   Separate: $Zn(s) \rightarrow Zn^{2+}(aq)$ and $Sn^{2+}(aq) \rightarrow Sn(s)$
        Balance elements: $Zn(s) \rightarrow Zn^{2+}(aq)$ and $Sn^{2+}(aq) \rightarrow Sn(s)$
        Add electrons: $Zn(s) \rightarrow Zn^{2+}(aq) + 2 \, e^-$ and $Sn^{2+}(aq) + 2 \, e^- \rightarrow Sn(s)$
        Equalize electrons: $Zn(s) \rightarrow Zn^{2+}(aq) + 2 \, e^-$ and $Sn^{2+}(aq) + 2 \, e^- \rightarrow Sn(s)$
        Add half-reactions: $Zn(s) + Sn^{2+}(aq) + \cancel{2 \, e^-} \rightarrow Zn^{2+}(aq) + \cancel{2 \, e^-} + Sn(s)$
        Cancel electrons: $Zn(s) + Sn^{2+}(aq) \rightarrow Zn^{2+}(aq) + Sn(s)$

Check:

Reactants	Products
1 Zn atom	1 Zn atom
1 Sn atom	1 Sn atom
+2 charge	+2 charge

(b)   Separate: $Mg(s) \rightarrow Mg^{2+}(aq)$ and $Cr^{3+}(aq) \rightarrow Cr(s)$
        Balance elements: $Mg(s) \rightarrow Mg^{2+}(aq)$ and $Cr^{3+}(aq) \rightarrow Cr(s)$
        Add electrons: $Mg(s) \rightarrow Mg^{2+}(aq) + 2 \, e^-$ and $Cr^{3+}(aq) + 3 \, e^- \rightarrow Cr(s)$
        Equalize electrons: $3 \, Mg(s) \rightarrow 3 \, Mg^{2+}(aq) + 6 \, e^-$ and $2 \, Cr^{3+}(aq) + 6 \, e^- \rightarrow 2 \, Cr(s)$
        Add half-reactions: $3 \, Mg(s) \rightarrow 2 \, Cr^{3+}(aq) + \cancel{6 \, e^-} \rightarrow 3 \, Mg^{2+}(aq) + \cancel{6 \, e^-} + 2 \, Cr(s)$
        Cancel electrons: $3 \, Mg(s) + 2 \, Cr^{3+}(aq) \rightarrow 3 \, Mg^{2+}(aq) + 2 \, Cr(s)$

Check:

Reactants	Products
3 Mg atoms	3 Mg atoms
2 Cr atoms	2 Cr atoms
+6 charge	+6 charge

(c)   Separate: $MnO_4^-(aq) \rightarrow Mn^{2+}(aq)$ and $Al(s) \rightarrow Al^{3+}(aq)$
        Balance non-H & O elements: $MnO_4^-(aq) \rightarrow Mn^{2+}(aq)$ and $Al(s) \rightarrow Al^{3+}(aq)$
        Balance O with H_2O: $MnO_4^-(aq) \rightarrow Mn^{2+}(aq) + 4 \, H_2O(l)$ and $Al(s) \rightarrow Al^{3+}(aq)$
        Balance H with H^+: $MnO_4^-(aq) + 8 \, H^+(aq) \rightarrow Mn^{2+}(aq) + 4 \, H_2O(l)$ and $Al(s) \rightarrow Al^{3+}(aq)$
        Add electrons: $MnO_4^-(aq) + 8 \, H^+(aq) + 5 \, e^- \rightarrow Mn^{2+}(aq) + 4 \, H_2O(l)$ and $Al(s) \rightarrow Al^{3+}(aq) + 3 \, e^-$
        Equalize electrons:
        $3 \, MnO_4^-(aq) + 24 \, H^+(aq) + 15 \, e^- \rightarrow 3 \, Mn^{2+}(aq) + 12 \, H_2O(l)$ and $5 \, Al(s) \rightarrow 5 \, Al^{3+}(aq) + 15 \, e^-$
        Add half-reactions:
        $3 \, MnO_4^-(aq) + 24 \, H^+(aq) + \cancel{15 \, e^-} + 5 \, Al(s) \rightarrow 3 \, Mn^{2+}(aq) + 12 \, H_2O(l) + 5 \, Al^{3+}(aq) + \cancel{15 \, e^-}$
        Cancel electrons: $3 \, MnO_4^-(aq) + 24 \, H^+(aq) + 5 \, Al(s) \rightarrow 3 \, Mn^{2+}(aq) + 12 \, H_2O(l) + 5 \, Al^{3+}(aq)$

Check:

Reactants	Products
3 Mn atoms	3 Mn atoms
12 O atoms	12 O atoms
24 H atoms	24 H atoms
5 Al atoms	5 Al atoms
+21 charge	+21 charge

18.3 **Conceptual Plan:** Separate the overall reaction into two half-reactions: one for oxidation and one for reduction. Balance each half-reaction with respect to mass in the following order: (1) Balance all elements other than H and O, (2) balance O by adding H_2O, and (3) balance H by adding H^+. → Balance each half-reaction with respect to charge by adding electrons. (The sum of the charges on both sides of the equation should be made equal by adding electrons as necessary.) → Make the number of electrons in both half-reactions equal by multiplying one or both half-reactions by a small whole number. → Add the two half-reactions together, canceling electrons and other species as necessary. → Verify that the reaction is balanced with respect to both mass and charge.

Solution:

(a)

Separate: $PbO_2(s) \rightarrow Pb^{2+}(aq)$ and $I^-(aq) \rightarrow I_2(s)$

Balance non-H & O elements: $PbO_2(s) \rightarrow Pb^{2+}(aq)$ and $2\,I^-(aq) \rightarrow I_2(s)$

Balance O with H_2O: $PbO_2(s) \rightarrow Pb^{2+}(aq) + 2\,H_2O(l)$ and $2\,I^-(aq) \rightarrow I_2(s)$

Balance H with H^+: $PbO_2(s) + 4\,H^+(aq) \rightarrow Pb^{2+}(aq) + 2\,H_2O(l)$ and $2\,I^-(aq) \rightarrow I_2(s)$

Add electrons: $PbO_2(s) + 4\,H^+(aq) + 2\,e^- \rightarrow Pb^{2+}(aq) + 2\,H_2O(l)$ and $2\,I^-(aq) \rightarrow I_2(s) + 2\,e^-$

Equalize electrons: $PbO_2(s) + 4\,H^+(aq) + 2\,e^- \rightarrow Pb^{2+}(aq) + 2\,H_2O(l)$ and $2\,I^-(aq) \rightarrow I_2(s) + 2\,e^-$

Add half-reactions: $PbO_2(s) + 4\,H^+(aq) + 2\,\cancel{e^-} + 2\,I^-(aq) \rightarrow Pb^{2+}(aq) + 2\,H_2O(l) + I_2(s) + 2\,\cancel{e^-}$

Cancel electrons & others: $PbO_2(s) + 4\,H^+(aq) + 2\,I^-(aq) \rightarrow Pb^{2+}(aq) + 2\,H_2O(l) + I_2(s)$

Check:

Reactants	Products
1 Pb atom	1 Pb atom
2 O atoms	2 O atoms
4 H atoms	4 H atoms
2 I atoms	2 I atoms
+2 charge	+2 charge

(b)

Separate: $MnO_4^-(aq) \rightarrow Mn^{2+}(aq)$ and $SO_3^{2-}(aq) \rightarrow SO_4^{2-}(aq)$

Balance non-H & O elements: $MnO_4^-(aq) \rightarrow Mn^{2+}(aq)$ and $SO_3^{2-}(aq) \rightarrow SO_4^{2-}(aq)$

Balance O with H_2O: $MnO_4^-(aq) \rightarrow Mn^{2+}(aq) + 4\,H_2O(l)$ and $SO_3^{2-}(aq) + H_2O(l) \rightarrow SO_4^{2-}(aq)$

Balance H with H^+:

$MnO_4^-(aq) + 8\,H^+(aq) \rightarrow Mn^{2+}(aq) + 4\,H_2O(l)$ and $SO_3^{2-}(aq) + H_2O(l) \rightarrow SO_4^{2-}(aq) + 2\,H^+(aq)$

Add electrons: $MnO_4^-(aq) + 8\,H^+(aq) + 5\,e^- \rightarrow Mn^{2+}(aq) + 4\,H_2O(l)$ and

$SO_3^{2-}(aq) + H_2O(l) \rightarrow SO_4^{2-}(aq) + 2\,H^+(aq) + 2\,e^-$

Equalize electrons: $2\,MnO_4^-(aq) + 16\,H^+(aq) + 10\,e^- \rightarrow 2\,Mn^{2+}(aq) + 8\,H_2O(l)$ and

$5\,SO_3^{2-}(aq) + 5\,H_2O(l) \rightarrow 5\,SO_4^{2-}(aq) + 10\,H^+(aq) + 10\,e^-$

Add half-reactions: $2\,MnO_4^-(aq) + 6\,\cancel{16}\,H^+(aq) + 10\,\cancel{e^-} + 5\,SO_3^{2-}(aq) + \cancel{5\,H_2O(l)} \rightarrow$

$2\,Mn^{2+}(aq) + 3\,\cancel{8}\,H_2O(l) + 5\,SO_4^{2-}(aq) + \cancel{10\,H^+(aq)} + \cancel{10\,e^-}$

Cancel electrons: $2\,MnO_4^-(aq) + 6\,H^+(aq) + 5\,SO_3^{2-}(aq) \rightarrow 2\,Mn^{2+}(aq) + 3\,H_2O(l) + 5\,SO_4^{2-}(aq)$

Check:

Reactants	Products
2 Mn atoms	2 Mn atoms
23 O atoms	23 O atoms
6 H atoms	6 H atoms
5 S atoms	5 S atoms
−6 charge	−6 charge

(c)

Separate: $S_2O_3^{2-}(aq) \rightarrow SO_4^{2-}(aq)$ and $Cl_2(g) \rightarrow Cl^-(aq)$

Balance non-H & O elements: $S_2O_3^{2-}(aq) \rightarrow 2\,SO_4^{2-}(aq)$ and $Cl_2(g) \rightarrow 2\,Cl^-(aq)$

Balance O with H_2O: $S_2O_3^{2-}(aq) + 5\,H_2O(l) \rightarrow 2\,SO_4^{2-}(aq)$ and $Cl_2(g) \rightarrow 2\,Cl^-(aq)$

Balance H with H^+: $S_2O_3^{2-}(aq) + 5\,H_2O(l) \rightarrow 2\,SO_4^{2-}(aq) + 10\,H^+(aq)$ and $Cl_2(g) \rightarrow 2\,Cl^-(aq)$

Add electrons:
$$S_2O_3^{2-}(aq) + 5\,H_2O(l) \rightarrow 2\,SO_4^{2-}(aq) + 10\,H^+(aq) + 8\,e^- \quad \text{and} \quad Cl_2(g) + 2\,e^- \rightarrow 2\,Cl^-(aq)$$

Equalize electrons:
$$S_2O_3^{2-}(aq) + 5\,H_2O(l) \rightarrow 2\,SO_4^{2-}(aq) + 10\,H^+(aq) + 8\,e^- \quad \text{and} \quad 4\,Cl_2(g) + 8\,e^- \rightarrow 8\,Cl^-(aq)$$

Add half-reactions:
$$S_2O_3^{2-}(aq) + 5\,H_2O(l) + 4\,Cl_2(g) + 8\,e^- \rightarrow 2\,SO_4^{2-}(aq) + 10\,H^+(aq) + 8\,e^- + 8\,Cl^-(aq)$$

Cancel electrons: $S_2O_3^{2-}(aq) + 5\,H_2O(l) + 4\,Cl_2(g) \rightarrow 2\,SO_4^{2-}(aq) + 10\,H^+(aq) + 8\,Cl^-(aq)$

Check:

Reactants	Products
2 S atoms	2 S atoms
8 O atoms	8 O atoms
10 H atoms	10 H atoms
8 Cl atoms	8 Cl atoms
−2 charge	−2 charge

18.4 **Conceptual Plan: Separate the overall reaction into two half-reactions: one for oxidation and one for reduction. → Balance each half-reaction with respect to mass in the following order: (1) Balance all elements other than H and O, (2) balance O by adding H_2O, and (3) balance H by adding H^+. → Balance each half-reaction with respect to charge by adding electrons. (The sum of the charges on both sides of the equation should be made equal by adding electrons as necessary.) → Make the number of electrons in both half-reactions equal by multiplying one or both half-reactions by a small whole number. → Add the two half-reactions together, canceling electrons and other species as necessary. → Verify that the reaction is balanced with respect to both mass and charge.**

Solution:

(a) Separate: $\quad NO_2^-(aq) \rightarrow NO(g) \quad$ and $\quad I^-(aq) \rightarrow I_2(s)$

Balance non-H & O elements: $NO_2^-(aq) \rightarrow NO(g) \quad$ and $\quad 2\,I^-(aq) \rightarrow I_2(s)$

Balance O with H_2O: $NO_2^-(aq) \rightarrow NO(g) + H_2O(l) \quad$ and $\quad 2\,I^-(aq) \rightarrow I_2(s)$

Balance H with H^+: $NO_2^-(aq) + 2\,H^+(aq) \rightarrow NO(g) + H_2O(l) \quad$ and $\quad 2\,I^-(aq) \rightarrow I_2(s)$

Add electrons: $NO_2^-(aq) + 2\,H^+(aq) + e^- \rightarrow NO(g) + H_2O(l) \quad$ and $\quad 2\,I^-(aq) \rightarrow I_2(s) + 2\,e^-$

Equalize electrons: $2\,NO_2^-(aq) + 4\,H^+(aq) + 2\,e^- \rightarrow 2\,NO(g) + 2\,H_2O(l) \quad$ and $\quad 2\,I^-(aq) \rightarrow I_2(s) + 2\,e^-$

Add half-reactions: $2\,NO_2^-(aq) + 4\,H^+(aq) + 2\,e^- + 2\,I^-(aq) \rightarrow 2\,NO(g) + 2\,H_2O(l) + I_2(s) + 2\,e^-$

Cancel electrons: $2\,NO_2^-(aq) + 4\,H^+(aq) + 2\,I^-(aq) \rightarrow 2\,NO(g) + 2\,H_2O(l) + I_2(s)$

Check:

Reactants	Products
2 N atoms	2 N atoms
4 O atoms	4 O atoms
4 H atoms	4 H atoms
2 I atoms	2 I atoms
0 charge	0 charge

(b) Separate: $\quad ClO_4^-(aq) \rightarrow ClO_3^-(aq) \quad$ and $\quad Cl^-(aq) \rightarrow Cl_2(g)$

Balance non-H & O elements: $ClO_4^-(aq) \rightarrow ClO_3^-(aq) \quad$ and $\quad 2\,Cl^-(aq) \rightarrow Cl_2(g)$

Balance O with H_2O: $ClO_4^-(aq) \rightarrow ClO_3^-(aq) + H_2O(l) \quad$ and $\quad 2\,Cl^-(aq) \rightarrow Cl_2(g)$

Balance H with H^+: $ClO_4^-(aq) + 2\,H^+(aq) \rightarrow ClO_3^-(aq) + H_2O(l) \quad$ and $\quad 2\,Cl^-(aq) \rightarrow Cl_2(g)$

Add electrons: $ClO_4^-(aq) + 2\,H^+(aq) + 2\,e^- \rightarrow ClO_3^-(aq) + H_2O(l) \quad$ and $\quad 2\,Cl^-(aq) \rightarrow Cl_2(g) + 2\,e^-$

Equalize electrons: $ClO_4^-(aq) + 2\,H^+(aq) + 2\,e^- \rightarrow ClO_3^-(aq) + H_2O(l) \quad$ and $\quad 2\,Cl^-(aq) \rightarrow Cl_2(g) + 2\,e^-$

Add half-reactions: $ClO_4^-(aq) + 2\,H^+(aq) + 2\,e^- + 2\,Cl^-(aq) \rightarrow ClO_3^-(aq) + H_2O(l) + Cl_2(g) + 2\,e^-$

Cancel electrons: $ClO_4^-(aq) + 2\,H^+(aq) + 2\,Cl^-(aq) \rightarrow ClO_3^-(aq) + H_2O(l) + Cl_2(g)$

Check:

Reactants	Products
3 Cl atoms	3 Cl atoms
4 O atoms	4 O atoms
2 H atoms	2 H atoms
−1 charge	−1 charge

(c) Separate: $\quad NO_3^-(aq) \rightarrow NO(g) \quad$ and $\quad Sn^{2+}(aq) \rightarrow Sn^{4+}(aq)$

Balance non-H & O elements: $NO_3^-(aq) \rightarrow NO(g) \quad$ and $\quad Sn^{2+}(aq) \rightarrow Sn^{4+}(aq)$

Balance O with H_2O: $NO_3^-(aq) \rightarrow NO(g) + 2\,H_2O(l) \quad$ and $\quad Sn^{2+}(aq) \rightarrow Sn^{4+}(aq)$

Balance H with H^+: $NO_3^-(aq) + 4\,H^+(aq) \rightarrow NO(g) + 2\,H_2O(l)$ and $Sn^{2+}(aq) \rightarrow Sn^{4+}(aq)$

Add electrons: $NO_3^-(aq) + 4\,H^+(aq) + 3\,e^- \rightarrow NO(g) + 2\,H_2O(l)$ and $Sn^{2+}(aq) \rightarrow Sn^{4+}(aq) + 2\,e^-$

Equalize electrons:

$$2\,NO_3^-(aq) + 8\,H^+(aq) + 6\,e^- \rightarrow 2\,NO(g) + 4\,H_2O(l) \text{ and } 3\,Sn^{2+}(aq) \rightarrow 3\,Sn^{4+}(aq) + 6\,e^-$$

Add half-reactions:

$$2\,NO_3^-(aq) + 8\,H^+(aq) + \cancel{6\,e^-} + 3\,Sn^{2+}(aq) \rightarrow 2\,NO(g) + 4\,H_2O(l) + 3\,Sn^{4+}(aq) + \cancel{6\,e^-}$$

Cancel electrons: $2\,NO_3^-(aq) + 8\,H^+(aq) + 3\,Sn^{2+}(aq) \rightarrow 2\,NO(g) + 4\,H_2O(l) + 3\,Sn^{4+}(aq)$

Check:

Reactants	Products
2 N atoms	2 N atoms
6 O atoms	6 O atoms
8 H atoms	8 H atoms
3 Sn atoms	3 Sn atoms
+12 charge	+12 charge

18.5 **Conceptual Plan: Separate the overall reaction into two half-reactions: one for oxidation and one for reduction. → Balance each half-reaction with respect to mass in the following order: (1) Balance all elements other than H and O, (2) balance O by adding H_2O, (3) balance H by adding H^+, and (4) neutralize H^+ by adding enough OH^- to neutralize each H^+. Add the same number of OH^- ions to each side of the equation. → Balance each half-reaction with respect to charge by adding electrons. (The sum of the charges on both sides of the equation should be made equal by adding electrons as necessary.) → Make the number of electrons in both half-reactions equal by multiplying one or both half-reactions by a small whole number. → Add the two half-reactions together, canceling electrons and other species as necessary. → Verify that the reaction is balanced with respect to both mass and charge.**

Solution:

(a)   Separate: $ClO_2(aq) \rightarrow ClO_2^-(aq)$ and $H_2O_2(aq) \rightarrow O_2(g)$

Balance non-H & O elements: $ClO_2(aq) \rightarrow ClO_2^-(aq)$ and $H_2O_2(aq) \rightarrow O_2(g)$

Balance O with H_2O: $ClO_2(aq) \rightarrow ClO_2^-(aq)$ and $H_2O_2(aq) \rightarrow O_2(g)$

Balance H with H^+: $ClO_2(aq) \rightarrow ClO_2^-(aq)$ and $H_2O_2(aq) \rightarrow O_2(g) + 2\,H^+(aq)$

Neutralize H^+ with OH^-:

$$ClO_2(aq) \rightarrow ClO_2^-(aq) \text{ and } H_2O_2(aq) + 2\,OH^-(aq) \rightarrow O_2(g) + \underbrace{2\,H^+(aq) + 2\,OH^-(aq)}_{2\,H_2O(l)}$$

Add electrons: $ClO_2(aq) + e^- \rightarrow ClO_2^-(aq)$ and $H_2O_2(aq) + 2\,OH^-(aq) \rightarrow O_2(g) + 2\,H_2O(l) + 2\,e^-$

Equalize electrons:

$$2\,ClO_2(aq) + 2\,e^- \rightarrow 2\,ClO_2^-(aq) \text{ and } H_2O_2(aq) + 2\,OH^-(aq) \rightarrow O_2(g) + 2\,H_2O(l) + 2\,e^-$$

Add half-reactions:

$$2\,ClO_2(aq) + \cancel{2\,e^-} + H_2O_2(aq) + 2\,OH^-(aq) \rightarrow 2\,ClO_2^-(aq) + O_2(g) + 2\,H_2O(l) + \cancel{2\,e^-}$$

Cancel electrons: $2\,ClO_2(aq) + H_2O_2(aq) + 2\,OH^-(aq) \rightarrow 2\,ClO_2^-(aq) + O_2(g) + 2\,H_2O(l)$

Check:

Reactants	Products
2 Cl atoms	2 Cl atoms
8 O atoms	8 O atoms
4 H atoms	4 H atoms
−2 charge	−2 charge

(b)   Separate: $MnO_4^-(aq) \rightarrow MnO_2(s)$ and $Al(s) \rightarrow Al(OH)_4^-(aq)$

Balance non-H & O elements: $MnO_4^-(aq) \rightarrow MnO_2(s)$ and $Al(s) \rightarrow Al(OH)_4^-(aq)$

Balance O with H_2O: $MnO_4^-(aq) \rightarrow MnO_2(s) + 2\,H_2O(l)$ and $Al(s) + 4\,H_2O(l) \rightarrow Al(OH)_4^-(aq)$

Balance H with H^+:

$MnO_4^-(aq) + 4\,H^+(aq) \rightarrow MnO_2(s) + 2\,H_2O(l)$ and $Al(s) + 4\,H_2O(l) \rightarrow Al(OH)_4^-(aq) + 4\,H^+(aq)$

Neutralize H^+ with OH^-: $MnO_4^- + \underbrace{4\,H^+(aq) + 4\,OH^-(aq)}_{2\,4\,H_2O\,(l)} \rightarrow MnO_2(s) + 2\,\cancel{H_2O(l)} + 4\,OH^-(aq)$

and $Al(s) + \cancel{4\,H_2O(l)} + 4\,OH^-(aq) \rightarrow Al(OH)_4^-(aq) + \underbrace{4\,H^+(aq) + 4\,OH^-(aq)}_{\cancel{4\,H_2O(l)}}$

Add electrons: $MnO_4^-(aq) + 2\,H_2O(l) + 3\,e^- \rightarrow MnO_2(s) + 4\,OH^-(aq)$ and

$Al(s) + 4\,OH^-(aq) \rightarrow Al(OH)_4^-(aq) + 3\,e^-$

Equalize electrons: $MnO_4^-(aq) + 2 H_2O(l) + 3 e^- \rightarrow MnO_2(s) + 4 OH^-(aq)$ and

$$Al(s) + 4 OH^-(aq) \rightarrow Al(OH)_4^-(aq) + 3 e^-$$

Add half-reactions:

$MnO_4^-(aq) + 2 H_2O(l) + 3e^- + Al(s) + 4OH^-(aq) \rightarrow MnO_2(s) + 4OH^-(aq) + Al(OH)_4^-(aq) + 3e^-$

Cancel electrons: $MnO_4^-(aq) + 2 H_2O(l) + Al(s) \rightarrow MnO_2(s) + Al(OH)_4^-(aq)$

Check:

Reactants	Products
1 Mn atom	1 Mn atom
6 O atoms	6 O atoms
4 H atoms	4 H atoms
1 Al atom	1 Al atom
−1 charge	−1 charge

(c) Separate: $Cl_2(g) \rightarrow Cl^-(aq)$ and $Cl_2(g) \rightarrow ClO^-(aq)$

Balance non-H & O elements: $Cl_2(g) \rightarrow 2 Cl^-(aq)$ and $Cl_2(g) \rightarrow 2ClO^-(aq)$

Balance O with H_2O: $Cl_2(g) \rightarrow 2 Cl^-(aq)$ and $Cl_2(g) + 2 H_2O(l) \rightarrow 2 ClO^-(aq)$

Balance H with H^+: $Cl_2(g) \rightarrow 2 Cl^-(aq)$ and $Cl_2(g) + 2 H_2O(l) \rightarrow 2 ClO^-(aq) + 4 H^+(aq)$

Neutralize H^+ with OH^-:

$Cl_2(g) \rightarrow 2 Cl^-(aq)$ and $Cl_2(g) + 2 H_2O(l) + 4 OH^-(aq) \rightarrow 2 ClO^-(aq) + \underline{4 H^+(aq) + 4 OH^-(aq)}$

$$2\ 4\ H_2O(l)$$

Add electrons: $Cl_2(g) + 2 e^- \rightarrow 2 Cl^-(aq)$ and $Cl_2(g) + 4 OH^-(aq) \rightarrow 2 ClO^-(aq) + 2 H_2O(l) + 2 e^-$

Equalize electrons: $Cl_2(g) + 2 e^- \rightarrow 2 Cl^-(aq)$ and $Cl_2(g) + 4 OH^-(aq) \rightarrow 2 ClO^-(aq) + 2 H_2O(l) + 2 e^-$

Add half-reactions: $Cl_2(g) + 2e^- + Cl_2(g) + 4 OH^-(aq) \rightarrow 2 Cl^-(aq) + 2 ClO^-(aq) + 2 H_2O(l) + 2e^-$

Cancel electrons: $2 Cl_2(g) + 4 OH^-(aq) \rightarrow 2 Cl^-(aq) + 2 ClO^-(aq) + 2 H_2O(l)$

Simplify: $Cl_2(g) + 2 OH^-(aq) \rightarrow Cl^-(aq) + ClO^-(aq) + H_2O(l)$

Check:

Reactants	Products
2 Cl atoms	2 Cl atoms
2 O atoms	2 O atoms
2 H atoms	2 H atoms
−2 charge	−2 charge

18.6 **Conceptual Plan: Separate the overall reaction into two half-reactions: one for oxidation and one for reduction. → Balance each half-reaction with respect to mass in the following order: (1) balance all elements other than H and O, (2) balance O by adding H_2O, (3) balance H by adding H^+, and (4) neutralize H^+ by adding enough OH^- to neutralize each H^+. Add the same number of OH^- ions to each side of the equation. → Balance each half-reaction with respect to charge by adding electrons. (The sum of the charges on both sides of the equation should be made equal by adding electrons as necessary.) → Make the number of electrons in both half-reactions equal by multiplying one or both half-reactions by a small whole number. → Add the two half-reactions together, canceling electrons and other species as necessary. → Verify that the reaction is balanced both with respect to mass and with respect to charge.**

Solution:

(a) Separate: $MnO_4^-(aq) \rightarrow MnO_2(s)$ and $Br^-(aq) \rightarrow BrO_3^-(aq)$

Balance non-H & O elements: $MnO_4^-(aq) \rightarrow MnO_2(s)$ and $Br^-(aq) \rightarrow BrO_3^-(aq)$

Balance O with H_2O: $MnO_4^-(aq) \rightarrow MnO_2(s) + 2 H_2O(l)$ and $Br^-(aq) + 3 H_2O(l) \rightarrow BrO_3^-(aq)$

Balance H with H^+:

$MnO_4^-(aq) + 4 H^+(aq) \rightarrow MnO_2(s) + 2 H_2O(l)$ and $Br^-(aq) + 3 H_2O(l) \rightarrow BrO_3^-(aq) + 6 H^+(aq)$

Neutralize H^+ with OH^-: $MnO_4^-(aq) + \underline{4 H^+(aq) + 4 OH^-(aq)} \rightarrow MnO_2(s) + 2 H_2O(l) + 4 OH^-(aq)$

$$2\ 4\ H_2O(l)$$

and $Br^-(aq) + 3 H_2O(l) + 6 OH^-(aq) \rightarrow BrO_3^-(aq) + \underline{6 H^+(aq) + 6 OH^-(aq)}$

$$3\ 6\ H_2O(l)$$

Add electrons: $MnO_4^-(aq) + 2 H_2O(l) + 3 e^- \rightarrow MnO_2(s) + 4 OH^-(aq)$ and

$$Br^-(aq) + 6 OH^-(aq) \rightarrow BrO_3^-(aq) + 3 H_2O(l) + 6 e^-$$

Equalize electrons: $2 MnO_4^-(aq) + 4 H_2O(l) + 6 e^- \rightarrow 2 MnO_2(s) + 8 OH^-(aq)$ and

$$Br^-(aq) + 6 OH^-(aq) \rightarrow BrO_3^-(aq) + 3 H_2O(l) + 6 e^-$$

Add half-reactions: $2\,MnO_4^-(aq) + 1\cancel{4}\,H_2O(l) + \cancel{6\,e^-} + Br^-(aq) + 6\,\cancel{OH^-(aq)} \longrightarrow$
$2\,MnO_2(s) + 2\,\cancel{8}\,OH^-(aq) + BrO_3^-(aq) + 3\,\cancel{H_2O(l)} + \cancel{6\,e^-}$

Cancel electrons & others: $2\,MnO_4^-(aq) + H_2O(l) + Br^-(aq) \longrightarrow 2\,MnO_2(s) + 2\,OH^-(aq) + BrO_3^-(aq)$

Check:

Reactants	Products
2 Mn atoms	2 Mn atoms
9 O atoms	9 O atoms
2 H atoms	2 H atoms
1 Br atom	1 Br atom
−3 charge	−3 charge

(b) Separate: $Ag(s) + CN^-(aq) \longrightarrow Ag(CN)_2^-(aq)$ and $O_2(g) \longrightarrow$

Balance non-H & O elements: $Ag(s) + 2\,CN^-(aq) \longrightarrow Ag(CN)_2^-(aq)$ and $O_2(g) \longrightarrow$

Balance O with H_2O: $Ag(s) + 2\,CN^-(aq) \longrightarrow Ag(CN)_2^-(aq)$ and $O_2(g) \longrightarrow 2\,H_2O(l)$

Balance H with H^+: $Ag(s) + 2\,CN^-(aq) \longrightarrow Ag(CN)_2^-(aq)$ and $O_2(g) + 4\,H^+(aq) \longrightarrow 2\,H_2O(l)$

Neutralize H^+ with OH^-:

$Ag(s) + 2\,CN^-(aq) \longrightarrow Ag(CN)_2^-(aq)$ and $O_2(g) + \underbrace{4\,H^+(aq) + 4\,OH^-(aq)}_{2\,\cancel{4}\,H_2O} \longrightarrow 2\,\cancel{H_2O(l)} + 4\,OH^-(aq)$

Add electrons: $Ag(s) + 2\,CN^-(aq) \longrightarrow Ag(CN)_2^-(aq) + e^-$ and $O_2(g) + 2\,H_2O(l) + 4\,e^- \longrightarrow 4\,OH^-(aq)$

Equalize electrons:

$4\,Ag(s) + 8\,CN^-(aq) \longrightarrow 4\,Ag(CN)_2^-(aq) + 4\,e^-$ and $O_2(g) + 2\,H_2O(l) + 4\,e^- \longrightarrow 4\,OH^-(aq)$

Add half-reactions:

$4\,Ag(s) + 8\,CN^-(aq) + O_2(g) + 2\,H_2O(l) + \cancel{4\,e^-} \longrightarrow 4\,Ag(CN)_2^-(aq) + \cancel{4\,e^-} + 4\,OH^-(aq)$

Cancel electrons: $4\,Ag(s) + 8\,CN^-(aq) + O_2(g) + 2\,H_2O(l) \longrightarrow 4\,Ag(CN)_2^-(aq) + 4\,OH^-(aq)$

Check:

Reactants	Products
4 Ag atoms	4 Ag atoms
8 C atoms	8 C atoms
8 N atoms	8 N atoms
4 O atoms	4 O atoms
4 H atoms	4 H atoms
−8 charge	−8 charge

(c) Separate: $NO_2^-(aq) \longrightarrow NH_3(g)$ and $Al(s) \longrightarrow AlO_2^-(aq)$

Balance non-H & O elements: $NO_2^-(aq) \longrightarrow NH_3(g)$ and $Al(s) \longrightarrow AlO_2^-(aq)$

Balance O with H_2O: $NO_2^-(aq) \longrightarrow NH_3(g) + 2\,H_2O(l)$ and $Al(s) + 2\,H_2O(l) \longrightarrow AlO_2^-(aq)$

Balance H with H^+: $NO_2^-(aq) + 7\,H^+(aq) \longrightarrow NH_3(g) + 2\,H_2O(l)$ and

$Al(s) + 2\,H_2O(l) \longrightarrow AlO_2^-(aq) + 4\,H^+(aq)$

Neutralize H^+ with OH^-: $NO_2^-(aq) + \underbrace{7\,H^+(aq) + 7\,OH^-(aq)}_{5\,\cancel{7}\,H_2O(l)} \longrightarrow NH_3(g) + 2\,\cancel{H_2O(l)} + 7\,OH^-(aq)$ and

$Al(s) + 2\,\cancel{H_2O(l)} + 4\,OH^-(aq) \longrightarrow AlO_2^-(aq) + \underbrace{4\,H^+(aq) + 4\,OH^-(aq)}_{2\,\cancel{4}\,H_2O(l)}$

Add electrons: $NO_2^-(aq) + 5\,H_2O(l) + 6\,e^- \longrightarrow NH_3(g) + 7\,OH^-(aq)$ and

$Al(s) + 4\,OH^-(aq) \longrightarrow AlO_2^-(aq) + 2\,H_2O(l) + 3\,e^-$

Equalize electrons: $NO_2^-(aq) + 5\,H_2O(l) + 6\,e^- \longrightarrow NH_3(g) + 7\,OH^-(aq)$ and

$2\,Al(s) + 8\,OH^-(aq) \longrightarrow 2\,AlO_2^-(aq) + 4\,H_2O(l) + 6\,e^-$

Add half-reactions: $NO_2^-(aq) + 1\cancel{5}\,H_2O(l) + \cancel{6\,e^-} + 2\,Al(s) + 1\cancel{8}\,OH^-(aq) \longrightarrow$
$NH_3(g) + \cancel{7\,OH^-(aq)} + 2\,AlO_2^-(aq) + \cancel{4\,H_2O(l)} + \cancel{6\,e^-}$

Cancel electrons & others: $NO_2^-(aq) + H_2O(l) + 2\,Al(s) + OH^-(aq) \longrightarrow NH_3(g) + 2\,AlO_2^-(aq)$

Check:

Reactants	Products
1 N atom	1 N atom
4 O atoms	4 O atoms
3 H atoms	3 H atoms
2 Al atoms	2 Al atoms
−2 charge	−2 charge

Voltaic Cells, Standard Cell Potentials, and Direction of Spontaneity

18.7   **Given:** voltaic cell overall redox reaction
        Find: Sketch voltaic cell, labeling anode, cathode, all species, and direction of electron flow
        Conceptual Plan: Separate the overall reaction into two half-cell reactions and add electrons as needed to balance reactions. Put the anode reaction on the left (oxidation = electrons as product) and the cathode reaction on the right (reduction = electrons as reactant). Electrons flow from anode to cathode.
        Solution:

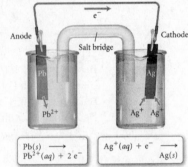

     (a) $2 \, Ag^+(aq) + Pb(s) \rightarrow 2 \, Ag(s) + Pb^{2+}(aq)$ separates to $2 \, Ag^+(aq)$
          $\rightarrow 2 \, Ag(s)$ and $Pb(s) \rightarrow Pb^{2+}(aq)$ then add electrons to balance to get
          the cathode reaction—$2 \, Ag^+(aq) + 2 \, e^- \rightarrow 2 \, Ag(s)$—and the anode
          reaction—$Pb(s) \rightarrow Pb^{2+}(aq) + 2 \, e^-$.
          Because we have $Pb(s)$ as the reactant for the oxidation, it will be our
          anode. Because we have $Ag(s)$ as the product for the reduction, it will be
          our cathode. Simplify the cathode reaction, dividing all terms by 2.

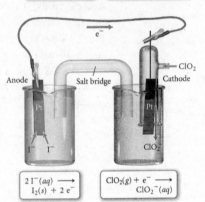

     (b) $2 \, ClO_2(g) + 2 \, I^-(aq) \rightarrow 2 \, ClO_2^-(aq) + I_2(s)$ separates to $2 \, ClO_2(g)$
          $\rightarrow 2 \, ClO_2^-(aq)$ and $2 \, I^-(aq) \rightarrow I_2(s)$ then add electrons to balance to
          get the cathode reaction—$2 \, ClO_2(g) + 2 \, e^- \rightarrow 2 \, ClO_2^-(aq)$—and
          the anode reaction—$2 \, I^-(aq) \rightarrow I_2(s) + 2 \, e^-$.
          Because we have $I^-(aq)$ as the reactant for the oxidation, we will
          need to use Pt as our anode. Because we have $ClO_2^-(aq)$ as the prod-
          uct for the reduction, we will need to use Pt as our cathode. Because
          $ClO_2(g)$ is our reactant for the reduction, we need to use an electrode
          assembly like that used for a SHE. Simplify the cathode reaction,
          dividing all terms by 2.

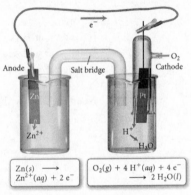

     (c) $O_2(g) + 4 \, H^+(aq) + 2 \, Zn(s) \rightarrow 2 \, H_2O(l) + 2 \, Zn^{2+}(aq)$ sepa-
          rates to $O_2(g) + 4 \, H^+(aq) \rightarrow 2 \, H_2O(l)$ and $2 \, Zn(s) \rightarrow 2 \, Zn^{2+}(aq)$
          then add electrons to balance to get the cathode reaction—
          $O_2(g) + 4 \, H^+(aq) + 4 \, e^- \rightarrow 2 \, H_2O(l)$—and the anode reaction—
          $2 \, Zn(s) \rightarrow 2 \, Zn^{2+}(aq) + 4 \, e^-$.
          Because we have $Zn(s)$ as the reactant for the oxidation, it will be our
          anode. Because we have $H_2O(l)$ as the product for the reduction, we will
          need to use Pt as our cathode. Because $O_2(g)$ is our reactant for the re-
          duction, we need to use an electrode assembly like that used for a SHE.
          Simplify the anode reaction, dividing all terms by 2.

18.8   **Given:** voltaic cell overall redox reaction
        Find: Sketch voltaic cell, labeling anode, cathode, all species, and direction of electron flow
        Conceptual Plan: Separate the overall reaction into two half-cell reactions and add electrons as needed to balance reactions. Put the anode reaction on the left (oxidation = electrons as product) and the cathode reaction on the right (reduction = electrons as reactant). Electrons flow from anode to cathode.

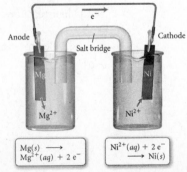

        Solution:

     (a) $Ni^{2+}(aq) + Mg(s) \rightarrow Ni(s) + Mg^{2+}(aq)$ separates to $Ni^{2+}(aq) \rightarrow$
          $Ni(s)$ and $Mg(s) \rightarrow Mg^{2+}(aq)$ then add electrons to balance to get
          the cathode reaction—$Ni^{2+}(aq) + 2 \, e^- \rightarrow Ni(s)$—and the anode
          reaction—$Mg(s) \rightarrow Mg^{2+}(aq) + 2 \, e^-$.

Because we have Mg(s) as the reactant for the oxidation, it will be our anode. Because we have Ni(s) as the product for the reduction, it will be our cathode.

(b) $2 H^+(aq) + Fe(s) \rightarrow H_2(g) + Fe^{2+}(aq)$ separates to $2 H^+(aq) \rightarrow$
$H_2(g)$ and $Fe(s) \rightarrow Fe^{2+}(aq)$ then add electrons to balance to get
the cathode reaction—$2 H^+(aq) + 2 e^- \rightarrow H_2(g)$—and the anode
reaction—$Fe(s) \rightarrow Fe^{2+}(aq) + 2 e^-$.
Because we have Fe(s) as the reactant for the oxidation, it will be our
anode. Because we have $H_2(g)$ as the product for the reduction, we will
need to use Pt as our cathode and the product can leave using an electrode assembly like that used for a SHE.

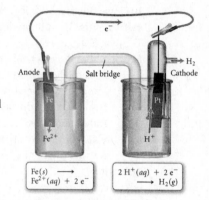

$$\begin{array}{cc} Fe(s) \longrightarrow & 2 H^+(aq) + 2 e^- \\ Fe^{2+}(aq) + 2 e^- & \longrightarrow H_2(g) \end{array}$$

(c) $2 NO_3^-(aq) + 8 H^+(aq) + 3 Cu(s) \rightarrow 2 NO(g) + 4 H_2O(l)$
$+ 3 Cu^{2+}(aq)$ separates to $2 NO_3^-(aq) + 8 H^+(aq) \rightarrow$
$2 NO(g) + 4 H_2O(l)$ and $3 Cu(s) \rightarrow 3 Cu^{2+}(aq)$ then
add electrons to balance to get the cathode reaction—
$2 NO_3^-(aq) + 8 H^+(aq) + 6 e^- \rightarrow 2 NO(g) + 4 H_2O(l)$—
and the anode reaction—$3 Cu(s) \rightarrow 3 Cu^{2+}(aq) + 6 e^-$.
Because we have Cu(s) as the reactant for the oxidation, it will
be our anode. Because we have $H_2O(l)$ and NO(g) as the products for the reduction, we will need to use Pt as our cathode
and the gaseous product can leave, using an electrode assembly like that used for a SHE.

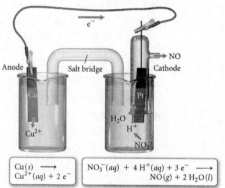

$$\begin{array}{cc} Cu(s) \longrightarrow & NO_3^-(aq) + 4 H^+(aq) + 3 e^- \longrightarrow \\ Cu^{2+}(aq) + 2 e^- & NO(g) + 2 H_2O(l) \end{array}$$

18.9   **Given:** overall reactions from Problem 7   **Find:** E°_{cell}
Conceptual Plan: Use Table 18.1 to look up half-reactions from the solution of Problem 7. Calculate the
standard cell potential by subtracting the electrode potential of the anode from the electrode potential of the
cathode: $E^\circ_{cell} = E^\circ_{cathode} - E^\circ_{anode}$.
Solution:
(a) $Ag^+(aq) + e^- \rightarrow Ag(s)\ E^\circ_{red} = 0.80\ V = E^\circ_{cathode}$ and $Pb(s) \rightarrow Pb^{2+}(aq) + 2 e^-\ E^\circ_{red} = -0.13\ V = E^\circ_{anode}$.
        Then $E^\circ_{cell} = E^\circ_{cathode} - E^\circ_{anode} = 0.80\ V - (-0.13\ V) = 0.93\ V$.
(b) $ClO_2(g) + e^- \rightarrow ClO_2^-(aq)\ E^\circ_{red} = 0.95\ V = E^\circ_{cathode}$ and $2 I^-(aq) \rightarrow I_2(s) + 2 e^-\ E^\circ_{red} = +0.54\ V = E^\circ_{anode}$.
        Then $E^\circ_{cell} = E^\circ_{cathode} - E^\circ_{anode} = 0.95\ V - 0.54\ V = 0.41\ V$.
(c) $O_2(g) + 4 H^+(aq) + 4 e^- \rightarrow 2 H_2O(l)\ E^\circ_{red} = 1.23\ V$ and $Zn(s) \rightarrow Zn^{2+}(aq) + 2 e^-\ E^\circ_{red} = -0.76\ V =$
        E°_{anode}. Then $E^\circ_{cell} = E^\circ_{cathode} - E^\circ_{anode} = 1.23\ V - (-0.76\ V) = 1.99\ V$.

Check: The units (V) are correct. All of the voltages are positive, which is consistent with a voltaic cell.

18.10   **Given:** overall reactions from Problem 8   **Find:** E°_{cell}
Conceptual Plan: Use Table 18.1 to look up half-reactions from the solution of Problem 8. Calculate the
standard cell potential by subtracting the electrode potential of the anode from the electrode potential of the
cathode: $E^\circ_{cell} = E^\circ_{cathode} - E^\circ_{anode}$.
Solution:
(a) $Ni^{2+}(aq) + 2 e^- \rightarrow Ni(s)\ E^\circ_{red} = -0.23\ V = E^\circ_{cathode}$ and $Mg(s) \rightarrow Mg^{2+}(aq) + 2 e^-\ E^\circ_{red} = -2.37\ V =$
        E°_{anode}. Then $E^\circ_{cell} = E^\circ_{cathode} - E^\circ_{anode} = -0.23\ V - (-2.37\ V) = 2.14\ V$.
(b) $2 H^+(aq) + 2 e^- \rightarrow H_2(g)\ E^\circ_{red} = 0.00\ V = E^\circ_{cathode}$ and $Fe(s) \rightarrow Fe^{2+}(aq) + 2 e^-\ E^\circ_{red} = -0.45\ V = E^\circ_{anode}$.
        Then $E^\circ_{cell} = E^\circ_{cathode} - E^\circ_{anode} = 0.00\ V - (-0.45\ V) = 0.45\ V$.
(c) $NO_3^-(aq) + 4 H^+(aq) + 3 e^- \rightarrow NO(g) + 2 H_2O(l)\quad E^\circ_{red} = 0.96\ V = E^\circ_{cathode}$ and $Cu(s) \rightarrow$
        $Cu^{2+}(aq) + 2 e^-\ E^\circ_{red} = -0.34\ V = E^\circ_{anode}$. Then $E^\circ_{cell} = E^\circ_{cathode} - E^\circ_{anode} = 0.96\ V - 0.34\ V = 0.62\ V$.

Check: The units (V) are correct. All of the voltages are positive, which is consistent with a voltaic cell.

18.11   **Given:** voltaic cell drawing
Find: (a) Determine electron flow direction, anode, and cathode; (b) write balanced overall reaction and calculate
E°_{cell}; (c) label electrodes as + and −; and (d) find directions of anions and cations from salt bridge.

Conceptual Plan: Look at each half-cell and write a reduction reaction by using electrode and solution composition and adding electrons to balance. Look up half-reactions and standard reduction potentials in Table 18.1. Because this is a voltaic cell, the cell potentials must be assigned to give a positive $E°_{cell}$. Calculate the standard cell potential by subtracting the electrode potential of the anode from the electrode potential of the cathode, $E°_{cell} = E°_{cathode} - E°_{anode}$, choosing the electrode assignments to give a positive $E°_{cell}$.

(a)   **Label the electrode where the oxidation occurs as the anode. Label the electrode where the reduction occurs as the cathode. Electrons flow from anode to cathode.**

(b)   **Take two half-cell reactions and multiply the reactions as necessary to equalize the number of electrons transferred. Add the two half-cell reactions and cancel electrons and any other species.**

(c)   **Label anode as ($-$) and cathode as ($+$).**

(d)   **Cations will flow from the salt bridge toward the cathode, and the anions will flow from the salt bridge toward the anode.**

Solution:

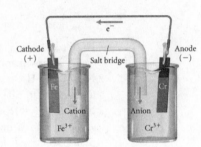

left side: $Fe^{3+}(aq) \rightarrow Fe(s)$; right side: $Cr^{3+}(aq) \rightarrow Cr(s)$. Add electrons to balance $Fe^{3+}(aq) + 3 e^- \rightarrow Fe(s)$ and right side—$Cr^{3+}(aq) + 3 e^- \rightarrow Cr(s)$. Look up cell standard reduction potentials: $Fe^{3+}(aq) + 3 e^- \rightarrow Fe(s)$ $E°_{red} = -0.036$ V and $Cr^{3+}(aq) + 3 e^- \rightarrow Cr(s)$ $E°_{red} = -0.73$ V.

To get a positive cell potential, the second reaction is the oxidation reaction (anode). $E°_{cell} = E°_{cathode} - E°_{anode} = -0.036$ V $- (-0.73$ V$) = + 0.69$ V (a, c, and d).

(b) Add two half-reactions with the second reaction reversed.

$Fe^{3+}(aq) + \cancel{3e^-} + Cr(s) \rightarrow Fe(s) + Cr^{3+}(aq) + \cancel{3e^-}$

Cancel electrons to get $Fe^{3+}(aq) + Cr(s) \rightarrow Fe(s) + Cr^{3+}(aq)$.

Check: All atoms and charge are balanced. The units (V) are correct. The cell potential is positive, which is consistent with a voltaic cell.

18.12   **Given:** voltaic cell drawing

Find: (a) Determine electron flow direction, anode, and cathode; (b) write balanced overall reaction and calculate $E°_{cell}$; (c) label electrodes as $+$ and $-$; and (d) find directions of anions and cations from salt bridge.

Conceptual Plan: Look at each half-cell and write a reduction reaction by using electrode and solution composition and adding electrons to balance. Look up half-reactions and standard reduction potentials in Table 18.1. Because this is a voltaic cell, the cell potentials must be assigned to give a positive $E°_{cell}$. Calculate the standard cell potential by subtracting the electrode potential of the anode from the electrode potential of the cathode, $E°_{cell} = E°_{cathode} - E°_{anode}$, choosing the electrode assignments to give a positive $E°_{cell}$.

(a)   **Label the electrode where the oxidation occurs as the anode. Label the electrode where the reduction occurs as the cathode. Electrons flow from anode to cathode.**

(b)   **Take two half-cell reactions and multiply the reactions as necessary to equalize the number of electrons transferred. Add the two half-cell reactions and cancel electrons and any other species.**

(c)   **Label anode as ($-$) and cathode as ($+$).**

(d)   **Cations will flow from the salt bridge toward the cathode, and the anions will flow from the salt bridge toward the anode.**

Solution: left side: $Pb^{2+}(aq) \rightarrow Pb(s)$; right side: $Cl_2(g) \rightarrow$ $2 Cl^-(aq)$. Add electrons to balance $Pb^{2+}(aq) + 2 e^- \rightarrow Pb(s)$ and right side—$Cl_2(g) + 2 e^- \rightarrow 2 Cl^-(aq)$. Look up cell standard reduction potentials: $Pb^{2+}(aq) + 2 e^- \rightarrow Pb(s)$ $E°_{red} = -0.13$ V and $Cl_2(g) + 2 e^- \rightarrow 2 Cl^- (aq)$ $E°_{red} = 1.36$ V. To get a positive cell potential, the first reaction is the oxidation reaction (anode). $E°_{cell} = E°_{cathode} - E°_{anode} = 1.36$ V $- (-0.13$ V$) = +1.49$ V (a, c, and d).

(b) Add two half-reactions with the first reaction reversed.

$Pb(s) + Cl_2(g) + \cancel{2e^-} \rightarrow Pb^{2+}(aq) + \cancel{2e^-} + 2 Cl^-(aq)$

Cancel electrons to get $Pb(s) + Cl_2(g) \rightarrow Pb^{2+}(aq) + 2 Cl^-(aq)$.

Check: All atoms and charge are balanced. The units (V) are correct. The cell potential is positive, which is consistent with a voltaic cell.

18.13   **Given:** overall reactions from Problem 7   **Find:** line notation
Conceptual Plan: Use the solution from Problem 7. Write the oxidation half-reaction components on the left and the reduction on the right. A double vertical line ($\|$), indicating the salt bridge, separates the two half-reactions. Substances in different phases are separated by a single vertical line ($|$), which represents the boundary between the phases. For some redox reactions, the reactants and products of one or both of the half-reactions may be in the same phase. In these cases, the reactants and products are separated from each other with a comma in the line diagram. Such cells use an inert electrode, such as platinum (Pt) or graphite, as the anode or cathode (or both).
Solution:
(a)   Reduction reaction: $Ag^+(aq) + e^- \rightarrow Ag(s)$; oxidation reaction: $Pb(s) \rightarrow Pb^{2+}(aq) + 2\,e^-$ so
$Pb(s)\,|\,Pb^{2+}(aq)\,\|\,Ag^+(aq)\,|\,Ag(s)$
(b)   Reduction reaction: $ClO_2(g) + e^- \rightarrow ClO_2^-(aq)$; oxidation reaction: $2\,I^-(aq) \rightarrow I_2(s) + 2\,e^-$ so
$Pt(s)\,|\,I^-(aq)\,|\,I_2(s)\,\|\,ClO_2(g)\,|\,ClO_2^-(aq)\,|\,Pt(s)$
(c)   Reduction reaction: $O_2(g) + 4\,H^+(aq) + 4\,e^- \rightarrow 2\,H_2O(l)$; oxidation reaction: $Zn(s) \rightarrow Zn^{2+}(aq) + 2\,e^-$
so $Zn(s)\,|\,Zn^{2+}(aq)\,\|\,O_2(g)\,|\,H^+(aq), H_2O(l)\,|\,Pt(s)$

18.14   **Given:** overall reactions from Problem 8   **Find:** line notation
Conceptual Plan: Use the solution from Problem 8. Write the oxidation half-reaction components on the left and the reduction on the right. A double vertical line ($\|$), indicating the salt bridge, separates the two half-reactions. Substances in different phases are separated by a single vertical line ($|$), which represents the boundary between the phases. For some redox reactions, the reactants and products of one or both of the half-reactions may be in the same phase. In these cases, the reactants and products are separated from each other with a comma in the line diagram. Such cells use an inert electrode, such as platinum (Pt) or graphite, as the anode or cathode (or both).
Solution:
(a)   Reduction reaction: $Ni^{2+}(aq) + 2\,e^- \rightarrow Ni(s)$; oxidation reaction: $Mg(s) \rightarrow Mg^{2+}(aq) + 2\,e^-$ so
$Mg(s)\,|\,Mg^{2+}(aq)\,\|\,Ni^{2+}(aq)\,|\,Ni(s)$
(b)   Reduction reaction: $2\,H^+(aq) + 2\,e^- \rightarrow H_2(g)$; oxidation reaction: $Fe(s) \rightarrow Fe^{2+}(aq) + 2\,e^-$ so
$Fe(s)\,|\,Fe^{2+}(aq)\,\|\,H^+(aq)\,|\,H_2(g)\,|\,Pt(s)$
(c)   Reduction reaction: $NO_3^-(aq) + 4\,H^+(aq) + 3\,e^- \rightarrow NO(g) + 2\,H_2O(l)$; oxidation reaction: $Cu(s)$
$\rightarrow Cu^{2+}(aq) + 2\,e^-$ so $Cu(s)\,|\,Cu^{2+}(aq)\,\|\,NO_3^-(aq), H^+(aq), H_2O(l)\,|\,NO(g)\,|\,Pt(s)$

18.15   **Given:** $Sn(s)\,|\,Sn^{2+}(aq)\,\|\,NO_3^-(aq), H^+(aq)\,|\,NO(g)\,|\,Pt(s)$
Find: Sketch voltaic cell, labeling anode, cathode, all species, direction of electron flow, and $E°_{cell}$
Conceptual Plan: Separate overall reaction into two half-cell reactions, knowing that the oxidation half-reaction components are on the left and the reduction half-reaction components are on the right. Add electrons as needed to balance reactions. Multiply the half-reactions by the appropriate factors so that an equal number of electrons are transferred. Add the half-cell reactions and cancel electrons. Put anode reaction on the left (oxidation = electrons as product) and cathode reaction on the right (reduction = electrons as reactant). Electrons flow from anode to cathode. Look up half-reactions in Table 18.1. Calculate the standard cell potential by subtracting the electrode potential of the anode from the electrode potential of the cathode:
$E°_{cell} = E°_{cathode} - E°_{anode}$.
Solution: Oxidation reaction (anode): $Sn(s) \rightarrow Sn^{2+}(aq) + 2\,e^-$ $E°_{red} =$
-0.14 V; reduction reaction (cathode): $NO_3^-(aq) + 4\,H^+(aq) + 3\,e^-$
$\rightarrow NO(g) + 2\,H_2O(l)$ $E°_{red} = 0.96$ V. $E°_{cell} = E°_{cathode} - E°_{anode} = 0.96$ V $-$
$(-0.14$ V$) = 1.10$ V. Multiply the first reaction by 3 and the second reaction
by 2 so that 6 electrons are transferred. $3\,Sn(s) \rightarrow 3\,Sn^{2+}(aq) + 6\,e^-$ and
$2\,NO_3^-(aq) + 8\,H^+(aq) + 6\,e^- \rightarrow 2\,NO(g) + 4\,H_2O(l)$. Add the two half-
reactions and cancel electrons. $3\,Sn(s) + 2\,NO_3^-(aq) + 8\,H^+(aq) + \cancel{6\,e^-} \rightarrow$
$3\,Sn^{2+}(aq) + \cancel{6\,e^-} + 2\,NO(g) + 4\,H_2O(l)$. So balanced reaction is
$3\,Sn(s) + 2\,NO_3^-(aq) + 8\,H^+(aq) \rightarrow 3\,Sn^{2+}(aq) + 2\,NO(g) + 4\,H_2O(l)$.

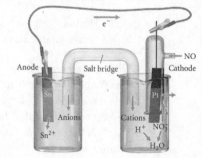

Check: All atoms and charge are balanced. The units (V) are correct. The cell
potential is positive, which is consistent with a voltaic cell.

18.16   **Given:** $Mn(s)\,|\,Mn^{2+}(aq)\,\|\,ClO_2(g)\,|\,ClO_2^-(aq)\,|\,Pt(s)$
Find: Sketch voltaic cell, labeling anode, cathode, all species, direction of electron flow, and $E°_{cell}$

Conceptual Plan: Separate the overall reaction into two half-cell reactions, knowing that the oxidation half-reaction components are on the left and the reduction half-reaction components are on the right. Add electrons as needed to balance reactions. Multiply the half-reactions by the appropriate factors so that an equal number of electrons are transferred. Add the half-cell reactions and cancel electrons. Put the anode reaction on the left (oxidation = electrons as product) and the cathode reaction on the right (oxidation = electrons as reactant). Electrons flow from anode to cathode. Look up half-reactions in Table 18.1. Calculate the standard cell potential by subtracting the electrode potential of the anode from the electrode potential of the cathode: $E°_{cell} = E°_{cathode} - E°_{anode}$.

Solution: Oxidation reaction (anode): $Mn(s) \rightarrow Mn^{2+}(aq) + 2\,e^-$
$E°_{red} = -1.18$ V; reduction reaction (cathode): $ClO_2(g) + e^- \rightarrow ClO_2^-(aq)$
$E°_{red} = 0.95$ V. $E°_{cell} = E°_{cathode} - E°_{anode} = 0.95$ V $- (-1.18$ V$) = 2.13$ V.
Multiply the second reaction by 2 so that 2 electrons are transferred.
$Mn(s) \rightarrow Mn^{2+}(aq) + 2\,e^-$ and $2\,ClO_2(g) + 2\,e^- \rightarrow 2\,ClO_2^-(aq)$. Add
the two half-reactions and cancel electrons. $Mn(s) + 2\,ClO_2(g) + 2\,e^- \rightarrow$
$Mn^{2+}(aq) + 2\,e^- + 2\,ClO_2^-(aq)$. So balanced reaction is
$Mn(s) + 2\,ClO_2(g) \rightarrow Mn^{2+}(aq) + 2\,ClO_2^-(aq)$.

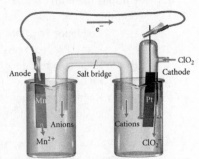

Check: All atoms and charge are balanced. The units (V) are correct. The cell potential is positive, which is consistent with a voltaic cell.

18.17   **Given:** overall reactions   **Find:** spontaneity in forward direction
Conceptual Plan: Separate the overall reaction into two half-cell reactions and add electrons as needed to balance reactions. Look up half-reactions in Table 18.1. Calculate the standard cell potential by subtracting the electrode potential of the anode from the electrode potential of the cathode: $E°_{cell} = E°_{cathode} - E°_{anode}$. If $E°_{cell} = 0$, the reaction is spontaneous in the forward direction.
Solution:

(a) $Ni(s) + Zn^{2+}(aq) \rightarrow Ni^{2+}(aq) + Zn(s)$ separates to $Ni(s) \rightarrow Ni^{2+}(aq)$ and $Zn^{2+}(aq) \rightarrow Zn(s)$. Add electrons. $Ni(s) \rightarrow Ni^{2+}(aq) + 2\,e^-$ and $Zn^{2+}(aq) + 2\,e^- \rightarrow Zn(s)$. Look up cell potentials. Ni is oxidized, so $E°_{red} = -0.23$ V $= E°_{anode}$. Zn^{2+} is reduced, so $E°_{cathode} = -0.76$ V. Then $E°_{cell} = E°_{cathode} - E°_{anode} = -0.76$ V $- (-0.23$ V$) = -0.53$ V, so the reaction is nonspontaneous.

(b) $Ni(s) + Pb^{2+}(aq) \rightarrow Ni^{2+}(aq) + Pb(s)$ separates to $Ni(s) \rightarrow Ni^{2+}(aq)$ and $Pb^{2+}(aq) \rightarrow Pb(s)$. Add electrons. $Ni(s) \rightarrow Ni^{2+}(aq) + 2\,e^-$ and $Pb^{2+}(aq) + 2\,e^- \rightarrow Pb(s)$. Look up cell potentials. Ni is oxidized, so $E°_{red} = -0.23$ V $= E°_{anode}$. Pb^{2+} is reduced, so $E°_{red} = -0.13$ V $= E°_{cathode}$. Then $E°_{cell} = E°_{cathode} - E°_{anode} = -0.13$ V $- (-0.23$ V$) = +0.10$ V, so the reaction is spontaneous.

(c) $Al(s) + 3\,Ag^+(aq) \rightarrow Al^{3+}(aq) + 3\,Ag(s)$ separates to $Al(s) \rightarrow Al^{3+}(aq)$ and $3\,Ag^+(aq) \rightarrow 3\,Ag(s)$. Add electrons. $Al(s) \rightarrow Al^{3+}(aq) + 3\,e^-$ and $3\,Ag^+(aq) + 3\,e^- \rightarrow 3\,Ag(s)$. Simplify the Ag reaction to $Ag^+(aq) + e^- \rightarrow Ag(s)$. Look up cell potentials. Al is oxidized, so $E°_{red} = -1.66$ V $E°_{anode}$. Ag^+ is reduced, so $E°_{red} = 0.80$ V $= E°_{cathode}$. Then $E°_{cell} = E°_{cathode} - E°_{anode} = 0.80$ V $- (-1.66$ V$) = +2.46$ V, so the reaction is spontaneous.

(d) $Pb(s) + Mn^{2+}(aq) \rightarrow Pb^{2+}(aq) + Mn(s)$ separates to $Pb(s) \rightarrow Pb^{2+}(aq)$ and $Mn^{2+}(aq) \rightarrow Mn(s)$. Add electrons. $Pb(s) \rightarrow Pb^{2+}(aq) + 2\,e^-$ and $Mn^{2+}(aq) + 2\,e^- \rightarrow Mn(s)$. Look up cell potentials. Pb is oxidized, so $E°_{red} = -0.13$ V $= E°_{anode}$. Mn^{2+} is reduced, so $E°_{red} = -1.18$ V $= E°_{cathode}$. Then $E°_{cell} = E°_{cathode} - E°_{anode} = -1.18$ V $- (-0.13$ V$) = -1.05$ V, so the reaction is nonspontaneous.

Check: The units (V) are correct. If the voltage is positive, the reaction is spontaneous. If the voltage is negative, the reaction is nonspontaneous.

18.18   **Given:** overall reactions   **Find:** spontaneity in reverse direction
Conceptual Plan: Separate the overall reaction into two half-cell reactions and add electrons as needed to balance reactions. Look up half-reactions in Table 18.1. Calculate the standard cell potential by subtracting the electrode potential of the anode from the electrode potential of the cathode: $E°_{cell} = E°_{cathode} - E°_{anode}$. If $E°_{cell} < 0$, the reaction is spontaneous in the reverse direction.
Solution:

(a) $Ca^{2+}(aq) + Zn(s) \rightarrow Ca(s) + Zn^{2+}(aq)$ separates to $Ca^{2+}(aq) \rightarrow Ca(s)$ and $Zn(s) \rightarrow Zn^{2+}(aq)$. Add electrons. $Ca^{2+}(aq) + 2e^- \rightarrow Ca(s)$ and $Zn(s) \rightarrow Zn^{2+}(aq) + 2\,e^-$. Look up cell potentials. Zn is oxidized, so $E°_{red} = -0.76$ V $= E°_{anode}$. Ca^{2+} is reduced, so $E°_{red} = -2.76$ V $= E°_{cathode}$. Then $E°_{cell} = E°_{cathode} - E°_{anode} = -2.76$ V $- (-0.76$ V$) = -2.00$ V, so the reaction is spontaneous in the reverse direction.

(b) $2 Ag^+(aq) + Ni(s) \rightarrow 2 Ag(s) + Ni^{2+}(aq)$ separates to $2 Ag^+(aq) \rightarrow 2 Ag(s)$ and $Ni(s) \rightarrow Ni^{2+}(aq)$.
Add electrons. $2 Ag^+(aq) + 2 e^- \rightarrow 2 Ag(s)$ and $Ni(s) \rightarrow Ni^{2+}(aq) + 2 e^-$. Simplify the Ag reaction to
$Ag^+(aq) + e^- \rightarrow Ag(s)$. Look up cell potentials. Ni is oxidized, so $E^\circ_{red} = -0.23$ V $= E^\circ_{anode}$. Ag^+ is reduced, so $E^\circ_{red} = 0.80$ V $= E^\circ_{cathode}$. Then $E^\circ_{cell} = E^\circ_{cathode} - E^\circ_{anode} = 0.80$ V $- (-0.23$ V$) = +1.03$ V, so
the reaction is nonspontaneous in the reverse direction.

(c) $Fe(s) + Mn^{2+}(aq) \rightarrow Fe^{2+}(aq) + Mn(s)$ separates to $Fe(s) \rightarrow Fe^{2+}(aq)$ and $Mn^{2+}(aq) \rightarrow Mn(s)$.
Add electrons. $Fe(s) \rightarrow Fe^{2+}(aq) + 2 e^-$ and $Mn^{2+}(aq) + 2 e^- \rightarrow Mn(s)$. Look up cell potentials.
Fe is oxidized, so $E^\circ_{red} = -0.45$ V $= E^\circ_{anode}$. Mn^{2+} is reduced, so $E^\circ_{red} = -1.18$ V $= E^\circ_{cathode}$. Then
$E^\circ_{cell} = E^\circ_{cathode} - E^\circ_{anode} = -1.18$ V $- (-0.45$ V$) = -0.73$ V, so the reaction is spontaneous in the reverse
direction.

(d) $2 Al(s) + 3 Pb^{2+}(aq) \rightarrow 2 Al^{3+}(aq) + 3 Pb(s)$ separates to $2 Al(s) \rightarrow 2 Al^{3+}(aq)$ and $3 Pb^{2+}(aq) \rightarrow 3 Pb(s)$.
Add electrons. $2 Al(s) \rightarrow 2 Al^{3+}(aq) + 6 e^-$ and $3 Pb^{2+}(aq) + 6 e^- \rightarrow 3 Pb(s)$. Simplify the reactions
to $Al(s) \rightarrow Al^{3+}(aq) + 3 e^-$ and $Pb^{2+}(aq) + 2 e^- \rightarrow Pb(s)$. Look up cell potentials. Al is oxidized, so
$E^\circ_{red} = -1.66$ V $= E^\circ_{cathode}$. Pb^{2+} is reduced, so $E^\circ_{red} = -0.13$ V $= E^\circ_{cathode}$. Then $E^\circ_{cell} = E^\circ_{cathode} -$
$E^\circ_{anode} = -0.13$ V $- (-1.66$ V$) = +1.53$ V, so the reaction is nonspontaneous in the reverse direction.

Check: The units (V) are correct. If the voltage is negative, the reaction is spontaneous in the reverse direction.

18.19   For a metal to be able to reduce an ion, it must be below it in Table 18.1 (need positive $E^\circ_{cell} = E^\circ_{cathode} - E^\circ_{anode}$). So
we need a metal that is below Mn^{2+} but above Mg^{2+}. Aluminum is the only one in the table that meets those criteria.

18.20   For a metal to be oxidized into an ion by another species, it must be below it in Table 18.1 (need positive
$E^\circ_{cell} = E^\circ_{cathode} - E^\circ_{anode}$). So we need a metal that is above Fe^{2+} but below Sn^{2+}. Nickel and cadmium meet those
criteria.

18.21   In general, metals whose reduction half-reactions lie below the reduction of H^+ to H_2 in Table 18.1 will dissolve in acids, while metals above it will not. (a) Al and (c) Pb meet that criterion. To write the balanced redox
reactions, pair the oxidation of the metal with the reduction of H^+ to $H_2 (2 H^+(aq) + 2 e^- \rightarrow H_2(g))$. For Al,
$Al(s) \rightarrow Al^{3+}(aq) + 3 e^-$. To balance the number of electrons transferred, we need to multiply the Al reaction
by 2 and the H^+ reaction by 3. So $2 Al(s) \rightarrow 2 Al^{3+}(aq) + 6 e^-$ and $6 H^+(aq) + 6 e^- \rightarrow 3 H_2(g)$. Adding the
two reactions: $2 Al(s) + 6 H^+(aq) + 6e^- \rightarrow 2 Al^{3+}(aq) + 6e^- + 3 H_2(g)$. Simplify to $2 Al(s) + 6 H^+(aq) \rightarrow$
$2 Al^{3+}(aq) + 3 H_2(g)$. For Pb, $Pb(s) \rightarrow Pb^{2+}(aq) + 2 e^-$. Because each reaction involves two electrons, we can
add the two reactions. $Pb(s) + 2 H^+(aq) + 2e^- \rightarrow Pb^{2+}(aq) + 2e^- + H_2(g)$. Simplify to $Pb(s) + 2 H^+(aq) \rightarrow$
$Pb^{2+}(aq) + H_2(g)$.

18.22   In general, metals whose reduction half-reactions lie below the reduction of H^+ to H_2 in Table 18.1 will dissolve
in acids, while metals above it will not. Only (b) Fe meets that criterion. To write the balanced redox reactions,
pair the oxidation of the metal with the reduction of H^+ to $H_2 (2 H^+(aq) + 2 e^- \rightarrow H_2(g))$. For Fe, there are
two possible reactions, $Fe(s) \rightarrow Fe^{3+}(aq) + 3 e^-$ and $Fe(s) \rightarrow Fe^{2+}(aq) + 2 e^-$. Because the second reaction
is lower in Table 18.1, the cell potential will be more positive. This means that this reaction will be more
spontaneous and thus preferred. Because each reaction involves two electrons, we can add the two reactions.
$Fe(s) + 2 H^+(aq) + 2e^- \rightarrow Fe^{2+}(aq) + 2e^- + H_2(g)$. Simplify to $Fe(s) + 2 H^+(aq) \rightarrow Fe^{2+}(aq) + H_2(g)$.

18.23   Nitric acid (HNO_3) oxidizes metals through the following reduction half-reaction: $NO_3^-(aq) + 4 H^+(aq) +$
$3 e^- \rightarrow NO(g) + 2 H_2O(l)$ $E^\circ_{red} = 0.96$ V. Because this half-reaction is above the reduction of H^+ in Table 18.1,
HNO_3 can oxidize metals (copper, for example) that cannot be oxidized by HCl. (a) Cu, which is below nitric acid
in the table, will be oxidized, but (b) Au, which is above nitric acid in the table (and has a reduction potential of 1.50
V), will not be oxidized. To write the balanced redox reactions, pair the oxidation of the metal with the reduction
of nitric acid: $NO_3^-(aq) + 4 H^+(aq) + 3 e^- \rightarrow NO(g) + 2 H_2O(l)$. For Cu, $Cu(s) \rightarrow Cu^{2+}(aq) + 2 e^-$. To balance the number of electrons transferred, we need to multiply the Cu reaction by 3 and the nitric acid reaction by 2.
So $3 Cu(s) \rightarrow 3 Cu^{2+}(aq) + 6 e^-$ and $2 NO_3^-(aq) + 8 H^+(aq) + 6 e^- \rightarrow 2 NO(g) + 4 H_2O(l)$. Adding the two
reactions: $3 Cu(s) + 2 NO_3^-(aq) + 8 H^+(aq) + 6e^- \rightarrow 3 Cu^{2+}(aq) + 6e^- + 2 NO(g) + 4 H_2O(l)$. Simplify to
$3 Cu(s) + 2 NO_3^-(aq) + 8 H^+(aq) \rightarrow 3 Cu^{2+}(aq) + 2 NO(g) + 4 H_2O(l)$.

18.24   Iodic acid (HIO_3) oxidizes metals through the following reduction half-reaction: $IO_3^-(aq) + 6 H^+(aq) +$
$5 e^- \rightarrow \frac{1}{2} I_2(aq) + 3 H_2O(l)$ $E^\circ_{red} = 1.20$ V. Because this half-reaction is above the reduction of H^+ in Table 18.1,

HIO$_3$ can oxidize metals (copper, for example) that cannot be oxidized by HCl. (a) Au (which has a reduction potential of 1.50 V) will not be oxidized, but (b) Cr (which has a reduction potential of -0.73 V) will be oxidized by both HCl and HIO$_3$. To write the balanced redox reactions, pair the oxidation of the metal with the reduction of iodic acid (IO$_3^-$(aq) + 6 H$^+$(aq) + 5 e$^-$ → $\frac{1}{2}$I$_2$(aq) + 3 H$_2$O(l)). For Cr, Cr(s) → Cr^{3+}(aq) + 3 e$^-$. To balance the number of electrons transferred, we need to multiply the Cr reaction by 5 and the iodic acid reaction by 3. So 5 Cr(s) → 5 Cr^{3+}(aq) + 15 e$^-$ and 3 IO$_3^-$(aq) + 18 H$^+$(aq) + 15 e$^-$ → 3/2 I$_2$(aq) + 9 H$_2$O(l). Adding the two reactions: 5 Cr(s) + 3 IO$_3^-$(aq) + 18 H$^+$(aq) + ~~15 e$^-$~~ → 5 Cr^{3+}(aq) + ~~15 e$^-$~~ + 3/2 I$_2$(aq) + 9 H$_2$O(l). Simplify to 5 Cr(s) + 3 IO$_3^-$(aq) + 18 H$^+$(aq) → 5 Cr^{3+}(aq) + 3/2 I$_2$(aq) + 9 H$_2$O(l).

18.25   **Given:** overall reactions   **Find:** $E°_{cell}$ and spontaneity in forward direction
Conceptual Plan: Separate the overall reaction into two half-cell reactions and add electrons as needed to balance reactions. Look up half-reactions in Table 18.1. Calculate the standard cell potential by subtracting the electrode potential of the anode from the electrode potential of the cathode: $E°_{cell} = E°_{cathode} - E°_{anode}$. If $E°_{cell} > 0$, the reaction is spontaneous in the forward direction.
Solution:

(a)   2 Cu(s) + Mn^{2+}(aq) → 2 Cu$^+$(aq) + Mn(s) separates to 2 Cu(s) → 2 Cu$^+$(aq) and Mn^{2+}(aq) → Mn(s). Add electrons. 2 Cu(s) → 2 Cu$^+$(aq) + 2 e$^-$ and Mn^{2+}(aq) + 2 e$^-$ → Mn(s). Simplify the Cu reaction to Cu(s) → Cu$^+$(aq) + e$^-$. Look up cell potentials. Cu is oxidized, so $E°_{red} = +0.52$ V = $E°_{anode}$. Mn^{2+} is reduced, so $E°_{red} = -1.18$ V = $E°_{cathode}$. Then $E°_{cell} = E°_{cathode} - E°_{anode} = -1.18$ V $- 0.52$ V $= -1.70$ V, so the reaction is nonspontaneous.

(b)   MnO$_2$(s) + 4 H$^+$(aq) + Zn(s) → Mn^{2+}(aq) + 2 H$_2$O(l) + Zn^{2+}(aq) separates to MnO$_2$(s) + 4 H$^+$(aq) → Mn^{2+}(aq) + 2 H$_2$O(l) and Zn(s) → Zn^{2+}(aq). Add electrons. MnO$_2$(s) + 4 H$^+$(aq) +2 e$^-$ → Mn^{2+}(aq) + 2 H$_2$O(l) and Zn(s) → Zn^{2+}(aq) + 2 e$^-$. Look up cell potentials. Zn is oxidized, so $E°_{red} = -0.76$ V = $E°_{anode}$. Mn is reduced, so $E°_{red} = 1.21$ V = $E°_{cathode}$. Then $E°_{cell} = E°_{cathode} - E°_{anode} = 1.21$ V $- (-0.76$ V) $= +1.97$ V, so the reaction is spontaneous.

(c)   Cl$_2$(g) + 2 F$^-$(aq) → 2 Cl$^-$(aq) + F$_2$(g) separates to Cl$_2$(g) → 2 Cl$^-$(aq) and 2 F$^-$(aq) → F$_2$(g). Add electrons. Cl$_2$(g) + 2 e$^-$ → 2 Cl$^-$(aq) and 2 F$^-$(aq) → F$_2$(g) + 2 e$^-$. Look up cell potentials. F$^-$ is oxidized, so $E°_{red} = 2.87$ V = $E°_{anode}$. Cl is reduced, so $E°_{red} = 1.36$ V = $E°_{cathode}$. Then $E°_{cell} = E°_{cathode} - E°_{anode} = 1.36$ V $- 2.87$ V $= -1.51$ V, so the reaction is nonspontaneous.

Check: The units (V) are correct. If the voltage is positive, the reaction is spontaneous.

18.26   **Given:** overall reactions   **Find:** $E°_{cell}$ and spontaneity in forward direction
Conceptual Plan: Separate the overall reaction into two half-cell reactions and add electrons as needed to balance reactions. Look up half-reactions in Table 18.1. Calculate the standard cell potential by subtracting the electrode potential of the anode from the electrode potential of the cathode: $E°_{cell} = E°_{cathode} - E°_{anode}$. If $E°_{cell} > 0$, the reaction is spontaneous in the forward direction.
Solution:

(a)   O$_2$(g) + 2 H$_2$O(l) + 4 Ag(s) → 4 OH$^-$(aq) + 4 Ag$^+$(aq) separates to O$_2$(g) + 2 H$_2$O(l) → 4 OH$^-$(aq) and 4 Ag(s) → 4 Ag$^+$(aq). Add electrons. O$_2$(g) + 2 H$_2$O(l) + 4 e$^-$ → 4 OH$^-$(aq) and 4 Ag(s) → 4 Ag$^+$(aq) + 4 e$^-$. Simplify the Ag reaction to Ag(s) → Ag$^+$(aq) + e$^-$. Look up cell potentials. Ag is oxidized, so $E°_{red} = +0.80$ V = $E°_{anode}$. O is reduced, so $E°_{red} = 0.40$ V = $E°_{cathode}$. Then $E°_{cell} = E°_{cathode} - E°_{anode} = 0.40$ V $- 0.80$ V $= -0.40$ V, so the reaction is nonspontaneous.

(b)   Br$_2$(l) + 2 I$^-$(aq) → 2 Br$^-$(aq) + I$_2$(g) separates to Br$_2$(g) → 2 Br$^-$(aq) and 2 I$^-$(aq) → I$_2$(g). Add electrons. Br$_2$(g) + 2 e$^-$ → 2 Br$^-$(aq) and 2 I$^-$(aq) → I$_2$(g) + 2 e$^-$. Look up cell potentials. I is oxidized, so $E°_{red} = 0.54$ V = $E°_{anode}$. Br is reduced, so $E°_{red} = 1.09$ V = $E°_{cathode}$. Then $E°_{cell} = E°_{cathode} - E°_{anode} = 1.09$ V $- 0.54$ V $= +0.55$ V, so the reaction is spontaneous.

(c)   PbO$_2$(s) + 4 H$^+$(aq) + Sn(s) → Pb^{2+}(aq) + 2 H$_2$O(l) + Sn^{2+}(aq) separates to PbO$_2$(s) + 4 H$^+$(aq) → Pb^{2+}(aq) + 2 H$_2$O(l) and Sn(s) → Sn^{2+}(aq). Add electrons. PbO$_2$(s) + 4 H$^+$(aq) + 2 e$^-$ → Pb^{2+}(aq) + 2 H$_2$O(l) and Sn(s) → Sn^{2+}(aq) + 2 e$^-$. Look up cell potentials. Sn is oxidized, so $E°_{red} = -0.14$ V = $E°_{cathode}$. Pb is reduced, so $E°_{red} = 1.46$ V = $E°_{cathode}$. Then $E°_{cell} = E°_{cathode} - E°_{anode} = 1.46$ V $- (-0.14$ V) $= +1.60$ V, so the reaction is spontaneous.

Check: The units (V) are correct. If the voltage is positive, the reaction is spontaneous.

18.27   (a)   Pb^{2+}. The strongest oxidizing agent is the one with the reduction reaction that is closest to the top of Table 18.1 (most positive, least negative reduction potential).

18.28   (a)   Al. The strongest reducing agent is the one with the reduction reaction that yields the metal that is closest to the bottom of Table 18.1 (most negative, least positive reduction potential).

Cell Potential, Free Energy, and the Equilibrium Constant

18.29   **Given:** overall reactions   **Find:** ΔG°_{rxn} and spontaneity in forward direction
Conceptual Plan: Separate the overall reaction into two half-cell reactions and add electrons as needed to balance reactions. Look up half-reactions in Table 18.1. Calculate the standard cell potential by subtracting the electrode potential of the anode from the electrode potential of the cathode: $E^\circ_{cell} = E^\circ_{cathode} - E^\circ_{anode}$. Then calculate ΔG°_{rxn} using $\Delta G^\circ_{rxn} = -nFE^\circ_{cell}$.
Solution:

(a) $Pb^{2+}(aq) + Mg(s) \rightarrow Pb(s) + Mg^{2+}(aq)$ separates to $Pb^{2+}(aq) \rightarrow Pb(s)$ and $Mg(s) \rightarrow Mg^{2+}(aq)$. Add electrons. $Pb^{2+}(aq) + 2\,e^- \rightarrow Pb(s)$ and $Mg(s) \rightarrow Mg^{2+}(aq) + 2\,e^-$. Look up cell potentials. Mg is oxidized, so $E^\circ_{red} = -2.37$ V $= E^\circ_{anode}$. Pb^{2+} is reduced, so $E^\circ_{red} = -0.13$ V $= E^\circ_{cathode}$. Then E°_{cell} $= E^\circ_{cathode} - E^\circ_{anode} = -0.13$ V $- (-2.37$ V$) = +2.24$ V. $n = 2$, so $\Delta G^\circ_{rxn} = -nFE^\circ_{cell}$

$= -2\ \text{mol e}^- \times \dfrac{96{,}485\ \text{C}}{\text{mol e}^-} \times 2.24\ \text{V} = -2 \times 96{,}485\ \text{C} \times 2.24\ \dfrac{\text{J}}{\text{C}} = -4.32 \times 10^5\ \text{J} = -432\ \text{kJ}.$

(b) $Br_2(l) + 2\,Cl^-(aq) \rightarrow 2\,Br^-(aq) + Cl_2(g)$ separates to $Br_2(g) \rightarrow 2\,Br^-(aq)$ and $2\,Cl^-(aq) \rightarrow Cl_2(g)$. Add electrons. $Br_2(g) + 2\,e^- \rightarrow 2\,Br^-(aq)$ and $2\,Cl^-(aq) \rightarrow Cl_2(g) + 2\,e^-$. Look up cell potentials. Cl is oxidized, so $E^\circ_{red} = 1.36$ V $= E^\circ_{anode}$. Br is reduced, so $E^\circ_{red} = 1.09$ V $= E^\circ_{cathode}$. Then $E^\circ_{cell} = E^\circ_{cathode}$ $-E^\circ_{anode} = 1.09$ V $- 1.36$ V $= -0.27$ V. $n = 2$, so $\Delta G^\circ_{rxn} = -nFE^\circ_{cell}$

$= -2\ \text{mol e}^- \times \dfrac{96{,}485\ \text{C}}{\text{mol e}^-} \times -0.27\ \text{V} = -2 \times 96{,}485\ \text{C} \times -0.27\ \dfrac{\text{J}}{\text{C}} = 5.2 \times 10^4\ \text{J} = 52\ \text{kJ}.$

(c) $MnO_2(s) + 4\,H^+(aq) + Cu(s) \rightarrow Mn^{2+}(aq) + 2\,H_2O(l) + Cu^{2+}(aq)$ separates to $MnO_2(s) + 4\,H^+(aq)$ $\rightarrow Mn^{2+}(aq) + 2\,H_2O(l)$ and $Cu(s) \rightarrow Cu^{2+}(aq)$. Add electrons. $MnO_2(s) + 4\,H^+(aq) + 2\,e^- \rightarrow$ $Mn^{2+}(aq) + 2\,H_2O(l)$ and $Cu(s) \rightarrow Cu^{2+}(aq) + 2\,e^-$. Look up cell potentials. Cu is oxidized, so $E^\circ_{red} = 0.34$ V $= E^\circ_{anode}$. Mn is reduced, so $E^\circ_{red} = 1.21$ V $= E^\circ_{cathode}$. Then $E^\circ_{cell} = E^\circ_{cathode} - E^\circ_{anode} =$ 1.21 V $- 0.34$ V $= +0.87$ V. $n = 2$, so $\Delta G^\circ_{rxn} = -nFE^\circ_{cell} = -2\ \text{mol e}^- \times \dfrac{96{,}485\ \text{C}}{\text{mol e}^-} \times 0.87\ \text{V} =$

$-2 \times 96{,}485\ \text{C} \times 0.87\ \dfrac{\text{J}}{\text{C}} = -1.7 \times 10^5\ \text{J} = -1.7 \times 10^2\ \text{kJ}.$

Check: The units (kJ) are correct. If the voltage is positive, the reaction is spontaneous and the free energy change is negative.

18.30   **Given:** overall reactions   **Find:** ΔG°_{rxn} and spontaneity in forward direction
Conceptual Plan: Separate the overall reaction into two half-cell reactions and add electrons as needed to balance reactions. Look up half-reactions in Table 18.1. Calculate the standard cell potential by subtracting the electrode potential of the anode from the electrode potential of the cathode: $E^\circ_{cell} = E^\circ_{cathode} - E^\circ_{anode}$. Then calculate ΔG°_{rxn} using $\Delta G^\circ_{rxn} = -nFE^\circ_{cell}$.
Solution:

(a) $2\,Fe^{3+}(aq) + 3\,Sn(s) \rightarrow 2\,Fe(s) + 3\,Sn^{2+}(aq)$ separates to $2\,Fe^{3+}(aq) \rightarrow 2\,Fe(s)$ and $3\,Sn(s) \rightarrow$ $3\,Sn^{2+}(aq)$. Add electrons. $2\,Fe^{3+}(aq) + 6\,e^- \rightarrow 2\,Fe(s)$ and $3\,Sn(s) \rightarrow 3\,Sn^{2+}(aq) + 6\,e^-$. Simplify reactions to $Fe^{3+}(aq) + 3\,e^- \rightarrow Fe(s)$ and $Sn(s) \rightarrow Sn^{2+}(aq) + 2\,e^-$. Look up cell potentials. Sn is oxidized, so $E^\circ_{red} = -0.14$ V $= E^\circ_{anode}$. Fe^{3+} is reduced, so $E^\circ_{red} = -0.036$ V $= E^\circ_{cathode}$. Then $E^\circ_{cell} = E^\circ_{cathode} - E^\circ_{anode} = -0.036$ V $- (-0.14$ V$) = +0.104$ V. $n = 6$, so $\Delta G^\circ_{rxn} = -nFE^\circ_{cell}$

$= -6\ \text{mol e}^- \times \dfrac{96{,}485\ \text{C}}{\text{mol e}^-} \times 0.104\ \text{V} = -6 \times 96{,}485\ \text{C} \times 0.104\ \dfrac{\text{J}}{\text{C}} = -6.0 \times 10^4\ \text{J} = -6.0 \times 10^1\ \text{kJ}.$

(b) $O_2(g) + 2\,H_2O(l) + 2\,Cu(s) \rightarrow 4\,OH^-(aq) + 2\,Cu^{2+}(aq)$ separates to $O_2(g) + 2\,H_2O(l) \rightarrow 4\,OH^-(aq)$ and $2\,Cu(s) \rightarrow 2\,Cu^{2+}(aq)$. Add electrons. $O_2(g) + 2\,H_2O(l) + 4\,e^- \rightarrow 4\,OH^-(aq)$ and $2\,Cu(s) \rightarrow$ $2\,Cu^{2+}(aq) + 4\,e^-$. Simplify the Cu reaction to $Cu(s) \rightarrow Cu^{2+}(aq) + 2\,e^-$. Look up cell potentials. Cu is oxidized, so $E^{\circ}_{red} = 0.34 \text{ V} = E^{\circ}_{anode}$. O is reduced, so $E^{\circ}_{red} = 0.40 \text{ V} = E^{\circ}_{cathode}$. Then $E^{\circ}_{cell} = E^{\circ}_{cathode}$

$- E^{\circ}_{anode} = 0.40 \text{ V} - 0.34 \text{ V} = +0.06 \text{ V}$. $n = 4$, so $\Delta G^{\circ}_{rxn} = -nFE^{\circ}_{cell} = -4 \text{ mol } e^{-} \times \dfrac{96{,}485 \text{ C}}{\text{mol } e^{-}} \times 0.06 \text{ V}$

$= -4 \times 96{,}485 \text{ C} \times 0.06 \dfrac{\text{J}}{\text{C}} = -2 \times 10^4 \text{ J} = -2 \times 10^1 \text{ kJ}$.

(c) $Br_2(l) + 2 \text{ I}^-(aq) \rightarrow 2 \text{ Br}^-(aq) + I_2(s)$ separates to $Br_2(g) \rightarrow 2Br^-(aq)$ and $2 \text{ I}^-(aq) \rightarrow I_2(s)$. Add electrons. $Br_2(g) + 2 e^- \rightarrow 2 \text{ Br}^-(aq)$ and $2 \text{ I}^-(aq) \rightarrow I_2(s) + 2 e^-$. Look up cell potentials. I is oxidized, so $E^{\circ}_{red} = +0.54 \text{ V} = E^{\circ}_{anode}$. Br is reduced, so $E^{\circ}_{red} = 1.09 \text{ V} = E^{\circ}_{cathode}$. Then $E^{\circ}_{cell} = E^{\circ}_{cathode} - E^{\circ}_{anode}$

$= 1.09 \text{ V} - 0.54 \text{ V} = +0.55 \text{ V}$. $n = 2$, so $\Delta G^{\circ}_{rxn} = -nFE^{\circ}_{cell} = -2 \text{ mol } e^{-} \times \dfrac{96{,}485 \text{ C}}{\text{mol } e^{-}} \times 0.55 \text{ V}$

$= -2 \times 96{,}485 \text{ C} \times 0.55 \dfrac{\text{J}}{\text{C}} = -1.1 \times 10^5 \text{ J} = -1.1 \times 10^2 \text{ kJ}$.

Check: The units (kJ) are correct. If the voltage is positive, the reaction is spontaneous and the free energy change is negative.

18.31   **Given:** overall reactions from Problem 29   **Find:** K

Conceptual Plan: $°C \rightarrow K$ **then** $\Delta G^{\circ}_{rxn}, T = K$

$\qquad\qquad K = 273.15 + °C \qquad \Delta G^{\circ}_{rxn} = -RT \ln K$

Solution: $T = 273.15 + 25 °C = 298 \text{ K}$ then

(a) $\Delta G^{\circ}_{rxn} = -RT \ln K$. Rearrange to solve for K.

$$K = e^{\frac{-\Delta G^{\circ}_{rxn}}{RT}} = e^{\dfrac{-(-432 \text{ kJ}) \times \frac{1000 \text{ J}}{1 \text{ kJ}}}{\left(8.314 \frac{\text{J}}{\text{K} \cdot \text{mol}}\right)(298 \text{ K})}} = e^{174.364} = 5.31 \times 10^{75}$$

(b) $\Delta G^{\circ}_{rxn} = -RT \ln K$. Rearrange to solve for K.

$$K = e^{\frac{-\Delta G^{\circ}_{rxn}}{RT}} = e^{\dfrac{-(+52 \text{ kJ}) \times \frac{1000 \text{ J}}{1 \text{ kJ}}}{\left(8.314 \frac{\text{J}}{\text{K} \cdot \text{mol}}\right)(298 \text{ K})}} = e^{-20.998} = 7.67 \times 10^{-10}$$

(c) $\Delta G^{\circ}_{rxn} = -RT \ln K$. Rearrange to solve for K.

$$K = e^{\frac{-\Delta G^{\circ}_{rxn}}{RT}} = e^{\dfrac{-(-170 \text{ kJ}) \times \frac{1000 \text{ J}}{1 \text{ kJ}}}{\left(8.314 \frac{\text{J}}{\text{K} \cdot \text{mol}}\right)(298 \text{ K})}} = e^{68.616} = 6.3 \times 10^{29}$$

Check: The units (none) are correct. If the voltage is positive, the reaction is spontaneous, the free energy change is negative, and the equilibrium constant is large.

18.32   **Given:** overall reactions from Problem 30   **Find:** K

Conceptual Plan: $°C \rightarrow K$ **then** $\Delta G^{\circ}_{rxn}, T = K$

$\qquad\qquad K = 273.15 + °C \qquad \Delta G^{\circ}_{rxn} = -RT \ln K$

Solution: $T = 273.15 + 25 °C = 298 \text{ K}$ then

(a) $\Delta G^{\circ}_{rxn} = -RT \ln K$. Rearrange to solve for K.

$$K = e^{\frac{-\Delta G^{\circ}_{rxn}}{RT}} = e^{\dfrac{-(-60 \text{ kJ}) \times \frac{1000 \text{ J}}{1 \text{ kJ}}}{\left(8.314 \frac{\text{J}}{\text{K} \cdot \text{mol}}\right)(298 \text{ K})}} = e^{24.217} = 3.3 \times 10^{10}$$

(b) $\Delta G^{\circ}_{rxn} = -RT \ln K$. Rearrange to solve for K.

$$K = e^{\frac{-\Delta G^{\circ}_{rxn}}{RT}} = e^{\dfrac{-(-20 \text{ kJ}) \times \frac{1000 \text{ J}}{1 \text{ kJ}}}{\left(8.314 \frac{\text{J}}{\text{K} \cdot \text{mol}}\right)(298 \text{ K})}} = e^{8.072} = 3 \times 10^3$$

(c) $\Delta G^\circ_{rxn} = -RT \ln K$. Rearrange to solve for K.

$$K = e^{\frac{-\Delta G^\circ_{rxn}}{RT}} = e^{\dfrac{-(-110 \text{ kJ}) \times \frac{1000 \text{ J}}{1 \text{ kJ}}}{\left(8.314 \frac{J}{K \cdot mol}\right)(298 \text{ K})}} = e^{44.398} = 1.9 \times 10^{19}$$

Check: The units (none) are correct. If the voltage is positive, the reaction is spontaneous, the free energy change is negative, and the equilibrium constant is large.

18.33   **Given:** $Ni^{2+}(aq) + Cd(s) \rightarrow$ **Find:** K

Conceptual Plan: Write two half-cell reactions and add electrons as needed to balance the reactions. Look up half-reactions in Table 18.1. Calculate the standard cell potential by subtracting the electrode potential of the anode from the electrode potential of the cathode: $E^\circ_{cell} = E^\circ_{cathode} - E^\circ_{anode}$, then

$^\circ C \rightarrow K$ then $E^\circ_{cell}, n, T \rightarrow K$.

$K = 273.15 + {}^\circ C$ $\Delta G^\circ_{rxn} = -RT \ln K = -nFE^\circ_{cell}$

Solution: $Ni^{2+}(aq) + 2 e^- \rightarrow Ni(s)$ and $Cd(s) \rightarrow Cd^{2+}(aq) + 2 e^-$. Look up cell potentials. Cd is oxidized, so $E^\circ_{red} = -0.40 \text{ V} = E^\circ_{anode}$. Ni^{2+} is reduced, so $E^\circ_{red} = -0.23 \text{ V} = E^\circ_{cathode}$. Then $E^\circ_{cell} = E^\circ_{cathode} - E^\circ_{anode} = -0.23 \text{ V}$ $-(-0.40 \text{ V}) = +0.17 \text{ V}$. The overall reaction is $Ni^{2+}(aq) + Cd(s) \rightarrow Ni(s) + Cd^{2+}(aq)$. $n = 2$ and $T = 273.15 + 25 \,^\circ C = 298 \text{ K}$ then $\Delta G^\circ_{rxn} = -RT \ln K = -nFE^\circ_{cell}$. Rearrange to solve for K.

$$K = e^{\frac{nFE^\circ_{cell}}{RT}} = e^{\dfrac{2 \text{ mol } e^- \times \frac{96,485 \text{ C}}{\text{mol } e^-} \times 0.17 \frac{J}{C}}{\left(8.314 \frac{J}{K \cdot mol}\right)(298 \text{ K})}} = e^{13.241} = 5.6 \times 10^5$$

Check: The units (none) are correct. If the voltage is positive, the reaction is spontaneous and the equilibrium constant is large.

18.34   **Given:** $Fe^{2+}(aq) + Zn(s) \rightarrow$ **Find:** K

Conceptual Plan: Write two half-cell reactions and add electrons as needed to balance the reactions. Look up half-reactions in Table 18.1. Calculate the standard cell potential by subtracting the electrode potential of the anode from the electrode potential of the cathode: $E^\circ_{cell} = E^\circ_{cathode} - E^\circ_{anode}$, then

$^\circ C \rightarrow K$ then $E^\circ_{cell}, n, T \rightarrow K$.

$K = 273.15 + {}^\circ C$. $\Delta G^\circ_{rxn} = -RT \ln K = -nFE^\circ_{cell}$

Solution: $Fe^{2+}(aq) + 2 e^- \rightarrow Fe(s)$ and $Zn(s) \rightarrow Zn^{2+}(aq) + 2 e^-$. Look up cell potentials. Zn is oxidized, so $E^\circ_{red} = -0.76 \text{ V} = E^\circ_{anode}$. Fe^{2+} is reduced, so $E^\circ_{red} = -0.45 \text{ V} = E^\circ_{cathode}$. Then $E^\circ_{cell} = E^\circ_{cathode} - E^\circ_{anode} = -0.45 \text{ V} - (-0.76 \text{ V}) = +0.31 \text{ V}$. The overall reaction is $Fe^{2+}(aq) + Zn(s) \rightarrow Fe(s) + Zn^{2+}(aq)$. $n = 2$ and $T = 273.15 + 25 \,^\circ C = 298 \text{ K}$ then $\Delta G^\circ_{rxn} = -RT \ln K = -nFE^\circ_{cell}$. Rearrange to solve for K.

$$K = e^{\frac{nFE^\circ_{cell}}{RT}} = e^{\dfrac{2 \text{ mol } e^- \times \frac{96,485 \text{ C}}{\text{mol } e^-} \times 0.31 \frac{J}{C}}{\left(8.314 \frac{J}{K \cdot mol}\right)(298 \text{ K})}} = e^{24.145} = 3.1 \times 10^{10}$$

Check: The units (none) are correct. If the voltage is positive, the reaction is spontaneous and the equilibrium constant is large.

18.35   **Given:** $n = 2$ and $K = 25$ **Find:** ΔG°_{rxn} and E°_{cell}

Conceptual Plan: $K, T \rightarrow \Delta G^\circ_{rxn}$ and $\Delta G^\circ_{rxn}, n \rightarrow E^\circ_{cell}$

$\Delta G^\circ_{rxn} = -RT \ln K$ $\Delta G^\circ_{rxn} = -nFE^\circ_{cell}$

Solution: $\Delta G^\circ_{rxn} = -RT \ln K = -\left(8.314 \dfrac{J}{K \cdot mol}\right)(298 \text{ K}) \ln 25 = -7.97500 \times 10^3 \text{ J} = -8.0 \text{ kJ}$ and

$\Delta G^\circ_{rxn} = -nFE^\circ_{cell}$. Rearrange to solve for E°_{cell}.

$$E^\circ_{cell} = \frac{\Delta G^\circ_{rxn}}{-nF} = \frac{-7.97500 \times 10^3 \text{ J}}{-2 \text{ mol } e^- \times \dfrac{96,485 \text{ C}}{\text{mol } e^-}} = 0.041 \frac{V \cdot C}{C} = 0.041 \text{ V}$$

Check: The units (kJ and V) are correct. If $K > 1$, the voltage is positive and the free energy change is negative.

18.36   **Given:** $n = 3$ and $K = 0.050$ **Find:** $\Delta G°_{rxn}$ and $E°_{cell}$

Conceptual Plan: $K, T \rightarrow \Delta G°_{rxn}$ and $\Delta G°_{rxn}, n \rightarrow E°_{cell}$

$$\Delta G°_{rxn} = -RT \ln K \qquad \Delta G°_{rxn} = -nFE°_{cell}$$

Solution: $\Delta G°_{rxn} = -RT \ln K = -\left(8.314 \dfrac{J}{K \cdot mol}\right)(298 \ K) \ln 0.050 = 7.4\underline{2}21 \times 10^3 \ J = 7.4 \ kJ$ and

$\Delta G°_{rxn} = -nFE°_{cell}$. Rearrange to solve for $E°_{cell}$.

$$E°_{cell} = \dfrac{\Delta G°_{rxn}}{-nF} = \dfrac{7.4\underline{2}21 \times 10^3 \ J}{-3 \ \cancel{mol \ e^-} \times \dfrac{96,485 \ C}{\cancel{mol \ e^-}}} = -0.026 \dfrac{V \cdot \cancel{C}}{\cancel{C}} = -0.026 \ V$$

Check: The units (kJ and V) are correct. If $K < 1$, the voltage is negative and the free energy change is positive.

Nonstandard Conditions and the Nernst Equation

18.37   **Given:** $Sn^{2+}(aq) + Mn(s) \rightarrow Sn(s) + Mn^{2+}(aq)$
Find: (a) $E°_{cell}$; (b) E_{cell} when $[Sn^{2+}] = 0.0100 \ M$; $[Mn^{2+}] = 2.00 \ M$; and (c) E_{cell} when $[Sn^{2+}] = 2.00 \ M$; $[Mn^{2+}] = 0.0100 \ M$

Conceptual Plan: (a) **Separate the overall reaction into two half-cell reactions and add electrons as needed to balance the reactions. Look up half-reactions in Table 18.1. Calculate the standard cell potential by subtracting the electrode potential of the anode from the electrode potential of the cathode:** $E°_{cell} = E°_{cathode} - E°_{anode}$. **(b) and (c)** $E°_{cell}, [Sn^{2+}], [Mn^{2+}], n \rightarrow E_{cell}$

$$E_{cell} = E°_{cell} - \dfrac{0.0592 \ V}{n} \log Q \quad \text{where} \quad Q = \dfrac{[Mn^{2+}]}{[Sn^{2+}]}$$

Solution:

(a)   Separate the overall reaction to $Sn^{2+}(aq) \rightarrow Sn(s)$ and $Mn(s) \rightarrow Mn^{2+}(aq)$. Add electrons. $Sn^{2+}(aq) + 2 \ e^- \rightarrow Sn(s)$ and $Mn(s) \rightarrow Mn^{2+}(aq) + 2 \ e^-$. Look up cell potentials. Mn is oxidized, so $E°_{red} = -1.18 \ V = E°_{anode}$. Sn^{2+} is reduced, so $E°_{red} = -0.14 \ V = E°_{cathode}$. Then $E°_{cell} = E°_{cathode} - E°_{anode} = -0.14 \ V - (-1.18 \ V) = +1.04 \ V$.

(b) $Q = \dfrac{[Mn^{2+}]}{[Sn^{2+}]} = \dfrac{2.00 \ M}{0.0100 \ M} = 200.$ and $n = 2$ then

$$E_{cell} = E°_{cell} - \dfrac{0.0592 \ V}{n} \log Q = 1.04 \ V - \dfrac{0.0592 \ V}{2} \log 200. = +0.97 \ V$$

(c) $Q = \dfrac{[Mn^{2+}]}{[Sn^{2+}]} = \dfrac{0.0100 \ M}{2.00 \ M} = 0.00500$ and $n = 2$ then

$$E_{cell} = E°_{cell} - \dfrac{0.0592 \ V}{n} \log Q = 1.04 \ V - \dfrac{0.0592 \ V}{2} \log 0.00500 = +1.11 \ V$$

Check: The units (V, V, and V) are correct. The Sn^{2+} reduction reaction is above the Mn^{2+} reduction reaction, so the standard cell potential will be positive. Having more products than reactants reduces the cell potential. Having more reactants than products raises the cell potential.

18.38   **Given:** $2 \ Fe^{3+}(aq) + 3 \ Mg(s) \rightarrow 2 \ Fe(s) + 3 \ Mg^{2+}(aq)$ **Find:** (a) $E°_{cell}$; (b) E_{cell} when $[Fe^{3+}] = 1.0 \times 10^{-3} \ M$; $[Mg^{2+}] = 2.50 \ M$; and (c) E_{cell} when $[Fe^{3+}] = 2.00 \ M$; $[Mg^{2+}] = 1.5 \times 10^{-3} \ M$

Conceptual Plan: (a) **Separate the overall reaction into two half-cell reactions and add electrons as needed to balance reactions. Look up half-reactions in Table 18.1. Calculate the standard cell potential by subtracting the electrode potential of the anode from the electrode potential of the cathode:** $E°_{cell} = E°_{cathode} - E°_{anode}$. **(b) and (c)** $E°_{cell}, [Fe^{3+}], [Mg^{2+}], n \rightarrow E_{cell}$

$$E_{cell} = E°_{cell} - \dfrac{0.0592 \ V}{n} \log Q \quad \text{where} \quad Q = \dfrac{[Mg^{2+}]^3}{[Fe^{3+}]^2}$$

Solution:

(a)   Separate the overall reaction to $2 \ Fe^{3+}(aq) \rightarrow 2 \ Fe(s)$ and $3 \ Mg(s) \rightarrow 3 \ Mg^{2+}(aq)$. Add electrons. $2 \ Fe^{3+} + 6 \ e^-(aq) \rightarrow 2 \ Fe(s)$ and $3 \ Mg(s) \rightarrow 3 \ Mg^{2+}(aq) + 6 \ e^-$. Look up cell potentials. Mg is oxidized, so

$E°_{red} = -2.37$ V $= E°_{anode}$. Fe^{3+} is reduced, so $E°_{red} = -0.036$ V $= E°_{cathode}$. Then $E°_{cell} = E°_{cathode} - E°_{anode}$ $= -0.036$ V $- (-2.37$ V$) = +2.3\underline{3}4$ V $= +2.33$ V.

(b) $Q = \dfrac{[Mg^{2+}]^3}{[Fe^{3+}]^2} = \dfrac{(2.50)^3}{(1.0 \times 10^{-3})^2} = 1.5625 \times 10^7$ and $n = 6$ then

$E_{cell} = E°_{cell} - \dfrac{0.0592 \text{ V}}{n}\log Q = 2.3\underline{3}4$ V $- \dfrac{0.0592 \text{ V}}{6}\log 1.5625 \times 10^7 = +2.26$ V

(c) $Q = \dfrac{[Mg^{2+}]^3}{[Fe^{3+}]^2} = \dfrac{(1.5 \times 10^{-3})^3}{(2.00)^2} = 8.4375 \times 10^{-10}$ and $n = 6$ then

$E_{cell} = E°_{cell} - \dfrac{0.0592 \text{ V}}{n}\log Q = 2.3\underline{3}4$ V $- \dfrac{0.0592 \text{ V}}{6}\log 8.4375 \times 10^{-10} = +2.42$ V

Check: The units (V, V, and V) are correct. The Fe^{3+} reduction reaction is above the Mg^{2+} reduction reaction, so the standard cell potential will be positive. Having more products than reactants reduces the cell potential. Having more reactants than products raises the cell potential.

18.39   **Given:** $Pb(s) \rightarrow Pb^{2+}(aq, 0.10$ M$) + 2$ e$^-$ and $MnO_4^-(aq, 1.50$ M$) + 4$ H$^+(aq, 2.0$ M$) + 3$ e$^- \rightarrow MnO_2(s) +$ 2 H$_2$O(l) **Find:** E_{cell}
Conceptual Plan: Look up half-reactions in Table 18.1. Calculate the standard cell potential by subtracting the electrode potential of the anode from the electrode potential of the cathode: $E°_{cell} = E°_{cathode} - E°_{anode}$. Equalize the number of electrons transferred by multiplying the first reaction by 3 and the second reaction by 2. Add the two half-cell reactions and cancel the electrons.
Then $E°_{cell}$, $[Pb^{2+}]$, $[MnO_4^-]$, $[H^+]$, $n \rightarrow E_{cell}$.

$$E_{cell} = E°_{cell} - \dfrac{0.0592 \text{ V}}{n}\log Q \quad \text{where} \quad Q = \dfrac{[Pb^{2+}]^3}{[MnO_4^-]^2[H^+]^8}$$

Solution: Pb is oxidized, so $E°_{red} = -0.13$ V $= E°_{anode}$. Mn is reduced, so $E°_{red} = 1.68$ V $= E°_{cathode}$. Then $E°_{cell} = E°_{cathode} - E°_{anode} = 1.68$ V $- (-0.13$ V$) = +1.81$ V. Equalizing the electrons: 3 Pb$(s) \rightarrow 3$ Pb$^{2+}(aq) + 6$ e$^-$ and 2 MnO$_4^-(aq) + 8$ H$^+(aq) + 6$ e$^- \rightarrow 2$ MnO$_2(s) + 4$ H$_2$O(l). Adding the two reactions: 3 Pb$(s) + 2$ MnO$_4^-(aq)$ $+ 8$ H$^+(aq) + \cancel{6e^-} \rightarrow 3$ Pb$^{2+}(aq) + \cancel{6e^-} + 2$ MnO$_2(s) + 4$ H$_2$O(l). Cancel the electrons: 3 Pb$(s) + 2$ MnO$_4^-(aq)$ $+ 8$ H$^+(aq) \rightarrow 3$ Pb$^{2+}(aq) + 2$ MnO$_2(s) + 4$ H$_2$O(l). So $n = 6$ and $Q = \dfrac{[Pb^{2+}]^3}{[MnO_4^-]^2[H^+]^8} = \dfrac{(0.10)^3}{(1.50)^2(2.0)^8}$

$= 1.\underline{7}361 \times 10^{-6}$. Then $E_{cell} = E°_{cell} - \dfrac{0.0592 \text{ V}}{n}\log Q = 1.81$ V $- \dfrac{0.0592 \text{ V}}{6}\log 1.\underline{7}361 \times 10^{-6} = +1.87$ V.

Check: The units (V) are correct. The MnO_4^- reduction reaction is above the Pb^{2+} reduction reaction, so the standard cell potential will be positive. Having more reactants than products raises the cell potential.

18.40   **Given:** $Sn(s) \rightarrow Sn^{2+}(aq, 2.00$ M$) + 2$ e$^-$ and $ClO_2(g, 0.100$ atm$) + $ e$^- \rightarrow ClO_2^-(aq, 2.00$ M$)$ **Find:** E_{cell}
Conceptual Plan: Look up half-reactions in Table 18.1. Calculate the standard cell potential by subtracting the electrode potential of the anode from the electrode potential of the cathode: $E°_{cell} = E°_{cathode} - E°_{anode}$. Equalize the number of electrons transferred by multiplying the second reaction by 2. Add the two half-cell reactions and cancel the electrons. Then $E°_{cell}$, $[Sn^{2+}]$, P_{ClO_2}, $[ClO_2^-]$, $n \rightarrow E_{cell}$.

$$E_{cell} = E°_{cell} - \dfrac{0.0592 \text{ V}}{n}\log Q \quad \text{where} \quad Q = \dfrac{[Sn^{2+}][ClO_2^-]^2}{P_{ClO_2}^2}$$

Solution: Sn is oxidized, so $E°_{red} = -0.14$ V $= E°_{anode}$. ClO_2 is reduced, so $E°_{red} = 0.95$ V $= E°_{cathode}$. Then $E°_{cell} = E°_{cathode} - E°_{anode} = 0.95$ V $- (-0.14$ V$) = +1.09$ V. Equalizing the electrons: Sn$(s) \rightarrow$ Sn$^{2+}(aq) + 2$ e$^-$ and 2 ClO$_2(g) + 2$ e$^- \rightarrow 2$ ClO$_2^-(aq)$. Adding the two reactions: Sn$(s) + 2$ ClO$_2(g) + \cancel{2e^-} \rightarrow$ Sn$^{2+}(aq) + \cancel{2e^-} +$ 2 ClO$_2^-(aq)$. Cancel the electrons: Sn$(s) + 2$ ClO$_2(g) \rightarrow$ Sn$^{2+}(aq) + 2$ ClO$_2^-(aq)$. So $n = 2$ and

$Q = \dfrac{[Sn^{2+}][ClO_2^-]^2}{P_{ClO_2}^2} = \dfrac{(2.00)(2.00)^2}{(0.100)^2} = 800$. Then

$E_{cell} = E°_{cell} - \dfrac{0.0592 \text{ V}}{n}\log Q = 1.09$ V $- \dfrac{0.0592 \text{ V}}{2}\log 800. = +1.00$ V.

Check: The units (V) are correct. The ClO_2 reduction reaction is above the Sn^{2+} reduction reaction, so the standard cell potential will be positive. Having more products than reactants lowers the cell potential.

18.41 **Given:** Zn/Zn^{2+} and Ni/Ni^{2+} half-cells in voltaic cell; initially, $[Ni^{2+}] = 1.50$ M and $[Zn^{2+}] = 0.100$ M
Find: (a) initial E_{cell}, (b) E_{cell} when $[Ni^{2+}] = 0.500$ M, and (c) $[Ni^{2+}]$ and $[Zn^{2+}]$ when $E_{cell} = 0.45$ V
Conceptual Plan:

(a) **Write two half-cell reactions and add electrons as needed to balance reactions. Look up half-reactions in Table 18.1. Calculate the standard cell potential by subtracting the electrode potential of the anode from the electrode potential of the cathode: $E^{\circ}_{cell} = E^{\circ}_{cathode} - E^{\circ}_{anode}$. Choose the direction of the half-cell reactions so that $E^{\circ}_{cell} > 0$. Add two half-cell reactions and cancel electrons to generate overall reaction. Define Q based on overall reaction. Then $E^{\circ}_{cell}, [Ni^{2+}], [Zn^{2+}], n \rightarrow E_{cell}$.**

$$E_{cell} = E^{\circ}_{cell} - \frac{0.0592 \text{ V}}{n} \log Q$$

(b) **When $[Ni^{2+}] = 0.500$ M, then $[Zn^{2+}] = 1.100$ M. (Because the stoichiometric coefficients for $Ni^{2+} : Zn^{2+}$ are 1:1 and the $[Ni^{2+}]$ drops by 1.00 M, the other concentration must rise by 1.00 M.) Then $E^{\circ}_{cell}, [Ni^{2+}], [Zn^{2+}], n \rightarrow E_{cell}$**

$$E_{cell} = E^{\circ}_{cell} - \frac{0.0592 \text{ V}}{n} \log Q$$

(c) $E^{\circ}_{cell}, E_{cell}, n \rightarrow [Zn^{2+}]/[Ni^{2+}] \rightarrow [Ni^{2+}], [Zn^{2+}]$

$$E_{cell} = E^{\circ}_{cell} - \frac{0.0592 \text{ V}}{n} \log Q \qquad [Ni^{2+}] + [Zn^{2+}] = 1.50 \text{ M} + 0.100 \text{ M} = 1.60 \text{ M}$$

Solution:

(a) $Zn^{2+}(aq) + 2 e^- \rightarrow Zn(s)$ and $Ni^{2+}(aq) + 2 e^- \rightarrow Ni(s)$. Look up cell potentials. For Zn, $E^{\circ}_{red} = -0.76$ V. For Ni, $E^{\circ}_{red} = -0.23$ V. To get a positive E°_{cell}, Zn is oxidized; so $E^{\circ}_{red} = -0.76$ V $= E^{\circ}_{anode}$. Ni^{2+} is reduced, so $E^{\circ}_{red} = -0.23$ V $= E^{\circ}_{cathode}$. Then $E^{\circ}_{cell} = E^{\circ}_{cathode} - E^{\circ}_{anode} = -0.23$ V $- (-0.76$ V$) = +0.53$ V. Adding the two half-cell reactions: $Zn(s) + Ni^{2+}(aq) + 2e^- \rightarrow Zn^{2+}(aq) + 2e^- + Ni(s)$. The overall reaction is $Zn(s) + Ni^{2+}(aq) \rightarrow Zn^{2+}(aq) + Ni(s)$. Then $Q = \dfrac{[Zn^{2+}]}{[Ni^{2+}]} = \dfrac{0.100}{1.50} = 0.0666667$ and $n = 2$. Then

$$E_{cell} = E^{\circ}_{cell} - \frac{0.0592 \text{ V}}{n} \log Q = 0.53 \text{ V} - \frac{0.0592 \text{ V}}{2} \log 0.0666667 = +0.56 \text{ V}.$$

(b) $Q = \dfrac{[Zn^{2+}]}{[Ni^{2+}]} = \dfrac{1.100}{0.500} = 2.20$ then

$$E_{cell} = E^{\circ}_{cell} - \frac{0.0592 \text{ V}}{n} \log Q = 0.53 \text{ V} - \frac{0.0592 \text{ V}}{2} \log 2.20 = +0.52 \text{ V}$$

(c) $E_{cell} = E^{\circ}_{cell} - \dfrac{0.0592 \text{ V}}{n} \log Q$ so 0.45 V $= 0.53$ V $- \dfrac{0.0592 \text{ V}}{2} \log Q \rightarrow 0.08 \text{ V} = \dfrac{0.0592 \text{ V}}{2} \log Q \rightarrow$

$\log Q = 2.70270 \rightarrow Q = 10^{2.70270} = 504.31$. Then $Q = 504.31 = \dfrac{[Zn^{2+}]}{1.60 \text{ M} - [Zn^{2+}]}$. Solving for $[Zn^{2+}]$:

$$(504.31)(1.60 \text{ M} - [Zn^{2+}]) = [Zn^{2+}] \rightarrow [Zn^{2+}] = \frac{806.896 \text{ M}}{505.31} = 1.59683 \text{ M} = 1.60 \text{ M then}$$

$[Ni^{2+}] = 1.60$ M $- 1.59683$ M $= 0.003$ M.

Check: The units (V, V, and M) are correct. The standard cell potential is positive, and because there are more reactants than products, this raises the cell potential. As the reaction proceeds, reactants are converted to products; so the cell potential drops for parts (b) and (c).

18.42 **Given:** Pb/Pb^{2+} and Cu/Cu^{2+} half-cells in voltaic cell; initially, $[Pb^{2+}] = 0.0500$ M and $[Cu^{2+}] = 1.50$ M
Find: (a) initial E_{cell}, (b) E_{cell} when $[Cu^{2+}] = 0.200$ M, and (c) $[Pb^{2+}]$ and $[Cu^{2+}]$ when $E_{cell} = 0.35$ V
Conceptual Plan:

(a) **Write two half-cell reactions and add electrons as needed to balance reactions. Look up half-reactions in Table 18.1. Calculate the standard cell potential by subtracting the electrode potential of the anode from the electrode potential of the cathode: $E^{\circ}_{cell} = E^{\circ}_{cathode} - E^{\circ}_{anode}$. Choose the direction of the half-cell reactions so that $E^{\circ}_{cell} > 0$. Add two half-cell reactions and cancel electrons to generate overall reaction. Define Q based on overall reaction. Then $E^{\circ}_{cell}, [Pb^{2+}], [Cu^{2+}], n \rightarrow E_{cell}$.**

$$E_{cell} = E^{\circ}_{cell} - \frac{0.0592 \text{ V}}{n} \log Q$$

(b)   When $[Cu^{2+}] = 0.200$ M, then $[Pb^{2+}] = 1.35$ M. (Because the stoichiometric coefficients for $Pb^{2+}: Cu^{2+}$ are 1:1 and the $[Cu^{2+}]$ drops by 1.30 M, the other concentration must rise by 1.30 M.) Then $E°_{cell}, [Pb^{2+}], [Cu^{2+}], n \rightarrow E_{cell}$

$$E_{cell} = E°_{cell} - \frac{0.0592 \text{ V}}{n} \log Q$$

(c) $E°_{cell}, E_{cell}, n \rightarrow [Pb^{2+}]/[Cu^{2+}] \rightarrow [Pb^{2+}], [Cu^{2+}]$

$$E_{cell} = E°_{cell} - \frac{0.0592 \text{ V}}{n} \log Q \quad [Pb^{2+}] + [Cu^{2+}] = 0.0500 \text{ M} + 1.50 \text{ M} = 1.55 \text{ M}$$

Solution:

(a) $Pb^{2+}(aq) + 2 e^- \rightarrow Pb(s)$ and $Cu^{2+}(aq) + 2 e^- \rightarrow Cu(s)$. Look up cell potentials. For Pb, $E°_{red} = -0.13$ V. For Cu, $E°_{red} = +0.34$ V. To get a positive $E°_{cell}$, Pb is oxidized; so $E°_{red} = -0.13$ V $= E°_{anode}$. Cu^{2+} is reduced, so $E°_{red} = 0.34$ V $= E°_{cathode}$. Then $E°_{cell} = E°_{cathode} - E°_{anode} = 0.34$ V $- (-0.13$ V$) = +0.47$ V. Adding the two half-cell reactions: $Pb(s) + Cu^{2+}(aq) + 2e^- \rightarrow Pb^{2+}(aq) + 2e^- + Cu(s)$. The overall reaction is $Pb(s) + Cu^{2+}(aq) \rightarrow Pb^{2+}(aq) + Cu(s)$. Then $Q = \dfrac{[Pb^{2+}]}{[Cu^{2+}]} = \dfrac{0.050}{1.50} = 0.033333$ and $n = 2$. Then

$$E_{cell} = E°_{cell} - \frac{0.0592 \text{ V}}{n} \log Q = 0.47 \text{ V} - \frac{0.0592 \text{ V}}{2} \log 0.033333 = +0.51 \text{ V}.$$

(b) $Q = \dfrac{[Pb^{2+}]}{[Cu^{2+}]} = \dfrac{1.35}{0.200} = 6.75$ then

$$E_{cell} = E°_{cell} - \frac{0.0592 \text{ V}}{n} \log Q = 0.47 \text{ V} - \frac{0.0592 \text{ V}}{2} \log 6.75 = +0.45 \text{ V}$$

(c) $E_{cell} = E°_{cell} - \dfrac{0.0592 \text{ V}}{n} \log Q$, so 0.35 V $= 0.47$ V $- \dfrac{0.0592 \text{ V}}{2} \log Q \rightarrow 0.12 \cancel{\text{V}} = \dfrac{0.0592 \cancel{\text{V}}}{2} \log Q \rightarrow$

$\log Q = 4.0541 \rightarrow Q = 10^{4.0541} = 1.1327 \times 10^4$. Then $Q = 1.1327 \times 10^4 = \dfrac{[Pb^{2+}]}{1.55 \text{ M} - [Pb^{2+}]}$. Solving

for $[Pb^{2+}]$: $(1.1327 \times 10^4)(1.55 \text{ M} - [Pb^{2+}]) = [Pb^{2+}] \rightarrow [Pb^{2+}] = \dfrac{1.7557 \times 10^4 \text{ M}}{1.1328 \times 10^4} = 1.5499 \text{ M} = 1.5 \text{ M}$

then $[Cu^{2+}] = 1.55$ M $- 1.5499$ M $= 0.0001$ M $= 0.0$ M.

Check: The units (V, V, and M) are correct. The standard cell potential is positive, and because there are more reactants than products, this raises the cell potential. As the reaction proceeds, reactants are converted to products; so the cell potential drops for parts (b) and (c).

18.43   **Given:** Zn/Zn^{2+} concentration cell, with $[Zn^{2+}] = 2.0$ M in one half-cell and $[Zn^{2+}] = 1.0 \times 10^{-3}$ M in other half-cell

Find: Sketch a voltaic cell, labeling the anode, the cathode, the reactions at electrodes, all species, and the direction of electron flow.

Conceptual Plan: In a concentration cell, the half-cell with the higher concentration is always the half-cell where the reduction takes place (contains the cathode). The two half-cell reactions are the same, but reversed. Put anode reaction on the left (oxidation = electrons as product) and cathode reaction on the right (reduction = electrons as reactant). Electrons flow from anode to cathode.
Solution:

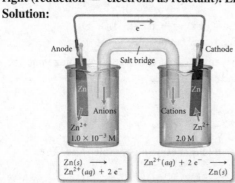

Check: The figure looks similar to the right side of Figure 18.10.

18.44   **Given:** Pb/Pb^{2+} concentration cell sketch
Find: (a) Label the anode and cathode, (b) indicate direction of electron flow, and (c) indicate what happens to $[Pb^{2+}]$ in each half-cell with time.
Conceptual Plan: (a) In a concentration cell, the half-cell with the higher concentration is always the half-cell where the reduction takes place (contains the cathode). (b) Electrons flow from anode to cathode. (c) Each half-cell reaction moves forward, so the direction of the concentration changes in each half-cell can be determined.
Solution:

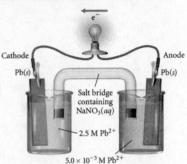

(c) As the reaction proceeds, the left half-cell (cathode = reduction reaction) will decrease in concentration and the right half-cell (anode = oxidation reaction) will increase in concentration. Eventually, the two concentrations will be the same and the flow of electrons will stop.

Check: The figure looks similar to the right side of Figure 18.10.

18.45   **Given:** Sn/Sn^{2+} concentration cell with $E_{cell} = 0.10$ V   **Find:** ratio of $[Sn^{2+}]$ in two half-cells
Conceptual Plan: Determine n, then $E°_{cell}, E°_{cell}, n \rightarrow Q = $ ratio of $[Sn^{2+}]$ in two half-cells.

$$E_{cell} = E°_{cell} - \frac{0.0592 \text{ V}}{n} \log Q$$

Solution: Because $Sn^{2+}(aq) + 2 e^- \rightarrow Sn(s), n = 2$. In a concentration cell, $E°_{cell} = 0$ V. So

$$E_{cell} = E°_{cell} - \frac{0.0592 \text{ V}}{n} \log Q, \text{ so } 0.10 \text{ V} = 0.00 \text{ V} - \frac{0.0592 \text{ V}}{2} \log Q \rightarrow 0.10 \cancel{V} = -\frac{0.0592 \cancel{V}}{2} \log Q \rightarrow$$

$$\log Q = -3.\underline{3}784 \rightarrow Q = 10^{-3.\underline{3}784} = 4.2 \times 10^{-4} = \frac{[Sn^{2+}](ox)}{[Sn^{2+}](red)}.$$

Check: The units (none) are correct. Because the concentration in the reduction reaction half-cell is always greater than the concentration in the oxidation half-cell in a voltaic concentration cell, the Q or ratio of two cells is less than 1.

18.46   **Given:** Cu/Cu^{2+} concentration cell with $E_{cell} = 0.22$ V and $[Cu^{2+}] = 1.5 \times 10^{-3}$ M   **Find:** $[Cu^{2+}]$ in other half-cell
Conceptual Plan: Determine n, then $E°_{cell}, E_{cell}, n \rightarrow Q = $ ratio of $[Cu^{2+}]$ in two half-cells then

$$E_{cell} = E°_{cell} - \frac{0.0592 \text{ V}}{n} \log Q$$

$[Cu^{2+}]$ one side, $Q \rightarrow [Cu^{2+}]$ other side.

$$Q = \frac{[Cu^{2+}](ox)}{[Cu^{2+}](red)}$$

Solution: Because $Cu^{2+}(aq) + 2 e^- \rightarrow Cu(s), n = 2$. In a concentration cell, $E°_{cell} = 0$ V. So

$$E_{cell} = E°_{cell} - \frac{0.0592 \text{ V}}{n} \log Q, \text{ so } 0.22 \text{ V} = 0.00 \text{ V} - \frac{0.0592 \text{ V}}{2} \log Q \rightarrow 0.22 \cancel{V} = -\frac{0.0592 \cancel{V}}{2} \log Q \rightarrow$$

$$\log Q = -7.\underline{4}324 \rightarrow Q = 10^{-7.\underline{4}324} = 3.\underline{6}949 \times 10^{-8} = \frac{[Cu^{2+}](ox)}{[Cu^{2+}](red)}.$$

$$[Cu^{2+}](red) = \frac{[Cu^{2+}](ox)}{Q} = \frac{1.5 \times 10^{-3} \text{ M}}{3.\underline{6}949 \times 10^{-8}} = 4.1 \times 10^4 \text{ M}. \text{ This concentration is not possible, so the given}$$

concentration must be the higher concentration. Therefore $[Cu^{2+}](ox) = [Cu^{2+}](red) \times Q$
$= (1.5 \times 10^{-3} \text{ M})(3.\underline{6}949 \times 10^{-8}) = 5.5 \times 10^{-11} \text{ M}$, which is low but possible.

Check: The units (M) are correct. Because the voltage is fairly high for a concentration cell, there must be a very small Q, which leads to an extremely low concentration on the oxidation side.

Batteries, Fuel Cells, and Corrosion

18.47   **Given:** alkaline battery   **Find:** optimum mass ratio of Zn to MnO_2
Conceptual Plan: Look up alkaline battery reactions. Use stoichiometry to get mole ratio. Then

$$Zn(s) + 2 OH^-(aq) \rightarrow Zn(OH)_2(s) + 2 e^- \qquad \frac{1 \text{ mol Zn}}{2 \text{ mol MnO}_2}$$

$$2 MnO_2(s) + 2 H_2O(l) + 2 e^- \rightarrow 2 MnO(OH)(s) + 2 OH^-(aq)$$

mol Zn → g Zn Zn then mol MnO$_2$ → g MnO$_2$.

$$\frac{65.38 \text{ g Zn}}{1 \text{ mol Zn}} \qquad\qquad \frac{1 \text{ mol MnO}_2}{86.94 \text{ g MnO}_2}$$

Solution: $\dfrac{1 \text{ mol Zn}}{2 \text{ mol MnO}_2} \times \dfrac{65.38 \text{ g Zn}}{1 \text{ mol Zn}} \times \dfrac{1 \text{ mol MnO}_2}{86.94 \text{ g MnO}_2} = 0.3760 \dfrac{\text{g Zn}}{\text{g MnO}_2}$

Check: The units (mass ratio) are correct. Because more moles of MnO$_2$ are needed and the molar mass is larger, the ratio is less than 1.

18.48   **Given:** lead storage battery, 1.00 g Pb oxidizes   **Find:** mass PbSO$_4$
Conceptual Plan: Look up lead acid battery reactions. Then g Pb → mol Pb → mol PbSO$_4$ → g PbSO$_4$.

$$\text{Pb}(s) + \text{HSO}_4^-(aq) \rightarrow \text{PbSO}_4(s) + \text{H}^+(aq) + 2\,e^- \qquad \frac{1 \text{ mol Pb}}{207.2 \text{ g Pb}} \quad \frac{2 \text{ mol PbSO}_4}{1 \text{ mol Pb}} \quad \frac{303.27 \text{ g PbSO}_4}{1 \text{ mol PbSO}_4}$$

$$\text{PbO}_2(s) + \text{HSO}_4^-(aq) + 3\,\text{H}^+(aq) + 2\,e^- \rightarrow \text{PbSO}_4(s) + 2\,\text{H}_2\text{O}(l)$$

Solution: $1.00 \text{ g Pb} \times \dfrac{1 \text{ mol Pb}}{207.2 \text{ g Pb}} \times \dfrac{2 \text{ mol PbSO}_4}{1 \text{ mol Pb}} \times \dfrac{303.27 \text{ g PbSO}_4}{1 \text{ mol PbSO}_4} = 2.93 \text{ g PbSO}_4$

Check: The units (g) are correct. Because more moles of PbSO$_4$ are generated and the molar mass is larger, the mass is larger.

18.49   **Given:** $\text{CH}_4(g) + 2\,\text{O}_2(g) \rightarrow \text{CO}_2(g) + 2\,\text{H}_2\text{O}(g)$ **Find:** $E°_{cell}$
Conceptual Plan: $\Delta G°_{rxn} = \sum n_p \Delta G°_f \text{(products)} - \sum n_r \Delta G°_f \text{(reactants)}$ and determine n then
$\Delta G°_{rxn}, n \rightarrow E°_{cell}$
$$\Delta G°_{rxn} = -nFE°_{cell}$$

Solution:

Reactant/Product	$\Delta G°_f$ (kJ/mol from Appendix IIB)
CH$_4$(g)	−50.5
O$_2$(g)	0.0
CO$_2$(g)	−394.4
H$_2$O(g)	−228.6

Be sure to pull data for the correct formula and phase.

$$\begin{aligned}
\Delta G°_{rxn} &= \sum n_p \Delta G°_f \text{(products)} - \sum n_r \Delta G°_f \text{(reactants)} \\
&= [1(\Delta G°_f(\text{CO}_2(g))) + 2(\Delta G°_f(\text{H}_2\text{O}(g)))] - [1(\Delta G°_f(\text{CH}_4(g))) + 2(\Delta G°_f(\text{O}_2(g)))] \\
&= [1(-394.4 \text{ kJ}) + 2(-228.6 \text{ kJ})] - [1(-50.5 \text{ kJ}) + 2(0.0 \text{ kJ})] \\
&= [-851.6 \text{ kJ}] - [-50.5 \text{ kJ}] \\
&= -801.1 \text{ kJ} = -8.011 \times 10^5 \text{ J}
\end{aligned}$$

Also, because one C atom goes from an oxidation state of −4 to +4 and four O atoms are going from 0 to −2, $n = 8$ and $\Delta G°_{rxn} = -nFE°_{cell}$. Rearrange to solve for $E°_{cell}$.

$$E°_{cell} = \frac{\Delta G°_{rxn}}{-nF} = \frac{-8.011 \times 10^5 \text{ J}}{-8 \text{ mol } e^- \times \dfrac{96,485 \text{ C}}{\text{mol } e^-}} = 1.038 \frac{\text{V} \cdot \text{C}}{\text{C}} = 1.038 \text{ V}$$

Check: The units (V) are correct. The cell voltage is positive, which is consistent with a spontaneous reaction.

18.50   **Given:** $\text{CH}_3\text{CH}_2\text{OH}(g) + \text{O}_2(g) \rightarrow \text{HC}_2\text{H}_3\text{O}_2(g) + \text{H}_2\text{O}(g)$ **Find:** $E°_{cell}$
Conceptual Plan: $\Delta G°_{rxn} = \sum n_p \Delta G°_f \text{(products)} - \sum n_r \Delta G°_f \text{(reactants)}$ and determine n then
$\Delta G°_{rxn}, n \rightarrow E°_{cell}$
$$\Delta G°_{rxn} = -nFE°_{cell}$$

Solution:

Reactant/Product	$\Delta G°_f$ (kJ/mol from Appendix IIB)
CH$_3$CH$_2$OH(g)	−167.9
O$_2$(g)	0.0
HC$_2$H$_3$O$_2$(g)	−374.2
H$_2$O(g)	−228.6

Be sure to pull data for the correct formula and phase.

$$\Delta G^\circ_{rxn} = \sum n_p \Delta G^\circ_f \,(\text{products}) - \sum n_r \Delta G^\circ_f \,(\text{reactants})$$

$$= [1(\Delta G^\circ_f\,(HC_2H_3O_2(g))) + 1(\Delta G^\circ_f\,(H_2O(g)))] - [1(\Delta G^\circ_f\,(CH_3CH_2OH(g))) + 1(\Delta G^\circ_f\,(O_2(g)))]$$

$$= [1(-374.2 \text{ kJ}) + 1(-228.6 \text{ kJ})] - [1(-167.9 \text{ kJ}) + 1(0.0 \text{ kJ})]$$

$$= [-602.8 \text{ kJ}] - [-167.9 \text{ kJ}]$$

$$= -434.9 \text{ kJ} = -4.349 \times 10^5 \text{ J}$$

Also, because two O atoms are going from 0 to −2, $n = 4$; then $\Delta G^\circ_{rxn} = -nFE^\circ_{cell}$. Rearrange to solve for E°_{cell}.

$$E^\circ_{cell} = \frac{\Delta G^\circ_{rxn}}{-nF} = \frac{-4.349 \times 10^5 \text{ J}}{-4 \text{ mol e}^- \times \dfrac{96{,}485 \text{ C}}{\text{mol e}^-}} = 1.127 \,\frac{\text{V} \cdot \cancel{C}}{\cancel{C}} = 1.127 \text{ V}$$

Check: The units (V) are correct. The cell voltage is positive, which is consistent with a spontaneous reaction.

18.51   When iron corrodes or rusts, it oxidizes to Fe^{2+}. For a metal to be able to protect iron, it must be more easily oxidized than iron or be below it in Table 18.1. (a) Zn and (c) Mn meet that criterion.

18.52   When iron corrodes or rusts, it oxidizes to Fe^{2+}. For a metal to be able to protect iron, it must be more easily oxidized than iron or be below it in Table 18.1. (a) Mg and (b) Cr meet that criterion.

Electrolytic Cells and Electrolysis

18.53   **Given:** electrolytic cell sketch

Find: (a) Label the anode and cathode and indicate half-reactions, (b) indicate direction of electron flow, and (c) label battery terminals and calculate minimum voltage to drive reaction.

Conceptual Plan: (a) Write two half-cell reactions and add electrons as needed to balance reactions. Look up half-reactions in Table 18.1. Calculate the standard cell potential by subtracting the electrode potential of the anode from the electrode potential of the cathode: $E^\circ_{cell} = E^\circ_{cathode} - E^\circ_{anode}$. **Choose the direction of the half-cell reactions so that** $E^\circ_{cell} < 0$. **(b) Electrons flow from anode to cathode. (c) Each half-cell reaction moves forward, so direction of the concentration changes can be determined.**

Solution:

(a) $Ni^{2+}(aq) + 2e^- \rightarrow Ni(s)$ and $Cd^{2+}(aq) + 2e^- \rightarrow Cd(s)$.

Look up cell potentials. For Ni, $E^\circ_{red} = -0.23$ V. For Cd, $E^\circ_{red} = -0.40$ V. To get a negative cell potential, Ni is oxidized; so $E^\circ_{red} = -0.23$ V $= E^\circ_{anode}$. Cd^{2+} is reduced, so $E^\circ_{red} = -0.40$ V $= E^\circ_{cathode}$. Then $E^\circ_{cell} = E^\circ_{cathode} - E^\circ_{anode} = -0.40$ V $- (-0.23$ V) $= -0.17$ V. Because oxidation occurs at the anode, Ni is the anode and the reaction is $Ni(s) \rightarrow Ni^{2+}(aq) + 2e^-$. Because reduction takes place at the cathode, Cd is the cathode and the reaction is $Cd^{2+}(aq) + 2e^- \rightarrow Cd(s)$.

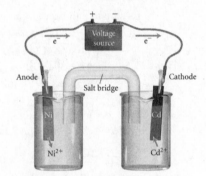

(c)   Because reduction is occurring at the cathode, the battery terminal closest to the cathode is the negative terminal. Because the cell potential from part (a) is $= -0.17$ V, a minimum of 0.17 V must be applied by the battery.

Check: The reaction is nonspontaneous because the reduction of Ni^{2+} is above Cd^{2+}. Electrons still flow from the anode to the cathode. The reaction can be made spontaneous with the application of electrical energy.

18.54   **Given:** electrolytic cell Mn^{2+} reduced to Mn and Sn oxidized to Sn^{2+}

Find: Draw a cell and label the anode and cathode, write half-reactions, indicate the direction of electron flow, and calculate the minimum voltage to drive reaction.

Conceptual Plan: Write two half-cell reactions and add electrons as needed to balance reactions. Look up half-reactions in Table 18.1. Calculate the standard cell potential by subtracting the electrode potential of the anode from the electrode potential of the cathode: $E^\circ_{cell} = E^\circ_{cathode} - E^\circ_{anode}$. **Anode is where oxidation occurs, so Sn is anode and Mn is cathode. Electrons flow from anode to cathode. The minimum potential needed is** E°_{cell}.

Solution: $Mn^{2+}(aq) + 2e^- \rightarrow Mn(s)$ and $Sn^{2+}(aq) + 2e^- \rightarrow Sn(s)$. Look up cell potentials. For Mn^{2+}, $E^\circ_{red} = -1.18$ V. For Sn, $E^\circ_{red} = -0.14$ V. Because Sn is oxidized, $E^\circ_{red} = -0.14$ V $= E^\circ_{anode}$. Then $E^\circ_{cell} = E^\circ_{cathode} - E^\circ_{anode} = -1.18$ V $- (-0.14$ V) $= -1.04$ V. Because oxidation occurs at the anode, the

Sn is the anode and the reaction is $Sn(s) \rightarrow Sn^{2+}(aq) + 2\,e^-$. Because reduction takes place at the cathode, Mn is the cathode and the reaction is $Mn^{2+}(aq) + 2\,e^- \rightarrow Mn(s)$. Electrons flow from the anode to the cathode. Because the cell potential is -1.04 V, a minimum of 1.04 V must be applied by the battery.

Check: The reaction is nonspontaneous because the reduction of Sn^{2+} is above Mn^{2+}. Electrons still flow from the anode to the cathode. The reaction can be made spontaneous with the application of electrical energy.

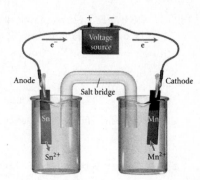

18.55 **Given:** electrolysis cell to electroplate Cu onto a metal surface
Find: Draw a cell and label the anode and cathode and write half-reactions.
Conceptual Plan: Write two half-cell reactions and add electrons as needed to balance reactions. The cathode reaction will be the reduction of Cu^{2+} to the metal. The anode will be the reverse reaction.
Solution:

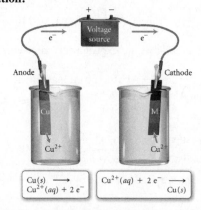

Check: The metal to be plated is the cathode because metal ions are converted to $Cu(s)$ on the surface of the metal.

18.56 **Given:** electrolysis cell to electroplate Ni onto a metal surface
Find: Draw a cell and label the anode and cathode and write half-reactions.
Conceptual Plan: Write two half-cell reactions and add electrons as needed to balance reactions. The cathode reaction will be the reduction of Ni^{2+} to the metal. The anode will be the reverse reaction.
Solution: Label the electrode where the oxidation occurs as the anode. Label the electrode where the reduction occurs as the cathode. Electrons flow from anode to cathode. Label anode as $(-)$ and cathode as $(+)$.

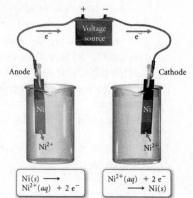

Check: The metal to be plated is the cathode because metal ions are converted to $Ni(s)$ on the surface of the metal.

18.57 **Given:** Cu electroplating of 225 mg Cu at a current of 7.8 A (7.8 C/s); $Cu^{2+}(aq) + 2\,e^- \rightarrow Cu(s)$ **Find:** time
Conceptual Plan: mg Cu → g Cu → mol Cu → mol e^- → C → s

$$\frac{1\ g}{1000\ mg} \quad \frac{1\ mol\ Cu}{63.55\ g\ Cu} \quad \frac{2\ mol\ e^-}{1\ mol\ Cu} \quad \frac{96{,}485\ C}{1\ mol\ e^-} \quad \frac{1\ s}{7.8\ C}$$

Solution: $225\ \text{mg Cu} \times \dfrac{1\ \text{g Cu}}{1000\ \text{mg Cu}} \times \dfrac{1\ \text{mol Cu}}{63.55\ \text{g Cu}} \times \dfrac{2\ \text{mol } e^-}{1\ \text{mol Cu}} \times \dfrac{96{,}485\ \text{C}}{1\ \text{mol } e^-} \times \dfrac{1\ s}{7.8\ \text{C}} = 88\ s$

Check: The units (s) are correct. Because far less than a mole of Cu is electroplated, the time is short.

18.58　　**Given:** Ag electroplating at a current of 5.8 A (5.8 C/s) for 55 min; $Ag^+(aq) + e^- \rightarrow Ag(s)$　　**Find:** mass of Ag

Conceptual Plan: $min \rightarrow s \rightarrow C \rightarrow mol\ e^- \rightarrow mol\ Ag \rightarrow g\ Ag$

$$\frac{60\ s}{1\ min} \quad \frac{5.8\ C}{1\ s} \quad \frac{1\ mol\ e^-}{96,485\ C} \quad \frac{1\ mol\ Ag}{1\ mol\ e^-} \quad \frac{107.87\ g\ Ag}{1\ mol\ Ag}$$

Solution: $55\ \cancel{min} \times \dfrac{60\ \cancel{s}}{1\ \cancel{min}} \times \dfrac{5.8\ \cancel{C}}{1\ \cancel{s}} \times \dfrac{1\ \cancel{mol\ e^-}}{96,485\ \cancel{C}} \times \dfrac{1\ \cancel{mol\ Ag}}{1\ \cancel{mol\ e^-}} \times \dfrac{107.87\ g\ Ag}{1\ \cancel{mol\ Ag}} = 21\ g\ Ag$

Check: The units (g) are correct. Because less than a mole of electrons is used, the mass is less than the molar mass of Ag.

18.59　　**Given:** Na electrolysis, 1.0 kg in one hour　　**Find:** current

Conceptual Plan: $Na^+(l) + e^- \rightarrow Na(l) \quad \dfrac{kg\ Na}{h} \rightarrow \dfrac{g\ Na}{h} \rightarrow \dfrac{mol\ Na}{h} \rightarrow \dfrac{mol\ e^-}{h} \rightarrow \dfrac{C}{h} \rightarrow \dfrac{C}{min} \rightarrow \dfrac{C}{s}$

$$\frac{1000\ g}{1\ kg} \quad \frac{1\ mol\ Na}{22.99\ g\ Na} \quad \frac{1\ mol\ e^-}{1\ mol\ Na} \quad \frac{96,485\ C}{1\ mol\ e^-} \quad \frac{1\ h}{60\ min} \quad \frac{1\ min}{60\ s}$$

Solution:

$$\frac{1.0\ \cancel{kg\ Na}}{1\ \cancel{h}} \times \frac{1000\ \cancel{g\ Na}}{1\ \cancel{kg\ Na}} \times \frac{1\ \cancel{mol\ Na}}{22.99\ \cancel{g\ Na}} \times \frac{1\ \cancel{mol\ e^-}}{1\ \cancel{mol\ Na}} \times \frac{96,485\ C}{1\ \cancel{mol\ e^-}} \times \frac{1\ \cancel{h}}{60\ \cancel{min}} \times \frac{1\ \cancel{min}}{60\ s} = 1.2 \times 10^3\ \frac{C}{s} = 1.2 \times 10^3\ A$$

Check: The units (A) are correct. Because the amount per hour is so large, we expect a very large current.

18.60　　**Given:** Al electrolysis at a current of 25 A for 1 hour; $Al^{3+}(aq) + 3e^- \rightarrow Al(s)$　　**Find:** mass of Al

Conceptual Plan: $h \rightarrow min \rightarrow s \rightarrow C \rightarrow mol\ e^- \rightarrow mol\ Al \rightarrow g\ Al$

$$\frac{60\ min}{1\ h} \quad \frac{60\ s}{1\ min} \quad \frac{25\ C}{1\ s} \quad \frac{1\ mol\ e^-}{96,485\ C} \quad \frac{1\ mol\ Al}{3\ mol\ e^-} \quad \frac{26.98\ g\ Al}{1\ mol\ Al}$$

Solution: $1\ \cancel{h} \times \dfrac{60\ \cancel{min}}{1\ \cancel{h}} \times \dfrac{60\ \cancel{s}}{1\ \cancel{min}} \times \dfrac{25\ \cancel{C}}{1\ \cancel{s}} \times \dfrac{1\ \cancel{mol\ e^-}}{96,485\ \cancel{C}} \times \dfrac{1\ \cancel{mol\ Al}}{3\ \cancel{mol\ e^-}} \times \dfrac{26.98\ g\ Al}{1\ \cancel{mol\ Al}} = 8.4\ g\ Al$

Check: The units (g) are correct. Because three moles of electrons are used per mole of Al^{3+}, the mass is less than the molar mass of Al.

Cumulative Problems

18.61　　**Given:** $MnO_4^-(aq) + Zn(s) \rightarrow Mn^{2+}(aq) + Zn^{2+}(aq)$, 0.500 M $KMnO_4$, and 2.85 g Zn

Find: balance equation and volume $KMnO_4$ solution

Conceptual Plan: Separate the overall reaction into two half-reactions: one for oxidation and one for reduction. → Balance each half-reaction with respect to mass in the following order: (1) Balance all elements other than H and O, (2) balance O by adding H_2O, and (3) balance H by adding H^+. → Balance each half-reaction with respect to charge by adding electrons. (The sum of the charges on both sides of the equation should be made equal by adding electrons as necessary.) → Make the number of electrons in both half-reactions equal by multiplying one or both half-reactions by a small whole number. → Add the two half-reactions together, canceling electrons and other species as necessary. → Verify that the reaction is balanced with respect to both mass and charge.

Then $g\ Zn \rightarrow mol\ Zn \rightarrow mol\ MnO_4^- \rightarrow L\ MnO_4^- \rightarrow mL\ MnO_4^-$.

$$\frac{1\ mol\ Zn}{65.38\ g\ Zn} \quad \frac{2\ mol\ MnO_4^-}{5\ mol\ Zn} \quad \frac{1\ L\ MnO_4^-}{0.500\ mol\ MnO_4^-} \quad \frac{1000\ mL\ MnO_4^-}{1\ L\ MnO_4^-}$$

Solution:

Separate:	$MnO_4^-(aq) \rightarrow Mn^{2+}(aq)$	and　$Zn(s) \rightarrow Zn^{2+}(aq)$
Balance non-H & O elements:	$MnO_4^-(aq) \rightarrow Mn^{2+}(aq)$	and　$Zn(s) \rightarrow Zn^{2+}(aq)$
Balance O with H_2O:	$MnO_4^-(aq) \rightarrow Mn^{2+}(aq) + 4\ H_2O(l)$	and　$Zn(s) \rightarrow Zn^{2+}(aq)$
Balance H with H^+:	$MnO_4^-(aq) + 8\ H^+(aq) \rightarrow Mn^{2+}(aq) + 4\ H_2O(l)$	and　$Zn(s) \rightarrow Zn^{2+}(aq)$
Add electrons:	$MnO_4^-(aq) + 8\ H^+(aq) + 5\ e^- \rightarrow Mn^{2+}(aq) + 4\ H_2O(l)$	and　$Zn(s) \rightarrow Zn^{2+}(aq) + 2\ e^-$

Equalize electrons:

$2\ MnO_4^-(aq) + 16\ H^+(aq) + 10\ e^- \rightarrow 2\ Mn^{2+}(aq) + 8\ H_2O(l)$　and　$5\ Zn(s) \rightarrow 5\ Zn^{2+}(aq) + 10\ e^-$

Add half-reactions:

$2\ MnO_4^-(aq) + 16\ H^+(aq) + \cancel{10\ e^-} + 5\ Zn(s) \rightarrow 2\ Mn^{2+}(aq) + 8\ H_2O(l) + 5\ Zn^{2+}(aq) + \cancel{10\ e^-}$

Cancel electrons: $2\ MnO_4^-(aq) + 16\ H^+(aq) + 5\ Zn(s) \rightarrow 2\ Mn^{2+}(aq) + 8\ H_2O(l) + 5\ Zn^{2+}(aq)$

$$2.85 \text{ g Zn} \times \frac{1 \text{ mol Zn}}{65.38 \text{ g Zn}} \times \frac{2 \text{ mol MnO}_4^-}{5 \text{ mol Zn}} \times \frac{1 \text{ L MnO}_4^-}{0.500 \text{ mol MnO}_4^-} \times \frac{1000 \text{ mL MnO}_4^-}{1 \text{ L MnO}_4^-} = 34.9 \text{ mL MnO}_4^- =$$

$$= 34.9 \text{ mL KMnO}_4$$

Check:	Reactants	Products
	2 Mn atoms	2 Mn atoms
	8 O atoms	8 O atoms
	16 H atoms	16 H atoms
	5 Zn atoms	5 Zn atoms
	+14 charge	+14 charge

The units (mL) are correct. Because far less than a mole of zinc is used, less than a mole of permanganate is consumed; so the volume is less than a liter.

18.62   **Given:** $Cr_2O_7^{2-}(aq) + Cu(s) \rightarrow Cr^{3+}(aq) + Cu^{2+}(aq)$ 0.850 M $K_2Cr_2O_7$ and 5.25 g Zn
Find: balance equation and volume $K_2Cr_2O_7$ solution
Conceptual Plan: Separate the overall reaction into two half-reactions: one for oxidation and one for reduction. → Balance each half-reaction with respect to mass in the following order: (1) Balance all elements other than H and O, (2) balance O by adding H_2O, and (3) balance H by adding H^+. → Balance each half-reaction with respect to charge by adding electrons. (The sum of the charges on both sides of the equation should be made equal by adding electrons as necessary.) → Make the number of electrons in both half-reactions equal by multiplying one or both half-reactions by a small whole number. → Add the two half-reactions together, canceling electrons and other species as necessary. → Verify that the reaction is balanced with respect to both mass and charge.
Then g Cu → mol Cu → mol $Cr_2O_7^{2-}$ → L $Cr_2O_7^{2-}$ → mL $Cr_2O_7^{2-}$.

$$\frac{1 \text{ mol Cu}}{63.55 \text{ g Cu}} \quad \frac{1 \text{ mol Cr}_2O_7^{2-}}{3 \text{ mol Cu}} \quad \frac{1 \text{ L Cr}_2O_7^{2-}}{0.850 \text{ mol Cr}_2O_7^{2-}} \quad \frac{1000 \text{ mL Cr}_2O_7^{2-}}{1 \text{ L Cr}_2O_7^{2-}}$$

Solution:
Separate: $Cr_2O_7^{2-}(aq) \rightarrow Cr^{3+}(aq)$ and $Cu(s) \rightarrow Cu^{2+}(aq)$
Balance non-H & O elements: $Cr_2O_7^{2-}(aq) \rightarrow 2\,Cr^{3+}(aq)$ and $Cu(s) \rightarrow Cu^{2+}(aq)$
Balance O with H_2O: $Cr_2O_7^{2-}(aq) \rightarrow 2\,Cr^{3+}(aq) + 7\,H_2O(l)$ and $Cu(s) \rightarrow Cu^{2+}(aq)$
Balance H with H^+: $Cr_2O_7^{2-}(aq) + 14\,H^+(aq) \rightarrow 2\,Cr^{3+}(aq) + 7\,H_2O(l)$ and $Cu(s) \rightarrow Cu^{2+}(aq)$
Add electrons: $Cr_2O_7^{2-}(aq) + 14\,H^+(aq) + 6\,e^- \rightarrow 2\,Cr^{3+}(aq) + 7\,H_2O(l)$ and $Cu(s) \rightarrow Cu^{2+}(aq) + 2\,e^-$
Equalize electrons:
$Cr_2O_7^{2-}(aq) + 14\,H^+(aq) + 6\,e^- \rightarrow 2\,Cr^{3+}(aq) + 7\,H_2O(l)$ and $3\,Cu(s) \rightarrow 3\,Cu^{2+}(aq) + 6\,e^-$
Add half-reactions:
$Cr_2O_7^{2-}(aq) + 14\,H^+(aq) + \cancel{6\,e^-} + 3\,Cu(s) \rightarrow 2\,Cr^{3+}(aq) + 7\,H_2O(l) + 3\,Cu^{2+}(aq) + \cancel{6\,e^-}$
Cancel electrons: $Cr_2O_7^{2-}(aq) + 14\,H^+(aq) + 3\,Cu(s) \rightarrow 2\,Cr^{3+}(aq) + 7\,H_2O(l) + 3\,Cu^{2+}(aq)$

$$5.25 \text{ g Cu} \times \frac{1 \text{ mol Cu}}{63.55 \text{ g Cu}} \times \frac{1 \text{ mol Cr}_2O_7^{2-}}{3 \text{ mol Cu}} \times \frac{1 \text{ L Cr}_2O_7^{2-}}{0.850 \text{ mol Cr}_2O_7^{2-}} \times \frac{1000 \text{ mL Cr}_2O_7^{2-}}{1 \text{ L Cr}_2O_7^{2-}} = 32.4 \text{ mL Cr}_2O_7^{2-} =$$

$$= 32.4 \text{ mL K}_2\text{Cr}_2\text{O}_7$$

Check:	Reactants	Products
	2 Cr atoms	2 Cr atoms
	7 O atoms	7 O atoms
	14 H atoms	14 H atoms
	3 Cu atoms	3 Cu atoms
	+12 charge	+12 charge

The units (mL) are correct. Because far less than a mole of copper is used, less than a mole of dichromate is consumed; so the volume is less than a liter.

18.63   **Given:** beaker with Al strip and Cu^{2+} ions   **Find:** Draw sketch after Al is submerged for a few minutes.
Conceptual Plan: Write two half-cell reactions and add electrons as needed to balance reactions. Look up half-reactions in Table 18.1. Calculate the standard cell potential by subtracting the electrode potential of the anode from the electrode potential of the cathode: $E°_{cell} = E°_{cathode} - E°_{anode}$. If $E°_{cell} > 0$, the reaction is spontaneous in the forward direction and Al will dissolve and Cu will deposit.

Solution: $Al(s) \rightarrow Al^{3+}(aq)$ and $Cu^{2+}(aq) \rightarrow Cu(s)$. Add electrons. $Al(s) \rightarrow Al^{3+}(aq) + 3 e^-$ and $Cu^{2+}(aq) + 2 e^- \rightarrow Cu(s)$. Look up cell potentials. Al is oxidized, so $E°_{anode} = E°_{red}$ = -1.66 V. Cu^{2+} is reduced, so $E°_{cathode} = E°_{red} = 0.34$ V. Then $E°_{cell} = E°_{cathode} - E°_{anode}$ = 0.34 V $- (-1.66$ V$) = 2.00$ V, so the reaction is spontaneous. Al will dissolve to generate $Al^{3+}(aq)$, and $Cu(s)$ will deposit.

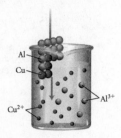

Check: The units (V) are correct. If the voltage is positive, the reaction is spontaneous; so Al will dissolve and Cu will deposit.

18.64   **Given:** Zn/Zn^{2+} and Ni/Ni^{2+} half-cells in voltaic cell
Find: Draw sketch after substantial amount of current generated.
Conceptual Plan: Write two half-cell reactions and add electrons as needed to balance reactions. Look up half-reactions in Table 18.1. Calculate the standard cell potential by subtracting the electrode potential of the anode from the electrode potential of the cathode: $E°_{cell} = E°_{cathode} - E°_{anode}$. Choose the direction of the half-cell reactions so that $E°_{cell} > 0$. Add two half-cell reactions and cancel electrons to generate overall reaction. Because reaction is spontaneous, it will move forward.
Solution: $Zn^{2+}(aq) + 2 e^- \rightarrow Zn(s)$ and $Ni^{2+}(aq) + 2 e^- \rightarrow Ni(s)$. Look up cell potentials. For Zn, $E°_{red} = -0.76$ V. For Ni, $E°_{red} = -0.23$ V. To get a positive $E°_{cell}$, the sign of the Zn potential must be reversed. Zn is oxidized, so $E°_{anode} = E°_{red} = -0.76$ V. Ni^{2+} is reduced, so $E°_{cathode} = E°_{red} = -0.23$ V. Then $E°_{cell} = E°_{cathode} + E°_{anode} = -0.23$ V $- (-0.76$ V$) = +0.53$ V. Adding the two half-cell reactions: $Zn(s) + Ni^{2+}(aq) + 2e^- \rightarrow Zn^{2+}(aq) + 2e^- + Ni(s)$. The overall reaction is $Zn(s) + Ni^{2+}(aq) \rightarrow Zn^{2+}(aq) + Ni(s)$. Zn will dissolve to generate $Zn^{2+}(aq)$, and $Ni(s)$ will deposit.

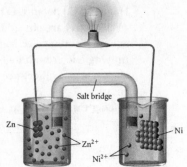

Check: The units (V) are correct. Because Ni is above Zn in Table 18.1, Ni is reduced. If the voltage is positive, the reaction is spontaneous; so Zn will dissolve, and Ni will deposit.

18.65   **Given:** (a) 2.15 g Al, (b) 4.85 g Cu, and (c) 2.42 g Ag in 3.5 M HI
Find: If metal dissolves, write a balanced reaction and the minimum amount of HI needed to dissolve the metal.
Conceptual Plan: In general, metals whose reduction half-reactions lie below the reduction of H^+ to H_2 in Table 18.1 will dissolve in acids, while metals above it will not. Stop here if metal does not dissolve. To write the balanced redox reactions, pair the oxidation of the metal with the reduction of H^+ to H_2 ($2H^+(aq) + 2e^- \rightarrow H_2(g)$). Balance the number of electrons transferred. Add the two reactions. Cancel electrons. Then g metal $\rightarrow$ mol metal $\rightarrow$ mol H^+ $\rightarrow$ L HI $\rightarrow$ mL HI.

$$\mathcal{M} \qquad \frac{x \text{ mol } H^+}{y \text{ mol metal}} \quad \frac{1 \text{ L HI}}{3.5 \text{ mol HI}} \quad \frac{1000 \text{ mL HI}}{1 \text{ L HI}}$$

Solution:
(a)   Al meets this criterion. For Al, $Al(s) \rightarrow Al^{3+}(aq) + 3 e^-$. We need to multiply the Al reaction by 2 and the H^+ reaction by 3. So $2 Al(s) \rightarrow 2 Al^{3+}(aq) + 6 e^-$ and $6 H^+(aq) + 6 e^- \rightarrow 3 H_2(g)$. Adding the half-reactions: $2 Al(s) + 6 H^+(aq) + 6e^- \rightarrow 2 Al^{3+}(aq) + 6e^- + 3 H_2(g)$. Simplify to $2 Al(s) + 6 H^+(aq) \rightarrow 2 Al^{3+}(aq) + 3 H_2(g)$. Then

$$2.15 \text{ g Al} \times \frac{1 \text{ mol Al}}{26.98 \text{ g Al}} \times \frac{6 \text{ mol } H^+}{2 \text{ mol Al}} \times \frac{1 \text{ L HI}}{3.5 \text{ mol HI}} \times \frac{1000 \text{ mL HI}}{1 \text{ L HI}} = 68.3 \text{ mL HI}$$

(b)   Cu does not meet this criterion, so it will not dissolve in HI.
(c)   Ag does not meet this criterion, so it will not dissolve in HI.

Check: Only metals with negative reduction potentials will dissolve. The volume of acid needed is fairly small because the amount of metal is much less than 1 mole and the concentration of acid is high.

18.66   **Given:** (a) 5.90 g Au, (b) 2.55 g Cu, and (c) 4.83 g Ni in 6.0 M HNO_3
Find: If the metal dissolves, write the balanced reaction and minimum amount of HNO_3 needed to dissolve the metal.
Conceptual Plan: Nitric acid (HNO_3) oxidizes metals through the following reduction half-reaction: $NO_3^-(aq) + 4 H^+(aq) + 3 e^- \rightarrow NO(g) + 2 H_2O(l)$ $E°_{red} = 0.96$ V. Because this half-reaction is above the reduction of H^+ in Table 18.1, HNO_3 can oxidize metals that can't be oxidized by HCl.

Solution:

(a) Au (which has a reduction potential of 1.50 V) will not be oxidized, so it will not dissolve in HNO_3.

(b) Cu (which has a reduction potential of 0.34 V) will be oxidized. To write the balanced redox reactions, pair the oxidation of the copper ($Cu(s) \rightarrow Cu^{2+}(aq) + 2\,e^-$) with the reduction of nitric acid ($NO_3^-(aq) + 4\,H^+(aq) + 3\,e^- \rightarrow NO(g) + 2\,H_2O(l)$). To balance the number of electrons transferred, we need to multiply the Cu reaction by 3 and the nitric acid reaction by 2. So $3\,Cu(s) \rightarrow 3\,Cu^{2+}(aq) + 6\,e^-$ and $2\,NO_3^-(aq) + 8\,H^+(aq) + 6\,e^- \rightarrow 2\,NO(g) + 4\,H_2O(l)$. Adding the two reactions: $3\,Cu(s) + 2\,NO_3^-(aq) + 8\,H^+(aq) + \cancel{6\,e^-} \rightarrow 3\,Cu^{2+}(aq) + \cancel{6\,e^-} + 2\,NO(g) + 4\,H_2O(l)$. Simplify to $3\,Cu(s) + 2\,NO_3^-(aq) + 8\,H^+(aq) \rightarrow 3\,Cu^{2+}(aq) + 2\,NO(g) + 4\,H_2O(l)$. Then

$$2.55\ \text{g}\,\cancel{Cu} \times \frac{1\ \text{mol}\,\cancel{Cu}}{63.55\ \text{g}\,\cancel{Cu}} \times \frac{8\ \text{mol}\,\cancel{H^+}}{3\ \text{mol}\,\cancel{Cu}} \times \frac{1\ \text{L}\,\cancel{HNO_3}}{6.0\ \text{mol}\,\cancel{HNO_3}} \times \frac{1000\ \text{mL}\ HNO_3}{1\ \text{L}\,\cancel{HNO_3}} = 18\ \text{mL}\ HNO_3.$$

Use stoichiometric coefficient of H^+ because it is larger than the NO_3^- stoichiometric coefficient.

(c) Ni (which has a reduction potential of -0.23 V) will be oxidized. To write the balanced redox reactions, pair the oxidation of the nickel ($Ni(s) \rightarrow Ni^{2+}(aq) + 2\,e^-$) with the reduction of nitric acid ($NO_3^-(aq) + 4\,H^+(aq) + 3\,e^- \rightarrow NO(g) + 2\,H_2O(l)$). To balance the number of electrons transferred, we need to multiply the Ni reaction by 3 and the nitric acid reaction by 2. So $3\,Ni(s) \rightarrow 3\,Ni^{2+}(aq) + 6\,e^-$ and $2\,NO_3^-(aq) + 8\,H^+(aq) + 6\,e^- \rightarrow 2\,NO(g) + 4\,H_2O(l)$. Adding the two reactions: $3\,Ni(s) + 2\,NO_3^-(aq) + 8\,H^+(aq) + \cancel{6\,e^-} \rightarrow 3\,Ni^{2+}(aq) + \cancel{6\,e^-} + 2\,NO(g) + 4\,H_2O(l)$. Simplify to $3\,Ni(s) + 2\,NO_3^-(aq) + 8\,H^+(aq) \rightarrow 3\,Ni^{2+}(aq) + 2\,NO(g) + 4\,H_2O(l)$. Then

$$4.83\ \text{g}\,\cancel{Ni} \times \frac{1\ \text{mol}\,\cancel{Ni}}{58.69\ \text{g}\,\cancel{Ni}} \times \frac{8\ \text{mol}\,\cancel{H^+}}{3\ \text{mol}\,\cancel{Ni}} \times \frac{1\ \text{L}\,\cancel{HNO_3}}{6.0\ \text{mol}\,\cancel{HNO_3}} \times \frac{1000\ \text{mL}\ HNO_3}{1\ \text{L}\,\cancel{HNO_3}} = 37\ \text{mL}\ HNO_3.$$

Use stoichiometric coefficient of H^+ because it is larger than the NO_3^- stoichiometric coefficient.

Check: Only metals with reduction potentials less than 0.96 V will dissolve. The volume of acid needed is fairly small because the amount of metal is much less than 1 mole and the concentration of acid is high.

18.67   **Given:** $Pt(s)\,|\,H_2(g, 1\ \text{atm})\,|\,H^+(aq, ?\ M)\,\|\,Cu^{2+}(aq, 1.0\ M)\,|\,Cu(s)$, $E_{cell} = 355$ mV   **Find:** pH

Conceptual Plan: Write half-reactions from line notation. Look up half-reactions in Table 18.1. Calculate the standard cell potential by subtracting the electrode potential of the anode from the electrode potential of the cathode: $E^{\circ}_{cell} = E^{\circ}_{cathode} - E^{\circ}_{anode}$. Add the two half-cell reactions and cancel the electrons.

Then mV $\rightarrow$ V then $E^{\circ}_{cell}, E_{cell}, P_{H_2}, [Cu^{2+}], n \rightarrow [H^+] \rightarrow$ pH.

$$\frac{1\ V}{1000\ mV} \qquad\qquad E_{cell} = E^{\circ}_{cell} - \frac{0.0592\ V}{n} \log Q \quad pH = -\log [H^+]$$

Solution: The half-reactions are $H_2(g) \rightarrow 2\,H^+(aq) + 2\,e^-$ and $Cu^{2+}(aq) + 2\,e^- \rightarrow Cu(s)$. H is oxidized, so $E^{\circ}_{red} = 0.00\ V = E^{\circ}_{anode}$. Cu is reduced, so $E^{\circ}_{red} = 0.34\ V = E^{\circ}_{cathode}$. Then $E^{\circ}_{cell} = E^{\circ}_{cathode} - E^{\circ}_{anode} = 0.34\ V - 0.00\ V = +0.34\ V$. Adding the two reactions: $H_2(g) + Cu^{2+}(aq) + \cancel{2\,e^-} \rightarrow 2\,H^+(aq) + \cancel{2\,e^-} + Cu(s)$.

Cancel the electrons: $H_2(g) + Cu^{2+}(aq) \rightarrow 2\,H^+(aq) + Cu(s)$. Then $355\ \cancel{mV} \times \dfrac{1\ V}{1000\ \cancel{mV}} = 0.355\ V$. So

$n = 2$ and $Q = \dfrac{[H^+]^2}{P_{H_2}[Cu^{2+}]} = \dfrac{(x)^2}{(1)(1.0)} = x^2$. Then $E_{cell} = E^{\circ}_{cell} - \dfrac{0.0592\ V}{n} \log Q$. Substitute values and

solve for x. $0.355\ V = 0.34\ V - \dfrac{0.0592\ V}{2} \log x^2 \rightarrow 0.015\ \cancel{V} = -\dfrac{0.0592\ \cancel{V}}{2} \log x^2 \rightarrow -0.50676 = \log x^2 \rightarrow$

$x^2 = 10^{-0.50676} = 0.31134 \rightarrow x = 0.55798$ then pH $= -\log [H^+] = -\log [0.55798] = 0.25338 = 0.3$

Check: The units (none) are correct. The pH is acidic, which is consistent with dissolving a metal in acid.

18.68   **Given:** $Pt(s)\,|\,H_2(g, 1\ \text{atm})\,|\,H^+(aq, 1.0\ M)\,\|\,Au^{3+}(aq, ?\ M)\,|\,Au(s)$, $E_{cell} = 1.22$ V   **Find:** $[Au^{3+}]$

Conceptual Plan: Write half-reactions from line notation. Look up half-reactions in Table 18.1. Calculate the standard cell potential by subtracting the electrode potential of the anode from the electrode potential of the cathode: $E^{\circ}_{cell} = E^{\circ}_{cathode} - E^{\circ}_{anode}$. Equalize the number of electrons transferred; then add the two half-cell reactions and cancel the electrons.

Then $E^{\circ}_{cell}, E_{cell}, P_{H_2}, [H^+], n \rightarrow [Au^{3+}]$.

$$E_{cell} = E^{\circ}_{cell} - \frac{0.0592\ V}{n} \log Q$$

Solution: The half-reactions are $H_2(g) \rightarrow 2\,H^+(aq) + 2\,e^-$ and $Au^{3+}(aq) + 3\,e^- \rightarrow Au(s)$. H is oxidized, so $E^{\circ}_{red} = 0.00\ V = E^{\circ}_{anode}$. Au is reduced, so $E^{\circ}_{red} = 1.50\ V = E^{\circ}_{cathode}$. Then $E^{\circ}_{cell} = E^{\circ}_{cathode} - E^{\circ}_{anode} = 1.50\ V - 0.00\ V = +1.50\ V$. Equalize the number of electrons transferred by multiplying the first reaction

by 3 and the second reaction by 2; so $3 H_2(g) \rightarrow 6 H^+(aq) + 6 e^-$ and $2 Au^{3+}(aq) + 6 e^- \rightarrow 2 Au(s)$.
Adding the two reactions: $3 H_2(g) + 2 Au^{3+}(aq) + 6e^- \rightarrow 6 H^+(aq) + 6e^- + 2 Au(s)$. Cancel the elec-

trons: $3 H_2(g) + 2 Au^{3+}(aq) \rightarrow 6 H^+(aq) + 2 Au(s)$. So $n = 6$ and $Q = \dfrac{[H^+]^6}{P_{H_2}^3[Au^{3+}]^2} = \dfrac{(1.0)^6}{(1)^3(x)^2} = x^{-2}$. Then

$E_{cell} = E°_{cell} - \dfrac{0.0592\ V}{n} \log Q$. Substitute values and solve for x. $1.22\ V = 1.50\ V - \dfrac{0.0592\ V}{6} \log x^{-2} \rightarrow 0.28\ V$

$= \dfrac{0.0592\ V}{6} \log x^{-2} \rightarrow 28.3784 = \log x^{-2} \rightarrow x^{-2} = 10^{28.3784} = 2.3900 \times 10^{28} \rightarrow x = 6.4685 \times 10^{-15}\ M$.

Check: The units (none) are correct. The concentration is expected to be low because the cell potential must be reduced.

18.69   **Given:** Mg oxidation and Cu^{2+} reduction; initially, $[Mg^{2+}] = 1.0 \times 10^{-4}$ M and $[Cu^{2+}] = 1.5$ M in 1.0 L
half-cells   **Find:** (a) initial E_{cell}, (b) E_{cell} after 5.0 A for 8.0 h, and (c) how long battery can deliver 5.0 A
Conceptual Plan:
(a)   **Write the two half-cell reactions and add electrons as needed to balance reactions. Look up half-reactions in Table 18.1. Calculate the standard cell potential by subtracting the electrode potential of the anode from the electrode potential of the cathode:** $E°_{cell} = E°_{cathode} - E°_{anode}$. **Add the two half-cell reactions, cancel electrons, and determine** n. **Then** $E°_{cell}, [Mg^{2+}], [Cu^{2+}], n \rightarrow E_{cell}$.

$$E_{cell} = E°_{cell} - \frac{0.0592\ V}{n} \log Q$$

(b)   **h** $\rightarrow$ **min** $\rightarrow$ **s** $\rightarrow$ **C** $\rightarrow$ **mol e$^-$** $\rightarrow$ **mol Cu reduced** $\rightarrow$ **[Cu^{2+}] and**

$\dfrac{60\ min}{1\ h}$ $\dfrac{60\ s}{1\ min}$ $\dfrac{5.0\ C}{1\ s}$ $\dfrac{1\ mol\ e^-}{96,485\ C}$ $\dfrac{1\ mol\ Cu^{2+}}{2\ mol\ e^-}$ since $V = 1.0\ L$ $[Cu^{2+}] = [Cu^{2+}] - \dfrac{mol\ Cu^{2+}\ reduced}{1.0\ L}$

mol Cu reduced $\rightarrow$ **mol Mg oxidized** $\rightarrow$ **[Mg^{2+}]**

$\dfrac{1\ mol\ Mg\ oxidized}{1\ mol\ Cu^{2+}\ reduced}$ because $V = 1.0\ L$ $[Mg^{2+}] = [Mg^{2+}] + \dfrac{mol\ Mg\ oxidized}{1.0\ L}$

(c)   **[Cu^{2+}]** $\rightarrow$ **mol e$^-$** $\rightarrow$ **C** $\rightarrow$ **s** $\rightarrow$ **min** $\rightarrow$ **h**

$\dfrac{1\ mol\ e^-}{2\ mol\ Cu^{2+}}$ $\dfrac{96,485\ C}{1\ mol\ e^-}$ $\dfrac{1\ s}{5.0\ C}$ $\dfrac{1\ min}{60\ s}$ $\dfrac{1\ h}{60\ min}$

Solution:
(a)   Write half-reactions and add electrons. $Cu^{2+}(aq) + 2 e^- \rightarrow Cu(s)$ and $Mg(s) \rightarrow Mg^{2+}(aq) + 2 e^-$.
Look up cell potentials. Mg is oxidized, so $E°_{red} = -2.37\ V = E°_{anode}$. Cu^{2+} is reduced, so
$E°_{red} = 0.34\ V = E°_{cathode}$. Then $E°_{cell} = E°_{cathode} - E°_{anode} = 0.34\ V - (-2.37\ V) = +2.71\ V$. Add
the two half-cell reactions: $Cu^{2+}(aq) + 2 e^- + Mg(s) \rightarrow Cu(s) + Mg^{2+}(aq) + 2 e^-$. Simplify to

$Cu^{2+}(aq) + Mg(s) \rightarrow Cu(s) + Mg^{2+}(aq)$. So $Q = \dfrac{[Mg^{2+}]}{[Cu^{2+}]} = \dfrac{1.0 \times 10^{-4}}{1.5} = 6.6667 \times 10^{-5}$ and $n = 2$.

Then $E_{cell} = E°_{cell} - \dfrac{0.0592\ V}{n} \log Q = 2.71\ V - \dfrac{0.0592\ V}{2} \log 6.6667 \times 10^{-5} = +2.83361\ V = +2.83\ V$.

(b) $8.0\ h \times \dfrac{60\ min}{1\ h} \times \dfrac{60\ s}{1\ min} \times \dfrac{5.0\ C}{1\ s} \times \dfrac{1\ mol\ e^-}{96,485\ C} \times \dfrac{1\ mol\ Cu^{2+}}{2\ mol\ e^-} = 0.74623\ mol\ Cu^{2+}$ and

$[Cu^{2+}] = [Cu^{2+}] - \dfrac{mol\ Cu^{2+}\ reduced}{1.0\ L} = 1.5\ M - \dfrac{0.74623\ mol\ Cu^{2+}}{1.0\ L} = 0.75377\ M\ Cu^{2+}$

and $0.74623\ mol\ Cu^{2+} \times \dfrac{1\ mol\ Mg\ oxidized}{1\ mol\ Cu^{2+}\ reduced} = 0.74623\ mol\ Mg\ oxidized$ and

$[Mg^{2+}] = [Mg^{2+}] + \dfrac{mol\ Mg\ oxidized}{1.0\ L} = 1.0 \times 10^{-4}\ M + \dfrac{0.74623\ mol\ Mg\ oxidized}{1.0\ L}$

$= 0.74633\ M\ Mg^{2+}$

$Q = \dfrac{[Mg^{2+}]}{[Cu^{2+}]} = \dfrac{0.74633}{0.75377} = 0.99013$ and $n = 2$ then

$E_{cell} = E°_{cell} - \dfrac{0.0592\ V}{n} \log Q = 2.71\ V - \dfrac{0.0592\ V}{2} \log 0.99013 = +2.71013\ V = +2.71\ V$

(c)   In 1.0 L, there are initially 1.5 moles of Cu^{2+}. So

$$1.5 \ \cancel{\text{mol Cu}^{2+}} \times \frac{2 \ \cancel{\text{mol e}^-}}{1 \ \cancel{\text{mol Cu}^{2+}}} \times \frac{96,485 \ \cancel{C}}{1 \ \cancel{\text{mol e}^-}} \times \frac{1 \ \cancel{s}}{5.0 \ \cancel{C}} \times \frac{1 \ \cancel{\text{min}}}{60 \ \cancel{s}} \times \frac{1 \ h}{60 \ \cancel{\text{min}}} = 16 \ h.$$

Check: The units (V, V, and h) are correct. The Cu^{2+} reduction reaction is above the Mg^{2+} reduction reaction, so the standard cell potential will be positive. Having more reactants than products increases the cell potential. As the reaction proceeds, the potential drops. The concentrations drop by $\frac{1}{2}$ in 8 hours (part (b)), so all of it is consumed in 16 hours.

18.70   **Given:** Ag/Ag^+ concentration cell; initially, $[Ag^+] = 1.25$ M and 1.0×10^{-3} M in 2.0 L half-cells
Find: (a) how long battery can deliver 2.5 A, (b) mass of Ag plated after 3.5 A for 5.5 h, and (c) how long to redissolve 1.00×10^2 g Ag with 10.0 A
Conceptual Plan:
(a)   **Write the two half-cell reactions and add electrons as needed to balance reactions.**
Then $[Ag^+], V \rightarrow$ **mol Ag^+** $\rightarrow$ **mol e^-** $\rightarrow$ **C** $\rightarrow$ **s** $\rightarrow$ **min** $\rightarrow$ **h**

$$M = \frac{\text{mol Ag}^+}{L} \qquad \frac{1 \ \text{mol e}^-}{1 \ \text{mol Ag}^+} \qquad \frac{96,485 \ C}{1 \ \text{mol e}^-} \quad \frac{1 \ s}{2.5 \ C} \quad \frac{1 \ \text{min}}{60 \ s} \quad \frac{1 \ h}{60 \ \text{min}}$$

(b)   **h** $\rightarrow$ **min** $\rightarrow$ **s** $\rightarrow$ **C** $\rightarrow$ **mol e^-** $\rightarrow$ **mol Ag** $\rightarrow$ **g Ag**

$$\frac{60 \ \text{min}}{1 \ h} \quad \frac{60 \ s}{1 \ \text{min}} \quad \frac{3.5 \ C}{1 \ s} \quad \frac{1 \ \text{mol e}^-}{96,485 \ C} \qquad \frac{1 \ \text{mol Ag}}{1 \ \text{mol e}^-} \qquad \frac{107.87 \ \text{g Ag}}{1 \ \text{mol Ag}}$$

(c)   **g Ag** $\rightarrow$ **mol Ag** $\rightarrow$ **mol e^-** $\rightarrow$ **C** $\rightarrow$ **s** $\rightarrow$ **min** $\rightarrow$ **h**

$$\frac{1 \ \text{mol Ag}}{107.87 \ \text{g Ag}} \qquad \frac{1 \ \text{mol e}^-}{1 \ \text{mol Ag}} \qquad \frac{96,485 \ C}{1 \ \text{mol e}^-} \quad \frac{1 \ s}{10.0 \ C} \quad \frac{1 \ \text{min}}{60 \ s} \quad \frac{1 \ h}{60 \ \text{min}}$$

Solution:

(a)   Write half-reactions and add electrons. $Ag(aq) + e^- \rightarrow Ag(s)$. $M = \dfrac{\text{mol Ag}^+}{L}$, so

$$\text{mol Ag}^+ = M \times L = 1.25 \frac{\text{mol Ag}^+}{\cancel{L}} \times 2.0 \ \cancel{L} = 2.50 \ \text{mol Ag}^+ \text{ then}$$

$$2.50 \ \cancel{\text{mol Ag}^+} \times \frac{1 \ \cancel{\text{mol e}^-}}{1 \ \cancel{\text{mol Ag}^+}} \times \frac{96,485 \ \cancel{C}}{1 \ \cancel{\text{mol e}^-}} \times \frac{1 \ \cancel{s}}{2.5 \ \cancel{C}} \times \frac{1 \ \cancel{\text{min}}}{60 \ \cancel{s}} \times \frac{1 \ h}{60 \ \cancel{\text{min}}} = 27 \ h$$

(b) $5.5 \ \cancel{h} \times \dfrac{60 \ \cancel{\text{min}}}{1 \ \cancel{h}} \times \dfrac{60 \ \cancel{s}}{1 \ \cancel{\text{min}}} \times \dfrac{3.5 \ \cancel{C}}{1 \ \cancel{s}} \times \dfrac{1 \ \cancel{\text{mol e}^-}}{96,485 \ \cancel{C}} \times \dfrac{1 \ \cancel{\text{mol Ag}}}{1 \ \cancel{\text{mol e}^-}} \times \dfrac{107.87 \ \text{g Ag}}{1 \ \cancel{\text{mol Ag}}} = 77 \ \text{g Ag}$

(c) $1.00 \times 10^2 \ \cancel{\text{g Ag}} \times \dfrac{1 \ \cancel{\text{mol Ag}}}{107.87 \ \cancel{\text{g Ag}}} \times \dfrac{1 \ \cancel{\text{mol e}^-}}{1 \ \cancel{\text{mol Ag}}} \times \dfrac{96,485 \ \cancel{C}}{1 \ \cancel{\text{mol e}^-}} \times \dfrac{1 \ s}{10.0 \ \cancel{C}} \times \dfrac{1 \ \cancel{\text{min}}}{60 \ \cancel{s}} \times \dfrac{1 \ h}{60 \ \cancel{\text{min}}} = 2.48 \ h$

Check: The units (h, g, and h) are correct. Because 2.5 moles need to be plated, we expect it to take a long time. The time is shorter by a factor of ~30, and the current is larger by about 1.5; so we expect less Ag to be plated in part (b) as compared to part (a). We expect a shorter time in part (c) than in part (b) because the current is so much larger. In parts (b) and (c), we are not exhausting the 2.5 moles initially in the half-cell.

18.71   **Given:** $Cu(s) \mid CuI(s) \mid I^-(aq, 1.0 \ M) \parallel Cu^+(aq, 1.0 \ M) \mid Cu(s)$, $K_{sp}(CuI) = 1.1 \times 10^{-12}$ **Find:** E_{cell}
Conceptual Plan: Write half-reactions from line notation. Because this is a concentration cell, $E^\circ_{cell} = 0.00$ V.
Then $K_{sp}, [I^-] \rightarrow [Cu^+](ox)$ then $E^\circ_{cell}, [Cu^+](ox), [Cu^+](red), n \rightarrow E_{cell}$.

$$K_{sp} = [Cu^+][I^-] \qquad\qquad E_{cell} = E^\circ_{cell} - \frac{0.0592 \ V}{n} \log Q$$

Solution: The half-reactions are $Cu(s) \rightarrow Cu^+(aq) + e^-$ and $Cu^+(aq) + e^- \rightarrow Cu(s)$. Because this is a concentration cell, $E^\circ_{cell} = 0.00$ V and $n = 1$. Because $K_{sp} = [Cu^+][I^-]$, rearrange to solve for $[Cu^+](ox)$.

$$[Cu^+](ox) = \frac{K_{sp}}{[I^-]} = \frac{1.1 \times 10^{-12}}{1.0} = 1.1 \times 10^{-12} \ M \text{ then}$$

$$Q = \frac{[Cu^+](ox)}{[Cu^+](red)} = \frac{1.1 \times 10^{-12}}{1.0} = 1.1 \times 10^{-12} \text{ then}$$

$$E_{cell} = E^\circ_{cell} - \frac{0.0592 \ V}{n} \log Q = 0.00 \ V - \frac{0.0592 \ V}{1} \log (1.1 \times 10^{-12}) = 0.71 \ V$$

Check: The units (V) are correct. Because [Cu$^+$](ox) is so low and [Cu$^+$](red) is high, the Q is very small; so the voltage increase compared to the standard value is significant.

18.72   **Given:** $Zn(OH)_2(s) + 2\,e^- \rightarrow Zn(s) + 2\,OH^-(aq)$, $K_{sp}(Zn(OH)_2) = 1.8 \times 10^{-14}$ **Find:** E for half-cell
Conceptual Plan: In Table 18.1, look up the half-reaction for the Zn reduction (E°_{red}), determine n, then $K_{sp} \rightarrow [OH^-]$ then E°_{cell}, $[OH^-]$, $n \rightarrow E_{cell}$.

$$K_{sp} = [Zn^{2+}][OH^-]^2 \qquad\qquad E_{cell} = E^\circ_{cell} - \frac{0.0592\ V}{n}\log Q$$

Solution: The reduction half-reaction is $Zn^{2+}(aq) + 2\,e^- \rightarrow Zn(s)$ and $E^\circ_{red} = -0.76\ V$ and $n = 2$. Because $K_{sp} = [Zn^{2+}][OH^-]^2 = S(2S)^2 = 4\,S^3$, rearrange to solve for $2\,S = [OH^-]$.

$$S = \frac{1}{2}[OH^-] = \sqrt[3]{\frac{K_{sp}}{4}} = \sqrt[3]{\frac{1.8 \times 10^{-14}}{4}} = 1.6\underline{5}096 \times 10^{-5}\ M \text{ then}$$

$$[OH^-] = 2 \times 1.65096 \times 10^{-5} = 3.\underline{3}0193 \times 10^{-5}\ M$$

$$Q = [OH^-]^2 = (3.\underline{3}0193 \times 10^{-5})^2 = 1.\underline{0}903 \times 10^{-9} \text{ then}$$

$$E_{cell} = E^\circ_{cell} - \frac{0.0592\ V}{n}\log Q = -0.76\ V - \frac{0.0592\ V}{2}\log(1.\underline{0}903 \times 10^{-9}) = -0.49\ V$$

Check: The units (V) are correct. Because [OH$^-$] is so low, the Q is very small; so the voltage increase is significant, but the half-reaction is nonspontaneous.

18.73   **Given:** (a) disproportionation of $Mn^{2+}(aq)$ to $Mn(s)$ and $MnO_2(s)$ and (b) disproportionation of $MnO_2(s)$ to $Mn^{2+}(aq)$ and $MnO_4^-(s)$ in acidic solution   **Find:** ΔG°_{rxn} and K
Conceptual Plan: Separate the overall reaction into two half-reactions: one for oxidation and one for reduction. $\rightarrow$ Balance each half-reaction with respect to mass in the following order: (1) Balance all elements other than H and O, (2) balance O by adding H_2O, and (3) balance H by adding H^+. $\rightarrow$ Balance each half-reaction with respect to charge by adding electrons. (The sum of the charges on both sides of the equation should be made equal by adding electrons as necessary.) $\rightarrow$ Make the number of electrons in both half-reactions equal by multiplying one or both half-reactions by a small whole number. $\rightarrow$ Add the two half-reactions together, canceling electrons and other species as necessary. $\rightarrow$ Verify that the reaction is balanced with respect to both mass and charge. Look up half-reactions in Table 18.1. Calculate the standard cell potential by subtracting the electrode potential of the anode from the electrode potential of the cathode: $E^\circ_{cell} = E^\circ_{cathode} - E^\circ_{anode}$. Then calculate ΔG°_{rxn} using $\Delta G^\circ_{rxn} = -nFE^\circ_{cell}$. Finally, °C $\rightarrow$ K then ΔG°_{rxn}, $T \rightarrow K$.

$$K = 273.15 + {}^\circ C \qquad\qquad \Delta G^\circ_{rxn} = -RT\ln K$$

Solution:

(a)   Separate: $Mn^{2+}(aq) \rightarrow MnO_2(s)$ and $Mn^{2+}(aq) \rightarrow Mn(s)$
Balance non-H & O elements: $Mn^{2+}(aq) \rightarrow MnO_2(s)$ and $Mn^{2+}(aq) \rightarrow Mn(s)$
Balance O with H_2O: $Mn^{2+}(aq) + 2\,H_2O(l) \rightarrow MnO_2(s)$ and $Mn^{2+}(aq) \rightarrow Mn(s)$
Balance H with H^+: $Mn^{2+}(aq) + 2\,H_2O(l) \rightarrow MnO_2(s) + 4\,H^+(aq)$ and $Mn^{2+}(aq) \rightarrow Mn(s)$
Add electrons: $Mn^{2+}(aq) + 2\,H_2O(l) \rightarrow MnO_2(s) + 4\,H^+(aq) + 2\,e^-$ and $Mn^{2+}(aq) + 2\,e^- \rightarrow Mn(s)$
Equalize electrons: $Mn^{2+}(aq) + 2\,H_2O(l) \rightarrow MnO_2(s) + 4\,H^+(aq) + 2\,e^-$ and $Mn^{2+}(aq) + 2\,e^- \rightarrow Mn(s)$
Add half-reactions: $Mn^{2+}(aq) + 2\,H_2O(l) + Mn^{2+}(aq) + 2\,\cancel{e^-} \rightarrow MnO_2(s) + 4\,H^+(aq) + 2\,\cancel{e^-} + Mn(s)$
Cancel electrons: $2\,Mn^{2+}(aq) + 2\,H_2O(l) \rightarrow MnO_2(s) + 4\,H^+(aq) + Mn(s)$
Look up cell potentials. Mn is oxidized in the first half-cell reaction, so $E^\circ_{anode} = E^\circ_{red} = +1.21\ V$. Mn is reduced in the second half-cell reaction, so $E^\circ_{cathode} = E^\circ_{red} = -1.18\ V$. Then
$E^\circ_{cell} = E^\circ_{cathode} - E^\circ_{anode} = -1.18\ V - 1.21\ V = -2.39\ V$. $n = 2$, so

$$\Delta G^\circ_{rxn} = -nFE^\circ_{cell} = -2\ \cancel{mol\ e^-} \times \frac{96{,}485\ C}{\cancel{mol\ e^-}} \times -2.39\ V = -2 \times 96{,}485\ \cancel{C} \times -2.39\ \frac{J}{\cancel{C}} =$$

$4.6\underline{1}198 \times 10^5\ J = 461\ kJ$ and $T = 273.15 + 25\ °C = 298\ K$ then
$\Delta G^\circ_{rxn} = -RT\ln K$. Rearrange to solve for K.

$$K = e^{\frac{-\Delta G^\circ_{rxn}}{RT}} = e^{\frac{-4.6\underline{1}198 \times 10^5\ \cancel{J}}{\left(8.314\frac{\cancel{J}}{K\cdot mol}\right)(298\ K)}} = e^{-186.149} = 1.43 \times 10^{-81}$$

Check: Reactants   Products
                     2 Mn atoms   2 Mn atoms
                     2 O atoms   2 O atoms
                     4 H atoms   4 H atoms
                     +4 charge   +4 charge

The units (kJ and none) are correct. If the voltage is negative, the reaction is nonspontaneous, the free energy change is very positive, and the equilibrium constant is extremely small.

(b)   Separate: $MnO_2(s) \rightarrow Mn^{2+}(aq)$ and $MnO_2(s) \rightarrow MnO_4^-(aq)$
       Balance non-H & O elements: $MnO_2(s) \rightarrow Mn^{2+}(aq)$ and $MnO_2(s) \rightarrow MnO_4^-(aq)$
       Balance O with H_2O: $MnO_2(s) \rightarrow Mn^{2+}(aq) + 2\,H_2O(l)$ and $MnO_2(s) + 2\,H_2O(l) \rightarrow MnO_4^-(aq)$
       Balance H with H^+:
       $MnO_2(s) + 4\,H^+(aq) \rightarrow Mn^{2+}(aq) + 2\,H_2O(l)$ and $MnO_2(s) + 2\,H_2O(l) \rightarrow MnO_4^-(aq) + 4\,H^+(aq)$
       Add electrons: $MnO_2(s) + 4\,H^+(aq) + 2\,e^- \rightarrow Mn^{2+}(aq) + 2\,H_2O(l)$ and $MnO_2(s) + 2\,H_2O(l) \rightarrow$
       $\qquad\qquad\qquad\qquad\qquad\qquad\qquad\qquad\qquad\qquad\qquad MnO_4^-(aq) + 4\,H^+(aq) + 3\,e^-$
       Equalize electrons: $3\,MnO_2(s) + 12\,H^+(aq) + 6\,e^- \rightarrow 3\,Mn^{2+}(aq) + 6\,H_2O(l)$ and
       $\qquad\qquad\qquad\qquad\qquad 2\,MnO_2(s) + 4\,H_2O(l) \rightarrow 2\,MnO_4^-(aq) + 8\,H^+(aq) + 6\,e^-$
       Add half-reactions: $3\,MnO_2(s) + \cancel{4}\,12\,H^+(aq) + \cancel{6\,e^-} + 2\,MnO_2(s) + \cancel{4}\,H_2O(l) \rightarrow$
       $\qquad\qquad\qquad\qquad\qquad\qquad\qquad\qquad\qquad \overset{2}{}$
       $\qquad\qquad\qquad\qquad 3\,Mn^{2+}(aq) + \cancel{6}\,H_2O(l) + 2\,MnO_4^-(aq) + \cancel{8}\,H^+(aq) + \cancel{6\,e^-}$
       Cancel electrons & species: $5\,MnO_2(s) + 4\,H^+(aq) \rightarrow 3\,Mn^{2+}(aq) + 2\,H_2O(l) + 2\,MnO_4^-(aq)$
       Look up cell potentials. Mn is reduced in the first half-cell reaction, so $E_{cathode}^\circ = E_{red}^\circ = 1.21$ V. Mn is oxidized in the second half-cell reaction, so $E_{anode}^\circ = E_{red}^\circ = +1.68$ V. Then $E_{cell}^\circ = E_{cathode}^\circ - E_{anode}^\circ$
       $= 1.21$ V $- 1.68$ V $= -0.47$ V. $n = 6$, so

$$\Delta G_{rxn}^\circ = -nFE_{cell}^\circ = -6\,\cancel{mol\,e^-} \times \frac{96{,}485\text{ C}}{\cancel{mol\,e^-}} \times -0.47\text{ V} = -6 \times 96{,}485\,\cancel{C} \times -0.47\,\frac{J}{\cancel{C}}$$

$= 2.\underline{7}209 \times 10^5$ J $= 270$ kJ $= 2.7 \times 10^2$ kJ. $T = 273.15 + 25\,°C = 298$ K then $\Delta G_{rxn}^\circ = -RT \ln K$.

Rearrange to solve for K. $K = e^{\frac{-\Delta G_{rxn}^\circ}{RT}} = e^{\dfrac{\overset{-2.\underline{7}209 \times 10^5\,\cancel{J}}{}}{\left(8.314\,\frac{\cancel{J}}{K\cdot mol}\right)(298\text{ K})}} = e^{-109.82} = 2.0 \times 10^{-48}$

Check: Reactants   Products
                     5 Mn atoms   5 Mn atoms
                     10 O atoms   10 O atoms
                     4 H atoms   4 H atoms
                     +4 charge   +4 charge

The units (kJ and none) are correct. If the voltage is negative, the reaction is nonspontaneous, the free energy change is very positive, and the equilibrium constant is extremely small. The voltage is less than in part (a), so the free energy change is not as large and the equilibrium constant is not as small.

18.74   **Given:** (a) reaction of $Cr^{2+}(aq)$ with $Cr_2O_7^{2-}(aq)$ in acidic solution to form $Cr^{3+}(aq)$ and (b) reaction of $Cr^{3+}(aq)$ with $Cr(s)$ to form $Cr^{2+}(aq)$ **Find:** ΔG_{rxn}° and K
         Conceptual Plan: Separate the overall reaction into two half-reactions: one for oxidation and one for reduction. → Balance each half-reaction with respect to mass in the following order: (1) Balance all elements other than H and O, (2) balance O by adding H_2O, and (3) balance H by adding H^+. → Balance each half-reaction with respect to charge by adding electrons. (The sum of the charges on both sides of the equation should be made equal by adding electrons as necessary.) → Make the number of electrons in both half-reactions equal by multiplying one or both half-reactions by a small whole number. → Add the two half-reactions together, canceling electrons and other species as necessary. → Verify that the reaction is balanced with respect to both mass and charge. Look up half-reactions in Table 18.1. Calculate the standard cell potential by subtracting the electrode potential of the anode from the electrode potential of the cathode: $E_{cell}^\circ = E_{cathode}^\circ - E_{anode}^\circ$.
         Then calculate ΔG_{rxn}° using $\Delta G_{rxn}^\circ = -nFE_{cell}^\circ$. Finally, $°C \rightarrow K$ then $\Delta G_{rxn}^\circ, T \rightarrow K$.

$$K = 273.15 + °C \qquad\qquad \Delta G_{rxn}^\circ = -RT \ln K$$

         Solution:
(a)   Separate: $Cr^{2+}(aq) \rightarrow Cr^{3+}(aq)$ and $Cr_2O_7^{2-}(aq) \rightarrow Cr^{3+}(aq)$
       Balance non-H & O elements: $Cr^{2+}(aq) \rightarrow Cr^{3+}(aq)$ and $Cr_2O_7^{2-}(aq) \rightarrow 2\,Cr^{3+}(aq)$
       Balance O with H_2O: $Cr^{2+}(aq) \rightarrow Cr^{3+}(aq)$ and $Cr_2O_7^{2-}(aq) \rightarrow 2\,Cr^{3+}(aq) + 7\,H_2O(l)$

Balance H with H^+: $Cr^{2+}(aq) \rightarrow Cr^{3+}(aq)$ and $Cr_2O_7^{2-}(aq) + 14\,H^+(aq) \rightarrow 2\,Cr^{3+}(aq) + 7\,H_2O(l)$

Add electrons: $Cr^{2+}(aq) \rightarrow Cr^{3+}(aq) + e^-$ and $Cr_2O_7^{2-}(aq) + 14\,H^+(aq) + 6\,e^- \rightarrow 2\,Cr^{3+}(aq) + 7\,H_2O(l)$

Equalize electrons:

$6\,Cr^{2+}(aq) \rightarrow 6\,Cr^{3+}(aq) + 6\,e^-$ and $Cr_2O_7^{2-}(aq) + 14\,H^+(aq) + 6\,e^- \rightarrow 2\,Cr^{3+}(aq) + 7\,H_2O(l)$

Add half-reactions:

$6\,Cr^{2+}(aq) + Cr_2O_7^{2-}(aq) + 14\,H^+(aq) + \cancel{6\,e^-} \rightarrow 6\,Cr^{3+}(aq) + \cancel{6\,e^-}(aq) + 2\,Cr^{3+}(aq) + 7\,H_2O(l)$

Cancel electrons: $6\,Cr^{2+}(aq) + Cr_2O_7^{2-}(aq) + 14\,H^+(aq) \rightarrow 8\,Cr^{3+}(aq) + 7\,H_2O(l)$

Look up cell potentials. Cr is oxidized in the first half-cell reaction, so $E^\circ_{red} = -0.50\,V = E^\circ_{anode}$. Cr is reduced in the second half-cell reaction, so $E^\circ_{red} = 1.33\,V = E^\circ_{cathode}$. Then $E^\circ_{cell} = E^\circ_{cathode} - E^\circ_{anode}$

$= 1.33\,V - (-0.50\,V) = +1.83\,V.$ $n = 6$, so $\Delta G^\circ_{rxn} = -nFE^\circ_{cell} = -6\,\cancel{mol\,e^-} \times \dfrac{96{,}485\,C}{\cancel{mol\,e^-}} \times 1.83\,V$

$= -6 \times 96{,}485\,\cancel{C} \times 1.83\,\dfrac{J}{\cancel{C}} = -1.05941 \times 10^6\,J = -1.06 \times 10^3\,kJ$ and $T = 273.15 + 25\,°C = 298\,K$

then $\Delta G^\circ_{rxn} = -RT \ln K$. Rearrange to solve for K.

$$K = e^{\frac{-\Delta G^\circ_{rxn}}{RT}} = e^{\frac{-(-1.05941 \times 10^6\,J)}{\left(8.314\frac{J}{K\cdot mol}\right)(298\,K)}} = e^{427.600} = 5.06 \times 10^{185}$$

Check:

Reactants	Products
8 Cr atoms	8 Cr atoms
7 O atoms	7 O atoms
14 H atoms	14 H atoms
+24 charge	+24 charge

The units (kJ and none) are correct. If the voltage is positive, the reaction is spontaneous, the free energy change is very negative, and the equilibrium constant is extremely large.

(b)

Separate:	$Cr^{3+}(aq) \rightarrow Cr^{2+}(aq)$	and	$Cr(s) \rightarrow Cr^{2+}(aq)$	
Balance:	$Cr^{3+}(aq) \rightarrow Cr^{2+}(aq)$	and	$Cr(s) \rightarrow Cr^{2+}(aq)$	
Add electrons:	$Cr^{3+}(aq) + e^- \rightarrow Cr^{2+}(aq)$	and	$Cr(s) \rightarrow Cr^{2+}(aq) + 2\,e^-$	
Equalize electrons:	$2\,Cr^{3+}(aq) + 2\,e^- \rightarrow 2\,Cr^{2+}(aq)$	and	$Cr(s) \rightarrow Cr^{2+}(aq) + 2\,e^-$	
Add half-reactions:	$2\,Cr^{3+}(aq) + \cancel{2\,e^-} + Cr(s) \rightarrow 2\,Cr^{2+}(aq) + Cr^{2+}(aq) + \cancel{2\,e^-}$			
Cancel electrons & species:	$2\,Cr^{3+}(aq) + Cr(s) \rightarrow 3\,Cr^{2+}(aq)$			

Look up cell potentials. Cr is reduced in the first half-cell reaction, so $E^\circ_{red} = E^\circ_{cell} = -0.50\,V = E^\circ_{cathode}$. Cr is oxidized in the second half-cell reaction, so $E^\circ_{red} = -0.91\,V = E^\circ_{anode}$. Then $E^\circ_{cell} = E^\circ_{cathode} - E^\circ_{anode}$

$= -0.50\,V - (-0.91\,V) = +0.41\,V.$ $n = 2$, so $\Delta G^\circ_{rxn} = -nFE^\circ_{cell} = -2\,\cancel{mol\,e^-} \times \dfrac{96{,}485\,C}{\cancel{mol\,e^-}} \times 0.41\,V$

$= -2 \times 96{,}485\,\cancel{C} \times 0.41\,\dfrac{J}{\cancel{C}} = -7.9118 \times 10^4\,J = -79\,kJ$ and $T = 273.15 + 25\,°C = 298\,K$

then $\Delta G^\circ_{rxn} = -RT \ln K$. Rearrange to solve for K.

$$K = e^{\frac{-\Delta G^\circ_{rxn}}{RT}} = e^{\frac{-(-7.9118 \times 10^4\,J)}{\left(8.314\frac{J}{K\cdot mol}\right)(298\,K)}} = e^{31.934} = 7.4 \times 10^{13}$$

Check:

Reactants	Products
3 Cr atoms	3 Cr atoms
+6 charge	+6 charge

The units (kJ and none) are correct. If the voltage is positive, the reaction is spontaneous, the free energy change is negative, and the equilibrium constant is large. The voltage and n are less than in part (a), so the free energy change is not as negative and the equilibrium constant is not as large.

18.75   **Given:** metal, M, 50.9 g/mol, 1.20 g of metal reduced in 23.6 minutes at 6.42 A from molten chloride
   Find: empirical formula of chloride
   Conceptual Plan: min $\rightarrow$ s $\rightarrow$ C $\rightarrow$ mol e^- and g M $\rightarrow$ mol M then mol e^-, mol M $\rightarrow$ charge $\rightarrow$ MCl_x

$$\dfrac{60\,s}{1\,min} \quad \dfrac{6.42\,C}{1\,s} \quad \dfrac{1\,mol\,e^-}{96{,}485\,C} \qquad \dfrac{1\,mol\,M}{50.9\,g\,M} \qquad \dfrac{1\,mol\,e^-}{1\,mol\,M}$$

Solution: $23.6 \, \text{min} \times \dfrac{60 \, \text{s}}{1 \, \text{min}} \times \dfrac{6.42 \, \text{C}}{1 \, \text{s}} \times \dfrac{1 \, \text{mol e}^-}{96{,}485 \, \text{C}} = 0.0942190 \, \text{mol e}^-$ and

$1.20 \, \text{g M} \times \dfrac{1 \, \text{mol M}}{50.9 \, \text{g M}} = 0.0235756 \, \text{mol M}$ then $\dfrac{0.0942190 \, \text{mol e}^-}{0.0235756 \, \text{mol M}} = 3.99646 \, \dfrac{\text{e}^-}{\text{M}}$

So the empirical formula is MCl_4.

Check: The units (none) are correct. The result was an integer within the error of the measurements. The formula is typical for a metal salt. It could be vanadium, which has a +4 oxidation state.

18.76   **Given:** molten MF_3 electrolysis, 1.25 g of metal reduced in 16.2 minutes at 3.86 A   **Find:** molar mass of metal

Conceptual Plan: min $\rightarrow$ s $\rightarrow$ C $\rightarrow$ mol e$^-$ $\rightarrow$ mol M then g M, mol M $\rightarrow$ molar mass

$$\dfrac{60 \, \text{s}}{1 \, \text{min}} \quad \dfrac{3.86 \, \text{C}}{1 \, \text{s}} \quad \dfrac{1 \, \text{mol e}^-}{96{,}485 \, \text{C}} \quad \dfrac{1 \, \text{mol M}}{3 \, \text{mol e}^-} \qquad \mathcal{M} = \dfrac{\text{g M}}{\text{mol M}}$$

Solution: $16.2 \, \text{min} \times \dfrac{60 \, \text{s}}{1 \, \text{min}} \times \dfrac{3.86 \, \text{C}}{1 \, \text{s}} \times \dfrac{1 \, \text{mol e}^-}{96{,}485 \, \text{C}} \times \dfrac{1 \, \text{mol M}}{3 \, \text{mol e}^-} = 0.0129620 \, \text{mol M}$ then

$\mathcal{M} = \dfrac{1.25 \, \text{g M}}{0.0129620 \, \text{mol M}} = 96.4 \, \dfrac{\text{g}}{\text{mol}}$

Check: The units (g/mol) are correct. The result was a number typical for metals, and it could be niobium, which is known to have a +3 oxidation state.

18.77   **Given:** 0.535 g impure Sn; dissolve to form Sn^{2+} and titrate with 0.0344 L of 0.0448 M NO_3^- to generate NO   **Find:** percent by mass Sn

Conceptual Plan: Use balanced reaction from Problem 18.4(c) then

L $\rightarrow$ mol NO_3^- $\rightarrow$ mol Sn $\rightarrow$ g Sn $\rightarrow$ percent by mass Sn.

$$M = \dfrac{\text{mol}}{\text{L}} \qquad \dfrac{3 \, \text{mol Sn}}{2 \, \text{mol NO}_3^-} \qquad \dfrac{118.71 \, \text{g Sn}}{1 \, \text{mol Sn}} \qquad \text{percent by mass Sn} = \dfrac{\text{g Sn}}{\text{g sample}} \times 100\%$$

Solution: $2 \, NO_3^-(aq) + 8 \, H^+(aq) + 3 \, Sn^{2+}(aq) \rightarrow 2 \, NO(g) + 4 \, H_2O(l) + 3 \, Sn^{4+}(aq)$

$0.0344 \, \text{L} \times \dfrac{0.0448 \, \text{mol NO}_3^-}{1 \, \text{L}} \times \dfrac{3 \, \text{mol Sn}}{2 \, \text{mol NO}_3^-} \times \dfrac{118.71 \, \text{g Sn}}{1 \, \text{mol Sn}} = 0.2744195 \, \text{g Sn}$ then

percent by mass Sn $= \dfrac{\text{g Sn}}{\text{g sample}} \times 100\% = \dfrac{0.2744195 \, \text{g Sn}}{0.535 \, \text{g sample}} \times 100\% = 51.3\%$ by mass Sn

Check: The units (% by mass) are correct. The result was a number less than 100%.

18.78   **Given:** 0.0251 L Cu^+ solution titrated with 0.0322 L of 0.129 M $KMnO_4$ to generate Cu^{2+} and Mn^{2+}

Find: concentration of Cu solution

Conceptual Plan: Use the balanced reaction from Problem 18.61, but change metal and stoichiometry by a factor of 2 then L MnO_4^- $\rightarrow$ mol MnO_4^- $\rightarrow$ mol Cu^+ $\rightarrow$ $[Cu^+]$.

$$M = \dfrac{\text{mol}}{\text{L}} \qquad \dfrac{5 \, \text{mol Cu}^+}{1 \, \text{mol MnO}_4^-} \qquad M = \dfrac{\text{mol}}{\text{L}}$$

Solution: $MnO_4^-(aq) + 8 \, H^+(aq) + 5 \, Cu^+(aq) \rightarrow Mn^{2+}(aq) + 4 \, H_2O(l) + 5 \, Cu^{2+}(aq)$

$0.0322 \, \text{L MnO}_4^- \times \dfrac{0.129 \, \text{mol MnO}_4^-}{1 \, \text{L MnO}_4^-} \times \dfrac{5 \, \text{mol Cu}^+}{1 \, \text{mol MnO}_4^-} = 0.020769 \, \text{mol Cu}^+$ then

$[Cu^{2+}] = \dfrac{0.020769 \, \text{mol Cu}^{2+}}{0.0251 \, \text{L}} = 0.827 \, \text{M Cu}^{2+}$

Check: The units (M) are correct. The Cu concentration is much higher than the $KMnO_4$ concentration because of the reaction stoichiometry.

18.79   **Given:** $[A^{2+}]$ and $[B^{2+}]$ in table and $\Delta G°_{\text{rxn}} = -14.0$ kJ   **Find:** $E°_{\text{cell}}$, K, Q, E_{cell}, and ΔG_{rxn}

Conceptual Plan: Determine n; $\Delta G°_{\text{rxn}}$, then $n \rightarrow E°_{\text{cell}}$ and $\Delta G°_{\text{rxn}}, T \rightarrow K$ and

$$A(s) + B^{2+}(aq) \rightarrow A^{2+}(aq) + B(s) \quad \Delta G°_{\text{rxn}} = -nFE°_{\text{cell}} \qquad \Delta G°_{\text{rxn}} = -RT \ln K$$

For each set of conditions: $[A^{2+}], [B^{2+}] \rightarrow Q$ then $E°_{\text{cell}}, [A^{2+}], [B^{2+}], n \rightarrow E_{\text{cell}}$ and $\Delta G°_{\text{rxn}}, Q, T \rightarrow \Delta G_{\text{rxn}}$

$$Q = \dfrac{[A^{2+}]}{[B^{2+}]} \qquad\qquad E_{\text{cell}} = E°_{\text{cell}} - \dfrac{0.0592 \, \text{V}}{n} \log Q \qquad \Delta G_{\text{rxn}} = \Delta G°_{\text{rxn}} + RT \ln Q$$

Solution: Since the charge of both A and B change by 2 in the reaction, $n = 2$. $\Delta G^\circ_{rxn} = -nFE^\circ_{cell}$ Rearrange to solve for E°_{cell}. $E^\circ_{cell} = \dfrac{\Delta G^\circ_{rxn}}{-nF} = \dfrac{-1.40 \times 10^4 \text{ J}}{-2 \text{ mol e}^- \times \dfrac{96{,}485 \text{ C}}{\text{mol e}^-}} = 0.0725501 \dfrac{\text{V} \cdot \cancel{\text{C}}}{\cancel{\text{C}}} = 0.0726 \text{ V}.$

$\Delta G^\circ_{rxn} = -RT \ln K$. Rearrange to solve for K. $K = e^{\frac{-\Delta G^\circ_{rxn}}{RT}} = e^{\frac{-(-1.40 \times 10^4 \text{ J})}{\left(8.314 \frac{\text{J}}{\text{K} \cdot \text{mol}}\right)(298 \text{ K})}} = e^{+5.650694} = 284.4888 = 284.$

1: $Q = \dfrac{[A^{2+}]}{[B^{2+}]} = \dfrac{1.00 \text{ M}}{1.00 \text{ M}} = 1.00$

$E_{cell} = E^\circ_{cell} - \dfrac{0.0592 \text{ V}}{n} \log Q = 0.0725501 \text{ V} - \dfrac{0.0592 \text{ V}}{2} \log (1) = +0.0726 \text{ V}$ and

$\Delta G_{rxn} = \Delta G^\circ_{rxn} + RT \ln Q = -14.0 \text{ kJ} + \left(8.314 \dfrac{\text{J}}{\text{K} \cdot \text{mol}}\right)\left(\dfrac{1 \text{ kJ}}{1000 \text{ J}}\right)(298 \text{ K}) \ln (1) = -14.0 \text{ kJ}$

These are standard state conditions, so $E^\circ_{cell} = E_{cell}$ and $\Delta G^\circ_{rxn} = \Delta G_{rxn}$.

2: $Q = \dfrac{1.00 \times 10^{-4} \text{ M}}{1.00 \text{ M}} = 1.00 \times 10^{-4}$

$E_{cell} = 0.0725501 \text{ V} - \dfrac{0.0592 \text{ V}}{2} \log (1.00 \times 10^{-4}) = +0.1909501 \text{ V} = +0.1910 \text{ V}$ and

$\Delta G_{rxn} = -14.0 \text{ kJ} + \left(8.314 \dfrac{\text{J}}{\text{K} \cdot \text{mol}}\right)\left(\dfrac{1 \text{ kJ}}{1000 \text{ J}}\right)(298 \text{ K}) \ln (1.00 \times 10^{-4}) = -36.8 \text{ kJ}$

3: $Q = \dfrac{1.00 \text{ M}}{1.00 \times 10^{-4} \text{ M}} = 1.00 \times 10^4$

$E_{cell} = 0.0725501 \text{ V} - \dfrac{0.0592 \text{ V}}{2} \log (1.00 \times 10^4) = -0.0458499 \text{ V} = -0.0458 \text{ V}$ and

$\Delta G_{rxn} = -14.0 \text{ kJ} + \left(8.314 \dfrac{\text{J}}{\text{K} \cdot \text{mol}}\right)\left(\dfrac{1 \text{ kJ}}{1000 \text{ J}}\right)(298 \text{ K}) \ln (1.00 \times 10^4) = +8.8 \text{ kJ}$

4: $Q = \dfrac{1.00 \text{ M}}{3.52 \times 10^{-3} \text{ M}} = 284.0909 = 284$

$E_{cell} = 0.0725501 \text{ V} - \dfrac{0.0592 \text{ V}}{2} \log (284.0909) = -0.00007224 \text{ V} = -0.0001 \text{ V}$ and

$\Delta G_{rxn} = -14.0 \text{ kJ} + \left(8.314 \dfrac{\text{J}}{\text{K} \cdot \text{mol}}\right)\left(\dfrac{1 \text{ kJ}}{1000 \text{ J}}\right)(298 \text{ K}) \ln (284.0909) = -0.00347 \text{ kJ} = +0.0 \text{ kJ}$

These are equilibrium conditions, so $E_{cell} = 0$ and $\Delta G_{rxn} = 0$.

Experiment	$[B^{2+}]$	$[A^{2+}]$	Q	E_{cell}	ΔG_{rxn}
1	1.00 M	1.00 M	1.00	+ 0.0726 V	− 14.0 kJ
2	1.00 M	1.00×10^{-4} M	1.00×10^{-4}	+ 0.1910 V	− 36.8 kJ
3	1.00×10^{-4} M	1.00 M	1.00×10^4	− 0.0458 V	+ 8.8 kJ
4	3.52×10^{-3} M	1.00 M	284	− 0.0001 V	+ 0.0 kJ

Check: The units (V, none, 4 sets of none, V, and kJ) are correct. ΔG°_{rxn} was negative, so $K > 1$ and $E^\circ_{cell} > 0$. At standard state conditions, $E^\circ_{cell} = E_{cell}$ and $\Delta G^\circ_{rxn} = \Delta G_{rxn}$. These are equilibrium conditions, so $E_{cell} = 0$ and $\Delta G_{rxn} = 0$.

18.80 **Given:** $[Cd^{2+}]$ and $[Cr^{2+}]$ in table and $Cr(s) + Cd^{2+}(aq) \rightarrow Cr^{2+}(aq) + Cd(s)$
Find: E°_{cell}, K, ΔG°_{rxn}, Q, E_{cell}, and ΔG_{rxn}
Conceptual Plan: Look up half-reactions in Table 18.1 or other source. Calculate the standard cell potential by subtracting the electrode potential of the anode from the electrode potential of the cathode:

$$E^\circ_{cell} = E^\circ_{cathode} - E^\circ_{anode}.$$

Determine n; then $E^\circ_{cell}, n \rightarrow \Delta G^\circ_{rxn}$ and $\Delta G^\circ_{rxn}, T \rightarrow K$ and

$Cr(s) + Cd^{2+}(aq) \rightarrow Cr^{2+}(aq) + Cd(s)$ $\Delta G^\circ_{rxn} = -nFE^\circ_{cell}$ $\quad\quad \Delta G^\circ_{rxn} = -RT \ln K$

For each set of conditions: $[Cd^{2+}], [Cr^{2+}] \rightarrow Q$ then $E°_{cell}, [Cd^{2+}], [Cr^{2+}], n \rightarrow E_{cell}$ and $\Delta G°_{rxn}, Q, T \rightarrow \Delta G_{rxn}$

$$Q = \frac{[Cr^{2+}]}{[Cd^{2+}]} \qquad\qquad E_{cell} = E°_{cell} - \frac{0.0592 \text{ V}}{n}\log Q \qquad \Delta G_{rxn} = \Delta G°_{rxn} + RT\ln Q$$

Solution: $Cr(s) + Cd^{2+}(aq) \rightarrow Cr^{2+}(aq) + Cd(s)$ separates to $Cr(s) \rightarrow Cr^{2+}(aq)$ and $Cd^{2+}(aq) \rightarrow Cd(s)$ add electrons $Cr(s) \rightarrow Cr^{2+}(aq) + 2\ e^-$ and $Cd^{2+}(aq) + 2\ e^- \rightarrow Cd(s)$. Look up cell potentials. Cr is oxidized so $E°_{red} = E°_{anode} = -0.91$ V. Cd^{2+} is reduced so $E°_{red} = E°_{anode} = -0.40$ V. Then $E°_{red} = E°_{cathode} = E°_{anode} = -0.40$ V $- (-0.91)$ V $= +0.51$ V. Since the charges of both Cr and Cd change by 2 in the reaction, $n = 2$.

$$\Delta G°_{rxn} = -nFE°_{cell} = -2 \ \cancel{mole^-} \times \frac{96{,}485 \text{ C}}{\cancel{mole^-}} \times 0.51 \text{ V} = -2 \times 96{,}485 \ \cancel{C} \times 0.51 \frac{\text{J}}{\cancel{C}} = -9.\underline{8}4147 \times 10^4 \text{ J}$$
$$= -98.\underline{4}147 \text{ kJ}$$

$\Delta G°_{rxn} = -RT\ln K$ Rearrange to solve for K.

$$K = e^{\frac{-\Delta G°_{rxn}}{RT}} = e^{\frac{-(-9.\underline{8}4147 \times 10^4 \text{ J})}{\left(8.314\frac{\text{J}}{\text{K}\cdot\text{mol}}\right)(298 \text{ K})}} = e^{+39.\underline{7}222} = 1.\underline{7}82986 \times 10^{17} = 1.8 \times 10^{17}.$$

1: $Q = \dfrac{[Cr^{2+}]}{[Cd^{2+}]} = \dfrac{1.00 \text{ M}}{1.00 \text{ M}} = 1.00 \quad E_{cell} = E°_{cell} - \dfrac{0.0592 \text{ V}}{n}\log Q = 0.51 \text{ V} - \dfrac{0.0592 \text{ V}}{2}\log (1) = +0.51$ V and

$$\Delta G_{rxn} = \Delta G°_{rxn} + RT\ln Q = -98.\underline{4}147 \text{ kJ} + \left(8.314\frac{\text{J}}{\text{K}\cdot\text{mol}}\right)\left(\frac{1 \text{ kJ}}{1000 \text{ J}}\right)(298 \text{ K})\ln (1) = -98 \text{ kJ}$$

These are standard state conditions, so $E°_{cell} = E_{cell}$ and $\Delta G°_{rxn} = \Delta G_{rxn}$.

2: $Q = \dfrac{1.00 \times 10^{-5} \text{ M}}{1.00 \text{ M}} = 1.00 \times 10^{-5} \quad E_{cell} = 0.51 \text{ V} - \dfrac{0.0592 \text{ V}}{2}\log (1.00 \times 10^{-5}) = +0.6\underline{5}8 \text{ V} = +0.66$ V and

$$\Delta G_{rxn} = -98.\underline{4}147 \text{ kJ} + \left(8.314\frac{\text{J}}{\text{K}\cdot\text{mol}}\right)\left(\frac{1 \text{ kJ}}{1000 \text{ J}}\right)(298 \text{ K})\ln (1.00 \times 10^{-5}) = -126.\underline{9}388 \text{ kJ} = -127 \text{ kJ}$$

3: $Q = \dfrac{1.00 \text{ M}}{1.00 \times 10^{-5} \text{ M}} = 1.00 \times 10^5 \quad E_{cell} = 0.51 \text{ V} - \dfrac{0.0592 \text{ V}}{2}\log(1.00 \times 10^5) = +0.3\underline{6}2 \text{ V} = +0.36$ V and

$$\Delta G_{rxn} = -98.\underline{4}147 \text{ kJ} + \left(8.314\frac{\text{J}}{\text{K}\cdot\text{mol}}\right)\left(\frac{1 \text{ kJ}}{1000 \text{ J}}\right)(298 \text{ K})\ln (1.00 \times 10^5) = -69.\underline{8}906 \text{ kJ} = -70. \text{ kJ}$$

4: $Q = \dfrac{1.00 \text{ M}}{4.18 \times 10^{-4} \text{ M}} = 23\underline{9}2.3445 = 2390$

$$E_{cell} = 0.51 \text{ V} - \frac{0.0592 \text{ V}}{2}\log(23\underline{9}2.3445) = +0.4\underline{0}9987 \text{ V} = +0.41 \text{ V} \text{ and}$$

$$\Delta G_{rxn} = -98.\underline{4}147 \text{ kJ} + \left(8.314\frac{\text{J}}{\text{K}\cdot\text{mol}}\right)\left(\frac{1 \text{ kJ}}{1000 \text{ J}}\right)(298 \text{ K})\ln (23\underline{9}2.3445) = -79.\underline{1}391 \text{ kJ} = -79 \text{ kJ}$$

Experiment	$[Cd^{2+}]$	$[Cr^{2+}]$	Q	E_{cell}	ΔG_{rxn}
1	1.00 M	1.00 M	1.00	+0.51 V	−98 kJ
2	1.00 M	1.00×10^{-5} M	1.00×10^{-5}	+0.66 V	−127 kJ
3	1.00×10^{-5} M	1.00 M	1.00×10^5	+0.36 V	−70. kJ
4	4.18×10^{-4} M	1.00 M	2390	+0.41 V	−79 kJ

Check: The units (V, none, kJ, 4 sets of none, V, and kJ) are correct. $\Delta G°_{rxn}$ was negative, so $K > 1$ and $E°_{cell} > 0$. At standard state conditions, $E°_{cell} = E_{cell}$ and $\Delta G°_{rxn} = \Delta G_{rxn}$. The larger the Q, the smaller the E_{cell} and the smaller the ΔG_{rxn}. All conditions are spontaneous because the $E°_{cell}$ is so positive.

Challenge Problems

18.81   **Given:** hydrogen–oxygen fuel cell; 1.2×10^3 kWh of electricity/month   **Find:** V of $H_2(g)$ at STP/month
Conceptual Plan: Write half-reactions. Look up half-reactions at pH 7. The reaction on the left is the oxidation. Calculate the standard cell potential by subtracting the electrode potential of the anode from the electrode potential of the cathode: $E°_{cell} = E°_{cathode} - E°_{anode}$. **Add the two half-cell reactions and cancel the electrons. Then**
kWh $\rightarrow$ J $\rightarrow$ C $\rightarrow$ mol e^- $\rightarrow$ mol H_2 $\rightarrow$ V.

$$\frac{3.60 \times 10^6 \text{ J}}{1 \text{ kWh}} \quad \frac{1 \text{ C}}{1.23 \text{ J}} \quad \frac{1 \text{ mol } e^-}{96{,}485 \text{ C}} \quad \frac{2 \text{ mol } H_2}{4 \text{ mol } e^-} \quad \text{at STP} \quad \frac{22.414 \text{ L}}{1 \text{ mol } H_2}$$

Solution: $2 H_2(g) + 4 OH^-(aq) \rightarrow 4 H_2O(l) + 4 e^-$ where $E°_{red} = -0.83$ V $= E°_{anode}$ and $O_2(g) + 2 H_2O(l) + 4 e^- \rightarrow 4 OH^-(aq)$ where $E°_{red} = 0.40$ V $= E°_{cathode}$. $E°_{cell} = E°_{cathode} - E°_{anode} = 0.40$ V $- (-0.83$ V$) = 1.23$ V $= 1.23$ J/C and $n = 4$. Net reaction is $2 H_2(g) + O_2(g) \rightarrow 2 H_2O(l)$. Then

$$1.2 \times 10^3 \text{ kWh} \times \frac{3.60 \times 10^6 \text{ J}}{1 \text{ kWh}} \times \frac{1 \text{ C}}{1.23 \text{ J}} \times \frac{1 \text{ mol } e^-}{96,485 \text{ C}} \times \frac{2 \text{ mol } H_2}{4 \text{ mol } e^-} \times \frac{22.414 \text{ L}}{1 \text{ mol } H_2} = 4.1 \times 10^5 \text{ L}$$

Check: The units (L) are correct. A large volume is expected because we are trying to generate a large amount of electricity.

18.82   **Given:** voltaic cell to measure $[Cu^{2+}]$; SHE electrode paired with Cu^{2+}/Cu cell
         Find: parameters to plot for a calibrations curve and the slope of the curve
         Conceptual Plan: Write the two half-cell reactions and add electrons as needed to balance reactions. Look up half-reactions in Table 18.1. Calculate the standard cell potential by subtracting the electrode potential of the anode from the electrode potential of the cathode: $E°_{cell} = E°_{cathode} - E°_{anode}$**. Add the two half-cell reactions and cancel electrons and determine** n**. Then** $E°_{cell}, P_{H_2}, [H^+], [Cu^{2+}], n \rightarrow E_{cell}$**.**

$$E_{cell} = E°_{cell} - \frac{0.0592 \text{ V}}{n} \log Q$$

Solution: Write half-reactions and add electrons. $H_2(g) \rightarrow 2 H^+(aq) + 2 e^-$ and $Cu^{2+}(aq) + 2 e^- \rightarrow Cu(s)$. Look up cell potentials. H is oxidized, so $E°_{red} = 0.00$ V $= E°_{anode}$. Cu^{2+} is reduced, so $E°_{red} = 0.34$ V $= E°_{cathode}$. Then $E°_{cell} = E°_{cathode} - E°_{anode} = 0.34$ V $- 0.00$ V $= +0.34$ V. Add the two half-cell reactions: $H_2(g) + Cu^{2+}(aq) + 2 e^- \rightarrow 2 H^+(aq) + 2 e^- + Cu(s)$. Simplify to $H_2(g) + Cu^{2+}(aq) \rightarrow 2 H^+(aq) + Cu(s)$. So $Q = \dfrac{[H^+]^2}{P_{H_2}[Cu^{2+}]}$ and $n = 2$. Then $E_{cell} = E°_{cell} - \dfrac{0.0592 \text{ V}}{n}\log Q = 0.34$ V $- \dfrac{0.0592 \text{ V}}{2}\log \dfrac{[H^+]^2}{P_{H_2}[Cu^{2+}]}$. If the anode half-cell is buffered at a constant pH and a constant P_{H_2} is used, two of the terms in Q are constant and can be pulled out of the expression so that

$$E_{cell} = 0.34 \text{ V} - \frac{0.0592 \text{ V}}{2}\left(\log \frac{[H^+]^2}{P_{H_2}} - \log[Cu^{2+}]\right)$$

$$= \left(0.34 \text{ V} - \frac{0.0592 \text{ V}}{2}\log \frac{[H^+]^2}{P_{H_2}}\right) + (0.0296 \text{ V})\log[Cu^{2+}].$$

If we plot $\log[Cu^{2+}]$ versus $E°_{cell}$, the slope will be 0.0296 V. Note: The value of both the slope and the y-intercept are needed to calculate the copper concentration.

18.83   **Given:** Au^{3+}/Au electroplating; surface area $= 49.8$ cm^2, Au thickness $= 1.00 \times 10^{-3}$ cm, density $= 19.3$ g/cm^3; at 3.25 A   **Find:** time
         Conceptual Plan: Write the half-cell reaction and add electrons as needed to balance reactions. Then surface area, thickness $\rightarrow$ **V** $\rightarrow$ **g Au** $\rightarrow$ **mol Au** $\rightarrow$ **mol** e^- $\rightarrow$ **C** $\rightarrow$ **s.**

$$V = surface\ area \times thickness \quad \frac{19.3 \text{ g Au}}{1 \text{ cm}^3 \text{ Au}} \quad \frac{1 \text{ mol Au}}{196.97 \text{ g Au}} \quad \frac{3 \text{ mol } e^-}{1 \text{ mol Au}} \quad \frac{96,485 \text{ C}}{1 \text{ mol } e^-} \quad \frac{1 \text{ s}}{3.25 \text{ C}}$$

Solution: Write the half-reaction and add electrons. $Au^{3+}(aq) + 3 e^- \rightarrow Au(s)$.
$V = surface\ area \times thickness = (49.8 \text{ cm}^2)(1.00 \times 10^{-3}\text{cm}) = 0.0498$ cm^3 then

$$0.0498 \text{ cm}^3 \text{ Au} \times \frac{19.3 \text{ g Au}}{1 \text{ cm}^3 \text{ Au}} \times \frac{1 \text{ mol Au}}{196.97 \text{ g Au}} \times \frac{3 \text{ mol } e^-}{1 \text{ mol Au}} \times \frac{96,485 \text{ C}}{1 \text{ mol } e^-} \times \frac{1 \text{ s}}{3.25 \text{ C}} = 435 \text{ s}$$

Check: The units (s) are correct. Because the layer is so thin, there is far less than a mole of gold; so the time is not very long. To be an economical process, it must be fairly quick.

18.84   **Given:** electrodeposit mixture Cu and Cd with 1.20 F (1 F $= 1$ mol e^-); total mass $= 50.36$ g
         Find: mass of $CuSO_4$
         Conceptual Plan: Write the half-cell reaction and add electrons as needed to balance reactions. Then
         F $\rightarrow$ **mol** e^- $\rightarrow$ **mol (Cu + Cd) then let** $x = $ **g Cu so that (50.36 g** $- x$ **g) = g Cd then g Cu** $\rightarrow$ **mol Cu.**

$$\frac{1 \text{ mol } e^-}{1 \text{ F}} \quad \frac{1 \text{ mol (Cu + Cd)}}{2 \text{ mol } e^-} \qquad\qquad\qquad\qquad\qquad\qquad \frac{1 \text{ mol Cu}}{63.55 \text{ g Cu}}$$

and g Cd $\rightarrow$ **mol Cd then solve for** $x = $ **g Cu** $\rightarrow$ **g** $CuSO_4$**.**

$$\frac{1 \text{ mol Cd}}{112.41 \text{ g Cd}} \qquad\qquad \frac{159.62 \text{ g } CuSO_4}{63.55 \text{ g Cu}}$$

Solution: $Cu^{2+}(aq) + 2e^- \rightarrow Cu(s)$ and $Cd^{2+}(aq) + 2e^- \rightarrow Cd(s)$, so $n = 2$ for both metals.

$$1.20 \text{ F} \times \frac{1 \text{ mole}^-}{1 \text{ F}} \times \frac{1 \text{ mol(Cu + Cd)}}{2 \text{ mole}^-} = 0.600 \text{ mol(Cu + Cd)} \text{ then let } x = \text{g Cu so that } (50.36 \text{ g} - x \text{ g}) = \text{g Cd}$$

then x g Cu $\times \dfrac{1 \text{ mol Cu}}{63.55 \text{ g Cu}} = \dfrac{x}{63.55}$ mol Cu and $(50.36 - x)$ g Cd $\times \dfrac{1 \text{ mol Cd}}{112.41 \text{ g Cd}} = \dfrac{(50.36 - x)}{112.41}$ mol Cd

then $0.600 \text{ mol(Cu + Cd)} = \dfrac{x}{63.55}$ mol Cu $+ \dfrac{(50.36 - x)}{112.41}$ mol Cd. Solve for x.

$$0.600 = 0.01573564x + 0.4480028 - 0.008896006x \rightarrow x = 22.2\underline{2}300 \text{ g Cu} \rightarrow$$

$$22.2\underline{2}300 \text{ g Cu} \times \frac{159.62 \text{ g CuSO}_4}{63.55 \text{ g Cu}} = 55.8 \text{ g CuSO}_4$$

Check: The units (g) are correct. The result is reasonable because 0.600 mol Cu = 38.1 g and 0.600 mol Cd = 67.4 g and the amount deposited is between the two values.

18.85 **Given:** $C_2O_4^{2-} \rightarrow CO_2$ and $MnO_4^-(aq) \rightarrow Mn^{2+}(aq)$, 50.1 mL of MnO_4^- to titrate 0.339 g $Na_2C_2O_4$, 4.62 g U sample titrated by 32.5 mL MnO_4^-; and $UO^{2+} \rightarrow UO_2^{2+}$ **Find:** percent U in sample

Conceptual Plan: Separate the overall reaction into two half-reactions: one for oxidation and one for reduction. → Balance each half-reaction with respect to mass in the following order: (1) Balance all elements other than H and O, (2) balance O by adding H_2O, and (3) balance H by adding H^+. → Balance each half-reaction with respect to charge by adding electrons. (The sum of the charges on both sides of the equation should be made equal by adding electrons as necessary.) → Make the number of electrons in both half-reactions equal by multiplying one or both half-reactions by a small whole number. → Add the two half-reactions together, canceling electrons and other species as necessary. → Verify that the reaction is balanced with respect to both mass and charge. Then

$$\text{mL MnO}_4^- \rightarrow \text{L MnO}_4^- \text{ and g Na}_2\text{C}_2\text{O}_4 \rightarrow \text{mol Na}_2\text{C}_2\text{O}_4 \rightarrow \text{mol MnO}_4^- \text{ then}$$

$$\frac{1 \text{ L MnO}_4^-}{1000 \text{ mL MnO}_4^-} \qquad \frac{1 \text{ mol Na}_2\text{C}_2\text{O}_4}{134.00 \text{ g Na}_2\text{C}_2\text{O}_4} \qquad \frac{2 \text{ mol MnO}_4^-}{5 \text{ mol Na}_2\text{C}_2\text{O}_4}$$

L MnO_4^-, mol $MnO_4^- \rightarrow$ M MnO_4^- then write U half-reactions and balance as above. →

$$M = \frac{\text{mol MnO}_4^-}{L}$$

Make the number of electrons in both half-reactions equal by multiplying one or both half-reactions by a small whole number. → Add the two half-reactions together, canceling electrons and other species as necessary. → Verify that the reaction is balanced with respect to both mass and charge. Then mL MnO_4^-, M $MnO_4^- \rightarrow$ mol $MnO_4^- \rightarrow$ mol U $\rightarrow$ g U then g U, g sample → % U.

$$M = \frac{\text{mol MnO}_4^-}{L} \qquad \frac{5 \text{ mol U}}{2 \text{ mol MnO}_4^-} \qquad \frac{238.03 \text{ g U}}{1 \text{ mol U}} \qquad \text{percent U} = \frac{\text{g U}}{\text{g sample}} \times 100\%$$

Solution:

Separate: $\qquad MnO_4^-(aq) \rightarrow Mn^{2+}(aq) \qquad$ and $\quad C_2O_4^{2-}(aq) \rightarrow CO_2(g)$

Balance non-H & O elements: $MnO_4^-(aq) \rightarrow Mn^{2+}(aq) \qquad$ and $\quad C_2O_4^{2-}(aq) \rightarrow 2 CO_2(g)$

Balance O with H_2O: $MnO_4^-(aq) \rightarrow Mn^{2+}(aq) + 4 H_2O(l) \quad$ and $\quad C_2O_4^{2-}(aq) \rightarrow 2 CO_2(g)$

Balance H with H^+: $MnO_4^-(aq) + 8 H^+(aq) \rightarrow Mn^{2+}(aq) + 4 H_2O(l)$ and $C_2O_4^{2-}(aq) \rightarrow 2 CO_2(g)$

Add electrons: $MnO_4^-(aq) + 8 H^+(aq) + 5 e^- \rightarrow Mn^{2+}(aq) + 4 H_2O(l)$ and $C_2O_4^{2-}(aq) \rightarrow 2 CO_2(g) + 2 e^-$

Equalize electrons:

$2 MnO_4^-(aq) + 16 H^+(aq) + 10 e^- \rightarrow 2 Mn^{2+}(aq) + 8 H_2O(l)$ and $5 C_2O_4^{2-}(aq) \rightarrow 10 CO_2(g) + 10 e^-$

Add half-reactions:

$2 MnO_4^-(aq) + 16 H^+(aq) + \cancel{10 e^-} + 5 C_2O_4^{2-}(aq) \rightarrow 2 Mn^{2+}(aq) + 8 H_2O(l) + 10 CO_2(g) + \cancel{10 e^-}$

Cancel electrons: $2 MnO_4^-(aq) + 16 H^+(aq) + 5 C_2O_4^{2-}(aq) \rightarrow 2 Mn^{2+}(aq) + 8 H_2O(l) + 10 CO_2(g)$

then $50.1 \text{ mL MnO}_4^- \times \dfrac{1 \text{ L MnO}_4^-}{1000 \text{ mL MnO}_4^-} = 0.0501 \text{ L MnO}_4^-$

$0.399 \text{ g Na}_2\text{C}_2\text{O}_4 \times \dfrac{1 \text{ mol Na}_2\text{C}_2\text{O}_4}{134.00 \text{ g Na}_2\text{C}_2\text{O}_4} \times \dfrac{2 \text{ mol MnO}_4^-}{5 \text{ mol Na}_2\text{C}_2\text{O}_4} = 0.001 1\underline{9}10448 \text{ mol MnO}_4^-$

$M = \dfrac{0.001 1\underline{9}10448 \text{ mol MnO}_4^-}{0.0501 \text{ L}} = 0.023\underline{7}73345 \text{ M MnO}_4^-$

Separate: $MnO_4^-(aq) \rightarrow Mn^{2+}(aq)$ and $UO^{2+}(aq) \rightarrow UO_2^{2+}(aq)$

Balance non-H & O elements: $MnO_4^-(aq) \rightarrow Mn^{2+}(aq)$ and $UO^{2+}(aq) \rightarrow UO_2^{2+}(aq)$

Balance O with H_2O: $MnO_4^-(aq) \rightarrow Mn^{2+}(aq) + 4\,H_2O(l)$ and $UO^{2+}(aq) + H_2O(l) \rightarrow UO_2^{2+}(aq)$

Balance H with H^+:

$MnO_4^-(aq) + 8\,H^+(aq) \rightarrow Mn^{2+}(aq) + 4\,H_2O(l)$ and $UO^{2+}(aq) + H_2O(l) \rightarrow UO_2^{2+}(aq) + 2\,H^+(aq)$

Add electrons: $MnO_4^-(aq) + 8\,H^+(aq) + 5\,e^- \rightarrow Mn^{2+}(aq) + 4\,H_2O(l)$ and

$$UO^{2+}(aq) + H_2O(l) \rightarrow UO_2^{2+}(aq) + 2\,H^+(aq) + 2\,e^-$$

Equalize electrons: $2\,MnO_4^-(aq) + 16\,H^+(aq) + 10\,e^- \rightarrow 2\,Mn^{2+}(aq) + 8\,H_2O(l)$ and

$$5\,UO^{2+}(aq) + 5\,H_2O(l) \rightarrow 5\,UO_2^{2+}(aq) + 10\,H^+(aq) + 10\,e^-$$

Add half-reactions: $2\,MnO_4^-(aq) + 6\,\cancel{16}H^+(aq) + \cancel{10\,e^-} + 5\,UO^{2+}(aq) + 5\cancel{H_2O(l)} \rightarrow$

$$2\,Mn^{2+}(aq) + 3\,\cancel{8}\,H_2O(l) + 5\,UO_2^{2+}(aq) + \cancel{10\,H^+(aq)} + \cancel{10\,e^-}$$

Cancel electrons & species:

$$2\,MnO_4^-(aq) + 6\,H^+(aq) + 5\,UO^{2+}(aq) \rightarrow 2\,Mn^{2+}(aq) + 3\,H_2O(l) + 5\,UO_2^{2+}(aq)$$

$$32.5 \text{ mL } \cancel{MnO_4} \times \frac{0.023773345 \text{ mol } \cancel{MnO_4}}{1000 \text{ mL } \cancel{MnO_4}} \times \frac{5 \text{ mol } \cancel{U}}{2 \text{ mol } \cancel{MnO_4}} \times \frac{238.03 \text{ g U}}{1 \text{ mol } \cancel{U}} = 0.459775\underline{0} \text{ g U then}$$

$$\text{percent U} = \frac{\text{g U}}{\text{g sample}} \times 100\% = \frac{0.459775\underline{0} \text{ g U}}{4.62 \text{ g sample}} \times 100\% = 9.95\%$$

Check: first reaction

Reactants	Products
2 Mn atoms	2 Mn atoms
28 O atoms	28 O atoms
16 H atoms	16 H atoms
10 C atoms	10 C atoms
+4 charge	+4 charge

second reaction

Reactants	Products
2 Mn atoms	2 Mn atoms
13 O atoms	13 O atoms
6 H atoms	6 H atoms
5 U atoms	5 U atoms
+14 charge	+14 charge

The reactions are balanced. The units (%) are correct. The percentage is between 0 and 100%.

18.86   **Given:** 1.25 L of a 0.552 M HBr solution, convert H^+ to $H_2(g)$ for 73 minutes at 11.32 A   **Find:** pH

Conceptual Plan: min $\rightarrow$ s $\rightarrow$ C $\rightarrow$ mol e^- $\rightarrow$ mol H^+ consumed and L, M $\rightarrow$ mol H^+ initially then

$$\frac{60 \text{ s}}{1 \text{ min}} \quad \frac{11.32 \text{ C}}{1 \text{ s}} \quad \frac{1 \text{ mol } e^-}{96{,}485 \text{ C}} \quad \frac{2 \text{ mol } H^+}{2 \text{ mol } e^-} \qquad\qquad M = \frac{\text{mol}}{L}$$

mol H^+ initially, mol H^+ consumed $\rightarrow$ mol H^+ remaining then mol H^+ remaining, L $\rightarrow$ $[H^+]$ $\rightarrow$ pH

mol H^+ initially $-$ mol H^+ consumed $=$ mol H^+ remaining $M = \frac{\text{mol}}{L}$ $pH = -\log [H^+]$

Solution: $2\,H^+(aq) + 2\,e^- \rightarrow H_2(g)$

$$73 \text{ min} \times \frac{60 \text{ s}}{1 \text{ min}} \times \frac{11.32 \text{ C}}{1 \text{ s}} \times \frac{1 \text{ mol } e^-}{96{,}485 \text{ C}} \times \frac{2 \text{ mol } H^+}{2 \text{ mol } e^-} = 0.51\underline{3}879 \text{ mol } H^+ \text{ consumed and}$$

$$1.25 \text{ L } H^+ \times \frac{0.552 \text{ mol } H^+}{1 \text{ L } H^+} = 0.690 \text{ mol } H^+ \text{ then mol } H^+ \text{ initially} - \text{mol } H^+ \text{ consumed} =$$

mol H^+ remaining $= 0.690 \text{ mol } H^+$ initially $- 0.51\underline{3}879 \text{ mol } H^+$ consumed $= 0.1\underline{7}612 \text{ mol } H^+$ remaining

then $[H^+] = \dfrac{0.1\underline{7}612 \text{ mol } H^+}{1.25 \text{ L}} = 0.1\underline{4}0896 \text{ M } H^+$ then $pH = -\log [H^+] = -\log 0.1\underline{4}0896 = 0.85$

Check: The units (none) are correct. The result is a pH higher than the initial pH ($-\log(0.552) = 0.258$), as expected.

18.87   **Given:** 215 mL of a 0.500 M NaCl solution, initially at pH $= 7.00$; after 15 minutes, a 10.0 mL aliquot is titrated with 22.8 mL 0.100 M HCl   **Find:** current (A)

Conceptual Plan: Titration is neutralizing base generated in the hydrolysis, so

mL HCl, M HCl, mL aliquot $\rightarrow$ mol OH^- in aliquot $\rightarrow$ mol OH^- in solution then min $\rightarrow$ s then

$$M_{Acid}V_{Acid} = M_{Base}V_{Base} \qquad\qquad M_1V_1 = M_2V_2 \qquad\qquad \frac{1 \text{ min}}{60 \text{ s}}$$

mol OH^- in solution, s → mol e^-/s → C/s.

$$\frac{2\ mol\ e^-}{2\ mol\ OH^-} \qquad \frac{96,485\ C}{1\ mol\ e^-}$$

Solution: $2\ NaCl(aq) + 2\ H_2O(l) \rightarrow H_2(g) + Cl_2(g) + 2\ Na^+(aq) + 2\ OH^-(aq)$

$M_{Acid}V_{Acid} = M_{Base}V_{Base}$ so $22.8\ mL\ HCl \times \dfrac{0.100\ mol\ HCl}{1000\ mL\ HCl} \times \dfrac{1\ mol\ OH^-}{1\ mol\ HCl} = 0.00228\ mol\ OH^-$

$0.00228\ mol\ OH^-$ in aliquot $\times \dfrac{215\ mL}{10.0\ mL} = 0.04902\ mol\ OH^-$ in solution

$\dfrac{0.04902\ mol\ OH^-\ in\ solution}{15\ min} \times \dfrac{1\ min}{60\ s} \times \dfrac{2\ mol\ e^-}{2\ mol\ OH^-} \times \dfrac{96,485\ C}{1\ mol\ e^-} = 5.2552\ \dfrac{C}{s} = 5.3\ A$

Check: The units (A) are correct. The current is reasonable for an electrolysis process.

18.88   **Given:** MnO_2/Mn^{2+} electrode at pH 10.24   **Find:** $[Mn^{2+}]$ to get half-cell potential = 0.00 V

Conceptual Plan: pH → $[H^+]$ then write half-cell reactions and look up half-reactions in Table 18.1.

$$pH = -\log [H^+]$$

Define Q based on half-cell reaction. Then $E^\circ_{\text{half-cell}}, n, [H^+] \rightarrow [Mn^{2+}]$.

$$E_{\text{half-cell}} = E^\circ_{\text{half-cell}} - \frac{0.0592\ V}{n} \log Q$$

Solution: Because $pH = -\log [H^+]$, $[H^+] = 10^{-pH} = 10^{-10.24} = 5.75440 \times 10^{-11}$ M

$MnO_2(s) + 4\ H^+(aq) + 2\ e^- \rightarrow Mn^{2+}(aq) + 2\ H_2O(l)$ $E^\circ_{\text{half-cell}} = 1.21$ V, $n = 2$, and $Q = \dfrac{[Mn^{2+}]}{[H^+]^4}$.

$E_{\text{half-cell}} = E^\circ_{\text{half-cell}} - \dfrac{0.0592\ V}{n} \log Q$, so $0.00\ V = 1.21\ V - \dfrac{0.0592\ V}{2} \log \dfrac{[Mn^{2+}]}{(5.75440 \times 10^{-11})^4} \rightarrow$

$1.21\ V = \dfrac{0.0592\ V}{2} \log \dfrac{[Mn^{2+}]}{(5.75440 \times 10^{-11})^4} \rightarrow 40.8784 = \log \dfrac{[Mn^{2+}]}{(5.75440 \times 10^{-11})^4} \rightarrow$

$\dfrac{[Mn^{2+}]}{(5.75440 \times 10^{-11})^4} = 10^{40.8784} = 7.55788 \times 10^{40} \rightarrow [Mn^{2+}] = 0.828705\ M = 0.83\ M\ Mn^{2+}$

Check: The units (M) are correct. The standard half-cell potential is very large and positive. Most of the shift toward 0.00 V is due to the fourth-order dependence in $[H^+]$ at a high pH; so the $[Mn^{2+}]$ is close to 1 M. So the concentration is reasonable.

18.89   **Given:** SHE   **Find:** pH to get half-cell potential = −0.122 V

Conceptual Plan: Write the half-cell reaction. The standard half-cell potential is 0.00 V. Define Q based on half-cell reaction. Then $E^\circ_{\text{half-cell}}, n \quad \rightarrow \quad [H^+] \quad \rightarrow \quad$ pH.

$$E_{\text{half-cell}} = E^\circ_{\text{half-cell}} - \frac{0.0592\ V}{n} \log Q \qquad pH = -\log [H^+]$$

Solution: $2\ H^+(aq) + 2\ e^- \rightarrow H_2(g)$ $E^\circ_{\text{half-cell}} = 0.00$ V, $n = 2$, and $Q = \dfrac{1}{[H^+]^2}$.

$E_{\text{half-cell}} = E^\circ_{\text{half-cell}} - \dfrac{0.0592\ V}{n} \log Q$, so $-0.122\ V = 0.00\ V - \dfrac{0.0592\ V}{2} \log [H^+]^{-2} \rightarrow$

$4.12162 = \log [H^+]^{-2} \rightarrow [H^+]^{-2} = 10^{4.12162} = 1.32318 \times 10^4 \rightarrow [H^+] = 0.00869342$ M

$pH = -\log [H^+] = -\log(0.00869342) = 2.06081 = 2.06$

Check: The units (none) are correct. There is an inverse second-order dependence in $[H^+]$, so we expect an acidic pH.

Conceptual Problems

18.90   (a)   If E°cell > 0 then the reaction is spontaneous under standard conditions and K > 1. If E°_{cell} > 0 and

$E_{\text{cell}} = E^\circ_{\text{cell}} - \dfrac{0.0592\ V}{n} \log Q < 0$, the second term dominates and is negative. This means that $Q > K$.

The value of K is dependent on the standard cell potential, which is greater than zero (or positive). Therefore the reaction is spontaneous under normal conditions and K > 1.

18.91   (a) . Looking for anion reductions that are between the reduction potentials of Cl_2 and Br_2. The only one that meets that criterion is the dichromate ion.

18.92   (b)   If the free energy change is negative, this is a spontaneous reaction. This translates to a positive cell potential and a large equilibrium constant.

18.93   Since $K < 1$, the reaction must be nonspontaneous under standard conditions. Therefore, E°_{cell} is negative and ΔG°_{rxn} is positive.

Questions for Group Work

18.94   **Conceptual Plan: Separate the overall reaction into two half-reactions: one for oxidation and one for reduction. → Balance each half-reaction with respect to mass in the following order: (1) balance all elements other than H and O; (2) balance O by adding H_2O; and (3) balance H by adding H^+. → Balance each half-reaction with respect to charge by adding electrons. (The sum of the charges on both sides of the equation should be made equal by adding electrons as necessary.) → Make the number of electrons in both half-reactions equal by multiplying one or both half-reactions by a small whole number. → Add the two half-reactions together, canceling electrons and other species as necessary. → In basic solutions, neutralize H^+ by adding enough OH^- to neutralize each H^+, adding the same number of OH^- ions to each side of the equation. → Verify that the reaction is balanced both with respect to mass and with respect to charge.**
Solution:

(a)   Separate (split cation and anion in salt): $Fe\,(s) \rightarrow Fe^{2+}(s)$ and $I_2(s) \rightarrow I^-(s)$

         Balance elements: $Fe\,(s) \rightarrow Fe^{2+}(s)$ and $I_2(s) \rightarrow 2\,I^-(s)$

         Add electrons: $Fe\,(s) \rightarrow Fe^{2+}(s) + 2\,e^-$ and $I_2(s) + 2\,e^- \rightarrow 2\,I^-(s)$

         Equalize electrons: $Fe\,(s) \rightarrow Fe^{2+}(s) + 2\,e^-$ and $I_2(s) + 2\,e^- \rightarrow 2\,I^-(s)$

         Add half-reactions: $I_2\,(s) + 2\,e^- + Fe\,(s) \rightarrow Fe^{2+}(s) + 2\,e^- + 2\,I^-\,(s)$

         Cancel electrons (and recombine salt): $I_2\,(s) + Fe\,(s) + FeI_2\,(s)$

Check:	Reactants	Products
	2 I atoms	2 I atoms
	1 Fe atom	1 Fe atom
	0 charge	0 charge

(b)   Separate: $H_2O_2(aq) \rightarrow O_2(g)$ and $Cl_2(g) \rightarrow Cl^-(aq)$

         Balance non-H & O elements: $H_2O_2(aq) \rightarrow O_2(g)$ and $Cl_2(g) \rightarrow 2\,Cl^-(aq)$

         Balance H with H^+: $H_2O_2(aq) \rightarrow O_2(g) + 2\,H^+(aq)$ and $Cl_2(g) \rightarrow 2\,Cl^-(aq)$

         Add electrons: $H_2O_2(aq) \rightarrow O_2(g) + 2\,H^+(aq) + 2\,e^-$ and $Cl_2(g) + 2\,e^- \rightarrow 2\,Cl^-(aq)$

         Equalize electrons: $H_2O_2(aq) \rightarrow O_2(g) + 2\,H^+(aq) + 2\,e^-$ and $Cl_2(g) + 2\,e^- \rightarrow 2\,Cl^-(aq)$

         Add half-reactions: $H_2O_2(aq) + Cl_2(g) + 2\,e^- \rightarrow O_2(g) + 2\,H^+(aq) + 2\,e^- + 2\,Cl^-(aq)$

         Cancel electrons: $H_2O_2(aq) + Cl_2(g) \rightarrow O_2(g) + 2\,H^+(aq) + 2\,Cl^-(aq)$

Check:	Reactants	Products
	2 H atoms	2 H atoms
	2 O atoms	2 O atoms
	2 Cl atoms	2 Cl atoms
	0 charge	0 charge

(c)   Separate: $H_2(g) \rightarrow H_2O(l)$ and $Hg^{2+}(aq) \rightarrow Hg(l)$

         Balance non-H & O elements: $H_2(g) \rightarrow H_2O(l)$ and $Hg^{2+}(aq) \rightarrow Hg(l)$

         Balance O with H_2O: $H_2(g) + H_2O(l) \rightarrow H_2O(l)$ and $Hg^{2+}(aq) \rightarrow Hg(l)$

         Balance H with H^+: $H_2(g) + H_2O(l) \rightarrow H_2O(l) + 2\,H^+(aq)$ and $Hg^{2+}(aq) \rightarrow Hg(l)$

         Neutralize H^+ with OH^-:

              $H_2(g) + \cancel{H_2O}(l) + 2\,OH^-(aq) \rightarrow \cancel{H_2O}(l) + \underbrace{2\,H^+(aq) + 2\,OH^-(aq)}_{2\,H_2O(l)}$ and $Hg^{2+}(aq) \rightarrow Hg(l)$

Add electrons: $H_2(g) + 2\ OH^-(aq) \rightarrow 2\ H_2O(l) + 2\ e^-$ and $Hg^{2+}(aq) + 2\ e^- \rightarrow Hg(l)$

Equalize electrons: $H_2(g) + 2\ OH^-(aq) \rightarrow 2\ H_2O(l) + 2\ e^-$ and $Hg^{2+}(aq) + 2\ e^- \rightarrow Hg(l)$

Add half-reactions: $H_2(g) + 2\ OH^-(aq) + Hg^{2+}(aq) + 2\ e^- \rightarrow 2\ H_2O(l) + 2\ e^- + Hg(l)$

Cancel electrons: $H_2(g) + 2\ OH^-(aq) + Hg^{2+}(aq) \rightarrow 2\ H_2O(l) + Hg(l)$

Check:	Reactants	Products
	4 H atoms	4 H atoms
	2 O atoms	2 O atoms
	1 Hg atom	1 Hg atom
	0 charge	0 charge

(d)　Separate: 　　　　　　　　　　$CH_3OH(l) \rightarrow CO_2(g)$ 　　and　$O_2(g) \rightarrow H_2O(l)$

Balance non-H & O elements: $CH_3OH(l) \rightarrow CO_2(g)$ 　　and　$O_2(g) \rightarrow H_2O(l)$

Balance O with H_2O: 　　　　$CH_3OH(l) + H_2O(l) \rightarrow CO_2(g)$ 　and　$O_2(g) \rightarrow 2\ H_2O(l)$

Balance H with H^+: $CH_3OH(l) + H_2O(l) \rightarrow CO_2(g) + 6\ H^+(aq)$ and $O_2(g) + 4\ H^+(aq) \rightarrow 2\ H_2O(l)$

Add electrons: $CH_3OH(l) + H_2O(l) \rightarrow CO_2(g) + 6\ H^+(aq) + 6\ e^-$ and $O_2(g) + 4\ H^+(aq) + 4\ e^- \rightarrow 2\ H_2O(l)$

Equalize electrons:

　$2\ CH_3OH(l) + 2\ H_2O(l) \rightarrow 2\ CO_2(g) + 12\ H^+(aq) + 12\ e^-$ and $3\ O_2(g) + 12\ H^+(aq) + 12\ e^- \rightarrow 6\ H_2O(l)$

Add half-reactions:

　$2\ CH_3OH(l) + 2\ H_2O(l) + 3\ O_2(g) + 12\ H^+(aq) + 12\ e^- \rightarrow 2\ CO_2(g) + 12\ H^+(aq) + 12\ e^- + 4\!6\ H_2O(l)$

Cancel electrons and others: $2\ CH_3OH(l) + 3\ O_2(g) \rightarrow 2\ CO_2(g) + 4\ H_2O(l)$

Check:	Reactants	Products
	2 C atoms	2 C atoms
	8 H atoms	8 H atoms
	8 O atoms	8 O atoms
	0 charge	0 charge

18.95　Choose any two half-reaction from Table 18.1 and follow the conceptual plan in Problem 18.17 to get a positive cell potential.

18.96　Using the cell potential from Problem 18.95, use the conceptual plan outlined in Problems 18.29–18.34. All of the examples should have $\Delta G° < 0$, $K > 1$, and $E°_{cell} > 0$ for a spontaneous process under standard conditions.

18.97　Specific answer will vary. In general, a device could have a known cell as one half-reaction, and the unknown copper sample as the other half cell. $E_{cell} = E°_{cell} + RT \ln Q$ can be solved for the unknown Cu^{2+}. 1 mV uncertainty in voltage may correspond to approximately 1×10^{-6} M uncertainty in concentration.

18.98　The reaction at the anode is: $2\ CH_3OH(l) + 2\ H_2O(l) \rightarrow 12\ H^+(aq) + 12\ e^- + 2\ CO_2(g)$; the reaction at the cathode is: $3\ O_2(g) + 12\ H^+(aq) + 12\ e^- \rightarrow 6\ H_2O(l)$; and the overall reaction is: $2\ CH_3OH(aq) + 3\ O_2(g) \rightarrow 2\ CO_2(g) + 4\ H_2O(l)$ (This reaction was balanced in Problem 18.94(d).)

The standard cell potential is 1.18 V (Lamy, H., Leger, J.-M. and Srinivasan, S. (2000), "Direct methanol fuel cells—from a 20th-century electrochemists' dream to a 21st century emerging technology," in *Modern Aspects of Electrochemistry*, 34 (eds J.O.M. Bockris and B.E. Conway), Plenum Press, New York, Ch 3, p. 53).

$$0.792\ \text{kg } CH_3OH \times \frac{1000\ \text{g } CH_3OH}{1\ \text{kg } CH_3OH} \times \frac{1\ \text{mol } CH_3OH}{32.04\ \text{g } CH_3OH} \times \frac{12\ \text{mol } e^-}{2\ \text{mol } CH_3OH} \times \frac{96{,}485\ C}{1\ \text{mol } e^-} \times \frac{1.18\ J}{1\ C} \times \frac{1\ \text{kWh}}{3.60 \times 10^6\ J}$$

$= 4.69$ kWh

19 Radioactivity and Nuclear Chemistry

Radioactive Decay and Nuclide Stability

19.1 **Conceptual Plan:** Begin with the symbol for a parent nuclide on the left side of the equation and the symbol for a particle on the right side (except for electron capture). → Equalize the sum of the mass numbers and the sum of the atomic numbers on both sides of the equation by writing the appropriate mass number and atomic number for the unknown daughter nuclide. → Using the periodic table, deduce the identity of the unknown daughter nuclide from the atomic number and write its symbol.

Solution:

(a) U-234 (alpha decay) $^{234}_{92}\text{U} \rightarrow {}^{?}_{?}? + {}^{4}_{2}\text{He}$ then $^{234}_{92}\text{U} \rightarrow {}^{230}_{90}? + {}^{4}_{2}\text{He}$ then $^{234}_{92}\text{U} \rightarrow {}^{230}_{90}\text{Th} + {}^{4}_{2}\text{He}$

(b) Th-230 (alpha decay) $^{230}_{90}\text{Th} \rightarrow {}^{?}_{?}? + {}^{4}_{2}\text{He}$ then $^{230}_{90}\text{Th} \rightarrow {}^{226}_{88}? + {}^{4}_{2}\text{He}$ then $^{230}_{90}\text{Th} \rightarrow {}^{226}_{88}\text{Ra} + {}^{4}_{2}\text{He}$

(c) Pb-214 (beta decay) $^{214}_{82}\text{Pb} \rightarrow {}^{?}_{?}? + {}^{0}_{-1}\text{e}$ then $^{214}_{82}\text{Pb} \rightarrow {}^{214}_{83}? + {}^{0}_{-1}\text{e}$ then $^{214}_{82}\text{Pb} \rightarrow {}^{214}_{83}\text{Bi} + {}^{0}_{-1}\text{e}$

(d) N-13 (positron emission) $^{13}_{7}\text{N} \rightarrow {}^{?}_{?}? + {}^{0}_{+1}\text{e}$ then $^{13}_{7}\text{N} \rightarrow {}^{13}_{6}? + {}^{0}_{+1}\text{e}$ then $^{13}_{7}\text{N} \rightarrow {}^{13}_{6}\text{C} + {}^{0}_{+1}\text{e}$

(e) Cr-51 (electron capture) $^{51}_{24}\text{C} + {}^{0}_{-1}\text{e} \rightarrow {}^{?}_{?}?$ then $^{51}_{24}\text{Cr} + {}^{0}_{-1}\text{e} \rightarrow {}^{51}_{23}?$ then $^{51}_{24}\text{Cr} + {}^{0}_{-1}\text{e} \rightarrow {}^{51}_{23}\text{V}$

Check: (a) $234 = 230 + 4$, $92 = 90 + 2$, and thorium is atomic number 90. (b) $230 = 226 + 4$, $90 = 88 + 2$, and radium is atomic number 88. (c) $214 = 214 + 0$, $82 = 83 - 1$, and bismuth is atomic number 83. (d) $13 = 13 + 0$, $7 = 6 + 1$, and carbon is atomic number 6. (e) $51 + 0 = 51$, $24 - 1 = 23$, and vanadium is atomic number 23.

19.2 **Conceptual Plan:** Begin with the symbol for a parent nuclide on the left side of the equation and the symbol for a particle on the right side (except for electron capture). → Equalize the sum of the mass numbers and the sum of the atomic numbers on both sides of the equation by writing the appropriate mass number and atomic number for the unknown daughter nuclide. → Using the periodic table, deduce the identity of the unknown daughter nuclide from the atomic number and write its symbol.

Solution:

(a) Po-210 (alpha decay) $^{210}_{84}\text{Po} \rightarrow {}^{?}_{?}? + {}^{4}_{2}\text{He}$ then $^{210}_{84}\text{Po} \rightarrow {}^{206}_{82}? + {}^{4}_{2}\text{He}$ then $^{210}_{84}\text{Po} \rightarrow {}^{206}_{82}\text{Pb} + {}^{4}_{2}\text{He}$

(b) Ac-227 (beta decay) $^{227}_{89}\text{Ac} \rightarrow {}^{?}_{?}? + {}^{0}_{-1}\text{e}$ then $^{227}_{89}\text{Ac} \rightarrow {}^{227}_{90}? + {}^{0}_{-1}\text{e}$ then $^{227}_{89}\text{Ac} \rightarrow {}^{227}_{90}\text{Th} + {}^{0}_{-1}\text{e}$

(c) Tl-207 (beta decay) $^{207}_{81}\text{Tl} \rightarrow {}^{?}_{?}? + {}^{0}_{-1}\text{e}$ then $^{207}_{81}\text{Tl} \rightarrow {}^{207}_{82}? + {}^{0}_{-1}\text{e}$ then $^{207}_{81}\text{Tl} \rightarrow {}^{207}_{82}\text{Pb} + {}^{0}_{-1}\text{e}$

(d) O-15 (positron emission) $^{15}_{8}\text{O} \rightarrow {}^{?}_{?}? + {}^{0}_{+1}\text{e}$ then $^{15}_{8}\text{O} \rightarrow {}^{15}_{7}? + {}^{0}_{+1}\text{e}$ then $^{15}_{8}\text{O} \rightarrow {}^{15}_{7}\text{N} + {}^{0}_{+1}\text{e}$

(e) Pd-103 (electron capture) $^{103}_{46}\text{Pd} + {}^{0}_{-1}\text{e} \rightarrow {}^{?}_{?}?$ then $^{103}_{46}\text{Pd} + {}^{0}_{-1}\text{e} \rightarrow {}^{103}_{45}?$ then $^{103}_{46}\text{Pd} + {}^{0}_{-1}\text{e} \rightarrow {}^{103}_{45}\text{Rh}$

Check: (a) $210 = 206 + 4$, $84 = 82 + 2$, and lead is atomic number 82. (b) $227 = 227 + 0$, $89 = 90 - 1$, and thorium is atomic number 90. (c) $207 = 207 + 0$, $81 = 82 - 1$, and lead is atomic number 82. (d) $15 = 15 + 0$, $8 = 7 + 1$, and nitrogen is atomic number 7. (e) $103 + 0 = 103$, $46 - 1 = 45$, and rhodium is atomic number 45.

19.3 **Given:** Th-232 decay series: $\alpha, \beta, \beta, \alpha$ **Find:** balanced decay reactions
Conceptual Plan: Begin with the symbol for a parent nuclide on the left side of the equation and the symbol for a particle on the right side. → Equalize the sum of the mass numbers and the sum of the atomic numbers on both sides of the equation by writing the appropriate mass number and atomic number for the unknown daughter nuclide. → Using the periodic table, deduce the identity of the unknown daughter nuclide from the atomic number and write its symbol. → Use the product of this reaction to write the next reaction.

Solution:

Th-232 (alpha decay) $^{232}_{90}\text{Th} \rightarrow\ ^{?}_{?}? + ^{4}_{2}\text{He}$ then $^{232}_{90}\text{Th} \rightarrow\ ^{228}_{88}? + ^{4}_{2}\text{He}$ then $^{232}_{90}\text{Th} \rightarrow\ ^{228}_{88}\text{Ra} + ^{4}_{2}\text{He}$

Ra-228 (beta decay) $^{228}_{88}\text{Ra} \rightarrow\ ^{?}_{?}? + ^{0}_{-1}\text{e}$ then $^{228}_{88}\text{Ra} \rightarrow\ ^{228}_{89}? + ^{0}_{-1}\text{e}$ then $^{228}_{88}\text{Ra} \rightarrow\ ^{228}_{89}\text{Ac} + ^{0}_{-1}\text{e}$

Ac-228 (beta decay) $^{228}_{89}\text{Ac} \rightarrow\ ^{?}_{?}? + ^{0}_{-1}\text{e}$ then $^{228}_{89}\text{Ac} \rightarrow\ ^{228}_{90}? + ^{0}_{-1}\text{e}$ then $^{228}_{89}\text{Ac} \rightarrow\ ^{228}_{90}\text{Th} + ^{0}_{-1}\text{e}$

Th-228 (alpha decay) $^{228}_{90}\text{Th} \rightarrow\ ^{?}_{?}? + ^{4}_{2}\text{He}$ then $^{228}_{90}\text{Th} \rightarrow\ ^{224}_{88}? + ^{4}_{2}\text{He}$ then $^{228}_{90}\text{Th} \rightarrow\ ^{224}_{88}\text{Ra} + ^{4}_{2}\text{He}$

Thus, the decay series is $^{232}_{90}\text{Th} \rightarrow\ ^{228}_{88}\text{Ra} + ^{4}_{2}\text{He},\ ^{228}_{88}\text{Ra} \rightarrow\ ^{228}_{89}\text{Ac} + ^{0}_{-1}\text{e},\ ^{228}_{89}\text{Ac} \rightarrow\ ^{228}_{90}\text{Th} + ^{0}_{-1}\text{e}$, $^{228}_{90}\text{Th} \rightarrow\ ^{224}_{88}\text{Ra} + ^{4}_{2}\text{He}$.

Check: $232 = 228 + 4, 90 = 88 + 2$, and radium is atomic number 88. $228 = 228 + 0, 88 = 89 - 1$, and actinium is atomic number 89. $228 = 228 + 0, 89 = 90 - 1$, and thorium is atomic number 90. $228 = 224 + 4, 90 = 88 + 2$, and radium is atomic number 88.

19.4   **Given:** Rn-220 decay series: $\alpha, \alpha, \beta, \alpha$ **Find:** balanced decay reactions
Conceptual Plan: Begin with the symbol for a parent nuclide on the left side of the equation and the symbol for a particle on the right side. → Equalize the sum of the mass numbers and the sum of the atomic numbers on both sides of the equation by writing the appropriate mass number and atomic number for the unknown daughter nuclide. → Using the periodic table, deduce the identity of the unknown daughter nuclide from the atomic number and write its symbol. → Use the product of this reaction to write the next reaction.
Solution:

Rn-220 (alpha decay) $^{220}_{86}\text{Rn} \rightarrow\ ^{?}_{?}? + ^{4}_{2}\text{He}$ then $^{220}_{86}\text{Rn} \rightarrow\ ^{216}_{84}? + ^{4}_{2}\text{He}$ then $^{220}_{86}\text{Rn} \rightarrow\ ^{216}_{84}\text{Po} + ^{4}_{2}\text{He}$

Po-216 (alpha decay) $^{216}_{84}\text{Po} \rightarrow\ ^{?}_{?}? + ^{4}_{2}\text{He}$ then $^{216}_{84}\text{Po} \rightarrow\ ^{212}_{82}? + ^{4}_{2}\text{He}$ then $^{216}_{84}\text{Po} \rightarrow\ ^{212}_{82}\text{Pb} + ^{4}_{2}\text{He}$

Pb-212 (beta decay) $^{212}_{82}\text{Pb} \rightarrow\ ^{?}_{?}? + ^{0}_{-1}\text{e}$ then $^{212}_{82}\text{Pb} \rightarrow\ ^{212}_{83}? + ^{0}_{-1}\text{e}$ then $^{212}_{82}\text{Pb} \rightarrow\ ^{212}_{83}\text{Bi} + ^{0}_{-1}\text{e}$

Bi-212 (alpha decay) $^{212}_{83}\text{Bi} \rightarrow\ ^{?}_{?}? + ^{4}_{2}\text{He}$ then $^{212}_{83}\text{Bi} \rightarrow\ ^{208}_{81}? + ^{4}_{2}\text{He}$ then $^{212}_{83}\text{Bi} \rightarrow\ ^{208}_{81}\text{Tl} + ^{4}_{2}\text{He}$

Thus, the decay series is $^{220}_{86}\text{Rn} \rightarrow\ ^{216}_{84}\text{Po} + ^{4}_{2}\text{He},\ ^{216}_{84}\text{Po} \rightarrow\ ^{212}_{82}\text{Pb} + ^{4}_{2}\text{He},\ ^{212}_{82}\text{Pb} \rightarrow\ ^{212}_{83}\text{Bi} + ^{0}_{-1}\text{e},\ ^{212}_{83}\text{Bi} \rightarrow\ ^{208}_{81}\text{Tl} + ^{4}_{2}\text{He}$.

Check: $220 = 216 + 4, 86 = 84 + 2$, and polonium is atomic number 84. $216 = 212 + 4, 84 = 82 + 2$, and lead is atomic number 82. $212 = 212 + 0, 82 = 83 - 1$, and bismuth is atomic number 83. $212 = 208 + 4, 83 = 81 + 2$, and thallium is atomic number 81.

19.5   **Conceptual Plan: Equalize the sum of the mass numbers and the sum of the atomic numbers on both sides of the equation by writing the appropriate mass number and atomic number for the unknown species. → Using the periodic table and the list of particles, deduce the identity of the unknown species from the atomic number and write its symbol.**
Solution:

(a) $^{?}_{?}? \rightarrow\ ^{217}_{85}\text{At} + ^{4}_{2}\text{He}$ becomes $^{221}_{87}? \rightarrow\ ^{217}_{85}\text{At} + ^{4}_{2}\text{He}$ then $^{221}_{87}\text{Fr} \rightarrow\ ^{217}_{85}\text{At} + ^{4}_{2}\text{He}$

(b) $^{241}_{94}\text{Pu} \rightarrow\ ^{241}_{95}\text{Am} + ^{?}_{?}?$ becomes $^{241}_{94}\text{Pu} \rightarrow\ ^{241}_{95}\text{Am} + ^{0}_{-1}?$ then $^{241}_{94}\text{Pu} \rightarrow\ ^{241}_{95}\text{Am} + ^{0}_{-1}\text{e}$

(c) $^{19}_{11}\text{Na} \rightarrow\ ^{19}_{10}\text{Ne} + ^{?}_{?}?$ becomes $^{19}_{11}\text{Na} \rightarrow\ ^{19}_{10}\text{Ne} + ^{0}_{+1}?$ then $^{19}_{11}\text{Na} \rightarrow\ ^{19}_{10}\text{Ne} + ^{0}_{+1}\text{e}$

(d) $^{75}_{34}\text{Se} + ^{?}_{?}? \rightarrow\ ^{75}_{33}\text{As}$ becomes $^{75}_{34}\text{Se} + ^{0}_{-1}? \rightarrow\ ^{75}_{33}\text{As}$ then $^{75}_{34}\text{Se} + ^{0}_{-1}\text{e} \rightarrow\ ^{75}_{33}\text{As}$

Check: (a) $221 = 217 + 4, 87 = 85 + 2$, and francium is atomic number 87. (b) $241 = 241 + 0, 94 = 95 - 1$, and the particle is a beta particle. (c) $19 = 19 + 0, 11 = 10 + 1$, and the particle is a positron. (d) $75 = 75 + 0, 34 - 1 = 33$, and the particle is an electron.

19.6   **Conceptual Plan: Equalize the sum of the mass numbers and the sum of the atomic numbers on both sides of the equation by writing the appropriate mass number and atomic number for the unknown species. → Using the periodic table and the list of particles, deduce the identity of the unknown species from the atomic number and write its symbol.**
Solution:

(a) $^{241}_{95}\text{Am} \rightarrow\ ^{237}_{93}\text{Np} + ^{?}_{?}?$ becomes $^{241}_{95}\text{Am} \rightarrow\ ^{237}_{93}\text{Np} + ^{4}_{2}?$ then $^{241}_{95}\text{Am} \rightarrow\ ^{237}_{93}\text{Np} + ^{4}_{2}\text{He}$

(b) $^{?}_{?}? \rightarrow\ ^{233}_{92}\text{U} + ^{0}_{-1}\text{e}$ becomes $^{233}_{91}? \rightarrow\ ^{233}_{92}\text{U} + ^{0}_{-1}\text{e}$ then $^{233}_{91}\text{Pa} \rightarrow\ ^{233}_{92}\text{U} + ^{0}_{-1}\text{e}$

(c) $^{237}_{93}\text{Np} \rightarrow\ ^{?}_{?}? + ^{4}_{2}\text{He}$ becomes $^{237}_{93}\text{Np} \rightarrow\ ^{233}_{91}? + ^{4}_{2}\text{He}$ then $^{237}_{93}\text{Np} \rightarrow\ ^{233}_{91}\text{Pa} + ^{4}_{2}\text{He}$

(d) $^{75}_{35}\text{Br} \rightarrow\ ^{?}_{?}? + ^{0}_{+1}\text{e}$ becomes $^{75}_{35}\text{Br} \rightarrow\ ^{75}_{34}? + ^{0}_{+1}\text{e}$ then $^{75}_{35}\text{Br} \rightarrow\ ^{75}_{34}\text{Se} + ^{0}_{+1}\text{e}$

Check: (a) $241 = 237 + 4, 95 = 93 + 2$, and the particle is an alpha particle. (b) $233 = 233 + 0, 91 = 92 - 1$, and protactinium is atomic number 91. (c) $237 = 233 + 4, 93 = 91 + 2$, and protactinium is atomic number 91. (d) $75 = 75 + 0, 35 = 34 + 1$, and selenium is atomic number 34.

19.7 (a) Mg-26: stable, N/Z ratio is close to 1, acceptable for low Z atoms

(b) Ne-25: not stable, N/Z ratio is much too high for low Z atom

(c) Co-51: not stable, N/Z ratio is less than 1, much too low

(d) Te-124: stable, N/Z ratio is acceptable for this Z

19.8 (a) Ti-48: stable, N/Z ratio is acceptable for this Z

(b) Cr-63: not stable, N/Z ratio is much too high for this Z

(c) Sn-102: not stable, N/Z ratio is close to 1, much too low for this Z

(d) Y-88: stable, N/Z ratio is acceptable for this Z

19.9 Sc, V, and Mn each have an odd number of protons. Atoms with an odd number of protons typically have fewer stable isotopes than those with an even number of protons.

19.10 Both aluminum and sodium, which have fewer stable isotopes, have an odd Z. Both of these atoms are small Z atoms, so the N/Z should be close to 1. Only one option meets both criteria for aluminum and sodium. Neon and magnesium have an even Z, so they have more options for stable isotopes.

19.11 (a) Mo-109, $N = 67$, $Z = 42$, $N/Z = 1.6$, beta decay, because N/Z is too high

(b) Ru-90, $N = 46$, $Z = 44$, $N/Z = 1.0$, positron emission, because N/Z is too low

(c) P-27, $N = 12$, $Z = 15$, $N/Z = 0.8$, positron emission, because N/Z is too low

(d) Rn-196, $N = 110$, $Z = 86$, $N/Z = 1.3$, positron emission, because N/Z is too low

19.12 (a) Sb-132, $N = 81$, $Z = 51$, $N/Z = 1.6$, beta decay, because N/Z is too high

(b) Te-139, $N = 87$, $Z = 52$, $N/Z = 1.7$, beta decay, because N/Z is too high

(c) Fr-202, $N = 115$, $Z = 87$, $N/Z = 1.3$, positron emission, because N/Z is too low

(d) Ba-123, $N = 67$, $Z = 56$, $N/Z = 1.2$, positron emission, because N/Z is too low

19.13 (a) Cs-125, $N/Z = 70/55 = 1.3$; Cs-113, $N/Z = 58/55 = 1.1$; Cs-125 will have the longer half-life because it is closer to the proper N/Z

(b) Fe-62, $N/Z = 36/26 = 1.4$; Fe-70, $N/Z = 44/26 = 1.7$; Fe-62 will have the longer half-life because it is closer to the proper N/Z

19.14 (a) Cs-149, $N/Z = 94/55 = 1.7$; Cs-139, $N/Z = 84/55 = 1.5$; Cs-139 will have the longer half-life because it is closer to the proper N/Z

(b) Fe-52, $N/Z = 26/26 = 1.0$; Fe-45, $N/Z = 19/26 = 0.7$; Fe-52 will have the longer half-life because it is closer to the proper N/Z

The Kinetics of Radioactive Decay and Radiometric Dating

19.15 **Given:** U-235, $t_{1/2}$ for radioactive decay $= 703$ million years **Find:** t to $\frac{1}{8}$ of initial amount

Conceptual Plan: radioactive decay implies first-order kinetics, $t_{1/2} \rightarrow k$ then

$$t_{1/2} = \frac{0.693}{k}$$

$m_{\text{U-235 }0}, m_{\text{U-235 }t}, k \rightarrow t$

$$\ln N_t = -kt + \ln N_0$$

Solution: $t_{1/2} = \dfrac{0.693}{k}$; rearrange to solve for k. $k = \dfrac{0.693}{t_{1/2}} = \dfrac{0.693}{703 \times 10^6 \text{ yr}} = 9.8\underline{5}7752 \times 10^{-10} \text{ yr}^{-1}$. Because

$\ln m_{\text{U-235 }t} = -kt + \ln m_{\text{U-235 }0}$, rearrange to solve for t.

$$t = -\frac{1}{k} \ln \frac{m_{\text{U-235 }t}}{m_{\text{U-235 }0}} = -\frac{1}{9.8\underline{5}7752 \times 10^{-10} \text{ yr}^{-1}} \ln \frac{1}{8} = 2.11 \times 10^9 \text{ yr}$$

Check: The units (yr) are correct. Because 1/2 will be left after one half-life, 1/4 will be left after two half-lives, and 1/8 will be left after three half-lives $= 3 \times 7.03 \times 10^8 = 2.11 \times 10^9$.

19.16   **Given:** initially 0.050 mg Tc-99m, $t_{1/2}$ for radioactive decay $= 6.0$ h   **Find:** t to 6.3×10^{-3} mg
    Conceptual Plan: radioactive decay implies first-order kinetics, $t_{1/2} \rightarrow k$ **then**

$$t_{1/2} = \frac{0.693}{k}$$

$m_{\text{Tc-99m 0}}, m_{\text{Tc-99m }t}, k \rightarrow t$
$$\ln N_t = -kt + \ln N_0$$

Solution: $t_{1/2} = \dfrac{0.693}{k}$; rearrange to solve for k. $k = \dfrac{0.693}{t_{1/2}} = \dfrac{0.693}{6.0 \text{ h}} = 0.1155 \text{ h}^{-1}$. Because

$\ln m_{\text{Tc-99m }t} = -kt + \ln m_{\text{Tc-99m 0}}$, rearrange to solve for t.

$$t = -\frac{1}{k} \ln \frac{m_{\text{Tc-99m }t}}{m_{\text{Tc-99m 0}}} = -\frac{1}{0.1155 \text{ h}^{-1}} \ln \frac{6.3 \times 10^{-3} \text{ mg}}{0.050 \text{ mg}} = 18 \text{ h}$$

Check: The units (h) are correct. The time is about three half-lives, and the amount is about 1/8, or $1/2^3$, of the original amount.

19.17   **Given:** $t_{1/2}$ for isotope decay $= 3.8$ days; 1.55 g isotope initially   **Find:** mass of isotope after 5.5 days
    Conceptual Plan: radioactive decay implies first-order kinetics, $t_{1/2} \rightarrow k$ **then**

$$t_{1/2} = \frac{0.693}{k}$$

$m_{\text{isotope 0}}, t, k \rightarrow m_{\text{isotope }t}$
$$\ln N_t = -kt + \ln N_0$$

Solution: $t_{1/2} = \dfrac{0.693}{k}$; rearrange to solve for k. $k = \dfrac{0.693}{t_{1/2}} = \dfrac{0.693}{3.8 \text{ days}} = 0.18237 \text{ day}^{-1}$. Because

$\ln N_t = -kt + \ln N_0 = -(0.18237 \text{ day}^{-1})(5.5 \text{ day}) + \ln(1.55 \text{ g}) = -0.56478 \rightarrow N_t = e^{-0.56478} = 0.57 \text{ g}$.
Check: The units (g) are correct. The amount is consistent with a time between one and two half-lives.

19.18   **Given:** $t_{1/2}$ for I-131 $= 8$ days; 58 mg dose at 8 a.m.   **Find:** mass of I-131 at 5 p.m. next day
    Conceptual Plan: radioactive decay implies first-order kinetics, $t_{1/2} \rightarrow k$ **and determine days since dose**

$$t_{1/2} = \frac{0.693}{k}$$

then $m_{\text{I-131 0}}, t, k \rightarrow m_{\text{I-131 }t}$
$$\ln N_t = -kt + \ln N_0$$

Solution: $t_{1/2} = \dfrac{0.693}{k}$; rearrange to solve for k. $k = \dfrac{0.693}{t_{1/2}} = \dfrac{0.693}{8 \text{ days}} = 0.086625 \text{ day}^{-1}$. The time since the

dose is one day plus 9 hours, or $(1 + 9/24)$ days $= 1.375$ days. Because $\ln m_{\text{I-131 }t} = -kt + \ln m_{\text{I-131 0}} = -(0.086625 \text{ day}^{-1})(1.375 \text{ day}) + \ln(58 \text{ mg}) = 3.9413 \rightarrow m = e^{3.9413} = 51 \text{ mg}$.
Check: The units (mg) are correct. The amount is consistent with a time less than one half-life.

19.19   **Given:** F-18 initial decay rate $= 1.5 \times 10^5$/s, $t_{1/2}$ for F-18 $= 1.83$ h   **Find:** t to decay rate of 1.0×10^2/s
    Conceptual Plan: radioactive decay implies first-order kinetics, $t_{1/2} \rightarrow k$ **then** Rate$_0$, Rate$_t$, $k \rightarrow t$

$$t_{1/2} = \frac{0.693}{k} \qquad\qquad \ln \frac{\text{Rate}_t}{\text{Rate}_0} = -kt$$

Solution: $t_{1/2} = \dfrac{0.693}{k}$; rearrange to solve for k. $k = \dfrac{0.693}{t_{1/2}} = \dfrac{0.693}{1.83 \text{ h}} = 0.378689 \text{ h}^{-1}$. Because

$\ln \dfrac{\text{Rate}_t}{\text{Rate}_0} = -kt$, rearrange to solve for t.

$$t = -\frac{1}{k} \ln \frac{\text{Rate}_t}{\text{Rate}_0} = -\frac{1}{0.378689 \text{ h}^{-1}} \ln \frac{1.0 \times 10^2/\text{s}}{1.5 \times 10^5/\text{s}} = 19.3 \text{ h}$$

Check: The units (h) are correct. The time is between 10 and 11 half-lives, and the rate is just under $1/2^{10}$ of the original amount.

19.20   **Given:** Tl-201 initial decay rate $= 5.88 \times 10^4$/s, $t_{1/2}$ for Tl-201 $= 3.042$ days   **Find:** t to decay rate of 55/s
    Conceptual Plan: radioactive decay implies first-order kinetics, $t_{1/2} \rightarrow k$ **then** Rate$_0$, Rate$_t$, $k \rightarrow t$

$$t_{1/2} = \frac{0.693}{k} \qquad\qquad \ln \frac{\text{Rate}_t}{\text{Rate}_0} = -kt$$

Solution: $t_{1/2} = \dfrac{0.693}{k}$; rearrange to solve for k. $k = \dfrac{0.693}{t_{1/2}} = \dfrac{0.693}{3.042 \text{ days}} = 0.227\underline{8}107 \text{ day}^{-1}$. Because

$\ln \dfrac{\text{Rate}_t}{\text{Rate}_0} = -k\,t$, rearrange to solve for t.

$t = -\dfrac{1}{k} \ln \dfrac{\text{Rate}_t}{\text{Rate}_0} = -\dfrac{1}{0.227\underline{8}107 \text{ day}^{-1}} \ln \dfrac{55/\cancel{s}}{5.88 \times 10^4/\cancel{s}} = 30.6\underline{1}56 \text{ days} = 30.6 \text{ days}$

Check: The units (days) are correct. The time is between 10 and 11 half-lives, and the rate is just under $1/2^{10}$ of the original amount.

19.21   **Given:** boat analysis, C-14/C-12 = 72.5% of living organism   **Find:** t
         Other: $t_{1/2}$ for decay of C-14 = 5730 years
         Conceptual Plan: radioactive decay implies first-order kinetics, $t_{1/2} \rightarrow k$ then 72.5% of $m_{\text{C-14}\,0}, k \rightarrow t$

$$t_{1/2} = \dfrac{0.693}{k} \qquad\qquad \ln N_t = -k\,t + \ln N_0$$

Solution: $t_{1/2} = \dfrac{0.693}{k}$; rearrange to solve for k. $k = \dfrac{0.693}{t_{1/2}} = \dfrac{0.693}{5730 \text{ yr}} = 1.20\underline{9}42 \times 10^{-4} \text{ yr}^{-1}$ then

$[\text{C-14}]_t = 0.725[\text{C-14}]_0$. Because $\ln m_{\text{C-14}\,t} = -k\,t + \ln m_{\text{C-14}\,0}$, rearrange to solve for t.

$t = -\dfrac{1}{k} \ln \dfrac{m_{\text{C-14}\,t}}{m_{\text{C-14}\,0}} = -\dfrac{1}{1.20\underline{9}42 \times 10^{-4} \text{ yr}^{-1}} \ln \dfrac{0.725 \, \cancel{m_{\text{C-14}\,0}}}{\cancel{m_{\text{C-14}\,0}}} = 2.66 \times 10^3 \text{ yr}$

Check: The units (yr) are correct. The time to 72.5% decay is consistent with a time less than one half-life.

19.22   **Given:** peat analysis, C-14/C-12 = 22.8% of living organism   **Find:** t
         Other: $t_{1/2}$ for decay of C-14 = 5730 years
         Conceptual Plan: radioactive decay implies first-order kinetics, $t_{1/2} \rightarrow k$ then 72.5% of $[\text{C-14}]_0, k \rightarrow t$

$$t_{1/2} = \dfrac{0.693}{k} \qquad\qquad \ln N_t = -k\,t + \ln N_0$$

Solution: $t_{1/2} = \dfrac{0.693}{k}$; rearrange to solve for k. $k = \dfrac{0.693}{t_{1/2}} = \dfrac{0.693}{5730 \text{ yr}} = 1.20\underline{9}42 \times 10^{-4} \text{ yr}^{-1}$ then

$[\text{C-14}]_t = 0.228[\text{C-14}]_0$. Because $\ln m_{\text{C-14}\,t} = -k\,t + \ln m_{\text{C-14}\,0}$, rearrange to solve for t.

$t = -\dfrac{1}{k} \ln \dfrac{m_{\text{C-14}\,t}}{m_{\text{C-14}\,0}} = -\dfrac{1}{1.20\underline{9}42 \times 10^{-4} \text{ yr}^{-1}} \ln \dfrac{0.228 \, \cancel{m_{\text{C-14}\,0}}}{\cancel{m_{\text{C-14}\,0}}} = 1.22 \times 10^4 \text{ yr}$

Check: The units (yr) are correct. The time to 22.8% decay is consistent with a time just more than two half-lives.

19.23   **Given:** skull analysis, C-14 decay rate = 15.3 dis/min · g C in living organisms and 0.85 dis/min · g C in skull
         Find: t **Other:** $t_{1/2}$ for decay of C-14 = 5730 years
         Conceptual Plan: radioactive decay implies first-order kinetics, $t_{1/2} \rightarrow k$ then $\text{Rate}_0, \text{Rate}_t, k \rightarrow t$

$$t_{1/2} = \dfrac{0.693}{k} \qquad\qquad \ln \dfrac{\text{Rate}_t}{\text{Rate}_0} = -k\,t$$

Solution: $t_{1/2} = \dfrac{0.693}{k}$; rearrange to solve for k. $k = \dfrac{0.693}{t_{1/2}} = \dfrac{0.693}{5730 \text{ yr}} = 1.20\underline{9}42 \times 10^{-4} \text{ yr}^{-1}$

Because $\ln \dfrac{\text{Rate}_t}{\text{Rate}_0} = -k\,t$, rearrange to solve for t.

$t = -\dfrac{1}{k} \ln \dfrac{\text{Rate}_t}{\text{Rate}_0} = -\dfrac{1}{1.20\underline{9}42 \times 10^{-4} \text{ yr}^{-1}} \ln \dfrac{0.85 \, \cancel{\text{dis/min} \cdot \text{g C}}}{15.3 \, \cancel{\text{dis/min} \cdot \text{g C}}} = 2.39 \times 10^4 \text{ yr}$

Check: The units (yr) are correct. The rate is 6% of initial value, and the time is consistent with a time just more than four half-lives.

19.24   **Given:** mammoth analysis C-14 decay rate = 15.3 dis/min · g C in living organisms and 0.48 dis/min · g C in mammoth
         Find: When did the mammoth live? **Other:** $t_{1/2}$ for decay of C-14 = 5730 years
         Conceptual Plan: radioactive decay implies first-order kinetics, $t_{1/2} \rightarrow k$ then $\text{Rate}_0, \text{Rate}_t, k \rightarrow t$

$$t_{1/2} = \dfrac{0.693}{k} \qquad\qquad \ln \dfrac{\text{Rate}_t}{\text{Rate}_0} = -k\,t$$

Solution: $t_{1/2} = \dfrac{0.693}{k}$; rearrange to solve for k. $k = \dfrac{0.693}{t_{1/2}} = \dfrac{0.693}{5730 \text{ yr}} = 1.20942 \times 10^{-4} \text{ yr}^{-1}$

Because $\ln \dfrac{\text{Rate}_t}{\text{Rate}_0} = -k\,t$, rearrange to solve for t.

$t = -\dfrac{1}{k} \ln \dfrac{\text{Rate}_t}{\text{Rate}_0} = -\dfrac{1}{1.20942 \times 10^{-4} \text{ yr}^{-1}} \ln \dfrac{0.48 \text{ dis/min} \cdot \text{g C}}{15.3 \text{ dis/min} \cdot \text{g C}} = 2.9 \times 10^4 \text{ yr ago}$

Check: The units (yr) are correct. The rate is 3% of initial value, and the time is consistent with a time just more than five half-lives.

19.25 **Given:** rock analysis, 0.438 g Pb-206 to every 1.00 g U-238, no Pb-206 initially **Find:** age of rock
Other: $t_{1/2}$ for decay of U-238 to Pb-206 $= 4.5 \times 10^9$ years
Conceptual Plan: radioactive decay implies first-order kinetics, $t_{1/2} \rightarrow k$ then

$$t_{1/2} = \frac{0.693}{k}$$

g Pb-206 $\rightarrow$ mol Pb-206 $\rightarrow$ mol U-238 $\rightarrow$ g U-238 then $m_{\text{U-238 }t}, k \rightarrow t$

$$\frac{1 \text{ mol Pb-206}}{206 \text{ g Pb-206}} \quad \frac{1 \text{ mol U-238}}{1 \text{ mol Pb-206}} \quad \frac{238 \text{ g U-238}}{1 \text{ mol U-238}} \qquad \ln N_t = -k\,t + \ln N_0$$

Solution: $t_{1/2} = \dfrac{0.693}{k}$; rearrange to solve for k. $k = \dfrac{0.693}{t_{1/2}} = \dfrac{0.693}{4.5 \times 10^9 \text{ yr}} = 1.54 \times 10^{-10} \text{ yr}^{-1}$ then

$0.438 \text{ g Pb-206} \times \dfrac{1 \text{ mol Pb-206}}{206 \text{ g Pb-206}} \times \dfrac{1 \text{ mol U-238}}{1 \text{ mol Pb-206}} \times \dfrac{238 \text{ g U-238}}{1 \text{ mol U-238}} = 0.506039 \text{ g U-238}$. Because

$\ln \dfrac{m_{\text{U-238 }t}}{m_{\text{U-238 }0}} = -k\,t$, rearrange to solve for t.

$t = -\dfrac{1}{k} \ln \dfrac{m_{\text{U-238 }t}}{m_{\text{U-238 }0}} = -\dfrac{1}{1.54 \times 10^{-10} \text{ yr}^{-1}} \ln \dfrac{1.00 \text{ g U-238}}{(1.00 + 0.506039) \text{ g U-238}} = 2.7 \times 10^9 \text{ yr}$

Check: The units (yr) are correct. The amount of Pb-206 is less than half the initial U-238 amount, and time is less than one half-life.

19.26 **Given:** meteor analysis, 0.855 g Pb-206 : 1.00 g U-238, no Pb-206 initially **Find:** age of meteor
Other: $t_{1/2}$ for decay of U-238 to Pb-206 $= 4.5 \times 10^9$ years
Conceptual Plan: radioactive decay implies first-order kinetics, $t_{1/2} \rightarrow k$ then

$$t_{1/2} = \frac{0.693}{k}$$

g Pb-206 $\rightarrow$ mol Pb-206 $\rightarrow$ mol U-238 $\rightarrow$ g U-238 then $m_{\text{U-238 }0}, m_{\text{U-238 }t}, k \rightarrow t$

$$\frac{1 \text{ mol Pb-206}}{206 \text{ g Pb-206}} \quad \frac{1 \text{ mol U-238}}{1 \text{ mol Pb-206}} \quad \frac{238 \text{ g U-238}}{1 \text{ mol U-238}} \qquad \ln N_t = -k\,t + \ln N_0$$

Solution: $t_{1/2} = \dfrac{0.693}{k}$; rearrange to solve for k. $k = \dfrac{0.693}{t_{1/2}} = \dfrac{0.693}{4.5 \times 10^9 \text{ yr}} = 1.54 \times 10^{-10} \text{ yr}^1$ then

$0.855 \text{ g Pb-206} \times \dfrac{1 \text{ mol Pb-206}}{206 \text{ g Pb-206}} \times \dfrac{1 \text{ mol U-238}}{1 \text{ mol Pb-206}} \times \dfrac{238 \text{ g U-238}}{1 \text{ mol U-238}} = 0.987816 \text{ g U-238}$. Because

$\ln \dfrac{m_{\text{U-238 }t}}{m_{\text{U-238 }0}} = -k\,t$, rearrange to solve for t.

$t = -\dfrac{1}{k} \ln \dfrac{m_{\text{U-238 }t}}{m_{\text{U-238 }0}} = -\dfrac{1}{1.54 \times 10^{-10} \text{yr}^{-1}} \ln \dfrac{1.00 \text{ g U-238}}{(1.00 + 0.987816) \text{ g U-238}} = 4.5 \times 10^9 \text{ yr}$

Check: The units (yr) are correct. The amount of Pb-206 is just less than the initial U-238 amount, and time is just under one half-life.

Fission and Fusion

19.27 **Given:** U-235 fission induced by neutrons to Xe-144 and Sr-90 **Find:** number of neutrons produced
Conceptual Plan: Write the species given on the appropriate side of the equation. $\rightarrow$ Equalize the sum of the mass numbers and the sum of the atomic numbers on both sides of the equation by writing the stoichiometric coefficient in front of the desired species.

Solution: $^{235}_{92}U + ^1_0n \rightarrow ^{144}_{54}Xe + ^{90}_{38}Sr + ?^1_0n$ becomes $^{235}_{92}U + ^1_0n \rightarrow ^{144}_{54}Xe + ^{90}_{38}Sr + 2^1_0n$, so two neutrons are produced.

Check: $235 + 1 = 144 + 90 + 2, 92 + 0 = 54 + 38 + 0$, and no other particle is necessary to balance the equation.

19.28   **Given:** U-235 fission to Te-137 and Zr-97   **Find:** number of neutrons produced
Conceptual Plan: Write the species given on the appropriate side of the equation. → Equalize the sum of the mass numbers and the sum of the atomic numbers on both sides of the equation by writing the stoichiometric coefficient in front of the desired species.
Solution: $^{235}_{92}U + ^1_0n \rightarrow ^{137}_{52}Te + ^{97}_{40}Zr + ?^1_0n$ becomes $^{235}_{92}U + ^1_0n \rightarrow ^{137}_{52}Te + ^{97}_{40}Zr + 2^1_0n$, so two neutrons are produced.

Check: $235 + 1 = 137 + 97 + 2, 92 + 0 = 52 + 40 + 0$, and no other particle is necessary to balance the equation.

19.29   **Given:** fusion of two H-2 atoms to form He-3 and one neutron   **Find:** balanced equation
Conceptual Plan: Write the species given on the appropriate side of the equation. → Equalize the sum of the mass numbers and the sum of the atomic numbers on both sides of the equation by writing the stoichiometric coefficient in front of the desired species.
Solution: $2^2_1H \rightarrow ^3_2He + ^1_0n$

Check: $2(2) = 3 + 1, 2(1) = 2 + 0$, and no other particle is necessary to balance the equation.

19.30   **Given:** fusion of H-3 and H-1 atoms to form He-4   **Find:** balanced equation
Conceptual Plan: Write the species given on the appropriate side of the equation. → Equalize the sum of the mass numbers and the sum of the atomic numbers on both sides of the equation by writing the stoichiometric coefficient in front of the desired species.
Solution: $^3_1H + ^1_1H \rightarrow ^4_2He$

Check: $3 + 1 = 4, 1 + 1 = 2$, and no other particle is necessary to balance the equation.

19.31   **Given:** U-238 bombarded by neutrons to form U-239, which undergoes two beta decays to form Pu-239
Find: balanced equations
Conceptual Plan: Write the species given on the appropriate side of the equation. → Equalize the sum of the mass numbers and the sum of the atomic numbers on both sides of the equation by writing the stoichiometric coefficient in front of the desired species. → Use the product of this reaction to write the next reaction until the process is complete.
Solution: $^{238}_{92}U + ?^1_0n \rightarrow ^{239}_{92}U$ becomes $^{238}_{92}U + ^1_0n \rightarrow ^{239}_{92}U$ then

beta decay $^{239}_{92}U \rightarrow ^{239}_?? + ^0_{-1}e$ becomes $^{239}_{92}U \rightarrow ^{239}_{93}? + ^0_{-1}e$ then $^{239}_{92}U \rightarrow ^{239}_{93}Np + ^0_{-1}e$ then

beta decay $^{239}_{93}Np \rightarrow ^{239}_?? + ^0_{-1}e$ becomes $^{239}_{93}Np \rightarrow ^{239}_{94}? + ^0_{-1}e$ then $^{239}_{93}Np \rightarrow ^{239}_{94}Pu + ^0_{-1}e$

The entire process is $^{238}_{92}U + ^1_0n \rightarrow ^{239}_{92}U, ^{239}_{92}U \rightarrow ^{239}_{93}Np + ^0_{-1}e, ^{239}_{93}Np \rightarrow ^{239}_{94}Pu + ^0_{-1}e$.

Check: $238 + 1 = 239, 92 + 0 = 92$, and no other particle is necessary to balance the equation. $239 = 239 + 0, 92 = 93 - 1$, and neptunium is atomic number 93. $239 = 239 + 0, 93 = 94 - 1$, and plutonium is atomic number 94.

19.32   **Given:** Al-27 bombarded by a neutron and then undergoes an alpha decay and a beta decay
Find: balanced equations
Conceptual Plan: Write the species given on the appropriate side of the equation. → Equalize the sum of the mass numbers and the sum of the atomic numbers on both sides of the equation by writing the stoichiometric coefficient in front of the desired species. → Use the product of this reaction to write the next reaction until the process is complete.
Solution: $^{27}_{13}Al + ^1_0n \rightarrow ^{28}_??$ becomes $^{27}_{13}Al + ^1_0n \rightarrow ^{28}_{13}?$ then $^{27}_{13}Al + ^1_0n \rightarrow ^{28}_{13}Al$ then

alpha decay $^{28}_{13}Al \rightarrow ^{24}_?? + ^4_2He$ becomes $^{28}_{13}Al \rightarrow ^{24}_{11}? + ^4_2He$ then $^{28}_{13}Al \rightarrow ^{24}_{11}Na + ^4_2He$ then

beta decay $^{24}_{11}Na \rightarrow ^{24}_?? + ^0_{-1}e$ becomes $^{24}_{11}Na \rightarrow ^{24}_{12}? + ^0_{-1}e$ then $^{24}_{11}Na \rightarrow ^{24}_{12}Mg + ^0_{-1}e$

The entire process is $^{27}_{13}Al + ^1_0n \rightarrow ^{28}_{13}Al, ^{28}_{13}Al \rightarrow ^{24}_{11}Na + ^4_2He, ^{24}_{11}Na \rightarrow ^{24}_{12}Mg + ^0_{-1}e$.

Check: $27 + 1 = 28, 13 + 0 = 13$, and aluminum is atomic number 13. $28 = 24 + 4, 13 = 11 + 2$, and sodium is atomic number 11. $24 = 24 + 0, 11 = 12 - 1$, and magnesium is atomic number 12.

Energetics of Nuclear Reactions, Mass Defect, and Nuclear Binding Energy

19.33 **Given:** 1.0 g of matter converted to energy   **Find:** energy

Conceptual Plan: g → kg → E

$$\frac{1\ kg}{1000\ g} \qquad E = mc^2$$

Solution: $1.0\ \cancel{g} \times \dfrac{1\ kg}{1000\ \cancel{g}} = 0.0010\ kg$ then $E = mc^2 = (0.0010\ kg)\left(2.9979 \times 10^8\ \dfrac{m}{s}\right)^2 = 9.0 \times 10^{13}\ J$

Check: The units (J) are correct. The magnitude of the answer makes physical sense because we are converting a large quantity of amus to energy.

19.34 **Given:** 1.0×10^3 kWh of electricity/month from nuclear reaction   **Find:** mass converted to energy/year

Conceptual Plan: kWh → J → kg → g then g/month → g/year

$$\frac{3.60 \times 10^6\ J}{1\ kWh} \qquad E = mc^2 \qquad \frac{1000\ g}{1\ kg} \qquad\qquad \frac{12\ months}{1\ year}$$

Solution: $1.0 \times 10^3\ \cancel{kWh} \times \dfrac{3.60 \times 10^6\ J}{1\ \cancel{kWh}} = 3.6 \times 10^9\ J$. Because $E = mc^2$, rearrange to solve for m.

$$m = \frac{E}{c^2} = \frac{3.6 \times 10^9\ kg\ \dfrac{m^2}{s^2}}{\left(2.9979 \times 10^8\ kg\ \dfrac{m}{s}\right)^2} = 4.0 \times 10^{-8}\ \cancel{kg} \times \frac{1000\ g}{1\ \cancel{kg}} = 4.0 \times 10^{-5}\ g\ \text{then}$$

$$\frac{4.0 \times 10^{-5}\ g}{1\ \cancel{month}} \times \frac{12\ \cancel{month}}{1\ year} = \frac{4.8 \times 10^{-4}\ g}{1\ year}$$

Check: The units (g) are correct. A small mass is expected because nuclear reactions generate a large amount of energy.

19.35 **Given:** (a) O-16 = 15.9949145 amu, (b) Ni-58 = 57.935346 amu, and (c) Xe-129 = 128.904780 amu
Find: mass defect and nuclear binding energy per nucleon

Conceptual Plan: $^A_Z X$**, isotope mass → mass defect → nuclear binding energy per nucleon**

$$\text{mass defect} = Z(\text{mass}\ {}^1_1 H) + (A\text{-}Z)(\text{mass}\ {}^1_0 n) - \text{mass of isotope} \qquad \frac{931.5\ MeV}{(1\ amu)(A\ nucleons)}$$

Solution: mass defect $= Z(\text{mass}\ {}^1_1 H) + (A\text{-}Z)(\text{mass}\ {}^1_0 n) - \text{mass of isotope}$

(a)   O-16 mass defect $= 8(1.00783\ amu) + (16 - 8)(1.00866\ amu) - 15.9949145\ amu =$

$0.1370055\ amu = 0.13701\ amu$ and $0.1370055\ \cancel{amu} \times \dfrac{931.5\ MeV}{(1\ \cancel{amu})(16\ nucleons)} = 7.976\ \dfrac{MeV}{nucleon}$

(b)   Ni-58 mass defect $= 28(1.00783\ amu) + (58 - 28)(1.00866\ amu) - 57.935346\ amu =$

$0.543694\ amu = 0.54369\ amu$ and $0.543694\ \cancel{amu} \times \dfrac{931.5\ MeV}{(1\ \cancel{amu})(58\ nucleons)} = 8.732\ \dfrac{MeV}{nucleon}$

(c)   Xe-129 mass defect $= 54(1.00783\ amu) + (129 - 54)(1.00866\ amu) - 128.904780\ amu = 1.16754\ amu$

and $1.16754\ \cancel{amu} \times \dfrac{931.5\ MeV}{(1\ \cancel{amu})(129\ nucleons)} = 8.431\ \dfrac{MeV}{nucleon}$

Check: The units (amu and MeV/nucleon) are correct. The mass defect increases with an increasing number of nucleons, but the MeV/nucleon does not change by as much (on a relative basis).

19.36 **Given:** (a) Li-7 = 7.016003 amu, (b) Ti-48 = 47.947947 amu, and (c) Ag-107 = 106.905092 amu
Find: mass defect and nuclear binding energy per nucleon

Conceptual Plan: $^A_Z X$**, isotope mass → mass defect → nuclear binding energy per nucleon**

$$\text{mass defect} = Z(\text{mass}\ {}^1_1 H) + (A\text{-}Z)(\text{mass}\ {}^1_0 n) - \text{mass of isotope} \qquad \frac{931.5\ MeV}{(1\ amu)(A\ nucleons)}$$

Solution: mass defect $= Z(\text{mass}\ {}^1_1 H) + (A\text{-}Z)(\text{mass}\ {}^1_0 n) - \text{mass of isotope}$

(a)   Li-7 mass defect $= 3(1.00783\ amu) + (7 - 3)(1.00866\ amu) - 7.016003\ amu =$

$0.042127\ amu = 0.04213\ amu$ and $0.042127\ \cancel{amu} \times \dfrac{931.5\ MeV}{(1\ \cancel{amu})(7\ nucleons)} = 5.606\ \dfrac{MeV}{nucleon}$

(b) Ti-48 mass defect $= 22(1.00783 \text{ amu}) + (48 - 22)(1.00866 \text{ amu}) - 47.947947 \text{ amu} =$

$0.449\underline{4}73 \text{ amu} = 0.44947 \text{ amu}$ and $0.449\underline{4}73 \text{ amu} \times \dfrac{931.5 \text{ MeV}}{(1 \text{ amu})(48 \text{ nucleons})} = 8.723 \dfrac{\text{MeV}}{\text{nucleon}}$

(c) Ag-107 mass defect $= 47(1.00783 \text{ amu}) + (107 - 47)(1.00866 \text{ amu}) - 106.905092 \text{ amu} =$

$0.982\underline{5}18 \text{ amu} = 0.98252 \text{ amu}$ and $0.982\underline{5}18 \text{ amu} \times \dfrac{931.5 \text{ MeV}}{(1 \text{ amu})(107 \text{ nucleons})} = 8.553 \dfrac{\text{MeV}}{\text{nucleon}}$

Check: The units (amu and MeV/nucleon) are correct. The mass defect increases with an increasing number of nucleons, but the MeV/nucleon does not change by as much (on a relative basis).

19.37 **Given:** $^{235}_{92}\text{U} + ^{1}_{0}\text{n} \rightarrow ^{144}_{54}\text{Xe} + ^{90}_{38}\text{Sr} + 2\,^{1}_{0}\text{n}$, U-235 = 235.043922 amu, Xe-144 = 143.9385 amu, and Sr-90 = 89.907738 amu **Find:** energy per g of U-235

Conceptual Plan: mass of products and reactants $\rightarrow$ mass defect $\rightarrow$ mass defect/g of U-235 then

$$\text{mass defect} = \sum \text{mass of reactants} - \sum \text{mass of products} \qquad \dfrac{\text{mass defect}}{235.043922 \text{ g U-235}}$$

g $\rightarrow$ kg $\rightarrow$ E

$$\dfrac{1 \text{ kg}}{1000 \text{ g}} \qquad E = mc^2$$

Solution: mass defect $= \sum \text{mass of reactants} - \sum \text{mass of products}$; notice that we can cancel a neutron from each side to get $^{235}_{92}\text{U} \rightarrow ^{144}_{54}\text{Xe} + ^{90}_{38}\text{Sr} + ^{1}_{0}\text{n}$ and

mass defect $= 235.043922 \text{ g} - (143.9385 \text{ g} + 89.907738 \text{ g} + 1.00866 \text{ g}) = 0.189024 \text{ g}$

then $\dfrac{0.189\underline{0}24 \text{ g}}{235.043922 \text{ g U-235}} \times \dfrac{1 \text{ kg}}{1000 \text{ g}} = 8.04\underline{2}07 \times 10^{-7} \dfrac{\text{kg}}{\text{g U-235}}$ then

$E = mc^2 = \left(8.04\underline{2}07 \times 10^{-7} \dfrac{\text{kg}}{\text{g U-235}} \right) \left(2.9979 \times 10^{8} \dfrac{\text{m}}{\text{s}} \right)^2 = 7.228 \times 10^{10} \dfrac{\text{J}}{\text{g U-235}}$

Check: The units (J) are correct. A large amount of energy is expected per gram of fuel in a nuclear reactor.

19.38 **Given:** $^{235}_{92}\text{U} + ^{1}_{0}\text{n} \rightarrow ^{137}_{52}\text{Te} + ^{97}_{40}\text{Zr} + 2\,^{1}_{0}\text{n}$, U-235 = 235.043922 amu, Te-137 = 136.9253 amu, and Zr-97 = 96.910950 amu **Find:** energy per mol of U-235

Conceptual Plan: mass of products and reactants $\rightarrow$ mass defect $\rightarrow$ mass defect/mol of U-235 then

$$\text{mass defect} = \sum \text{mass of reactants} - \sum \text{mass of products} \qquad \dfrac{\text{mass defect}}{235.043922 \text{ g U-235}}$$

g $\rightarrow$ kg $\rightarrow$ E

$$\dfrac{1 \text{ kg}}{1000 \text{ g}} \qquad E = mc^2$$

Solution: mass defect $= \sum \text{mass of reactants} - \sum \text{mass of products}$; notice that we can cancel a neutron from each side to get $^{235}_{92}\text{U} \rightarrow ^{137}_{52}\text{Te} + ^{97}_{40}\text{Zr} + ^{1}_{0}\text{n}$ and

mass defect $= 235.043922 \text{ g} - (136.9253 \text{ g} + 96.910950 \text{ g} + 1.00866 \text{ g}) = 0.199012 \text{ g/mol U-235}$

then $\dfrac{0.199\underline{0}12 \text{ g}}{\text{mol U-235}} \times \dfrac{1 \text{ kg}}{1000 \text{ g}} = 1.99\underline{0}12 \text{ g} \times 10^{-4} \dfrac{\text{kg}}{\text{mol U-235}}$ then

$E = mc^2 = \left(1.99\underline{0}12 \text{ g} \times 10^{-4} \dfrac{\text{kg}}{\text{mol U-235}} \right) \left(2.9979 \times 10^{8} \dfrac{\text{m}}{\text{s}} \right)^2 = 1.789 \times 10^{13} \dfrac{\text{J}}{\text{mol U-235}}$

Check: The units (J) are correct. A large amount of energy is expected per gram of fuel in a nuclear reactor.

19.39 **Given:** $2\,^{2}_{1}\text{H} \rightarrow ^{3}_{2}\text{He} + ^{1}_{0}\text{n}$, H-2 = 2.014102 amu, and He-3 = 3.016029 amu **Find:** energy per g reactant

Conceptual Plan: mass of products and reactants $\rightarrow$ mass defect $\rightarrow$ mass defect/g of H-2 then

$$\text{mass defect} = \sum \text{mass of reactants} - \sum \text{mass of products} \qquad \dfrac{\text{mass defect}}{2(2.014102 \text{ g H-2})}$$

g $\rightarrow$ kg $\rightarrow$ E

$$\dfrac{1 \text{ kg}}{1000 \text{ g}} \qquad E = mc^2$$

Solution: mass defect $= \sum \text{mass of reactants} - \sum \text{mass of products}$ and mass defect $= 2(2.014102 \text{ g}) - (3.016029 \text{ g} + 1.00866 \text{ g}) = 0.003\underline{5}15 \text{ g}$

then $\dfrac{0.003515 \text{ g}}{2(2.014102 \text{ g H-2})} \times \dfrac{1 \text{ kg}}{1000 \text{ g}} = 8.72597 \times 10^{-7} \dfrac{\text{kg}}{\text{g H-2}}$ then

$E = mc^2 = \left(8.72597 \times 10^{-7} \dfrac{\text{kg}}{\text{g H-2}}\right)\left(2.9979 \times 10^8 \dfrac{\text{m}}{\text{s}}\right)^2 = 7.84 \times 10^{10} \dfrac{\text{J}}{\text{g H-2}}$

Check: The units (J) are correct. A large amount of energy is expected per gram of fuel in a fusion reaction.

19.40   **Given:** $^3_1\text{H} + ^1_1\text{H} \rightarrow ^4_2\text{He}$, H-3 = 3.016049 amu, H-1 = 1.007825 amu, and He-4 = 4.002603 amu
Find: energy per g reactant
Conceptual Plan: mass of products and reactants $\rightarrow$ mass defect $\rightarrow$ mass defect/g reactant then

$$\text{mass defect} = \sum\text{mass of reactants} - \sum\text{mass of products} \qquad \dfrac{\text{mass defect}}{\text{g reactant}}$$

g $\rightarrow$ kg $\rightarrow$ E

$\dfrac{1 \text{ kg}}{1000 \text{ g}} \qquad E = mc^2$

Solution: mass defect $= \sum\text{mass of reactants} - \sum\text{mass of products}$ and
mass defect $= (3.016049 \text{ g} + 1.007825 \text{ g}) - 4.002603 \text{ g} = 4.023874 \text{ g} - 4.002603 \text{ g} = 0.021271 \text{ g}$

then $\dfrac{0.021271 \text{ g}}{4.023874 \text{ g reactants}} \times \dfrac{1 \text{ kg}}{1000 \text{ g}} = 5.2861993 \times 10^{-6} \dfrac{\text{kg}}{\text{g reactants}}$

then $E = mc^2 = \left(5.2861993 \times 10^{-6} \dfrac{\text{kg}}{\text{g reactants}}\right)\left(2.9979 \times 10^8 \dfrac{\text{m}}{\text{s}}\right)^2 = 4.7509 \times 10^{11} \dfrac{\text{J}}{\text{g reactants}}$

Check: The units (J) are correct. A large amount of energy is expected per gram of fuel in a fusion reaction.

Effects and Applications of Radioactivity

19.41   **Given:** 75 kg human exposed to 32.8 rad and falling from chair   **Find:** energy absorbed in each case
Conceptual Plan: rad, kg $\rightarrow$ J and assume $d = 0.50$ m chair height then mass, $d \rightarrow$ J

$1 \text{ rad} = \dfrac{0.01 \text{ J}}{1 \text{ kg body tissue}}$ $\qquad\qquad E = F \cdot d = mgd$

Solution: $32.8 \text{ rad} = 32.8 \dfrac{0.01 \text{ J}}{1 \text{ kg body tissue}} \times 75 \text{ kg} = 25 \text{ J}$ and

$E = F \cdot d = mgd = 75 \text{ kg} \times 9.8 \dfrac{\text{m}}{\text{s}^2} \times 0.50 \text{ m} = 370 \text{ kg} \dfrac{\text{m}^2}{\text{s}^2} = 370 \text{ J}$

Check: The units (J and J) are correct. Allowable radiation exposures are low because the radiation is very ionizing and thus damaging to tissue. Falling may have more energy, but it is not ionizing.

19.42   **Given:** 55 g mouse exposed to 20.5 rad   **Find:** energy absorbed
Conceptual Plan: g $\rightarrow$ kg then rad, kg $\rightarrow$ J

$\dfrac{1 \text{ kg}}{1000 \text{ g}} \qquad\qquad \dfrac{0.01 \text{ J}}{1 \text{ kg body tissue}}$

Solution: $55 \text{ g} \times \dfrac{1 \text{ kg}}{1000 \text{ g}} = 0.055 \text{ kg}$ then $20.5 \text{ rad} = 20.5 \dfrac{0.01 \text{ J}}{1 \text{ kg body tissue}} \times 0.055 \text{ kg} = 0.011 \text{ J}$

Check: The units (J) are correct. Allowable radiation exposures are low because the radiation is very ionizing and thus damaging to tissue.

19.43   **Given:** $t_{1/2}$ for F-18 = 1.83 h, 65% of F-18 makes it to the hospital traveling at 60.0 miles/hour   **Find:** distance between hospital and cyclotron
Conceptual Plan: $t_{1/2} \rightarrow k$ then $m_{\text{F-18 0}}, m_{\text{F-18 t}}, k \rightarrow t$ then h $\rightarrow$ mi

$t_{1/2} = \dfrac{0.693}{k} \qquad\qquad \ln\dfrac{m_{\text{F-18 }t}}{m_{\text{F-18 }0}} = -kt \qquad\qquad \dfrac{60.0 \text{ mi}}{1 \text{ h}}$

Solution: $t_{1/2} = \dfrac{0.693}{k}$; rearrange to solve for k. $k = \dfrac{0.693}{t_{1/2}} = \dfrac{0.693}{1.83 \text{ h}} = 0.378689 \text{ h}^{-1}$. Because

$\ln\dfrac{m_{\text{F-18 }t}}{m_{\text{F-18 }0}} = -kt$, rearrange to solve for t.

$$t = -\frac{1}{k} \ln \frac{m_{\text{F-18}\,t}}{m_{\text{F-18}\,0}} = -\frac{1}{0.378689 \text{ h}^{-1}} \ln \frac{0.65 m_{\text{F-18}\,0}}{m_{\text{F-18}\,0}} = 1.\underline{1}376 \text{ h then}$$

$$1.\underline{1}376 \cancel{\text{ h}} \times \frac{60.0 \text{ mi}}{1 \cancel{\text{ h}}} = 68 \text{ mi}$$

Check: The units (mi) are correct. The time is less than one half-life, so the distance is less than 1.83 times the speed of travel.

19.44   **Given:** I-131, 155 mg, $t_{1/2} = 8.0$ days   **Find:** exposure (in Ci) after 4.0 h
     Conceptual Plan: h → day and $t_{1/2}$ → k then $m_{\text{I-131}\,0}, t, k$ → $m_{\text{I-131}\,t}$

$$\frac{1 \text{ day}}{24 \text{ h}} \qquad\qquad t_{1/2} = \frac{0.693}{k} \qquad\qquad \ln N_t = -kt + \ln N_0$$

then mg$_0$, mg$_t$ → mg decayed → g decayed → mol decayed → beta decays then h → min → s

$$\text{mg}_0 - \text{mg}_t = \text{mg decayed} \quad \frac{1 \text{ g}}{1000 \text{ mg}} \quad \frac{1 \text{ mol I-131}}{131 \text{ g I-131}} \quad \frac{6.022 \times 10^{23} \text{ beta decays}}{1 \text{ mol I-131}} \quad \frac{60 \text{ min}}{1 \text{ h}} \quad \frac{60 \text{ s}}{1 \text{ min}}$$

then beta decays, s → beta decays/s → Ci

$$\text{take ratio} \qquad \frac{\dfrac{1 \text{ Ci}}{3.7 \times 10^{10} \text{ decays}}}{s}$$

Solution: $4.0 \cancel{\text{ h}} \times \dfrac{1 \text{ day}}{24 \cancel{\text{ h}}} = 0.1\underline{6}667 \text{ day then } t_{1/2} = \dfrac{0.693}{k}$; rearrange to solve for k.

$$k = \frac{0.693}{t_{1/2}} = \frac{0.693}{8.0 \text{ days}} = 0.08\underline{6}625 \text{ day}^{-1}. \text{ Because}$$

$$\ln m_{\text{I-131}\,t} = -kt + \ln m_{\text{I-131}\,0} = -(0.086625 \cancel{\text{day}^{-1}})(0.16667 \cancel{\text{day}}) + \ln (155 \text{ mg}) = 5.02\underline{8}99 \rightarrow$$

$$m_{\text{I-131}\,t} = e^{5.02899} = 152.\underline{7}79 \text{ mg then mg}_0 - \text{mg}_t = \text{mg decayed} = 155 \text{ mg} - 152.\underline{7}79 \text{ mg} = 2.\underline{2}21 \text{ mg I-131 then}$$

$$2.\underline{2}21 \text{ mg I-131} \times \frac{1 \text{ g I-131}}{1000 \text{ mg I-131}} \times \frac{1 \text{ mol I-131}}{131 \text{ g I-131}} \times \frac{6.022 \times 10^{23} \text{ beta decays}}{1 \text{ mol I-131}} = 1.\underline{0}210 \times 10^{19} \text{ beta decays}$$

$$\text{then } 4.0 \cancel{\text{ h}} \times \frac{60 \cancel{\text{ min}}}{1 \cancel{\text{ h}}} \times \frac{60 \text{ s}}{1 \cancel{\text{ min}}} = 1.44 \times 10^4 \text{ s then}$$

$$\frac{1.\underline{0}210 \times 10^{19} \cancel{\text{ beta decays}}}{1.44 \times 10^4 \cancel{\text{ s}}} \times \frac{1 \text{ Ci}}{\dfrac{3.7 \times 10^{10} \cancel{\text{ decays}}}{\cancel{\text{s}}}} = 1.\underline{9}163 \times 10^4 \text{ Ci} = 2 \times 10^4 \text{ Ci}$$

Check: The units (Ci) are correct. The amount that decays is large because the half-life is fairly short; so the dose is high.

Cumulative Problems

19.45   **Given:** (a) Ru-114, (b) Ra-216, (c) Zn-58, and (d) Ne-31   **Find:** Write a nuclear equation for the most likely decay.
     Conceptual Plan: Referring to the Valley of Stability graph in Figure 19.4, decide on the most likely decay mode depending on N/Z (too large = beta decay, too low = positron emission). → Write the symbol for the parent nuclide on the left side of the equation and the symbol for a particle on the right side. → Equalize the sum of the mass numbers and the sum of the atomic numbers on both sides of the equation by writing the appropriate mass number and atomic number for the unknown daughter nuclide. → Using the periodic table, deduce the identity of the unknown daughter nuclide from the atomic number and write its symbol.
     Solution:

(a)   Ru-114 ($N/Z = 1.6$) will undergo beta decay $^{114}_{44}\text{Ru} \rightarrow ^{?}_{?}? + ^{0}_{-1}\text{e}$ then $^{114}_{44}\text{Ru} \rightarrow ^{114}_{45}? + ^{0}_{-1}\text{e}$ then
     $^{114}_{44}\text{Ru} \rightarrow ^{114}_{45}\text{Rh} + ^{0}_{-1}\text{e}$

(b)   Ra-216 ($N/Z = 1.4$) will undergo positron emission $^{216}_{88}\text{Ra} \rightarrow ^{?}_{?}? + ^{0}_{+1}\text{e}$ then $^{216}_{88}\text{Ra} \rightarrow ^{216}_{87}? + ^{0}_{+1}\text{e}$ then
     $^{216}_{88}\text{Ra} \rightarrow ^{216}_{87}\text{Fr} + ^{0}_{+1}\text{e}$

(c)   Zn-58 ($N/Z = 0.9$) will undergo positron emission $^{58}_{30}\text{Zn} \rightarrow ^{?}_{?}? + ^{0}_{+1}\text{e}$ then $^{58}_{30}\text{Zn} \rightarrow ^{58}_{29}? + ^{0}_{+1}\text{e}$ then
     $^{58}_{30}\text{Zn} \rightarrow ^{58}_{29}\text{Cu} + ^{0}_{+1}\text{e}$

(d)   Ne-31 ($N/Z = 2$) will undergo beta decay $^{31}_{10}\text{Ne} \rightarrow ^{?}_{?}? + ^{0}_{-1}\text{e}$ then $^{31}_{10}\text{Ne} \rightarrow ^{31}_{11}? + ^{0}_{-1}\text{e}$ then $^{31}_{10}\text{Ne} \rightarrow ^{31}_{11}\text{Na} + ^{0}_{-1}\text{e}$

Check: (a) $114 = 114 + 0$, $44 = 45 - 1$, and rhodium is atomic number 45. (b) $216 = 216 + 0$, $88 = 87 + 1$, and francium is atomic number 87. (c) $58 = 58 + 0$, $30 = 29 + 1$, and copper is atomic number 29. (d) $31 = 31 + 0$, $10 = 11 - 1$, and sodium is atomic number 11.

19.46 **Given:** (a) Kr-74, (b) Th-221, (c) Ar-44, and (d) Nb-85
Find: Write a nuclear equation for the most likely decay.
Conceptual Plan: Referring to the Valley of Stability graph in Figure 19.4, decide on the most likely decay mode depending on N/Z (too large = beta decay, too low = positron emission). → Write the symbol for the parent nuclide on the left side of the equation and the symbol for a particle on the right side. → Equalize the sum of the mass numbers and the sum of the atomic numbers on both sides of the equation by writing the appropriate mass number and atomic number for the unknown daughter nuclide. → Using the periodic table, deduce the identity of the unknown daughter nuclide from the atomic number and write its symbol.
Solution:

(a)   Kr-74 ($N/Z = 1$) will undergo positron emission $^{74}_{36}\text{Kr} \rightarrow {}^{?}_{?}? + {}^{0}_{+1}\text{e}$ then $^{74}_{36}\text{Kr} \rightarrow {}^{74}_{35}? + {}^{0}_{+1}\text{e}$ then $^{74}_{36}\text{Kr} \rightarrow {}^{74}_{35}\text{Br} + {}^{0}_{+1}\text{e}$

(b)   Th-221 ($N/Z = 1.5$) will undergo positron emission $^{221}_{90}\text{Th} \rightarrow {}^{?}_{?}? + {}^{0}_{+1}\text{e}$ then $^{221}_{90}\text{Th} \rightarrow {}^{221}_{89}? + {}^{0}_{+1}\text{e}$ then $^{221}_{90}\text{Th} \rightarrow {}^{221}_{89}\text{Ac} + {}^{0}_{+1}\text{e}$

(c)   Ar-44 ($N/Z = 1.4$) will undergo beta decay $^{44}_{18}\text{Ar} \rightarrow {}^{?}_{?}? + {}^{0}_{-1}\text{e}$ then $^{44}_{18}\text{Ar} \rightarrow {}^{44}_{19}? + {}^{0}_{-1}\text{e}$ then $^{44}_{18}\text{Ar} \rightarrow {}^{44}_{19}\text{K} + {}^{0}_{-1}\text{e}$

(d)   Nb-85 ($N/Z = 1.1$) will undergo positron emission $^{85}_{41}\text{Nb} \rightarrow {}^{?}_{?}? + {}^{0}_{+1}\text{e}$ then $^{85}_{41}\text{Nb} \rightarrow {}^{85}_{40}? + {}^{0}_{+1}\text{e}$ then $^{85}_{41}\text{Nb} \rightarrow {}^{85}_{40}\text{Zr} + {}^{0}_{+1}\text{e}$

Check: (a) $74 = 74 + 0, 36 = 35 + 1$, and bromine is atomic number 35. (b) $221 = 221 + 0, 90 = 89 + 1$, and actinium is atomic number 89. (c) $44 = 44 + 0, 18 = 19 - 1$, and potassium is atomic number 19. (d) $85 = 85 + 0, 41 = 40 + 1$, and zirconium is atomic number 40.

19.47 **Given:** Bi-210, $t_{1/2} = 5.0$ days, 1.2 g Bi-210, 209.984105 amu, 5.5% absorbed
Find: beta emissions in 13.5 days and dose (in Ci)
Conceptual Plan: $t_{1/2} \rightarrow k$ then $m_{\text{Bi-210 0}}, t, k \rightarrow m_{\text{Bi-210 }t}$ then

$$t_{1/2} = \frac{0.693}{k} \qquad \ln N_t = -kt + \ln N_0$$

$g_0, g_t \rightarrow$ g decayed $\rightarrow$ mol decayed $\rightarrow$ beta decays then day $\rightarrow$ h $\rightarrow$ min $\rightarrow$ s then

$$g_0 - g_t = \text{g decayed} \quad \frac{1 \text{ mol Bi-210}}{209.984105 \text{ g Bi-210}} \quad \frac{6.022 \times 10^{23} \text{ beta decays}}{1 \text{ mol Bi-210}} \quad \frac{24 \text{ h}}{1 \text{ day}} \quad \frac{60 \text{ min}}{1 \text{ h}} \quad \frac{60 \text{ s}}{1 \text{ min}}$$

beta decays, s $\rightarrow$ beta decays/s $\rightarrow$ Ci available $\rightarrow$ Ci absorbed

$$\text{take ratio} \qquad \frac{1 \text{ Ci}}{\frac{3.7 \times 10^{10} \text{ decays}}{\text{s}}} \qquad \frac{5.5 \text{ Ci absorbed}}{100 \text{ Ci emitted}}$$

Solution: $t_{1/2} = \dfrac{0.693}{k}$; rearrange to solve for k. $k = \dfrac{0.693}{t_{1/2}} = \dfrac{0.693}{5.0 \text{ days}} = 0.1\underline{3}86 \text{ day}^{-1}$. Because

$\ln m_{\text{Bi-210 }t} = -kt + \ln m_{\text{Bi-210 0}} = -(0.1\underline{3}86 \text{ day}^{-1})(13.5 \text{ day}) + \ln (1.2 \text{ g}) = -1.6\underline{8}88 \rightarrow$

$m_{\text{Bi-210 }t} = e^{-1.6\underline{8}88} = 0.18\underline{4}74 \text{ g}$ then $g_0 - g_t = \text{g decayed} = 1.2 \text{ g} - 0.18\underline{4}74 \text{ g} = 1.0\underline{1}53 \text{ g Bi-210}$

then $1.0\underline{1}53 \text{ g Bi-210} \times \dfrac{1 \text{ mol Bi-210}}{209.984105 \text{ g Bi-210}} \times \dfrac{6.022 \times 10^{23} \text{ beta decays}}{1 \text{ mol Bi-210}} = 2.9\underline{1}17 \times 10^{21} \text{ beta decays}$

$= 2.9 \times 10^{21}$ beta decays then $13.5 \text{ day} \times \dfrac{24 \text{ h}}{1 \text{ day}} \times \dfrac{60 \text{ min}}{1 \text{ h}} \times \dfrac{60 \text{ s}}{1 \text{ min}} = 1.1\underline{6}64 \times 10^6 \text{ s}$ then

$\dfrac{2.9\underline{1}17 \times 10^{21} \text{ beta decays}}{1.1\underline{6}64 \times 10^6 \text{ s}} \times \dfrac{1 \text{ Ci}}{\frac{3.7 \times 10^{10} \text{ decays}}{\text{s}}} = 6.7\underline{4}68 \times 10^4 \text{ Ci emitted} \times \dfrac{5.5 \text{ Ci absorbed}}{100 \text{ Ci emitted}} = 3700 \text{ Ci}$

Check: The units (decays and Ci) are correct. The amount that decays is large because the time is over three half-lives and we have a relatively large amount of the isotope. Because the decay is large, the dosage is large.

19.48 **Given:** Po-218, $t_{1/2} = 3.0$ minutes, 55 mg Po-218, 218.008965 amu
Find: alpha emissions in 25.0 min and dose (in Ci)
Conceptual Plan: $t_{1/2} \rightarrow k$ then $m_{\text{Po-218 0}}, t, k \rightarrow m_{\text{Po-218 }t}$ then

$$t_{1/2} = \frac{0.693}{k} \qquad \ln N_t = -kt + \ln N_0$$

$mg_0, mg_t \rightarrow$ mg decayed $\rightarrow$ g decayed $\rightarrow$ mol decayed $\rightarrow$ alpha decays then min $\rightarrow$ s

$$mg_0 - mg_t = \text{mg decayed} \quad \frac{1 \text{ g}}{1000 \text{ mg}} \quad \frac{1 \text{ mol Po-218}}{218.008965 \text{ g Po-218}} \quad \frac{6.022 \times 10^{23} \text{ alpha decays}}{1 \text{ mol Po-218}} \quad \frac{60 \text{ s}}{1 \text{ min}}$$

then beta decays, s → **beta decay/s → Ci**

$$\text{take ratio} \quad \frac{1\ \text{Ci}}{3.7 \times 10^{10}\ \text{decays}}$$

Solution: $t_{1/2} = \dfrac{0.693}{k}$; rearrange to solve for k. $k = \dfrac{0.693}{t_{1/2}} = \dfrac{0.693}{3.0\ \text{min}} = 0.231\ \text{min}^{-1}$. Because

$\ln m_{\text{Po-218}\ t} = -kt + \ln m_{\text{Po-218}\ 0} = -(0.231\ \text{min}^{-1})(25.0\ \text{min}) + \ln(55\ \text{mg}) = -1.7677 \rightarrow$

$m_{\text{Po-218}\ t} = e^{-1.7677} = 0.17073\ \text{mg}$ then

$\text{mg}_0 - \text{mg}_t = \text{mg decayed} = 55\ \text{mg} - 0.17073\ \text{mg} = 54.829\ \text{mg Po-218}$ then $54.829\ \text{mg Po-218}$

$$54.829\ \text{mg Po-218} \times \frac{1\ \text{g Po-218}}{1000\ \text{mg Po-218}} \times \frac{1\ \text{mol Po-218}}{218.008965\ \text{g Po-218}} \times \frac{6.022 \times 10^{23}\ \text{alpha decays}}{1\ \text{mol Po-218}} =$$

1.5145×10^{20} alpha decays $= 1.5 \times 10^{20}$ alpha decays then

$$25.0\ \text{min} \times \frac{60\ \text{s}}{1\ \text{min}} = 1.5 \times 10^3\ \text{s then} \quad \frac{1.5145 \times 10^{20}\ \text{alpha decays}}{1.5 \times 10^3\ \text{s}} \times \frac{1\ \text{Ci}}{\dfrac{3.7 \times 10^{10}\ \text{decays}}{\text{s}}} = 2.7 \times 10^6\ \text{Ci}$$

Check: The units (decays and Ci) are correct. The amount that decays is large because the time is over eight half-lives; so almost the entire isotope has decayed. Because the decay rate is large (small half-life), the dosage is large.

19.49   **Given:** Ra-226 (226.025402 amu) decays to Rn-224, $t_{1/2} = 1.6 \times 10^3$yr, 25.0 g Ra-226, $T = 25.0\ °\text{C}$, $P = 1.0$ atm
      Find: V of Rn-224 gas produced in 5.0 day
      Conceptual Plan: day → yr then $t_{1/2}$ → k then $m_{\text{Ra-226}\ 0}\ t, k$ → $m_{\text{Ra-226}\ t}$

$$\frac{1\ \text{yr}}{365.24\ \text{day}} \qquad t_{1/2} = \frac{0.693}{k} \qquad \ln N_t = -kt + \ln N_0$$

      then g_0, g_t → **g decayed** → **mol decayed** → **mol Rn-224 formed then** $°\text{C}$ → K then P, n, T → V

$$g_0 - g_t = \text{g decayed} \quad \frac{1\ \text{mol Ra-226}}{226.025402\ \text{g Ra-226}} \quad \frac{1\ \text{mol Rn-224}}{1\ \text{mol Ra-226}} \qquad\qquad K = °\text{C} + 273.15 \qquad PV = nRT$$

      Solution: $5.0\ \text{day} \times \dfrac{1\ \text{yr}}{365.24\ \text{day}} = 0.013690\ \text{yr}$ then $t_{1/2} = \dfrac{0.693}{k}$; rearrange to solve for k.

$k = \dfrac{0.693}{t_{1/2}} = \dfrac{0.693}{1.6 \times 10^3\ \text{yr}} = 4.33125 \times 10^{-4}\ \text{yr}^{-1}$. Because

$\ln m_{\text{Ra-226}\ t} = -kt + \ln m_{\text{Ra-226}\ 0} = -(4.33125 \times 10^{-4}\ \text{yr}^{-1})(0.013690\ \text{yr}) + \ln(25.0\ \text{g}) = 3.21887 \rightarrow$

$m_{\text{Ra-226}\ t} = e^{3.21887} = 24.999854\ \text{g}$ then

$g_0 - g_t = \text{g decayed} = 25.0\ \text{g} - 24.999854\ \text{g} = 0.000146\ \text{g Ra-226}$ then

$0.000146\ \text{g Ra-226} \times \dfrac{1\ \text{mol Ra-226}}{226.025402\ \text{g Ra-226}} \times \dfrac{1\ \text{mol Rn-224}}{1\ \text{mol Ra-226}} = 6.5584 \times 10^{-7}\ \text{mol Rn-224}$ then

$T = 25.0\ °\text{C} + 273.15 = 298.2\ \text{K}$ then $PV = nRT$. Rearrange to solve for V.

$$V = \frac{nRT}{P} = \frac{6.5584 \times 10^{-7}\ \text{mol} \times 0.08206\ \dfrac{\text{L} \cdot \text{atm}}{\text{mol} \cdot \text{K}} \times 298.2\ \text{K}}{1.0\ \text{atm}} = 1.6049 \times 10^{-5}\ \text{L} = 1.6 \times 10^{-5}\ \text{L}.\ \text{Two}$$

significant figures are reported as requested in the problem.

Check: The units (L) are correct. The amount of gas is small because the time is so small compared to the half-life.

19.50   **Given:** U-235 (235.043922 amu) neutron-induced fission to Ba-140 and Kr-93, 1.00 g U-235, $T = 25.0\ °\text{C}$,
      $P = 1.0$ atm   **Find:** V of Kr-93 gas produced
      Conceptual Plan: Write the species given on the appropriate side of the equation. → Equalize the sum of the mass numbers and the sum of the atomic numbers on both sides of the equation by writing the stoichiometric coefficient in front of the desired species. Then

      g U-235 → mol U-235 → mol Kr-93 formed then $°\text{C}$ → K then P, n, T → V

$$\frac{1\ \text{mol U-235}}{235.043922\ \text{g U-235}} \quad \frac{1\ \text{mol Kr-93}}{1\ \text{mol U-235}} \qquad\qquad K = °\text{C} + 273.15 \qquad PV = nRT$$

      Solution: $^{235}_{92}\text{U} + ^{1}_{0}\text{n} \rightarrow ^{140}_{56}\text{Ba} + ^{93}_{36}\text{Kr} + ?^{1}_{0}\text{n}$ becomes $^{235}_{92}\text{U} + ^{1}_{0}\text{n} \rightarrow ^{140}_{56}\text{Ba} + ^{93}_{36}\text{Kr} + 3\ ^{1}_{0}\text{n}$

      then $1.00\ \text{g U-235} \times \dfrac{1\ \text{mol U-235}}{235.043922\ \text{g U-235}} \times \dfrac{1\ \text{mol Kr-93}}{1\ \text{mol U-235}} = 4.25452 \times 10^{-3}\ \text{mol Kr-93}$

then $T = 25.0\,°C + 273.15 = 298.2$ K then $PV = nRT$ Rearrange to solve for V.

$$V = \frac{nRT}{P} = \frac{4.25452 \times 10^{-3}\ \text{mol} \times 0.08206\ \dfrac{L \cdot atm}{mol \cdot K} \times 298.2\ K}{1.0\ atm} = 0.104109\ L = 0.10\ L$$

Check: $235 + 1 = 140 + 93 + 3(1)$, $92 + 0 = 56 + 36 + 3(0)$, and no other particle is necessary to balance the equation. The units (L) are correct. About 1/200 mole of gas is generated, so we expect the volume to be about 22/200 L.

19.51 **Given:** $_{+1}^{0}e + _{-1}^{0}e \rightarrow 2\,_{0}^{0}\gamma$ **Find:** energy (in kJ/mol)
Conceptual Plan:
mass of products and reactants $\rightarrow$ mass defect (g) $\rightarrow$ kg $\rightarrow$ kg/mol $\rightarrow$ E (J/mol) $\rightarrow$ E (kJ/mol)

$$\text{mass defect} = \sum\text{mass of reactants} - \sum\text{mass of products} \qquad \frac{1\ \text{kg}}{1000\ \text{g}} \qquad 2\ \text{mol} \qquad E = mc^2 \qquad \frac{1\ \text{kJ}}{1000\ \text{J}}$$

Solution: mass defect $= \sum$ mass of reactants $- \sum$ mass of products $= (0.00055\ g + 0.00055\ g) - 0\ g =$

0.00110 g then $\dfrac{0.00110\ g}{2\ mol} \times \dfrac{1\ kg}{1000\ g} = 5.50 \times 10^{-7}\ \dfrac{kg}{mol}$ then

$$E = mc^2 = \left(5.50 \times 10^{-7}\ \frac{kg}{mol}\right)\left(2.9979 \times 10^8\ \frac{m}{s}\right)^2 = 4.94307 \times 10^{10}\ \frac{J}{mol} \times \frac{1\ kJ}{1000\ J} = 4.94 \times 10^7\ \frac{kJ}{mol}$$

Check: The units (kJ/mol) are correct. A large amount of energy is expected per mole of mass lost. The photon is in the gamma ray region of the electromagnetic spectrum.

19.52 **Given:** 1.0 MW power/day **Find:** minimum rate of mass loss required
Conceptual Plan: MW $\rightarrow$ MWh $\rightarrow$ kWh $\rightarrow$ J $\rightarrow$ kg $\rightarrow$ g

$$\frac{24\ h}{1\ day} \qquad \frac{1000\ kWh}{1\ MWh} \qquad \frac{3.60 \times 10^6\ J}{1\ kWh} \qquad E = mc^2 \qquad \frac{1000\ g}{1\ kg}$$

Solution: $1.0\ MW \times \dfrac{24\ h}{1\ day} \times \dfrac{1000\ kWh}{1\ MWh} \times \dfrac{3.60 \times 10^6\ J}{1\ kWh} = 8.64 \times 10^{10}\ \dfrac{J}{day}$. Because $E = mc^2$, rearrange to solve

for m. $m = \dfrac{E}{c^2} = \dfrac{8.64 \times 10^{10}\ \dfrac{kg\ m^2}{day\ s^2}}{\left(2.9979 \times 10^8 \dfrac{m}{s}\right)^2} = 9.6 \times 10^{-7}\ \dfrac{kg}{day} \times \dfrac{1000\ g}{1\ kg} = 9.6 \times 10^{-4}\ \dfrac{g}{day}$

Check: The units (g/day) are correct. A large amount of energy is expected per gram of mass lost.

19.53 **Given:** ^{3}He $= 3.016030$ amu **Find:** nuclear binding energy per atom
Conceptual Plan: $_Z^A X$, **isotope mass $\rightarrow$ mass defect $\rightarrow$ nuclear binding energy per nucleon**

$$\text{mass defect} = Z(\text{mass } _1^1\text{H}) + (A-Z)(\text{mass } _0^1\text{n}) - \text{mass of isotope} \qquad \frac{931.5\ \text{MeV}}{1\ \text{amu}}$$

Solution: mass defect $= Z(\text{mass } _1^1\text{H}) + (A-Z)(\text{mass } _0^1\text{n}) - \text{mass of isotope}$
He-3 mass defect $= 2(1.00783\ \text{amu}) + (3 - 2)(1.00866\ \text{amu}) - 3.016030\ \text{amu} = 0.00829\ \text{amu}$

and $0.00829\ \text{amu} \times \dfrac{931.5\ \text{MeV}}{1\ \text{amu}} = 7.72\ \text{MeV}$

Check: The units (MeV) are correct. The number of nucleons is small, so the MeV is not that large.

19.54 **Given:** $4\,_1^1\text{H} \rightarrow\,_2^4\text{He}$ **Find:** energy (in J/mol reactant)
Conceptual Plan: mass of products and reactants $\rightarrow$ mass defect in g $\rightarrow$ mass defect in kg $\rightarrow$ E

$$\text{mass defect} = \sum\text{mass of reactants} - \sum\text{mass of products} \qquad \frac{1\ \text{kg}}{1000\ \text{g}} \qquad E = mc^2$$

Solution:
mass defect $= \sum$ mass of reactants $- \sum$ mass of products $= 4(1.00783\ g) - 4.002603\ g = 0.028717\ g$

then $\dfrac{0.028717\ g}{4\ \text{mol reactants}} \times \dfrac{1\ kg}{1000\ g} = 7.17925 \times 10^{-6}\ \dfrac{kg}{\text{mol reactants}}$ then

$$E = mc^2 = \left(7.17925 \times 10^{-6}\ \frac{kg}{mol\ reactants}\right)\left(2.9979 \times 10^8\ \frac{m}{s}\right)^2 = 6.4523 \times 10^{11}\ \frac{J}{mol\ reactants}$$

Check: The units (J/mol) are correct.

19.55 **Given:** $t_{1/2}$ for decay of ^{238}U $= 4.5 \times 10^9$ years, 1.6 g rock, 29 dis/s all radioactivity from U-238
Find: percent by mass ^{238}U in rock
Conceptual Plan: $t_{1/2} \to k$ and s $\to$ min $\to$ h $\to$ day $\to$ yr then Rate, $k \to N \to$ mol ^{238}U $\to$ g ^{238}U

$$t_{1/2} = \frac{0.693}{k} \qquad \frac{1\ min}{60\ s} \quad \frac{1\ h}{60\ min} \quad \frac{1\ day}{24\ h} \quad \frac{1\ yr}{365.24\ day} \qquad Rate = kN \quad \frac{1\ mol\ dis}{6.022 \times 10^{23}\ dis} \quad \frac{238\ g\ ^{238}U}{1\ mol\ ^{238}U}$$

then g ^{238}U, g rock $\to$ **percent by mass ^{238}U**

$$percent\ by\ mass\ ^{238}U = \frac{g\ ^{238}U}{g\ rock} \times 100\%$$

Solution: $t_{1/2} = \frac{0.693}{k}$; rearrange to solve for k. $k = \frac{0.693}{t_{1/2}} = \frac{0.693}{4.5 \times 10^9\ yr} = 1.54 \times 10^{-10}\ yr^{-1}$ and

$$1\ s \times \frac{1\ min}{60\ s} \times \frac{1\ h}{60\ min} \times \frac{1\ day}{24\ h} \times \frac{1\ yr}{365.24\ day} = 3.16889554 \times 10^{-8}\ yr.\ Rate = kN.\ \text{Rearrange to}$$

solve for N.

$$N = \frac{Rate}{k} = \frac{\dfrac{29\ dis}{3.16889554 \times 10^{-8}\ yr}}{1.54 \times 10^{-10}\ yr^{-1}} = 5.9425 \times 10^{18}\ dis\ then$$

$$5.9425 \times 10^{18}\ dis \times \frac{1\ mol\ dis}{6.022 \times 10^{23}\ dis} \times \frac{238\ g\ ^{238}U}{1\ mol\ ^{238}U} = 2.3486 \times 10^{-3} g\ ^{238}U\ then$$

$$percent\ by\ mass\ ^{238}U = \frac{g\ ^{238}U}{g\ rock} \times 100\% = \frac{2.3486 \times 10^{-3}\ g\ ^{238}U}{1.6\ g\ rock} \times 100\% = 0.15\%$$

Check: The units (%) are correct. The mass percent is low because the dis/s is low.

19.56 **Given:** $t_{1/2}$ for decay of ^{232}Th $= 1.4 \times 10^{10}$ years **Find:** number of dis emitted by 1.0 mol ^{232}Th in 1 min
Conceptual Plan: $t_{1/2} \to k$ then $N, k \to$ Rate (dis/yr) $\to$ dis/day $\to$ dis/h $\to$ dis/min

$$t_{1/2} = \frac{0.693}{k} \qquad Rate = kN \qquad \frac{1\ yr}{365.24\ day} \quad \frac{1\ day}{24\ h} \quad \frac{1\ h}{60\ min}$$

Solution: $t_{1/2} = \frac{0.693}{k}$; rearrange to solve for k. $k = \frac{0.693}{t_{1/2}} = \frac{0.693}{1.4 \times 10^{10}\ yr} = 4.95 \times 10^{-11}\ yr^{-1}$ then

$$Rate = kN = (4.95 \times 10^{-11}\ yr^{-1})(6.022 \times 10^{23}\ dis) \times \frac{1\ yr}{365.24\ day} \times \frac{1\ day}{24\ h} = 3.4 \times 10^9\ dis/h$$

$$3.4 \times 10^9\ dis/h \times \frac{1\ h}{60\ min} = 5.7 \times 10^7\ dis/min$$

Check: The units (dis/h and dis/min) are correct. The rate is high because the amount of ^{232}Th is high.

19.57 **Given:** $V = 1.50$ L, $P = 745$ mmHg, $T = 25.0\ °C$, 3.55% Rn-220 by volume, $t_{1/2} = 55.6$ s
Find: number of alpha particles emitted in 5.00 min
Conceptual Plan: mmg $\to$ atm and °C $\to$ K then $P, V, T \to n_{Total} \to n_{Rn\text{-}220}$ and min $\to$ s

$$\frac{1\ atm}{760\ mmHg} \qquad K = °C + 273.15 \qquad PV = nRT \quad \frac{3.55\ mol\ Rn\text{-}220\ particles}{100\ mol\ gas\ particles} \quad \frac{60\ s}{1\ min}$$

then $t_{1/2} \to k$ then $n_{Rn\text{-}220\ 0}, t, k \to n_{Rn\text{-}220\ t} \to$ **number of particles remaining** $\to$ **particles emitted**

$$t_{1/2} = \frac{0.693}{k} \qquad \ln N_t = -kt + \ln N_0 \qquad \frac{6.022 \times 10^{23}\ particles}{1\ mol}$$

Solution: $745\ mmHg \times \frac{1\ atm}{760\ mmHg} = 0.9802632\ atm$ and $T = 25.0\ °C + 273.15 = 298.2\ K$ then

$PV = nRT$. Rearrange to solve for n.

$$n = \frac{PV}{RT} = \frac{0.9802632\ atm \times 1.50\ L}{0.08206\ \frac{L \cdot atm}{mol \cdot K} \times 298.2\ K} = 0.06008898\ mol\ gas\ particles$$

then $0.06008898 \text{ mol gas particles} \times \dfrac{3.55 \text{ mol Rn-220 particles}}{100 \text{ mol gas particles}} = 0.002133159 \text{ mol Rn-220 particles}$

$5.00 \text{ min} \times \dfrac{60 \text{ s}}{1 \text{ min}} = 300. \text{ s then } t_{1/2} = \dfrac{0.693}{k}$ and rearrange to solve for k.

$k = \dfrac{0.693}{t_{1/2}} = \dfrac{0.693}{55.6 \text{ s}} = 0.01246403 \text{ s}^{-1}$. Because

$\ln m_{\text{Rn-220 } t} = -k\,t + \ln m_{\text{Rn-220 } 0} = -(0.01246403 \text{ s}^{-1})(300. \text{ s}) + \ln (0.002133159 \text{ mol}) = -9.889360 \rightarrow$

$m_{\text{Rn-220 } t} = e^{-9.889360} = 5.071139 \times 10^{-5} \text{ mol alpha particles remaining}$

The number of alpha particles emitted would be the difference between this and the initial number of moles.

$0.002133158 \text{ mol} - 0.00005071139 \text{ mol} = 0.002082447 \text{ mol}$

$0.002082447 \text{ mol} \times \dfrac{6.022 \times 10^{23} \text{ particles}}{1 \text{ mol}} = 1.254050 \times 10^{21} \text{ particles} = 1.25 \times 10^{21} \text{ particles}$

Check: The units (particles) are correct. The number of particles is far less than a mole, because we have far less than a mole of gas.

19.58   **Given:** 228 mL of 2.35% by mass $MgCl_2$; exactly $\frac{1}{2}$ of Mg is Mg-28, $t_{1/2} = 21$ h, $d = 1.02$ g/mL
 Find: decay rate after 4.00 days
 Conceptual Plan: mL $\rightarrow$ g solution $\rightarrow$ g $MgCl_2$ $\rightarrow$ mol Mg $\rightarrow$ atoms Mg $\rightarrow$ atoms Mg-28 and

$\dfrac{1.02 \text{ g}}{1 \text{ mL}} \quad \dfrac{2.35 \text{ g } MgCl_2}{100 \text{ g solution}} \quad \dfrac{1 \text{ mol Mg}}{95.21 \text{ g } MgCl_2} \quad \dfrac{6.022 \times 10^{23} \text{ Mg atoms}}{1 \text{ mol Mg}} \quad \dfrac{1 \text{ Mg-28 atom}}{2 \text{ Mg atoms}}$

days $\rightarrow$ h then $t_{1/2} \rightarrow k$ then $N_{\text{Mg-28 } 0}, t, k \rightarrow N_{\text{Mg-28 } t} \rightarrow$ Rate

$\dfrac{1 \text{ day}}{24 \text{ h}} \qquad t_{1/2} = \dfrac{0.693}{k} \qquad \ln N_t = -k\,t + \ln N_0 \quad \text{Rate} = kN$

Solution: $228 \text{ mL solution} \times \dfrac{1.02 \text{ g solution}}{1 \text{ mL solution}} \times \dfrac{2.35 \text{ g } MgCl_2}{100 \text{ g solution}} \times \dfrac{1 \text{ mol Mg}}{95.21 \text{ g } MgCl_2} \times \dfrac{6.022 \times 10^{23} \text{ Mg atoms}}{1 \text{ mol Mg}} \times$

$\dfrac{1 \text{ Mg-28 atom}}{2 \text{ Mg atoms}} = 1.728348 \times 10^{22} \text{ Mg-28 atoms}$

and $21 \text{ h} \times \dfrac{1 \text{ day}}{24 \text{ h}} = 0.875 \text{ day then } t_{1/2} = \dfrac{0.693}{k}$; rearrange to solve for k.

$k = \dfrac{0.693}{t_{1/2}} = \dfrac{0.693}{0.875 \text{ day}} = 0.792 \text{ day}^{-1}$. Because

$\ln N_{\text{Mg-28 } t} = -k\,t + \ln N_{\text{Mg-28 } 0} = -(0.792 \text{ day}^{-1})(4.00 \text{ day}) + \ln (1.728348 \times 10^{22}) = 48.03604 \rightarrow$

$N_{\text{Mg-28 } t} = e^{48.03604} = 7.2742 \times 10^{20} \text{ Mg-28 atoms. Finally, Rate} = kN, \text{ so}$

Rate $= 0.792/\text{day} \times 7.2742 \times 10^{20} = 5.8 \times 10^{20}$ atoms/day.

Check: The units (atoms) are correct. The number of particles is far less than a mole because we have a dilute solution.

19.59   **Given:** $_{+1}^{0}e + _{-1}^{0}e \rightarrow 2\,_{0}^{0}\gamma$ **Find:** wavelength of gamma ray photons
 Conceptual Plan:
 mass of products and reactants $\rightarrow$ mass defect (g) $\rightarrow$ kg $\rightarrow$ kg/mol $\rightarrow$ E (J/mol) $\rightarrow$ E (kJ/mol)

$\text{mass defect} = \sum \text{mass of reactants} - \sum \text{mass of products} \quad \dfrac{1 \text{ kg}}{1000 \text{ g}} \quad 2 \text{ mol} \quad E = mc^2 \quad \dfrac{1 \text{ kJ}}{1000 \text{ J}}$

This energy is for 2 moles of γ, so E(J/2 mol γ) $\rightarrow$ E(J/γ photon) $\rightarrow$ λ.

$\dfrac{1 \text{ mol } \gamma}{6.022 \times 10^{23} \gamma \text{ photons}} \qquad E = \dfrac{hc}{\lambda}$

Solution: mass defect $= \sum \text{mass of reactants} - \sum \text{mass of products} = (0.00055 \text{ g} + 0.00055 \text{ g}) - 0 \text{ g} =$

$0.00110 \text{ g then } \dfrac{0.00110 \text{ g}}{2 \text{ mol}} \times \dfrac{1 \text{ kg}}{1000 \text{ g}} = 5.50 \times 10^{-7} \dfrac{\text{kg}}{\text{mol}} \text{ then}$

$E = mc^2 = \left(5.50 \times 10^{-7} \dfrac{\text{kg}}{\text{mol}}\right)\left(2.9979 \times 10^{8} \dfrac{\text{m}}{\text{s}}\right)^2 = 4.94307 \times 10^{10} \dfrac{\text{J}}{\text{mol}} \times \dfrac{1 \text{ kJ}}{1000 \text{ J}} = 4.94 \times 10^{7} \dfrac{\text{kJ}}{\text{mol}}$

$$E = 4.9\underline{4}307 \times 10^{10} \frac{J}{\text{mol } \gamma} \times \frac{1 \text{ mol } \gamma}{6.022 \times 10^{23} \gamma \text{ photons}} = 8.2\underline{0}835 \times 10^{-14} \frac{J}{\gamma \text{ photons}}. \text{ Then } E = \frac{h\,c}{\lambda}. \text{ Rearrange}$$

$$\text{to solve for } \lambda. \ \lambda = \frac{h\,c}{E} = \frac{(6.626 \times 10^{-34} \, J \cdot s)\left(2.9979 \times 10^8 \, \frac{m}{s}\right)}{8.2\underline{0}835 \times 10^{-14} \frac{J}{\gamma \text{ photons}}} = 2.42 \times 10^{-12} \text{ m} = 2.42 \text{ pm}$$

Check: The units (m or pm) are correct. A large amount of energy is expected per mole of mass lost. The photon is in the gamma ray region of the electromagnetic spectrum.

19.60   **Given:** 1.0 mg U-235, $t_{1/2} = 7.1 \times 10^8$ yr
Find: alpha particles emitted in 1.0 min
Conceptual Plan: Because the time is so small compared to the half-life, use Rate $= kN_0$ and calculate the number of particles emitted based on the initial rate.

mg $\rightarrow$ g $\rightarrow$ mol $\rightarrow$ atoms (N_0) and

$$\frac{1 \text{ g}}{1000 \text{ mg}} \quad \frac{1 \text{ mol}}{235 \text{ g}} \quad \frac{6.022 \times 10^{23} \text{ atoms}}{1 \text{ mol}}$$

min $\rightarrow$ h $\rightarrow$ days $\rightarrow$ yr then $t_{1/2} \rightarrow k$ then $N_{\text{U-235 0}}, t, k \rightarrow$ alpha particles emitted

$$\frac{1 \text{ h}}{60 \text{ min}} \quad \frac{1 \text{ day}}{24 \text{ h}} \quad \frac{1 \text{ yr}}{365.24 \text{ days}} \qquad t_{1/2} = \frac{0.693}{k} \qquad \qquad \text{Rate} = kN_0$$

Solution: $1.0 \text{ mg} \times \dfrac{1 \text{ g}}{1000 \text{ mg}} \times \dfrac{1 \text{ mol}}{235 \text{ g}} \times \dfrac{6.022 \times 10^{23} \text{ atoms}}{1 \text{ mol}} = 2.5\underline{6}255 \times 10^{18}$ atoms and

$1.0 \text{ min} \times \dfrac{1 \text{ h}}{60 \text{ min}} \times \dfrac{1 \text{ day}}{24 \text{ h}} \times \dfrac{1 \text{ yr}}{365.24 \text{ day}} = 1.9\underline{0}1337 \times 10^{-6}$ yr then $t_{1/2} = \dfrac{0.693}{k}$; rearrange to solve for k.

$k = \dfrac{0.693}{t_{1/2}} = \dfrac{0.693}{7.1 \times 10^8 \text{ yr}} = 9.7\underline{6}056 \times 10^{-10} \text{ yr}^{-1}$ then

Rate $= -k \, N_{\text{U-235 0}} = (9.7\underline{6}056 \times 10^{-10} \text{ yr}^{-1})(2.5\underline{6}255 \times 10^{18} \text{ particles}) = 2.5\underline{0}1192 \times 10^9$ particles/yr then $\rightarrow$

$\dfrac{2.5\underline{0}1192 \times 10^9 \text{ particles}}{1 \text{ yr}} \times 1.9\underline{0}1337 \times 10^{-6} \text{ yr} = 4\underline{7}55.6$ particles $= 4800$ particles emitted

Check: The units (particles) are correct. The number of particles is small because the half-life is long and the observation time is small.

19.61   **Given:** $^2_1\text{H} + ^2_1\text{H} \rightarrow ^3_2\text{He} + ^1_0\text{n}$ releases 3.3 MeV; $^2_1\text{H} + ^2_1\text{H} \rightarrow ^3_1\text{H} + ^1_1\text{p}$ releases 4.0 MeV
Find: The energy change for $^3_2\text{He} + ^1_0\text{n} \rightarrow ^3_1\text{H} + ^1_1\text{p}$ and explain why this can happen at a much lower temperature.
Conceptual Plan: Use Hess's law to calculate the energy change and give the two reactions.
Solution:

$$\begin{array}{ll} ^3_2\text{He} + ^1_0\text{n} \rightarrow ^2_1\text{H} + ^2_1\text{H} & \Delta E = 3.3 \text{ MeV} \\ ^2_1\text{H} + ^2_1\text{H} \rightarrow ^3_1\text{H} + ^1_1\text{p} & \Delta E = -4.0 \text{ MeV} \\ \hline ^3_2\text{He} + ^1_0\text{n} \rightarrow ^3_1\text{H} + ^1_1\text{p} & \Delta E = -0.7 \text{ MeV} \end{array}$$

The energy change is much less, and there is no coulombic barrier for collision with a neutron; so the process can occur at lower temperatures.

Check: The units (MeV) are correct. Because one reaction releases energy and one requires energy, the resulting energy change is much smaller in magnitude.

19.62   **Given:** $^{18}_9\text{F} + ^0_{-1}\text{e} \rightarrow ^{18}_8\text{O}$ and $^{18}_9\text{F} \rightarrow ^{18}_8\text{O} + ^0_{+1}\text{e}$ **Find:** difference in energy released
Other: $^{18}_9\text{F} = 18.000950$ g and $^{18}_8\text{O} = 17.9991598$ g
Conceptual Plan: For each reaction, calculate mass of products and reactants $\rightarrow$ mass defect in amu then

$$\text{mass defect} = \sum \text{mass of reactants} - \sum \text{mass of products}$$

calculate the difference between the two mass defects in amu $\rightarrow$ E.

$$\frac{931.5 \text{ MeV}}{1 \text{ amu}}$$

Solution: Because mass defect $= \sum$ mass of reactants $- \sum$ mass of products
for $^{18}_9\text{F} + ^0_{-1}\text{e} \rightarrow ^{18}_8\text{O}$

mass defect $= (18.000950 \text{ amu} + 0.0005486 \text{ amu}) - (17.9991598 \text{ amu}) = +0.0023388 \text{ amu}$ and for
$^{18}_{9}\text{F} \rightarrow ^{18}_{8}\text{O} + ^{0}_{+1}\text{e}$, mass defect $= (18.000950 \text{ amu}) - (17.9991598 \text{ amu} + 0.0005486) = +0.0012416 \text{ amu}$
The mass defect difference between the two reactions is $0.0023388 - 0.0012416 = 0.0010972 \text{ amu} = $ mass of two
electrons then $0.0010972 \text{ amu} \times \dfrac{931.5 \text{ MeV}}{1 \text{ amu}} = 1.022 \text{ MeV}$

Check: The units (MeV) are correct. The energy is smaller than that of most nuclear reactions because the mass difference is small.

Challenge Problems

19.63   (a)   **Given:** 72,500 kg Al(s) and $10 \text{ Al}(s) + 6 \text{ NH}_4\text{ClO}_4(s) \rightarrow 4 \text{ Al}_2\text{O}_3(s) + 2 \text{ AlCl}_3(s) + 12 \text{ H}_2\text{O}(g) + 3 \text{ N}_2(g)$
and 608,000 kg $\text{O}_2(g)$ that reacts with hydrogen to form gaseous water
Find: energy generated (ΔH°_{rxn})
Conceptual Plan: Write a balanced reaction for $\text{O}_2(g)$ then

$$\Delta H^{\circ}_{rxn} = \sum n_p \Delta H^{\circ}_f (\text{products}) - \sum n_r \Delta H^{\circ}_f (\text{reactants}) \text{ then}$$

kg $\rightarrow$ g $\rightarrow$ mol $\rightarrow$ energy then add the results from the two reactions.

$$\dfrac{1000 \text{ g}}{1 \text{ kg}} \qquad \mathcal{M} \qquad \Delta H^{\circ}_{rxn}$$

Solution:

Reactant/Product	ΔH°_f (kJ/mol from Appendix IIB)
Al(s)	0.0
$\text{NH}_4\text{ClO}_4(s)$	−295
$\text{Al}_2\text{O}_3(s)$	−1675.7
$\text{AlCl}_3(s)$	−704.2
H_2O (g)	−241.8
$\text{N}_2(g)$	0.0

Be sure to pull data for the correct formula and phase.

$$\Delta H^{\circ}_{rxn} = \sum n_p \Delta H^{\circ}_f (\text{products}) - \sum n_r \Delta H^{\circ}_f (\text{reactants})$$
$$= [4(\Delta H^{\circ}_f (\text{Al}_2\text{O}_3(s))) + 2(\Delta H^{\circ}_f (\text{AlCl}_3(s))) + 12(\Delta H^{\circ}_f (\text{H}_2\text{O}(g))) + 3(\Delta H^{\circ}_f (\text{N}_2(g)))] +$$
$$-[10(\Delta H^{\circ}_f (\text{Al}(s))) + 6(\Delta H^{\circ}_f (\text{NH}_4\text{ClO}_4(s)))]$$
$$= [4(-1675.7 \text{ kJ}) + 2(-704.2 \text{ kJ}) + 12(-241.8 \text{ kJ}) + 3(0.0 \text{ kJ})] - [10(0.0 \text{ kJ}) + 6(-295 \text{ kJ})]$$
$$= [-11012.8 \text{ kJ}] - [-1770. \text{ kJ}]$$
$$= -9242.8 \text{ kJ}$$

then $72{,}500 \text{ kg Al} \times \dfrac{1000 \text{ g Al}}{1 \text{ kg Al}} \times \dfrac{1 \text{ mol Al}}{26.98 \text{ g Al}} \times \dfrac{9242.8 \text{ kJ}}{10 \text{ mol Al}} = 2.483703 \times 10^9 \text{ kJ}$

balanced reaction: $\text{H}_2(g) + \frac{1}{2}\text{O}_2(g) \rightarrow \text{H}_2\text{O}(g)$ $\Delta H^{\circ}_{rxn} = \Delta H^{\circ}_f (\text{H}_2\text{O}(g)) = -241.8 \text{ KJ/mol}$ then

$608{,}000 \text{ kg O}_2 \times \dfrac{1000 \text{ g O}_2}{1 \text{ kg O}_2} \times \dfrac{1 \text{ mol O}_2}{32.00 \text{ g O}_2} \times \dfrac{241.8 \text{ kJ}}{0.5 \text{ mol O}_2} = 9.1884 \times 10^9 \text{ kJ}$. So the total is

$2.483703 \times 10^9 \text{ kJ} + 9.1884 \times 10^9 \text{ kJ} = 1.1672103 \times 10^{10} \text{ kJ} = 1.167 \times 10^{10} \text{ kJ}$.

Check: The units (kJ) are correct. The answer is very large because the reactions are very exothermic and the weight of reactants is so large.

(b)   **Given:** $^{1}_{1}\text{H} + ^{-1}_{1}\text{p} + ^{0}_{+1}\text{e} \rightarrow ^{0}_{0}\gamma$
Find: mass of antimatter to give same energy as part (a)
Conceptual Plan: Because the reaction is an annihilation reaction, no matter will be left; so the mass of antimatter is the same as the mass of the hydrogen. So kJ $\rightarrow$ J $\rightarrow$ kg $\rightarrow$ g

$$\dfrac{1000 \text{ J}}{1 \text{ kJ}} \qquad E = mc^2 \qquad \dfrac{1000 \text{ g}}{1 \text{ kg}}$$

Solution: $1.1672103 \times 10^{10} \text{ kJ} \times \dfrac{1000 \text{ J}}{1 \text{ kJ}} = 1.1672103 \times 10^{13} \text{ J}$. Because $E = mc^2$, rearrange to solve for m.

$$m = \frac{E}{c^2} = \frac{1.1672103 \times 10^{13} \, \text{kg} \, \frac{\text{m}^2}{\text{s}^2}}{\left(2.9979 \times 10^8 \, \frac{\text{m}}{\text{s}}\right)^2} = 1.299 \times 10^{-4} \, \text{kg} \times \frac{1000 \, \text{g}}{1 \, \text{kg}} = 0.1299 \, \text{g total matter, } 0.0649 \, \text{g}$$

each of matter and antimatter.

Check: The units (g) are correct. A small mass is expected because nuclear reactions generate a large amount of energy.

19.64   **Given:** 85.0 g animal, ingests 10.0 mg of substance with 2.55% by mass Pu-239, alpha emitter, $t_{1/2} = 24{,}110$ years
Find: (a) initial exposure in Ci and (b) all radiation absorbed and 7.77×10^{-12} J/emission, RBE = 20, dose in rads in the first 4.0 hours and dose in rems in the first 4.0 hours
Conceptual Plan:

(a) $t_{1/2} \rightarrow k$ and mg $\rightarrow$ g $\rightarrow$ g Pu-239 $\rightarrow$ mol Pu-239 $\rightarrow$ atoms Pu-239

$t_{1/2} = \dfrac{0.693}{k}$ $\dfrac{1 \, \text{g}}{1000 \, \text{mg}}$ $\dfrac{2.55 \, \text{g Pu-239}}{100 \, \text{g substance}}$ $\dfrac{1 \, \text{mol Pu-239}}{239 \, \text{g Pu-239}}$ $\dfrac{6.022 \times 10^{23} \, \text{Pu-239 atoms}}{1 \, \text{mol Pu-239}}$

then $N, k \rightarrow$ **Rate (dis/yr)** $\rightarrow$ **dis/day** $\rightarrow$ **dis/h** $\rightarrow$ **dis/min** $\rightarrow$ **dis/s** $\rightarrow$ **Ci**

Rate = kN $\dfrac{1 \, \text{yr}}{365.24 \, \text{day}}$ $\dfrac{1 \, \text{day}}{24 \, \text{h}}$ $\dfrac{1 \, \text{h}}{60 \, \text{min}}$ $\dfrac{1 \, \text{min}}{60 \, \text{s}}$ $\dfrac{1 \, \text{Ci}}{\dfrac{3.7 \times 10^{10} \, \text{decays}}{\text{s}}}$

(b)   **h** $\rightarrow$ **min** $\rightarrow$ **s** then **dis/s, s** $\rightarrow$ **alpha decays** $\rightarrow$ **J** and **g** $\rightarrow$ **kg** then **J, animal mass** $\rightarrow$ **rad** $\rightarrow$ **rem**

$\dfrac{60 \, \text{min}}{1 \, \text{h}}$ $\dfrac{60 \, \text{s}}{1 \, \text{min}}$ multiply terms $\dfrac{7.77 \times 10^{-12} \, \text{J}}{\text{decay}}$ $\dfrac{1 \, \text{kg}}{1000 \, \text{g}}$ $\dfrac{1 \, \text{rad}}{\dfrac{0.01 \, \text{J}}{\text{kg animal}}}$ rem = RBE $\times$ rad

Solution:

(a) $t_{1/2} = \dfrac{0.693}{k}$; rearrange to solve for k. $k = \dfrac{0.693}{t_{1/2}} = \dfrac{0.693}{24{,}110 \, \text{yr}} = 2.874326 \times 10^{-5} \, \text{yr}^{-1}$ then

$10.0 \, \text{mg} \times \dfrac{1 \, \text{g}}{1000 \, \text{mg}} \times \dfrac{2.55 \, \text{g Pu-239}}{100 \, \text{g substance}} \times \dfrac{1 \, \text{mol Pu-239}}{239 \, \text{g Pu-239}} \times \dfrac{6.022 \times 10^{23} \, \text{Pu-239 atoms}}{1 \, \text{mol Pu-239}}$

$= 6.425146 \times 10^{17} \, \text{Pu-239 atoms}$

Rate = $kN = (2.874326 \times 10^{-5} \, \text{yr}^{-1})(6.425146 \times 10^{17} \, \text{Pu-239 atoms}) \times$

$\dfrac{1 \, \text{yr}}{365.24 \, \text{day}} \times \dfrac{1 \, \text{day}}{24 \, \text{h}} \times \dfrac{1 \, \text{h}}{60 \, \text{min}} \times \dfrac{1 \, \text{min}}{60 \, \text{s}} = 5.85230 \times 10^5 \, \dfrac{\text{dis}}{\text{s}} \times \dfrac{1 \, \text{Ci}}{\dfrac{3.7 \times 10^{10} \, \text{decays}}{\text{s}}} =$

$1.58170 \times 10^{-5} \, \text{Ci}$

(b) $4.0 \, \text{h} \times \dfrac{1 \, \text{day}}{24 \, \text{h}} \times \dfrac{1 \, \text{yr}}{365.24 \, \text{day}} = 4.5632 \times 10^{-4} \, \text{yr}$. Because the time is so much less than the $t_{1/2}(10^{-6}\%)$, the concentration is essentially constant. Use dis/s and time to get dose,

so $4.0 \, \text{h} \times \dfrac{60 \, \text{min}}{1 \, \text{h}} \times \dfrac{60 \, \text{s}}{1 \, \text{min}} = 1.44 \times 10^4 \, \text{s}$

$5.85230 \times 10^5 \, \dfrac{\text{dis}}{\text{s}} \times 1.44 \times 10^4 \, \text{s} = 8.42731 \times 10^9 \, \text{decays} \times \dfrac{7.77 \times 10^{-12} \, \text{J}}{\text{decays}} = 6.54802 \times 10^{-2} \, \text{J}$

and $85.0 \, \text{g} \times \dfrac{1 \, \text{kg}}{1000 \, \text{g}} = 0.0850 \, \text{kg}$ then $\dfrac{6.54802 \times 10^{-2} \, \text{J}}{0.0850 \, \text{kg}} \times \dfrac{1 \, \text{rad}}{\dfrac{0.01 \, \text{J}}{\text{kg animal}}} = 77 \, \text{rad}$ and

rem = RBE $\times$ rad = 20×77 rad = 1.5×10^3 rem and the animal will die.

Check: The units (Ci, rem, and rad) are correct. The number of curies is small because of the conversion factor. The doses in rems and rad are high because it is an alpha emitter and the isotope was ingested.

19.65   **Given:** $^{235}_{92}\text{U} \rightarrow ^{206}_{82}\text{Pb}$ and $^{232}_{90}\text{Th} \rightarrow ^{206}_{82}\text{Pb}$ **Find:** decay series

Conceptual Plan: Write the species given on the appropriate side of the equation. → **Equalize the sum of the mass numbers and the sum of the atomic numbers on both sides of the equation by writing the stoichiometric coefficient in front of the desired species.**

Solution: $^{235}_{92}\text{U} \rightarrow ^{?}_{82}\text{Pb} + ?\,^{4}_{2}\text{He} + ?\,^{0}_{-1}\text{e}$ becomes $^{235}_{92}\text{U} \rightarrow ^{207}_{82}\text{Pb} + 7\,^{4}_{2}\text{He} + 4\,^{0}_{-1}\text{e}$.

$^{232}_{90}\text{Th} \rightarrow ^{?}_{82}\text{Pb} + ?\,^{4}_{2}\text{He} + ?\,^{0}_{-1}\text{e}$ becomes $^{232}_{90}\text{Th} \rightarrow ^{208}_{82}\text{Pb} + 6\,^{4}_{2}\text{He} + 4\,^{0}_{-1}\text{e}$.

U-235 forms Pb-207 in 7 α-decays and 4 β-decays, and Th-232 forms Pb-208 in 6 α-decays and 4 β-decays.

Check: $235 = 207 + 7(4) + 4(0)$, and $92 = 82 + 7(2) + 4(-1)$. $232 = 208 + 6(4) + 4(0)$, and $90 = 82 + 6(2) + 4(-1)$. The mass of the Pb can be determined because alpha particles are large and need to be included as integer values. To make the masses balance requires more alpha particles than can be supported by the number of protons in the total equation. To account for this, an appropriate number of beta decays is added.

Conceptual Problems

19.66   **Given:** $^{21}_{9}\text{F} \rightarrow ^{?}_{?}? + ^{0}_{-1}\text{e}$ **Find:** missing nucleus

Conceptual Plan: Write the species given on the appropriate side of the equation. → **Equalize the sum of the mass numbers and the sum of the atomic numbers on both sides of the equation by writing the stoichiometric coefficient in front of the desired species.**

Solution: $^{21}_{9}\text{F} \rightarrow ^{?}_{?}? + ^{0}_{-1}\text{e}$ becomes $^{21}_{9}\text{F} \rightarrow ^{21}_{10}\text{Ne} + ^{0}_{-1}\text{e}$.

Check: $21 = 21 + 0$, and $9 = 10 - 1$. Neon is atomic number 10, and no other species are needed to balance the equation.

19.67   7. Because $1/2^6 = 1.6\%$ and $1/2^7 = 0.8\%$.

19.68   Nuclide A is more dangerous because the half-life is shorter (18.5 days), so it decays faster.

19.69   The gamma emitter is a greater threat while you sleep because it can penetrate more tissue. The alpha particles will not penetrate the wall to enter your bedroom. The alpha emitter is a greater threat if you ingest it because it is more ionizing.

Questions for Group Work

19.70 $^{A}_{Z}\text{X}$: A is the mass number (number of protons + neutrons) and is the superscript on the left; Z is the atomic number (number of protons) and is the subscript on the left; the charge is the superscript on the right; and X is the chemical symbol of the element.

Particle Name	Symbol	Mass Number	Atomic Number or Charge
alpha particle	$^{4}_{2}\text{He}$	4	2
beta particle	$^{0}_{-1}\text{e}$	0	−1
gamma ray	$^{0}_{0}\gamma$	0	0
positron	$^{0}_{+1}\text{e}$	0	+1
neutron	$^{1}_{0}\text{n}$	1	0
proton	$^{1}_{1}\text{p}$	1	1

19.71   See Table 19.1; All processes conserve total mass number and total charge, but they differ in the specific particles consumed and produced.

19.72   The first student is correct in that the total mass number is conserved during any nuclear process. The second student is correct in that there will also be a small (<1 amu) mass defect (difference in exact masses between reactants and products) that is converted into energy according to $E = mc^2$.

19.73 $^{238}_{92}\text{U} \rightarrow ^{234}_{90}\text{Th} + ^{4}_{2}\text{He};$ $^{234}_{90}\text{Th} \rightarrow ^{234}_{91}\text{Pa} + ^{0}_{-1}\text{e};$ $^{234}_{91}\text{Pa} \rightarrow ^{234}_{92}\text{U} + ^{0}_{-1}\text{e}.$

19.74   The number of atoms will decrease by one-half each 55.6 s.

Time (s)	Rn-220 Atoms*
0	16,000
55.6	8,000
111.2	4,000
166.8	2,000
222.4	1,000
278.0	500
50	8,578.5
100	4,599.4
200	1,322.1

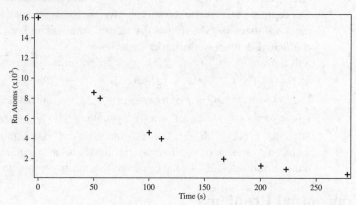

*Values are not displayed with the correct number of significant figures.

For the times that are not a multiple of the half-life, calculate k using $k = \dfrac{0.693}{t_{1/2}} = \dfrac{0.693}{55.6 \text{ s}} = 0.012\underline{4}6403 \text{ s}^{-1}$. For each time, calculate $\ln[\text{Rn-220}]_t = -k\,t + \ln[\text{Rn-220}]_0 = -(0.012\underline{4}6403 \text{ s}^{-1})\,t + \ln(16{,}000 \text{ atoms})$.